The PLANT FINDER

Devised & Compiled by Chris Philip

Edited by Tony Lord

British Library Cataloguing in Publication Data.

Philip, Chris *1928-*
The Plant Finder. - 7th. ed.
1. Great Britain. Gardens. Hardy plants
I. Title II. Lord, Tony *1949-*
635.9

ISBN 0-9512161-5-5
ISSN 0961-2599

First edition April 1987
Second edition April 1988
Reprinted August 1988
Third edition April 1989
Reprinted September 1989
Fourth edition April 1990
Fifth edition April 1991
Reprint September 1991
Sixth edition April 1992
Reprint September 1992
Seventh edition April 1993

Compiled, Produced and Computer typeset by:
Headmain
Lakeside
Whitbourne
Worcs. WR6 5RD

Agents for the book trade:
Moorlands Publishing Co Ltd.
Moor Farm Road West
Airfield Estate
Ashbourne DE6 1HD

Maps by:
à la carte
13 Lloyd Street
Llandudno
Gwynedd LL30 2UU

Printed by:
Richard Clay Ltd.
Bungay
Suffolk NR35 1ED

Cover:
DAHLIA: 'Geerling's Elite' (Trial at Wisley)
Harry Smith Horticultural Picture Library

Contents

Symbols and Abbreviations

*	Name not validated. Not listed in the appropriate International Registration Authority checklist nor in works cited in the Bibliography. For fuller discussion see **Nomenclature** on page 11
¶	New plant entry in this year's Edition, (or reinstated from list of previously deleted plants)
®	Registered Trade Mark or Selling name
♦	New or amended synonym or cross-reference included for the first time this year
§	Plant listed elsewhere in the **PLANT DIRECTORY** under a synonym
†	National Council for the Conservation of Plants and Gardens (NCCPG) Collection exists for all or part of this genus.
C	Culinary (for Fruit)
cv(s)	Cultivar(s)
D	Dessert (for Fruit)
d	Double flowered
F	Fruit
f.	forma (botanical form)
g	grex
gr	Group
(g.&cl.)	grex and clone (Rhododendron)
I	Invalid name. See International Code of Nomenclature for Cultivated Plants 1980. For fuller discussion see **Nomenclature** on page 11
N	Refer to **Nomenclature Notes** on page 14
nm.	nothomorph (hybrid form)
nssp.	nothosubspecies (hybrid ssp.)
nvar.	nothovarietas (hybrid var.)
S	Shrubby
(s-p)	Self-pollinating
sp.	species
ssp.	subspecies
svar.	subvarietas (botanical subvariety)
(v)	Variegated plant
var.	varietas (botanical variety)

For **Collector's References** see page 25

For abbreviations relating to individual genera see **Classification of Genera** page 20

IMPORTANT NOTE TO USERS

This, the Sixth Edition of **THE PLANT FINDER,** contains over 60,000 plants and details of the nurseries which have advised us that they can supply them. No nursery, by the very nature of its business, will be able to provide everything in its list at all times. This is, of course, particularly true of plants which are rare, seldom asked for, or difficult to propagate.

To avoid disappointment, we suggest that you always:

CHECK WITH THE NURSERY BEFORE VISITING OR ORDERING

THE PLANT FINDER exists to put gardeners in touch with nurserymen. It does *not* offer value judgements on the nurseries or the plants it lists nor intend any reflection on any other nursery or plant *not* listed.

In addition, **THE PLANT FINDER** tries to cross-reference plant names to their correct *valid* name, although in some cases it is all too easy to understand why British nurserymen have preferred a more immediately comprehensible English name! *Every* name, apart from 'Common' names, that has been shown in a Catalogue has been listed, which is why there are so may cross-references. It is, clearly, the nursery's responsibility to ensure that its stock is accurately named both in its catalogue and on the plant when it is sold.

Caveat Emptor.

The Compiler and Editor of **THE PLANT FINDER** have taken every care, in the time available, to check all the information supplied to them by the nurseries concerned. Nevertheless, in a work of this kind, containing as it does, almost half-a-million separate computer encodings, errors and omissions will, inevitably, occur. Neither The Hardy Plant Society nor the Compiler or Editor can accept responsibility for any consequences that may arise from such errors.

If you find mistakes we hope that you will let us know so that the matter can be corrected in the next edition.

Preface - 1993/94 Edition

During the last twelve months two important developments have taken place which will affect, directly or indirectly, every nursery and gardener in Europe.

On January 1st 1993 the European Community became one large single marketplace which now enables a virtually unrestricted movement of plants between the Member States without costly formality. (There are however restrictions on certain plants known to harbour harmful pests and diseases such as Fireblight).

In the summer of 1992 the Royal Horticultural Society's ***New RHS Dictionary of Gardening*** was published.

The Common Market

This new enlarged market and the freedom of movement will mean, in theory, that the British nurseryman has more to gain than that of his European counterpart because he can now provide gardeners in the rest of Europe with a far greater range of plants than has hitherto been possible.

It will, of course, also become much easier for nurseries and garden centres to obtain material from Europe than in the past and this could, in some cases, mean cheaper plants.

With the increasing number of European countries now publishing their own national equivalent of **THE PLANT FINDER**, (currently France, Belgium, Germany & Switzerland, see Bibliography for details), there will be far greater opportunities for the small specialist nursery to increase its sales should it wish to do so.

Exports

In order to undertake any Mail Order operation a nursery must first have notified the Ministry of Agriculture, Fisheries and Food so that they can establish what degree of inspection, if any, it will have to undergo. Nurseries who propagate plants that are known to harbour certain specific pests and diseases may have to be inspected and provide records of what they grow. In general, however, the small specialist nursery will not have to register and be inspected.

Once having been registered and inspected, if required to do so, the nursery will then be free to undertake Mail Order to *anywhere* within the Community without the need, as in the past, of having to obtain individual Phytosanitary Certificates for each consignment.

As a result of these changes we are now quoting, in this edition, under the heading *Mail Order* the minimum order value that a nursery will accept for its plants on the assumption that this will apply to both UK and European destinations. To this, of course, must be added any postage, carriage, packing or insurance charge which will obviously vary greatly depending on the weight and destination. In such cases we have added "+ p&p" to cover all these charges. In some cases nurseries do not set any minimum charge for plant orders so the words "No minimum charge" are used. It must however be realised that the cost of sending even one small plant can often involve charges several times higher than the price of the plant itself.

Although all nurseries listed as undertaking Mail Order are now permitted to sell to Member States, under certain circumstance they may refuse to send plants a long distance as some kinds will not survive more than a short transit.

In such cases, members of the Hardy Plant Society might care to be reminded of the facility that exists by which members arrange to collect, care for, and pass on plants until they reach their final destination.

Some larger nurseries, especially those listed as "Both" under *W/sale or Retail* may also be prepared to export to countries outside the Community if the order value is sufficiently large, although they will have to obtain a Phytosanitary Certificate and Customs documents which will add substantially to the cost and will have to be born by the customer.

The New RHS Dictionary of Gardening

This substantially revised publication, the first for over 30 years, has both solved and caused a number of problems for the compiler and editor of **THE PLANT FINDER**.

The RHS Dictionary has published details of a number of new generic names to which many well known and widely available plants may be transferred. We are concerned that if we follow slavishly these recommendations it will cause considerable confusion and cost to all those whose business is connected with the correct naming of plants. These include, not only nurserymen and gardeners, but also photographic and bibliographic libraries, label makers, and publishers of books, magazines and catalogues not only in the UK but worldwide.

In the past, before improved communications, and indeed before the annual publication of **THE PLANT FINDER**, it would have taken many years for a published name change to be disseminated to any except readers of botanical journals and the average gardener or nursery often remained unaware of these changes. For example, several veronicas were transferred to *Hebe* in the 1920's but 60 years later they were often still listed under *Veronica.*

A similar problem arose a few years ago when it was proposed that *Erica carnea* be changed to *E. herbacea.* However, because it was appreciated that the cost of making such a change could not be justified, even though both the genus and cultivar name would remain the same, the proposal was dropped.

For this reason we are not at this stage making some of the changes that are proposed, although these new names will be listed for the time being as synonyms. (This matter is discussed further in the Nomenclature chapter.)

Of particular concern to us is the fact that any botanist can publish a proposal to change the name of a genus or species providing it is done in a way that complies with the requirements of the International Code of Botanical Nomenclature. Furthermore, this can be done without any verification by his peers and, as a result, such a change may be acceptable to some but not to others.

Because taxonomy is, in general, a subjective study rather than a scientific discipline it relies to a great extent on opinion rather than fact; indeed some plant names see-saw back and forth with the prevailing fashions of the day. To the poor gardener, however, the plant remains the same.

One unfortunate result of this is that when an influential source book, such as the RHS Dictionary is published, some writers will adopt a new generic or specific name and others will ignore it. For example, Plant Finders in different countries will also have differing views on these changes and thus plant names in American catalogues may differ from those in Germany which may again differ from those in the UK.

In an attempt to resolve this problem we are currently having discussions with other international publishers and organisations with a view to the stabilisation, for horticultural purposes at least, of names of cultivated plants.

Introduction

How to use the Directory

Look up the plant you require in the alphabetical **Plant Directory.** Against each plant you will find a four-letter Code, or Codes, for example 'ECha SDix', each code representing one nursery offering that plant. The first letter of each Code indicates the main area of the country in which the nursery is situated:

C = South West England

Avon, Devon, Dorset, Channel Isles, Cornwall, Isles of Scilly, Somersetshire & Wiltshire.

E = Eastern England

Cambridgeshire, Essex, Lincolnshire, Norfolk & Suffolk.

G = Scotland

Borders, Central, Dumfries & Galloway, Fife, Grampian, Highlands, Inverness, Strathclyde.

I = Northern Ireland & Republic of Ireland.

L = London area

Bedfordshire, Berkshire, Buckinghamshire, Hertfordshire, London, Middlesex, Surrey.

M = Midlands

Cheshire, Derbyshire, Isle of Man, Leicestershire, Northamptonshire, Nottinghamshire, Oxfordshire, Staffordshire, Warwickshire, West Midlands.

N = Northern England

Cleveland, Cumbria, Durham, East Yorkshire, Greater Manchester, Humberside, Lancashire, Merseyside, Northumberland, North Yorkshire, South Yorkshire, Tyne & Wear, West Yorkshire.

S = Southern England

East Sussex, Hampshire, Isle of Wight, Kent, West Sussex.

W = Wales & Western England

Dyfed, Clywd, Glamorganshire, Gloucestershire, Gwent, Gwynedd, Herefordshire & Worcestershire, Powys, Shropshire.

Turn to the **Code-Nursery Index** on page 574 where, in alphabetical order of Codes, you will find details of each nursery which offers the plant in question. If you wish to visit any of these nurseries you can find its *approximate* location on one of the maps at the back. Those few nurseries which sell *only* by Mail Order are not shown on the maps. Always check that the nursery you select has the plant in stock before you set out.

Widely available plants

If more than 30 nurseries offer any plant the Directory gives no Code and the plant is listed as 'Widely available'. This has been done to prevent **THE PLANT FINDER** becoming too bulky. In this Edition there are just under 1000 plants listed as 'Widely available' and you should have little difficulty in finding these in local nurseries or Garden Centres. However, if any readers do have difficulty in finding such plants, we will be pleased to send them a full list of all the nurseries that we have listed and this could include anything from 31 to a maximum of 50. Please write to:

THE PLANT FINDER,
Lakeside, Whitbourne, Worcester WR6 5RD

All such enquiries *must* include the full name of the plant being sought, as shown in **THE PLANT FINDER**, together with a *stamped addressed envelope*.

Nursery-Code Index

For convenience, a reverse **Nursery-Code Index** is included on page 567. This gives the names of the nurseries listed in the **Plant Directory** in alphabetical order of nursery names together with their relevant Codes.

Additional Nursery Index

There is also an **Additional Nursery Index**, on page 628, containing brief details of other nurseries that have not been included in the **Plant Directory**. They may be listed in this Index for a number of reasons, for example, their stock is small and changes too quickly for them to be able to issue a viable catalogue, or the major part of their stock would have to be listed as 'Widely available', or simply because their latest Catalogue was not received in time for inclusion. Again, their catalogues may either give mainly English names, (and this particularly applies to Herb nurseries) or Latin names which do not provide sufficient information to establish easily the genus or species of the plant concerned. The location of these nurseries on the maps are marked by their listed numbers.

How to find your plant

If you cannot immediately find the plant you seek in the **Plant Directory**, look through the various species of the genus. You may be using an incomplete name. The problem is most likely to arise in very large genera such as *Phlox* where there are a number of possible species, each with a large number of cultivars. A search through the whole genus may well bring success.

New Cross-references

Major new cross-references and synonyms have been marked with a ♦. This sign has only been used when the genus, species or cultivar name has been altered, but not where there have been merely minor typographic or orthographic changes.

If the plant you seek is not listed in the **Plant Directory,** it is possible that a nursery in the **Additional Nursery Index** which specialises in similar plants may be able to offer it. In addition to the plants listed in their catalogues, many nurseries are often able to supply other plants of the same general type that they specialise in. They may not list them if they only have a few available. In some cases they can arrange to propagate special items from their stock plants.

Nurseries

The details given for each nursery (listed in the Indices at the back) have been compiled from information supplied to us in answer to a questionnaire. In some cases, because of constraints of space, the entries have been slightly abbreviated and blanks have been left where no information has been provided.

Opening Times

The word 'daily' implies every day including Sunday and Bank Holidays. Although opening times have been given as provided and where applicable, it is *always* advisable, especially if travelling a long distance, to check with the nursery first.

Mail Order

Many nurseries provide a Mail Order service which now extends to all members of the European Community. Where it is shown that there is no minimum charge it should be realised that to send even one plant may involve the nursery in substantial postage and packing costs. Some nurseries may not be prepared to send tender or bulky plants.

Catalogue Cost

Some nurseries offer their catalogue free, or for a few stamps (the odd value quoted can usually be made up from a combination of first or second class stamps), but a *large*, at least (A5) stamped addressed envelope is always appreciated as well. Overseas customers should use an equivalent number of International Reply Coupons (IRCs) in place of stamps.

Wholesale or Retail

The main trading method is indicated, but it should be stressed that some wholesalers do have retail outlets and many retailers also have a wholesale trade and would frequently be prepared to offer discounts for large single orders.

Export

We have not indicated this year which nurseries are prepared to export to countries outside the European Community because of the administrative difficulties connected with the implementation of the various new EC regulations. However several of the larger nurseries that are marked 'Both' under the heading *W/Sale or Retail* are prepared to export to such providing, of course, all the additional costs of Phytosanitary Certificates and Customs are met by the purchaser.

Variegated Plants

Following a suggestion from the Variegated Plant Group of the Hardy Plant Society, we have added a (v) to those plants which are 'variegated' although this may not be apparent from their name. Plants named 'Variegata' or 'Marginata' (in combination) are not coded as all except *Iris variegata, Rosa* 'Variegata di Bologna' and *R.* 'Centrifolia Variegata' have variegated leaves rather than flowers. The dividing line between variegation and less distinct colour marking is necessarily arbitrary and plants with light veins, pale, silver or dark zones or leaves flushed in paler colours are not shown as being variegated unless there is an absolutely sharp distinction between paler and darker zones.

For further details of the Variegated Plant Group, please write to:

Stephen Tafler, 18 Hayes End Manor, South Petherton, Somerset TA13 5BE.

Hardy Plant Society Search List

During the last few years the Hardy Plant Society has instigated several searches in Europe for scarce and desirable plants that may not be available in this country. As a result, several new plants have been introduced into cultivation in the UK, and the HPS has built up a list of about 1000 plants that it is keen to obtain further information about. This list appears on page 732.

Fire Blight Warning

We have been asked to draw attention to the prevalence of this disease, especially in the centre and east of England, which has already destroyed crops of several members of the Rosaceae family. These include:-

Cotoneaster *salicifolius* 'Pendulus'
C. *floccosus*

C. *salicifolius* 'Repens'
All **Cotoneaster** in Standard Form
Sorbus *hupehensis*
S. 'Joseph Rock'
Photinia *davidiana*

New Nursery entries

Nurseries that are appearing in **THE PLANT FINDER** for the first time this year are printed in **bold type** in the **Nursery-Code Index** starting on page 567.

We are always grateful for suggestions for new inclusions but it should however be realised, that if your favourite nursery has not been included, it may be that it has specifically asked that we should not do so.

Deleted Nurseries

Every year a couple of dozen nurseries ask to be deleted. This may be because they are about to move or close, or they are changing the way in which they trade.

There are also some nurseries who, despite several reminders from us, have not responded in any way, so we have no idea if their details and plant lists are still correct and current.

Please, never use old editions.

Deleted Plants

The **Plant Deletions Index** contains some 8000 plant names that were listed in one or other of the six previous editions of **THE PLANT FINDER**, but are now no longer represented. As a result there are a few instances where a Genus exists in the main **Plant Directory** but with no apparent entries for either species or cultivars. These will be found in the **Plant Deletions Index**. It is also possible that some cross-references may not apparently refer to an entry in the main Directory. Again this is because the plant in question had a supplier or suppliers but is now in the **Plant Deletions Index.** These references are deliberately kept so as to provide an historic record of synonyms and plant availability and to aid those who wish to try and find and reintroduce any of these 'deleted' plants.

These deletions arise, not only because the nursery that supplied the plants may have gone out of business, but also because a few nurseries who were included previously have not responded to our latest questionnaire and have thus had to be deleted. Such plants may well be still available but we have no current knowledge of their whereabouts. Furthermore, some items may have been misnamed by nurseries in previous editions, but are now appearing under their correct name.

New Nurseries

We are well aware that there are a number of nurseries that have not been included simply because either we do not know about them or they have asked not to be included. If any wish to be considered for inclusion in the next edition of **THE PLANT FINDER** (1994/95) they should write, in the first instance to:

The Plant Finder
Lakeside
Gaines Road
Whitbourne
Worcs WR6 5RD

The closing date for new entries will be January 31st 1994.

Nomenclature

"The question of nomenclature is always a vexed one. The only thing certain is, that it is impossible to please everyone."
W J Bean - Preface to First Edition of
Trees & Shrubs Hardy in the British Isles."

As in previous editions, we remain committed to the use of plant names which are as correct as possible and agree with the current opinions of botanists. Of course, gardeners and nurserymen can still use whatever names they want and many will prefer a more conservative approach to naming. However, to adopt any middle course for **THE PLANT FINDER**, keeping some old (but wrong) names and introducing some new ones, would be a recipe for chaos and confusion. Such a course would ultimately result in botanists and gardeners speaking different, mutually incomprehensible languages and we would all be the poorer.

This does not mean that we will change a name the moment we hear that one botanist considers it to be wrong; name changes once they are considered correct by the great majority of experts are likely to become permanent and to be used by gardeners and botanists alike. Only then do we accept new names and we do not inflict them on gardeners or nurseries purely out of perversity.

Except for those names in which we have made corrections of only a couple of letters to bring them in line with the codes of nomenclature, we are responsible for ***none*** of the name changes in this or any other edition of **THE PLANT FINDER**.

Several important new works have been published during the last year which propose drastic changes to the names of garden plants and threaten a divergence between plant names used by botanists and those familiar to gardeners. Foremost among these is *The New RHS Dictionary of Gardening*: though in most respects this is an admirable and much-needed work, it adopts substantial changes to the names of a great many garden plants without giving the least discussion or reason for doing so. The splitting of *Eupatorium* into a number of unfamiliar genera and the moving of the most popular sedums to the genus *Hylotelephium* are examples of taxonomic treatments which seem to us to be too hasty, costly to implement and ill-advised; we will not be following them in this edition.

A publication from Kew, *Vascular Plant Families and Genera*, lists all generic and family names accepted at Kew. We have used it, along with Piers Trehane's proposed treatment of families, to standardise families given in this edition; however, for generic names, again we feel that some of treatments here involve too many changes to established names for us to adopt them before they are fully proven and accepted.

Though we are generally reluctant to change well-known names, there are a few major changes in this edition. *Alyssum saxatile* becomes *Aurinia saxatilis* and *Cheiranthus* is transferred to *Erysimum*. Both of these changes are endorsed by the *New RHS Dictionary*, *Vascular Plant Families and Genera* and the new edition of *Flora Europaea*. However, we have decided not to transfer *Ledum* to *Rhododendron*, *Jovibarba* to *Sempervivum*, nor will we, at present, split off four new genera from *Sorbus* as suggested by Robertson, Phipps, Rohrer and Smith in their paper *A Synopsis of Genera in Maloideae (Rosaceae)* (Systematic Botany (1991), 16(2): pp. 376-394).

Dr McAllister's researches with Alison Rutherford on ivies are incorporated in the *New RHS Dictionary of Gardening* and will also appear in *European Garden Flora*. Their treatment of the Algerian and Canary Island ivies and recognition of *Hedera hibernica* as a separate species are retained in this edition.

One highlight of the year has been the appearance of *The International Camellia Register* by T J Savige, bringing together in two weighty volumes an astonishing quantity of information. The third volume of the *International Conifer Manual* covering cypresses has also made a welcome appearance; we look forward to the publication of *The World Checklist of Conifers* by Humphrey Welch and Gordon Haddow (?August 1993) for yet more information.

Verification of names

Although we find that many nurseries have greatly improved the accuracy of their plant names, plants which are new entries often appear under a bewildering variety of wrong names and misspellings. This is partly a reflection on the rarity of the plants and nurserymen are not to be blamed for not finding correct names for plants which do not appear in recent authoritative garden literature. Some plants are simply too new for valid names and descriptions yet to have appeared in print.

Although we try to verify every name which appears in these pages, the amount of time which can be allotted to checking each of over 60,000 entries must be limited. There is always a proportion which do not appear in any of the reference sources used (i.e. those listed in the

Bibliography) and those unverified names for which there may be scope for error are marked with an asterisk. Such errors may occur with species we cannot find listed (possibly synonyms for more recent and better known names) or may include misspellings (particularly of names transliterated from Japanese or Chinese, or commemorating a person). We are especially circumspect about names not known to the International Registrar for a particular genus. We are always grateful to receive information about the naming and origin of any asterisked plant and once we feel reassured about the plant's pedigree, the asterisk will be removed. Of course, many such names will prove to be absolutely correct and buyers can be reassured if they know that the selling nursery takes great care with the naming of its plants.

Rules of Nomenclature

Throughout **THE PLANT FINDER** we try to follow the rules of nomenclature set out in the *International Code of Botanical Nomenclature* 1988 (ICBN) and the *International Code of Nomenclature for Cultivated Plants* 1980 (ICNCP). Cultivar names which are clearly not permissible under this code and for which there seems to be no valid alternative are marked "I" (for invalid). The commonest sorts of invalid names seem to be those that are wholly or partly in Latin (not permissible since 1959, eg 'Pixie Alba', 'Superba', 'Variegata') and those which use a latin generic name as a cultivar name (eg *Rosa* 'Corylus', *Viola* 'Gazania'). If no prior valid name exists, an enterprising nurseryman may publish a new valid name for any such plant. This would be considered validly published if it appeared in a dated catalogue with a clear description of the plant; the originator, if still alive, must be willing to accept the new name.

Apart from being discourteous to the plants' originators and their countries, the translating of foreign plant names into English is a bad and insular practice that is likely to cause confusion; it may be years yet before we make sense of the host of German names and apparent English translations for a genus such as *Coreopsis*, many of which must be synonyms. Throughout **THE PLANT FINDER**, we have tried to give preference to the original name in every case, although English names are also given.

The substitution of slick selling names by nurseries which do not like, or have not bothered to find out, the correct names of the plants they sell is sharp practice not expected of any reputable nursery; it is also a probable breach of the Trades Description Act.

Orthography

The recent ruling on orthography, that is retention, in commemorative names, of a person's name in its original form, is discussed in the supplement to Bean's *Trees and Shrubs Hardy in the British Isles* (1988) and is given in ICBN Article 73.10, further clarified by Article 73.7 Example 10, 1988. The gist of this is, that except for full-scale latinisations of names (eg *brunonius* for Brown, thus *Rosa brunonii*), the name of the person commemorated should remain in its original form. Some names falling into this category were corrected in our previous three editions and further corrections will be found this year. Names ending in -er (eg Solander, Faber) may be become *solandri* (as in pure Latin, because -er is a usual Latin termination) or *solanderi*, if the specific name was originally spelt in this way. I am grateful to Susyn Andrews and Nigel Taylor of Kew for confirming that according to ICBN, names such as *backhousiana, catesbaei, mackaiana, glazoviana, manescavii and bureavii* are **not** allowed and, according to the Code, must be corrected to *backhouseana, catesbyi, mackayana, glaziouana, manescaui and bureaui* respectively.

Some authorities, including some International Registrars, choose not to follow the ruling on orthography and indeed there are not only proposals to strengthen it but counter-proposals to abolish it at the next International Botanical Congress at Tokyo in August 1993. However, this applies equally to a number of the rules of the Code: we cannot use this as an argument for picking and choosing which parts of the Code it suits us to follow but must uphold the Code in its entirety; ICBN and ICNCP are great forces for stability in plant names and generally help to minimise the number of irritating and confusing name changes which beset gardeners.

Botanical epithets

Botanical epithets commemorating someone whose name has been transliterated from script other than Roman (e.g. Cyrillic or Japanese) present great problems and the ruling on orthography is difficult to apply to these: although there is widespread acceptance of Hepburn's system of transliteration from Japanese, there is no apparent universal approval for a system for transliteration from Cyrillic; without this it seems difficult to reach any concensus on the orthography of, for instance, Russian commemorative names. However, implementation of this rule has been assisted by another new publication from Kew, *Authors of Plant Names*, which is particularly helpful in giving acceptable transliterations of names which were originally in Cyrillic.

We have great sympathy for gardeners who want to find a particular cultivar but are not sure to which species it belongs. The problem is acute for genera such as Juniperus and readers must search through all the entries to find their plants; even nurseries seem uncertain of the species of 'Skyrocket'. We have felt that saxifrages, astilbes (and a few others), were so impossible that they must be listed by cultivar first, giving the species in parentheses.

Adjectival names

Latin adjectival names, whether for species, subspecies, cultivar etc., must agree in gender with the genus, *not* with the specific name if the latter is a noun (as for *Phyllitis scolopendrium, Lonicera caprifolium* etc.). Thus azaleas have to agree with *Rhododendron*, their true genus (neuter), rather than *Azalea* (feminine). For French cultivar names, adjectives should agree with whatever is being described; for roses, this is almost always *la rose* (feminine) but on rare occasions *le rosier* (when describing vegetative characteristics such as climbing forms), *l'oeillet* or *le pompon* (all masculine).

It is often the case that gardeners consider two plants to be distinct but botanists, who know of a whole range of intermediates linking the two, consider them to be the same species. The most notable example is for the rhododendrons, many species of which were "sunk" in Cullen and Chamberlain's recent revision. In such cases we have always tried to provide names that retain important horticultural entities, even if not botanically distinct, often by giving the sunk species a Group name, such as *Rhododendron rubiginosum* Desquamatum Group. Rhododendrons and orchids are also blessed with grex names for swarms of hybrids with the same parentage such as *R*. Polar Bear or *Pleione* Shantung. Such names are not enclosed in quotes but, particularly for rhododendrons, a single clone from the grex may be given the same cultivar name, ie 'Polar Bear'. In many cases nursery catalogues do not specify whether the named clone is being offered or other selections from the hybrid swarm and entries are therefore given as eg *Rhododendron* Polar Bear (g.&cl.) (i.e. grex and clone).

There are a few cases in which it is difficult to tell whether a "sunk" species remains horticulturally distinct enough to merit a group name, as for many of the rhododendrons; we would be grateful if users would let us know of any plants that we have "sunk" in synonymy but which still need to be distinguished by a separate name. In many cases, the plants gardeners grow will be the most extreme variants of a species; although one "end" of the species will seem to be quite a different plant from the other "end" to the gardener, the botanist will see them as the outer limits of a continuous range of variation and will give them the same species name. We often hear gardeners complain "How can these two plants have the same name? They are different!"; in such cases, although the botanist may have to "lump" them under the same name, we will always try to provide an acceptable name to distinguish an important horticultural entity, even if it is not botanically distinct.

Taxonomic rank

This edition is the second in which we have included taxonomic rank for infraspecific taxa. Thus subspecies, varietas and forma are shown as ssp., var. and f. respectively. For hybrid species, the corresponding ranks are nothosubspecies, nothovarietas and nothomorph (nssp., nvar. and nm.), e.g. *Mentha villosa* nm. *alopecurodes*. Each of these ranks indicates a successively less significant change in the characteristics of the plant from the original type on which the species was based; in general terms, a subspecies may be expected to be more markedly different from the typical species than a forma which may differ in only one characteristic such as flower colour, hairiness of leaf or habit. In rare cases, taxonomists have felt the need to impose another "layer" in this heirarchy, the subvarietas, shown here as svar.

Though we have shown the rank of a considerably greater proportion of infraspecific epithets, some remain to be added in future editions. In many cases, it is not at all clear whether a colour form shown as, say, *alba* is a true botanical forma or a cultivar of garden origin. Our inclination here is not to treat such plants as cultivars if they are recorded as being naturally occurring, nor if they embrace considerable variation: forma *alba* would be preferred if a valid publication is recorded, otherwise a suitable Group name. In the absence of conclusive evidence we will leave such names styled as they are at present.

In many cases the same species name has been used by two or more authors for quite different plants. Thus *Bloomingthingia grandiflora* of Linnaeus might be an altogether different species from *B. grandiflora* of gardeners (*B. grandiflora* hort.). In such circumstances it becomes necessary to define whose *Bloomingthingia* we are considering by quoting the author of the name directly after the species name. Generally the more recent name will be invalid and may be cross referenced to the plant's first validly published name. Author's names appear directly after the species name and are usually spelled in full here, except for longer citations for which abbreviations are listed in e.g. Mabberley's *The Plant-Book* or given in full in *Index Hortensis*. Such names do not appear in quotes so should not be confused with cultivar names.

Hyphenation

Some items of the International Code of Botanical Nomenclature have been "more honour'd in the breach than in the observance". One such is the ruling on hyphenation (Article 73.9) which forbids the use of hyphens after a "compounding form" (i.e. albo, pseudo, aureo, neo). In this edition we have tried to eliminate any remaining illegitimate hyphens from any botanical or cultivar names, although hyphens are still permitted to divide separate words such as *novae-angliae* or *bella-donna.*

Commemorative names

Another item of the code which is often ignored is that covering terminations of commemorative names (Article 73.10, referring to Recommendation 73C). A botanical epithet commemorating Helena must be styled *helenae* whereas one commemorating Helen may be styled either *heleniae* or, following Helena as an established Latin form of the same name or, quite frequently, of Ellen, *helenae*; in such cases when either spelling could be legitimate, the original is followed. When there is no accepted Latin alternative, the *-iae* ending is used and this seems to be more correct for *murieliae* and *edithiae*. The genitive form of names ending in -a is always -ae, even if a man is being commemorated (as for *Picea koyamae*). It is this same article which requires that the well known *Crocosmia* be spelt *masoniorum* and not *masonorum.*

International Registration Authorities

International Registration Authorities (IRAs) have been a great help and although it is perhaps invidious to single out any for special praise, the International Registrars acting for the Royal Horticultural Society have all been exceptionally helpful and have shown just how valuable such schemes can be when well organised with up-to-date and complete records. We have had much help from other Registrars mentioned in the acknowledgments and have followed their rulings implicitly in almost every case.

THE PLANT FINDER is useful not only as a directory of plant sources but as a "menu" of plants grown by British gardeners. Such a list is of great value not only to private gardeners; landscapers can use it to check the range of plants they can incorporate in designs; botanists can discover the species grown in Britain, some of them from recorded natural sources; nurserymen can use it to select for propagation first-rate plants that are still not readily available; horticultural authors, who often only want to write about plants the public are able to buy, will find it invaluable. For all such users, **THE PLANT FINDER** can be recommended as a source of standard, up-to-date and reliable nomenclature.

Chris Philip and Tony Lord
April 1993

Nomenclature Notes

These notes refer to plants in the main **PLANT DIRECTORY** that are marked with a 'N'.

'Bean Supplement' refers to W J Bean *Trees & Shrubs Hardy in the British Isles* (Supplement to the 8th edition) edited by D L Clarke 1988.

Acer *palmatum coreanum*
This has nothing to do with A. *p.* 'Koreanum'

Acer *palmatum* 'Sango-kaku'/ 'Senkaki'
These names once thought to be synonyms seem to refer to distinct plants. 'Sango-kaku' has richer red stems.

Acer *pseudoplatanus* 'Leopoldii;
True 'Leopoldii' has leaves stained with yellowish pink and purple. Plants are often A. *p.* f. *variegatum.*

Acer *p.* 'Spaethii'
Has large leaves with light yellow specks.

Aconitum *autumnale*
A synonym of A. *napellus* and A. *carmichaelii wilsonii.*

Acorus *gramineus* 'Oborozuki' & 'Ogon'
Although these seem to be the same clone in British gardens, 'Oborozuki' is a distinct brighter yellow cultivar in the USA.

Alchemilla *alpina*
The true species is very rare in cultivation. Plants under this name are usually A. *plicatula* or A. *conjuncta.*

Alchemilla *splendens*

The true species is probably not in cultivation in the British Isles.

Alopecurus *pratensis* 'Aureus'
Name applies only to plants with all gold leaves, not with green & gold striped forms.

Anemone *magellanica*
According to *European Garden Flora* this is a form of the very variable A. *multifida.*

Anemone *nemorosa* 'Alba Plena'
This name is used for several double white forms including A. *n.* 'Flore Pleno' and A. *n.* 'Vestal'.

Anthemis *tinctoria* 'Grallach Gold'
The true cultivar of this name has golden yellow flowers. Plants with orange yellow flowers are **A.** *t.* 'Beauty of Grallach'.

Aquilegia *vulgaris* Vervaeneana Group 'Woodside'.
This name applies only to plants with variegated foliage & deep indigo blue single flowers.

Artemisia 'Faith Raven' & 'Powis Castle'
Most, if not all plants labelled 'Faith Raven' are identical with 'Powis Castle'. It is not clear which is the valid name.

Arum *i. marmoratum* and **A.** *italicum pictum* are synonyms for subspecies *italicum* which has white-veined leaves. **A.** *pictum* is a distinct species.

Aster *amellus* 'Violet Queen'
It is probable that more than one cultivar is sold under this name.

Aster *dumosus*
Many of the Asters listed under *A. novi-belgii* contain varying amounts of A. *dumosus* blood in their parentage. It is not possible to allocate these to one species or the other and they are therfore listed under A. *novi-belgii.*

Aster x *frikartii* 'Mönch'
The true plant is very rare in British gardens. Most plants are another form of A. x *frikartii* usually 'Wunder von Stafa'.

Aster *novi-belgii*
See note under A. *dumosus.*

Aubrieta *deltoidea* 'Variegata'
This name may refer to any of the variegated cultivars of Aubrieta.

Berberis *aristata*
Plants so named may be either B. *chitria* or B. *floribunda.*

Berberis x *ottawensis* f. *purpurea*/ 'Superba'
'Superba' is a clonal selection from f. *purpurea*

Berberis x *ottawensis* 'Superba'
See note in Bean Supplement, p 109.

Berberis *stenophylla* 'Lemon Queen'
This sport from 'Pink Pearl' was first named in 1982. The same mutation occured again and was named 'Cream Showers'. The older name has priority.

Bergenia Ballawley Hybrids
The name 'Ballawley' refers only to plants vegetatively propagated from ther original clone. Seed raised plants, which may differ considerably, should be called Ballawley Hybrids.

Betula *pendula* 'Dalecarlica'
The true plant of this name is rare in cultivation in the British Isles and is probably not available from nurseries.

Betula *utilis* var. *jacquemontii*
Plants are often the clone 'Inverleith' which may or may not be a form of B. *utilis.*

Brachyscome
Originally published as BRACHYSCOME by Cassini who later revised his spelling to BRACHYCOME. The original spelling has been internationally adopted.

Brachyglottis *greyi* and *laxifolia*
Both these species are extremely rare in cultivation. Plants under these names usually being B. 'Sunshine'.

Buddleja *davidii* Petite Indigo ®, Petite Plum ® 'Nanho Blue', 'Nanho Purple'
These cultivars or hybrids of B. *d. nanhoensis* are claimed by some to be synonyms while others claim the 'Nanho' plants were raised in Holland and the 'Petite' plants in the USA. We are not yet certain whether these names are synonyms and if so which have priority.

Buddleja *fallowiana*
Many plants in cultivation are not the true species but the hybrid 'West Hill'.

Camassia *leichtlinii* 'Plena'
This has starry, transparent creamy-white flowers, creamy-white 'Semiplena' is sometimes offered under this name.

Camellia 'Campbellii'
This name is used for five cvs. including 'Margherita Coleoni' but applies correctly to Guichard's 1894 cultivar, single to semi-double full rose pink.

Camellia 'Cleopatra'
There are three cultivars with this name.

Camellia 'Perfecta'
There are three cultivars under this name. This is 'Perfecta' of Jury.

Campanula *persicifolia*
Plants under 'cup and saucer white' are not definitely ascribed to a particular cultivar. 'White Cup and Saucer' is a cultivar named by Margery Fish.

Carex *conica* 'Hime-kansuge'/ 'Hino-kansuge'/ 'Variegata'
This variegated sedge is listed under over a dozen variants of the above names, none of which is legitimate. Dr Alan Leslie has proposed the cultivar name 'Snowline' for this plant.

Carex *morrowii* 'Variegata'
C. *oshimensis* 'Evergold' is sometimes sold under this name.

Carya *illinoinensis*
The correct spelling of this name is discussed in Baileya Vol 10. No. 1 1962.

Cassia *corymbosa*
See note in Bean Supplement, p 148.

Cedrus *deodara* 'Prostrata'
The true plant is extremely rare if not lost to cultivation. Most plants under this name are in fact C. *d.* 'Pendula'.

Chamaecyparis *lawsoniana* 'Columnaris Glauca'
Plants under this name may be C. *l.* 'Columnaris' or a new illegitimately named cultivar.

Chamaecyparis *lawsoniana* 'Elegantissima'
This name has ben applied to two cultivars, 'E.' of Schelle and subsequently (illegitimately) 'E.' of Hillier.

Chamaecyparis *lawsoniana* 'Smithii'
May include some which are C. *l.* 'Darleyensis'.

Chamaecyparis *squarrosa* 'Argentea'
There are two plants of this name, one (valid) with variegated foliage, the other (illigitimate) with silvery foliage.

Cistus *hirsutus* and C. *h. psilosepalus*
These do not appear to be distinct in cultivation.

Cistus x *loretii*
Plants in cultivation under this name are usually forms of C. *dansereauii.*

Cistus x *purpureus*
Most plants in cultivation may be the cultivar 'Betty Taudevin'

Clematis *chrysocoma*
The true C. *chrysocoma* is a non-climbing erect plant with dense yellow down on the young growth, still uncommon in cultivation.

Clematis *heracleifolia* 'Campanile'
May be *C.*x *bonstedtii* 'C'.

Clematis *heracleifolia* 'Cote d'Azur'
May be C. x *bonstedtii* 'C. d'A.'

Clematis *jackmanii* 'Superba'
Plants under this name are usually C. 'Gipsy Queen'

Clematis *montana*
This name should refer to the white-flowered form only. Pink-flowered forms are referrable to C. *m.*var. *rubens.*

Colchicum 'Autumn Queen'
Entries here may refer to the slightly different *C.* 'Prinses Astrid'.

Cornus 'Norman Hadden'
See note in Bean Supplement. p 184.

Cotoneaster *buxifolius*
Plants in gardens under this name may be C. *astrophoros* or C. *lidjiangensis*

Cotoneaster *dammeri*
Plants sold under this name are usually C. *d.*'Major'.

Crataegus *coccinea*
Plants may be CC. *intricata, pedicellata* or *bilmoreana.*

Crocosmia x *crocosmiiflora 'Citronella'*
The true plant of this name has a dark eye and grows at Wisley. The plant usually offered may be more correctly *C.* 'Golden Fleece'.

Crocosmia x *crocosmiiflora 'Honey Angels'*
Also wrongly referred to as 'Citronella'. May be correctly 'Golden Fleece'.

Crocosmia x *crocosmiiflora 'Solfaterre'*
This the original spelling.

Crocus *cartwrightianus albus*
The plant offered is the true form and not C. *hadriaticus.*

Cuphea *platycentra*
Usually C. *ignea*, otherwise C. *microphylla.*

Cupressus *arizonica* var. *bonito*
See discussion in *International Conifer Register* Part 3.

Dendranthema 'Anastasia Variegata'
Despite its name, this seems to be derived from 'Mei-kyo' not 'Anastasia'

Dianthus 'Musgrave's Pink' (p)
This is the registered name of this white-flowered cultivar.

Dryopteris *affinis polydactyla*
This name covers at least three different clones.

Elymus *magellanicus*
Although this is a valid name Mr Roger Grounds has suggested that many plants might belong to a different, perhaps unnamed species.

Erigeron *salsuginosus*
Is a synonym of ASTER *sibiricus* but plants in cultivation under this name may be E. *peregrinus callianthemus*

Erodium *cheilanthifolium*
Most plants under this name are hybrids.

Erodium *glandulosum*
Plants under this name are often hybrids.

Erodium *guttatum*
Doubtfully in commerce, plants under this name are usually E. *heteradenum*, E. *cheilanthifolium* or hybrids.

Erodium *petraeum*
Many are hybrids, often E. 'Merstham Pink'.

Erysimum *cheiri* 'Baden-Powell'
Plant of uncertain origin differing from E. *c.* 'Harpur Crewe' only in its shorter stature.

Erysimum 'Variegatum'
This name may refer to any of the variegated cultivars of *Erysimum*.

Eucryphia 'Penwith'
The cultivar name 'Penwith' was originally given to a hybrid of E. *cordifolia* x E. *lucida*, not E. x *hillieri*.

Euphorbia *longifolia*
E. *cornigera* is sometimes offered under this name.

Euphorbia *wallichii*
Many plants are E. *longifolia* or E. *cornigera*.

Fagus *sylvatica* Copper Group / Purple Group
It is desirable to provide a name, Copper Group, for less richly coloured forms, used in historic landscapes before the purple clones appeared.

Fagus *sylvatica* 'Pendula'
This name refers to the Knap Hill clone, the most common weeping form in English gardens. Other clones occur, particularly in Ireland.

Forsythia 'Beatrix Farrand'
The true plant may not be in cultivation.

Fragaria *chiloensis* 'Variegata'
Most, possibly all, plants under this name are F. x *ananassa* 'Variegata'.

Freesia *refracta alba*
Plants may be F. *lactea* or F. *sparrmannii*.

Fuchsia
All names, except the following, marked N refer to more than one cultivar or species.

Fuchsia *decussata*
A hybrid form of F. *magellanica* is also offered under this name.

Fuchsia loxensis
For a comparison of the true species with the hybrids 'Speciosa' and 'Loxensis' commonly grown under this name, see Boulemier's *Check List* (2nd ed.) p.268.

Fuchsia *minimiflora*
Some plants may be F. x *bacillaris*.

Fuchia 'Pumila'
Plants under this name may be F. *magellanica* var. *pumila*.

Gentiana *cachemirica*
Most plants sold are not true to type.

Geum 'Borisii'
This name refers to cultivars of G. *coccineum* Sibthorp & Smith, especially G. *c.* 'Werner Arends' and not to G. x *borisii* Kelleper.

Halimium *alyssodes* and H. *halimifolium*
Plants under these names are sometimes H. x *pauanum or H.* x *santae*.

Hebe 'Amy'
May include entries which refer to H. 'Purple Queen'.

Hebe 'C P Raffill'
See note in Bean Supplement, p 265.

Hebe 'Carl Teschner'
See note in Bean Supplement, p 264.

Hebe 'Glaucophylla'
This plant is a green reversion of the hybrid H. 'Glaucophylla Variegata'.

Hedera *helix helix* 'Caenwoodiana'/ 'Pedata'
Some authorities consider these to be distinct cultivars whilst others think them different morphological forms of the same unstable clone.

Helleborus *orientalis*
Plants under this name are almost invariably hybrids and have been named H. x *hybridus*.

Hemerocallis *fulva* 'Kwanso', 'Kwanso Variegata', 'Flore Pleno' and 'Green Kwanso'
For a discussion of these plants see *The Plantsman* (Vol. 7 Pt. II).

Heuchera *micrantha* 'Palace Purple'
This cultivar name refers only to plants with deep purple-red foliage. Seed-raised plants of inferior colouring should not be offered under this name.

Hosta 'Marginata Alba'
This name is wrongly used both for H. *crispula* and, more commonly, for H. *fortunei* 'Albomarginata'.

Hosta *montana*
This name refers only to plants long grown in Europe, which differ from H. *elata*.

Hosta 'Venusta Variegated'
In spite of its name this plant is not a form of H. *venusta*.

Hypericum *fragile*
The true H. *fragile* is probably not available from British nurseries.

Hypericum *leschenaultii*
Plants are usually HH. *addingtonii*, *choisyana* or *augustinii*.

Ilex x *altaclerensis*
The argument for this correct spelling is given by Susyn Andrews (*The Plantsman* Vol.5, Pt.II) and is not superceded by the more recent but erroneous comments in the Supplement to Bean's *Trees and Shrubs*.

Iris *pallida* 'Variegata'
The white-variegated I. *p*. 'Argentea Variegata' is sometimes wrongly supplied under this name, which refers only to the gold-variegated form.

Lamium *maculatum* 'Chequers'
This name refers to two plants; the first, validly named, is a large and vigorous form of L. *maculatum* with a stripe down the centre of the leaf; the second is silver-leaved and very similar to L. *m*. 'Beacon Silver'.

Lavandula 'Alba'
May be either L. *angustifolia* 'Alba' or L. x *intermedia* 'Alba'

Lavandula 'Twickel Purple'
There are two cultivars called 'Twickel Purple', one a form of L. x *intermedia*, the other of L. *angustifolia*.

Lavatera *olbia & thuringiaca*
Although L. *olbia* is usually shrubby and L. *thuringiaca* usually herbaceous, both species are very variable. Cultivars formally ascribed to one species or the other are quite possibly hybrids and are listed by cultivar name alone pending the results of further research.

Leptospermum *flavescens*
This name is usually applied to plants correctly named L. *glaucescens*.

Lobelia
PRATIA (fruit a berry) and LOBELIA (fruit a capsule) are here united because L. *angulata* has fruits that are intermediate between a berry and a capsule (cf. PERNETTYA and GAULTHERIA). The two genera cannot therefore satisfactorily be separated.

Lonicera x *americana*
Most plants offered by nurseries under this name are correctly L. x *italica*. The true *americana* is still widely grown but is hard to propagate. See *The Plantsman* (Vol. 12 Pt. II).

Lonicera *periclymenum* 'Belgica'
L. x *italica* is sometimes offered under this name.

Lonicera *periclymenum* 'Serotina'
See note in Bean Supplement, p 315.

Lonicera *sempervirens* f. *sulphurea*
Plants in the British Isles usually a yellow-flowered form of L. *periclymenum*.

Macleaya *cordata*
Most, if not all plants offered are M. x *kewensis*.

Magnolia x *highdownensis*.
Believed to fall within the range of variation of M. *wilsonii*.

Magnolia *obovata*
This name refers to either M. *hypoleuca* or M. *officinalis*. The former is more common in cultivation.

Magnolia x *soulangeana* 'Burgundy'
Most plants under this name are M. x *s*. 'Purpliana'

Mahonia *pinnata*
Plants in cultivation are believed to belong to M. x *wagneri* 'Pinnacle'.

Malus *domestica* 'Dumeller's Seedling'
The phonetic spelling 'Dumelow's Seedling' contravenes the ICBN ruling on orthography, i.e. that commemorative names should retain the original spelling of the person's name.

Melissa *officinalis* 'Variegata'
The true cultivar of this name was striped with white.

Nemesia *fruticans*
The lavender blue clone 'Joan Wilder', described and illustrated in *The Hardy Plant*, Vol.14 No.1 pp 11-14, does not come true from seed; it may only be propagated from cuttings. Blue & lilac flowered plants including those grown as N. *foetens* and N. *umbonata* might be N. *caerulea*.

Papaver *orientale* 'Trkenlouis'/ 'Turkish Delight'
These names are definitely synonymous. However, other wrongly named cultivars are often sold as 'Turkish Delight'.

Pelargonium 'Beauty of Eastbourne'
This should not be confused with P. 'Eastbourne Beauty', a different cultivar.

Pelargonium 'Lass o'Gowrie'
The American plant of this name has pointed, not rounded leaf lobes.

Pelargonium *quercifolium*
Plants under this name are mainly hybrid. The true species has pointed, not rounded leaf lobes.

Penstemon 'Apple Blossom'
There are two cvs. of this name, one with narrow leaves.

Pernettya
Botanists now consider that PERNETTYA (fruit a berry) is not separable from GAULTHERIA (fruit a capsule) because in some species the fruit is intermediate bewteen a berry and a capsule. For a fuller explanation see D. Middleton *The Plantsman*. 1991 (Vol 12 Pt. III).

Picea *pungens* 'Glauca Pendula'
This name may be one of several blue cultivars.

Pinus *aristata*
May include plants referrable to P. *longaeva.*

Pinus *ayacahuite*
P. *a.* var. *veitchii* (syn P. *veitchii*) is occasionally sold under this name.

Pinus *nigra* 'Cebennensis Nana'
A doubtful and illegitimate name, probably a synonym for P. *n.* 'Nana'.

Polygonatum *odoratum* 'Variegatum'
Plants under this name be P. x *falcatum* 'Variegatum.

Polystichum *setiferum* 'Wollaston'
Incomplete name which may refer to either of two cultivars.

Populus *nigra italica*
See note in Bean Supplement, p 393.

Pratia
See Note under LOBELIA.

Prunus *cerasifera* 'Nigra'
Plants under this name may be referrable to P. *c.* 'Woodii'.

Prunus *laurocerasus* 'Castlewellan'
We are grateful to Dr Charles Nelson for informing us that the name 'Marbled White' is not valid because although it has priority of publication it does not have the approval of the originator who asked for it to be called 'Castlewellan'

Prunus *laurocerasus* 'Variegata'
The true 'Variegata', (marginal variegation), dates from 1811 but this name is also used for the relatively recent cultivar P. *l.* 'Castewellan'.

Prunus *serrulata* var. *pubescens*
See note in Bean Supplement, p 398.

Prunus x *subhirtella* 'Rosea'
Might be P. *pendula* var. *ascendens* 'Rosea', P. *p.* 'Pendula Rosea', or P. x *subhirtella* 'Autumnalis Rosea'.

Pyracantha 'Orange Charmer'
Possibly a synonym of 'Golden Charmer'

Rheum x *cultorum*
The name R. x *cultorum* was published without adequate description and must be abandoned in favour of the validly published R. x *hybridum.*

Rhododendron Azalea
All names marked N refer to more than one cultivar.

Rhododenron Hybrid Loderi/Kewense
The grex name Kewense has priority of 13 years over the name Loderi for hybrids of R. *griffithianum* x *fortunei* ssp. *fortunei* and would, under normal circumstances be considered correct. However, the RHS as IRA for Rhododendron has declared Loderi as a name to be conserved.

Rhus *typhina*
Linnaeus published both R. *typhina* and R. *hirta* as names for the same species but R. *hirta* has priority and should be used in preference to the newer name.

Robinia *hispida* 'Rosea'
This name is applied to R. *hispida*, (young shoots with bristles), R. *elliottii*, (young shoots with grey down) and R. *boyntonii*, (young shoot with neither bristles nor down).

Rosa
New cultivar names, the first three letters of which normally derive from the name of the breeder, are not given for ROSA. These are usually sold under Registered Trade Marks '®'. Roses often known by common names, eg. Rosa Mundi, Hume's Blush are referred to botanical names as given in Bean.

Rosa *gentiliana*
Plants may be RR. *multiflora* 'Wilsonii', *multiflora* var. *cathayensis*, *henryi* or a hybrid.

Rosa 'Gros Choux de Hollande' (Bb)
It is doubtful if this name is correctly applied.

Rosa 'Maiden's Blush'
R. 'Great Maiden's Blush' may be supplied under this name.

Rosa 'Marchesa Boccella'
For a discussion on the correct identity of this rose see *Heritage Rose Foundation News* Oct 1989 & Jan 1990.

Rosa 'Professeur Emile Perrot'
For a discussion on the correct identity of this rose see *Heritage Roses* Nov 1991.

Rosa Sweetheart ®
This is not the same as the Sweetheart Rose, a common name for R. 'Cécile Brunner'.

Salix *alba* 'Tristis'
This cultivar should not be confused with S. *tristis*, which is now correctly S. *humilis.* Although this cultivar is distinct in European gardens, most plants under this name in the British Isles are S. x *sepulcralis* var. *chrysocoma.*

Salix x *smithiana*
See note in Bean Supplement, p 486.

Salvia *officinalis* 'Aurea'
S. *o. aurea* is a rare form of the common sage with leaves entirely of gold. It is represented in cultivation by the cultivar 'Kew Gold'. The plant usually offered as S. *o.* 'Aurea' is the gold variegated sage S. *o.* 'Icterina'.

Salvia *sclarea* var. *turkestanica*
Plants in gardens under this name are not S. *s. turkistaniana* of Mottet.

Sambucus *nigra* 'Aurea'
Plants under this name are usually not S. *nigra.*

Sedum *nevii*
The true species is not in cultivation. Plants under this name are usually either S. *glaucophyllum*, occasionally S. *beyrichianum.*

Sedum *spathulifolium* 'Cape Blanco'
This is the correct spelling.

Sempervivum *arachnoideum tomentosum*
Entries here may include plants classified as *S.* 'Hookeri'.

Skimmia *japonica* 'Foremanii'
The true cultivar, which belongs to S. *japonica* Rogersii Group, is believed to be lost to cultivation. Plants offered under this name are usually S. *japonica* 'Veitchii'.

Sophora *prostrata*
Plants may be the hybrid S. 'Little Baby'.

Staphylea *holocarpa* var. *rosea*
This botanical variety has woolly leaves. The cultivar 'Rosea', with which it is often confused, does not.

Stewartia *ovata* var. *grandiflora.*
Most, possibly all, plants available from British nurseries under this name are not true to name but are derived from the improved Nymans form.

Thymus 'Silver Posie'
The cultivar name 'Silver Posie' is applied to several different plants, not all of them T. *vulgaris.*

Tricyrtis Hototogisu
This is the common name applied generally to all Japanese Tricyrtis and specifically to T. *hirta.*

Tricyrtis *macropoda*
This name has been used for at least five different species.

Uncinia *rubra*
This name is loosely applied to UU. *egmontiana* and *unciniata.*

Verbena 'Kemerton'
Origin unknown, not from Kemerton.

Viburnum *opulus* 'Fructu Luteo'
See note below.

Viburnum *opulus* 'Xanthocarpum'
Entries here include the closely similar V. *o.* 'Fructu Luteo'.

Viburnum *plicatum*
Entries may include the "Snowball" form, V. *plicatum* 'Sterile'.

Classification of Genera

CHRYSANTHEMUM

(Now correctly DENDRANTHEMA)

(By the Floral Committee of the National Chrysanthemum Society)

Indoor Cultivars

Section 1 LARGE EXHIBITION

Section 2 MEDIUM EXHIBITION

Section 3 INCURVED
- (a) Large-flowered
- (b) Medium-flowered
- (c) Small-flowered

Section 4 REFLEXED
- (a) Large-flowered
- (b) Medium-flowered
- (c) Small-flowered

Section 5 INTERMEDIATE
- (a) Large-flowered
- (b) Medium-flowered
- (c) Small-flowered

Section 6 ANEMONES
- (a) Large-flowered
- (b) Medium-flowered
- (c) Small-flowered

Section 7 SINGLES
- (a) Large-flowered
- (b) Medium-flowered
- (c) Small-flowered

Section 8 POMPONS
- (a) True Poms
- (b) Semi-Poms

Section 9 SPRAYS
- (a) Anemones
- (b) Pompons
- (c) Reflexed
- (d) Singles
- (e) Intermediate
- (f) Spider, Quills, Spoons and any other type

Section 10
- (a) Spiders
- (b) Quills
- (c) Spoons

Section 11 ANY OTHER TYPES

Section 12
- (a) Charms
- (b) Cascades

October-flowered Chrysanthemums

Section 13 INCURVED
- (a) Large-flowered
- (b) Medium-flowered
- (c) Small-flowered

Section 14 REFLEXED
- (a) Large-flowered
- (b) Medium-flowered
- (c) Small-flowered

Section 15 INTERMEDIATE
- (a) Large-flowered
- (b) Medium-flowered
- (c) Small-flowered

Section 16 LARGE OCTOBER FLOWERING

Section 17 SINGLES
- (a) Large-flowered
- (b) Medium-flowered
- (c) Small-flowered

Section 18 POMPONS
- (a) True Poms
- (b) Semi-poms

Section 19 SPRAYS
- (a) Anemones
- (b) Pompons
- (c) Reflexed
- (d) Singles
- (e) Intermediate
- (f) Spider, Quills, Spoons and any other type

Section 20 ANY OTHER TYPES

Early-flowering Chrysanthemums

Outdoor Cultivars

Section 23 INCURVED
- (a) Large-flowered
- (b) Medium-flowered
- (c) Small-flowered

Section 24 REFLEXED
- (a) Large-flowered
- (b) Medium-flowered
- (c) Small-flowered

Section 25 INTERMEDIATE

(a)	Large-flowered
(b)	Medium-flowered
(c)	Small-flowered

Section 26 ANEMONE

(a)	Large-flowered
(b)	Medium-flowered

Section 27 SINGLES

(a)	Large-flowered
(b)	Medium-flowered

Section 28 POMPONS

(a)	True Poms
(b)	Semi-poms

Section 29 SPRAYS

(a)	Anemones
(b)	Pompons
(c)	Reflexed
(d)	Singles
(e)	Intermediate
(f)	Spider, Quills, Spoons and any other type
K	Korean
Rub	Rubellum

Section 30 ANY OTHER TYPE

BEGONIA

C	Cane
R	Rex
S	Semperflorens
T	x tuberhybrida (Tuberous)

CLEMATIS

(A)	Alpina Group (Section Atragene)
(D)	Diversifolia Group
(F)	Florida Group
(Fo)	Fosteri Group
(J)	Jackmanii Group
(L)	Languinosa Group
(P)	Patens Group
(T)	Texensis Group
(Ta)	Tangutica Group
(Vt)	Viticella Group

DAHLIAS

(By The National Dahlia Society)

1	Single	Sin
2	Anemone-flowered	Anem
3	Collerette	Col
4B	Waterlily, large	LWL
4C	Waterlily, medium	MWL
4D	Waterlily, small	SWL
4E	Waterlily, miniature	MinWL
5A	Decorative, giant	GD
5B	Decorative, large	LD
5C	Decorative, medium	MD
5D	Decorative, small	SD
5E	Decorative, miniature	MinD
6A	Small ball	SBa
6B	Miniature ball	MinBa
7	Pompon	Pom
8A	Cactus, giant	GC
8B	Cactus, large	LC
8C	Cactus, medium	MC
8D	Cactus, small	SC
8E	Cactus, miniature	MinC
9A	Semi-cactus, giant	GSC
9B	Semi-cactus, large	LSC
9C	Semi-cactus, medium	MSC
9D	Semi-cactus, small	SSC
9E	Semi-cactus, miniature	MinSC
10	Miscellaneous	Misc
-	Orchid flowering	O
-	Botanical	B
-	Dwarf bedding	DwB
-	Fimbriated	Fim
	Lilliput	Lil

DIANTHUS

(p)	Pinks
(p,a)	Annual pinks
(pf)	Perpetual flowering
(b)	Border
(m)	Malmaison

GLADIOLUS

(B)	Butterfly
(Colv)	Colvillei
(G)	Giant
(L)	Large
(M)	Medium
(Min)	Miniature
(N)	Nanus
(P)	Primulinus
(S)	Small
(Tub)	Tubergenii

HYDRANGEA macrophylla

H	Hortensia
L	Lacecap

IRIS

(AB)	Arilbred
(BB)	Border Bearded
(Cal-Sib)	Series Californicae x Series Sibiricae
(CH)	Californian Hybrid
(DB)	Dwarf Bearded
(Dut)	Dutch
(IB)	Intermediate Bearded

(MDB)	Miniature Dwarf Bearded
(MTB)	Miniature Tall Bearded
(SDB)	Standard Dwarf Bearded
(Sp)	Spuria
(TB)	Tall Bearded

LILIUM

'International Lily Register' (Third Edition)
The Royal Horticultural Society 1982

I	Hybrids derived from LL.*lancifolium cernuum, davidii, leichtlinii,* x *maculatum,* x *hollandicum, amabile, pumilum, concolor,* & *bulbiferum*
I(a)	Early flowering with upright flowers, single or in an umbel
I(b)	Outward facing flowers
I(c)	Pendant flowers
II	Hybrids of Martagon type, one parent having been a form of LL. *martagon* or *hansonii*
III	Hybrids from LL. *candidum, chalcedonicum* and other related European species (ex. L. *martagon*)
IV	Hybrids of American species
V	Hybrids derived from LL. *longiflorum* & *formosanum*
VI	Hybrid Trumpet Lilies & Aurelian Hybrids from Asiatic species, incl. L. *henryi* but excluding those from LL. *auratum, speciosum, japonicum* & *rubellum*
VI(a)	with trumpet-shaped flowers
VI(b)	with bowl-shaped & outward-facing
VI(c)	with pendant flowers
VI(d)	with flat, star-shaped flowers
VII	Hybrids of Far Eastern species as, LL *auratum, speciosum, rubellum,* & *japonicum*
VII(a)	with trumper-shape flowers
VII(b)	with bowl-shaped flowers
VII(c)	with flat flowers
VII(d)	with recurved flowers
VIII	All Hybrids not in another division
IX	All species & their varieties & forms

NARCISSUS

Classification by The Royal Horticultural Society (Revised 1977)

Division 1	Trumpet
Division 2	Large-cupped
Division 3	Small-cupped
Division 4	Double
Division 5	Triandrus
Division 6	Cyclamineus
Division 7	Jonquilla
Division 8	Tazetta
Division 9	Poeticus
Division 10	Species and wild forms & hybrids
Division 11	Split-corona
Division 12	Miscellaneous

NYMPHAEA (Waterlilies)

H	Hardy
D	Day-blooming
N	Nigth-blooming
T	Tropical

PELARGONIUM

A	Angel
C	Coloured foliage (in combination)
Ca	Cactus (in combination)
d	Double (in combination)
Dec	Decorative
Dw	Dwarf
DwI	Dwarf Ivy-leaved
Fr	Frutetorum
I	Ivy-leaved
Min	Miniature or Dwarf
MinI	Miniature Ivy-leaved
R	Regal
Sc	Scented-leaved
St	Stellar (in combination)
T	Tulip (in combination)
U	Unique
Z	Zonal

PRIMULA

(1)	Amethystina
(2)	Auricula
(3)	Bullatae
(4)	Candelabra
(5)	Capitatae
(6)	Carolinella
(7)	Cortusoides
(8)	Cuneifolia
(9)	Denticulata
(10)	Dryadifolia
(11)	Farinosae
(12)	Floribundae
(13)	Grandis
(14)	Malacoides
(15)	Malvacea
(16)	Minutissimae
(17)	Muscarioides
(18)	Nivales
(19)	Obconica
(20)	Parryi
(21)	Petiolares
(22)	Pinnatae
(23)	Pycnoloba
(24)	Reinii
(25)	Rotundifolia

(26) Sikkimensis
(27) Sinenses
(28) Soldenelloideae
(29) Souliei
(30) Vernales
(A) Alpine Auricula
(B) Border Auricula
(D) Double
(Poly) Polyanthus
(Prim) Primrose
(S) Show Auricula

RHODODENDRON (Azalea)

(E) Evergreen
(G) Ghent
(K) Knaphill or Exbury
(M) Mollis
(O) Occidentalis
(R) Rustica
(Vs) Viscosa

RHODODENDRON

(A) Azalea species
(EA) Evergreen azalea species

ROSA

(A) Alba
(Bb) Bourbon
(Bs) Boursault
(Ce) Centifolia
(Ch) China
(Cl) Climbing
(Co) Compacta
(D) Damask
(DPo) Damask Portland
(F) Floribunda or Cluster-flowered
(G) Gallica
(Ga) Garnette
(GC) Ground Cover
(HScB) Hybrid Scots Briar
(HSwB) Hybrid Sweet Briar
(HM) Hybrid Musk
(HP) Hybrid Perpetual
(HT) Hybrid Tea or Large-flowered
(Min) Miniature
(Mo) Moss
(N) Noisette
(Patio) Patio or Miniature Floribunda
(Poly) Polyanthus
(Ra) Rambler
(Ru) Rugosa
(S) Shrub
(T) Tea

SAXIFRAGA

1 Micranthes
2 Hirculus
3 Gymnopera
4 Diptera
5 Trachyphyllum
6 Xanthizoon
7 Aizoonia
8 Porophyllum
9 Porophyrion
10 Miscopetalum
11 Saxifraga
12 Trachyphylloïdes
13 Cymbalaria
14 Discogyne

TULIPA

'Revised Classification of Tulips' by Koninklijke Algemeene Vereening voor Bloembollenculture 1981

Early Flowering

1 Single Early
2 Double Early

Mid-Season

3 Triumph
4 Darwin Hybrid

Late Flowering

5 Single Late (incl. Darwin)
6 Lily-Flowered
7 Fringed
8 Viridiflora
9 Rembrandt
10 Parrot
11 Double Late

Species and their Hybrids

12 Kaufmanniana
13 Fosteriana
14 Greigii

VIOLA

(C) Cornuta hybrid
(dVt) Double Violet
(ExVa) Exhibition Viola
(FP) Fancy Pansy
(SP) Show Pansy
(T) Tricolor
(Va) Viola
(Vt) Violet
(Vtta) Violetta

VITIS

B Black
G Glasshouse
O Outdoor
R Red
W White

Acknowledgements

For the compilation of this edition, we are particularly indebted to Messrs J Carter, G Dunlop, G Hutchins, J Irons, A C Leslie, N Noblett, R Poulett, G Spencer, G S Thomas, T Weston, Mrs K Dryden, Mrs J Hewitt, Mrs E Parker-Jervis, Miss E Strangman & Sandra Bond for many helpful comments on plant nomenclature. Views on ivy names have come from P Q Rose, R Whitehouse, Hazel Key and Alison Rutherfords. The opinions of the members of the Horticultural Taxonomy Group on both general and particular points of taxonomy have been extremely useful; Piers Trehane has been a much valued 'sounding-board' for treatments of some of the most vexing plant names and a source of much information. The Royal Horticultural Society's Technical Liaison Officer, Mike Pollock, has kept me informed of research on names of plants trialled at Wisley, particularly *Argyranthemum, Artemisia, Aster* and *Penstemon*. Once again, I am most grateful to Hatton Gardner for so diligently comparing names in **The Plant Finder** with those in some of the major encyclopaedic works on garden plants and bringing differences to my attention.

Alchemilla	Dr. S M Walters ('90)
Australian Plants	G Butler, Registrar, Australian Cultivar Registration Authority. ('89)
Bamboos	D McClintock ('90-'93)
Bulbs	Ing. J R Stuurman, Royal General Bulbgrowers Society, Holland. ('89)
Camellia	T J Savige, The International Registrar, New South Wales & J Gallagher, International Camellia Society, Dorset ('90 & '93)
Cimicifuga	J Compton ('92)
Conifers	J Lewis, The International Registrar, RHS, Wisley. ('90 & '93) H J Welch, World Conifer Data Pool, Devon. ('90-'93)
Cotoneaster	Jeanette Fryer, NCCPG National Collection holder. ('91 & '92)
Dahlia	D Pycraft, The International Registrar, Royal Horticultural Soc.('90 & '91)
Delphinium	Dr A C Leslie, The International Registrar, Royal Horticultural Society ('90 & '91)
Dianthus	Dr A C Leslie, The International Registrar, Royal Horticultural Society ('90-'93)
Erodium	J Ross. ('90)
Euphorbia	R Turner. ('91)
Ferns	P Barnes, Royal Horticultural Society. ('89)
Fuchsia	Mrs D A Logan, The International Registrar, American Fuchsia Soc. ('91)
Gesneriaceae	J D Dates, The International Registrar, American Gloxinia and Gesneriad Society. ('91)
Gladiolus	F N Franks ('92)
Heathers	D McClintock ('92)
Hedera	P Q Rose & Mrs H Key. ('91, '93). Alison Rutherford ('92, '93)'
Helianthemum	H Gardner, formerly of Hilliers Arboretum ('88 -'91)
Hoya	D Kent. ('91)
Ilex	Susyn Andrews ('92, '93)
Jovibarba & Sempervivum	P J Mitchell, The International Registrar, The Sempervivum Society. ('91-'93)
Kalmia	R A Jaynes, The International Registrar, Broken Arrow Nursery, Connecticut, USA. ('89)
Lavandula	S Andrews ('92)
Mentha	Dr R Harley, Royal Botanic Gardnes, Kew ('90)
Narcissus	Mrs Sally Kington, The International Registrar, RHS Wisley ('90-'93)
Oleaceae	P S Green, Royal Botanic Gardens, Kew. ('89)
Passiflora	D Kent. ('91)
Pelargonium	Mrs H Key. ('91-'93)
Pelargonium ssp.	Mrs D Miller ('93)
Pelargonium	Dr A Hamilton
Phormium	L J Metcalf, The International Registrar, New Zealand. ('90 & '91)
Polygonum (Persicaria)	D H Kent. ('90)
Rhododendron	Dr A C Leslie, The International Registrar, RHS Wisley. ('90-'93)
Salix	Dr R D Meikle ('93)
Salvia	J Compton ('92)

To all these, as well as the many readers and nurseries who have also made comments and suggestions, we are, once again, sincerely grateful.

Collectors' References

AB&S	Archibald, Blanchard & Salmon. Morocco 1980's
AC&H	Apold, Cox & Hutchinson. 1962 expedition to NE Turkey
ACL	A C Leslie
AC&W	Albury, Cheese & Watson
AGS/ES	Alpine Garden Society expedition to Sikkim
AGSJ	Alpine Garden Society expedition to Japan
AL&JS	Sharman & Leslie. Yugoslavia 1990
A&L	Ala & Lancaster expedition to N Iran 1972
B	Len Beer
BB	B Bartholemew
BC&W	Beckett, Cheese & Watson
BL&M	Beer, Lancaster & Morris
B&L	Brickell & Leslie, China
BL&M	Beer, Lancaster & Morris. 1971 NE Nepal
BM	Brian Mathew
B&M	Chris Brickell & Brian Mathew
BM&W	Binns, Mason & Wright
B&S	Peter Bird & Mike Salmon
BSBE	Bowles Scholarship Botanical Expedition
CC	Chris Chadwell
CC&MR	Chris Chadwell & Magnus Ramsey 1985 to Kashmir, 1989 to Himachal Pradesh & W Himalaya
CDB	C D Brickell
CD&R	Compton, D'Arcy & Rix. China & Drakensburg
CE&H	Christian, Elliott & Hoog. Yugoslavia & Greece 1982
CH&M	Cox, Hutchinson & MacDonald
CL	Dr C Lovell
CLD	Kew, Edinburgh & RHS. China 1990
CM&W	M Cheese, J Mitchel & J Watson
Cooper	Roland Edgar Cooper (1890-1962)
C&Mc	Chadwell & McKelvie 1990/1/2. To Nepal & W. Himalaya
C&H	Cox & Hutchinson. 1965 expediton to Assam, NE Frontier & N Bengal
C&R	Christian & Roderick. (California, Oregon, Washington).
C&W	Cheese & Watson
CT	Carla Teune
DF	Derek Fox
DS&T	Drake, Sharman & Thompson. Turkey 1989
EGM	E G Millais
EKB	E K Balls
EM	East Malling Research Station. Clonal selection scheme
EMR	E Martyn Rix
F	George Forrest (1873-1932)
Farrer	Reginald Farrer (1880-1920)
FMB	F M Bailey
F&W	Anita Flores & John Watson. Chile 1992
G	M Gardner
GS	George Sherriff (1898-1967)
G&K	M Gardner & S Knees
G-W&P	Grey-Wilson & Phillips
G&P	Gardner & Page, Chile '92
Guitt	Prof. G G Guittonneau
Guiz	Guizhou Expedition 1985
H	Paul Huggins. Oxford University Expedition to the Tehri-Garwal, Central Himalaya
Harry Smith	Karl August Harald Smith (1889-1971)
H&B	Hilliard & Burtt
HM&S	Halliwell, Mathew & Smallcombe
H&W	Hedge & Wendelbo. 1969 to Afghanistan
JCA	J C Archibald
JLS	J L Sharman. USA 1988
JR	J Russell
JRM	Dr John Marr. Expedition to Greece & Turkey 1975
JW	J Watson
K	G Kirkpatrick
KBE	Kashmir Botanical Expedition, Chadwell, Howard, Powell & Wright 1983
K&E	Kew & Edinburgh. Chine 1989
K&Mc	George Kirkpatrick and Ron McBeath.
KR	Keith Rushforth
KW	Frank Kingdon-Ward (1885-1958)
L	Roy Lancaster
LA	Long Ashton Research Station. Clonal Selection scheme.
L&S	Ludlow (1885-1972) & G Sherriff
LS&E	Ludlow, Sherriff & Elliott
LS&H	Ludlow, Sherriff & Hicks, 1949 to Bhutan
LS&T	Ludlow Sherriff & Taylor. 1938 to SE Tibet
Mac&W	MacPhail & Watson
McB	Ron McBeath
McLaren	Henry McLaren, 2nd Baron Aberconway (1879-1953)
MS	Mike Salmon
MSF	M S Fillan. Tenerife 1988, South Korea 1989
NS	Nick Turland (Northside Seeds)
M&T	B Mathew & J Tomlinson
PB	Peter Bird
PD	Peter Davis

PF	Paul Furse
PJC	P J Christian
PJC&AH	P J Christian & A Hoog. Greece & Yugoslavia 1985
Pras	Milan Prasil
PS&W	Polunin, Sykes & Williams. 1952 W. Nepal
P&W	Polastri & Watson
R	J F C Rock (1884-1962)
RV	Richard Valder
SBEC	Sino-British expedition to Cangshan, SW China (1981)
Sch	A D Schilling
SEP	Swedish expedition to Pakistan
S&B	Mike Salmon & John Blanchard
SF	S Forde, Bhutan Oct '90
SH	Sheila & Spencer Hannay. Lesotho & NW Cape Province 1989 & '91
S&L	Mike Salmon & Dr Chris Lovell
SS&W	Stainton, Sykes & Williams 1954 to Central Nepal
T	Nigel Taylor
TSS	T Spring-Smyth
T&K	Taylor & Knees
TW	Tony Weston
USNA	United States National Arboretum
VH	Professor Vernon Heywood
W	E H Wilson, (1876-1930)
W A	E H Wilson, for Arnold Arboretum - (1906-1919)
WM	Will McLewin.
Wr	David & Anke Wraight
W V	E H Wilson, for Veitch - (1899-1905)
Yu	Tse Tsun Yu (1908-1986)

NOTE: Collectors' numbers which do not appear to relate to the species listed are given an asterisk after the number. For the Collections of Joseph Rock, a number of nurseries quote United States Department of Agriculture numbers rather than Rock's own collection number. We have tried to make clear which of the two numbers is quoted and to give Rock's own numbers wherever possible.

PLANT DIRECTORY

ABELIA † (Caprifoliaceae)

chinensis	CB&S CBow CChu CCla CGre CPle SGil SHil SLon SPer SReu WHCG WPat WSHC WWat
'Edward Goucher'	CB&S CBot CBow CChu CCla CDoC CFis CPle CSco CWit EBre ELan ESma LBre MGos SHil SPla WOld WPat WWeb
engleriana	CPle CSam ECtt EPla NWyt SGil WWat
floribunda	CB&S CBot CBow CChu CDoC CGle CLan CMHG CPle CSco CTrw EBre ELan IMal IOrc LBre MRav SHer SHil SPer SSpi SSta WAbe WBod WSHC WWat
graebneriana	CHan CPle
§ x ***grandiflora***	Widely available
– 'Aurea'	See A. x ***g.*** 'Goldsport'
– 'Francis Mason' (v)	CB&S CBra CMHG CPle CSco EBre ELan ENot IJoh IOrc LBre LHop MBal MBri MPla MWat NKay SApp SBla SFis SHBN SPer SReu SSpi SSta WBod WDin WOld WPat WSHC
– 'Gold Strike'	See A. x ***g.*** 'Goldsport'
§ – 'Goldsport'	CAbb CB&S CCla CDoC CHal EBre IOrc LBre MPla SBod SCro WPat WWat
– 'Prostrata'	CBot WHCG
– 'Variegata'	CLan WWat WWin
rupestris hort.	See A. x ***grandiflora***
– Lindley	See A. ***chinensis***
schumannii	CB&S CBot CBra CChu CGle CLan CMHG CPle CSam CSco EBre ELan ENot LBre SDry SHBN SLon SPer SPla SReu SSta WAbe WHCG WOld WPat WSHC
triflora	CBot CHan CPle EPla SPla SSta WPat WWat

ABELIOPHYLLUM (Oleaceae)

distichum	CB&S CBot CBow CChu CCor CHan CMHG CPle CSco ELan ENot GWht MBri MUlv NWyt SGil SHBN SHil SPer SPla SReu SSpi SSta WBod WPat WSHC WWat WWin
– Roseum Group	CB&S CCor CPMA CSam ELan MPla MUlv SSpi

ABELMOSCHUS (Malvaceae)
See Plant Deletions

ABIES † (Pinaceae)

alba	CDoC LCon MBar WDin
– 'Compacta'	CKen
– 'Green Spiral'	CKen
¶ – 'Pendula'	LPan
¶ – 'Tortuosa'	CKen
amabilis	WFro
balsamea f. ***balsamea***	EHar WCoo WFro
– f. ***hudsonia***	CDoC CKen CMac EHul ENHC GDra IOrc LCon LLin MBal MBar MGos NHar NHol SIng SLim SPla WDin WThu
– 'Nana'	CKen EBlo EBre EHul IDai IJoh LBee LBre LCon MBri MPla NHar NRoo SPer WAbe WDin WStI
– 'Prostrata'	LCon
bornmuelleriana	See A, ***nordmanniana equi-trojani***
– 'Archer'	CKen
brachyphylla dwarf form	See A. ***homolepis*** 'Prostrata'
bracteata	ISea LCon WCoo
cephalonica	EHar LCon
§ – 'Meyer's Dwarf'	EBre EHar LBre LCon LLin MBar
I – 'Nana'	See A. ***c.*** 'Meyer's Dwarf'
concolor	CDoC CGre EHar GRei IJoh IOrc ISea LBee LCon MBal MBar NWea SPer WCoo WDin WFro
– 'Archer's Dwarf'	CKen MGos
§ – 'Argentea'	LCon LPan
– 'Candicans'	See A. ***c.*** 'Argentea'
§ – 'Compacta'	CBra CKen EBre LBre LCon LLin MBal MBar MGos SHil SLim SSta
– 'Fagerhult'	CKen
– 'Gable's Weeping'	CKen
– 'Glauca'	See A. ***c.*** 'Violacea'
– 'Glauca Compacta'	See A. ***c.*** 'Compacta'
¶ – 'Hillier Broom'	CKen
– var. ***lowiana*** 'Creamy'	CKen
– 'Masonic Broom'	CKen
– 'Piggelmee'	CKen
§ – 'Violacea'	CBra EBre LBre LCon MAsh MBar MBri MGos SSta
– 'Wattezii'	CKen LCon LLin MAsh
delavayi var. ***delavayi***	IBar IOrc
– – Fabri Group	See A. ***fabri***
– 'Headfort'	MBar NHol
¶ – 'Inverleith'	CKen
¶ – 'Major Neishe'	CKen
ernestii	See A. ***recurvata e.***
§ ***fabri***	WCoo
fraseri	LCon MBal
– 'Klein's Nest'	CKen
grandis	CB&S EHar ENot GRei IOrc LCon MBar NWea SHBN SMad WDin WMou
– 'Compacta'	CKen
holophylla	CMCN LCon WCoo
homolepis	ISea LCon MBlu NWea WCoo
§ – 'Prostrata'	CKen
koreana	Widely available
– 'Aurea'	See A. ***k.*** 'Flava'
¶ – 'Blaue Zwo'	CKen
– 'Compact Dwarf'	LLin MGos SSta WAbe
§ – 'Flava'	CDoC CKen EBre GAri LBre LCon MBar MBri NHol
¶ – 'Golden Wonder'	COtt
¶ – 'Inverleith'	CKen
– 'Nisbet'	CKen LCon

– 'Piccolo'	CKen
– 'Silberlocke'	CBra CKen EBre GAri IOrc LBre LCon LLin MBar MBri MGos NHol SEng SHil SLim SPer SSta
¶ – 'Silberperl'	CKen
¶ – 'Silver Show'	CKen
– 'Starker's Dwarf'	CKen
lasiocarpa	LCon WDin
– var. ***arizonica***	LCon SSta
– 'Compacta'	CDoC CKen CMac COtt EBlo EBre EHar EHul IOrc LBee LBre LCon LLin LPan MAsh MBar MBri MGos NHar NHol SLim SMad SSta WDin WStI
– 'Glauca'	See A. ***concolor*** 'Violacea'
– 'Globe'	CKen
– 'Green Globe'	CKen LCon
– 'Kenwith Blue'	CKen
magnifica	EHar EHul LCon LPan WCoo
I – 'Nana'	CKen
marocana	See A. ***pisapo marocana***
nephrolepis	CMCN LRHS
nobilis	See A. ***procera***
nordmanniana	CDoC EHar EHul LBuc LCon LPan MBal MBar MGos NWea SLim WDin WFro
I – 'Barabit's Compacta'	MBar
§ – ssp. ***equi-trojani***	LCon
– 'Golden Spreader'	CKen EBlo EBre LBre LCon MAsh MBar MGos NHol SLim SSta
¶ – 'Pendula'	LPan
I – 'Reflexa'	LPan
numidica	LPan
– 'Lawrenceville'	LCon
– 'Pendula'	CKen
pindrow	CGre EHal
pinsapo	EHar LCon MBar
– 'Aurea'	CKen EBre LBre WThu
– 'Glauca'	CDoC EHar ELan IOrc LCon LPan MBar MBlu MBri NHol SHil WDin
– 'Hamondii'	CKen
I – 'Horstmann'	CKen MBar
– 'Kelleriis'	LCon
¶ – var. ***marocana***	CGre
§ ***procera***	CDoC CGre EHul GAri GRei IDai ISea LCon MBal MBar NWea STre WCoo WDin WMou
– 'Blaue Hexe'	CKen
– 'Compacta'	See A. ***p.*** 'Prostrata'
– 'Glauca'	CDoC CMac EBre EHar IOrc LBre LCon LPan MBar MBri MGos NHar SLim
– 'Glauca Prostrata'	EBlo EBre EHul ENHC GAri IOrc LBee LBre LPan MAsh MBal MBar MGos NHol SSta WDin
– 'Mount Hood'	CKen
§ – 'Prostrata'	LCon
¶ ***recurvata*** var. ***ernestii***	CMCN LCon
¶ ***religiosa***	GAri
sachalinensis	LCon
sibirica	NWea
spectabilis	GWht WCoo
squamata	CMCN LCon
sutchuenensis	See A. ***fargesii***
veitchii	GRei IOrc LCon MBar NWea
– 'Hedergott'	CKen
– 'Heine'	CKen

ABROMEITIELLA (Bromeliaceae)
See Plant Deletions

ABRONIA (Nyctaginaceae)
See Plant Deletions

ABROTANELLA (Compositae)
See Plant Deletions

ABUTILON † (Malvaceae)

'Amsterdam'	ERea
'Ashford Red'	CBot CCan CTre EBre IBlr IJoh IOrc LAbb LBre SLMG WOMN WOld
'Boule de Neige'	CBot CBrk CGre ERea LRHS MBri SLMG
'Canary Bird'	CB&S CBar CBot CBow CBrk CGre CPle CSun CTre CTro ERea LGre LHop MBri NWyt SHBN SLMG
'Cannington Carol' (v)	CAbb CBrk CCan CSun ERea
'Cannington Peter' (v)	CBrk CCan CHal ERea
¶ 'Cannington Sonia' (v)	ERea
¶ 'Cerise Queen'	CCan
'Cloth of Gold'	EPla IJoh
'Fireball'	CBrk EPla LGre LHop
¶ 'Glenroy Snowdrift'	MBal
globosum	See A. × ***hybridum***
'Golden Fleece'	CKni ERea GCal IBlr
'Hinton Seedling'	CBow CBrk CDoC CTre EMil LHop MUlv SLMG WEas
§ × ***hybridum***	CTro MBri MNew
¶ ***indicum***	GCra
'Kentish Belle'	CAbb CB&S CBot CBra CCan CLan CMHG CPle CSco CTre EBre ENot IOrc ISea LBre NTow SBra SHBN SLMG SPer WWye
'Louise Marignac'	CBrk CCan CSun
'Master Michael'	CBow CCla CKni EMil ERea
megapotamicum	Widely available
¶ – 'Compactum'	CBrk
¶ – 'Joy Bells'	CBrk
– 'Variegatum'	CB&S CBot CBow CBrk CCla CLan CSco CWit ECtt ELan GCal GCra IBar IBlr IOrc LHil MBri NWyt SBra SHBN SLMG SLon
– 'Wisley Red'	CBow CDoC CTre
× ***milleri***	CB&S CBot CCla CGre CSun ELan ERea IBar IOrc SBra SHBN WSHC
– 'Variegatum'	CB&S CBrk CCan CDoC CKni SHBN SLMG
'Nabob'	CBrk CCan CGre CHal CSun CTre CTro CWit ERea LHop LRHS MBri SLMG WEas WOld
'Orange King'	CB&S
'Patrick Synge'	CBrk CGre CMHG CSco CSun CTro ERav ERea LBlm LGre SLMG
§ ***pictum***	ERea MBri
– 'Thompsonii' (v)	CBot CBrk CHal CSun CTro EFol ERea IBlr ISea LHil SLMG
*– ***variegatum***	EFol
¶ 'Pink Lady'	CB&S EMil

'Savitzii' (v)	CB&S CBar CBot CBrk ERea IReg LHil SRms
sellowianum var. *marmoratum*	ERea SLMG
'Souvenir de Bonn'	CBar CBrk CGre CSun ERea IBlr
striatum	See A. ***pictum***
x *suntense*	CB&S CBow CCan CCla CGle CHEx CMHG CPle CSco CWSG EBre ELan ERav LAbb LBre MBal NRar SHer SLMG SPer SSta WBod WEas WPat WWye
– 'Jermyns'	CAbb CCla CDoC CPMA CWSG CWit EBre ECtt ISea LBre LGre MGos MUlv NWyt SFis SGil SHer SHil SMrm SSta WWat
– 'Violetta'	CAbb CBot CTre NSti NWyt SPer
theophrasti	NSal WHer
vitifolium	CB&S CBot CCan CCla CFis CGle GWht IOrc LHop MNew SHer SPer WCru WWat WWin WWye
– *album*	CAbb CB&S CBot CFis CGle CMHG CSco CTrw CWit ELan ERav IMal LHop MBal NRar NTow SPer SSpi SSta WBod WSHC WWat WWye
– 'Ice Blue'	CBot
– 'Tennant's White'	CAbP CBot CCan CGre LGre NWyt SHBN SHil
– 'Veronica Tennant'	CB&S CCan CGle ERav ISea LGre NSti NWyt SHil SMrm

ACACIA † (Leguminosae)

¶ *acinacea*	CGre
alpina	WCel
♦ *armata*	See A. ***paradoxa***
baileyana	CB&S CBow CSun CWSG ERea LBlm
– 'Purpurea'	CAbb CB&S CBow CDoC CGre CPle CTro CWSG CWit LAbb MBlu MUlv SFai SMad SSpi
¶ *beckleri*	CGre
¶ *burkittii*	CGre
cultriformis	ERea IOrc
dealbata	CAbb CB&S CBow CBra CDoC CGre CHEx CHan CPle CSco CSun CTre CWSG ELan ERea IDai IOrc ISea LAbb LHil MBal MBlu NPal SHBN SIgm SPer SSpi WNor
– 'Mirandole'	ERea
– *subalpina*	SArc WCel
Exeter hybrid	CGre ERea
¶ *extensa*	CGre
filicifolia	SArc WCel
floribunda 'Lisette'	ERea
frigescens	SArc WCel
genistifolia	CSun LBlm
¶ *gillii*	CGre
julibrissin	See ALBIZIA *j.*
♦ *juniperina*	See A. ***ulicifolia***
¶ *karroo*	CArn CTro
kybeanensis	WCel
longifolia	CB&S CHEx CPle CTro IOrc
mearnsii	WCel
melanoxylon	IBar IOrc ISea LRHS WCel
¶ *motteana*	ERea
mucronata	CB&S GWht
obliquinervia	WCel
§ *paradoxa*	ERea IMal IOrc MBri
– *angustifolia*	CSun LBlm
pendula	MBri
podalyriifolia	CMHG CPle
pravissima	CB&S CDoC CGre CHEx CMHG CPle CSun CWit ERea ISea LBlm LHop MBal SArc SFai SSpi WCel WNor
retinodes	CDoC CGre ERea MNew SRms
riceana	CB&S WCel
rubida	SArc
saligna	IOrc
sentis	See A. ***victoriae***
sophorae	GWht
§ *ulicifolia*	CGre CPle CWit
verticillata	CB&S
§ *victoriae*	ERea

ACAENA (Rosaceae)

* *acris*	CSun
§ *adscendens*	CNic CRiv CRow ECha ECro ECtt EHoe EMon ESis GGar MFir NNor NNrd SDix WWin
– 'Glauca'	LHop NBir NNor
affinis	See A. ***adscendens***
anserinifolia Druce	CGle CLew ECha GCHN NCat NHol NRar NRed WEas WPer WWin
– hort.	See A. ***novae-zelandiae***
argentea	SBla
§ 'Blue Haze'	CCla CGle CLew CMea CPar CRow CShe EBre ECha ELan EPar EPot GCHN LBre MBar NNrd NPer NRed NSti SDix SIng SPer WHal WHoo
buchananii	CNic CRiv CRow CShe CTom ECro EPar EPot GTou MBar MBri MCas MFir NKay NMir NNor SIng SSmi STre WByw WCla WHoo WMer WPer WWye
caerulea	See A. ***caesiiglauca***
§ *caesiiglauca*	CBar CLew CMer CNic CRiv ECro GGar MWat NCat NNor NSti WEas WPer
fissistipula	GGar
glaucophylla	See A. ***magellanica***
inermis	CGle CLew CMer ECha ELan LAbb LWad NNrd SIng SSmi SSou WPer
§ *magellanica*	ECro GCal LAbb WMer
microphylla	CMer EBre ECar ECro EPar ESis GGar LBre MBar MBri MBro MFir MRav MWat NGre NMen NRed SHer SIng SSmi WByw WCla WEas WHoo WPer
– 'Glauca'	See A. ***caesiiglauca***
§ – 'Kupferteppich' ('Copper Carpet')	CPar CRiv CRow ECro EHoe GAbr GAri MBri MFir MRav NCat NVic SIng WPat
– 'Pallidolivacea'	CRow
– 'Pulchella'	CTom EBre ECha GAri LBre MRav NHol
¶ *myriophylla*	WPer
§ *novae-zelandiae*	CHun CRiv CRow ECro MFir NRed SDix SIgm SIng WPer
ovalifolia	CNic CRow CTom MFir NCat NRed WPer

'Pewter'	See A. 'Blue Haze'
'Purple Carpet'	See A. ***microphylla*** 'Kupferteppich'
saccaticupula	WPer
♦*sanguisorbae*	See A. ***anserinifolia*** Druce
sericea	CLew NMen WPer
¶ sp. CC 451	NWCA WDav
¶ sp. CC 577	NWCA

ACALYPHA (Euphorbiaceae)

hispida	MBri
– 'Hispaniola'	ERea
wilkesiana	MBri
– 'Can-Can'	MBri
– 'Gold Cant'	MBri
– *pudsiana*	MBri

ACANTHOCALYX See MORINA

ACANTHOLIMON (Plumbaginaceae)

androsaceum	See A. ***ulicinum***
¶ *armenum*	WDav
glumaceum	MDHE SHer SRms
¶ *hohenackeri*	WDav
litvinovii	WDav
§ *ulicinum*	EPot NWCA WDav

ACANTHOPANAX See ELEUTHEROCOCCUS

ACANTHUS † (Acanthaceae)

¶ *australis*	SLMG
balcanicus	See A. ***hungaricus***
dioscoridis perringii	CChu CGle CHan CMil LGre
hirsutus	EMon LGre
¶ – *syriacus* JCA 106.500	CGle SBla
§ *hungaricus*	CCla CHan ECED EMon EPla GCal LGan MFir SBla SDix SPer WCru WRus
– AL&JS 90097YU	EMon
longifolius	See A. ***hungaricus***
mollis	Widely available
– Latifolius Group	CMGP CSco EBre ECro EFou EGol EPla LBre LHil MRav MUlv NHol SChu SHer SPer SSpi WWat
spinosus	Widely available
– 'Lady Moore'	IFer
– Spinosissimus Group	CFis CGle ECha EOrc EPla LGre MUlv NOak SBla

ACCA (Myrtaceae)

F *sellowiana*	CB&S CCla CHan CMHG CPle CSam ELan EPla ERea ESim LAbb LHop MBrk SEng SHBN SLon SSpi WPat WSHC
F – 'Apollo'	ERea ESim
F – 'Coolidge'	ERea
F – 'Mammoth'	ERea
F – 'Triumph'	ERea ESim
F – 'Variegata'	CGre

ACER † (Aceraceae)

acuminatum	CMCN WAce WNor
albopurpurescens	CMCN
amplum	CMCN
argutum	CMCN WAce WCoo WNor
barbinerve	CMCN
buergerianum	CB&S CLnd CMCN EHar GAri MUlv SSpi STre WAce WCoo WMou WNor
– 'Goshiki-kaede' (v)	SSpi
caesium	CMCN
campbellii	CB&S CMCN
– SF 29	ISea
– *yunnanense*	CMCN
campestre	CBra CDoC CKin CLnd CMCN CPer CSco EBre ENot GRei IOrc LBre LBuc MBar MBri MGos NBee NRoo NWea SHBN SPer STre WAce WCoo WDin WMou WNor
¶ – 'Autumn Red'	WMou
– 'Carnival'	MBri SHBN SMad
– 'Elsrijk'	CLnd EBre LBre SSpi WMou
¶ – 'Nanum'	WMou
– 'Postelense'	CMCN LMer SHil WAce WMou
– 'Pulverulentum' (v)	CMCN
¶ – 'Queen Elizabeth'	WMou
– 'Red Shine'	MGos WMou
– 'Rockhampton Red Stem'	WMou
¶ – 'Royal Ruby'	CTho WMou
– 'Schwerinii'	CMCN WMou
¶ – 'Weeping'	WMou
– 'William Caldwell'	CTho MBri WMou
capillipes	CB&S CBra CMCN CSam EHar ELan ENot IBar IJoh IOrc LMer MBar MBri MGos MPar SPer SSpi SSta STre WAce WDin WNor WWat
cappadocicum	CMCN WAce WCoo WDin WNor
– 'Aureum'	CAbP CDoC CLnd CMCN COtt CSco EBre EHar ELan ENot ESma GAbr IOrc LBre LNet MBri MUlv NSel SHBN SHil SPer SSpi WAce WMou
– *mono*	See A. ***mono***
– 'Rubrum'	CCla CDoC CLnd CMCN EHar ENot IHos IOrc MBlu MUlv SPer SSpi SSta WDin
– *sinicum*	CMCN
carpinifolium	CB&S CCor CLnd CMCN SHil SSpi WAce WCoo
catalpifolium	See A. ***longipes c.***
§ *caudatifolium*	CMCN WCoo
§ *caudatum*	CMCN
cinerascens	CMCN
§ *cinnamomifolium*	CMCN
circinatum	CChu CMCN CSam ECtt EHar ESma GWht IBar LNet SHil SReu SSpi SSta WAbe WAce WCoo WNor WWat
– 'Little Gem'	CMCN LRHS LTil
– 'Monroe'	CMCN LNet WAce
cissifolium	CMCN WAce WCoo
¶ *conspicuum* 'Phoenix'	CPMA
§ *cordatum*	CMCN
coriaceifolium	See A. ***cinnamomifolium***
x *coriaceum*	CMCN CSam WAce
crataegifolium	CMCN SSpi
– 'Veitchii' (v)	CMCN CPMA LNet SSpi
creticum	See A. ***sempervirens***
dasycarpum	See A. ***saccharinum***

davidii	CAbP CB&S CBow CCla CDoC CMCN CMHG CSco EBre EHar ENot IBar IOrc LBre MBal MBar MGos MRav SHBN SPer SPla SSta WAce WCoo WDin WFro WNor
– 'Ernest Wilson'	CB&S CBow CMCN ELan MBrk WNor
– 'George Forrest'	CB&S CMCN ELan MUlv SSpi WThu
– 'Karmen'	MBri MGos SSpi
– 'Rosalie'	MBri
– 'Serpentine'	CB&S CBow CPMA EHar ELan EPla LTil MBri NSel SSpi
¶ – 'Silver Cardinal'	CPMA SSpi
diabolicum	CMCN
x ***dieckii***	CMCN
distylum	CMCN WAce
divergens	CMCN
elegantulum	CMCN
erianthum	CLnd CMCN SSpi WNor
fabri	CMCN
flabellatum	CMCN
forrestii	CMCN SSpi WAce WCoo WNor
– 'Alice'	CB&S CCla CDoC CPMA LNet MBri SSpi
franchetii	CMCN
fulvescens	See A. ***longipes***
ginnala	See A. ***tataricum ginnala***
giraldii	CMCN
glabrum	CMCN WAce WNor
– douglasii	CMCN WAce
globosum	See A. ***platanoïdes*** 'Globosum'
grandidentatum	See A. ***saccharum g.***
griseum	Widely available
¶ – 'Tilgates'	LTil
grosseri	CMCN WFro
– hersii	CB&S CBra CDoC CLnd EBre ECtt EHar ELan ENot LBre MBal MBri MRav MUlv NWea SHil SMad SPer SSpi SSta WAce WDin WNor WWat
heldreichii	CLnd CMCN SSpi WAce WCoo
henryi	CGre CMCN ENot LNet SSpi WNor
x ***hillieri***	CMCN
hookeri	CMCN
hyrcanum	CMCN
japonicum	CMCN LNet MBal MBar SSta WAbe WAce WDin WFro WNor WWat
§ – 'Aconitifolium'	CAlt CMCN CPMA CSco CShe EHar ELan ENot IHos IOrc LNet MBar MBri MGos MMor NBee NHip NJap NSel SHBN SPer SReu SSpi SSta WAce WDin WNor WWat
– f. ***aureum***	See A. ***shirasawanum aureum***
– 'Ezo-no-momiji'	CMCN
– 'Green Cascade'	CAlt CMCN CPMA SSpi WAce WPat
– 'Laciniatum'	See A. ***j.*** 'Aconitifolium'
– f. ***microphyllum***	See A. ***shirasawanum m.***
– 'Ogurayama'	LNet WNor
– 'O-isami'	CMCN LRHS
¶ – 'O-taki'	WAce
¶ – ***viride***	WDin

– 'Vitifolium'	CAlt CDoC CMCN CSco ELan IOrc LNet NPal NSel SHil SPer SSpi SSta WAce WDin
kawakamii	See A. ***caudatifolium***
laevigatum	CMCN
lanceolatum	CMCN
laxiflorum	CB&S CLnd CMCN SSpi
lobelii	CLnd CMCN EHar ENot NWea SHil SSpi WAce WNor
§ ***longipes***	CMCN
¶ – ssp. ***catalpifolium***	CMCN
macrophyllum	CMCN EHar IOrc ISea LHyd SSpi WAce WCoo
– 'Kimballae'	CMCN
– 'Seattle Sentinel'	CMCN
§ ***maximowiczianum***	CDoC CLnd CMCN CSam EHar ELan IOrc MBal MBri MUlv SReu SSpi WNor WThu
*– ***morifolium***	WCoo
maximowiczii	CMCN EHal MGos WNor
micranthum	CMCN SSpi WAce WCoo WNor
miyabei	CMCN WAce WNor
§ ***mono***	CMCN WAce
– 'Hoshiyadori' (v)	CMCN
– 'Shufu-nishiki'	CMCN
– var. ***tricuspis***	CMCN
monspessulanum	CMCN WAce
morrisonense	See A. ***caudatifolium***
negundo	CCor CLnd CMCN EBre ELan ENot ISea LBre NHip WDin WNor
– 'Argenteovariegatum'	See A. ***n.*** 'Variegatum'
– 'Auratum'	CMCN EPla SPer WDin
– 'Aureovariegatum'	CB&S ELan MBar MUlv NJap SHBN
§ – 'Elegans' (v)	CDoC CLnd CMCN COtt EBre ELan ENot EPla LBre NJap NKay SHBN SPer SSpi
– 'Elegantissimum'	See A. ***n.*** 'Elegans'
– 'Flamingo' (v)	Widely available
– 'Kelly's Gold'	CB&S SEng
§ – 'Variegatum'	CB&S CBra CLnd CSco EGol EHoe ENot IDai MBri MGos NBee SPer WDin
– var. ***violaceum***	CMCN ELan EPla SHil
nikoense	See A. ***maximowiczianum***
nipponicum	CMCN
oblongum	CMCN
§ ***obtusifolium***	CMCN LRHS WAce
okamotoanum	CMCN
oliverianum	CMCN LTil SSpi WAce WNor
opalus	CMCN WAce WNor
orientale	See A. ***sempervirens***
palmatum	CBow CLan CMCN CMHG ENot ESis GAbr LNet LTil MBal MBar MMor SHBN SPer SPla SSta STre WAbe WAce WCoo WDin WFro WNor WPat WThu WWat
– 'Aka Shigitatsusawa'	CMCN LNet LTil NHip NJap NSel WAce
§ – 'Akaji-nishiki'	CPMA
– 'Akegarasu'	CMCN WAce
– 'Aoshime-no-uchi'	See A. ***p.*** 'Shinobugaoka'
– 'Aoyagi'	CMCN LNet NJap NSel WAce
♦– 'Arakawa'	See A. ***p.*** 'Rough Bark Maple'
– 'Asahi-zuru' (v)	CBow CMCN CPMA LNet LTil MMor NSel SHil SSta WAce WNor

Name	Suppliers
– f. ***atropurpureum***	Widely available
– 'Atropurpureum Superbum'	CMCN MBri MRav
– 'Aureum'	CAlt CBow CMCN CPMA CSco LNet MBri SBod SReu SSpi SSta WAce
– Autumn Glory Group	SSpi
– 'Awakawa'	CMCN WAce
¶– 'Azahi-zuru'	MGos
– 'Azuma-murasaki'	CMCN WAce
– 'Beni-kagami'	CMCN LNet NJap NSel WAce
¶– 'Beni-kawa'	LTil
– 'Beni-komachi'	CB&S CMCN LNet LTil NSel WNor
– 'Beni-maiko'	CBow CMCN CPMA LNet LTil NSel SHil SSpi WNor
¶– 'Beni-otake'	NHip
– 'Beni-schichihenge' (v)	CAbP CMCN LNet LTil NHip NSel SHil SSta WAce WNor
– 'Beni-shidare Variegated'	CMCN LNet
– 'Beni-tsukasa' (v)	LNet LTil NJap NSel SSpi WAce
– 'Bloodgood'	Widely available
♦– 'Bonfire'	See A. ***p.*** 'Akaji-nishiki'
– 'Brocade'	CMCN NSel WPat
– 'Burgundy Lace'	CAlt CBow CMCN COtt CPMA CSPN IOrc LNet MGos NHip NJap NSel SSpi WAce
– 'Butterfly' (v)	Widely available
– 'Chirimen-nishiki' (v)	CMCN LNet
– 'Chishio'	See A. ***p.*** 'Shishio'
– 'Chishio Improved'	See A. ***p.*** 'Shishio Improved'
– 'Chitoseyama'	CAlt CMCN CPMA LNet MBri MMor NHip SSpi SSta WAce WNor WPat
– 'Coonara Pygmy'	CMCN IMal LNet WAce
– 'Corallinum'	CBow CMCN CPMA LTil NHip WAce WPat
N– var. ***coreanum***	NJap SSpi WNor WWat
– 'Crimson Queen'	CAlt CDoC CMCN CPMA CSco ENot IOrc LAbb LNet MAsh MBal MBri MGos MMor NHip NJap NSel SPer SReu SSpi WAce WNor WPat
– 'Crippsii'	SEng
– 'Deshôjô'	CMCN CPMA SEng WAce
– var. ***dissectum***	CBow CBra CDoC CShe CTho ENot IJoh IOrc LHyd MBar MBri MGos NWea SHBN SReu WDin WFro WNor WPat WStI WWat
– – Dissectum Atropurpureum Group	Widely available
– – Dissectum Viride Group	CAlt CB&S CBra CMCN CPMA CSco ELan GRei IDai LNet LTil MAsh MMor NHip NJap NKay NSel SPer SPla SSta WBod
– – 'Dissectum Flavescens'	CMCN NHip NSel
§– – 'Dissectum Nigrum'	CAlt EHoe LNet MAsh MGos SPer SSpi WBod
– – 'Dissectum Ornatum'	CDoC COtt ELan MGos
– – 'Dissectum Palmatifidum'	LNet
§– – 'Dissectum Variegatum'	CPMA ELan LNet SEng SSta
*– 'Eddisbury'	MMor SSta WAce
– 'Ever Red'	See A. ***p. dissectum*** 'Dissectum Nigrum'
– 'Filigree'	CAlt CMCN EHar LNet LTil MGos NHip NJap NSel SMad SSpi
¶– 'Filigree Lace'	LTil
– 'Fireglow'	CBow CPMA MBri NHip WPat
¶– 'Flamingo'	NHip
– 'Frederici Guglielmi'	See A. ***p.*** 'Dissectum Variegatum'
– 'Garnet'	CCla CMCN CPMA CSam EBlo EBre ECtt EHar ELan IHos LBre LPan LTil MAsh MBal MBar MBri MMor NHip NJap NSel SMad SPer SSpi SSta WDin WPat WStI WWat
– 'Goshiki-kotohime' (v)	CMCN
– 'Goshiki-shidare' (v)	CMCN LNet
¶– 'Green Trompenburg'	NHip
§– 'Hagoromo'	LNet WAce WNor
– 'Hanami-nishiki'	CMCN
– 'Harusame' (v)	LNet
– 'Hazeroino' (v)	CMCN NSel
– var. ***heptalobum***	CMCN
§– 'Heptalobum Elegans'	CBow CMCN CPMA NSel SHBN SPer SReu SSpi WAce
– 'Heptalobum Elegans Purpureum'	See A. ***p.*** 'Hessei'
– 'Heptalobum Lutescens'	NSel
§– 'Hessei'	CMCN CSco LNet NHip SReu WAce
– 'Higasayama' (v)	CB&S CBow CMCN CPMA LNet LTil NHip NJap NSel SSpi WAce WNor WPat
– 'Hôgyoku'	CMCN NHip NJap NSel WAce
– 'Ichigyôji'	CMCN NJap WAce
– 'Improved Shishio'	See A. ***p.*** 'Shishio Improved'
– 'Inaba-shidare'	CDoC CPMA CSam CSco EBlo GRei IMal LNet LTil MBar MBri MGos MMor NHip NJap NSel SPer SReu SSta
– 'Inazuma'	CMCN NHip NJap NSel SSpi WAce
– 'Jirô-shidare'	SSpi
¶– 'Kagero' (v)	CPMA
§– 'Kagiri-nishiki' (v)	CB&S CMCN COtt CPMA CSco LNet LTil MGos NJap NSel SHil SSpi SSta WNor
– 'Kamagata'	CMCN LTil NHip SSpi SSta WAce WNor
– 'Karaori-nishiki' (v)	LNet NJap NSel WAce
– 'Karasugawa' (v)	CMCN NSel SHil WAce
– 'Kasagiyama'	CAlt CMCN LRHS NJap SSpi
¶– 'Kasen-nishiki'	NHip NSel
– 'Kashima'	CMCN NJap NSel WNor
– 'Katsura'	CB&S CMCN CPMA EBlo EBre ELan LBre LTil MAsh MBri NJap NSel SEng SPla SSpi SSta WAce WNor
– 'Kinran'	CMCN LNet NHip SSpi WAce
– 'Kinshii'	CMCN LRHS MAsh SSpi SSta
– 'Kiyohime'	CMCN NSel
– 'Ki-hachijô'	CMCN NJap NSel WAce
N– 'Koreanum'	CMCN SHil
¶– 'Koshibori-nishiki'	CPMA
– 'Kotohime'	CMCN
¶– 'Koto-no-ito'	CMCN
– 'Kurui-jishi'	LNet

– 'Linearilobum'	CAlt CMCN LHyd LNet LTil NHip NJap SHil SSpi WAce WNor WPat
– 'Linearilobum Atropurpureum'	SSta WNor
– 'Little Princess'	See A. ***p.*** 'Mapi-no-machihime'
¶ – 'Mama'	CMCN
§ – 'Mapi-no-machihime'	LRHS LTil MAsh MBri NHol SSta WWat
¶ – 'Masukagami' (v)	CAlt NHip WAce
– 'Matsukaze'	COtt CPMA NJap NSel SSpi WAce
– 'Mirte'	LNet
¶ – 'Mizu-kuguri'	WAce
¶ – 'Monzukushi'	WAce
– 'Moonfire'	CMCN LNet NHip NJap NSel WAce
– 'Mure-hibari'	CMCN
– 'Murogawa'	CMCN WAce
– 'Nicholsonii'	CMCN WAce
– 'Nigrum'	CMCN NSel SEng WPat
– 'Nishiki-gawa'	See A. ***p.*** 'Pine Bark Maple'
– 'Nomurishidare'	CBow LRHS NHip SSpi WAce
– 'Nuresagi'	CMCN LNet
¶ – 'Ogon-sarasa'	WAce
– 'Okushimo'	CMCN LNet NHip NSel SSpi SSta WAce WNor
– 'Omurayama'	LNet LRHS NJap SSta WNor
– 'Orido-nishiki' (v)	CAlt CMCN CPMA ELan LNet LTil MGos NHip WAce WNor
– 'Ornatum'	CDoC MBri NHip NJap NSel SPer WAce
– 'Osakazuki'	Widely available
– 'Oshû-beni'	CMCN WAce
– 'Oshû-shidare'	CMCN
– 'O-kagami'	COtt LNet MBri NHip NSel
§ – 'O-nishiki'	LNet NHip NJap
– 'Pendulum Julian'	CMCN WAce
§ – 'Pine Bark Maple'	CMCN LRHS NSel
– 'Red Dragon'	COtt NSel SEng
¶ – 'Red Filigree Lace'	LTil
– 'Red Pygmy'	CAlt CBow CDoC CMCN COtt CPMA CSco LNet LTil MAsh MBri MGos NHip NJap NSel SSpi SSta WAce
– 'Reticulatum'	See A. ***p.*** 'Shigitatsu-sawa'
– 'Ribesifolium'	See A. ***p.*** 'Shishigashira'
– 'Roseomarginatum'	See A. ***p.*** 'Kagiri-nishiki'
§ – 'Rough Bark Maple'	CMCN GAri
– 'Rubrum'	CMCN MBal NJap SSpi WPat
– 'Rufescens'	CMCN WAce
– 'Sagara-nishiki' (v)	CMCN
– 'Samidare'	CMCN NJap NSel WAce
N – 'Sango-kaku'	CDoC CMCN CPMA CSam CSco CShe ENot LNet MBal MBar MBri MGos NHip NJap NSel SHer SReu SSpi SSta WAce
– 'Saoshika'	CMCN WAce
– 'Sazanami'	CMCN NJap NSel WNor
¶ – 'Schichihenge'	WAce
¶ – 'Seigen'	CMCN
– 'Seiryû'	CAlt CB&S CMCN CPMA EHar ELan LNet MBri MGos MMor NBee NHip NHol NJap NSel SEng SPer SSpi SSta WDin WNor
N – 'Senkaki'	Widely available
– 'Septemlobum Elegans'	See A. ***p.*** 'Heptalobum Elegans'
– 'Septemlobum Purpureum'	See A. ***p.*** 'Hessei'
– 'Sessilifolium' (dwarf)	See A. ***p.*** 'Hagoromo'
– 'Sessilifolium' (tall)	See A. ***p.*** 'Koshimino'
– 'Sherwood Flame'	CBow CMCN CPMA LNet LTil MBri MGos NHip NJap NSel WAce WPat
§ – 'Shigitatsu-sawa' (v)	CB&S CMCN NHip WAce
– 'Shime-no-uchi'	CMCN LNet WAce
– 'Shindeshôjô'	CBow CDoC CMCN CPMA ELan LNet MAsh MBri NHol NJap NSel SBod SPer SSta WNor
§ – 'Shinobugaoka'	CBow CMCN CPMA LNet
– 'Shinonome'	CMCN COtt CSco
§ – 'Shishigashira'	CMCN EHar MBri MGos MMor NHip SSta WPat
§ – 'Shishio'	CB&S CMCN COtt LHyd LNet LTil NJap NSel SEng SSpi WAce
§ – 'Shishio Improved'	CAlt LNet MAsh MGos MMor NHip NJap NSel WAce WNor WPat
– 'Shôjô-nomura'	COtt
¶ – 'Stella Rossa'	NHip
– 'Suminagashi'	CMCN LNet NSel
– 'Takinogawa'	LRHS SSpi SSta WAce
– 'Tamahime'	NJap NSel WAce WNor
– 'Tamukeyama'	CMCN
– 'Tana'	CMCN NHip NJap NSel WAce WNor
¶ – 'Tatsuta-gawa'	WAce
– 'Trompenburg'	CAbP CBow CMCN COtt CPMA LNet LTil MAsh MBri NHip NJap NSel SHil SSpi SSta WAce WBod WNor WPat
¶ – 'Tsuchigumo'	CMCN
– 'Tsukubane'	CMCN
– 'Tsukushigata'	LRHS WAce
– 'Tsuma-beni'	CMCN NSel SSta WAce
– 'Tsuma-gaki'	CMCN
– 'Ukigumo' (v)	CAlt CB&S COtt CPMA LNet LTil MGos NHip NJap NSel SSpi SSta WAce
– 'Ukon'	CMCN NHip NJap WAce WNor
– 'Umegae'	CMCN
– 'Utsu-semi'	CMCN SSpi WAce
– 'Versicolor' (v)	LNet NJap
– 'Villa Taranto'	CMCN LNet MBlu MGos NJap NSel SSpi WAce
– 'Volubile'	CMCN NSel WAce
– 'Wabito'	CMCN NSel WAce
– 'Wada's Flame'	SSta
– 'Waterfall'	CMCN LNet MGos NJap NSel
– 'Wou-nishiki'	See A. ***p.*** 'O-nishiki'
¶ – 'Yasmine'	LTil
– 'Yezo-nishiki'	NHip
¶ – 'Yûgure'	MGos NHip WAce
papilio	See A. ***caudatum***
paxii	CMCN
pectinatum	CMCN
– 'Sirene'	MGos
– 'Sparkling'	MBri
pensylvanicum	CCla CDoC CMCN ISea MGos MRav NWea SHBN SHil SMad SPer SReu SSpi WAce WCoo WDin WNor WWeb
– 'Erythrocladum'	CBow CMCN CPMA LNet LTil MAsh MBlu NHol SHil SSpi
pentaphyllum	CMCN SHil WAce

§ ***pentapotamicum***	CMCN EBre LBre
pictum	See A. ***mono***
platanoïdes	CKin CLnd CMCN CPer ELan ENot GRei IDai IJoh ISea LBuc LPan MGos NWea SPer STre WAbe WAce WDin WMou WNor
¶ – 'Autumn Blaze'	WMou
– 'Cleveland'	CB&S ENot
– 'Columnare'	CDoC CMCN ENot IOrc
– 'Crimson King'	CB&S CBra CCla CMCN CSam CSco CTho EBre ECtt ELan GRei IDai IJoh LBre LBuc LNet MBar NBar NBee NSel NWea SHBN SPer SReu SSta WAbe WDin
– 'Crimson Sentry'	COtt IHos LNet MBri SHil SMad
– 'Deborah'	CDoC CLnd CTho SHBN WMou
– 'Drummondii' (v)	CB&S CBra CCla CLnd CMCN CSco CTho EBre ELan ENot GRei IDai IJoh LBre LBuc LNet LPan MBar MBri MGos NSel NWea SHBN SPer SPla SReu SSta WAbe WDin WStI
– 'Emerald Queen'	CDoC CLnd ENot SHBN
– 'Erectum'	CMCN
§ – 'Globosum'	CLnd CMCN ENot LPan
– 'Goldsworth Purple'	CFis CLnd MGos WAbe
– 'Laciniatum'	CMCN ENot SPer
– 'Lorbergii'	See A. ***p.*** 'Palmatifidum'
– 'Olmstead'	ENot LNet
§ – 'Palmatifidum'	CSam
¶ – 'Reitenbachii'	CTho
– 'Royal Red'	CBra ENot MBri
– 'Schwedleri'	CBra CLnd CSco ENot MGos SPer WDin WMou
pseudoplatanus	CB&S CKin CLnd CMCN CPer ELan ENot GRei IDai LBuc LPan MBar MGos NWea SHer WDin WMou
§ – 'Atropurpureum'	CDoC CLnd CTho ENot IOrc NWea
– 'Brilliantissimum'	CB&S CBra CCla CLnd CMCN CSco CTho EBre EGol EHar ELan IJoh LBre LNet MBar MBri MGos NBar NHip NSel NWea SHBN SMad SPer SPla SReu SSta WDin WMou WPat
– 'Corstorphinense'	CMCN
– 'Erectum'	ENot
N– 'Leopoldii' (v)	CB&S CBra CDoC CFis CLnd CMCN COtt CSco CTho ELan ENot IOrc LPan MBar MBri NBee SHBN SPer WDin
– 'Negenia'	CDoC
– 'Nizetii' (v)	EHar ENot MBri SHil
– 'Prinz Handjery'	CAbP CB&S CBow CBra CDoC CMCN CSco CTho EBre EHar LBre LNet LPan MBar NJap SHBN SSpi STre
– 'Simon-Louis Frères' (v)	CBra CDoC CLnd CTho ELan LNet MBri MGos NJap NSel SHer
N– 'Spaethii' hort. (v)	See A. ***p.*** 'Atropurpureum'
¶ – f. ***variegatum***	WCot
– 'Worleei'	CB&S CBra CDoC CLnd CMCN COtt CSco ECtt EHar ENot GRei IOrc MBri NWea SHBN SHil SPer WDin WMou
pseudosieboldianum	CMCN WAce WNor
pycnanthum	CMCN
regelii	See A. ***pentapotamicum***
rubescens	CBra CSam
rubrum	CB&S CBow CBra CDoC CGre CLnd CMCN COtt EBre LBre NBee NWea SPer WAbe WAce WBod WDin WNor
– 'Morgan'	MBri
– 'October Glory'	CBra CDoC CMCN CMHG CSam EHar IOrc MBlu MBri MBrk MUlv SHil SSpi SSta WAce WWeb
– 'Red Sunset'	CMCN MBri MUlv SHil SSpi WAce
– 'Scanlon'	CDoC CMCN SHil
– 'Schlesingeri'	CMCN
– 'Tridens'	CMCN
rufinerve	CB&S CDoC CLnd CMCN CMHG EBre EHar ENot IOrc LBre LPan MBri NWea SMad SPer WAce WNor WStI
♦– 'Albolimbatum'	See A. ***r.*** 'Hatsuyuki'
– 'Albomarginatum'	See A. ***r.*** 'Hatsuyuki'
§ – 'Hatsuyuki' (v)	CB&S CMCN CPMA MBri MUlv SSpi
§ ***saccharinum***	CB&S CGre CLnd CMCN EBre EHar ENot LBre MGos NWea SPer SSpi SSta WDin
– 'Elegans'	CDoC CMCN
– 'Fastigiatum'	See A. ***s.*** 'Pyramidale'
– f. ***laciniatum***	CDoC CMCN COtt EHar ENot MBlu MGos NBee SPer WDin
– ***lutescens*** f.	CMCN EBre EHar ENot LBre SHil SPer WMou
§ – ***pyramidale*** f.	CDoC CLnd CMCN EHar ENot IOrc
– 'Wieri'	CLnd
saccharum	CBra CDoC CLnd CMCN EHar SHil SPer STre WNor
*– 'Aureum'	IOrc
¶ – ***barbatum***	CMCN
¶ – ssp. ***leucoderme***	CMCN
– 'Newton Sentry'	CMCN
– ssp. ***nigrum***	CMCN
– 'Temple's Upright'	CMCN
§ ***sempervirens***	CMCN
serrulatum	CMCN
shirasawanum	CMCN CSco SSpi WAce WNor
§ – f. ***aureum***	CAlt CB&S CCla CMCN CPMA EHar ENot IDai IJoh LHyd LNet LTil MAsh MBar MBri MGos MMor NBee NHip NHol NJap NSel NWea SMad SPer SSta WBod WPat WStI WWat
§ – ***microphyllum***	CMCN LNet WNor
– 'Palmatifolium'	CMCN CPMA MGos WAce WStI
sieboldianum	CLnd CMCN EHar WAce WNor
¶ – 'Kinugasayama'	WAce
– 'Miyami-nishiki'	LRHS
– 'Sode-no-uchi'	CMCN WAce
'Silver Vein'	CMCN CPMA EBre LBre LRHS LTil MBri SHil
sinense	CMCN
sinopurpurascens	CMCN
spicatum	CB&S CMCN WAce WNor
stachyophyllum	See A. ***tetramerum***
§ ***sterculiaceum***	CMCN
syriacum	See A. ***obtusifolium***
takesimense	CMCN WAce
taronense	CMCN

¶ ***tataricum*** SSpi
§ – ssp. ***ginnala*** CLnd CMCN CMHG EBar EHar ENot IOrc MBal MGos NHip NJap NSel SPer SReu SSta WAce WCoo WNor WTyr WWat
*– – 'Fire' LNet
– – 'Flame' CMCN
– ***grandidentatum*** CMCN
– ssp. ***semenowii*** CMCN
tegmentosum CMCN WCoo
– ssp. ***glaucorufinerve*** See A. ***rufinerve***
tenuifolium CMCN WAce
§ ***tetramerum*** CMCN SSpi
thomsonii CMCN
trautvetteri CMCN SSpi WAce WNor
triflorum CMCN SSpi WAce
truncatum CMCN WAce WFro WNor
– 'Akikaze-nishiki' (v) LNet
tschonoskii CMCN EHar
turkestanicum CMCN CTho
ukurunduense CMCN WNor
velutinum CMCN
villosum See A. ***sterculiaceum***
wilsonii CMCN
x ***zoeschense*** CMCN
– 'Annae' IOrc

ACERIPHYLLUM (Saxifragaceae)

rossii See MUKDENIA ***rossii***

ACHILLEA † (Compositae)

abrotanoïdes ELan EMon NGre
ageratifolia CGle CLew ECha EFol LGre MBro MHig MTho NHol NMen NNor NWCA SHer SIgm SSmi WByw WPer
– JCA 110.031 WDav
§ – ssp. ***aïzoön*** NKay WPer
§ ***ageratum*** CArn CHal CSFH Effi GPoy LGan LHol MChe NSal SIde WWye
– 'W B Child' CBos CChu CPar ECha EFou ELan EMon LGre MMil WEas
'Alabaster' EMon MBel
'Anthea' EBlo LRHS MBel MUlv
'Apfelblüte' ('Appleblossom') CGle CMGP CPar CSco CSun EBre ECtt EFol EFou ELan EOrc EPla LBlm LBre LHop MBri NHol SHer SPer WMer
argentea hort. See AA. ***clavennae, umbellatum***
– Lamarck See TANACETUM ***argenteum***
aurea 'Grandiflora' See A. ***chrysocoma*** 'G.'
¶ 'Bahama' NFai
cartilaginea EFou LHop NCat
chrysocoma CHal ELan ESis GAbr MCas MWat NKay NMen NRya NTow SHer SSmi
§ – 'Grandiflora' CFis CHad EHal NTow SIng
§ ***clavennae*** CFis CGle CHal CPar CShe CTom EPot GCHN LHil MCas MHig MPla MWat NMen NNor NRoo NTow SBla SHer SRms WAbe WHil WOld
– ssp. ***integrifolia*** NHol WDav

¶ ***coarctata*** WPer
'Coronation Gold' CBre CDoC CKel CSco CShe EBre ECED EFou ELan ENot LBre MBri MWat NKay SPer WEas
'Credo' CGle EFou EMon WCot
'Croftway' SCro
♦***decolorans*** See A. ***ageratum***
§ ***distans*** ssp. ***tanacetifolia*** MTol
erba-rotta ssp. ***rupestris*** CLew ESis MDHE MHig NKay SIng WPer
§ 'Fanal' CHad CHal COtt CPar CSco CSev CSun EBre ELan EOrc EPla LBlm LBre LHop MTho NCat NHol SChu SCro SHer SPer WWin
¶ 'Feuerland' EMon
filipendulina MFir MHew WWin
– 'Cloth of Gold' CBow CDoC CHun EBar EBre ECED ECtt EJud EPad LAbb LBre MBel MBri MPit NFai NMir NNor NRoo SPla SSvw WByw WHoo WPer
– 'Gold Plate' CBow CChu CDec CGle CSco CShe CTom EBre ECha ECtt EFou ELan GAbr LBre MBel NKay NOrc SCro SPer WDav WEas WHil
– 'Parker's Variety' EJud NOak
'Forncett Beauty' EFou
'Forncett Candy' EFou
'Forncett Fletton' EFou SCro
'Forncett Ivory' EFou
¶ ***glaberrima*** WPer
grandifolia CHan CMil CPou CRDP EMon EPad LGre MUlv NCat WCot
'Great Expectations' See A. 'Hoffnung'
'Hartington White' EMon LRHS MSte SCro
§ 'Hoffnung' CBre COtt CPar CSco CSev CSun EBre ECtt EFou EOrc EPla LBlm LBre MBro NHol SCro SPer WPer WWin
x ***huteri*** CHal CLew CMHG CMea CNic CSam CShe ECtt ELan EPot ESis MBro MCas MHig MPlt NCat NHol NMen NNor NNrd NTow SChu SGil SSmi SSou WAbe WEas WPer WWin
x ***jaborneggii*** GCHN NKay
x ***kellereri*** MBro MCas MHig SSmi
x ***kolbiana*** EOrc EPad LHop MHig MWat NHol NMen NNrd NRoo SSmi WDav WPat WWin
§ – 'Weston' CMHG NRoo NTow
§ 'Lachsschönheit' ('Salmon Beauty') CHad CMea COtt CPar CSco CSev CSun CTom EBar EBre ECha ECtt EFol EFou ELan EPla LBlm LBre LHop NHol NSti SChu SCro SHer SPer WHal WMer WPer WWin
x ***lewisii*** NMen
– 'King Edward' CMea CNic CSam EBre ECha EFol EFou ELan ESis LBee LBre MTho NBir NHol NKay NNrd NRoo NTow NVic SBla SHer SIgm SIng SSmi WPer
¶ 'Libella' NFai
'Martina' EHal EMon LRHS SCro

millefolium	CArn CGle CSFH EEls EJud Effi GPoy IEde LHol MHew NLan NMir NSel SHer SIde WByw WNdy WOak WWye
– var. ***borealis***	NSal
– 'Burgundy'	EOrc
– 'Cerise Queen'	CB&S CGle CHal CHun CKel CNic CPar CRDP CSco CShe EBre ECha ELan EPar EPla GCHN LBre MPit MWat NBee NFai NKay NNor NOrc SPer SSvw WEas WHil WOld WPer
– 'Fire King'	CHal
– 'Kelwayi'	LHil
– 'Lansdorferglut'	MBri NBar
– 'Lavender Beauty'	See A. ***m.*** 'Lilac Beauty'
§ – 'Lilac Beauty'	CB&S CGle CKel CTom EBre ECha EFol EFou EOrc LBre MBel SHer WMer
– 'Lilac Queen'	MBri NFai
¶ – 'Melanie'	WMer
– 'Paprika'	CBow CDoC EBar EBre EPar LBre MBri NBar
¶ – 'Red Beauty'	EPar NCat SRms
– f. ***rosea***	CPar EJud MBal NMir NRoo SRms WOMN
– 'Sammetriese'	EFou ELan EMon WHoo
– 'White Queen'	WMer
'Moonbeam'	EOrc SHer
'Moonshine'	CGle CHad CKel CPar CRDP CSco CSev CShe EBar EBlo EBre ECha EFol EFou ELan ENot EOrc LBre MBri MWat NBar NNor NRoo NSti SAxl SDix SPer WByw WEas WRus
¶ 'Moonwalker'	CBow
nana	EPot LGan WHil
nobilis ssp. ***neilreichii***	EMon LHil WCot
x ***obristii***	NMen
'Peter Davis'	See HIPPOLYTIA ***herderi***
ptarmica	CArn CKin LHol MChe MHew NSal NSel SIde SPer SSvw WHil WWye
*– 'Ballerina'	EFou
§ – 'Boule de Neige'	Widely available
¶ – 'Major'	WCot
– 'Nana Compacta'	ECha ECro
– 'Perry's White'	CBre EMon EPla GCal MBri MUlv NCat SPla WByw WCot WMer
– 'The Pearl'	See A. ***p.*** 'Boule de Neige'
– 'Unschuld' ('Innocence')	NBir NRoo
pumila	See A. ***distans tanacetifolia***
'Salmon Beauty'	See A. 'Lachsschönheit'
'Schwefelblüte' ('Flowers of Sulphur')	CSco EFol ELan NBir WCot
'Schwellenburg'	EFou SCro
sibirica	CLew CSun LBlm
¶ – AGS 1241	CNic
– 'Kiku-san'	CRDP EMon
¶ 'Smiling Queen'	NFai
Summer Pastels	CBow CDoC CHun ECro GAbr MFir MSte MWil NMir NNor NOak NRoo SSvw WFro WHen WHil WPer WWye
'Taygetea'	CGle CSam EBre ECha ELan EOrc EPar LBre MBel MBri MUlv MWat NRar NSti SChu SDix SPer WByw WCot WHer WKif WRus WSHC WSun
'The Beacon'	See A. 'Fanal'
'Theo Ploeger'	EMon
tomentosa	CGle CMer CTom ECha ECtt ELan IDai LHop MBal MPit NKay NNor NNrd NRoo WByw WHil
§ – 'Aurea'	CFis CHal CLew ECro ECtt EMon LHol MHew MPit NHol NMir NSti SCro SIde WHen WHil WPer WWin
– 'Maynard's Gold'	See A. ***t.*** 'Aurea'
umbellata	GTou MFos NTow SIgm
– NS 390	NWCA
– 'Weston'	See A. x ***kolbiana*** 'Weston'
'Wesersandstein'	EMon MBri WCot
x ***wilczekii***	CRiv SBod SGil SHer SPla SRms

X ACHIMENANTHA (Gesneriaceae)

'Cerulean Mink'	See X SMITHICODONIA 'C.M'
'Dutch Treat'	NMos
'Ginger Peachy'	NMos
'Inferno'	NMos
*'Rose Bouquet'	NMos
'Royal'	NMos

ACHIMENES (Gesneriaceae)

'Adelaide'	NMos
'Adèle Delahaute'	NMos
'Admiration'	LAma NRog
'Adonis Blue'	NMos
'Almandine'	NMos
'Ambleside'	NMos
'Ambroise Verschaffelt'	LAma NMos
'Ami Van Houtte'	NMos
'Ann Marie'	NMos
'Apricot Glow'	NMos
'Aquamarine'	NMos
'Bassenthwaite'	NMos
'Bea'	NMos
bella	See EUCODONIA ***verticillata***
'Bernice'	NMos
'Blauer Planet'	NMos
'Bloodstone'	NMos
'Blue Gown'	NMos
'Brilliant'	NMos
'Butterfield Bronze'	NMos
'Buttermere'	NMos
'Camberwell Beauty'	NMos
'Cameo Rose'	NMos
'Cameo Triumph'	NMos
'Camille Brozzoni'	NMos
candida	NMos
'Carmine Queen'	NMos
'Cascade Cockade'	NMos
'Cascade Evening Glow'	NMos
'Cascade Fairy Pink'	NMos
'Cascade Fashionable Pink'	NMos
'Cascade Rosy Red'	NMos

'Cascade Violet Night'	NMos
'Cattleya'	LAma NMos
'Chalkhill Blue'	NMos
'Charm'	LAma NMos
'Clouded Yellow'	NMos
'Compact Great Rosy Red'	NMos
'Coniston Water'	NMos
'Copeland Boy'	NMos
'Copeland Girl'	NMos
'Coral Sunset'	NMos
'Cornell Favourite 'A''	NMos
'Cornell Favourite 'B''	NMos
'Crimson Beauty'	NMos
'Crimson Glory'	NMos
'Crimson Tiger'	NMos
'Crummock Water'	NMos
'Cupido'	NMos
'Dentoniana'	NMos
'Derwentwater'	NMos
'Dorothy'	NMos
'Dot'	NMos
dulcis	NMos
'Early Arnold'	NMos
ehrenbergii	See EUCODONIA ***e.***
'Elke Michelssen'	NMos
'English Waltz'	NMos
erecta	WEfe
'Escheriana'	NMos
'Flamenco'	NMos
'Flamingo'	SDeJ
flava	NMos
'Fritz Michelssen'	NMos
'Gary John'	NMos
'Gary/Jennifer'	NMos
'Germanica'	LAma
'Grape Wine'	NMos
'Grasmere'	NMos
'Harry Williams'	LAma
§ 'Harveyi'	NMos
'Haweswater'	NMos
'Hilda Michelssen'	NMos
'Honey Gold'	NMos
'Ida Michelssen'	NMos
'India'	NMos
§ 'Jaureguia Maxima'	NMos
'Jennifer Goode'	NMos
'Jewell Blue'	NMos
'Johanna Michelssen'	NMos
'Jubilee Gem'	NMos
'Lake City'	LAma
'Lakeland Lady'	NMos
'Lavender Fancy'	NMos
'Little Beauty'	LAma NMos
'Little Red Tiger'	NMos
longiflora	LAma NMos
– 'Alba'	See A. 'Jaureguia Maxima'
– 'Major'	NMos
'Magnificent'	NMos
'Margaret White'	LAma
'Marie'	NMos
'Master Ingram'	LAma
'Masterpiece'	NMos
'Mauve Queen'	LAma
'Maxima'	LAma NRog
'Menuett '80'	NMos
'Milton'	NMos
'Minute'	LAma
misera	NMos
'Miss Blue'	LAma
'Moonstone'	NMos
'Nessida'	LAma
'Old Rose Pink'	LAma NMos
'Orange Queen'	NMos
'Pally'	NMos
'Panic Pink'	NMos
'Patens Major'	NMos
'Patricia'	NMos
'Paul Arnold'	LAma NMos SDeJ
'Peach Blossom'	LAma NMos SDeJ
'Peach Glow'	NMos
'Peacock'	NMos
'Pearly Queen'	NMos
'Pendant Blue'	NMos
'Pendant Purple'	NMos
'Petticoat Pink'	NMos
'Pink Beauty'	NMos
'Pinocchio'	NMos
'Prima Donna'	LAma NMos
'Pulcherrima'	LAma
'Purple King'	LAma NMos
'Queen of Sheba'	NMos
'Quickstep'	NMos
'Rachael'	NMos
'Red Admiral'	NMos
'Red Giant'	NMos
'Red Imp'	NMos
'Red Top Hybrid'	NMos
'Robin'	NMos
'Rosenelfe'	NMos
'Rosy Doll'	NMos
'Rosy Frost'	NMos
'Ruby'	LAma
'Rydal Water'	NMos
'Scafell'	NMos
'Shirley Dwarf White'	NMos
'Shirley Fireglow'	See A. 'Harveyi'
'Show-Off'	NMos
'Silver Wedding'	NMos
'Snow Princess'	SDeJ
'Sparkle'	NMos
'Stan's Delight'	NMos
'Sue'	NMos
'Tango'	NMos
'Tantivvy'	NMos
'Tarantella'	NMos
'Teresa'	NMos
'Tiny Blue'	NMos
'Topsy'	LAma NMos
'Troutbeck'	NMos
'Ullswater'	NMos
'Vanessa'	NMos
'Viola Michelssen'	NMos
'Violacea Semiplena'	NMos
'Violetta'	LAma
'Vivid'	LAma NMos NRog
'Warren'	NMos
'Wastwater'	NMos
'Wetterflow's Triumph'	NMos
'White Admiral'	NMos
'White Rajah'	NMos
'Wilma'	NMos

'Windermere'	NMos

ACHLYS (Berberidaceae)

¶ ***triphylla***	WDav

ACHNATHERUM See STIPA

ACIDANTHERA See GLADIOLUS

ACINOS (Labiatae)

§ ***alpinus***	CLew CShe MHig MWat NMen NNrd SChu WTyr
– ssp. ***meridionalis***	NHol
arvensis	See CLINOPODIUM ***acinos***
§ ***corsicus***	CHal CHun ESis GArf SFis WPat WWin

ACIPHYLLA (Umbelliferae)

aurea	CAbb MBal MBro NHar NHol WDav
¶ ***colensoi***	WAbe
glacialis	NHol WDav
glaucescens	GDra MBal NHar NHol SArc
hectorii	GArf GDra
monroi	EPot GDra NTow WHal
pinnatifida	NHar
¶ ***procumbens***	NHar
scott-thomsonii	ECou GCal NHar NHol WCot
squarrosa	ECar
¶ ***subflabellata***	ECar

ACNISTUS (Solanaceae)

australis	See DUNALIA ***a.***

ACONITUM (Ranunculaceae)

anglicum	See A. ***napellus napellus*** Anglicum Group
N ***autumnale***	NBir
'Blue Sceptre'	CSco EBre LBre NOak NRoo SRms
'Bressingham Spire'	CBow CDoC CKel CMGP CSco CShe EBlo EBre ECtt EFou ELan ERav GAbr LBre MBel MBri MWat NDea NKay NOrc NRoo SHer SPer
x ***cammarum*** 'Bicolor'	CBow CCla CDoC CGle CMGP CRow EBlo EBre ECro EFou EGol ELan EOrc GCal GCra GDra LBre MBri NBar NFai NRoo NSti SChu SPer WByw WEas
– 'Grandiflorum Album'	ELan NRoo SPer
§ ***carmichaelii***	CArn CBot CGle CHad CKel EBre ECED ECro EFou ELan LBre MBro MPar MRav NRoo SUsu WCra WHoo WRus
– 'Arendsii'	CCla CPar EBre ECha ECro ECtt EOrc LBre MBri MNFA MSte NBar NDea NFai NRoo SChu SFis SPer SPla WCot WEas
carmichaelii Wilsonii Group	CChu CHan ECro GCra GGar LGan MTol SChu SPer WPer
§ – – 'Barker's Variety'	CRow EFou MFir NDea NHol NSti WMer WRus
– – 'Kelmscott'	EBre ELan LBre MUlv SBla WByw
cilicicum	See ERANTHIS ***hyemalis*** Cilicica Group
♦ ***compactum***	See A. ***napellus vulgare***
¶ 'Eleonara'	EFou
elwesii	GGar
fischeri hort.	See A. ***carmichaelii***
§ ***hemsleyanum***	CArn CBot CChu CGle CRDP CRow ECro EMar ERav GCra LHol MFir MPar MTho NTow SAxl SBla SMrm WCru WEas WOld
hyemalis	See ERANTHIS ***hyemalis***
'Ivorine'	Widely available
lamarckii	See A. ***lycoctonum neapolitanum***
¶ ***lycoctonum***	WDav
§ – ssp. ***lycoctonum***	ECED ECro NSal SRms
§ – ssp. ***neapolitanum***	CBow ELan
§ – ssp. ***vulparia***	CArn CFis CGle CRow CTom ECha ECro EFou GPoy LHol LWad NDea NRoo NSal SUsu WByw WCra
napellus	CArn CShe CTom ECro ECtt EFou GAbr GPoy LGan LHol MBro MHew MPit MWat NFai NNor NSel SIde WHoo WOld WRus WWye
– 'Albidum'	MBri NSti WByw
§ – ***napellus*** Anglicum Group	CBre CKin CRow NSal NSti WCot
– 'Sphere's Variety'	NOrc
¶ – ssp. ***vulgare*** 'Albidum'	CMGP ECha
§ – – 'Carneum'	CGle EBre ECha EFou ELan LBre NRoo NSti SChu WByw WDav WEas WHer WRus
neapolensis	See A. ***lycoctonum neapolitanum***
'Newry Blue'	CBos CPar EHal ELan LWad MBri MPit NHol NKay WMer WPer
orientale hort.	See A. ***lycoctonum vulparia***
♦ ***pyrenaicum***	See A. ***lycoctonum neapolitanum***
septentrionale	See A. ***lycoctonum lycoctonum***
smithii	CBrd
'Spark's Variety'	CDoC CHan CSco EBre ECED ELan EOrc GCal LBre LWad MBel MBri MRav NKay NOrc NRoo NSti SChu SCro SDix SHig SMad
¶ ***spicatum***	SAxl
x ***tubergenii***	See ERANTHIS ***hyemalis*** Tubergenii Group
volubile hort.	See A. ***hemsleyanum***
vulparia	See A. ***lycoctonum v.***

ACONOGONON See PERSICARIA

ACORUS (Araceae)

calamus	CArn CBen CGle CRow CWGN EHon EWav Effi GPoy LMay MSta NDea SHig SWat WChe WHol

– 'Variegatus'	CB&S CBen CGle CRDP CRow CWGN EBre ECha ECtt EGol EHon EMFW EPla EWav GAbr GCal LBre LMay MBal MSta NDea SHig SLon SPer SWat WChe WHol WWye
gramineus	CBen CGle CRow EFou EMFW LMay SWat WWye
N– 'Oborozuki'	CRow
N– 'Ogon' (v)	CBen CChu CElw CGle CHan COtt CRow CWit EBlo EBre ECha ECtt EFou EGol EHal EHoe EPar EPla EPot GCal LBre LHil MUlv NRar SAxl SMad WRus WWye
– 'Pusillus'	CLew CRiv CRow
– 'Variegatus'	Widely available
– 'Yodo-no-yuki'	CRow

ACRADENIA (Rutaceae)

frankliniae	CAbb CChu CPle CTre IBar IBlr LTil SArc SBor SSpi WBod WSHC

ACRIDOCARPUS (Malpighiaceae)

¶ *natalitius*	CTro

ACROCLADIUM See **CALLIERGON**

ACTAEA (Ranunculaceae)

§ *alba*	CBrd CCMG CChu CCla CHan CRow ECha ECro EPar GPoy IBlr MBri MUlv NHar NSal SAxl SMad WOMN WWat WWye
§ *erythrocarpa* Fischer	CHan ECro GDra GPoy MMil MSte NHol SDix WEas WOMN WWin
– hort.	See A. ***rubra***
pachypoda	See A. ***alba***
§ *rubra*	CBro CCla CHan CMHG CRow ECha ECro ELun EPar GCal IBlr MBri MUlv NHar NHol NRar NSti SAxl SFar SHer SSpi WByw WHal WWat
– *alba*	See A. ***r. neglecta***
– ssp. *arguta*	NHol
§ – f. *neglecta*	CHan NHar NRar
spicata	CLew CRDP ECro GPoy MHew MSte NHol NSal NSti
– var. *alba*	See A. ***spicata***
– var. *rubra*	See A. ***erythrocarpa*** Fischer

ACTINELLA (Compositae)

scaposa	See TETRANEURIS ***scaposa***

ACTINIDIA † (Actinidiaceae)

arguta	CB&S CCla CDoC
– (m)	CB&S SHBN
¶ – 'Blaek'	LBuc
– 'Issai' (s-p)	ERea ESim LBuc WHig
chinensis hort.	See A. ***deliciosa***
§ *deliciosa*	CBow CGre CLan CMac CSco CWit ELan ENot ISea LHol MGos NBar SSpi WCru WSHC WStI
F– (f)	IJoh SHBN SPer WDin WHig
– (m)	IJoh SDea SPer WDin WHig
– 'Atlas'	MBri
F– 'Bruno' (f)	ISea
F– 'Hayward' (f)	CB&S CBow CDoC CMac COtt EBre ELan EPla ERea IOrc ISea LBre MBri MGos MMor MWat NPal SBra SDea SHBN WWeb
F– hermaphrodite	SSpi
F– 'Jenny' (s-p)	MGos
– 'Tomuri' (m)	CB&S CBow CDoC CMac COtt EBre ELan EPla ERea IOrc ISea LBre MWat NPal SBra SHBN WWeb
kolomikta (v)	Widely available
pilosula	GCal
polygama	WSHC

ACTINOTUS (Umbelliferae)

helianthi	SMrm

ADELOCARYUM See **LINDELOFIA**

ADENOPHORA † (Campanulaceae)

aurita	CCMG SBla
bulleyana	CHan CSev ECro IBlr NCat NOak WPer
confusa	LAbb
coronopifolia	EPad
forrestii	CHan LHil
himalayana	CLew CSam CSun ECro EPad LHil NRed WHil
khasiana	CHan GCal
latifolia Fischer	GCra WHCG
– hort.	See A. ***pereskiifolia***
liliifolia	CBrd CDec CRDP ECro ELan EMar EPad GCal LAbb MNFA NBro NCat NSti SAxl SCro SHer SMrm SUsu WHCG WHoo WPer
nikoensis	CLew ECro EPad WPer
¶ – *stenophylla*	MHig
nipponica	See A. ***nikoensis stenophylla***
§ *pereskiifolia*	CCMG CRDP ECro EPad MNFA MTol NRed SSou WCot WPer
– var. *heterotricha*	EPad
polyantha	CHan EPad
♦ *polymorpha*	See A. ***nikoensis***
potaninii	CHan ECro EPad GCal MNFA NBro WPer
– 'Alba'	CHan
– dark form	EFol
remotiflora	ECro
sp. AGSJ 227	GArf
¶ *sublata*	CHan
takedae	ECro EPad LAbb LWad WPer
– var. *howozara*	EPad NTow
tashiroi	CHan CNic CRDP ECro EPad MBel MTol NTow SCro SIgm SMrm WHal WHoo WOld
triphylla	EPad
– var. *hakusanensis*	NHar
– var. *japonica*	ECro EPad

ADIANTUM † (Adiantaceae)

capillus-veneris	CHEx NMar SRms
– 'Banksianum'	NMar
– 'Mairisii'	See A. x ***mairisii***
– 'Pointonii'	NMar
concinnum	NMar

cuneatum	See A. ***raddianum***
diaphanum	NMar
edgeworthii	NMar
formosum	NMar
henslowianum	NMar
§ x ***mairisii***	NMar
monochlamys	NKay
* ***monocolor***	MBri
pedatum	CGle CHEx CHal CPar CRDP EBre ECha EFou ELan GAri LBre LWad MBal MBri NHol NKay NOrc SApp SBar SPer SSpi SWat
– var. ***aleuticum***	See A. ***p. subpumilum***
§ – Asiatic form	CMil CRDP CWGN EBre ELan LBre LWad MBri NBir NHol NKay SApp SMad SRms SSpi SWas WCot
– 'Imbricatum'	NHar NHol NMar SBla SRms
– ***japonicum***	See A. ***p.*** Asiatic form
– 'Laciniatum'	CHal NKay SRms
– var. ***minus***	See A. ***p. subpumilum***
– 'Miss Sharples'	NMar SRms
– ***roseum***	See A. ***p.*** Asiatic form
§ – var. ***subpumilum***	CRDP ELan GDra IOrc MBri NBro NHar NHol NKay SBla SSpi WRic
– – f.***minimum***	NMar
peruvianum	MBri
pubescens	MBri NMar
§ ***raddianum***	CHal NMar SSpi
– 'Brilliantelse'	MBri NMar
– 'Crested Majus'	NMar
– 'Crested Micropinnulum'	NMar
– 'Deflexum'	NMar
– 'Elegans'	NMar
– 'Feltham Beauty'	NMar
– 'Fragrans'	See A. ***r.*** 'Fragrantissimum'
§ – 'Fragrantissimum'	MBri NMar
– 'Fritz Luthi'	CHal MBri NMar
– 'Gracilis'	See A. ***r.*** 'Gracillimum'
§ – 'Gracillimum'	NMar
– 'Grandiceps'	NMar
– 'Gympie Gold'	NMar
– 'Kensington Gem'	NMar
– 'Legrand Morgan'	NMar
– 'Legrandii'	NMar
– 'Micropinnulum'	NMar
– 'Pacific Maid'	NMar
– 'Pacottii'	NMar
– 'Triumph'	NMar
– 'Tuffy Tips'	NMar
– 'Variegated Tessellate'	NMar
– 'Victoria's Elegans'	NMar
– 'Weigandii'	NMar
venustum	CBos CDoC CGle CRDP EBul ECha EPot MBal MPar NKay NMar SApp SBla SDix SFar SSpi SWat WAbe WCot WEas WFib WOMN WRic

ADLUMIA (Papaveraceae)

fungosa	CGle CNic CRDP ECro EMar GCra LWad NSti SAxl WCot WCru WMar

ADONIS (Ranunculaceae)

aestivalis	SMrm
amurensis	EBre EPar EPot LAma LBre MUlv
– 'Flore Pleno'	COtt EBlo EBre EGol EPar LBre MBri MUlv SPer SRms
– 'Fukujukai'	EBre ECha ECro LBre LRHS SPer
¶ ***annua***	MHew
brevistyla	NTow
vernalis	EPar EPot GPoy SMrm SRms

ADOXA (Adoxaceae)

moschatellina	CKin MTho WHer WWye

AECHMEA † (Bromeliaceae)

caerulea	See A. ***lueddemanniana***
chantinii	MBri
fasciata	MBri
Foster's Favorite	SLMG
* 'Grand Prix'	MBri
'Romero'	MBri

AEGLE (Rutaceae)

sepiaria	See PONCIRUS ***trifoliata***

AEGOPODIUM (Umbelliferae)

podagraria 'Variegatum'	Widely available

AEONIUM (Crassulaceae)

arboreum	CHEx GAri SLMG
– 'Albovariegatum'	NRar
– 'Atropurpureum'	CHEx CHal ERea IBlr MBri SHer SLMG WEas
– var. ***rubrolineatum***	NRar
balsamiferum	CHEx NRar
canariense	CHEx
cuneatum	CHEx
x ***domesticum***	See AICHRYSON x ***d.***
haworthii	CHEx CTro GAri
– 'Variegatum'	CHEx
holochrysum	IBlr
lindleyi	CHal
nobile	CHEx SLMG
percarneum	SLMG
simsii	CHEx
tabuliforme	CHEx NBro SLMG
undulatum	CHEx
'Zwartkop'	CBar CHEx CHal CTre NWyt WEas

AESCHYNANTHUS (Gesneriaceae)

'Big Apple'	WEfe
'Greensleeves'	WEfe
hildebrandii	WEfe
'Hot Flash'	WEfe
'Little Tiger'	WEfe
lobbianus	See A. ***radicans***
§ ***longicaulis***	CHal MBri
♦ ***marmoratus***	See A. ***longicaulis***
'Mira'	MBri
'Mona'	MBri
♦ ***parvifolius***	See A. ***radicans***
'Pulobbia' I	MBri
'Purple Star'	MBri
§ ***radicans***	EBak MBri

– *lobbianus*	See A. *radicans*
'Rigel'	MBri
* *rigidus*	SLMG
speciosus	CHal CTro LAbb
*– *rubens**	MBri
'Topaz'	MBri

AESCULUS † (Hippocastanaceae)

x *arnoldiana*	CMCN
californica	CChu CCla CTho CTrw EArb SMad SSpi WWat
x *carnea*	CDoC EArb EBre ELan GRei ISea LBre MBal MBar
– 'Aureomarginata'	EMon
– 'Briotii'	CBra CDoC CLnd COtt CSco EBre EHar ELan ENot IHos IJoh IOrc LBre LBuc LPan MBri MGos NBee NWea SHBN SHer SPer SSta WDin WStI
– 'Plantierensis'	CTho ENot SSpi
¶ *chinensis*	EArb ISea
§ *flava*	CCla CMCN CSco CTho EHar ENot MBri SSpi SSta WCoo
– *vestita*	CDoC
♦ *georgiana*	See A. *sylvatica*
glabra	CLnd CMCN EArb EHar MUlv
¶ – 'October Red'	WMou
hippocastanum	CB&S CBra CKin CLnd CPer CSco EBre ELan ENot GRei IDai IJoh ISea LBre LBuc MBal MBar MBri NBee NWea SHBN SPer WDin WMou WStI
§ – 'Baumannii' (d)	CDoC CLnd COtt CSco ENot MBri MGos SPer WDin WStI
¶ – 'Digitata'	SMad
– 'Flore Pleno'	See A. *h.* 'Baumannii'
– 'Pyramidalis'	EHar EMon
indica	CCla CHEx CLnd CSam CSco CTrw EBre ELan ENot IHos IOrc ISea LBre MBri SPer SSpi SSta WCoo WDin WMou
– 'Sydney Pearce'	CMCN EHar MBri MMea SHil
x *mutabilis* 'Induta'	MBlu MBri SHil SMad
– 'Penduliflora'	CDoC CTho
¶ x *neglecta*	CLnd
– 'Erythroblastos'	CLnd CMCN CTho EHar MBlu SHil SSpi WMou WWat
♦ x *neglecta georgiana*	See A. *sylvatica*
octandra	See A. *flava*
parviflora	CB&S CCla CGre CMCN COtt CSco CTho EHar ELan ENot ERav LNet MBal MBlu MBri MUlv NBee SHil SMad SPer SSpi WDin WWat
§ *pavia*	CChu CCla CMCN CTho EArb EHar ISea SSpi
– 'Atrosanguinea'	CDoC MBri NPal SHil SSpi
– 'Koehnei'	MBri
– 'Rosea Nana'	CMCN MBlu SSpi
splendens	See A. *pavia*
§ *sylvatica*	SSpi
turbinata	CLnd CMCN CTho EArb EHar ISea SSpi

AETHIONEMA (Cruciferae)

armenum	CHun CSam ECro EPot ESis MBro MPlt SIng WDav WPer
coridifolium	ESis MFir WPer
¶ *diastrophis*	NWCA
graecum	See A. *saxatile*
grandiflorum	CMHG CShe LBee MFir MHig NHol NNor NTow NWCA SBla SSou WPer
– Pulchellum Group	CGle CNic EPot LHop MBro MCas MNFA NHol NKay NMen WHoo WWin
iberideum	MWat NKay SRms WPat
oppositifolium	EPot MBro MWat NHar NKay NMen NNrd WDav WHoo
§ *saxatile*	NHol
schistosum	CNic SBar WDav WPer
thomasianum	NHol
'Warley Rose'	CGle CLew CNic CPar CShe EBre EFou ELan EPot LBre MCas MHig MPla MTho MWat NGre NHol NKay NMen NNor SBla WHil WHoo WPat WPer WWin
'Warley Ruber'	CNic MHig NHol

AGAPANTHUS † (Liliaceae/Alliaceae)

§ *africanus*	ESma IBlr NRog SLMG WPer
*– *albus**	CB&S CBow WPer
¶ – *minor*	CTro
* *alboroseus*	WThi
Ardernei hybrid	CBot ECha GCal IBlr MUlv
'Ben Hope'	MUlv
¶ 'Blue Baby'	CB&S
'Blue Giant'	EBlo MUlv
'Blue Imp'	ESma
'Blue Moon'	CBro ECha MUlv SHig
'Blue Star'	ERav MUlv
'Blue Triumphator '	LBow WMer
'Bressingham Blue'	EBlo EBre GCal LBre MRav MUlv NRoo
¶ 'Bressingham Bounty'	EBlo
'Bressingham White'	CGle EBlo EBre ECtt EFol GAbr GAri GCHN LBre MRav MUlv NRoo WRus
'Buckingham Palace'	SSpi
§ *campanulatus*	CB&S CGle CHad CKel CMon CRDP EBre ELan ERav GDra IDai ISea LBre SCro SHig SPla WDav
– var. *albidus*	CB&S CBos CCla CHad CMGP CRDP EBre ECha EFou ELan GCal IBlr IDai ISea LBre MPlt MSte NHol NRoo NSti NVic SGil SHer SHig SPer
– *albovittatus*	CRow LGre
– bright blue	GCal
– cobalt blue	ECha
– 'Isis'	CBro EBlo EBre ECha GCal IBlr LBre MUlv SApp SPer
– ssp. *patens*	EBre LBre SApp SHig SPer WWat
– 'Profusion'	ECha MUlv
– 'Ultramarine'	CKel
– variegated form	ECha WCot
'Castle of Mey'	LGre LHyd MUlv
¶ *caulescens*	IBlr
¶ *comptonii*	CMon
¶ – forms	SLMG
¶ 'Donau' ('Danube')	CBow
¶ 'Findlay's Blue'	SWas
Giant hybrids	ERav
§ Headbourne hybrids	Widely available
– 'Golden Rule' (v)	CRow EHoe ELan LGre

'Holbrook' CSam
'Hydon Mist' LHyd
¶ ***inapertus hollandii*** CChu GCal
¶ – ssp. ***intermedius*** CHan
¶ 'Kew White' SDix
'Kingston Blue' ECha SWas
'Lady Moore' MPar
'Lilliput' Widely available
'Loch Hope' CKel MUlv
* 'Marjorie' SBla
'Midnight Blue' CGle ELan ERav GCal IBlr LHil MBel MUlv SHig
'Midnight Star' ERav MUlv
¶ 'Moonstar' SApp
'Mooreanus' SUsu
'Norman Hadden' EBul
¶ ***nutans*** 'Albus' GCal
Palmer's hybrids See A. Heabourne hybrids
'Peter Pan' CBow CRow EFou GCal SApp
praecox CDoC IBlr
¶ – 'Flore Pleno' EMon
– 'Maximus Albus' IBlr
– ***minimus*** ssp. IBlr
§ – ssp. ***orientalis*** CHEx CHan ERea GAri LHil NPal WWat
– – var.***albiflorus*** CDoC LBow NPal
¶ – – 'Mount Thomas' CHan
¶ – ssp. ***praecox*** EBre LBre
¶ – 'Variegatus' SLMG
– ***vittatus*** (v) CHan
'Purple Cloud' CB&S
'Sapphire' CB&S
'Sky Star' ERav MUlv
'Snowy Owl' CCla CKel MUlv
¶ 'Tinkerbell' WMer
'Torbay' MUlv SBla SHig
umbellatus See AA. ***campanulatus, praecox orientalis***
'Underway' CMon
¶ 'White Dwarf' EFou
'White Star' ERav MUlv
'White Starlet' ERav MUlv
'Windsor Castle' SSpi
'Zella Thomas' LHyd

AGAPETES (Ericaceae)

buxifolia WBod
'Ludgvan Cross' CB&S CGre MBal
serpens CGre LTil MBal
– 'Nepal Cream' CGre MBal

AGARISTA (Ericaceae)

See Plant Deletions

AGASTACHE (Labiatae)

anethiodora See A. ***foeniculum***
anisata See A. ***foeniculum***
barberi CSun LBlm WWye
– 'Firebird' CBot CGle CRDP GCal LGre SBla
§ ***foeniculum*** Widely available
– 'Alabaster' CChu CCla CCor CGle CRDP ECha ECro EFou EMon GCal LGan LGre SAxl WWye
§ ***mexicana*** CFis CHan ECro EFol ELan EMon EOrc GCal LHop MHew NTow SUsu WHer WWye
¶ – 'Carille Carmine' WPer
¶ – 'Champagne' WPer
– 'Rosea' CGle WCot
nepetoïdes MHew NSal WWye
pallidiflora LGre WWye
rugosa CArn CSev ECro GPoy MHew NSal SWat WPer WWye
¶ ***urticifolia*** MHew NSal
– 'Alba' ECro EGol EHal EOrc WPer

AGATHAEA (Compositae)

coelestis See FELICIA ***amelloïdes***

AGATHIS (Araucariaceae)

australis CTre

AGAVE (Agavaceae)

affinis See A. ***sobria sobria***
americana CB&S CGre CHEx CTro IBlr LHil LPal LPan MUlv SArc SLMG SMad
– 'Marginata' CGre CHal IBlr LHop
– 'Mediopicta' CHEx SArc SLMG
– 'Variegata' CB&S CHEx MBri SArc SCro SLMG SSpi
¶ ***angustifolia*** SLMG
avellanidens See A. ***sebastiana***
celsii CHEx SArc
cerulata See A. ***sobria sobria***
coarctata See A. ***mitriiformis***
ellemeetiana CHEx
ferox CHEx SLMG
filifera CHEx SLMG
franzosinii SArc
gigantea See FURCRAEA ***foetida***
¶ ***neomexicana*** SIgm
parryi CHEx CTro SArc SIgm
– ***couesii*** See A. ***p. parryi***
– var. ***parryi*** SArc
schottii SIgm
* ***striata rubra*** SIgm
utahensis SIgm
– ssp. ***kaibabensis*** SArc
victoriae-reginae WMar
weberi CHEx
xylonacantha CHEx

AGERATINA See EUPATORIUM

AGERATUM (Compositae)

See Plant Deletions

AGLAONEMA (Araceae)

§ ***crispum*** MBri
* – 'Marie' MBri
'Malay Beauty' MBri
roebelinii See A. ***crispum***
'Silver Queen' MBri

AGRIMONIA (Rosaceae)

eupatoria CArn CKin Effi GPoy LHol MChe MHew NLan NSel SHer SIde SWat WCla WGwy WOak WWye
odorata See A. ***repens***

§ *repens* MHew NSal WGwy WNdy

AGROPYRON (Gramineae)

glaucum See ELYMUS *hispidus*
magellanicum See ELYMUS *magellanicus*
pubiflorum See ELYMUS *magellanicus*
♦*scabrum* See ELYMUS *scabrus*

AGROSTEMMA (Caryophyllaceae)

coronaria See LYCHNIS *coronaria*
githago CSFH MHew NMir NSal WCla

AGROSTIS (Gramineae)

canina 'Silver Needles' (v) CNic EHoe EMon ETPC GCal SApp
♦*karsensis* See A. *stolonifera*
¶ *stolonifera* ETPC

AGROSTOCRINUM (Liliaceae/Phormiaceae)

See Plant Deletions

AICHRYSON (Crassulaceae)

§ x *domesticum* CHEx CHal SLMG
– 'Variegatum' CHal EBak ESis SLMG

AILANTHUS (Simaroubaceae)

§ *altissima* CB&S CBra CChu CHEx CLnd CSco CWSG EBre ELan ENot IOrc LBre LPan MGos NBee SPer WCoo WDin WNor WStI
glandulosa See A. *altissima*

AIPHANES (Palmae)

¶ *caryotifolia* LPal

AJANIA (Compositae)

tibetica CNic MFos

AJUGA (Labiatae)

'Brockbankii' CHal
genevensis 'Tottenham' MBri WMer
metallica See A. *pyramidalis*
§ *pyramidalis* CHal CKel CRow ECha EGol SCro SSou WHer
– 'Metallica Crispa' CLew CMHG CRDP CRow CShe ESma NEgg NMir NNrd WMer WThu
reptans CFis CHan CKin CSFH ECtt GPoy LHol LMay MChe MHew MPla NMen NMir NSal WChe WTyr
– 'Alba' CArn CBre CCot CGle CHal CHan CNat CNic CRiv CRow CTom CWGN ECar ECha EFou EGol EMar GCal SMrm SPer SSou WBon WByw WHal WMer WPer WWye
§ – 'Atropurpurea' Widely available
– 'Braunherz' CB&S CElw CGle CHad CHal CRow CSam EBar EBre ECtt EFol EFou EGol EHoe ELan EPot GAbr LBre LHop MBri MFir MRav MSte NEgg NOak NSti SPer WHal WHen WMer
– 'Burgundy Glow' (v) Widely available
*– 'Burgundy Red' GDra
§ – 'Catlin's Giant' Widely available
– 'Delight' (v) EFol EFou ELan EMon EPot IBar MBri MFir NMir NNrd SBod SHer WCHb WCra WEas
¶ – 'Harlequin' WMer
¶ – 'Jumbo' EGol
– 'Jungle Beauty' CCor CElw CGle CHan CRDP CRow CWGN EBre EFou EOrc EPar GCal LBre NFai SApp SAxl SPer SSpi SUsu WHen WHer
– 'Macrophylla' See A. *r.* 'Catlin's Giant'
– 'Multicolor'/ 'Rainbow'/ 'Tricolor' (v) Widely available
– 'Pink Elf' CNic CRow CTom EBre EBur ECha EFol ELan ESis LBlm LBre NNor NOak NSti SHer SUsu WBon WHoo WPer
– 'Pink Surprise' CElw CGle EFol EFou EGol EHoe EMar EMon LRHS MMil NGre WBon WCHb WHal
– 'Purple Torch' CGle ECha ESis MBal MBri WBon WEas WMer
– 'Purpurea' See A. *r.* 'Atropurpurea'
– 'Silver Shadow' EMon WCHb
– 'Tortoiseshell' (v) CGle
– 'Variegata' ('Argentea') Widely available

AKEBIA (Lardizabalaceae)

x *pentaphylla* CBow ERea SBra
quinata CB&S CBot CBra CChu CCla CMac CSam CSco EBre ELan ENot IJoh LBre LHop MBri MWat NHol NSti SBra SHBN SLon SPer SReu SSpi SSta WDin WSHC WWat
trifoliata CB&S CChu MUlv SBra SSpi WSHC

ALANGIUM (Alangiaceae)

¶ *chinense* CB&S
platanifolium CBot CLan CMCN EPla LTil

ALBIZIA (Leguminosae)

distachya See PARASERIANTHES *d.*
§ *julibrissin* CB&S CHan CWit EHal ELan ERea ISea LGan SArc SEng WFro
– var. *rosea* CAbb CGre CHEx CPle EHar ESma IOrc MUlv SArc SDry SHil SMad SSpi WCru WNor WSHC WWeb
lophantha See PARASERIANTHES *distachya*

ALBUCA (Liliaceae/Hyacinthaceae)

canadensis NRog
¶ *caudata* CMon
humilis CAvo EPot ESis MHig NRog SIng WOMN
¶ *juncifolia* CMon
nelsonii CAvo CMon NRog

ALCEA (Malvaceae)

ficifolia CGle SSvw

§ ***rosea***	CGle CHad EJud LWad MBri SSvw WEas
– Chater's Double Group	CB&S CBow EBre ECtt ELan LBre LWad MBri MFir NNor SHer SRms
¶ – deep yellow	LWad
¶ – forms	LWad
– Majorette Group	ECtt
– 'Nigra'	CArn CCMG CGle CHad CMil EFou GCal GCra LWad MFir MSte MUlv NNor NRoo SMad WEas WHal
– Powder Puff Group	ELan
¶ – 'Summer Carnival'	NMir SRms
§ ***rugosa***	CGle CHad CMil CSam ELan EOrc EPad LGan MSte SDix WCot WEas WHil WOMN WOld WRus

ALCHEMILLA † (Rosaceae)

abyssinica	CDoC CElw CRiv CRow NCat NSti SHer SIng
****affinis venosa***	EPla
N***alpina***	CBro CCla CFis CHad CPar CRow EFol ELan EMNN EPar LAbb MHig MTho NEgg NHol NLan NMir NNor NRoo SIng SPer SSpi WCla WHil WOak WOld WPbr WWin
arvensis	See APHANES ***a.***
conjuncta	CBot CBre CElw CHan CLew CNic ECha ECro EFou EGol ELan ELun EMar GAbr LHop MTho NBro NHol NOak NRya SMrm WByw WEas WGwy
elisabethae	EMon EPad EPla WCHb
ellenbeckii	CElw CLew CMHG CNic CTom EBre EFol ELan ESis GCHN LBee LBre MFir MHig MPlt MRav NMen NMir NNor NNrd NRoo NSti NWCA SFis WByw WEas WPer WWat
erythropoda	CArn CBro CCla CElw CHan CRow CSco CShe ECha EFol EFou EGol EHoe ELan EOrc ESis MBri MCas NHol NSti SPer SSpi SWas WEas WRus WWat WWin
faeroensis	EPla LBee MDHE MMil NHol SWas WWat
glaucescens	CNat
lapeyrousei	NMir
mollis	Widely available
*– 'Grandiflora'	MUlv
*– 'Robusta'	ECro ESma WHal
'Mr Poland's Variety'	See A. ***venosa***
plicatula	EPad
¶ ***pumila***	ECro
¶ ***saxatilis***	NHol
¶ ***scalaris***	CCor
N***splendens***	CArn CPar CRiv ECro EOrc GAri LGan NHol NRoo
§ ***venosa***	SAxl SPer WWat
vulgaris hort.	See A. ***xanthochlora***
§ ***xanthochlora***	ECro EGol Effi GGar GPoy MHew NMir NSal

ALECTRYON (Sapindaceae)

excelsus	CHEx

ALETRIS (Liliaceae/Melanthiaceae)

farinosa	NSal

ALISMA (Alismataceae)

lanceolatum	WChe
plantago-aquatica	CBen CKin CRDP CRow CWGN EHon EMFW LMay MSta NDea SHig SWat WChe WHol
– ***parviflorum***	CBen CRDP CWGN EMFW LMay MSta NDea SHig SRms SWat WChe

ALKANNA (Boraginaceae)

orientalis	WCru
tinctoria	MChe NSal

ALLAMANDA (Apocynaceae)

§ ***blanchetii***	MNew
cathartica	MBri
– 'Birthe'	MBri
*– 'Chocolate Swirl'	MNew
– 'Stansill's Double'	MNew
♦ ***neriifolia***	See A. ***schottii***
♦ ***violacea***	See A. ***blanchetii***

ALLARDIA (Compositae)

§ ***glabra***	WPer

ALLIARIA (Cruciferae)

petiolata	CArn CKin CSev WCla WHer

ALLIUM † (Liliaceae/Alliaceae)

acuminatum	GCHN MFos NBir WChr WCot
aflatunense hort.	See A. ***stipitatum***
aflatunense Fedtschenko	CBro CGle CMon ECha ECtt EFou EPar ETub LAma LBow MBri MNFA NBro NEgg NRog NSti SIng SUsu WCra WPer
– 'Purple Sensation'	CAvo CBro CGle ECha EFou EPot ETub LAma LBow MBri NRog SApp SMad SUsu WPer
akaka	EPot LAma
♦ ***albidum***	See A. ***denudatum***
albopilosum	See A. ***christophii***
altissimum	LRHS
amabile	See A. ***mairei a.***
ampeloprasum	ECha WPer
– var. ***babingtonii***	CCor IEde
amphibolum	CNic
amplectens	GDra WChr
§ ***angulosum***	MMil WCot
atropurpureum	ECha EPar LBow NHol SPou
azureum	See A. ***caeruleum***
'Beau Regard'	LAma
beesianum hort.	See A. ***cyaneum***
– W W Smith	CGle EBre EBur EPot ESis LBre MBal MHig MNFA MPar MPlt MSte NBir NHol NRya NWCA SPou WCot WOMN
¶ – phyllodic form	SPou
¶ ***bucharicum***	CMon
bulgaricum	See NECTAROSCORDUM ***siculum bulgaricum***

§ ***caeruleum***	CArn CAvo CBro CGle ELan EPar ETub LAma LBlo LBow MBri MNFA NBir NRog NSti SGil SSpi SUsu WHal WHil WPer WSun
♦– ***azureum***	See A. ***c.***
caesium	SPou
callimischon	CBro CMon EPot MHig WChr
– ssp. ***haemostictum***	EBul MPar SIng SPou SWas
canadense	CLew CSam WHal
§ ***carinatum***	GCHN
§ – ssp. ***pulchellum***	CArn CAvo CBos CBro CGle CHan CMil CNic CRDP CRiv CTom EBul ECar ECha EFou EPar EPot LAma LBow MBal MBro MNFA MPar MTho MWat NHol NNor NTow SUsu WPer
– – f.***album***	CAvo CBro CMon ECha EFou EMon EPar EPot ETub MBal MBro MPar NSti NTow SUsu WWin
cepa	CHal CSFH
– Aggregatum Group	MPlt WHil
– 'Perutile'	CArn CHal EJud GPoy ILis SHer SIde
– Proliferum Group	CArn CSev EJud GPoy IEde ILis MChe MFir NSel SHer SIde WCHb WGwy WOak
cernuum	Widely available
– 'Hidcote'	EMon WCot
– var. ***neomexicanum***	EBul
¶ ***chamaemoly littorale*** AB&S 4387	CMon
§ ***christophii***	CAvo CBro CGle EBre ECha EFou ELan EOrc EPar EPot ERav ETub LAma LBlo LBow LBre MBri NRog NSel NSti SIng SSpi WEas WHoo WKif
cirrhosum	See A. ***carinatum pulchellum***
cowanii	See A. ***neapolitanum*** Cowanii Group
¶ ***cupanii***	CMon
§ ***cyaneum***	CBro CGle CHal CTom EBre ECar EFol ELan EPot LBre LGan MCas MFos NHol NNrd NRya NWCA SGil SPou SUsu WEas WOMN WRus WWin
¶– ***album***	SPou
– 'Cobalt Blue'	SSou
cyathophorum	CArn
– var. ***farreri***	CArn CAvo CBro CHal CMon CNic CRiv CSun ECar ELan EPot ESis MBal MHig NHol NNrd SIng WAbe WDav WEas WHil WOMN WThu
§ ***denudatum***	SIng
dichlamydeum	CBro SPou WChr
§ ***drummondii***	CMon
elatum	See A. ***macleanii***
falcifolium	WChr
farreri	See A. ***cyathophorum f.***
fimbriatum var. ***purdyi***	WChr
fistulosum	CArn CHal CHun CSFH EJud ELan EPla GPoy IEde ILis MChe MFir MHew SHer SIde WGwy WOak WPer WWye
flavum	CArn CAvo CBro CGle CHal CMon CRDP CTom EBar ECha ELan EPar LBow MHig MPar MWat NHol NMen SIng SUsu SWas WCla WHil WPer WRus
§ – 'Blue Leaf'	EBar EPot MFir
– forms	SPou
♦– ***glaucum***	See A. ***f.*** 'Blue Leaf'
– 'Golden Showers'	EBar
– var. ***minus***	CNic ELan MTho NHol NWCA
¶ – var. ***nanum***	MFos
– ssp. ***tauricum***	CMon SIng
geyeri	WChr WDav
giganteum	CArn CB&S CBot CBow CFis EFou ELan EPar ETub GCra LAma LBlo LBow MBri MFir MRav NNor NRog NSel SIng WCra
'Gladiator'	LAma
glaucum	See A. ***senescens montanum glaucum***
'Globus'	EPot
¶ ***goodingii***	CNic
heldreichii	SPou
¶ ***hierochuntinum*** S&L 79	CMon
¶ ***humile***	ESis
¶ ***hyalinum***	CMon
§ ***insubricum*** forms	CNic MS&S NBir
kansuense	See A. ***sikkimense***
karataviense	CArn CAvo CBro CElw CGle CLew CRDP ECha EFou ELan EMon EOrc EPar EPot ETub LAma LBow MBri MTho NBir NHol NRar NRog NSti SIng WCra WHil WPat WPer
kharputense	LAma
¶ ***libani***	WPer
¶ ***libonicum***	WPer
¶ ***loratum***	EPar
'Lucy Ball'	LAma
§ ***macleanii***	EMon EPar ETub LAma LBow
macranthum	GCHN MPar MSte NHol SWas WDav
macrochaetum	LAma
mairei	CBro CNic CRiv EPot ESis GCHN MCas MDHE SGil WAbe WHal WOMN
§ – var. ***amabile***	MBal MFos MHig MPar NHol NNrd NRya NTow SGil WOMN
– – pink form	NBir SPou
maximowiczii	SIng
moly	CAvo CBro CCla CGle CNic CRiv ELan EPar ETub LAma LBlo LBow MBri NHol NMen NRog NRoo NRya NSti SIng WCla WEas WPer WThu WWin
– 'Jeannine'	CBro
multibulbosum	See A. ***nigrum***
murrayanum hort.	See A. ***unifolium***
narcissiflorum hort.	See A. ***insubricum***
– Villars	EPot MHig MPar NHol NMen NSti SIng SSou SUsu WAbe
– pink form	NHar
neapolitanum	CArn CGle CLew EBul ELan EPar LAma MBri MBro MNFA NHol NRog NSti SIng WHil WPer
§ – Cowanii Group	CBro NHol WPer
– 'Grandiflorum'	ETub

§ ***nigrum*** EBul EFou EPar ETub LAma MNFA MPar NRog WCot WHal WPer
nuttallii See A. ***drummondii***
obliquum CAvo ECha SWas WPer
odorum Linnaeus See A. ***ramosum***
olympicum MBro SPou WThu
¶ – ACW 1956 CMon
§ ***oreophilum*** CAvo CBro CMea CRDP CRiv ECar ECha ECtt LAma LBlo LBow MBro MFos MHig MNFA NHol NRog NRoo SIng WCla WHil WHoo WPer WSun
– 'Zwanenburg' CBro EPot ETub NMen
orientale EPot LAma
ostrowskianum See A. ***oreophilum***
pallens CBre EFol LGre MTho NBir
paniculatum CAvo MMil SChu
– CDB SPou
paradoxum NBir SPou
¶ – PF 5085 CMon
pedemontanum See A. ***narcissiflorum*** Villars
peninsulare SPou WChr
polyastrum GCHN
pskemense SPou
pulchellum See A. ***carinatum p.***
pyrenaicum hort. See A. ***angulosum***
– Costa & Vayreda CAvo EBlo ELan MNFA
§ ***ramosum*** LAma NCat WPer
'Rien Poortvliet' LAma
rosenbachianum CBro EPar EPot ETub LAma LBow NSti WCra
– 'Album' EPar LAma SIng
roseum CAvo CElw ECtt EMon ETub LAma MPlt NHol NRog SIng WPer WWin
¶ – B&S 396 CMon
§ – var. ***bulbiferum*** MPlt
– 'Grandiflorum' See A. ***r. bulbiferum***
sativum CArn EEls EJud GPoy IEde MHew NSel SHer SIde WOak
– var. ***ophioscordon*** GPoy ILis
¶ ***scabriscapum*** CMon
¶ ***schmitzii*** CMon
schoenoprasum CArn CHal CSFH CSev CTom GPoy IEde LHol MBal MBri MBro MChe MFir MPit NCat NFai NHol NNor NSel SHer SIde WEas WHil WPer WThu WWye
¶ – 'Corsican White' EMon
– fine leaf form MWil
– 'Forescate' COtt EBlo EBre ECha EFou EPla LBre LHol MBal MBri MMil MUlv NHol SHer WCot
– 'Polyphant' CBre
– ***roseum*** GPoy
– 'Shepherds Crooks' WThu
– var. ***sibiricum*** EJud GPoy IEde MBri NSel SDix SIde
– 'Wallington White' EMon
– white form EPla MSte SApp WBon
schubertii CAvo CBro EPar ETub LAma LBow
scorodoprasum ssp. ***jajlae*** CSun MBel NHol NMen WPer
¶ ***scorzonerifolium*** var. ***xericense*** CMon

senescens CArn CElw EBre ECro ELan EPar GCHN LBre MNFA NMen NSti SSpi
§ – ssp. ***montanum*** CCor CLew EBul ELan EPot ERav MBro MCas MHig SDix SIng SUsu WThu
§ – – ssp.***glaucum*** CHan CMea CRiv CTom ECar ECha EPla ESis GCHN MBel NHol WEas WHal WPer
– ssp. ***senescens*** EMon
siculum See NECTAROSCORDUM ***siculum***
§ ***sikkimense*** CSun ECar EPot GDra MBro MPar NFai NHol NNrd NTow NWCA SHer SPou SSou WDav WEas WHil WOMN WPer
sphaerocephalon CArn CAvo CHad CRDP ECha ELan EPar ETub LAma LBlo LBow LHop MNFA NLan NOak NRog NSti SIng SMrm SUsu WEas WPer WShi
stellerianum GCHN WCot WHal WPer
– var. ***kurilense*** CAvo SPou WThu
§ ***stipitatum*** LAma LBow SUsu WCot
– ***album*** CBro ETub LAma LBow
subhirsutum CSam WPer
¶ ***subvillosum*** CMon
tanguticum GCHN
thunbergii CMon EPot NBir WChr
tibeticum See A. ***sikkimense***
triquetrum CAvo CGle CTom ELan ETub GGar IBlr IEde ILis LAma NBir NLan SIng WCru WPer WWin
tuberosum CArn CAvo CHal CLew CSFH CSev EBul ECha EFou EJud EPar GPoy IEde ILis LHol MBri MChe MFir MHew NSel SHer SIde WCHb WHal WHil WPer WWye
§ ***unifolium*** CBro CGle CMon CRDP EBul EPot ESma ETub LAma LBlo LBow MBri MNFA NBir NCat SSpi SWas WChr WCla WDav WPer WRus
ursinum CArn CAvo CKin ETub GPoy IEde LAma LHol NMir WCru WGwy WHen WPer WShi
¶ ***validum*** WDav
vineale CArn
violaceum See A. ***carinatum***
wallichii CMon EMon LAma NBir
¶ – B 445 WDav
zebdanense ETub LAma NHol NRog WCla WPer

ALLOCASUARINA (Casuarinaceae)

distyla ISea

ALMOND See PRUNUS *dulcis*

ALNUS † (Betulaceae)

cordata CB&S CDoC CKin CLnd CPer CSto EBre EHar ELan ENot GRei IJoh IOrc LBre LBuc SHBN SPer SSta WDin WFro WMou
– wild origin CSto
cremastogyne CMCN
fauriei CSto
firma EPla MBlu

– var. ***multinervis***	See A. ***pendula***
– var. ***sieboldiana***	See A. ***sieboldiana***
¶ ***formosana***	EArb
glutinosa	CB&S CBow CDoC CKin CLnd CPer CSam CSto EBre ENot GRei IDai IOrc LBre LBuc MGos NBee NRoo NWea SHBN SPer WDin WMou WStI
– 'Aurea'	EBre EHar LBre WMou
– var. ***barbata***	CSto
– 'Imperialis'	CBow CLnd CPMA CSco CTho EGol EHar ELan ENot MBri SHil SPer SSpi WDin WMou WWat
– f. ***incisa***	ELan
– 'Laciniata'	CDoC CSco CTho IOrc MBlu WMou
– 'Pyramidalis'	WMou
hirsuta	CMCN CSto
incana	CDoC CKin CLnd CPer CSto EBre ENot GRei IOrc LBre LBuc MBar NWea SHBN WDin WMou
– 'Aurea'	CB&S CCla CLnd COtt CSco CTho EBre EHar ELan ENot IOrc LBre MBar MBlu MBri SEng SHBN SHer SPer WDin WMou
– 'Laciniata'	COtt CTho EHar ENot SSpi WDin WMou
– 'Pendula'	CTho EHar SHil WMou
japonica	CSto
maritima	CSto
maximowiczii	CCor CSto
nepalensis	CSto
oblongifolia	CSto
oregona	See A. ***rubra***
§ ***pendula***	CSto EBre LBre
* ***pinnatisecta***	EHar
rhombifolia	CSto
§ ***rubra***	CDoC CKin CLnd CSto ELan ENot GAri GCHN GRei IOrc WDin WMou
§ ***rugosa***	CMCN CSto
serrulata	See A. ***rugosa***
§ ***sieboldiana***	CSto
sinuata	CSto CTho
x ***spaethii***	CTho SHil WMou
¶ ***subcordata***	CLnd EArb
tenuifolia	CSto
viridis	CSto GAri NWea WMou

ALOCASIA (Araceae)

x ***amazonica***	CTro MBri
¶ ***sanderiana***	CTro

ALOË (Liliaceae/Aloëaceae)

arborescens	CHEx
aristata	CBow CHEx CHal MBri SArc SCro SLMG
barbadensis	See A. ***vera***
brevifolia	CHEx
camperi 'Maculata'	MBri
ciliaris	CHEx CTro ERea
¶ ***descoingsii***	SGil
ferox	CHEx
humilis	IBlr
karasbergensis	LHil
mitriformis	CHEx LHil
saponaria	SLMG
sp. yellow flowered	IBlr
striata	CHEx
§ ***vera***	ERea GPoy ILis LHil SHer SIde SLMG WHer
'Walmsley's Blue'	MBri

ALONSOA (Scrophulariaceae)

¶ ***acutifolia***	LHil
¶ ***meridionalis***	CNic
¶ 'Pink Beauty'	SUsu
warscewiczii	CBar CMHG CSam CSun ELan ERav ERea IBlr LAbb LGan LHil SAxl SChu SMrm SUsu WEas WOMN WPer WWin
– pale form	See A. ***w.*** 'Peachy-Keen'
§ – 'Peachy-Keen'	CBar CHad CMHG CSam EMon ERea LHop SAxl SGil SUsu WHal WPer

ALOPECURUS (Gramineae)

alpinus	CElw EHoe EMon EPla ETPC SFar
– ssp. ***glaucus***	EHoe
¶ ***arundinaceus***	ETPC
geniculatus	ETPC
lanatus	NHol SGil SIng
pratensis	MWil
– 'Aureovariegatus'	EHal EHoe EMon EPla ETPC GCal IBlr MSte NBar NEgg NRar SCro SPer SPla WRus
N– 'Aureus'	CMGP CNic CRiv ECha EFou EPar EPot GAbr LHil MBal MPar NBro NHol NSti SCob SFar SSpi WWin

ALOPHIA (Iridaceae)

♦ ***lahue***	See HERBERTIA ***l.***

ALOYSIA (Verbenaceae)

citriodora	See A. ***triphylla***
§ ***triphylla***	Widely available

ALPINIA (Zingiberaceae)

purpurata	MNew
sanderae	See A. ***vittata***
speciosa	See A. ***zerumbet***
§ ***vittata***	MNew
§ ***zerumbet***	MNew

ALSOBIA See EPISCIA

ALSTROEMERIA † (Liliaceae/Alstroemeriaceae)

aurantiaca	See A. ***aurea***
§ ***aurea***	CGle CGre ELan EMar MUlv NCat NSti WCru
– 'Dover Orange'	CB&S CBow CGle CMGP EBre LBre NBar SFis SHer SMrm SPla
– 'Orange King'	CDoC CKel SRms WStI
¶ Beatrix ® / 'Stadoran'	SSmt
brasiliensis	CBro CChu WCot
Diana ®	See A. Mona Lisa ®
¶ Doctor Salter's Hybrids	EFou
¶ Frederika ® / 'Stabrons'	SSmt
Grace ®	See A. King Cardinal ®

hookeri	WOMN
Ileana ®	See A. 'Rita'
Inca hybrids	CB&S
¶ King Cardinal ® / 'Starodo'	SSmt
Ligtu hybrids	CAvo CB&S CBow CDoC CGle CKel CMea CRDP CShe EBlo EBre ECha ELan ERav GArf LBre LHop MBri MFir NPer SDeJ SDix SUsu WRus
¶ Manon ® / 'Zelanon'	SSmt
¶ Margaret ® / 'Stacova'	SSmt
Marie-Louise ®	See A. Manon ®
Meyer hybrids	SMrm
'Ohio'	LRHS MBri
pelegrina	CMon MTho
§ ***psittacina***	CAvo CChu CGle CGre CHad CHan CRDP CTro ELan EPar ERav GCal LHil LHop MUlv NCat NTow SAxl SLMG SMrm WSHC
*– ***variegata***	ELan
pulchella	See A. ***psittacina***
¶ ***pulchra*** BC&W 4751	CMon
– BC&W 4762	SBla
'Purple Joy'	COtt
pygmaea	MTho NNrd NTow SWas
¶ 'Red Beauty'	NBir
'Rosy Wings'	COtt LRHS MBri WMer
¶ 'Saffier'	LRHS MBri
¶ Sarah ® / 'Stalicamp'	SSmt
'Saxony'	LRHS MBri
Sophia ®	See A. Yellow King ®
'Sovereign'	COtt LRHS MBri
¶ sp. ex Patagonia	GCra
sp. Wr 8893	SIgm
'Sunrise'	LRHS MBri
I 'Vanitas'	LRHS MBri
¶ Victoria ® / 'Regina'	SSmt
¶ Yellow King ® / 'Stajello'	SSmt

ALTHAEA (Malvaceae)

armeniaca	CCor EMon LRHS
cannabina	CFis GCal LRHS MUlv WHoo WRus
officinalis	CArn CHan CHun CKin CSFH CSev ELan EMon Effi GPoy GTou LBlm LHol LHop MChe MHew MMil NDea NFai NSal NSel SHer SIde SMad SMrm WOak WWye
rosea	See ALCEA ***rosea.***
♦***rugosostellulata***	See ALCEA ***rugosa***

ALYOGYNE (Malvaceae)

hakeifolia	CSun ERea LAbb LBlm LHop
huegelii	CAbb CSun LBlm
– 'Santa Cruz'	CTro ERea ESma LAbb LHop NWyt SMad

ALYSSOÏDES (Cruciferae)

utriculata	CMHG CNic CTom EBar ELan GTou NGre SIng STre WByw WDav WOld WPer WWin
– NS 431	NWCA
– var. ***graeca***	MSte NHol

ALYSSUM (Cruciferae)

argenteum hort.	See A. ***murale***
¶ ***caespitosum***	WDav
cuneifolium	WAbe
*– ***pyrenaeum***	MHig NGre
♦***gemonense***	See AURINIA ***petraea***
idaeum	LBee MWat WThi
moellendorfianum	EPad EPot NMen
montanum	CNic CShe ECha ELan EMNN MPit MPla NMen SChu SHer SIng
– 'Berggold' ('Mountain Gold')	CB&S LAbb LBee MCas NNrd NRoo NVic
§ ***murale***	CHal WHoo
♦***petraeum***	See AURINIA ***petraea***
¶ ***propinquum***	WDav
pulvinare	MHig NGre WDav
pyrenaicum	MHig NMen NWCA WDav
repens	NGre
♦***saxatile***	See AURINIA ***saxatilis***
serpyllifolium	MBro MHig NHol NKay NTow NWCA SIgm
spinosum	LHil MBro MHig MTho NKay NNrd STre WAbe
– ***roseum***	CLew CMHG CPar CShe ECar ECha EFol ELan EPad EPot LHop MPla MWat NGre NMen NTow NWCA SBla WAbe WHal WOMN WPat WPer WSHC WTyr WWin
stribrnyi	LRHS MHig NHar NTow
tortuosum	ESis MHig NMen SIgm WAbe WCla
wulfenianum	CMHG MHig NWCA SIng WHil

AMANA See TULIPA

X AMARCRINUM (Liliaceae/Amaryllidaceae)

¶ ***howardii***	CMon

X AMARINE (Liliaceae/Amaryllidaceae)

tubergenii	LBow
– 'Zwanenburg'	CAvo LBow WHil

X AMARYGIA (Liliaceae/Amaryllidaceae)

parkeri	LBow
§ – 'Alba'	CAvo LBow

AMARYLLIS (Liliaceae/Amaryllidaceae)

§ ***bella-donna***	CB&S CBro CHEx CMon EPar IHos LAma LHop MBri MUlv NHol NRog SDeJ SIng WHil WThu
– 'Johannesburg'	CAvo LAma LBow
– 'Kimberley'	LAma LBow
– 'Major'	CAvo
– 'Parkeri Alba'	See X AMARYGIA ***parkeri*** 'Alba'

AMBROSINA (Araceae)

¶ ***bassii*** S&L 315	CMon

AMELANCHIER † (Rosaceae)

alnifolia	CBow CPle EPla ESim WWat

'Ballerina'	CB&S CBow CCla CDoC CPMA CSPN CSco EBre EHar ELan ESim LBre LNet MAsh MBri MGos MRav MWat NBee NHol SHBN SPer SPla SSpi SSta WPat WWat
¶ *bartramiana*	SSta
canadensis	CB&S CBra CCla CLnd CMHG CPle EBre ELan GRei IJoh ISea LAbb LBre LHop LNet MBar NRoo NWea SHBN SPer SSta WBod WDin WNor WPat WStI WWat
– 'Micropetala'	MUlv NHol
florida	See A. ***alnifolia semiintegrifolia***
x *grandiflora* 'Rubescens'	SSta
laevis	CB&S CBot CChu CSco MBal NBee NNor SPer
lamarckii	CB&S CBow CChu CCla CDoC CPMA CSco EBre EGol ELan ENot IDai IHos IOrc LBre LBuc MGos NBee NKay SHBN SHer SPer SReu WDin
pumila	GDra MBal MGos MSte NTow WAbe WDav WNor WThu

AMICIA (Leguminosae)

zygomeris	CBot CBrd CHEx CPle GCal GCra SMrm WSHC

AMOMUM (Zingiberaceae)

cardamomum	See A. ***compactum***
§ *compactum*	CTro MNew

AMOMYRTUS (Myrtaceae)

§ *luma*	CLan CMHG CPle CTrw ELan ISea WBod

AMORPHA (Leguminosae)

canescens	CAbb CB&S CBow CPle ECro ELan ESma MBel
fruticosa	CB&S CBot CLew CPle ECro EHal IOrc
¶ *nana*	WDav

AMORPHOPHALLUS (Araceae)

bulbifer	NRog
rivierei	EPot

AMPELODESMOS (Gramineae)

mauritanicus	EHoe ETPC

AMPELOPSIS † (Vitaceae)

glandulosa var. *brevipedunculata*	CBra CHan GAri SAxl SIgm SPer WCru WOMN WWat
§ – – 'Elegans' (v)	Widely available
– – 'Tricolor'	See A. ***g. b.*** 'Elegans'
henryana	See PARTHENOCISSUS ***h.***
megalophylla	CBot CGre ELan ISea SHil
sempervirens hort.	See CISSUS ***striata***
tricuspidata 'Veitchii'	See PARTHENOCISSUS ***t.*** 'V.'

AMPHICOME See INCARVILLEA

AMSONIA (Apocynaceae)

ciliata	WCot WMer WPer
orientalis	CGle EBlo EBre ECha EMon EPar ERea LBre LHop SWas WHal WOld WPer WWin
tabernaemontana	CHan ECro ELan EMon MBel SUsu SWas WCot
– var. *salicifolia*	CGre CLew CShe EBre ECha ECro LBre

AMYGDALUS See PRUNUS

ANACYCLUS (Compositae)

pyrethrum	CSam GPoy
– var. *depressus*	CGle CLew CNic CPar CSam EBre EFou EHoe ELan ESis LBre LGan MBel MFir MHig NHol NNor NWCA SAxl SBla SIng WCru WEas WHoo WOMN WPer WWin
*– – 'Golden Gnome'	EBar EHal NMir NNrd WHil
– – 'Silberkissen'	NHol

ANAGALLIS (Primulaceae)

**alternifolia repens*	ECou GArf
arvensis	GPoy MHew NSal WEas WWye
– var. *latifolia*	CHal
foemina	CRDP NSal
linifolia	See A. ***monelli***
§ *monelli*	CElw CNic CRiv ELan EPot LBee SAxl SBla SIng SUsu WCla WCru WPer WWin
– 'Sunrise'	CRiv EBur EPot MTho SUsu WCot WCru WOMN
tenella	NHar SFis
– 'Studland'	CRDP EPot NGre NMen NTow NWCA SIng WAbe WCru WOMN WPer

ANANAS (Bromeliaceae)

comosus var. *variegatus*	MBri

ANAPHALIS (Compositae)

alpicola	EPot NCat NTow
cinnamomea	See A. ***margaritacea c.***
margaritacea	CLew CSco CTom ECtt EFou EJud GCHN MBri MPlt NBro NKay NOak NSti SPer WByw WHal
§ – var. *cinnamomea*	CGle CHan CKel CLew CSco ECED EFou EJud ELan NHol NKay SCro SHer WEas
– 'Neuschnee' ('New Snow')	CSam NHol NRoo SFis SPla WPer
¶ – var. *yedoensis*	ECha EMar EPar NRar SDix WHil
nepalensis B&L 12606	EMon
§ – var. *monocephala*	CB&S CGle CMea CTom ELan EMon MNFA MWat NSti SChu SHer
¶ – – C&Mc 550	GCHN
♦ *nubigena*	See A. ***nepalensis monocephala***
sinica ssp. *morii*	ECha EPla LRHS SBar
sp. CLD 1322	EMon

§ *subrigida*	ECou
§ *trinervis*	CBow
triplinervis	CBos CBre CFis CGle CKel CNic CSco CShe EBre EFol EFou ELan GDra IDai LBre LGan NBro NHol NKay NNor SCro WByw WEas WHoo WOld WRus WTyr WWin
– var. *intermedia*	See A. ***nepalensis***
– 'Sommerschnee' ('Summer Snow')	CCla CHad CKel CPar EBlo EBre ECha EHal EOrc EPla LBre MBel MBri NCat NNor SPer WPer
yedoensis	See A. ***margaritacea y.***

ANARRHINUM (Scrophulariaceae)

bellidifolium	WHil WPer

ANCHUSA (Boraginaceae)

angustissima	See A. ***leptophylla incana***
arvensis	MHew NSal
§ *azurea*	NBee NOrc NSel WHal
– 'Dropmore'	CBow CDoC EBar EHal NMir SIde SRms WPer
– 'Feltham Pride'	CBot CBow CPar ECtt MBro NRoo NVic SFis SPla WHoo WPer WTyr
¶ – 'Italian Pride'	LAbb
– 'Little John'	CSco CSev EBre GCal LBre LWad NRoo SHer SPer SRms WMer
– 'Loddon Royalist'	CB&S CCla CDoC CGle CHad CKel CSco CSev CShe EBre ECED EFou ELan LBre LHop MBri MWat NBar NRoo NWyt SChu SPer WMer
– 'Morning Glory'	CKel CSco SFis
– 'Opal'	CGle CSco EFou GCal MWat NRoo SPer
– 'Royal Blue'	CPou ECro GAbr WMer
barrelieri	WPer
caespitosa hort.	See A. ***leptophylla incana***
– Lamarck	EBre ECar ELan EPad EPot LBre LHop NHar WAbe WThu
¶ *capensis*	WPer
italica	See A. ***azurea***
♦ *laxiflora*	See BORAGO ***pygmaea***
§ *leptophylla* ssp. *incana*	CLew EMon MPlt NTow SHer WCot WCru
myosotidiflora	See BRUNNERA ***macrophylla***
officinalis	CArn CSFH EJud LHol MHew NSal SIde
sempervirens	See PENTAGLOTTIS ***sempervirens***

ANDROCYMBIUM (Liliaceae/Colchicaceae))

¶ *europaeum* MS 510	CMon
¶ *punicum* S&L 325	CMon

ANDROMEDA (Ericaceae)

glaucophylla	ECar IOrc MBar WDav
– 'Latifolia'	ECar
polifolia	CBow CRiv CSam EBre EPla IOrc LBre NBar NLan SLon WBod
– 'Alba'	EBre ECar ELan ESis GArf LBre MBal MBar MGos MHig NHar NRya SBar SBod SGil SHer SIng SSta WDav WPat WThu
– 'Compacta'	EBre ECar ELan EMNN EPot ESis LBre MBal MBar MBlu MBri MGos MPla NHar NMen NRya SDeJ SGil SHer SIng SPer SReu WPat WWin
– 'Grandiflora'	ITim MAsh MBal MGos NNrd SBod SPer WThu
– 'Hayachine'	ECar GArf NHol
– 'Iwasugo'	ECar
– 'Kiri-Kaming'	ECar ELan MAsh MBal MGos NHol SSta WAbe WPat
– 'Macrophylla'	ECar EPot ESis GArf GDra ITim MBal MHig NHar NHol SSta WAbe WPat WThu
– 'Major'	MBal
– 'Minima'	ECar MBal
– 'Nana'	ECar ELan EPot GAbr LNet LTil MAsh MGos STre WRus WStI WWat WWeb
– 'Nikko'	ECar IJoh MBal MBar MGos MHig NHol WPat
– 'Red Winter'	CNic LRHS
– 'Shibutsu'	ECar GArf MGos NHol SPer SSta

ANDROPOGON (Gramineae)

gerardii	EMon EPla ETPC
♦ *scoparius*	See SCHIZACHYRIUM ***scoparium***

ANDROSACE (Primulaceae)

albana	CNic GTou NHol NNrd NWCA
armeniaca macrantha	CNic MHig NGre NWCA
carnea	CMea CNic CWes EMNN EPot LBee MCas MTho NHar NHol NMen SIng WCla WDav WHal
– *alba*	LBee MBro MFir NGre NHar NHol NWCA WDav WHoo WThu
¶ – 'Andorra'	GArf
– ssp. *brigantiaca*	EMNN ESma GTou MCas MHig NGre NHar NHol NKay NMen NRed NTow NWCA WAbe WDav
– var. *halleri*	See A. ***c. rosea***
– ssp. *laggeri*	EMNN EPot GDra NHar NWCA
– x *pyrenaica*	EPot GDra MHig NHar WAbe WDav
§ *carnea* ssp. *rosea*	CNic ESma GDra GTou MCas NGre NHol NTow WCla
– – ssp. x *laggeri*	NHol
chaixii	GCHN
ciliata	CNic EPot GArf GTou MCas NMen NTow WAbe
cylindrica	CNic EPot GDra GTou LBee MCas NGre NHar NHol NMen NNrd NWCA SBla
– x *hirtella*	EPot GDra MCas NGre NHar NWCA WAbe
delavayi	EPot ITim NWCA
elongata	EBar
foliosa	SIng
geraniifolia	CRDP ECha GCHN MTho
globifera	EPot NHar
¶ – EMAK 0460	NHol
¶ – x *muscoidea*	NHar
hausmannii	NGre NTow

hedraeantha	CNic EPot MBro NGre NNrd SIng WAbe WDav
x ***heeri*** 'Alba'	EPot ITim NHar WDav
¶ ***helvetica***	GTou
hirtella	CNic EPot GTou NGre NHar NTow NWCA WDav
jacquemontii	See A. ***villosa jacquemontii***
¶ ***kochii tauricola***	NWCA
lactea	GTou NGre NNrd WAbe WDav
laevigata	EPad EPot WDav
– var. ***ciliolata***	EPad NWCA
lanuginosa	CGle CLew CMHG CNic CRiv CShe ELan EPad EPot LHop MBro MHig MWat NMen NRoo SBar SIng SWas WAbe WDav WPat WWin
– 'Leichtlinii'	WThu
¶ – 'Wisley Variety'	SIgm
limprichtii	See A. ***sarmentosa watkinsii***
mathildae	MBro NGre NHar NHol NNrd NTow
– x ***carnea***	NMen
microphylla	See A. ***mucronifolia*** Walt
mollis	See A. ***sarmentosa yunnanensis***
montana	EPad WDav
mucronifolia hort.	See A. ***sempervivoïdes***
§ – Watt	ITim NGre NWCA
muscoidea	MHig NWCA
¶ ***nortonii*** EMAK 0480	NHol
obtusifolia	NNrd
primuloïdes Duby	CWes NCat SFis WDav
– hort.	See A. ***sarmentosa***
– 'Salmon's Variety'	See A. ***sarmentosa*** 'S.V.'
pubescens	EPot GDra GTou LBee MBro MFos NHar SBla WDav
pyrenaica	CNic EPot GTou ITim MCas NGre NHar NHol NTow NWCA SBla SIng WAbe WThu
rotundifolia	CNic ESma GCHN GTou NHol WCru
salicifolia	See A. ***lactiflora***
§ ***sarmentosa***	CLew CNic EBro ELan EPar GTou ITim LBee MBro MFir MHig MWat NGre NMen NNrd SChu SHer SSmi SSou WAbe WCla WEas WHal WHoo
– 'Brilliant'	CNic ELan
– 'Chumbyi'	CLew CRDP CRiv MBro MCas NHar NHol NKay NTow NWCA SBla SHer SIng SUsu WDav WPat WThu WTyr
– ***monstrosa***	NHol
§ – 'Salmon's Variety'	CMea CWes MCas NTow SIgm
– 'Sherriff's'	CGle CNic CShe EPot GCHN MBro MCas NHar NHol NTow SBla SIgm SIng WDav WHal WPat
§ – var. ***watkinsii***	EPot MBro NHar NMen WDav WThu
§ – var. ***yunnanensis***	EPot MBro NHar NHol NNrd NTow SIng WDav
sempervivoïdes	CLew EBro ECha ELan EPot GCHN GDra LBee MBro MCas MHig NGre NHar NNrd NRed NWCA SBod SIgm SIng WAbe WHoo WOMN WPat WThu WWin
septentrionalis puberulenta	NHol
spinulifera	SWas
– CLD 744	NHol
strigillosa	EPad
¶ ***studiosorum***	GCHN
¶ ***uliginosa***	WOMN
vandellii	EPot GTou MHig NGre NHar NTow SIng WAbe WDav
villosa	MHig NTow
– var. ***arachnoidea*** 'Superba'	EPot
§ – var. ***jacquemontii***	CMea CWes EPot GArf MHig NTow SBla SIgm SIng WAbe WThu
– – pink form	EPot NHol
¶ – var. ***taurica*** 'Palandoken'	WDav
vitaliana	See VITALIANA ***primuliflora***
watkinsii	See A. ***sarmentosa watkinsii***

ANDRYALA (Compositae)

agardhii	EFol ESis MCas MFos MHig NHol NTow NWCA WHil
lanata	See HIERACIUM ***lanatum***

ANEMIA (Schizaeaceae)

phyllitidis	NMar

ANEMONE † (Ranunculaceae)

altaica	CNic EBar EPot NNrd NRya
apennina	CBro EPar NTow SCro
– CE&H 538	LRHS
baicalensis	LBee NHol SUsu
baldensis	CGle CSam ECro ESis GAbr LBee MNFA NHol NMen NNrd NOak NWCA SHer WOMN
biarmiensis	CNic
blanda	CBow EFou EOrc LAma LBow LHop MBri MBro MHig MPlt NHar NNrd NRog NRya SChu SHer WHil WPat WPer
– 'Atrocaerulea'	See A. ***b.*** 'Ingramii'
– blue	CAvo CBro CMea CRDP CRiv ELan EPot ETub LAma MBri MNFA SHer WCru WPat
– 'Blue Mist'	LBlo NNor
– 'Charmer'	CAvo CBro CCla EPar EPot ETub NMen NNrd SIng WCru WPat
§ – 'Ingramii'	CCla ELan EPar LAma MBal NRog SDeJ SIng WHoo
– 'Pink Star'	CMea CRDP CRiv EPot LAma LBlo LBow NBir NHar NNor NRog WHil WHoo
– 'Radar'	CAvo CBro CRDP ELan EPar EPot ETub LAma LBlo LBow NBir NRog SHer WChr WCru WPat
– var. ***rosea***	CAvo EFou ELan ETub LAma NEgg WCru WPat WPer
– 'Violet Star'	CBro EPot SHer
– 'White Splendour'	CAvo CBro CCla CGle CMea CRDP ECha EFou ELan EOrc EPar EPot ETub LAma LBlo LBow MHig NHar NMen NRog NRya SChu SHer SIng WCru WPat WPer
canadensis	CCla
caroliniana	CGle CNic EPot ESis MNFA SHer

caucasica	EPot
coronaria De Caen Group	CKel CRDP ETub LAma WCru
– –'Die Braut' ('The Bride')	CGle NRog
– – forms	NRog
– – 'Hollandia'	WCru
– – 'Mister Fokker'	LAma NRog
– – 'The Governor'	NHol NRog WCru
coronaria Mona Lisa Group 'Sylphide'	NRog
coronaria Saint Brigid Group	CKel CSut ETub LAma LBlo MBri NRog SApp SDeJ
– – 'Lord Lieutenant'	NRog
– – 'Mount Everest'	ETub NHol NRar
– – 'The Admiral'	NHol NRog
coronaria Saint Piran Group	SDeJ
cylindrica	CAvo CGle CLew CPar EMar EMon MNFA NHol WCru
¶ ***decapetala***	GCal
drummondii	CPar MHig NWCA WCla
flaccida	CBro EPot SIng
x ***fulgens***	ECha LAma NWCA SRms
– 'Annulata Grandiflora'	CBro CMon LBlo
– 'Multipetala'	CBro NRog
– Saint Bavo Group	CBro CNic LAma SIng
globosa	See A. ***multifida***
¶ ***heldreichiana*** MS 690	CMon
hepatica	See HEPATICA ***nobilis***
§ ***hortensis***	CMon ECro SSvw
¶ – MS 958	CMon
¶ – ***alba***	CMon
hupehensis	CBos CBot CBow CCla LWad NOrc WCot
§ – 'Bowles' Pink'	CRDP MBri MPar MUlv MWat
– 'Eugenie'	CGle
– 'Hadspen Abundance'	CHad CRDP EBlo ECha ELun GCal LGre NTow SAxl WAbb
– var. ***japonica***	CBos CGle CHan CRDP ERav GCal LGro NMir NNor WCru WEas WRus
§ – – 'Bressingham Glow'	CB&S CMHG CSco CShe EBre EGol ELan ELun EOrc EPot GCra LBre LHop MBri MPit MRav NBar NHol NOrc NRoo NVic SHer SPer SSpi WAbb WAbe WOld WTyr
§ – – 'Prinz Heinrich'	CB&S CCla CHad ECha EFou LGre LHop MBri MBro NJap SAxl SHer SPla SSpi WAbe WHoo WOld
– 'Praecox'	CMea EFou MBri WAbb WAbe WHal
– 'Rosenschale'	GCal MBal
– 'September Charm'	CBow CCla CDoC CKel CMil ECha EFol EFou EGol ELan EOrc MBri NBar NSti SChu SDix SPer
– 'Splendens'	CBow EFou WHal
§ x ***hybrida***	CAvo CBos CGle CHad CKel EFou ERav IHos MBro NBar NOak NRar SChu SPla WAbe WCru WHil WHoo WOld
♦– 'Alba' hort. (UK)	See A. x ***h.*** 'Honorine Jobert'
♦– 'Alba' hort. (USA)	See A. x ***h.*** 'Lady Ardilaun'
– 'Alba Dura'	WCot
– 'Bowles' Pink'	See A. ***hupehensis*** 'B.P.'
– 'Bresssingham Glow'	See A. ***hupehensis japonica*** 'B.G.'
– 'Coupe d'Argent'	CSco GCal
– 'Elegans'	EFou
§ – 'Géante des Blanches'	ECro ECtt EFou NNor NRoo SPer WCru
§ – 'Honorine Jobert'	Widely available
¶ – 'King George V'	WKif
– 'Königin Charlotte' ('Queen Charlotte')	CB&S CBow CGle CKel CMea CPar CSco EBlo ECha ECro EFou EGol ELan MBel MBri MPit NBar NBir NHol NMir NRoo SBla SPer SSpi WAbe WHoo WRus WTyr
– 'Kriemhilde'	NJap WCot
– 'Lady Gilmour'	See A. x ***h.*** 'Margarete'
– 'Loreley'	CMea WCot
– 'Luise Uhink'	CDoC CGle CSco EBre ENot LBre NBir SSpi WCot WEas
§ – 'Margarete'	CCla CDec CMGP EBre ECtt EFou EGol ELan EOrc LBre MPar MWat NHol NJap SCro SPer WHoo WTyr
– 'Max Vogel'	CDoC CSco
– 'Monterosa'	CBos CGle ECro EOrc GCal MBal NBar WCot
– 'Pamina'	CGle GCal MBri WHoo WOld
– 'Prinz Heinrich' ('Prince Henry')	See A. ***hupehensis japonica*** 'P.H.'
– 'Profusion'	WCot WOld WRus
– 'Richard Ahrens'	MBri SAxl WAbe
§ – 'Superba'	SBla WKif
– 'Whirlwind' ('Wirbelwind')	CB&S CDoC CGle CMea EFou EGol ELan EOrc LHop MBel MBri NHol NJap NRoo NSti SApp SCro SFis SHer SPer WAbe WCot WCru WHoo WOld WRus
– 'White Queen'	See A. x ***h.*** 'Géante des Blanches'
japonica	See AA. x ***hybrida, hupehensis***
x ***lesseri***	Widely available
¶ ***leveillei***	WDav
§ x ***lipsiensis***	CBro CMon ECha EPar EPot GCHN MNFA MPar MTho NHar NHol NTow SWas WAbe WChr WThu
– 'Pallida'	SPou
N ***magellanica*** hort.	See A. ***multifida***
mexicana	WHil
§ ***multifida***	Widely available
– 'Major'	CLew CNic CPar LGan MTol NKay SBla SUsu SWas WSun
– pink form	CLew
¶ – red form	WDav
narcissiflora	CNic CPou LGan
nemorosa	CBro CGle CKin CRDP EPar EPot LAma LBow LGan MBal MHew MPlt NGar NHar NHol NLan NSal SIng SSpi WGwy WHil WMer WShi

N– 'Alba Plena' CAvo CBro CChu ECha EPot GAbr MHig NHol SBla SIng WAbb WChr WCru WEas WMar WRus
– 'Allenii' CAvo CBro ECar ECha EOrc EPot MBal MCas MNFA NGar NHar NTow SIng SSpi SWas WAbe WChr WCru
– 'Atrocaerulea' EPar EPot MNFA NGar NHol
– 'Blue Beauty' EPot MBal NGar NHol NNrd SPou
– 'Blue Bonnet' CChu GAbr
– 'Blue Queen' EPot
– 'Bowles' Purple' EPar EPot GAbr NGar NTow SIng SWas WAbe WChr WMar
– 'Bracteata Pleniflora' EPot LHop MBal NGar
– 'Caerulea' EPot
¶– 'Cedric's Pink' NGar
¶– 'Celestial' SPou
– 'Danica' MBal
– 'Flore Pleno' CTre ECar EOrc EPar GArf MBal NGar SBla WAbe
¶– forms CMon
– 'Green Fingers' SPou WChr
– 'Hannah Gubbay' EPar MBal SIng
– 'Hilda' EPar EPot MBal NGar
– 'Lady Doneraile' MPar NGar
– 'Leeds' Variety' EPot NGar NHar NHol SBla WChr
– 'Lychette' EPar EPot MBal
– 'Monstrosa' EPar EPot NGar
¶– 'Parlez Vous' NGar
– 'Pentre Pink' WChr
– 'Purity' LBlo
– x ***ranunculoïdes*** See A. x ***lipsiensis***
– 'Robinsoniana' CBro CChu CGle CHad CRDP ECha EPar EPot MBal MBro MCas MHig MNFA MTho NGar NRya NSti NTow SBla SIng
– 'Rosea' CGle EPot LAma NHol WChr
– 'Royal Blue' CNic EPot LAma NHol SBla SWas WAbe
– 'Vestal' CGle EPot LGre MNFA MPar NGar NMen SBla
¶– 'Virescens' NGar
– 'Viridiflora' CRDP WChr WCru
– 'Wilks' White' ECar EPar EPot MBal NGar
– 'Wyatt's Pink' SWas WAbe
obtusiloba EPot GDra GTou NHar
– ***alba*** GDra NHar NHol
¶***palmata*** MS 413 CMon
¶– 'Alba' CMon
parviflora ESis ESma
patens See PULSATILLA ***p.***
pavonina LGre NBir SIng SWas
pseudoaltaica EPot
pulsatilla See PULSATILLA ***vulgaris***
ranunculoïdes CAvo CBro CMon CRDP ECar EPar EPot GArf LAma MHig MNFA NGar NHar NHol NKay NNrd SIng WAbe WChr WCru WEas WOMN
– 'Pleniflora' ECha EPar EPot MPar NGar WChr WMar
reflexa EPot
rivularis CAvo CBro CCMG CElw CGle CHan CNic CRDP EBul ECha ELun EMon LGre MBro MPar NHar NHol SAxl SBla SSpi SUsu WDav WEas WHil WKif WOld
rupicola NHol
x ***seemannii*** See A. x ***lipsiensis***
sp. CLD 573 NHol
♦***stellata*** See A. ***hortensis***
sulphurea See PULSATILLA ***alpina apiifolia***
sylvestris Widely available
tetrasepala NHol
§ ***tomentosa*** CGle CMGP ECha NHol NRoo NSti SCro WCot WEas
– 'Robustissima' CDoC CGle CSco ECro EFou EGol EPla GCal MBri MBro SPla WAbb WRus
trifolia CRDP ECha EPot MBal NGar NHol NMen SPou SUsu SWas
trullifolia SBEC 797 EPla GTou NHar NHol NTow
– ***alba*** NHar NTow
tschernjaewii EPot
vernalis See PULSATILLA ***vernalis***
virginiana ECro MSte NHol WCru
vitifolia hort. See A. ***tomentosa***
– De Candolle ECro EJud ESma GGar MPar
– C&Mc 43 CGle MBro

ANEMONELLA (Ranunculaceae)

thalictroïdes CRDP LAma LBow NGar NRog NTow SSpi SWas

ANEMONOPSIS (Ranunculaceae)

macrophylla CCMG CRDP EBre ECha ECro LBre MUlv NTow SBla WEas WOld

ANETHUM (Umbelliferae)

graveolens CArn GPoy IEde LHol MChe MHew MPit NSel SHer SIde WPer
¶– 'Dukat' CSFH GPoy

ANGELICA (Umbelliferae)

archangelica CArn CBow CFis CGle CSFH CSco CSev ECha EEls EFou ELan Effi GPoy IEde LHol MBri MChe MHew NBro NFai NRoo NSel SChu SHer SIde WEas WOak WPer WWye
atropurpurea NSal
curtisii See A. ***triquinata***
gigas CGle CRDP ECha EMon MSte WHal
montana See A. ***sylvestris***
§ ***sylvestris*** CArn CKin NSal WHer
§ ***triquinata*** NSal
ursina SMrm

ANIGOZANTHOS (Haemodoraceae)

flavidus CSev MBri
– red form CRDP CTro LHil
– yellow form CRDP LHil
manglesii CTro WPer
*– 'Bush Dawn' CB&S
preissii CSun

ANISODONTEA (Malvaceae)

capensis	CB&S CBar CBrk CHad CSpe CTro ELan ERea ESis ESma IBlr IMal LHil LHop MPla SAxl SChu SFis SGil SHer SMrm WEas WWin
§ x *hypomandarum*	CElw CMHG CSev CSun CTre ECtt EOrc LAbb LBlm MUlv NPer NRar NTow SMad SUsu WAbe WHal WOMN WOld WPer WRus
malvastroïdes	GCal LHil WCot
scabrosa	CAbb CDoC SLon

ANISOTOME (Umbelliferae)

haastii	NHol
imbricata	GDra

ANNONA (Annonaceae)

¶ *cherimola*	CTro

ANODA (Malvaceae)

cristata 'Opal Cup'	EMon LRHS

ANOIGANTHUS See **CYRTANTHUS**

ANOMATHECA (Iridaceae)

cruenta	See A. *laxa*
§ *laxa*	CAvo CBro CNic CRDP ECar ECha ELan EPot LBee LGre LHop MFir MFos MTho NWCA SAxl SChu SDix SSpi WAbe WCla WCru WHal WOMN WPat WWin
– *alba*	CAvo CRDP ECar ELan EPot LBee LGre MFir MPit NWCA SChu WAbe WOMN WThu
– 'Joan Evans'	EPot
¶ *moisii*	WCru
viridis	CAvo CMon CNic LBow SSad

ANOPTERUS (Escalloniaceae)

glandulosus	CHEx IBlr

ANREDERA (Basellaceae)

§ *cordifolia*	LHop NHex SLMG WCot

ANTENNARIA (Compositae)

alpina	SIng
aprica	See A. *parvifolia*
dioica	CPar CRiv ECro ELan EPad GCHN GPoy LHol MBro MFir MHew NLan NSal SHer WCla WHal WHil WHoo WWye
– 'Alba'	EHoe
– 'Aprica'	See A. *parvifolia*
§ – var. *hyperborea*	CLew LGro MNFA SSmi WAbe
– 'Minima'	CGle CLew CPar ECar EPot GDra MHig MPla MWat NHar NHol NMen NNrd
– 'Nyewoods Variety'	CNic EPot GDra MHig NHol NTow
¶ – red form	WDav
♦– *rosea*	See A. *rosea*
*– 'Rubra'	CKel CPar ECha GAri NHol NKay NNrd SBla SSmi WAbe
– *tomentosa*	See A. *d. hyperborea*
macrophylla	NTow WEas WOMN
– hort.	See A. *microphylla*
neglecta var. *gaspensis*	NHol
§ *parvifolia*	CNic EMNN EPot ESis GCHN GDra LBee MBar MPla NHar NNrd NSti SBod WCla WHil WPer WWin
♦– *rosea*	See A. *rosea*
rosea	Widely available
– 'Plena'	CGle NKay

ANTHEMIS (Compositae)

aïzoön	See ACHILLEA *ageratifolia a.*
biebersteinii	See A. *marschalliana*
cretica ssp. *carpatica*	CGle GCHN LGre NBro SMrm
– – 'Karpatenschnee'	WHil
¶ – ssp. *cretica*	SWas WDav
'Eva'	LGan NCat WEas
frutescens	See ARGYRANTHEMUM *frutescens*
§ *marschalliana*	CGle CHan CKel CShe ECha ELan EPot ESis LBee LHil LHop NEgg NKay NNor NNrd NOak NPer SIgm SSmi WHil WPer WWin
♦ *montana*	See A. *cretica cretica*
nobilis	See CHAMAEMELUM *nobile*
punctata ssp. *cupaniana*	Widely available
– – 'Nana'	NPer
rudolphiana	See A. *marschalliana*
sancti-johannis	CBow CGle CLew CSFH CSam CSco EBar EBre EMon LBre MBri MFir NFai NOak NPer NTow SHer SMad SPer WHal WHil WPer
'Tetworth'	ECha ELan EMon WCot
tinctoria	CArn CGle CSFH ECED EJud ELan EMon GPoy LHol MBel MChe MHew MPit NBee NKay NPer NSel SIde WAbe WByw WGwy WSun WWin WWye
– 'Alba'	CGle ECha EFol EMar EMon GCal LGre MBel NCat NPer SChu SMrm WCot
– 'E C Buxton'	Widely available
N– 'Grallach Gold'	CDoC CGle ECha EMon EOrc IDai LRHS MBel MUlv MWat NCat NHol NPer SCro SHer WDav WEas WMer
– 'Kelwayi'	CGle CPar CRiv EBar ECtt ESma GAbr GCHN LAbb LHop MFir NBro NFai NMir NPer NRoo SPla SSvw WHal WHen WPer
– 'Powis White'	CHan
– 'Pride of Grallach'	EMon GCal
– 'Sauce Hollandaise'	CBre CGle ECtt EFou EMon EOrc GAbr GCal LRHS MBel MMil NBro NCat NPer SMrm WByw
– 'Wargrave'	CBre CElw CGle CLew CSam ECha ECtt EFol EFou ELan EMon GAbr GCal MUlv MWat NBro NFai NPer SAxl SChu SDix SMrm WRus

tuberculata	EBre LBre MCas SBla SIng SMrm SUsu

ANTHERICUM (Liliaceae/Anthericaceae)

algeriense	See A. ***liliago major***
¶ *baeticum*	CMon WDav
liliago	CBro CGle EBul ECED ELan ESis GCal GDra LGan LHop MBro MSte SMrm WCla WOld WPer
§ – var. ***major***	CAvo ECha EPot GDra IBlr LGre WDav WOld
ramosum	CMon EBul ECha ELan EMon GDra LGre MBro NHol NWCA WCla WPer
– JCA 166.300	CAvo
– ***plumosum***	CBro

ANTHOCERCIS (Solanaceae)
See Plant Deletions

ANTHOLYZA (Iridaceae)

coccinea	See CROCOSMIA ***paniculata***
paniculata	See CROCOSMIA ***paniculata***

ANTHOXANTHUM (Gramineae)

odoratum	CSFH GPoy MWil SIde

ANTHRISCUS (Umbelliferae)

cerefolium	CArn CHun CSFH CSev EJud GPoy IEde ILis LHol MChe NSel SHer SIde WOak WPer
¶ *sylvestris* 'Moonlight Night'	EHoe
– 'Ravenswing'	CBot CElw CGle CHad CSun EMar EMon EPla LGre LRHS MBri MUlv NBir NSti SAxl SIgm SMad SUsu SWas WBon WByw WCHb WCot WDav WRus

ANTHURIUM (Araceae)

amazonicum	MBri
andreanum	MBri
¶ – 'Acropolis'	MBri
¶ – 'Flamingo'	MBri
– 'Rose'	See A. × ***ferrierense*** 'Roseum'
clarinervium	MBri
cordatum	See A. ***leuconeurum***
§ × *ferrierense* 'Roseum'	MBri
scherzerianum	MBri
– 'Rosemarie'	MBri

ANTHYLLIS (Leguminosae)

hermanniae	CHan CMHG CSam MCas NHar SHil WAbe
♦– *compacta*	See A. ***h.*** 'Minor'
– 'Minor'	EPot NMen NTow WDav
¶ – prostrate form	LGre
montana	CLew ELan LBee LHil MPlt
– 'Rubra'	EPot NKay NNrd NTow SHer SIng WOMN WWin
¶ – 'Rubra Compacta'	WThu
vulneraria	CKin GTou MChe MHew NKay NLan NMir NSal WCla WNdy WPer
– var. *coccinea*	CMil CNic EBar EFol GAbr MSte MTho NHar NHol NNrd NTow NWCA SUsu

ANTIGONON (Polygonaceae)

leptopus	CTro MNew SLMG

ANTIRRHINUM (Scrophulariaceae)

asarina	See ASARINA ***procumbens***
'Black Prince'	CHad
braun-blanquetii	ECro GCal GGar LHop MTol NCat
glutinosum	See A. ***hispanicum hispanicum***
§ *hispanicum*	CFis CGle GCal MDHE NTow WCla
§ – ssp. *hispanicum roseum*	CFis CSam CSpe ELan NRar NTow SBla WOld WPer
majus	ECro
– ssp. *linkianum*	WOMN
– 'Taff's White' (v)	CBot CElw CFis CHal EMon LGre LHil MTho SMrm SUsu WHil WRus
molle	CElw CLew CPar CSpe ELan EOrc ESis GCal LHop MSte MTho NMen NPer NRar NTow SUsu WCru WPer
– pink form	CRiv EOrc WCru
pulverulentum	CCMG LGre LHop SMrm WEas WHil WKif WOMN WPer
sempervirens	CRiv EPad MDHE MTol SWas WOMN

APHANES (Rosaceae)

§ *arvensis*	GPoy MHew NHex NSal WWye

APHELANDRA (Acanthaceae)

alexandri	SLMG
squarrosa (v)	MBri
– 'Dania' (v)	MBri

APHYLLANTHES (Liliaceae/Aphyllanthaceae)

monspeliensis	CLew MCas WOMN WOld

APIOS (Leguminosae)

§ *americana*	EMon WCru WSHC
tuberosa	See A. ***americana***

APIUM (Umbelliferae)

graveolens	EJud GPoy NSal SIde WWye

APOCYNUM (Apocynaceae)

androsaemifolium	NSal
cannabinum	CArn GPoy NSal

APONOGETON (Aponogetonaceae)

distachyos	CBen CHEx CRow CWGN EBre EHon ELan EMFW EWav IMal LBre LMay MBal MSta NDea SHig SLon SWat WChe WHol
krausseanus	See A. ***desertorum***

APPLE See **MALUS** ***domestica***

APPLE, Crab See **MALUS**

APRICOT See **PRUNUS** ***armeniaca***

APTENIA (Aizoaceae)

cordifolia	CHEx CSev LHil
– 'Variegata'	CBrk CHEx CHal LHil

AQUILEGIA † (Ranunculaceae)

akitensis hort.	See A. ***flabellata pumila***
alpina	Widely available
¶– 'Alba'	NOak
*– 'Carl Ziepke'	EDra GCal
– 'Hensol Harebell'	See A. 'H.H.'
'Alpine Blue'	CSco SIde
amaliae	WAbe
§ ***atrata***	CGle CHad ECro EDra ESis GAbr GCHN MSte NOak WEas WHal WPer
aurea	EDra
baicalensis	See A. ***vulgaris*** Baicalensis Group
barnebyi	EDra LGre NWCA SIgm WDav
bertolonii	CGle CLew CRiv EDra EPot GAbr GTou LBee MBro NHar NNrd NOak NRoo SBla SSmi SWas WAbe WDav WHoo
– ***alba***	NWCA
¶– var. ***australis***	WPer
– 'Blue Berry'	ESis MBro MPla WHoo
'Betty Barton'	MFir
'Biedermeier'	CBow EDra MTol NOrc SHer WHil WPer
¶ 'Blue Berry'	NHar WDav
'Blue Spurs'	EDra
buergeriana	EDra ESis GCra GGar NHol WPer
caerulea	CHun ECro EDra EPad GAri GCHN GDra LAbb NCat SIgm
– 'Kristall'	WMer
– 'Mrs Nicholls'	MBri WMer
– var. ***ochroleuca***	EDra GCHN
canadensis	CGle CMil EBar EBre EDra ELan EPad ESma GAbr GDra LBre MBal MHew NBro NGre NHol NOak NSal NSti SFis WByw WEas WPer
– 'Corbett'	EDra
– 'Nana'	CSam EDra GArf NHol
cazorlensis	CMea CWes EDra ESis GCHN
'Celestial Blue'	ELan
chrysantha	EDra EPad GCHN GCal LGre LRHS MNFA MSte NHar SIgm WDav WPer WRus
– var. ***chaplinei***	CBot ECro EDra GCal LGre NBir NHol WCra
¶– double dark red	CMil
– 'Yellow Queen'	CMil EDra EFou GCal NHol WHil
clematiflora	See A. ***vulgaris stellata***
*'Coronato'	EDra
'Crimson Star'	CBow CCla CKel EBre EDra ELan LBre NBar SPer SUsu WHil
desertorum	CNic LGre WAbe WDav
dinarica	EDra
discolor	CLew CMea CNic CRiv EDra ESis GDra MBro MPla NGre NKay NRoo NTow NWCA WDav WOMN WPat WThu
'Dragonfly'	CB&S CBow GAbr GAri LAbb LWad MBri MPit MRav NMir NOak NVic SMrm WPer WRus WSun
'Eastgrove'	WEas
ecalcarata	See SEMIAQUILEGIA ***ecalcarata***
einseleana	CBot EDra MNFA SHer
* ***elegantissima***	CMea ESis GDra WHal
elegantula	LGre NHar WOMN WPer
eximia	EDra
flabellata	CGle CHad EDra EMNN GAbr GAri GCHN MPlt NMen WHal WPat WPer
§ – f. ***alba***	CBot CPar ELan EMNN GCHN GGar NGre NHol NWCA SBla WEas
– 'Ministar'	CNic EBar EBre EDra EFou ESis LBre MRav NMen NOak NRoo SIng WHoo WPer WWin
– var. ***nana***	See A. ***f. pumila***
– 'Nana Alba'	See A. ***f. pumila alba***
§ – var. ***pumila***	CNic CSam CShe CWGN ECha EDra EFol ESis GArf GCal GDra GTou LBee MBal MHig MTho NHol NKay NNrd NOak NRed NRoo SBla SGil SHer SIng WAbe WCla
– – f. ***alba***	CBot CGle CHun EBar EBre ECha EDra EFol ESis GAbr GCal GDra LBre MBal MBro MSte NHol NNrd NRoo NRya SBla SGil SHer SIng WHil WPer WRus WWin
– – f. ***kurilensis***	GDra MSte NKay NNrd WCla
– – Mount Hakkado form	EDra
*– 'White Angel'	EFou
flavescens	EDra
formosa	CBot CNic EBar ECha EDra EFol ELan GAbr GCHN GCal GGar GTou LGan NHol NNrd NRar NRoo NWCA SBla SHer SMrm SUsu WCru WDav WHal WPer
– x ***longissima***	EDra
– var. ***truncata***	EDra GCra
§ ***fragrans***	CArn CGle CHad CNic EDra EPad ESis GCHN GTou LGan LGre MTho NOak NWCA SBla WCra WDav WEas WHoo
¶– CC 57	CNic
glandulosa	CSam EDra GCra GDra ITim NHol WEas
– var. ***jucunda***	EDra
♦ ***glauca***	See A. ***fragrans***
grata	CPar EDra GCHN LGre
'Hensol Harebell'	CGle CHan EDra LGan MBro NHol NKay SPer WHil WHoo WSun
hinckleyana	See A. ***chrysantha h.***
japonica	See A. ***flabellata pumila***
Jewel hybrids	NRoo WHil WPer
jonesii	MFos NHar NKay
– x ***saximontana***	EPad
laramiensis	EDra ESis GTou NHar NTow SBla SSpi

longissima	CGle CHad CSam EDra MMil MTho SBla WCla WDav WEas WHal WHil
Lowdham strain	EDra
'Maxi Star'	EDra
McKana hybrids	CBow CKel CSco CShe EBlo EBre ECED EDra ELan ENot GAbr GCHN IDai LBre MFir MWat NBee NNor NOak NVic SPer WPer
* *melange pygmaea*	NHol
micrantha	GCHN WDav
microphylla	EDra NHol
* 'Modra Pisen'	EDra
Mrs Scott-Elliot Hybrids	CBow EDra GAbr MBri SMrm
'Mrs Shaw's Double'	WEas
Music Series Hybrids	NOak NRoo SHer SMrm SPla SRms WByw
nevadensis	See A. ***vulgaris n.***
nigricans	See A. ***atrata***
nivalis	SBla SWas WAbe
§ *olympica*	EDra LGre
– JCA 173.600	NHol
ottonis	EDra LRHS
oxysepala	CChu EDra WHal
¶ 'Phyll's Bonnet'	GCal
¶ 'Pink Bonnet'	GCal
pubiflora	GCHN GCra
– CC&MR 96	WDav
pyrenaica	CNic CSam EDra NHol NTow WCla WDav WWin
¶ *rockii* CLD 0437	NHol
* *saxatilis*	EDra
saximontana	EDra EPot GAbr GCHN LBee NHar NHol NMen NTow NWCA WOMN WPer
§ 'Schneekönigin' ('Snow Queen')	CCla ELan GCHN NOak WEas WHen WRus
scopulorum	CLew EDra GAbr MFos NRed WDav
shockleyi	CNic EDra MBel NHar WAbe WOMN
sibirica	EDra
¶ 'Silver Queen'	CKel
skinneri	CHun EDra NHol NRed SIgm WCru WHil
'Snow Queen'	See A. 'Schneekönigin'
sp. ACL 7781	NHol
sp. from Zigana Pass	EDra
stellata	See A. ***vulgaris s.***
thalictrifolia	NRed
– JCA 174.400	WDav
transsilvanica	EBar EDra
triternata	EDra ESis GTou LGre NHol NTow SIgm
viridiflora	CBot CGle CHad CMea CPar CRow EDra EFol EPad ESma GCHN GCal GDra LBee MFir MTho NGre NRoo NTow SBla SMad SUsu SWas WCru WEas WHal WOMN WPer WThu
viscosa	EDra
vulgaris	CArn CFis CWGN EDra GPoy IEde LHol MChe MHew NBro NLan NMir NNor SIde WBon WOak WPer WWye
– 'Adelaide Addison'	CBro CGle ECha EDra ELan LGan MNFA NFai NHol NRoo SFis SUsu SWas WEas WHal WMer
– *alba*	CArn CRDP CRow MPar WByw
– 'Anne Calder'	EDra
¶ – 'Aureovariegata'	ELan
§ – Baicalensis Group	EDra GCHN
– 'Belhaven Blue'	EDra
– 'Blue Star'	ECtt EFou GAbr GCHN NMir SPer SUsu WPer
– from Brno Czechoslovakia	EDra
– *clematiflora*	See A. ***v. stellata***
– double black	NRar
– double blue	LWad SWas WDav
¶ – double pink	LWad NFai
– double red	CHal EDra GAbr GCra MNFA
¶ – double white	LGre SWas
– var. *flore-pleno*	ECro ECtt EFol NOak SMrm SSvw WByw WHil WPer WSun
– – 'Warwick'	WCot
– 'Gisela Powell'	EDra
¶ – golden-leaved	EFou
¶ – 'Heidi'	WPer
– var. *hispanica*	EDra
¶ – 'Jane Hollow'	CRow
* – 'Mathew Strominger'	ECro EDra
¶ – 'Miss Coventry'	SWas
§ – ssp. *nevadensis*	EPad
– 'Nivea' ('Munstead White')	CBot CCla CHad CMil ECha ELan EMon GAbr MNFA NCat NRoo SAxl SBla SHig SSpi WCla WRus
– 'Nora Barlow'	Widely available
– Olympica Group	See A. ***olympica***
– 'Patricia Zavros'	EDra
– 'Pink Spurless'	See A. ***vulgaris stellata rosea***
– 'Red Star'	ECtt EFou GAbr GCHN NMir NOak WPer WRus
– 'Reverend E Baty'	EDra
– from Rize, Turkey	EDra
¶ – 'Robin'	NRoo
– 'Ruby Port'	GCal
– scented form	EDra
– 'Snowdust'	EHoe
§ – var. *stellata*	CBot CGle CHal CLew CRow EBar ECro EDra ESma GCHN LWad MTol NBro NFai NHol NNrd WDav WHal WHer WHil WHoo WPer WRus WWin
§ – – pink	EDra EFou MBel
§ – – white	CGle CMil EDra EFou GCHN LHop NBro NCat
– 'Tom Fairhurst'	EDra
– variegated foliage	See A. ***v.*** Vervaeneana Group
§ – Vervaeneana Group (v)	CBos CBot CGle CHad CHan CPar CRDP CRow ECha ECro EDra EFol EFou EMar EMon MBel NBir NPer NSti SRms WCla WHal WHil WPbr WPer WRus
¶ – Vervaeneana Group 'Graeme Iddon'	GCra LGre NFai

N– Vervaeneana Group	
'Woodside' (v)	CChu CHun CNic CRow CSco EPad EPla GAbr LHop LWad NFai SAxl SMad WCot WCra WHoo WRus
– 'White Spurless'	See A. *v.* ***stellata*** white
– 'White Star'	ECtt EFou GAbr GCHN LWad NMir NRoo SPer WPer WRus
¶– 'William Guiness'	WPer

ARABIS † (Cruciferae)

albida	See A. ***caucasica***
alpina	CB&S CLew MWat NMen
– 'Flore Pleno'	See A. ***caucasica*** 'F.P.'
– ***rosea***	See A. ***caucasica rosea***
– 'Snow Cap'	See A. ***caucasica*** 'Schneehaube'
*– 'Snow White'	NGre
– 'Spring Charm'	See A. ***blepharophylla*** 'Frühlingszauber'
androsacea	EPar GTou MBro MCas MHig MPla NGre NMen NTow SSou WDav
x ***arendsii*** 'Compinkie'	CBow CDoC ECtt NOak NRoo SRms STre
– 'La Fraicheur'	WMer
– 'Rosabella'	CMHG ECha LHop MRav
blepharophylla	ESma GAbr MFir NTow WCot
§– 'Frühlingszauber' ('Spring Charm')	CB&S CPar GDra MPit NGre NKay NRoo SRms STre WCla
bryoïdes	NGre WDav
§ ***caucasica***	EBar MBar
– 'Corfe Castle'	ECtt
§– 'Flore Pleno'	CElw CGle CHal CNic CShe EBre ECha ECtt ELan EOrc EPar IDai LBre LGro MCas MFir MTho MWat NKay NRoo SBod SHer SIng WBon WByw WDav WEas WHil WWin
– 'Gillian Sharman' (v)	EMon
– 'Pink Pearl'	CGle GAbr LAbb
– 'Rose Frost'	EMNN SHer
§– ***rosea***	CHal LAbb NBir NMen SRms WByw WSun
§– 'Schneehaube' ('Snowcap')	ECtt EMNN MBar NKay NRoo SRms
– 'Snowdrop'	CPar GAbr MCas MRav
– 'Variegata'	CBot CGle CHal CPar CRow CShe ECha EFol EFou EHoe ELan EOrc EPar EPot GAbr IDai LBee LHop MBri MCas MTho NRoo SHer WByw WEas WHil WPbr WPer WWin
¶ ***collina***	WHil
cypria	LRHS WOMN
ferdinandi-coburgii	CGle CRow EOrc EPot LGro MPla NBro NRed NVic SBod WCla WEas WWin
– 'Aureovariegata'	CMea CRiv EHoe NRar
– 'Old Gold'	Widely available
– 'Variegata'	Widely available
x ***kellereri***	MBro NHol WDav
* ***lucida*** 'Variegata'	EFol
muralis	See A. ***collina***
'Pink Snow'	NGre
rosea	See A. ***collina***
soyeri	NRed NTow
– ssp. ***jacquinii***	NRed WHil
– 'Variegata'	MFir
¶ ***stelleri*** var. ***japonica***	NWCA
stricta	CNat
x ***sturii***	MHig NGre NTow WHil
x ***suendermannii***	MPla

ARACHNIODES (Dryopteridaceae)

¶ ***aristata***	WRic
– 'Variegata'	NMar
¶ ***simplicior*** C&L 236	SBla
standishii	WRic

ARAIOSTEGIA (Davalliaceae)

See Plant Deletions

ARALIA (Araliaceae)

cachemirica	CHad CHan MUlv SDix
californica	NSal
chinensis	CB&S EPla MBel NHol SPer WWye
– hort.	See A. ***elata***
continentalis	CHan
cordata	GCal
§ ***elata***	CBow CBra CDoC CHEx CHad CHan CLan CLnd CWSG EBre ELan ENot IOrc LBre LNet MBal NBee NNor SArc SMad SPer SSpi WDin WNor
– 'Albomarginata'	See A. ***e.*** 'Variegata'
– 'Aureovariegata'	CB&S CBow CDoC CSco EHar ELan ENot IJoh IOrc LNet MBri SHil WDin WPat
§– 'Variegata'	CB&S CBot CBow CDoC CSco EHar ELan ENot IBar IOrc LNet MBlu MBri NPal SEng SHBN SHer SHil WDin WPat
racemosa	GCal GPoy MSte NSal SAxl
sieboldii hort.	See FATSIA ***japonica***

ARAUCARIA (Araucariaceae)

angustifolia	CHEx GAri
§ ***araucana***	CB&S CBra CDoC CHEx CMac CSco EHar ELan ENot GRei IJoh LCon LLin LNet MBal MBar MBri MGos NHol SArc SHBN SLim SMad SPer WDin WMou WThu
excelsa	See A. ***heterophylla***
§ ***heterophylla***	EBre LBre MBri
imbricata	See A. ***araucana***

ARAUJIA (Asclepiadaceae)

grandiflora	SLMG
sericifera	CAbb CB&S CDoC CGre CMHG CTro EMil ERea LHop MGos

ARBUTUS † (Ericaceae)

andrachne	LAbb WCoo
x ***andrachnoïdes***	CB&S CBot CBow CChu CCla CDoC CGre CMHG CPMA EHar ELan GWht IJoh IOrc ISea LNet LTil MBal MUlv SArc SHBN SHer SHil SPer SReu SSpi SSta WWat

glandulosa See ARCTOSTAPHYLOS *g.*
¶ *marina* SMad
menziesii CBot MBal SHil SMad WBod WCoo WWat
unedo Widely available
– 'Compacta' CBow CChu CDoC CPMA CSco EBre LBre MGos SHBN SSpi
– 'Elfin King' CB&S
– 'Quercifolia' MBal WPat
– f. *rubra* CB&S CBow CBra CChu CCla CDoC CMHG CPMA CSco EBre ECtt EHar ELan IOrc LBre LNet MBal MBri MUlv SPer SReu SSpi SSta WAbe WBod WPat WSHC

ARCHONTOPHOENIX (Palmae)

cunninghamiana NPal

ARCTANTHEMUM (Compositae)

§ *arcticum* EPla MSte
– 'Schwefelglanz' ECha EPla WCot

ARCTERICA See PIERIS

ARCTIUM (Compositae)

lappa CArn CKin Effi GPoy LHol MChe NHex NSal SIde WHer
minus CKin MHew NSal
pubens CKin

ARCTOSTAPHYLOS (Ericaceae)

* *californica* MBal
§ *glandulosa* SArc
x *media* 'Snow Camp' CMHG ELan MAsh MBal SSta
– 'Wood's Red' GGGa MBal MGos SSta WAbe
myrtifolia GAri SSta WSHC
nevadensis MBal MBar SPer SReu SSta
nummularia MBal
patula LRHS LTil SMad
pumila ECar
¶ *stanfordiana* LTil
– C&H 105 GGGa
uva-ursi ECar ELan ENot GPoy IDai IOrc MBal MBar MGos MHig MPla NLan NNor SBod SEng SHBN SPer SSta WBod WDin
– 'Clyde Robin' SSta
– 'Massachusetts' EBre ELan LBre
– 'Point Reyes' SReu SSta
– 'Vancouver Jade' IJoh MAsh MBar MGos MUlv SSta

ARCTOTIS (Compositae)

x *hybrida* 'Apricot' CBow CBrk LHop SMrm
¶ – 'China Rose' SAxl SMrm
– cream and green SMrm
– 'Flame' CBar CBrk CHad LHop SChu SMrm SUsu WPer
– 'Pink' CHad SChu SMrm
– 'Wine' CBar CBrk CHad LHop SMrm
¶ – 'Yellow' CBrk

ARDISIA (Myrsinaceae)

crenata MBri

ARECA (Palmae)

catechu MBri

ARECASTRUM See SYAGRUS

ARENARIA (Caryophyllaceae)

aggregata CNic
balearica CHal CNic CSpe ELan EPar EPot GTou LBee MBro MFir MPlt MTho NGre NHol NMen NNrd SBod SHer SIng WEas WHoo WWin
bertolonii WPer
caespitosa See MINUARTIA *verna c.*
¶ *canescens* WDav
¶ *festucoïdes* WDav
¶ – C&Mc 405 GTou
grandiflora ESis WAbe
¶ *hookeri* MFos NWCA
ledebouriana EPot MWat NHol NTow WAbe WThu
§ *lithops* WOld WWin
¶ *longifolia* MNFA
* *magellanica* NWCA
montana CGle CLew CPar ECha ECtt EFou ELan EMNN EOrc EPar GCHN IDai MTho NNor NNrd NRoo SIng WEas WHil WHoo WPat WPbr WPer WWin
nevadensis ITim WAbe
norvegica WHil
– ssp. *anglica* WOMN
♦ *obtusiloba* See MINUARTIA *o.*
pinifolia See MINUARTIA *circassica*
pulvinata See A. *lithops*
purpurascens CHal ECtt ELan EMNN EPot ESis GArf LBee MBro MCas NKay NNrd NRoo WOMN
¶ *scariosa* WDav
tetraquetra EPad GDra MFos MTho MWat NTow NWCA SIng SSmi WThu
¶ – JJA 188.450 SBla
– var. *granatensis* EPot LBee MHig NGre NNrd NRed NTow SIng WHil
tmolea NNrd
verna See MINUARTIA *verna*

ARENGA (Palmae)

See Plant Deletions

ARGEMONE (Papaveraceae)

grandiflora EJud ELan
mexicana WOMN

ARGYRANTHEMUM † (Compositae)

♦ 'Blizzard' (d) See A. 'Snoflake'
broussonetii CCan NSty NWyt
callichrysum 'Etoile d'Or' ('Yellow Star') CBrk EBre ECtt IHos LBre LHop
– 'Prado' CB&S CSpe EDon NFai
canariense ca aSe A fru eria sce s
♦ 'Cheek's Peach' See A. 'Peach Cheeks'
'Chelsea Princess' EOrc
coronopifolium CCan
¶ double cream CCan
double white CCan ESma

'Edelweiss' (d) CBar CBrk CCan CElw CHal CSpe EBar EDon ERav GCal LHil LHop WEas WHal WHen
'Flamingo' See PYRETHROPSIS ***gayanum***
foeniculaceum hort. CBos CBrk CCan CElw CHad CHal CMHG CMer CSev ECha ELan ERav LAbb NRar NSty NTow SDix SHer SIgm SMrm SUsu WAbe WHen WKif WOMN
♦– pink form See A. 'Petite Pink'
– Webb 'Royal Haze' CB&S CCan CSpe LHil NRoo SFis
§***frutescens*** CBar CCla CGle CHEx CMea EBre ECha EDon ELan EOrc ERea LAbb LBre LHil NFai SCro WCru WEas
*– 'Album Plenum' EOrc
¶– ssp. ***canariae*** CBrk
§– ssp. ***frutescens*** CCan
– ssp. ***pumilum*** GCal
– ssp. ***succulentum*** 'Margaret Lynch' CBrk CCan EDon
'Gill's Pink' EDon NRar
§***gracile*** CB&S CBar CBrk CCan CHal CMea CMer CSev EBar ESma GCal LHil MFir NFai SHer WEas WHal WKif
– 'Chelsea Girl' CElw ERav SIgm
'Hopley's Double Yellow' LHil LHop NSty
§'Jamaica Primrose' Widely available
*'Jamaica Snowstorm' CB&S CBar WHal
*'Lemon Meringue' CElw ECtt EOrc
'Levada Cream' EDon EOrc
¶'Leyton Treasure' CBrk
§***maderense*** CB&S CBrk CCan CHad CMHG CMer CSev CSpe EOrc GCal IBlr LGre LHil LHop MSte NFai NRoo NSty NTow SAxl SDix SFis SUsu WEas WOMN WPer
¶'Mary Cheek' (d) CCan
'Mary Wootton' (d) CBrk CCan CElw CFis CGle CRDP CSev ECtt ELan EOrc ERav GCal LHil LHop MFir NBro NSty NWyt SChu WHal
mawii See PYRETHROPSIS ***gayanum***
'Mrs F Sander' (d) CBrk CCan EDon EFol LHop NSty
'Nevada Cream' See A. 'Qinta White'
ochroleucum See A. ***maderense***
¶'Peach Cheeks' CB&S CBrk CSev NRoo SIgm SMrm SRms
'Penny' CBrk LHop SUsu
¶'Petite Pink' CB&S CBrk CSpe MSte NFai SIgm
'Pink Australian' LHil
'Pink Break' CCan CHal
♦'Pink Delight' See A. 'Petite Pink'
¶'Pink Silver Queen' WEas
'Powder Puff' (d) CBrk CCan CKni CSpe EDon EFol EOrc LHop MRav MSte NFai
§'Qinta White' CCan EDon
'Rollason's Red' CBrk CCan CSev LHop NFai
'Rosali' (d) LHop
¶'Royal Haze' See A. ***foeniculaceum*** Webb 'Royal Haze'
'Sark' CBrk CCan CSpe ECha LHil LHop NRar NSty NWyt
*'Silver Queen' WEas
single pink CBos CElw CGle LHil NSty
§'Snowflake' (d) CB&S CBrk CCan CFis CHEx CMer CMil CSev CSpe ECtt EDon EOrc IHos LGre LHil SMad WAbe WHen
¶'Stydd Rose' NWyt
¶'Tony Holmes' CCan
'Vancouver' (d) Widely available
*'Vera' IHos
'Wellwood Park' CBrk CCan EBre GCal LBre LHop NFai

ARGYROCYTISUS See CYTISUS

ARISAEMA (Araceae)

amurense CBro CRDP EPot GDra NHar WChr WThu
candidissimum CBro CChu CHan CRDP EBre ECha EPar EPot IMal LAma LBow LBre MPar NHar NHol NKay NRog NRoo SPou WChr WCot WCru WHal
¶***ciliatum*** CT 369 SWas
concinnum EBul NHol NRog
consanguineum CBro CChu CGle LAma MUlv NHol WCot WCru
costatum EBul NRog
dracontium LAma NHol NRog NSal WCru
erubescens NRog
flavum CBro EBul EPot GCal LBow MPar NHol NNrd WCru WThu
griffithii CBro LAma NHol NRog WCot WCru WHal
¶– var. ***pradhanii*** WCru
helleborifolium See A. ***tortuosum***
intermedium NRog
jacquemontii CBro GDra LAma NHar NHol
japonicum See A. ***serratum***
§***nepenthoïdes*** LAma NHar NHol NRog WCot WCru
♦***ochraceum*** See A. ***nepenthoïdes***
propinquum EPot NRog WCru
ringens hort. See A. ***robustum***
– (Thunberg) Schott CBro LAma NHol WChr WCru
§***serratum*** LAma
sikokianum CBro CRDP EPot LAma LBow NHar NHol NRog SHer WChr WCru
speciosum CKel ELan LAma LBow MUlv NHol WCru WHil
thunbergii ssp. ***urashima*** LAma NHol NRog WCru
§***tortuosum*** ECha LAma MBal NHol WCru WHal
triphyllum CBro ECou EPar EPot GCra LAma LBow NHol NRog SHer WChr WCru WHil

ARISARUM (Araceae)

proboscideum CB&S CBos CBro CMea CRDP CRow ECha EFol ELan ELun EPar EPot GCal GDra LAma LBow MBal MCas MHig MTho NBro NHol NKay NRog NSti SIng SUsu WOld WRus
¶– MS 958 CMon
vulgare CB&S EPot LAma

¶ – ssp. ***simorrhinum*** SF 396/347 | CMon
¶ – ssp. ***vulgare*** JRM 1396 | CMon

ARISTEA (Iridaceae)

ecklonii CBot CHan CTro EBar LAbb SAxl WAbe WPer
ensifolia ELan EMon WThi
¶ – SH 88 CHan

ARISTOLOCHIA (Aristolochiaceae)

baetica SSpi
clematitis GPoy MBro MHew NHex NSal
contorta SSpi
§ ***durior*** CB&S CBot CDoC CGre CHEx CSco ELan MBri NPal SHBN SHer SHil SPer
♦ ***elegans*** See A. ***littoralis***
¶ ***gigantea*** CTro
§ ***littoralis*** CHal SLMG
macrophylla See A. ***durior***
sipho See A. ***durior***
tomentosa NSal
trilobata GCra

ARISTOTELIA (Elaeocarpaceae)

§ ***chilensis*** CB&S CGre CPle
– 'Variegata' CAbb CB&S CBra CCla CGre CHan CPle CTre EPla LHop LNet WEas WSHC
fruticosa (f) ECou
– (m) ECou
macqui See A. ***chilensis***
¶ ***peduncularis*** GWht
serrata ECar ECou

ARMERIA (Plumbaginaceae)

§ ***alliacea*** ECha WPer
– Formosa hybrids ELan IBlr NBar NCat NMir NOak SFis SIde WHil WHoo WPbr
– f. ***leucantha*** CBot
alpina NHol
'Bee's Ruby' CLew ECED GCal MFir MUlv WMer WPer
caespitosa See A. ***juniperifolia***
¶ Carlux hybrids GAbr
¶ ***filicaulis*** MFir
§ ***girardii*** EPot NHol
§ ***juniperifolia*** CMHG CMea EBre ECtt EMNN ESis LBre LHop MBro MHig MPla MTho NGre NKay NMen NNor NNrd NRoo NTow NWCA SBla SGil SHer WCla WWin
– 'Alba' CLew CRiv EBre ECar ELan EPar ESis LBee LBre MCas MHig MPla NHar NRoo SGil SHer WHil WThu WWin
– 'Ardenholme' NKay
– 'Beechwood' NHol SBla WThu
– 'Bevan's Variety' CMHG CRiv EBre ECar ECha ELan EPar EPot LBre MBro MFir MHig MRav MWat NHar NHol NKay NNrd NRoo NRya SHer SIng SWas WAbe WHil WHoo WPat WThu
– dark form ECar GDra
– rose form CLew EPot
¶ – spiny dwarf form EPot
leucocephala MPlt
– 'Corsica' ECha NBir
maritima CArn CBow CKin CMHG CRow CShe EBre EPar LAbb LBre LGro LHol MBar MPlt MRav NCat NLan NMen NNor NRed NSel SIde SPla WByw WWye
– 'Alba' CHal CNic EBre ECha EFou ELan EPar EPot ESis LBre MBal MBar MBri MFir NHol NNor NNrd NRoo NRya WAbe WByw WHen WPat WPer WWin
– ssp. ***alpina*** See A. ***a.***
– 'Bloodstone' CShe ECar ELan EPar EPot MWat SHer SPla
– 'Düsseldorfer Stolz' ('D. Pride') CHal CShe CTom EBre ECha ELan LBre MBri MBro MHig NHar NHol NMen NNrd NRoo SGil SHer WHen WPat WWye
– 'Glory of Holland' EPot
– 'La Pampa' NOak
– 'Laucheana' MFir NNrd NOak NTow WHoo
– 'Ruby Glow' NMen NNrd
– 'Snowball' NOak
– 'Splendens' CPar EMNN GCHN NHar NNrd SFis WCla WPer WWin
– 'Splendens Alba' CPar
– 'Vindictive' CHal CKel ELan MBal SHer SRms WAbe
'Ornament' ECtt ELan GAbr NRoo WCra WHen WPer WTyr
plantaginea See A. ***alliacea***
pseudarmeria ELan WEas
setacea See A. ***girardii***
tweedyi CRDP ECar EPot GTou NWCA SHer WHal
welwitschii CMHG SRms

ARMORACIA (Cruciferae)

§ ***rusticana*** CArn CHal CSFH CSev Effi GPoy IEde ILis LHol MBar MBri NSal NSel SIde WGwy WOak WWye
– 'Variegata' CRDP EMon LRHS WCHb

ARNEBIA (Boraginaceae)

echioïdes See A. ***pulchra***
§ ***pulchra*** EBlo EBre ECED LBre

ARNICA (Compositae)

§ ***angustifolia*** NHol
*– 'Iljinni' NBir
chamissonis GGar LHol MHew NRoo NSal WPer WWye
longifolia WWye
montana CArn CSFH EBar ECro GAbr GPoy MChe MHew NHol NSal NSel SHer SWat WPer WWye

ARONIA (Rosaceae)

arbutifolia CB&S CBow CGre CPle EPla GWht IJoh IOrc MBal MGos NBar NHol SHBN SHer SPer WAbe WBod WDin WSHC WWat
– 'Brilliant' ELan MUlv SHil SPer

– 'Erecta'	CCla CCor EBre ENot GWht LBre SRms WThu WWat
melanocarpa	CCla CCor CHan CMHG EBre LBre MBar MRav NHol SReu SSpi WBod WDin WHCG WThu WWat
– 'Viking'	LBuc MUlv
x ***prunifolia***	CCla CCor CDoC CMHG CSco NHol WHCG WWat

ARRHENATHERUM (Gramineae)

elatius ssp. ***bulbosum*** 'Variegatum'	CHan CNic EFol EFou EHoe ELan EMar EMon EPla ETPC MCas MPar NCat NRya SCob SFar WEas WRus

ARTEMISIA † (Compositae)

§ ***abrotanum***	Widely available
absinthium	CArn CFis CHad CHal CSFH CTom EEls Effi GPoy LHol MBar MBri MChe MPit NNor NSti SHer SIde SPer WHal WNdy WOak WPer WWye
– 'Lambrook Silver'	Widely available
§ ***alba***	CFis CSev EEls LHol NSel NSti SIde WPer WWye
– 'Canescens'	CBos CCla CFis CGle CHan CLew CSev CShe EBre ECha EEls EFou EGol EOrc EPla GCal LBre MBri NTow SBla SDix SGil SMrm SPer SSvw WMer WPer WWat
annua	EEls NSal SIde WWye
arborescens	CArn CFis CGle CGre CMHG CMer ECha EEls EFou ELan EPla IJoh NFai NSti SDix SDry SGil SMad SPer WDin WHer
– 'Brass Band'	See A. 'Faith Raven'
– 'Porquerolles'	EEls LHop SAxl
armeniaca	EEls WWin
assoana	See A. ***caucasica***
atrata	EEls
brachyloba	CFis CMHG EEls SHer WCHb
♦***caerulescens***	See SERIPHIDIUM ***c.***
campestris	CFis
– ssp. ***borealis***	CMer EEls Effi LHol MBri MChe NSel
– ssp. ***campestris***	CNat EEls
– ssp. ***maritima***	EEls
camphorata	See A. ***alba***
canariensis	See A. ***thuscula***
capillaris	EEls
§ ***caucasica***	CFis CGle CHal CPar CRDP CShe EBre EEls EFol GCHN IDai LBre LGro MTol NKay NNrd NRed NSel SIng SMrm WCHb WEas WHer WHil WPer WWat
¶– ***caucasica***	SGil SIgm
chamaemelifolia	CArn CHal EEls LHol NSti SIde WPer WWye
♦***cretacea***	See SERIPHIDIUM ***nutans***
discolor	See A. ***ludoviciana incompta***
douglasiana 'Valerie Finnis'	See A. ***ludoviciana latiloba***
dracunculus	CArn CFis CGle CHad CRiv CSFH CSev ECha EEls ELan Effi GPoy IEde LHol MBar MBri MChe NRoo NSel SDix SIde WEas WOak WPer WWye
– ***dracunculoïdes***	EEls EJud MChe
eriantha	EEls
'Faith Raven'	CFis CMea CShe CWit EBar EEls EFou EGol ELan MBri NFai WHal WHer WMer WRus WSHC
frigida	EEls EOrc ILis WEas WHCG WWin
glacialis	CMHG CRiv EEls LGan NRar NSti SFar SIng
gmelinii	EEls
gnaphalodes	See A. ***ludoviciana***
gracilis	See A. ***scoparia***
granatensis	NSti WOMN
¶ ***kitadakensis***	EEls
¶– 'Guizhou'	CGle EBlo EFou EOrc LGre WCot
laciniata	EEls
lactiflora	CFis CGle CHad CKel CSco ECha ECtt EEls EFou ELan EPar GCal IDai NKay NNor NSel NSti SCro SDix SHer SPer WBon WWye
¶– dark form	EFol
*– ***purpurea***	CBre SAxl
lanata	See A. ***caucasica***
♦***laxa***	See A. ***umbelliformis***
§ ***ludoviciana***	CArn CBre CFis CGle CHal CPle CSFH CShe CSun ECED EEls ELan IJoh LGre LGro MWat NFai NNor NOak NOrc NSal SIde WHil WOld WWin WWye
§ – var. ***incompta***	CFis ECha EEls EFol EPla MNFA NFai
– var. ***latifolia***	See A. ***l. latiloba***
§ – var. ***latiloba***	CCla CHad CLew CMer CMil ECha EEls EFol EFou EHoe EOrc EPla GCal LHop MBri MBro MPar MRav MTol NBro NFai NOak NRoo WCot WEas WHal WHer WMer WPbr WPer
– 'Silver Queen'	CCla CFis CGle CKel CLew CMea CSco EBre ECtt EEls ELan ENot EPar EPla LBre MBri NBro NFai NHol NNor NSti SBla SPer SPla WHal WHen WHil WPer WWat
♦***maritima***	See SERIPHIDIUM ***maritimum***
molinieri	EEls LHol
mutellina	See A. ***umbelliformis***
niitakayamensis	EEls
♦***nutans***	See SERIPHIDIUM ***n.***
♦***palmeri*** A Gray	See SERIPHIDIUM ***p.***
– hort.	See A. ***ludoviciana***
pedemontana	See A. ***caucasica***
pontica	CArn CBre CElw CFis CGle CHad CHal CMea COtt CSFH ECha EEls EHoe ELan EOrc EPar GPoy LHol NBro NNor NSti SDix SIde WEas WHer WHil WRus WWat WWin WWye
N'Powis Castle'	Widely available
♦***procera***	See A. ***abrotanum***
purshiana	See A. ***ludoviciana***
rupestris	EEls

schmidtiana	CFis ECha EFou EPad LHop MPar MWat SHer WHen
– 'Nana'	Widely available
§ ***scoparia***	CFis EEls
splendens	CMHG CShe EBre EFol ELan LBre LGre MTol NSti SHer WEas WRus WSHC
– var. ***brachyphylla***	CHan
¶ sp. CLD 1531	EMon
sp. Guiz 137	CBos EPla
stelleriana	CBrk CFis CGle CMer CShe CTom EBre ECha IJoh LAbb LBre LHop MFir MNFA MTho NBro NMir NNor NSti SHer SIng SPer WHoo WPer WRus WSHC WWye
– 'Boughton Silver'	See A. *s.* 'Mori'
§ – 'Mori'	CCla CFis CHad CMHG EEls EFou EHoe ELan EMNN LBlm LGre MBri NBar NHol NNrd NRar NTow SCro SGil SMrm WHil WMer WPer WWat WWeb
– 'Nana'	ECha EEls EPla GTou
– ***prostrata***	See A. *s.* 'Mori'
¶ – 'Silver Brocade'	SHil
§ ***thuscula***	EEls
tridentata	See SERIPHIDIUM ***tridentatum***
§ ***umbelliformis***	EEls LBee WDav
♦ ***vallesiaca***	See SERIPHIDIUM ***vallesiacum***
verlotiorum	EEls
versicolor	NNor
vulgaris	CArn CSFH EEls Effi GPoy IEde LHol MChe NSel SIde WHer WOak WWye
– 'Cragg-Barber Eye' (v)	CNat
– 'Crispa'	SIde
– 'Variegata'	CBos CBre CElw CFis CLew CRDP CWit EFol EHoe EMon WHer
* ***xerganensis***	EEls

ARTHROPODIUM (Liliaceae/Anthericaceae)

candidum	CBot CHan CMea CRow EBar EBul ECha ECou EFol EPla EPot LHil MPit NCat NMen NWCA SAxl SHer SUsu WEas WHal
– ***maculatum***	CNic
– ***purpureum***	CRDP CRiv ELan EMar EMon EPot NHol WCru
cirrhatum	CAbb CPle CRDP CTre CTro EBul ECou GCal IBar LHop
milleflorum	CAvo EBul ECou NWCA SAxl WAbe

ARTICHOKE, Globe See CYNARA *scolymus*

ARTICHOKE, Jerusalem See HELIANTHUS *tuberosus*

ARUM (Araceae)

§ ***concinnatum***	CMon SSpi WChr
conophalloïdes	See A. ***detruncatum detruncatum***
cornutum	See SAUROMATUM ***venosum***
creticum	CAvo CBot CBro CHan ECha EPar EPot IBlr LAma NHol NTow SSpi WOld
– FCC form	WChr
– white form	SPou
– yellow form	NBir SDix
§ ***detruncatum*** var. ***detruncatum***	CAvo
dioscoridis	CAvo MTho WChr WCot
dracunculus	See DRACUNCULUS ***vulgaris***
elongatum	EPot WChr
hygrophilum	CAvo WChr
idaeum	See A. ***maculatum*** Idaeum Group
italicum	CBow CGle ECro EOrc ETub LAma MBri NCat NNrd NRog SDeJ SHer WAbe WByw WOMN
¶ – NL 1234	CMon
– ssp. ***albispathum***	CMon EMon EPot LAma WChr WDav
¶ – 'Chameleon'	CHad
§ – ssp. ***italicum***	Widely available
– – 'Tiny'	GCal MPar SWas
§ – – 'White Winter'	EMon WRus
– ***marmoratum***	See A. ***i. italicum***
– 'Nancy Lindsay'	EMon
– ssp. ***neglectum***	LRHS
N– ***pictum***	See A. ***i. italicum***
korolkowii	EPot WChr
maculatum	CKin CRDP EPar EPot GDra GPoy LAma MHew NHex NSal WWye
§ – Idaeum Group	WChr
– ***variegatum***	GPoy
♦ ***nickelii***	See A. ***concinnatum***
§ ***nigrum***	EMon
orientale	EPot NHol
palaestinum	CAvo
♦ ***petteri*** hort.	See A. ***nigrum***
N ***pictum***	CAvo EPot LAma SPou WChr
– ACL 321/78	EMon
¶ – CL 28	CMon
– 'Taff's Form'	See A. ***italicum italicum*** 'White Winter'
¶ ***purpureospathum***	EMon

ARUNCUS (Rosaceae)

aethusifolius	CCla CDoC CLew COtt CRDP CRow CSco CTom EBar ECha EFou EGol ELan EPar EPla LHil MBro MRav MUlv NHar NHol NNor NOak SMad SUsu WDav WEas WHil WPer WWin
§ ***dioicus***	Widely available
– 'Glasnevin'	CChu CCla CSco EBre ECtt EGol EOrc GAbr GCal LBre LGan MBri MUlv NHol SFis WMer
– var. ***kamtschaticus***	NHol WDav
¶ – – AGSJ 59	NHol
– 'Kneiffii'	Widely available
– 'Zweiweltenkind' ('Child of Two Worlds')	COtt NHol WMer
japonicus AGSJ 238	NHol
plumosus	See A. ***dioicus***
sp. CLD 718	EMon
sylvester	See A. ***dioicus***

ARUNDINARIA † (Gramineae(Bambuseae))

amabilis	See PSEUDOSASA ***a.***
anceps	See YUSHANIA ***a.***
angustifolia	See PLEIOBLASTUS ***chino a.***
auricoma	See PLEIOBLASTUS ***auricomus***
chino	See PLEIOBLASTUS ***c.***
disticha	See PLEIOBLASTUS ***pygmaeus distichus***
falconeri	See HIMALAYACALAMUS ***f.***
fastuosa	See SEMIARUNDINARIA ***f.***
fortunei	See PLEIOBLASTUS ***variegatus***
♦*funghomii*	See SCHIZOSTACHYUM ***f.***
gigantea	SBam SDry WJun
hindsii	See PLEIOBLASTUS ***h.***
hookeriana hort.	See DREPANOSTACHYUM 'Damarapa'
humilis	See PLEIOBLASTUS ***h.***
japonica	See PSEUDOSASA ***j.***
jaunsarensis	See YUSHANIA ***anceps***
maling	See YUSHANIA ***m.***
marmorea	See CHIMONOBAMBUSA ***m.***
murieliae	See FARGESIA ***spathacea***
nitida	See FARGESIA ***n.***
♦*oedogonata*	See CLAVINODUM ***oedogonatum***
palmata	See SASA ***p.***
pumila	See PLEIOBLASTUS ***humilis pumilus***
pygmaea	See PLEIOBLASTUS ***pygmaeus***
quadrangularis	See CHIMONOBAMBUSA ***q.***
simonii	See PLEIOBLASTUS ***s.***
spathiflora	See THAMNOCALAMUS ***spathiflorus***
§ *tecta*	SDry
tessellata	See THAMNOCALAMUS ***tessellatus***
vagans	See SASAELLA ***ramosa***
variegata	See PLEIOBLASTUS ***variegatus***
veitchii	See SASA ***v.***
viridistriata	See PLEIOBLASTUS ***auricomus***
'Wang Tsai'	See BAMBUSA ***multiplex*** 'Fernleaf'

ARUNDO (Gramineae)

donax	CBen CHEx CRow EPla GAri LMay LPan SApp SArc SMad
– 'Macrophylla'	CRow
– 'Variegata'	See A. ***d. versicolor***
§ – var. *versicolor* (v)	CB&S CBen CBot CBrk CHEx CRDP CRow CSun ECha EFol EHoe LBlm LHop MSta MSte MUlv SApp SArc SMad WOld
pliniana	EMon EPla LRHS

ASARINA (Scrophulariaceae)

antirrhiniflora	CSpe SFis
barclayana	See MAURANDYA ***b.***
erubescens	See MAURANDYA ***e.***
hispanica	See ANTIRRHINUM ***h.***
lophantha	See MAURANDYA ***l.***
lophosperma	See MAURANDYA ***l.***
§ *procumbens*	CGle CLew CMHG CMea CPar CSun ECha ELan GCal GDra GTou LHop MBal MPar MPit MTho NBro NSti NWCA SAxl SIng SPer SUsu WCla WEas WHer WHoo WOMN WPbr WWin
¶ – 'Alba'	SRms

ASARUM (Aristolochiaceae)

arifolium	EPar
canadense	GPoy MTol NSal WCru WWye
caudatum	CRDP CRow ECar EMon EPla GCal LHop MBri NSal WCru WHal
europaeum	CAvo CBos CBow CHEx CHan CRDP EBlo ECha EFol EFou ELan EPar EPla EPot GPoy MFir MHew MPar MWat NGar NSal NSel NSti SAxl WCru WEas WHer WWye
hartwegii	CAvo ECar ECha EPot NBir NSal SPou SWas WCru
lemmonii	EPla

ASCLEPIAS (Asclepiadaceae)

albicans	NSal
¶ 'Cinderella'	SIgm
curassavica	EBar LAbb NSal SLMG SLon
fruticosa	WHer
incarnata	CGre CPle ECro ELan GAbr MRav MUlv NSal SAxl SFis SPer WPer
physocarpa	CArn CPle
purpurascens	LHop
speciosa	NSal
subulata	NSal
syriaca	CArn CGre CHan ECro GCal MPlt MSte NSal WPer
tuberosa	CArn CB&S CDoC CHad CPar CRDP EBar EBre ECED ECro GPoy LAbb LBre MHew MRav NSal SFis SMrm WPer
¶ – Gay Butterflies Group	WHil
viridiflora	NSal

ASPARAGUS (Liliaceae/Asparagaceae)

asparagoïdes	ERea SLMG
– 'Myrtifolius'	CHal
densiflorus 'Myers'	CHal MBri
– Sprengeri Group	CHal MBri NBee
falcatus	CHal MBri
officinalis	CHEx NSal WByw WNdy
– 'Backlim'	ESor
– 'Boonlim'	ESor MBen
– 'Connover's Collosal'	ESor MBen
– 'Franklim'	ESor
– 'Gijnlim'	ESor
– 'Lucullus'	MBen
¶ – *pseudoscaber* 'Spitzenschleier'	GCal
– 'Venlim'	ESor
setaceus	CHal MBri
– 'Pyramidalis'	MBri
¶ *verticillatus*	GCal SRms

ASPERULA (Rubiaceae)

arcadiensis	
JCA 210.100	NTow
aristata ssp. ***scabra***	ELan EMon
– ssp. ***thessala***	See A. ***sintenisii***
gussonii	CLew CNic CRiv EPot ESis GAbr GDra MBro MCas MFir MPit MTho MWat NHol NKay NWCA SBla SIng SSmi WDav WPat WThu
hexaphylla	ECED
hirta	CHal CNic MCas MHig NHol NRed
§ ***lilaciflora***	LBee MHig NWCA SIng
– var. ***caespitosa***	See A. ***l. lilaciflora***
– ssp. ***lilaciflora***	CLew CMHG EBre ELan EPot LBre MTho NHar NHol NKay NMen NNrd NRoo SHer SSmi WPat WWin
nitida	ELan MCas MTho NNrd
– ssp. ***puberula***	See A. ***sintenisii***
odorata	See GALIUM ***odoratum***
§ ***perpusilla***	CShe
§ ***sintenisii***	EPot LBee MBro NHar NHol NKay NTow SBla SHer SIng SSou SWas WDav WHoo WThu
suberosa hort.	EBre ELan EPot LBre MTho NHol NKay NMen NTow SGil SHer SSmi WOMN WThu
taurina ssp. ***caucasica***	NSti SAxl WCot WHal
tinctoria	GPoy LHol MChe MHew NSal SIde SRms

ASPHODELINE (Liliaceae/Asphodelaceae)

¶ ***brevicaulis***	SWas
liburnica	CChu CHan CMon ECha EMar GAbr LRHS MBro MNFA SDix WCot WHoo WRus
§ ***lutea***	Widely available
*– 'Gelbkerze' ('Yellow Candle')	EBar EBlo EPot

ASPHODELUS † (Liliaceae/Asphodelaceae)

acaulis	SSpi SWas
¶– SF 37	CMon
§ ***aestivus***	CSam ECro GCal SAxl
albus	CChu EBul ECha ECro LGre SAxl WPbr
brevicaulis	See ASPHODELINE ***b.***
cerasiferus	See A. ***ramosus***
fistulosus	CAvo CRDP ECro EFol ELan EMon EOrc ESis LGan LGre LHop LWad MFir MTho NBir NBro NHol WPer WWin
lusitanicus	See A. ***ramosus***
luteus	See ASPHODELINE ***lutea***
microcarpus	See A. ***aestivus***
§ ***ramosus***	CHan CMon ECro SAsh

ASPIDISTRA (Liliaceae/Convallariaceae)

elatior	CHEx CHal EBak ERav MBri NRog SAxl SGil WOak
– 'Variegata'	CHal LAbb MTho NBir
* ***lurida*** 'Irish Mist'	IBlr

ASPLENIUM † (Aspleniaceae)

adiantum-nigrum	CTom
alternans	See A. ***dalhousieae***
bulbiferum	NMar WEas
§ ***ceterach***	EPot
cuneifolium	NKay
dareoïdes	GDra
§ ***delthiopicum***	EFou NBar
* ***fimbriatum***	MBri
¶ ***flabellifolium***	NMar
♦ ***furcatum*** Thunberg	See A. ***aethiopicum***
lepidum	NKay
¶ ***marinum***	NMar
nidus	CHal MBri
oblongifolium	NMar
officinarum	See A. ***ceterach***
¶ ***rhizophyllum***	NMar
ruta-muraria	CNat SRms
– ssp. ***dolomiticum*** var. ***eberlei***	NKay
§ ***scolopendrium***	CKin CPar CWGN EBre ECha EGol EHon EPar GPoy LBre LMay MBal MBri MSta NBro NHol NKay NLan NMar NOrc SApp SDix SMad SPer SRms SSpi WFib
– 'Angustatum'	EFou
¶ – 'Conglomeratum'	SRms
¶ – Crispum Fimbriatum Group	WRic
– Crispum Group	CRDP ECha ELan EPla MBri NHar NHol NKay SSpi WFib
– 'Crispum Nobile'	NBro NMar WEas
¶ – 'Crispum Robinson'	WRic
– Cristatum Group	ELan IOrc MBal MBri MRav NHar NHol NKay NMar SPer SRms SWat WFib
– 'Digitatum'	WFib
– 'Kaye's Lacerated'	EGol ELan MBri NHar NHol NMar WRic
¶ – Laceratum Group	SRms
– Marginatum Group	CWGN NMar SWat
– Marginatum Group 'Irregulare'	CRDP NHar NHol SRms WFib
– 'Muricatum'	CRDP NMar
– 'Ramocristatum'	NMar WRic
– 'Ramomarginatum'	CWGN ELan SRms
– 'Sagittatocristatum'	NKay
– 'Undulatum'	CMil EGol EPla GGar NHar NMar SPla SRms SSpi SWat WRic
¶ ***septentrionale***	SRms
trichomanes	CHal EBre EFou ELan GGar LBre MBal MBri NHar NHol NKay NMar SApp SCob WFib
– Cristatum Group	NMar WRic
– Incisum Group	IOrc NHar SApp
¶ ***viride***	SRms

ASTELIA (Liliaceae/Asteliaceae)

¶ ***banksii***	CB&S
cunninghamii	See A. ***solandri***
fragrans	ECou
grandis	EBul
nervosa	CAbb CB&S CHEx EBul ECou SSpi
¶ – var. ***chathamica***	GCal
– – 'Silver Spear'	CB&S CHEx IMal LHop SDry SSpi WCru
§ ***solandri***	CHEx

ASTER † (Compositae)

acris	See A. ***sedifolius***
§ ***albescens***	CGre CPle CPou EHal EMon EPla ISea MBal MPla WCru WSHC
¶ ***alpigenus***	CNic
alpinus	CPar CWGN EBar EBre EMNN GCHN LBre MBro MCas MFir MPit MWat NHar NHol NKay NMen NWCA SBla SHer SIng SSou WOMN WOld WPer WWin
– var. ***albus***	CNic GCHN NCat NHol WPer
– 'Beechwood'	NKay
– 'Dunkle Schöne' ('Dark Beauty')	EFou NOak
– 'Happy End'	NHol NOak NRoo
– 'Roseus'	EPad
– 'Trimix'	CSam ESis LAbb NBir NMir NRoo NVic SFis WHil
– violet	WPer
– 'White Beauty'	EFou MWil SSou
amelloïdes	See FELICIA ***amelloïdes***
amellus	CHal NNor
– 'Blue King'	EFou SFis
– 'Breslau'	EFou WOld
– 'Brilliant'	CAll CKel CLew CMGP CPar CSco EBre ECtt EFou EOrc LBre MNFA MWat NRoo SChu SPer WByw WMer WOld
– 'Empress'	WOld
– 'Framfieldii'	WOld
– 'Jacqueline Genebrier'	SMrm SWas WOld
– 'King George'	CAll CElw CKel CShe EBlo EBre ECED EFou ELan EOrc EPla ERav LBre MWat NRoo SChu SPer SPla WEas WHoo WOld
– 'Kobold'	WOld
– 'Lac de Genève'	CSco CShe LRHS MBri WCot
– 'Lady Hindlip'	MUlv WEas
*– 'Marie Anne Neill'	SFis
– 'Moerheim Gem'	CAll WEas WOld
– 'Nocturne'	CAll CSco EBlo ECED WByw WOld
– 'Peach Blossom'	CDoC EFou MUlv WOld
– 'Pink Pearl'	EFou WOld
– 'Pink Zenith' ('Rosa Erfüllung')	CAll CBos CLew CRDP CShe EBre ECtt EFou ELan EOrc LAbb LBre MBri MRav NNor NRoo NVic SBla SChu SPer SPla WAbe WEas WHil WOld WRus
– 'Praecox Junifreude'	EFou
– 'Rudolph Goethe'	CCla EFou MUlv SHBN WEas WMer WOld
– 'Schone von Ronsdorf'	WOld
– 'September Glow'	ECha EFou EHal EOrc
– 'Sonia'	CAll ECha EFou SFis SUsu WByw WMer WOld
– 'Sonora'	WOld
– 'Sternkugel'	WOld
– 'Ultramarine'	CAll EFou WAbb
N– 'Veilchenkönigin' ('Violet Queen')	CAll CGle CKel CMGP EBar EBlo EBre ECha ECtt EFou ELan LBre MBri SBla SChu SDix SGil SUsu SWas WEas WHoo WOld
– 'Weltfriede'	WOld
♦***asper***	See A. ***bakerianus***
§ ***bakerianus***	CHan NOak WOld WPer
'Barbara Worl'	SAsh
batangensis CLD 956	EMon
'Blue Star'	CBre EFou SAxl SChu WOld
canus	See A. ***sedifolius c.***
capensis 'Variegata '	See FELICIA ***amelloïdes*** variegated
§ ***carolinianus***	CHan
coelestis	See FELICIA ***amelloïdes***
'Coombe Fishacre'	CAll CBre CGle EFou GCal LHil MBel MBri MNFA MTol MUlv NCat NSti SFis SPla SWas WByw WEas WHer WOld
cordifolius 'Aldebaran'	SAxl
– 'Elegans'	CAll EFou EHal NSti WOld
– 'Ideal'	CDoC EFou LRHS WOld
– 'Little Carlow'	See A. 'L. C.'
– 'Little Dorrit'	See A. 'Little Dorrit'
– 'Photograph'	See A. 'Photograph'
– 'Silver Queen'	CAll EOrc
– 'Silver Spray'	CAll CCla CDoC EFou MBri MWat SFis WEas WHoo WMer WOld WPer
– 'Sweet Lavender'	CAll MNFA SFis WOld
corymbosus	See A. ***divaricatus***
'Deep Pink Star'	WOld
♦***diffusus***	See A. ***lateriflorus***
§ ***divaricatus***	CAll CBos CBre CCla CElw CGle CHad CHan CLew CMea CPar CRDP ECha EFol EFou ELan EOrc GCal MPar MRav NHol NSti SAxl SChu SHig SUsu WByw WOld WWin
N***dumosus***	NKay
ericoïdes	CGle ERav NCat SChu SIng SMrm WHil WWin
¶– 'Blue Heaven'	COtt
– 'Blue Star'	NFai WOld
– 'Blue Wonder'	CGle MNFA WOld
– 'Brimstone'	CAll EOrc MNFA WOld
– 'Cinderella'	CTom EHal EOrc EPad MNFA NRoo NSti SAxl SChu SPer SPla
– 'Constance'	CAll WOld
*– 'Dainty'	CLew CRDP
– 'Enchantress'	CAll
– 'Erlkönig'	CAll EFou EJud GAbr MBri MSte SChu WOld
– 'Esther'	CAll CGle CLew ECha EFou EHal EOrc ESma MNFA NCat NSti SChu SDix SFis WOld
– 'Golden Spray'	CAll CBre EFou LHil NSti WMer WOld
– 'Herbstmyrte'	EFou SAxl
– 'Hon. Edith Gibbs'	CAll EOrc MSte WCot
– 'Ideal'	CAll
– 'Maidenhood'	SFis WOld
– 'Monte Cassino'	See A. ***pringlei*** 'M.C.'
– 'Perfection'	CAll
– 'Pink Cloud'	CAll CBre CChu CGle CTom EBlo EFou EOrc ERav ESma MBro MNFA MSte MTol MUlv NFai NRoo SPla WHoo WOld WRus
– prostrate form	EFol SCro
– 'Rosy Veil'	CAll WByw WOld
– 'Schneegitter'	CAll MSte
– 'Vimmer's Delight'	CAll

– 'White Heather'	CAll CBre CGle CSco MNFA SAxl SFis SPla WByw WCot WEas WHoo WOld
– 'Yvette Richardson'	WOld
farreri	SMrm
§ *flaccidus*	MDHE MPlt
foliaceus cusickii	EMon
x *frikartii*	CAll CCla CKel CLew CMea CSco CSev EBre EFou EGol ELan ENot EOrc EPar GCHN LBre LHop MRav NBar NKay SAxl SBla SChu SGil SHBN SPer WByw WEas WOld WWin
– 'Eiger'	WOld
– 'Flora's Delight'	EBre EOrc LBre NRoo
– 'Jungfrau'	CHan MUlv WOld
N– 'Mönch'	Widely available
– 'Wunder von Stäfa'	CCla CElw CSco EFol EOrc MBri MUlv NSti SAxl SFis WOld WStI WSun
¶ 'Herfstweelde'	EMon SWas
himalaicus	GCHN GTou
– BM&W 12	NHol
– C&Mc 145	GCHN WDav
– EMAK 0952	NHol
'Hon. Vicary Gibbs' (*ericoïdes* x)	CAll CGle EOrc ESma MNFA SFis WOld
hybridus luteus	See X SOLIDASTER ***luteus***
§ 'Kylie'	EMon WOld
laevis	CBre MSte
– 'Arcturus'	CBos
– 'Calliope'	SWas WOld
lanceolatus 'Edwin Beckett'	CAll CBre MNFA SFis WOld
lateriflorus	CGle ECha EJud EOrc WOld
– 'Delight'	CAll MUlv NSti WOld
– 'Horizontalis'	Widely available
– 'Lovely'	SFis
– 'Prince'	EFou EHal EMon EPla LRHS SWas WCot
♦ *likiangensis*	See A. ***asteroïdes***
§ *linosyris*	CAll SFis SPer WCot WMer
– 'Goldilocks'	See A. ***linosyris***
§ 'Little Carlow' (*cordifolius* x)	CAll CBre CGle EFou EHal EJud EOrc GCal MNFA MRav NSti SAxl SBla SFis WEas WHal WOld WPer
§ 'Little Dorrit' (*cordifolius* x)	CAll NSti SAxl WCot WOld
macrophyllus	CAll ELan EMon NSti SPer WOld
– 'Albus'	EMon LRHS WCot
– 'Twilight'	CGle EBar SUsu SWas WCot WOld
♦ *mongolicus*	See KALIMERIS ***mongolica***
natalensis	See FELICIA ***rosulata***
novae-angliae 'Andenken an Alma Pötschke'	Widely available
– 'Andenken an Paul Gerber'	EMon
– 'Barr's Blue'	CGle EFou EMon MUlv SChu SHer SMrm WMer WOld
– 'Barr's Pink'	CAll EFou EMon ERav SFis WEas WMer WOld
– 'Barr's Violet'	CAll CGle SAxl SRms WCot WOld
– 'Crimson Beauty'	CAll WOld
– 'Ernie Moss'	SFis
– 'Festival'	SFis
– 'Forncett Jewel'	EFou
– 'Harrington's Pink'	CAll CBre CElw CGle CKel CMea EBre ECED EFou EMon EOrc IDai LBre MWat NBro NOak SChu SCro SGil SPer WByw WEas WOld WSun WWin
§ – 'Herbstschnee' ('Autumn Snow')	CAll CBre CGle CShe EBre EFou EMon EOrc LBre LHil LHop MBel MWat NHol NSti SChu SFis SGil WOld WPer WWin
– 'Lye End Beauty'	CAll CGle EFou EMon EOrc MFir MNFA MSte MUlv NOak SAxl SChu WOld
– 'Lye End Companion'	CAll CGle
– 'Mrs S T Wright'	CAll EFou EMon LHil WByw WOld
*– 'Mrs S W Stern'	WOld
– 'Purple Cloud'	CAll EMon
– 'Quinton Menzies'	CAll EMon EOrc MUlv WOld
– 'Red Cloud'	EFou
– 'Rosa Sieger'	EMon SChu WOld
¶ – 'Roter Stern'	EFou
– 'Rubinschatz'	EFou
– 'Rudelsburg'	EFou EMon
– 'Sayer's Croft'	WCot
– 'Septemberrubin' ('September Ruby')	CAll CKel CMea EBre ECED ECtt EMon LBre LHop MRav MUlv NFai SChu SGil WByw WEas WOld WPer WWin
– 'Treasure'	CAll EFou EMon WOld
– 'Violetta'	EMon WOld
– 'W Bowman'	EMon
N *novi-belgii* 'Ada Ballard'	CAll CKel CMGP CPar CSco EBre ECED LBre MBel NHol SPer WOld
– 'Albanian'	CAll EJud WOld
– 'Alderman Vokes'	CAll WOld
– 'Alex Norman'	CAll WOld
– 'Algar's Pride'	CAll LHil MUlv WOld
– 'Alice Haslam'	CAll CMGP ECtt EFou MBal MBri MFir NBar NKay NOrc SPla WByw WOld WPer
– 'Alpenglow'	CAll WOld
– 'Anita Ballard'	CAll WOld
– 'Anita Webb'	WEas WOld WPer
– 'Anneke'	WHer
– 'Antwerpse Parel' ('Antwerp Pearl')	CAll
– 'Apollo'	CB&S MBri WHil
– 'Apple Blossom'	CAll EFou WOld
¶ – 'Archbishop'	WOld
– 'Arctic'	CAll WOld
– 'Audrey'	CAll CKel CLew CMGP CPar EBre ECED ECtt EFou GCHN LBre MBri MNFA NBar NBro NKay NOrc SPla WByw WMer WOld
– 'Autumn Beauty'	CAll WOld
– 'Autumn Days'	CAll WOld
– 'Autumn Glory'	CAll WOld
– 'Autumn Rose'	CAll WOld
– 'Autumn Snow'	See A. ***n-a*** 'Herbstschnee'
– 'Baby Climax'	CAll WOld

– 'Beechwood Beacon'	CAll
– 'Beechwood Challenger'	CAll CDoC NKay WMer WOld
– 'Beechwood Charm'	CAll MNFA WOld
– 'Beechwood Rival'	WMer
– 'Beechwood Supreme'	CAll WOld
– 'Belmont Blue'	CAll
– 'Bewunderung'	EFou
– 'Blandie'	CAll CKel CMGP CSco ECED EFou MWat NHol NMir NVic WOld
– 'Blauglut'	EFou
– 'Blue Baby'	SHer WPer
– 'Blue Bouquet'	CAll CKel ECED SRms WByw WOld
– 'Blue Boy'	WOld
– 'Blue Danube'	CAll WOld
– 'Blue Eyes'	CAll EFou WOld
– 'Blue Gem'	CAll CBre
– 'Blue Gown'	CAll GCal MBri SHig WOld
– 'Blue Patrol'	CAll CKel WOld
– 'Blue Plume'	CAll
– 'Blue Radiance'	CAll MNFA WOld
– 'Blue Whirl'	CAll WOld
– 'Bonanza'	CAll MBal WOld
– 'Bonningdale Blue'	CAll WOld
– 'Bonningdale White'	CAll WOld
– 'Borealis'	CAll
– 'Bridesmaid'	CAll WOld
– 'Bridgette'	EFou
– 'Brightest and Best'	WOld
– 'Cameo'	CAll WOld
– 'Cantab'	WOld
– 'Carlingcot'	CAll WOld
– 'Carnival'	CAll CMGP CPar CSco EFou MBri MUlv NBar NOrc SFis SPer WOld
– 'Cecily'	CAll WOld
– 'Charles Wilson'	WCot WOld
– 'Chatterbox'	CAll CSco ECtt MNFA MWat SChu SRms WEas WOld
– 'Chelwood'	CAll WOld
– 'Chequers'	CAll CPar ECED NBar NHol WOld
– 'Chilcompton'	CAll
– 'Choristers'	CAll CShe WOld
– 'Christina'	See A. ***n-b.*** 'Kristina'
– 'Christine Soanes'	EFou
– 'Cliff Lewis'	CAll CShe WOld
– 'Climax'	CAll CBre CSco ECha GCal MBri MNFA MUlv NSti SHig SPer WOld
– 'Climax Albus'	See A. ***n-b.*** 'White Climax'
– 'Cloudy Blue'	CAll CBre EFou WOld
– 'Colin Bailey'	CAll
– 'Colonel F R Durham'	CAll WMer
– 'Coombe Gladys'	WOld
– 'Coombe Joy'	WOld
– 'Coombe Margaret'	CAll WOld
– 'Coombe Queen'	CAll WOld
– 'Coombe Radiance'	WOld
– 'Coombe Ronald'	MWat WOld
– 'Coombe Rosemary'	CDec CPar EBre ECtt LBre MUlv SGil WByw WCot WOld
– 'Coombe Violet'	MWat WOld
– 'Countess of Dudley'	CAll CKel WOld WPer
– 'Court Herald'	CAll CSco WOld
– 'Crimson Brocade'	CAll CKel ECED ELan ENot MBri MWat WMer WOld
– 'Crimson Velvet'	CAll
– 'Dandy'	CAll CKel CPar CTom EFou ELan LHil NHol WByw WOld
– 'Daniela'	EFou
– 'Daphne Anne'	WOld
– 'Dauerblau'	EFou WOld
– 'Davey's True Blue'	WOld
– 'David Murray'	WOld
– 'Dazzler'	CAll EFou WOld
– 'Destiny'	CAll WOld
– 'Diana'	CNic WOld
– 'Diana Watts'	CAll WOld
– 'Dietgard'	WOld
– 'Dolly'	EFou
– 'Dora Chiswell'	CAll
– 'Dorothy Bailey'	CAll
– 'Dusky Maid'	CAll WOld
– 'Dymbro'	CAll
– 'Elizabeth'	CAll WOld
– 'Elizabeth Bright'	CAll WOld
– 'Elizabeth Hutton'	CAll WOld
– 'Elsie Dale'	CAll WOld
– 'Elta'	WOld
– 'Erica'	CAll MWat WCot WOld
– 'Ernest Ballard'	CAll CKel MRav WOld
– 'Ernie Moss'	EFou
– 'Eva'	CAll WOld
– 'Eventide'	CAll CB&S CElw ECED ENot SPer WOld
– 'Fair Lady'	CAll MWat WOld
– 'Faith'	CAll WOld
– 'Farrington'	CAll WOld
– 'Felicity'	CAll
– 'Fellowship'	CAll CB&S CElw CMGP ECED EFou MBri MNFA MUlv MWat NCat NMir NVic SPer WEas WOld
– 'Festival'	EFou
– 'Flair'	CAll
– 'Flamingo'	CAll CSco
– 'Fontaine'	WOld
– 'Freda Ballard'	CAll EBre ECED EFou LBre LHil MUlv MWat NHol WOld
– 'Fuldatal'	EFou
– 'Gayborder Beauty'	CAll
– 'Gayborder Blue'	CAll
– 'Gayborder Royal'	CAll WOld
– 'Gayborder Spire'	CAll
– 'Gayborder Splendour'	WOld
– 'Goliath'	CAll WOld
– 'Guardsman'	CAll WOld
– 'Gulliver'	EFou
– 'Gurney Slade'	CAll EJud MBri WOld
– 'Guy Ballard'	CAll NNor
– 'Harrison's Blue'	CAll SAxl WEas WOld WPer
– 'Heather'	CAll
– 'Heinz Richard'	CAll CMGP ECha EFou ESma LHop MBri MUlv NBir NHol SBla SChu WOld
– 'Helen'	WOld
– 'Helen Ballard'	CAll CSco WOld
– 'Herbstpurzel'	EFou WMer
– 'Hey Day'	CAll
– 'Hilda Ballard'	CAll EFou WOld
– 'Ilse Brensell'	EFou
– 'Irene'	CAll WOld

¶– 'Isabel Allen' WOld
– 'Janet McMullen' CAll EJud
– 'Janet Watts' CAll WOld
– 'Janice Stephenson' CAll
– 'Jean' CAll CSco MWat SChu SPla WEas WOld
– 'Jean Gyte' CAll WOld
– 'Jenny' CAll CKel CLew CRDP CSco EBre ECED ECtt EFou ERav IDai LBre LHil LHop MBri MBro MRav MWat NBar NHol SHBN SPer WByw WEas WHil WHoo WOld WPer
– 'Jollity' CAll WOld
– 'Judith' EFou
– 'Julia' CAll
– 'Juliet' CAll
– 'Karen' CAll
– 'Karminkuppel' EFou
– 'King of the Belgians' CAll WOld
– 'King's College' CAll WOld
– 'Kristina' CAll EBre ECha ECtt EFou GAbr LBlm LBre LHil MRav MUlv NCat WCot WHil WOld
– 'Lady Evelyn Drummond' WOld
– 'Lady Frances' CAll CPar WOld
– 'Lady in Blue' CAll CHal CLew CPar CRDP CSco EBre ECtt EFou ELan ENot EPla IHos LBre LHil MBro MWat NBar NHol NMir NVic SPer SPla WByw WHoo WOld WPer WWin
– 'Lady Paget' CAll WOld
– 'Lassie' CAll CKel MWat SFis WOld
– 'Lavender Dream' CAll WOld
– 'Lawrence Chiswell' CAll WOld
– 'Leuchtfeuer' EFou
– 'Lilac Time' CAll WByw WOld
– 'Lilakönigin' EFou
– 'Lisa Dawn' CAll WOld
– 'Little Blue Baby' CTom
– 'Little Boy Blue' CAll CB&S CKel SHBN WByw WMer WOld
– 'Little Pink Beauty' CAll CKel CPar CRDP CTom EBar ECtt EFou ELan GAbr GCHN IHos LHop MBri MBro MWat NHol NKay NMir NVic SHer SPer WEas WHil WOld WWin
– 'Little Pink Lady' CAll ECED
– 'Little Pink Pyramid' CSco SFis SRms
– 'Little Red Boy' CAll CB&S CSco MBel MTol WOld
– 'Little Treasure' CAll WOld
– 'Lucy' CAll WOld
– 'Mabel Reeves' CAll CShe
– 'Madge Cato' CAll WOld
– 'Mammoth' CAll WOld
– 'Margaret Murray' CAll
– 'Margaret Rose' CAll ELan NKay NOrc WOld
– 'Margery Bennett' CAll WOld
– 'Marie Ann Neil' EFou
– 'Marie Ballard' CAll CB&S CElw CKel CSco CShe EBre ECED ENot EPla ERav GCal LBre LWad MBri MFir MWat NHol NKay NOrc SChu SHBN SPer WEas WOld WPer
¶– 'Marie's Pretty Please' EFou
– 'Marjorie' CAll WOld WPer
¶– 'Marjory Ballard' WOld
– 'Mars' CAll
– 'Martonie' WOld WPer
– 'Mary' CAll
– 'Mary Dean' CAll WEas WOld WPer
– 'May Louise' CAll
– 'Melbourne' CAll
– 'Melbourne Belle' CAll WOld
– 'Melbourne Lad' CAll
– 'Melbourne Magnet' WOld
– 'Melbourne Mauve' CAll
– 'Melbourne Sparkler' CAll
– 'Michael Watts' CAll WOld
– 'Michelle' CAll
– 'Miranda' CAll
– 'Miss Muffet' CAll
– 'Mistress Ford' CAll
– 'Mistress Quickly' CAll MBel WOld
– 'Mount Everest' CAll CDoC WMer WOld WPer
– 'Mrs J Sangster' CAll
– 'Mrs Leo Hunter' CAll WOld
– 'My Smokey' CAll
– 'Nancy' CAll
– 'Nightfall' CAll
– 'Niobe' CAll CLew ELan WMer WOMN WOld
¶– 'Nobilis' WOld
– 'Norman Thornely' CAll
– 'Norman's Jubilee' CAll ECtt WOld
– 'Norton Fayre' CAll CShe
– 'Nursteed Charm' CAll WOld
– 'Oktoberschneekuppel' LRHS
– 'Orchid Pink' CAll
– 'Orlando' CAll WCot WOld
– 'Pamela' CAll WOld
– 'Patricia Ballard' CAll CLew CMGP CSco CShe ECED MBri MFir MWat NBro NHol NKay NVic WOld WPer
– 'Peace' CAll WOld
– 'Peerless' CAll
– 'Pensford' CAll
– 'Percy Thrower' CAll CKel EFou WOld
– 'Perry's White' CAll
– 'Peter Chiswell' MTol WOld
– 'Peter Harrison' CAll CSco MBal MBri WOld WPer
– 'Peter Pan' CAll MPlt SHer WHil WOld WSun
– 'Picture' CAll WOld
– 'Pink Buttons' CAll
– 'Pink Gown' WOld
– 'Pink Lace' CAll CKel CRDP CSco EBar ECtt NHol WByw WEas WOld WPer
– 'Pink Perfection' CAll
– 'Pink Profusion' CAll
– 'Pink Pyramid' EJud WOld
– 'Plenty' CBre WOld
– 'Pride of Colwall' CSco
– 'Priory Blush' CAll WOld
– 'Priory Maid' CAll
– 'Professor Anton Kippenberg' CAll CSco CShe EBre ECtt EFou EJud LBre MBri MBro MPlt WAbe WOld
– 'Prosperity' CAll CKel WOld
– 'Prunella' CAll WOld
– 'Purple Dome' EBlo EFou WOld

– 'Purple Emperor' CAll
– 'Queen Mary' CAll WMer WOld
– 'Queen of Colwall' CAll WOld
– 'Rachel Ballard' CAll
¶– 'Ralph Picton' WOld
– 'Raspberries and Cream' CAll
– 'Raspberry Ripple' CAll CKel CMGP EFou ERav MBri NHol WOld
– 'Rebecca' CAll
¶– 'Rector' WOld
– 'Red Greetings' CAll
– 'Red Robin' MWat
– 'Red Sunset' CAll CB&S WOld
– 'Rembrandt' CAll CSco NHol
– 'Remembrance' CAll EFou SAxl WOld
– 'Reverend Vincent Dale' CAll WOld
– 'Richness' CAll SAxl WOld
– 'Robert' CAll
– 'Robin Adair' CAll WOld
– 'Rose Bonnet' CKel CMGP CTom EFou ENot IHos MTol MWat NBar NHol SChu SHBN SPla
– 'Rose Bouquet' CAll CLew SAxl WOld
– 'Rosebud' CAll ELan WOld
– 'Rosenwichtel' CAll EFou EMar MBri NBar NHol WOld
– 'Rosie Nutt' CAll
– 'Royal Blue' CAll WMer
– 'Royal Ruby' CAll CSco ECtt WOld
– 'Royal Velvet' CAll CSco ECED ENot WHil WOld
– 'Royal Violet' CAll
– 'Royalty' CAll
– 'Rozika' EFou
– 'Rufus' CAll WOld
– 'Sailing Light' CAll
– 'Sailor Boy' CAll CBre SFis WOld
– 'Saint Egwyn' CAll WOld
– 'Sandford White Swan' EJud MBel MTol WPer
– 'Sandford's Purple' CAll
– 'Sarah Ballard' CAll MUlv MWat WOld
– 'Saturn' CAll
– 'Schneekissen' ('Snow Cushion') CLew CPar CSco EBre ECtt EHal LBre LHop MBal MBri MBro NMir SBla SHer SPer WOld
– 'Schöne von Dietlikon' CDoC WMer WOld
– 'Schoolgirl' CAll CShe MUlv WOld
– 'Sheena' WCot WOld
– 'Silberblaukissen' EFou
– 'Silver Mist' CAll
– 'Sir Edward Elgar' CAll
– 'Snowdrift' CAll WOld
– 'Snowsprite' CAll CB&S CKel CMGP CTom EBre ECED ELan IDai LBre MWat NBar NOrc SChu SPer SPla WByw WHoo WOld
– 'Sonata' CAll EFou EJud ERav LHil NHol SPer WOld
– 'Sophia' WOld
– 'Sputnik' CAll
– 'Starlight' CAll EFou ENot WOld
– 'Steinebrück' EFou
– 'Stella Lewis' CAll
– 'Sterling Silver' CAll WByw WOld
– 'Storm Clouds' EFou SFis
– 'Strawberries and Cream' CAll
– 'Sunset' CAll WOld
– 'Sussex Violet' CAll
– 'Sweet Briar' WOld
– 'Symbol' CAll
– 'Tapestry' CAll WOld
– 'Terry's Pride' CAll WOld
– 'The Archbishop' CAll
– 'The Bishop' CAll WOld
– 'The Cardinal' CAll ECED SFis WOld
– 'The Dean' CAll WOld
– 'The Rector' CAll
– 'The Sexton' CAll
– 'Thundercloud' CAll SAxl WOld
– 'Timsbury' CAll WOld
– 'Tony' CAll WOld
– 'Tosca' SFis
– 'Tovarich' CAll WOld
– 'Triumph' SFis
– 'Trudi Ann' EFou SFis
– 'True Blue' CAll
– 'Twinkle' EFou SFis
– 'Victor' CAll MBal WOld
– 'Violet Lady' CAll CKel WOld
*– 'Violet Queen' EBre LBre LWad SFis SMad
– 'Violetta' CB&S EFou
– 'Waterperry' MWat
– 'Weisse Wunder' EFou
§– 'White Climax' CAll EFou MUlv WOld
– 'White Ladies' CAll CPar EBre ECtt EFou ERav LBre MUlv NOrc SPer
– 'White Swan' CAll CBre CKel EMon NOak SFis WEas WOld
– 'White Wings' CAll MNFA WCot WOld
– 'Wickwar Crimson' CAll
– 'Winford' CAll
– 'Winston S Churchill' CAll CKel CSco ECED ELan ENot LWad MNFA MTol MWat NOrc SHBN SPer WEas WHil WOld
oblongifolius CCor
'Ochtendgloren' (***pringlei*** x) EFou EMon
paniculatus hort. See A. ***lanceolatus***
pappei See FELICIA ***amoena***
'Pearl Star' WOld
perfoliatus NCat
petiolatus See FELICIA ***petiolata***
§ 'Photograph' CAll CHan EFou MNFA SAxl WOld
§ ***pilosus*** var. ***demotus*** CBos CBre GAbr MSte SCro SGil SPla SWas
'Pink Star' CBre EFou NSti WCot WOld
§ ***pringlei*** 'Monte Cassino' CChu CGle COtt EBlo EBre ECha EFou EHal ESma LBre LHop MUlv NHol NRoo SChu SGil SPla SWas WCot WHil WOld
procumbens CMer CTre
ptarmicoïdes CAll EFou EMon WCot WPer
pyrenaeus 'Lutetia' ECha EFou GCal WCot WOld
'Ringdove' (***ericoïdes*** x) CAll SPer WEas WOld
'Rosa Star' WOld
rotundifolius 'Variegatus' See FELICIA ***amelloïdes*** 'Variegata'

**sativus atrocaeruleus*	NRoo
scandens	See A. ***carolinianus***
§ ***sedifolius***	CAll CBos CPar EJud ELan EMon MWat SDix SFis SPer SUsu WEas WOld WPer WSun
– 'Nanus'	CAll ECED ECha EFol EFou MBri NBir NSti SFis SMrm WByw WOld
– 'Roseus'	CAll
'Snow Star'	WOld
spathulifolius	CHan CRDP
spectabilis	CChu WOld
sp. BM&W 18	See ERIGERON ***multiradiatus*** BM&W 18
¶ ***stracheyi***	WDav
thomsonii 'Nanus'	CGle COtt CSam EBre ECha EFou EMon EOrc GAbr LBre MNFA MRav NKay NRoo SAxl SBla SHBN SUsu WEas WHoo WMer WOld WSHC WWin
♦ ***tibeticus***	See A. ***flaccidus***
§ ***tongolensis***	CHan MRav SRms WEas WOMN WWin
– 'Berggarten'	EFou EOrc GCal MBri NRoo SCro SFis SPla WMer
– 'Lavender Star'	CLew EFou NMir SRms
– 'Napsbury'	ECha EPla MBri NSti NVic SFis SPla
– 'Sommergrüss' ('Summer Greeting')	EFou
– 'Wartburgstern'	SFis WPer
tradescantii hort.	See A. ***pilosus demotus***
– Linnaeus	CAll CBre CGle EBar ECha EFou ELan ERav GCal LHil MFir MNFA MRav MUlv NOak NSti SAxl SHig SMad WEas WOld
tripolium	CKin
turbinellus	CAll EFou MNFA SChu WCot WOld
umbellatus	CBre EMon EOrc SAxl WOld
vahlii	ECar ECou GAbr LHop WPer
♦ ***vimineus*** Lamarck	See A. ***lateriflorus***
– 'Ptarmicoides'	See A. ***ptarmicoïdes***
¶ 'Yvonne'	CBre

ASTERANTHERA (Gesneriaceae)

ovata	CGre ELan GGar MBal SArc SHil SSpi WBod WSHC WWat

ASTERISCUS (Compositae)

♦ 'Gold Coin'	See A. ***maritimus***
¶ ***intermedius***	GCal
§ ***maritimus***	IHos LHop MPit
¶ ***spinosus***	WHer

ASTILBE † (Saxifragaceae)

'Amethyst' (x ***arendsii***)	CMGP CMHG CTom EGol NBar NRoo NTow SApp SHig SPer
'Anita Pfeifer' (x ***arendsii***)	MBri MUlv WMer
'Aphrodite' (***simplicifolia*** x)	COtt EBre EGol LBre MBri NHol NOrc SSpi WAbe
x ***arendsii***	NNor SHer WHil WPer
astilboïdes	NHol
'Atrorosea' (***simplicifolia*** x)	CSco ECha
'Bergkristall' (x ***arendsii***)	CMHG
'Betsy Cuperus' (***thunbergii*** x)	CMHG EFou
biternata	WDav
'Bonn' (***japonica*** x)	CB&S CKel EPar SRms
'Brautschleier' ('Bridal Veil') (x ***arendsii***)	CMHG ECtt EFou EGol ENot EPla GCHN IDai MWat SGil
'Bressingham Beauty' (x ***arendsii***)	CGle CKel CMHG CSco CShe EBlo EBre ECtt EHon ELan ELun ENot EPGN EPar LBre MBri NBee NHol NRoo SChu SCro SGil SHig SPer
'Bronce Elegans' (***simplicifolia*** x)	COtt CSco EBar EBre ECha EFou EPGN EPar LBre MBal MBri MNFA MPlt NBar NHar NHol NKay NOrc NRoo SChu SCro SPer WAbe
'Bumalda' (x ***arendsii***)	CDoC MBri MSte MUlv NBee NHol
* 'Carmine King'	SFis
¶ 'Catherine Deneuve'	EBlo
'Cattleya' (x ***arendsii***)	CMHG EFou
'Ceres' (x ***arendsii***)	CDoC CMHG MWat NHol NKay
¶ 'Cherry Ripe'	ECha
chinensis	CMCN CMHG IBlr
– var. ***pumila***	Widely available
* 'Crimson Feather'	ECha
x ***crispa***	GAbr IBlr SSpi
'Deutschland' (***japonica*** x)	CB&S CBow CMHG CRDP EBre ECED EGol ELan EPGN EPla GAbr GCHN LBre MBri NHol NKay SApp SBla SCro SHer SPer SPla SSpi WAbe WEas WHal WWin
'Diamant' ('Diamond') (x ***arendsii***)	CDoC CMHG MFir SFis
'Drayton Glory' (x ***arendsii***)	See A. 'Peach Blossom'
'Dunkellachs' (***simplicifolia*** x)	COtt EBre ECha EGol EPGN LBre LWad MBri NHol NOrc SHig SPla WAbe
'Düsseldorf' (***japonica*** x)	CMGP CMHG EPla GAbr GGar SPer
'Elizabeth Bloom'	EBlo
¶ 'Ellie'	EBlo
'Emden' (***japonica*** x)	MWat
'Erica' (x ***arendsii***)	CMHG GGar MBri
'Etna' (***japonica*** x)	CB&S CDoC CKni CMHG CSev EPGN MBal SCro
'Europa' (***japonica*** x)	CMHG EPGN MBal NBar NOak SGil SHer
'Fanal' (x ***arendsii***)	CB&S CGle CMHG CRDP CShe EBlo EBre ECha EFou ELan ELun EPGN IBar LBre MBal MBri MWat NBar NDea NHol NKay NNrd NOrc NRoo SBla SCro SDix SPer WAbe WEas
'Federsee' (x ***arendsii***)	CB&S CGle CKel CMGP CMHG CPar CSco EBre ECha EHon ELan EPGN LBre LHop MBri NBar NKay SCro SHig SPer WAbe

'Feuer' ('Fire')
(x *arendsii*) CB&S CKni CMGP CMHG CShe EBre ECha ELan GGar LBre MBri NHol NTow NVic SGil SHer SPer SPla WPbr
'Finale' (*chinensis*) CMHG CSco NHol NKay NOrc SPer WEas
'Frankentroll' (*chinensis pumila*) CMHG
'Gertrud Brix'
(x *arendsii*) CB&S CMHG COtt EPar GAbr
glaberrima EPar SSpi
– var. *saxatilis* CNic CRow ECar ELan EPGN GCHN MBal NHol NKay NNrd NOak NRoo NTow SChu
– *saxosa* See A. 'Saxosa'
*– – *minor* NNrd
¶ 'Glenroy Elf' MBal
'Gloria' (x *arendsii*) CMHG MBri
'Gloria Purpurea'
(x *arendsii*) CKni CMHG MUlv NHol
'Glut' ('Glow')
(x *arendsii*) CKel CMHG CPar EPGN EPar EPla MBri NHol SCro SGil SHer SRms
'Gnom' (x *crispa*) CRow NHar
'Granat' (x *arendsii*) CDoC CElw CMHG EPGN MBal NHol NKay SDix SGil SHer WWin
grandis CMHG
'Grete Püngel'
(x *arendsii*) MBri WMer
'Harmony' (x *arendsii*) CMHG
'Hyazinth' ('Hyacinth')
(x *arendsii*) CMHG EGol ELan EPGN GAbr LWad NBee NFai NHol NOrc SCro SHer WTyr
'Inshriach Pink'
(*simplicifolia* x) CBro CMHG EBre EGol ELan EPla GDra LBre MBri MUlv NHar NHol NNrd NOak SGil
'Irrlicht' (x *arendsii*) CCla CGle CKel CMHG CPar CSco CShe EBre ECha EGol EHon ELan ELun EPGN EPla LBre LHop MBal MBri NBar NDea NHol NRoo SChu SCro SDix SPer
'Jo Ophorst' (*davidii* x) CMHG CPar EBre ECha ECtt EPGN LBre MBel NDea SCro SGil SHer SPer
'Koblenz' (*japonica* x) IDai NHol
'Köln' ('Cologne')
(*japonica* x) CPar WAbe
'Kvele' (x *arendsii*) MBri
'Lachskönigin' ('Salmon Queen') (x *arendsii*) CMHG MWat
'Lilli Goos' (x *arendsii*) CMHG
'Lilliput' (x *crispa*) MPlt
microphylla CMCN CMHG NHol
– pink form CMHG NHol
¶ – *saisuensis* MHig
'Moerheimii (*thunbergii* x) CMHG
'Montgomery' (*japonica* x) CCla CKel EBre ECha EPGN LBre NBee NFai NHol
'Nana' (*simplicifolia* x) CRow EGol NNrd
'Obergärtner Jürgens'
(x *arendsii*) CMHG
'Peach Blossom'
(x *rosea*) CB&S CCla CDoC CKni CMHG EGol EPar GAbr GCHN MBal NBar NFai NHol WMer
'Perkeo' (x *crispa*) COtt CRDP CRow EBre ECha EPGN GDra GGar LBre MBel MBri NBir NHar NKay NRoo SApp
'Peter Barrow'
(*glaberrima* x) EPGN MBel SRms
¶ 'Pink Curtsy' (x *arendsii*) EBre LBre
'Praecox Alba'
(*simplicifolia*) EBre ECha LBre LWad NHol
'Professor van der Wielen' (*thunbergii* x) CGle CMHG ECha GCal GGar SPer SRms
'Purple Glory'
(*chinensis*) CMHG
'Purpurlanze' ('Purple Lance') (*chinensis taquetii*) CMHG EBre EFou LBre MBri MRav MUlv NBir NOrc WCot WMer WWin
'Queen Alexandra'
(x *rosea*) SFis
¶ 'Red Admiral' NNor
'Red Sentinel' (*japonica* x) CB&S CSco CTom EBre EFou EGol ELun EPGN EPar EPla GCHN LBre NBee NHar NHol NOrc NSti SGil SHer SPla WAbe
'Rheinland' (*japonica* x) CMHG EBre GCHN LBre MBri SBla WAbe WEas
rivularis CCla CMHG
'Rosa Perle' ('Pink Pearl') (x *arendsii*) CMHG ECha NHol
'Rosea' (*simplicifolia* x) NHol
'Rotlicht' ('Red Light')
(x *arendsii*) MBri
'Salmon Queen'
(x *arendsii*) See A. 'Lachskönigin'
§ 'Saxosa' EPot ESis
'Serenade' (*chinensis pumila*) CMHG SHig
simplicifolia CGle CRow MHig MTho NHar NKay WEas
– 'Alba' EFou GGar NHol
– x *glaberrima* GDra NHar NHol
'Snow Queen' (x *crispa*) CRow NHar
'Snowdrift' (x *arendsii*) CMHG EBar EBre ECha EFou EGol ELun EPla GAri LBre LWad MUlv NOak NOrc NRoo SApp
* 'Spartan' (x *arendsii*) CMHG NHol
'Spinell' (x *arendsii*) MWat
'Sprite' (*simplicifolia* x) Widely available
sp. CLD 1559 NHol
'Straussenfeder'
('Ostrich Plume')
(*thunbergii* x) CSco EBre EFou ELun EPGN EPla GCHN GCal LBre NHol NTow SCro SHig WPbr WTyr

'Superba' (*chinensis taquetii*)	CGle CMHG CRow CSco CTom EBre ECha ELan EPGN LBre MSte NDea NHol NNor NSti NTow SDix SHig SPer WAbe WEas WOld
'Venus' (x *arendsii*)	CCla CKel CMHG CSco CShe CTom EBre ECED ECha ECtt EFou EGol ELun EPGN GAbr LBre MBel NHol NKay NOrc NVic SChu SCro SPer
'Veronica Klose' (*chinensis*)	CMHG MBri
'Vesuvius' (*japonica* x)	CB&S EPla MBel
'W E Gladstone' (*japonica* x)	CB&S CDoC WAbe WMer
'Weisse Gloria' ('White Gloria') (x *arendsii*)	CCla CHad CMHG ECha EPGN EPar MBel MBri NFai NSti SCro SGil SPla WRus
'Weisse Perle' (x *arendsii*)	CMHG
'White Queen' (x *arendsii*)	CElw NNrd
'William Buchanan' (*simplicifolia* x)	CGle EBre ECar ECtt EGol EMNN EPGN EPar GAbr GCHN GGar LBre MBal MBar MBri MCas MFir MHig MPlt NDea NHar NHol NKay NMen NRed SCro
'William Reeves' (x *arendsii*)	CKni COtt NHol
¶ 'Yakusima'	SRms

ASTILBOÏDES (Saxifragaceae)

§ *tabularis*	CChu CCla CGle CHEx CHad CRDP CRow CSco CWGN ECha EFol EFou EGol ELan EOrc MBro MSta NHol NSti SBla SMad SPer SSpi WHoo WWat

ASTRAGALUS (Leguminosae)

glycyphyllos	MHew NSal
¶ *thompsoniae*	WDav
¶ *utahensis*	WDav
¶ *whitneyi sonneanus*	MFos

ASTRANTIA (Umbelliferae)

carniolica	CRDP NKay
– *major*	See A. *major*
– var. *rubra*	CB&S CBot CBro CCla CKel CRow CSam EBre ECED ECro EPar LBre LWad MFir NFai SPer WAbe WByw WCru WOMN WTyr
– 'Variegata'	See A. *major* 'Sunningdale Variegated'
helleborifolia hort.	See A. *maxima*
§ *major*	Widely available
– *alba*	CRow ECha ECro EFol EGol ERav NBir NCat
– *biebersteinii*	NBir
¶ – 'Buckland'	SWas
– 'Hadspen Blood'	CBos CHad EGol MSta WMer
¶ – 'Hillview Red'	WHil
– ssp. *involucrata*	CDec ELan NHol NVic
– – 'Barrister'	MUlv SApp SSpi
– – 'Margery Fish'	See A. *m. i.* 'Shaggy'
§ – – 'Shaggy'	CBos CChu CMGP CMea CShe ECro EFou EGol ELan ERav ESma MPar NDea NOak SApp SHer SPer SPla WEas WHoo WRus
– 'Primadonna'	CBow CSam EMar WPer
¶ – 'Proctor'	MUlv
– *rosea*	CBre CCla CGle CMGP CPar EBlo ECro EFou EGol LHop NBee NHol NSel SGil SPer
¶ – 'Rosensinfonie'	EPar GCal WDav
– *rubra*	CCla CDoC CGle CHan COtt CSco ECha ECtt EGol ELan ELun EOrc ERav GCal LGre LHop MBri MPar NBar NHol NOrc NRoo SGil SPla SUsu WCru WEas WHal
– 'Ruby Wedding'	CGle ESma LWad SMrm WHoo
§ – 'Sunningdale Variegated'	Widely available
– 'Variegata'	See A. *m.* 'Sunningdale Variegated'
§ *maxima*	Widely available
¶ – 'Mark Fenwick'	NBir
minor	LGre
rubra	See A. *major r.*

ASYNEUMA (Campanulaceae)

canescens	EBar EPad WWin
limonifolium	GDra WDav
pulvinatum	SIng
– Mac&W 5880	EPot MHig NMen

ASYSTASIA (Acanthaceae)

bella	See MACKAYA *bella*
§ *gangetica*	CPle MNew SLMG
♦ *violacea*	See A. *gangetica*

ATHAMANTA (Umbelliferae)

cretensis	NHol
macedonica	ESma
¶ – ssp. *arachnoïdea*	GTou SIgm

ATHEROSPERMA (Monimiaceae)

moschatum	CB&S CGre CLan CPle CTre LTil WBod

ATHROTAXIS (Taxodiaceae)

cupressoïdes	GAri MBar
x *laxifolia*	CMHG EBre LBre LCon MBar MBri WThu

ATHYRIUM † (Dryopteridaceae)

filix-femina	CBar CPar CRow CTom EBre ECha EFou ELan LBre MBal MBri MSta NBro NEgg NHol NLan NMar NOrc SPer SPla SSpi SWat WBon WFib
¶ – 'Clarissimum'	WRic
– 'Corymbiferum'	NKay NMar SRms
– Cristatum Group	CWGN ELan MBri NHol SCob SPer SWat WFib WRic
– Cruciatum Group	EGol
– 'Fieldii'	CRow EFou NHar NHol WFib

– 'Frizelliae' CBar CDoC CMil CRDP CWGN EFou ELan IOrc MBri NHar NHol NMar NOrc SApp SCob SMad SMrm SPla SRms WFib WHal WRic WWat
– 'Frizelliae Capitatum' NKay SApp SRms WFib
– 'Grandiceps' NMar SRms
– 'Minutissimum' CBos CRDP CWGN ECha EFou EGol EHon ELan GCHN MBri NMar SAxl SCob SSpi
– Percristatum Group NKay
– 'Plumosum Axminster' CRDP SMrm
– 'Plumosum Cristatum' NMar
– Plumosum Group NMar SAxl
– 'Plumosum Percristatum' NMar
– Ramocristatum Group NMar
– 'Setigerum Cristatum' NKay NMar
– 'Vernoniae Cristatum' MBal NHol NMar NNrd SPer WFib
– Vernoniae Group ELan MBri
– Victoriae Group & clone CBar CRDP CRow EGol ELan GAri MBri NHol SApp SRms WFib WRic
frangulum NMar
goeringianum 'Pictum' See A. ***niponicum pictum***
niponicum EBre LBre NMar
– ***metallicum*** See A. ***n. pictum***
§ – var. ***pictum*** CBar CDoC CGle CHan CMil CPar CRDP CRow EBre ECha EFou EGol ELan EPar IOrc LBre LGre LHop MBal MBri NHar NHol SApp SBla SMad SPer SRms SSpi SWas WFib
otophorum NMar
– var. ***okanum*** SBla SSpi
palustre NKay WRic
¶ sp. ACL 290 SMrm
¶ ***vidalii*** SApp

ATRAGENE See CLEMATIS

ATRAPHAXIS (Polygonaceae)
See Plant Deletions

ATRIPLEX (Chenopodiaceae)
canescens WDin
halimus CB&S CBot CCla CFis CGle CHan CPle CRow CSco CShe EHoe ENot LAbb LHil MWat SLon SPer SSpi WDin WHCG WHer WSHC WStI
¶ ***hortensis*** MChe
– var. ***rubra*** CArn CFis CGle CRow ELan EMon LHol MChe MHew NRar SIde SUsu WEas WHer WOak WWye

ATROPA (Solanaceae)
bella-donna CArn GPoy LHol NSal WWye
– ***lutea*** NSal
mandragora See MANDRAGORA ***officinarum***

ATROPANTHE (Solanaceae)
¶ ***sinensis*** NSal

AUBRIETA † (Cruciferae)
albomarginata See A. 'Argenteovariegata'
'Alida Vahli' ELan
'Alix Brett' EBre ECtt ELan LBee LBre NHar SHer
'April Joy' CMHG ELan MPla NHol SHer SRms
§ 'Argenteovariegata' ELan LHop NHol NRoo SBla SHer SSmi WAbe
'Astolat' CLew ECar EFol ELan SBla SHer WAbe WEas WPer
¶ 'Astolat Variegated' NHar
§ 'Aureovariegata' CLew CMea CNic CRiv EBar EBre ECar ECha ECtt EFol ELan LBre MHig MPla NHol NKay NRar NRoo NVic SBla SChu SIng WAbe WHil WPer
'Belisha Beacon' ECtt LBee MBri NHol
Bengal hybrids GAbr
¶ 'Blaue Schönheit' ('Blue Beauty') NHol
'Blue Cascade' ECtt
'Blue Emperor' WMer
'Blue King' WMer
'Bob Sanders' CKel CMHG EBre ECtt LBee LBre MCas NEgg NVic
'Bonfire' NHol NKay
* 'Bonsul' CShe
'Bordeaux' WMer
'Bressingham Pink' EBre ECtt ELan EPar LBre LHop MCas MHig SHer
'Bressingham Red' EBre LBre WMer
'Britannia' NKay
canescens NTow SIgm
– JCA 225.150 CNic
'Carnival' See A. 'Hartswood Purple'
¶ 'Church Knowle' NHol
'Claret Cascade' CPar
¶ ***cumulus*** NCat
* ***deltoidea*** 'Gloria' WPat
– 'Nana Variegata' EPot MPla MTho WEas WHil
– ***rosea*** MHig
– 'Tauricola' WMer
– 'Tauricola Variegata' CShe
N– 'Variegata' CRiv CShe ECtt EFol EPot ESis LHop MFir MHig MTho NMen NTow SChu SIng WPat
¶ – ***variegata*** 'Shaw's Red' WDav
'Doctor Mules' CDoC CHal CKel CPar EBre ECtt EPot IHos LBee LBre MHig MPit NEgg NKay SHer SIng
'Doctor Mules Variegata' MHig WPer
'Dream' ECtt SIng
'Elsa Lancaster' CLew EPot MHig NGre
'Fire King' WMer
¶ 'Frühlingszauber' ('Spring Charm') SRms
'Gloriosa' CMHG CRiv SIng
'Golden Carpet' SHer SIng
'Golden King' See A. 'Aureovariegata'
gracilis scardica NTow
'Greencourt Purple' CMHG CRiv EBre ECtt ELan EPar EPot GAbr LBre MHig NKay SHer SIng WEas
'Gurgedyke' ELan MHig SHer SIng SRms
'Hartswood' SIng
§ 'Hartswood Purple' CShe NHol WHil

¶ 'Hendersonii'	SRms
¶ 'Henslow Purple'	EBre LBre
'Ina den Ouden'	WMer
¶ 'J S Baker'	SRms
'Joan Allen'	CMHG ECtt NHar SHer
'Joy'	NRar SIng
'Lavender Gem'	CMHG
'Leichtlinii'	NOak
'Lilac Cascade'	LBee
'Little Gem'	MHig
'Lodge Crave'	SIng
'Lucy'	NKay
¶ ***macedonica***	EPot
'Magician'	ECtt NHol NKay
'Mars'	ELan SHer SRms
'Mary Poppins'	MHig NKay
* ***mastichina***	WPat
'Maurice Prichard'	CKel ECtt
'Mrs Lloyd Edwards'	CHal ECtt
'Mrs Rodewald'	CMHG ECtt ELan NHol NKay NMen WHal
'Novalis Blue'	NOak SRms
'Oakington Lavender'	ELan EPar IHos MPit
'Pennine Glory'	CShe
'Pennine Heather'	CShe
¶ 'Pike's Variegated'	SRms
pinardii	WHil
'Pink Gem'	NKay
'Prichard's A1'	WMer
'Purple Cascade'	CNic ECtt EMNN LBee SRms
¶ 'Purple Charm'	SRms
'Red Carpet'	CKel CMHG CNic CRiv EBre EFol ELan EMNN EPar EPot IHos LBee LBre MCas MFir MHig MPla NEgg NHol NKay NMen SChu SHer SIng WEas WHil
'Red Cascade'	ECtt EMNN GAbr NMen
'Red Dyke'	SIng
'Riverslea'	NHol SIng
'Rose Queen'	CMea LBee SMrm
'Rosea Splendens'	MPla
'Royal Blue'	NRoo
'Royal Red'	ESis MCas MPit NRoo SRms
'Royal Violet'	ESis NRoo
'Schloss Eckberg'	WMer
'Schofield's Double'	ELan EPot SHer
'Silberrand'	ECha ECtt SAxl
'Triumphante'	CHal NEgg NMen
'Wanda'	ELan IHos SHer SIng
'Whitewell Gem'	EBar LBee SRms
Wisley hybrid	WEas

AUCUBA (Aucubaceae)

japonica	CB&S CChu CDoC CHEx EBre ELan ENot LBre SCob SPer SReu
– 'Crassifolia' (m)	CHig MBal SArc WMar
– 'Crotonifolia' (f/v)	CB&S CDoC CHEx CSco EBre ENot IJoh LAbb LBre MBal MBar MBri MGos MRav NWea SCob SDix SHBN SPer WDin WMar WStI
– 'Fructu Albo'	CGre
– 'Gold Dust' (f/v)	CLan CShe SHil WMar
– 'Golden King' (m/v)	CB&S CDoC CSco CTrw LNet MUlv
– 'Golden Spangles' (v)	CB&S MBal SHer
– 'Hillieri' (f)	CLan SHil
– 'Lance Leaf' (m/v)	MUlv SHil
– 'Latiomaculata' (v)	SCob
– f. ***longifolia***	CHig SArc SDix SHil
– 'Maculata' (v)	See A. *j.* 'Variegata'
– 'Nana Rotundifolia' (f)	MAsh MUlv SCob WMar
– 'Picturata' (m/v)	CB&S CDoC CSco CTre EBre EFol ELan ENot LBre MBal MBri MGos SCob SHBN SPer
– 'Rozannie' (m/f)	CB&S CDoC COtt ENot MAsh MBal MBlu MBri MGos MUlv NBee NHol SCob SPer SReu WDin WStI
– 'Salicifolia' (f)	ENot MBri MUlv SCob SHil SPer
– 'Sulphurea Marginata' (f/v)	CB&S CSco EFol MBri
§ – 'Variegata' (f)	CPle CShe ELan ENot GRei IDai IJoh ISea LBuc MBal MBar MBri MGos MRav MWat NBee NNor SCob SHBN SLon SPer SReu WBod WDin WStI
* 'Mr Goldstrike' (v)	CSco LNet

AURINIA (Cruciferae)

§ ***petraea***	CNic WDav
saxatilis	CB&S CShe EBre GAbr GDra IDai LBre MBar NKay SHer SIng SPer WWin
– 'Argentea'	WPer
– var. ***citrina***	CHal CShe ECha ECtt MBel MPla MWat SDix SRms
– 'Compacta'	CDoC CKel CPar EBre ECtt ENot LBre NEgg NHol NNor SSou WHoo
– 'Dudley Nevill'	CCMG CLew CNic CRiv CShe EBre ECha EFol GAbr LBee LBre MPla MWat NEgg SBla SChu WDav
– 'Dudley Nevill Variegated'	EBre ECED ERav GAbr LBre MPla MUlv NRoo SIng SUsu WOld WPer WRus
– 'Flore Pleno'	CLew NRoo SBla WEas
– 'Gold Dust'	EBre ECtt LBre LGro NGre SRms
– 'Golden Queen'	CDoC ECtt NNrd
– 'Goldkugel' ('Gold Ball')	CHal ELan EMNN MPit NRoo NVic SHer SRms STre
– 'Silver Queen'	EBre ELan LBre NRoo SPer WEas
– 'Variegata'	CLew SBla

AUSTROCEDRUS (Cupressaceae)

§ ***chilensis***	CGre CKen GAri LCon MBal

AVENA (Gramineae)

candida	See HELICTOTRICHON ***sempervirens***
sterilis	EHoe

AVENULA See **HELICTOTRICHON**

AVOCADO See **PERSEA *americana***

AYAPANA See **EUPATORIUM**

AZALEA See **RHODODENDRON** Azalea

AZALEODENDRON See
RHODODENDRON Azaleodendron

AZARA † (Flacourtiaceae)

dentata	CB&S CDoC CGre CLan CMCN CMac CPle CTrw ERea MBal WSHC
– 'Variegata'	CMac
integrifolia	CTre SArc
– 'Variegata'	CB&S CGre SHil
lanceolata	CB&S CLan CPle IBar IOrc ISea SLon SPer SSpi WBod WWat
microphylla	CB&S CBow CDoC CGre CMCN CMHG CPle CSPN CSco CShe CTre EPla IBar IDai IOrc ISea LAbb MBal SArc SBra SDry SHil SPer SSpi WBod WStI
– 'Variegata'	CAbb CDoC CHan CMac EHar ERav IDai IOrc ISea MBal SArc SSpi WCru
paraguayensis	CGre CTre GAri
petiolaris	CGre IBar WBod WCru WWat
serrata	CBot CBow CChu CCla CGre CHEx CHan CMCN CMHG CPle EBre EPla GWht ISea LAbb LBre NTow SArc SBra SDix SLon SPer WDin WPat

AZOLLA (Azollaceae)

caroliniana	CBen CHEx CRow CWGN EHon EMFW EWav LMay MSta SHer SWat WHol WStI
¶*filiculoïdes*	SWat

AZORELLA (Umbelliferae)

glebaria hort.	See A. *trifurcata*
gummifera	See BOLAX *g.*
lycopodioïdes	ECou GCHN
§ *trifurcata*	CLew CRiv ELan EPot GAbr GDra MBro MTho NHol NKay NRoo SHer SIng SSmi WAbe WByw WPat
– 'Nana'	CNic GGar MHig MTho MWat NHol NMen NNrd SIng WOld WPat WThu

AZORINA (Campanulaceae)

§ *vidalii*	CAbb CBot CGre CPle CSpe CSun EPad GCHN GCal LGan SGil SIgm WPer WTyr
– 'Rosea'	EPad

BABIANA (Iridaceae)

ambigua	NRog
hybrids	CKel LBow
rubrocyanea	CMon NRog
stricta	NRog
¶ – 'Purple Star'	ETub
¶ – 'Tubergen's Blue'	ETub
tubulosa	NRog
villosa	NRog
villosula	NRog

BACCHARIS (Compositae)

crispa	GCal
genistelloïdes	GCal
halimifolia	CB&S EMon
¶ – 'Twin Peaks'	SDry
magellanica	ECar ECou
patagonica	CAbb CMHG CPle CTre IBar SArc SDry SLon WBod

BAECKEA (Myrtaceae)
See Plant Deletions

BAILLONIA (Verbenaceae)

juncea	CPle WSHC

BALLOTA (Labiatae)

acetabulosa	CDec CHan CWes ECha EFol EFou EHal EMar MBel SChu SDix SDry SPer
'All Hallows Green'	CChu CCla CGle CMGP EBre ECro ECtt EFou EGol EOrc GCal LBre LHil LHop MBel MTol SAxl SChu SFar SGil SUsu WHen WSun WWat
¶ *hirsuta*	CHan
nigra	CArn CKin LHol MHew NSal SIde WWye
§ – 'Archer's Variety' (v)	CHan CSpe CSun CWes EBar EFol EHal EJud EMon MBel NHex NPer NSti SIde WRus
– 'Dingle Gold'	EFol
– 'Dingle Gold Variegated'	EFol
– *variegata*	See B. *n.* 'Archer's Variety'
– 'Zanzibar' (v)	EMon MBel
pseudodictamnus	Widely available

BALSAMITA See **TANACETUM**

BAMBUSA † (Gramineae(Bambuseae))

glaucescens	See B. *multiplex*
* *gracillima*	CB&S CBar COtt CPMA GAri SBam
§ *multiplex*	EFul LBam SBam WJun
– 'Alphonse Karr'	CB&S CBra EFul EPla ISta SBam SCob SDry WJun
§ – 'Fernleaf'	CB&S CBar COtt EFul GAri ISta LBam MUlv NPal SBam SCob SDry WJun
– 'Wang Tsai'	See B. *m.* 'Fernleaf'
oldhamii	SBam
tuldoïdes	CB&S GAri
ventricosa	LBam SBam SDry WJun
vulgaris	SBam
– 'Vittata'	SBam
– 'Wamin'	SBam WJun

BANANA See **MUSA**

BANKSIA (Proteaceae)

baueri	CSun
baxteri	CSun LBlm
benthamiana	CSun
blechnifolia	CSun LBlm
canei	CSun
dryandroïdes	CSun LBlm
ericifolia	CSun
grandis	CSun LBlm
hookeriana	CSun
integrifolia	CB&S CSun NBar WDin
marginata	CSun ECou
media	CSun
ornata	CSun
petiolaris	CSun
praemorsa	CSun
quercifolia	CGre CSun
repens	CSun
robur	CSun
saxicola	CSun
serrata	CSun
speciosa	CSun LBlm SIgm
spinulosa collina	CSun
violacea	CSun

BAPTISIA (Leguminosae)

australis	Widely available
– 'Exaltata'	ECro ELan LHop
§ *bracteata*	NSal SMad
§ *lactea*	CChu CPle NBir NSal
♦ *leucantha*	See B. ***lactea***
♦ *leucophaea*	See B. ***bracteata***
¶ *sphaerocarpa*	GCra
tinctoria	CPle NSal WCot WThi

BARBAREA (Cruciferae)

praecox	See B. ***verna***
¶ *rupicola*	WPer
§ *verna*	CArn GPoy SIde WWye
vulgaris	CKin
– 'Variegata'	CGle CPar CRow ECha ECro EFol EHoe ELan ELun EMon EPla ERav LHil MFir MPar NBro NFai NOak NSti NVic SUsu WHal WHil WPbr WWin

BARLERIA (Acanthaceae)

obtusa	CTro MNew

BARTLETTINA See **EUPATORIUM**

BARTSIA (Scrophulariaceae)
See Plant Deletions

BASHANIA (Gramineae(Bambuseae))

¶ *fargesii*	EPla WJun

BAUERA (Cunoniaceae)
See Plant Deletions

BEAUCARNEA (Dracaenaceae)

recurvata	CHal LPal MBri

BEAUFORTIA (Myrtaceae)

¶ *sparsa*	CTre

BEAUMONTIA (Apocynaceae)

grandiflora	CTro MNew

BEAUVERDIA See **TRISTAGMA**, IPHEION, LEUCOCORYNE

BECKMANNIA (Gramineae)

eruciformis	ETPC

BEDFORDIA (Compositae)

¶ *salicina*	ECou

BEGONIA † (Begoniaceae)

♦ *acerifolia*	See B. ***vitifolia***
albopicta (C)	CHal CTro EBak ER&R
¶ – 'Rosea'	WEfe
'Allan Langdon' (T)	CBla
¶ 'Alleryi' (C)	ER&R
¶ 'Amy' (T)	CBla
angularis	See B. ***stipulacea***
¶ 'Anita Roseanna' (C)	ER&R
'Anniversary' (T)	CBla
¶ *annulata*	WEfe
'Apricot Delight' (T)	CBla
'Argentea' (R)	EBak MBri
¶ 'Baby Perfection'	WEfe
¶ 'Barclay Griffiths'	ER&R
'Beatrice Haddrell'	CHal ER&R WEfe
¶ 'Bernat Klein' (T)	CBla
¶ 'Bethlehem Star'	ER&R WEfe
'Billie Langdon' (T)	CBla
'Black Knight'	CHal
¶ 'Bokit'	ER&R
'Bonaire'	CHal
¶ 'Boomer' (C)	ER&R
'Bouton de Rose' (T)	NRog SDeJ
bowerae	CHal
¶ 'Burle Marx'	ER&R MNew
'Bush Baby'	CHal
'Buttermilk' (T)	CBla
'Camelliiflora (T)	NRog
'Can-Can' (T)	CBla
'Carol Wilkins of Ballaarat' (T)	CBla
§ x *carrierei*	MBri
x *carrierei flore-pleno*	CHal LHop
¶ 'Cathedral'	ER&R
'Chantilly Lace'	CHal
x *cheimantha* 'Gloire de Lorraine'	MBri
'Clara' (R)	MBri
'Cleopatra'	CHal ER&R SLMG
¶ *coccinea* (C)	ER&R
compta (C)	See B. ***stipulacea***
x *corallina*	EBak

§ – 'Lucerna' (C) CHal CTro EBak ER&R
– 'Lucerna Amazon' (C) CHal IBlr
'Corbeille de Feu' CHal
¶ 'Cowardly Lion' (R) ER&R
'Crimson Cascade' CBla
¶ ***cubensis*** (C) ER&R
cucullata CHal ER&R
'Curly Locks' (S) CHal
'Dannebo' MBri
¶ 'Dawnal Meyer' (C) ER&R
¶ 'Di-anna' (C) ER&R
'Druryi' ER&R SLMG
¶ ***echinosepala*** (C) ER&R
¶ 'Elaine Wilkerson' ER&R
'Emma Watson' CHal ER&R
¶ ***epipsila*** ER&R
x ***erythrophylla*** 'Bunchii' ER&R SLMG
§ – 'Helix' CHal ER&R
¶ 'Esther Albertine' (C) ER&R
'Fairylight' (T) CBla
feastii helix See B. x ***erythrophylla*** 'Helix'
'Festiva' (T) CBla
¶ 'Fire Flush' (R) WEfe
¶ 'Five and Dime' ER&R
¶ 'Florence Rita' (C) ER&R
¶ ***foliosa*** ER&R WEfe
¶ – var. ***amplifolia*** ER&R
§ – var. ***miniata*** 'Rosea' CHal
¶ 'Fred Bedson' ER&R
fuchsioïdes CBar CHal CSev CTro EBak ER&R GCra LHil NWyt WEas WEfe
– 'Rosea' See B. ***foliosa miniata*** 'Rosea'
'Full Moon' (T) CBla
¶ ***gehrtii*** CTro
glaucophylla See B. ***procumbens***
'Gold Cascade' CBla
'Goldilocks' (T) CBla
grandis dark form SApp
– ssp. ***evansiana*** CAvo CDec CGle CHEx CHal CRDP CTro ECar ER&R ESma GCal LHil LHop MTho SBar SChu SDix SSpi WCru
– – ***alba*** CAvo CHal CRDP ER&R LHil MTho NBir SMad SSpi
♦ ***griffithii*** See B. ***annulata***
'Gustav Lind' (S) CHal GCra SSad WEas
haageana See B. ***scharffii***
¶ 'Honeysuckle' (C) ER&R
hybrids CKel
¶ ***incarnata*** (C) ER&R
– 'Metallica' CHal SLMG
'Jean Blair' (T) CBla
'Joe Hayden' ER&R SLMG
¶ 'Lady Clare' ER&R
'Lady France' MBri
'Leopard' ER&R MBri
¶ 'Libor' (C) ER&R
♦ ***limmingheana*** See B. ***radicans***
¶ ***lindeniana*** ER&R
listada CHal MBri
¶ 'Little Darling' ER&R
¶ 'Looking Glass' (C) ER&R
'Lou Anne' CBla
¶ 'Lubbergei' (C) ER&R
'Lucerna' See B. x ***corallina*** 'Lucerna'
¶ ***luxurians*** ER&R
¶ – 'Ziesenhenne ER&R
¶ ***maculata*** 'Wightii' (C) ER&R
¶ 'Mac's Gold' ER&R
'Madame Richard Gallé' (T) SDeJ
'Majesty' (T) CBla
¶ ***manicata*** ER&R
'Maphil' MBri
'Marmorata' (T) NRog SDeJ
masoniana CHal ER&R ERea MBri SLMG WEas WEfe
¶ ***mazae*** ER&R
¶ 'Medora' (C) ER&R
'Melissa' (T) CBla
¶ ***metallica*** ER&R
¶ 'Mirage' ER&R
¶ ***natalensis*** (T) ER&R
nigramarga See B. ***bowerae*** 'Nigramarga'
¶ 'Norah Bedson' ER&R
¶ 'Odorata Alba' CTro MNew
¶ 'Old Gold' (T) ER&R
¶ 'Ophelia' (T) CBla
'Orange Cascade' (T) CBla
¶ 'Orange Rubra' (C) ER&R
¶ ***partita*** CTro
'Picotee' (T) CSut NRog
¶ 'Pinafore' (C) ER&R
¶ ***polyantha*** ER&R
'Président Carnot' (C) ER&R SLMG
'Primrose' (T) CBla
♦ ***procumbens*** See B. ***radicans***
¶ ***pustulata*** 'Argentea' ER&R
§ ***radicans*** CHal CTro ER&R MBri
¶ 'Raquel Wood' ER&R
¶ 'Raspberry Swirl' (R) WEfe
¶ 'Raymond George Nelson' ER&R
¶ 'Red Planet' ER&R WEfe
rex MBri
¶ 'Richard Robinson' ER&R
¶ 'Richmondensis' ER&R
'Ricky Minter' ER&R SLMG
'Roy Hartley' (T) CBla
'Royalty' (T) CBla
¶ 'Sachsen' ER&R
'Sandersonii' WEas
¶ ***sanguinea*** ER&R
¶ 'Scarlet Pimpernel' (T) CBla
'Scarlett O'Hara' (T) CBla
'Sceptre' (T) CBla
§ ***scharffii*** CHal CTro EBak ER&R
'Scherzo' CHal ER&R
'Sea Coral' (T) CBla
semperflorens hort. See B. x ***carrierei***
serratipetala EBak ER&R MBri
¶ Skeezar ER&R
¶ ***Skeezar*** Brown Lake ER&R
solananthera CHal ER&R
sonderiana ERea
¶ 'Sophie Cecile' (C) ER&R
¶ 'Spellbound' WEfe
§ ***stipulacea*** CHal CTro ER&R
§ – 'Bat Wings' SLMG

'Sugar Candy' (T)	CBla
sutherlandii	CAvo CHal CRDP EBak ER&R LHil MBri NBir NPer SAxl SLMG SSad SSpi
'Sweet Dreams' (T)	CBla
'Sweet Magic'	CHal ER&R
'Switzerland' (T)	LAma SDeJ
'Tahiti' (T)	CBla
'Thrush' (R)	SLMG
'Thunderclap'	CHal
'Thurstonii'	CHal CTro ER&R
'Tiger Paws'	CHal ER&R MBri
¶ 'Tom Ment' (C)	ER&R
¶ 'Tom Ment II' (C)	ER&R
¶ 'Tondelayo' (R)	ER&R
¶ ***tripartita*** (T)	ER&R
'Trout' (C)	CHal SLMG
¶ ***undulata*** (C)	ER&R
'Venus'	CHal
¶ x ***verschaffeltii***	ER&R
¶ ***vitifolia***	ER&R
¶ 'Weltoniensis'	ER&R
¶ 'Withlacoohee'	ER&R
¶ 'Zuensis'	ER&R
'Zulu' (T)	CBla

BELAMCANDA (Iridaceae)

chinensis	CBot CBro CDoC CHal CHan CMHG CRDP ECro LHop MHew NBir NBro NRar NSal NTow SLMG SMrm WHil WHoo WOMN WOld WPer WWye
– 'Hello Yellow'	EMar

BELLEVALIA (Liliaceae/Hyacinthaceae)

¶ ***dubia***	CMon
forniculata	SPou
¶ – JCA 227.770	CNic
¶ ***hackelii*** MS 439	CMon
¶ ***maura*** SF 387	CMon
¶ ***nivalis*** CL 101	CMon
paradoxa	See B. ***pycnantha***
§ ***pycnantha***	ETub NHol SIng SUsu
romana	MPar
¶ – JCA 523	CMon
¶ ***sessiliflora***	CMon
sp. PD 20493	WOMN

BELLIS † (Compositae)

perennis	CKin
– 'Alba Plena'	CBos CWes ELan EPla NHol NNrd NSti SHer SIng
– 'Alice'	CBos CCot CGle NSti WHer
¶ – 'Annie'	CGle
– 'Aucubifolia' (v)	GAbr
– 'Dresden China'	CElw CMer CMil CTom ELan GAbr MCas MTho NHol SHer WEas WOMN WOld WPer WRus
– 'Miss Mason'	CGle EOrc GAbr WRus
– 'Monstrosa'	MWat
– 'Parkinson's Great White'	GAbr
– 'Pomponette'	NRoo
– 'Prolifera' (Hen and Chickens)	CBos CCot CGle CMil CRDP CRow GAbr MTho NSti
– 'Rob Roy'	GAbr MCas NHol
– 'Robert'	CCot CMil GAbr MCas
– 'Single Blue'	See B. ***rotundifolia*** 'Caerulescens'
– 'Stafford Pink'	GAbr WHer
¶ – 'White Pearl'	MTho
rotundifolia	CLew CRiv
§ – 'Caerulescens'	CCot CNic EMar GAbr GArf ILis MCas MHig MTho NHol NMen NNrd NSti WEas WHer WOMN WRus

BELLIUM (Compositae)

bellidioïdes	EPla NHol
crassifolium canescens	WOMN WPer WTyr
minutum	CLew GAbr MHig NGre NRya NTow

BELOPERONE See JUSTICIA

BENSONIELLA (Saxifragaceae)

oregona	EMon LRHS MHig

BERBERIDOPSIS (Flacourtiaceae)

corallina	CB&S CDoC CMac CPle CSam CSco EBre ELan EPla IOrc ISea LBre LHop MBal MBri SArc SBra SGil SLon SPer SSta WAbe WBod WDin WSHC WWat

BERBERIS † (Berberidaceae)

aggregata	MBal SPer SRms WDin
x ***antoniana***	MBri NHol WWeb
aquifolium	See MAHONIA ***aquifolium***
– ***fascicularis***	See MAHONIA ***pinnata***
N ***aristata***	CMCN EHal
¶ ***atrocarpa***	LRHS
bealei	See MAHONIA ***japonica*** Bealei Group
¶ ***bergmanniae***	SLPl SSpi
'Blenheim'	LRHS NHol WWat
¶ ***brachypoda***	NHol
brevipedunculata Bean	See B. ***prattii***
x ***bristolensis***	CSco MBri NHol SLon SPla
buxifolia	MBal SCob SLon
§ – 'Nana'	CAbP CB&S CPMA CPle CSco ELan ENot IJoh MBal MBar MBri MPla NFai NHol NRoo SPer STre WStI
– 'Pygmaea'	See B. ***b.*** 'Nana'
calliantha	CChu CSam CSco MBri MWat NHol SGil SLPl WWat
candidula	CPle CSam EBre ELan ENot IJoh IOrc LBre MBal MBar MWat NHol NNor SBod SCob SLon SPer WBod WDin WStI WTyr WWat
x ***carminea*** 'Barbarossa'	CLan
– 'Buccaneer'	CDoC ENot ISea NKay SBod SHer SPer
– 'Pirate King'	CDoC CSco CShe ENot MBal SCob SPer
chrysosphaera	CChu WWat
congestiflora	CB&S CLew
coryi	See B. ***wilsoniae subcaulialata***
coxii	CSam NTow SSpi

darwinii	Widely available
dictyophylla	CBot CCla CHad CPMA CPle EBre EHar ELan LBre LGre MBri MBrk SLon SMad SPer SSpi SSta WSHC WWat
dulcis 'Nana'	See B. ***buxifolia*** 'Nana'
empetrifolia	CGre CLew NNor SIng WHCr
x *frikartii* 'Amstelveen'	CSam EBar ENot IJoh SCob SLon
– 'Telstar'	CPle CSco ELan ENot LBuc MBal MBri MRav SCob WStI
gagnepainii hort.	See B. ***g. lanceifolia***
¶ – 'Fernspray'	MBri SBod SRms
§ – var. *lanceifolia*	CB&S CPle ENot EPla IOrc MBar MGos NNor NWea SLPl SLon SPer SSta
– 'Purpurea'	See B. x ***interposita*** 'Wallich's Purple'
¶ 'Georgei'	CMHG SHil
glaucocarpa	SSpi
'Goldilocks'	CAbP CDoC CPMA CTre EHar MBlu SHil SMad SSpi WWat
¶ *gracilis*	WFro
hookeri	SCob
– var. *latifolia*	See B. ***manipurana***
x *hybridogagnepainii* 'Chenault'	ELan MWat SPer WAbe
hypokerina	CLan SHil
§ x *interposita* 'Wallich's Purple'	EGol ENot MBal MBar MBri SGil SPer WStI
jamesiana	NTow
julianae	CBra CDoC CPle CSco EBre EGol ELan ENot IOrc LBre MBal MBar MBri MGos MRav NBee NHol NNor NWea SCob SLPl SPer SPla WDin WSHC
– 'Mary Poppins'	MBri MUlv
kawakamii	SLPl
knightii	See B. ***manipurana***
koreana	CMCN CSam ECtt EPla SPer
lempergiana	CB&S CMCN CMHG
linearifolia	CBra GRei SLon
– 'Orange King'	CAbP CB&S CChu CDoC CPMA CSco ELan ENot IJoh LHop LTil MBri MGos MWat NBar NBee NKay SCob SDry SHBN SPer WDin WStI
'Little Favourite'	See B. ***thunbergii*** 'Atropurpurea Nana'
x *lologensis*	IOrc MGos SPla WDin
– 'Apricot Queen'	CAbP CB&S CDoC COtt CPMA CSco IJoh LHop LTil MBal MBri MRav NBee SCob SDry SLon SPer WDin WStI WWeb
– 'Mystery Fire'	CAbP CDoC CKni COtt CPMA CSco ECtt IOrc LTil MAsh MBar MBlu MBri MGos MUlv NBee SCob SReu
– 'Stapehill'	CB&S ENot MAsh MBri MUlv SSpi SSta WWeb
lycium	EHal
§ *manipurana*	CGre ENot
x *media* 'Parkjuweel' ('Park Jewel')	CB&S CBra CDoC EHal MAsh MRav NHol SGil SPer WWeb
– 'Red Jewel'	CBra CDoC CSco EBre EGol IJoh LBre MBri MGos SGil SHer SPer SPla WAbe WWeb
x *ottawensis*	CSco GRei LAbb WStI
– 'Auricoma'	WWeb
– 'Decora'	SPer
– 'Lombart's Purple'	SLon
N x *ottawensis purpurea*	IJoh MBri SBod WDin
§ x *ottawensis* 'Silver Mile' (v)	COtt EFol ELan EPla LHop LNet SDry SGil SSpi SSta WPat
N – 'Superba'	CB&S CDoC CPle CShe ECar ELan ENot GWht IDai LHop MBal MBar MGos NBee NHol NNor NRoo SLon SPer SPla WDin
§ *panlanensis*	ENot ESis MBar MBel SCob SLon
patagonica	NNor
polyantha Hemsley	MRav
– hort.	See B. ***prattii***
§ *prattii*	MBri NHol NTow
pruinosa	CPle EGol SLPl
'Red Tears'	CDoC COtt CPMA CSam MBlu MBri MGos SSpi
replicata	CB&S SLPl SLon SSpi
'Rubrostilla'	CDoC CSco ENot ISea MBri SCob
♦ *sanguinea* hort.	See B. ***panlanensis***
sargentiana	ELan ENot NNor SLPl SLon SSpi WWat
* – 'Nana'	WPat
sherriffii	CLew NHol NTow
sieboldii	CBot EHar
x *stenophylla*	CB&S CPle CSco CShe ELan GRei IDai IJoh LBuc MBar MBri MGos MWat NHol NKay NNor NRoo NWea SCob SLon SPer SReu WBod WDin WPat WWin
– 'Autumnalis'	SCob
– 'Claret Cascade'	CCla CSco ELan MAsh MBri MGos SPer WWeb
– 'Coccinea'	EPla IBar SPer
– 'Corallina'	WWeb
– 'Corallina Compacta'	CCla CHal CLew ENot EPla EPot ESis GArf IDai IMal MBal MBro MPla NHar NKay SBla SBod SChu SHer SIng SPer SPla SSpi WPat WThu
– 'Crawley Gem'	CMHG COtt CPle ECar LNet MBar MBri MPla NHol NKay NRoo SPer WStI
– Cream Showers ®	See B. x ***s.*** 'Lemon Queen'
– 'Irwinii'	CMHG CSco CShe ENot EPla IOrc MBri MGos MWat NKay SCob SIgm SLon SPer WDin WWeb
N – 'Lemon Queen'	CCla EBre EHal LBre NHol SPer
– 'Nana'	EPla NHol WPat
– 'Pink Pearl'	CBra CShe EPla SHBN
temolaica	CCla EBre EHar ELan LBre LGre SHil SLon SPer SSpi SSta WWat
thunbergii	ENot GRei IDai LBuc MBal NHol NKay NWea SPer WDin WStI
– f. *atropurpurea*	Widely available
§ – 'Atropurpurea Nana'	Widely available
– 'Atropurpurea Superba'	See B. x ***ottawensis*** 'Superba'
– 'Aurea'	Widely available
– 'Bagatelle'	COtt EBlo ECtt ELan ENot EPla EPot ESma IDai IOrc MBar MBri MGos MPla MRav NBee NHar NRoo SGil SHer SPer SSpi WDin WPat
– 'Carpetbagger'	IOrc MGos

– 'Crimson Pygmy'	See B. *t.* 'Atropurpurea Nana'
– 'Dart's Purple'	ENot MAsh MBri WWeb
– 'Dart's Red Lady'	CCla EBlo EBre ECtt EHal ELan ENot EPla ESma IJoh IOrc LBre MBri MPla MRav NRoo SPer SPla WAbe
– 'Erecta'	ENot MAsh MBar MGos NHol SCob WDin
– 'Golden Ring'	CB&S CCla CPle CSco EBar ECtt EFol EHoe ELan EPla LAbb LHop MBar MBri MGos MWat NHar NHol NRoo SChu SHBN SPer SPla SReu WPat WSHC
¶– 'Golden Ring'	WDin
– 'Green Carpet'	EBre ENot IOrc LBre MAsh MBal MBar NRoo SPer SSta
*– 'Green Mantle'	SBod
*– 'Green Marble'	NHar
– 'Green Ornament'	MWat SPer
– 'Green Ring'	EGol
– 'Harlequin'	CB&S CPle CSco EBre ECtt EHar EHoe ELan ENot EPla IJoh IOrc LBre LTil MBal MBri MGos NBee NHar NHol SApp SCob SHBN SPer SPla SSpi WBod WDin WPat WStI
– 'Helmond Pillar'	CMHG CPMA CSco EBlo EBre EGol EHoe ELan ENot EPla IJoh IOrc LBre MBri NBee NFai NRoo SCob SGil SMad SPer SReu WEas WPat WSHC
– 'Kelleriis'	COtt EPla MBar MBri SSpi WStI
– 'Kobold'	ENot EPla MBar MBri MGos MPla NBee NRoo SPer WPat
– 'Pink Queen'	CB&S MAsh MBri MGos NHol SHer WWeb
– 'Red Chief'	CMHG CSco CShe EBre ECtt EHar ELan ENot EPla GRei LBre LHop MBal MGos MRav MWat NBee NRoo SChu SCob SGil SHBN SLon SPer SPla SReu WDin WStI
– 'Red King'	ELan WDin
– 'Red Pillar'	CB&S CLan CPle CSco EBre ECtt EPla LBre MBal MBar MBri MGos MWat NBee NHol SHBN SPla WDin WPat WStI WWeb
¶– 'Red Rocket'	EMil
¶– 'Robin Hood'	MBrk
– 'Rose Glow' (v)	Widely available
– 'Silver Beauty'	CB&S CCla CDoC CMHG CPle EGol EHal ELan MBel MGos NFai SBod SChu SPer WWeb
– 'Silver Mile'	See B. x ***ottawensis*** 'S.M.'
– 'Somerset'	CSco WWat
*– 'Tricolor' (v)	EHoe MUlv WEas WPat WSHC WWeb
*– 'Variegata'	SReu
– 'Vermilion'	CSco
tsangpoensis	SLPl SLon
valdiviana	CBot EHar
veitchii	SLPl SRms SSpi
verruculosa	CBra CLan CSco ELan ENot IDai LHop MBal MBar MBel MBri MGos MWat NHol NKay NNor NWea SCob SLon SPer SPla SReu SSta WBod WDin WWat
vulgaris	CArn NSal
wardii	CB&S
wilsoniae	CB&S CBra CLan CSam CSco EBre EGol ELan ENot IOrc LBre MBar MPla MWat NFai NHol NKay NNor NTow NWea SCob SPer WDin WStI
– L 1738	SSpi
– 'Graciella'	MBri NHol
§ – var. ***subcaulialata***	CPMA

BERCHEMIA (Rhamnaceae)

racemosa	SPer SSpi WSHC

BERGENIA † (Saxifragaceae)

'Abendglocken'	CLew MBri SHig SPla
§ 'Abendglut'	CBow CGle CSco CShe EBar EBlo EBre ECha ECtt EGol ELan ELun EPla IBar LBre MBal MBri NBee NHol NKay NOrc NSti SHig SPer
*****acanthifolia***	CRow
'Admiral'	ECha MUlv
*****afgahanica***	CRow
'Apple Court White'	SApp
'Baby Doll'	CCla CDoC COtt CSco EBre ECha EFou EGol EOrc EPla GCal LBre MBri MUlv NBir NHol NOrc NTow SApp SGil SHer SHig SPla WAbe WRus
§ 'Ballawley'	CRow ECha IBlr MUlv NDea SAxl SHig
N Ballawley hybrids	CB&S CBot CCla CMHG CShe EBre EGol EPar ERav LBre LGro MUlv MWat NHol SDix SGil SPer
'Bartok'	MUlv
beesiana	See B. ***purpurascens***
'Beethoven'	CHad EBre ECha EPla LBre SSpi
'Borodin'	MUlv
'Brahms'	CRow MUlv
'Bressingham Bountiful'	MUlv SPer
'Bressingham Ruby'	CDec COtt EBlo EBre EPla ERav GAri LBre MUlv NRoo SPla WCot
'Bressingham Salmon'	CMil EBre EFol ELan ERav LBre LWad MBri MMil NHol NMir SAxl SGil SHer SPer SSpi WCot
'Bressingham White'	CBot CBow CCla CMHG COtt CSco EBlo EBre ECha ECtt EGol ELan ELun EOrc ERav LBre LHop MBri MRav MUlv NCat NDea NFai NHol NRoo SApp SPer SSpi WRus WWin
'Britten'	MBal MUlv
ciliata	CHEx CHad CHan CMil CRow ECha EPla GCra LGre MBal NBir NSti SAxl SDix WDav WEas WPer WThu
– f. ***ligulata***	EMar EPla SSpi
cordifolia	Widely available
– 'Purpurea'	CB&S CPar CSco CShe EBlo EBre ECha EGol EHal ELan ENot EPla LBre LBuc LGro LWad MBri MRav NKay SDix SHig SPer
– 'Redstart'	NMir NOak SGil
crassifolia	CB&S CGle CKel CWGN EBul EPla LGro MFir SHig SRms WByw
– DF 90028	EMon
– 'Autumn Red'	ECha EPla
– ***orbicularis***	See B. x ***schmidtii***
'Croesus'	IDai

delavayi	See B. ***purpurascens***
'Delbees'	See B. 'Ballawley'
'Eric Smith'	ECha EPla
'Evening Glow'	See B. 'Abendglut'
'Glockenturm' ('Bell Tower')	EPla MUlv
¶ 'Jo Watanabe'	ECha
'Lambrook'	See B. 'Margery Fish'
§ 'Margery Fish'	CDoC COtt CSco CShe SPer SPla
'Morgenröte' ('Morning Red')	CBow CDoC COtt CSco CShe EBar ECha EPla MBri NHol NKay SHig SPer SPla SRms WAbe
'Mrs Crawford'	ECha EPla
¶ 'Opal'	ECha
'Profusion'	SPer
'Pugsley's Pink'	CMGP CMil ECha MUlv
'Pugsley's Purple'	LRHS
§ *purpurascens*	CDec CMHG CMil CRow CSco EBre ECha EPla ERav GDra LBre MBal SAxl SDix SPer WByw WWin
– var. *delavayi* CLD 1366	EMon LRHS WPer
– hybrid	SSpi
'Purpurglocken'	ECha
¶ 'Rosette'	NFai
'Rosi Klose'	ECha EPla GCal LRHS SApp
'Rotblum'	ECtt LRHS SFis
§ x *schmidtii*	CFis LGro NBir SApp SAxl SDix SHig
¶ 'Schneekissen'	LRHS SGil
'Schneekönigin' ('Snow Queen')	ECha EPla
'Silberlicht' ('Silverlight')	CB&S CGle CHad CPar CSco CWGN EBre ECha EFol EFou EGol EOrc EPar GCal IBar LBre LHop MBal MBri NFai NHol NMir NSti SDix SHig SPer WByw WEas
'Snowblush'	MBal SSpi
x *spathulata*	SApp
stracheyi	CBot CCla CLew CRow ECha EFol EGol EPla MNFA NHol NNrd SDix SHig WDav WHCr WHil WHoo
– KBE 151	NHol
– KBE 209	NHol
– *alba*	CChu ECha EPla GCal SDix
'Sunningdale'	CB&S CMGP EBre ECha EGol EHal EPar EPla LBre NBar NBir NHol NSti SAxl SChu SPer WMer
'Wintermärchen'	CBow ECha ECtt EFou EGol ELan EPla ERav MBri MUlv NBee NHol NOrc NSti SHer SPla WRus

BERKHEYA (Compositae)

¶ *macrocephala*	WCot

BERLANDIERA (Compositae)

lyrata	WCru

BERULA (Umbelliferae)

erecta	EHon

BESCHORNERIA (Agavaceae)

tubiflora	CHEx
yuccoïdes	CB&S CHEx IBlr IFer SArc

BESSERA (Liliaceae/Alliaceae)

¶ *elegans*	CKel

BESSEYA (Scrophulariaceae)

¶ *ritteriana*	WDav

BETA (Chenopodiaceae)

trigyna	EMon LRHS

BETONICA See STACHYS

BETULA † (Betulaceae)

aetnensis	CSto
alba Linnaeus	See B. ***pubescens, pendula***
albosinensis	CB&S CGre ELan GAri WCoo WFro WHCr WMou WNor
– W 4106	CSto
¶ – 'Conyngham'	CTho SSpi WWat
– var. *septentrionalis*	CDoC CLnd CSto CTho EHar ENot GAri LNet MBri SEng SHil SPer SReu SSpi WWat
§ *alleghaniensis*	CBow CDoC CGre CLnd CMCN CSam CSto IOrc MBal NWea WCoo WNor
apoiensis	CSto
borealis	CSto
x *caerulea*	CSto CTho
caerulea-grandis	See B. x ***caerulea***
¶ *calcicola*	EMon
– B&L 12268	WHCr
celtiberica	CSto
chichibuensis	EPla
chinensis	WCoo WHCr
¶ *cordifolia*	CSto
costata hort.	See B. ***ermanii*** 'Blush'
– Trautvetter	CCla CDoC CLnd CMCN COtt CSam CSco CSto CTho EBre EHar ELan ENot IBar IOrc LBre MSte WCoo WDin WFro WNor
davurica	CLnd WCoo
ermanii	CB&S CBra CLnd CMCN CMHG COtt CSam CSco CSto CTho EBre EHar ELan ENot IOrc LBre MBal MBlu MBri MGos NWea SPer SReu WCoo WDin WFro WMou WNor
¶ – 'Blush'	MGos
– 'Grayswood Hill'	CMHG CSto MBal SPer SSpi WWat
'Fetisowii'	CLnd CTho SHil SSpi WHCr
§ *fontinalis*	CSto WHCr
glandulifera	CLnd CSto EArb
¶ *glandulosa*	EArb
grossa	CSto
¶ 'Hergest'	WHCr
humilis	CDoC
'Inverleith'	EHar MBri SFai SSpi
jacquemontii	See B. ***utilis jacquemontii***
'Jermyns'	CMHG CTho EHar MUlv SHil SSpi
lenta	CSto EHar MBal WCoo
litvinovii	WNor

lutea	See B. ***alleghaniensis***
maximowicziana	CB&S CBra CDoC CLnd CMCN CSto EBar GAri MBal SSta WCoo WFro WNor
medwedewii	CLnd CMCN CTho GAri SEng SMad SSpi SSta WCoo
michauxii	WAbe WPat
minor	CSto
nana	CLew CSto EHar ELan EPla ESis IOrc MBal MBar MBro MPla MPlt NLan NRoo NWea SIng SReu SSpi SSta STre WPat WPer
– 'Glengarry'	EPla EPot GAri MPlt WAbe WDin
§ *neoalaskana*	CSto
nigra	CBra CDoC CLnd CMCN CSto CTho EHar ENot IHos IOrc LMer MBal MSte SHil SMad SPer SSpi WCoo WDin WFro WMou WNor
occidentalis	See B. ***fontinalis***
§ *ovalifolia*	CSto
papyrifera	CB&S CBra CCla CLnd CMCN CSco CSto EBre EHar ELan ENot IOrc ISea LBre LBuc MBal MBar MGos NWea SHBN SPer SReu WCoo WDin WNor WWat
¶ – var. *commutata*	CLnd
– var. *kenaica*	CDoC CTho SHil WHCr
¶ – var. *minor*	EArb
¶ – 'Saint George'	CTho SSpi WWat
§ *pendula*	CB&S CBra CKin CLnd CPer CSco CSto EBre EHar ELan ENot GRei IDai IJoh IOrc LBre LBuc MBal MBar MBri MGos NWea SPer SPla SReu WAbe WDin WMou
– f. *crispa*	See B. ***p.*** 'Laciniata'
N– 'Dalecarlica'	See B. ***p.*** 'Laciniata'
– 'Fastigiata'	CLnd CSco CTho EBre EHar ELan ENot LBre LPan MGos SHil SPer SReu
– 'Golden Cloud'	CB&S CBow CLnd COtt EHar IOrc MBar NBar SEng SPer WDin WStI
§ – 'Laciniata'	CLnd COtt CSco CTho EBre EHar ENot GRei IOrc LBre MBar MBri MGos NBee NWea SHBN SPer SSpi SSta WAbe WDin WHCr WMou
¶ – var. *pendula* 'Dissecta'	WFro
– 'Purpurea'	CBra CLnd CSco CTho CWSG EBre EFol EHar ELan ENot EPla IOrc LBre MBal MBar MBlu MBri MGos NBar NBee SEng SHBN SHil SPer SReu SSpi WDin
– 'Tristis'	CDoC CLnd CSco CTho EHar ENot GRei IOrc MBal MBar MBri NWea SPer SSpi WAbe WDin WHCr WMou
– 'Youngii'	CB&S CBra CCla CLnd CSco EBre EGol EHar ELan ENot GRei IDai IJoh LBre LBuc LNet MBal MBar MBri MGos NBar NWea SHBN SPer SReu SSta WAbe WDin
platyphylla	CMCN CSto CTho GAri LHop WFro
– var. *japonica*	CLnd MBrk WFro WNor
populifolia	CSto GAri SEng
§ *pubescens*	CKin CLnd CPer CSto EBre IOrc ISea LBre LNet MBal NBar NWea WDin WMou
¶ – 'Arnold Brembo'	CTho
pumila	CMCN CSto
♦ *resinifera* Britton	See B. ***neoalaskana***
saposhnikovii	WNor
schmidtii	CSto WCoo WNor
szechuanica	CSto SHil WAbe
– W 983	CSto
♦ *tatewakiana*	See B. ***ovalifolia***
tianschanica	LMer MGos
'Trost's Dwarf'	CB&S CCla COtt CWSG EHal EHar EPla ESis IJoh IOrc ISea LHop MBar MBro MGos MPla NBee NHar NHol SEng SMad SPer WPat WWat
x *utahensis*	CSto EArb WHCr
utilis	CBow CBra CCla CLnd CMCN CMHG CTho EHar ELan ENot GRei LNet MBal MBar MGos MRav MSte NBar NHol SPer SSpi WAbe WCoo WDin WFro WNor
¶ – BL&M 100	CTho
– B&L 5380	WHCr
– F 19505	CSto
– G-W&P 760	CSto
– PF 48	ISea
– SS&W 4382	CSto
¶ – 'Buckland'	CTho
¶ – 'Grayswood Ghost'	CTho
N– var. *jacquemontii*	Widely available
¶ – – 'Silver Shadow'	SSpi WWat
¶ – 'Kyelang'	SSpi
¶ – 'Trinity College'	IMal
verrucosa	See B. ***pendula***

BIARUM (Araceae)

¶ *arundanum*	CMon
¶ *bovei* S&L 132	CMon
carduchorum	EPot LAma WChr
¶ *carratracense* SF 233	CMon
davisii	EPot LAma WChr WCru
¶ – ssp. *davisii* MS 785/735	CMon
¶ – ssp. *marmarisense*	CMon
dispar	WChr
¶ – AB&S 4455	CMon
¶ – S&L 295	CMon
ditschianum	WChr
¶ *eximium* FF 1024	CMon
¶ – PD 26644	CMon
ochridense	WChr
¶ – M&T 4629	CMon
¶ *pyrami* PB	CMon
tenuifolium	CBro CMon EPot LAma WChr
¶ – AB&S 4356	CMon
*– *idomeneanum* MS 758	CMon
– var. *zeleborii*	CBro

BIDENS (Compositae)

atrosanguinea	See COSMOS ***atrosanguineus***
aurea	CGle ECtt EPad MSte NFai
cernua	MHew NSal

ferulifolia	CBrk CSev CSpe ECtt ERav ERea GCal LHil LHop MFir NRoo SBor SChu WEas WHal WOMN WPer
¶ – 'Golden Goddess'	SAxl
¶ *heterophylla* CD&R 1230	CHan
¶ *ostruthioïdes*	CBrk
¶ sp. CD&R 1515	CHan
tripartita	NSal

BIGNONIA (Bignoniaceae)

capreolata	CBow SBra SHil SPer WSHC WWeb
♦ *lindleyana*	See CLYTOSTOMA ***callistegioïdes***
unguis-cati	See MACFADYENA ***u-c.***

BILDERDYKIA See **FALLOPIA**

BILLARDIERA (Pittosporaceae)

longiflora	CB&S CGre CHan CMHG CMac CPle CSam CSun CTro CWit EBre ECou ELan EOvi ERea IDai ISea LBre LGre LHop MGos NHar SApp SBra SLMG SPer SSta SUsu WSHC WWat
– 'Cherry Berry'	ECou
– *fructu-albo*	MBal SWas
– red berried	CSam EBul
– 'Rosea'	CSun LBlm
scandens	ECou

BILLBERGIA (Bromeliaceae)

¶ × *albertii*	CTro
nutans	CHEx CHal CSun EBak ELan ERav IBlr LAbb LBlm MBri SArc SFar SLMG
pyramidalis var. *striata* (v)	SLMG
saundersii	See B. ***chlorosticta***
× *windii*	CHal EBak SLMG

BISCUTELLA (Cruciferae)

frutescens	MHig WWin

BISTORTA See **PERSICARIA**

BLACKBERRY See **RUBUS *fruticosus***

BLACKCURRANT See **RIBES *nigrum***

BLACKSTONIA (Gentianaceae)

perfoliata	WCru

BLANDFORDIA (Liliaceae/Blandfordiaceae)

punicea	ECar SIgm

BLECHNUM (Blechnaceae)

alpinum	See B. ***penna-marina alpinum***
chilense	See B. ***tabulare***
gibbum	MBri
§ *glandulosum*	NMar
magellanicum	See B. ***tabulare***
♦ *occidentale nanum*	See B. ***glandulosum***
penna-marina	CBos CBro CNic CTom EBul ECou EPar GGar MBal MFos NGar NHar NMar SDix SHer SIng SPer SSpi WAbe WOMN WRic
§ – ssp. *alpinum*	NKay NMar SSpi
– *cristatum*	EBre GDra LBre MBal NHar NKay WRic
spicant	CKin GGar IOrc MBal NBro NMar SApp SIng SMad SPer SPla SSpi WRic
§ *tabulare*	CB&S CHEx EBul IBlr LTil MBal NKay SApp SArc SAxl SDix SHig SSpi

BLETILLA (Orchidaceae)

¶ *formosana*	EFEx SWes
hyacinthina	See B. ***striata***
¶ *ochracea*	EFEx SWes
§ *striata*	CAvo CKel COtt CRiv CRow CSut ECtt EFEx ERea GAbr IBlr LAma MBri MTho NHol NRog SDeJ SHer SSpi SWes WAbe WChr
– *alba*	See B. ***s. gebina***
– *albostriata*	CBot EFEx ELan LAma NHol NRog SMad SWes WChr
§ – f. *gebina*	CAvo CBot CKel ECtt GAbr LAma NHol NRog SDeJ SWes WChr
¶ *szetschuanica*	SWes
¶ 'Yokohama'	EFEx SWes

BLOOMERIA (Liliaceae/Alliaceae)

crocea	WChr

BLUEBERRY See **VACCINIUM *corymbosum***

BOCCONIA (Papaveraceae)

cordata	See MACLEAYA ***c.***
microcarpa	See MACLEAYA ***m.***

BOEHMERIA (Urticaceae)

nivea	CB&S

BOENNINGHAUSENIA (Rutaceae)
See Plant Deletions

BOLAX (Umbelliferae)

§ *gummifera*	ITim

BOLTONIA (Compositae)

asteroïdes	CGle CHan CLew CSev EHal EMar GCal MUlv NSti WSun
– var. *latisquama*	CBre CCor CGle CHan CRDP ECro EFou EMon GCal LRHS MSte NWyt SHer SMad SSvw
– – 'Nana'	CBre CLew CRDP ECha NHol SFis WPer
– 'Snowbank'	EFol LHop MBel
incisa	See KALIMERIS ***incisa***

BOLUSANTHUS (Leguminosae)

speciosus	CPle

BOMAREA (Liliaceae/Alstroemeriaceae)

caldasii	CHEx CTro ERea
¶ *edulis*	ERea
multiflora	CSun
volubilis	IBar

BONGARDIA (Berberidaceae)

chrysogonum	LAma LBow NRog

BORAGO † (Boraginaceae)

alba	LHol MChe WCHb
laxiflora	See B. *pygmaea*
officinalis	CArn CSFH CSev GPoy IEde LHol MBri MChe MHew NFai NSel SHer SIde WEas WHal WHer WOak WPer WWye
– 'Alba'	CBos CBre CGle CHun EJud WHal WHer
§ *pygmaea*	Widely available

BORNMUELLERA (Cruciferae)

See Plant Deletions

BORONIA (Rutaceae)

'Heaven Scent'	CB&S EMil
heterophylla	CB&S CMHG CSun ERea LAbb LBlm LHop MUlv
megastigma	CB&S EMil

BOTHRIOCHLOA (Gramineae)

§ *bladhii*	ETPC
caucasica	See B. *bladhii*
ischaemum	CHan ETPC
saccharoïdes	CHan

BOTRYOSTEGE (Ericaceae)

bracteata	See ELLIOTTIA *bracteata*

BOUGAINVILLEA (Nyctaginaceae)

'Afterglow'	See B. 'Mrs Helen McLean'
'Albo d'Ora'	MNew
'Alexandra'	CSun MBri MNew SLMG
'Amethyst'	LBlm MBri SLMG
¶ 'Apple Blossom'	ERea
¶ 'Asia'	ERea
'Barbara Karst'	CB&S ERea
'Betty Lavers'	ERea
¶ 'Brilliant'	ERea
'California Gold'	See B. 'Golden Glow'
'Dania'	LAbb MBri
'Danica Rouge'	MNew SLMG
¶ 'Daphne Masson'	ERea
¶ 'Dixie'	ERea
¶ 'Doctor David Barry'	CTro ERea
¶ 'Donyo'	ERea
¶ double orange	CTro
¶ double pink	CTro
'Elizabeth Angus'	ERea
¶ 'Flamingo Pink'	ERea
¶ 'Gillian Greensmith'	ERea
glabra	CB&S LAbb MBri
¶ – *harissii*	ERea
– *variegata*	LAbb
§ 'Golden Glow' (x *buttiana*)	CTro MNew
¶ 'Harlequin'	ERea
¶ 'Isabel Greensmith'	CTro
'Jamaica White'	CB&S
¶ 'James Walker'	ERea
¶ 'Jane Snook'	ERea
'Jennifer Fernie'	ERea MNew SLMG
¶ 'Juanita Hatten'	CTro
¶ 'Kaual Royal'	ERea
'Killie Campbell'	ERea MBri SLMG
¶ 'La Jolla'	ERea
'Lady Mary Ralney'	ERea
¶ 'Limberlost Beauty'	ERea
¶ 'Mardi Gras'	CTro ERea
¶ 'Mary Palmer' (x *buttiana*)	CTro ERea
¶ 'Mary Palmer's Enchantment'	ERea
¶ 'Meriol Fitzpatrick'	ERea
'Mrs Butt' (x *buttiana*)	ERea SLMG
¶ 'Mrs H C Buck'	ERea
§ 'Mrs Helen McLean' (x *buttiana*)	ERea LBlm SLMG
'Muril Fitzpatrick'	SLMG
'Nina Milton'	ERea
'Orange Glow'	CSun LAbb SLMG
'Orange King'	See B. 'Mrs Helen McLean'
¶ 'Pagoda Pink'	ERea
¶ 'Pearl'	ERea
¶ 'Pink Cluster'	ERea
¶ 'Pink Pixie'	CTro
'Poultonii Special'	CTro ERea MNew SLMG
'Raspberry Ice' (v)	CPle CTro ERea
'Red Diamond'	CSun LBlm SLMG
¶ 'Rosenka'	ERea
¶ 'Royal Bengal Orange'	ERea
¶ 'Royal Bengal Red'	ERea
'San Diego Red'	See B. 'Scarlett O'Hara'
'Sanderiana' (*glabra*)	ERea NRog SLMG
'Sanderiana Variegata' (*glabra*)	MBri
§ 'Scarlett O'Hara'	CSun CTro ERea LBlm MNew SLMG
'Sea Foam'	CTro SLMG
¶ 'Smartipants'	ERea
spectabilis 'Brasiliensis'	See B. *s.* 'Lateritia'
– 'Camarillo Fiesta'	ERea
– 'Elizabeth'	ERea
– 'Variegata'	MNew
¶ 'Summer Snow'	CTro
Surprise ® (x *buttiana*)	See B. 'Mary Palmer'
'Tahitian Maid'	SLMG
¶ 'Tango'	ERea
¶ 'Temple Fire'	ERea MNew
'Texan Dawn'	ERea
¶ 'Thai Gold'	ERea
¶ 'Thimbra'	MNew
¶ 'Weeping Beauty'	CTro ERea
'White Empress'	MNew

BOUSSINGAULTIA (Basellaceae)
baselloïdes See ANREDERA *cordifolia*

BOUTELOUA (Gramineae)
curtipendula EMon ETPC
gracilis See CHONDROSUM *gracile*

BOUVARDIA (Rubiaceae)
bouvardioïdes CSun
x *domestica* ERea
longiflora MNew
scabrida CPle CSun
§ *ternifolia* CGre CSun SLMG
triphylla See B. *ternifolia*

BOWENIA (Boweniaceae)
serrulata LPal WNor

BOWIEA (Liliaceae/Hyacinthaceae)
volubilis CHal

BOWKERIA (Scrophulariaceae)
citrina CGre
gerrardiana CGre

BOYKINIA (Saxifragaceae)
aconitifolia CGle CRDP CSam EBar ECro EFol ELan EMon GDra MFir MTol SSpi WCru WPer
heucheriformis See B. *jamesii*
§ *jamesii* CNic EPot GTou LBee MBro MHig NHar NHol NNrd NTow NWCA SIng WDav WThu
– JCA 9623 NHol
rotundifolia CSam ECro ELan GAbr NHol NSti WCru
– JLS 86269LACA EMon
tellimoïdes See PELTOBOYKINIA *t.*

BOYSENBERRY See **RUBUS**

BRACHYCHILUM (Zingiberaceae)
¶ *horsfieldii* CTro

BRACHYGLOTTIS † (Compositae)
§ *bidwillii* CChu CGle SDry WAbe WCru
§ *buchananii* CHan SDry WCru WSHC
§ *compacta* CB&S CDec ECha ECou MPla NRoo SDry SPer WCru WEas WWat
'Drysdale' SDry WCru
§ *elaeagnifolia* ISea NNor SHil
N *greyi* CLan CPle CSco CShe ERav GRei IDai IJoh ISea LAbb MBar MPla NKay NNor NRoo SLon WEas WWin
§ *hectorii* LHop
§ *huntii* CAbb CBot CPle WCru
§ *kirkii* CGre CPle CSpe WCot
N *laxifolia* CFis CLan LHop NNor WCru
§ 'Leonard Cockayne' CHEx SDry
§ 'Moira Read' (v) CPMA CPle CSco EFol ELan EPla ERav LHop MBal MUlv SDry WCru WEas
§ *monroi* CFis CLan CMHG CMil CPle CSam CSco ECar ECou ELan EPla ERav IBlr IDai IOrc ISea LHop MBal MRav NNor NTow SLon SPer SUsu WCru WEas WSHC WWat
– 'Clarence' ECou
'New Zealand' CBot
repanda CHEx CPle
– 'Purpurea' CBot CHEx
– x *greyi* CPle SArc
§ *rotundifolia* CAbb CDoC CGre CPle IBlr IDai MBlu WCru WEas
¶ *spedenii* GTou WCru
§ 'Sunshine' CB&S CDec CFis CMHG ELan ENot IBlr LGro LHop MBal MBri MGos NBee SDix SGil SPer SPla SSta WAbe WWat
'Sunshine Variegated' See B. 'Moira Read'

BRACHYPODIUM (Gramineae)
¶ *phoenicoïdes* ETPC
pinnatum CKin ETPC
sylvaticum CKin ETPC

BRACHYSCOME (Compositae)
'Harmony' IHos
iberidifolia CGre ELan SHer
multifida CSpe IHos LHop MBri
nivalis var. *alpina* See B. *tadgellii*
rigidula CRDP CRiv ECou MCas NNrd NTow SIng
§ *tadgellii* WPer
'Tinkerbell' CBar IHos NRoo

BRACHYSTACHYUM (Gramineae(Bambuseae))
densiflorum SDry

BRACTEANTHA (Compositae)
acuminata NHol
bracteata 'Dargan Hill Monarch' CBrk CSev ERav LHil LHop NOak WEas WPer
– 'Skynet' CBrk LHil LHop NOak WPer

BRAHEA (Palmae)
armata LPal NPal
brandegeei LPal
edulis LPal

BRASSAIA See **SCHEFFLERA**

BRASSICA (Cruciferae)
japonica See B. *juncea crispifolia*
§ *juncea* var. *crispifolia* CArn

BRAVOA (Agarvaceae)
♦ *geminiflora* See POLIANTHES *g.*

BRAYA (Cruciferae)
alpina GAbr NMen WPer

BREYNIA (Euphorbiaceae)
See Plant Deletions

X BRIGANDRA (Gesneriaceae)
* *calliantha* NTow

BRIGGSIA (Gesneriaceae)
muscicola MHig NTow

BRIMEURA (Liliaceae/Hyacinthaceae)
§ *amethystina* CAvo LRHS MPar WThu
– 'Alba' CAvo ETub LRHS MPar NHol NRog WHil WPer WThu

BRIZA (Gramineae)
maxima CSFH EHoe EPla NBee NSti SIng WWye
media CKin EBar EFou EHoe ELan EOrc EPla ETPC GAbr GCHN GCal NBee NLan NMir SPer
– Elatior Group ETPC
– 'Limouzi' ETPC
minor CLew EHoe
triloba EHoe ETPC

BROCCHINIA (Bromeliaceae)
¶ *reducta* EFEx

BRODIAEA (Liliaceae/Alliaceae)
capitata See DICHELOSTEMMA *pulchellum*
elegans EBul ESma MFos WChr
♦ *ida-maia* See DICHELOSTEMMA *i.-m.*
laxa See TRITELEIA *laxa*
peduncularis See TRITELEIA *p.*
stellaris WChr
terrestris WChr
volubilis WChr

BROMUS (Gramineae)
¶ *commutatus* ETPC
§ *lanceolatus* ETPC
macrostachys See B. *lanceolatus*
ramosus EHoe ETPC

BROUSSONETIA (Moraceae)
papyrifera CB&S CBot CCla CHEx CPle EHar SMad WCoo WMou WWat

BROWALLIA (Solanaceae)
speciosa 'Major' MBri
– 'Silver Bells' MBri

BRUCKENTHALIA (Ericaceae)
spiculifolia CLew CNic EDen EPot GArf GWht MBal MBar MPlt NHol SSpi WThu
– 'Balkan Rose' CNic ECar LTil

BRUGMANSIA (Solanaceae)
§ *arborea* CArn CHEx NPal SLMG
aurea MNew SLMG
x *candida* EBak
– 'Grand Marnier' CBot MBri SHil SLMG WKif
§ – 'Knightii' CBot CBrk CHEx CTro EBak ERea MNew
¶ – 'Plena' CKel
¶ – 'Variegata' CKel
¶ x *candida* x *aurea* CTro
* *chlorantha* CHEx LHil MBri MNew SLMG
– apricot ERea
¶ 'Golden Queen' CBrk
§ hybrids SDeJ
¶ x *insignis* 'Orange' CSun
§ – pink CHEx MNew SHil
meteloïdes See DATURA *inoxia*
'Panache' CBot CKel
rosei See B. *sanguinea*
§ *sanguinea* CHEx CTro ERea GCal ISea LHil MBri MNew NRar SHil SLMG
§ *suaveolens* CHEx EBar ELan ERea ISea SHil
– 'Flore Pleno' SHil
– *rosea* See B. x *insignis* pink
§ *versicolor* CBrk CTro ERea MNew SLMG

BRUNFELSIA (Solanaceae)
americana CPle CTro MNew SLMG
calycina See B. *pauciflora*
♦ *eximia* See B. *pauciflora*
pauciflora CTro ELan LAbb MBri MNew SLMG
– 'Floribunda' MNew
– 'Macrantha' CTro SLMG
undulata MNew

BRUNNERA (Boraginaceae)
§ *macrophylla* Widely available
– *alba* See B. *m.* 'Betty Bowring'
§ – 'Betty Bowring' CBos CHad CLew CRow
§ – 'Dawson's White' (v) CBot CChu CCla CGle CHEx CRow CSco EBre ECha EFol EGol EOrc EPar EPla LBre LGre LHop MBri MTho NHol NRoo NSti SHer SPer WPbr WRus WWat WWin
– 'Hadspen Cream' (v) CBot CBro CHad CPou CRow CShe CSpe EBlo EBre ECha EFol EPar LBre LGre MBri MRav MTho NBir NRoo SAxl WByw WCru WRus
– 'Langtrees' CChu CElw CFis CRow EBre ECha EFol EFou ELun EPar EPla GAbr LBre MTho MTol SFis SSpi WByw WCru WHer WPbr WRus WSHC
– 'Variegata' See B. *m.* 'Dawson's White'

X BRUNSCRINUM
(Liliaceae/Amaryllidaceae)
¶ 'Dorothy Hannibel' CMon

BRUNSVIGIA (Liliaceae/Amaryllidaceae)
♦ *multiflora* See B. *orientalis*
§ *orientalis* CMon NRog
¶ – 'Alba' CMon
♦ *rosea* 'Minor' See AMARYLLIS *bella-donna*

BRYANTHUS (Ericaceae)
gmelinii GArf

BRYONIA (Cucurbitaceae)

dioica	GPoy MHew NSal

BRYUM (moss)

¶ *truncorum*	LFle

BUCHLOË (Gramineae)

¶ *dactyloïdes*	ETPC

BUDDLEJA † (Buddlejaceae)

agathosma	CHan WSHC
alternifolia	Widely available
– 'Argentea'	CBot CDoC CPMA CPle CSam CSco EBar ELan EPla ERav LHol SGil SHBN SPer SPla SSpi WPat WSHC WWeb
asiatica	CBot ERea ISea MNew
auriculata	CAbb CB&S CBow CChu CCla CHan CMCN CPle CWit ERea GCal SBor SDix SSpi SSta WCru WEas WHCG WSHC WWeb
bhutanica	CGre
* 'Butterfly Ball'	LHop WPer
caryopteridifolia	CCla CPle EHar ENot WSHC
colvilei	CAbb CB&S CHEx CHan CPle CTre CWit GCal ISea MBal SBor SPer SSpi WAbe WBod WCru WEas
– 'Kewensis'	CBot CCla CPMA CSam IBlr MUlv SBla SHil WBod WSHC
§ *crispa*	CBot CBow CDoC CHal CPle CSco ECha ELan ERav GCal LHop MSte SBor SDry SHBN SHil SPer SSpi SSta SUsu WCru WEas WHCG WKif WSHC WWat
– L 1544	NHex
davidii	CArn CKin LHol NWea WDin
– 'African Queen'	ESma MAsh SCob SMad SPer
– –	CFis SHBN SLon
– 'Black Knight'	Widely available
¶ – 'Blue Horizon'	WCot
– 'Border Beauty'	ESma SBod SHer SPer SPla WWeb
¶ – 'Calanadrina'	SBod
§ – 'Charming'	ELan SCob
– 'Dartmoor'	CBot CMHG CRow ECtt EFol ELan ENot EPla GCal LAbb LHop MMil NPer SCob SDix SHBN SMad SPer SPla SSta WEas WHCG
– 'Dart's Blue Butterfly'	MBri MUlv
– 'Dart's Ornamental White'	MBri MUlv
¶ – 'Dart's Papillon Blue'	SLPl
– 'Dart's Purple Rain'	MBri MUlv
– 'Dubonnet'	SMad
– 'Empire Blue'	CB&S CCla CSco CShe ECtt ELan ENot EPla GRei IDai IJoh MBal MBar MUlv MWat NPer NWea SCob SHBN SPer SPla WDin WStI
– 'Fascinating'	EPla GCal MAsh MWat NPer SBod WHCG WWeb
– 'Fortune'	NNor
– 'Glasnevin'	SDix SHBN SPer
¶ – 'Golden Sunset'	SPla
– 'Gonglepod'	ELan
– 'Harlequin' (v)	Widely available
– 'Ile de France'	CB&S ELan EPla MGos MWat NWea SCob WHCG
¶ – 'Les Kneale'	MBal
– 'Masquerade'	ENot MGos SPla
§ – 'Nanho Blue'	CBow CDoC CPle CSPN CSco EBre ECtt EFol EHar ELan EMon ENot EPar EPla ESma IOrc ISea LBre LHil LHop MBar MGos NNor SBod SHBN WDin WSHC
– 'Nanho Petite Indigo'	See B. *d.* 'Nanho Blue'
– 'Nanho Petite Purple'	See B. *d.* 'Nanho Purple'
§ – 'Nanho Purple'	CDoC CSco EBlo EHar ELan ENot EPla GAri ISea LHol MBar MBri NRoo SPer SUsu WSHC WStI
– var. ***nanhoensis***	CHan CMHG CPle ERav MWat SLon SPer
– – ***alba***	EFol ELan EMon MMil SRms WWat
– – blue	CShe IJoh MBri SPer SPla WEas WWat
¶ – 'Operetta'	WDin
– 'Orchid Beauty'	SCob WWeb
– 'Peace'	CLan CTre ECtt ENot ISea NPer SPer
– Petite Indigo ®	See B. *d.* 'Nanho Blue'
– Petite Plum ®	See B. *d.* 'Nanho Purple'
– 'Pink Beauty'	SCob SHBN
– 'Pink Charming'	See B. *d.* 'Charming'
* – 'Pixie Blue'	EPla
* – 'Pixie White'	EPla
– 'Purple Prince'	CB&S SCob
¶ – 'Purple Rain'	SLPl
– 'Royal Purple'	MGos
– 'Royal Red'	Widely available
¶ – 'Summer Beauty'	CPle WPat
– 'Variegata'	CRow NKay WWeb
– 'Variegated Royal Red'	SCob SHBN
– 'White Bouquet'	CPle EPla GRei MBal MPla MRav MWat NRoo NWea SBod SCob SPer SReu WWeb
¶ – 'White Butterfly'	EBlo
– 'White Cloud'	EPar IOrc ISea LHil SMad
– 'White Harlequin' (v)	CRow EFol EMon EPla LHop WCot WCru WEas WWat
– 'White Perfection'	NKay
– 'White Profusion'	CB&S CDoC CHal CRow CSam CSco CShe ECtt ELan ESma IDai IJoh LAbb LHol MBal MBar MGos NBee NNor SCob SHBN SHer SPla WDin WEas WStI
N *fallowiana*	CB&S CBow CGre CPle LAbb NNor SReu
– var. ***alba***	CBot CBow CChu CDoC CGre CLan CMil CPle CRow CSco ELan ENot EPla ERav GCal ISea LHop MBel NSti SHBN SHil SPer SSpi WBod WCru WSHC WWat
farreri	CBot CHan SIgm WBod
forrestii	CBot CHEx CPle SArc
globosa	CB&S CBra CDoC CFis CLan CPle CSco CShe CTre EBre ELan ENot IJoh ISea LBre LHol MBel MBri MGos MRav NNor SBod SHBN SMad SPer WCru WDin WSun WTyr
– 'Cannington Gold'	MUlv
¶ – 'Lemon Ball'	CB&S
heliophila	CGre CHan CPle ERea WCru
japonica	CPle WCru
x *lewisiana*	CPle
– x ***asiatica***	MNew
– 'Margaret Pike'	CBot WCru

lindleyana	CAbb CB&S CBot CChu CCla CDoC CGre CHan CMCN CMHG CPle CTro ELan EPla ERea GCal GWht MBel SBor SChu SPla SSpi WCru WHCG WSHC
'Lochinch'	Widely available
loricata	CBot CChu CGre CHan CPle EPla MSte
¶– CD&R 190	EPla
macrostachya SBEC 360	NHex
§ ***madagascariensis***	CB&S CGre CHEx CPle CTro ERea LAbb LHop WWat
myriantha	CPle
nicodemia	See B. ***madagascariensis***
nivea	CBot CGre CMHG CPle ELan SSpi WCru
– var. ***yunnanensis***	GCal MSte
officinalis	CBot CGre CPle CTro ERea
§ x ***pikei*** 'Hever'	CHal CPle EHar SPer
'Pink Delight'	Widely available
pterocaulis	CGre
saligna	CPle
salviifolia	CAbb CBot CBow CMHG CPle CTre ELan EPla GCal SDry SLon SSta WCru WHCG
stenostachya	CPle
♦***sterniana***	See B. ***crispa***
tubiflora	CBot ERea
'West Hill'	CGre
x ***weyeriana***	CBow CFis CLan CPle CSam ECtt EFol ELan EPar EPla ESma ISea MFir MRav MWat SBod SHer WCru WEas WSHC
– 'Golden Glow'	CB&S CBow CDoC CHan CMCN CSco CTre EBre ERav LBre MBri MPla NKay NNor SBla SGil SHil SMad SReu WAbe WWeb WWin
– 'Lady de Ramsey'	WPer
– 'Moonlight'	CPle CRow EPla MFir SCob SLon
– 'Sungold'	CB&S CRow ELan IJoh IOrc MBal MBel MBlu MGos NBee SHBN SPer SPla
– 'Trewithen'	CB&S CTrw
*'White Butterfly'	WWat

BUGLOSSOÏDES (Boraginaceae)

§ ***purpurocaerulea***	CCla CFis CKin CMea CRDP ECha ELan EMon GCal MHew MSte NSal SAxl SUsu WCru WEas WHal WOld WWin

BULBINE (Liliaceae/Asphodelaceae)

annua	EMon
bulbosa	WCot
♦***caulescens***	See B. ***frutescens***
§ ***frutescens***	EBul
¶ ***semibarbata***	NBro

BULBINELLA (Liliaceae/Asphodelaceae)

angustifolia	EPot NHol
¶ ***caudata***	GCal
hookeri	CRiv ECar ECou ELan EPot GDra GGar ITim LBee MFir MTho NGre NHar NHol SUsu WThu
rossii	GDra

BULBINOPSIS See BULBINE

BULBOCODIUM (Liliaceae/Colchicaceae)

vernum	CAvo ETub LAma LBlo MBri NRog SIng WChr

BULLACE See PRUNUS *institia*

BUPHTHALMUM (Compositae)

§ ***salicifolium***	CBow CKel CLew CPar CSam CSev ELan EMon LHil MBri NBro NOrc NSti SPer SSvw WByw WHil WMer
¶ – 'Golden Beauty'	SCro
speciosum	See TELEKIA ***speciosa***

BUPLEURUM (Umbelliferae)

angulosum	CRDP LGan LGre SIgm WCru WDav
¶ ***barceloi***	SIgm
falcatum	CGle CNat ECha MUlv NKay NRar NSti SBar SChu WCru WWat
fruticosum	CAbb CB&S CBot CBow CChu CCla CCor CHad CHan ECha ELan ERav LAbb LGre LHop SBla SChu SHil SPer SSpi WCru WEas WSHC WWat
longifolium	CDoC CHan ECha GGar
rotundifolium	NSal
¶ ***stellatum***	GArf

BURCHARDIA (Liliaceae/Colchicaceae))

umbellata	CMon

BURSARIA (Pittosporaceae)

spinosa	CBot CGre CPle

BUTIA (Palmae)

capitata	CHEx LPal NPal SArc

BUTOMUS (Butomaceae)

umbellatus	CBen CRDP CRow CWGN ECha ECtt EHon ELan EMFW EWav LMay MSta NDea SHig SWat WChe WHol

BUXUS † (Buxaceae)

aurea 'Marginata'	See B. ***sempervirens*** 'Marginata'
balearica	EPla SArc SDry SGil SLan WSHC WWat
bodinieri	EPla SLan
*'David's Gold'	WEas WSHC
'Green Gem'	NHar NWyt SLan
'Green Mountain'	SLan
'Green Velvet'	SLan
harlandii hort.	EPla GAri SIng SLan
– 'Richard'	SLan
japonica 'Nana'	See B. ***microphylla***
macowanii	SLan
§ ***microphylla***	GDra LHol NHol SIng SLan
¶ – 'Asiatic Winter'	SLPl
– 'Compacta'	CChu MPlt SLan WThu
– 'Curly Locks'	EPla GAri SLan
– 'Faulkner'	ESma LHop MUlv SGil SLan

– 'Grace Hendrick Phillips'	SLan
– 'Green Pillow'	SLan
– 'Helen Whiting'	SLan
– var. ***insularis***	See B. ***sinica insularis***
¶ – var. ***japonica***	SLan
– – 'Green Jade'	SLan
– – 'Morris Dwarf'	SLan
– – 'Morris Midget'	SLan
– – 'National'	SLan
– – 'Variegata'	CMHG
– 'John Baldwin'	SLan
– var. ***koreana***	See B. ***sinica insularis***
– var. ***riparia***	See B. ***riparia***
– var. ***sinica***	See B. ***sinica***
natalensis	SLan
'Newport Blue'	LRHS
§ ***riparia***	SLan
sempervirens	Widely available
§ – 'Angustifolia'	EPla SGil SLan SMad
– 'Argentea'	See B. ***s.*** 'Argenteovariegata'
§ – 'Argenteovariegata'	EPla MBal MRav SHig SLan WSHC
– 'Aurea'	See B. ***s.*** 'Aureovariegata'
– 'Aurea Maculata'	See B. ***s.*** 'Aureovariegata'
– 'Aurea Marginata'	See B. ***s.*** 'Marginata'
– 'Aurea Pendula' (v)	EHar EPla SLan SMad
§ – 'Aureovariegata'	CB&S CRow EBre LBre MBar MGos MRav MWat SChu SGil SLan SMad SPer WDin
– 'Blauer Heinz'	SLan
– clipped ball	CSco ERea SPer
– clipped pyramid	CSco ERea MGos NBar SPer
§ – 'Elegantissima' (v)	Widely available
– 'Gold Tip'	See B. ***s.*** 'Notata'
– 'Greenpeace'	SLan
¶ – 'Handsworthiensis'	SLan
– 'Handsworthii'	EHar ERea NWea SLon SPer
– ssp. ***hyrcana***	SLan
– 'Kingsville'	WCot
– 'Lace'	NSti NWyt
I – 'Langley Pendula'	SLan
– 'Latifolia'	See B. ***s.*** 'Bullata'
– 'Latifolia Macrophylla'	CHan ELan EPla NWyt SLan
§ – 'Latifolia Maculata'	CAbP CSco EFol EPla ESma GDra ISea MBal MPla NHol NRoo SLan STre WMou WOak
– 'Lawson's Golden'	MAsh
– 'Longifolia'	See B. ***s.*** 'Angustifolia'
§ – 'Marginata'	CPMA ECtt GCHN LHop MRav NHol SHBN SLan SPla WHil
– 'Memorial'	SLan
– 'Myosotidifolia'	CMHG EPla NHar SLan WWat
– 'Myrtifolia'	CBot NHar NWyt SLan SLon
§ – 'Notata' (v)	CDec CLan CPMA CRow EHal ERea SGil
– 'Pendula'	CGre EHar NWyt SLan
*– 'Pendula Esveld'	SLan
– 'Prostrata'	SLan
– 'Pyramidalis'	ENot NWyt SLan WMou
– 'Rosmarinifolia'	SLan
– 'Rotundifolia'	CLnd EPla LHol MAsh SLan WDin
– 'Salicifolia Elata'	SLan
*– 'Silver Beauty' (v)	CB&S MGos
– 'Silver Variegated'	See B. ***s.*** 'Elegantissima'
– 'Suffruticosa'	CArn CLan CSev CShe EHar ELan ERea ESis IEde LBuc LHol MBri MWat NRoo SCro SHer SLan SPer SPla STre WMou WOak
– 'Suffruticosa Variegata'	CB&S EHal SRms
– 'Vardar Valley'	NHar NHol NWyt SLan
§ ***sinica***	SLan
– 'Filigree'	SLan
§ – var. ***insularis***	CLew EPla NHol
– – 'Justin Brouwers'	SLan
– – 'Pincushion'	SLan
– – 'Tide Hill'	SLan
– – 'Winter Beauty'	LRHS MUlv
wallichiana	SBor SLan

CAESALPINIA (Leguminosae)

gilliesii	CBot CHEx CPle ESma SHil SMad
¶ ***sappan***	CTro

CAIOPHORA (Loasaceae)

¶ ***laiteritia*** F&W 7177	MFos

CALADIUM (Araceae)

§ ***bicolor*** (v)	MBri
– forms	NRog
x ***hortulanum***	See C. ***bicolor***
§ ***lindenii*** (v)	MBri

CALAMAGROSTIS (Gramineae)

§ x ***acutiflora*** 'Karl Foerster'	CDoC ECha EFol EPla ETPC GCal SApp SDix
*– 'Overdam'	CElw EBre ECha EHoe EMon EPla ETPC LBre LRHS SApp SGil
– 'Stricta'	See C. x ***a.*** 'Karl Foerster'
epigejos	ETPC

CALAMINTHA † (Labiatae)

alpina	See ACINOS ***alpinus***
clinopodium	See CLINOPODIUM ***vulgare***
cretica	CSam LHol LHop MTho NHol SIng WDav WHer WHil WPer WTyr WWye
– ***variegata***	WThi
§ ***grandiflora***	CArn CBre CCMG CCla CGle CHal CHan CLew CSev CShe CTom EBar ECha ELan EMon Effi GPoy LHol MPar MWat NSel SAxl SUsu WByw WCot WHal WHoo WPer WRus WWye
– 'Variegata'	CCor CGle CRDP EFol EHoe ELan EMon LHop NSti WByw WCHb WHal WHer WHil WHoo WOld WPer
§ ***nepeta***	CArn CBre CCla CHad CMGP CMil CSFH ECha IEde LAbb LGre MFir MHew MRav MSte NBir NBro NSal SBla SHer WEas WHoo WNdy WPer WWin
– ssp. ***glandulosa*** ACL 1050/90	EMon
– – 'White Cloud'	CGle EFou EMon LGre MSte SAxl SChu

– ssp. ***nepeta*** CCla CGle CHal CPar CSev CShe EFou EGol ELan EMon LHol LHop MBri MPla MRav MTho NOak SAxl SCro SIde SPer SUsu WRus WSHC WWat
¶ – – 'Blue Cloud' CGle ECha EFou SMrm SUsu
nepetoïdes See C. ***nepeta nepeta***
§ ***sylvatica*** CNat NSal WCla
¶ – ssp. ***ascendens*** MHew

CALAMONDIN See X CITROFORTUNELLA

CALANDRINIA (Portulacaceae)

caespitosa MHig NGre NMen NWCA WPer
– P&W 6229 MSte
¶ ***colchaguensis*** F&W 7210 MFos
¶ ***compressa*** WPer
grandiflora EBar ELan NWCA
megarhiza ssp. ***nivalis*** See CLAYTONIA ***m. n.***
rupestris NGre NTow
sericea NGre
sibirica See CLAYTONIA ***sibirica***
skottsbergii NGre
¶ sp. JCA 12317 WDav
¶ sp. JCA 12570 WDav
umbellata EBar ELan EPot NTow NWCA SHer WOMN WPer WWin

CALANTHE (Orchidaceae)

aristulifera EFEx LAma NHol NRog SWes WChr
bicolor See C. ***discolor flava***
discolor EFEx LAma NHol NRog SWes WChr
§ – var. ***flava*** LAma NHol
reflexa EFEx LAma NHol NRog SWes WChr
§ ***sieboldii*** EFEx LAma NHol NRog SWes WChr
striata See C. ***sieboldii***
tricarinata EFEx LAma NHol SWes

CALATHEA † (Marantaceae)

albertii MBri
albicans See C. ***micans***
§ ***bella*** MBri
burle-marxii MBri
crocata MBri
'Exotica' MBri
'Greystar' MBri
kegeljanii See C. ***bella***
lietzei MBri
– 'Greenstar' MBri
§ ***majestica*** MBri
makoyana (v) MBri
* 'Mavi Queen' MBri
metallica MBri
* 'Misto' MBri
oppenheimiana See CTENANTHE ***o.***
orbiculata See C. ***truncata***
ornata See C. ***majestica***
* ***pendula*** MBri
picturata 'Argentea' MBri
– 'Vandenheckei' MBri
roseopicta MBri
§ ***truncata*** MBri
veitchiana MBri
warscewiczii MBri
'Wavestar' MBri
zebrina MBri

CALCEOLARIA † (Scrophulariaceae)

acutifolia See C. ***polyrhiza***
arachnoidea EPot NWCA
x ***banksii*** GCal MFir
bicolor ECar GCal GCra
§ ***biflora*** CNic CRiv EBar ELan GCHN GDra GTou MBal NHol NKay NMen NMir NRed SHer SSou WCla WDav WHil WWin
– 'Goldcrest Amber' GCra SRms
'Brownii' CHal
'Camden Hero' CBrk CKni ELan MAsh WOld
chelidonioïdes MTho
¶ x ***clibranii*** CBrk
¶ ***crenatiflora*** GTou
darwinii GAbr GCra GTou MHig NCat NMen NTow SIng
falklandica CPar ECtt ELan EOrc EPot GTou LHop MPit NHol NMen NRed NTow NWCA SHer WWin
fothergillii GAbr GDra MHig NTow WHil
'Goldcrest' GCHN NGre WDav
'Hort's Variety' MTho
integrifolia CB&S CDec CFis CHal CPle CRDP ELan ERav ISea MBal MFir NRog SChu SLon SPer WCru WEas WOMN WOld WWat WWye
– var. ***angustifolia*** CGre SDry
– bronze form WAbe
– 'Gaines' Yellow' GCal
'John Innes' CHal CRDP EBur ECar ELan EPot ESis GAri GCal LHop NMen NNrd NRoo NTow SHer SIng
'Kentish Hero' CBot CBrk CMHG CPle ELan EMon GCal LHop MFir SChu WOMN WPat
¶ ***mexicana*** WCru
plantaginea See C. ***biflora***
§ ***polyrhiza*** CNic CPar CRDP ECar ELan EMNN MBal NHol NMen NRoo NRya NWCA SHer SSou WAbe WCla WHil
scabiosifolia See C. ***tripartita***
'Sir Daniel Hall' SAsh
tenella EBar ECtt EPot ESis GAri GDra MHig MTho NHar NHol NTow NWCA SHer WAbe WWin
'Walter Shrimpton' ECtt ELan EPot NHar NTow SBla SHer SIng

CALENDULA (Compositae)

officinalis CArn CSFH GPoy LHol MChe MHew NSal NSel SHer SIde WOak WWye
– 'Prolifera' WHer
– 'Variegata' NSal

CALLA (Araceae)

aethiopica See ZANTEDESCHIA ***aethiopica***

palustris	CBen CHEx CRiv CRow CWGN EBre EHon EWav GAri GGar LBre LMay MSta NDea SHig SWat WChe WHol

CALLIANDRA (Leguminosae)
See Plant Deletions

CALLIANTHEMUM (Ranunculaceae)

coriandrifolium	GDra

CALLICARPA (Verbenaceae)

bodinieri	CBow CBra NBir
– var. ***giraldii***	CBow CDec CGre CShe MAsh MRav SLon SSta WBod WDin WWat WWeb
– – 'Profusion'	Widely available
cathayana	CMCN
dichotoma	ELan EPla WBod WSHC WWat WWin
japonica 'Leucocarpa'	CPle EPla SLon WWat
x ***shirasawana***	NBar

CALLIERGON (moss)

¶ ***giganteum***	LFle

CALLIRHOË (Malvaceae)

involucrata	WPer

CALLISIA (Commelinaceae)

elegans	CHal
§ ***navicularis***	CHal
repens	CHal MBri

CALLISTEMON † (Myrtaceae)

'Burning Bush'	CB&S CSun LBlm MUlv
citrinus	CBow CPle CShe EArb ECou GWht ISea LAbb SLMG SPer WWin
– ***albus***	CGre
– 'Mauve Mist'	CB&S LBlm NPal
– 'Perth Pink'	CB&S
– 'Red Clusters'	CB&S ELan ERea
– 'Splendens'	CB&S CBow CDoC CHEx CSam EBre ELan IOrc LBre NPal SDry SHBN SHil SLon SSta WBod WStI WWat
linearis	CBow CMac CTre ELan IOrc ISea MBal SLMG SLon
pallidus	CChu CMHG CMac CPle CWit GWht WBod
paludosus	See C. ***sieberi***
¶ 'Perth Pink'	MUlv
phoeniceus	IDai
pinifolius	IBar
pityoïdes	CGre
rigidus	CB&S CBra CDoC CHEx CLan CMHG CSun CWSG ELan ESis IBar ISea MBlu MGos MUlv SHer SLMG SPer SSpi WBod WCru WDin
salignus	CChu CHEx CHan CMHG CSam IOrc ISea MBal MUlv SAxl SDry SHil WSHC
sieberi	CChu CGre ECou GWht IBar ISea LAbb NBir NHol WSHC WWat
speciosus	See C. ***glaucus***
subulatus	CMHG MBal SArc
viminalis 'Captain Cook'	CB&S CBow EBre ECou LBre MUlv
– 'Hannah Ray'	CB&S
– 'Little John '	CB&S COtt
'Violaceus'	CPle
viridiflorus	CChu CPle ECou IBlr

CALLITRICHE (Callitrichaceae)

♦ ***autumnalis***	See C. ***hermaphroditica***
¶ ***hermaphroditica***	EMFW
§ ***palustris***	CBen EHon SAWi
verna	See C. ***palustris***

CALLITRIS (Cupressaceae)

oblonga	ECar ECou
rhomboidea	ECou

CALLUNA † (Ericaceae)

vulgaris	CKin
¶ – 'Adrie'	EDen
– 'Alba Argentea'	ENHC
– 'Alba Aurea'	EDen ENHC MBar NWin WGre
– 'Alba Dumosa'	EDen ENHC
– 'Alba Elata'	CNCN EDen ENHC MBar
– 'Alba Elegans'	EDen
– 'Alba Elongata'	See C. ***v.*** 'Mair's Variety'
¶ – 'Alba Erecta'	EDen
– 'Alba Jae'	EDen MBar
¶ – 'Alba Minor'	EDen
– 'Alba Plena'	CB&S CMac CNCN EDen ENHC GPen GSpe IDai IJoh MBal MBar SBod WRid
– 'Alba Praecox'	EDen WGre
– 'Alba Pumila'	EDen MBar
§ – 'Alba Rigida'	CMac CNCN EBre EDen ENHC LBre MBar MBri WGre WRid
– 'Alex Warwick'	EDen SBod
– 'Alison Yates'	MBar
¶ – 'Allegretto'	EDen
– 'Allegro'	CMac EBlo EBre EDen ENHC LBre MBar MBri MOke SBod
– 'Alportii'	EDen ENHC GAng GBla GDra GSpe IDai MBar MBri MOke SBod WGre
– 'Alportii Praecox'	CNCN EDen ENHC MBar SBod WGre
¶ – 'Alys Sutcliffe'	EDen
¶ – 'Amilto'	EDen
– 'Andrew Proudley'	EDen ENHC
– 'Angela Wain'	EDen
¶ – 'Anna'	EDen
– 'Annabel'	EDen
¶ – 'Anneke'	EDen
– 'Annemarie'	EDen MBri MGos WGre
¶ – 'Annemarie'	EBlo SBod
– 'Anthony Davis'	CNCN EDen ENHC GAng GPen MBar MGos MOke NWin SBod WRid
– 'Anthony Wain'	EDen MGos
¶ – 'Anton'	EDen
– 'Apollo'	EDen
– 'Applecross'	CNCN EDen SHBN
– 'Argentea'	EDen MBar
– 'Arina'	EDen MBri MOke
– 'Arran Gold'	EDen ENHC GBla GSpe MBar NRoo
¶ – 'Ashgarth Amber'	EDen

¶ – 'Asterix'	EDen
– 'Atalanta'	EDen
– 'August Beauty'	CNCN EDen ENHC GBla MOke NWin WRid
– 'Aurea'	EDen ENHC GSpe IJoh
¶ – 'Autumn Glow'	EDen
– 'Baby Ben'	CMac CNCN
– 'Barbara Fleur'	EDen SBod
¶ – 'Barja'	EDen
– 'Barnett Anley'	CNCN EDen ENHC GSpe MBal
– 'Battle of Arnhem'	CNCN EDen MBar WGre
– 'Beechwood Crimson'	CNCN EDen ENHC
– 'Ben Nevis'	EDen
– 'Beoley Crimson'	CB&S CNCN EDen ENHC GAng GAri GDra MBar MGos NWin SBod WRid
– 'Beoley Gold'	CB&S CMHG CMac CNCN EBre EDen ENHC EPot GAng GBla GPen GRei GSpe IDai LBre MBal MBar MBri MGos MOke NRoo NWin SBod SHBN SPla WBod WGre WRid
¶ – 'Beoley Silver'	EDen
– 'Bernadette'	EDen
– 'Betty Baum'	EDen
– 'Blazeaway'	CMac CNCN EBre EDen ENHC GAng GBla GDra GRei GSpe IJoh LBre MBal MBar MBri NHar NRoo SBod SHBN WBod WGre WRid
¶ – 'Blueness'	EDen
– 'Bognie'	CNCN EDen ENHC GRei
– 'Bonfire Brilliance'	CMHG CNCN EDen MBar NHar NRoo SBod
– 'Boreray'	CNCN EDen
– 'Boskoop'	EBre EDen ENHC LBre MBar MBri SBod SPla
– 'Braemar'	EDen GBla
– 'Braeriach'	EDen
– 'Bray Head'	CNCN EDen GPen MBar SBod WGre
– 'Bud Lyle'	EDen WGre
– 'Bunsall'	CMac CNCN EDen
– 'Buxton Snowdrift'	CMHG EDen
– 'C W Nix'	CNCN EDen ENHC GPen GSpe IJoh MBar WRid
– 'Caerketton White'	EDen ENHC GAng GBla GPen GSpe MBal WGre
– 'Caleb Threlkeld'	EDen
– 'Calf of Man'	EDen ENHC
– 'Californian Midge'	CNCN EDen ENHC EPot GAri GPen GSpe MBar MGos NHol WGre
¶ – 'Carl Röders'	EDen
– 'Carmen'	EDen
– 'Carole Chapman'	CMHG EDen ENHC GPen MBar MGos SBod SHBN WRid
– 'Carolyn'	EDen
¶ – 'Catherine Anne'	EDen
¶ – 'Celtic Gold'	EDen IDai
¶ – 'Chindit'	EDen
– 'Christina'	EDen
– 'Citronella'	EDen GPen
– 'Clare Carpet'	EDen
¶ – 'Coby'	EDen
– 'Coccinea'	CMac EDen ENHC MBal MBar SBod WGre
¶ – 'Colette'	EDen
¶ – 'Con Brio'	EDen
¶ – 'Copper Glow'	EDen
– 'Coral Island'	EDen MBar MGos SBod
– 'Corries's White'	EDen
– 'Cottswood Gold'	EDen
– 'County Wicklow'	CMac CNCN EBre EDen ENHC GAng GBla GPen GSpe IJoh LBre MBal MBar MBri MGos MOke NHar NHol NWin SBod SHBN SPla WBod WGre WRid
– 'Craig Rossie'	EDen
– 'Cramond'	EDen ENHC GBla GDra MBar WGre
– 'Crimson Glory'	EDen GDra GSpe MBal MBar NWin WGre
– 'Crimson Sunset'	CNCN EDen SBod
– 'Crowborough Beacon'	EDen
– 'Cuprea'	CMac CNCN EBre EDen ENHC GAng GBla GDra GRei GSpe LBre MBal MBar MBri MOke NHol NWin SBod WGre
– 'Dainty Bess'	CNCN ECar MBar SBod WGre
– 'Dark Beauty'	EBlo MGos NRoo
– 'Dark Star'	EDen MOke NHar
– 'Darkness'	CB&S CMHG CNCN EBre EDen ENHC GAng GBla GPen GSpe IDai IJoh LBre MBal MBar MBri MGos MOke NHar NHol NRoo NWin SBod SHBN SPla WGre
¶ – 'Dart's Amethyst'	EDen
– 'Dart's Brilliant'	EDen
– 'Dart's Flamboyant'	CNCN EDen
– 'Dart's Gold'	GBla MBar NHar NRoo
– 'Dart's Hedgehog'	EDen WGre
– 'Dart's Parakeet'	CNCN EDen
– 'Dart's Parrot'	EDen NHar
– 'Dart's Silver Rocket'	EDen GBla
– 'David Eason'	CNCN EDen ENHC MBal
– 'David Hutton'	MBar
¶ – 'David Platt'	EDen
¶ – 'Desiree'	EDen
– 'Dickson's Blazes'	EDen GSpe
– 'Dirry'	EDen GSpe
– 'Doctor Murray's White'	See C. *v.* 'Mullardoch'
– 'Doris Rushworth'	EDen
– 'Drum-ra'	EDen ENHC GAng GBla GDra GSpe MBal MBar SBod WGre
– 'Dunnet Lime'	EDen SPla
– 'Dunnydeer'	EDen ENHC
– 'Dunwood'	MBar
– 'Durfordii'	EDen
– 'E F Brown'	CNCN EDen ENHC
– 'E Hoare'	EDen MBar
¶ – 'Easter-bonfire'	EDen
– 'Edith Godbolt'	CNCN EDen ENHC
– 'Elegant Pearl'	EDen MBar SBod
– 'Elegantissima'	EDen ENHC GSpe MBri MOke
– 'Elegantissima Walter Ingwersen'	See C. *v.* 'Walter Ingwersen'
¶ – 'Elizabeth'	SPla
– 'Elkstone'	CNCN EDen ENHC MBal MBar SBod WGre
– 'Else Frye'	EDen
– 'Elsie Purnell'	CMac CNCN EDen ENHC GAng GBla GPen GSpe MBal MBar MBri MGos MOke NHol SBod WBod WGre WRid
– 'Emerald Jock'	EDen SBod
– 'Fairy'	CMHG CMac EDen MBri MOke
¶ – 'Falling Star'	EDen

§ – 'Finale'	EDen ENHC GPen MBar WGre
¶ – 'Findling'	EDen
– 'Fire King'	MBar
¶ – 'Fire Star'	EDen
– 'Firebreak'	EDen MBar MBri
– 'Firefly'	CMac CNCN EBre EDen ENHC GAng GBla GSpe LBre MBal MBar MBri MOke NHar NRoo NWin SBod SHBN SPla WBod WGre WRid
– 'Flamingo'	CMac CNCN EBre EDen LBre MBar MBri MOke NHar
– 'Flatling'	EDen
– 'Flore Pleno'	ENHC MBar
– 'Foxhollow Wanderer'	CNCN EDen ENHC GSpe MBal MBar MOke SBod
– 'Foxii Floribunda'	EDen ENHC GSpe MBar
♦ – 'Foxii Lett's Form'	See CC. *v.* 'Mousehole', 'Velvet Dome'
– 'Foxii Nana'	CMac CNCN ENHC GAng GBla GSpe MBal MBar NHar NHol SBod SPla WGre WRid
– 'Fred J Chapple'	CNCN EBre EDen ENHC GAng GBla GDra GPen IDai LBre MBal MBar MBri MOke SBod WBod WGre
– 'Fréjus'	EDen
– 'French Grey'	CNCN EDen
– 'Gerda'	EBre LBre SPla
– 'Ginkel's Glorie'	EDen
– 'Glencoe'	EDen ENHC GBla GSpe MBal MBar MBri MGos MOke NHar WGre
– 'Glenfiddich'	EDen MBar MBri
– 'Glenlivet'	EDen MBar
– 'Glenmorangie'	EDen MBar
– 'Gold Flame'	EDen GAng MBar MBri SBod
– 'Gold Haze'	CB&S CMac CNCN EBre EDen ENHC GAng GBla GSpe IJoh LBre MBal MBar MBri MOke NHol SBod WBod WGre WRid
– 'Gold Knight'	MBri SBod
– 'Gold Kup'	MBar
– 'Gold Mist'	EDen
¶ – 'Gold Spronk'	EDen
– 'Golden Carpet'	CB&S CMac CNCN EBre EDen ENHC GAng GBla GDra GPen LBre MBal MBar MBri MGos MOke NHar NRoo NWin WBod WGre WRid
– 'Golden Feather'	CB&S CMHG CMac CNCN EBlo EBre EDen ENHC GAng GBla GDra GPen GRei IDai LBre MBal MBar MGos NWin SBod SHBN WGre WRid
¶ – 'Golden Fleece'	EDen
– 'Golden Max'	EDen NHar
– 'Golden Rivulet'	CMac EDen ENHC MBar
– 'Golden Turret'	EDen ENHC GBla GRei
– 'Goldsworth Crimson'	ENHC WGre
– 'Goldsworth Crimson Variegated'	CNCN EDen ENHC MBar SBod
– 'Grasmeriensis'	MBar
– 'Great Comp'	MBar
– 'Grey Carpet'	EDen GBla MBar SBod
– 'Grijsje'	EDen
– 'Grizzly'	EDen
– 'Guinea Gold'	EDen MBar MBri WGre
§ – 'H E Beale'	CB&S CMac CNCN EBre EDen ENHC GAng GBla GDra GPen GSpe IDai IJoh LBre MBal MBar MBri MGos MOke NHar NWin SBod SHBN WBod WGre WRid
– 'Hamlet Green'	CNCN EDen MBar
– 'Hammondii'	CNCN EDen GPen SBod WGre
– 'Hammondii Aureifolia'	CNCN EBre EDen GAng GAri GBla LBre MBal MBar MBri MOke
– 'Hammondii Rubrifolia'	CNCN EDen GAng MBal MBar MBri MOke NHar
– 'Harlekin'	EDen
– 'Heideteppich'	EDen
– 'Herbert Mitchell'	EDen
– 'Hester'	EDen
– 'Hibernica'	EDen GPen MBar WGre
– 'Hiemalis'	EDen ENHC MBar
– 'Hiemalis Southcote'	See C. *v.* 'Durfordii'
– 'Highland Rose'	EDen ESis GBla
– 'Hilda Turberfield '	EDen
– 'Hillbrook Orange'	EDen MBar
– f. ***hirsuta***	GPen NWin WGre WRid
– 'Hirsuta Albiflora'	EDen MBar
– 'Hirsuta Typica'	CNCN EDen WGre
– 'Hirta'	CNCN ECar MBar SBod WGre
– 'Hookstone'	GPen MBar WGre
– 'Hugh Nicholson'	CNCN EDen ENHC NHar SPla
– 'Humpty Dumpty'	CNCN EDen ENHC NHol WRid
– 'Hypnoïdes'	EDen
¶ – 'Ide's Double'	SBod
– 'Inchcolm'	GPen
– 'Ineke'	CNCN EDen ENHC MBar
– 'Inshriach Bronze'	CMac EDen ENHC GDra GRei GSpe MBar NRoo SBod WRid
– 'Isobel Frye'	MBar
– 'Isobel Hughes'	EDen MBar
– 'J H Hamilton'	CNCN EDen ENHC GAng GBla GDra GPen GSpe MBal MBar MBri MGos NHol SBod WGre WRid
– 'Jan'	EDen
– 'Jan Dekker'	EDen SBod WGre
– 'Janice Chapman'	EDen MBar WGre
– 'Jenny'	EDen
¶ – 'Jimmy Dyce'	EDen SBod
– 'Joan Sparkes'	CMac CNCN EDen ENHC GBla GPen GRei IDai MBal MBar WGre
– 'John F Letts'	CMac CNCN EDen ENHC GAng GBla GRei GSpe MBal MBar MGos NWin SBod SHBN
– 'Johnson's Variety'	CNCN EDen MBar WGre
– 'Joy Vanstone'	CMac CNCN EBre EDen ENHC GAng GBla LBre MBal MBar MBri MGos MOke SHBN WRid
– 'Julia'	CNCN EDen
– 'Kerstin'	SPla
– 'Kinlochruel'	CMHG CMac CNCN EBlo EBre EDen ENHC GAng GBla GDra GPen GRei GSpe IJoh LBre MBar MBri MGos MOke NHar NHol NRoo NWin SBod SHBN SPla WBod WGre WRid
– 'Kirby White'	CNCN EDen GAng GBla GPen MBar MBri NWin
– 'Kirsty Anderson'	MBri MOke
– 'Kit Hill'	EDen MBar
– 'Kuphaldtii'	EDen MBar

– 'Kynance'	CNCN EDen ENHC MBar
– 'Lambstails'	EDen MBal MBar MGos SBod
¶ – 'Lemon Gem'	EDen
– 'Leslie Slinger'	EBre EDen ENHC GBla LBre MBar
– 'Lewis Lilac'	EDen WGre
– 'Llanbedrog Pride'	CNCN EDen MBar
– 'Loch Turret'	CNCN EDen ENHC GBla GSpe MBar MBri MOke NWin
– 'Loch-na-Seil'	EDen MBar
– 'Long White'	EDen GSpe MBar
– 'Lyle's Late White'	CNCN EDen GPen
– 'Lyle's Surprise'	MBar
– 'Lyndon Proudley'	EDen ENHC GPen
§ – 'Mair's Variety'	CNCN EDen ENHC GAng GBla GDra GSpe IDai MBal MBar NRoo SBod WGre WRid
¶ – 'Marie'	EDen
– 'Marion Blum'	MBar
– 'Marleen'	EDen SBod
– 'Masquerade'	MBar
– 'Mauvelyn'	EDen
– 'Mazurka'	EDen
¶ – 'Mies'	EDen
– 'Minima'	GPen MBar SBod
– 'Minima Smith's Variety'	EDen ENHC MBar WRid
– 'Mirelle'	CNCN EDen
– 'Miss Muffet'	NHol
– 'Molecule'	EDen MBar
§ – 'Mousehole'	CMac CNCN ENHC GBla GSpe MBar MGos MOke NHol WGre
– 'Mousehole Compact'	See C. *v.* 'Mousehole'
– 'Mrs Alf'	EDen
– 'Mrs E Wilson'	EDen
– 'Mrs Pat'	CNCN EDen ENHC GAri GPen MBar MBri MOke NWin WGre WRid
– 'Mrs Ronald Gray'	CMac CNCN EDen GDra IJoh MBar WGre WRid
– 'Mullach Mor'	ECar EDen SBod
§ – 'Mullardoch'	EDen GPen MBar
– 'Mullion'	CNCN EDen ENHC MBar MOke SBod
– 'Multicolor'	CB&S CMac CNCN EBre EDen ENHC GAng GBla GDra GPen GSpe IDai LBre MBal MBar MBri MOke NHol NRoo NWin SBod SPla WBod WGre WRid
– 'Murielle Dobson'	EDen MBar
§ – 'My Dream'	CNCN EBre EDen ENHC GSpe LBre MBar NHol WGre
– 'Nana'	ENHC
– 'Nana Compacta'	CMac CNCN EDen EPot GAng GPen GSpe MBal MBar MBri MOke NWin SBod WRid
– 'Naturpark'	EDen ENHC MBar
– 'October White'	CNCN EDen ENHC
– 'Oiseval'	EDen
¶ – 'Old Rose'	EDen
– 'Olive Turner'	EDen
¶ – 'Orange Carpet'	EDen
– 'Orange Max'	CNCN GBla
– 'Orange Queen'	CMac CNCN EBre EDen ENHC GAng GBla GRei GSpe LBre MBal MBar SBod WRid
– 'Öxabäck'	MBar
– 'Oxshott Common'	CNCN EDen ENHC MBar SBod WGre
– 'Pallida'	EDen
– 'Pearl Drop'	MBar
¶ – 'Penhale'	EDen
– 'Penny Bun'	EDen
¶ – 'Perestrojka'	EDen
– 'Peter Sparkes'	CB&S CMac CNCN EBre EDen ENHC GAng GBla GDra GPen GSpe IDai IJoh LBre MBal MBar MBri MGos MOke NHar NWin SBod WBod WGre WRid
– 'Petra'	EDen
– 'Pewter Plate'	GPen MBar MBri NWin
– 'Pink Beale'	See C. *v.* 'H E Beale'
– 'Pink Dream'	EDen
– 'Pink Gown'	CNCN EDen
– 'Prizewinner'	CNCN EDen
– 'Prostrate Orange'	CNCN EDen GSpe MBal MBar WRid
¶ – 'Punch's Delight'	EDen
– 'Pygmaea'	ENHC MBar
– 'Pyramidalis'	EDen ENHC
– 'Pyrenaica'	EDen GPen MBar
– 'Radnor'	CMac CNCN EDen ENHC GAng GBla GSpe MBal MBar MBri MGos MOke NHar NRoo SBod WGre WRid
– 'Radnor Gold'	MBar
– 'Ralph Purnell'	CNCN EDen ENHC MBal MBar NHar SBod
¶ – 'Ralph's Red'	EDen
– 'Red Carpet'	CNCN EDen MBri MOke WBod WGre
– 'Red Favorit'	EBre EDen LBre NRoo SBod WGre
– 'Red Fred'	MGos
– 'Red Haze'	CMHG CMac CNCN EDen ENHC GAng MBal MBar MBri MOke NHol SBod WBod WGre
¶ – 'Red Hugh'	IDai
– 'Red Pimpernel'	EDen
– 'Red Star'	EBre EDen LBre MOke
¶ – 'Reini'	EDen
– 'Richard Cooper'	EDen MBar
– 'Rigida Prostrata'	See C. *v.* 'Alba Rigida'
¶ – 'Robber Knight'	EDen
– 'Robert Chapman'	CB&S CMac CNCN EBlo EBre EDen ENHC GAng GBla GDra GPen GRei GSpe IDai IJoh LBre MBal MBar MBri MGos MOke NHar NHol NWin SBod WBod WGre WRid
– 'Roland Haagen'	EDen MBar MBri MOke NHar SBod
– 'Roma'	EDen ENHC GPen MBar
– 'Ronas Hill'	GDra
¶ – 'Roodkapje'	EDen
– 'Rosalind'	CNCN EPot GBla GPen GSpe MBal MBar MOke NRoo WGre
– 'Rosalind Underwood's Variety'	EDen
I – 'Rosalind, Crastock Heath Variety'	EDen
– 'Ross Hutton'	EDen GBla GPen
– 'Ruby Slinger'	EBre GAng GBla LBre MBar SBod WGre
– 'Rusty Triumph'	EDen SBod
– 'Ruth Sparkes'	CMac CNCN EDen ENHC GAng GPen MBal MBar MBri MOke NWin SBod WRid
– 'Saint Kilda'	GPen GRei GSpe
– 'Saint Nick'	CNCN EDen ENHC MBar

– 'Sally Anne Proudley' CNCN EDen ENHC MBar SBod WGre
– 'Salmon Leap' CNCN GSpe MBar NHol NWin
– 'Sampford Sunset' CSam
– 'Sandwood Bay' EDen
– 'Schurig's Sensation' EBre EDen GAri GBla GSpe LBre MBar MBri MOke NHar SBod
– 'Scotch Mist' EDen
– 'Serlei' CNCN EDen ENHC GPen MBal MBar MBri MOke SBod
– 'Serlei Aurea' CNCN EBre EDen ENHC GAng GPen GSpe LBre MBal MBar SBod WGre WRid
– 'Serlei Grandiflora' EDen GPen MBar
– 'Serlei Lavender' EDen WGre WRid
– 'Serlei Rubra' EDen
– 'Sesam' EDen
– 'Shirley' CMac MBar
– 'Silver Cloud' CNCN MBar MBri NWin
– 'Silver King' CMac CNCN MBar
– 'Silver Knight' CMHG CMac EBre EDen ENHC EPot GAng GBla GDra GPen GRei GSpe LBre MBal MBar MBri MGos MOke NHar NHol NRoo SBod SHBN WBod WRid
– 'Silver Queen' CMHG CMac CNCN EBre EDen ENHC GAng GBla GRei GSpe IJoh LBre MBal MBar MBri MOke NHar NHol SBod WGre WRid
– 'Silver Rose' CNCN EDen ENHC GBla GSpe MBar NWin SBod WGre WRid
– 'Silver Sandra' EDen
– 'Silver Spire' CNCN EDen ENHC MBal MBar
– 'Silver Stream' ENHC MBar NWin SBod
– 'Sir John Charrington' CMac CNCN EBre EDen ENHC GAng GBla GDra GPen GSpe LBre MBal MBar MBri MGos MOke NHol SBod SHBN WGre WRid
– 'Sirsson' EDen MBri NWin
– 'Sister Anne' CMac CNCN EBre EDen ENHC EPot GAng GBla GDra LBre MBal MBri MGos MOke NHol SBod SHBN SPla WRid
– 'Skipper' MBar WGre
– 'Snowball' See C. *v.* 'My Dream'
– 'Soay' ECar EDen MBar SBod
– 'Spicata' EDen
– 'Spicata Aurea' CNCN MBar
– 'Spitfire' CMac CNCN EDen ENHC GAng GPen GSpe MBal MBar WGre WRid
– 'Spring Cream' CMHG EBre EDen ENHC ESis GAng GBla GSpe LBre MBar MBri MGos MOke NHar SBod WGre WRid
– 'Spring Glow' CMac CNCN EDen GAng MBar MBri MOke NHar NWin SBod
– 'Spring Torch' CB&S CMHG CNCN EBre EDen ENHC GAng GDra GSpe IJoh LBre MBal MBar MBri MGos MOke NHar SBod SHBN WGre WRid
– 'Springbank' MBar
– 'Summer Elegance' EDen
– 'Summer Orange' CNCN EDen GAng GPen MBal MBar
– 'Sunningdale' See C. *v.* 'Finale'
– 'Sunrise' EBre EDen ENHC GAng LBre MBar MGos MOke NHol SBod WGre
– 'Sunset' CB&S CMHG CMac CNCN EBre ENHC GAng GBla GDra GPen GRei GSpe LBre MBal MBar NHol NRoo NWin SBod SPla WGre WRid
– 'Tenuis' CNCN ENHC MBar NWin
– 'Terrick's Orange' EDen
– 'Tib' CMHG CMac CNCN EBre EDen ENHC GAng GBla GPen GSpe IJoh LBre MBal MBar MBri MOke NWin SBod WGre WRid
– 'Tom Thumb' MBar
– 'Torulosa' EDen ENHC GPen
– 'Tricolorifolia' CNCN EBre EDen ENHC GAng GBla GDra IDai LBre MBal SBod
– 'Underwoodii' EDen ENHC GBla GPen MBar
– 'Velvet Dome' MBal MBar SBod
¶ – 'Velvet Fascination' NRoo
– 'Visser's Fancy' EDen
§ – 'Walter Ingwersen' EDen MBar
– 'White Carpet' GPen MBar
– 'White Gown' ENHC GDra WRid
– 'White Lawn' CMac CNCN EBre EDen LBre MBar MGos NHol NWin SHBN
– 'White Mite' ENHC MBar
– 'White Princess' See C. *v.* 'White Queen'
§ – 'White Queen' EDen MBal MBar
– 'Whiteness' CNCN EDen
– 'Wickwar Flame' CB&S CMac CNCN EBlo EBre EDen ENHC GAng GBla GDra GPen IJoh LBre MBal MBar MBri MOke NHar NHol NRoo SBod WBod WRid
– 'Wingate Gem' NWin
– 'Wingate Gold' NWin
– 'Winter Chocolate' CMHG CMac CNCN EBre EDen ENHC ESis GAng GBla GPen LBre MBal MBar MBri MGos MOke NHol NRoo SBod WGre WRid
¶ – 'Winter Red' EDen
¶ – 'Yellow One' EDen

CALOCEDRUS (Cupressaceae)

§ ***decurrens*** CB&S CDoC CMHG CMac CSco EHar EHul ENot IBar IDai IOrc LCon MBal MBar MBri MUlv NWea SGil SLim SPer WFro WMou WWat
– 'Aureovariegata' CDoC CKen EHar IOrc LCon LNet MAsh MBar MBlu NHol SEng SHil SLim SMad WDin
– 'Berrima Gold' CKen SHil
¶ – 'Depressa' CKen
– 'Intricata' CKen
– 'Nana' See C. ***d.*** 'Depressa'
– 'Pillar' EHar
formosana WBod

CALOCEPHALUS (Compositae)

brownii ECou LHil MRav SChu SLon

CALOCHORTUS (Liliaceae/Liliaceae)

albus WChr
amabilis WChr
¶ ***barbatus*** EBul MFos
catalinae WChr
clavatus WChr
luteus EBul WChr

splendens	WChr
superbus	WChr
uniflorus	MFos WChr WOMN
venustus	WChr
vestae	WChr

CALOMERIA (Compositae)

§ ***amaranthoïdes***	LHol

CALOSCORDUM (Liliaceae/Alliaceae)

§ ***neriniflorum***	EBur SUsu SWas

CALOTHAMNUS (Myrtaceae)

validus	CPle CTro

CALTHA † (Ranunculaceae)

¶ 'Auenwald'	CRow
¶ 'Honeydew'	CRow
introloba	EPot SWat
♦ ***laeta***	See C. ***palustris palustris***
leptosepala	CGle NGre SRms
¶ ***natans***	CRow
palustris	CBen CChu CGle CHEx CHad CKin CMHG CRDP CRiv CRow CWGN EBre EHon EPot GPoy LBre LMay MSta NDea NHol NLan NMir NSel SHig SLon SWat WByw WChe WCru WHol
– var. ***alba***	Widely available
– 'Flore Pleno'	Widely available
¶ – var. ***himalensis***	NGre
¶ – 'Multiplex'	NSel
§ – ***palustris***	CBen CRow CWGN EBre ECha EHon ELan EMFW EMon EPar EWav GAri GGar LBre LMay MSta NDea SHig SPer SSpi SWat WChe WHol
¶ – var. ***radicans***	CRow EMFW
¶ – 'Tyermannii'	CRow
– 'Wheatfen'	CNat
♦ ***polypetala***	See C. ***palustris palustris***
¶ 'Susan'	CRow

CALYCANTHUS (Calycantheaceae)

fertilis	CBot CCla MUlv SEng WSHC
floridus	CArn CB&S CBow CChu CCla CPle EBar EGol ELan ENot IOrc SHil WBod
– ***glaucus***	See C. ***fertilis laevigatus***
occidentalis	CBow CCla ELan LTil SSpi

CALYDOREA (Iridaceae)

♦ ***speciosa***	See C. ***xiphioïdes***
¶ ***xiphioïdes***	WPer

CALYPTRIDIUM (Portulacaceae)

umbellatum	See SPRAGUEA ***umbellata***

CALYSTEGIA (Convolvulaceae)

hederacea	ELan
§ – 'Flore Pleno'	CRDP ECha ELan EMon EOrc EPar EPla GCal LHop MTho SAxl SMad WCot WCru
japonica 'Flore Pleno'	See C. ***hederacea*** 'F.P.'
¶ ***silvatica*** 'Incarnata'	CRDP EMon MBel
tuguriorum	ECou

CALYTRIX (Myrtaceae)

alpestris	See LHOTZKYA ***alpestris***

CAMASSIA † (Liliaceae/Hyacinthaceae)

cusickii	CAvo CBro CCla ECha ELan EPar ETub LAma LBow MBri MTho NHol NRog WHal
esculenta	See C. ***quamash***
fraseri	See C. ***scilloïdes***
leichtlinii	CAvo ECha EFou EPar ERav ETub LBow MUlv NHol
– Alba Group	CAvo CBro EFou ELan ETub LAma NCat NHol
– 'Blauwe Donau' ('Blue Danube')	LAma LBow
– Caerulea Group	CBro CHad ELan EMon EPar LAma NRog SIng SSpi
– 'Electra'	ECha SWas
N– 'Plena'	ECED ECha WCot
– 'Semiplena'	CAvo CBro EPar
§ ***quamash***	CAvo CBro CCla CMea ECha ELan EPar ETub LAma LBlo LBow MBri MTho NHol NRog SIng WBod WByw
– ***linearis***	NHol
– 'Orion'	CBro EMon
§ ***scilloïdes***	CMon MBri

CAMELLIA † (Theaceae)

'Aaron's Ruby' (***japonica***)	CMHG CTre SCog
'Ada Pieper' (***japonica***)	CTrh
'Adelina Patti' (***japonica***)	CB&S CTre SCog
'Adolphe Audusson' (***japonica***)	CB&S CMac CSco CTre CTrh CTrw EBre ELan ENot IJoh IOrc LBre LHyd LNet MBal MBri MGos NKay SBod SCog SExb SHBN SHer SLon SPer SReu SSta WBod WStI
'Adolphe Audusson Special' (***japonica***)	CB&S SCog
§ 'Akashigata' ('Lady Clare') (***japonica***)	CMac CSco CTre CTrw ELan ENot IHos SCog SExb SPer SPla SReu SSta WBod WWat
§ 'Akebono' (***japonica***)	CTrw
'Alba Plena' (***japonica***)	CGre CMac CTre ENot IHos IOrc ISea LNet MGos SBod SCog SPer
'Alba Simplex' (***japonica***)	CB&S CGre CMac CTre ELan IOrc LNet MBal SBod SCog SExb SHBN SPer SSta
'Alex Blackadder' (***japonica***)	CMHG SCog
'Alexander Hunter' (***japonica***)	CTre CTrh MAsh SBod SCog SExb
'Alice Wood' (***japonica***)	CTrh SCog
§ 'Althaeiflora' (***japonica***)	CB&S CGre CMac CTre SCog
'Ama-no-gawa' (***japonica***)	SCog
'Anemone Frill' (x ***williamsii***)	CTrh
'Anemoniflora' (***japonica***)	CB&S CTre ELan IHos ISea SBod SPer WBod
'Angel' (***japonica***)	CMHG CTre SCog

'Angela Cocchi' (*japonica*)	SCog
'Ann Sothern' (*japonica*)	CB&S CTrh
'Annie Wylam' (*japonica*)	CTrh SCog
'Anticipation' (x *williamsii*)	CB&S CMHG CSam CSco CTre CTrh CTrw EBre GGGa GWht IDai IJoh IOrc ISea LBre LHyd MBri MGos SBod SCog SExb SGil SHBN SHer SSpi WBod
¶ 'Anticipation Variegated' (x *williamsii*)	SCog
'Apollo' (*japonica*)	CB&S CTrh CTrw ELan IHos MBri SHBN SLon SPer WBod
§ 'Apple Blossom' (*japonica*)	CGre CMac MAsh MBal MBri
– (*saluenensis*)	See C. 'Shôwa-wabisuke'
¶ – (*sasanqua*)	MAsh
'Arabella' (*japonica*)	SCog
'Arajishi' (*rusticana*)	CB&S CMac CTre ISea SCog SExb SPla WBod
'Arbutus Gum' (*reticulata* x *japonica*)	CTrh
'Arch of Triumph' (*reticulata*)	CB&S CTrh
'Auburn White'	See C. 'Mrs Bertha A Harms'
* 'Augustine Supreme' (*japonica*)	CMac
'Augusto Leal de Gouveia Pinto' (*japonica*)	SCog
'Ave Maria' (*japonica*)	CTrh SCog
'Azumakagami' (*japonica*)	CSco
'Azurea (*japonica*)	CGre
'Baby Face'	See C. 'Tongzimian'
'Ballet Dancer' (*japonica*)	MBri SCog
'Ballet Queen' (x *williamsii*)	CB&S CTrh MBri MGos SExb WBod
'Ballet Queen Variegated' (x *williamsii*)	SCog
'Barbara Clark' (*saluenensis* x *reticulata*)	MBri MGos
'Barbara Hillier' (*reticulata* x *japonica*)	CTre
'Barbara Woodroof' (*japonica*)	SCog
'Barchi'	See C. 'Contessa Samailoff'
'Baron Gomer' (*japonica*)	See C. 'Comte de Gomer'
'Baronesa de Soutelinho' (*saluenensis*)	SCog
'Bartley Number Five' (x *williamsii*)	CMac
'Beatrice Michael' (x *williamsii*)	CB&S CMac CTre SCog
'Bellbird'	SCog
'Belle of the Ball' (*japonica*)	CMHG
'Ben' (*sasanqua*)	SCog
'Benten' (*japonica*)	CTrw MBri
'Benten-kagura' (*japonica*)	CTrh
'Berenice Boddy' (*japonica*)	CB&S CTrh SCog SLon
'Berenice Perfection' (*japonica*)	CTrh SCog
'Bernadette Karsten' (*reticulata* x *japonica*)	CTrh
'Bert Jones' (*sasanqua*)	CTrh
'Bertha Harms Blush'	See C. 'Mrs Bertha A Harms'
'Bettie Patricia' (*sasanqua*)	SCog
'Betty Foy Sanders' (*japonica*)	CTrh
'Betty Sheffield' (*japonica*)	CGre CTre ISea SBod SCog SHBN WBod
'Betty Sheffield Blush' (*japonica*)	SExb
'Betty Sheffield Coral' (*japonica*)	SCog
'Betty Sheffield Pink' (*japonica*)	CMHG
'Betty Sheffield Supreme' (*japonica*)	CB&S CGre CMac CTrh SCog SHer
'Betty Sheffield White' (*japonica*)	SCog
'Bienville' (*japonica*)	SCog
'Black Lace' (x *williamsii* x *reticulata*)	CTrh MBal SCog
'Blackburnia' (*japonica*)	See C. 'Althaeiflora'
'Blaze of Glory' (*japonica*)	CGre CTrh SCog
§ 'Blood of China' (*japonica*)	CMac MBri SBod SCog SExb SPer WBod
'Blue Danube' (x *williamsii*)	CTrh
'Bob Hope' (*japonica*)	CGre CTre CTrh MAsh SCog
'Bob's Tinsie' (*japonica*)	CGre CTre CTrh CTrw MBri SCog SExb
'Bokuhan' (*japonica*)	CGre CTre CTrh MBri
'Bonnie Marie' (hybrid)	CGre CTre
'Bow Bells' (x *williamsii*)	CGre CMac CTre CTrh IJoh LHyd SCog WWat
'Bowen Bryant' (x *williamsii*)	CGre CTre CTrh CTrw GGGa SCog
'Bridal Gown' (x *williamsii*)	CTrh SCog
'Brigadoon' (x *williamsii*)	CMHG CTre CTrh CTrw GGGa IOrc ISea LHyd MAsh MBal SCog
'Bright Buoy' (*japonica*)	CTrh
'Brilliant Butterfly' (*reticulata*)	CTrh
'Brushfield's Yellow' (*japonica*)	CB&S ISea MBal MBlu SGil
'Bryan Wright' (*japonica*)	CMHG
'Burncoose' (x *williamsii*)	CB&S

'Burncoose Apple Blossom' (x ***williamsii***) CB&S
'Bush Hill Beauty' (***japonica***) See C. 'Lady de Saumarez'
'C F Coates' (x ***williamsii***) CTre SCog
§ 'C M Hovey' (***japonica***) CMHG CMac CTrh MAsh MBal SCog SHBN WBod
'C M Wilson' (***japonica***) CMac CTre SCog
'Caerhays' (x ***williamsii***) CB&S CTre SCog SReu
¶ 'Caleb Cope' (***japonica***) CMHG
N 'Campbellii' (***japonica***) CMac
'Campsii Alba' (***japonica***) ELan WStI
'Can Can' (***japonica***) CMHG SCog
'Captain Rawes' (***reticulata***) CMac CTre CTrh SHil
'Cara Mia' (***japonica***) CB&S CTre
'Cardinal's Cap' (***japonica***) CGre
'Carolyn Williams' (x ***williamsii***) CB&S
'Carter's Sunburst' (***japonica***) CB&S CTrh SCog
* 'Cascade' (***rosiflora***) CTrh
caudata CTrh
'Cécile Brunazzi' (***japonica***) CMac SCog
'Chandleri Elegans' (***japonica***) See C. 'Elegans'
'Chansonette' (***hiemalis***) SPla
§ 'Charity' (x ***williamsii***) CTrh
'Charlean' (x ***williamsii***) SCog
'Charles Colbert' (x ***williamsii***) CTrh CTrw SCog
'Charles Michael' (x ***williamsii***) CB&S CGre CMac CTrh
'Charlotte de Rothschild' (***japonica***) CTrh SExb
'Charming Betty' (***japonica***) See C. 'Funny Face Betty'
'Cheerio' (***japonica***) SCog
'Cheryll Lynn' (***japonica***) CTrh SCog
'China Clay' (x ***williamsii***) CB&S CSam CTre SBod SCog
'China Lady' (***reticulata*** x ***granthamiana***) SCog
'Christmas Beauty' (***japonica***) SCog
♦ ***chrysantha*** See C. ***nitidissima nitidissima***
'Cinderella' (***japonica***) CTre SCog
§ 'Citation' (x ***williamsii***) CB&S CGre CMac CTrw SCog WBod
'Clarise Carleton' (***japonica***) CMHG CTre CTrh SCog
¶ 'Clarissa' (***japonica***) SExb
'Clarrie Fawcett' (x ***williamsii***) CTre
N 'Cleopatra' (***japonica***) CTrh SBor
'Colonel Firey' (***japonica***) See C. 'C M Hovey'
'Colonial Dame' (***japonica***) MBri SCog
'Commander Mulroy' (***japonica***) CTrh
'Compton's Brow' (***japonica***) See C. 'Gauntlettii'
§ 'Comte de Gomer' (***japonica***) CGre MBri
'Conrad Hilton' (***japonica***) SCog
'Conspicua' (***japonica***) CSco
'Contessa Lavinia Maggi' See C. 'Lavinia Maggi'
¶ 'Contessa Samailoff' (***japonica***) CTre
§ 'Coquettii' (***japonica***) CTre SCog
'Coral Delight' (x ***williamsii***) CTrh
¶ 'Cornish Clay' ISea
'Cornish Snow' (***saluenensis*** x ***cuspidata***) CB&S CGre CMac CSam CTre CTrh GGGa IJoh IOrc ISea LNet MBal SHBN SPer SPla SReu SSpi WWat
'Cornish Spring' (***japonica*** x ***cuspidata***) CTre CTrh WWat
'Coronation' (***japonica***) SCog WBod
'Countess of Orkney' (***japonica***) CTre
'Crimson King' (***sasanqua***) CGre MBal SBod SHBN SPer WBod WStI
'Crinkles' (x ***williamsii***) CGre
cuspidata CB&S CGre CTre SSpi
'Czar' See C. 'The Czar'
'Daikagura' (***japonica***) CMHG SCog
'Daintiness' (x ***williamsii***) CTre CTrh MBri SCog
'Daitairin' (***japonica***) See C. 'Dewatairin'
'Daphne du Maurier' (***japonica***) SCog
'Dark Nite' (x ***williamsii***) CMHG
'Daviesii' (***japonica***) SCog
♦ 'Dawn' See C. 'Ginryû'
'Dazzler' (***hiemalis***) CTre CTrh SCog
'Dear Jenny' (***japonica***) CB&S CTre SCog
'Debbie' (x ***williamsii***) CB&S CGre CMHG CMac CSam CSco CTre CTrh CTrw ELan ENot IJoh IOrc ISea LHyd MBal MBri MGos MRav SBod SCog SExb SHBN SPer SPla SSpi SSta WBod
'Debbie's Carnation' (x ***williamsii***) CMHG SCog
'Debut' (***reticulata*** x ***japonica***) CTrh
'Debutante' (***japonica***) CB&S CGre CMac CTre CTrh IDai MBri SCog SGil SPer SReu SSta WBod
♦ 'Delia Williams' See C. 'Citation'
'Desire' (***japonica***) CMHG CTrh SCog
'Devonia' (***japonica***) CGre LHyd MBal MBri
§ 'Dewatairin' (***japonica***) CMac SCog SExb WBod
'Diamond Head' (***japonica*** x ***reticulata***) MBri
¶ 'Dixie Knight' (***japonica***) SExb
'Dobreei' (***japonica***) CMac
'Doctor Burnside' (***japonica***) CMHG CTre CTrh SCog

'Doctor Clifford Parks' (*reticulata* x *japonica*)	CTre CTrh SCog
'Doctor Louis Polizzi' (*saluenensis* x *reticulata*)	CTrh
'Doctor Tinsley' (*japonica*)	CGre CTrh SCog
'Dona Herzilia de Freitas Magalhaes' (*japonica*)	CTre SCog
'Dona Jane Andresson' (*japonica*)	CMHG
'Donation' (x *williamsii*)	Widely available
'Donckelaeri'	See C. 'Masayoshi'
'Doris Ellis' (*japonica*)	CMHG
'Double Rose' (*japonica*)	SCog
'Doutor Balthazar de Mello' (*japonica*)	CMHG
'Drama Girl' (*japonica*)	CB&S CGre CTre CTrw IOrc MBal SBod SCog SExb WBod
'Dream Boat' (x *williamsii*)	CTrh MBri SCog
'Dream Girl' (*sasanqua* x *reticulata*)	CTrh SCog
'Duc de Bretagne' (*japonica*)	SCog
'Duchesse Decazes' (*japonica*)	CTre MGos SCog
'E G Waterhouse' (x *williamsii*)	CB&S CGre CMHG CTrh CTrw MAsh MBal SBod SCog SExb WBod WWeb
'E T R Carlyon' (x *williamsii*)	CB&S CTre ISea MBal MBri SCog
'Eclipsis'	See C. 'Press's Eclipse'
'Eden Roc' (*reticulata*)	CTrh
♦ 'Effendee' (*japonica*)	See C. 'Rosea Plena'
'El Dorado' (*pitardii* x *japonica*)	CTrh SCog SExb
§ 'Elegans' (*japonica*)	CB&S CGre CHig CMac CSco CTre CTrh ENot IHos IOrc ISea LHyd MBal MBri NBee SBod SCog SExb SHBN SHer SReu SSta WBod
'Elegans Champagne' (*japonica*)	CTrh SCog
'Elegans Splendor' (*japonica*)	CTre CTrh
'Elegans Supreme' (*japonica*)	CGre CTre CTrh SCog
'Elegant Beauty' (x *williamsii*)	CB&S CTre CTrh CTrw IHos MBal MBri SBod SCog SExb
'Elisabeth' (*japonica*)	SCog
'Elizabeth Arden' (*japonica*)	CTre
¶ 'Elizabeth Bolitho'	CTre
'Elizabeth Dowd' (*japonica*)	CB&S SCog
'Elizabeth Hawkins' (*japonica*)	CTre
'Elizabeth Le Bey' (*japonica*)	SCog
'Ella Drayton' (*japonica*)	SCog
'Ellamine' (x *williamsii*)	CTrh
'Ellen Sampson' (*japonica*)	SCog
'Elsie Dryden' (*reticulata* x *japonica*)	CTrh
'Elsie Jury' (x *williamsii*)	CB&S CDoC CGre CMac CSam CSco CTrh CTrw IHos IOrc LHyd MBal MGos SBod SCog SExb SGil SHer SSta WBod
Emmett Pfingstl ® (*japonica*) (v)	SCog
'Emperor of Russia' (*japonica*)	MBri SCog WBod
'Erin Farmer' (*japonica*)	CB&S SCog
'Eugène Lizé' (*japonica*)	WBod
euphlebia	CTrh
'Evalina' (*japonica*)	SCog
'Exaltation' (x *williamsii*) (hybrid)	CB&S SCog
¶ 'Exbury Trumpet' (*saluenensis*)	CTre
¶ 'Eximia' (*japonica*)	SExb
'Extravaganza' (*japonica* x)	CTrh SBod SCog
'Faith' (*japonica*)	SCog
¶ 'Fascination'	IDai
'Fatima' (*japonica*)	CTre
§ 'Faustina' (*japonica*)	SCog
♦ 'Faustina Lechi'	See C. 'Faustina'
'Felice Harris' (*sasanqua* x *reticulata*)	CTrh SCog
§ 'Fimbriata' (*japonica*)	SCog
'Fimbriata Alba' (*japonica*)	See C. 'Fimbriata'
'Finlandia Variegated' (*japonica*)	SCog
'Fire Dance' (*japonica*)	CTrh
'Fire Falls' (*japonica*)	CMHG
'Firebird' (*japonica*)	CTrw
'First Flush' (*cuspidata* x *saluenensis*)	SCog
* 'Fishtail White'	SCog
'Flame' (*japonica*)	CB&S
'Flamingo' (*sasanqua*)	See C. 'Fukuzutsumi'
¶ 'Fleur Dipater' (*japonica*)	SExb WBod
'Flora' (*japonica*)	WBod
'Flore Pleno' (*reticulata*)	See C. 'Songzilin'
'Flower Girl' (*sasanqua* x *reticulata*)	CTrh
'Flowerwood' (*japonica*)	SCog
¶ 'Forest Green' (*japonioca*)	MAsh SCog
forrestii	CTrh
'Forty-Niner' (*reticulata* x *japonica*)	SCog
'Fragrant Pink' (*rusticana* x *lutchuensis*)	CTrh
'Fran Homeyer' (*japonica*)	CTrh
'Francie L' (*saluenensis* x *reticulata*)	CGre CTre CTrh CTrw SCog
'Francis Hanger' (x *williamsii*)	CB&S CMac CSam CTre CTrh CTrw IJoh IOrc ISea MBal MBri SBod SCog SExb SPer SSpi WBod
fraterna	CTrh

'Frau Minna Seidel' See C. 'Otome'
'Free Style' (x *williamsii*) CTrh SCog
'Freedom Bell' (hybrid) CTre CTrh GGGa ISea SCog
'Frosty Morn' (*japonica*) SCog
§ 'Fukuzutsumi' (*sasanqua*) CB&S CBot SBod SPer WBod
§ 'Funny Face Betty' (*japonica*) CMHG
'Furo-an' (*japonica*) MAsh SCog
'Galaxie' (x *williamsii*) CB&S CTrh ISea
'Garden Glory' (x *williamsii*) CTre CTrh
§ 'Gauntlettii' ('Lotus') (*japonica*) SCog
'Gay Chieftain' (*japonica*) SCog
'Gay Time' (x *williamsii*) CTre CTrh
'George Blandford' (x *williamsii*) CB&S CMac CTre CTrh
* 'George Orman' (*japonica*) CTrh
'Giardino Franchetti' (*japonica*) CGre
'Gigantea' (*japonica*) SCog
¶ 'Gigantea Red' (*japonica*) IOrc
¶ 'Ginryû' (x *vernalis*) CB&S
'Gladys Wannamaker' (*japonica*) SCog
♦ 'Glen 40' (*japonica*) See C. 'Coquettii'
'Glenn's Orbit' (x *williamsii*) CB&S CGre CTre CTrw SCog
'Gloire de Nantes' (*japonica*) CTrh SCog SExb SRms WBod
'Golden Spangles' (x *williamsii*) (v) CB&S CTre ELan IJoh IOrc ISea LHyd MBal MBri MGos SCog SDry SPla SReu SSta
'Grace Bunton' (*japonica*) SCog
'Grace Caple' (*pitardii* x *japonica*) CMHG
'Granada' (*japonica*) SCog
'Grand Jury' (x *williamsii*) CTre CTrw MGos SCog
'Grand Prix' (*japonica*) CMHG CTrh CTrw MBri SCog
'Grand Slam' (*japonica*) CMHG CMac CTre CTrh CTrw ISea MAsh SCog
granthamiana CGre CTrh
grijsii CTrh
'Guest of Honor' (*japonica*) CB&S SCog
'Guilio Nuccio' (*japonica*) CB&S CTre CTrh EBre LBre SCog SPla
'Gwavas' (x *williamsii*) CB&S CTre
'Gwenneth Morey' (*japonica*) CMHG
§ 'Hagoromo' (*japonica*) CMac ELan ENot IHos MBal MBri SPer WBod WWat
'Hakurakuten' (*japonica*) CTre CTrh ISea SBod SCog SLon
'Hanafûki' (*japonica*) CTre SCog
'Hanatachibana' (*japonica*) CTrh SExb
'Harold L Paige' (*japonica* x *reticulata*) CTrh
'Hassaku' (*japonica*) See C. 'Hassaku-shibori'
'Hatsuzakura' (*japonica*) See C. 'Dewatairin'
'Hawaii' (*japonica*) CB&S CMac CTre CTrh SCog
'Henry Turnbull' (*japonica*) CTrh
'High Hat' (*japonica*) CTrw SCog
'Hikarugenji' ('Herme') (*japonica*) SCog
'Hilo' (x *williamsii*) CTrw
'Hinomaru' (*japonica*) CMac
'Hiraethlyn' (x *williamsii*) CTre WBod
'Hope' (x *williamsii*) CTrh SCog
'Howard Asper' (*reticulata* x *japonica*) SCog
'Hugh Evans' (*sasanqua*) CB&S CBot CDoC CTre CTrh WBod
'Ice Queen' (*japonica*) SCog
¶ 'Ichisetsu' (*japonica*) SExb
§ 'Imbricata' (*japonica*) CTre ENot IHos MGos SCog SExb WBod
'Imbricata Alba' (*japonica*) SExb SLon SSta
'Imbricata Rubra' See C. 'Imbricata'
'In the Pink' (*japonica*) CMHG
'Innovation' (x *williamsii* x *reticulata*) CB&S CTre CTrh GGGa IJoh ISea MGos SCog
'Inspiration' (*reticulata* x *saluenensis*) CB&S CGre CMHG CMac CSam CSco CTre CTrh GGGa IDai IJoh ISea LHyd MBri MGos SBod SCog SExb SGil SHBN SSpi WBod
'Interval' (*reticulata* x) CTrh
'J C Williams' (x *williamsii*) CB&S CGre CMac CSam CTre CTrh CTrw GGGa GWht IDai IHos IJoh IOrc ISea LHyd MBal MBri MRav SBod SCog SExb SPer SSpi WBod
'J J Whitfield' (*japonica*) CMac CTrh SCog
'Jack Jones Scented' (*japonica*) SCog
¶ 'James Allan' (*japonica*) SPer
'Janet Waterhouse' (*japonica*) CTrh SCog
japonica CTrh
'Jean Clere' (*japonica*) CTrh NBar
'Jean Lyne' (*japonica*) SCog
'Jean May' (*sasanqua*) CB&S CDoC CTre SBod SCog
'Jenefer Carlyon' (x *williamsii*) CTre SCog
'Jill Totty' (x *williamsii*) CTrh
'Jingle Bells' (*japonica*) CTrh SCog
'Joan Trehane' (x *williamsii*) CTrh CTrw
'Joseph Pfingstl' (*japonica*) CGre CMHG CTre CTrh SCog SExb
'Joshua E Youtz' (*japonica*) SCog
'Jovey Carlyon' (*japonica*) (hybrid) SCog
'Joy Sander' (*japonica*) See C. 'Apple Blossom'

'Joyful Bells' (x *williamsii*) CTrh
'Jubilation' (x *williamsii*) GGGa MBri SCog
'Julia France' (*japonica*) CB&S SCog
'Julia Hamiter' (x *williamsii*) CB&S CGre CTre CTrh CTrw ELan SCog
'Juno' (*japonica*) SCog
'Jupiter' (*japonica*) CB&S CMac CTre CTrh CTrw ISea LHyd LNet MBal MGos SCog SHBN SPla WBod
♦ 'Jury's Charity' See C. 'Charity'
¶ 'Jury's Sunglow' (*williamsii*) SCog
'Jury's Yellow' (x *williamsii* x *japonica*) CB&S CTrh CTrw IDai IJoh IOrc MAsh MBri MGos SBod SCog SExb SPer SSta
'Just Darling' (*japonica*) CTrh
'K O Hester' (*reticulata*) CTrh
'K Sawada' (*japonica*) SCog
'Kate Thrash' (*japonica*) SCog
'Katie' (*japonica*) SCog
'Kellingtoniana' (*japonica*) See C. 'Gigantea'
'Kenkyô' (*sasanqua*) SCog SPla
'Kenny' (*japonica*) CB&S WBod
'Kewpie Doll' (*japonica*) CTrh SCog
'Kick-Off' (*japonica*) CTrh ELan SCog
'Kimberley' (*japonica*) WBod
§ 'Kingyo-tsubaki' (*japonica*) SBor SExb WBod
'King's Ransom' (*japonica*) CMac SExb
kissi CTrh
'Kitty' (*japonica*) CMHG SCog
§ 'Konronkoku' (*japonica*) CTrh SBor SCog
'Kouron-jura' (*japonica*) See C. 'Konronkoku'
¶ 'Kramer's Beauty' (*japonica*) SCog SExb
'Kramer's Supreme' (*japonica*) CB&S CGre CMac CTre CTrh LNet MBal MGos SBod SCog SExb WBod WStI
§ 'Kumasaka' (*japonica*) CMac CSco SExb WBod
'Kyô-nishiki' (x *vernalis*) SCog
'Lady Campbell' (*japonica*) SExb
'Lady Clare' See C. 'Akashigata'
§ 'Lady de Saumarez' (*japonica*) CMac ELan ISea LNet SBod SCog SExb WBod
'Lady Loch' (*japonica*) CTre CTrh MGos SCog
'Lady Mackinnon' (*japonica*) SCog
'Lady Marion' (*japonica*) See C. 'Kumasaka'
'Lady McCulloch' (*japonica*) SCog WStI
'Lady McCulloch Pink' (*japonica*) SCog
'Lady Vansittart' (*japonica*) CB&S CMac CSam CTre ELan ENot IHos ISea LNet MBal MBri SBod SCog SExb SGil SHer SPer WBod WStI
§ 'Lady Vansittart Pink' (*japonica*) CMac MGos MPla SBod SHBN WBod
'Lady Vansittart Red' (*japonica*) See C 'Lady Vansittart Pink'
'Lady's Maid' (x *williamsii*) CTrh
'Lalla Rookh' (*japonica*) See C. 'L'Avvenire'
'Lanarth' (*japonica*) CTre
'Lasca Beauty' (*reticulata* x *japonica*) CTrh SCog
'Latifolia' (*japonica*) CTre ENot ISea SCog
'Laura Boscawen' (x *williamsii*) CTrh
'Laurie Bray' (*japonica*) CGre CTrh SCog
§ 'Lavinia Maggi' (*japonica*) CMac CTre CTrh ELan GAri IHos IOrc LHyd MBri MRav SBod SCog SExb SGil SHBN SLon SReu WBod
'Lavinia Maggi Rosea' (*japonica*) SCog
'L'Avvenire' (*japonica*) CMac SCog SExb
§ 'Le Lys' (*japonica*) SCog
'Leonard Messel' (*reticulata* x *williamsii*) CB&S CDoC CGre CMHG CSco CTre CTrh ENot GGGa IDai IHos IJoh ISea LHyd MBal MBri MGos SBod SCog SExb SHBN SPer SReu WBod WStI
'Lila Naff' (*reticulata* x) CTre SCog
'Lily Pons' (*japonica*) CTrh SCog
'Little Bit' (*japonica*) CTrh SCog SPla
'Little Bo Peep' (*japonica*) CTrh
'Little Lavender' (x *williamsii*) (hybrid) SCog
'Little Pearl' (*sasanqua*) CTrh
'Look-Away' (*japonica*) SCog
'Lovelight' (*japonica*) CTrh
'Lucy Hester' (*japonica*) CTre MBal SCog
'Lulu Belle' (*japonica*) SCog SExb
lutchuensis CTrh
'Ma Belle' (*japonica*) CMHG SCog
'Madame Charles Blard' (*japonica*) SCog
'Madame de Strekaloff' (*japonica*) CMac
'Madame Lebois' (*japonica*) CB&S
'Madame Lourmand' (*japonica*) WBod
'Madame Martin Cachet' (*japonica*) CMHG SCog
'Madame Victor de Bisschop' See C. 'Le Lys'
'Madge Miller' (*japonica*) CTre ELan
'Magic City' (*japonica*) SCog
'Magic Moments' (*japonica*) SExb
♦ 'Magnolia Queen' See C. 'Priscilla Brooks'
'Magnoliiflora' (*japonica*) See C. 'Hagoromo'
'Maiden's Blush' (*japonica*) CMac SCog

'Man Size' (*japonica*) SCog
'Mandalay Queen' (*reticulata*) CTrh
¶ 'Marchioness of Exeter' (*japonica*) SExb
'Margaret Davis Picotee' (*japonica*) CB&S CGre CMHG CTrh CTrw MGos SCog SExb
'Margaret Waterhouse' (x ***williamsii***) CTre SCog
'Margarete Hertrich' (*japonica*) SCog
'Margherita Coleoni' (*japonica*) CB&S SBod SPla WBod
'Marguérite Gouillon' (*japonica*) ISea SCog
'Marinka' (*japonica*) CB&S
* 'Mariottii' (*japonica*) CMac
'Mark Alan' (*japonica*) NBar SExb
'Maroon and Gold' (*japonica*) SCog
'Mars' (*japonica*) CB&S CTre SExb WBod
'Martha Brice' (*japonica*) CMHG
'Mary Charlotte' (*japonica*) SCog
'Mary Christian' (x ***williamsii***) CB&S CSco CTre CTrh LHyd MBri WBod
'Mary Costa' (*japonica*) CGre CTrh
'Mary J Wheeler' (*japonica*) CTrw MBri
'Mary Jobson' (x ***williamsii***) CB&S CTre
'Mary Larcom' (x ***williamsii***) CTrh
'Mary Phoebe Taylor' (x ***williamsii***) CB&S CTre CTrh CTrw MBri SBod SCog WBod
§ 'Masayoshi' (*japonica*) CGre CMac ENot IOrc LHyd LNet MBri SCog SPla WBod
§ 'Mathotiana' (*japonica*) CTrw MBal SCog SExb WBod
'Mathotiana Alba' (*japonica*) CB&S MBal SCog SReu WBod
'Mathotiana Purple King' (*japonica*) See C. 'Julia Drayton'
'Mathotiana Rosea' (*japonica*) CB&S CMac CTre ELan ENot LNet SBod SCog SExb SGil SHBN SPer
'Mathotiana Supreme' (*japonica*) SCog
'Matterhorn' (*japonica*) CTrh
'Mattie Cole' (*japonica*) CGre CTre CTrh SCog
'Mattie O'Reilly' (*japonica*) CTre
'Maud Messel' (x ***williamsii*** x ***reticulata***) MBri
'Melinda Hackett' (*japonica*) SCog
'Melody Lane' (*japonica*) SCog
'Mercury' (*japonica*) CMac ENot GGGa NKay SExb SGil SHBN SLon WBod
'Mercury Variegated' (*japonica*) CMHG
'Midnight' (*japonica*) CB&S CGre SCog
'Midnight Serenade' (*japonica*) CTrh
'Midsummer's Day' (*japonica*) CB&S
§ 'Mikenjaku' (*japonica*) CMac ENot LNet MGos SExb
'Mildred Veitch' (x ***williamsii***) CGre CTre CTrh
'Ming Temple' (*reticulata*) CTre
'Minnie Maddern Fiske' (*japonica*) SExb
'Mirage' (x ***williamsii***) CTrh
'Miss Charleston' (*japonica*) CB&S SCog
'Miss Frankie' (*japonica*) SCog
'Miss Tulare' (*reticulata*) CTrh
'Miss Universe' (*japonica*) CGre CTrh SCog
'Miya' (*japonica*) SCog
'Momiji-gari' (*japonica*) CTrh
'Mona Jury' (x ***williamsii***) CTrh MBri SCog
'Monica Dance' (x ***williamsii***) CB&S
'Monstruosa Rubra' (*japonica*) See C. 'Gigantea Red'
'Monte Carlo' (*japonica*) SCog WBod
'Moonlight Bay' (*japonica*) SCog
'Morning Glow' (*japonica*) WBod
'Moshio' (*japonica*) MBri
§ 'Mrs Bertha A Harms' (*japonica*) CGre CMHG CTrw SCog
'Mrs D W Davis' (*japonica*) CB&S CGre CTrh CTrw SCog SPer
'Muskoka' (x ***williamsii***) CB&S CMHG ISea
* 'Mutabilis' (*japonica*) SCog
* 'Mywoods' (*sasanqua*) CMac
'Nagasaki' (*japonica*) See C. 'Mikenjaku'
'Nanbankô' (*japonica*) CTrh
'Narumigata' (*sasanqua*) CBot CDoC CMac CTrh CTrw MAsh MBal MBlu SBod SCog SLeo WBod
'Navajo' (*sasanqua*) CTrh
'New Venture' (x ***williamsii***) CB&S
'Nigra' (*japonica*) See C. 'Konronkoku'
¶ 'Nijinski' (*reticulata* x) ISea
§ ***nitidissima*** var. ***nitidissima*** CGre CTre CTrh
'Nobilissima' (*japonica*) CB&S CMac CTre ELan IHos ISea SBod SCog SExb SHBN SPer SPla WBod WWeb
'Nodami-ushiro' (*sasanqua*) CTrh
'November Pink' (x ***williamsii***) CB&S CTre CTrh
'Nuccio's Gem' (*japonica*) CB&S CMHG CTrh MBri SCog SExb
'Nuccio's Jewel' (*reticulata*) CMHG CTre MGos SCog SExb SPer
'Nuccio's Pearl' (*japonica*) CTrh SCog SExb

'Nuccio's Ruby' (*reticulata*) CTrh
oleifera CSam CTre CTrh
'Onetia Holland' (*japonica*) CB&S CTre CTrw SCog
'Optima Rosea' (*japonica*) CTre
§ 'Otome' (*japonica*) CMac SExb SLon WBod
'Otto Hopfer' (*reticulata* x *japonica*) CTrh
'Overture' (*reticulata*) CTrh
'Owen Henry' (*japonica*) CTrh
§ 'O-niji' (*japonica*) MBal WBod
'Painted Lady' (*japonica*) CMac
'Paolina' (*japonica*) SCog
'Paolina Maggi' (*japonica*) SCog
¶ 'Parkside' (*williamsii*) CTre
'Paul Jones Supreme' (*japonica*) CMHG SCog
'Pauline Winchester' (*japonica*) SCog
♦ 'Peachblossom' (*japonica*) See C. 'Fleur Dipater'
'Pearl Maxwell' (*japonica*) CMHG
'Pensacola Red' (*japonica*) SCog
N 'Perfecta' (x *williamsii*) CTrh
'Phillippa Forward' (x *williamsii*) CMac WBod
'Pink Champagne' (*japonica*) CMHG CTre SBod SCog
'Pink Clouds' (*japonica*) SCog
'Pink Diddy' (*japonica*) MBri
'Pink Pagoda' (*japonica*) SCog
'Pink Perfection' (*japonica*) See C. 'Otome'
♦ 'Pink Spangles' See C. 'Mathotiana Rosea'
'Pirate's Gold' (*japonica*) (v) SCog
pitardii* x *cuspidata SExb
'Plantation Pink' (*sasanqua*) CTrh SCog SExb SPer SSta
'Pompone' (*japonica*) SCog
'Pope Pius IX' (*japonica*) See C. 'Prince Eugène Napoléon'
'Powder Puff' (*japonica*) CTre MBri
§ 'Press's Eclipse' (*japonica*) ISea SCog
'Preston Rose' (*japonica*) CB&S CGre CMac CTre ELan MBal MGos SExb SPer WBod WWat
'Pride of Descanso' (*japonica*) See C. 'Yukibotan'
'Primavera' (*japonica*) CTrh SCog
§ 'Prince Eugéne Napoléon' (*japonica*) SCog
'Prince of Orange' (*japonica*) SCog
* 'Princess du Mahe' (*japonica*) CMac
§ 'Priscilla Brooks' (*japonica*) SCog
'Professor Sargent' (*japonica*) SCog
'Purity' (*japonica*) See C. 'Shiragiku'
'Purple Emperor' (*japonica*) See C. 'Julia Drayton'
'Quercifolia' See C. 'Kingyo-tsubaki'
'R L Wheeler' (*japonica*) CB&S CGre CTre CTrh CTrw EBre LBre MBal SCog SExb
'Rainbow' (*japonica*) See C. 'O-niji'
'Rebel Yell' (*japonica*) SCog
'Red Cardinal' (*japonica*) SExb
¶ 'Red Dahlia' (x *williamsii*) SCog
'Red Dandy' (*japonica*) CTrh SCog
'Red Ensign' (*japonica*) SCog
'Red Rogue' (*japonica*) CTrh SCog
'Reg Ragland' (*japonica*) SCog
'Rendezvous' (x *williamsii*) SCog SPla
reticulata CGre CTre CTrh
♦ 'Robert Fortune' See C. 'Songzilin'
'Roger Hall' (*japonica*) SCog SExb
'Rôgetsu' (*japonica*) CGre
'Roman Soldier' (*japonica*) CB&S
'Rose Court' (x *williamsii*) WBod
'Rose Holland' (x *williamsii*) CMHG
'Rose Parade' (x *williamsii*) CGre CTrh SCog
'Rose Quartz' (x *williamsii*) ELan
§ 'Rosea Plena' (*sasanqua*) CB&S CMac CTre CTrw
'Rosemary Williams' (x *williamsii*) CB&S CTre CTrh CTrw
'Rosie Anderson' (x *williamsii*) MBri
rosiflora CTre
'Royalty' (*japonica* x *reticulata*) CTre CTrh SCog
'Rubescens Major' (*japonica*) CB&S CGre CMac CTrh ISea SCog SReu WBod
'Rubra' (*sasanqua*) See C. 'Sasanqua Rubra'
'Ruby Bells' (x *williamsii*) CMHG
'Ruddigore' (*japonica*) CTrh
'Sabrina' (*japonica*) SCog
'Saint André' (*japonica*) CMac
'Saint Ewe' (x *williamsii*) CB&S CDoC CGre CMac CTre CTrh CTrw ELan ENot GGGa GWht IJoh ISea MBal MBri MGos MRav SBod SCog SExb SHBN SPer SPla WBod
'Saint Michael' (x *williamsii*) CB&S
'Salonica' See C. 'Shimna'
saluenensis CTre CTrh SReu
– x ***japonica*** See C. x ***williamsii***
'Salutation' (*saluenensis* x *reticulata*) CB&S CGre CSco CTre ISea SCog WBod
'Samantha' (*reticulata*) CTrh
'San Dimas' (*japonica*) CTrh SCog
'Sarah Frost' (*japonica*) SExb
sasanqua CTrh ISea SEng
¶ 'Sasanqua Rubra' CMac
§ 'Sasanqua Variegata' (*sasanqua*) SPla SSta

'Satan's Robe' (*reticulata* x)	CMHG CTre CTrh SCog
'Saturnia' (*japonica*)	SCog WStI
'Sayonara' (x *williamsii*)	CTre CTrh
'Scentsation' (*japonica*)	CMHG CTre SCog
'Scentuous' (*japonica* x *lutchuensis*)	SCog
'Sea Foam' (*japonica*)	CMHG
'Sea Gull' (*japonica*)	CTrh
'Seiji' (*japonica*)	CMac
'Senator Duncan U Fletcher' (*japonica*)	CTrw
'Senorita' (x *williamsii*)	CTrh
'Serenade' (*japonica*)	CMHG SCog
§ 'Shimna' (x *williamsii*)	ISea
'Shinonome' (*sasanqua*)	CTrh
'Shin-akebono' (*japonica*)	See C. 'Akebono'
§ 'Shiragiku' (*japonica*)	SExb
'Shirobotan' (*japonica*)	MBri SCog
'Shiro-daikagura' (*rusticana*)	SCog WBod
'Shiro-wabisuke' (Wabisuke)	CTrh
'Show Girl' (*sasanqua* x *reticulata*)	CTre CTrh SBod SCog SExb WBod
'Shôwa-no-sakae' (*hiemalis*)	SCog
'Shôwa-wabisuke' (Wabisuke)	CTrh
'Sierra Spring' (*japonica*)	SCog
'Silver Anniversary' (*japonica*)	CB&S CMHG ELan MAsh SBod SCog SReu SSta
'Silver Waves' (*japonica*)	SCog
§ *sinensis*	CGre CTre CTrh EMil GAri
'Snow Goose' (*japonica*)	SCog
'Snowflake' (*sasanqua*)	CTrh
¶ 'Songzilin' (*reticulata*)	SHil
'Souvenir de Bahuaud-Litou' (*japonica*)	CGre CTre SCog SLon WBod WWat
'Sparkling Burgundy' (*hiemalis*)	CB&S CTre SCog
'Speciosissima' (*japonica*)	SCog
'Spencer's Pink' (*japonica*)	CB&S CTre CTrw
♦ 'Splendens'	See C. 'Coccinea'
'Spring Festival' (*cuspidata* x)	CHig CTrh SCog
'Spring Mist' (*japonica* x *lutchuensis*)	CMHG
'Spring Sonnet' (*japonica*)	SCog
'Stella Polare'	See C. 'Etoile Polaire'
¶ 'Strawberry Swirl' (*japonica*)	SCog
'Sunset Glory' (*japonica*)	SCog
¶ 'Swan Lake' (hybrid)	SCog SExb
'Sweet Delight' (*japonica*)	CMHG
'Sylvia' (*japonica*)	CMac WBod
taliensis	CGre CTre CTrh
'Tammia' (*japonica*)	SCog
'Tanya' (*sasanqua*)	CTrh
'Tarô'an' (*japonica*)	CTrh SCog
'Taylor's Perfection' (x *williamsii*)	CDoC CTrw
'Teresa Ragland' (*japonica*)	SCog
¶ 'Teringa' (*japonica*)	CTre
'The Czar' (*japonica*)	CB&S CTrw ISea MBri SCog WBod
'The Duchess of Cornwall' (x *williamsii*)	CTre
¶ 'The Mikado' (*japonica*)	CTre
'The Pilgrim' (*japonica*)	SCog
thea	See C. ***sinensis***
'Thomas Cornelius Cole' (*japonica*)	CTre
'Tick Tock' (*japonica*)	SCog
'Tickled Pink' (*japonica*)	SCog
'Tiffany' (*japonica*)	CB&S CTre CTrh LNet SCog SExb SHBN SHer SPla WBod
'Tinker Bell' (*japonica*)	CGre CTrh SCog
'Tinker Toy' (*japonica*)	CTrh
'Tiny Princess' (*japonica* x *fraterna*)	CGre CTrh
'Tiptoe' (x *williamsii*)	CTrh SCog
'Tom Knudsen' (*reticulata* x *japonica*)	CTre CTrh SExb
'Tom Thumb' (*japonica*)	CTrh
'Tomorrow' (*japonica*)	CB&S CMHG CMac CSam CTre CTrh CTrw ISea MAsh SCog SExb WBod
'Tomorrow Park Hill' (*japonica*)	CTrh SCog
'Tomorrow Supreme'	See C. 'Tomorrow Variegated'
§ 'Tomorrow Variegated' (*japonica*)	SCog
'Tomorrow's Dawn' (*japonica*)	CB&S CTrh SCog
§ 'Tongzimian' (*reticulata*)	CTrh
¶ *transnokoensis*	CTre
¶ 'Tregrehan' (x *williamsii*)	ISea
'Tregye' (*japonica*)	CB&S
'Trewithen Red' (*saluenensis*)	CTrw
'Trewithen White' (*japonica*)	CSam CTrw
'Tricolor' (*japonica*)	CB&S CGre CMHG CMac CTrh ENot IHos IJoh IOrc ISea SCog SExb SSta WBod
♦ 'Tricolor Red' (*japonica*)	See C. 'Lady de Saumarez'
'Tricolor Sieboldii'	See 'Tricolor'
'Tricolor Superba' (*japonica*)	WBod
'Tristrem Carlyon' (*reticulata* x)	CB&S CTre MBri SCog WBod
tsaii	CTrh
'Twilight' (*japonica*)	SCog
¶ 'Twinkle Star' (x *williamsii*)	SCog
♦ 'Usu-ôtome'	See C. 'Otome'
'Valentine Day' (*reticulata* x *japonica*)	CTrh

'Valley Knudsen' (***saluenensis*** × ***reticulata***)	SCog
'Valtevareda' (***japonica***)	CGre
♦'Variegata' (***sasanqua***)	See C. 'Sasanqua Variegata'
'Victor de Bisschop' (***japonica***)	See C. 'Le Lys'
'Victor Emmanuel' (***japonica***)	See C. 'Blood of China'
'Virginia Carlyon' (***japonica***)	CB&S CTre
'Virginia Robinson' (***japonica***)	WBod
'Vittorio Emanuele II' (***japonica***)	CTrh
'Warrior' (***japonica***)	CTre SCog
'Water Lily' (× ***williamsii***)	CB&S CTre CTrh CTrw ISea SSta
'Waterloo'	See C. 'Etherington White'
'White Nun' (***japonica***)	SCog
'White Swan' (***japonica***)	CB&S CMac CTre MAsh SExb
'Wilamina' (***japonica***)	CTrh SExb
'Wilber Foss' (× ***williamsii***)	CB&S CGre CTre CTrh CTrw SExb
'Wildfire' (***japonica***)	SCog
'William Bartlett' (***japonica***)	CTrh
'William Carylon' (***williamsii***)	CTre MBal
'William Hertrich' (***reticulata***)	CGre CTre SCog
'William Honey' (***japonica***)	CMHG CTrh SCog
§ × ***williamsii***	CGre
'Winter Cheer' (***japonica***)	CTrh SCog
'Winton' (***cuspidata*** × ***saluenensis***)	CB&S
'Wood Nymph' (***japonica***)	CTre ISea MBal WBod
'Woodville Red' (***japonica***)	CTre
'Yae-arare' (***sasanqua***)	CTrh
'Yesterday' (× ***williamsii***)	CTre MAsh SCog
'Yoibijin' (***japonica***)	See C. 'Suibijin'
'Yours Truly' (***japonica***)	CMac CTre CTrh MGos SBod SCog
yuhsienensis	CTrh
§ 'Yukibotan' (***japonica***)	SCog
♦'Yukihaki'	See C. 'Yukishiro'
'Yukimi-guruma' (***japonica***)	SPla WBod
§ 'Yukishiro' (***japonica***)	CTrw
'Yuletide' (× ***vernalis***)	CTrh
'Zoraide Vanzi' (***japonica***)	WBod

CAMPANULA † (Campanulaceae)

alaskana	See C. ***rotundifolia alaskana***
§ ***alliariifolia***	Widely available
– 'Ivory Bells'	See C. ***alliariifolia***
allionii	See C. ***alpestris***
§ ***alpestris***	EPad GArf MBro
– 'Grandiflora'	EPad EPot WDav
– 'Rosea'	EPad
alpina	CMea EPad GDra GTou WPer
¶ – var. ***bucegiensis***	EPad
– ***orbelica***	See C. ***o.***
americana	EPad
anchusiflora	EPad MFir MFos
andrewsii	EPad MFir MFos
– ssp. ***andrewsii***	EPad
– ssp. ***hirsutula***	EPad WDav
argyrotricha	ECro EPad
arvatica	CLew EPad GCHN LBee MBro MHig MNFA NGre NHar NHol NMen NTow SSmi WAbe WDav
– 'Alba'	EPad LBee MBro MHig NMen WDav WHil
atlantis	EPad
aucheri	CNic EBur EPad EPot GArf GDra
autraniana	EPad
'Avalon'	EPad
'Balchiniana'	EPad WEas WPbr
barbata	CNic ECro ELan EPad GCHN GDra MBro MCas MSte MTol NMen NNrd NRya NWCA WCla WDav WHal WHoo WNdy WPer
– var. ***alba***	MBro MCas NNrd WDav
baumgartenii	EPad
bellidifolia	CNic EPad GDra NBir
bertolae	EPad
§ ***betulifolia***	CPar CSam ECtt EPad EPot GCHN GDra MBro MPar NGre NHar NHol NRed SIng WDav WPer WThu
¶ – JCA 252.005	SBla
¶ ***biebersteiniana***	EPad
'Birch Hybrid'	CMHG CNic CPar ECtt ELan EMNN EPad ESis GCHN GDra MBal MBro MCas MNFA NHar NHol NMen NNrd NRoo SCro SHer SIng WHil
bononiensis	EPad WOld
bornmuelleri	EPad WDav
'Burghaltii'	Widely available
§ ***buseri***	WThi
caespitosa	EPad NWCA WPer
calaminthifolia	CBrd CLew CNic EPad GTou MFir MHig NRed NWCA WAbe WOMN
§ ***carnica***	MBro NHol NWCA
carpatha	EPad
carpatica	CGle CRiv CShe GAri GDra LAbb MBar MBri MHig NBro NNor SIng SPer SUsu WHoo WKif WWin
– –	CGle CRiv CShe NNor NOak SIng SPer WEas WHoo
– 'Bees' Variety'	NKay
– 'Blaue Clips' ('Blue Clips')	CDoC CLew ECtt ELan EMNN EPad EPar ESis GTou LAbb MCas MPla NGre NHol NKay NMen NMir NNrd NRoo SCro SHer SPla WByw WDav WPat WPer
– 'Blue Moonlight'	CKel EBre EOrc EPad LBee LBre NEgg NHar NRoo
– 'Bressingham White'	CKel CLew EBre EPad GAri GCHN GDra LBee LBre NEgg NNrd SBla WHoo
– 'Caerulea'	CB&S
– 'Chewton Joy'	EBre EOrc EPad ESis GAri GCHN LBre NHar NRoo
– 'Ditton Blue'	EPad GDra

– dwarf form	EPot
– 'Harvest Moon'	EPad
¶ – 'Kathy'	SAsh
– 'Lavender'	NKay WHil
– 'Maureen Haddon'	EBre EPad GAri GCHN LBre NEgg NRoo
– 'Molly Pinsent'	CKel CShe EPad WMar
– 'Queen of Sheba'	EPad
– 'Queen of Somerville'	EPad NKay NNrd
– 'Riverslea'	EPad NKay
– 'Snowdrift'	EPad SFis
– 'Suzie'	SBla
– var. ***turbinata***	GDra MPar MTho SIng SSou
– – f.***alba***	ECha NNrd
– – 'Craven Bells'	EPad WDav
– – 'Georg Arends'	SAsh
– – 'Hannah'	CPar EBre EPad GCHN GDra LBee LBre SHer WMar
– – 'Isabel'	CPar EPad GCHN NKay NNrd
– – 'Jewel'	CLew EPad LBee SSmi
– – 'Karl Foerster'	EBre EPad GCHN LBre MBri MNFA NHar NRoo
– – 'Pallida'	GDra NHol SSmi
– – 'Snowsprite'	EBre LBre LRHS NHar NRoo
– – 'Wheatley Violet'	CPar EBre EPad ESis GCHN LBre NHol NMen NRoo SBla WPer
– 'Weisse Clips' ('White Clips')	CDoC ECtt ELan EMNN EPad EPar GTou LAbb MCas NGre NHol NKay NMen NMir NNrd NRoo SCro SHer SPla WByw WPat WPer
cashmeriana	EBur EPad GCHN ITim MFos MPlt NBir NWCA WAbe WOMN WThu
celsii	EPad
– ssp. ***carystea***	EPad
cephalenica	See C. ***garganica c.***
cervicaria	EPad
§ ***chamissonis***	EPad EPot
§ – 'Major'	EMNN EPad EPot
– 'Oyobeni'	EPad
§ – 'Superba'	GArf GDra MBal MTho NHol NMen NNrd NTow
§ ***cochleariifolia***	CElw CMea CPar CShe ELan EMNN EPad ESis GCHN MBal MBro MCas MFir MHig MTho MWat NGre NHar NKay NRed NRoo SIng WAbe WCla WDav WEas WHoo WPat WWin
– var. ***alba***	CLew CMea CPar CShe EMNN EOrc EPad GCHN MBal MBro MCas MHig MPar NGre NHar NKay NMen NNrd NRed NRya NVic SBla SSmi SUsu WAbe WCla WHil WPer
– 'Annie Hall'	WHal
– x ***arvatica***	NHar
– 'Blue Tit'	EBre EPad LBre
– 'Cambridge Blue'	EBre EPad GCHN LBre NMen NNrd SSmi WAbe WPer
– 'Elizabeth Oliver' (d)	Widely available
– 'Flore Pleno'	CHal ECtt EFol EMNN EPad MBro NHar NHol NMen NNrd
– 'Miss Willmott'	EBur EPad NBir SSmi
– 'Oakington Blue'	CElw EPad NHol NNrd NTow SSmi
– var. ***pallida***	SRms
– – 'Miranda'	CNic CPar CSpe EPad MBro MHig NNrd SSmi
– 'R B Loder' (D)	EPad
– 'Silver Chimes'	EMNN EPad NBir NNrd WPat WThu
¶ – 'Temple Bells'	WPer
– 'Tubby'	EPad GCHN NKay NNrd SRms
– ***warleyensis***	See C. x ***haylodgensis*** 'Warley White'
collina	CRiv EPad MBro MCas MFir MPlt NHar WAbe WHoo WPer
'Constellation'	EPad NCat NNrd
coriacea	WThu
– JCA 253.800	EPad
'Covadonga'	CTom EPad WPat
crispa	WDav
– JCA 253.901	EPad
dasyantha	See C. ***chamissonis***
divaricata	CHun EPad
'E K Toogood'	CHal CHun ECtt EPad MDHE MWat NHar NHol NKay NNrd SBla SCro WHil
elatines	EPad NNrd
– var. ***elatinoïdes***	EPad GDra WPer
¶ – – JCA 254.300	SBla
§ 'Elizabeth'	CBro CHan EBlo ECtt EPad LGre MBri MSte NHar SMad SMrm SUsu SWas WBon WPbr
ephesia	EPad
¶ ***erinus***	EPad
eriocarpa	See C. ***latifolia*** 'Eriocarpa'
excisa	EPad ITim LBee MDHE NNrd NWCA
¶ 'Faichem'	EPad
fenestrellata	EPad MBro MDHE MNFA MTho NCat NHol NNrd NSti SSmi SSou WDav
– ssp. ***fenestrellata***	EPad
– ssp. ***istriaca***	EPad
finitima	See C. ***betulifolia***
¶ ***foliosa***	EPad
formanekiana	EBur EPad EPot MFos NTow NWCA SIng WPer
fragilis	EBur ECro ELan EPad EPot GTou SHer SIng WPer
– ssp. ***cavolinii***	EPad
– 'Hirsuta'	ELan EPad SHer
'G F Wilson'	EMNN EPad MBal NCat NHol NKay
garganica	CLew CNic EFol ELan EOrc EPad ESis MBro MCas MFir MPit MTho NHar NKay NMen NNrd NRed NRoo SIde SIng SSou WByw WCla WDav WHoo WPer
– 'Aurea'	See C. ***g.*** 'Dickson's Gold'
– 'Blue Diamond'	CRiv ELan EPad ESis LHop MPit SHer SIng
§ – ssp. ***cephalenica***	EPad MDHE NHol NKay
§ – 'Dickson's Gold'	CElw CGle CHal CMea EBre ECtt EFol ELan EPad EPar EPla EPot ESis GArf GCal LBee LBre LHop MBro MCas MHig NHar NHol NRoo SAxl SHer SIng WDav WPat WPer
¶ – 'Hirsuta'	SRms
– 'W H Paine'	EBre EPad LBre NCat SHer
'Glandore'	EPad NCat
glomerata	CB&S CBot CFis CGle CKin CRDP CShe CTom EBar EOrc EPad GTou MBal MFir MHew MTho MWat NBro NMir NRar NRed NRya NSel SUsu WByw WEas WHal WNdy WWin

– var. ***acaulis***	CDoC CHal CNic CRiv EBar ECro EPad GCHN GCal MCas MPit NMen NOak NRoo SPla SSou WHil WHoo WPer WWin
– var. ***alba***	CCla CSev EFol ELan EMon EPad MBal MBri MBro MNFA MUlv NBar NBro NFai NHol SPer SPla SSvw WCot WHal WHil WHoo WNdy WPer
– 'Alba Nana'	EPad SSou WWin
– var. ***dahurica***	CSco EPad LBlm LGan NNrd NOak WPer
– 'Joan Elliott'	ECha EPad
– 'Purple Pixie'	EBre ECtt EPad LBre MBel
– 'Schneekrone' ('Crown of Snow')	CGle ECha ECro EFou EPad GCal NNor NOak NRoo WRus
– 'Superba'	CCla CGle CKel CPar CRiv EBlo EFol EFou ELan ENot EPad EPar MBri MBro MNFA NBar NFai NHol NNor NOrc NRoo SCro SPer SPla SSvw WHoo WPer WTyr
– 'White Barn'	ECha
grossekii	EPad SSou
¶ ***grossheimii***	EPad
¶ ***hakkiarica***	EPad
x ***hallii***	EPad EPot ESis MBro MPla NGre NHol NRed NRoo SIng SSou WDav WPat
x ***haylodgensis***	CElw CNic CRiv CSpe ECar ELan EPad EPot ESis IHos MBal MCas MHig NHar NNrd SBla WAbe WHal WHil WOMN WPat WThu
– 'Plena'	CHal CLew CSam CShe LHop NHol WEas WKif WPer
§ – 'Warley White' (d)	CGle CNic CRiv CSpe EBur ECar ECro ELan EPad GArf GDra LHop SBla SFis SGil SHer WOMN
¶ ***hemschinica***	EPad
'Hemswell Starlight'	EPad NMen WPer
hercegovina	EPad EPot
– 'Nana'	CNic WAbe
herminii	EPad
heterophylla	EPad NTow
§ ***incurva***	CBot CGle EPad LWad MRav NHol WByw WDav WMar WPer
– JCA 256.800	MBro
innesii	See C. 'John Innes'
isophylla	CHal EPad EPot ERav LAbb MBri SGil SHer SIng SLMG WEas
– 'Alba'	CHal EPad LAbb SGil SHer SIng SLMG
¶ – 'Flore Pleno'	EPad
– 'Mayi'	CSpe
– 'Pamela'	EPad
– 'Variegata'	See C. 'Balchiniana'
'Joe Elliott'	CNic EPad LBee NMen NNrd
§ 'John Innes'	CShe EPad
kemulariae	CNic EPad GCHN MBro MCas NCat NHol NKay NNrd SSmi WDav WEas WHil
¶ – ***alba***	EPad
¶ 'Kent Belle'	SWas
kladniana	EPad
kolenatiana	EPad GCHN WPer
¶ ***laciniata***	EPad
lactiflora	CFis CGle CHad CHan CPar CSev EBar EBre ECha EFou ELan EOrc EPad GCHN LBre MWat NVic SChu SPer SSpi WBon WByw WDav WEas WHal WHoo WNdy WOld WWin
– white	CBot CKel CMGP EBre ECha EFou EOrc EPad LBre MBro NBir SPer SPla SSpi WEas WHoo WOld
– ***alba***	See C. ***l.*** white
– 'Loddon Anna'	Widely available
– 'Pouffe'	CDoC CFis CKel CMGP CSco EBre ECha EFou ELan EOrc EPad LBre MNFA NHol NRoo SCro SPer SPla WHoo WPer WRus
– 'Prichard's Variety'	CCla CDoC CFis CGle CKel CLew CRDP CSam CSco CShe EBre EFou ELan EOrc EPad LAbb LBre MBri MWat NBar NRoo NSti SDix SHer SMad SPer SPla WAbe WRus WTyr
– 'Violet'	WPer
– 'White Pouffe'	CCla CHad EBlo EBre EFou EHal EOrc EPad LBre NHol NSti SCro SPer WByw WRus
lanata	ELan EPad WByw WDav
lasiocarpa	EBur EPad GArf GTou MHig WOMN WPer
§ ***latifolia***	CElw CHan CKin CMea CRDP CSev ECha EFou EPad LGan MPar NMir NNor NOrc NRed NTow SPer SSpi WCla WEas WHoo WPer
– 'Arthur Wood'	EPad
– 'Brantwood'	CChu CMGP CMil EPad GAbr MFir MSte NHol NOak SChu SCro SFis SPer WPer
¶ – 'Eriocarpa'	CHan
– 'Gloaming'	EBre EPad LBre MUlv SIde
– var. ***macrantha***	CSco EFou EPad LHil MBri MNFA MSte NSti SFis SMad WCot WOld WPer WWat
– – ***alba***	CChu CSco ECtt LBlm LGre MBro SCro SSvw WDav WPer WWat
– white	CChu CElw CGle CHan ECha EOrc EPad MBri MNFA MSte NNor NSti NTow SPer WCru WEas WNdy WPer WRus
– 'White Ladies'	EBre EPad LBre
§ ***latiloba***	CFis CGle EBre EPad LBre LGro MFir WByw WEas WHoo WNdy WWin
– ***alba***	CBre CChu CFis CHan CLew CMil EBre EFou EMon EPad GAbr GCal LBre LGre LHil MBri MRav SCro WBon WEas WMar WNdy WOld
– 'Hidcote Amethyst'	Widely available
– 'Highcliffe Variety'	CChu ECha EFou EPad MBri NHol SGil WEas WKif WNdy WOld
– 'Percy Piper'	CElw CMil CSam ECED ECha EFou ELan EPad GAbr GCal MBri MRav NSti NVic SCro SHer SMrm WByw
ledebouriana pulvinata	EPad WDav
lingulata	EPad WDav
linifolia	See C. ***carnica***
longestyla	EPad
lusitanica	WPer
'Lynchmere'	EPad MNFA NKay NNrd NTow SHer

Plant	Suppliers
¶ ***lyrata***	EPad
makaschvilii	EPad
¶ 'Marion Fisher'	EPad
mirabilis	EPad
'Mist Maiden'	CShe EPad ESis LBee MCas MNFA NKay NNrd SBla WDav WMar
moesiaca	EPad MBel
mollis	EPad
– var. ***gibraltarica***	EPad NTow WOMN
muralis	See C. ***portenschlagiana***
nitida	See C. ***persicifolia planiflora***
– var. ***planiflora***	See C. ***persicifolia planiflora***
'Norman Grove'	EBur EPad LBee MCas MHig NNrd NTow
ochroleuca	EPad WHal
olympica Boissier	EPad GCra
– hort.	See C. ***rotundifolia*** 'Olympica'
orbelica	EPad
oreadum	CNic EPad
orphanidea	EPad MFos
pallida	EPad
parryi	EPad
patula	CNic EPad MHew NRed NSal WCla WGwy
– ssp. ***abietina***	EPad MFir
pelviformis	EPad WDav
peregrina	CHan
persicifolia	Widely available
– ***alba***	CCla CGle CHan CLew CPar CRDP CSco CShe ECha EHon EPad EPar GCHN LHop MBri MBro NHol NMir NNor NRoo SPer SUsu WByw WHoo WNdy WOMN WPbr WRus WWat
§ – 'Alba Coronata' (d)	CDec CElw EMon EPad LGan MBal MBel NBir NSti
– 'Alba Plena'	See C. ***p.*** 'Alba Coronata'
– Ashfield double ice blue	NRar
¶ – 'Bennett's Blue'	EOrc EPad
– blue	EOrc MBel WEas WPbr
¶ – blue cup-in-cup	WDav WHil
– 'Boule de Neige' (d)	CBre CDec CHad CHan CRDP ECha EMon EPad GAbr GCra MBel NOak SAxl SPla WEas WHil WNdy
– 'Caerulea Coronata'	See C. ***p.*** 'Coronata'
*– 'Caerulea Plena'	CBos CBre EBar EFol WEas WPbr
– 'Carillon'	CB&S CKel EPad
¶ – 'Chettle Charm'	EFou
*– 'China Blue'	SFis
§ – 'Coronata' (d)	EFou GAbr
N– cup & saucer white	CChu CElw CMil ELan LGre NFai WBon WByw WMar WPer
– double blue	CElw CHad EOrc LGre MBal MPar NFai NSti WByw WEas WRus
– double white	CChu CTom EFol ELan MBel NFai WByw WRus
– 'Fleur de Neige'	CGle CLew CSam EFou MBri MPar NCat WDav WHoo WRus
– 'Flore Pleno'	CHan EPad SApp WNdy
– 'Frances'	EMon
¶ – 'Frank Lawley'	EFou EMon
– 'Gawen' (d)	CBre CGle
– 'George Chiswell'	CChu CHad CHan CMil CRDP CSam EFol EOrc EPad LGre MUlv SApp SAsh SAxl WAbb WEas
– 'Grandiflora'	NHol WDav WWat
¶ – 'Grandiflora Alba'	SCro
¶ – 'Grandiflora Caerulea'	SCro
§ – 'Hampstead White' (d)	CDec CHan EFou EPad EPar GCal MBri MNFA NBir SBla WEas WHal WNdy
– 'Hetty'	See C. ***p.*** 'Hampstead White'
– 'Moerheimii' (d)	EOrc EPad EPar MBel MUlv NBir
– var. ***nitida***	See C. ***p. planiflora***
– – ***alba***	See C. ***p. planiflora alba***
*– 'Peach Bells'	EBar NOak
– 'Perry's Boyblue'	NPer
– 'Pike's Supremo'	LHop NBir
§ – var. ***planiflora***	CHan CPar EPad GDra MCas MNFA NHol NNrd WAbe
§ – – f.***alba***	EPad MCas MWat NHol WAbe WWin
– 'Pride of Exmouth'	CBre CGle CLew CMil CSam EFou EMon EPad MBel MNFA NNor NVic WDav WHil WHoo WNdy WRus
– ssp. ***sessiliflora***	See C. ***latiloba***
– 'Telham Beauty'	CDoC CKel COtt CTom ECED EFou ELan EOrc EPad LGan LHop LWad MFir NSti SMad SMrm SPer SSvw WDav WPer WRus WWat
– 'Wedgwood'	MBal
N– 'White Cup and Saucer'	CMil EMon MPar NCat SAxl WDav WRus
– 'White Queen'	ECro EFou EPad NFai NVic SApp WEas
petraea	EPad WHil
petrophila	NNrd
pilosa	See C. ***chamissonis***
– ***superba***	See C. ***chamissonis*** 'Superba'
piperi	NNrd WHal
planiflora	See C. ***persicifolia p.***
§ ***portenschlagiana***	CBar CElw CFis CKel CMea EBar ELan EPad EPar LGro MBro MCas MHig MWat NNor NRoo SBla SDix SHer SIng SPer SSvw WEas WHil WWin
– 'Bavarica'	CHal IDai NHol
– 'Major'	CShe NKay SRms
– 'Resholdt's Variety'	CGle CLew CMea CNic CRiv CSam CShe EBre EFol EFou ELan EPad EPla GCHN LBre MPit MUlv NCat NHol NNrd
poscharskyana	CCla CElw CFis CKel ELan EPad ESis IDai LBuc LGro MBal MBri MCas MFir NGre NKay NMen NRoo SHer SIng SPer SPla SSmi WAbe WByw WPer
– 'Blauranke'	CNic EBlo EPad GAri GCHN MDHE MNFA
– 'E H Frost'	CElw CHal CLew CShe ECtt EMNN EPad ESis MBro MCas MHig MPla MWat NCat NHol NKay NMen NNrd NRed SCro SSmi WHil WWin
– 'Glandore'	See 'G.'
– 'Lilacina'	SIng WThi
– 'Lisduggan'	CElw CGle CHal CNic EBur EPad ESis MBal MBro MCas MWat NCat NNrd SBla WAbe WHil

– 'Stella'	CShe EMNN EPad GCHN MCas MNFA MRav NCat NMen NRed NRoo NVic SChu SDix SHer SIng SSpi WEas
– variegated	EHoe IBlr
primulifolia	CPou EPad SUsu WHer WHoo WPer WWin
x ***pseudoraineri***	ELan EPad NGre NNrd SSou
pulla	CHal CLew CMea CPar CRDP ELan EPad EPot ESis MBro MCas MHig MPar MTho NGre NHar NHol SHer SSmi SSou WHal WPat WPer WWin
x ***pulloïdes***	EBre EPad EPot LBre NMen NNrd SSmi
punctata	CBot CBrd CMHG CMil ECro EFol EFou EPad EPar GArf GCHN GTou LGan LGre MBel MBro MFir MRav MTho NBro NGre NSti SBla WCla WEas WPer WWin
– f. ***albiflora***	CHan EFol EPad LGan LGre MBri MNFA NCat NMen WDav WHal
– var. ***hondoensis***	EPad MBel WDav
– f. ***impunctata***	EPad
– 'Pallida'	EPad
– pink	CChu CGle CMea LRHS MBri MPar NKay SRms
– 'Rubriflora'	CChu CCla CDec CHad CMGP ECtt EGol ELan EPad GCal LHop MBro MNFA NBar NHol NOak NOrc NRoo SCro SPer WHal WHoo WPer WRus
pusilla	See C. ***cochleariifolia***
pyramidalis	CBot CHan CSam EFou EPad LWad NOrc SUsu WByw WEas WPer
– ***alba***	EFou EPad SIde WPer
*– ***rhomboidea***	WEas
x ***pyraversi***	EPad
radchensis	EPad
raddeana	CHal CRiv EPad GCHN LBee MBro MNFA NGre NHar NMen NNrd NRed SSmi SSou WCla WDav WPer
raineri	EPad EPot GArf LBee NMen NWCA WAbe WThu
§ ***rapunculoïdes***	CArn EPad LGan NSti SBla SSvw WHer WHil WPer
– 'Alba'	EMon EPad
rapunculus	EPad MWil
recurva	See C. ***incurva***
rhomboidalis	See C. ***rapunculoïdes***
rigidipila	ECar
rotundifolia	CArn CBos CGle CKin CLew CNic CRDP EPad GTou LBlm MHew NLan NMir NNrd NRoo SSvw WCla WGwy WOak WPer
§ – var. ***alaskana***	EPad NBir NWCA
– ***alba***	EPad MBro WHoo
– ***caerulea plena***	See C. ***r.*** 'Flore Pleno'
§ – 'Flore Pleno'	CBos CGle
§ – 'Olympica'	CShe EBar EPad GCHN MBro NHol SFis
rupestris	CBot CNic EBur EPad EPot MFos NHol NWCA WAbe WDav WThu
– NS 401	NWCA
rupicola	EPad WEas
– JCA 262.400	CNic
samarkandensis	EPad
sarmatica	CGle CHan CNic EPad MBro MNFA NRoo NSti WCla WPer
sartorii	EPad SIng
saxatilis	EPad MBro NRed WDav WHal
– ssp. ***saxatilis***	EPad
saxifraga	EPad GCHN NWCA
¶ ***scabrella***	EPad MFos
¶ ***serrata***	EPad
shetleri	EPad
sibirica	EPad WPer
– ssp. ***taurica***	EPad
'Southern Seedling'	EPad
spathulata	EPad
– ssp. ***spruneriana***	EPad
¶ ***spatulata*** ssp. ***spatulata***	GTou NWCA
speciosa	EPad
spicata	EPad WHil
sp. ex Furze	MPar
sp. JCA 6872	EPad
sp. JCA 8363	EPad
sp. JJH 918638	EPad
'Stansfieldii'	EPad EPot NNrd NTow
sulphurea	EPad
takesimana	Widely available
– 'Elizabeth'	See C. 'Elizabeth '
thessala	EPad NWCA
thyrsoïdes	EPad GAbr GCra GDra GTou MNFA NWCA SBar SMrm WCla WPer
– ssp. ***carniolica***	EPad
tommasiniana	EPad LBee NHar SAsh WOMN
topaliana	EPad
– ssp. ***cordifolia***	CNic EPad
– – NS 409	NWCA
trachelium	CGle CKin CRDP EBar EJud EOrc EPad GTou LBlm MFir MHew NCat NHol NSal NSti SSvw WByw WCla WDav WHer WPer
– var. ***alba***	CElw CGle EPad MBro SSvw WEas WNdy WPer
– 'Alba Flore Pleno'	CBos CChu CGle CRow ECha EFou ELan EMon EPad LGre MUlv SBla
– 'Bernice' (d)	CElw CGle CHad CMil CRow EFou ELan EMon EOrc EPad EPar MBri MNFA MUlv NSti SCro SPer WByw WHal WHoo WNdy WRus
transsilvanica	EPad
tridentata	EPad
troegerae	EPad LBee LRHS MBro SBla
– JCA 265.500	WDav
tubulosa	See C. ***buseri***
'Tymonsii'	EBur EPad ESis MCas MHig NBir NKay NNrd NTow WHil
'Van-Houttei'	CBos CHan EMon EPad GCal MSte SBla WCot
versicolor	CHan EPad MBel MHig NHol NSti WEas WOMN WPer
– G&K 3347	EMon
♦ ***vidalii***	See AZORINA ***v.***
waldsteiniana	CPar EPad EPot LBee NNrd NTow WOMN
– JCA 266.000	MBro
'Warley White'	See C. x ***haylodgensis*** 'W.W.'
'Warleyensis'	See C. x ***haylodgensis*** 'Warley White'
witasekiana	CHun

x *wockei*	See C. x *w.* 'Puck'
§ – 'Puck'	CHun CRiv EPad GDra LBee MBro MCas NHar NMen NNrd WOMN WPat
xylocarpa	EPad
* 'Yvonne'	NEgg WHoo WPer
zoysii	EPad MHig

CAMPANULA X SYMPHYANDRA (Campanulaceae)

¶ C. *punctata* x S. *ossetica*	EPad

CAMPHOROSMA (Chenopodiaceae)

monspeliaca	NHol

CAMPSIS (Bignoniaceae)

grandiflora	CB&S CBow CBra CPle CSco EBre ELan ENot EPla LBre NPal SHil SPer SReu SSpi SSta WStI
radicans	CArn CBot CBow CDoC CHEx CLew CMac CPle ECtt ELan ENot EPla GCHN MWat SHBN SPer SReu WDin
¶ – 'Flamenco'	CB&S CCor IOrc LHop NWyt SMad WPat
§ – f. *flava*	CDoC CMac ELan IHos IJoh IOrc MBri MWat NPal SBra SHer SPer SSpi SSta
– 'Yellow Trumpet'	See C. *r. flava*
x *tagliabuana* 'Guilfoylei'	CB&S NBar
– 'Madame Galen'	CB&S CChu CCla CMac CSco CShe EBre ECtt EPla IJoh IOrc LBre LHop MBri MGos MRav NBar NFai SBra SHBN SMad SPer SReu SSpi SSta WSHC

CAMPTOSORUS See ASPLENIUM

CAMPYLOTROPIS (Leguminosae)

See Plant Deletions

CANARINA (Campanulaceae)

canariensis	ERea WOMN

CANDOLLEA See HIBBERTIA

CANNA † (Cannaceae)

¶ 'Assaut'	CBrk
'Black Knight'	CBrk LAma
¶ 'City of Portland'	CKel
¶ *coccinea*	CBrk
¶ Crozy hybrids	WCot
¶ *edulis*	CMon
x *ehemanii*	CHEx CTro
'Endeavour'	CBrk MSta
'Erebus'	CBrk MSta
¶ 'Fireside'	CBrk
¶ 'General Eisenhower'	CBrk
x *generalis*	CHEx
¶ *glauca*	CBrk CMon
'Golden Lucifer'	CKel LAma MBri
hybrids	LBow
indica	CBrk CChu CHEx CMon ERav GCra LBow LHil LHop SLMG WCot
– 'Purpurea'	CBrk CChu CMon ECha ERav SDix WCot
– *variegata*	LBow LHil
iridiflora	CBrk CChu ECha LHil SDix
¶ 'King Hakon'	CBrk
¶ 'King Midas'	CBrk
¶ 'Louis Cayeux'	CBrk
¶ 'Lucifer'	CBrk CKel SLMG
lutea	WCot
malawiensis 'Variegata'	LHil LHop
musifolia	CBrk SDix
'Oiseau de Feu' ('Firebird')	MBri
¶ 'Oiseau d'Or'	CBrk
'Orchid'	CBrk LAma MBri
'Perkeo'	CBrk LHil
'Picasso'	CBrk LAma
'President'	CKel LAma MBri
'Ra'	CBrk MSta
'Roi Humbert'	CBrk LHil SLMG
'Rosemond Coles'	LHil SLMG
¶ 'Shenandoah'	CBrk
¶ 'Strasbourg'	CBrk
¶ *striata*	CBrk
¶ 'Striped Beauty'	CBrk
¶ 'Tirol'	CBrk
'Verdi'	CBrk LHil
warscewiczii	CBrk SLMG
'Wyoming'	CBrk CKel LAma LHil
'Yellow Humbert'	LAma LHil

CANTUA (Polemoniaceae)

buxifolia	CB&S CGre CPle CTre CTro SHil SIgm

CAPPARIS (Capparaceae)

See Plant Deletions

CAPSICUM (Solanaceae)

annuum	MBri
* – 'Janne'	MBri

CARAGANA (Leguminosae)

arborescens	CChu CPle ENot MBar SPer WDin WFro WStI WTyr
– 'Lorbergii'	CDoC CLnd CSco IOrc MBlu MPla MUlv SHil SPer WDin
– 'Pendula'	CBow CLnd CSco EBre EHal ELan GRei LBre MBar MUlv NBee SEng SPer WDin WStI
– 'Walker'	CB&S CDoC COtt CPMA EBre IOrc LBre MBlu MBri MGos MUlv NBar SMad SPer WStI
brevispina	CHan
franchetiana	CLnd
frutex 'Globosa'	SPer

CARDAMINE (Cruciferae)

alba	WEas
asarifolia hort.	See PACHYPHRAGMA *macrophyllum*
– Linnaeus	CRow SSpi WCru
bulbifera	CHan CRDP CTom EMon
enneaphyllos	CRDP ECha NHar
§ *heptaphylla*	ECro ELan EPar IBlr WHoo
§ *kitaibelii*	WCot
latifolia	See C. *raphanifolia*

¶ ***microphylla***	SWas
§ ***pentaphyllos***	CGle CRDP CWGN ECha ECro ELan EPla GArf GGar MRav NSti SIgm
pratensis	CArn CKin CRDP CRow CWGN MHew NDea NLan NMir NSal WCla WHer WOak
– 'Edith' (d)	CGle EMon LRHS WCot WRus
– 'Flore Pleno'	CBre CChu CElw CGle CLew CRDP CRow CWGN ECha EFol ELan EMon GArf LRHS MPar MSta MTho NBro NNrd NSti SBla WByw WCla WEas WHoo WOMN WRus
– 'Improperly Dressed'	EMon
– 'William' (d)	CGle EMon LRHS
quinquefolia	CGle SWas
§ ***raphanifolia***	CBre CGle CLew CRow CWGN ECha EMon GAbr GCal GGar NCat NVic WSun
trifolia	CBos CCla CGle CRDP CWGN ECar ECha ECro EPar EPla GCal LGan MBar MFir NBro NHol NKay NNor NNrd NRya NTow SBla SWas WBon WByw WCru WEas WHer WHil
*– ***digitata***	MTho
¶ ***waldsteinii***	SWas

CARDIOCRINUM (Liliaceae/Liliaceae)

cordatum	EBul ERav
– var. ***glehnii***	EBul
giganteum	CB&S CBot CBrd CBro CHEx CRDP EBul EPar EPla GGGa IBlr LAma MBal MBlu NRog SSpi WChr WCru
– var. ***yunnanense***	EBul EPla GGGa NHar

CARDIOSPERMUM (Sapindaceae)

grandiflorum	CPle

CARDUNCELLUS (Compositae)

See Plant Deletions

CARDUUS (Compositae)

benedictus	See CNICUS ***b.***
nutans	CKin

CAREX (Cyperaceae)

albida	CElw EHoe EMon EPla ETPC MBal
atrata	EHoe EPla ETPC LHil SIng
¶ ***aurea***	ETPC
berggrenii	CElw CGle CMil CRow ECar ECou EHoe EMon EPar GCHN LGre MNFA NCat NHol NMir NNrd NSti NWyt SBar SBla WHil WPer
– narrow-leaved form	EHoe EPla
boottiana	GGar
brunnea 'Variegata'	GGar SCob WCot
buchananii	Widely available
– 'Viridis'	CB&S EGol ELan EPla ETPC WHer WPbr
comans	CLew EFol EGol EHoe EMon EPar EPla GCHN GCal GGar IBlr LHil MBal NBro SMrm SSpi WHal WWat
– bronze form	CB&S CElw CGle CRDP CRow CWGN EBar EBre ECar ECou EFol EHoe EMon EPar EPla EPot ESis ETPC LBre LGan MBri NHar NMir NSti SSpi WOMN WPbr WPer WWat WWye
§ ***conica***	EFol LHil LHop MBri SIng SSpi WPbr
– 'Hime-kan-suge'	See C. ***c.*** 'Snowline'
§ – 'Snowline' (v)	CAbb CElw CGle CRow CTom CWGN EBre ECha EHoe ELan EMon EPar EPla ESma ETPC GCHN GDra LBre MBri MDHE NBro NFai NHol NMir NWCA WPbr WRus WWye
crus-corvi	ETPC
dallii	ECou
demissa	EHoe
depauperata	CElw EMon EPla ETPC
¶ ***digitata***	WWye
dipsacea	CB&S CElw CPMA CRow ECou EHoe EMon EOrc EPla ETPC GCal NHar SFar SSpi WHal WWye
§ ***elata*** 'Aurea' (v)	Widely available
* 'Everbright' (v)	CB&S
firma	MHig NNrd
– 'Variegata'	CLew CRiv EHoe EPar MCas MDHE MFir MTho NTow NWCA SGil SIng WRus
flagellifera	CB&S CHad CRow ECar ECou EGol EHoe EMon EPar EPla ESma ETPC GGar LGan MFir NHol NWCA SUsu WEas WPbr
flava	ETPC
♦ ***forsteri***	See C. ***pseudocyperus***
fortunei 'Variegata'	See C. ***morrowii*** 'V.'
'Frosted Curls'	Widely available
grayi	CHan EHoe EMon EPla ETPC GCal MTho
hachijoensis	EPla
– 'Evergold' (v)	Widely available
N 'Hime-kan-suge'	See C. ***conica***
hirta	CKin
hispida	ETPC
humilis 'Hexe'	ETPC
kaloïdes	ECou EHoe EPla LGan
¶ ***macloviana***	ETPC
morrowii Boott	EBre EOrc GArf IBlr LBre MDHE NSti SPer
– hort.	See CC. ***oshimensis, hachijoensis***
– 'Fisher's Form' (v)	CBrd CHan EFou EGol EHoe EOrc EPla ESma ETPC GCHN MBri MUlv NHar SMad SSpi WCot
*– 'Nana Variegata'	NBir
N– 'Variegata'	CElw CGle CHan CMHG CRiv CRow EFol EHoe ELan ELun EMon EPla ETPC MBal MBar NEgg NMir NNor SApp SCob SLon SSpi WWat
muricata	CKin
muskingumensis	CB&S CElw EHoe EMon EPla ETPC GAbr MBri SApp SMad WWye
¶ – 'Small Red'	CB&S
– 'Wachtposten'	ETPC GCal MFir
nigra	CKin EHon ETPC GAbr
– ssp. ***tornata***	SIng
ornithopoda	CLew EPot LGan

– ***aurea***	See C. ***o.*** 'Variegata'
§ – 'Variegata'	CNic CRiv EBre EGol EPar EPla ETPC GCHN GCal LBre LHil MBal MCas NHar NHol NMir SCob SSmi WRus WWat WWye
¶ ***oshimensis***	IBlr
– 'Evergold'	See C. ***hachijoensis*** 'E.'
– 'Variegata'	CElw
¶ ***otrubae***	ETPC
¶ ***pallescens***	WWye
– 'Wood's Edge'	CNat
¶ ***panicea***	ETPC
pendula	Widely available
– 'Variegata'	LGan
petriei	CElw CNic CRow CTom EBar ECha EGol EPla ESis ETPC GAbr NNrd NSti NVic
pilulifera 'Tinney's Princess' (v)	EHoe EPot IBlr SApp SSpi
plantaginea	EHoe EMar EMon EPla ETPC
§ ***pseudocyperus***	CKin EHoe ETPC GCHN MSta SRms WWye
¶ ***remota***	WWye
¶ ***riparia***	EMFW
– 'Variegata'	CBen CGle CHan CMGP CRDP CRiv CRow CWGN EBre ECha EFol EHoe EHon EMFW EPar EPla ETPC GCHN GCal LBre MBri MUlv NBro SApp SCro SSpi WAbb WByw
* ***saxatilis*** 'Variegata'	SApp
secta	EHoe ETPC NHol
– var. ***tenuiculmis***	EHoe ETPC
siderosticha	CHan ECar EPot SMad WSHC
– 'Variegata'	CElw CGle CHal CHan CMHG CRow EBar EHoe EMon EPla ETPC GCHN IBar LHil LHop MBri NBro NHol NVic SAxl SIng WByw WRus WWat WWye
spicata	CKin
¶ sp. ex Chile	GCal
¶ sp. ex Uganda	GCal
stricta 'Bowles' Golden'	See C. ***elata*** 'Aurea'
sylvatica	CKin WWye
testacea	CB&S ECou EFol EGol EHoe ELan ELun EMar EMon EPla ETPC LHil MBri SFar SSpi WPbr WWye
trifida	CTom EHoe EPla ETPC GAbr GCHN GCal NCat
umbrosa 'The Beatles'	EHoe ETPC GCal
uncifolia	ECou EHoe
vulpina	CKin

CARICA (Caricaceae)

¶ ***chrysopetala***	CTro
pubescens	SArc

CARISSA (Apocynaceae)

bispinosa	SLMG
♦ ***grandiflora***	See C. ***macrocarpa***
F ***macrocarpa***	CTro ERea MNew

CARLINA (Compositae)

acanthifolia	ECro GCal SMad
acaulis	ECro SFis SGil SHer WEas WPer
¶ – bronze form	LGre
– ***caulescens***	See C. ***a. simplex***
§ – ssp. ***simplex***	CBrd CDec ECha ECro GCal LGan MBri NRar NRoo WHoo
vulgaris	CKin

CARMICHAELIA (Leguminosae)

aligera	ECou
angustata	ECou
§ ***arborea***	WBod
arenaria	ECou
astonii	ECou
♦ ***australis***	See C. ***arborea***
curta	ECou
enysii	ITim
– var. ***ambigua***	ECou
– 'Pringle'	ECou
exsul	ECou
glabrata	CPle ECou NNor
kirkii	ECou
– x ***astonii***	ECou
¶ – hybrid	SIgm
monroi	ECou MHig
nigrans	ECou
odorata	ECou
orbiculata	ECou
ovata	ECou
petriei	ECou SPer
uniflora	ECou
violacea	ECou
williamsii	ECou

X CARMISPARTIUM (Leguminosae)

astens	See X C. ***hutchinsii***
§ ***hutchinsii***	ECou
– 'County Park'	ECou

CARPENTERIA (Hydrangeaceae)

californica	CBot CBra CCla CGre CSco EHar ELan ERea IJoh IOrc LAbb LHop LNet MBri MGos SBla SHBN SLPl SLon SPer SReu SSpi SSta WDin WSHC WWat
– 'Bodnant'	SHil
– 'Ladhams' Variety'	CB&S LGre

CARPINUS † (Corylaceae)

betulus	CB&S CBow CBra CDoC CKin CLnd CPer EBre ELan ENot GRei IHos IJoh ISea LBre LBuc LPan MBar MBri NBee NWea SPer SReu STre WDin WMou WNor WStI
– 'Columnaris'	CLnd CTho ENot
§ – 'Fastigiata'	CB&S CDoC CLnd CSco CTho EBre ENot GRei IJoh IOrc LBre LPan MBar MGos NBee NWea SPer WDin WMou
¶ – 'Frans Fontaine'	CTho MBri SHil WMou
¶ – 'Incisa'	GAri LPan
– 'Pendula'	CTho EBre GAri LBre WMou
– 'Purpurea'	ENot
– 'Pyramidalis'	See C. ***b.*** 'Fastigiata'
– 'Quercifolia'	WMou
– 'Variegata'	WMou
caroliniana	CLnd CMCN GAri SHil WMou WNor
coreana	WNor
fargesii	See C. ***laxiflora macrostachya***

japonica	GAri SMad SSpi WCoo WMou
laxiflora	CMCN ELan SSpi WMou WNor
orientalis	CMCN EArb EHal GAri STre WCoo WNor
x *schuschaensis*	ELan
turczaninowii	CTho WNor

CARPOBROTUS (Aizoaceae)

§ *edulis*	CHEx IBlr NGre SLMG WEas WHer

CARPODETUS (Grossulariaceae)

¶ *serratus*	CPle

CARTHAMUS (Compositae)

tinctorius	MChe NSal SIde WHer

CARUM (Umbelliferae)

carvi	CArn CHun CSFH Effi GPoy IEde LHol MChe NSel SHer SIde WOak WPer WWye
petroselinum	See PETROSELINUM ***crispum***

CARYA † (Juglandaceae)

cordiformis	CMCN EHar SSpi WCoo
glabra	CMCN WCoo
N *illinoinensis*	CMCN EArb EHar
laciniosa	CMCN
¶ *myristiciformis*	CMCN
ovata	CMCN EHar ESim MBrk SHil SSpi WCoo
tomentosa	CMCN

CARYOPTERIS † (Verbenaceae)

x *clandonensis*	CB&S CBot CBra CPle CSco CTrw EFol ELan ENot ERav GRei IDai ISea LAbb LHop MBro MWat NBir NKay NNor WBod WCru WDin WEas WSHC WStI WWat WWeb WWin WWye
– 'Arthur Simmonds'	CDoC ECha EGol EHal MBal MBri SFis SLon SPer
– 'Ferndown'	CArn CBow CDoC CSco CShe EBre EGol ELan LBre LHop NKay SPer SReu SSpi WDin WSHC WWeb
– 'Heavenly Blue'	CB&S CBra CSco EBre ECha EHoe ELan ENot ERav IJoh LBre MBar MGos MWat NKay NRoo SLon SMad SPer SPla SReu SSpi SSta WDin WRus
– 'Kew Blue'	CB&S CBot CBow CBra CCla CDoC CShe EBre ECar EFou EGol ELan ENot LAbb LBre LGre MGos SHBN SHer SMad SPer SPla SSta WRus WSHC WWat WWeb WWye
– 'Worcester Gold'	Widely available
¶ *divaricata*	SSpi
incana	CBow CDoC CSco CShe ERav GCal LHop MSte SDry SPla WSHC
– weeping form	GCal
odorata	CPle

CARYOTA (Palmae)

mitis	LPal

CASSANDRA See **CHAMAEDAPHNE**

CASSIA (Leguminosae)

–	See also SENNA

CASSINIA (Compositae)

leptophylla	CPle EBar SPer WThu
– ssp. ***fulvida***	CB&S CMHG CPle ECou EHoe ESis IBar IOrc ISea MBar MBlu MPla MRav NNor NTow SBor SHil SPer STre WBod WDin WStI
– ssp. ***vauvilliersii***	CKni CMHG NNor WDav WSHC
– – var.***albida***	CB&S SHil SPer WBod
retorta	ECou IBar NNor SPer
'Ward Silver'	CBot ECou LGre NNor

CASSINIA X HELICHRYSUM (Compositae)

	WKif

CASSIOPE † (Ericaceae)

'Askival'	ITim
'Badenoch'	CNic ESis GDra GGGa GWht MBal MBar NHar
'Bearsden'	GAri GDra GGGa GWht MBal NHar NKay WPat WThu
'Edinburgh'	CMHG EPot GAbr GDra GGGa GWht MBal MBar MBri NHar NHol SEng WBod WDin WPat WThu
fastigiata	GGGa NHar
– B 542	MBal
– LS&H 17451	MBal
'George Taylor'	WAbe
¶ 'Inverleith'	WThu
'Kathleen Dryden'	GDra MBal
lycopodioïdes	ECar EPot ESis GAbr GDra GGGa GWht MBal MBar MBri MGos NHar NHol NKay SReu WAbe WBod WThu
– 'Beatrice Lilley'	CRiv ECar EPot GAri GGGa MBal MBar MHig NHar NHol WPat
*– ***crista pilosa***	ECar
– var. ***globularis***	GArf GGGa
– 'Major'	WBod
– ***minima***	GArf
'Medusa'	EPot GDra GGGa MAsh MBal MHig WPat WThu
mertensiana	CRiv ESis GGGa GWht MBal MBar WAbe WBod
– ***californica***	GArf
– dwarf form	MBal
– ssp. ***gracilis***	CNic ELan GAbr GGGa MGos MHig NHar NHol
'Muirhead'	EPot GDra GGGa GWht LTil MBal MBar MHig NHar NHol NKay SHer WAbe WBod WDin WPat WThu
'Randle Cooke'	EPot ESis GDra GGGa MBal MBar MBri MHig NHar NKay WPat WThu
selaginoïdes	NHol
– LS&E 13284	GArf GAri GGGa
stelleriana	GArf SSta
tetragona	MAsh MBal MBar MBri NHol SRms
– var. ***saximontana***	EPot GGGa MBal NHol

CASTANEA † (Fagaceae)

mollissima	GAri ISea
sativa	CB&S CBow CBra CDoC CHEx CKin CLnd CPer ENot GRei IJoh IOrc ISea LBuc MBar MBri NBee NRog NWea SHBN SPer WCoo WDin WMou WOMN WStI
§ – 'Albomarginata'	CDoC CSco EBre EHar LBre MBlu SHil SMad SSpi SSta WMou
– 'Argenteovariegata'	See C. *s.* 'Albomarginata'
– 'Aureomarginata'	See C. *s.* 'Variegata'
F – 'Marron de Lyon'	ESim
§ – 'Variegata'	CB&S COtt ELan IMal SMad SPer
¶ – 'Vincent van Gogh'	SMad

CASTANOPSIS (Fagaceae)

cuspidata	SArc WCoo

CASUARINA (Casuarinaceae)

cunninghamiana	CGre ISea
¶ *equisetifolia*	CTro
¶ *muelleriana*	CGre
stricta	See ALLOCASUARINA *verticillata*
torulosa	ECar

CATALPA † (Bignoniaceae)

bignonioïdes	CB&S CBot CBow CBra CDoC CGre CHEx CLnd CSco ELan ENot IBar IOrc ISea LPan MBri NPal SPer WCoo WDin
– 'Aurea'	CB&S CBot CBow CBra CCla CLnd CSco EBre EHar ELan ENot IOrc LBre LHop LNet LPan MBlu MBri MGos NHol SEng SHBN SMad SPer SReu SSta WDin WMou WPat
– 'Purpurea'	See C. x *erubescens* 'P.'
– 'Variegata'	CWit LNet SGly SPer SSpi SSta WPat
bungei	LPan SEng
– 'Purpurea'	ELan LPan
x *erubescens* 'Purpurea'	CB&S CBot CBow CDoC CHEx CLnd EBre EHar EPla IOrc LBre MBlu MBri SHBN SHil SMad SPer SSpi WPat
¶ *fargesii*	CLnd
ovata	CBot CGre CHEx EHar WCoo
speciosa	CB&S CHEx CMCN EHar WMou

CATANANCHE (Compositae)

caerulea	Widely available
– 'Alba'	CCla CGle CPou CSev ECha EFou GCal LHop MUlv NBir NOak SAxl SHer SPer SUsu WHal WRus WSun WTyr
– 'Bicolor'	EMon
– 'Major'	CKel CShe ENot GCal MBri MWat SRms WEas

CATAPODIUM (Gramineae)

§ *rigidum*	ETPC

CATHARANTHUS (Apocynaceae)

roseus	MBri
– *ocellatus*	MBri

CAULOPHYLLUM (Berberidaceae)

thalictroïdes	NSal

CAUTLEYA † (Zingiberaceae)

spicata	CHEx IBlr
– 'Robusta'	CCla CKni CRDP EBlo

CAYRATIA (Vitaceae)

See Plant Deletions

CEANOTHUS † (Rhamnaceae)

'A T Johnson'	CMHG CMac CPle ENot LNet NFai NKay SHBN SPer SPla SReu WAbe WBod WTyr WWeb
americanus	CArn CMHG CPle NSal
– 'Fincham'	EPla
arboreus	CGre SArc
– 'Trewithen Blue'	CB&S CCla CGre CLan CMHG CMac CPle CSco CTre CTrw ELan IDai IOrc ISea LHop LNet MRav NKay NSti SLon SPer SReu WBod WSHC WWat
'Autumnal Blue'	CB&S CCla CMHG CMac CSco CShe EGol ELan ENot IDai IJoh MBri MGos MWat NFai NKay SHBN SLon SPer SReu SSta WDin WEas WWat WWin
azureus	See C. *coeruleus*
'Basil Fox'	EPla
* 'Blue Cushion'	CB&S ECtt ESis ESma LHop MGos NHol NWyt
¶ 'Blue Jeans'	CAbP
'Blue Mound'	CDoC CGre CLan CPMA CPle CSco CShe CTre CTrw EBlo EBre EGol ERav ESma IJoh LAbb LBre LHop MGos MRav NHol NNor NWyt SPer SPla SReu SSpi WSHC WWat
'Burkwoodii'	CB&S CBra CDoC CGre CMHG CMac CPle CSco EBre GRei IDai IOrc LBre LTil MBal MBri MPit NWea SBla SHBN SLon SPer SReu
'Burtonensis'	CGre CMHG ENot
'Cascade'	CB&S CBow CBra CDoC CLan CMHG CMac CSam CSco CShe ELan ENot IOrc ISea LAbb LNet MBri MWat NSti SHer SLon SPer SSta WBod WSHC
§ *coeruleus*	WBod
'Concha'	CAbP CAbb CB&S CBow CMHG CPMA CPle CSam CSco CTre EGol ERav ESma LHop LTil MBri MUlv NWyt SHer SMad SPla SReu SSpi SSta WEas WWat
cyaneus	CGre CPle
¶ 'Cynthia Postan'	EBlo
'Dark Star'	LRHS
'Delight'	EPla IDai IOrc LAbb NNor SChu SPer WAbe WBod WWat
x *delileanus* 'Gloire de Versailles'	CB&S CBot CMHG CMac CPle CSam CSco CShe ELan ENot GRei IDai IJoh ISea LAbb MBri MGos MWat NKay NWea SHBN SLon SPer SReu SSta WBod WDin WWin
– 'Henri Desfossé'	CSco ELan SPer WDin WKif WStI
– 'Topaze'	CDoC CPle CSco CShe ENot NSti SLon
dentatus hort.	See C. x *lobbianus*

– Torrey & A Gray	CB&S CBra CMHG CMac CPle CSam CSco EBre EGol ELan ENot GRei IJoh IOrc LBre MBal MGos NKay NNor SChu SLon SPer WBod
– var. ***floribundus***	CSco ELan SDix
*– 'Prostratus'	MBal
****depressus***	CPle
'Dignity'	CGre CLan CSco WWeb
divergens	CMac CPle SPer WBod
'Edinburgh'	CMHG CMac ELan ENot MBri SGil SHer WBod WKif WWeb
¶ 'Edward Stevens'	CGre
fendleri	CGre
foliosus	CGre CPle
– ***austromontanus***	CB&S CLan CPle CTrw IDai
¶ 'Frosty Blue'	MSta
'Gentian Plume'	LTil
gloriosus	CCla CDoC CPMA CPle IOrc SDry WSHC WWat
– 'Emily Brown'	CB&S IJoh
griseus var. ***horizontalis***	SDry
– – 'Hurricane Point'	CB&S
– – 'Yankee Point'	CB&S CChu CMHG CMac CPle CSPN CSam CSco ECtt ERav LHop LNet MAsh MBri MPit NFai SHBN SHer SLon SPer SPla WWeb
impressus	CB&S CCla CDoC CGre CLan CMHG CPMA CPle CSco CShe ELan ENot IJoh MBal MBri MRav MWat SHer SLon SPer SPla SReu SSpi WAbe WBod WEas
integerrimus macrothyrsus	CPle
'Italian Skies'	CDoC CGre CLan CMHG CMac CSam CSco ELan ESma LHop LTil MBri MRav NWyt SHer SPer WBod WWeb
'Joyce Coulter'	CB&S
¶ 'Julia Phelps'	CMHG WEas
'Ken Taylor'	LRHS
x ***lobbianus***	CGre EHal
– 'Russellianus'	SHBN SLon WBod
¶ x ***mendocinensis***	CPle
¶ ***oliganthus***	CPle
x ***pallidus*** 'Marie Simon'	CB&S CPle ELan ERav IJoh LHop MBri MRav NNor SHer SLon SPer WAbe WKif WSHC
– 'Perle Rose'	CB&S CDoC CMac CPle EHal IOrc LTil SGil SHBN SHer SPer WAbe WKif
papillosus	CBra CGre CLan CMac CPle ECtt ELan
– var. ***roweanus***	CGre CMac CPle GAri LRHS SDry SHil WWat
– x ***thyrsiflorus***	CPle
¶ 'Percy Picton'	CGre
'Pin Cushion'	LRHS LTil
¶ 'Point Millerton'	LRHS
prostratus	CDoC ECar EPla IDai LGro MAsh SDry SHBN SHil WAbe WEas WWin
'Puget Blue'	CB&S CBra CCla CHad CLan CMHG CMac CPMA CPle CSam CSco EBlo EBre ELan IBar LBre LHop MBri MGos MWat NTow SDix SGil SHer SPer SSpi SSta WBod WKif WSHC
purpureus	CGre CHan CPle SDry SGil WWeb
'Ray Hartman'	SMad
x ***regius***	LHop
repens	See C. ***thyrsiflorus r.***
rigidus	CBow CPle MGos SDry SRms WBod
'Sierra Blue'	WBod
'Snow Flurries'	CB&S CBow CPle ELan ERav MSta SLon SMad
¶ ***sorediatus***	CPle
'Southmead'	CB&S CMac IJoh IOrc ISea MBri WBod WWat
¶ ***spinosus***	CPle
thyrsiflorus	CB&S CMac CPle ELan IJoh LNet MBal MBri NFai NHol SArc SHBN SPer WBod WDin
§ – var. ***repens***	Widely available
– 'Skylark'	LRHS SReu
x ***veitchianus***	CB&S CBra CMac CSam CSco CShe EBre ELan ENot LBre LNet MBar MWat NHol SLon SPer WBod WTyr
verrucosus	CPle
¶ 'White Cascade'	MSta

CEDRELA (Meliaceae)

sinensis	See TOONA ***s.***

CEDRONELLA (Labiatae)

§ ***canariensis***	CArn CFis CGle CHun CMer CSFH CSev CTre GCal GPoy IBlr ILis LHol NSal NSel SHer SIde SWat WHer WOMN WOak WPer WWye
mexicana	See AGASTACHE ***m.***
triphylla	See C. ***canariensis***

CEDRUS (Pinaceae)

atlantica	See C. ***libani a.***
brevifolia	See C. ***libani brevifolia***
deodara	Widely available
– 'Albospica' (v)	LCon MAsh MBri
– 'Argentea'	MBar MGos
– 'Aurea'	CB&S CBra CDoC CGre CPMA CSco EHar EHul IJoh LCon LPan MBar MBri SEng SLim SPer SReu SSta WAbe WDin WFro WMou
– 'Aurea Pendula'	ENHC
– 'Blue Dwarf'	CKen LCon
¶ – 'Blue Triumph'	LPan
– 'Cream Puff'	EBre LBre LCon LLin MBri MGos
– 'Feelin' Blue'	CDoC CKen COtt EBre LBee LBre LCon LLin LPan LRHS MAsh MBar MBri MGos NBar NHol SLim SPer
– 'Gold Cone'	MGos
– 'Gold Mound'	GAri LCon MAsh MBar MBri MPla NHol
– 'Golden Horizon'	CBra CDoC CGre CKen CMac CSco EBlo EBre EHar EHul ENHC IJoh IOrc LBee LBre LCon LLin LTil MBar MBri MGos NBee NHol SHBN SLim SPer SSta WDin
– 'Karl Fuchs'	EBre LBre LCon LRHS MBri
– 'Kashmir'	LCon MBri
– 'Klondyke'	NHol
– 'Lime Glow'	CKen
*– 'MacPenny's Seedling'	CMac

– 'Nana Aurea'	EBlo LCon
– 'Nivea'	CKen
– 'Pendula'	CMac EHul LPan MBar MBri MGos MWat NHol SEng
– 'Pygmy'	CKen
– 'Robusta'	LCon
– 'Scott'	CKen
– 'Verticillata Glauca'	CDoC MBri SEng
§ ***libani*** var. ***atlantica***	CDoC CGre EHar EHul GAri ISea LCon MBar NWea SLim WDin WMou WWat
– – 'Aurea'	CB&S CDoC CMac CSco EHar LCon LLin LPan MBar MBri MGos SHil SSta WDin
– – 'Fastigiata'	CDoC CMac EHar EHul LCon LPan MBar MBri SLim WMou
– – 'Glauca Fastigiata'	CB&S CKen EHar LCon MBri SMad
– – Glauca Group	Widely available
– – 'Glauca Pendula'	CBow CDoC CKen CPMA CSco EHar EHul IOrc LCon LNet LPan MBar MBri MGos SEng SHil SLim SMad SPer SSta WAbe
– – 'Pendula'	CMac EHar GAri MGos NBee
§ – ssp. ***brevifolia***	EHar ELan GAri LCon MBar MBlu SSta
– – 'Epsteiniana'	MBar
– – 'Hillier Compact'	CKen
– – 'Kenwith'	CKen
– ssp. ***libani***	CB&S CBow CBra CDoC CMac CSco EHar EHul ENot IJoh IOrc LCon MBar MBri NWea SHBN SMad SPer STre WDin WFro WMou WNor WWat
– – 'Comte de Dijon'	EHul SHil SLim
– – 'De Creffe'	CDoC
– – 'Nana'	CKen LCon SEng
– – 'Sargentii'	CDoC CKen CMac CSco EHar EHul LCon LLin MAsh MBal MBar MBri MGos NHar SHil SLim SSta
– – 'Taurus'	MBar

CELASTRUS (Celastraceae)

loeseneri (f)	SBra
– (m)	SBra
orbiculatus	CB&S CBra CHan CMCN CSco ECar ELan EMon MPla MPlt MRav MWat NWyt SPer SReu SSta WBod WSHC
– 'Diana' (f)	SSta
– hermaphrodite form	ELan EOvi EPla SBra SDix SHil SSpi WWat
scandens	CMac ELan EOvi MWat NSal
– (f)	SBra
– (m)	SBra

CELMISIA (Compositae)

alpina	NNrd WCru
argentea	ECar GArf MHig NHar
bellidioïdes	CNic CRiv EMNN GArf GDra ITim NHar NHol NMen NRed WAbe
brevifolia	IBlr
coriacea	IBlr NHar NNor SBar WDav WEas
¶ ***dallii***	WAbe
densiflora	GDra NHol
gracilenta	GArf MFir MHig NHol SIng WDav
hectorii	IBlr ITim MHig
¶ ***incana***	IBlr
Inshriach hybrids	GAbr MBal NHar WCru
¶ Jury hybrids	GCal
longifolia	GDra
ramulosa	GArf IBlr ITim MHig NHar
semicordata	WAbe WDav
sessiliflora	GArf ITim
– 'Mount Potts'	GDra
¶ ***traversii***	WAbe
§ ***walkeri***	IBlr IDai WAbe
webbiana	See C. ***walkeri***

CELOSIA (Amaranthaceae)

argentea var. ***cristata***	MBri
– – Plumosa Group	MBri

CELSIA See VERBASCUM

X CELSIOVERBASCUM See VERBASCUM

CELTIS (Ulmaceae)

australis	CB&S CCor EHal LPan
bungeana	CMCN
jessoensis	CMCN
¶ ***laevigata***	CMCN
occidentalis	CPle EHar ELan WCoo
¶ – var. ***pumila***	CMCN
reticulata	WCoo
sinensis	CMCN WCoo

CENTAUREA (Compositae)

atropurpurea	EMon
bella	Widely available
benoistii	EMon
¶ 'Blue Dreams'	EMon
cana	See C. ***triumfettii cana***
♦ ***candidissima*** hort.	See C. ***cineraria cineraria***
cheiranthifolia	ECha
§ – var. ***purpurascens***	EMon
§ ***cineraria*** ssp. ***cineraria***	CBrk CFis CSpe IDai WPer
¶ – 'Colchester White'	CBrk
cyanus	CNat CSFH MHew NSal
cynaroïdes	See LEUZEA ***centauroïdes***
dealbata	CHad CHan CPar EBar ECtt LGan LWad MFir NBro NCat NFai NKay NMir NOak NOrc NRoo SChu SCro SHer SSvw SUsu WByw WHil WHoo WWin
– 'Steenbergii'	CDoC CGle CMGP CSco EBre ECED ELan EPad GCal LBre MBel MBri NOak NRya NSti SCro SPer WByw WCot WHer
debeauxii ssp. ***nemoralis***	CKin
fischeri	See C. ***cheiranthifolia purpurascens***
glastifolia	EMon GCal
gymnocarpa	See C. ***cineraria cineraria***
hypoleuca 'John Coutts'	Widely available
jacea	NBir WHil
macrocephala	CBre CChu CElw CGle CKel CPar CSco ECha ELan GCal MBri MChe MFir NBee NBro NMir NOak NOrc NRoo SDix SPer WByw WHal WHil WHoo WMer WPer

montana	CBow CBre EFol ELan ESma IDai LGan MBro MFir NBro NNor NOak NOrc NVic SSvw WByw WCra WEas WHal WOak WOld WPer WWin
– ***alba***	CBow CBre CElw CGle CSev CTom ECha EFol EGol ELan EMar EMon EOrc EPar LGre MBri MFir MPar MSte NCat NRar SChu SPer SPla WByw WEas WHal WMer
§ – ***carnea***	CBre CElw CTom ECha EMon WBon WHal WWin
– 'Grandiflora'	MBri
– 'Ochroleuca'	CElw EMon
– 'Parham'	CBre EMon SChu SMrm SPer
– ***purpurea***	CTom
– ***rosea***	See C. ***m. carnea***
– 'Violetta'	NBir
nigra	CArn CKin MHew NLan NMir NSal WCla
– var. ***alba***	CArn
– 'Breakaway' (v)	EMon
– ssp. ***rivularis***	WHil
orientalis	EMon
¶ ***parilica***	NWCA
pulcherrima	ECha EFol EMon
'Pulchra Major'	CGle EBre ECha EGol ELan EPla GCal LBre LGre MUlv WByw
rutifolia	EBar
¶ ***salonitana***	EMon
scabiosa	CKin CNat EHal MChe MHew NLan NSal SFis SIde WCla WGwy WPer
simplicicaulis	CMea CNic LGan MFir MRav MTho NRoo SFis SWas WAbe WCla WEas WHil WOMN WPer
sp. DS&T 89061T	EMon
sp. DS&T 89073T	EMon
sp. DS&T 89075T	EMon
§ ***triumfettii*** ssp. ***cana*** 'Rosea'	CMea CNic ECha EFol EMon NNrd WHil WWin
– ssp. ***stricta***	CTom EMar EMon LHil SFis SPla WOMN
– – 'Macedonia'	SFis
uniflora ssp. ***nervosa***	CPar
– – JCA 287.000	CLew EMon

CENTAURIUM (Gentianaceae)

erythraea	CArn GPoy MChe NSal NSel SIde WCla WWye
scilloïdes	CNic CRiv CShe ELan MBro MCas MPit MPla MTho NGre NHol NMen NNrd NTow NWCA SHer WCla WHoo WOMN WWin

CENTELLA (Umbelliferae)

¶ ***asiatica***	CArn

CENTRADENIA (Melastomataceae)

inaequilateralis 'Cascade'	CAbb ERea IHos LHil MBri NFai SFis
¶ – 'Mini Cascade'	LHil

CENTRANTHERA (Scrophulariaceae)

See Plant Deletions

CENTRANTHUS (Valerianaceae)

§ ***ruber***	CArn CBow CKin CSFH CTom EBre ECtt EFol EFou EMon GPoy LBre LWad MChe MHew MNFA MPlt NMir NPer NRoo NSel NSti SHer WByw WDin WHen WWye
§ – ***albus***	Widely available
– ***atrococcineus***	CSco ECha SPer WPer
– ***coccineus***	CCla CDoC ELan EMon MWat NFai SMrm SPla WHil WTyr

CEPHALANTHUS (Rubiaceae)

occidentalis	CCla CPle EBar ELan EPla MBlu MPla NSal SPer WPat

CEPHALARIA (Dipsacaceae)

§ ***alpina***	CElw CGle CPar ECha EPot ESis GCHN GCal MBro MPit NRoo SHer SUsu WAbe WDav WPer WWin
– 'Nana'	CShe NMir NWCA WPer
§ ***gigantea***	Widely available
leucantha	ECro
tatarica	See C. ***gigantea***

CEPHALOTAXUS (Cephalotaxaceae)

fortunei	CGre
– 'Prostrate Spreader'	CGre LTil SHil
harringtonia var. ***drupacea***	CChu LCon WWat
– 'Fastigiata'	CB&S CChu CDoC CKen EHul LTil MBar MBri SHil SLim
– 'Gimborn's Pillow'	MBar
– 'Gnome'	LCon
– 'Nana'	CMCN

CEPHALOTUS (Cephalotaceae)

follicularis	EFEx MSte WHal WMEx

CERASTIUM (Caryophyllaceae)

alpinum	ELan SRms SSou WThi
– ssp. ***lanatum***	CLew CNic GTou MHig NGre NNrd NTow NWCA SHer SIng WCru WDav WHil WPer
¶ ***candidissimum***	SIgm
tomentosum	CFis CRiv ELan LGro NNor NRoo SIng SPer WPer WWin
– var. ***columnae***	CRiv EBre ECha EHoe GGar LBre SHer SRms
– 'Silberteppich'	SFis

CERATONIA (Leguminosae)

See Plant Deletions

CERATOPHYLLUM (Ceratophyllaceae)

demersum	CBen CRow EHon EMFW NDea SAWi SWat WChe

CERATOSTIGMA † (Plumbaginaceae)

abyssinicum	ELan ERav
griffithii	Widely available
– SF 149/150	ISea
larpentae	See C. ***plumbaginoïdes***

§ ***plumbaginoïdes*** Widely available
willmottianum Widely available

CERATOTHECA (Pedaliaceae)

triloba alba ELan

CERCIDIPHYLLUM † (Cercidiphyllaceae)

japonicum CB&S CBra CCla CFis CLnd CMCN CMHG CSco ELan ENot IBar IDai IJoh IOrc LHop LTil MBal MBri NBar NHol NJap SHBN SPer SSta WBod WCoo WDin WPat WSHC WWat
– var. ***magnificum*** CMCN EHar MBlu MBri MGos SEng WWat
– f. ***pendulum*** CBow CCla CDoC CPMA CSco EHar ELan ESma LTil MBri NBar SHil SPer SSpi
– 'Rotfuchs' SSpi WMou
– 'Ruby' CPMA LRHS SSpi

CERCIS (Leguminosae)

canadensis CBot MGos SPer SSpi
– 'Forest Pansy' CAbP CB&S CBow COtt CPMA CSco EHar LRHS LTil MBlu MBri MGos MUlv SHil SMad SPer SSpi WPat
chinensis CBow CSam SPer SSpi WCoo
– f. ***alba*** ELan
– 'Avondale' CB&S CBow CPMA LNet LTil MBri SSpi
griffithii CMCN
¶ ***racemosa*** SHil
siliquastrum Widely available
– f. ***albida*** CBot CBow CChu CCla CDoC CGre CLnd CMCN CPMA EHar IOrc MBlu MSta SHil SMad SPer SSpi WBod WWat
– 'Bodnant' LTil

CERCOCARPUS (Rosaceae)

♦ ***breviflorus*** See C. ***montanus paucidentatus***
¶ ***montanus*** CB&S CCor
§ – ***paucidentatus*** CCor

CERINTHE (Boraginaceae)

glabra WCru WPer

CEROPEGIA (Asclepiadaceae)

¶ ***armandii*** SGil
barklyi CHal
lanceolata See C. ***longifolia***
linearis ssp. ***woodii*** CHal IBlr MBri SLMG
§ ***longifolia*** SLMG
radicans SLMG
stapeliiformis SLMG

CEROXYLON (Palmae)

¶ ***alpinum*** LPal
quindiuense LPal
¶ ***utile*** LPal

CESTRUM (Solanaceae)

aurantiacum CB&S CPle CTro ERea GCal IBlr SLMG
§ ***elegans*** CBot CHal CPle CSev CTre CTro IBlr ISea LHil SHil SLMG
fasciculatum CB&S CGre IBlr LHil NRar SLMG
'Newellii' CB&S CHEx CLan CPle CSev CTro ELan ERea IBlr ISea LAbb LHop MBal SCog SHil SLMG WAbe WSHC
nocturnum CB&S CPle CSun CTro ERea LBlm LHil SLMG
parqui CAbb CBot CChu CDec CDoC CGre CLan CMHG CPle CTro ECha EFou EPla ERea GCal IBlr LHil LHop LWad SDix SUsu WBod WOld WSHC
psittacinum CGre SLMG
purpureum See C. ***elegans***
roseum 'Ilnacullin' CB&S CGre CPle ERea IBlr LHil
violaceum CB&S

CETERACH See ASPLENIUM

CHAENACTIS (Compositae)

See Plant Deletions

CHAENOMELES (Rosaceae)

x ***californica***
'Enchantress' CShe
cathayensis CPou
¶ – var. ***wilsonii*** CPle CTho
§ ***japonica*** CDoC ENot GRei IJoh LBuc MAsh MBal MBar MPla NNor NRoo SHer WCoo WDin WWeb
– f. ***alba*** CShe
– var. ***alpina*** CSco MPla
– 'Sargentii' COtt CShe
♦ ***lagenaria*** See C. ***speciosa***
maulei See C. ***japonica***
sinensis See PSEUDOCYDONIA ***s.***
§ ***speciosa*** CSam ISea MBal MBar NNor NWea WFro WNor
♦ – 'Apple Blossom' See C. ***s.*** 'Moerloosei'
– 'Aurora' MBar
– 'Cardinalis' CGre
– 'Choshan' See C. x ***superba*** 'Yaegaki'
– 'Falconnet Charlet' CShe
– 'Geisha Girl' CDoC CPMA CSco EBre EPla ESis ESma LBre MAsh MPla MRav MUlv NHol NWyt SHBN SHer SPer SPla STre WWat WWeb
– 'Knap Hill Radiance' CShe SHer
§ – 'Moerloosei' CBow CChu CCla CPMA CSam CSco CShe CWit EHar ELan GWht MBri MPla MRav NSti SHBN SIng SPer SPla WWat WWeb
– 'Nivalis' CB&S CBow CCla CShe CTre EBre EGol EHar ELan ENot GRei IJoh IOrc LBre LHop MBar MBri MPla SChu SHBN SPer SPla SReu SSta WBod WDin WSHC WWat
– 'Phylis Moore' CLan
*– 'Port Eliot' CDoC CGre MBal MBrk SHer WBod WWeb
– 'Rosea Plena' CShe
¶ – 'Rosemoor Seedling' GAri
– 'Rubra Grandiflora' CShe

– 'Simonii'	CPMA CSco CShe ENot MBal MBri MGos MPla SHer SPer WBod WWat
– 'Snow'	CPle CSam ISea MBal MWat SHer SSpi WBod WStI WWeb
– 'Tortuosa'	CCor WWat
– 'Umbilicata'	CDoC CSco ENot MBel SPer SRms
x *superba* 'Boule de Feu'	CBra CDoC SCob
¶– 'Cameo'	CAbP CBow CDec EHar SLPl
– 'Coral Sea'	CSco CShe NNor
– 'Crimson and Gold'	CBra CCla CSco EBre EHar ELan ENot IJoh IOrc LBre LHop MBal MBar MBri MGos MRav MWat NBee NKay NRoo SHBN SLon SPer SReu WBod WDin WStI
– 'Elly Mossel'	CB&S CDoC CSco CShe
– 'Etna'	CB&S SPla
– 'Fire Dance'	CShe EBre ECtt ELan ENot LBre NHol SCob SPer
– 'Hever Castle'	CPMA CShe WWat
– 'Hollandia'	CDoC CSco CShe ELan MBel MGos NEgg WStI
– 'Issai White'	MBri MUlv
– 'Jet Trail'	CB&S CPMA CSco EBre ENot LBre MBri SCob SLPl
– 'Knap Hill Scarlet'	CB&S CBow CLan CSam CShe CTre IOrc LAbb SHBN SPer STre WDin WStI WWat
– 'Lemon and Lime'	CCla CPMA CSco ENot
– 'Nicoline'	CB&S CSco EHar ENot GRei IDai MBri MWat NHol SCob SSpi WStI
– 'Ohio Red'	SCob WBod
– 'Pink Lady'	Widely available
– 'Rowallane'	CSam CSco ELan ENot GAri IDai MBal MRav MWat SHBN SPer
– 'Texas Scarlet'	MBri WWin
§– 'Yaegaki'	CDoC CShe SPer

CHAENORHINUM (Scrophulariaceae)

'Blue Pygmy'	SChu
glareosum	MCas MHig WCla WPer
§ *origanifolium*	EPot ESis MFir MPar NTow NWCA WPer WWin
¶– 'Blue Dream'	WPer
§– 'Blue Sceptre'	MCas

CHAEROPHYLLUM (Umbelliferae)

hirsutum	CRow ELan
– roseum	CBre CChu CHan CLew CRDP ECha EFol EMar EPla MFir MPar MRav MUlv NRoo NSti SMrm SSpi SUsu WByw WEas WHal WSHC

CHAMAEBATIARIA (Rosaceae)

millefolium	CCor EPla GCal LGre WThu

CHAMAECYPARIS † (Cupressaceae)

¶*formosensis*	CKen
§*funebris*	CMCN ISea
lawsoniana	CTre EHar EHul GAri GRei GWht IDai ISea MBar NWea SLim WDin WFro WMou
– 'Albospica' (v)	CBra CMac EBre EHul LBre MBal MBar MBri MRav MWat SBod
– 'Albospica Nana' (v)	See C. *l.* 'Nana Albospica'
– 'Albovariegata'	EHul IDai LBee MBar MPlt NBee
– 'Albrechii'	ENot
– 'Allumii Aurea'	See C. *l.* 'Alumigold'
I – 'Allumii Green'	ISea
– 'Allumii Magnificent'	CB&S NBee WWeb
§– 'Alumigold'	CB&S CDoC CKen EHar ENHC LBee LCon MBal MBar MBri MGos MWat SBod SLim SPer SPla SReu WDin WStI WWeb
– 'Alumii'	CDoC CMac CSco EBre EHar EHul ENot GRei IDai LBre LBuc MBal MBar MGos MWat NWea SLim SPer SReu WDin WStI
¶– 'Annesleyana'	ISea
– 'Argentea'	See C. *l.* 'Argenteovariegata'
§– 'Argenteovariegata'	CMac LCon NEgg SLim WThu
I – 'Aurea Compacta'	MPlt
– 'Aurea Densa'	CKen CMac EBar EBre EHar EHul GAri LBre LCon MBar MBri MGos SBod SHer SLon
– 'Aureovariegata'	EBre IJoh LBre MBal MBar NRoo SIng
§– 'Barabits' Globe'	MBar MWat
– 'Bleu Nantais'	CBra CKen CMHG CMac CSco EHul ENHC EPla LBee LCon LLin LNet MBal MBar MBri MGos MPla MWat SBod SHBN SLim SPla SReu SSmi SSta WDin
– 'Blom'	CKen EHul MBri SLim
– 'Blue Gem'	LBee NHol
§– 'Blue Gown'	EHul GRei LBee MBar MGos MPla SRms WWeb
§– 'Blue Jacket'	CSco
– 'Blue Surprise'	CBra CKen CMHG EHoe EHul EPla GPen LBee LCon MBal MBar MBri MPla NBee
¶– 'Bowleri'	LCon
– 'Broomhill Gold'	CBra CDoC CMac CSco EBre EHul ENot LBre LCon LNet MBal MBar MBri MGos MPla MRav MWat NBee NHol SBod SLim SPer WDin
*– 'Burkwood's Blue'	MBar
– 'Caudata'	CKen MBar
– 'Chantry Gold'	CKen EHul LCon SLim
– 'Chilworth Silver'	CBra CDoC CKen CMHG EBre EHar ENHC EPot IJoh ITim LBee LBre LLin MBar MBri MCas MGos MPla MWat NRoo SBod SHBN SLim SLon SPer WDin WStI WThu WWeb
– 'Chingii'	CDoC
– 'Columnaris'	CB&S CBra CDoC CMac EBre EHar ENHC ENot GRei GWht IDai IHos LBee LBre MBal MBar MBri MGos MOke NBee NWea SHBN SLim SReu
– 'Columnaris Aurea'	See C. *l.* 'Golden Spire'
N– 'Columnaris Glauca'	EBre EHul IJoh LBre LCon LPan MGos MPla MWat NRoo SBod SGil SPer WBod WDin WStI WWeb
I – 'Cream Crackers'	EHul
– 'Croftway'	EHul SRms
– 'Dik's Weeping'	MBri
– 'Drummondii'	EHul NBee
– 'Duncanii'	EHul LCon MBal
– 'Dutch Gold'	EHul GAri MAsh
– 'Dwarf Blue'	EHul
N– 'Elegantissima'	CKen CMac SHil
– 'Elfin'	EPla

– 'Ellwoodii'	Widely available
– 'Ellwood's Empire'	MBri
– 'Ellwood's Gold'	Widely available
– 'Ellwood's Nymph'	CKen MBar SHBN
– 'Ellwood's Pillar'	CBra CDoC CKen CMac CSco EBlo EBre EHul ENHC EPot ISea LBee LBre LCon LLin MBar MBri MGos MPla MWat NBee NHol SBod SLim SSmi WAbe WDin
– 'Ellwood's Pygmy'	CMac EPot MBar
– 'Ellwood's Silver'	CGre ISea MAsh WStI
– 'Ellwood's Variegata'	See C. *l.* 'Ellwood's White'
§ – 'Ellwood's White' (v)	CKen CMac EHul MBal MBar MBri MWat SHBN SSmi WAbe
I – 'Emerald'	CKen MBar MBri NHol
– 'Emerald Spire'	CDoC CMac MAsh
♦– 'Erecta'	See C. *l.* 'Erecta Viridis'
– 'Erecta Argenteovariegata'	MPla
– 'Erecta Aurea'	CKen EHul LBee MAsh SBod SReu
– 'Erecta Filiformis'	MBar
§ – 'Erecta Viridis'	CB&S CDoC CMac EHar GRei LCon MBal MBar MPla MRav MWat NEgg NWea SBod SLim SPer SReu WDin WWeb
– 'Ericoides'	EHul
– 'Erika'	LCon MBar MWat SLim
– 'Fantail'	MWat
¶ – 'Filiformis Compacta'	EBar
– 'Fleckelwood'	CKen EHul GPen LBee LLin MBar MGos MPla SBod SLim WStI
– 'Fletcheri'	CB&S CBra CMac CSco EHar EHul ENHC ENot IDai ISea LBee LCon MBar MGos MPla MRav NBee NWea SBod SHBN SLim SLon SPer SPla SReu WBod WDin WStI WThu
– 'Fletcheri Aurea'	See C. *l.* 'Yellow Transparent'
– 'Fletcher's White'	EHul MBar
– 'Forsteckensis'	CDoC CMac CNic EBar EBre EHul ENHC ESis ISea LBre LCon LLin MBar MGos MWat NBee NWea SLim SLon SSmi
I – 'Forsteckensis Aurea'	LCon
– 'Fraseri'	CMac EHar ENHC LCon MBar NWea WDin WStI
– 'Gail's Gold'	CKen
– 'Gilt Edge'	CKen
– 'Gimbornii'	CDoC CMHG CMac CSco EBar EBlo EBre EHul ENHC LBee LBre LCon LLin MBar MBri MPla NBee SBod SLim SLon
– 'Glauca Spek'	See C. *l.* 'Spek'
– 'Globus'	See C. *l.* 'Barabits' Globe'
– 'Gnome'	CDoC CMac CNic EBre EHul ENHC EPot GAri LBre LCon MBal MBar MGos MPla NHol SBod SHer SLim SPer
– 'Gold Flake'	MBar
– 'Gold Splash'	CKen
– 'Golden King'	MBar SRms
§ – 'Golden Pot'	CDoC CKen CMac EBre EHul EPla LBee LBre LCon LLin MBar MBri MGos MOke MPla MPlt MWat NRoo SBod SLim WAbe
¶ – 'Golden Queen'	CMHG EHul
– 'Golden Showers'	CKen EHul
§ – 'Golden Spire'	CB&S LBee MBar MBri SBod
– 'Golden Triumph'	CB&S EHul
– 'Golden Wonder'	CDoC CMHG CMac EBre EHul IDai LBee LBre LBuc LCon LNet MAsh MBal MBar MBri MGos MRav WStI
¶ – 'Goldgren'	SMad
– 'Grayswood Feather'	CDoC CKen CMac CSco EBre EHul ESma LBee LBre LCon MBar MGos MPla SLim SLon WWeb
– 'Grayswood Gold'	CDoC CKen EHul LBee MBar MPla
– 'Grayswood Pillar'	CKen CMac LBee LCon MBal MBar MGos SIng
– 'Green Globe'	CDoC CKen EBlo EBre EHul EPot LBee LBre LCon LTil MBar MBri MCas MPla NHar NHol SBod WAbe WDin
§ – 'Green Hedger'	CMac CSco EHar EHul ENot GRei LBuc SBod SReu WAbe WStI
§ – 'Green Pillar'	CKen CSco EBre GAri GWht IJoh LBee LBre LPan MBal MBar MBri MGos MWat SHBN SReu WStI WWeb
♦– 'Green Spire'	See C, *l.* 'Green Pillar'
– 'Green Wall'	EHul
– 'Greycone'	CKen LBee
– 'Hillieri'	MBar
♦– 'Hogger's Blue Gown'	See C. *l.* 'Blue Gown'
*– 'Hogger's Gold'	CMHG EHul
– 'Howarth's Gold'	EBre GAri LBre MBri
I – 'Imbricata Pendula'	SMad
– 'Intertexta'	CMHG EHar EHul ISea LTil SMad
♦– 'Jackman's Green Hedger'	See C. *l.* 'Green Hedger'
– 'Jackman's Variety'	See C. *l.* 'Green Pillar'
– 'Kelleriis Gold'	EHar EHul LPan
¶ – 'Kilbogget Gold'	ISea
– 'Killiney Gold'	CMac
– 'Kilmacurragh'	CMac EHar ENHC ENot GRei IDai MBal MBar SLim SPer WBod
– 'Knowefieldensis'	CMHG CMac IDai LLin WWeb
§ – 'Lane'	CBra CDoC CGre CKen CMHG CMac EBre EHar EHul ENot GRei LBre LCon MBal MBar MGos MRav NWea SLon SReu WStI WTyr
– 'Lanei'	See C. *l.* 'Lane'
– 'Lanei Aurea'	See C. *l.* 'Lane'
– 'Lemon Flame'	NHol
– 'Lemon Queen'	EHul LBee LCon NBee
– 'Limelight'	CKen EHul
– 'Little Spire'	CDoC CMHG EBlo EBre EPla LBee LBre LCon LLin MBar MBri MGos MPla NHar NHol SLim
– 'Lombartsii'	CDoC CMHG EHul LCon
– 'Lutea'	CMac EHar EHul LCon MAsh MBal MGos SBod SPer SPla SReu
§ – 'Lutea Nana'	CKen CMac EHul IBar IDai MAsh MBar
– 'Luteocompacta'	CKen EHar LBee SHBN
– 'Lycopodioides'	CMHG EHul MBar SSmi WThu
*– 'MacPenny's Gold'	CMac
– 'Magnifica Aurea'	ENHC
– 'Milford Blue Jacket'	See C. *l.* 'Blue Jacket'
§ – 'Minima'	MBar SRms WAbe
– 'Minima Aurea'	Widely available

I – 'Minima Densa'	See C. *l.* 'Minima'
– 'Minima Glauca'	Widely available
– 'Moonlight'	CBra EPla MBar MGos MPla
– 'Naberi'	EHar LPan SHil
– 'Nana'	CMac MBar
§ – 'Nana Albospica'	CKen EHul ENHC LBee LCon LLin MAsh MBal MBar MGos MPla NBar NBee SGil SLim
– 'Nana Argentea'	CKen CMHG EHul SGil
– 'Nana Lutea'	See C. *l.* 'Lutea Nana'
§ – 'Nana Rogersii'	MBar SRms WStI
– 'Nidiformis'	EHul GWht LBee MBal MBar SLim SLon SPla WStI
– 'Nivea'	MBar
♦– 'Nyewoods'	See C. *l.* 'Chilworth Silver'
– 'Nymph'	EBre LBre LCon LLin MAsh MBri NHol
– 'Parsons'	IHos SLon WDin
– 'Pelt's Blue'	CKen LBee LPan
– 'Pembury Blue'	CBra CDoC CKen CMHG CMac CSco EBre EHar EHul ENHC ENot IDai LBee LBre LCon MBar MBri MPla MWat NHol NRoo SBod SHBN SLim SLon SPer SReu WDin
– 'Pendula'	MBar
– 'Pendula Vera'	CBra
– 'Pick's Dwarf Blue'	LCon MBar MBri NHol
– Pot of Gold ®	See C. *l.* 'Gold Pot'
– 'Pottenii'	CDoC CMac CSco EBre EHar EHul ENHC IJoh LBee LBre LCon MBal MBar MGos MPla MWat NWea SBod SHBN SPer SReu WBod WDin WStI
– 'Pygmaea Argentea' (v)	CKen CMac EBar EBlo EBre EHar EHul ENHC EPla ESis GPen IDai LBee LBre LCon LLin MBal MBar MBri MPla MWat NBee NHol SBod SLim SPer SPla WAbe WDin WThu
– 'Pygmy'	CNic EHul ESis GAri LBee LCon MBar MPla SLim
– 'Pyramidalis Lutea'	CKen
I – 'Reid's Own Number One'	GRei
¶ – 'Rijnhof'	GAri LBee
– 'Rock Gold'	SLim
♦– 'Rogersii'	See C. *l.* 'Nana Rogersii'
I – 'Romana'	MBri
– 'Royal Gold'	EHul
– 'Silver Queen' (v)	CKen EHar GRei IDai MBal MBar NWea
– 'Silver Threads' (v)	CBra CKen CMac EBlo EBre EHar EHoe EHul ENot EPla GPen IJoh LBee LBre LCon LLin MBar MBri MCas MGos MPla MWat NHol SBod SGil SHer SLim SLon
– 'Silver Tip'	EHul SLim
I – 'Slocockiana'	EHul SHBN
N– 'Smithii'	CMHG EHul ISea LCon MBar
– 'Snow Flurry' (v)	CKen EHul LBee
– 'Snow White' (v)	CDoC EBre EHul IJoh LBee LBre LCon LLin MAsh MBar MBri MGos MPla NHol SLim
– 'Somerset'	CMHG CMac CSco IDai LCon MBar SLon WWeb
§ – 'Spek'	CB&S
– 'Stardust'	CDoC CKen CMHG CMac ENHC ENot ESis GRei GWht IHos IJoh LCon MBal MBar MBri MGos MPla MWat NRoo SBod SHBN SIng SLim SPer SReu WDin
– 'Stewartii'	CMac ENot MBal MBar MGos MPla NWea SBod SGil SHBN WStI
– 'Stilton Cheese'	MBar
*– 'Summer Cream'	EHul
– 'Summer Snow'	CDoC CMHG CMac EHoe EHul ENot IJoh LBee LCon LLin MBal MBar MBri MGos MPla MRav SBod SLim SPla SReu WAbe WTyr WWeb
– 'Sunkist'	CKen EBre LBre LCon MAsh
– 'Tamariscifolia'	CDoC EBre EHul ENHC IDai LBre LCon MBal MBar NBee SBod SIng WDin
– 'Temple's White'	CKen
– 'Tharandtensis Caesia'	CDoC LCon MBar NBee SLon SMad
– 'Tilford'	EHul
– 'Treasure'	CKen CNic CRiv EBre EHoe EHul EPla LBee LBre LCon LLin MAsh MBar MBri MGos NHol
– 'Triomf van Boskoop'	EHul MBar
– 'Van Pelt's Blue'	CB&S CBra EHar EHoe EHul LCon MGos NHol SHBN SLim SLon SReu
– 'Versicolor' (v)	EHul MBar
– 'Westermannii'	CMac EHar EHul LCon MAsh MBal SBod SHil SLim SLon SPer SReu
– 'White Spot' (v)	CDoC CKen EBre EHar EHul ENHC IDai ISea LBee LBre LCon MAsh MBal MBar MBri SLim WStI
– 'Winston Churchill'	CMHG EHar LCon MAsh MBar MGos MPla NWea SBod SLim SPer
– 'Wisselii'	CDoC CKen CMac EHar EHul ENHC ENot IDai LBee LCon LTil MBar NWea SBod SIng SLon SMad SPer WDin
– 'Wisselii Nana'	CKen
– 'Wissel's Saguaro'	LRHS
– 'Witzeliana'	MBar MGos NBee
– 'Wyevale Silver'	MBar
♦– 'Yellow Success'	See C. *l.* 'Golden Queen'
§ – 'Yellow Transparent'	CMac EHul LCon LPan MBar MGos MWat SBod SHBN SLim SPer
*– 'Yvonne'	MBri
leylandii	See X CUPRESSOCYPARIS ***leylandii***
nootkatensis	EHar MBar SLim WDin
– 'Aureovariegata'	EHar EHul EPla SLim
– 'Compacta'	LCon MBar
– 'Glauca'	ENHC MBar
– 'Gracilis'	EHul
– 'Jubilee'	SMad WMou
– 'Lutea'	CDoC CMHG CMac IDai LCon MBal MBar NWea SHil
– 'Nidifera'	MBar
– 'Pendula'	CDoC CSco EBre EHar ENHC ENot IJoh LBre LCon LNet LTil MBal MBar MBri MBrk MGos NBee NWea SLim SMad WDin WMou
– 'Variegata'	EHar LCon MBar SLim
obtusa 'Albospica'	EHul

– 'Albovariegata'	CKen
– 'Aurea'	CDoC
I – 'Aureovariegata'	See C. *o.* 'Opaal'
– 'Aurora'	CKen SHil
*– 'Autumn Gold'	MBar
– 'Bambi'	CKen
– 'Bartley'	CKen EPot
– 'Basset'	CKen
– 'Caespitosa'	CKen EPot
– 'Chabo-yadori'	CDoC CMHG EPot LCon LLin MAsh MBal MBar MGos NHar NHol SBod SHer SLim
– 'Chilworth'	CKen EBre LBre LCon MAsh MBar MBri
♦– 'Chima-anihiba'	See C. *l.* 'Pygmea Densa'
– 'Contorta'	EPot LCon MBri
– 'Coralliformis'	LLin MBal MBar NHol SLim
§ – 'Crippsii'	CB&S CKen CMac EBar EHar EHul ENot EPot IDai LCon MBal MBar MBri MGos MPla SBod SHil SLim SPer
– 'Crippsii Aurea'	See C. *o.* 'Crippsii'
– 'Dainty Doll'	CKen
♦– 'Densa'	See C. *o.* 'Nana Densa'
*– 'Ellie B'	CKen
– 'Ericoides'	CKen
– 'Erika'	CDoC MPla MPlt
– 'Fernspray Gold'	CDoC CMHG CMac EHul ENot LCon LLin MBar MBri MPla NHol SBod SPer
– 'Filicoides'	LCon LTil
– 'Flabelliformis'	CKen
– 'Gimborn Beauty'	EBre LBre LCon MBri
– 'Golden Fairy'	CKen
– 'Golden Filiment'	CKen
– 'Golden Nymph'	CKen LCon MBri
– 'Golden Sprite'	EBre EPot LBre LCon MAsh MBri
– 'Goldilocks'	EBre EHul LBre MAsh MBri
– 'Gracilis Aurea'	CKen
♦– 'Graciosa'	See C. *o.* 'Loenik'
– 'Hage'	CKen EPot LCon LTil MBri MPla
– 'Hypnoides Nana'	CKen
– 'Intermedia'	CKen EPot
– 'Juniperoides Compacta'	CKen EPot MAsh MBri
¶ – 'Kamakurahiba'	CKen
¶ – 'Kanaamihiba'	MAsh
– 'Kosteri'	CDoC CKen CMac EBre EHul ENHC EPot ESis LBee LBre LCon LLin MBar MBri MGos MPla NHar NHol SHBN SIng SLim WAbe
– 'Little Marky'	CKen
§ – 'Loenik'	CDoC EHul ENHC MBar NHol
– 'Lycopodioides'	CDoC EPot
§ – 'Mariesii' (v)	CKen LCon MAsh MBri SHBN
– 'Minima'	CKen EPot WTyr
– 'Nana'	CKen CMHG CMac EPot GAri LBee LCon MBar MBri MPla MRav NHol SIng SLim SSmi
– 'Nana Aurea'	CDoC CMac CSco EBre EHul ENHC EPot LBre LLin MBar MBri MCas MRav MWat NHol SHBN SHil SIgm SLim SLon SPer WStI
– 'Nana Compacta'	LCon MAsh MBri NHol
§ – 'Nana Densa'	CKen CMac
– 'Nana Gracilis'	Widely available
I – 'Nana Gracilis Aurea'	EHul
– 'Nana Lutea'	CKen EBlo EBre EHul ENHC EPot ESis LBee LBre LCon LLin MAsh MBar MBri MPla MRav NHol NRoo SBod SHer SLim SPla SReu SSmi WAbe
– 'Nana Rigida'	See C. *o.* 'Rigid Dwarf'
– 'Nana Variegata'	See C. *o.* 'Mariesii'
§ – 'Opaal'	EPot LCon MBar MBri
– 'Pygmaea'	CDoC EBre EHul ENHC ENot EPot ESis IDai LBre LCon MBal MBar MPla NHar NHol SBod SLim SPer SPla
– 'Pygmaea Aurescens'	ENHC MBar MWat
– 'Pygmaea Densa'	CKen MBri
– 'Reis Dwarf'	EPla LCon
§ – 'Rigid Dwarf'	CKen EHul EPot LBee MBar MBri
– 'Snowkist' (v)	CKen
– 'Spiralis'	CKen EPla MBar
– 'Stoneham'	CKen MAsh MBar
– 'Tempelhof'	CDoC CKen EBre EHar EHul EPot LBre LCon MBar MBri MGos MPla NHar SBod SLim SLon WWeb
– 'Tetragona Aurea'	CDoC EHar EHul ENHC EPot GWht IDai LCon MBar MGos MWat SBod SLim SPer
– 'Tonia' (v)	EBre EHul ESis LBre MBar MBri SLim WWeb
– 'Verdon'	MBar MBri
– 'Wissel'	CKen
– 'Yellowtip' (v)	CKen EBre LBre LCon MBar MGos
pisifera	GAri LMer
– 'Aurea Nana'	See C. *p.* 'Strathmore'
– 'Avenue'	EHul LCon MPla NHol SPla
– 'Boulevard'	Widely available
– 'Compacta Variegata'	EHul MBar
– 'Devon Cream'	EHoe GPen LCon LLin MBar MPla NHol SBod
– 'Filifera'	CMac EBre LBre MBal MBar MRav SBod SLim SLon WBod
– 'Filifera Aurea'	CBra CKen CMHG CMac EBre EHul ENHC ENot GPen IDai IJoh LBre LCon LLin LNet MBal MBar MBri NWea SBod SIng SLim SPer WBod WDin WThu WWin
– 'Filifera Aureomarginata'	CMac EBre EPla GAri LBre MBal MBar MBri SLim
– 'Filifera Nana'	CDoC CGre EBar EBre EHul ENHC EPla LBre LCon MBal MBar MBri MWat SLim SPer SSmi WDin
I – 'Filifera Sungold'	See C. *p.* 'Sungold'
I – 'Filifera Variegata'	EHul
– 'Gold Cushion'	CKen
– 'Gold Dust'	See C. *p.* 'Plumosa Aurea'
– 'Gold Spangle'	CMHG EPla MBar MGos SBod SLim WBod
¶ – 'Golden Dwarf'	SPla
– 'Golden Mop'	CKen LCon LRHS LTil MAsh MPla
– 'Hime-himuro'	CKen
– 'Hime-sawara'	CKen
– 'Nana'	CDoC CKen EBre EHul GAri GPen LBre LLin MBal MBar MBri MWat NHol SBod SPer SSmi WThu
I – 'Nana Albovariegata'	CDoC LBee MBar MBri SBod
– 'Nana Aurea'	CKen

§ – 'Nana Aureovariegata' CDoC CMac EBar EHul EPot ESis LCon MBal MBar MBri MPla MPlt MWat NHol SBod SPer WWeb
I – 'Nana Compacta' CMac IDai
I – 'Parslorii' CKen EPot NHol
– 'Pici' CKen
– 'Plumosa' MBal SLon SPla SRms
– 'Plumosa Albopicta' ENHC MAsh MBal MBar MPlt SBod
§ – 'Plumosa Aurea' CDoC CKen EHul ENHC GPen GWht IDai IJoh MBal MBar NWea WBod WDin
– 'Plumosa Aurea Compacta' CKen CMHG CMac GAri LCon MPla MPlt NBee SLon WTyr
I – 'Plumosa Aurea Compacta Variegata' CMac
– 'Plumosa Aurea Nana' ENot MBal MBar MGos MPla
I – 'Plumosa Aurea Nana Compacta' CMac SBod
– 'Plumosa Aurescens' CMac
§ – 'Plumosa Compressa' CDoC CKen EHul EPot ESis GPen LBee LCon MAsh MBar MBri MCas MGos SIng SLim WThu
*– 'Plumosa Densa' See C. *p.* 'Plumosa Compressa'
– 'Plumosa Flavescens' CDoC CMac EHul MBar MPla MWat SLim SLon
I – 'Plumosa Juniperoides' CKen EBre EHul ITim LBre LCon MBri MPla MPlt
– 'Plumosa Purple Dome' See C. *p.* 'Purple Dome'
I – 'Plumosa Pygmaea' EPot MBar MGos MPlt SLon
– 'Plumosa Rogersii' CDoC EHul ENHC EPot MBar MCas MGos MPla SBod SLim WThu
– 'Purple Dome' EBre EHul LBre MBar MGos NHol SBod
♦– 'Pygmaea' See C. *p.* 'Plumosa Pygmaea'
♦– 'Rogersii' See C. *p.* 'Plumosa Rogersii'
– 'Silver and Gold' MBar MCas SLim
– 'Silver Lode' CKen
– 'Snow' (v) CKen CMHG CMac EPot GAri GPen LLin MBal MBar MBri MCas MPla SBod SSmi WDin
– 'Snowflake' EHul
§ – 'Squarrosa' CDoC GAri GPen GWht MBal MBar NWea SLon WBod WDin
N– 'Squarrosa Argentea' MBal
I – 'Squarrosa Blue Globe' CKen
– 'Squarrosa Dumosa' CKen EHul MBar MWat
– 'Squarrosa Intermedia' EHul LCon MBar MGos SLon
I – 'Squarrosa Lombarts' CMac EBre EHul ENHC EPla LBre LCon LLin MPla MWat SBod SIng SSmi
– 'Squarrosa Lutea' EPla GPen MAsh MBar
– 'Squarrosa Sulphurea' CMHG CMac CTre EBlo EBre EHul EPot GPen IDai LBee LBre LCon MBal MBar MPla MWat SBod SLim WDin WTyr
– 'Squarrosa Veitchii' See C. *p.* 'Squarrosa'
§ – 'Strathmore' CKen EHul GPen IDai LBee LLin MAsh MBar MBri NHol SIng
§ – 'Sungold' CDoC CKen CMHG EHul ENot EPla GPen LBee LCon MBar MBri MPla MPlt SBod SLim SPla
– 'Tama-himuro' CKen LLin MBri MGos SLim
– 'White Beauty' CKen
*– 'White Brocade' CMac
– 'White Pygmy' EPot LCon MAsh
thyoïdes SLim WThu
– 'Andelyensis' CDoC CMac EHul ENHC GAri GPen LCon LLin MAsh MBal MBar MPla NHol SLim
– 'Andelyensis Nana' CKen
– 'Aurea' EHul MBar MPlt
– 'Conica' CKen LCon MAsh
– 'Ericoïdes' CDoC CKen CMHG CMac CSam EBar EHul ENHC ENot GPen GWht LBee LCon LLin MBal MBar MWat NBee SBod SLim SPer WBod WDin
§ – 'Glauca' EHul LCon MBar
– 'Kewensis' See C. *t.* 'Glauca'
– 'Rubicon' CKen CMac EBlo EBre EHul EPla ESis ESma GPen IJoh LBee LBre LCon LLin MAsh MBar MBri MGos MPla MPlt MRav NHol SBod SLim SPla
– 'Schumacher's Blue Dwarf' EPla MBar
*– 'Top Point' IJoh SLim
– 'Variegata' EHul MBar SLim

CHAMAECYTISUS (Leguminosae)

§ ***albus*** CB&S CBow CLan ECtt ENot NNor SDix SIng SPer WDin WStI
§ ***purpureus*** CAbP CBow EBre ELan IDai IOrc LBre MBal MBar MBri MGos MPla NRoo SHBN SHil SPer SReu WAbe WBod WDin WOMN WRus WWin
– f. ***albus*** CB&S MBar MPla SHBN SHil SPer SUsu
§ – 'Atropurpureus' CB&S EBlo ENot MPla NHol SHil SPer SSta
– ***incarnatus*** See C. *p.* 'Atropurpureus'
§ ***supinus*** LHop SRms

CHAMAEDAPHNE (Ericaceae)

§ ***calyculata*** CB&S CPle MUlv SHBN WBod WSHC
– 'Nana' CNic ECar MBal MBar MGos NHar

CHAMAEDOREA (Palmae)

costaricana LPal
elegans LPal MBri
erumpens NPal
metallica LPal
seifrizii LPal MBri

CHAMAELIRIUM (Liliaceae/Melanthiaceae)

luteum NSal

CHAMAEMELUM (Compositae)

§ ***nobile*** CArn CHad CHal CSFH CSev Effi GPoy LHol MBar MBri NNrd NRoo SIde WEas WOak WPer WWye
– 'Flore Pleno' CGle CHal CHan CMea CSev CShe CTom ECha ELan GArf GPoy LHol LHop MBri MCas NCat NSti SChu SHer SIde SIng SSvw SUsu WEas WHal WPer

- 'Treneague' CArn CHal CLew CMea CPar CSFH CSev CShe CTom ELan GPoy IEde LGro LHol LMor MBri NNor NRoo NSti SHer SIde SIng WHal WOak WPer WWye

CHAMAENERION See EPILOBIUM

CHAMAEPERICLYMENUM See CORNUS

CHAMAEROPS (Palmae)

excelsa hort. See TRACHYCARPUS ***fortunei***
– Thunberg See RHAPIS ***excelsa***
humilis CHEx GAri IOrc LPal NPal NRog SArc SDry SHil SPer WCot

CHAMAESPARTIUM See GENISTA

CHAMOMILLA See MATRICARIA

CHARA (stonewort)

¶ ***vulgaris*** SAWi

CHASMANTHE (Iridaceae)

aethiopica CHan GCal LHop MBel NRog
¶ ***bicolor*** CMon
floribunda NRog
– var. ***duckittii*** NRog

CHASMANTHIUM (Gramineae)

§ ***latifolium*** ECha EFou EHoe ELan EPla ETPC GAbr GCal NHar SDix SMad WBon

CHEILANTHES (Adiantaceae)

argentea NMar
eatonii SIgm
farinosa NMar
¶ ***hirta*** var. ***ellisiana*** NMar
lanosa CMil NMar SIgm SMad
myriophylla NMar

CHEIRANTHUS See ERYSIMUM

CHELIDONIUM (Papaveraceae)

¶ ***japonicum*** ECro WPer
majus CKin CRDP CRow CSFH GPoy GTou LHol MChe MHew MPit NHex NSal SIde WHer WWye
– 'Flore Pleno' CGle CRow CWGN ELan GCHN GCal NSti
– 'Laciniatum Flore Pleno' CRDP CRow GCal IBlr NHol WHer WPer

CHELONE (Scrophulariaceae)

barbata See PENSTEMON ***barbatus***
§ ***glabra*** CChu CCla CHan CLew CPar EBre ECha EFou EGol ELan EOrc GPoy LBre LHop MBri MHew MUlv NHol NSal SChu SCro SFis SPer WPer WRus WWat
obliqua Widely available
– var. ***alba*** See C. ***glabra***

CHENOPODIUM (Chenopodiaceae)

bonus-henricus CArn CHun CSev EJud Effi GPoy IEde ILis LHol MChe NSel SIde WOak WPer WWye
botrys MHew NSal

CHERRY, Duke See PRUNUS × *gondouinii*

CHERRY, Sour or Morello See PRUNUS *cerasus*

CHERRY, Sweet See PRUNUS *avium*

CHESTNUT, Sweet See CASTANEA *sativa*

CHEVREULIA (Compositae)

See Plant Deletions

CHIASTOPHYLLUM (Crassulaceae)

§ ***oppositifolium*** Widely available
♦– 'Frosted Jade' See C. ***o.*** 'Jim's Pride'
§ – 'Jim's Pride' (v) CBos CElw CLew CRDP CRow EFol EMon EPla LAbb LBee MUlv SMad WCot
simplicifolium See C. ***oppositifolium***

CHILIOTRICHUM (Compositae)

diffusum CGre CPle ECar ECou GDra GWht IBar MBlu SLon SPer

CHIMAPHILA (Ericaceae)

maculata NSal

CHIMONANTHUS (Calycanthaceae)

fragrans See C. ***praecox***
§ ***praecox*** Widely available
– 'Grandiflorus' ENot SSpi
– 'Luteus' CPMA CSco MBlu SHil SSpi WWat
– 'Trenython' CBow SSpi
yunnanensis CAbb
zhejiangensis GCal

CHIMONOBAMBUSA (Gramineae(Bambuseae))

falcata See DREPANOSTACHYUM ***falcatum***
hookeriana hort. See DREPANOSTACHYUM 'Damarapa'
¶ ***macrophylla*** f. ***intermedia*** SDry
§ ***marmorea*** EPla ISta LBam SBam SDry WJun
– 'Variegata' EFul EPla ISta LBam SBam SDry WJun
§ ***quadrangularis*** EFul EPla GAri ISta SBam SDry WJun
¶ – 'Svow' SDry
§ ***tumidissinoda*** EPla SBam SDry WJun

CHIOGENES See GAULTHERIA

CHIONANTHUS (Oleaceae)

retusus SHil SSta
virginicus CB&S CBow CCla CPMA EHar ELan IOrc LTil MBri MUlv SEng SMad SSpi SSta WWat

CHIONOCHLOA (Gramineae)

¶ *beddiei* SMad
conspicua CElw GCal MBal MFir NBir NHar
– 'Rubra' See C. ***rubra***
¶ *flavescens* GCal
flavicans EPla MUlv
§ *rubra* CElw EMon EPla ETPC

CHIONODOXA † (Liliaceae/Hyacinthaceae)

♦ *cretica* See C. ***nana***
§ *forbesii* CAvo CBro CMon LRHS WPer
– 'Alba' EPar ETub LAma NRog
– 'Pink Giant' CAvo CBro CCla LAma LBlo SIng WPer
– 'Rosea' EPar ETub LAma LBow NEgg NRog
§ – Siehei Group CBro
gigantea See C. ***luciliae*** Gigantea Group
luciliae Boissier CAvo CBro CCla ELan EPar EPot ETub LAma LBlo LBow MBal MBri NEgg NMen NNrd NRog SIng WAbe WHil
– hort. See C. ***forbesii***
§ – Gigantea Group ELan ETub LAma NEgg NRog SIng WHil
* *mariesii* LAma
§ *nana* CBro CMon
sardensis CAvo CBro CCla EPar EPot ETub LAma LBlo LBow MBal NRog SIng WChr WPer
siehei See C. ***forbesii*** Siehei Group
tmolusi See C. ***forbesii*** 'Tmoli'

CHIONOHEBE (Scrophulariaceae)

armstrongii ITim
densifolia ECar ECou ITim
x *petrimea* 'Margaret Pringle' EPot
pulvinaris ECou EPot GArf ITim MHig NHar NHol NTow NWCA WDav WThu

X CHIONOSCILLA (Liliaceae/Hyacinthaceae)

§ *allenii* CMon LAma LRHS

CHIRITA (Gesneriaceae)

¶ *sinensis* WEfe

CHIRONIA (Gentianaceae)

See Plant Deletions

CHLIDANTHUS (Liliaceae/Amaryllidaceae)

fragrans CKel LBow NHol NRog SDeJ WChr

CHLOROPHYTUM (Liliaceae/Anthericaceae)

comosum 'Mandaianum' (v) CHal
– 'Variegatum' CHal MBri NRog
– 'Vittatum' (v) MBri

CHOISYA (Rutaceae)

arizonica SDry
'Aztec Pearl' Widely available
¶ *mollis* CGre
ternata Widely available
– 'Moonsleeper' NBee
– 'Sundance' Widely available

CHONDROSUM (Gramineae)

§ *gracile* ECha EFou EMon EPla MMil MPar NBar NBro SFar SMad

CHORDOSPARTIUM (Leguminosae)

muritai ECou
stevensonii CGre CHEx CPle ECou SArc SMad SSpi
– 'Duncan' ECou
– 'Kiwi' ECou
– 'Miller' ECou

CHORISIA (Bombacaceae)

See Plant Deletions

CHORIZEMA (Leguminosae)

ilicifolium CB&S CBow ERea

CHRYSALIDOCARPUS (Palmae)

lutescens LPal MBri

CHRYSANTHEMOPSIS See PYRETHROPSIS

CHRYSANTHEMUM

See also ARGYRANTHEMUM
alpinum See LEUCANTHEMOPSIS ***alpina***
arcticum Linnaeus See ARCTANTHEMUM ***a.***
argenteum See TANACETUM ***a.***
balsamita See TANACETUM ***b.***
cinerariifolium See TANACETUM ***c.***
clusii See TANACETUM ***corymbosum c.***
coccineum See TANACETUM ***c.***
coronarium CArn
corymbosum See TANACETUM ***c.***
foeniculaceum See ARGYRANTHEMUM ***frutescens f.***
frutescens See ARGYRANTHEMUM ***f.***
haradjanii See TANACETUM ***h.***
hosmariense See PYRETHROPSIS ***h.***
leucanthemum See LEUCANTHEMUM ***vulgare***
macrophyllum See TANACETUM ***m.***
mawii See PYRETHROPSIS ***gayanum***
maximum hort. See LEUCANTHEMUM x ***superbum***
– Ramond See LEUCANTHEMUM ***m.***
nankingense See DENDRANTHEMA ***n.***
nipponicum See NIPPONANTHEMUM ***n.***
pacificum See DENDRANTHEMA ***p.***
parthenium See TANACETUM ***p.***
ptarmiciflorum See TANACETUM ***p.***
roseum See TANACETUM ***coccineum***
rubellum See DENDRANTHEMA ***zawadskii***

§ ***segetum*** NMir WHer WOak WThu
uliginosum See LEUCANTHEMELLA ***serotina***
welwitschii See C. ***segetum***
weyrichii See DENDRANTHEMA ***w.***
yezoense See DENDRANTHEMA ***y.***

CHRYSOCOMA (Compositae)
See Plant Deletions

CHRYSOGONUM (Compositae)
virginianum CRDP EBre ECha EMar EPla LBre LGan MRav SPer

CHRYSOLEPIS (Fagaceae)
See Plant Deletions

CHRYSOPOGON (Gramineae)
gryllus EMon EPla ETPC

CHRYSOPSIS (Compositae)
villosa See HETEROTHECA ***v.***

CHRYSOSPLENIUM (Saxifragaceae)
davidianum CBre CRDP CTom ECha EMon EPar EPot GCHN NBir NCat NRar SBla SWas WAbe WCru
– SBEC 231 NHol
oppositifolium EMNN GDra GGar NKay WCla WCru

CHRYSOTHAMNUS (Compositae)
See Plant Deletions

CHRYSOTHEMIS (Gesneriaceae)
pulchella CHal MBri

CHUNIOPHOENIX (Palmae)
¶ ***hainanensis*** LPal

CHUSQUEA † (Gramineae(Bambuseae))
culeou CBot CBow CDoC CGre CHEx CMCN EFul EHar ELan EPla GCal ISta LBam MBri MUlv SArc SBam SDry SSta WJun WNor
– ***breviglumis*** See C. ***c.*** 'Tenuis'
§ – 'Tenuis' LBam SBam SDry WJun
montana LTil SArc SBam WJun WWat
quila LTil SArc SBam SDry WJun
ramosissima SBam SDry WJun

CICERBITA (Compositae)
plumieri WCot

CICHORIUM (Compositae)
intybus CHal CKin CRDP CSFH EBre ECro Effi LBre LHol LHop MChe NMir SHer SIde WGwy WHer WOak WPer
– ***album*** CPou ECha EMon LRHS SHer
– ***roseum*** CPou CRDP ECha ECro ELan EMon MRav MTho NRoo SHer SMrm SPer
'Rosso di Verona' ELan
spinosum ELan EMon

CICUTA (Umbelliferae)
See Plant Deletions

CIMICIFUGA † (Ranunculaceae)
acerina See C. ***japonica***
americana NHol NSal SRms
¶ ***dahurica*** CHan GCal
foetida GPoy LGan
heracleifolia GCal
§ ***japonica*** CHan CRow EBre GCal LBre WCot WRus
– ***compacta*** CHan
racemosa CArn CChu CCla CHan CKel CPar CRDP CRow CSam EBre ECro EGol ELan ELun GCal GPoy LBre LGan MBal MRav NDea NHol NSal NSti SFis SPer WByw WWye
– var. ***cordifolia*** See C. ***rubifolia***
*– 'Purple Torch' WEas
*– 'Purpurea' CDoC CMea EFol ELun NBar SPer
ramosa See C. ***simplex*** 'Prichard's Giant'
§ ***rubifolia*** CChu CHan EBre ECro LBre SBla SPer
simplex CSam LBre MBri WCot
– Atropurpurea Group CAbb CChu CCla CHan CRDP CRow EBre ECha ECro EFou ELan EPar LBre LGre MBri MUlv NBar NOak NSti SBla SMad SMrm SSpi WRus
– 'Brunette' EBlo EBre LBre LRHS MUlv
– 'Elstead' CChu EBre ECha ELun EPar LBre LGre MBri SBla
¶ – 'Frau Herms' LRHS
§ – 'Prichard's Giant' CHan CRow EBre GAri GCal LBre MBri NHol WCot
– 'White Pearl' Widely available

CINERARIA (Compositae)
maritima See SENECIO ***cineraria***

CINNAMOMUM (Lauraceae)
camphora CB&S CHEx ERea

CIONURA (Asclepiadaceae)
oreophila GCal

CIRCAEA (Onagraceae)
lutetiana CKin NLan NSal WHer

CIRSIUM (Compositae)
acaule CKin ECro
¶ ***candelebrum*** NWCA
diacantha See PTILOSTEMON ***d.***
dissectum CKin
eriophorum CKin NMir
¶ ***falconeri*** ECro
forrestii CLD 1000 NHol
heleniöides See C. ***heterophyllum***
§ ***heterophyllum*** CKin ECro NLan
japonicum MFir
*– 'Pink Beauty' CBow ECro EGol ELan SHer WHil
– 'Rose Beauty' CBow CPar ECha ECro ELan GCal MBri NMir SHer WHil

¶– 'Snow Beauty'	GCal
mexicanum	EMon
oleraceum	ECro
palustre	CKin
rivulare atropurpureum	CCla CElw COtt CSco ECha ECro EGol ELan EPla MUlv NBir NSti WByw WCra WEas WHal
¶ ***spinosissimum***	GCal
vulgare	CKin

CISSUS (Vitaceae)

antarctica	MBri
discolor	CHal MBri
rhombifolia	MBri
– 'Ellen Danica'	MBri
§ ***striata***	CB&S CGre CHEx CSPN IBar MUlv WCru WSHC WWat

CISTUS † (Cistaceae)

x ***aguilarii***	CHan EPla LAbb LGre SIgm WSHC
– 'Maculatus'	CB&S CBot CDoC CHan CSco EBre ELan ENot LBre LGre MBri SDry SHil SLMG SPer SPla SSpi WKif WWin
albanicus	GCHN NTow
albidus	CFis CRiv EBar LGre NTow SDry WEas WWat
algarvensis	See HALIMIUM ***ocymoïdes***
'Anne Palmer'	CChu CDoC CHan CSco LGre LHop SAxl SBla SChu SMrm
atriplicifolius	See HALIMIUM ***atriplicifolium***
'Barnsley Pink'	See C. 'Grayswood Pink'
'Blanche'	CHan SIgm WKif
x ***canescens***	CB&S SLMG
– 'Albus'	CFis CMHG CShe EPla LGre NSti SAxl SIgm
¶ 'Chelsea Bonnet'	WAbe
'Chelsea Pink'	EBar
§ ***clusii***	CKni CSam MAsh SAxl SCro SPla
♦ ***coeris***	See C. x ***hybridus***
x ***corbariensis***	See C. x ***hybridus***
crispus hort.	See C. x ***pulverulentus***
– Linnaeus	CB&S CHan ECha GAbr LGre NNor SIgm SSpi WEas WRus WWeb
– 'Prostratus'	See C. ***c.*** Linnaeus
– 'Sunset'	See C. x ***pulverulentus*** 'S.'
§ x ***cyprius***	CCla CCor CMHG CSco CShe ELan ENot IBar MBri MGos MWat SDix SHBN SHil SMrm SPer SPla SSpi WBod WDin
– 'Albiflorus'	CDoC CPle
§ x ***dansereaui***	CHan CShe IOrc SLMG WAbe WDin
– 'Decumbens'	CB&S CCla CHan CMHG CSco EBre ELan GCal IJoh LBre MBal MBri NFai NKay SHBN SIgm SPer WAbe WHCG WStI WWat
'Elma'	CGre ERav LGre MBri NTow SDix SDry SIgm SPer WAbe WHCG WWat
§ x ***florentinus***	CDoC IOrc LAbb MRav NNor SAxl SChu WSHC
formosus	See HALIMIUM ***lasianthum***
§ 'Grayswood Pink'	CBow CDoC CMHG ELan EPla ESma LHil MBri MPla NSti SIgm SMrm SSpi WAbe
halimifolius	See HALIMIUM ***halimifolium***
hirsutus	SDry SPer WKif WWeb
N– var. ***psilosepalus***	CFis EBar
§ x ***hybridus***	Widely available
§ ***incanus***	SChu SIde WPer WSHC
– ssp. ***creticus***	CFis CMHG EBar ELan ERav LAbb LGre NTow SIgm SPer SUsu WAbe WSHC WWin
– ssp. ***incanus***	LGre SIgm
ingwerseniana	See X HALIMIOCISTUS ***ingwersenii***
ladanifer hort.	See C. x ***cyprius***
– Linnaeus	CB&S CHal CHan CPle CSco EBre ECha ELan ERav IJoh IOrc LAbb LBre MBal MRav NNor NTow SBla SChu SLon SPer WCru WEas WSHC
– Palhinhae Group	LGre NTow SDry SHil SIgm WAbe
– 'Pat'	CGre WEas
lasianthus	See HALIMIUM ***lasianthum***
laurifolius	CDec CHan CPle CSco EBre ENot EPla LBre LGre MBal MBri MGos SBla SLPl SPer SSpi WEas WSHC WWat
x ***laxus***	SPla
– 'Snow White'	CCla CFis CHan EPla LGre MBri NPer SAxl SSvw WBod WKif
libanotis	CSam ECar ELan NNor
N x ***loretii*** Rouy & Fouc.	CBra CHan CMHG CSam ENot IBar LGre NSti SDry SHBN SPer SPla WCru WKif WPat WWat
x ***lusitanicus*** Maund.	See C. x ***dansereaui***
'Merrist Wood Cream'	See X HALIMIOCISTUS ***wintonensis*** 'Merrist Wood Cream'
monspeliensis	CCor CHan CMHG CSev EPla GWht SChu SDry SPer
x ***obtusifolius***	CBow CHan ELan MBri SBla SLPl WTyr
ocymoïdes	See HALIMIUM ***ocymoïdes***
osbeckiifolius	GCal
♦ ***palhinhae***	See C. ***ladanifer*** Palhinhae Group
parviflorus hort.	See C. 'Grayswood Pink'
– Lamarck	CBot CCla CFis CNic ECha EPla ERav LGre LHil LHop NSti SAxl SChu SPer WSHC
'Peggy Sammons'	CBot CDoC CSco CShe EBre ECha EGol ELan ERav IOrc LAbb LBre LHop MBri NSti SAxl SGil SHer SIgm SLon SPer SSvw SUsu WBod WSHC WWat
populifolius	CMHG SLon SMad SPer
– var. ***lasiocalyx***	CChu ERav IOrc LGre SHil SLon SMrm
– ssp. ***major***	CFis CHan LGre
§ x ***pulverulentus***	CBow CCla CGre CHal CHan CPle EPla ERav LAbb LTil SChu SCro SPer SUsu WDin WKif WSHC
§ – 'Sunset'	CFis CSco EBre EFol ELan ENot IBar IDai IJoh IOrc LBre LHop MBri MGos MWat NKay SDix SHBN SLon SPer SPla SReu SSpi SSta SUsu WAbe WBod WDin WEas WPat
– 'Warley Rose'	CDoC CFis CSam CSco CShe EBar EBre LBre SAxl SHBN SIgm
N x ***purpureus***	Widely available

– 'Alan Fradd'	CBra CKni CSco SAxl SCro SGil SHer SIgm SMrm
– 'Betty Taudevin'	CB&S CFis LGre LHop NCat NFai SBar WAbe WCru
rosmarinifolius	See C. ***clusii***
sahucii	See X HALIMIOCISTUS ***sahucii***
salviifolius	CB&S CBow CDoC CHan CPle CSam CSco ERav LGre WEas
– 'Avalanche'	WAbe WCru
♦– x ***monspeliensis***	See C. x ***florentinus***
– 'Prostratus'	CMHG ELan LGre LHop NTow WCru
'Silver Pink'	Widely available
x ***skanbergii***	CB&S CBra CCla CHal CHan CMHG CMil CSam CSco ELan ENot ERav MGos MWat NFai NSti SAxl SDix SHBN SLon SPer SPla SSpi WEas WWat WWin
symphytifolius	GCal LGre
tomentosus	See HELIANTHEMUM ***nummularium tomentosum***
x ***verguinii***	LGre MBri SDix SIgm
villosus	See C. ***incanus***
wintonensis	See X HALIMIOCISTUS ***wintonensis***

CITHAREXYLUM (Verbenaceae)

¶ ***ilicifolium***	CGre
♦ ***quadrangulare***	See C. ***spinosum***
§ ***spinosum***	CGre CPle

X CITROFORTUNELLA (Rutaceae)

F ***floridana*** 'Eustis'	ERea
F – 'Lakeland'	ERea
Limequat	See X C. ***floridana***
F ***microcarpa***	CGOG MBri WFou
F – 'Tiger' (v)	CB&S LHop
mitis	See X C. ***microcarpa***
F ***swinglei*** 'Tavares'	ERea

CITRON See **CITRUS *medica***

X CITRONCIRUS (Rutaceae)

'Zehnder' (***paradisi*** x)	ESim

CITRONELLA (Icacinaceae)

§ ***gongonha***	CAbb
mucronata	See C. ***gongonha***

CITRUS † (Rutaceae)

F ***aurantiifolia*** 'Bearss'	CGOG ERea
F – x ***limon*** 'Indian Lime'	ERea
F – x ***limon*** 'La Valette'	ERea
F – 'Tahiti'	CB&S ERea MNew
F ***aurantium***	CGOG ERea
F – 'Bouquet'	ERea
F – var. ***myrtifolia*** 'Chinotto'	ERea
– 'Seville'	See C. ***a.***
Calamondin	See X CITROFORTUNELLA ***microcarpa***
F ***ichangensis***	SArc
japonica	See FORTUNELLA ***j.***
Kumquat	See FORTUNELLA ***margarita***
F ***limon***	LPan MBri
F – 'Fino'	CGOG
F – 'Garey's Eureka'	CGOG ERea MBri
F – 'Imperial'	ERea
F – 'Lemonade'	ERea
F – 'Lisbon'	ERea
F – 'Quatre Saisons'	See C. ***l.*** 'Garey's Eureka'
F – x ***sinensis*** 'Meyer'	CB&S CGOG CTro GTwe LHop MBri MNew NPal SEng SLMG SPer SSta WFou WHig
F – 'Variegata'	ERea MBri
F – 'Verna'	CGOG
F – 'Villafranca'	ERea MNew
F x ***limonia*** 'Rangpur'	ERea
F ***maxima***	ERea
F ***medica*** 'Ethrog'	ERea
F – var. ***sarcodactylis***	ERea
mitis	See X CITROFORTUNELLA ***microcarpa***
F x ***nobilis***	LPan
F – 'Blida'	ERea
F – 'Murcott'	ERea
F – Ortanique Group	CTro
F – 'Silver Hill Owari'	ERea
F – Tangor Group	ERea
F x ***paradisi***	LPan
F – 'Foster '	ERea
F – 'Golden Special'	CB&S ERea IOrc MNew SEng
F – 'Red Blush'	CGOG
F – 'Wheeny'	MNew
F 'Ponderosa'	ERea MNew
reticulata x ***paradisi***	See C. x ***tangelo***
F ***reticulata*** Mandarin Group	WFou
F – – 'Clementine'	CB&S ERea IOrc SEng
F – – 'Comun'	CGOG
F – – 'De Mules'	CGOG
F – – 'Encore'	ERea
F – – 'Fortune'	CGOG
F – – 'Nova'	CGOG
F – – 'Tomatera'	CGOG
F ***reticulata*** Satsuma Group	ERea
F – – 'Clausellina'	CGOG
F – – 'Okitsu'	CGOG
F – – 'Owari'	CGOG
F ***sinensis***	LPan MBri
F – 'Arnci Alberetto'	SEng
F – 'Egg'	ERea
F – 'Embiguo'	ERea
F – 'Jaffa'	See C. ***s.*** 'Shamouti'
F – 'Malta Blood'	ERea
F – 'Moro Blood'	ERea
F – 'Navelina'	CGOG
F – 'Newhall'	CGOG
F – 'Prata'	ERea
F – 'Ruby'	ERea
F – 'Saint Michael'	ERea
F – 'Salustiana'	CGOG
F – 'Sanguinelli'	CGOG
F – 'Shamouti'	ERea
F – 'Valencia'	ERea MBri
F – 'Valencia Late'	CGOG ERea
F – 'Washington'	CB&S CGOG CTro ERea GTwe MBri MNew
F x ***tangelo*** 'Mapo'	WFou
F – 'Seminole'	CTro ERea

CLADOTHAMNUS See ELLIOTTIA

CLADRASTIS (Leguminosae)

**hirsuta*	CSPN
lutea	CB&S CCla CLnd CMCN CPle EHal ELan SHil SSpi WWat

CLARKIA (Onagraceae)

¶ *amoena*	CRDP
concinna	WOMN
**repens*	CSpe

CLAVINODUM (Gramineae(Bambuseae))

oedogonatum	SDry

CLAYTONIA (Portulacaceae)

australasica	See NEOPAXIA *australasica*
caroliniana	LAma NRog
§ *megarhiza* var. *nivalis*	GArf GDra GTou MAsh NGre NTow NWCA WThu
§ *parvifolia*	CLew CNic
§ *perfoliata*	CArn GPoy WHer WWye
§ *sibirica*	CElw CFis CLew CNic CRDP CRow ELan NGre WWye
virginica	LAma NRog WEas

CLEMATIS † (Ranunculaceae)

'Abundance' (Vt)	CBow CCla CDoC CHad CPev CSCl CSPN EBre EOvi ETho EVal IOrc LBre LPri MBea MBri MCad MRav NBea NHol SBra SDix SHBN SPer WSHC
'Acton Pride'	LPri
addisonii	EOvi SBra WOMN
aethusifolia	CB&S CHan CSCl CSPN EBre EOrc EOvi EVal LBre LPri MBri MCad SBra SSpi
afoliata	CPev ECou EOvi ETho MCad
akebioïdes	CCla CHan CSCl ELan ETho LRHS MCad SBra SGly SHBN SPer
'Alabast' (F)	MCad
'Alba Luxurians' (Vt)	CBar CBow CCla CDoC CGle CHad CMac CPev CSCl CSPN EBre ELan EOrc EOvi ERav ETho EVal IOrc LBre LPri MBri MCad MGos SBla SBra SDix SHil SPer SPla
¶ *albicoma*	CSCl
'Albiflora'	CBow EVal MCad
'Alice Fisk' (P)	CSCl EOvi EVal LPri MCad NBea SBra
¶ 'Aljonushka'	EOvi MGos
'Allanah' (J)	CSCl EOvi ETho EVal LPri MCad MGos NBea SBra
§ *alpina*	CBow CMac CPev CRDP CSCl CSco GDra MBal MBar MBea MCad NBar NEgg NHol NPer NRar NRoo SGly SHBN SIng SUsu WAbe WStI WWat
¶ – 'Blush Queen'	CSCl NWyt
– 'Burford White'	EOvi LPri MCad NBea WSHC
– 'Columbine'	CBow CCMG CPev EOrc EOvi ETho EVal LPri MBea MCad NBea SBra SDix SPer
– 'Columbine White'	CHan EOvi ETho EVal MBri MCad NBea
¶ – 'Constance'	CSPN EBlo
– 'Frances Rivis'	Widely available
– 'Frankie'	CBow CDoC CSPN EBlo ELan EOrc EOvi ETho EVal LRHS MBri MCad SGly
– 'Inshriach'	CGle MSte NHol
– 'Jacqueline du Pré'	CPev CSPN MGos
– 'Jan Lindmark'	EBre LBre NBir
– 'Maria'	MCad
§ – 'Pamela Jackman'	CBow CCMG CCla CDoC CSCl CSPN EBre ELan EOrc EOvi EVal IOrc LBre LPri MBea MBri MCad MGos NBar NBea NHol NRoo SBra SDix SPer
¶ – 'Pink Flamingo'	CSPN EBlo EVal
– 'Ria'	MBea MCad
– 'Rosy Pagoda'	CBow CHan CSPN EOvi EVal LPri MCad NBea NBir NRoo WWat
– 'Ruby'	CCla CMac CPev CSCl CSco EGol ELan EOrc EOvi ETho EVal LPri MBea MBri MCad MGos NBea NEgg NHol SBla SBra SDix SGly SHBN SPer SReu SSpi SSta WWat
– ssp. *sibirica*	CPev EOvi MCad NBea
§ – – 'White Moth'	CCMG CCla CMac CSCl CSPN CSam CSco EBre ELan EOvi EVal LAbb LBre LPri MBri MCad MGos MPar NBea NHol NRoo SBla SBra SHil SMad SPer WWat
– 'Willy'	CCMG CPev CSCl CSPN EBlo EGol EOrc EOvi ETho EVal LPri MBea MBri MCad MGos NBea NRar SBod SBra SDix SGly SPer SPla
'André Devillers' (P)	MCad
'Anna' (P)	MCad
¶ 'Anna Louise'	EVal
'Annabel' (P)	MCad
*'Anniversary'	LPri
apiifolia	CCla CPev EHal EOvi EVal MCad SBra
¶ – var. *biternata* GR 0008	SBra
'Arabella'	CPev
aristata	ECou MCad
armandii	Widely available
– 'Apple Blossom'	CCMG CCla CHad CPev CSCl CSco EHar ELan EOvi ETho EVal IOrc LPri MBea MBri MCad MGos NBea NHol SBra SGly SHBN SPer SReu SSpi SSta
– var. *biondiana*	CMac EOvi SBla
¶ – 'Jeffries'	EVal
– 'Snowdrift'	CPev CSCl CSam CSco EOvi LPri MCad SBla SHil SReu WStI
x *aromatica*	EOvi MCad SBra SPla
'Asao' (P)	CBow CSCl CSPN EBre ELan EOvi ETho EVal LBre LPri MBea MCad NBea SBra SGly SPer WWat
'Ascotiensis' (Vt)	CCMG CCla CPev CSCl CSPN EBre EOvi ETho EVal LBre LPri MCad SBra SDix SGly SPer
**atrata*	WCru
§ 'Aureolin' (Ta)	CDoC CSCl EBre EVal LBre MBar MBri MCad MGos NHol NWyt SBra WWeb
'Aurora Borealis'	MCad
¶ *australis*	WAbe
'Barbara Dibley' (P)	CBow CCla CMac CPev CSCl EOvi ETho EVal LPri MBea MBri MCad NBea SBod SBra SDix SGly WBod

'Barbara Jackman' (P)	CBow CCMG CCla CPev CSCl CSPN CSco ENot EOvi ETho EVal LPri MBar MBea MBri MCad MRav NBar NBea SBra SDix SGly SPer WBod
barbellata (A)	GDra MCad
– 'Pruinina'	See C. 'Pruinina'
'Beauty of Richmond' (L)	EOvi ETho EVal MCad SBra SDix
'Beauty of Worcester' (F/L)	CCMG CCla CPev CSPN EBre EGol ELan EOvi ETho EVal LBre LPri MAsh MBar MBea MCad NBea SBra SDix SGly SPer
'Bees' Jubilee' (P)	CB&S CMac CPev CSCl CSPN EBre ELan ENot EOvi ETho EVal IHos LBre LPri MBar MBea MBri MCad MGos NBar NBea NRoo SBra SDix SGly SPer WBod
'Belle Nantaise' (L)	CPev CSCl CSPN EOvi ETho EVal LPri MCad
'Belle of Woking' (F/P)	CBow CCMG CPev CSCl CSPN EBlo EBre ELan EOvi ETho EVal LBre LPri MBar MBea MBri MCad NBea SBra SDix SGly SPer
¶ 'Benedictus'	EOvi
'Bessie Watkinson'	MCad
'Betty Corning' (Vt)	CSCl CSPN EOvi ETho EVal LRHS MBri
§ 'Bill Mackenzie' (Ta)	Widely available
'Blue Belle' (Vt)	CBar CSCl CSPN EBlo EOvi EVal LPri MBri MCad NBea SBra
'Blue Bird' (A)	CCla CMac CSCl EOrc EOvi EVal IOrc LPri MBea MCad NBar NBea NHol NRoo SBod SBra SGly SPer SPla SReu
¶ 'Blue Boy'	EVal
'Blue Dancer'	CAbP MBal MWat
'Blue Gem' (L)	EOvi MCad SBra SHil
x ***bonstedtii***	MCad
– 'Crépuscule'	CCla NSti SRms
'Bracebridge Star' (L/P)	CSCl EOvi ETho EVal MCad SBra
brachiata	CHan CPou CSCl EOvi LPri SBra SDix
brevicaudata	CB&S MCad WCru
* 'Broughton's Star'	EOvi ETho MCad NBea SBra
¶ 'Brunette'	MGos
buchananiana De Candolle	EVal MCad
– Finet & Gagnepain	See C. ***rehderiana***
'Burford Variety' (Ta)	EGol EOrc EVal LPri MBri MCad NBea WAbe
'Burma Star'	CPev
'C W Dowman' (P)	MCad SBra
calycina	See C. ***cirrhosa***
campaniflora	CBot CBow CCMG CCla CHan CPev CSCl CSPN EBre EOrc EOvi ETho EVal LBre LGan MBri MCad NBea SBra SDix SGly SSpi
– hybrid	MPar
¶ – 'Lisboa'	EVal
'Candy Stripe'	CSCl MCad
'Capitaine Thuilleaux'	See C. 'Souvenir du Capitaine Thuilleaux'
'Cardinal Wyszynski'	See C. 'Kardynal Wyszynski'
¶ 'Carmencita'	EOvi
'Carnaby' (L)	CCMG CSPN EBre ELan EOvi ETho EVal LBre LPri MBar MBri MCad MRav SBod SBra SGly WBod WWeb
'Caroline'	CPev
x ***cartmanii*** (Fo)	ECou
– 'Joe' (Fo)	LBee MCad NHar WAbe WDav
¶ 'Cassiopeia' (PxL)	EOvi
'Centre Attraction'	MCad
'Chalcedony' (FxL)	CPev CSCl EOvi MCad
'Charissima' (P)	CBow CMac CPev CSCl EOvi LPri MCad
'Cherry Brandy'	LPri SBra
chiisanensis	MCad NBea
chinensis	CSCl EOvi MCad
¶ ***chrysantha***	EOvi
♦– var. ***paucidentata***	See C. ***hilariae***
N ***chrysocoma***	CCMG CCla CHad CHan CPev CSCl EBar ELan EOvi ETho EVal LPri MBar MBea MCad MGos MRav NHol SBla SBra SDix SPer SSpi SSta WWat
– B&L 12237	NBea SBra
– B&L 12324	SBra
¶ – hybrid	CSCl
– ***sericea***	See C. ***montana sericea***
– ***spooneri***	See C. ***montana sericea***
§ ***cirrhosa***	CBot CBow CHan CPev CSCl EBre ELan EOvi LBre LPri MCad SGly SPer WSHC
– var. ***balearica***	Widely available
– – forms	CPev MCad SGly WCru
– 'Freckles'	CB&S CBow CCMG CCla CDoC COtt CSCl CSPN EBlo EBre ELan EOrc EOvi ERav ETho EVal LBre LPri MBri MCad NBea NHol SBra SGly SPer SPla WWat
¶ – 'Ourika Valley'	SBla
– 'Wisley Cream'	CCMG CSCl CSPN ECtt EGol ELan EVal LPri LRHS MAsh MCad NHol SBra SGly SPer SPla
coactilis	CSCl MCad
'Colette Deville' (J)	CSCl MCad SBra
columbiana	MCad
'Comtesse de Bouchaud' (J)	Widely available
connata	CBot EVal MCad SBra
'Continuity'	EOvi EVal MBri MCad SBra WSHC
'Corona' (PxL)	CPev CSPN ELan EOvi ETho EVal LPri MBar MCad NBea SGly
'Corry' (Ta)	EVal MCad NBea
'Countess of Lovelace' (P)	CB&S CCla CHan CMac CSCl CSPN EBre ELan EOvi ETho EVal LBre LPri MBar MBea MBri MCad NBea SBod SBra SDix SPer WBod
County Park hybrids (Fo)	ECou
'Crimson King' (L)	EOvi ETho EVal MAsh MBea MCad SBod SBra
crispa	CSCl EOvi EVal MCad SBra
§ – 'Cylindrica'	CSCl MCad
I – 'Rosea'	See C. *c.* 'Cylindrica'
x ***cylindrica***	CSCl EOvi ETho EVal LRHS MCad SBra
'Daniel Deronda' (P)	CB&S CBow CCMG CPev CSCl CSPN EBre ELan EOvi ETho EVal LBre LPri MBea MBri MCad NBea NWyt SBod SBra SDix SGly SPer SSta WBod
'Darlene'	LPri
'Dawn' (L/P)	CCMG CPev CSCl CSPN EBre EOvi ETho EVal LBre LPri MCad NBea SBra SGly SPer SPla

'Debutante'	MCad
'Denny's Double'	MCad
¶ ***denticulata***	WCru
– P&W 6287	MCad
* 'Dilly Dilly'	MCad
dioscoreifolia	See C. ***terniflora***
'Doctor Ruppel' (P)	CBow CCMG CMac CPev CSCl CSPN EBre ELan EOvi ETho EVal LBre LPri MBar MBea MBri MCad MGos NBea NWyt SBod SBra SDix SGly SHBN SPer WSHC
'Donna'	MCad
¶ 'Dorothy Tolver'	ETho
'Dorothy Walton' (J)	EOvi ETho EVal LPri MCad SBra
douglasii	See C. ***hirsutissima***
drummondii	MCad
'Duchess of Albany' (T)	CBar CCla CPev CSCl CSPN EBre EGol ELan EOrc EOvi ETho EVal LBre LPri MBar MBea MBri MCad NBea NHol SBla SBra SDix SGly SHil SPer SReu SSpi SSta WSHC
'Duchess of Edinburgh' (F)	CB&S CCla CMac CPev CSCl CSPN EBre ELan EOrc EOvi ETho EVal LBre LPri MBar MBea MBri MCad MGos NBea SBra SDix SGly SHBN SPer SSta WSHC
'Duchess of Sutherland' (Vt)	CPev CSCl CSPN EOvi ETho EVal LPri MAsh MBri MCad SBra SDix SPla WBod
x ***durandii*** (D)	CB&S CBot CCla CHad CPev CSCl CSPN CSco EBlo EBre EGol EHar ELan EOrc EOvi ETho EVal LBre LPri MBar MBri MCad NBea SBla SBra SDix SGly SPer SSpi WSHC
'East Sunset'	MCad
'Ebba'	MCad
'Edith' (L)	CCMG CSPN EBre EOvi ETho EVal LBre LPri MAsh MBri MCad NBea WWat
'Edomurasaki' (L)	CSPN EVal LPri
'Edouard Desfossé' (P)	MCad NBea
'Edward Prichard'	EOvi MCad NBea SBra SDix
§ 'Elsa Späth' (L/P)	CB&S CCMG CCla CPev CSCl CSPN CSco EBre ELan ENot EOvi ETho EVal LBre LPri MBar MBea MBri MCad MGos MRav NBea SBra SDix SGly SPer WBod
'Elvan' (Vt)	CBar CHan CPev EOvi MCad NBea
¶ 'Emajogi' (L)	EOvi
'Empress of India' (P)	EBlo EOvi EVal LPri MCad NBea
x ***eriostemon*** (D)	CCla CSCl CSPN EOvi EVal MCad NWyt SBla SBra SGly SPer SPla
– 'Blue Boy' (D)	MBri MCad SBra
§ – 'Hendersonii' (D)	CCMG CCla CPev CSco EBre EGol EHar ELan EOvi ETho LBre MCad MRav MUlv NBea NBir NHol SBra SDix SHil SPer SPla WSHC
'Ernest Markham' (J/V)	Widely available
¶ 'Esperanto' (J)	EOvi
'Etoile de Malicorne' (P)	CSPN EOvi ETho MBri MCad NBea SBra
'Etoile de Paris' (P)	EOvi ETho MCad SBra
'Etoile Rose' (T)	CCla CHan CPev CSCl EBre EOrc EOvi ETho EVal IOrc LBre LPri MCad NBea SBla SBra SHil
'Etoile Violette' (Vt)	CCla CHad CMac CSCl CSPN EGol ELan ENot EOrc EOvi ETho EVal LPri MBar MBea MBri MCad NBea SBla SBod SBra SDix SHBN SHil SPer SSta WSHC WWat
'Fair Rosamond' (L/P)	CCMG CPev CSCl CSPN EBre EOvi ETho EVal LBre LPri MBri MCad NBea SBod SBra SDix
'Fairy' (x ***indivisa***) (Fo)	ECou
'Fairy Queen' (L)	EOvi ETho EVal LPri MCad SBra
fargesii	See C. ***potaninii***
x ***fargesioïdes***	See C. 'Paul Farges'
'Farrago'	MCad
fasciculiflora	CBot CCMG CGre CHan CMHG CSCl MCad NBea SBla SBra SSpi WCru WSHC
finetiana	MCad
'Fireworks'	CBow COtt CSPN EBlo EOvi EVal MCad NBea
flammula	Widely available
– 'Rubra Marginata'	See C. x ***triternata*** 'Rubromarginata'
'Floralia'	CSPN EBlo EVal LRHS MBri MCad SGly
florida bicolor	See C. ***f.*** 'Sieboldii'
– 'Flore Pleno'	CBow CCMG CCla CHan CPev CSCl CSPN EBlo EOrc EOvi ETho EVal MCad NBea NHol SBla SBra SGly SHBN SHil SMad SPer SPla
§ – 'Sieboldii'	CB&S CBot CBow CCMG CCla CHan CPev CSCl CSPN EBlo EBre ELan EOrc ETho EVal LBre LPri MBri MCad NHol NSti SBra SGly SHBN SHil SMad SPer SPla SSpi SSta
foetida	ECou MCad WAbe
forrestii	See C. ***napaulensis***
§ ***forsteri***	CHan CMHG CSCl CSPN CSam EBlo EPot EVal LGre LPri MCad NBea SBod SBra SPou WCru WOMN WSHC
'Four Star' (L)	LPri MCad
'Fuji-musume' (L)	EOvi LPri MCad SHil
♦ ***fusca*** hort.	See C. ***japonica***
– Turczaninow	MCad
§ – ssp. ***fusca***	CSCl
– var. ***kamtschatica***	See C. ***fusca fusca***
– var. ***mandshurica***	CSCl
– var. ***violacea***	CSCl EVal MCad SBra
¶ 'G Steffner' (A)	EOvi
'Général Sikorski' (L)	CCMG CMac CSCl CSPN CSam EBre ELan EOvi ETho EVal LBre LPri MBea MBri MCad MGos NBea NWyt SBra SDix SGly SPer WBod WWat
gentianoïdes	CSPN EVal MBri MCad
¶ 'Georg' (A)	EOvi
'Gillian Blades' (P)	CSCl CSPN EBlo EBre ELan EOvi EVal LBre MBea MBri MCad NBea SBra SGly
'Gipsy Queen' (J)	CB&S CBra CMac CPev CSCl CSPN CSco EBre ELan ENot EOvi ETho EVal LBre LPri MBar MBea MBri MCad NBea NKay NRoo SBod SBra SDix SGly SHBN SPer WBod WWat
'Gladys Picard' (P)	MCad

glauca hort.	See C. ***intricata***
'Glynderek' (L)	MCad
gouriana	CCla EVal SBra
¶ ***gracilifolia***	EOvi EVal
'Grandiflora Sanguinea' (Vt)	CB&S CSPN EBre EVal LBre MCad SBod SBra SGly
grata hort.	See C. × ***jouiniana***
– Wallich	CPev MBea MCad WEas
'Gravetye Beauty' (T)	CCla CHad CPev CSCl CSPN EBre ELan EOrc EOvi ETho EVal LBre LPri MBea MBri MCad NBea SBra SDix SGly SHBN SHil SMad SPer SPla SReu SSpi SSta WSHC WWat
'Gravetye Seedling' (T)	EOvi
'Green Velvet' (Fo)	ECou
'Guernsey'	CSPN EBlo EVal MCad
'Guiding Star'	MCad
'H F Young' (L/P)	CCMG CCla CPev CSCl CSPN CSam CSco EBre ELan EOvi ETho EVal LBre LPri MBar MBea MBri MCad MGos NBea NRoo SBod SBra SDix SHBN SPer SSta WWin
'Hagley Hybrid' (J)	Widely available
¶ 'Hainton Ruby'	EVal
'Haku-ôkan' (L)	CPev CSCl CSPN EOvi ETho EVal LPri MAsh MBea MCad SBod SBra SGly
'Harlequin'	MCad
Havering hybrids (Fo)	ECou
'Heirloom'	MCad
'Helios' (Ta)	CSCl EVal MBri MCad MGos SBra
'Helsingborg' (A)	CB&S CBow CSCl CSPN EBre ELan EOrc EOvi ETho EVal LBre LPri MBri MCad SBra SGly SMad
'Henryi' (L)	CCMG CCla CPev CSCl CSPN EBre ELan EOvi ETho EVal IOrc LBre LPri MBar MBea MBri MCad NBea SBra SDix SGly SPer WBod WSHC
heracleifolia	CBot CBow CCMG CSCl ETho MCad NRoo NWyt WCru
N– 'Campanile'	CCla CPev CSCl EOvi LPri MCad NBea NBir SBra SDix
N– 'Côte d'Azur'	CBot CCMG EBre EFol EOvi LBre MCad NBea SHil
– var. ***davidiana***	CCMG CHad CPev ELan EOvi NHol WByw WHCr
– – 'Wyevale'	CBot CCla CHan CPev CSCl CSPN CSco EGol ELan EOrc EVal IHos LHop LPri MBri MCad MUlv NBea SBra SDix SGly SMad SPer SSpi WEas
– 'Jaggards'	CBot
'Herbert Johnson' (P)	CMac CPev EOvi MCad SBra
hexapetala De Candolle	See C. ***forsteri***
♦– hort.	See C. ***recta recta lasiosepala***
'Hidcote Purple' (L)	MCad
§ ***hilariae***	CSCl SBra
'Hint of Pink'	MCad
§ ***hirsuta***	EVal LRHS
¶ ***hirsutissima***	LGre WDav
– var. ***scottii***	MCad MPar MUlv NBea
'Horn of Plenty' (L/P)	CBow CCMG CSCl CSPN EOvi ETho EVal MBea MBri MCad SBra SDix SGly
'Huldine' (Vt)	CCla CGle CHad CPev CSCl CSPN CSco EBre ELan EOvi ERav EVal LBre LPri MBea MBri MCad MRav NBea SBra SDix SGly SPer SPla WBod
§ 'Hybrida Sieboldii' (L)	CMac CSCl CSPN EOvi EVal LPri MBea MCad NBea SBod SBra SGly SPer
ianthina	See C. ***fusca violacea***
¶ 'Ilka' (P)	EOvi
§ ***indivisa***	CGre CPev ECou MCad WSHC
– (f)	CGre MCad MFos NHar
– (m)	MCad
integrifolia	CBow CHad CHan CSCl EOrc EVal LGan LHop LPri MBri MBro MCad MGos NHol NRoo NSti SFis SGly SPer WCra WPer WTyr
§ – var. ***albiflora***	EOvi EVal LPri MCad NBea NBir SBra
*– 'Finnis Form'	WSHC
– 'Hendersonii'	See C. × ***eriostemon*** 'H.'
– 'Olgae'	CCMG CCla CDoC CPev CSCl CSPN EOvi ETho EVal LPri MCad NBea NWyt SBra SDix
¶ – 'Pangbourne Pink'	EVal SBra
– 'Pastel Blue'	CPev
– 'Pastel Pink'	CPev
– 'Rosea'	CBot CBow CCla CDoC CPev CSCl CSPN EOvi ETho EVal LGan LPri MBri NBea SHil WPer
– 'Tapestry'	CPev MCad
– white form	See C. ***i. albiflora***
§ ***intricata***	CB&S CGre CSCl CSPN EVal LGan MCad WCru WWat
'Ishobel'	EOvi LPri MCad
ispahanica	See C. ***orientalis*** Linnaeus
× ***jackmanii***	CBra CMac CSCl EBre ENot EOvi GRei IHos LBre MCad NBea NEgg NRoo NWea SBod SBra SGly SPer SPla
'Jackmanii Alba' (J)	CCMG CCla CPev CSCl CSPN EBre ELan EOvi ETho EVal IJoh LBre LPri MBar MBea MBri MCad NBea SBra SDix SGly SPer
'Jackmanii Rubra' (J)	CPev CSCl EOvi LPri MAsh NBea SBra SPer
N 'Jackmanii Superba' (J)	Widely available
'James Mason'	CPev EVal MCad
§ 'Jan Pawel II' (J)	CCla CSCl CSPN EBlo EBre ELan EOvi ETho EVal LBre LPri MCad NBea SBra SGly SPer
japonica	CPev CSCl EOvi ETho MCad NBea SGly
'Jim Hollis' (F)	EOvi
'Joan Picton' (P)	CSCl EOvi ETho LPri MAsh MBea MCad
¶ 'John Gould Veitch' (F)	EOvi
'John Huxtable' (J)	CDoC CPev EBre EOvi ETho EVal LBre LPri MBri MCad NBea NRoo SBra SDix SPla
'John Paul II'	See C. 'Jan Pawel II'
'John Warren' (L)	CCla CSCl EOvi ETho EVal LPri MCad NBea SBod SBra SDix SGly SPer
§ × ***jouiniana***	CBow CHad EOvi EVal ISea MBal MBea MCad MUlv SGly SHil SPer WSHC
§ – 'Mrs Robert Brydon'	CBow CCMG CDoC CSco CShe EGol EVal MCad NBea NHol NSti SPer

– 'Praecox'	CBow CCMG CCla CPev CSCl ECro EFol EFou EGol EHar ELan EPla ETho EVal LPri MBri MCad NBea NBir NHol NWyt SBla SBra SDix SMad SPer SPla SSpi SUsu
'Kacper' (L)	CSCl EOvi LPri MCad
§ 'Kakio' (P)	CCMG CSCl CSPN EBlo ETho EVal LPri MBri MCad SBra SGly SPer
'Kaleidoscope'	MCad
§ 'Kardynal Wyszynski' (J)	CBow CSCl EOvi LPri MBea MCad NBea SBra
'Kathleen Dunford' (F)	CSCl EOvi ETho EVal LPri MAsh MBea MCad NBea SBra
'Kathleen Wheeler' (P)	CCMG CMac CPev CSco EOvi ETho EVal LPri MBri MCad NBea SBra SDix
'Keith Richardson' (P)	CPev EOvi LPri MCad SBra
'Ken Donson' (L)	CMac CSPN EOvi EVal MCad SBod
§ 'Kermesina' (Vt)	CCla CMac CPev CSam CSco EBre ELan EOvi ERav ETho EVal LBre LPri MBea MBri MCad MRav NBea NHol SBla SBra SDix SGly SPer SSta SUsu WSHC WWat
'King Edward VII' (L)	EOvi EVal LPri MCad NBea SBra
'King George V' (L)	EOvi ETho EVal MBea MCad NBea SBra
'Kiri Te Kanawa'	CPev MCad
¶ ***kirilovii***	SBra
koreana	CSCl MCad SBra
– var. ***fragrans***	CSCl
– f. ***lutea***	CSCl MCad
'Kosmiczeskaja Melodija' (J)	MCad
ladakhiana	CHan CPev CSCl EHal EOvi EVal MCad NBea NBir SBra WEas WSHC
'Lady Betty Balfour' (J/Vt)	CBow CCMG CCla CMac CPev CSCl CSPN CSco EBre ELan EOvi EVal GRei LBre LPri MBea MBri MCad NBea NWyt SBra SDix SGly WSHC WStI
'Lady Caroline Nevill' (L)	CPev EOvi EVal LPri MCad NBea SBra
'Lady Londesborough' (P)	CPev CSCl CSPN EGol ELan EOvi ETho EVal LPri MCad NBea SBra SDix
'Lady Northcliffe' (L)	CCMG CMac CPev CSCl ELan EOvi EVal LPri MAsh MCad NBea SBra SDix SPer
'Ladybird Johnson' (T)	CPev CSCl MCad
♦ 'Lagoon'	See C. ***macropetala*** 'Maidwell Hall'
lasiandra	MBea
¶ ***lasiantha*** G 10174	SBra
'Lasurstern' (P)	CCla CMac CPev CSCl CSPN CSco EBre ELan ENot EOvi ETho EVal GRei IJoh LBre LPri MBar MBea MBri MCad NBea NKay NRoo SBod SBra SDix SGly SPer WBod
'Laura Denny'	EOvi MCad
'Lavender Lace'	MCad
'Lawsoniana' (L)	CCMG CMac CSCl EBre ETho LBre LPri MAsh MBar MBea MCad NBea SBra WStI
§ ***ligusticifolia***	EVal MCad NBea SBra
'Lilacina Floribunda' (L)	CSCl CSPN ELan EOvi EVal LPri MBea MCad SBra SGly SPla WSHC
* 'Lilactime'	EVal LPri
'Lincoln Star' (P)	CCMG CPev CSPN CSco ELan EOvi ETho EVal LPri MBar MBea MBri MCad MRav NBea SBra SDix SGly SPer WBod
'Little Nell' (Vt)	CBow CCMG CCla CDoC CPev CSCl CSPN ELan EOvi EVal LPri MBea MBri MCad NBea NHol SBod SBra SDix SGly SPer SReu SSta WSHC
'Lord Nevill' (P)	CBow CCMG CPev CSCl EBre ELan EOvi ETho EVal LBre LPri MBea MBri MCad NBea SBod SBra SDix SGly SPer WStI
'Louise Rowe' (F)	CSCl EOvi ETho LPri MCad SBra
'Lunar Lass' x ***foetida***	ECou
¶ 'Luther Burbank' (J)	EOvi
macropetala (A)	Widely available
¶ – 'Alborosea'	EOvi
– 'Anders' (A)	EOvi EVal
– 'Ballerina' (A)	MCad
– 'Ballet Skirt' (A)	MCad MGos
– 'Blue Lagoon' (A)	See C. ***m.*** 'Maidwell Hall'
– forms	CPev
¶ – 'Harry Smith'	EVal
– 'Jan Lindmark' (A)	EBre ETho EVal LBre LRHS MBri MCad MGos SGly
§ – 'Maidwell Hall' (A)	CBow CCMG CCla CDoC CMac CSCl CSco EBre EOvi ETho EVal LBre LPri LRHS MBea MBri MCad MGos NHol NWyt SBla SBra SHBN SPer SPla SSpi SSta WSHC WStI WWat
– 'Markham's Pink' (A)	Widely available
– 'Pauline' (A)	MCad SBra
– 'Pearl Rose' (A)	MCad
– 'Rödklokke (A)	MCad
– 'Snowbird' (A)	CPev EOvi ETho MCad NBea NHol
¶ – 'Vicky'	CSCl
¶ – 'Westleton'	NHol
– 'White Moth'	See C. ***alpina sibirica*** 'W. M.'
– 'White Swan'	See C. 'White Swan'
'Madame Baron Veillard' (J)	CPev CSCl CSPN EBlo EOvi ETho EVal LPri MBar MBea MCad NBea SBra SDix SGly
'Madame Edouard André' (J)	CCMG CCla CDoC CMac CPev CSCl EOvi ETho EVal LPri MBea MCad NBea SBra SDix SGly WSHC
'Madame Grangé' (J)	CPev CSPN CSco EOvi ETho EVal LPri MBea MCad NBea SBod SBra SDix SGly
'Madame Julia Correvon' (Vt)	Widely available
'Madame le Coultre'	See C. 'Marie Boisselot'
mandschurica	CSCl MCad SBra
marata	SBra SPou WAbe
– 'Temple Prince' (m)	ECou
– 'Temple Queen' (f)	ECou
'Marcel Moser' (P)	CPev EOvi EVal MCad NBea SBra SDix
'Margaret Hunt' (J)	CSPN EOvi ETho EVal LPri MCad SBra

Name	Suppliers
'Margot Koster' (Vt)	CDoC CSCl EBre EOvi EVal LBre LPri MBea MCad NBea NWyt SBla SBra SSta WSHC
§ 'Marie Boisselot' (L)	CB&S CCla CGle CMac CPev CSCl CSPN ELan ENot EOrc EOvi ETho EVal LPri MBar MBea MBri MCad MGos NBea NKay NRoo SBod SBra SDix SHBN SPer WSHC WWat
¶ 'Marie Louise Jensen' (J)	EOvi
marmoraria	ECou EPot ESis GArf MCad NBir NHar NHol NRed SBla WAbe WDav WPat
¶ 'Matthais' (PxL)	EOvi
'Maureen' (L)	CPev CSCl CSPN EOvi ETho EVal LPri MBri MCad NBea SBra SDix SPer
maximowicziana	See C. ***terniflora***
microphylla	ECou MCad
¶ 'Minister' (P)	EOvi
'Minuet' (Vt)	CCla CSCl CSPN EBre EGol EOvi ETho EVal IOrc LBre LPri MBea MBri MCad NBea NHol NRoo SBra SDix SMad SPer
'Miriam Markham' (J)	CPev MCad
'Miss Bateman' (P)	CCMG CCla CMac CPev CSCl CSPN EBre ELan EOrc EOvi ETho EVal LBre LPri MBar MBea MBri MCad MPla NBea NRoo SBod SBra SDix SGly SPer SPla WSHC
'Miss Crawshay' (P)	CPev CSCl EOvi EVal MBea MCad NBea SBra SDix
N ***montana***	Widely available
– ***alba***	See C. ***montana***
– 'Alexander'	CBow CCMG CDoC CSCl CSPN CSco EOrc EOvi EVal LPri MBea MBri MCad MGos SBra WCru
¶ – 'Boughton Beauty'	NRoo
– 'Elizabeth'	Widely available
– 'Freda'	CSCl EBre EOvi ETho EVal LBre LPri MBri MCad MGos NBea NHol SBra SHBN SMad SPer SPla WBod
– f. ***grandiflora***	CCMG CCla CMac CSco EBre ECtt ELan EOvi ETho ISea LBre LPri MBea MBri MCad MGos NBea SBra SDix SGly SPer SReu WBod WSHC WWat
– 'Marjorie' (d)	CB&S CBow CDoC CSCl EBre ECtt EOvi ETho EVal LBre LPri MBal MBri MCad MGos MRav NBea NHol SBra SGly SHBN SPer SPla WCru
– 'Mayleen'	CHad CSCl EOvi EVal LPri MBea MBri MCad MGos NBea SBra SHBN SPer
– 'Mrs Margaret Jones'	ETho MCad SBra
– 'Odorata'	CDoC CSCl EOvi EVal LRHS MBea MCad MGos SBra SGly WCru
– 'Peveril'	CPev
– 'Picton's Variety'	CBow CDoC CHan CPev CSCl EOrc EOvi EPla ETho LPri MBri MCad NBea SBra SDix SHBN SPer
– 'Pink Perfection'	CBow CCMG CDoC CSCl CSco EBre ELan EOvi ETho EVal LBre LPri MBea MBri MCad NBea NHol SBra
– var. ***rubens***	Widely available
– 'Rubens Superba'	See C. ***m.*** 'Superba'
§ – var. ***sericea***	CBot CHan CPev EOvi EVal LPri MCad NBea NHol SBra SGly
– 'Snow'	EOvi
– 'Spooneri'	See C. ***montana sericea***
§ – 'Superba'	CSco ECtt GAri SGly SHBN
– 'Tetrarose'	Widely available
– 'Veitch's Form'	CBot
– 'Vera'	CBow EOvi EVal MCad NBea NBir SBra WCru
¶ – 'Warwickshire Rose'	CHan
– var. ***wilsonii***	CBar CBot CCMG CCla CHad CLan CPev CSCl CSco EBre ELan EOvi ETho EVal LBre LHol LPri MBar MBea MBri MCad MRav MWat NBea SDix SPer WSHC
'Monte Cassino' (J)	MCad
§ 'Moonlight' (P)	CPev EOvi MCad NBea SBra SDix SPer
'Mrs Bush' (L)	EOvi EVal LRHS MCad NBea
'Mrs Cholmondeley' (L)	CBra CCla CMac CPev CSCl CSPN EBre ELan ENot EOvi ETho EVal IJoh LBre LPri MBar MBea MBri MCad NBar NBea NRoo SBra SDix SGly SPer WBod WSHC
'Mrs George Jackman' (P)	CCla CPev EOvi EVal LPri MBea MCad NBea SBra SDix WBod
'Mrs Hope' (L)	CPev EOvi EVal MAsh MCad NBea SBra SDix
'Mrs James Mason'	CPev EOvi ETho EVal MCad SBra
'Mrs N Thompson' (P)	CBow CCMG CMac CPev CSCl CSPN EBre ELan EOvi ETho EVal LBre LPri MBar MBea MBri MCad NBea NRoo SBod SBra SDix SGly SHBN SPla SSta WBod WStI
'Mrs P B Truax' (P)	CSPN EOvi ETho EVal LPri MCad NBea SBra SDix
'Mrs Robert Brydon'	See C. x ***jouiniana*** 'Mrs R.B.'
'Mrs Spencer Castle' (Vt)	CPev CSCl EOvi ETho EVal LPri MAsh MBea MCad NBea SBra SDix
'Mrs T Lundell'	EOvi MCad
'Multi Blue'	CSCl EBlo EBre ELan EOvi EVal LBre LPri MCad SGly SHil
'Myôjô' (P)	CSCl EOvi LPri MBea MCad NBea
§ ***napaulensis***	CPev EOvi EVal IBlr LPri MBea MCad SBra SGly
'Natacha'	MCad
¶ 'Negritjanka' (J)	EOvi
'Nelly Moser' (L/P)	Widely available
New Zealand hybrids	ECou
'Nikolaj Rubtzov'	EOvi MCad
'Niobe' (J)	CCla CHad CMac CPev CSCl CSPN EGol ELan ENot EOrc EOvi ETho EVal IJoh LPri MBea MBri MCad MGos NBea NHol SBra SDix SGly SPer WBod WSHC
'North Star'	MCad
occidentalis ssp. ***grosseserrata***	CSCl
orientalis hort.	See C. ***tibetana vernayi***
§ – Linnaeus	MCad NHol SBod SBra SReu
– 'Bill Mackenzie'	See C. 'Bill Mackenzie'
– 'Orange Peel'	See C. ***tibetana vernayi*** 'O.P.'
* – 'Rubromarginata'	CPev

– 'Sherriffii'	See C. ***tibetana vernayi*** LS&E 13342
'Otto Froebel' (L)	MCad
'Paddington'	MCad
'Pagoda' (Vt)	CBar CCla CDoC CPev CSCl CSam EOvi EVal MBea MCad SBra SGly WSHC
'Pamela Jackman'	See C. ***alpina*** 'P.J.'
paniculata Gmelin	See C. ***indivisa***
– Thunberg	See C. ***terniflora***
'Parasol'	MCad
'Pat Ann'	MCad
patens	EVal SBra
'Patricia Ann Fretwell'	CPev
§ 'Paul Farges'	CSPN EVal SBra SGly SPer
'Percy Picton' (P)	MAsh MCad NBea
'Perle d'Azur' (J)	CCla CHad CMac CPev CSCl CSPN CSco EBre ELan EOrc EOvi ETho EVal LBre LPri MBar MBea MBri MCad NBea SBra SDix SGly SHBN SPer SSta WSHC
petriei	ECou EOvi WAbe
– x ***foetida***	ECou
– x ***forsteri***	ECou
– 'Limelight' (m)	CSCl ECou
– x ***parviflora***	ECou
– 'Princess' (f)	ECou
'Peveril Pearl' (P)	CPev CSPN ETho EVal LPri MCad SGly
¶ ***pierotii***	EVal
'Pink Champagne'	See C. 'Kakio'
'Pink Fantasy' (J)	CMac CPev CSCl EBre EOvi ETho EVal IJoh LBre LPri MAsh MCad
'Pink Flamingo'	MBea
'Pink Pearl'	EOvi MCad NRoo
pitcheri	CBow CHan CPev CSCl EBre EOrc EOvi ETho EVal LBre LRHS MBri MCad NBea WSHC
'Polish Spirit' (Vt)	CDoC CSPN EBre ELan EOrc EOvi EVal LBre MBri MCad NHol SBra SGly SPer
§ ***potaninii***	CSCl EOvi EVal GCra LGan MBri MCad NBea SBra
§ – var. ***potaninii***	CCla CGle CHan CMHG CPev ISea LGan MBri MCad NBea NHol SBra SDix SPer WSHC
– var. ***souliei***	See P. ***p. potaninii***
'Prince Charles' (J)	CHad EOvi ETho LPri MCad NBea NBir SBra SDix
'Princess of Wales' (T)	CPev CSCl EOvi ETho LPri MCad SBra WSHC
'Prins Hendrik' (L/P)	CMac CSCl EOvi MBea MCad NBea SBra
'Proteus' (F)	CB&S CBow CCMG CPev CSCl CSPN EBre ELan EOvi ETho EVal LBre LPri MCad NBea NWyt SBra SDix SGly SPer SPla WSHC WWat
quadribracteolata	ECou EOvi NBea WAbe
'Radiant'	MCad
'Ramona'	See C. 'Hybrida Sieboldii'
recta	CBow CHad CHan CPev CSPN EBar ELan EOvi ETho EVal LPri MBri MCad MFir NBea NHol NRoo NWCA NWyt SAxl SPer WByw WCra
¶ – 'Grandiflora'	CSCl
– 'Peveril'	CPev
– 'Purpurea'	CB&S CBos CBot CBrd CCla CHad CSCl EFol EHoe ELan ERav ETho EVal LGan LGre MCad NBea NHol SBla SBod SBra SCro SDix SMad SPer SPla SSpi WByw WSHC
§ ***recta*** ssp. ***recta*** var. ***lasiosepala***	WWat
rehderiana	CBot CCla CHad CPev CSCl CSPN CSam CSco EBre ELan EOvi ERav ETho EVal LBre LPri MBri MCad NBea SBla SBra SDix SHil SPer SSpi SUsu WSHC WWat
'Rhapsody'	CPev MCad WSHC
'Richard Pennell' (P)	CBow CCla CMac CPev CSCl CSPN EOvi ETho EVal LPri MBri MCad NBea SBra SDix SGly
'Rose Supreme'	MCad
'Rosie O'Grady' (A)	ELan EOrc EOvi EVal LPri MBar MBea MBri MCad NBea NHol SBra SPla
'Rouge Cardinal' (J)	CCla CMac CPev CSCl CSPN EBre ELan EOvi ETho EVal LBre LPri MBar MBea MBri MCad NBea NKay SBod SBra SDix SGly SHBN SPer SReu SSta WBod
'Royal Velours' (Vt)	CCMG CCla CDoC CPev CSCl CSPN EOvi ETho EVal IOrc LPri MBea MCad NBea NHol SBla SBod SBra SDix SHBN SHil WWat
¶ 'Royal Velvet'	EVal
'Royalty' (LxP)	CSCl CSPN EBre EOvi ETho EVal LBre LPri MBri MCad NBea NBir SBra SDix SGly WBod
'Ruby Anniversary'	MCad
'Ruby Glow' (L)	EOvi EVal MCad SBra
'Ruby Lady'	LPri
'S Ruczehet'	MCad
'Sally Cadge' (P)	MCad
'Saturn' (Vt)	EVal MCad SBra
'Scartho Gem' (P)	CMac CPev CSCl EOvi EVal MCad SBra
'Sealand Gem' (L)	CCMG CPev CSCl CSPN EOvi ETho EVal MBea MCad NBar NBea NWyt SBod SBra SGly
'Serenata' (J)	CSCl EBlo EOvi ETho EVal LPri MBea MCad NBea NBir SBra
serratifolia	CCla CHan CPev CSCl CSPN EBre EGol EOvi ETho EVal LBre LPri MBea MBri MCad NBea NSti SBra SDix SPer
'Shogun'	MCad
'Signe' (P)	MCad
'Silver Lining'	MCad
'Silver Moon' (L)	CSCl EOvi EVal LPri MAsh MCad NBea SBra
'Sir Garnet Wolseley' (P)	EOvi EVal MCad NBea SBod SBra SDix
'Sir Trevor Lawrence' (T)	CCla CPev CSCl CSam EOrc EOvi ETho EVal LPri MCad NBea SBod SBra SDix SPer
¶ 'Sizaja Ptitsa' (T)	EOvi
'Snow Queen'	CSCl CSPN EOvi ETho EVal LPri MCad NBea SBra
songarica	CSCl CSPN EBar EBre EOvi EVal LBre MBri MCad SBra WSHC
'Souvenir de J L Delbard' (P)	EVal MCad SBra

§ 'Souvenir du Capitaine Thuilleaux' (P)	CPev EOvi ETho EVal LPri MBea MBri MCad SBra SGly SPer
spooneri	See C. ***montana sericea***
– 'Rosea'	See C. x ***vedrariensis*** 'Rosea'
'Sputnik' (J)	MGos SBra
¶ sp. EMAK 1029	NHol
stans	ESis EVal SIng WCra
'Star of India' (P/J)	CBow CPev CSCl ELan EOvi ETho EVal LPri MBri MCad NBea NWyt SBra SDix
'Strawberry Roan'	EOvi EVal
'Susan Allsop' (L)	CPev EOvi MCad
'Sylvia Denny' (F)	CBow CCMG CCla CHad CSPN EBre ELan EOvi ETho EVal LBre LPri MBar MBea MBri MCad MRav NBea SBod SBra SGly SPer
'Sympatia' (Vt)	CSCl MCad
¶ 'Tage Lundell' (A)	CSPN EVal
tangutica	Widely available
– 'Aureolin'	See C. 'Aureolin'
– 'Bill Mackenzie'	See C. 'B. M.'
– 'Gravetye Variety'	CCMG CSCl NBea NHol
– 'Lambton Park'	EOvi ETho EVal LPri MCad NBea NBir SBra SPla
– ssp. ***obtusiuscula***	NBea
– 'Warsaw'	EOrc MBri
§ ***terniflora***	CCla CPev CSCl EOrc EOvi EVal LPri MCad NBea SBra SGly SPer WSHC
– Caddick's form	CHan
ternifolia mandshurica	See C. ***m.***
'Teshio' (F)	LPri
texensis	CGre CHan CSPN MCad SReu
'The Comet'	LPri
'The President' (P)	Widely available
'The Vagabond'	LPri MCad
thunbergii hort.	See C. ***terniflora***
– Steudel	See C. ***hirsuta***
§ ***tibetana***	CMac CPev CSPN ELan EOrc ETho EVal MBal MBar MBea MCad NHol NNor SPer WSHC WWat
§ – ssp. ***vernayi***	CCla CHan CMHG CSCl EBar EGol ELan EOvi ESis LMer MPla SBra WCru WWin
– – C&Mc 193	NWCA
§ – – LS&E 13342	CPev EOrc EOvi EVal MBri MCad NBea NHol SBla SBra SDix SPer
¶ – – var. ***laciniifolia***	WCru
§ – – 'Orange Peel'	ENot EVal IOrc MCad MGos
'Trianon' (P)	MCad
§ x ***triternata*** 'Rubromarginata'	CBow CCla CDoC CPev CSCl CSPN CSco EBre ETho EVal LBre LPri MCad NBea NHol SBod SBra SDix SGly SHil SPer SPla WCru WSHC
¶ 'Tuczka' (J)	EOvi
'Twilight' (J)	CSCl EOvi ETho EVal MAsh MCad NBea SBra SPer
uncinata	CPev EOvi
¶ 'Vanilla Cream'	ECou
x ***vedrariensis***	EVal MCad SPer WAbe
– 'Dovedale'	CPev
– 'Highdown'	CCMG CCla CSCl LPri MBea MCad NBea NHol SBra
§ – 'Rosea'	CTrw EVal MCad MGos WSHC

'Venosa Violacea' (Vt)	CCla CSCl CSPN EHal ELan EOrc EOvi EVal LPri MBri MCad NBar NBea SBla SBra SDix SHil SPer
'Veronica's Choice' (L)	CBow CPev EOvi ETho EVal MBri MCad MGos SBra
versicolor	CSCl
'Victoria' (J)	CPev CSCl EBre ELan EOvi ETho EVal LBre LPri MBea MCad NBea SBra SDix SGly
'Ville de Lyon' (Vt)	Widely available
'Vino' (J)	EBlo EOvi EVal MCad
'Violet Charm' (L)	CSPN EVal LRHS
'Violet Elizabeth' (P)	CSCl MCad SBra
viorna	CSCl LPri NBea SDix
virginiana Hooker	See C. ***ligusticifolia***
– hort.	See C. ***vitalba***
§ ***vitalba***	CKin CPev CSCl EVal MBar MBea MCad WHer
viticella	CHan CPev CSCl EOvi EVal LAbb LGan LPri MCad SBra SDix WStI
– 'Mary Rose'	CPev EOvi ETho MCad
– 'Purpurea Plena Elegans'	CCMG CCla CGle CHad CPev CSCl EBre EGol EHar ELan EOrc EOvi ETho EVal LBre LHol LPri MBea MBri MCad NHol SBla SBra SDix SGly SHBN SPer SReu SSta
'Viticella Rubra' (Vt)	See C. 'Kermesina'
'Voluceau' (Vt)	CBow CSPN EBlo EOvi EVal MBea MCad NBea SBra SPer WStI
'Vyvyan Pennell' (F/P)	Widely available
'W E Gladstone' (L)	CPev EOvi EVal LPri MBea MCad NBea SBra SDix SPer
'W S Callick'	MCad
'Wada's Primrose' (P)	CBow CCMG CCla CDoC CHad CSCl CSPN EBre ELan EOvi ETho EVal LBre LPri MBea MBri MCad MRav NBea SBra SGly SHil SPer SPla WSHC
'Walter Pennell' (F/P)	CMac CPev EOvi ETho EVal LPri MCad SBra
'Warszawska Nike' (J)	CCMG CSCl ETho EVal LPri MCad SBra
§ 'White Swan' (A)	CBow CCMG CCla CSCl EVal LPri MBri MCad MGos NHol SBra SHil SPer SPla
¶ 'White Tokyo' (A)	MGos
'Wilhemina Tull' (L)	CSCl EOvi MCad
'Will Goodwin' (L)	CB&S CSPN ELan EOvi ETho EVal LPri MBea MBri MCad NBea SBra SGly
'William Kennett' (L)	CCMG CMac CPev CSCl CSPN CSco ELan EOvi ETho EVal LPri MBar MBea MBri MCad MGos MRav NBea NKay NRoo SBod SBra SDix SGly SPer
'Xerxes'	See C. 'Elsa Späth'
'Yellow Queen'	See C. 'Moonlight'
'Yorkshire Pride'	MCad
'Yvette Houry' (L)	MCad
'Zato'	MCad

CLEOME (Capparaceae)

§ ***hassleriana***	SMrm
spinosa hort.	See C. ***hassleriana***
– Jacquin	SMrm

CLERODENDRUM (Verbenaceae)

bungei	CAbb CB&S CBot CCla CGre CHEx CHad CHan CPle CSco CWit ELan EPla ERea LTil NPal SBor SDix SHil SLMG SMad SPer WBod WOMN WWat
fragrans var. ***pleniflorum***	See C. ***philippinum***
§ ***philippinum***	ERea
¶ x ***speciosum***	MNew
splendens	CTro SLMG
thomsoniae	CTro LAbb MBri SLMG
trichotomum	CAbb CB&S CBow CChu CCla CGre CHEx CTrw CWit EBar EBre ENot IOrc ISea LBre NWyt SHer SMad SPer SReu SSpi SSta WBod WCoo WDin WFro WStI
– var. ***fargesii***	CAbb CBra CCla CPMA CPle CSco ELan EPla IOrc LHop LTil MBri MGos SBor SHBN SLon SPer WEas WPat WWat
*– – 'Variegatum'	ELan
ugandense	CTro LHil MNew SLMG

CLETHRA (Clethraceae)

acuminata	LTil
alnifolia	CB&S CBot CBow CChu CCla CGre CLan CMHG CSam CWSG ELan IOrc MBar NBee SBor SHer SPer SReu WBod WDin WWat WWin
¶ – 'Fingle Dwarf'	SSta
– 'Paniculata'	CDoC CSco ENot MBri SSpi WWat
– 'Pink Spire'	CB&S CDoC CKni CWSG ELan MPla MRav
– 'Rosea'	CBot CBow CChu CCla CSco GWht IJoh IOrc MBal MBar MBlu MBri MGos SEng SHBN SPer SSpi WAbe WBod WSHC WWat
arborea	CChu CHEx CPle CTre SSpi
barbinervis	CB&S CBra CCla CGre CLan CSam CWSG ECar GGGa SHil SPer WCoo WSHC WWat
delavayi	CCla GGGa MBal NHol WWat
– B&L 12547	WHCr
– CLD 1508	NHol
fargesii	CB&S CCla EHal MGos SHil SSpi WWat
monostachya	CChu CCla GGGa SBor
tomentosa	CCla

CLEYERA (Theaceae)

fortunei	See C. ***japonica*** 'Fortunei'
– 'Variegata'	See C. ***japonica*** 'Fortunei'
¶ ***japonica*** 'Fortunei'	CAbb CBot IBar SBor SReu SSpi SSta WWat
– var. ***japonica***	MBal
– 'Tricolor' (v)	CDec CGre SHil

CLIANTHUS (Leguminosae)

§ ***puniceus***	CAbb CB&S CBot CHEx CHan CMac CPle CTre CTro CTrw ECou ELan ERea IDai IHos IJoh IOrc LHop MBal MNew SArc SLMG SMad SPer WBod WCru WDin
§ – 'Albus'	CB&S CBot CBow CDoC CGre CHan CPle CTre CTro CTrw ELan ERea IHos IMal IOrc LHop MNew SAxl SDry SLMG SPer WBod
– 'Flamingo'	See C. ***p.*** 'Roseus'
– 'Red Admiral'	See C. ***p.***
– 'Red Cardinal'	See C. ***p.***
§ – 'Roseus'	CB&S CBow CBra CWit ELan ERea IHos
– 'White Heron'	See C. ***p.*** 'Albus'

CLINOPODIUM (Labiatae)

§ ***acinos***	CArn CHun LHol MBri MChe NSal SIde WHer WWye
ascendens	See CALAMINTHA ***sylvatica***
calamintha	See CALAMINTHA ***nepeta***
grandiflorum	See CALAMINTHA ***grandiflora***
§ ***vulgare***	CArn CKin LHol MHew NMir NSal SIde WCla WNdy

CLINTONIA (Liliaceae/Convallariaceae)

andrewsiana	CBro GDra GGGa NKay WThi
borealis	EBul EPot NSal
umbellulata	EPot NSal SWas

CLIVIA (Liliaceae/Amaryllidaceae)

miniata hybrids	CHal CTro ERea LAma MBri NPal SLMG

CLUSIA (Guttiferae)

See Plant Deletions

CLYTOSTOMA (Bignoniaceae)

§ ***callistegioïdes***	CB&S CTro ERea

CNEORUM (Cneoraceae)

See Plant Deletions

CNICUS (Compositae)

§ ***benedictus***	CArn CHan GPoy LHol NSal NSel SIde WHer WWye

COBAEA (Cobaeaceae)

scandens	IBlr SMrm WHal
– ***alba***	ELan ERea IBlr SUsu

COBNUT See **CORYLUS** ***avellana***

COCCULUS (Menispermaceae)

See Plant Deletions

COCHLEARIA (Cruciferae)

armoracia	See ARMORACIA ***rusticana***
glastifolia	EMon
officinalis	NSal WHer

COCONUT See **COCOS** ***nucifera***

COCOS (Palmae)

nucifera 'Dwarf Golden Malay'	MBri

plumosa	See SYAGRUS ***romanzoffiana***
weddelliana	See LYTOCARYUM ***weddellianum***

CODIAEUM (Euphorbiaceae)

variegatum var. *pictum*	
'Gold Moon' (v)	MBri
– – 'Gold Sun' (v)	MBri
– – 'Goldfinger' (v)	MBri
– – 'Juliette' (v)	MBri
– – 'Louise' (v)	MBri
– – 'Mrs Iceton' (v)	MBri
– – 'Nervia' (v)	MBri
– – 'Petra' (v)	MBri
– – 'Sunny Star' (v)	MBri

CODONANTHE (Gesneriaceae)

gracilis	CTro EBak WEfe
'Paula'	WEfe

X CODONATANTHUS (Gesneriaceae)

'Aurora'	WEfe
'Tambourine'	MBri WEfe

CODONOPSIS (Campanulaceae)

bulleyana	GCra NSti SSpi WThu
cardiophylla	GDra NHol WDav
clematidea	Widely available
convolvulacea	CChu ECar ESma GAbr GDra MBro MTho NHar NHol NKay SDix WCru WHal WHoo WPer WWye
– 'Alba'	GDra NHar NHol SBla SWas
– Forrest's form	See C. ***forrestii***
dicentrifolia	SIng
§ *forrestii*	SBla WBod
♦ *handeliana*	See C. ***tubulosa***
§ *lanceolata*	ECro GCra NHol WCru WPer WWye
meleagris	GCra GDra NHar NHol SUsu WDav WPer
mollis	ECro EPad NHol
ovata	CBot CGle ECro ELan EPad ESma GCra GDra LGan MTho NHar NHol NWCA SBla SHer WEas WPer
– KBE 225	NHol
pilosula	CNic ECro GCra MTho NSti SBla SSpi
rotundifolia	SBla WDav
– *angustifolia*	CDoC NHol
subsimplex	NHol NRed NWCA
tangshen	CCMG CChu CGre EPad GPoy MTho NHar NHol NSal NSti SBla WCru WDav WPer
thalictrifolia	GArf
§ *tubulosa*	NHol SSpi WPer
ussuriensis	See C. ***lanceolata***
vinciflora	CNic ECar ECro GDra GTou MBro SBla WCru WMar
viridiflora	ECro WPer WThu
¶ *viridis* C&Mc 618	GCHN

COFFEA (Rubiaceae)

arabica	MBri

COFFEE See **COFFEA** ***arabica***

COIX (Gramineae)

lacryma-jobi	EHoe

COLCHICUM † (Liliaceae/Colchicaceae)

agrippinum	CAvo CBro CMon ECha EPar EPot LAma LBow MBal MPar NBir NRog SIng WAbe WChr WThu
¶ *algeriense* AB&S 4353	CMon
¶ *alpinum*	CMon SPou
'Antares'	LAma
atropurpureum	LAma WChr
'Attlee'	LAma LBlo NRog WCru WHil
'Autumn Herald'	LAma
N 'Autumn Queen'	CBro LAma MPar
§ *autumnale*	CArn CAvo CBro CMon ELan EPot ETub GPoy LAma LBow MBal MHew NLan NMen NRar WShi
§ – 'Alboplenum'	CBro ETub LAma LBlo WChr
– *album*	CAvo CBro CMon ECha EPar ETub GDra LAma LBlo LBow MBal NBir NHol SIng WHil
– *atropurpureum*	CBro LAma
– *major*	See C. ***byzantinum***
– *minor*	See C. ***autumnale***
– – *album plenum*	See C. ***a.*** 'Alboplenum'
– 'pannonicum'	CBro LRHS
– pink form	MPar
§ – 'Pleniflorum'	CBro EPar ETub LAma LBlo LBow WCot WCru WHil
– *roseum plenum*	See C. ***a.*** 'Pleniflorum'
baytopiorum	EPot LAma WChr
¶ – PB 224	CMon
'Beaconsfield'	MPar
§ *bivonae*	CBro EPot LAma NHar SPou WChr
¶ – S&L 467	CMon
§ *boissieri*	CMon SPou
– CE&H 628	WChr
¶ – S&L 468	CMon
bornmuelleri	CAvo CBro EPar EPot ETub LAma NHar NHol SIng
bowlesianum	See C. ***bivonae***
burttii	EPot WChr
§ *byzantinum*	CAvo CBro CMon ECha EPar EPot ETub LAma LBlo LBow MBri MPar NRog SIng WChr WCot
– *album*	EPot SPou
chalcedonicum	WChr
cilicicum	CBro EPot ETub LAma LBow MPar WChr WCru
– 'Purpureum'	LAma NHar
'Conquest'	See C. 'Glory of Heemstede'
corsicum	EPar LAma MPar WChr WThu
cupanii	CBro EPot LAma WChr
¶ – MS 977	CMon
* – *glossophyllum*	CMon
'Daendels'	LAma MPar
'Darwin'	MPar
'Dick Trotter'	LAma MPar
doerfleri	See C. ***hungaricum***
'E A Bowles'	LAma MPar
fasciculare	LAma

§ *giganteum* CAvo CMon EPot LAma LBlo NHar SIng
¶– ACW 2337 CMon
§ 'Glory of Heemstede' LAma MPar
hierosolymitanum EPot LAma WChr
§ *hungaricum* LAma LBow SPou WChr
'Huxley' MPar
♦ *illyricum* See C. ***giganteum***
kesselringii CBro EPot
kotschyi EPot LAma SPou
laetum hort. See C. ***parnassicum***
'Lilac Wonder' CBro EPot ETub LAma MBri MPar NHol NRog SIng WCot WHil
lingulatum EPot LAma NRog
¶– S&L 217 CMon
'Little Woods' MPar
§ *longiflorum* EPot LAma
lusitanicum LAma WChr
¶– HC 2273 CMon
luteum CBro ETub LAma LBlo LBow NRog WChr
macrophyllum CMon EPot LAma WChr
micranthum EPot LAma
'Nancy Lindsay' MPar
♦ *neapolitanum* See C. ***longiflorum***
¶ *parlatoris* Rix 2127 CMon
parnassicum CMon EPot MPar
– CE&H 630 WChr
'Pink Goblet' EPot LAma MPar
* *polyphyllum* LAma
'Prinses Astrid' CAvo LAma MPar
♦ *procurrens* See C. ***boissieri***
¶ *psaridis* S&L198 CMon
pusillum CBro SPou
¶– MS 803/833 CMon
'Rosy Dawn' CBro ECha EPot LAma MPar WChr
sibthorpii See C. ***bivonae***
speciosum CAvo CBro CMon CNic EPot ETub LAma LBow MBal MPar NBir NRar SIng WAbe WCru
– 'Album' CAvo CBro ECha EPar EPot ETub LAma LBlo LBow MBri MPar NBir NHol SIng SPou SSpi WChr
– 'Atrorubens' ECha GDra LAma MPar
¶– *bornmuelleri* hort. CMon
– 'illyricum' See C. ***giganteum***
– 'Maximum' LAma
– 'Ordu' LRHS
tenorei LAma MPar
'The Giant' CAvo CBro ECha EPot LAma LBlo MPar NRog SIng
troodii CMon EPot LAma
turcicum EPot LAma WChr
umbrosum CBro EPot
variegatum CBro LAma SPou WChr
'Violet Queen' CBro LAma MPar SIng WHil
'Waterlily' CAvo CBro ECha ELan EPar EPot ETub LAma LBlo LBow MBal MBri MPar NBir NRog SIng WAbe WHil
'William Dykes' LAma MPar
'Zephyr' LAma

COLEONEMA (Rutaceae)

pulchrum CSun
virgatum CTro

COLEUS See SOLENOSTEMON, PLECTRANTHUS

COLLETIA (Rhamnaceae)

armata See C. ***hystrix***
cruciata See C. ***paradoxa***
§ *hystrix* CB&S IBar LAbb MPar SArc SBor SLon SMad WAbe WBod WDin
– 'Rosea' CGre MBlu MPla SArc
§ *paradoxa* CB&S CDoC CGre CHEx CTre SArc SHil SMad SSpi WBod

COLLINSONIA (Labiatae)

canadensis ELan NSal

COLLOMIA (Polemoniaceae)

debilis NWCA

COLOBANTHUS (Caryophyllaceae)

acicularis EPot ITim
¶ *apetalus* NRya
buchananii ECou
canaliculatus ECou EPot ITim MPlt NHol
muscoïdes NHol

COLOCASIA (Araceae)

esculenta CHEx

COLQUHOUNIA (Labiatae)

coccinea CAbb CArn CCla CHal CHan MBal MRav MSte NTow SDry SSpi WBod WSHC
– *mollis* See C. ***c. vestita***
§ – var. *vestita* CB&S CGre CPle IReg NHol SLon WPat

COLUMNEA (Gesneriaceae)

'Aladdin's Lamp' NMos WEfe
'Apollo' WEfe
x *banksii* CPle CTro MBri WEfe
§ 'Broget Stavanger' (v) WEfe
'Chanticleer' CHal CTro MBri WEfe
'Early Bird' WEfe
'Flamingo' WEfe
gloriosa EBak LAbb
'Heidi' MBri
hirta MBri WEfe
♦– 'Variegata' See C. 'Light Prince'
* *hosta* MBri
'Inferno' WEfe
'Katsura' MBri WEfe
I 'Kewensis Variegata' MBri
§ 'Light Prince' (v) MBri
'Mary Ann' WEfe
¶ 'Merkur' WEfe
* *microphylla variegata* CHal MBri
I 'Midnight Lantern' WEfe
schiedeana CHal MBri WEfe
'Starburst' NMos
'Stavanger' CHal EBak MBri WEfe
'Stavanger Variegated' See C. 'Broget Stavanger'
Yellow Dragon Group CHal

COLUTEA † (Leguminosae)

arborescens	CArn CPle EBre ELan ENot GCHN IBlr IHos LBre MBar MGos NNor NSal SHBN SPer WCru WDin WHer WWin
x ***media***	CGre EHal WCru
– 'Copper Beauty'	CB&S CSco ELan MBri MGos SPer WPat
multiflora	CPle
orientalis	SDry
persica	SLon

COLUTEOCARPUS (Cruciferae)

vesicaria	WPer

COMARUM See POTENTILLA

COMMELINA (Commelinaceae)

coelestis	See C. ***tuberosa*** Coelestis Group
dianthifolia	CGle CRDP GCal ITim MCas MPar MPit MSte MTho NGre NTow SSad WCru WPer
tuberosa	CAvo CKel ELan
– 'Alba'	CKel CPou CRDP ELan EMon EOrc GCal LHop NBro SUsu WHer WPer
§ – Coelestis Group	CGle CHan CMea CPar CRDP ECha ECro EMon EOrc GCal LHop NBro SLMG SMrm SUsu WCru WHal WHer WOMN WPer WWin WWye
¶ – 'Snowmelt'	EMon
♦ ***virginica*** hort.	See C. ***erecta***
– Linnaeus	ECro IBlr WCru

COMPTONIA (Myricaceae)

peregrina	SHil

CONIUM (Umbelliferae)

See Plant Deletions

CONOCEPHALUM (liverwort)

¶ ***supradecompositum***	LFle

CONOPODIUM (Umbelliferae)

majus	CKin

CONRADINA (Labiatae)

¶ ***canescens***	LGre
verticillata	LGre WPer

CONSOLIDA (Ranunculaceae)

§ ***ajacis***	CArn NSal
ambigua	See C. ***ajacis***
regalis	NSal

CONVALLARIA † (Liliaceae/Convallariaceae)

japonica	See OPHIOPOGON ***jaburan***
majalis	Widely available
§ – 'Albostriata'	CBot CChu CRDP CRiv CRow CSin ELan EPar LGre MCas MPar NBir SAxl SPou SSpi WCru WEas WHer
¶ – 'Berlin Giant'	CSin
– 'Fortin's Giant'	CBro CHad CRDP CSco CSin ECro ELan EMon EPar EPla ERav SSpi
– 'Hardwick Hall' (v)	CRow CSin EHoe
¶ – 'Hofheim' (v)	CRow
– 'Prolificans'	CAvo CRow ELan EPar EPot MCas MPar SPou SSpi
– var. ***rosea***	CAvo CBos CRDP CRiv CRow CSco CShe CSin ELan EPar EPot ERav GCal NBir NHol NSti SIng SPou WEas WHil
¶ – ***variegata***	CRow
* – 'Variegata'	CRow
– 'Vic Pawlowski's Gold' (v)	CRow CSin

CONVOLVULUS (Convolvulaceae)

althaeoïdes	CBot CHad CHan CMil CSam ECha EPla LGre MNFA MTho SBla SChu SCro SSpi SUsu WAbb WCru WEas WHal
§ – ssp. ***tenuissimus***	CRDP CSpe EOrc GCal MWat SAxl WCot
cneorum	Widely available
♦ ***elegantissimus***	See C. ***althaeoïdes tenuissimus***
lineatus	ELan EPot LBee LHop MTho NHar NMen NNrd NWCA SBla SIng SSou
mauritanicus	See C. ***sabatius***
nitidus	See C. ***boissieri***
§ ***sabatius***	Widely available
– dark form	CSpe GCal LHil LHop SMrm SUsu WCru

X COOPERANTHES (Liliaceae/Amaryllidaceae)

¶ ***lancasterae***	CMon

COOPERIA See ZEPHYRANTHES

COPROSMA † (Rubiaceae)

acerosa (f)	See C. ***brunnea***
areolata	ECou
atropurpurea (m)	ECou ITim WDav
baueri 'Picturata'	See C. ***repens*** 'P.'
'Beatson's Gold' (f/v)	CB&S CBra CDec CDoC CMHG CMer CTrw ERea ESma GWht IBar IOrc ISea LHop NFai SChu SGil STre WBod WSHC
§ ***billardierei***	GCal
'Blue Pearls' (f)	ECou
'Brunette' (f)	ECou
§ ***brunnea*** (f)	ECar ECou MHig
– x ***kirkii*** (m)	ECou
cheesemanii	ECou NTow
'Chocolate Soldier' (m)	ECou
'Coppershine'	CB&S CMer ERea ESma
repens (m)	ECou
x ***cunninghamii*** (f)	ECou
depressa	ECou
foetidissima Forster	ECou
'Green Girl' (f)	ECou
'Green Globe'	CTre
'Hinerua' (f)	ECou
'Indigo Lustre' (f)	ECou
'Jewel' (f)	ECou
x ***kirkii*** 'Kirkii' (f)	ECou

– 'Kirkii Variegata' (f) CB&S CBot CHal CHan CMer CPle CTre ECou ERea ESma LAbb LHop NTow STre WSHC
'Kiwi-Gold' (v) CB&S CMer ECou
linariifolia ECou
lucida ECou
macrocarpa ECou
nitida (m) ECou
parviflora (m) ECou
'Pearly Queen' (f) EBar ECou
'Pearl's Sister' (f) ECou
petriei ECou MHig NTow WDav
– 'Don' (m) ECou
– 'Lyn' (f) ECou
propinqua SDry WSHC
– (f) ECou
– (m) ECou
'Prostrata' (m) ECou
pumila ECar ECou
♦***quadrifida*** See C. ***billardierei***
repens (f) CHEx ECou
– (m) CB&S ECou
– 'Apricot' (f) ECou
– 'Brownie' (f) ECou
– 'County Park Purple' (f) ECou ERea ESma
– 'Exotica' (f/v) ECou LHop SGil
– 'Marble King' (m/v) ECou ESma
– 'Marble Queen' (m/v) ECou ESma IBar LHil LHop SGil SLMG
– 'Orangeade' (f) ECou
§ – 'Picturata' (m/v) ECou ERea
– 'Pink Splendour' (v) CB&S CSpe ERea ESma LHop
– 'Silver Queen' (m/v) ECou
– 'Variegata' (m) CPle ECou LHil
rhamnoïdes ECou
rigida (f) ECou
robusta (m&f) ECou GWht SDry
– 'Williamsii Variegata' (m/f) LHop
rotundifolia (m&f) ECou
'Roy's Red' ECou
rugosa ECou IBar
tenuifolia (m) ECou
¶ 'Tuffet' (f) MUlv
'Violet Drops' (f) ECou
virescens (f) ECou
¶ 'Walter Brockie' CChu

COPTIS (Ranunculaceae)

¶ ***quinquefolia*** CBos

CORALLOSPARTIUM (Leguminosae)

crassicaule ECar ECou
– x CARMICHAELIA ***kirkii*** ECou

CORDYLINE † (Agavaceae)

australis CB&S CBot CBra CHEx CLan CTre EBre ELan ENot ERea IBar IDai IHos IJoh ISea LBre LNet LPal MBal MBri NPal NRog SArc SHBN SPer WBod
– 'Albertii' (v) CB&S CHEx CTro ERea IOrc LNet MBri NPal SArc
– Purpurea Group CB&S CBar CBot CBra CHEx CHal EBre ENot ERea IBar IOrc ISea LBre SPer WStI WWeb
¶ – 'Red Star' CTor
– 'Sundance' CAbb CB&S CBar CTor CTro CWit IJoh ISea WStI
– 'Torbay Dazzler' (v) CAbb CB&S CBar CDoC CHEx COtt CTor CWit EBre ELan IJoh ISea LBre MAsh MBal SHBN SHer WWeb
¶ – 'Torbay Green' CTor
– 'Torbay Red' CAbb CB&S CBar COtt CTor CTro ELan IJoh ISea MAsh
– 'Torbay Sunset' CDoC CTor ELan IOrc
¶ – 'Torbay Surprise' CTor
– 'Variegata' CBot CHEx
banksii CAbb CB&S
fruticosa 'Atom' MBri
– 'Baby Ti' MBri
– 'Calypso Queen' MBri
– 'Kiwi' CHal MBri
– 'Orange Prince' MBri
– 'Red Edge' CHal MBri
– 'Yellow King' MBri
¶ 'Green Goddess' CB&S
§ ***indivisa*** CHEx CLan EBak GAri MBri SArc
kaspar CHEx SArc
'Purple Tower' CB&S IBar
stricta CHEx MBri
terminalis See C. ***fruticosa***

COREOPSIS † (Compositae)

auriculata 'Schnittgold' ('Cutting Gold') CSam MWat NRoo SFis SSvw WPer
– 'Superba' CTom EBre LBre SFis
¶ 'Gold Child' SGil
'Goldfink' CKel EBre ECED ECha LBre MRav NKay SRms
grandiflora EHal WOld
– 'Badengold' CB&S CDoC
– 'Domino' NOak
– 'Early Sunrise' CBow CDoC CSam ECtt EFou LAbb LWad MWat NBar NFai NMir NPer NRoo SFis SGil WHen WHil WHoo WPer
– 'Mayfield Giant' CBow MBel NBar NVic SHer SRms
– 'Rotkehlchen' ('Ruby Throat') ECha
¶ ***integrifolia*** EMon WCot
lanceolata 'Lichtstad' MBri
– 'Sterntaler' EFou EPar NOrc NRoo WTyr
¶ ***maximillion*** WPer
rosea CElw CLew CRDP EPla LAbb MBel SMrm WCot
¶ – 'American Dream' EBlo EFou EMil EPar
'Sonnenkind' ('Baby Sun') EPar MBri MDHE MHig MPit NBro NMen NNor NNrd SFis
'Sunburst' EJud ELan NNor NOak SHer WFro
'Sunray' CBow CKel CLew CRiv EFol EFou LHil LWad MBel MBri MFir MPit NBar NMir NNor NOak NRoo SCro SFis SHer SSvw WByw WPer WWin
tinctoria NSal
– ***atkinsoniana*** MBel WPer
tripteris ECha EMon WCot

verticillata	CBow CLew CMea CSam CShe ECha EFol ENot EOrc LHil MBal MFir MWat NKay NPer SAxl SDix WAbe WEas WHal WOld WRus
– 'Golden Shower'	See C. *v.* 'Grandiflora'
§ – 'Grandiflora'	CB&S CKel COtt CPar CSco CTom EBlo EBre EFou ELan EMon EPla LBre MBri NBar NHol NNor NOak NVic SChu SMad SPer SPla WPbr WWin
– 'Moonbeam'	Widely available
– 'Zagreb'	CCla CMGP COtt CSco EBlo EBre ECtt EFol EPar EPla GCal LBre LHop MBri MUlv NBar NHol NRoo SPla WCra WMer WPbr WRus

CORETHROGYNE (Compositae)

californica	CWes ESma LHil SLon WSHC

CORIANDRUM (Umbelliferae)

sativum	CArn CSFH CSev GPoy IEde ILis LHol MChe MHew NSel SHer SIde WOak WPer WWye
– 'Cilantro'	CSev GPoy
– 'Morocco'	CSev

CORIARIA (Coriariaceae)

japonica	GCal SDry WCru WWat
kingiana	ECou
§ *microphylla*	SDry WCru
myrtifolia	CB&S SDry WCru
¶ *napalensis*	GCal WWat
terminalis	
var. *xanthocarpa*	CB&S ECha GCal IBlr MBal SDry WCot WCru WWat
thymifolia	See C. *microphylla*

CORIS (Primulaceae)

See Plant Deletions

CORNUS † (Cornaceae)

alba	CBow CDoC CKin CLnd CPer ENot IHos IJoh IOrc MBar MBri NWea WDin WMou WStI
*– 'Albovariegata'	ENot
– 'Aurea'	CB&S CMCN CSco EBlo EBre ECtt EFol EGol EHar EHoe ELan EPla IJoh IOrc LBre MBar MBri MRav NRoo SHBN SPer SSpi WAbe WDin WMou WPat
– 'Elegantissima' (v)	Widely available
– 'Gouchaultii' (v)	CB&S CDoC MBar NKay SRms WDin
– 'Kesselringii'	CAbP CB&S CCor EBlo EBre EGol EHar EHoe ENot EPla IOrc LBre MBar MBri MWat SMad SPer SPla SSta WBod WDin
§ – 'Sibirica'	Widely available
*– 'Sibirica Variegata'	CDoC CPMA EBlo EBre EPla IJoh IOrc LBre MBri MGos MWat SHBN SSpi WPat
– 'Spaethii' (v)	Widely available
*– 'Variegata'	CB&S CCla EFol ISea SPer WWin
– 'Westonbirt'	See C. *a.* 'Sibirica'
alternifolia	CBow CCla CMHG EHar IJoh MSte MWat SPer SSpi WMou WWat
§ – 'Argentea' (v)	CBow CBra CCla CDoC CPMA CSco CShe EBre EGol EHar ELan IMal LBre LTil MMor SHil SLeo SMad SPer SReu SSpi SSta WDin WHCG WKif WPat WWat
– *variegata*	See C. *a.* 'Argentea'
amomum	CB&S CCla CCor NHol WCoo
§ 'Ascona'	CB&S CBow CPMA ELan MBlu MBri SPer SSpi
australis	EPla
baileyi	See C. ***stolonifera*** 'B.'
§ *canadensis*	Widely available
candidissima	See C. ***racemosa***
capitata	CB&S CChu CDec CGre CHan CPMA CPle ECtt ESma IOrc SSpi WAbe WCru
chinensis	CBra LPan
controversa	CAbP CB&S CBow CDoC CMCN CPMA CPle CSam CSco EHar ESma IJoh IOrc LPan MBar MBlu MBrk MSte SEng SPer SReu SSpi SSta WCoo WDin WMou WWat
– 'Pagoda'	CPMA CSco MBlu SMad SSpi
– 'Variegata'	Widely available
'Eddie's White Wonder'	CB&S CBow CCla CPMA CSco EHar ELan ESma IMal LTil MBal MBlu MBri MGos SHBN SHer SHil SReu SSpi SSta WDin
florida	CBow CCla CGre CTre EBre ECtt ELan IOrc LBre MSte SPer SReu SSta WCoo WNor
– 'Alba Plena'	CBow CPMA SSpi
– 'Apple Blossom'	CBow CPMA
– 'Cherokee Chief'	CAbP CB&S CBow CDoC CPMA CSco LPan MBlu MGos SPer SSpi
– 'Cherokee Princess'	CBow CPMA LPan MBlu SSta
– 'Clear Moon'	LPan
– 'Cloud Nine'	CB&S CDoC COtt CPMA CSco LPan MBal MGos SSpi
– 'Daybreak'	COtt CPMA MBlu
– 'First Lady'	CPMA LPan SSpi
– 'Fragrant Cloud'	LPan
– 'G H Ford'	CPMA
¶ – 'Pendula'	CPMA
– 'Purple Glory'	CPMA
– 'Rainbow'	CAbP CB&S CBow CCla CDoC COtt CPMA CSco EHoe ELan ESma LPan LTil MBri MGos SEng SPer SSpi SSta
– 'Red Giant'	CPMA MGos
– 'Royal Red'	CPMA
– f. *rubra*	CB&S CBot CBow CBra CDoC CSco ELan IDai IJoh LPan MGos SHer SPer SReu SSpi SSta WBod WNor
– 'Spring Song'	CBow CPMA MBri SSpi
– 'Stoke's Pink'	CPMA SSpi
– 'Sunset'	COtt CPMA MBlu
– 'Sweetwater'	CBow CCla CPMA SSpi
– 'Tricolor'	See C. *f.* 'Welchii'
§ – 'Welchii' (v)	CPMA SHil
– 'White Cloud'	SHil SPer SSpi
♦ *foemina*	See C. ***stricta***
glabrata	CCor
hemsleyi	EPla
'Kelsey's Dwarf'	See C. ***stolonifera*** 'Kelseyi'
kousa	CB&S CBow CBra CDec CDoC CMCN ELan ISea LNet MBal MBar MWat NKay NNor SHBN SPer SPla SReu SSpi SSta WAbe WBod WCoo WDin WFro WStI

– ***angustata*** CCla MBal SPer SSpi
– var. ***chinensis*** CBot CBow CChu CCla CMHG CPle CSam CSco EBlo EBre ECtt EHar ELan IBar IJoh IOrc LBre MBri MGos NBee SMad SPer SReu SSpi SSta WDin WNor WWat
– – 'Bodnant Form' CPMA
– – 'China Girl' CAbP CBow CDoC COtt CPMA CSco LPan MBri MGos SEng SHBN SPer SPla SSpi
– – 'Milky Way' CBow CPMA SPer
– – Spinners form CCla CPMA LTil SSpi
– 'Gold Star' (v) CAbP CBow CCla CPMA CSco ELan ESma IOrc MBri MGos SHBN SPer SSpi
– 'Madame Butterfly' CPMA LRHS LTil SPer SSpi
– 'Satomi' CCla CDoC CPMA CSco ELan LTil MBri SMad SPer SReu SSpi
¶ – 'Snowboy' (v) CPMA CSco ELan SMad SSpi SSta
¶ – 'Tilgates' LTil
– 'Weaver's Weeping' CPMA
macrophylla CMCN
mas Widely available
– 'Aurea' (v) CBow CBra CCla CPMA EBre EGol EHar ERav LBre MAsh MBri SHBN SPer SPla SSpi SSta WWat
§ – 'Aureoelegantissima' (v) CPMA EHar ELan ERav LTil MBri SPer SSpi SSta WSHC
– 'Elegantissima' (v) See C. ***m.*** 'Aureoelegantissima'
– 'Golden Glory' CBow CPMA SSpi
– 'Variegata' CBot CBra CCla CDoC CPMA CShe EGol EHar ELan ERav IOrc MBri MGos NPal SHBN SHil SPer SSpi WWat
N 'Norman Hadden' CBot CCla CPMA CSam EHar EPla MBlu MBri NKay SHil SReu SSpi SSta WAbe WBod WThu WWat
nuttallii CB&S CBot CBow CCla CSam CSco ELan LPan MBal MBri SEng SHBN SPer SSpi SSta WCoo WDin WNor WWat
– 'Ascona' See C. 'Ascona'
– 'Colrigo Giant' SHil
– 'Gold Spot' (v) CPMA IOrc SSpi
– 'Monarch' CBow CPMA SSpi
– 'North Star' CPMA MBri SSpi
– 'Portlemouth' CPMA SHil SSpi
obliqua EPla
¶ ***occidentalis*** EPla
officinalis CMCN EHal LTil SHil WWat
'Ormonde' CPMA LTil SPer SSpi
paucinervis CMCN EPla
♦ ***pubescens*** See C. ***occidentalis***
pumila EPla NHol SPla
§ ***racemosa*** CCor WWat
sanguinea CKin CLnd CPer EBre ENot EPla LBre LBuc NNor NWea WDin
– 'Compressa' WPat
* – 'Midwinter Fire' EGol EPla LBuc MAsh MBar MGos MWat NBar NBee SMad WPat
§ – 'Winter Beauty' CB&S CDoC EBlo EBre IJoh IOrc LBre MBri MGos NHol SPer WWat
– 'Winter Flame' See C. ***s.*** 'Winter Beauty'
stolonifera CBow CLan EGol MGos
– 'Baileyi' CCla CCor EHar
– 'Flaviramea' Widely available
§ – 'Kelseyi' CB&S CBow CDoC CWit EBar EGol ESis ESma IOrc LHop MBar NHol SEng SLPl SPer WWat
§ – 'White Gold' (v) CAbP ENot EPla IOrc MAsh MBri NHol SHil WPat
♦ – 'White Spot' (v) See C. ***s.*** 'White Gold'
¶ ***stricta*** CLnd
walteri CMCN

COROKIA (Escalloniaceae)

buddleioïdes CB&S CChu CDoC CMHG CPle WBod
'Coppershine' CB&S LAbb
cotoneaster CDoC CLan CTrw ECou ELan ENot EPot IMal ISea LGre MBlu MUlv SDry SPer SReu SSpi SSta WBod WSHC WStI WWat
– 'Little Prince' CB&S ELan
– 'Ohau Scarlet' ECou
– 'Ohau Yellow' ECou
¶ – 'Swale Stream' ECou
¶ – 'Wanaka' ECou
macrocarpa CDoC CPle ISea SDix SPer WSHC
x ***virgata*** CAbP CB&S CBra CChu CDec CMHG CPle CTrw ECou GWht IBar IJoh IOrc ISea MBlu MCas MGos MUlv SArc SGil SPer SReu WBod WSHC WStI
– 'Bronze King' CTre CWit IHos MBrk SPer
– 'Bronze Lady' MBal
¶ – 'Cheesemanii' ECou
– 'County Park Lemon' ECou
¶ – 'County Park Purple' ECou
¶ – 'Havering' ECou
– 'Red Wonder' CB&S CBra CMHG EHal ERea IHos IMal SDry SHil WBod
¶ – 'Virgata' ECou
– 'Yellow Wonder' CB&S CMHG EBar ECou SHil

CORONILLA (Leguminosae)

♦ ***cappadocica*** See C. ***orientalis***
emerus See HIPPOCREPIS ***e.***
glauca See C. ***valentina g.***
¶ ***globosa*** SUsu
minima LRHS NTow SBla WAbe
§ ***orientalis*** NWCA WWin
valentina CDoC CMac ECha LHop MNew SBra SDix WCot WSHC
– 'Citrina' CAbb CB&S CBot CChu CCla CDoC CGre CMHG CSam CSco ECha ELan ERav LAbb LHop MTho NPer SAxl SBla SChu SPer SSpi SUsu WAbe WKif WRus WSHC
§ – ssp. ***glauca*** CB&S CBot CBra CDoC CGle CLan CMac CPle CSam CSco ECha ELan ENot ERea IJoh IOrc MBal NTow SPer WAbe WBod WWin
– 'Variegata' CAbb CB&S CBot CBra CFis CGle CHan CMac CPle CSam CSco EBre ECha ELan ERav ERea IBar LAbb LBre LHil LHop MTho SBra SDix SPer SSpi SSta WEas WSHC WWin
§ ***varia*** WCot

CORREA (Rutaceae)

alba	CB&S CGre CMHG CPle CSev ECou ERea SDry
– 'Pinkie'	CPle ECou ERea LHop SAxl
backhouseana	CAbb CB&S CCla CPle CSam CSun CTre GCal IBar IBlr IReg ISea LGre MBel SIgm SLMG WAbe WBod WSHC
calycina	CMHG ERea
decumbens	CB&S CGre CPle ECou ISea WSHC
'Dusky Bells'	CHan CPle ECou SAxl
'Harrisii'	See C. 'Mannii'
lawrenceana	CAbb CB&S CBow CCla IBlr LHil
– *rosea*	CMHG LAbb MBel
§ 'Mannii'	CB&S CBot CCla CGre CMHG CSam CSev CTre CWit ECou ERea IBar IReg ISea LHil LHop LTil MNew NTow SHil SLMG WAbe WEas WSHC WWat
pulchella	CAbb CB&S CCla CMHG CWit ERea
§ *reflexa*	CB&S CPle CSun ECou LBlm
– *virens*	WEas
– 'Yanakie'	CPle
speciosa	See C. ***reflexa***

CORTADERIA † (Gramineae)

argentea	See C. ***selloana***
fulvida	CGre IBar MPlt SSpi WCot
♦*richardii* hort.	See C. ***fulvida***
§ – (Endlicher) Zotov	CAbb CElw CHEx CHan EBre EFou EHoe ELan ETPC GAri GGar IBlr LBre MBal SArc
§ *selloana*	CB&S CHEx CRDP CTre CWGN EBre ELan IBar ISea LBre LNet MBar MWat NBee NEgg NHol NKay NNor SArc SPer WStI
§ – 'Albolineata' (v)	EMon EPla SMad
§ – 'Aureolineata' (v)	Widely available
– 'Gold Band'	See C. ***s*** 'Aureolineata'
– 'Pink Feather'	EBar EBre EPla ESma LBre NMir NOrc SRms WStI
– 'Pumila'	CB&S CCla CDoC CSco ECtt EGol EHoe ELan EMon ENot EPla GAbr IDai ISea MBal MBri MGos MUlv NFai NHol NTow SCob SCro SDix SHBN SPer SPla WPat WStI
– 'Rendatleri'	CB&S CDoC CGre CSco EHoe ELan GAbr GRei MBal MUlv SCob SMad SPer
– 'Rosea'	CHEx EPla ISea MBal MBar MBri NBee
– 'Silver Fountain'	ELan MAsh SApp SSpi
– 'Silver Stripe'	See C. ***s.*** 'Albolineata'
– 'Sunningdale Silver'	CB&S CBra CSco EBre ECtt EGol EHoe ELan ENot EOrc EPla IBar IHos ISea LBre MBal MBri MGos MUlv MWat NFai NHol SCob SHBN SMad SPer SSpi
– 'White Feather'	CHEx CLan ECtt EPla NEgg NMir
Toe Toe	See C. ***richardii***

CORTUSA (Primulaceae)

¶ *brotheri* C&R	NHar WDav
matthioli	CGle CNic GTou LBee LGan MBal MFir MHig MSte NGre NMen NTow NWCA SAxl SHer SIng WCla WCru WHal
– *alba*	MBal NHar NNrd SAxl WDav
– ssp. *pekinensis*	GAbr GCra GDra MBro MSte NHar NHol NTow WCra WDav
turkestanica	CNic NHar NTow WDav

CORYDALIS (Papaveraceae)

alexeenkoana	EPot
ambigua hort.	EPot GDra LAma MHig MTho NHar NRog SMad WChr WCot WCru
angustifolia	EPot LAma SPou WChr
bracteata	EPot LRHS NHar
♦*bulbosa*	See C. ***cava***
cashmeriana	EBre GArf GTou LAma LBre MHig NHar SBla SPou SWas WHil
– 'Kailash'	SPou
caucasica	EPot GDra LAma NHol NTow SPou WChr
– *alba*	EPot NBir SPou
§ *cava*	CGle EPar EPot LAma MNFA NHar
– *albiflora*	EPar EPot MPar SPou
cheilanthifolia	CAvo CLew CMea CRiv CRow ECha EFol ELan EPar EPot GCHN GDra MBri MBro MFir MPar NBro NSti NWCA SApp WBon WCot WDav WEas WHil WHoo WKif WOMN
chionophila	EPot
decipiens	MTho SPou WChr
decumbens	EPot
diphylla	EPot
ecristata	NHar
¶ *fargesii*	ERav
firouzii	EPot
flexuosa	CBos CChu CElw CHan CMil CRDP CRow ELan EPar MBro MTho SPou WKif
– CD&R 528	CAvo CGle CHad ECha LGre MDHE NHar SAxl SCro SHer SIgm SMrm SUsu WCot WCru
¶ – 'China Blue' CD&R 528c	CGle EPot MDHE SAxl SMrm SWas WCru
¶ – 'Père David' CD&R 528b	CGle SAxl
¶ – 'Purple Leaf' CD&R 528a	MDHE SAxl SWas
glauca	See C. ***sempervirens***
glaucescens	EPot WChr
integra	SPou WChr
intermedia	EPot WChr
kashgarica	EPot WChr
ledebouriana	CBro EPot WChr
lutea	See PSEUDOFUMARIA ***l.***
marschalliana	EPot
nobilis	LRHS
nudicaulis	WChr
ochroleuca	See PSEUDOFUMARIA ***alba***
ophiocarpa	CGle ELan EMar GAri GCal GGar IBlr MBel WCot WHil
paczoskii	EPot LRHS WChr
parnassica	See C. ***bulbosa***
pumila	EPot NTow WChr
rutifolia	GCHN
schanginii schanginii	WChr
§ *sempervirens*	NBro SUsu WEas WHer WOMN WPer WWin

solida CAvo CBro CGle CMea CRDP CRow EPar EPot ETub IBlr LAma LBlo LBow NGar NHar NRog SHer WAbe WCot WCru WHil
¶– MS 881 CMon
– ssp. *densiflora* MHig NHol
– forms EPot
– 'George P Baker' CAvo CBro NHol SPou SWas
¶– ssp. *incisa* SPou
¶– ssp. *tauricola* SPou
– f. *transsylvanica* EPot GArf NBir NHar NHol SPou WChr
¶– – pink form NHol
sp. Gökce Beli SPou
sp. Yayladag SPou
thalictrifolia Franchet See C. ***saxicola***
tomentella EPot NBro WAbe WDav WPer
wendelboi SPou
– 'Kartal Tepe' SPou WChr
wilsonii CBot GCHN GDra GTou IBlr MBro MTho NHol NMen NTow NWCA SBla WAbe WDav WEas WHal WOMN

CORYLOPSIS † (Hamamelidaceae)

§ *glabrescens* CB&S CBow CDoC CMCN CPMA EBre ELan GCal LAbb LBre MBal SPer SSpi SSta WNor
– var. *gotoana* ELan MAsh SPer
pauciflora CB&S CBow CCla CMCN CPMA ECtt EHar ENot IBar IDai IJoh IOrc MBal MBar MBri MGos MPla NBee NKay SHBN SPer SReu SSta WBod WRus WWat
platypetala See C. ***sinensis calvescens***
– *laevis* See C. ***sinensis calvescens***
sinensis EHal MBri SSta
§ – var. *calvescens* CBow CPMA MBal MBri SSpi SSta
§ – – f.*veitchiana* CGre CMCN CPMA CSam GCal MBal MBri SHil SSpi SSta WBod WWat
§ – var. *sinensis* CBow CCla CDoC CLan CWit ECtt ESma ISea MBal MBri MGos SPer SReu SSta WBod WWat
– – 'Spring Purple' CAbP CBow CCla CDoC CPMA CSco EHar ELan LTil MBlu MBri SHBN SHil SPer SSpi SSta WWat
spicata CDoC CPMA ELan ENot IDai IHos IJoh ISea MBal MBlu MBri MPla SPer SSta WBod
veitchiana See C. ***sinensis calvescens v.***
willmottiae See C. ***sinensis sinensis***

CORYLUS † (Corylaceae)

F *avellana* (cobnut) CBow CKin CLnd CPer EBre ENot ERea GRei LBre LBuc MBal MBar MBri NBee NRog NWea SHil SKee SPla WDin WMou WStI
– 'Aurea' COtt ELan MBlu MGos MWat NBee SPer SSta WDin
– 'Bollwyller See C. ***maxima*** 'Halle'sche Riesennuss'
– 'Contorta' CBra CMac CSco CShe CTrw EGol EHar ELan ENot GRei GTwe IBar IJoh MBal MBar MBri MGos MWat NBar NHol NWea SDea SHBN SPer SReu SSpi WDin WMou WPat WWat
F – 'Cosford Cob' CDoC ERea ESim GTwe LBuc MBri MGos NRog SDea SKee SPer WHig
F – 'Fuscorubra' CBow CMac CSco EGol ELan ENot IOrc WMou
– 'Halle Giant' See C. ***maxima*** 'Halle'sche Riesennuss'
§ – 'Heterophylla' EGol SSta WMou
– *laciniata* See C. ***a.*** 'Heterophylla'
– 'Merveille de Bollwiller' See C. ***maxima*** 'Halle'sche Riesennuss'
– 'Nottingham Prolific' See C. ***a.*** 'Pearson's Prolific'
F – 'Pearson's Prolific' EHar ERea ESim GTwe LBuc MBri SDea
– 'Pendula' WMou
– 'Purpurea' See C. ***a.*** 'Fuscorubra'
F – 'Webb's Prize Cob' CMac ERea IJoh LHol MBri NRog SDea WMou
colurna CLnd CMCN EBre EHar ENot ESim IOrc LBre MGos NBee NWea SMad SPer SSpi WDin WMou
– x *avellana* See C. x ***colurnoïdes***
– variegated WMou
§ x *colurnoïdes* ESim
F *maxima* (filbert) CLnd GTwe SDea WDin
F – 'Butler' SKee
F – 'Ennis' SKee
– 'Fertile de Coutard' See C. ***m.*** 'White Filbert'
F – 'Frizzled Filbert' ERea
– 'Frühe van Frauendorf' See C. ***m.*** 'Red Filbert'
– 'Grote Lambertsnoot' See C. ***m.*** 'Kentish Cob'
F – 'Gunslehert' SKee
F – 'Halle'sche Riesennuss' GTwe LHol SDea SKee
F – 'Kentish Cob' CDoC CSam EHar ERea ESim GTwe LBuc MBri NRog SDea SFam SKee SPer WHig
– 'Lambert's Filbert' See C. ***m.*** 'Kentish Cob'
¶ – 'Longue d'Espagne' SKee
– 'Purple Filbert' See C. ***m.*** 'Purpurea'
F – 'Purpurea' Widely available
F – 'Red Filbert' EHar ERea EWar GTwe MBlu MBri NRog
– 'Red Zellernut' See C. ***m.*** 'Red Filbert'
F – 'Tonda Giffon' SKee
F – 'White Filbert' ERea NRog SKee
– 'White Spanish Filbert' See C. ***m.*** 'White Filbert'
– 'Witpit Lambertsnoot' See C. ***m.*** 'White Filbert'
sieboldiana WMou
¶ x *vilmorinii* WMou

CORYNEPHORUS (Gramineae)

canescens EHoe ETPC

CORYNOCARPUS (Corynocarpaceae)

laevigata	CGre CHEx ECou MBri
– 'Picturata'	CHEx
– 'Variegata'	CB&S CHEx

COSMOS (Compositae)

§ *atrosanguineus*	Widely available

COSTUS (Costaceae)

curvibracteatus	MNew
§ *cuspidatus*	MNew
igneus	See C. ***cuspidatus***
speciosus	MNew NRog
spiralis	MNew

COTINUS † (Anacardiaceae)

americanus	See C. ***obovatus***
§ *coggygria*	CBra CDoC CSco EBre ELan ENot IOrc LBre LHop MBar MBri MWat NBee NNor NRoo SHBN SPer WAbe WDin WFro WMou WStI
– 'Foliis Purpureis'	See C. ***c.*** Rubrifolius Group
– 'Notcutt's Variety'	CCla ELan ENot SPla
– 'Purpureus Group'	CLan CSco
– 'Red Beauty'	COtt MBri
– 'Royal Purple'	Widely available
§ – Rubrifolius Group	CCla MBal NNor SChu SDix SPer SPla WWeb
– 'Velvet Cloak'	CBow CCla CPMA CSam MBri MGos MUlv SHil SSpi SSta WPat
'Flame'	CDoC CPMA CSco CShe SHil SMad SPer SSpi WBod
'Grace'	CAbP CB&S CBow CDoC COtt CPMA CSam CSco EBre ELan LBre MAsh MBri MGos MUlv SHil SPer SSpi SSta WDin
§ *obovatus*	CBow CChu CDoC CGre CKni CPMA CPle ENot MBri MUlv SHil SPer SPla SSpi WWat

COTONEASTER † (Rosaceae)

adpressus	CDoC CLew EPla GDra MGos MWat NHar NNor NWea SIng WWat
§ – 'Little Gem'	GAri MBri MBro SRms WDav
– var. *praecox*	See C. ***nanshan***
♦– 'Tom Thumb'	See C. ***a.*** 'Little Gem'
¶ *amoenus*	SLPl SRms
§ *ascendens*	CMCN
¶ *assamensis*	SRms
§ *astrophoros*	CDoC CSco NKay SRms WBod
¶ *atropurpureus*	SRms
¶ – 'Variegatus'	Widely available
¶ *boisianus*	SRms
§ *bullatus*	CCor CMHG CPle CSam ELan ENot GRei IDai ISea MGos NNor SPer SRms WAbe WSHC WWat
¶ – 'Firebird'	SRms
– f. *floribundus*	See C. ***b.***
– var. *macrophyllus*	See C. ***rehderi***
N *buxifolius* Wallich ex Lindley	ESis
♦– f. *vellaeus*	See C. ***astrophoros***
cashmiriensis	LMer
cavei	SLon
¶ *chailaricus*	SRms
§ *cochleatus*	CPar EPot ESis GAri GDra MBal MBar MBro NMen SFis SReu SRms WDav WEas WWat
§ *congestus*	CLew CMHG EPla IDai IJoh IOrc LHop MBal MBar MBri MBro MGos MRav NHol NKay NNor NRoo SBla WAbe WHal WHoo WWat WWeb WWin
– 'Menai'	CCla
– 'Nanus'	CDoC CMHG ELan IBar MPla NCat SPla SRms WHoo WPat
conspicuus	EPla IDai SRms
– 'Decorus'	CLew CMHG CSco ELan ENot GDra GRei IOrc MBar MGos MRav NHol NNor NRoo NWea SPer SPla SReu WDin WStI
– 'Flameburst'	ECtt MBal MBri SHBN
– 'Red Glory'	LRHS SRms
– 'Red Pearl'	SReu
¶ *cuspidatus*	SRms
N *dammeri*	CBra CMHG CSco EBre ELan ENot EPla EPot GRei IJoh ISea LBre LBuc LGro MBal MBar MGos NNor NWea SLon SPer SPla SReu SRms WDin WWat WWin
– 'Oakwood'	See C. ***radicans*** 'Eichholz'
– var. *radicans* hort.	CShe NKay SIng
– – Schneider	See C. ***radicans***
– 'Streibs Findling'	See C. ***procumbens***
¶ *declinatus*	SRms
dielsianus	CCla NWea SRms
¶ – 'Rubens'	SRms
distichus	See C. ***nitidus***
– var. *tongolensis*	See C. ***splendens***
divaricatus	ENot EPla GRei SPer
floccosus	ECtt EHal GRei IDai MBri NRoo NWea SPer WWat
franchetii	CB&S CLan CMHG CSco EBre ELan IDai IOrc LBre MBal MGos MRav MWat NBee NWea SHBN SPer SPla SRms WDin WMou WStI WTyr
– Yu 14144	MBal
frigidus	ENot GAri NKay NWea WBod
§ – 'Cornubia'	CBra CLan CLnd CSco EBre ELan ENot GCHN IDai ISea LBre LHop LNet MBar MBri MGos MRav MWat NBee NKay NWea SHBN SLon SPer SReu SRms WDin WStI WWat
– 'Fructu Luteo'	IBlr
– 'Notcutt's Variety'	ENot
– 'Sherpa'	LMer
¶ *froebelii*	SRms
¶ *giraldii*	SRms
¶ *glaucophyllus*	SRms
§ *glomerulatus*	ESis MBar SRms
¶ *harrovianus*	SRms
henryanus	CDoC CSco WWat
§ *hjelmqvistii*	CDoC CSco ENot SPla
– 'Robustus'	See C. ***h.***
– 'Rotundifolius'	See C. ***h.***
horizontalis	Widely available
♦– 'Variegatus'	See C. ***atropurpureus*** 'V.'
– var. *wilsonii*	See C. ***ascendens***
humifusus	See C. ***dammeri***
'Hybridus Pendulus'	See C. ***salicifolius*** 'Pendulus'
¶ *hylmoei*	SRms
ignavus	CCla EHal

§ ***integrifolius***	CCla CHan CMHG CSam ECar ELan EPla ESis IDai LNet LTil MBal MBar MBri NHol NKay NNor NRoo SRms WWat WWin
¶ ***kitiabelii***	SRms
lacteus	CCla CMHG CSam CSco CShe ELan ENot LBuc MGos MRav SHBN SPer SPla SRms WDin WWat
¶ ***laxiflorus***	SRms
¶ ***linearifolius***	SRms
lucidus	EHar
marquandii	EPla NNor SRms
¶ ***melanocarpus***	SRms
melanotrichus	See C. ***cochleatus***
microphyllus	CBow CHal CLan CMCN CPle CSco EBre EFol ELan ENot GRei IJoh ISea LBre MBar MBri MGos NNor NRoo SDix SHBN SLon SRms STre WAbe WBod WDav WDin
– 'Donard Gem'	See C. ***astrophoros***
– 'Teulon Porter'	See C. ***astrophoros***
– ***thymifolius***	See C. ***integrifolius***
¶ ***mucronatus***	SRms
multiflorus	NWea
¶ ***nagaensis***	SLPl
§ ***nanshan***	CDoC EHal GRei LHop NWea SPer
– 'Boer'	MBri SPla
nitidifolius	See C. ***glomerulatus***
§ ***nitidus***	SLon SPer
¶ ***nivalis***	SRms
pannosus	ESis
¶ ***parneyi***	SRms
¶ ***permutatus***	SRms
perpusillus	GAri MBri
¶ ***polyanthemus***	SRms
§ ***procumbens***	EPla ESis GAri NRoo SRms
– 'Queen of Carpets'	MBri MGos NHar SRms
prostratus 'Arnold Forster'	CDoC
pyrenaicus	See C. ***congestus***
¶ ***radicans***	SRms
§ – 'Eichholz'	CDoC ECtt ENot MBri MGos
§ ***rehderi***	SRms
rotundifolius	SRms
'Royal Beauty'	See C. x ***suecicus*** 'Coral Beauty'
¶ ***rugosus***	SLPl
salicifolius	CBra CLnd CPle NBee NNor SPer WDin
– 'Elstead'	SPer
– 'Exburyensis'	CBra CSam CSco CTrw LNet MBri MGos MWat SHBN SPer SReu SRms WAbe WDin WWat WWin
– 'Fructu Luteo'	EHal MBri
– 'Gnom'	EHar EPla LNet MBal MBri MGos NNor NRoo SLon SPer SRms WWat
– 'Herbstfeuer' ('Autumn Fire')	ECtt MBal MGos MRav MWat NKay NNor SPer SPla SRms
– 'Merriott Weeper'	CDoC CSco WWat
– 'Parkteppich' ('Park Carpet')	EBar NWea SLon SPer
§ – 'Pendulus'	CSco CShe ELan EPot GRei IDai IJoh ISea LNet LPan MBal MBar MBri MGos MRav MWat NBar NKay NWea SHBN SHer SPer SRms WAbe WPat WStI
– 'Red Flare'	SPer
– 'Repens'	CShe IDai MBal MWat NNor NRoo NWea SPer SPla SRms WAbe
– 'Rothschildianus'	CLan CPMA CShe EBre ECtt ELan ENot IJoh LBre LHop MBal MBar MBri MRav NKay SPer
– 'Scarlet Leader'	MBri
¶ ***salwinensis***	SRms
¶ ***schlechtendalii*** 'Blazovice'	SRms
¶ – 'Brno'	SRms
serotinus	CCla EPla SHil SLPl SRms
¶ ***shansiensis***	SRms
aff. ***sheriffii*** 'Highlight'	ECtt SRms
sikangensis	CCor EPla
simonsii	CKin CPer CSco EBre ELan IDai IOrc LBre LBuc MBar MBri MGos NBee NHol NWea SPer SRms WBod WDin WStI
§ ***splendens***	CDoC CGre ECtt ELan SHil SRms
¶ – 'Glasnevin'	SRms
– 'Sabrina'	See C. ***splendens***
sternianus	CShe ENot MBar MBri SLPl SPer SRms WBod
¶ ***suavis***	SRms
§ x ***suecicus*** 'Coral Beauty'	CSco EBre ENot EPla GRei IJoh IOrc LBre LBuc MBal MBri MGos NBar NHol NNor SPer SReu SRms WDin WStI WWeb
– 'Skogholm'	CLew CPle CSco GWht MBal MBar MGos MWat NHol NRoo NWea SLon SPer SRms WDin WStI WWin
¶ ***turbinatus***	SRms
vestitus	SRms
wardii	CDoC CSco IDai IJoh IOrc NBee SPer
x ***watereri***	CSco CShe EBre ELan EPla LBre LNet MGos NBar SHer WDin WWat WWeb
– 'Cornubia'	See C. ***frigidus*** 'C.'
– 'Goscote'	MGos
– 'John Waterer'	CBra SRms WBod
♦– 'Pendulus'	See C. ***salicifolius*** 'P'
– 'Pink Champagne'	CMer EHal MBri SHil SPer
¶ ***zabelii***	SRms

COTULA (Compositae)

atrata	See LEPTINELLA ***a.***
– var. ***dendyi***	See LEPTINELLA ***dendyi***
coronopifolia	CBen CSev CWGN LMay MSta NDea SWat WChe
goyenii	See LEPTINELLA ***g.***
hispida	CMHG CNic CRDP CRiv EBar ECtt EFol EPot GCHN MBar MCas MHig MTho NHol NMen NNor NRya NTow NWCA SIgm SSmi SUsu WCru WEas WHil WPer
lineariloba	CPar NSti SBla
minor	ECou NHol WCru
pectinata	See LEPTINELLA ***p.***
§ ***perpusilla***	SSmi
potentilloïdes	See LEPTINELLA ***potentillina***
pyrethrifolia	See LEPTINELLA ***p.***
reptans	See LEPTINELLA ***scariosa***
rotundata	See LEPTINELLA ***r.***
scariosa	See LEPTINELLA ***s.***
sericea	See LEPTINELLA ***albida***

¶ sp. C&H 452 — WDav
squalida — See LEPTINELLA *s.*

COTYLEDON (Crassulaceae)

chrysantha — See ROSULARIA *c.*
oppositifolia — See CHIASTOPHYLLUM *oppositifolium*
orbiculata SH 40 — CHan
**pomedosa* — MBri
*– 'Variegata' — MBri
simplicifolia — See CHIASTOPHYLLUM *oppositifolium*
undulata — CHal WEas

COWANIA (Rosaceae)

See Plant Deletions

CRAB APPLE See MALUS

CRAIBIODENDRON (Ericaceae)

yunnanense — CTre MBal

CRAMBE (Cruciferae)

cordifolia — Widely available
¶ *filiformis* — WHil
koktebelica — CHan ECha EPla GCal
maritima — CGle CSco ECha EMar EPla ERav GPoy MNFA NNor NSal NSti WHoo
– 'Lilywhite' — ILis
¶ *orientalis* — ECha

CRANBERRY See VACCINIUM *macrocarpon*

CRASPEDIA (Compositae)

glauca — NHol
richea — See C. *glauca*

CRASSULA (Crassulaceae)

arborescens — CHal GAri SLMG
argentea — See C. *ovata*
coccinea — CHEx SLMG
dejecta x *coccinea* — CHEx
falcata — IBlr MBri
**galanthea* — SLMG
§ *helmsii* — CBen EHon EMFW NDea WChe WHol
justi-corderoyi — CHal CPle
§ *milfordiae* — CHal CLew CNic CPar EPot MCas MFir NGre NHar NHol NMen SBod SSmi WPer
¶ – *nana* — CLew
¶ *monstrosa* — SLMG
moschata — ECou
multicaulis — ECar ECou
¶ *muscosa* 'Variegata' — SLMG
§ *ovata* — CHal EBak MBri SLMG
– 'Basutoland' — MPla
– 'Hummel's Sunset' (v) — CHal SLMG
– 'Variegata' — EBak SLMG
pellucida ssp. *marginalis* — CHal
perforata — CHal SLMG
– 'Variegata' — CHal
♦ *portulacea* — See C. *ovata*
♦ *recurva* — See C. *helmsii*
rupestris — MBri
¶ *rupicola* — GAri
§ *sarcocaulis* — CRiv CShe ELan EPot ESis GAbr ITim MCas MPla MTho NGre NHar NHol NKay NMen NNrd NWCA SBod SSmi STre WAbe WEas WPat WSHC WWin
– *alba* — CHal CNic CRiv ELan EPot NGre SIng STre WAbe WPer WSHC
– dark form — NHol
– 'Ken Aslet' — GAbr NGre NHol NNrd
schmidtii — CHal MBri
sedifolia — ELan MBar MFir NBir WWin
sediformis — See C. *milfordiae*
socialis — CHal ITim
tetragona — SLMG

CRATAEGUS (Rosaceae)

arnoldiana — CTho EHal
'Autumn Glory' — CLnd CWSG EBre LBre MGos
azarolus — WMou
F – 'White Italian' — ESim
¶ *champlainensis* — CTho
chlorosarca — SHil
N *coccinea* — NWea WDin
♦ *cordata* — See C. *phaenopyrum*
crus-galli hort. — See C. *persimilis* 'Prunifolia'
– Linnaeus — CB&S CDoC CLnd CTho EHal LBuc SPer WDin WMou
¶ – var. *pyracanthifolia* — CTho
x *durobrivensis* — CLnd CTho EArb WWat
¶ *eriocarpa* — CLnd
¶ *gemmosa* — CTho
x *grignonensis* — CB&S CLnd EBar ENot SPer
§ *laciniata* — CLnd SHil STre WMou
§ *laevigata* — NBee WMou
– 'Coccinea Plena' — See C. *l.* 'Paul's Scarlet'
– 'Crimson Cloud' — CBow CLnd ENot MBri SPer
– 'Gireoudii' — CDoC ELan EPla MGos SMad WMou WPat
¶ – 'Mutabilis' — CTho
§ – 'Paul's Scarlet' — CB&S CBow CBra CDoC CLnd CTho EBre ELan ENot GRei IDai IJoh IOrc LBre LBuc MBar MBri MGos MRav NBee NWea SHBN SPer SReu WAbe WDin WMou WStI
¶ – 'Pink Corkscrew' — GAri
– 'Plena' — CB&S CDoC IHos MBri NWea SHBN SPer SPla WMou
– 'Rosea Flore Pleno' — CB&S CBow CDoC CLnd CTho EBre ELan ENot GRei LBre LBuc MBar MBri MGos NWea SHBN SPer WAbe WDin WMou
x *lavallei* — CBra CLnd ENot SPer WDin
– 'Carrierei' — CDoC CSam CTho MBri NBee NWea
monogyna — CB&S CBow CDoC CKin CLnd CPer EBre ELan ENot GRei LBre LBuc MBar MBri MGos NWea SPer WDin WMou
– 'Biflora' — SHil WMou
– 'Compacta' — MBlu WMou
– 'Flexuosa' — WMou
– 'Pendula Rosea' — WMou
– 'Stricta' — CLnd CTho ENot MBri SHil
– 'Variegata' — CPMA EFol WMou
x *mordenensis* 'Toba' — CDoC CTho ENot
F *opaca* — ESim
orientalis — See C. *laciniata*
oxyacantha — See C. *laevigata*

pedicellata	CLnd CTho
§ *persimilis* 'Prunifolia'	CB&S CBow CDoC CSam CTho EBar ELan ENot IHos MBar MBri MGos NBee NWea SHBN SMad SPer SPla SSpi WCoo WDin WMou
§ *phaenopyrum*	CLnd CTho GAri MBrk SHil WWat
pinnatifida	WWat
– var. *major*	SHil
prunifolia	See C. ***persimilis*** 'Prunifolia'
punctata	EArb EHal
F 'Red Italian'	ESim
¶ *schraderiana*	CTho
tanacetifolia	CLnd CTho EArb WMou
wattiana	CLnd CTho

X CRATAEMESPILUS (Rosaceae)

¶ *grandiflora*	CTho

CRAWFURDIA (Gentianaceae)

speciosa	WCru

CREMANTHODIUM (Compositae)

See Plant Deletions

CREPIS (Compositae)

aurea	CNic CPar ECha EPar GAri GGar IBlr NMen NNrd SHer SPer WHer
incana	CGle CLew CRow CShe EBre ECha EPar LBre LHop MPit MTho NHol NKay NRar SAxl SDix SIng SPer SUsu WAbe

CRINITARIA See ASTER

CRINODENDRON (Elaeocarpaceae)

§ *hookerianum*	Widely available
patagua	CAbb CB&S CBot CDec CDoC CGre CPle CSam EPla GCal GWht IBar ISea LHop LTil MBal SBar SHil SLon SPer WBod WSHC

CRINUM (Liliaceae/Amaryllidaceae)

amoenum	NRog WCot
aquaticum	See C. ***campanulatum***
§ *bulbispermum*	EBlo EBre ELan LBre
¶ – 'Album'	ECha
capense	See C. ***bulbispermum***
moorei	NRog
– f. *album*	CTro EBre LBre
§ x *powellii*	CAvo CB&S CCla CKel CMil CTro EBak EBlo ECha ELan ERav LAma LBow LHop MBal MBri MSta MUlv NRog SDeJ SDix SGil SLMG SPer WCru
– 'Album'	CAvo CB&S CHEx CHan CKel EBlo ECha ELan ERav LBow MUlv NRog SApp SDeJ SHig SLMG
– 'Longifolium'	See C. ***bulbispermum***
– 'Roseum'	See C. x ***powellii***
¶ *yemense*	CMon

CRITHMUM (Umbelliferae)

maritimum	GPoy NSal

CROCOSMIA † (Iridaceae)

'Bressingham Beacon'	EBlo EBre GAri LBre MUlv NBee SPer
'Bressingham Blaze'	GAri GCal NCat NOak
'Castle Ward Late'	CRow GCal IBlr
x *crocosmiiflora*	EPla MBel NOrc SRms WCot
– 'Canary Bird'	CBro CRDP CRow EGol GAbr GAri GCal IBlr NBar SChu SSpi
– 'Carmin Brillant'	CRow GCal IBlr LAma LRHS MBri SRms WCot
N– 'Citronella'	CB&S CBos CBot CBro CChu CElw CGle CPar CRow CSam EFou ELun EOrc LAma LHop NNor NRoo NSti SAxl SBla SChu SDix SHer SUsu WAbe WEas WHal WPer
§ – 'Emily McKenzie'	Widely available
– 'Fire King'	SAxl
– 'George Davison'	CAvo CB&S ECha IBlr MBro
– 'His Majesty'	CRow GCal IBlr LRHS MBri WCot
– 'Jackanapes'	CBro CRow ECha GCal IBlr LAma MBri SUsu WCot WHal
– 'James Coey'	CChu CMHG CRDP CRow ECha EFou IBlr LAma LBlm LBow LHop MBel NHol NOrc NRog SBla SUsu WCot WHil
– 'Lady Hamilton'	CBos CChu CRow GCal IBlr MBri NTow SAxl WMer
– 'Lady McKenzie'	See x ***c.*** 'Emily McKenzie'
¶ – 'Lady Oxford'	IBlr
– 'Lady Wilson'	CRow ECha EPar LAma NHol NOrc NRog SDeJ
¶ – 'Marcotijn'	IBlr
– 'Mrs Geoffrey Howard'	CGle CRow IDai
¶ – 'Mrs Morrison'	SWas
– 'Norwich Canary'	CAvo CChu CSam ECha EFou IBlr LAma LBlm LBow LHop MMil NOrc WCot WHil WHoo WWin
– 'Queen Alexandra'	LAma LBlm LHop NFai WHal
– 'Rheingold'	EPar WCot
N– 'Solfaterre'	CAvo CBro CChu CMHG CRDP CRow CShe ECha EFou EGol ELan GCal IBlr IDai LAma MBel MBri MUlv NFai NHol NRoo SApp SAxl SBla SMad SPer SUsu WCot WEas WMer
¶ – 'Venus'	IBlr
¶ 'Dusky Maiden'	WCot
'Eldorado'	GCal
'Emberglow'	CBro CChu CMHG CRow CSam EBlo EBre EFou GAri GCal LAma LBre MBal MBri NBar NHol NOrc SAxl SPer WCot
¶ 'Firebird'	ECha SPer
¶ 'Firebrand'	WCot
'Flamenco'	CChu CShe MUlv SBla
¶ 'Flamethrower'	WCot
¶ 'Golden Fleece'	GCal MBri
N 'Honey Angels'	WCot
'Jenny Bloom'	COtt EBlo EBre GCal LBre MUlv NBir NRoo
* 'Jesse van Dyke'	CRow
¶ 'Jupiter'	LRHS MMil NFai
¶ 'Kiatschou'	IBlr
¶ 'Lana de Savary'	CRow
'Lucifer'	Widely available
¶ 'Lutea'	IBlr
'Mars'	GCal

masoniorum	CB&S CBro CHEx CKel CRow CSco CShe ECha EFou ELan EOrc EPar GAbr IDai LAma MWat NHol NNor NRog SFis SIng SPer SPla WAbe WByw
– 'Dixter Flame'	SDix
– 'Firebird'	EBlo EBre LBre MUlv NRoo SMrm
¶ – 'Rowallane'	LRHS
¶ 'Morning Light'	WCot
'Mount Stewart'	GCal IBlr WCot
¶ 'Mount Usher'	IBlr
* 'Orangeade'	CB&S
§ ***paniculata***	CAvo CFis CPar CSco EMar GAbr IDai LBow MBal MUlv NHol NKay NOrc NRar NTow SChu SIng WCot WHoo
– 'Major'	SPer
pottsii	CB&S CChu CCor CRDP CRow IBlr
'Queen of Spain'	LRHS MBri
* 'Red Star'	CB&S
rosea	See TRITONIA ***rubrolucens***
¶ 'Rowden Bronze'	CRow
¶ 'Rowden Chrome'	CRow
¶ 'Severn Sunrise'	LRHS WMer
'Spitfire'	CBot CRow EBre ECha GAri LBre MBri MRav MSta NRoo WByw WEas
'Star of the East'	CBos CChu CRow GCal IBlr MBri SBla SSpi
¶ 'Sultan'	WCot
'Vulcan'	CB&S EOrc SBla SPer SSpi
¶ 'Zeal Tan'	CChu

CROCUS † (Iridaceae)

abantensis	EPot LAma WChr
'Advance'	CAvo CBro EPar EPot ETub EWal LAma NHol NRog SIng
§ ***aerius***	LAma WChr
– 'Cambridge'	WChr
alatavicus	CBro EPot WChr
§ ***ancyrensis***	CAvo CBro EPar EPot ETub LAma LBlo LBow NRog SIng WChr
– 'Golden Bunch'	See C. ***a.***
§ ***angustifolius***	CAvo CBro CMon EPot ETub LAma LBow NRog SIng WChr
– 'Minor'	EPot LAma WChr
antalyensis	LAma WChr
asturicus	See C. ***serotinus salzmannii***
asumaniae	EPot LAma WChr
aureus	See C. ***flavus flavus***
banaticus	CBro EPot LAma NHol SPou WChr WThu
¶ – JRM 3630	CMon
¶ – 'John Marr'	SPou
baytopiorum	EPot LAma SPou WChr
biflorus	CBro EPar LAma NRog
– ssp. ***adamii***	EPot LAma WChr
– ssp. ***alexandri***	CAvo CBro EPot LAma LBow NRog WChr
– 'Argenteus'	See C. ***b. biflorus***
§ – ssp. ***biflorus***	CMon LAma LBow SIng
¶ – – MS 984/957	CMon
– ssp. ***crewei***	LAma WChr
– ssp. ***isauricus***	WChr
¶ – ssp. ***melantherus*** S&L 226	CMon
– 'Miss Vain'	CAvo LAma
– var. ***parkinsonii***	See C. ***b. biflorus***
– ssp. ***pulchricolor***	CAvo LAma LBow SPou WChr
– sulphur	SPou
– ssp. ***tauri***	LRHS WChr
– ssp. ***weldenii*** 'Albus'	EPot LAma LBow
– – 'Fairy'	CAvo CBro LAma LBow
biliottii	See C. ***aerius***
boryi	CAvo EPot LAma LBow SPou
– PJC 168	WChr
¶ – VH 1546	CMon
cambessedesii	SPou
§ ***cancellatus*** ssp. ***cancellatus***	CBro LAma LBow NHol
– var. ***cilicicus***	See C. ***c. cancellatus***
– ssp. ***mazziaricus***	CAvo
– ssp. ***pamphylicus***	WChr
candidus var. ***subflavus***	See C. ***olivieri olivieri***
¶ ***carpetanus*** B&S 399	CMon
cartwrightianus	CBro LAma SPou
– CE&H 613	WChr
¶ – S&L 484	CMon
N – 'Albus'	CMon EPot ETub SPou
¶ ***caspius*** PF 5036	CMon
chrysanthus	WChr
– 'Ard Schenk'	EPot LAma
– 'Blue Bird'	EPar EPot EWal LAma LBlo LBow MBri SIng
– 'Blue Giant'	LAma
– 'Blue Pearl'	CAvo CBro EPar ETub LAma LBlo LBow MBri NRog SIng
– 'Blue Peter'	CBro LAma
– 'Brass Band'	LAma
– 'Canary Bird'	NRog
– 'Cream Beauty'	CAvo CBro EPar EPot ETub EWal LAma LBlo LBow MBri NRog SIng
– 'Dorothy'	LAma NRog
– 'E A Bowles'	EPot LAma LBlo SIng
– 'E P Bowles'	CAvo CBro CRiv LAma LBow MBri NRog SIng
– 'Elegance'	CBro LAma
– 'Eye-catcher'	EPot ETub LAma
– var. ***fuscotinctus***	CBro LAma MBri NRog SIng
– 'Gipsy Girl'	CBro LAma MBri NRog SIng
– 'Gladstone'	LAma
– 'Goldilocks'	CBro LAma
– 'Herald'	LAma
– 'Jeannine'	ETub LRHS
– 'Ladykiller'	CAvo CBro EPar EPot LAma LBlo LBow MBri NRog SIng WCru
– 'Moonlight'	EPot LAma NRog SIng
– 'Prins Claus'	EPot LAma SIng
– 'Prinses Beatrix'	EPot LAma NRog SIng
– 'Romance'	EPot LAma
– 'Saturnus'	LAma NRog
– 'Sky Blue'	LAma
– 'Skyline'	CBro EPot
– 'Snow Bunting'	CAvo CBro EPar EWal LAma LBlo LBow NRog SIng
– 'Snowwhite'	LBlo
– 'Spring Pearl'	CBro LAma
– 'Sunkist'	LAma
– 'Warley'	NRog
– 'White Beauty'	LAma
– 'White Triumphator'	EPot ETub LAma NRog
– 'Zenith'	LAma LBlo
– 'Zwanenburg Bronze'	CAvo EPar ETub EWal LAma NRog SIng
'Cloth of Gold'	See C. ***angustifolius***

clusii	See C. *serotinus c.*
corsicus	EPar EPot ETub LAma LBow SIng WChr
– PJC 657	SPou
cvijicii	WChr
– CE&H 560	LRHS SPou
dalmaticus	LAma MPar
– CEH	SPou
danfordiae	CAvo LAma WChr
¶ *etruscus*	CAvo
– 'Zwanenburg'	EPot ETub LAma
flavus	See C. *f. flavus*
¶ – M&T 4578	CMon
§ – ssp. *flavus*	EPot LAma MPlt WChr
fleischeri	EPot LAma WChr
gargaricus	EPot LAma MPar WThu
– ssp. *gargaricus*	SPou
– ssp. *herbertii*	CBro SPou WChr
– *minor* JRM 3299/75	WThu
'Golden Mammoth'	See C. × *luteus* 'Golden Yellow'
goulimyi	CAvo CBro EPar EPot ETub LAma LBow NHol SIng SPou WChr WThi
¶ – S&L 197	CMon
– 'Albus'	CAvo SPou WChr
¶ 'Haarlem Gem'	ETub LAma
§ *hadriaticus*	CAvo EPot LAma LBow NHol SPou WChr
¶ – BM 8124	CMon
– B&M 8039	WChr
– AM form	SPou
– var. *chrysobelonicus*	See C. *hadriaticus*
– f. *hadriaticus*	CBro
– f. *lilacinus*	LRHS
– 'Tom Blanchard'	LRHS
heuffelianus	See C. *vernus vernus* Heuffelianus Group
imperati	SIng SPou
– ssp. *imperati*	LRHS SPou
¶ – – MS 965	CMon
– – 'De Jager'	EPot LAma LBow
– ssp. *suaveolens*	SPou
¶ – – MS 962	CMon
karduchorum	CBro LAma NRog SIng SPou WChr
'Keith Rattray'	SPou
korolkowii	CBro EPar EPot ETub LAma NHol SIng WChr
¶ – 'Golden Nugget'	EPot
– 'Kiss of Spring'	EPot LRHS WChr
¶ – 'Yellow Princess'	EPot
kosaninii	LRHS WChr
kotschyanus	CAvo SPou
¶ – CM&W 2720	CMon
– 'Albus'	SPou SRms WChr
– ssp. *cappadocicus*	WChr
§ – ssp. *kotschyanus*	CBro EPot LAma LBlo LBow NHol NRog SIng
– var. *leucopharynx*	CMon NHol
– ssp. *suworowianus*	SPou
laevigatus	LBlo SPou WChr
¶ – CE&H 612	CMon
– 'Fontenayi'	CBro EPot ETub LAma WChr
– form	LAma
– white	SPou
'Large Yellow'	See C. × *luteus* 'Golden Yellow'
lazicus	See C. *scharojanii*
longiflorus	CAvo CBro EPot SPou WChr WThu
¶ – MS 968/974/967	CMon
§ × *luteus*	CMon EPot ETub WChr
§ – 'Golden Yellow'	ETub LAma LBlo
malyi	LAma SPou
– CE&H 519	WChr
'Mammoth Yellow'	See C. × *luteus* 'Golden Yellow'
medius	CBro CMon EPot LAma NRog SPou
minimus	CAvo CBro EPar EPot ETub LAma LBow SIng
¶ *nevadensis* AB&S 4415	CMon
niveus	CAvo CBro LAma LBow SPou
– PJC 164	WChr
¶ – S&L 194	CMon
– blue	WChr
nudiflorus	CAvo CBro EPot LAma NHol WChr
¶ – MS 872	CMon
ochroleucus	CAvo CBro EPot LAma LBlo LBow NHol NRog SIng WChr
olivieri	EPar EPot LAma
– ssp. *balansae*	WChr
– ssp. *istanbulensis*	EPot WChr
§ – ssp. *olivieri*	CMon LAma SPou WChr
oreocreticus	SPou WChr
pallasii	LAma WChr
– ssp. *pallasii*	CAvo
pestalozzae	EPot LAma WChr
– var. *caeruleus*	WChr
pulchellus	CAvo CBro ETub LAma SPou
– CE&H 558	WChr
¶ – M&T 4584	CMon
– *albus*	SPou WChr
– 'Zephyr'	CBro EPot ETub ITim LAma NHol
'Purpureus'	See C. *vernus* 'Purpureus Grandiflorus'
reticulatus	
ssp. *reticulatus*	EPot
robertianus	CAvo SPou WChr
sativus	CArn CAvo CBro CHun CSFH ELan EPot ETub GPoy LAma LBow MBri NHol NRog NSal SIde SIng WHil
– *cartwrightianus* 'Albus'	See C. *cartwrightianus* 'Albus'
¶ – var. *cashmirianus*	CMon ETub
scardicus	LRHS WChr
§ *scharojanii*	EPot WChr
– var. *flavus*	EPot WChr
§ *serotinus* ssp. *clusii*	CBro EPot LAma NHol WChr
– forms	MPar
§ – ssp. *salzmanii*	CBro EPar EPot LAma LBow MPar
¶ – – AB&S 4326	CMon
¶ – – MS 343	CMon
¶ – – SF 218	CMon
– ssp. *salzmannii* 'Albus'	WChr
sibiricus	See C. *sieberi*
§ *sieberi*	EPot LAma
§ – 'Albus'	CAvo CBro EPot ETub LAma LBow
– ssp. *atticus*	CBro EPot LAma LBow
– 'Bowles' White'	See C. *s.* 'Albus'
– 'Firefly'	CBro EPot LAma LBow NRog SIng
– 'Hubert Edelsten'	CBro EPot LAma LBow SIng

*– *pallidus* CMon
– ssp. *sublimis* 'Tricolor' CBro EPot ETub LAma LBow SPou WChr
– 'Violet Queen' CAvo CBro LAma LBlo LBow MBri NRog
speciosus CAvo CBro ELan EPar ETub LAma LBlo LBow MPar NHol NRog SIng WCru WHil
– 'Aitchisonii' CBro ETub LAma NHol SIng
– 'Albus' CMon ECha EPar EPot
– 'Artabir' CBro EPot ETub SIng
– 'Cassiope' EPot LAma
– 'Conqueror' CBro LAma LBlo NHol SIng WCru
– ssp. *ilgazensis* EPot
– 'Oxonian' EPot ETub LAma SPou
– x *pulchellus* 'Big Boy' SPou
– ssp. *xantholaimos* SPou
x *stellaris* See C. x *luteus*
susianus See C. *angustifolius*
suterianus See C. *olivieri olivieri*
¶ *thomasii* B&S 364 CMon
¶ – MS 978/982 CMon
tommasinianus CAvo CBro CRiv EPar EPot ETub LAma LBow MBri MPar MPlt SIng
¶ – PF 6584 CMon
– f. *albus* CBro EPot LAma LBow SPou WChr
– 'Barr's Purple' LAma SIng
– 'Bobbo' MPar SPou WChr
– 'Eric Smith' CAvo WChr
– 'Lilac Beauty' LAma
– var. *pictus* LAma WChr
– var. *roseus* CBro LAma SPou WChr
– 'Ruby Giant' CAvo CBro CNic EPar EPot ETub LAma NRog SIng
– 'Whitewell Purple' CAvo CBro EPot LAma LBlo LBow MBri NRog
tournefortii CAvo CBro CMon EPot LAma LBow SPou
vallicola LAma
veluchensis SPou WChr
§ *vernus* ssp. *albiflorus* EPot LAma MPar WChr
– 'Enchantress' ETub LAma
– 'Glory of Limmen' LRHS
– 'Graecus' EPot
– 'Grand Maître' LAma NRog
– 'Jeanne d'Arc' CBro ETub LAma LBow NRog
– 'Kathleen Parlow' LBlo
– 'King of the Blues' LAma NRog
– 'Little Dorrit' LAma
– 'Negro Boy' LAma
– 'Paulus Potter' LAma NRog
– 'Peter Pan' NRog
– 'Pickwick' ETub LAma LBlo NRog
§ – 'Purpureus Grandiflorus' CBro ETub LAma LBlo NRog
– 'Queen of the Blues' CBro LBlo LBow NRog
– 'Remembrance' ETub LAma LBlo NRog
– 'Sky Blue' NRog
– 'Snowstorm' LAma
– 'Striped Beauty' LAma LBlo NRog
– 'Vanguard' CBro ETub LAma NRog SIng
– ssp. *vernus* var. *scepusiensis* EPot
– – 'Grandiflorus' See C. *v.* 'Purpureus Grandiflorus'
§ – – Heuffelianus Group EPot
– 'Victor Hugo' LAma NRog

¶ *versicolor* MS 941/935 CMon
¶ – S&B 384 CMon
– 'Picturatus' LAma
'Yellow Mammoth' See C. x *luteus* 'Golden Yellow'
zonatus See C. *kotschyanus kotschyanus*

CROSSANDRA (Acanthaceae)

infundibuliformis MBri

CROTALARIA (Leguminosae)

capensis CPle

CROWEA (Rutaceae)

See Plant Deletions

CRUCIANELLA (Rubiaceae)

stylosa See PHUOPSIS *stylosa*

CRUCIATA (Rubiaceae)

§ *laevipes* CKin NMir

CRYPTANTHUS (Bromeliaceae)

bivittatus CHal
– 'Pink Starlight' (v) MBri
– 'Roseus Pictus' CHal
bromelioïdes MBri
* 'Red Starlight' (v) MBri
x *roseus* 'Le Rey' MBri
– 'Marian Oppenheimer' MBri
* *zonatus argyraeus* CHal

X CRYPTBERGIA (Bromeliaceae)

See Plant Deletions

CRYPTOGRAMMA (Adiantaceae)

crispa SRms

CRYPTOMERIA (Taxodiaceae)

fortunei See C. *japonica sinensis*
japonica CDoC EHar GAri IOrc ISea MBar SLim SPer WDin WFro WMou WNor
§ – 'Araucarioïdes' EHul
– 'Aritaki' SLim
§ – 'Aurea' EPla
– 'Bandai-sugi' CDoC CKen CMac EBar EHul IJoh LCon MBar MGos MPla NBee SGil SIng SLim SLon SSmi WStI
– 'Compressa' CKen CSam EBar EHul EPla LBee LCon MBar MBri MPla NHar SLim
§ – 'Cristata' CDoC CMac EHar ELan ISea LCon LLin MBal MBar SEng SGil SHer SLim WBod
– 'Elegans' CB&S CDoC CHig CMac CSco EHar EHul ENHC ENot GRei IDai IJoh ISea LCon LNet MBal MBar MWat SBod SHBN SLim SPer SReu SSta WDin WWin
– 'Elegans Aurea' CDoC CGre EHul LCon LTil MBal MBar MPla SBod SPer WDin
– 'Elegans Compacta' CDoC CSco EBar EHul LBee LCon MBar MPla MUlv SLim WThu WWeb

– 'Elegans Nana'	LBee SLim
– 'Elegans Viridis'	EHar SLim
– 'Enko-sugi'	See C. *j.* 'Araucarioïdes'
¶ – 'Globosa'	SRms
– 'Globosa Nana'	EPla LBee LCon LLin MBar SHBN SLim
– 'Jindai-sugi'	CMac MBal MBar MPla
– 'Kilmacurragh'	CKen MBar NHol SLim WThu
– 'Koshiji-yatsubusa	LCon MBar
– 'Lobbii'	CDoC
– 'Lobbii Nana'	See C. *j.* 'Nana'
¶ – 'Mankichi-sugi'	LTil
– 'Midare-sugi'	See C. *j.* 'Viridis'
– 'Monstrosa'	CMHG MBar MGos SEng
– 'Monstrosa Nana'	See C. *j.* 'Mankichi-sugi'
§ – 'Nana'	CDoC CMac EBlo EBre EHul ENHC IJoh LBre LLin MBal MBar MPla MWat SBod SLon SPer SReu WThu
– 'Pygmaea'	LCon SRms
– 'Rasen-sugi'	EHar GAri LCon LTil
– 'Sekkan-sugi'	CB&S CDoC CMHG EBre EHul EPla GAri LBee LBre LCon LLin MAsh MBar MBri MGos MPla NHol SHil SLim SMad
– 'Sekka-sugi'	See C. *j.* 'Cristata'
§ – var. ***sinensis***	CMCN
§ – 'Spiralis'	CB&S CDoC CGre CKen CMHG CMac CSco EHar GWht IOrc LBee LCon LLin MBal MBar MBri MGos SLim SPer SSmi WBod WWeb
– 'Tenzan-sugi'	CKen
– 'Tilford Gold'	EHul LLin
– 'Vilmorin Gold'	CKen
– 'Vilmorin Variegated'	EPla
– 'Vilmoriniana'	Widely available
¶ – 'Viminalis'	NHol
– 'Wogon'	See C. *j.* 'Aurea'
– 'Yatsubasa'	See C. *j.* 'Tansu'
– 'Yokohama'	EHul LCon MBar NHar NHol SLim
– 'Yore-sugi'	See CC. *j.* 'Spiralis', j. 'Spiraliter Falcata'
– 'Yoshino'	CKen

CRYPTOTAENIA (Umbelliferae)

japonica	CArn CPou GPoy
– 'Atropurpurea'	CChu CElw CGle CRDP ECha ECro EFol EMon GCal WCot

CTENANTHE (Marantaceae)

§ ***amabilis***	CHal MBri
* 'Greystar'	MBri
lubbersiana	CHal MBri
§ ***oppenheimiana***	MBri
setosa	MBri
'Stripe Star'	MBri

CUMINUM (Umbelliferae)

cyminum	CArn GPoy IEde MHew SIde

CUNILA (Labiatae)

See Plant Deletions

CUNNINGHAMIA (Taxodiaceae)

§ ***lanceolata***	CB&S CGre CMCN EHar ISea LBee LCon LLin LTil MBar MPla MUlv SBor SEng SLim SMad WNor
I – 'Compacta'	CChu EBre EHar EPla LBre LTil MPla SMad
♦ ***sinensis***	See C. ***lanceolata***

CUPHEA (Lythraceae)

aequipetala	WOMN
caeciliae	CBrk CKni CMHG LHil LHop
cyanea	CAbb CBrk CMHG CMer CSev CTre ESma LHil LHop SBor SDix SLon WPer
hyssopifolia	CBrk CHan CMer CPle CSev CTre CTro ERea ESma IBlr LAbb LHil LHop MBri SLon WWye
– 'Alba'	CDoC CPle LHop
¶ – 'Riverdene Gold'	CBrk
¶ – 'Rob's Mauve'	CB&S
ignea	CAbb CBrk ELan GCal IBlr ISea MBri SLMG WPer WWye
– 'Variegata'	CBrk CTro
macrophylla	CBrk LHil
¶ ***maculata***	CTro
* ***signata variegata***	CMer IBlr LAbb LHil

X CUPRESSOCYPARIS (Cupressaceae)

§ ***leylandii***	CB&S CBra CDoC CMac CSco EBre EHar EHul ENHC ENot IDai ISea LBre LBuc LCon LPan MBal MBar MBri MGos SBod SLim SPer WMou WStI
§ – 'Castlewellan'	Widely available
– 'Galway Gold'	See X C. *l.* 'Castlewellan'
– 'Golconda'	EBre LBre
– 'Gold Rider'	CDoC EHul IOrc LBee MBar MBri MGos SLim WStI
– 'Golden Sun'	LCon
– 'Harlequin'	CMHG CTrw LCon
– 'Hyde Hall'	EHar EPla LBee MBar SBod SPla
– 'Naylor's Blue'	CMac
– 'New Ornament'	SMad
– 'Robinson's Gold'	CBra CDoC CMHG CMac CSco EBre EHar EHul GAri ISea LBee LBre LCon MBal MBar MBri NWea SBod SLim WMou WStI
– 'Silver Dust' (v)	EHar ISea MBri SRms
I – 'Variegata'	MBar SEng WStI
notabilis	WBod
– 'Brookhill'	ISea
ovensii	CMHG

CUPRESSUS (Cupressaceae)

N ***arizonica*** var. ***arizonica***	CMCN CSco EHar ISea MBal SLon
– var. ***arizoniva*** 'Arctic'	MBri
♦ – var. ***bonito***	See C. ***a. a.***
– 'Conica Glauca'	CMCN ENot MBar WDin
I – 'Fastigiata'	LCon LPan MBar
– var. ***glabra*** 'Aurea'	EHul LCon MAsh MBar SLim
– – 'Blue Ice'	CB&S CDoC CKen CMHG CSco EHar EHul LCon MAsh MBar MBri MGos SLim
– – 'Compacta'	CKen LCon
– – 'Conica'	CDoC CKen EHar SBod WWat

– 'Pyramidalis'	CMac CSco EHar IOrc SLim SPer
¶ – 'Sulfurea'	CKen
bakeri	CMHG WCoo
cashmeriana	See C. ***torulosa*** 'Cashmeriana'
duclouxiana	CMHG LTil
♦ ***funebris***	See CHAMAECYPARIS ***f.***
glabra	See C. ***arizonica g.***
goveniana	EArb GAri MBar
– ***abramsiana***	GWht
lusitanica	CMCN ISea
– 'Glauca Pendula'	CPMA LCon MAsh SHil
¶ – 'Pygmy'	CKen
macnabiana	CMCN
macrocarpa	CDoC EHar EHul SArc SLim
¶ – 'Barnham Gold'	SBod
I – 'Compacta'	CKen CMac
– 'Crippsii'	LLin
– 'Donard Gold'	CMac ISea MBal MBar
♦ – 'Globe'	See C. ***m.*** 'Compacta'
– 'Gold Spire'	CMHG
– 'Gold Spread'	CDoC EHul LBee LCon SLim
– 'Goldcrest'	CB&S CBra CDoC CMac CSco EHar EHul ENot EPot IOrc LBee LCon LPan LTil MBal MBar MBri MGos MPla SBod SLim SLon SPer WAbe WDin
– 'Golden Cone'	CMac MBal SHil
– 'Golden Pillar'	CDoC CMac CSco EHul LBee LCon MBar MPla MWat SLim WDin
– 'Greenstead Magnificent'	EBre LBre LCon MAsh MBri
– 'Horizontalis Aurea'	CSco EHul MBar
– 'Lutea'	CB&S CDoC CMac EHar EHul LCon MWat
– 'Pygmaea'	CKen
¶ – 'Sulphur Cushion'	CKen
sargentii	CMCN WCoo
sempervirens	CB&S CMCN EHar EHul IOrc SArc SEng WBod WCoo
– 'Green Pencil'	See C. ***s.*** 'Green Spire'
§ – 'Green Spire'	SHil
– 'Pyramidalis'	See C. ***s.*** 'Stricta'
– var. ***sempervirens***	See C. ***s.*** 'Stricta'
§ – 'Stricta'	CArn CGre CSam CSco EHul GAri IJoh ISea LBee LCon LPan MPla SArc
– 'Swane's Gold'	CB&S CDoC CKen CMHG EBre EHar LBee LBre LCon MAsh MPla SHil SLim
– 'Totem Pole'	EHar MGos
§ ***torulosa*** 'Cashmeriana'	CBar CDoC CGre CHEx CSam GAri ISea MAsh SHil SLim SMad

CURRANT, Black See **RIBES** Black Currant Group

CURRANT, Pink See **RIBES** Pink Currant Group

CURRANT, Red See **RIBES** Red Currant Group

CURRANT, White See **RIBES** White Currant Group

CURTONUS See **CROCOSMIA**

CYANANTHUS (Campanulaceae)

* ***canus***	EPad
integer x ***lobatus*** 'Sherriff's Variety'	GDra NBir NHar NHol
lobatus	CWes ELan EPad LBee MBel NGre NKay SBla SHer WCru
– 'Albus'	EPot
– dark seedling	GDra
– giant form	EPot GDra NHar SBla WCru
– var. ***insignis***	CNic WThi
¶ – x ***microphyllus***	NWCA WCru
microphyllus	CLew CWes EPad EPot GDra ITim LBee NHol SBla WCru
sherriffii	NHar WThi
¶ sp. CLD 1492	GArf

CYANELLA (Liliaceae/Tecophilaeaceae)

♦ ***capensis***	See C. ***hyacinthoïdes***
¶ ***hyacinthoïdes***	CMon
orchidiformis	CMon LBow

CYANOTIS (Commelinaceae)

somaliensis	CHal

CYATHEA (Cyatheaceae)

cooperi	CB&S
dealbata	CB&S CHEx NMar SArc
¶ ***dealgardii***	WRic
medullaris	CB&S CHEx NPal
smithii	CHEx

CYATHODES (Epacridaceae)

§ ***colensoi***	CBow ECou EPot GCal GGGa GWht MBal MBar MBri MPla NHar SDry SSpi WAbe WPat WSHC WThu WWat
empetrifolia	WThu
fasciculata	See LEUCOPOGON ***fasciculatus***
fraseri	See LEUCOPOGON ***fraseri***
juniperina	ECou
§ ***parviflora***	ECou GWht

CYBISTETES (Liliaceae/Amaryllidaceae)

longifolia	NRog

CYCAS (Cycadaceae)

cairnsiana	LPal
circinalis	LPal
♦ ***kennedyana***	See C. ***papuana***

media	LPal
& *papuana*	LPal
revoluta	CHEx LPal MBri NPal SArc
rumphii	LPal

CYCLAMEN † (Primulaceae)

africanum	CAvo CBro CLCN CMon EBre EPot LAma LBow LBre MAsh NHol SSou STil WMar
balearicum	CAvo CBro CLCN EBre EPot LAma LBre MBal SBla STil WAbe WThu
cilicium	Widely available
– f. *album*	CBro CLCN EBre LAma LBre STil WChr WMar
§ *coum*	Widely available
¶ – M&T 4051	CMon
– var. *abchasicum*	See C. *c. caucasicum*
¶ – 'Boothman's'	WDav
– ssp. *coum*	CBro MBal
– – *album*	CAvo CDoC CRDP EPot LAma MBro NGre NHol SPou STil WChr WDav WHoo WNor
– – *album* (patterned leaved)	STil
§ – – ssp. *caucasicum*	CLCN EPot LAma STil
– – *roseum*	CAvo LAma LBow STil WChr
– – *roseum* plain-leaved red	STil
– – 'Atkinsii'	CBro EPot MBro MPlt
– – 'Nymans' ex EKB 371	EPot SBla SPou
– – pewter-leaved red	CBro CLCN CRDP LAma MAsh WThu
– – silver-leaved red	CAvo EBre EPot LBre MTho NHar NHol SIng SPou SSpi STil WHoo WMar
– dark pink	CAvo
– Elegans Group from Iran	SPou
– forms	CRDP LAma MBro MS&S SPou
– *ibericum album*	See C. *c. caucasicum album*
– 'Maurice Dryden'	CAvo CBro CGle
– red	CRDP WChr
– from Russia	SPou
– 'Tile Barn Elizabeth'	SPou
– from Turkey	SPou
– 'Urfa'	EPot
creticum	CAvo CBro CLCN EPot LAma MAsh SSpi STil WMar WThu
cyprium	CAvo CBro CLCN CRiv EBre EPot ETub LAma LBre MAsh MFir MFos SBla STil WChr WMar WThu
– 'E.S.'	SPou STil WThu
europaeum	See C. *purpurascens*
fatrense	See C. *purpurascens purpurascens*
graecum	CAvo CBro CLCN CNic CRiv EPot LAma MFos MPlt SSou STil WMar WThu
– f. *album*	CBro LAma LRHS STil WCru
§ *hederifolium*	Widely available
– *album*	Widely available
¶ – 'Antiochus'	SPou
– 'Bowles' Apollo'	SBla SSpi
¶ – 'Daley Thompson'	SPou
– forms	LAma MS&S NRed SPou WCru
– 'Perlenteppich'	NHol
– red	SPou
– 'Rosenteppich'	NHol
– scented	CLCN SBla STil WMar
– 'Silver Cloud'	CLCN SPou
– silver leaved	EPot STil
¶ – 'White Bowles' Apollo'	CLCN
ibericum	See C. *coum caucasicum*
intaminatum	CAvo CBro CDoC CLCN CRiv EPot LAma MAsh MS&S NHol NRya SBla SPou SSou SSpi STil
– EKB 628	EPot
– 'E K Balls'	CAvo CBro
– patterned-leaved	NGre SPou STil WMar WThu
– plain-leaved	NGre STil WMar WThu
latifolium	See C. *persicum*
libanoticum	CAvo CBro CLCN EBre EPot LAma LBow LBre MAsh MBal NGre SBla SSpi STil WChr WMar WThu
mirabile	CAvo CBro CLCN EBre EPot LAma LBre NGre SIng STil WChr WDav WMar WThu
neapolitanum	See C. *hederifolium*
orbiculatum	See C. *coum*
parviflorum	EPot LAma
§ *persicum*	CAvo CBro CLCN CRiv CSam EPot ESis LAma LBow MAsh STil
¶ – RRL N8/65	CMon
¶ – S&L 55	CMon
pseudibericum	CAvo CBro CLCN CRiv EBre EPot ETub LAma LBow LBre MAsh SBla SIng SPou STil WChr WThu
– *roseum*	CLCN STil
§ *purpurascens*	CBro CKel CLCN EBre EPot ETub GDra LAma LBow LBre MAsh MS&S NHol SBla SIng SPou SSpi STil WPat WThu WWat
– *fatrense*	See C. *purpurascens purpurascens*
– form	LAma
– 'Lake Garda'	SSpi
¶ – Limone form	SBla
§ – ssp. *purpurascens*	CAvo EPot LAma NGre NHol STil
repandum	CAvo CBro CLCN CRiv EBre ECop LAma LBre MBal SBla SIng SPou SSpi STil WChr WCru WThu
– JCA 5157	SSpi
– 'Album'	EPot SBla SPou STil
¶ – x *balearicum*	CLCN
– ssp. *peloponnesiacum*	CAvo CLCN EPot SPou STil
– ssp. *rhodense*	CLCN LAma STil
rohlfsianum	CAvo CBro CLCN EPot MAsh NGre STil WChr WThu
trochopteranthum	CAvo CBro CLCN EPot LAma MAsh NHol NRog SBla SIng SPou STil WChr

CYCLOSORUS (Thelypteridaceae)

pennigerus	NMar

CYDISTA (Bignoniaceae)

¶ *aequinoctialis*	MNew

CYDONIA (Rosaceae)

japonica	See CHAENOMELES *speciosa*
F *oblonga*	ESim IMal LHol
F – 'Champion'	CSco GTwe SFru
¶ – 'Early Prolific'	SKee
F – 'Le Bourgeaut'	GTwe

F – 'Meech's Prolific' CDoC CSam CSco ERea ESim GTwe MWat SDea SFam SIgm SKee WHig WMou
– pear shaped EHar NRog
F – 'Portugal' CSco GTwe NRog
F – 'Vranja' CDoC CMac CSco EBre EHar ERea ESim EWar GChr GTwe LBre LBuc MBri MGos MMor NElm NRog SDea SFam SFru SIgm SKee SPer WHig WMou
* *seibosa* SKee

CYMBALARIA (Scrophulariaceae)

aequitriloba WAbe
– alba MPar
§ *hepaticifolia* CHun EFol EPot MDHE NGre NMen NNrd SIng SSou WCru WHil WPer
– alba CNic CRDP
§ *muralis* CKin CMea EBar EPla MBar MPit NMir WTyr
– albiflora CHal EPla ESis MBar NHar SHer WHil WOMN WWin
– 'Globosa Alba' CRiv EPot WPer
– 'Globosa Rosea' CNic MPar NNrd WCla WHil
– 'Nana Alba' CLew ELan MDHE MPlt NMen NNrd NWCA WPer
§ *pallida* CElw CHun CMea CNic GAri LBee MCas NHar NKay SAxl SBla SHer WCla WCru WHil WPer
pilosa CHun CRDP ECtt EMNN NGre NSti

CYMBIDIUM (Orchidaceae)

See Plant Deletions

CYMBOPOGON (Gramineae)

citratus CArn SIde

CYMOPHYLLUS (Cyperaceae)

See Plant Deletions

CYNARA (Compositae)

baetica ssp. *maroccana* ECha LGre SWas
§ *cardunculus* Widely available
– ACL 380/78 EMon
cardunculus Scolymus Group CB&S CCla CHad CSco EBre ERav GCal ILis LBre LHol MBri SMrm WByw WEas WHer
– – 'Green Globe' CBow CSev NPer
– – 'Gros Camus de Bretagne' WCot
– – 'Gros Vert de Lâon' CSco MBen WCot
– – 'Purple Globe' CArn
♦ *hystrix* See C. ***baetica maroccana***

CYNOGLOSSUM (Boraginaceae)

amabile EBar ELan EMon
– roseum EMon GCal NSti
¶ *creticum* WHer
dioscoridis CGle CHan MFir NBro WCot WPer
germanicum CKin
grande SCro
nervosum CCla CGle CLew CSco EBlo ECED EFou EGol ELan EPar EPla GCal MRav MTol MUlv NSel SPer SUsu WCra WHal WHoo WRus WSun WTyr WWin
– roseum CCla WSun
officinale CKin LHol MChe MHew NMir NSal NSti WHer WNdy
zeylanicum EMon WOMN

CYNOSURUS (Gramineae)

cristatus MWil

CYPELLA (Iridaceae)

¶ *coelestis* CMon WThi
herbertii CGle CMon LAma LBow MHig NWCA SAxl WCru WThi
plumbea See C. ***coelestis***

CYPERUS (Cyperaceae)

§ *albostriatus* CHal MBri
alternifolius See C. ***involucratus***
§ *cyperoïdes* MBri
diffusus See C. ***albostriatus***
§ *eragrostis* CHal ECha EPla ETPC NBro NRar SWat
esculentus GCal IBlr
haspan See C. ***papyrus*** 'Nana'
§ *involucratus* CBen CHEx CHal CKni CRDP CWGN EBak EMFW ERea ETPC MBri MSta SWat WChe WWye
– 'Flabelliformis' ETPC
– gracilis EBak MBri
– 'Nanus' ETPC
longus CBen CRow CWGN EBre EHoe EHon EMFW ETPC EWav LBre LMay MSta NDea SMad SWat WChe WHol WNdy
nanus CHEx
papyrus CHEx ERea ETPC MBri MSta
§ – 'Nanus' ERea
♦ *sumula* hort. See C. ***cyperoïdes***
* *variegatus* ERea
vegetus See C. ***eragrostis***

CYPHOMANDRA (Solanaceae)

betacea See C. ***crassicaulis***
F *crassicaulis* 'Goldmine' ERea SLMG
F – 'Oratia Red' ERea

CYPRIPEDIUM (Orchidaceae)

acaule CKel MPhe
debile LAma SWes
formosanum SWes
guttatum var. *yatabeanum* See C. ***guttatum***
japonicum LAma

CYRILLA (Cyrillaceae)

racemiflora WBod

CYRTANTHUS (Liliaceae/Amaryllidaceae)

¶ *brachyscyphus* CAvo
§ *elatus* CAvo CBro CKel ERea LAma LBow LHop MBri NRog SBar WChr
falcatus CMon LBow

flavidus	LHop
luteus	SWas
mackenii	NRog WOMN
parviflorus	See C. ***brachyscyphus***
♦*purpureus*	See C. ***elatus***
¶ *sanguineus*	CMon
speciosus	See C. ***elatus***

CYRTOMIUM See POLYSTICHUM

CYRTOSPERMA (Araceae)

See Plant Deletions

CYSTOPTERIS † (Dryopteridaceae)

bulbifera	CMGP EPot NMar NNrd NVic SBla SCob WEas
dickieana	NKay NMar NNrd
fragilis	EBul MBal NBro NKay NMar SHig SRms WRic
¶ – *sempervirens*	WRic
montana	NKay
regia	NKay

CYTISUS † (Leguminosae)

♦*albus*	See CHAMAECYTISUS ***a.***
'Andreanus'	ENot GRei IJoh MGos MRav NNor SPer WAbe
'Andreanus Splendens'	CB&S CDoC CSco
ardoinoi	GDra MBal MBro MCas MHig MPla NHar NHol NKay NNrd NRoo SIng WDav
battandieri	Widely available
– 'Yellow Tail'	SHil
x *beanii*	CBow CMHG CPMA CSam ELan ENot GDra MBal MBar MPla MPlt MWat NBee NNor NRya NTow SPer SPla SReu WAbe WBod WDin WRus WWat
– 'Osiris'	NBar
'Boskoop Glory'	CSco ECtt SPer
'Burkwoodii'	CB&S CSco ENot IDai IJoh ISea MBlu MBri MWat NBee SPla WStI
'Butterfly'	CB&S
♦*canariensis*	See GENISTA ***c.***
¶ 'College Girl'	NWyt
'Compact Crimson'	CDoC EBlo EBre LBre MAsh
'Cornish Cream'	CB&S CSco LHop MBri SPer SPla
'Cottage'	CNic CPMA EHal EPot GDra MBri MBro MMil MPla NHar NHol SGil SIng SPla WAbe WDav
¶ 'Crimson King'	SPla
'Criterion'	CPMA MBri MRav NBar
'Daisy Hill'	IDai LRHS SPla
§ *decumbens*	CDoC CRiv EPot IOrc MAsh MBro NHar NKay WDav WHil WWin
demissus	EPot GDra MHig NHol WAbe
'Dorothy Walpole'	CMHG CTrw EHal
'Dragonfly'	IOrc
'Dukaat'	CDoC EBre LBre MAsh MBri NBee NRoo SHBN
'Enchantress'	SPla
'Firefly'	MAsh MBal
'Fulgens'	CDoC CSco ELan IDai MAsh MBar MBri SPer WWeb
'Garden Magic'	LRHS
'Golden Cascade'	CB&S CPMA ELan MWat NNor SPla WWeb
'Golden Showers'	MBal
'Golden Sunlight'	CDoC ECtt ELan ENot SHBN WStI
'Goldfinch'	CB&S CDoC ENot MBri MWat WWeb
hirsutus	See CHAMAECYTISUS ***h.***
'Hollandia'	CB&S CSco CShe EBre GRei LBre MBar MGos MRav SHBN SPer WBod WDin WWeb WWin
x *kewensis*	Widely available
– 'Niki'	MBri SHBN SHil
'Killiney Red'	CDoC CPMA ENot GRei IJoh IOrc ISea MBal MBri MWat NBee SHBN
'Killiney Salmon'	CPMA CSco ENot MAsh MGos MPla
'La Coquette'	CDoC CMHG MBar SHil
'Lena'	CBow CMHG CPMA EBlo EBre ECtt EPla EPot GAri IJoh LBre MBar MBri MGos NHar NRoo SMad SPla WStI
leucanthus	See C. ***albus***
'Lord Lambourne'	LRHS
'Luna'	ENot IJoh WStI
'Maria Burkwood'	CSco IDai NBee SHBN
'Minstead'	CPMA CSco EBre ECar EPla LBre MBal SPer WAbe WDin
'Moonlight'	SPer
'Moyclare Pink'	CGle CLan CMHG
'Muldean'	MAsh NBar SPla WWeb
multiflorus	CGre MBal SHil SMad SPer SSpi WBod
– 'Toome's Variety'	SPla
¶ – 'White Bouquet'	MBri
'Newry Seedling'	LRHS MBri NBee
nigrescens	See C. ***nigricans***
§ *nigricans*	ENot SDry SHil SPer SReu SSpi
nubigenus	See C. ***supranubius***
'Palette'	CDoC CSco ECtt ELan ISea SPer
'Porlock'	CDoC CSPN CTre CWSG CWit ELan SHil SPla WBod WStI
x *praecox*	See C. x ***p.*** **'Warminster'**
– 'Albus'	CBow CCla CPMA CSco EBre ELan ENot GRei IJoh IOrc LBre MBar MBri MGos MWat NRoo SHBN SHil SPer SPla WAbe WBod WWat
– 'Allgold'	CB&S CBra CCla CMHG CPMA CSam CSco CShe EBre ENot GRei IDai IJoh LAbb LBre MBar MBri MPla MRav NKay NRoo SHBN SPla SReu SSta WAbe WBod WDin
– 'Canary Bird'	See C. x ***p.*** **'Goldspeer'**
– 'Frisia'	CB&S GAri MBar
§ – 'Goldspeer'	ENot SPer
§ – 'Warminster'	CSco CShe ELan ENot GDra GRei IDai LHop MBal MBar MBri MGos MPla MWat NRoo NWea NWyt SHBN SPer SPla SSta WAbe WThu WWat WWin
'Princess'	MBri MPla
procumbens	LHop MBal SReu SSmi WWat
purgans	CDoC MBal NNor SPer WBod
♦*purpureus*	See CHAMAECYTISUS ***p.***
racemosus	See CHAMAECYTISUS x ***spachianus***
'Red Wings'	CCla CDoC EPot GDra IJoh MGos SPer WBod WStI
'Roter Favorit' ('Red Favourite')	MBar
'Royal Standard'	LRHS
scoparius	CDoC CKin ENot GRei LHol MHew NSal NWea SReu WDin WWye

– f. ***indefessus*** EMon
§ – ssp. ***maritimus*** CB&S MBri NNor NTow WBod
¶ – 'Pastel Delight' CB&S
– var. ***prostratus*** See C. ***s. maritimus***
♦ x ***spachianus*** See GENISTA x ***spachiana***
'Sunset' ENot
♦ ***supinus*** See CHAMAECYTISUS ***s.***
'Windlesham Ruby' CCla ELan GRei ISea MBar MPla SHBN SPer WBod WDin WWeb
'Zeelandia' CB&S CCla CPMA ENot MBar MRav WAbe WBod WTyr

DABOECIA † (Ericaceae)

§ ***cantabrica*** GAri GRei MBal NLan
§ – f. ***alba*** CB&S CMac CNCN CNic EBre ENHC ENot GAng GBla GDra GPen GRei GSpe IDai IJoh LBre MBal MBar MBri MOke NHol NRoo SBod SHBN SPla WBod WRid WStI
– 'Alba Globosa' EDen ENHC MBar WGre
– 'Atropurpurea' CNCN COCH EBre EDen ENHC ENot GAng GBla GPen GSpe IDai IJoh LBre MBal MBri MGos MOke NHol NWin SBod WBod WRid WStI
– 'Barbara Phillips' MBar
– 'Bicolor' CNCN COCH EDen ENHC GPen GRei GSpe MBal MBri MGos MOke NHar WGre WRid
– 'Blueless' COCH NWin
– 'Charles Nelson' EDen MBar MOke
– 'Cinderella' CNCN EDen GPen GSpe MBar
– 'Covadonga' CNCN COCH EDen ENHC MBar
– 'Cupido' MGos
– 'David Moss' CMac EDen GAng GBla MBal MBar SBod WGre
♦ – 'Donard Pink' See D. c. 'Pink'
– 'Early Bride' COCH ENHC
– 'Eskdale Baron' ENHC
– 'Heather Yates' CNCN EDen ENHC GBla MBri MOke NWin SBod
– 'Hookstone Pink' WBod
– 'Hookstone Purple' EDen ENHC GBla GPen MBar MBri MGos MOke NHol WGre
– 'Lilacina' EDen ENHC GPen MBar WRid
§ – 'Pink' EDen GBla GPen MBar NMen
– 'Pink Lady' MBar
– 'Polifolia' CB&S EDen GBla GDra MBri MOke SBod SHBN SPla
– 'Porter's Variety' GBla MBar MBri MOke NHar
– 'Praegerae' CB&S CMac CNCN EDen ENHC GBla GPen GRei GSpe IDai MBal MBar MGos NWin SBod WGre WRid
– 'Purpurea' GBla MBar
– 'Rainbow' CNCN MBar
– 'Rosea' MBar
– 'Snowdrift' GPen MBar
– 'Waley's Red' COCH EDen ENHC GPen MBar NWin
– 'White Carpet' EDen
– 'William Buchanan' See D. x ***scotica*** 'William Buchanan'
x ***scotica*** 'Bearsden' EDen MBar
– 'Cora' ENHC GAng GPen GSpe MBar
– 'Goscote' MGos
– 'Jack Drake' EDen ENHC GDra GPen GSpe MBal MBar MBri MOke WGre
– 'Silverwells' CNCN EDen GAng MBar MBri MGos NHar NWin
– 'Tabramhill' EDen MBar NWin
§ – 'William Buchanan' CMac CNCN EDen ENHC GAng GBla GDra GPen GSpe MBal MBar MBri MGos MOke NHar NHol NMen NRoo NWin SBod WGre
– 'William Buchanan Gold' CNCN EDen MBar MBri NWin

DACRYCARPUS (Podocarpaceae)

§ ***dacrydioïdes*** ECou
– 'Dark Delight' ECou

DACRYDIUM (Podocarpaceae)

bidwillii See HALOCARPUS ***bidwillii***
cupressinum CTre ECou
franklinii See LAGAROSTROBOS ***f.***
laxifolium See LEPIDOTHAMNUS ***l.***

DACTYLIS (Gramineae)

glomerata 'Variegata' ETPC IBlr NBro NCat NMir NSti

DACTYLORHIZA (Orchidaceae)

§ ***elata*** EPar SPou
§ ***foliosa*** CBro CRow ECar MBri NGar NHar NTow WAbe
§ ***fuchsii*** ELan EPot NGar NHar SSou SWes WChe WCru
– 'Bressingham Bonus' EBre LBre NTow SBar
¶ ***incarnata*** NGar SWes
§ ***maculata*** EPar IBlr LAma MSta NRog SBla SWes WChe WCru WHer
§ ***majalis*** CCla LAma WCru
mascula See ORCHIS ***m.***
purpurella NGar

DAHLIA † (Compositae)

'Abingdon Ace' (SD) NHal
'Abridge Bertie' (MinD) CSut
'Abridge Natalie' (SWL) NHal
'Adelaide Fontane' (LD) CSut
'Alloway Cottage' (MD) CSut MTiv NHal
'Alltami Apollo' (GSC) MTiv NHal
'Alltami Cherry' (SBa) NHal
'Alltami Classic' (MD) MTiv NHal
'Alltami Corsair' (MSC) NHal
'Alltami Cosmic' (LD) NHal
'Almand's Climax' (GD) MTiv
'Alstergruss' (Col) LAma NRog
'Alva's Supreme' (GD) MTiv NHal
'Amber Banker' (MC) MTiv NHal
'Anatol' CSut
'Andrew Lockwood' (Pom) MTiv
'Appenzell' (MSC) MTiv
'Apricot Honeymoon Dress' (SD) NHal
'Arabian Night' (SD) CHad LAma NRog SDeJ
'Athalie' (SC) MTiv NHal
¶ 'Autumn Fairy' (D) CKel
'B J Beauty' (MD) NHal
'Banker' (MC) MTiv NHal
'Barbarry Banker' (MinD) NHal
'Barbarry Climax' (SB) NHal
¶ 'Barbarry Glamour' (SB) NHal

'Barbarry Lavender' (MinD) NHal
¶ 'Barbarry Pinky' (SD) NHal
¶ 'Barbarry Standard' (MinD) NHal
¶ 'Barbarry Trend' (MinD) NHal
'Bednall Beauty' (DwB) CBos CBrk CRDP NBir WCot
'Berwick Wood' (MD) NHal
'Betty Bowen' (SD) ECtt MTiv
'Bill Homberg' (GD) NHal
'Bishop of Llandaff' (Misc) Widely available
'Black Jack' (SD) MTiv
'Black Monarch' (GD) NHal
'Bonaventure' (GD) NHal
¶ 'Bonny Blue' (SB) ECtt
'Border Princess' (SC) SDeJ
'Border Triumph' (DwB) MTiv NHal
'Calgary' (SD) CSut
¶ 'Camano Choice' (SD) ECtt
¶ 'Candy Cupid' (MinB) NHal
'Candy Keene' (LSC) MTiv NHal
'Carstone Cobblers' (SBa) NHal
'Carstone Sunbeam' (SD) NHal
'Catherine Ireland' (MinD) NHal
'Charlie Kenwood' (MinD) NHal
'Charlie Two' (MD) NHal
'Charmant' CSut
'Cheerio' (SSC) MTiv
¶ 'Cherry Fire' (SC) CKel
'Christopher Nickerson' (MSC) NHal
'Christopher Taylor' (SWL) NHal
'Clarion' (MC)(MSC) SDeJ
¶ 'Clint's Climax' (LD) NHal
'Cloverdale' (SD) NHal
coccinea (Misc) CAvo CBot GCal NBro SSpi SUsu
– hybrids GCal SSpi
¶ – ***palmeri*** CD&R 1367 CHan
'Connie Bartlam' (MD) NHal
'Corona' (SSC)(DwB) MTiv NHal
'Cream Alvas' (GD) MTiv
'Cream Beauty' (SWL) NHal
'Crichton Honey' (SBa) NHal
'Croydon Supreme' (LD) MTiv
'Cryfield Bryn' (SSC) NHal
¶ 'Cryfield Keene' (LSc) NHal
'Daleko Gold' (MD) MTiv
'Daleko Jupiter' (GSC) MTiv NHal
'Daleko National' (MD) NHal
'Daleko Olympic' (LD) MTiv
'Dana Iris' (SSC) NHal
'Dana Louise' (MD) MTiv
'Danum Cream' (MSC) MTiv
'Danum Pinky' (MSC) MTiv
'Davenport Anita' (MinD) NHal
'Davenport Honey' (MinD) NHal
'Davenport Pride' (MSC) NHal
'Davenport Sunlight' (MSC) NHal
'David Howard' (MinD) CCMG ELan LAma NHal
'Debra Anne Craven' (GSC) NHal
'Deepest Yellow' (MinBa) CSut
'Denise Willow' (Pom) MTiv
¶ 'Diana Nelson' (SD) ECtt
'Doc van Horn' (LSC) MTiv NHal
'Doctor Caroline Rabbitt' (SD) MTiv
'Doris Day' (SC) LAma MTiv NHal NRog
'Duet' (MD) CKel CSut LAma NRog
'Dusky Lilac' (SWL) NHal
'Dutch Baby' (Pom) MTiv
'Eastwood Moonlight' (MSC) MTiv NHal
'Edinburgh' (SD) ECtt LAma MTiv NRog
'Edith Arthur' (SSC) MTiv
'Edna C' (MD) NHal
¶ 'Ellen Houston' (DwB) CHad CKel SFis
'Emmenthal' (SD) CSut NHal
'Eveline' (SD) CKel LAma SDeJ
'Evelyn Foster' (MD) NHal
'Evelyn Rumbold' (GD) CSut MTiv
'Evening Mail' (GSC) NHal
'Extase' (MD) CKel
¶ 'Ezau' (GD) CSut
'Feu Céleste' (Col) LAma
'Figurine' (SWL) NHal
'Fille du Diable' (LSC) MTiv
'Fiona Stewart' (SB) MTiv
'Firebird' LAma NRog
'Frank Holmes' (Pom) ECtt
'Frank Hornsey' (SD) MTiv
'Freestyle' (SC) NHal
* 'Friquolet' LAma
'Frits' (MinBa) MTiv
'G F Hemerik' (Sin) LAma
¶ 'Garden Festival' (SWL) NHal
'Gateshead Festival' (SD) NHal
'Gateshead Galaxy' (DwB) NHal
'Gay Mini' (MinD) MTiv
'Gerrie Hoek' (SWL) CSut LAma MTiv NRog SDeJ
'Gilt Edge' (MD) MTiv
'Gina Lombaert' (MSC) LAma
'Giraffe' (Misc) MTiv
'Gloria Romaine' (SD) MTiv
'Glorie van Heemstede' (SWL) LAma MTiv NHal NRog
¶ 'Glorie van Naardwijk' (SD) CKel
'Go American' (GD) MTiv NHal
'Gold Crown' (LSC) LAma NRog
'Golden Emblem' (MD) SDeJ
'Golden Impact' (MSC) MTiv NHal
'Golden Willo' (Pom) MTiv
'Good Earth' (MC) LAma
'Good Hope' (MinD) MTiv
'Gordon Lockwood' (Pom) NHal
'Grenadier' WCot
'Grenidor Pastelle' (MSC) MTiv NHal
'Gypsy Boy' (LD) MTiv
'Hamari Accord' (LSC) NHal
'Hamari Bride' (MSC) MTiv

'Hamari Fiesta' (SD) NHal
'Hamari Girl' (GD) MTiv NHal
'Hamari Gold' (GD) NHal
'Hamari Katrina' (LSC) CSut
'Hartenaas' LAma NRog
'Hayley Jane' (SSC) CKel CSut MTiv NHal
'Hazard' (MSC) LAma NRog
'Helga' (MSC) LAma
¶ 'Henriette' (Sin) CSut
'Herbert Smith' (D) LAma
'Hillcrest Albino' (MSC) NHal
¶ 'Hillcrest Blaze' (SC) NHal
¶ 'Hillcrest Hillton' (LSC) NHal
'Hillcrest Royal' (MC) NHal
'Hillcrest Suffusion' (SD) NHal
'Hit Parade' (MSC) CSut LAma NRog
'Holland Festival' (GD) CSut MTiv
'Honey' (Anem/DwB) LAma NRog
'Honeymoon Dress' (SD) MTiv NHal
'House of Orange' (MD) SDeJ
imperialis (Misc) GCal
'Inca Dambuster' (GSC) MTiv NHal
'Inca Matchless' (MD) MTiv
'Indian Summer' (SC) MTiv NHal
'Irene van der Zwet' (Sin) LAma
'Iris' (Pom) NHal
'Jacqueline Tivey' (SD) MTiv
'Janet Goddard' (SD) MTiv
¶ 'Jeanette Carter' (MinD) NHal
'Jescot Julie' (O) MTiv
'Jim Branigan' (LSC) MTiv NHal
¶ 'Jo Anne' (MSC) NHal
'Joan Beecham' (SWL) MTiv NHal
'Jocondo' (GD) NHal
'Johann' (Pom) MTiv NHal
'John Prior' (SD) NHal
'Just Julia' (MSC) MTiv
'Just Mary' (SD) MTiv
'Karenglen' (MinD) MTiv NHal
'Kathleen's Alliance' (SC) NHal
'Kathryn's Cupid' (MinBa) MTiv NHal
'Katisha' (MinD) MTiv
'Kelvin Floodlight' (GD) CSut
'Kennermerland' (SC) CKel LAma
¶ 'Kenora Challenger' (LSC) NHal
'Kenora Fireball' (MinB) NHal
'Key West' (MBa) CSut
'Kidd's Climax' (GD) MTiv NHal
'Kiwi Gloria' (SC) MTiv NHal
'Klankstad Kerkrade' (SC) ECtt MTiv NHal
'Kochelsee' (MinD) LAma
'Kung Fu' (SD) MTiv
¶ 'Kym Willo' (Pom) ECtt
'La Gioconda' (Col) LAma
'Lady Kerkrade' (SC) MTiv NHal
'Lady Linda' (SD) MTiv NHal
'LAncresse' (MinBa) NHal
'Laura Marie' (MinBa) NHal
'Lavender Athalie' (SC) NHal
'Lavender Perfection' (GD) LAma
'Lavender Symbol' (MSC) MTiv NHal
'Lavengro' (GD) NHal
I 'Lemon Elegans' (SSC) MTiv NHal
'Lemon Puff' CSut
'Liberator' (GD) MTiv
* 'Life Force' MTiv
'Life Size' (LD) NHal
¶ 'Lilac Shadow' (SC) CSut
'Lilian Ingham' (SSC) NHal
'Lilianne Ballego' (MinD) MTiv NHal
'Linda Lusardi' (SSC) MTiv
'Linda's Cheter' (SC) NHal
'Lismore Peggy' (Pom) ECtt
¶ 'Little Laura' (MinB) NHal
'Little Tiger' LAma NRog
'Majuba' (MD) LAma NRog SDeJ
'Margaret Ann' (MinD) MTiv
'Mark Damp' (LSC) NHal
'Mark Hardwick' (GD) NHal
'Mark Lockwood' (Pom) MTiv
'Martin's Yellow' (Pom) NHal
'Match' (SSC) MTiv
'Matterhorn' (SWL) MTiv
'Meiro' (SD) MTiv
merckii (Misc) CAvo CBos CBot CDec CGle CGre CHad CMon CPar CRDP CTom ECha EFol ESma GCal MTho MUlv NBro NSti SAxl SMad SSpi SUsu WCru WEas WHal WPer WRus WWin
– ***alba*** WCru WRus
– – 'Hadspen Star' CHad CRDP
'Mi Wong' (Pom) ECtt NHal
¶ 'Mies' (Sin) CKel
'Minder' (GD) MTiv
'Minley Carol' (Pom) NHal
'Minley Linda' (Pom) ECtt MTiv NHal
'Miss Blanc' (SD) MTiv
'Mistill Delight' (MinD) MTiv NHal
'Monk Marc' (SC) MTiv
'Moor Place' (Pom) ECtt MTiv NHal
'Morning Dew' (SC) SDeJ
'Morning Kiss ' (LSD) SDeJ
'Mrs McDonald Quill' (LD) NHal
'Mummies Favourite' (SD) MTiv
'Murillo' LAma NRog
'My Love' (SSC) CKel ECtt LAma NRog
'Nationwide' (SD) MTiv
'Neal Gillson' (MD) NHal
'Nellie Birch' (MinBa) MTiv
'New Baby' (MinBa) LAma NRog
'Nijinsky' (SBa) MTiv
'Nina Chester' (SD) MTiv NHal
'Noreen' (Pom) ECtt NHal
'Nunton Harvest' (SD) ECtt
¶ 'Onslow Michelle' (SD) ECtt
'Orange Nugget' (MinBa) LAma
'Orfeo' (MC) LAma NRog
'Park Princess' (DwB)(SC) CKel LAma MTiv SDeJ
'Paul Chester' (SC) NHal
'Paul Damp' (MSC) NHal
'Pearl of Heemstede' (SWL) MTiv NHal

'Pensford Marion' (Pom) ECtt
'Periton' (MinB) NHal
'Peter' LAma
'Pied Piper' (MinBa) MTiv
*'Pink Cloud' (SSC) NHal
'Pink Frank Hornsey' (SD) MTiv
'Pink Giraffe' (O) MTiv
'Pink Honeymoon Dress' (SD) NHal
'Pink Jupiter' (GSC) MTiv NHal
'Pink Katisha' (MinD) MTiv
'Pink Kerkrade' (SC) NHal
¶ 'Pink Pastelle' (MSC) NHal
'Pink Paul Chester' (SC) NHal
'Pink Risca Miner' (SBa) MTiv
'Pink Shirley Alliance' (SC) MTiv
'Pink Surprise' (LSC) SDeJ
'Pink Symbol' (MSC) ECtt
pinnata soft yellow GCal
'Pioneer' (MSC) SDeJ
'Piper's Pink' (SSC)(DwB) MTiv
'Playboy' (GD) MTiv
'Pontiac' (SC) MTiv
'Pop Willo' (Pom) NHal
'Potgieter' (MinBa) LAma NRog
'Prefect' (MSC) MTiv
'Preference' (SSC) LAma
'Preston Park' (Sin)(DwB) NHal
'Pride of Berlin' See D. 'Stolze von Berlin'
'Primrose Rustig' (MD) NHal
'Procyon' (SD) LAma
'Promotion' (MC) SDeJ
'Purple Gem' CKel LAma NRog
'Queeny' (SSC) NHal
'Quel Diable' (LSC) MTiv
'Radfo' (SSC) NHal
'Raiser's Pride' (MC) NHal
'Red Alert' (LBa) MTiv
'Red and White' (SD) SDeJ
'Red Diamond' (MD) NHal
'Red Sensation' (MD) MTiv NHal
'Reginald Keene' (LSC) MTiv NHal
¶ 'Reverend P Holian' (GSC) NHal
'Rhonda' (Pom) MTiv NHal
'Rhonda Suzanne' (Pom) ECtt MTiv
'Richard Marc' (SC) MTiv
'Risca Miner' (SBa) MTiv
'Robin Hood' (SBa) MTiv
'Rose Jupiter' (GSC) NHal
'Rosella' (MD) LAma
'Rothesay Castle' (DwB) MTiv NHal
'Rothesay Reveller' (MD) CSut
'Rothesay Robin' (SD) NHal
'Rotterdam' (MSC) MTiv NHal SDeJ
¶ 'Royal Ivory' (SWL) NHal
'Ruby Wedding' (MinD) NHal
¶ ***rupicola*** SAxl
'Ruskin Diane' (SD) ECtt MTiv NHal
¶ 'Ruskin Dynasty' (SD) ECtt
'Ruskin Petite' (MinBa) MTiv
'Rustig' (MD) MTiv NHal
'Rusty Hope' (MinD) MTiv
'Safe Shot' (MD) LAma NRog
¶ 'Saiva' CKel
'Salmon Beauty' (D) SDeJ
'Salmon Keene' (LSC) NHal
'Satellite' (MD) SDeJ
'Scarlet Beauty' (SwL) NHal
'Scarlet Kokarde' (MinD) NHal
'Schweitzer's Kokarde' (MinD) NHal
'Scottish Relation' (SSC) NHal
'Scottish Rhapsody' (MSC) NHal
'Senzoe Ursula' (SD) NHal
'Shandy' (SSC) NHal
'Sherwood Monarch' (GSC) MTiv
'Sherwood Standard' (MD) NHal
'Sherwood Titan' (GSC) MTiv
'Shirley Alliance' (SC) MTiv
¶ 'Shooting Star' CSut
'Siemen Doorenbos' (Anem) LAma NRog
'Silver City' (LD) CSut NHal
'Silver Slipper' (SSC) MTiv
'Sky High' (SD) MTiv
'Small World' (Pom) ECtt MTiv NHal
'Sneezy' (Sin) LAma
'Snowflake' (SWL) LAma
'Snowstorm' (MD) LAma SDeJ
¶ 'Sonia' (MinBa) CSut
§ 'Stolze von Berlin (MinBa) NRog
'Stylemaster' (MC) MTiv
'Suffolk Bride' (MSC) NHal
'Suffolk Spectacular' (MD) NHal
'Summer Night' (MC) CSut
'Sunney Boy' CSut
'Sunray Glint' (MSC) NHal
'Swanvale' (SD) MTiv NHal
'Sweet Content' (SD) ECtt MTiv
'Symbol' (MSC) MTiv NHal
'Syston Sophia' (LBa) MTiv
'Syston Zone' (LSC) MTiv
'Tahiti Sunrise' (MSC) MTiv
'Thais' (Col) MTiv
'Thelma Clements' (LD) MTiv
'Thomas A Edison' (MD) CSut LAma
'Tiger Tiv' (MD) MTiv
'Tommy Doc' (SSC) NHal
'Top Choice' (GSC) LAma SDeJ
'Trendy' (SD) MTiv SDeJ
'Trengrove Jill' (MD) MTiv NHal
'Trengrove Summer' (MD) NHal
¶ 'Trengrove Tauranga' (MD) NHal
'Union Jack' (Sin) LRHS
'Vaguely Noble' (SBa) NHal
'Vantage' (GSC) NHal
¶ 'Venlo' (D) CKel
'Veritable' (MSC) SDeJ
'Violet' SDeJ
'Violet Davies' (MSC) MTiv

'W J N' (Pom)	ECtt NHal
'Wanda's Capella' (GD)	MTiv NHal
'Wanda's Sunshine' (GD)	MTiv
'Welcome Guest' (MSC)	ECtt MTiv
'Wendy's Place' (Pom)	NHal
'White Alva's' (GD)	MTiv NHal
'White Hornsey' (SD)	ECtt MTiv
'White Kerkrade' (SC)	ECtt NHal
'White Linda' (SD)	NHal
'White Moonlight' (MSC)	MTiv NHal
'White Perfection' (GD)	SDeJ
'White Rustig' (MD)	NHal
'White Swallow' (SSC)	NHal
'William John' (Pom)	ECtt
¶ 'Willo's Flecks' (Pom)	ECtt
¶ 'Willo's Night' (Pom)	ECtt
'Willo's Surprise' (Pom)	ECtt MTiv NHal
'Willo's Violet' (Pom)	ECtt
'Wootton Carol' (SD)	MTiv
'Wootton Cupid' (MinBa)	CSut MTiv NHal
'Wootton Impact' (MSC)	MTiv NHal
'Yellow Frank Hornsey' (SD)	ECtt
'Yellow Hammer' (Sin)(DwB)	NHal SChu
'Yes Sir' (MD)	MTiv
'Yvonne'	CSut
'Zorro' (GD)	MTiv NHal

DAISWA (Liliaceae/Trilliaceae)

§ *polyphylla*	CRDP NRog SMad SPou WCru

DAMSON See PRUNUS *institia*

DANAË (Liliaceae/Ruscaceae)

§ *racemosa*	CBow CCla CSco EBre ECro EMon IHos LBre LTil MBri MUlv NTow SDry SEng SHil SPer SSpi

DAPHNE † (Thymelaeaceae)

acutiloba	CBow CCla CPMA EPot SBla SSta WCru
albowiana	CPMA SBla WCru WSHC
alpina	GAbr MHig NHol SBla WOMN
arbuscula	EB&P SBla SIgm WPat
bholua	CBow CDoC EB&P ELan NHar SSta WCru WWat
– –	CB&S CBow SBla SSta
– Darjeeling form	CBow CPMA SBla SSpi
– 'Gurkha'	CPMA CSco MGos SHil
– 'Jacqueline Postill'	CPMA CSco LAbb LRHS MAsh MGos SGil SHil
blagayana	CBow CNic CShe EB&P ELan EPot GAbr MBal MBri MHig MPla NHol NRoo NSti SBla SHBN SLeo SPer SSpi SSta WBod WDin WWat
x *burkwoodii*	CB&S CBot CBow CSam ELan IBar IJoh IOrc LHol MBal MWat NHar SHBN SHer SPla WCru WDin WWat
– 'Albert Burkwood'	NWea
– 'Astrid'	COtt ELan MGos MWat
§ – 'Carol Mackie'	CBot EGol ERav GAbr LGre LHop MPla SGil SIgm SSpi WWat
– 'G K Argles'	CPMA SBla WPat
– 'Somerset'	CB&S CShe EHar ELan ENot GAbr IHos LAbb LGre LHop MBar MBlu MGos MPla SBla SHBN SPer SReu SSpi SSta WBod WDav WDin WThu
– 'Somerset Gold Edge' (v)	CSco WCru
– 'Variegata'	See D x *b.* 'Carol Mackie'
caucasica	CBow SBla WWat
¶ – x *petraea*	SBla
¶ 'Cheriton'	SBla
cneorum	CB&S CBow CCla CSam EB&P GAbr IJoh LAbb LHol MBal MBar MWat NBee SBla SReu SSta WAbe WBod WCru WDin WWat WWin
– –	SBla
– 'Eximia'	CDoC EB&P ELan EPot GAbr IMal IOrc LGre LNet MAsh MGos MPla SBla SGil SHBN SIng SPer SSta WCru WWat
*– 'Poszta'	LRHS SBla SSpi
– var. *pygmaea*	SBla SIng WPat WThu
– – 'Alba'	WPat
– 'Variegata'	CPMA EB&P EPot LGre MBar MPla NRar SBla SGil SHer SPer SPla SSta WAbe WCru WRus WThu WWat
♦ *collina*	See D. *sericea*
genkwa	CB&S CPMA ELan SSpi WCru
giraldii	CBot EPot LGre NHol SBla SIgm SSpi
gnidioïdes	SIgm
¶ x *hendersonii*	SBla
x *houtteana*	CBot EB&P IBar NBir NHar SBla SSta WCru
x *hybrida*	SBla
japonica 'Striata'	See D. *odora* 'Aureomarginata'
jasminea	EPot SBla WPat
jezoensis	SBla SSta
juliae	SBla
'Kilmeston'	SBla
laureola	GPoy MGos MPla NPer SPou WWat WWye
– var. *cantabrica*	SChu
– 'Margaret Mathew'	EPot SWas
– ssp. *philippi*	CDoC CPMA CShe ELan MPla SChu SGil SHBN SHer SPer SReu SSpi SSta WAbe WWat
longilobata	NHol
– 'Peter Moore'	SHil
x *mantensiana*	SGil SMrm WThu
mezereum	Widely available
– f. *alba*	CChu CCla CSco CShe ELan IBar IOrc MBar MCas MHig MPla MTho NHol SEng SHBN SMad SPer SReu SSpi SSta SUsu WDav WDin WThu WWat
– var. *autumnalis*	ELan
– 'Bowles' Variety'	CBot EPot MPar WOMN
♦– 'Grandiflora'	See D. *m. autumnalis*
– 'Rosea'	MGos SRms
– var. *rubra*	CB&S CBow CPMA CSco EGol GAbr IOrc LNet MPla NBee SEng SReu WDin WWeb
x *napolitana*	CChu CMHG CPMA CSam EB&P ELan IOrc LNet MGos NHol SChu SPer WCru WEas
odora	CBow CBra CPle EB&P ERea LHol MGos SBla SChu SSpi SSta WAbe WCru
§ – f. *alba*	CB&S CBot CPMA EB&P ENot ERea NSti

§ – 'Aureomarginata' Widely available
– var. ***leucantha*** See D. ***o. alba***
– 'Marginata' See D. ***o.*** 'Aureomarginata'
– var. ***rubra*** CPMA EB&P SMrm
– 'Walburton' (v) LRHS
oleoïdes GDra MPar NTow
papyracea SBla
petraea 'Grandiflora' EPot SBla WPat
pontica CBow CCla CPMA CPle CTre EHar ELan LAbb MPar SDix SMad SPer SSpi SUsu WCru WThu WWat
retusa See D. ***tangutica*** Retusa Group
'Rosy Wave' SBla
§ ***sericea*** CB&S CPMA CSco EB&P ELan EPot LGre NTow SBla SIng SPer SPou SReu SSta WAbe WCru WRus WThu
tangutica Widely available
– Retusa Group CB&S CCla CSco CShe ECha ELan EPot GAbr GDra IDai ITim LHop MAsh MBri MBro MHig MPla NHol SBla SHBN SPou SReu SSta WBod WDav WPat WSHC WThu WWat
x ***thauma*** SBla WPat

DAPHNIPHYLLUM (Daphniphyllaceae)

humile JR 902 EMon
macropodum CChu CCla CGre CHEx EHar GWht MUlv SArc SHil SPer SSpi

DARLINGTONIA (Sarraceniaceae)

californica EFEx EPot MSte WHal WMEx

DARMERA (Saxifragaceae)

§ ***peltata*** Widely available
– 'Nana' CCla ECha ECro NHar NHol WOld

DASYLIRION (Dracaenaceae)

§ ***acrotrichum*** CHEx SArc
gracile Planchon See D. ***acrotichum***
longissimum SIgm

DASYPHYLLUM (Compositae)

dicanthoïdes CGre LTil

DASYPYRUM (Gramineae)

villosum ETPC

DATE See PHOENIX *dactylifera*

DATISCA (Datiscaceae)

cannabina EMon

DATURA (Solanaceae)

arborea See BRUGMANSIA ***a.***
chlorantha See BRUGMANSIA ***c.***
cornigera See BRUGMANSIA ***c.***
§ ***inoxia*** CTro ERea GCra LBlm LHil NSal SLMG
meteloïdes See DATURA ***inoxia***
rosea See BRUGMANSIA x ***insignis*** pink
rosei See BRUGMANSIA ***sanguinea***
sanguinea See BRUGMANSIA ***s.***
signata LHil
stramonium CArn GPoy LHol MHew NSal SIde WHer WWye
– Tatula Group NSal
suaveolens See BRUGMANSIA ***s.***
versicolor See BRUGMANSIA ***v.***

DAUCUS (Umbelliferae)

carota CArn CKin MHew MWil NSal WHer

DAVALLIA (Davalliaceae)

bullata See D. ***mariesii***
fejeenis MBri
§ ***mariesii*** CBos CNic CRDP MBri SDix WRic
¶ – var. ***stenolepis*** SDix
pyxidata NMar
solida NMar
trichomanoïdes NMar
– ***lorrainei*** NMar
tyermannii NMar

DAVIDIA (Cornaceae)

involucrata Widely available
– var. ***vilmoriniana*** CChu CGre EHar ELan LNet MGos MWat NBee SMad SPer SSta WCoo WSHC

DEBREGEASIA (Urticaceae)

longifolia CAbb CPle

DECAISNEA (Lardizabalaceae)

fargesii CBow CChu CGre CHad CMHG CPle CSco EBar ELan ENot EPla GCal IBar ISea LHop MBri MGos MUlv SBla SHil SPer SReu SSpi SSta WCoo WDin WWat

DECODON (Lythraceae)

¶ ***verticillatus*** EHon EMon

DECUMARIA (Hydrangeaceae)

barbara CBot CChu CCla CGre CHEx CMac EOvi IBar NBar SBra SHBN SHil SPer WCru WSHC
sinensis CHEx SArc

DEGENIA (Cruciferae)

velebitica NTow

DEINANTHE (Hydrangeaceae)

bifida ECro NKay WCru
caerulea WCru

DELAIREA (Compositae)

¶ ***odorata*** CHEx CTro

DELONIX (Leguminosae)

regia CPle

DELOSPERMA (Aizoaceae)

§ ***aberdeenense***	CB&S CHEx WEas WOMN
* ***album***	CHEx
ashtonii	WPer
'Basutoland'	See D. ***nubigenum***
cooperi	CHal EPot LHop NGre NMen NTow WPat WPer
§ ***lehmannii***	CB&S
lineare	NBir
lydenburgense	IBlr
macellum	NGre
§ ***nubigenum***	CLew CMHG CPar ELan MFos NGre NHol NNrd NRed SBod SHer STre WHil WHoo WOMN WPer WThu WWin
§ ***pallidum***	CB&S
sutherlandii	NGre NNrd NRed NTow WPat
'Wilson'	WWin

DELPHINIUM (Ranunculaceae)

¶ 'After Midnight'	LHar
¶ 'Agnes Brookes'	ERou
'Alice Artindale'	CBos CChu ECha LGre LHop SChu WEas
'Ann Woodfield'	MWoo
¶ 'Anne Page'	ERou
Astolat Group	CB&S CBow CDoC CHad CMea CPar CSco EBre ECED EFou ELan GAbr LAbb LBre MBri MRav MWat NNor NRoo SCro SHer SPer WEas
¶ 'Atholl'	LHar
Avon strain	MWoo
¶ 'Basil Clitheroe'	EBlo
x ***belladonna*** 'Andenken an August Koeneman'	See D. B. 'Wendy'
– 'Bellamosum'	EFou SPla
– 'Casa Blanca'	CBow CDoC CMGP EFou SFis
– 'Cliveden Beauty'	CDoC CMGP EFou NBar NRoo SSvw
– hybrids	ELan
¶ – 'Moerheimii'	EFou SPla
¶ – 'Peace'	EBlo EBre LBre
¶ – 'Piccolo'	EFou
– 'Pink Sensation'	See D. x ***ruysii*** 'P.S.'
– 'Völkerfrieden'	CSco EFou LWad MUlv SPla WMer
¶ – 'Wendy'	ECED
x ***bellamosum***	CMGP NBar SMrm
¶ 'Beryl Burton'	ERou
¶ 'Betty Baseley'	ERou
Black Knight Group	CB&S CBow CDoC CPar CSco EBre ECtt EFou ELan GAbr LAbb LBre LWad MBri MRav MWat NMir NNor NRoo NVic SCro SHer SPer SPla WEas
'Blauwal'	EFou
'Blue Bird'	CB&S CBow CDoC CMea CPar GAbr LGre LWad MBri MRav NMir NNor NRoo NVic SCro SHer SPer SPla
'Blue Butterfly'	See D. ***grandiflorum*** 'B. B.'
'Blue Dawn'	CBla ERou SOgg
Blue Fountains Group	CPar CSco ELan LAbb MBri MPit MRav MWat NBee NMir NOak NRoo SHer SPer SPla WHil WStI
Blue Heaven Group	NOak
Blue Jade Group	CBla ERou NNor SOgg SPer
'Blue Jay'	CBow CDoC EFou ENot SCro
'Blue Mirror'	CSun SMrm
'Blue Nile'	CBla ERou MWoo SOgg
'Blue Tit'	CBla ERou SOgg
'Browne's Lavender'	SOgg
'Bruce'	ERou LHar MWoo SOgg
brunonianum	LBee MTho NHol SBla WOMN
'Butterball'	CBla LHar SOgg
californicum	WWin
Cameliard Group	CBow EBre ECtt EFou ELan GAbr LBre LWad SCro SPer
'Can-Can'	ERou LHar
cardinale	GCra LGre WPer
'Carl Topping'	ERou MWoo
cashmerianum	CHan EFol ELan EPot LGan MTho NWCA SHer SIng WOMN
'Cassius'	CBla ERou LHar SOgg
♦ ***caucasicum***	See D. ***speciosum***
'Chelsea Star'	CBla ERou LHar MWoo SOgg
'Cherub'	CBla ERou LHar MWoo SOgg
chinense	See D. ***grandiflorum***
¶ 'Circe'	ERou
¶ 'Clack's Choice'	ERou
'Clifford Lass'	MWoo
'Clifford Pink'	CBla LHar MWoo SOgg
'Clifford Sky'	MWoo SOgg
Connecticut Yankees Group	NMir NNor NOak SMrm
'Conspicuous'	CBla ERou LHar MWoo SOgg
¶ 'Constance Rivett'	ERou
'Cressida'	ERou
'Cristella'	ERou MWoo
'Crown Jewel'	CBla ERou LHar SOgg
¶ ***cryophyllum***	MFos
'Cupid'	CBla ERou SOgg
¶ 'Daily Express'	ERou
¶ 'Darling Sue'	LHar
¶ 'David's Giant'	WEas
delavayi	SFis
'Demavand'	ERou LHar SOgg
'Diana Grenfell'	LHar
'Dolly Bird'	CBla ERou SOgg
'Dora Larkan'	LHar SOgg
¶ 'Dorothy Ash'	LHar
¶ 'Dreaming Spires'	NMir
¶ 'Duchess of Portland'	ERou
¶ 'Eamon Andrews'	ERou
* 'Eastgrove White'	WEas
elatum	SRms WOMN
'Emily Hawkins'	ERou LHar MWoo SOgg
¶ 'Eva Gower'	ERou
¶ 'Evita'	LHar
'F W Smith'	EFou WMer
'Fanfare'	CBla ERou LHar SOgg
'Father Thames'	ERou SOgg
'Faust'	CBla ERou MWoo SOgg
'Fenella'	CBla LHar MWoo SOgg
¶ 'Finsteraarhorn'	EFou
'Foxhill Lady'	LHar
¶ 'Foxhill Nina'	LHar
¶ 'Foxhill Oscar'	LHar
¶ 'Foxhill Pinta'	LHar
¶ 'Fred Yule'	ERou
Galahad Group	CB&S CBow CDoC CHad CPar CSco EBre ECED EFou ELan ENot GAbr LAbb LBre LGre LWad MBri MRav MWat NBir NMir NNor NRoo NVic SCro SGil SHer SPer WEas
¶ 'Garden Party'	CBla

'Gemma'	MWoo
¶ *geraniifolium*	MBro WDav
¶ 'Ghitto'	LHar
'Gillian Dallas'	CBla ERou LHar MWoo SOgg
glaucum	CNic NHol
'Gordon Forsyth'	CBla ERou LHar MWoo SOgg
'Gossamer'	LHar
§ *grandiflorum*	CBow CHad EPad GAbr LRHS SMrm
§ – 'Blue Butterfly'	CBow CMea EBre EBur LBre LGan NBro SBla WWin
Guinevere Group	CB&S CBow CMea ECtt GAbr LWad MBri NBir NNor NRoo SCro SGil SHer SPer SPla WEas
¶ 'Guy Langdon'	ERou
'Harmony'	ERou SOgg
¶ 'Iceman'	LHar
Ivory Towers Group	ECtt
'James Nuttall'	ECha
¶ 'Jill Curley'	LHar
¶ 'Joyce Roffey'	ERou
¶ 'Judy Knight'	ERou
'Kathleen Cooke'	LHar
'Kestrel'	ERou SOgg
King Arthur Group	CB&S CBow CDoC CPar CSco ECtt ENot GAbr LWad MBri MRav NNor SCro SHer WEas
¶ 'Lady Guinevere'	ERou
'Lady Hambleden'	See D. 'Patricia Lady Hambleden'
'Layla'	MWoo
'Leonora'	ERou LHar SOgg
'Lilian Bassett'	ERou LHar MWoo SOgg
¶ 'Loch Katrine'	LHar
'Loch Leven'	CBla ERou LHar MWoo SOgg
¶ 'Loch Torridon'	LHar
'Lord Butler'	CBla LHar SOgg
'Lorna'	ERou SOgg
¶ *luteum*	GCra
Magic Fountains	CBow EFou GAbr NRoo WPbr
'Margaret Farrand'	ERou SOgg
¶ 'Marie Broan'	ERou
'Michael Ayres'	CBla ERou MWoo
'Mighty Atom'	CBla ERou LHar MWoo SOgg
¶ 'Min'	ERou LHar
'Molly Buchanan'	CBla ERou SOgg
'Moonbeam'	CBla SOgg
¶ 'Morning Cloud'	ERou
¶ 'Mother Teresa'	ERou LHar
'Mrs Newton Lees'	EFou ERou
¶ 'Mrs T Carlile'	ERou
muscosum	WOMN
* 'Mystic'	LHar
* 'Mystique'	CBla ERou
New Century hybrids	CB&S EBlo EBre LBre NRoo
'Nicholas Woodfield'	MWoo SOgg
'Nimrod'	CBla ERou
'Nobility'	CBla ERou
nudicaule	CBot CBow ELan GDra LGan NBro NRoo WPer
– *luteum*	See D. *l.*
'Olive Poppleton'	CBla MWoo SOgg
'Oliver'	ERou MWoo SOgg
'Our Deb'	MWoo SOgg
Pacific hybrids	CKel EBre ENot LBre MFir NOak SPer SRms WByw
¶ *parishii* JJA 12737	SIgm
¶ 'Patricia Johnson'	ERou LHar
'Pericles'	CBla LHar SOgg
'Pink Ruffles'	CBla ERou SOgg
¶ 'Polar Sun'	ERou
¶ 'Purity'	ERou
¶ 'Purple Ruffles'	ERou
'Purple Triumph'	ERou SOgg
pylzowii	EPot ESma NRoo WPer
'Pyramus'	ERou SOgg
'Radiance'	SOgg
requienii	CBos CBot GCra LGan LHil SMrm WEas WHer
– variegated	CBos
'Romany'	LHar
'Rosemary Brock'	ERou LHar MWoo SOgg
¶ 'Royal Copenhagen'	EBlo
'Royal Flush'	CBla LHar MWoo SOgg
'Ruby'	CBla LHar
x *ruysii* 'Piccolo'	NBar
§ – 'Pink Sensation'	EBlo EBre ERou LBre MUlv NBar WMer WRus
'Sabrina'	CBla ERou
'Samantha'	ERou LHar
'Sandpiper'	LHar SOgg
§ *semibarbatum*	CBot SFis
¶ 'Sentinel'	ERou
'Shimmer'	CBla ERou LHar SOgg
¶ 'Silver Jubilee'	ERou
'Silver Moon'	ERou SOgg
'Skyline'	CBla ERou SOgg
Snow White Group	NBir NOak SRms
'Snowdon'	LHar
¶ 'Solomon'	ERou
Southern Aristocrats Group	LHar
Southern Consort Group	LHar
¶ Southern Countess Group	LHar
Southern Countrymen Group	LHar
¶ Southern Debutante Group	LHar
Southern Jesters Group	LHar
Southern Ladies Group	LHar
¶ Southern Maidens Group	LHar
Southern Minstrels Group	LHar
Southern Noblemen Group	EFol LHar
Southern Royals Group	LHar
§ *speciosum*	WOMN
¶ 'Spindrift'	LHar
sp. CLD 1476	EMon
sp. CLD 349	EMon
¶ *stachydeum*	MFos
staphisagria	MHew NSal WEas WWye
'Strawberry Fair'	CBla ERou SOgg
¶ 'Summer Haze'	ERou
Summer Skies Group	CB&S CBow CHad CNic CSco ECtt EFou LWad MBri MWat NNor NRoo SCro SHer SPer SPla WEas
¶ 'Summerfield Miranda'	LHar
'Sungleam'	CBla ERou LHar SOgg
'Sunkissed'	MWoo
¶ 'Swan Lake'	ERou
tatsienense	CNic ELan EMon GDra LHop MBro MFir MPar MTho NBro NWCA SHer SUsu WHoo WOMN

– 'Album'	SBla
– 'Blue Ice'	SMrm
¶ 'Tessa'	ERou
'Thamesmead'	LHar
'Thundercloud'	ERou SOgg
'Tiddles'	CBla LHar SOgg
¶ ***tricorne***	MFos
'Turkish Delight'	CBla ERou LHar SOgg
'Vespers'	ERou SOgg
'Walton Beauty'	MWoo
'Walton Gemstone'	MWoo
¶ 'Watkin Samuel'	ERou
¶ ***xantholeucum***	MFos
yunnanense	GDra
♦***zalil***	See D. ***semibarbatum***

DENDRANTHEMA † (Compositae)

¶ 'Abbygates' (25b)	NHal
'Adorn'	MRil
'Agnes Ann' (29K)	MCol
'Albert Broadhurst' (24b)	MWol NHal
'Albert's Yellow' (Rub)	MCol MMil
'Alexis' (5a)	MRil
'Alfreton Cream' (5b)	MRil
'Aline' (29K)	EHMN
'Alison' (29c)	EHMN
'Alison Kirk' (23b)	MCol NHal
'Allouise' (25b)	MCol NHal
'Allure' (22d)	MRil
'Amy Shoesmith' (15a)	MCol
'Anastasia' (28)	CMil ECtt EFou EOrc ERav LHil LHop MCol MMil MNFA MRav NFai NSti SChu SCro SPla SUsu WEas WPer WWin
N 'Anastasia Variegated' (28)	CSam EFol EHal ELan EMon ERav NSti SMrm WCot
'Angelic' (28)	MCol
'Angora' (25b)	MCol
'Ann Brook' (23b)	MCol
'Anna Marie' (18c)	EHMN MCol MWol
'Anne' (29K)	EHMN
'Anne, Lady Brockett'	EFou EMon NBro
'Apricot' (Rub)	CKel ECtt EFou MFir MMil MRav SFis SGil SMad SSvw
'Apricot Alexis' (5a)	MRil
'Apricot Cassandra' (5b)	NHal
'Apricot Chessington' (25a)	MRil NHal
'Apricot Courtier' (24a)	MRil MWol NHal
¶ 'Apricot Enbee Wedding' (29d)	MWol NHal
'Apricot Madeleine' (29c)	NHal
'Apricot Margaret' (29c)	EHMN
'Apricot Vedova'	MCol
'Arthur Hawkins' (24b)	MRil NHal
'Aucklander' (23b)	NHal
'Audrey Shoesmith' (3a)	NHal
'Aunt Millicent' (29K)	MCol
'Aurora' (4a)	MCol
'Autumn Days' (25b)	MCol
'Babs'	MMil
'Balcombe Perfection' (5a)	MCol MRil MWol NHal
'Barbara Ward' (7b)	MWol
'Beacon' (5a)	MRil NHal
'Belair' (9c)	MCol
'Belle' (29K)	EHMN
'Bertos'	EHMN
'Bessie Rowe' (25a)	MCol
¶ 'Betty' (29K)	MCol
'Betty Wiggins' (25b)	MCol
'Bill Bye' (1)	MWol NHal
'Bill Wade' (25a)	MRil NHal
'Black Magic' (24b)	MCol
'Bonnie Jean' (9d)	MCol
'Bo-Peep' (28)	CElw EMon MCol WByw
¶ 'Bravo'	NHal
'Brenda Rowe' (5a)	MCol
'Bridget' (6b)	MWol
'Brierton Festival' (7b)	MWol
'Brierton Lad' (7b)	MWol
'Brietner' (24b)	MCol
'Bright Eye' (28)	MCol WPer
'Bright Golden Princess Anne' (4b)	NHal
'Brightness' (29K)	EHMN SChu SUsu WEas
'Broadacre' (7a)	MCol
'Broadway Sovereign ' (29c)	EHMN
'Bronze Belair' (9c)	MCol
'Bronze Bornholm' (14b)	MCol
'Bronze Bridget' (6b)	MWol
'Bronze Cassandra' (5b)	NHal
'Bronze Elegance' (28)	CElw CMil CRDP CSco EFou ELan EMon ERav SHer SIng SPer SPla SUsu WAbe WByw WEas WRus WWat
'Bronze Elite' (29d)	EHMN
¶ 'Bronze Enbee Wedding' (29d)	NHal
'Bronze Fairweather' (3b)	MWol
'Bronze Fairy' (28a)	MCol MWol
¶ 'Bronze Majestic' (2)	MWol
'Bronze Margaret' (29c)	EHMN MCol MRil NHal
'Bronze Maria' (18a)	MCol
'Bronze Mayford Perfection' (5a)	MCol NHal
'Bronze Yvonne Arnaud (24b)	MCol
'Bronzetti'	EHMN
'Brown Eyes' (29K)	EHMN
'Bruera' (24a)	MWol NHal
'Bryan Kirk' (4b)	MWol NHal
'Buff Peter Rowe' (23b)	NHal
'Bullfinch' (12a)	EHMN MWol
'Bunty' (28)	ECha SMrm
'Cameo' (28a)	EBar MCol
'Candid' (15b)	MCol
'Candylite' (14b)	MCol
'Canopy' (24a)	NHal
'Carlene Welby' (25b)	MRil NHal
¶ 'Cassandra' (5b)	NHal
'Chaffinch' (22a)	EHMN
'Charles Fraser' (25a)	NHal
'Charles Tandy' (5a)	MRil
'Cheddar' (13a)	MCol
'Cherry Dynasty' (14a)	MRil
'Cherry Margaret' (29c)	EHMN MRil NHal
'Cherry Venice' (24b)	MRil
'Chessington' (25a)	MRil NHal
¶ 'Chester Globe' (23b)	NHal

'Christine Hall' (25a) MCol
'Christmas Carol' (5a) MWol
'Christmas Wine' (5a) MWol
I 'Citrus' (29K) EFou
'Clara Curtis' (Rub) CGle CKel CLew CMea CSco ECha EFou EGol EHMN ELan EMon LHop MBri MCol MFir MNFA MRav NBir NFai SChu SFis SMad SPer SPla SUsu WEas WHoo WPer WRus WWin
'Clare Dobson' (25b) MWol
'Clare Louise' (24b) MRil
'Claudia' (24c) EHMN MCol
'Cloudbank' (9a) MWol
'Columbine' (29K) EHMN
'Connie Meyhew' (5a) NHal
'Cooper Nob' (29K) EHMN
'Copeland' (14b) NHal
'Copper Hedgerow' (7b) MWol
'Copper Margaret' (29c) EHMN MWol
'Coral Rynoon' (9d) MWol
'Corngold' (5b) MWol NHal
'Cornish' (25b) MRil
'Cossack' (2) MWol
'Cottage Apricot' LHop SMrm
'Cottage Pink' See D. 'Emperor of China'
'Cottingham' (25a) NHal
'Courtier' (24a) MRil MWol NHal
'Cream Allouise' (25b) NHal
'Cream Elegance' (9c) NHal
'Cream John Hughes' (3b) MRil NHal
'Cream Margaret' (29c) NHal
'Cream West Bromwich' (14a) MRil
'Creamist' (25b) MCol MWol
'Cricket' (25b) MCol
'Crimson Yvonne Arnaud' (24b) MCol
'Cropthorne' EHMN
¶ 'Daniel Cooper' (Rub) MCol
'Daphne' EHMN
'David Shoesmith' (25a) MCol MWol
'Debbie' (29K) EHMN
'Debonair' (15a) MRil NHal
¶ 'Dee Crimson' (29c) NHal
'Dee Lemon' (24c) MCol
'Dee Pink' (29c) MCol
'Denise' (28) MCol MWol
'Dennis Fletcher' (25a) MRil
'Derek Bircumshaw' (28a) MCol
'Deva Glow' (25a) NHal
'Diamond Wedding' (25a) MWol
§ 'Doctor Tom Parr' (28) EFou ELan EMon GCal LGre SMrm WByw
'Donna' (3b) MRil
'Doreen Hall' (15a) MRil
'Doris' (29K) EHMN
¶ 'Dorothy Stone' (25b) NHal
'Dorridge Beauty' (24a) MRil MWol NHal
'Dorridge Candy' (4b) MWol
'Dorridge Choice' (5b) MWol
'Dorridge Crystal' (24a) MRil MWol NHal
'Dorridge Dream' (23b) MWol
¶ 'Dorridge Flair' (3b) MWol
'Dorridge King' (4b) MWol
'Dorridge Velvet' (4b) MWol
'Duchess of Edinburgh' (Rub) CCla CDec CGle CKel CSam CSco EBlo ECtt ELan EMon ERav LGre LHop MBri MCol MFir MNFA MRav NFai SChu SMad WEas WRus
'Duke of Kent' (1) MWol
¶ 'Dulverton' (24c) NHal
'East Riding' (25a) NHal
'Eastleigh' (24b) MWol
'Eddie Wilson' (25b) MRil
'Edelgard' EFou
'Edelweiss' (29K) EFou LHop
'Edwin Painter' (7b) MWol
'Elegance' (9c) MCol NHal
'Elizabeth Burton' (5a) MWol
'Elizabeth Shoesmith' (1) NHal
'Ellen' (29c) NHal
'Emma Lou' (23a) MCol NHal
§ 'Emperor of China' (Rub) CDec CGle CMil CSam ECha EFou EMon GAbr GCal LGre MCol MRav MSte MUlv NFai SChu SFis SGil SMad SUsu WEas WRus
¶ 'Enbee Dell' (29d) NHal
'Enbee Frill' (29d) MCol
'Enbee Wedding' (29d) MRil MWol NHal
¶ 'Encore' NHal SFis
'Epic' (6b) MWol
'Ermine' (23a) MCol NHal
'Evelyn Bush' (25a) MCol
'Eye Level' (5a) MRil NHal
'Fair Lady' (5a) MRil
'Fairweather' (3b) MCol MRil MWol
'Fairy' (28) MCol MWol
'Fairy Rose' (4b) MCol MMil
'Fieldfare' EHMN
'Flash Point' EFou
§ 'Fleet Margaret' (29c) MRil MWol NHal
'Flying Saucer' (6a) MCol
'Folk Song' (4b) MWol
'Formcast' (24a) NHal
'Fortune' (24b) MRil
'Fred Brocklehurst' (25a) MRil
'Fred Shoesmith' (5a) MRil MWol NHal
'Frolic' (25b) MRil
'Gala Princess' (24b) MWol
'Galaxy' (9d) MCol
'Gambit' (24a) MRil NHal
'Gay Anne' (4b) NHal
'Gazelle' (23a) MCol NHal
'George Griffiths' (24b) MRil NHal
'Gertrude' (19c) MCol
'Gigantic' (1) NHal
'Gingernut' (5b) MCol MRil NHal
'Gladys' (24b) ELan
'Gladys Homer' (24a) MWol
'Gloria' (25a) EHMN
– (30K) MCol
'Gold Foil' (5a) MRil NHal
'Gold Margaret' See D. 'Golden Margaret'
'Golden Anemone' EHMN
'Golden Angora' (25b) MCol
'Golden Cassandra' (5b) NHal
¶ 'Golden Courtier' (24a) NHal
'Golden Creamist' (25b) MCol

'Golden Fred Shoesmith' (5a) NHal
'Golden Gigantic' (1) MWol
'Golden Honeyball' (15b) MCol
'Golden Ivy Garland' (5b) MCol NHal
'Golden Lady' (3b) MWol
§ 'Golden Margaret' (29c) EHMN MCol MRil NHal
'Golden Mayford Perfection' (5a) MRil NHal
'Golden Orfe' (29c) MCol
'Golden Pamela' (29c) NHal
'Golden Pennine Pink' (29c) NHal
'Golden Pixton' (25b) MCol
'Golden Plover' EHMN
'Golden Queen' (3b) MWol
'Golden Quill Elegance' (9f) MWol
'Golden Saskia' MCol
'Golden Seal' (7b) MCol
'Golden Taffeta' (9c) NHal
'Golden Treasure' (28a) MCol MWol
'Golden Wedding' (30K) MCol
'Goldmarianne' EFou
¶ 'Goldmine' NHal
¶ 'Goodlife Sombrero' (29a) NHal
'Gordon Taylor' (7b) MWol
¶ 'Grace Lovell' (25a) NHal
'Grace Riley' (24a) MCol MRil MWol
'Grandchild' (29c) EHMN MCol
¶ x ***grandiflorum*** WOMN
'Green Chartreuse' (5b) MWol
'Green Nightingale' (10) MWol
'Green Satin' (5b) MWol
'Grenadine' (22c) MRil NHal
'Halloween' (4b) NHal
¶ 'Handford Pink' (29K) MCol
'Happy Geel' EHMN
'Hardwick Bronze' EHMN
'Hardwick Lemon' (29c) EHMN
'Hardwick Primrose' (29c) EHMN
'Hardwick Yellow' (19b) EHMN
'Harry Gee' (1) MWol
¶ 'Harry Woolman' (3b) MWol
'Harvest Dawn' (25) MCol
'Harvey' (29K) MCol
'Hazel' (30,K) EHMN
'Hazy Days' (25b) MCol NHal
'Heather James' (3b) MCol NHal
'Hedgerow' (7b) MCol
'Heide' (29c) MCol NHal
'Helmsman' (24a) MWol
'Honey' (25b) EHMN
¶ 'Honeyball' (25b) MCol
'Illusion' MRil
'Imp' (28) MCol MWol
¶ 'Inkberrow' (24b) NHal
'Innocence' (Rub) CElw CFis CGle EFou EHal ELan EMon MUlv WEas
'Irene' (29K) CElw EHMN SMad
'Iris Coupland' (5a) NHal
'Ivy Garland' (5b) MCol NHal
'James Kelway' NBir
'Jan Okum' (24b) MRil MWol NHal
'Jan Wardle' (5a) MWol
'Jante Wells' (28) CRDP EMon MCol WEas
'Jessie Cooper' (Rub) EOrc SChu
'Joan' (25b) EHMN
'John Hughes' (3b) MCol MRil NHal
'John Lewis' (24b) MWol
'John Murray' NBir
'John Riley' (14a) MRil
'John Wingfield' (14b) MRil MWol NHal
'Jules la Graveur' EMon LRHS SMrm WByw
'Julia' EFou
'June Wakley' (25b) MCol
'Karen Riley' (25a) MRil
¶ 'Kento-homari' (9f) MWol
'Keystone' (25b) MCol MRil NHal
'Kimberley Marie' (15b) MRil NHal
'Kingfisher' (12a) EHMN MWol
'Kismet' (4c) MWol
'Kleiner Bernstein' EFou
¶ 'Kokinran' (9f) MWol
¶ 'Komaki-zukura' (9f) MWol
♦x ***koreanum*** See D. x ***grandiflorum***
'Lady Clara' (Rub) SPer
'Lady in Pink' (Rub) EMon
'Lakelanders' (3b) MRil MWol NHal
'Leading Lady' (25b) MWol
'Lemon Blanket' EHMN
'Lemon Margaret' (29c) EHMN MRil MWol NHal
'Len Futerill' (25b) MCol
'Lilian Hoek' (29c) EHMN MWol NHal
'Lilian Jackson' (7b) MCol
'Lilian Shoesmith' (5b)_ MRil
'Lindy' EFou
'L'Innocence' (29K) SMrm
'Little Dorrit' (29K) EHMN MCol
'Liverpool Festival' (23b) MCol NHal
'Long Island Beauty' (6a) MCol
'Long Life' (25b) MCol
'Lorraine' (24b) MRil MWol NHal
'Louise' (25b) EHMN
'Louise Etheridge' (23a) NHal
'Lucida' (29c) MWol
'Lucy Simpson' (29K) MCol MMil
'Lundy' (2) NHal
'Lyndale' (25b) MCol NHal
'Lynmal's Choice' (13b) NHal
'Mac's Delight' (25b) MCol MRil
'Madeleine' (29c) EBlo NHal
'Malcolm Perkins' (25a) MRil NHal
'Mandarin' CGle EFou
'Margaret' (29c) EHMN MCol MRil MWol NHal
'Margaret Riley' (25a) NHal
'Maria' (28a) MCol
'Marion' (25a) EHMN
'Marlene Jones' (25b) MWol
'Martin Riley' (23b) MCol MRil
'Martin Walker' (25b) MCol
'Mary' (29K) EHMN MCol
'Mary Stevenson' (25b) MCol
'Mary Stoker' (Rub) CGle CKel CMea CRDP CSco ECha ECtt EFou EGol ELan EMon ERav LGre MBri MCol MNFA MRav NFai SChu SMad SPer WEas WRus
'Mason's Bronze' (7b) MCol
'Matlock' (24b) MRil NHal
'Mauve Gem' (29K) EHMN

'Mauve Mist' (30K) MCol
'Mavis' (28a) MCol MWol
'Max Riley' (23b) MRil MWol NHal
'May Shoesmith' (5a) MCol NHal
'Mayford Perfection' (5a) MCol NHal
'Megan Woolman' (3b) MWol
'Mei-kyo' (28) CGle CKel CLew CMea CMil CPar CSam CSco ECtt ELan EMon EOrc ERav MRav NHol NJap SCro SHer SIng SPer SPla SSvw WAbe WEas WRus WWat
'Membury' (24b) MCol NHal
'Michelle Walker' (24b) MCol
'Midnight' (24b) MRil
'Milltown' (24b) MRil
'Minaret' (3b) MWol
'Minstrel Boy' (3b) MRil NHal
'Mirage' (22b) MRil NHal
'Moira' (29K) EHMN
'Molly Lambert' (36) MWol
'Moonlight' (29K) EHMN
'Morning Star' (12a) MWol
'Mottram Barleycorn' (29d) MCol
'Mottram Lady' MCol
'Mottram Melody' MCol
'Mottram Minstrel' MCol
'Mottram Sentinel' MCol
'Mottram Twotone' (29d) MCol
'Mrs Jessie Cooper' (Rub) EFou ELan EMon LRHS
'Muriel Vipas' (25b) MRil
¶ 'Music' (23b) NHal
'My Love' (7a) MWol
¶ 'Myako-no-suki' (9f) MWol
§ ***naktongense*** EMon
'Nancy Perry' (Rub) CSam ELan EMon LGan LRHS MCol SChu
§ ***nankingense*** EFou EMon
'Nantyderry Sunshine' EFou SIng SUsu WEas WWat
'Naomi' (22f) MRil
'Nathalie' (19c) MWol
'Nell Gwyn' (Rub) MCol
'New Stylist' (24b) MRil
'Nicole' (22c) EHMN MRil
'Niederschlesien' EFou
¶ 'Noshi-no-nuki' (9f) MWol
'Nu Dazzler' (9d) MCol
'Nu-Rosemary' (9d) NHal
'Oakfield Bride' (24b) NHal
'Ogmore Vale' (12a) MWol
'Olga Patterson' (5b) MWol
'Orange Allouise' (25b) MWol NHal
'Orange Fair Lady' (5a) MRil NHal
'Orange Margaret' (29c) See D. 'Fleet Margaret'
'Orange Pennine Pink' (29c) NHal
'Orangeade' (24b) MCol
'Orno' (29b) MCol
'Overbury' EHMN
§ ***pacificum*** CCla CElw CHad CHan CMea COtt ECha ECtt EFol EFou ELan EPla ESma GCal LGan MFir NBir NBro NFai SBor SUsu WCot WEas
*– 'Hakai' SChu
'Packwell' (24b) MCol
'Pamela' (29c) NHal
'Panache' (5a) NHal
'Pat' (6b) EHMN
'Pat Addison' (24b) MWol NHal
'Patricia' EHMN
'Patricia Millar' (14b) MRil NHal
'Paul Boissier' (Rub) CElw CGle ELan EMon LGre MCol SChu SMrm WByw WEas
'Pavilion' (25a) MCol
'Payton Dale' (29c) MRil NHal
¶ 'Payton Glow' (29c) NHal
'Payton Lady' (29c) NHal
¶ 'Payton Plenty' (29c) NHal
'Payton Prince' (29c) NHal
'Payton Rose' (29c) NHal
'Peach Allouise' (25b) NHal
'Peach Margaret' See D. 'Salmon Margaret'
'Pearl Celebration' (24a) MRil MWol NHal
'Peggy' (28a) EHMN
'Pennine Ace' (29f) MRil
'Pennine Amber' (29c) MRil NHal
'Pennine Brenda' (29d) MRil NHal
'Pennine Bride' (29c) MRil NHal
'Pennine Calypso' (29b) MRil
'Pennine Canary' (29c) MRil
'Pennine Clarion' (29c) MRil
'Pennine Copper' (29c) MRil
'Pennine Crimson' (29c) NHal
'Pennine Crystal' (29c) MCol
'Pennine Cupid' (29c) MWol
'Pennine Dell' (29d) MCol
'Pennine Dove' (29d) NHal
'Pennine Eagle' (29c) MCol
'Pennine Gambol' (29a) MRil
'Pennine Hannah' (29d) MRil NHal
'Pennine Harmony' (29f) MRil
'Pennine Jade' (29d) MRil MWol NHal
'Pennine Jude' (29a) MRil
'Pennine Light' (29d) MRil
'Pennine Magic' (29c) MRil
'Pennine Mavis' (29f) MRil
¶ 'Pennine Nectar' (29c) NHal
'Pennine Oriel' (29a) MCol MRil MWol NHal
'Pennine Pink' (29c) NHal
¶ 'Pennine Polo' (29d) NHal
'Pennine Punch' (29a) MCol
'Pennine Purple' (29c) EHMN MCol NHal
'Pennine Rascal' (29c) MRil
'Pennine Serene' (29d) MRil
'Pennine Sergeant' (29c) MWol
'Pennine Signal' (29d) MCol
'Pennine Silk' (29c) MRil
'Pennine Ski' (29c) MCol MRil
'Pennine Smoke' (29d) MRil
'Pennine Soldier' (29d) MRil MWol NHal
'Pennine Tango' (29d) NHal
'Pennine Trill' (29c) MWol
'Pennine Twinkle' (29a) MCol
'Pennine Waltz' (29c) EHMN
'Pennine Whistle' (29f) MRil
'Pennine White' (29c) MWol
'Pennine Wine' (29c) MRil
'Percy Salter' (24b) MCol
¶ 'Perry's Peach' NPer
'Peter Rowe' (23b) MCol NHal
¶ 'Peter Sare' EBlo
'Peter White' (23a) MCol
'Peterkin' ECtt EMon MUlv SMrm WRus

'Phil Houghton' (1)	MWol
'Piecas'	EHMN
'Pink Champagne' (4b)	NHal
'Pink Duke' (1)	MWol NHal
'Pink Gin' (9c)	MWol NHal
'Pink Margaret' (29c)	EHMN NHal
'Pink Overture'	MCol
'Pink Progression'	EBlo ECtt NBir
'Pink World of Sport' (25a)	MRil
'Pixton' (25b)	MCol
'Playmate' (29K)	MCol
'Plessey Snowflake' (29d)	NHal
'Polar Gem' (3a)	MWol NHal
'Polaris' (9c)	MCol
'Primrose Alison Kirk' (23b)	NHal
'Primrose Anemone' (29K)	CHal EHMN
'Primrose Angora' (25b)	MCol
'Primrose Bill Wade' (25a)	MRil NHal
'Primrose Chessington (25a)	MRil NHal
'Primrose Cricket' (25b)	MCol
'Primrose Ermine' (23a)	NHal
'Primrose John Hughes' (3b)	MRil MWol NHal
'Primrose Margaret' (29c)	See D. 'Buff Margaret'
'Primrose Mayford Perfection' (5a)	MCol MRil NHal
'Primrose Muriel Vipas' (5a)	MRil
'Primrose Pennine Oriel' (29a)	MRil
'Primrose Polaris' (9c)	MCol
'Primrose Sam Vinter' (5a)	MRil
'Primrose Tennis' (25b)	MRil NHal
'Primrose West Bromwich (14a)	MRil NHal
'Primrose World of Sport' (25a)	MRil
'Princess' (29K)	CHal EHMN MCol
'Princess Anne' (4b)	MCol NHal
'Promise' (25a)	MCol
'Purleigh White'	EFou SIng SUsu
'Purple Fairie' (28b)	MCol
'Purple Gerrie Hoek'	EHMN
'Purple Glow' (5a)	NHal
'Purple Margaret' (29c)	EHMN NHal
'Purple Payton Lady' (29c)	NHal
'Purple-Pink'	EFou
'Queenswood' (5b)	MCol
'Quill Elegance' (9f)	MWol
'Rachel Fairweather' (3a)	NHal
'Raquel' (29K)	MCol
'Rayonnante' (11)	MCol
'Red Admiral' (6b)	MWol
'Red Balcombe Perfection' (5a)	MWol NHal
'Red Claudia' (29c)	EHMN
'Red Eye Level' (5a)	MRil
'Red Formcast' (24a)	NHal
'Red Gambit' (24a)	MRil NHal
'Red Hoek' (29c)	MWol
'Red Keystone' (25a)	MRil
'Red Mayford Perfection'	MCol
'Red Pamela' (29c)	NHal
'Red Payton Dale' (29c)	MRil
'Red Pheasant'	EHMN
'Red Rosita' (29c)	MCol
'Red Shirley Model' (3a)	MWol NHal
'Red Wendy' (29c)	MCol NHal
'Redall' (4c)	MCol
'Regal Mist' (25b)	MCol
¶ 'Regalia' (24b)	MCol
'Remarkable' (30)	MRil NHal
'Riley's Dynasty' (14a)	MRil NHal
'Ringdove' (12a)	MWol
'Robeam' (9c)	MWol
'Roblaze' (9c)	MWol NHal
'Roblush' (9c)	MWol
'Rockwell' (14b)	NHal
'Rolass' (9c)	NHal
'Romano Mauve'	EHMN
'Romantika'	EFou
'Romark' (9c)	MWol NHal
'Ron James' (4a)	NHal
'Rose Enbee Wedding' (29d)	MCol NHal
'Rose Mayford Perfection' (5a)	MCol
¶ 'Rose Payton Lady' (29c)	NHal
'Rosita' (28b)	MCol
'Roy Coopland' (5b)	MRil NHal
'Royal Command' (Rub)	NBro SMad
'Rozette'	EHMN
♦ ***rubellum***	See D. ***zawadskii***
'Ruby Mound' (29K)	EFou EHMN LGre LHop MCol NHal SFis WEas
'Ruby Raynor' (Rub)	MCol
'Ryfinch' (9d)	MCol
'Ryflare' (9c)	MWol NHal
'Ryflash' (9d)	MCol
'Rylands Gem' (24b)	MCol NHal
'Rylands Victor' (23c)	MCol
'Rynoon' (9d)	MWol
'Rytorch' (9d)	MCol
'Salmon Cassandra' (5b)	NHal
'Salmon Fairie' (28)	MCol
'Salmon Fairweather' (3b)	MWol
§ 'Salmon Margaret' (29c)	MCol MRil
'Salmon Rylands Gem' (24b)	MCol NHal
'Salmon Shirley McMinn' (15a)	MRil
'Salmon Susan Rowe' (24b)	MCol
'Salmon Tracy Waller' (24a)	MRil
'Salmon Venice' (24b)	MRil
'Salurose'	EHMN
'Sam Oldham' (24a)	MWol
'Sam Vinter' (5a)	MRil NHal
¶ 'Samuri Bronze' (Rub)	WCot
'Sandra Burch' (24b)	MWol NHal
'Sandy'	MRil
'Sarah'	MRil

'Sarah's Yellow' CSam
'Saskia' MCol
'Satin Pink Gin' (9c) NHal
'Sea Urchin' (29c) MCol
'Seagull' EHMN
'Seashell' (28b) MCol
'Sefton' (4a) MRil NHal
'Setron' EHMN
'Sheila' (29K) EHMN
'Shining Light' (29K) EHMN MCol
¶ 'Shirley' (25b) MWol
'Shirley Glorious' (24a) MWol
'Shirley McMinn' (15a) MRil
'Shirley Model' (3a) MWol
'Shirley Primrose' (1) MWol
'Shoesmith's Salmon' (4a) MWol
'Sid Griffiths' (29c) MCol
'Silver Gigantic' (1) MWol
'Silver Jubilee' (24a) MWol
¶ 'Silver Stan Addison' (5b) MWol
'Simon Mills' (2) NHal
'Snow Bunting' EHMN
'Snowbound' (30K) MCol
'Snowflake' (24a) CTre
'Snowshine' (5a) MWol
'Solarama' (9e) NHal
'Sonnenschein' LHop
'Southway Sovereign' (29d) NHal
¶ 'Southway Sure' (29d) NHal
'Spartan Flame' (29c) MWol
¶ 'Spartan Glory' (25b) MWol
'Spartan Legend' (29c) MWol
'Spartan Leo' (29c) MWol
¶ 'Spartan Magic' (29d) MWol
¶ 'Spartan Moon' (25b) MWol
'Spartan Orange' (29d) MWol
'Spartan Pink' (29c) MWol
'Spartan Rose' (29c) MWol
'Spartan Sunrise' (29c) MWol
¶ 'Spartan Sunset' (29d) MWol
'Spartan Wendy' (29c) MWol
'Spartan White' (29c) MWol
'Spencer's Cottage' (13b) MCol
* 'Spoons' SCro
'Springtime' (24a) MCol
'Stan Addison' (5b) MWol NHal
¶ 'Stan's Choice' (29K) MCol
'Star Centenary' (3b) NHal
'Starlet' (29K) EHMN MCol
¶ 'Stockton' (3b) NHal
'Stoke Festival' (25b) MCol
'Sun Spider' (29K) CHal EHMN
'Sun Valley' (5a) MCol
'Sunbeam' (25a) ECtt EFou
'Suncharm Bronze' (22a) MWol
'Suncharm Pink' (22a) MWol
'Suncharm Red' (22a) MWol
'Suncharm White' (22a) MWol
'Suncharm Yellow' (22a) MWol
¶ 'Sundora NHal
'Sundoro' MRil
'Sunflight' (25b) MCol
'Sunny Margaret' (29c) NHal
'Susan Dobson' (25b) MWol
'Susan Riley' (23a) NHal
'Susan Rowe' (24b) MCol
'Sussex County' (15a) MRil MWol NHal
'Swallow' EHMN
'Swalwell' (25b) NHal
'Swansdown' (25b) MWol
'Taffeta' (9c) MCol NHal
'Talbot Bolero' (29c) NHal
¶ 'Talbot Bouquet' (29a) NHal
'Talbot Jo' (29d) NHal
'Talbot Parade' (29c) NHal
'Tanaga' MRil
'Tang' (12a) MWol
'Tapestry Rose' CGle EMon
'Tapis Blanc' EHMN
'Target' (24b) MRil
¶ 'Tenerife' (23b) MWol
'Tennis' (25b) MRil NHal
'The Favourite' MCol
'Tickled Pink' (29K) EHMN
'Tinkerbelle' (24b/12a) EHMN
'Toledo' (25a) MWol
'Tolima' MRil
'Tom Parr' See D. 'Doctor Tom Parr'
'Tommy Trout' (28) MCol
'Tracy Waller' (24b) MRil NHal
¶ 'Triumph' NHal
'Truro' (24a) MWol
'Tundra' (4a) NHal
'Universiade' (25a) MRil NHal
'Vanity Pink' MCol
'Vanity Primrose' MCol
'Vedova' (6a) MCol
'Venice' (24b) MRil NHal
'Veria' EHMN
'Vesuvius' EFou
'Virginia' (29K) EHMN
'Vision On' (24b) MRil
'Wedding Day' CElw EMon SRms WCot WRus
'Wedding Sunshine' EHMN MUlv
'Wendy' (29c) MCol NHal
'Wendy Tench' (29d) MCol
¶ 'Wessex Amber' (29d) NHal
'Wessex Cream' (29d) NHal
'Wessex Glory' (29d) NHal
'Wessex Gold' (29d) NHal
'Wessex Ivory' (29d) NHal
'Wessex Melody' (29d) NHal
¶ 'Wessex Solo' (29d) NHal
'Wessex Tang' (29d) NHal
'West Bromwich' (14a) MRil NHal
§ ***weyrichii*** CLew CNic EFol ELan LBee LHop MCas MHig MNFA MTho NHol NKay NMen SBla SBod SIng SSou WAbe WOMN WPat WPer WRus WThu
'White Allouise' (25b) NHal
'White Bouquet' (28) MCol MWol
'White Cassandra' (5b) NHal
'White Fairweather' (3b) MRil MWol
'White Gem' (25b) EHMN
'White Gerrie Hoek' (29c) EHMN NHal
'White Gloss' (29K) EHMN
'White Lilac Prince' (1) MWol
'White Margaret' (29c) EHMN MCol MRil MWol NHal

'White Margaret Riley (25a)	NHal
'White Nu Rosemary' (9d)	NHal
'White Pamela' (29c)	EHMN
'White Pearl Celebration' (24a)	MRil
'White Spider' (10)	MCol
'White Taffeta' (9c)	MCol NHal
'Win' (9c)	NHal
'Winchcombe' (29c)	EHMN
¶ 'Windermere' (24a)	NHal
'Winnie Bramley' (23a)	MCol MRil MWol NHal
'Winning's Red' (Rub)	NBro SMad
¶ 'Woolman's Century' (1)	MWol
'Woolman's Giant" (14a)	MWol
¶ 'Woolman's Glory' (7a)	MWol
'Woolman's Perfecta' (3a)	NHal
¶ 'Woolman's Prince' (3a)	MWol
'Woolman's Queen' (24a)	MWol
'Woolman's Star' (3a)	MWol NHal
'World of Sport' (25a)	MRil
'Yellow Alfreton Cream' (5b)	MRil
'Yellow Balcombe Perfection' (5a)	MWol
'Yellow Dorridge Crown' (25b)	MWol
¶ 'Yellow Fairweather' (3b)	MWol
'Yellow Flying Saucer' (6a)	MCol
'Yellow Fred Shoesmith' (5a)	MWol
'Yellow Galaxy' (9d)	MCol
'Yellow Gingernut' (25b)	MCol MRil NHal
'Yellow Hammer'	EHMN WCot
'Yellow Hazy Days' (25b)	NHal
'Yellow Heather James' (3b)	MCol
'Yellow Heide' (29c)	MCol NHal
'Yellow John Hughes' (3b)	MCol MRil NHal
'Yellow John Wingfield' (14b)	MRil NHal
'Yellow Lilian Hoek' (29c)	EHMN MCol NHal
'Yellow Margaret' (29c)	EHMN MCol MRil MWol NHal
¶ 'Yellow Margaret Riley' (25a)	NHal
'Yellow May Shoesmith' (5a)	NHal
'Yellow Mayford Perfection' (5a)	MCol MRil
'Yellow Pennine Oriel' (29a)	MCol MRil MWol NHal
'Yellow Polaris' (9c)	MCol
'Yellow Spider' (10)	MCol
'Yellow Starlet' (29K)	EHMN MCol
'Yellow Taffeta' (9c)	MCol
'Yellow Tennis' (25b)	NHal
'Yellowmoor' (25b)	MCol
§ *yezoense*	CRDP EFou ELan EMon LHop NKay SIng WCot WEas WRus
– 'Roseum'	NSti
'Yvonne Arnaud' (24b)	MCol MWol
¶ *zawadskii*	SUsu WRus
♦– *latilobum*	See D. ***naktongense***

DENDRIOPOTERIUM See **SANGUISORBA**

DENDROBENTHAMIA See **CORNUS**

DENDROCALAMUS (Gramineae(Bambuseae))

giganteus	SBam
strictus	SBam

DENDROMECON (Papaveraceae)
See Plant Deletions

DENDROSERIS (Compositae)

littoralis	CHEx

DENTARIA (Cruciferae)

californica	EPar
digitata	See CARDAMINE ***pentaphyllos***
diphylla	LAma
pinnata	See CARDAMINE ***heptaphylla***
polyphylla	See CARDAMINE ***kitaibelii***

DERMATOBOTRYS (Scrophulariaceae)

saundersii	CSun

DERWENTIA See **PARAHEBE**

DESCHAMPSIA (Gramineae)

cespitosa	CKin CNat CTom CWGN ETPC MNFA NHol SMrm
– ssp. ***alpina***	EMon
– 'Bronzeschleier' ('Bronze Veil')	CHan COtt EBlo EBre EFou EPla ETPC GAbr GCHN GCal IBlr LBre MNFA MSte MUlv NBro NEgg NHar NMir SApp SMad SMrm WCot WRus
– 'Fairy's Joke'	See D. ***c. vivipara***
– 'Goldgehänge' ('Golden Pendant')	EHoe ETPC GCal IBlr MFir SAxl
– 'Goldschleier' ('Golden Veil')	CElw CWGN EBlo EBre ECha EFou EHoe EMon EPla ETPC GAri GCHN IBlr LBre MUlv NHar SMad
– 'Goldstaub' ('Gold Dust')	EFou ETPC GCal NCat
– 'Goldtau' ('Golden Dew')	CElw EBlo EHoe EMon EPla ETPC GCHN NBro NHar NMir NRoo
¶ – var. ***parviflora***	ETPC
§ – var. ***vivipara***	CRDP EHoe EMon ETPC GCal NBro NCat
flexuosa	EHoe ETPC MBri SApp
– 'Tatra Gold'	CDoC CHal CNic CPMA CRDP ECha EFol EHoe EMon EPla ETPC LHop MBri MCas MNFA NCat NFai NHol NMir NNor SAxl SGil SMad SUsu WHal WPat
media	ETPC

DESFONTAINIA (Loganiaceae)

§ *spinosa* CB&S CCla CLan CMHG CSco CTre CTrw CWSG GRei IDai IJoh ISea MBal MBar MBri MBrk MPla NKay SArc SBor SDry SHBN SHil SPer SReu SSta WAbe WBod WDin WWat

– 'Harold Comber' MBal WBod WCru

– *hookeri* See D. ***spinosa***

DESMAZERIA (Gramineae)

♦*rigida* See CATAPODIUM ***rigidum***

DESMODIUM (Leguminosae)

§ *elegans* CB&S CChu CCla CGre CHan CMHG CPle EHal ELan WSHC

♦*praestans* See D. ***yunnanense***

tiliifolium See D. ***elegans***

§ *yunnanense* WSHC

DEUTZIA † (Hydrangeaceae)

♦*chunii* See D. ***ningpoensis***

compacta CHan WBod WWat

– 'Lavender Time' CCla CMHG CPle ESma MPla NSti WSHC

corymbosa CBow CCla

crenata 'Flore Pleno' See D. ***scabra*** 'F. P.'

– var. *nakaiana* 'Nikko' CB&S CCla CDoC CPle EFol ESis LHop MBar MGos MPla SEng SGil SHer SPla SUsu WOMN WRus WSHC

discolor 'Major' CLan

x *elegantissima* CLan CMHG CSco CShe IDai MRav NKay NNor SPla SReu

– 'Fasciculata' SPer WWin

– 'Rosealind' CB&S CBow CCla CSco EBlo EBre ECtt ELan ENot IOrc LBre MBri MPla NSti SEng SLon SPer SReu SSta WBod WKif WSHC

gracilis CBow CCla CSco GRei GWht MBal MBar MBel MPla MRav MWat NBee NNor SHBN SHer SPer WBod WDin WHCG WStI WWat

– 'Carminea' See D. x ***rosea*** 'Carminea'

– 'Marmorata' WHCG

*– 'Variegata' CPMA ECro

hookeriana GGGa ISea WWat

x *hybrida* 'Contraste' CB&S CDoC CLan SPer

– 'Joconde' CLan SMad WKif

¶– 'Lavender Time' SHil WPat

– 'Magicien' CChu CLan CMHG CSam CShe EBlo EBre ECtt ENot EPla LBre MBal SGil SHBN SLon SPer SSpi WHCG WPat

– 'Mont Rose' CB&S CBow CLan CShe ENot GRei MBal MBar MGos MPla MRav NBee SHBN SPer SPla SReu SSta WDin WSHC WStI WWin

– 'Perle Rose' CLan CSco

– 'Pink Pompon' See D. x ***h.*** 'Rosea Plena'

§– 'Rosea Plena' CB&S CBow MBri SSta WWeb

– 'Strawberry Fields' MBri SHil

x *kalmiiflora* CB&S CLan CMHG CSco EBre EHar EPla LAbb LBre MBar MBri MGos MRav NKay NNor SLPl SPer SWas WAbe WDin WRus WWeb

longifolia CLan

– 'Veitchii' MRav

x *magnifica* CDoC CSco ELan IOrc MRav SHil WStI WWeb WWin

*– 'Rubra' EPla SBar

¶– 'Staphyleoïdes' SBla

monbeigii CChu ENot SBor WKif WWat

§ *ningpoensis* CB&S CBow CChu CCla CGre CLan CWSG ECtt ESma GAbr MBrk NSti SBla SLPl SPer SSpi WWat

¶– L 146 EPla

– 'Pink Charm' SHil

pulchra CBow CChu CHan CLan CPle CShe EBre EHal ESma LBre NSti SHil SPer SSpi WHCG WWat

x *rosea* CBow CBra CMHG CTrw EBre ENot GRei IJoh LBre MBar MPla MWat NNor SHBN SHer WKif WStI WWin

– 'Campanulata' CCla ENot

§– 'Carminea' CB&S CShe ELan LAbb MBal SDix SLon SPer SSpi SSta WDin

– 'Floribunda' CBra ELan

scabra CDoC CLan MGos

§– 'Candidissima' CMHG ELan IDai MBri SPer SPla WBod

– 'Codsall Pink' MGos

– 'Plena' CB&S CPle ECtt ELan MSte NNor NRar SEng SHBN SPer

– 'Pride of Rochester' CBow CDoC CSco EHal ENot MBar MRav SHer SPla WDin

– 'Punctata' (v) CMHG EFol EHoe WThu

– 'Variegata' ELan EPla

setchuenensis CBow EPla GGGa SLon SSpi WPat WSHC

– var. *corymbiflora* CBot CCla CLan SBla SDry WKif WWat

staminea CLan

x *wellsii* See D. ***scabra*** 'Candidissima'

¶ x *wilsonii* SRms

DIANELLA † (Liliaceae/Phormiaceae)

caerulea EBul ECou GCal LHil SBar SWas WOld

– var. *petasmatodes* LHil WCot

– 'Variegata' See D. ***tasmanica*** 'V.'

¶ *intermedia* MUlv WCot

nigra CDoC EBul ECou GCal NHol SSpi

revoluta ECou SBar WCot

tasmanica CGle CHan CMon CPar CRow ECou GCal IBlr MBri MUlv NOrc SArc SAxl SBor SSpi WWat

§– 'Variegata' ECou IBlr WOld

DIANTHUS † (Caryophyllaceae)

ACW 2116 EMFP EMNN LBee MPlt NMen NRed WPer

'Ada Wood' (pf) NPin

'Admiral Crompton' (pf) MBel MWoo NPin SBai SHay

'Admiration' (b) SHay

'Afton Water' (b) SBai SHay

'Alan Titchmarsh' (p) CHal SBai

'Albatross' (p) SChu

'Alder House' (p) MBro NRoo

'Aldersey Rose' (p) WMar WWin

'Aldridge Yellow' (b) SAll SBai

'Alfred Galbally' (b) SBai

'Alice' (p) CDoC CThr SAll SHay SSvw

'Alice Forbes' (b) SAll SHay

¶ 'Alick Sparkes' (pf) SHay

'Allen's Ballerina' (p) CThr NCra NPin

§ 'Allen's Huntsman' (p)	CThr NCra NPin
§ 'Allen's Maria' (p)	CHal CThr EMFP NCra SRms
'Alloway Star' (p)	EMFP WPer
'Allspice' (p)	CFis CMil CThr EMFP GAbr GCal MBro MPar NCra SChu SSvw WHoo WMar WPer
¶ 'Allwood's Crimson' (pf)	SHay
alpinus	CGle CKel EMFP GDra GTou LAbb LBee MBal MHig NGre NHol NKay NMen NNrd NWCA SBla SIgm WPer
– 'Albus'	LBee NNrd SBla
– Correvon's form	NHol
– 'Drake's Red'	NGre
– 'Joan's Blood'	CRiv ECha EPot GAbr LHop NHol NRed SBla SIng WDav WHoo WMar WWin
– 'Millstream Salmon'	GAbr
– salmon form	NGre
'Amarinth' (p)	EMar ESis MBel WPer
amurensis	EMon ITim LRHS WCla WPer
anatolicus	ELan LBee NHol SBla SWas WPer
'Andrew' (p)	SHay
'Anna Wyatt' (p)	CThr NCra
'Annabelle' (p)	MCas NKay SChu WHil
'Anniversay' (p)	CHal NPin SBai
'Ann's Lass' (pf)	NPin
¶ 'Apricale' (pf)	SAll
'Apricot Sue' (pf)	NPin SHay
¶ 'Arbel' (pf)	SAll
'Archfield'	CShe
arenarius	CHal CLew CNic EMFP GCHN MCas MTol SIng SSvw WPer WWin
'Argus'	CMil MPar WPer
'Ariel' (p)	NKay
armeria	CKin WOak
arpadianus	EMNN MPla NGre NHol NMir NNrd
'Arthur' (p)	EMFP
'Arthur Leslie' (b)	SAll
x ***arvernensis*** (p)	CMHG CNic CRiv ECha EMNN EPot GAbr GDra MBro MHig MPla NGre NHar NMen NMir NRoo SHer WPat
¶ – 'Albus'	SIng
atrorubens	See D. ***carthusianorum*** Atrorubens Group
'Audrey Robinson' (pf)	MWoo NPin SBai
'Aurora' (b)	SHay
'Baby Treasure' (p)	GAbr NHol NNrd WHil
'Badenia' (p)	LBee SBla SMrm
¶ 'Bailey's Apricot' (pf)	SHay
'Bailey's Splendour' (pf)	SBai
'Ballerina' (p)	CSut EBre LBre SBai SHay
barbatus Nigrescens Group (p,a)	CBos CHad CRDP LGre LHil
¶ – 'Wee Willie'	CFis
'Barleyfield Rose' (p)	GArf MTho
¶ 'Barlow' (pf)	SHay
§ 'Bat's Double Red' (p)	CCot CKel EMFP EMon MPar NCra SHig SSvw WPer
'Beauty of Cambridge' (b)	SAll
'Beauty of Healey' (p)	CMil EMFP MPar NCra
'Becka Falls' (p)	CGle CHal CThr EBre LBre NCra SBai SHay
'Becky Robinson' (p)	CHal CSut CThr ELan EMFP MBel NPin SBai SHay SSvw WPbr
¶ 'Becky's Choice' (p)	EMFP
'Bet Gilroy' (b)	SHay
'Betty Buckle' (p)	SChu
'Betty Day' (b)	SHay
'Betty Norton' (p)	CShe ECar MBro MHig NCra SBla SMrm SSvw WHoo WPer WThu
'Betty Tucker' (b)	SHay
'Betty Webber' (p)	SBai
¶ 'Bibby's Cerise' (pf)	SHay
'Binsey Red' (p)	MPar SChu SSvw
¶ 'Blaby Joy'	MUlv
* 'Blue Carpet'	WPer
'Blue Hills' (p)	ELan LBee MCas SHer SIng
'Blue Ice' (b)	SHay
♦ 'Blush' (m)	See D. 'Souvenir de la Malmaison'
'Bobby' (p)	SAll
'Bobby Ames' (b)	SHay
'Bombadier' (p)	CFis CTom NRoo WMar
'Bookham Fancy' (b)	SAll SHay
'Bookham Grand' (b)	SHay
'Bookham Heroine' (b)	SHay
'Bookham Lad' (b)	SAll SHay
'Bookham Lass' (b)	SHay
'Bookham Perfume' (b)	SBai SHay
'Bookham Sprite' (b)	SAll SHay
§ 'Bourboule' (p)	CPar CSam ELan EMNN EPot ESis GDra ITim LBee MBar MBel MCas MHig MPla NKay NMen NNrd NRed NRoo SFis SIng WAbe WDav WPat WPer WThu WWin
'Bourboule Albus' (p)	CPar CRiv CSam EMNN EPot MCas MHig NHol NRed NRoo SGil SHer WAbe WDav WMar WThu WWin
'Bovey Belle' (p)	CGle CHal CSam CThr EBre EMFP LBre NCra NPin NRoo SBai
'Boydii' (p)	NTow
'Bransgore' (p)	WHoo
brevicaulis Mac&W 5849	WOMN
'Bridal Veil' (p)	CThr EMFP MBel MPar NCra SChu SSvw
'Bridesmaid' (p)	SHay
'Brigadier' (p)	WPer WThu
'Brilliant'	See D. ***deltoïdes*** 'Brilliant'
'Brimstone' (b)	SHay
¶ 'Brymos' (p)	CMHG
'Brympton Red' (p)	CFis CMil CThr ECha EFou EMFP EOrc MPar NCra NSti SBla SChu SSvw SUsu WEas
'Bryony Lisa' (b)	MBel SBai
'Caesar's Mantle' (p)	MPar NGre SChu SSvw
caesius	See D. ***gratianopolitanus***
– 'Compactus'	See D. ***gratianopolitanus*** 'Compactus Eydangeri'
callizonus	GArf GDra LBee MHig NGre NKay NRed WAbe
¶ 'Calypso' (pf)	SHay
'Camelford' (p)	NCra WPer
'Camilla' (b)	CMea CThr EMFP SSvw
'Candy Clove' (b)	SAll SHay
¶ 'Cannup's Pride' (pf)	SHay
¶ 'Can-Can' (pf)	SHay
'Carinda' (p)	SHay
'Carlotta' (p)	SHay
'Carmen' (b)	EBar SHay
'Caroline Bone' (b)	SHay
'Caroline Clove' (b)	SHay

Name	Suppliers
'Carolyn Hardy' (pf)	MWoo
carthusianorum	CSev ECar EMFP GTou MBel NCat SSvw WPer
– var. ***humilis***	WAbe
caryophyllus	CArn CSFH CSev NSel SIde WOak
'Casser's Pink' (p)	ELan EMFP MPit MTho
'Catherine Glover' (b)	SAll SHay
* 'Catherine Tucker'	WEas
'Catherine's Choice'	See D. 'Rhyan's Choice'
§ 'Cedric's Oldest' (p)	ECha MPar
'Charles' (p)	SAll
'Charles Musgrave' (p)	See D. 'Musgrave's Pink'
'Charm' (b)	SHay
'Chastity' (p)	GAbr MBro SChu SSvw WDav WHoo
§ 'Chelsea Pink' (p)	EMFP
¶ 'Cherry Clove' (b)	SAll
'Cherryripe' (p)	SAxl SHay
'Cheryl' (p)	See D. 'Houndspool Cheryl'
'Chetwyn Doris' (p)	NPin
chinensis (p,a)	MBri
'Chris Crew' (b)	SBai
'Christine Hough' (b)	SAll SBai
'Christopher' (p)	EBre GCHN LBre SAll SHay
'Cindy' (p)	LHop
cinnabarinus	See D. ***biflorus***
¶ 'Circular Saw' (p)	SHer
'Clara' (pf)	MWoo NPin SBai SHay
'Clara Lucinda' (pf)	NPin
'Clara's Choice' (pf)	NPin
'Clara's Flame' (pf)	NPin SHay
'Clara's Glow' (pf)	NPin
'Clara's Lass' (pf)	MWoo NPin SBai SHay
'Clare' (p)	MBel SAll SBai SHay
'Claret Joy' (p)	CThr EBre ELan EMFP GAri LBre NPin NRoo WPbr
'Clarinda' (b)	SAll
'Clunie' (b)	SAll SHay
§ 'Cockenzie Pink' (p)	EMFP SChu SSvw WEas WThu
'Cocomo Sim' (pf)	SHay
'Constance' (p)	EMFP SAll
'Constance Finnis' (p)	CHad CThr ECha ELan ESma NRoo SChu SMrm SSvw WEas WPer
'Consul' (b)	SAll SHay
'Copperhead' (b)	SHay
'Cornish Snow' (p)	CMHG CSam SIng
'Coste Budde' (p)	ECha WMar
'Cranmere Pool' (p)	CGle CHal CMea CThr EBre ELan GAri LBre NCra NHol NPin NRoo SHay SMrm SPla WPbr
'Cream Sue' (pf)	MWoo NPin SHay
'Crimson Ace' (p)	SHay
'Crimson Velvet' (b)	SHay
¶ ***crinitus***	CMil
'Crompton Classic' (pf)	NPin
'Crompton Princess' (pf)	MWoo NPin SBai
'Crossways' (p)	ESis GDra LBee MHig NHar SHer
¶ 'Crowley's Pink Sim' (pf)	SHay
cruentus	LHop
* 'D D R'	LBee
'Dad's Choice' (p)	CHal CSut SBai
'Dad's Favourite' (p)	CFis CGle CHal CThr ECha ELan EMFP EOrc MPar NCra NPin SAll SAxl SBai SHay SSvw WDav WEas WPer WTyr
'Daily Mail' (p)	SBai

Name	Suppliers
'Dainty Clove' (b)	SHay
'Dainty Lady' (b)	SBai
'Daisy Hill Scarlet' (b)	IDai
'Damask Superb' (p)	EMFP MHig SSvw WHil WPer
'Dark Pierrot' (pf)	SBai
'Dartington Double' (p)	ELan ESis LBee NHol SGil SHer
¶ 'Dartington Laced'	CMil
'Dartmoor Forest' (p)	SBla
'David' (p)	SAll SHay
'David Saunders' (b)	SBai
'Dawlish Charm' (p)	CThr
'Dawn' (b)	SAll SHay
¶ – (pf)	SAll
* 'Dazzler'	MPla
'Debi's Choice' (p)	SBai
¶ 'Deep Purple' (pf)	SHay
deltoïdes	CArn CGle CKin CSev CShe EBar ECha ELan IDai LGro LHol MBar MPla NGre NLan NNor NRed WCla WOak WWin
– 'Albus'	CFis CGle CMea CRiv ECha EMFP EPot MBar MPla MTol NNor NNrd NOak NRed NSel SSvw WByw WCla WPer
– 'Bright Eyes'	CTom MRav
§ – 'Brilliant'	CGle CSev CTom LAbb NNor NNrd NOak WPbr
– 'Broughty Blaze'	GDra
– 'Erectus'	ELan WEas
– 'Leuchtfunk' ('Flashing Light')	CMea CRiv EBre EMNN EMar ESma GDra LBre LHil LHop MPit NHar NKay NNrd WEas WPbr WPer
– 'Microchip'	CDoC LAbb LBee MPit NHar NKay NOak
– 'Samos'	CDoC
– ***splendens***	WOMN
– 'Wisley Variety'	WCla
'Denis' (p)	CSut CThr EBre ELan EMFP LBre NCra NHol SRms
'Devon Blossom' (p)	CThr
'Devon Blush' (p)	CHal CThr EBre LBre NHol NPin NRoo
'Devon Cream' (p)	CThr EBre EMFP GAri LBre NHol NPin NRoo SPla
'Devon Dove' (p)	CThr EBre LBre NHol NPin NRoo
'Devon General' (p)	CThr EBre LBre NHol NPin NRoo
'Devon Glow' (p)	CHal CThr EBre LBre NPin NRoo SFis
'Devon Maid' (p)	CThr EBre LBre NHol NPin
¶ 'Devon Pearl' (p)	NHol
¶ 'Devon Pride' (p)	EBre LBre NHol NPin SFis WPbr
'Dewdrop' (p)	CMea ESis GCHN LBee NHol NRoo SMrm SUsu
'Diane' (p)	CGle CRiv CSam CSco CShe CThr EBre ELan EMFP LBre NCra NHol NPin NRoo SAll SBai SChu SFis SHay SMrm SPla SSvw WEas WPbr WPer
'Dianne Hewins' (pf)	MWoo
'Doctor Archie Cameron' (b)	SHay
¶ 'Dora'	NHol
'Doris' (p)	Widely available
'Doris Allwood' (pf)	MBel NPin SHay
'Doris Elite' (p)	SAll
¶ 'Doris Galbally' (b)	MBel
'Doris Majestic' (p)	SAll
'Doris Ruby'	See D. 'Houndspool Ruby'
'Doris Supreme' (p)	SAll

Plant	Suppliers
double dark red	CFis
'Double Irish' (p)	See D. 'Irish Pink'
'Downs Cerise' (b)	SHay
'Downs Glory' (b)	SHay
'Dubarry' (p)	CMil CShe ITim MCas MHig NHol NMir SBla WPer
¶ 'Duchess of Fife' (p)	CFis
¶ 'Duchess of Westminster' (m)	SBor WMal
'Duke of Argyll'	EMon
'Dunkirk' (b)	MWoo
'Dusky' (p)	NCra SChu
'E J Baldry' (b)	SHay
'Earl of Essex' (p)	CCot CMil CThr EMFP NCra SAll SHay SSvw WPer
'Ebor II' (b)	SAll SHay
¶ ***echiniformis***	MFos
'Edan Lady' (pf)	NPin SHay
'Edenside Scarlet' (b)	SHay
'Edenside White' (b)	SBai
'Edith Johnson' (pf)	NPin
'Edna' (p)	SAll
'Edward' (p)	SAll
'Eileen' (p)	EMFP
¶ 'Eileen O'Connor' (b)	MBel
'Elizabeth' (p)	CElw CGle
'Elizabeth Anne' (pf)	MWoo
♦ 'Ember Rose' (pf)	See D. 'Le Rêve'
'Emile Paré' (p)	ESis LHop MTho WMar
'Emma Sarah' (b)	SBai
'Emperor'	See D. 'Bat's Double Red'
'Enid Anderson' (p)	MPar NNrd SChu SHig SSvw
erinaceus	CLew CPar EMNN EPad GCHN ITim LBee MBro MPla MSte NHar NHol NMen NRoo NWCA SSmi WAbe WDav WPer WThu WWin
– var. ***alpinus***	EPot
'Erycina' (b)	EBar SAll SHay
¶ 'Esperance' (pf)	SAll SHay
* 'Ethel Hurford'	WHoo
'Eudoxia' (b)	SAll
'Eva Humphries' (b)	SAll SBai SHay
'Excelsior' (p)	CKel CPar CRiv CSco CThr EPad NMir NNor NSti WThu
'Exquisite' (b)	SBai SHay
'Fair Folly' (p)	CMil EMFP SSvw WHil WMar WPer
'Faith Raven' (p)	EMon
'Fanal' (p)	CPar CRiv CShe NBir NNrd SAsh WAbe
'Farnham Rose' (p)	MBel SChu
'Fascination' (b)	SHay
¶ 'Fashino' (pf)	SAll
'Fenbow Nutmeg Clove' (b)	SChu
'Fettes Mount ' (p)	EMon EPad GAbr MBel NSti SSvw
'Fiery Cross' (b)	SAll SHay
'Fimbriatus' (p)	WHoo
'Fingo Clove' (b)	SAll
'Fiona' (p)	SAll
¶ 'Firecrest Rose'	CCot
'First Lady' (b)	SAll
'Flame' (p)	SHay
¶ 'Flame Sim' (pf)	SHay
'Forest Glow' (b)	SAll SBai
'Forest Sprite' (b)	SAll SBai
'Forest Treasure' (b)	SAll SBai
'Fortuna' (p)	SAll
'Fountain's Abbey' (p)	MPar WMar
'Fragrant Ann' (pf)	MWoo NPin SBai SHay
'Fragrant Lace' (p)	CThr
'Fragrant Rose' (pf)	SBai SHay
'Frances Isabel' (p)	NCra SAll
'Frances King' (pf)	NPin
'Frances Sellars' (b)	SHay
'Frank's Frilly' (p)	MPar SSvw
'Freckles' (p)	CHal CPar CThr SBai SHay
'Freda' (p)	SAll SHay
'Freeland Crimson Clove' (b)	SAll SHay
'French'	CShe
freynii	CLew CRiv EPot ITim MBro NGre
* 'Fringed Pink'	See D. ***superbus***
furcatus	NWCA
'Fusilier' (p)	CMea CNic CSam LBee MCas NHol NRoo SGil SHer WHoo
¶ 'G J Sim' (pf)	SHay
'G W Haywood' (b)	SHay
'Gail Tilsey' (b)	SHay
Gala ® (pf)	SBai
¶ 'Galil' (pf)	SAll
'Garland' (p)	CHal CMea NHar NNrd NRoo
'Garnet' (p)	EFol SChu
'Gertrude' (p)	SSvw
giganteus	EMFP IBlr
'Gingham Gown' (p)	MPar NBir NCat NKay SBar
'Gipsy Clove' (b)	SHay
glacialis	GTou LBee MCas NHar NMen NRed
– ssp. ***gelidus***	NGre
'Gloriosa' (p)	WPer
'Glorious' (p)	SHay
'Golden Cross' (b)	MBel SBai
¶ 'Golden Rain' (pf)	SHay
'Gran's Favourite' (p)	CElw CFis CKel CSam CSco EBre ELan EMFP GAri LBre MPar MTho NHol NPin NRoo SBai SChu SFis SHay SSvw WEas WMar WPer
§ ***gratianopolitanus***	CArn CHal CPar CSev EPad GCHN GTou LHol MBel MBro MFir MHig NLan NOak NRoo NSel SIde SSmi WOak WPer
– 'Albus'	EPad
¶ – 'Compactus Eydangeri' (p)	WHil
¶ – 'Corinne Tremaine'	WHer
– 'Flore Pleno'	CBre EMFP
* – 'Karlik'	NWCA
– red form	GAbr
§ – 'Tiny Rubies'	WAbe
'Gravetye Gem' (b)	CPar CRiv ECar MBel NRoo SHer WHil WPat
¶ – (p)	NCra WHoo
'Grenadier' (p)	EPot SGil SHer
'Gwendolen Read' (p)	SHay
* 'Gypsy Lass'	SFis
haematocalyx	CPar EMFP ITim LHil NRed NWCA WDav
– 'Alpinus'	See D. ***h. pindicola***
§ – ssp. ***pindicola***	EPot MFos WOMN
'Hannah Louise' (b)	MBel SBai
'Happiness' (b)	SBai
'Harlequin' (p)	ECtt EMFP EMNN NCra NRoo NRya WPer
'Harmony' (b)	SAll SBai SHay

'Harvest Moon' (pf) SAll
'Haytor' (p) See D. 'Haytor White'
'Haytor Rock' (p) CHal CSut CThr EBre GAri LBre NCra SHay SPla WPer
§ 'Haytor White' (p) CGle CHal CSam CThr EBre EMFP ERav GAbr GAri GCHN LBre NCra NHol NPin NSti SAll SBai SChu SHay SSvw WEas WPbr
'Hazel Ruth' (b) MBel SBai
'Heidi' (p) SRms
'Helen' (p) CThr SAll SHay WEas
'Henry of Essex' (p) EMFP SSvw
'Hidcote' (p) CNic CShe ELan EMFP ESis MBel MHig NKay NMen NNrd SBla SHer SIng WWin
'Highland Chieftain' (p) NKay
'Highland Fraser' (p) CNic CShe MHig NHol NKay NRoo WEas WKif WPat WThu WWin
'Highland Queen' (p) CMil SAsh
♦*hispanicus* See D. ***pungens***
'Hollycroft Fragrance' (p) SAll
'Hope' (p) EMFP ESis MPar SChu SSvw SUsu WMar WPer WTyr
'Horsa' (b) SHay
*'Horton' MPar
§ 'Houndspool Cheryl' (p) CGle CSco CThr EMFP GAbr NHol NPin SBai SSvw
§ 'Houndspool Ruby' (p) CGle CSam CThr EMFP MWat NHol NOak NPin SBai SChu SSvw WEas
'Howard Hitchcock' (b) SBai
'Huntsman' See D. 'Allen's Huntsman'
'Ian' (p) CThr NPin SHay
'Ibis' (p) SHay
'Iceberg' (p) EMFP MPar
'Icomb' (p) CLew SRms WHoo WPer WWin
'Imperial Clove' (b) SHay
'Ina' (p) CHal CMea GDra SRms
'Inchmery' (p) CCot CHad CThr EMFP MBel MPar NCra NKay NNor NSti SAll SChu SHay SSvw WEas WHoo WPer
'Indios' (pf) SBai
'Inglestone' (p) CSam MCas WDav WHil
'Inshriach Dazzler' (p) CHal CMea EBre ECar EMFP EPot ESis GArf GCHN GDra ITim LBee LBre MBro MSte NCra NHar NHol NNrd NRoo SBla SHer WAbe WDav WHal WMar
'Inshriach Startler' (p) GDra NRoo
'Irene Della-Torré' (b) SBai
¶ 'J M Bibby' (pf) NPin SHay
'Jacqueline Ann' (pf) MWoo NPin SBai SHay
¶ 'Jaffa' (pf) SAll
¶ 'James' (pf) NPin
'Jane Austen' (p) NCra SChu SSvw WMar WPer WSun
'Jane Coffey' (b) SHay
'Jenny Wyatt' (p) CHal CThr EBre LBre NCra SHay
'Jess Hewins' (pf) MWoo NPin SHay
¶ 'Jessica' (pf) SAll
'Joanne' (pf) NPin SHay
'Joanne Taylor' (pf) MWoo
'Joanne's Highlight' (pf) NPin SHay
'Joan's Blood' See D. ***alpinus*** 'J. B.'
'Joe Vernon' (pf) MWoo NPin SBai
'John Ball' (p) EMFP MPar
'John Gray' (p) SSvw
'Joker' (pf) SHay
'Joy' (p) CKel CMea CSut CThr EBre EMFP LBre NCra NHol NPin SBai SHay WPbr
'Julian' (p) EMFP
'Kesteven Chambery' (p) EMNN WPer
'Kesteven Chamonix' (p) CPar ECar EMNN NMen WPer WThu
'Kestor' (p) CThr GCHN NCra NOak
kitaibelii See D. ***petraeus petraeus***
knappii CPar CPou ECro EMFP GCHN LGan LHil NBro NFai NOak SUsu WCla WHil WPer WTyr WWin
'La Bourbrille' See D. 'Bourboule'
'Laced Hero' (p) CMil MBel SChu WPer
laced hybrids WCla
'Laced Joy' (p) CGle CHal CMHG CThr EMFP NCra NOak SAll SChu SHay WHoo WPer
'Laced Monarch' (p) CGle CHal CSam CThr EMFP ESis GCHN MBel NBro NHol NPin NRoo SAll SBai SSvw WDav WPer
'Laced Prudence' See D. 'Prudence'
'Laced Romeo' (p) CCot EMFP NCra SChu SHay SSvw WEas
'Laced Treasure' (p) CThr EPad SAll
'Lady Diana' (p) NKay
'Lady Granville' (p) CMil CPar EMFP MPar NCra SSvw
'Lady Salisbury' (p) CMil
§ 'Lady Wharncliffe' (p) CMil EMFP MBel MPar SSvw WMar WPer
'Lancing Lady' (b) SAll
'Lancing Monarch' (b) SAll SHay
langeanus NWCA SIng
'Laura' (p) SAll SHay
'Lavender Clove' (b) SAll SBai SHay
¶ 'Lavender Lady' (pf) NPin
§ 'Le Rêve' (pf) SAll
¶ 'Leatham Pastel' (pf) NPin
'Leiden' (b) SBai
'Lemsii' (p) CMHG CRiv CSam EMFP ESis LBee MBal MCas NHar NMen NVic WHoo WPer WTyr
¶ 'Lena Sim' (pf) SHay
'Leslie Rennison' (b) SAll SHay
'Letitia Wyatt' (p) CThr NPin NRoo SFis
¶ 'Lightning' (pf) SAll
'Lilac Clove' (b) SHay
'Lilian' (p) CFis
'Little Diane' (p) MWoo
'Little Gem' (pf) LHil
'Little Jock' (p) Widely available
'Little Old Lady' See D. 'Chelsea Pink'
'Liz Rigby' (b) SHay
'London Brocade' (p) CFis EMFP NCra SChu WMar
'London Delight' (p) CCot CThr EMFP EOrc MPar NCra SHay WPer WTyr
'London Glow' (p) CThr SAll
*'London Joy' WEas
'London Lovely' (p) CPar EPad NCra SAll SSvw
'London Poppet' (p) CRiv CThr EOrc SAll WHoo
§ 'Lord Chatham' (b) EMon
'Louise's Choice' (p) EMFP
'Loveliness' (p) CBre GAbr WEas
¶ *lumnitzeri* EPot WPer
'Lustre' (b) SAll SBai SHay
'Madame Dubarry' (p) GAbr NRya
'Madonna' (p) CThr MPar NCra SHay SSvw

'Mandy' (p)	EMFP SAll
'Manningtree Pink' (p)	See D. 'Cedric's Oldest'
¶ 'Mannion' (pf)	NPin
'Manon' (pf)	SBai
¶ 'Marg's Choice' (p)	EMFP
'Maria'	See D. 'Allen's Maria'
'Mars' (p)	CGle CHal CMHG ELan EPad ITim LBee MPlt NRoo SAll SChu SHer WAbe WDav
'Marshwood Mystery' (p)	CThr
* 'Martin Nest'	ITim
'Mary Jane Birrel' (pf)	MWoo NPin
'Mary Simister' (b)	SAll SHay
* 'Mary's Gilliflower'	CPar SSvw
'Master Stuart' (b)	SBai
'Matador' (b)	SHay
'Maudie Hinds' (b)	MBel SBai
'May Jones' (p)	EMFP
'Maybole' (b)	SAll SHay
¶ 'Maythorne' (p)	SRms
'Mendip Hills' (b)	SHay
¶ 'Mercury' (p)	SAll
'Merlin Clove' (b)	SBai SHay
'Messines Pink' (p)	SAll
'Michael Saunders' (b)	SBai
'Microchip' (p)	NRed SFis
microlepis	ITim NMen NRed NWCA
– ***albus***	LBee
– var. ***musalae***	EPot WDav
'Mida'	See D. 'Melody'
'Milley' (p)	CRiv
§ ***minutiflorus***	GCHN
'Miss Sinkins' (p)	NCra
* 'Molly Blake'	WDav
'Monica Wyatt' (p)	CGle CHal CThr EBre LBre MRav NCra NPin NRoo SBai SFis
¶ ***monspessulanus***	NWCA
– ssp. ***sternbergii***	ESis NGre
'Montrose Pink' (p)	See D. 'Cockenzie Pink'
'Mrs Clark'	See D. 'Nellie Clark'
'Mrs Elmhurst' (p)	NCra
'Mrs Jackson' (p)	SAsh SBla
'Mrs Macbride' (p)	CMil SSvw
'Mrs N Clark'	See D. 'Nellie Clark'
'Mrs Shaw' (p)	NCra
'Mrs Sinkins' (p)	Widely available
'Murcia' (pf)	SBai
N 'Musgrave's Pink' (p)	CBre CFis CGle CShe CThr CTom ECha EMFP EOrc LHop MPar NCra SChu SIng SSvw WDav WEas WHoo WMar
'Musgrave's White'	See D. 'Musgrave's Pink'
myrtinervius	CBar CHal CNic ECha ESis ITim MBro MFir MHig NMen NRoo NWCA WCla WHil WPer
'N M Goodall' (p)	LHop
'Nan Bailey' (p)	SBai
'Nancy Lindsay' (p)	MPar SSvw
'Napoleon III' (p)	IBar WKif
nardiformis	WPer
'Nautilus' (b)	SHay
neglectus	See D. ***pavonius***
§ 'Nellie Clark' (p)	CHal CShe ESis MBal NMen SChu SGil SHer
¶ 'Neptune' (pf)	SAll
'Nicola Jane' (pf)	NPin
I 'Nina' (pf)	SBai
nitidus	GDra NBir NGre WPer
noeanus	See D. ***petraeus n.***
¶ 'Nonsuch'	CMil EMFP
'Norman Hayward' (b)	SHay
'Nyewood's Cream' (p)	CHal CKel CMHG CMea EMFP EMNN EPot ESis GArf MBar MBro MFir MHig MPla MRav NCra NGre NHar NHol NMen NNrd NRed NRoo SHer SIng SUsu WDav WPat WPer
'Oakfield Clove' (b)	SAll
§ 'Oakington' (p)	CHal CRiv CSam EBre EMNN GCHN LBre MBal MRav MWat NCra NKay NMen NNrd NRoo SChu WDav
'Oakington Rose'	See D. 'Oakington'
¶ 'Oakwood Billy Boole' (p)	NPin
♦ 'Old Blush'	See D. 'Souvenir de la Malmaison'
'Old Clove Red' (b)	CMil EMFP SFis WThu
'Old Dutch Pink' (p)	CMil NCra SChu SSvw
'Old Fringed Pink' (p)	EMFP MPar
'Old Fringed White' (p)	SAxl SSvw
'Old Irish'	NSti
'Old Mother Hubbard' (p)	ESis
§ 'Old Square Eyes' (p)	MPar SAxl SBla WEas
'Old Velvet' (p)	CBre CMil CPar CThr MPar SChu SSvw SUsu
'Oliver' (p)	SAll
¶ 'Omagio' (pf)	SAll
'Orange Maid' (b)	SAll
¶ 'Orchid Beauty' (pf)	SHay
'Oscar' (b)	SAll
'Osprey' (b)	SHay
'Paddington' (p)	CMil CThr EMFP NCra SChu SSvw
'Painted Beauty' (p)	EMFP NBir
'Painted Lady' (b)	EMon MBel NHol SSvw WPat
'Paisley Gem' (p)	CThr MBel NCra SChu SSvw
'Patchwork'	SAsh
'Patricia' (b)	SHay
'Patricia Bell '	See D. ***turkestanica*** 'P.B.'
'Paul' (p)	CHal EMFP NPin
'Paul Hayward' (p)	SHay
§ ***pavonius***	CNic CSam ESis LBee MBro MCas MRav NWCA SBla WAbe WPer WWin
– 'Nancy Lindsay'	See D. 'N.L.'
– ***roysii***	See D. 'Roysii'
'Peach' (p)	SHay
'Perfect Clove' (b)	SHay
§ ***petraeus***	LBee LRHS NHol NRed
§ – ssp. ***noeanus***	WHal WPer
'Petticoat Lace' (p)	SHay
'Phantom' (b)	SHay
'Pheasant's Eye' (p)	CPar CThr EMFP MPar NCra WDav WPer
'Philip Archer' (b)	SHay
'Phyllis Marshall' (b)	EMon
'Picture' (b)	SHay
'Pierrot'	See D. 'Kobusa'
'Pike's Pink' (p)	Widely available
pindicola	See D. ***haematocalyx p.***
¶ ***pinifolius***	WDav
'Pink Bizarre' (b)	SHay
'Pink Calypso'	See D. 'Truly Yours'
'Pink Damask' (p)	GAbr SSvw WPer
¶ 'Pink Galil' (pf)	SAll

'Pink Jewel' (p)	CSam ECar ECha EPad ESis ITim LBee NHol NMen NRar NRoo SChu SHer WEas
¶ 'Pink Mist Sim' (pf)	SHay
¶ 'Pink Monica Wyatt' (p)	NRoo
'Pink Mrs Sinkins' (p)	ECha EMFP SAll SChu WHoo
'Pink Pearl' (b)	SRms
'Pink Sim' (pf)	SAll
'Pixie' (b)	EMNN EPot ITim MCas NHol NNrd
plumarius	CHal NLan NMir NRed SRms WByw WOak WPer
¶ – 'Albiflorus'	NOrc WPer
¶ ***pontederae***	SIng
'Portsdown Fancy' (b)	EBar SHay
'Portsdown Lass' (b)	EBar SHay
'Portsdown Perfume' (b)	SHay
preobrazhenskii	NNrd
'Preston Pink'	SChu
'Pretty Lady' (p)	NRoo SMrm
'Prince Charming' (p)	CRiv ELan EMNN ESis GAbr ITim MCas NHol NMen NNrd NRoo SIng WAbe WPer
'Prince of Wales'	EPad
* 'Princess Charming'	LHil
¶ 'Princess of Wales' (m)	SBor WMal
¶ 'Priory Pink' (p)	SAll
§ 'Prudence' (p)	CThr EMFP NCra NSti SBai WHoo WMar
¶ 'Pummelchen' (p)	EPot
§ ***pungens***	CNic
'Purley King' (p)	CThr
¶ 'Purple Frosted' (pf)	SHay
¶ 'Purple Jenny' (p)	SAll
'Queen of Hearts' (p)	ESis MBro SAxl SGil WHil WPer
'Queen of Henri'	ECar NHol NRoo SChu SFis SHer
'Queen of Sheba' (p)	CFis CMil CThr EMFP NCra SChu SSvw WMar
'Queen's Reward' (pf)	MWoo SBai
'Raby Castle'	See D. 'Lord Chatham'
'Rachel' (p)	EBre LBre NRoo
'Raggio di Sole' (pf)	SBai
'Rainbow Loveliness' (p,a)	WCla
'Red and White' (p)	WPer
¶ 'Red Denim' (p)	SIng
'Red Emperor' (p)	SAll WPer
'Red Penny' (p)	ESis MBel MBro NBro NRoo SAsh WPat
¶ 'Red Velvet'	SAsh
¶ 'Red-Edged Skyline' (pf)	SHay
¶ 'Reiko' (pf)	SAll
'Renoir' (b)	SAll SHay
§ 'Revell's Lady Wharncliffe'	See D. 'Lady Wharncliffe'
§ 'Rhian's Choice' (p)	EMFP
'Riccardo' (b)	SBai
'Richard Gibbs' (p)	MRav NRoo WWin
¶ 'Rimon' (pf)	SAll
'Robert' (p)	CThr SAll SHay
¶ 'Robert Allwood' (pf)	SHay
'Robert Baden-Powell' (b)	SHay
¶ 'Roberta' (pf)	SAll
'Robin Thain' (b)	EBar SAll SBai SHay
'Ron's Joanne' (pf)	NPin SHay
¶ 'Roodkapje' (p)	SSvw
'Rosalind Linda' (pf)	MWoo
'Rose de Mai' (p)	CBre CMil CPar EMFP MMil NCra SChu SSvw
'Rose Joy' (p)	CSam CSut CThr NCra NHol NPin NRoo SBai SHay WPbr
'Rose Monica Wyatt' (p)	CHal CThr NRoo
¶ 'Rose Perfection ' (pf)	SHay
'Rosealie' (p)	SHay
'Royal Scot' (pf)	MWoo
'Royalty' (p)	SHay
§ 'Roysii' (p)	EMFP LHil MPla MPlt NNrd NWCA WPer
'Rubin' (pf)	WEas
'Ruby' (p)	See D. 'Houndspool Ruby'
'Ruby Doris'	See D. 'Houndspool Ruby'
¶ 'Ruffles' (p)	SIng
¶ 'Rupert Lambert'	MBel
rupicola	CNic
'Russling Robin'	See D. 'Fair Maid of Kent '
¶ 'Sabra' (pf)	SAll
¶ 'Sahara' (pf)	SAll
'Saint Nicholas' (p)	CMil MPar NCra SHer SSvw WThu
'Sally Anne Hayward' (b)	SHay
'Salmon Clove' (b)	SAll SHay
'Sam Barlow' (p)	CMil EMFP MPar NCra SAll SChu SHay SSvw WEas WMar WWin
'Samantha Holtom' (pf)	MWoo
'Sandra Neal' (b)	SBai
'Santa Claus' (b)	SAll SHay
'Sappho' (b)	SHay
'Scania' (pf)	SHay
'Scarlet Fragrance' (b)	SAll SHay
'Scarlet Joanne' (pf)	MWoo NPin SHay
'Scaynes Hill' (p)	WSun
* ***scopulorum perplexans***	EPot
'Sean Hitchcock' (b)	SBai
seguieri	GAbr MBro NWCA WPer
'Shaston' (b)	SHay
'Shaston Scarletta' (b)	SHay
'Shaston Superstar' (b)	SHay
¶ 'Shegange' (pf)	SAll
¶ 'Sheila's Choice' (p)	EMFP
'Shocking Pink Sim' (pf)	SAll
'Show Aristocrat' (p)	SAll
'Show Portrait' (p)	NNor
'Sir Arthur Sim' (pf)	SAll SHay
'Sir Cedric Morris'	See D. 'Cedric's Oldest'
'Sir David Scott' (p)	MPar SMrm
* 'Six Hills'	MBel MBro WPat
'Snow Clove' (b)	SHay
'Snowflake' (p)	NNrd
'Solomon' (p)	SSvw WMar
'Sonata' (p)	MWil
'Sops-in-Wine' (p)	CSam CThr ECha EMFP GAbr MBel NCra SChu SHay SSvw WHil
'Southmead' (p)	CPar MHig
¶ 'Souvenir de la Malmaison' (m)	SBor WMal
'Spangle' (b)	SAll
'Spark' (p)	ITim NRoo
'Spencer Bickham' (p)	EMFP EPot ESis SSvw
'Spotty' (p)	ITim
'Spring Beauty' (p)	NBir NRoo WCla
¶ sp. NS 643	WDav
'Square Eyes'	See D. 'Old Square Eyes'

squarrosus	CPar EPot LBee MHig NGre NWCA
'Squeeks' (p)	SChu
'Stan Stroud' (b)	SHay
'Startler' (p)	SHay
'Storm' (pf)	SBai SHay
'Strathspey' (b)	SHay
'Strawberries and Cream' (p)	CGle CHal CSut CThr EBre EMFP GAri LBre MBel NHol NOrc NPin SBai SHay SMrm WPbr
strictus	
var. *brachyanthus*	See D. *minutiflorus*
§ *subacaulis*	EPot MBro NWCA
– var. *brachyanthus*	See D. *subacaulis*
suendermannii	See D. *petraeus*
* 'Sullom Voe'	NRoo
'Sunray' (b)	SHay
'Sunstar' (b)	SAll SHay
§ *superbus*	CHad CHal CPou GCra LWad MBel MTho WCla WOMN WPer WSun WWin
'Susan' (p)	EMFP IBar SAll
'Susannah' (p)	SAll
'Swanlake' (p)	EMFP SHay
'Swansdown' (p)	NNor
'Sway Belle' (p)	CThr MBel SBai
'Sway Candy' (p)	SBai
'Sway Gem' (p)	SBai
'Sway Mist' (p)	CSut SBai
'Sway Pearl' (p)	SBai
'Sweet Sue' (b)	SAll SHay
'Sweetheart Abbey' (p)	CCot CMil CThr EMFP ESis MPar NCra SChu SSvw WThu
sylvestris	EPot NNrd
'Tamsin Fifield' (b)	SBai
'Tangerine Sim' (pf)	SAll SHay
¶ 'Taunton' (p)	WPat
'Tayside Red' (m)	EMon SBor WMal
¶ 'Telstar' (pf)	SAll SHay
* *tenerifa*	MBri
'Terry Sutcliffe' (p)	MPar SSvw WMar WPer
'The Bloodie Pink'	See D. 'Caesar's Mantle'
'Thomas' (p)	CFis CGle EFou NVic SAll SChu WEas
'Thomas Lee' (b)	SAll
'Thora'	EPad WMal
¶ *tianschanicus*	NWCA
'Tiny Rubies'	See D. *gratianopolitanus* 'T. R.'
¶ 'Toledo' (p)	EMFP
'Tony Langford' (pf)	NPin SBai
¶ 'Torino' (pf)	SAll
'Tracy Barlow' (b)	SHay
'Treasure' (p)	SHay
¶ 'Trisha's Choice' (p)	EMFP
turkestanicus	NBir NRed NWCA
¶ – 'Patricia Bell'	SBla
'Uncle Teddy' (b)	SBai
¶ *uniflorus*	WDav
'Unique' (p)	SSvw WMar
'Ursula Le Grove' (p)	MPar SSvw WMar
'Valda Wyatt' (p)	CCla CGle CHal CSam CThr ELan EMFP GCHN LHop MBel NCra NHol NPin NRoo NSti SBai SChu SSvw WPbr
'Valencia' (pf)	SBai
'Valerie' (p)	SChu
'Vera Woodfield' (pf)	MWoo NPin SHay
'Victoria' (p)	ITim
'Violet Carson' (b)	SAll
'Violet Clove' (b)	SHay
¶ 'Visa' (pf)	SAll
'W A Musgrave' (p)	See D. 'Musgrave's Pink'
¶ 'W H Brooks' (b)	SAll
'Waithman Beauty' (p)	CCot CGle CNic CTom ECha EMNN ESis GAbr ITim MBar MHig MPar MPla NCra NNrd NRoo SAll SSvw WEas WHoo WMar WPat WPer
'Waithman's Jubilee' (p)	CCot CFis CRiv GCHN NCat NKay NNrd NSti WDav WPer
'Warden Hybrid' (p)	CRiv EMNN GAbr MHig NHol NRoo WAbe WDav
'Warrior' (b)	SAll SHay
'Weetwood Double' (p)	CNic WPer
'Welcome' (b)	SHay
'Wells-next-the-Sea' (p)	EOrc
weyrichii	ITim NMen SIng WAbe WOMN WPer
'Whatfield Anona' (p)	ECar ELan ESis LBee SAll SHer
'Whatfield Beauty'	EPot LBee
'Whatfield Brilliant'	LBee LRHS
¶ 'Whatfield Cyclops'	EPot SAll
¶ 'Whatfield Dorothy Mann' (p)	SAll
¶ 'Whatfield Fuchsia' (p)	SAll
'Whatfield Gem' (p)	CHal EBre ELan EMFP EPad ESis LBre MCas MPit NMen NNrd NRoo NRya SAll SGil SHer WPer WThu
'Whatfield Joy' (p)	CHal CLew EPot GAbr MCas NHol NMen NRoo NTow SAll SHer
'Whatfield Magenta' (p)	EPad ESis LBee LRHS SGil SHer WEas
'Whatfield Mini' (p)	LBee SAll WPer
¶ 'Whatfield Miss' (p)	SAll
¶ 'Whatfield Peach' (p)	SAll
¶ 'Whatfield Polly Anne' (p)	SAll
'Whatfield Pom Pom' (p)	SAll SMrm
'Whatfield Pretty Lady' (p)	EPot LBee SHer
¶ 'Whatfield Rose' (p)	ESis
'Whatfield Ruby' (p)	CHal EMFP ESis LBee LRHS NRoo SAll SHer
¶ 'Whatfield Supergem'	EPot
'Whatfield White' (p)	ELan EPad ESis LBee LRHS SHer
'Whatfield Wisp' (p)	CLew ELan EPad GAbr LHil MPit SHer WMar
'White Barn' (p)	ECha
'White Ladies' (p)	CMea CThr ELan ENot SSvw
¶ 'White Lighning' (pf)	SAll
'White Sim' (pf)	SAll SHay
'Whitecliff' (b)	SAll SHay
'Whitehills' (p)	CGle CShe EPot NKay NMen NRoo NWCA WThu WWin
'Widecombe Fair' (p)	CGle CHal CThr EBre LBre LHop MBel NCra NHol SPla
'William Brownhill' (p)	CMil EMFP SChu SSvw
'William Sim' (pf)	SHay
¶ 'Winnie Lesurf' (b)	MBel
'Winsome' (p)	SHay
'Woodfield's Jewel' (p)	MWoo
'Yellow Dusty Sim' (pf)	SHay
'Yorkshireman' (b)	SAll SHay
¶ 'Young Marie' (pf)	NPin
'Zebra' (b)	SAll SBai SHay

zederbaueri	SIng
¶ 'Zodiac' (pf)	SAll

DIAPENSIA (Diapensiaceae)
See Plant Deletions

DIARRHENA (Gramineae)

japonica	ETPC

DIASCIA (Scrophulariaceae)

anastrepta	CHan CMHG ESma GCal MCas MFir MPit SChu WEas WPer WRus
'Apricot'	CBrk ELan EOrc GCal SMrm WPbr
barberae	EBlo EBre ELan EMar ESis ESma GCal LBre LHop MUlv
¶ 'Blackthorn Apricot'	LBee LGre SBla SIng SWas
§ *cordata*	CGle CLew CMHG CShe ECha EMNN EMon EOrc ERav GDra IHos ITim MBal MPit MPla NHar NHol NMen NRar SFis SUsu WEas WHil WThu WWin
elegans	See D. ***vigilis***
felthamii	See D. ***fetcaniensis***
§ *fetcaniensis*	CBrk CFis CHan CMHG CMea CSam CSun EMon ESma GCal LBee LGre MBal MTho MUlv NPer SBla SBor SChu SCro SIgm WAbe WCru WEas WHal WHoo WOld WPer WWin
flanaganii	See D. ***stachyoïdes***
♦ 'Hector Harrison'	See D. 'Salmon Supreme'
¶ 'Hopley's Apricot'	CMGP CSev EFou LRHS NHol NPer NSti SHer
§ *integerrima*	Widely available
¶ – 'Harry Hay'	CGle
integrifolia	See D. ***integerrima***
'Jack Elliott'	ESma LHop MTho NBro NTow SMrm
'Katherine Sharman' (v)	EMon
'Lilac Belle'	ECtt ELan EPot ERav LHil SMrm SUsu WCru WPbr
lilacina	CHan CLew CMHG CSev CSpe ECtt EMar EMon EOrc ESis ESma GCal LGan NCat NPer SHer WEas WPer
* *linaria*	SFis
megathura	EMon
* *nastopsin*	CLew
patens	CBrk CDoC CSev EOrc ESis LHil LHop SAxl SMrm SWas WCru WPer
* *pentandra*	CBot
¶ 'Pink Queen'	SFis
¶ 'Pink Spot'	EPot
rigescens	Widely available
– 'Forge Cottage'	WPer
– x *lilacina*	NCat SIgm
'Ruby Field'	Widely available
– x *stachyoïdes*	SIgm
'Rupert Lambert'	EMar EMon ESma GCal NPer SChu SCro SMrm SUsu WCru WPer
§ 'Salmon Supreme'	CGle CHad EBlo ECtt ELan EOrc EPot ERav LGre LHil MTho SCro SMrm SUsu SWas WCru WPbr WRus
§ *stachyoïdes*	CFis CMHG CSun EBar EHal ELan ERav ESma LBlm LHop NPer SMrm WHCG WPer WRus
¶ 'Twinkle'	EPot
§ *vigilis*	Widely available

DIASCIA X LINARIA See NEMESIA *fruticans*

DICENTRA † (Papaveraceae)

'Adrian Bloom'	CDoC CSco EPot GCal MTho NCat NOak NSti SAxl SPla WCot WHoo WRus
'Adrian Bloom Variegated'	WCot
'Bacchanal'	CMHG CRow CTom CWit EBlo EBre ECar ECtt EPar EPla LBre LGre MBri MTho NBir NOak NRoo NSti SAxl SBla SChu SSpi SUsu WBon WCru WHCG WRus WSHC
'Boothman's Variety'	See D. ***formosa*** 'Stuart Boothman'
'Bountiful'	CBos CCla CGle CMHG CMil CRow CSco EGol EMar MBro MHig MTho NHar NNor NRoo NSti SChu SPer WHoo
'Brownie'	CWGN NCat SAxl SCro SMrm
canadensis	CRDP ECar EPot MTho NSal NSti
cucullaria	CBre CRDP CRow ECar ELun EPot GArf LGre MTho NHar NHol NNrd NSal NSti NTow SIng SWas WAbe WChr WCru WDav WHil
eximia hort.	See D. ***formosa***
¶ *eximia* (Ker-Gawler) Torrey	CRow NSti
♦– 'Alba'	See D. ***e.*** 'Snowdrift'
¶– 'Snowdrift'	CRow NSti SPou
§ *formosa*	Widely available
§ – *alba*	Widely available
– 'Furse's Form'	EBre LBre NSti
– ssp. *oregona*	CHan CRDP CRow CWGN EPar GCal MBal NCat NOak NSti SChu WAbb WAbe WByw WCru WHCG WWin
– 'Paramount'	NSti
§ – 'Stuart Boothman'	CAvo CCla CGle CHad CMea CSam CShe ECha EGol EPar LGre LHop MBri MFir MRav NBro NHar NHol NMen NNrd NOak NSti SChu SUsu WEas WKif WMar WOMN WRus
'Langtrees'	CBos CElw CHad CLew CMHG CMil CRow CWGN CWit ECha ELun EMar EOrc GCal LHil NSti SAxl SBla SChu SMad SUsu SWas WByw WCru WEas WMar WMer
'Luxuriant'	CB&S CCla CGle CRow CShe EBlo EBre ECtt EGol ELan ELun EOrc EPar EPla LBre LGan MBri NBar NHol NJap NKay NOak NRoo NSti SPer SSpi WAbe WEas WRus
macrantha	CGle CHan CRow ECha EPot LGre SSpi WCru
macrocapnos	CB&S COtt CRDP CRow EBre LBre MFir MTho NSti WCru WSHC
'Pearl Drops'	CBro CDec CRow EBre EGol ELan EOrc EPar LBre MBri MRav MSte NHar NOak NRoo SAxl SCro SPer WAbb WAbe WEas WHCG WHoo WMer WRus WSun WWin
§ *scandens*	CBot CHan CRow ELan MTho NBir NOak NSti SSpi SUsu WAbe WCru WHoo WSHC

'Silver Beads'	ECar SGil
'Snowflakes'	COtt EBlo EBre ELun GCHN LBre NRoo SPer
spectabilis	Widely available
– *alba*	Widely available
'Spring Morning'	CBos CElw CGle CMHG CRow ECha IBlr SChu SPer
¶ sp. CLD 685	WCru
♦ *thalictrifolia*	See D. ***scandens***

DICHELOSTEMMA (Liliaceae/Alliaceae)

congestum	CAvo ECro ETub
§ *ida-maia*	CMon ECro
multiflorum	ECro WChr
§ *pulchellum*	ECro WChr
volubile	ECro WChr

DICHORISANDRA (Commelinaceae)

¶ *thyrsiflora*	CTro

DICHROA (Hydrangeaceae)

febrifuga	CAbb CB&S CCla SSpi WCru
versicolor	CPle

DICKSONIA (Dicksoniaceae)

antarctica	CB&S CHEx CTre LPan MMea NPal SArc WRic
fibrosa	CB&S CHEx MMea SArc
squarrosa	CB&S CHEx MMea SArc WRic

DICLIPTERA (Acanthaceae)

§ *suberecta*	CBot CHal ERea LHop

DICOMA (Compositae)
See Plant Deletions

DICRANOSTIGMA (Papaveraceae)

lactucoïdes	WCru

DICTAMNUS (Rutaceae)

albus	CArn CBow CChu CCla CSco EBlo EBre ECha ECro EFou ELan EOrc GCal LBre LGan MBri MUlv NHol NSel NSti SBla SChu SFis SGil SPer SSpi WHoo WMer WRus WWye
§ – var. *purpureus*	Widely available
fraxinella	See D. ***albus purpureus***

DICTYOLIMON (Plumbaginaceae)

¶ *macrorrhabdos*	NTow NWCA

DICTYOSPERMA (Palmae)

album	MBri

DIDYMOCHLAENA (Dryopteridaceae)

lunulata	See D. ***truncatula***
§ *truncatula*	CHal MBri

DIDYMOSPERMA (Palmae)

caudatum	See ARENGA ***caudata***

DIEFFENBACHIA (Araceae)

'Camille' (v)	MBri
'Candida' (v)	MBri
'Compacta' (v)	MBri
'Jeanette' (v)	MBri
'Jupiter' (v)	MBri
'Mars' (v)	MBri
'Neptune' (v)	MBri
'Saturnus' (v)	MBri
'Schott Gitte' (v)	MBri
seguine 'Amoena' (v)	MBri
– 'Carina' (v)	MBri
– 'Katherine' (v)	MBri
– 'Tropic Snow' (v)	MBri
'Triumph' (v)	MBri
'Tropic Sun' (v)	MBri
'Tropic White' (v)	MBri
'Veerie' (v)	MBri

DIERAMA (Iridaceae)

cooperi	SSpi
§ *dracomontanum*	CBro CChu CCor CGle CHan CRDP CSun ECha ELan GAbr GArf GCal LGre LRHS NBir SBar SBla SChu SMrm SPer WOMN
– dwarf lilac	GCal
– dwarf pale pink	EPla GCal
– dwarf pink	GCal
♦ *ensifolium*	See D. ***pendulum***
¶ *igneum*	CSam
– CD&R 278	CHan
latifolium	GCal
* *ochroleucum*	CGle
pauciflorum	CHan LGre
§ *pendulum*	CKel CMGP EBre EFou ELan EPla LAbb LBre MBri MFir MPar NCat NHol SChu SMrm SPer WAbe WByw WRus
– var. *pumilum*	See D. ***dracomontanum***
'Puck'	GCal LRHS NCat
pulcherrimum	Widely available
– 'Blackbird'	CGle CRDP GAbr LRHS WDav
– dwarf forms	GCal
¶ – forms	IBlr
– 'Peregrine'	GAbr
– Slieve Donard hybrids	GCal LHop MUlv
robustum	CHan
¶ sp. SH 20	CHan
¶ sp. SH 49	CHan
¶ sp. SH 63	CHan
¶ sp. SH 85	CHan
'Titania'	LRHS MUlv NCat

DIERVILLA † (Caprifoliaceae)

lonicera	WWat
middendorffiana	See WEIGELA ***middendorffiana***
rivularis	CCor SLon
sessilifolia	CB&S CCla CHan CPle EBre EPar IOrc LBre MUlv SChu SLPl WBod WKif WRus WSHC WTyr WWin
x *splendens*	CBra CCla CDoC CMHG CPMA CPle EBar EBre ECha EHoe ELan EPla ERav GWht IJoh LBre MBar MPla MRav MUlv SEng SLPl SPer SSta WAbe WDin WStI

DIETES (Iridaceae)

§ *iridioïdes*	CGle WPer WThi

DIGITALIS † (Scrophulariaceae)

ambigua	See D. ***grandiflora***
apricot hybrids	See D. ***purpurea*** 'Sutton's Apricot'
ciliata	CHal ELan NOak
cream hybrids	EFou
davisiana	CChu ECro GAbr NOak SUsu WDav WHil WPer
dubia	CBot CMea ECro ECtt NBir SMrm
eriostachya	See D. ***lutea***
ferruginea	Widely available
– 'Gelber Herold'	LBlm LGre NHol WCra WDav
¶ ***fontanesii***	WHoo
¶ x ***fulva***	NBir
'Glory of Roundway'	CBot CHan
§ ***grandiflora***	Widely available
¶ – 'Dropmore Yellow'	SUsu
– 'Temple Bells'	EMar NHol WCla WHer WHoo WPer WSun
heywoodii	See D. ***purpurea heywoodii***
¶ ***kishinoskyi*** AGS 1273	EMon
kishinskyi	See D. ***parviflora***
laevigata	CAbb CBot CHal CHan CSam ECro EPad ESma GTou LGre MSte NHol SBla SIng WCHb WCra WDav WHer WPer
– ssp. ***graeca***	ECro GAbr
lamarckii hort.	See D. ***lanata***
§ ***lanata***	CAbb CBot CCla CGle CHad CHan CMea CMil CRDP CSam EBar EFou EGol GCal GPoy GTou LHol MBri NMir NSel SFis WEas WHen WHer WHil
– JCA 408.300	CChu
¶ – x ***grandiflora*** 'John Innes Tetra'	WPer
§ ***lutea***	Widely available
– Brickell's form	MSte
x ***mertonensis***	Widely available
obscura	CBot CChu EBar ECro ECtt ELan EPad LGan LGre LHop NOak SAxl SBla SMrm WHal WHil WPer
§ ***parviflora***	CBot CChu CCla CHan EBar ECha ECro EFol EFou EPad EPar ESis LGan MFir MWat NBro NOak NSti SMrm SSvw SUsu WDav WEas WHil WMer WPer
purpurea	CArn CBow CKin EBre EFou ENot GPoy LBre LHol MPit NBro NLan NMir NNor NSel SIde WCla WHal WHil WNdy WOak WPer WWye
– ***alba***	Widely available
– 'Chedglow'	CNat
– Excelsior Hybrids Group	CB&S CBow CKel CPar CSam CSco EBlo EBre LAbb LBre LWad MBri MWat NBar NFai NMir NNor SPer SSvw WHen
– Excelsior White Group	CKni
– Foxy Hybrids Group	CBow EBar NFai NRoo SRms WHen WPer
¶ – Giant Spotted Group	SSvw
– Glittering Prizes Group	CBow GCra
– Gloxiniiflora Group 'The Shirley'	ECtt EFou
§ – ssp. ***heywoodii***	CBot CSam ECro ELan LGre SFis WCHb WPer WRus WWin
– 'Isabelina'	SSvw
– ssp. ***mariana***	NHol WPer
– 'Sutton's Apricot'	CBot CBow CDoC CHad CHan CMil CSam EFou ELan EMon GAbr LWad NBir NRoo SGil SMrm SPer SSvw WCra WDav WHen WPer WRus
¶ ***sibirica***	ECro WHer WPer
thapsi	ECro ELan EPad SBla WPer
trojana	ECro ECtt EMar NRoo SFis SSvw SUsu WDav WHil WPer
viridiflora	CAbb CArn EBar ECro ECtt EGol EMar EPad ERav ESma GCra SFis SUsu WDav WHal WHer WHil WPer WWye

DIMORPHOTHECA (Compositae)

–	See also OSTEOSPERMUM

DIONAEA (Droseraceae)

muscipula	EFEx EPot MSte WHal WMEx

DIONYSIA (Primulaceae)

aretioïdes	EPot MCas NTow WThu
– 'Gravetye'	ECar NHar NWCA
– 'Phyllis Carter'	ECar EPot NHar NMen
involucrata	NTow NWCA WDav
tapetodes 'Peter Edwards' (Hewer 1164)	WThu

DIOÖN (Zamiaceae)

edule	LPal NPal
¶ ***mejiae***	LPal
spinulosum	LPal

DIOSCOREA (Dioscoreaceae)

japonica	SSpi
villosa	NSal

DIOSMA (Rutaceae)

ericoïdes	IHos LWad

DIOSPHAERA (Campanulaceae)

asperuloïdes	See TRACHELIUM ***asperuloïdes***

DIOSPYROS (Ebenaceae)

F ***kaki***	CB&S CBot CGre GWht SSpi
lotus	EArb EHal SSpi
F ***virginiana***	EArb LRHS SSpi WCoo

DIPCADI (Liliaceae/Hyacinthaceae)

¶ ***lividum*** SF 1	CMon
¶ ***serotinum*** MS 877	CMon

DIPELTA (Caprifoliaceae)

floribunda	SHil WBod
ventricosa	LRHS

DIPHYLLEIA (Berberidaceae)

cymosa	ECha NSal WCru

DIPIDAX See **ONIXOTIS**

DIPLACUS See **MIMULUS**

DIPLADENIA See **MANDEVILLA**

DIPLARRHENA (Iridaceae)

§ *latifolia*	SWas
moraea	CChu CDoC ECha ECou ECro GCal GGar GWht IBar IBlr ILis ITim LHil MHig MTho NHol NOrc SAxl SBla SSpi WAbe WHal WOld WWin
– *minor*	SWas
– West Coast form	See D. *latifolia*

DIPLAZIUM (Dryopteridaceae)

¶ *japonicum*	WRic

DIPLOTAXIS (Cruciferae)

¶ *tenuifolia*	WPer

DIPSACUS (Dipsacaceae)

§ *fullonum*	CArn CKin CSFH CWGN ECro EJud IEde LHol MChe NBro NLan NMir NSal SIde SSvw WByw WNdy WOak WPer WWye
– ssp. *fullonum*	EMon
inermis	CHan ECro
pilosus	CKin ECro
♦ *sylvestris*	See D. *fullonum*

DIPTERACANTHUS See **RUELLIA**

DIPTERONIA (Aceraceae)

sinensis	CB&S CCla CMCN CPle CSam EHar ELan MBri SSpi WCoo WNor

DISANTHUS (Hamamelidaceae)

cercidifolius	CAbP CCla CSco ELan LTil MBlu MBri MGos SBor SHil SPer SReu SSpi SSta WBod WSHC WWat

DISCARIA (Rhamnaceae)
See Plant Deletions

DISELMA (Cupressaceae)

archeri	CKen CNic LCon MBar

DISPOROPSIS (Liliaceae/Convallariaceae)

pernyi	CRDP SAxl SBla SGil SWas WCru

DISPORUM (Liliaceae/Convallariaceae)

flavens	EBlo EPar SWas
hookeri	ECar WCru
– var. *oreganum*	CBro CRow CTom IBlr LGre NHol NRya SBar
lanuginosum	CBro
maculatum	LGre
sessile	EPla
– 'Variegatum'	CBro CChu CHan CRDP CRow ECar ECha ELan EPar EPla ERav LGre SAxl SBla SGil SUsu SWas WCru WPbr
smithii	CHan EBul EPar EPot MPar NHar NRya NSal WCru
trachycarpum	EPla

DISTICTIS (Bignoniaceae)

buccinatoria	CPle CTro

DISTYLIUM (Hamamelidaceae)

racemosum	CB&S CShe CTre ELan SHBN SReu SSpi SSta WBod WSHC WWat
§ – *tutcheri*	CWit SSta

DIURANTHERA (Liliaceae/Anthericaceae)

major	See CHLOROPHYTUM *majus*

DIZYGOTHECA See **SCHEFFLERA**

DODECADENIA (Lauraceae)

¶ *grandiflora*	CTre

DODECATHEON † (Primulaceae)

alpinum	CLew CNic MPhe NHar NHol NRya WDav WThi
¶ – JCA 11744	SBla
¶ – JCA 9542	NHol
♦ *amethystinum*	See D. *pulchellum*
clevelandii	CBro GAbr NRed NTow SWas
– ssp. *insulare*	CNic LRHS NHol NWCA
– ssp. *patullum*	LRHS
conjugens	CNic NTow
cusickii	See D. *pulchellum cusickii*
dentatum	CBro CNic EPar LBee LGre MBal MBro MCas MPar MTho NMen NNrd NTow SBla SSou SWas WAbe WThi
– ssp. *dentatum*	NHol
– ssp. *ellisiae*	MBri MPhe NGre NRya
hendersonii	CBro EPar ESma MBal MPhe NHol NNrd SGil
§ *jeffreyi*	CRDP EPot MPhe NHar NMen NNrd NWCA SGil WAbe WCla
¶ – 'Rotlicht'	NHar WDav
* x *lemoinei*	EPot
meadia	Widely available
– f. *album*	CB&S CBre CBro CLew CPar ECha EFou ELan EOrc EPar GAbr GDra LAma MTho NHol NNrd NRed NRoo NRya SHer SPer SSou SUsu WCru WWat
– 'Alpenglow'	NHol
– 'Millard's Clone'	EPar NHol
¶ – 'Rose Farben'	NHol
pauciflorum	See D. *pulchellum*
poeticum	MBro NHar NTow WDav
§ *pulchellum*	CNic CRDP EPar EPot GDra LBee LRHS MBal MPhe NGre NHar NHol NKay NNrd NRed NRya SBla WAbe WDav WEas
¶ – JCA 9174	NHol
¶ – ssp. *cusickii*	NWCA
– ssp. *macrocarpum*	NNrd
– ssp. *pulchellum* 'Red Wings'	CNic CRDP EBre EPot GAbr GDra LBre MBro MCas NHol NNrd NTow WDav WHoo WRus
radicatum	See D. *pulchellum*
tetrandrum	See D. *jeffreyi*

DODONAEA (Sapindaceae)

humilis (f)	ECou
– (m)	ECou
viscosa	ECou IBlr
– ***angustifolia***	ISea
– 'Purpurea'	CB&S CGre CPle CSun ECou ERea ISea LBlm MUlv SDry

DOLICHOS (Leguminosae)

lablab	See LABLAB ***purpureus***

DOLICOTHRIX (Compositae)
See Plant Deletions

DOMBEYA (Sterculiaceae)

¶ ***burgessiae***	CTro

DONDIA See **HACQUETIA**

DOODIA (Blechnaceae)

caudata	NMar SUsu
media	MMea NMar WRic

DORONICUM † (Compositae)

austriacum	NCat
caucasicum	See D. ***orientale***
§ ***columnae***	CB&S COtt GDra NHol NNrd NOak
cordatum	See D. ***columnae***
'Finesse'	ESma NOak
'Frühlingspracht' ('Spring Beauty')	CKel CRDP CSam EBre ECtt ELan GDra LBre LWad NHar NHol SHer SPer SPla WEas WWin
'Harpur Crewe'	See D. ***plantagineum*** 'Excelsum'
'Miss Mason'	CDoC CSco CShe ENot MBri MUlv NBro
§ ***orientale***	CBow CBre EHal MBro NBar WByw WDav WHil
– 'Goldzwerg'	CMGP CSco EBre LBre
– 'Magnificum'	CBow CLew CPar EBlo EBre ESma LBre MFir MPit NMir NOak NRoo WHil WPer WWin
pardalianches	GCra WByw WCot
plantagineum	ELan
§ – 'Excelsum'	CGle CKel ECED EFou EMon MWat NKay SPer SPla WCot WEas
'Riedels Goldkranz'	MBri

DORYANTHES (Liliaceae/Doryanthaceae)

palmeri	CHEx

DORYCNIUM See **LOTUS**

DORYOPTERIS (Adiantaceae)

pedata	MBri

DOUGLASIA See **ANDROSACE**

DOXANTHA See **MACFADYENA**

DRABA (Cruciferae)

acaulis	WDav
aïzoïdes	CSam CShe EBre ECha ELan EPar GCHN GDra LBre MHig MPla MPlt NGre NHol NKay NMen NMir NWCA SIng WCla WHoo WWin
– 'Compacta'	ELan
aïzoön	See D. ***lasiocarpa***
Alaskan species	NTow
arabisans canadensis	NRed
§ ***aspera***	GDra GTou NHar NHol NNrd
athoa	WDav WMar
aurea var. ***leiocarpa***	NHol
* ***balcanica***	NHol
bertolonii	See D. ***aspera***
breweri	ITim NHol
bruniifolia	EBre LBre MHig MTho NHol NTow NWCA SSmi
– ssp. ***olympica***	MBro WDav
bryoïdes	See D. ***rigida b.***
cappadocica	WOMN
– JCA 419.500	CNic
compacta	NNrd NWCA
crassifolia	NHol
cretica	SPou
cuspidata	EPot
daurica	NNrd
dedeana	MBro MCas WPer WWin
– ssp. ***mawii***	NNrd
densifolia	NGre NHol NTow
dubia	NWCA
haynaldii	NMen WDav
hispanica	MBro NHol NWCA SIng
– ***brevistyla***	NRed NTow
– ***segurensis***	WDav
hoppeana	NWCA SIng
imbricata	See D. ***rigida imbricata***
incana	NWCA
incerta	CNic
kitadakensis	GCHN NHol WPer
§ ***lasiocarpa***	MBro MPit NHol NRoo NVic NWCA WHal
longisiliqua	MHig NTow NWCA WOMN
– EMR 2551	EPot
magellanica	GGar MDHE
mollissima	ECar EPot GTou LBee MHig NTow NWCA
§ ***norvegica***	CNic NWCA
oligosperma	EPot MBro NHol NTow NWCA SIng WDav WThu
oreades	CNic
parnassica	GCHN GTou NHar NRed WDav
paysonii	GArf NGre
¶ – var. ***treleasii***	WDav
polytricha	GDra GTou WDav
repens	See D. ***sibirica***
rigida	EPot GDra MBro MTho NHol NVic SIng SSmi
§ – var. ***bryoides***	GDra MBro NHar NHol NTow NWCA WDav WThu
§ – var. ***imbricata***	EPot GArf ITim MBro MFos NHar NHol SIng SSmi WDav WThu
– – f.***compacta***	EPot
rosularis	GDra MHig SIng
rupestris	See D. ***norvegica***
sakuraii	ESis GTou SIng
x ***salomonii***	EPot
sauteri	GCHN
scardica	See D. ***lasiocarpa***

sp. AGS/J 214 NHol
sp. CLD 348 NHol
¶ sp. JJH 171 WDav
stylaris MBro MHig WPat WWin
ussuriensis NHol WPer
ventosa NGre NTow SIng WDav

DRACAENA (Dracaenaceae)

cincta 'Tricolor' (v) CHal MBri
congesta See CORDYLINE ***stricta***
deremensis MBri
– 'Compacta Purpurea' MBri
– 'Compacta Variegata' MBri
– 'Janet Craig' (v) MBri
– 'Lemon and Lime' (v) MBri
– 'Warneckei' (v) MBri
– 'Yellow Stripe' (v) MBri
fragrans MBri
*– ***glauca*** MBri
– 'Massangeana' (v) MBri
indivisa See CORDYLINE ***i.***
marginata (v) MBri
– 'Colorama' (v) MBri
sanderiana (v) MBri
****schrijveriana*** MBri
steudneri MBri
stricta See CORDYLINE ***s.***
surculosa 'Wit' (v) MBri
surculosa surculosa 'Florida Beauty' (v) MBri

DRACOCEPHALUM (Labiatae)

♦***altaiense*** See D. ***imberbe***
argunense LBee LGre LRHS MHig SCro SWas WPer WWin
botryoïdes CNic NTow NWCA
bullatum EHal NSti
calophyllum var. ***smithianum*** NGre WDav
forrestii EPot ESis SIng
grandiflorum MHig SPou
¶ ***hemsleyanum*** SIng
mairei See D. ***renatii***
moldavicum NSal WWye
♦***prattii*** See NEPETA ***p.***
§ ***renatii*** MHew NSal WPer
ruyschianum ELan EMon ESis LGan MBro MTol NOak NSti NWCA WHoo WPer
sibiricum See NEPETA ***sibirica***
virginicum See PHYSOSTEGIA ***virginiana***

DRACOPHYLLUM (Epacridaceae)

See Plant Deletions

DRACUNCULUS (Araceae)

canariensis EMon GCra
¶ – MS 934 CMon
§ ***vulgaris*** CGle CHEx CRDP CWit EMon EPar SMad SSpi WCru WHal
¶ – MS 790 CMon

DRAPETES (Thymelaeaceae)

dieffenbachii GArf GDra
lyallii GDra NHar

DREGEA (Asclepiadaceae)

§ ***sinensis*** CBot CChu CGre CMac CSam CTro ELan ERav ERea MNew SHBN SHil SSpi WSHC WWat
¶ – 'Variegata' CTro

DREPANOSTACHYUM (Gramineae(Bambuseae))

§ 'Damarapa' EPla ISta LBam SArc SBam SCob WJun
§ ***falcatum*** WJun
falconeri hort. See HIMALAYACALAMUS ***falconeri*** 'Damarapa'
¶ ***hookerianum*** WJun
¶ ***khasianum*** ISta
****microphyllum*** WJun

DRIMIOPSIS (Liliaceae/Hyacinthaceae)

¶ ***maculata*** CMon

DRIMYS (Winteraceae)

♦***aromatica*** See D. ***lanceolata***
colorata See PSEUDOWINTERA ***c.***
§ ***lanceolata*** CAbb CCla CGre CMHG CPle CTrw ECou ELan GCal GWht IDai ISea MBal SBor SDry SPer SSta WAbe WBod WCru WSHC WWat
– (f) CTre
– (m) CTre
winteri CAbb CB&S CBow CBra CCla CDoC CGre CHEx CMHG CPle CTre CTrw GWht IDai IOrc ISea MUlv SArc SHBN SHil SPer SReu SSpi WDin WSHC
– var. ***andina*** CMHG CSam GGGa
§ – var. ***chilensis*** CB&S CHEx CLan ISea MBal WBod
– 'Glauca' ISea
– Latifolia Group See D. ***w. chilensis***
– ***punctata*** See D. ***w. winteri***

DROSANTHEMUM (Aizoaceae)

floribundum CHEx WEas
hispidum CHEx CRiv EBre ELan EPot LBre LHop MHig MTho NGre NMen NNrd NTow NWCA SBod SHer SIng WPat

DROSERA (Droseraceae)

¶ ***adelae*** WMEx
aliciae WHal WMEx
¶ ***andersoniana*** EFEx
anglica WMEx
¶ 'Beermullah' WMEx
§ ***binata*** EPot MSte WHal WMEx
– 'Extremis' WHal
– 'Multifida' EPot WHal WMEx
¶ ***browiana*** EFEx
¶ ***bulbosa bulbosa*** EFEx
¶ – ***major*** EFEx
burmannii WMEx
'Californian Sunset' WMEx
capensis EPot MSte WHal WMEx
– ***alba*** WHal WMEx
– narrow leaf form WMEx
capillaris WMEx
cuneifolia WMEx

♦*dichotoma*	See D. *binata*
dielsiana	WMEx
¶ *erythrorrhiza collina*	EFEx
¶ – *imbecilia*	EFEx
¶ – *magna*	EFEx
¶ – *squamosa*	EFEx
filiformis ssp. *filiformis*	WHal WMEx
– ssp. *tracyi*	WMEx
¶ *gigantea*	EFEx
¶ *graniticola*	EFEx
hamiltonii	WMEx
¶ *heloïdes*	WHil
indica	WMEx
intermedia	WMEx
– x *rotundifolia*	WMEx
'Lake Badgebup'	WMEx
¶ *leucoblasta*	WMEx
¶ *loureirii*	EFEx
¶ *lovelliae*	WMEx
¶ *macrantha eremaea*	EFEx
¶ *macrophylla*	EFEx
¶ – *marchantii*	EFEx
¶ – *monantha*	EFEx
¶ – *prophylla*	EFEx
'Marston Dragon'	WMEx
¶ *menziesii basifolia*	EFEx
¶ – ssp. *menziesii*	EFEx
'Nagamoto'	WMEx
natalensis	WMEx
nitidula	WMEx
x *obovata*	WMEx
¶ *orbiculata*	EFEx
¶ *paleacea*	WHil
¶ *platypoda*	EFEx
¶ *prostratoscaposa*	EFEx
pulchella	WHal WMEx
– giant form	WMEx
pygmaea	WMEx
¶ *radicans*	EFEx
¶ *ramellosa*	EFEx
¶ *rosulata*	EFEx
rotundifolia	CRDP WHal WMEx
¶ *salina*	EFEx
scorpioïdes	WMEx
slackii	MSte WMEx
spathulata	WHal WMEx
– Kansai form	WMEx
– Kanto form	WMEx
¶ *stolonifera* ssp. *compacta*	EFEx
¶ – ssp. *humilis*	EFEx
¶ – *porrecta*	EFEx
¶ – ssp. *rupicola*	EFEx
¶ – ssp. *stolonifera*	EFEx
¶ *strictcaulis*	EFEx
¶ *subhirtella subhirtella*	EFEx
¶ *tubaestylus*	EFEx
*x *wateri*	WMEx
¶ *whittakeri*	EFEx

DRYANDRA (Proteaceae)

formosa	CSun
obtusa	CSun
praemorsa	CSun
pteridifolia	CSun

DRYAS (Rosaceae)

drummondii	NBir NHol WAbe
– 'Grandiflora'	EPot GDra WThu
§ *integrifolia*	CLew GDra MBro NHar NHol NRoo SIng WAbe WWin
octopetala	CGle CPar CSam ECha EFol ELan GDra IDai LHop MBal MBro MHig MWat NGre NHar NHol NKay NNor NNrd SBla SIng SLon WAbe WDav WEas WHil WHoo WOld WWin
– 'Minor'	CNic LBee MBro MHig NMen SWas WAbe WDav WHoo WPat
x *suendermannii*	CPar EBre ELan GAri GCal LBre MBal NHol NKay NRoo NWCA WAbe WEas WHoo WPat
tenella	See D. *integrifolia*

DRYOPTERIS † (Dryopteridaceae)

§ *affinis*	CRow ECha EFou EPar GGar LWad MBal NHol NKay NMar WFib
– 'Congesta Cristata'	EBre LBre NHar NHol
§ – 'Crispa Congesta'	CDoC CMil CPMA ELan NBir NKay SMrm SPla SRms
¶ – 'Crispa Cristata'	WRic
– Crispa Group	IOrc NKay SCob
– 'Cristata Angustata'	ELan IOrc NHol NKay NMar SRms WFib WRic
– 'Cristata Grandiceps Askew'	NKay NMar SMad WFib
– Cristata Group	CRow NMar SIng SMad SPla WFib WHer
– 'Cristata Ramosissima Wright'	NKay
– 'Cristata The King'	CBar CDoC CHal CRDP EBre EGol ELan IOrc LBre MBri NBro NCat NHol NMar NOrc SApp SCob SRms
– 'Pinderi'	EFou ELan
N– *polydactyla*	NMar
– 'Stableri'	NMar
atrata hort.	See D. *cycadina*
austriaca hort.	See D. *dilatata*
borreri	See D. *affinis*
carthusiana	NMar WRic
¶ x *complexa* 'Stablerae'	WRic
¶ *crassirhizoma*	WRic
§ *cycadina*	CRDP CWGN EFou ELan IOrc MBri NHol NMar SApp SMad SSpi WFib WWat
§ *dilatata*	CBar CKin CMGP CTom ECha ELan MBal NHol NKay NLan NMar SCob SIng WFib WRic
– 'Crispa'	NKay
– 'Crispa Whiteside'	ELan NHol SAxl SMad SMrm
– 'Grandiceps'	CRDP CRow NHol NNrd WFib
– 'Lepidota Cristata'	CHal CMil CRDP CWGN IOrc NHol NMar SCob SPer SRms WFib WRic
– 'Lepidota Grandiceps'	NMar
erythrosora	CBar CPMA CPar CRDP CWGN EBre EGol ELan LBre MBri MRav NEgg NHar NHol NMar SBla SCob SIng SMad SPer SPla SSpi WFib WHal WRic WWat
– *prolifera*	CMil CRDP NBir NHar NHol
filix-mas	CBar CKin CPar CRow CTom CWGN EBre ECha EFou EHon ELan IOrc LBre LHol MBal MBri MSta NHol NKay NLan NMar NOrc SCob SPer SPla SSpi SWat WFib WRic WWye

– 'Barnesii'	NMar WRic
– 'Crispa'	EHon NHol SCob WFib
– 'Crispa Congesta'	See D. *affinis* 'C. C.'
– 'Crispa Cristata'	CBar CMil CRDP EBre EGol ELan LBre MBri NBar NHol NMar SMad SPer SPla SWat WFib
– Cristata Group	NMar SCob WFib WRic
– Cristata Group 'Fred Jackson'	NHol WFib
– 'Cristata Martindale'	CRDP CRow NHol NKay NMar SApp SRms WFib
¶ – 'Decomposita'	WRic
– 'Depauperata'	CRDP WFib
* – ***fluctuosa***	NKay SRms
– Grandiceps Group	CBar
– 'Grandiceps Wills'	NHol NMar SApp WFib WRic
– 'Linearis'	CBar EBre EHon ELan IOrc LBre MBri SCob SRms
– 'Linearis Congesta'	NKay
– 'Linearis Cristata'	EBre LBre NKay NMar SApp WRic
– 'Linearis Polydactyla'	NMar SMad
– 'Mapplebeck'	CRDP CRow NHol SApp WFib WRic
– 'Multicristata'	NMar
– 'Polydactyla Dadds'	IOrc WFib
– Polydactyla Group	NKay NMar WFib
¶ ***fuscipes***	SBla
goldieana	NMar
hirtipes	See D. ***cycadina***
¶ ***lepidopoda***	WRic
marginalis	NKay NMar SCob
pseudomas	See D. ***affinis***
¶ × ***remota***	SRms
shiroumensis	NMar
sieboldii	CBar
¶ ***stewartii***	WRic
¶ ***sublacera***	WRic
× ***tavelii***	IOrc WFib
¶ × ***uliginosa***	WRic
wallichiana	CBar CKni ECha EFou EHal MBri NMar SApp SBla SCob SSpi WFib WHal WRic

DRYPIS (Caryophyllaceae)

See Plant Deletions

DUCHESNEA (Rosaceae)

chrysantha	See D. ***indica***
§ ***indica***	CCor CFis CHal CLew CTom ECro IBar IBlr MPar NSti
§ – 'Harlequin' (v)	CHal EFol EMon EPla MPar MTho NSti
– 'Variegata'	See D. *i.* 'Harlequin.

DUDLEYA (Crassulaceae)

¶ ***cymosa***	WDav
– JCA 11777	CNic
farinosa	CHEx IBlr

DUMORTIERA (liverwort)

¶ ***hirsuta***	LFle

DUNALIA (Solanaceae)

§ ***australis***	CGre CHan CTro EMon
– blue	CSun
– white	CBot CSun

DURANTA (Verbenaceae)

§ ***erecta***	CPle CTro SLMG
plumieri	See D. ***erecta***
repens	See D. ***erecta***

EBENUS (Leguminosae)

cretica	LGre SIgm WOMN

ECBALLIUM (Curcurbitaceae)

elaterium	MHew NSal WHer

ECCREMOCARPUS (Bignoniaceae)

¶ ***ruber***	SUsu
scaber	CB&S CGle CGre CMea CNic CPar CPle CSev ELan ENot EOrc GAbr GCHN IMal MBal MBri NBar NBro NPer SLon SPer SUsu WCru WHal WHoo WWye
– ***aurantiacus***	CB&S CMHG CSam LHop NPer NTow
– ***coccineus***	CB&S CHan CMHG CSam EBar GCHN WOMN WSHC
– ***roseus***	CB&S CBot CGle CSam ELan WWin

ECHEVERIA † (Crassulaceae)

affinis	MBri
agavoïdes	MRav
– 'Metallica'	MBri WEas
* 'Black Knight'	SLMG
derenbergii	CHEx SLMG
* 'Duchess of Nuremberg'	SLMG
elegans	CHEx MBri
harmsii	WEas
'Imbricata'	CHEx
'Paul Bunyon'	CHal
pulvinata	CHal
secunda var. ***glauca***	ESma IBlr NBir SLMG
setosa	CHEx SLMG WEas
¶ 'Warfield Wonder'	WEas

ECHINACEA (Compositae)

angustifolia	CArn GPoy MHew NSal WDav WWye
pallida	CCMG ESma LGan NSal SMad
paradoxa	NSal
§ ***purpurea***	Widely available
– Bressingham hybrids	EBlo EBre ELan LBre SPer
– dark stemmed form	EFou
¶ – 'Leuchtstern'	SPla SSvw
– 'Magnus'	CSco EBre ESma LAbb LBre LGre LHil LWad MBel MUlv NRoo SFis SMad SSvw WHen WPer
– 'Robert Bloom'	CShe EBlo ECED LHop MUlv
– 'White Lustre'	CSco EBlo EBre ECha EGol LBre MBri MRav MUlv SPer SPla WCot WMer
– 'White Swan'	Widely available
* ***simulata***	NSal

ECHINOPS (Compositae)

♦ ***albus***	See E. 'Nivalis'
§ ***bannaticus*** 'Blue Globe'	CHan CSco GCal NRoo
– 'Taplow Blue'	CHad CHan CKel CSco EBlo EBre ECro ELan GCal IDai LBre LHop MUlv NHol NKay NOrc NPer NSti SGil SPer SPla

exaltatus	NBir
giganteus	LWad
humilis	EMon
microcephalus	EMon
§ 'Nivalis'	CBre CCla CHan ECro EFou ELan EPla GCal NSti SGil SPer
* *perringii*	GCal
ritro hort.	See E. ***bannaticus***
– Linnaeus	CB&S CHan CMea CPar CRow EBar ECha ECtt EGol ELan ENot GCHN MWat NBar NBee NBro NKay NMir NNor NRoo SPer SSvw SUsu WEas WHil WOak WPer WWin
– ACL 149/75	EMon
– 'Blue Ball'	See E. ***bannaticus*** 'Blue Globe'
¶ – ssp. ***ruthenicus***	EMon
– 'Veitch's Blue'	CCla CDoC CHad CMGP CSco EMon GCal LWad MBri NCat SGil SHer
sphaerocephalus	CHan ECro ELan EMon GCra IBlr MUlv WByw

ECHINOSPARTUM See GENISTA

ECHIUM (Boraginaceae)

§ *candicans*	CAbb CB&S CHEx SArc WHal
♦ *fastuosum*	See E. ***candicans***
§ *pininana*	CGre CHEx CHan CTre IMal ISea LWad SArc WAbe
– x *wildpretii*	MSte SMrm
pinnifolium	See E. ***pininana***
x *scilloniense*	CAbb
vulgare	CArn CKin CRDP GPoy LHol MChe MHew NMir NSal SFis SIde WHer WNdy WWye
webbii	CAbb CGre
wildpretii	CBot CHEx LHol SArc WHal

EDGEWORTHIA (Thymelaeaceae)

§ *chrysantha*	CB&S
papyrifera	See E. ***chrysantha***

EDRAIANTHUS (Campanulaceae)

dalmaticus	SBla
dinaricus	MCas NHol
graminifolius	EBur ECtt EPad GDra NHol NKay NWCA SBar SSou SSvw WCru WDav WHil WPat WPer WWin
– *albus*	See E. ***g. niveus***
§ – ssp. ***niveus***	NKay
§ *pumilio*	CLew EPad MPit NGre NHar NHol NKay NMen SBla WCru WDav WOMN
serpyllifolius	CLew EPot
– 'Major'	EPot
tenuifolius	MPlt NHol

EGERIA (Hydrocharitaceae)

¶ *densa*	SAWi

EHRETIA (Boraginaceae)

§ *acuminata*	CGre
♦ *ovalifolia*	See E. ***acuminata***
thyrsiflora	See E. ***acuminata***

EICHHORNIA (Pontederiaceae)

crassipes	CBen CHEx CWGN EMFW EWav LMay MSta WHol
¶ – 'Major'	SAWi

ELAEAGNUS † (Elaeagnaceae)

angustifolia	CB&S CBot CCla CPle EHar ESim LAbb MRav NTow SHBN SPer SSpi SSta WCoo WDin WEas WWat
♦ – Caspica Group	See E. 'Quicksilver'
argentea	See E. ***commutata***
§ *commutata*	CB&S CBot CBow CCor CDoC CPle EGol EHoe ELan ENot EPar IOrc LHop NNor NRoo NTow SHil SLPl SPer SSpi WDin WHCG WRus WStI WWat
x *ebbingei*	Widely available
I – 'Aurea'	LPan
– 'Coastal Gold'	CDoC ENot MGos MUlv
– 'Gilt Edge' (v)	Widely available
– 'Limelight' (v)	CB&S CBra CPle CSco CShe EBre EGol EHar ELan ENot ERav IJoh IOrc LBre LHop LNet MBal MBri MGos MPla SHBN SLon SPer SPla SSpi SSta WDin WPat WWat
– 'Salcombe Seedling'	EGol LHop MBri MUlv
¶ – 'Southern Seedling'	CHEx
glabra 'Reflexa'	See E. x ***reflexa***
macrophylla	CChu CCla CLan CSam ENot NNor SDry SHil
multiflora	CChu CCla MBlu SPer SSpi
– 'Gigantea'	ELan
parvifolia	CChu CCla EGol ENot EPla
pungens	
'Argenteovariegata'	See E. ***p.*** 'Variegata'
– 'Aureovariegata'	See E. ***p.*** 'Maculata'
– 'Dicksonii' (v)	CB&S CDoC CLan CSco EHar IDai LNet SLon SPer SPla SSpi
– 'Frederici' (v)	CB&S CDoC CLan CMHG EBre EHar EHoe ELan EPla ERav LBre MBal MBri MPla MSta SCob SGil SHBN SHer SPer SSpi WPat WWat
– 'Goldrim' (v)	CKni CSam EPla IJoh MBri MGos SCob SHBN SHil WDin
§ – 'Maculata' (v)	Widely available
§ – 'Variegata'	CB&S CCla CDoC CLan CSco EFol EGol IOrc MBal MBri NBir SCob SHBN SPer WAbe
§ 'Quicksilver'	CChu CHad CPMA ECha EGol EHar ELan LGre SBla SPla SSta SUsu WHCG WSHC WWat
§ x ***reflexa***	CB&S CChu WWat
umbellata	CCla CPle MBlu SPer WCoo WHCG WWat

ELAEOCARPUS (Elaeocarpaceae)

See Plant Deletions

ELATOSTEMA (Urticaceae)

♦ *daveauana*	See E. ***repens***
pulchra	CHal MBri
§ *repens*	CHal

ELDERBERRY See SAMBUCUS *nigra*

ELEOCHARIS (Cyperaceae)

acicularis	CBen ELan EMFW NDea WChe

palustris	EMFW MSta

ELETTARIA (Zingiberaceae)

cardamomum	CSun LBlm MBri

ELEUTHEROCOCCUS (Araliaceae)

pictus	See KALOPANAX ***septemlobus***
senticosus	GPoy NSal
♦*septemlobus*	See KALOPANAX ***s.***
§ *sieboldianus*	CB&S
§ – 'Variegatus'	CB&S CBot CCla CHan CRow EFol ELan IOrc LHop MBlu MGos SChu WSHC

ELINGAMITA (Myrsinaceae)

johnsonii	CHEx

ELISENA (Liliaceae/Amaryllidaceae)

longipetala	See HYMENOCALLIS ***l.***

ELLIOTTIA (Ericaceae)

♦*bracteata*	See TRIPETALEIA ***b.***
**pyroliflora*	ECar

ELMERA (Saxifragaceae)

racemosa	EPot MFir NHol WPer

ELODEA (Hydrocharitaceae)

¶ *callitrichoïdes*	SAWi
canadensis	EHon EMFW SAWi SWat WChe WHol
crispa	See LAGAROSIPHON ***major***
♦*densa*	See EGERIA ***d.***

ELSHOLTZIA (Labiatae)

fruticosa	CArn WWye
stauntonii	CArn CB&S CBot CBow CChu CCla CDoC CPle ECha ENot LWad SFis SHil WPat WSHC WWye
– 'Alba'	CBot

ELYMUS (Gramineae)

arenarius	See LEYMUS ***a.***
canadensis	EHoe ETPC
giganteus	See LEYMUS ***racemosus***
glaucus hort.	See E. ***hispidus***
§ *hispidus*	CHan EHoe EPla LHil LHop MBri MUlv SApp SBla SPer SSpi SUsu
N *magellanicus*	CChu CElw CHad CRDP CRow CSam CTom EFol EHoe ELan EOrc ERav GCHN GCal IBar MFir MNFA NCat NFai NMir NSti SAxl SSpi WDav WEas WPer
§ *scabrus*	EMon EPla ETPC

ELYTROPUS (Apocynaceae)

chilensis	CGre

EMBOTHRIUM † (Proteaceae)

coccineum	CB&S CBow CBra CCla CGre CHEx CLan CSco ELan IDai IOrc MBal SBor SDry SHil SReu WNor
– Lanceolatum Group	CBra CCla CDec CGre CMHG CSam ELan IJoh ISea MBal MUlv SArc SHBN SPer SSta
¶ – Lanceolatum Group 'Inca Flame'	CPMA CSco
– Lanceolatum Group 'Norquinco Form'	CAbb CB&S CCla CDoC ELan IOrc MBal MBri SSpi WBod WWat
– Longifolium Group	CB&S CBra CDoC CMHG CTrw CWSG IBlr IJoh IOrc ISea SPer

EMILIA (Compositae)

§ *coccinea*	EMon
♦*javanica* hort.	See E. ***coccinea***

EMINIUM (Araceae)

albertii	LAma WChr
lehmannii	EPot WChr
rauwolffii	LAma WChr

EMMENOPTERYS (Rubiaceae)

henryi	CBrd

EMPETRUM (Empetraceae)

luteum	MBar
nigrum	ECar GAri GPoy MBal MBar MGos NLan WDav
– var. *japonicum*	GDra
– 'Lucia'	ECar MGos NHol
rubrum	ECar GArf WDav
¶ – 'Tomentosum'	WThu

ENCEPHALARTOS (Zamiaceae)

lebomboensis	LPal
natalensis	LPal

ENDYMION See HYACINTHOIDES

ENGELMANNIA (Compositae)

See Plant Deletions

ENKIANTHUS † (Ericaceae)

campanulatus	Widely available
– f. *albiflorus*	CCla CFis CWSG ELan GGGa MBal SPer SSpi WBod WWeb
¶ – Nymans form	MAsh
– var. *palibinii*	CGre GAri GGGa MBal MBri MGos SSpi WPat
– 'Red Bells'	CCla LTil SSpi
– *sikokianus*	GAri GGGa
¶ *cernuus matsudae*	GAri
– f. *rubens*	CB&S CCla CDoC CGre CPMA GAri GGGa MAsh MBal MBri NTow SHil SPer SSpi SSta WDin WSHC WWat
chinensis	CB&S CCla CGre CPMA EBre ELan GAri GCHN GGGa LBre MAsh MBar SPer SReu SSpi WWat
deflexus	CCla CKni LTil SSpi
perulatus	CB&S CBra CMHG CWSG GAri MBar SSpi SSta WBod
tectus	WBod

ENSETE (Musaceae)

§ *ventricosum*	CBot CHEx CTro LPal SArc

ENTELEA (Tiliaceae)

arborescens	CHEx ECou

EOMECON (Papaveraceae)

chionantha	CBot CElw CHEx CHan CPar CRDP CSam EBre ECha ELan EMon EPar EPot GCal IBlr LBre MTho MUlv NGre NSti SApp SAxl SFar WAbe WCot WCru WHal WWye

EPACRIS (Epacridaceae)

¶ *impressa*	ECar

EPHEDRA (Ephedraceae)

distachya	GPoy NFai NNor
fragilis	EPla SDry
gerardiana	CNic NHex SBor
– var. *sikkimensis*	ECar EPla SDry WBod
§ *major*	SDry
minima	WThu
nebrodensis	See E. ***major***
nevadensis	NSal
viridis	NSal

EPIDENDRUM (Orchidaceae)

* *crinatum*	SLMG
¶ *ibaguense*	CTro
♦ *radicans*	See E. ***ibaguense***

EPIGAEA (Ericaceae)

¶ *asiatica*	MBal
gaultherioïdes	GGGa MBal
¶ *repens*	MBal

EPILOBIUM (Onagraceae)

§ *angustifolium*	CGle CKin CRDP NNrd
§ – *album*	CBot CBre CElw CHan CMea ECha EPot GCal MBri MFir NCat SAxl SUsu WCla WHal WPer WRus WSHC WWat
♦ – *leucanthum*	See E. ***a. album***
– 'Stahl Rose'	EMon WCot
californicum	See EPILOBIUM ***canum***
– 'Glasnevin'	See EPILOBIUM ***canum*** 'Dublin'
– ssp. *latifolia*	See EPILOBIUM ***canum latifolium***
– ssp. *mexicana*	See EPILOBIUM ***canum mexicanum***
§ *canum*	CHal CHan CNic CSam ECha ELan EPla IOrc LAbb LGan MCas MPla NKay SChu SIgm SIng SUsu WCru WEas WPer WThu
– ssp. *angustifolium* 'Albiflorum'	CBot CSpe LHop MSte WCru WOMN WPer
§ – – 'Dublin'	Widely available
– – 'Sir Cedric Morris'	ELan EMon LHop
§ – ssp. *latifolium*	CCla CPle EMon ESis MPlt NMen
§ – ssp. *mexicanum*	CPar SRms WCru WOMN
¶ – 'Olbrich Silver'	SBla WCru
– 'Solidarity Pink'	CBrk CRDP CSpe ELan LGre LHop LRHS MTho SChu SIng SUsu
– *villosum*	LBee
¶ – 'Western Hills'	SBla WCru
¶ *caucasicum*	WDav
§ *chlorifolium*	CLew CTom ELan
– var. *kaikourense*	See E. ***c.***
crassum	CLew CNic EBar MPlt NGre NMen NTow SIng WCla WWin
§ *dodonaei*	CGle CLew ECro EOrc LGan MFir MTho NCat WCot WSHC WWin
fleischeri	CRDP LGre MTho SUsu SWas WCru WPat WSHC
¶ *garretiae*	NTow
glabellum	CGle CLew CMea CShe CSpe ECha ELan EMon EOrc LGre LHop NBir NMen SAxl SPer SUsu WAbe WEas WHil WOMN WPat WRus WWat WWin
– 'Sulphureum'	CNic EMar GTou NCat SUsu WBon WWin
hirsutum	CKin WCla
luteum	WCla
microphyllum	See EPILOBIUM ***canum***
montanum	CKin
obcordatum	CNic ELan NNrd SRms
rosmarinifolium	See E. ***dodonaei***
¶ *rostratum*	NGre
* *spathulifolium*	SSou
villosum	See EPILOBIUM ***canum mexicanum***
♦ *wilsonii*	See E. ***chlorifolium***

EPIMEDIUM † (Berberidaceae)

acuminatum L 575	CChu SBla SSpi SWas
alpinum	CMGP COtt CPar EPar MBal NGre NHol NJap SAxl SHig SPer WCru WPbr WRus
x *cantabrigiense*	CBro CCla CTom EBre ECtt ELun EOrc EPla GCHN GDra LBre MBal MBri NHol SPer SUsu WAbb WCru WPbr
davidii	ECar SWas
– EMR 4125	SBla
diphyllum	CChu LGre SBla SWas
¶ *dolichostemon*	SWas
¶ 'Enchantress'	SWas
§ *grandiflorum*	CHan CTom ECar ECha ELan EPar GDra MBal MBri NBir NMen SBla SPer SWas WCru WPbr WRus
– 'Album'	EPot
– 'Crimson Beauty'	CBos CChu LGre SBla SWas
– ssp. *koreanum*	LGre SBla
– lilac seedling	CBos SAxl SBla SWas
¶ – 'Lilofee'	SWas
– 'Nanum'	CChu CRDP ECar LGre NTow SBla SSou SWas WAbe WCru
– 'Rose Queen'	CBos CBro CCla CMil EPla GGar LGre NOak NRoo SBla SChu SHer SPla SWas WAbe
§ – 'Roseum'	EBre LBre NKay NTow
¶ – 'Shikinomai'	SWas
– f. *violaceum*	LGre
– 'White Queen'	ECha NOak SAxl SBla SWas
leptorrhizum	SWas
macranthum	See E. ***grandiflorum***
x *perralchicum*	CRDP MBal MBel MFir SChu SIng SPer WSHC
– 'Frohnleiten'	CBro CSco CTom EBlo EBre ECha ECtt ELun EOrc EPla EPot ERav GCHN LBre MBri MRav MSte MTol MUlv NBar NRoo SBla SMad SPer SUsu WAbb WCra WPbr

- 'Wisley' MUlv SBla
perralderianum CChu CCla CSam CWGN EBre EFou ELan ELun EPar EPot LBre LGro MBal MRav SAxl SBla SHig SSpi WAbe WCru WWin
pinnatum CChu CLew CMea MSta WHal
§ – ssp. ***colchicum*** CCla CKel CRDP CSco EBlo ELan ELun EPar EPot ERav MBal MBro NHol NKay NRoo NRya SDix SHig SPer SSpi WHoo WRus
– ***elegans*** See E. ***p. colchicum***
pubigerum ECha EPla MBal
x ***rubrum*** Widely available
setosum CChu ECar SBla SWas
x ***versicolor*** MBal
– 'Cupreum' SBla SSpi SWas
– 'Neosulphureum' CBro MTol SSpi
– 'Sulphureum' CB&S CBos CChu CCla CElw CSco CShe EBre ECha EOrc EPar EPot LBre MBri MFir MHig MMil NJap NRoo NSti SBla SChu SPer SUsu WAbe WDav WPbr WWin
– 'Versicolor' LGre
x ***warleyense*** CBos CBro CChu CElw CMea CRDP CSco ECha EFou ELan EPla EPot GCHN LGan LGre MBal SAxl SBla SFis SWas WRus WWin
– 'Orangekönigin' SWas
x ***youngianum*** CB&S EPot SBla SMrm
– 'Lilacinum' See E. x ***y.*** 'Roseum'
– 'Merlin' ECar EMon SWas
– 'Niveum' Widely available
§ – 'Roseum' CBow CCla CSco CTom ECar EFou ELun EPar LGan MBal MBri MTol MUlv NSti NTow SBla SPer WHil WPbr

EPIPACTIS (Orchidaceae)

gigantea CAvo CChu ECar ECha ELan EPar EPot LBee MBal MTho NGar SBla SIgm SWes WChr
palustris NGar SWes WChe

EPIPREMNUM (Araceae)

§ ***aureum*** CHal EBak MBri
– 'Marble Queen' (v) CHal
§ ***pinnatum*** MBri

EPISCIA (Gesneriaceae)

§ ***dianthiflora*** MBri MNew WEfe
* 'Iris August' MBri
* ***primeria*** MBri
* 'San Miguel' CHal MBri WEfe

EQUISETUM (Equisetaceae)

arvense NSal
hyemale CHEx CNat EBre LBre
– var. ***robustum*** ELan EPla
ramosissimum CNat
scirpoïdes EBre EMFW LBre MCas
sylvaticum CNat

ERAGROSTIS (Gramineae)

chloromelas ETPC
curvula EHoe ETPC

ERANTHIS (Ranunculaceae)

§ ***hyemalis*** CAvo CBro ELan EMon EPar ETub LAma LBlo LBow MBri MHew NGar NLan NRog NSal SIng WChr WCot
§ – Cilicica Group CBro EPar EPot LAma LBlo LBow NMen NRog SIng WHil
¶ – 'Flore Pleno' EPot
§ – Tubergenii Group LBlo
– Tubergenii Group 'Guinea Gold' MPar WChr
longistipitata WChr

ERCILLA (Phytolaccaceae)

volubilis CChu CGre CPle CSam LHop WCru WSHC

EREMAEA (Myrtaceae)

See Plant Deletions

EREMURUS (Liliaceae/Asphodelaceae)

§ ***aitchisonii*** LAma SBla
bungei See E. ***stenophyllus stenophyllus***
elwesii See E. ***aitchisonii***
himalaicus EPar LAma LBow SMad SMrm WCra
x ***isabellinus*** 'Cleopatra' LAma LBow SGil
– 'Pinokkio' ETub LAma
– Ruiter hybrids EFou ELan EPar ETub LAma MBri NFai SHer SPer
– Shelford hybrids CB&S CKel ELan LAma LBow NOak SDeJ
'Moneymaker' LAma
robustus CB&S CBot CBow CCMG CDoC CHEx CRDP EPar ETub GGar LAma LBow MBri NRog SGil SIgm SMad SMrm SPer WCra
stenophyllus
ssp. ***aurantiacus*** SFis
§ – ssp. ***stenophyllus*** CB&S CDoC CKel CMGP CRDP ELan EPar ETub LAma LBow NEgg NFai NNor NOak NRog SPer SPla

ERIANTHUS See SACCHARUM

ERICA † (Ericaceae)

arborea CAbb CBow CDoC CNCN MBal SArc SBar SHBN
§ – 'Albert's Gold' CB&S CBow CNCN EBlo EBre EDen ELan ENHC GBla IDai IOrc LBre MBal MBar MBri MOke NHol SBod SPer SPla SSpi WGre WRid
– var. ***alpina*** CMac CNCN EBlo EDen ENHC ENot GAng GBla GPen IDai IOrc MBal MBar MGos MPlt NHar NHol NWin SBod SLon SPer SReu SSta WBod WGre WRid WWat
*– 'Arbora Gold' See E. ***a.*** 'Albert's Gold'
– 'Arnold's Gold' See E. ***a.*** 'Albert's Gold'
– 'Estrella Gold' CDoC CNCN EBre EDen ELan ENHC GPen LBre MBal MBar NBar NHar NHol NWin SBar SBod SPer SPla SSta WGre WRid WStI
– 'Spring Smile' EDen
australis CB&S ELan GAng GBla MBar SBar SHBN SPer WRid
¶ – ***aragonensis*** SRms

– 'Castellar Blush'	CNCN
– 'Holehird'	EDen
– 'Mr Robert'	CNCN EDen MBar SBod WGre
– 'Riverslea'	CNCN EDen ENHC GAng GAri GBla GPen IOrc MBal MBar MBri MOke NHol SBod WBod WGre
canaliculata	CB&S CGre MBal MUlv
carnea 'Accent'	EDen
– 'Adrienne Duncan'	COCH EDen ENHC GAng GBla GPen MBar MBri MOke NHol NWin SBod SPla WGre
– 'Alan Coates'	CMac CNCN COCH EDen ENHC MBal MBar WGre
– 'Alba'	COCH EDen
– 'Altadena'	CNCN COCH EDen MBar
♦– 'Amy Doncaster'	See E. *c.* 'Treasure Trove'
– 'Ann Sparkes'	CMac CNCN COCH EBlo EBre EDen ENHC GAng GBla GPen LBre MBal MBar MBri MGos MOke MPla MWat NHol NWin SBod SPla WBod WGre WRid WThu
– 'Atrorubra'	CMac COCH EBre ENHC LBre MBal MBar
– 'Aurea'	CB&S CMac CNCN COCH EBre EDen ENHC ENot GAng GBla GPen LBre LGro MBal MBar MBri MOke MPla NBar NRoo SBod SLon WBod WGre WRid
– 'Barry Sellers'	COCH EDen
– 'Beoley Pink'	CNCN COCH EDen SBod
– 'C J Backhouse'	ENHC GPen
– 'Carnea'	CNCN COCH EBre EDen ENHC LBre MBar MBri MOke NBar NWin WGre
– 'Cecilia M Beale'	CNCN COCH ENHC GBla MBar NHol NWin
– 'Challenger'	CNCN COCH EBre EDen LBre MBri MGos NBar NRoo SBod
– 'Christine Fletcher'	COCH EDen WGre
– 'Clare Wilkinson'	CNCN COCH EDen
– 'David's Seedling'	COCH EDen
– 'December Red'	CB&S CMac CNCN COCH EBre EDen ENHC ENot ESis GAng GBla GPen IJoh LBre MBar MBri MOke MPla MWat NBar NHol SBod SPla WBod WGre WRid
¶– 'Dommesmoen'	EDen
– 'Early Red'	COCH
– 'Eileen Porter'	CMac COCH EDen ENHC GBla GDra IDai MBar MBri NWin WRid
– 'Foxhollow'	Widely available
– 'Foxhollow Fairy'	CB&S CNCN COCH EDen ENHC EPot GAng GPen MBar NWin WGre
– 'Gelber Findling'	COCH
– 'Golden Starlet'	EBre EDen LBre SPla WGre
– 'Gracilis'	ENHC GPen MBar NWin WGre
– 'Heathwood'	CB&S CNCN COCH ENHC ENot GAng MBar MBri NHol SBod
– 'Hilletje'	COCH EDen
¶– 'Isabel'	NRoo
– 'Jack Stitt'	COCH MBar WGre
– 'James Backhouse'	CMac EDen MBri
¶– 'January Sun'	COCH
– 'Jennifer Anne'	CNCN COCH EDen ENHC MBar
– 'John Kampa'	CNCN COCH EBre EDen ENHC LBre MBar MBri NHol WGre
– 'John Pook'	MGos
– 'King George'	CMac CNCN COCH EBre EDen GAng GBla GPen GRei GSpe IDai IJoh LBre MBar MGos MWat NBar NHar NHol NRoo NWin SBod SHBN SLon SPla WBod WGre WRid
– 'Lake Garda'	COCH EDen SPla
– 'Late Pink'	COCH
– 'Lesley Sparkes'	COCH EDen ENHC GPen MBal MBar NWin WGre WRid
– 'Lohses Rubin'	COCH WGre
– 'Loughrigg'	CMac CNCN COCH EBre EDen ENHC ESis GAng GBla GDra GRei GSpe IJoh LBre MBal MBar MBri MGos MOke NHol NRoo NWin SBod SPla WGre
– 'March Seedling'	CB&S CNCN COCH EBre EDen ENHC ENot GAng GBla GDra GSpe LBre MBar MBri MGos MOke MPla NHol NWin SBod SPla WGre
– 'Mrs Sam Doncaster'	CNCN COCH MBar SBod WGre
– 'Myretoun Ruby'	Widely available
– 'Orient'	COCH
– 'Pallida'	COCH GPen
– 'Pink Beauty '	See E. *c.* 'Pink Pearl'
– 'Pink Cloud'	COCH EDen
§– 'Pink Pearl'	COCH EDen GPen MBar WGre
– 'Pink Spangles'	CB&S CMac CNCN COCH EBlo EBre EDen ENHC ENot GAng GBla GDra GPen IJoh LBre MBal MBar MBri MGos MOke MPla NBar NHol NRoo NWin SBod WGre WRid
– 'Pirbright Rose'	COCH EDen ENHC MBri MPla SBod
– 'Polden Pride'	COCH EDen
– 'Porter's Red'	COCH EDen MBar
– 'Praecox Rubra'	CB&S COCH EBre EDen ENHC GAng GBla GDra GPen IJoh LBre LGro MBar MBri MGos MOke MPla NBar NHol NWin WRid
– 'Prince of Wales'	CNCN COCH EDen ENHC
– 'Queen Mary'	CNCN EDen ENHC MPla SBod
– 'Queen of Spain'	COCH EDen ENHC GPen MBri MOke
– 'R B Cooke'	CNCN COCH EDen ENHC MBar MBri NWin SBod WGre
¶– 'Red Jewel'	NRoo
– 'Red Rover'	COCH EDen
– 'Rosalinde Schorn'	COCH EDen
¶– 'Rosea'	EDen
– 'Rosy Gem'	EDen MBar SPla WRid
¶– 'Rosy Morn'	EDen
– 'Rubinteppich'	CNCN COCH EDen MBri SBod
– 'Ruby Glow'	CB&S CNCN COCH EBre EDen ENHC ENot GAng GBla GPen GSpe IJoh LBre LGro MBal MBar MBri MOke NHol
– 'Schneekuppel'	COCH EDen
¶– 'Schneesturm'	COCH
§– 'Sherwood Creeping'	EDen ENHC MBar
– 'Sherwoodii'	See E. *c.* 'Sherwood Creeping'
– 'Smart's Heath'	CNCN ENHC GPen
– 'Snow Queen'	CMac CNCN COCH EDen ENHC GPen MBar NBar NWin SBod SPla WGre
– 'Spring Cottage Crimson'	COCH EDen MBar
– 'Spring Day'	EDen

– 'Springwood Pink'	CMHG CMac CNCN COCH EDen ENHC ENot GAng GBla GDra GPen GRei GSpe IDai LGro MBal MBar MBri MGos MOke MPla MWat NHol SBod SHBN WBod WGre WRid
– 'Springwood White'	Widely available
– 'Startler'	COCH EBre EDen ENHC LBre MBar SBod SPla
– 'Sunshine Rambler'	CNCN COCH EBre EDen EPot GPen LBre MBar MGos MPla NWin WGre
– 'Thomas Kingscote'	CNCN COCH EDen ENHC MBar
¶ – 'Treasure Trove'	COCH EDen
– 'Tybesta Gold'	CNCN COCH
– 'Viking'	COCH EBre EDen IJoh LBre
– 'Vivellii'	Widely available
– 'Vivellii Aurea'	COCH EDen
– 'Walter Reisert'	CNCN COCH
– 'Wanda'	COCH EDen MBar
– 'Wentwood Red'	COCH EDen
– 'Westwood Yellow'	CNCN COCH EBlo EBre EDen ENHC GAng GBla LBre MBar MBri NHar NHol SBod SPla
– 'Winter Beauty'	CNCN COCH EBre GRei IDai IJoh LBre MBri MOke MPla NBar NHol NWin WGre
– 'Winter Gold'	COCH
cerinthoïdes	CSun
ciliaris	NLan
– 'Aurea'	CMac CNCN EDen ENHC GPen MBar NWin WGre
– 'Camla'	ENHC GPen MBar WGre
– 'Corfe Castle'	CMac CNCN EDen ENHC GPen MBar NWin SBod WGre
– 'David McClintock'	CMac CNCN EDen ENHC GPen MBar MGos NWin WGre
– 'Egdon Heath'	EDen WGre
– 'Globosa'	CNCN ENHC WGre
– 'Mrs C H Gill'	CMac CNCN ENHC GPen MBal WGre
– 'Stoborough'	CMHG CNCN EDen ENHC MBal MBar
– 'White Wings'	CNCN EDen ENHC GPen
– 'Wych'	GPen
cinerea	NLan
– f. ***alba***	CMac GRei
– 'Alba Major'	MBal MBar WGre
– 'Alba Minor'	CNCN EBre EDen GAng GPen GSpe LBre MBal MBar MBri MOke NHar NHol NRoo SBod WGre WRid
– 'Ann Berry'	CNCN EDen ENHC MBar SBod WGre
– 'Apple Blossom'	EDen WGre
– 'Apricot Charm'	EDen GAng GPen MBar SBod WGre
– 'Ashgarth Garnet'	MBar WGre
– 'Atrococcinea'	CB&S
– 'Atropurpurea'	CNCN MBar
– 'Atrorubens'	CMac EDen ENHC GPen GRei GSpe MBar NHar
– 'Atrosanguinea'	CNCN ENHC GAng GBla GSpe MBar MGos NWin SBod WGre WRid
– 'Atrosanguinea Smith's Variety'	EDen GAri
– 'Baylay's Variety'	EDen MBar
– 'Blossom Time'	MBar
– 'C D Eason'	CMac CNCN EBre EDen ENHC ENot GAng GBla GDra GPen GRei GSpe IJoh LBre MBal MBar MBri MGos MOke NHol NWin SBod WBod WGre WRid
§ – 'C G Best'	CMac CNCN EDen ENHC GBla GPen IDai MBal MBar SBod WGre
– 'Cairn Valley'	EDen GSpe
– 'Caldy Island'	MBar NWin
– 'Carnea'	GPen
– 'Carnea Underwood's Variety'	EDen
– 'Cevennes'	CMac CNCN EDen ENHC GAng GSpe IDai MBar MBri MGos MOke SBod WGre
– 'Cindy'	CNCN EDen ENHC GSpe MBal MBar MBri MOke
– 'Coccinea'	ENHC GRei IDai WGre
– 'Colligan Bridge'	GPen MBar
– 'Constance'	EDen ENHC MBar
– 'Contrast'	EDen GSpe MBar WGre
– 'Daphne Maginess'	CNCN
– 'Domino'	CB&S CNCN ENHC GBla GPen MBar MBri MGos MOke WBod
– 'Duncan Fraser'	CNCN EDen ENHC GSpe MBar
– 'Dunwood Sport'	MBar
– 'Eden Valley'	CMac CNCN EDen ENHC GAng GBla GPen GSpe MBar MGos NRoo SBod WGre WRid
– 'England'	ENHC
– 'Fiddler's Gold'	CNCN EDen ENHC GAng GAri GBla GPen MBar MBri MOke NHar NHol NWin
– 'Flamingo'	EDen WGre
– 'Foxhollow Mahogany'	EBre EDen ENHC GPen GSpe LBre MBal MBar NWin WGre WRid
– 'Frances'	EDen ENHC GBla
– 'G Osmond'	ENHC GPen MBar MOke
– 'Glasnevin Red'	MBar NHar WGre
– 'Glencairn'	EDen GAng GPen MBar MBri NHol NWin
– 'Godrevy'	EDen SBod
– 'Golden Charm'	NHol
– 'Golden Drop'	CMac CNCN EDen ENHC GAng GPen GSpe IJoh MBal MBar MBri MGos MOke NHol NWin SBod WGre WRid
– 'Golden Hue'	CB&S CNCN EDen ENHC GAng GPen GSpe IJoh MBar MBri MOke WBod WGre WRid
– 'Golden Sport'	MBri MGos NHar
♦ – 'Graham Thomas'	See E. *c.* 'C G Best'
– 'Grandiflora'	EDen MBar
– 'Guernsey Lime'	EDen ENHC MBar SBod
– 'Guernsey Plum'	EDen
– 'Guernsey Purple'	EDen SBod
– 'Hardwick's Rose'	CNCN EDen MBar
– 'Harry Fulcher'	CNCN EDen ENHC MBri MOke
– 'Heidebrand'	EDen GPen MBar
– 'Hermann Dijkhuizen'	EDen
– 'Honeymoon'	ENHC GSpe MBar
– 'Hookstone Lavender'	ENHC GPen GSpe
– 'Hookstone White'	CNCN EBre EDen ENHC GBla GDra GPen IJoh LBre MBal MBar SBod WGre WRid
– 'Jack London'	CNCN EDen
– 'Janet'	CNCN EDen ENHC MBar MGos NWin WGre
– 'John Ardron'	SBod WGre
– 'John Eason'	ENHC NHol
– 'Joseph Murphy'	EDen GAng GBla GSpe MBar WGre
– 'Josephine Ross'	GPen GSpe MBar NWin WGre
– 'Joyce Burfitt'	CNCN ENHC WGre

– 'Katinka'	CNCN EBre EDen ENHC GRei LBre MBar NHol WGre
– 'Kerry Cherry'	EDen
– 'Knap Hill Pink'	CNCN EDen ENHC GAng GBla MBar WGre
– 'Lady Skelton'	MBar
– 'Lavender Lady'	EDen NWin
– 'Lilac Time'	ENHC GAng GSpe MBar
– 'Lilacina'	EDen ENHC GSpe MBar MBri MOke
– 'Lime Soda'	CNCN EDen ENHC MBri
– 'Lorna Anne Hutton'	EDen
¶ – 'Michael Hugo'	CNCN
– 'Miss Waters'	EDen MBar NWin
– 'Mrs Dill'	ENHC MBar
– 'Mrs E A Mitchell'	EBre EDen LBre MBri MGos MOke
– 'Mrs Ford'	EDen ENHC GAng GPen MBar
– 'My Love'	EDen ENHC IJoh MBar MBri MOke WBod
– 'Nell'	GPen MBar
– 'Newick Lilac'	EDen MBar MBri MOke
– 'Novar'	EDen
– 'P S Patrick'	CNCN EDen ENHC GAng GBla GPen GSpe MBal MBar MGos SBod WRid
– 'Pallas'	GSpe IJoh
– 'Pentreath'	EDen ENHC GPen MBar MBri MOke NWin WBod
– 'Peñaz'	EDen
– 'Pink Foam'	EDen GBla GPen MBar
– 'Pink Ice'	CB&S CMac CNCN EBlo EBre EDen ENHC GAng GBla GDra GPen GRei GSpe IJoh LBre MBar MBri MGos MOke NHar NHol NRoo NWin SBod WBod WGre WRid
– 'Plummer's Seedling'	EDen GAng GBla GSpe MBar WRid
– 'Prostrate Lavender'	EDen ENHC GPen MBal
– 'Purple Beauty'	CB&S CNCN EBlo EDen ENHC GBla GSpe IJoh MBar MBri MGos MOke NHol NWin WGre
– 'Purple Robe'	CMac ENHC
– 'Purpurea'	GPen
– 'Pygmaea'	GBla MBar
– 'Red Pentreath'	EDen
– 'Rijneveld'	EDen
– 'Robert Michael'	EDen
– 'Rock Pool'	EDen GSpe MBal MBar NWin WGre
– 'Romiley'	EDen ENHC MBar MBri MOke
– 'Rosabella'	CNCN EDen ENHC MBar
– 'Rose Queen'	CMac GSpe WGre WRid
– 'Rosea'	EDen ENHC GAng GPen GSpe WGre
– 'Rozanne Waterer'	CMac NWin
– 'Ruby'	CMac CNCN EDen ENHC GAng GBla GSpe MBar
– 'Sandpit Hill'	MBar WGre
– 'Schizopetala'	CNCN EDen GPen MBar
– 'Sea Foam'	CNCN ENHC MBar
– 'Sherry'	CMac CNCN EDen ENHC GAng GBla GPen GRei GSpe MBar WGre
– 'Smith's Lawn'	EDen
– 'Snow Cream'	EDen GPen MBar
¶ – 'Son of Cevennes'	MGos
¶ – 'Spicata'	EDen
– 'Splendens'	EDen ENHC
– 'Startler'	CB&S ENHC GSpe MBri MOke
– 'Stephen Davis'	CNCN EBlo EBre EDen ENHC GAng GBla GPen GSpe LBre MBal MBar MBri MOke NHol NRoo SBod WBod WGre
– 'Strawberry'	EDen
– 'Sue Lloyd'	EDen WGre
– 'Summer Gold'	CNCN EBre LBre
– 'Tilford'	ENHC
– 'Tom Waterer'	MBar
– 'Velvet Night'	CB&S CMac CNCN ENHC GAng GBla GPen GSpe IDai IJoh MBal MBar MBri MOke NHar NHol NWin SBod WBod WGre WRid
– 'Victoria'	CMac EDen MBar WGre
– 'Vivienne Patricia'	ENHC GAng GBla GPen GSpe MBar NWin
– 'W G Notley'	EDen ENHC
– 'White Dale'	EDen MBar WGre
– 'Windlebrooke'	EDen ENHC GPen MBar SBod WGre
colorans	CSun
conspicua	CSun
cruenta	CSun EDen
curviflora	CSun EDen
x ***darleyensis*** 'Ada S Collings'	CNCN COCH EBre EDen ENHC GAng GBla LBre MBal MBar MPla NWin SBod SHBN
– 'Alba'	See E. x ***d.*** **'Silberschmelze'**
– 'Archie Graham'	COCH EDen
§ – 'Arthur Johnson'	CB&S CMac CNCN COCH EBlo EBre EDen ENHC ENot GAng GBla GPen GSpe LBre MBal MBar MBri MGos MOke MPla NHol NWin SBod SHBN SPla WGre WRid
– 'Cherry Stevens'	See E. x ***d.*** **'Furzey'**
– 'Darley Dale'	CMac CNCN COCH EBlo EBre EDen ENHC ENot GBla GPen GSpe LBre MBal MBar MBri MOke MPla NHol NRoo SBod SPla WGre WRid
– 'Dunreggan'	EDen
– 'Dunwood Splendour'	See E. x ***d.*** **'Arthur Johnson'**
– 'Erecta'	COCH EDen
§ – 'Furzey'	CB&S CMHG CMac CNCN COCH EBlo EDen ENHC ESis GAng GBla GPen GSpe MBal MBar MBri MGos MOke MPla NHar NHol NRoo SBod SHBN SPla WGre WRid
– 'George Rendall'	CB&S CMac CNCN COCH EDen ENHC GAng GDra GPen GSpe MBri MPla NHol SPla WGre WRid
– 'Ghost Hills'	CNCN COCH EBre EDen ENHC ESis GAng GDra LBre MBal MBar MBri MOke MPla NHol NWin SBod SHBN WBod WGre WRid
– 'J W Porter'	CNCN COCH EBre EDen ENHC GAng GBla GPen IJoh LBre MBal MBar MBri MOke NHol NWin WRid
§ – 'Jack H Brummage'	CB&S CMHG CMac CNCN COCH EBre EDen ENHC EPot GAng GBla GPen IJoh LBre MBal MBar MBri MGos MOke MPla NHar NHol NWin SBod SHBN SPla WGre WRid
– 'James Smith'	COCH ENHC ESis MBar
– 'Jenny Porter'	CMac CNCN COCH EDen ENHC GPen MBar MBri MOke NHol NWin WGre WRid

– 'Kramer's Rote' CNCN COCH EBlo EBre EDen GPen LBre MBri MGos MOke NRoo SPla WGre
– 'Margaret Porter' CB&S CMHG CNCN COCH EDen ENHC GAng IJoh MBri MPla NHol SBod WGre WRid
– 'Mary Helen' CNCN COCH EDen NHol
– 'Norman R Webster' COCH EDen NWin
§ – 'Silberschmelze' ('Molten Silver') CB&S CKel CNCN COCH EBlo EBre EDen ENHC ENot GAng GBla GDra GPen GSpe IDai LBre MBal MBar MBri MGos MOke MPla NHol NRoo NWin SBod SHBN WBod WGre WRid
– 'W G Pine' COCH
– 'White Glow' CNCN COCH EDen ENHC MBal MBri NHol WGre WRid
– 'White Perfection' CNCN COCH EBre EDen GPen LBre MBar MBri SPla WGre WRid
densifolia CSun
discolor CGre CSun EDen
doliiformis CSun EDen
§ ***erigena*** ELan ENot SBar SHBN SPer
– 'Alba' CMac COCH ENHC MBar NWin
– 'Alba Compacta' COCH GPen
– 'Brian Proudley' CNCN COCH EDen ENHC MBar SBod WRid
– 'Brightness' CB&S CMac CNCN COCH EBre EDen ENHC EPot GAng GBla GPen LBre MBal MBar MBri MOke MWat NHar NHol NWin SBod WRid
– 'Coccinea' COCH EDen ENHC NWin
– 'Ewan Jones' CNCN COCH EDen ENHC IOrc MBar
– 'Glauca' ENHC GPen
– 'Golden Lady' CMac CNCN COCH EBlo EBre EDen ENHC ESis GAng GPen LBre MBar MBri MGos MOke NHol SBod SPla WGre WRid
– 'Hibernica' GPen
– 'Hibernica Alba' MBar
– 'Irish Dusk' CMHG CNCN COCH EBlo EBre EDen ENHC GAng GBla GPen IDai IJoh LBre MBar MBri MGos MOke NHar NHol NWin SBod SPla WGre WRid
– 'Irish Salmon' CB&S CMac CNCN COCH GPen IJoh MBal MBar NWin
– 'Irish Silver' COCH GPen MBar MBri NWin
¶ – 'Ivory' COCH
– 'Mrs Parris' Lavender' WRid
– 'Mrs Parris' Red' WRid
– 'Mrs Parris' White' WRid
– 'Nana Alba' CNCN COCH GPen MBar
– 'Rosea' ENHC MBar NWin
– 'Rubra Compacta' ENHC
– 'Superba' CMac CNCN COCH EDen ENHC ENot GPen MBal MBar MGos MOke NWin SBod SPla WGre WRid
– 'W T Rackliff' CB&S CNCN COCH EBlo EBre EDen ENHC ENot EPot GAng GBla GPen LBre MBal MBar MBri MGos MOke NHol NWin SHBN SPla WGre WRid
– 'W T Rackliff Variegated' ENHC
glandulosa EDen WBod
gracilis EDen MBri
– red CSun
herbacea See E. ***carnea***
hibernica See E. ***erigena***
x ***hiemalis*** 'Limelight' EDen
lusitanica CB&S CMac CNCN COCH CPle EDen ELan MBar NHol SBod SPer SSpi WBod WRid
– 'George Hunt' CAbb CDoC CNCN EBre EDen ELan ENHC LBre NHol SBod SPer SPla
mackayana NLan
¶ – ssp. ***andevalensis*** EDen
– 'Ann D Frearson' CNCN EDen
– 'Doctor Ronald Gray' CNCN EDen ENHC GAng GPen MBar MBri MOke SBod WGre WRid
– 'Galicia' CNCN EDen
– 'Lawsoniana' ENHC
– 'Maura' EDen ENHC
– 'Plena' CMHG CNCN ENHC GPen MBal MBar MBri MOke SBod WGre
– 'Shining Light' EDen SPla
– 'William M'Calla' ENHC
manipuliflora CDoC COCH EDen GPen MBar SPla
– ssp. ***anthura*** 'Corfu' COCH
– – 'Don Richards' COCH EDen
– – 'Elegant Spike' EDen
– – 'Heaven Scent' COCH EDen
– – 'Ian Cooper' COCH EDen
– – 'Korcula' EDen
manipuliflora ssp. ***manipuliflora*** 'Aldburgh' COCH
– x ***vagans*** 'Valerie Griffiths' COCH EDen
mauritanica EDen
mediterranea See E. ***erigena***
mollis EDen
pageana CSun
persoluta CSun
perspicua CSun
x ***praegeri*** See E. x ***stuartii***
scoparia ssp. ***platycodon*** 'Lionel Woolner' EDen
§ – ssp. ***scoparia*** 'Minima' EDen ENHC MBar
– – 'Pumila' See E. ***s. s.*** 'Minima'
sessiliflora CSun
speciosa CSun EDen
§ x ***stuartii*** CMHG ENHC GPen MBar SBod
♦ – 'Charles Stuart ' See E. x ***s.*** 'Stuartii'
– 'Connemara' EDen
– 'Irish Lemon' CMHG CNCN EBre EDen ENHC GAng GDra GPen GSpe LBre MBar MBri NHar NHol NWin SBod SPla WBod WGre WRid
– 'Irish Orange' CNCN EBre EDen ENHC GAng GSpe LBre MBar MBri NHol SBod SPla WGre
§ – 'Stuartii' CNCN EDen
subdivaricata CSun EDen
§ ***terminalis*** CNCN COCH EDen ENHC ENot EPot GAng IOrc MBal MBar NWin SBod SPer WSHC
– ***stricta*** See E. ***terminalis.***
– 'Thelma Woolner' CMac CNCN COCH ENHC MBar NHol WGre
tetralix CKin NLan WCla
– 'Alba' EDen

– 'Alba Mollis'	CMac CNCN EDen ENHC ENot GAng GBla GDra GPen GSpe IJoh MBal MBar MBri MOke NHar NHol NRoo NWin SBod SPla WBod WGre WRid
– 'Ardy'	ENHC
– 'Bala'	CNCN EDen
– 'Bartinney'	EDen MBar
– 'Con Underwood'	CMac CNCN EBre EDen ENHC ENot GAng GBla GPen GSpe LBre MBal MBar MBri MOke NHol SBod SPla WBod WGre WRid
– 'Daphne Underwood'	EDen NWin WGre
– 'Delta'	EDen ENHC MBar
– 'Foxhome'	EDen ENHC GPen MBar NWin
– 'Hailstones'	ENHC MBar NWin
– 'Helma'	EDen ENHC
– 'Hookstone Pink'	CNCN EDen ENHC GPen MBal MOke NHar NWin SBod SHBN WGre
– 'Ken Underwood'	CNCN ENHC GDra GPen MBar NWin SHBN WGre
– 'L E Underwood'	CMac ENHC EPot GAng GPen MBal MBar NHol NWin WGre WRid
– 'Melbury White'	CNCN EDen ENHC GPen MBar NWin
– 'Morning Glow'	See E. x *watsonii* 'F White'
– 'Pink Star'	CMac CNCN EBre EDen ENHC GAng GBla GSpe LBre MBal MBar NHol NWin WGre WRid
– 'Rubra'	GPen
§ – 'Ruby's Variety'	GPen MBar NWin
– 'Ruby's Velvet'	See E. *t.* 'Ruby's Variety'
– 'Ruth's Gold'	EBre LBre MBar MBri NHol WGre
– 'Salmon Seedling'	GPen
– 'Silver Bells'	CMac ENHC GPen MBar WGre
– 'Terschelling'	EDen
– 'Tina'	CNCN EDen
– 'White House'	EDen
transparens	CSun
umbellata	CNCN EDen ENHC GAng GPen MBal MBar NWin WAbe WGre
vagans* f. *alba	MBal
– 'Birch Glow'	EDen ENHC NWin SBod WGre
– 'Carnea'	EDen
– 'Cornish Cream'	EDen ENHC GAri GPen MBar NHol NRoo NWin WBod WGre
– 'Cream'	CNCN EDen ENHC IDai MOke NHar
– 'Diana Hornibrook'	CNCN EDen ENHC GSpe MBal MBar MBri MOke NHar NRoo SHBN WGre
– 'Fiddlestone'	CNCN EDen ENHC GPen GSpe MBar NWin SBod WGre
– 'French White'	CNCN EDen MBar SBod
– 'George Underwood'	EDen ENHC GPen MBar WBod WGre
– 'Grandiflora'	CNCN EDen GPen IJoh MBal MBar NWin SPla WGre
– 'Holden Pink'	EDen MBri MOke NHar SBod SPla WBod
– 'Hookstone Rosea'	MBar
– 'Ida M Britten'	EDen MBar
– 'J C Fletcher'	EDen
– 'Kevernensis Alba'	EDen ENHC GPen IDai MBar NHol SBod
– 'Lilacina'	CMac CNCN EDen GSpe MBar
– 'Lyonesse'	CB&S CMac CNCN EBre EDen ENHC ENot GAng GBla GDra GPen GSpe IJoh LBre MBal MBar MBri MGos MOke NHol NRoo NWin SBod SPla WBod WGre WRid
– 'Miss Waterer'	EDen MBar
– 'Mrs D F Maxwell'	CB&S CMac CNCN EBlo EBre EDen ENHC GAng GBla GDra GPen GSpe IDai IJoh LBre MBal MBar MBri MGos MOke NBar NHar NHol NRoo NWin SBod SPla WBod WGre WRid
– 'Mrs Donaldson'	GPen
– 'Nana'	EDen MBal MBar
– 'Pallida'	EDen ENHC NHol
– 'Peach Blossom'	MBar
– 'Pyrenees Pink'	CMac CNCN EDen GBla MBal MBar MBri MOke NHar WGre
– 'Rubra'	CNCN EDen GBla MBal MBar
– 'Rubra Grandiflora'	ENHC
– 'Saint Keverne'	CB&S CMac CNCN EDen ENHC GAng GBla GPen MBal MBar MBri MGos MOke NHar NHol NRoo SBod SPla WGre WRid
– 'Summertime'	CNCN EDen GPen MBar
– 'Valerie Proudley'	CB&S CMac CNCN EBre EDen ENHC GAng GBla GDra GPen GSpe IJoh LBre MBal MBar MBri MGos MOke MWat NHar NHol NRoo NWin SBod SHBN SPla WGre WRid
– 'Viridiflora'	CNCN EDen MBar
– 'White Lady'	ENHC MBar NWin
– 'White Rocket'	EDen MBar
– 'White Spire'	EDen
– 'Yellow John'	GBla
x ***veitchii***	GPen MBal
– 'Exeter'	CNCN COCH EDen GAri MBar WGre
– 'Gold Tips'	CNCN EDen ENHC GAng MBal MBar MBri MGos MOke NHar SPla WGre WRid
– 'Pink Joy'	EDen ENHC GAri MBal MBri MOke NBar NHar NHol WGre
versicolor	CSun
x ***watsonii*** 'Cherry Turpin'	EDen SPla
– 'Dawn'	CMHG CNCN EDen GAng GDra GPen GSpe MBal MBar MBri NHar NWin SBod SHBN WGre WRid
– 'Dorothy Metheny'	EDen
§ – 'F White'	EDen ENHC GPen MBar
– 'Gwen'	CNCN EDen MBar
– 'H Maxwell'	CNCN GPen GSpe MBal NWin WGre
– 'Rachel'	MBal
– 'Truro'	EDen
¶ x ***williamsii*** 'David Coombe'	EDen
– 'Gwavas'	EDen EPot GAng GPen MBar SBod WGre
– 'P D Williams'	CNCN EDen MBal MBar NWin WGre WRid

ERIGERON † (Compositae)

acer	CKin MHew NSal WCla WNdy
'Adria'	EBre LBre SPer
alpinus	CNic CRDP GCHN LBee LGan MCas NGre SFis WCra
'Amity'	CMGP EOrc SPer
annuus	CBre
atticus	MHig
aurantiacus	CBow CSam EBar ECtt LGan MPit NBro NCat NOak NSti SHer WCot WHil WPer
§ *aureus*	WOMN
§ – 'Canary Bird'	ECar MSta NBir WAbe WDav
'Azurfee' ('Azure Fairy')	CBow CSam EBar EFol ELan ESma LWad MBro NFai NOak NRoo SPla SSvw WHen WHil WHoo WMer WPer WWin
'Birch Hybrid'	SIng
¶ 'Blue Beauty'	NMir
borealis	GCHN GTou WHil
'Charity'	CGle CKel CMGP CSco EFou SPer WTyr
chrysopsidis 'Grand Ridge'	EPot GArf WAbe
compositus	CLew CNic CPar GArf MCas NGre NMir NWCA SIng WPer
§ – var. *discoïdeus*	CLew CNic EBur
– 'Lavender Dwarf'	NHol
'Dignity'	CShe EBre ECED EFou EGol ELan GCHN LBre MWat NFai SChu SFis SPer WEas WPbr
'Dimity'	CGle EBre ECha EFou LBre NCat SFis SUsu WRus WWin
'Doctor Worth'	SHer
'Dunkelste Aller' ('Darkest of All')	CGle CKel CMGP CPar CSco CSev EBlo ECED ECtt ELan ENot MBri MRav NFai SPer SSvw WEas WOld WRus WTyr
elegantulus	GArf MBro WDav
'Felicity'	CShe EFou GAbr MMil SRms WOld
'Festivity '	SFis
flettii	GCHN MFir NCat
'Foersters Liebling'	CSev EFou ENot MBri MUlv MWat SFis SPla WCot WMer
'Four Winds'	CHal CLew CMil CShe EFou ELan EPad NMen NNrd SHer SMad WCot WMer WPer
'Gaiety'	CSco LHop SPer
glaucus	CFis CMer EPad IDai NCat NRed NVic SMrm WHil
– 'Albus'	WPer
– 'Elstead Pink'	CShe SPla WByw WEas
– 'Roseus'	CB&S CHal CMer
'Goliath'	CHal
* 'H E Beale'	LHil
¶ *hyssopifolius*	WHil
§ *karvinskianus*	CBos CFis CHal CHan CLew CMea CNic CTre ECha IDai LGan LHop MPar MWat NKay NMen NRed NSti SAxl SDix SIng SPer SPla SUsu WCla WEas WHil WRus
leiomerus	CNic MHig NKay NRed NTow NWCA WCla WOMN
linearis	MBro NRed WDav
'Mrs F H Beale'	SCro
mucronatus	See E. ***karvinskianus***
multiradiatus	CLew WCot WPer
'Nachthimmel'	LRHS
nanus	ESis MBro MHig NRed SHer WDav WPat WPer
¶ 'Pamela'	CKel
peregrinus	NHol WEas WPer
philadelphicus	CBre CElw CGle CHal CLew ECha NBir NSti SAxl SFis SMrm SUsu WCot WRus
'Pink Jewel'	See E. 'Rosa Juwel'
pinnatisectus	CNic LBee MBro NRed NWCA WPer
polymorphus	NCat NHol
'Prosperity'	CGle CShe EFou WOld
pumilis intermedius	GDra
'Quakeress'	CGle CSam EBre ECha EFou EMon EOrc LBre NCat SMrm SUsu WCot
radicatus	NRed
* *rhydbergii*	CBow
§ 'Rosa Juwel' ('Pink Jewel')	CBow CHal CPar CSam EBar EFou EPad ESma GAbr GCHN LHil LWad NBir NFai NMir NNrd NOak NRoo SPla SSvw WHen WHil WPbr WPer
¶ 'Rosa Triumph' ('Pink Triumph')	EFou SPla
¶ *roseus*	ECha
'Rotes Meer'	EFou ELan EMon LRHS MBri
rotundifolius 'Caerulescens'	See BELLIS ***rotundifolia*** 'C.'
N *salsuginosus*	NOak
'Schneewittchen' ('Snow White')	CGle CMGP EFou ELan LHop LRHS NSti SChu
'Schwarzes Meer' ('Black Sea')	EFou EGol EHal LHop MUlv NSti SPer SPla WMer
'Serenity'	CSco NCat SFis
simplex	EPad GDra LBee LHil MBro MCas MFir MWat NGre NHol NRed NTow SHer WDav WWin
'Sincerity'	CSco
¶ 'Sommerabend'	MUlv
'Sommerneuschnee'	CDoC
speciosus	MPit MWil NNrd WWye
¶ sp. Bald Mountains	NWCA
'Strahlenmeer'	EOrc LRHS WCot
¶ *thunbergii*	CLew
trifidus	See E. ***compositus discoïdeus***
uniflorus	CNic NHol NNrd NRed NWCA
'Unity'	MWat
vagus	EBur NWCA
– JCA 8911	CNic MFos NRed
'Wuppertal'	LRHS MMil SFis

ERINACEA (Leguminosae)

§ *anthyllis*	EPot MBro NHol SHer SIng SSpi WDav
pungens	See E. ***anthyllis***

ERINUS (Scrophulariaceae)

alpinus	CLew CMea CPar CRDP CRiv CSam ELan ESis GTou IDai LAbb MBal MBar MBro MPla MWat NGre NHol NKay NNor NRed NRoo SIng WCla WEas WHil WPat WThu WWin

– var. *albus*	CBot CHal CNic CRDP CRiv GGar GTou LGan MBro MCas MPar NKay NMen NNrd NTow NWCA SIng SSou WCla WDav WHoo WPat
– dark purple	NKay
– 'Dr Hähnle'	CHal CNic EBre LBre MBro MCas MHig MPit NHol NKay NMen NNrd NWCA SHer WHoo
– 'Mrs Charles Boyle'	CHal GDra MBro NKay SHer WHoo WOld

ERIOBOTRYA (Rosaceae)

¶ *deflexa*	CB&S CDoC CPle MUlv SMad
F *japonica*	CAbb CB&S CBar CBot CChu CDoC CGre CHEx CLan CPle CWit EPla ERea ESim ISea LGre LPan SArc SBor SDea SDry SEng SHil SLon SMad SPer SSpi SSta WWat
F – 'Benlehr'	ESim
F – 'Mrs Cookson'	ESim

ERIOCEPHALUS (Compositae)

See Plant Deletions

ERIOGONUM (Polygonaceae)

¶ *brevicaule nanum*	NWCA
caespitosum	MHig NTow NWCA SIgm WDav
– ssp. *douglasii*	GArf NTow WDav
flavum	WPer
jamesii	WDav WHil WPat
¶ *kennedyi*	WDav
¶ – *gracilipes*	MFos
¶ *lobbii robustum*	SIgm
* *multiceps*	WDav
ovalifolium	MFos NWCA SIgm SIng WDav
¶ – var. *depressum*	MFos
soredium	MFos
¶ *thymoïdes*	WDav
umbellatum	ECha EFol EPot MFir MFos NHol NTow NWCA SIgm SIng WCru WPer
– var. *porteri*	NWCA
– var. *subalpinum*	GArf MHig WDav
– var. *torreyanum*	EPot GArf MBro MHig NHol SIng WDav WPat

ERIOPHORUM (Cyperaceae)

angustifolium	CBen EHon EMFW EPla ETPC EWav GCHN LMay MSta NDea SWat WChe WHol
latifolium	LMay MSta
vaginatum	See SCIRPUS *fauriei vaginatus*

ERIOPHYLLUM (Compositae)

lanatum	CFis CHan CLew CNic CSam EBar ECha LHil MFir MNFA MWat NCat NGre NSti NTow NVic SBla SChu SFis WWin
¶ – var. *integrifolium*	WDav

ERITRICHIUM (Boraginaceae)

§ *canum*	MBro WCru WDav
¶ *howardii*	GTou
nanum	GTou
♦ *rupestre*	See E. *canum*
strictum	See E. *canum*

ERODIUM † (Geraniaceae)

absinthoïdes	GCHN LRHS WThi
acaule	GCHN NRog NRoo NRya
alnifolium	GCHN
balearicum	See E. x *variabile* 'Album'
battandierianum	GCHN SCou
boissieri	GCHN
brachycarpum	GCHN
carvifolium	CCor CElw CLew GCHN SCou WThu
§ *castellanum*	EPad GCHN LRHS MBri NRog NRoo SCou SCro WMar
chamaedryoïdes	See E. *reichardii*
§ *cheilanthifolium*	CSam GCHN GGar SIng
chium Guitt 88042202	GCHN
chrysanthum	CBot CGle CLew CMea CPar CSun EFol EFou ELan EOrc EPot GCHN GCal LGre MPar MTho NHol NKay NRog NRoo SAxl SBla SCou WAbe WEas WRus WWin
– *sulphureum*	CHan
ciconium Guitt 85051602	GCHN
§ *cicutarium* ssp. *cicutarium*	GCHN
corsicum	CGle CNic EBur EPot MDHE MHig MTho NCat NNrd NRog WAbe WOMN
– 'Album'	GCHN MMil WAbe
'County Park'	CLew ECou
crinitum	GCHN
daucoïdes hort.	See E. *castellanum*
foetidum	GCHN NRog
N *glandulosum*	CMea CShe ELan GCHN GCal LHop MBro MPar NRog SAxl SBla SCou SWas WEas WHal WHoo WKif WPat WPer WSHC WThi
gruinum	CMea ECro GCHN MTol SCou SMrm WHCG WPer
N *guttatum*	CGle CNic CPar CSun EPot LHop MPla MWat NKay NMen NNrd NTow WAbe WHal WPer
♦ *heteradenum*	See E. *petraeum*
x *hybridum*	EFol EPar NRoo WAbe WCru WHal WPbr
hymenodes hort.	See E. *trifolium*
jahandiezianum	GCHN
'Katherine Joy'	NRog
x *kolbianum*	MDHE NHol
– 'Natasha'	CNic CRiv ELan EPot GCHN MDHE MNFA NRog NRoo SGil SHer
¶ x *lindavicum*	CLew
– 'Charter House'	GCHN
macradenum	See E. *glandulosum*
malacoïdes	GCHN
malviflorum	SFis
manescaui	Widely available
'Merstham Pink'	CElw CLew ESis GCHN MDHE MMil MNFA NHol NRog NRoo SAxl SUsu WKif
moschatum Guitt 88041904	GCHN
munbyanum	GCHN

neuradifolium	
Guitt 86040601	GCHN
pelargoniiflorum	CBot CChu CGle CLew CMea ECro EFol EMar EPla ERav ESis GCHN LGre LWad MTho NBro NFai SCou SFis SUsu WCra WEas WHal WHil WHoo WOMN WPbr WPer WRus WWin
N***petraeum***	CMea CWes MFir NGre NMen NRoo SFis WAbe WCra WOld WThu
– 'Burgundy'	WHCG
– ssp. ***crispum***	See E. ***cheilanthifolium***
– ssp. ***glandulosum***	See E. ***glandulosum***
¶ – hybrids	ECha
– 'Pallidum'	CElw CSam MNFA
– 'Roseum'	GCal SBla SCro WAbe WMar WPer WRus
'Pickering Pink'	GCHN NRog
pimpinellifolium	GCHN
'Rachel'	GCHN
recorderi	GCHN
§ ***reichardii***	CHal CLew CMea CRDP CRiv EPad ESis LBee MPla MTho NGre NHol NRar NRog NRoo SBla SCou SIng SUsu WCla WHal WOMN
– cvs	See E. x ***variabile***
§ ***rupestre***	CBot CMea CNic ECtt GCHN GCal MPar NKay NNor SIng
salzmannii	See E. ***cicutarium cicutarium***
saxatile	GCHN
x ***sebaceum*** 'Polly'	GCHN
'Stephanie'	GCHN MDHE
supracanum	See E. ***rupestre***
tordylioïdes	GCHN
trichomanifolium	SAsh WHil
§ ***trifolium***	CElw ELan GCal MMil NSti SCou SIng SWas WCru WHCG
– Guitt 85051701	GCHN
– var. ***montanum***	GCHN SCou
valentinum	GCHN NRog
§ x ***variabile*** 'Album'	Widely available
– 'Bishop's Form'	CRiv CShe EMNN EPot ESis GArf MBar MBro MHig MPla MPlt NBro NGre NHar NHol NMen NRog NRoo NTow SAxl SFis SIng WEas WHil WHoo WPat WThu
– 'Flore Pleno'	CHal CLew CNic ELan GArf LHop MCas MFir MHig MPla NCat NGre NNrd NRog NRoo SAxl SHer SIng WOld WPer WTyr
– 'Roseum'	CBot CLew CPar CSev ECro EFol ELan EPar EPot IDai MFir MHig NGre NHol NKay NRed NRog NWCA SFis SIng WAbe WHal WOld WThu WWin
x ***wilkommianum***	NRog

ERPETION See VIOLA

ERUCA (Cruciferae)

vesicaria ssp. ***sativa***	CArn CSFH GPoy LHol MChe SIde WHer WOak WWye

ERYNGIUM † (Umbelliferae)

§ ***agavifolium***	CB&S CBot CChu CGle CHEx CHan ECha ECro ECtt ELan EMon EPla GCal IBar LHil MFir NBir NNor NSti SArc SAxl SMad SPer SSpi SSvw SUsu WDav WMer WWye
alpinum	CB&S CChu CDec CGle CHad CHan EBre ECha EFou ERav GDra LBre MBal MBro MTho NBir NSti SAxl SChu SPer WEas WHal
– 'Amethyst'	ELan GCal LGre MBri MPar MUlv NSti WMer
– 'Blue Star'	CMea ESma GCal LGre LWad NRoo SPla WPer
– 'Holden Blue'	GCal
– 'Opal'	CShe ELan LRHS MBri
– 'Slieve Donard'	GCal IBlr
– 'Superbum'	CBot ECro MBro NRoo SBla SMad
– 'Violet Lace'	GCal
amethystinum	CChu ECha EMon LGre MBri SGil WDav
♦ ***biebersteinianum***	See E. ***caucasicum***
bourgatii	Widely available
¶ – 'Forncett Ultra'	EFou
– 'Oxford Blue'	CHan LGre MPar NTow SMrm WEas
bromeliifolium hort.	See E. ***agavifolium***
caeruleum	CHan
campestre	NHol
¶ ***caucasicum***	WDav
¶ ***creticum***	ECro WHer
♦ ***decaisneanum***	See E. ***pandanifolium***
Delaroux	See E. ***proteiflorum***
¶ ***dichotomum*** Caeruleum Group	ECro
ebracteatum	GCal
– var. ***poterioïdes***	EMon LWad
§ ***eburneum***	CElw ECha ECro EMon SAxl SSpi
§ ***giganteum***	Widely available
– 'Silver Ghost'	EMon GCal LRHS SMrm
glaciale	EPad SPou WThi
maritimum	CArn CBot ECha ECro GPoy LGre NTow SIde SMrm
Miss Willmott's Ghost	See E. ***giganteum***
x ***oliverianum***	CHan CKel CSam EBlo ELan IDai LHop MBri MBro SDix SPer WByw WDav WMer WWin
§ ***pandanifolium***	CCla CElw CGre GCal IBlr SDix
paniculatum	See E. ***eburneum***
planum	Widely available
– 'Blauer Zwerg' ('Blue Dwarf')	CCla CSco EFou NBar SPla WMer
– 'Flüela'	CGle CMGP ECro EFou GCal LGre NHol SApp SGil SHer
– 'Seven Seas'	NRoo WPer
§ ***proteiflorum***	ECha ECro GCal LGre SGil SPer SRms
spinalba	ECro LGre SSpi
– 'Silbermannstreu'	NHol
x ***tripartitum***	Widely available
¶ – 'Variegatum'	EMon
variifolium	Widely available
yuccifolium	ECro EFou NSal SIgm WHil
x ***zabelii***	ECha ECro ELan GCal MFir NBir
– 'Jewel'	EMon MNFA SUsu
– 'Violetta'	CGle ELan GCal MBri MUlv

ERYSIMUM † (Cruciferae)

♦*alpinum* hort.	See E. ***hieraciifolium***
¶*amoenum*	NWCA
¶*arenicola*	NHol
– *torulosum*	See E. ***torulosum***
arkansanum	MDHE NTow
'Aunt May'	WRus
'Bowles' Mauve'	Widely available
'Bredon'	EFou ELan EMon EOrc GAbr GCHN LAbb LHop MRav NBro NPer NSti NTow SAxl SHer SMrm SPla SUsu WCru WKif WRus
'Butterscotch'	CBre CCMG CGle CLew CMHG CMil CPar CSam EMar LHop MFir NBro SFis SGil SSvw SUsu WHil WKif WMer
capitatum	MDHE NKay WHil WOMN WPer
'Changeling'	LRHS NPer
'Cheerfulness'	CHan
cheiri	CKin CRow CSFH GPoy IBlr LHol SIde WEas WSun WWye
N– 'Baden-Powell' (d)	ELan EOrc LHop WPer
– 'Bloody Warrior' (d)	CBot CCot CDec CElw CLew ELan EOrc GCal GCra LHop MFir MPla MTho NBro NFai NPer SUsu WHer WHil WPer
– 'Chevithorne'	SHBN
– 'Deben'	CBot
– 'Harpur Crewe' (d)	Widely available
– 'Jane's Derision'	CNat
– 'Malmesbury'	CNat
'Chelsea Jacket'	EFou GAbr NSti WRus
'Chequers'	ELan MBro WCra WMer WOMN WPer WRus
♦*concinnum*	See E. ***suffrutescens***
'Constant Cheer'	CBre CCot CElw CPar CSam CShe GAbr NBro NPer NSti SAxl SPer SUsu WKif WMar WMer WPer WRus WSun
'Devon Gold'	CPla
'Devon Sunset'	CPla CSam
♦'Dorothy Elmhirst'	See E. 'Mrs L K Elmhirst'
'Emm's Variety'	NBro
'Gold Flame'	MCas MWat NMen
'Golden Gem'	GGar MDHE SBla SIng WPer
'Golden Jubilee'	NTow WSun
§ ***helveticum***	CHal CNic GAbr LHil NCat NTow
§ ***hieracliifolium***	CRiv CSam MBal NBee WHil
'Jacob's Jacket'	CCot CElw CGle CMil CSam EBar EFou EPot GAbr GCHN LAbb LHop NBro NPer NRoo SAxl SChu WMer WPer WRus WSun WWin
'John Codrington'	CCMG CElw CGle CMHG EMar EMon NBro NPer NSti SBla SChu SHBN SMad SUsu
¶ 'Joseph's Coat'	CCot
'Jubilee Gold'	CHal EJud ELan MCas NCat
'Julian Orchard'	SAxl SUsu
kotschyanum	MCas MHig NTow SBla
'Lady Roborough'	CElw SWas
linifolium	EBur MDHE NBee NCat NWCA SHer SRms
§ – 'Variegatum'	CBar CCla CFis CGle CMer CPar CRDP CSam EFol ELan EOrc LHil LHop MBri MRav NBro NPer NRoo NSti SAxl SCro SPer SUsu WEas WHoo WPer WSun
'Miss Hopton'	CFis NTow WDav
'Moonlight'	CB&S CCot CElw CFis CGle CGre CMHG CPar CSam EFou LAbb LBee MTho NBro NNor NSti SChu SDix SFis SUsu WDav WEas WOMN WOld WPer WRus WSun
§ 'Mrs L K Elmhirst'	CFis CHal CLew EHal LHop NPer
mutabile	CB&S CCot CFis CMHG CRiv CShe EMon EOrc GAbr NBir NBro NCat NPer NSti SPla SSvw WEas WKif WOMN
– 'Variegatum'	CBot CElw CPar EFol ELan EMon IMal LHop NRar WEas WHoo
'Newark Park'	CHal
'Orange Flame'	CHal CLew CMHG CNic CRiv CSam EFol ELan EPad EPot ESis GAbr LAbb MBro MHig MPla MRav NBro NHol NKay NRar NRoo NTow SHer SMad WDav WPer
perofskianum	WEas
'Perry's Pumpkin'	NPer
'Primrose'	CMHG EFol EMar LHop NSti SSvw WPer
pulchellum	CRiv MWat SUsu WEas WHil WPat
pumilum	See E. ***helveticum***
'Rufus'	CCMG CCot CMHG CPar CPle CSam ELan EOrc GAbr LHop MBel MRav MTho NBro NSti SSvw WEas WMar WRus WSun
rupestre	See E. ***pulchellum***
§ ***scoparium***	CElw ESis GCal LHop NBro NPer NTow WHil WPer
semperflorens	NPer
'Sissinghurst Variegated'	See E. ***linifolium*** 'Variegatum'
'Sprite'	CLew CMHG CMea CShe EOrc EPot GAbr MHig MPla NCat NKay NMen NNrd NPer
§ ***suffrutescens***	ESis LHop MPlt NPer SUsu
'Sunbright'	CPar MCas NCat NMen NNrd NRoo
'Sunshine'	ELan
§ ***torulosum***	EPad NPer NSti
¶ ***uritimanii***	WPer
N 'Variegatum'	CB&S SHBN SPla WWin
'Wenlock Beauty'	CMHG CSam ELan GAbr MTho NBro NCat NFai NPer NSti SAxl SChu SHer SPer SSvw SUsu SWas WHil WMar WMer WOMN WPer WRus WSun
'Wenlock Beauty Variegated'	CMil
¶ ***wheeleri***	SFis
¶ ***witmannii***	WPer

ERYTHRAEA See CENTAURIUM

ERYTHRINA (Leguminosae)

crista-galli	CAbb CB&S CBot CGre CHEx CPle CSun CTro ERea ESma LAbb MUlv SHil SMad SSpi
¶ ***humeana***	CGre
lysistemon	CPle CTro

ERYTHRONIUM † (Liliaceae/Liliaceae)

albidum	LAma LBow NRog WChr

americanum	CArn CAvo CBro CHEx CRDP EPot GDra LAma LBow NRog NSal SSpi SUsu SWas WAbe WChr WCru
californicum	CHEx MPhe MS&S NRog SWas WChr
– 'White Beauty'	CAvo CBro CNic CRiv CWGN ECha ELan EPar EPot ETub ITim LAma LBlo LBow MBal MHig MTho NHar SHer SIng WAbe WChr WCru WKif
caucasicum	CBro EPot LBow NHol NRog WChr
citrinum	EPot MPhe
'Citronella'	CBro EPar LAma LBow NHar NHol NRog SIng WAbe WChr WCru WHil
cliftonii	See E. ***multiscapoideum*** Cliftonii Group
dens-canis	CAvo CBro CHEx CMea CRDP CRiv ECar ECha ELan EPar EPot ETub LAma LBow MBal MBri MHig MS&S MTho NHol NRog SIng SPou SSpi SWas WAbe WChr
– 'Frans Hals'	EPar EPot LAma NHol NRog WChr WHil
– 'Lilac Wonder'	CBro EPar EPot LAma NHol NRog WChr
– ***niveum***	LAma WChr
– 'Old Aberdeen'	WChr
*– 'Pajares Giant'	LRHS
– 'Pink Perfection'	EPar LAma NHol NRog SUsu WChr WHil
– 'Purple King'	EPar EPot LAma LBlo NHol NRog WChr
– 'Rose Queen'	CRDP ELan EPar EPot ETub LAma MNFA MTho NHol NRog WChr
– 'Snowflake'	ECha EPar EPot LAma MNFA NHol NRog WChr
– 'White Splendour'	CBro
grandiflorum	MPhe MS&S
helenae	MPhe
hendersonii	LAma WChr
japonicum	CBro CRDP CWGN EPar EPot LAma LBow NHol NRog SIng WChr
'Jeannine'	CBro CRDP LAma LRHS WChr
'Kondo'	EPot LAma MHig MNFA MS&S NHar NHol NRog NRoo SIng SSpi SUsu WAbe WCru
¶ ***montanum***	CAvo
§ ***multiscapoïdeum***	MHig MPhe MS&S WChr
§ – Cliftonii Group	MPhe WChr
oregonum	EPar EPot MPhe MS&S
'Pagoda'	Widely available
purdyi	See E. ***multiscapoideum***
revolutum	CBro ECar EPot IBlr LAma MS&S SSpi
– Johnsonii Group	MBal MS&S WChr
– 'Rose Beauty'	CBro LAma
'Sundisc'	NRog
tuolumnense	CAvo CBro CRiv ECar EPar EPot LAma LBow MBal MPhe NHar NRog SIng WAbe WChr
umbilicatum	MS&S WChr

ESCALLONIA † (Escalloniaceae)

'Alice'	CGre MBri SPer
§ ***alpina***	CGre CPle
'Apple Blossom'	Widely available
§ ***bifida***	CGre CPle WSHC WWat
'C F Ball'	CSco CTre ELan ENot GRei IOrc LBuc MGos NRoo NWea SReu WAbe WDin WStI
'Compacta Coccinea'	CLan CMer
'Dart's Rosy Red'	LRHS MBri
'Donard Beauty'	CDoC CMer CSco MBel SRms
'Donard Brilliance'	CMer ISea MGos
'Donard Gem'	CBow
'Donard Radiance'	CB&S CDoC CSco CShe ELan ENot IDai IJoh ISea MGos MRav MWat NKay SBod SGil SHer SPer WBod WDin WSHC
'Donard Scarlet'	CMer SRms
'Donard Seedling'	CB&S CBow CDoC CLan CMer CPle CSco EBre ECtt ELan ENot IDai LBre LBuc MBal MBel MBri MRav NBee NNor NRoo NWea SBod SHBN SPla SReu SRms STre
'Donard Star'	CShe ENot IOrc MGos
'Donard Suprise'	NNor
'Donard White'	IDai ISea SRms
'Edinensis'	CMHG CSco ECtt ENot ISea MBar NNor WDin WWat
'Erecta'	CBow LRHS
¶ × ***exoniensis***	SRms
♦ ***fonkii***	See E. ***alpina***
¶ 'Glasnevin Hybrid'	IDai
'Glory of Donard'	CDoC CSco ENot
¶ ***gracilis alba***	CPle
'Gwendolyn Anley'	CDoC CHal CMHG CMer CSco ECar ESis MAsh MGos NTow SBod SGil SHer SPer WTyr WWat WWeb
♦ 'Hopleys Gold'	See E. ***laevis*** 'Gold Brian'
illinita	CGre CMer CPle
'Iveyi'	Widely available
§ ***laevis***	CGre CMer SDry
¶ – 'Gold Brian'	CB&S MSta
'Lanarth Hybrid'	CMer
'Langleyensis'	CB&S CDoC CMer IJoh MWat NNor NWea SBod SPla WDin WSHC
leucantha	CGre CMer
littoralis	CPle
macrantha	See E. ***rubra m.***
¶ ***mexicana***	CBot CHan
montevidensis	See E. ***bifida***
'Newryensis'	SPer
organensis	See E. ***laevis***
'Peach Blossom'	CDoC CPle CSco EBar ELan ENot MGos SHBN SPer
'Pink Elf'	ECtt LRHS MBri
'Pink Pearl'	CMer SRms
'Pride of Donard'	CB&S CDoC CLan CSco IDai IOrc ISea LHop MAsh SGil SReu WWeb
pulverulenta	CGre
punctata	See E. ***rubra***
'Rebecca'	CMer ESma
'Red Dwarf'	WAbe
'Red Elf'	CMHG CMer EBlo EBre ECtt ELan ESma IJoh ISea LBre MBar MBri MGos MPla MWat NHol SLPl SLon SPer SPla WPat
'Red Hedger'	CDoC CMer MRav
resinosa	CPle SArc
revoluta	CGre CPle SDry
'Rose Queen'	IDai

rosea	CGre CPle
§ *rubra*	CGre SPer
– 'Crimson Spire'	CB&S CDoC CLan CSco CShe EBar EBre ENot GRei LBre MGos MRav MWat NNor SBod SHBN SHer SLon SPer SPla SRms WStI WTyr
– 'Ingramii'	CMHG CMer CSco SBod SHBN
§ – var. *macrantha*	CB&S CBow CHEx CSco CTre GRei GWht IDai IJoh ISea SArc SLon SPer SPla WAbe WBod WDin WPat WStI WTyr
– 'Pubescens'	CMer SLon
– 'Pygmaea'	See E. *r.* 'Woodside'
– var. *uniflora*	SDry
§ – 'Woodside'	CPle ESis GAbr IDai LHop MGos NHol SHer WBod WHCG
'Saint Keverne'	CMer
¶ 'Silver Anniversary'	CGre LRHS SMad SPla
'Slieve Donard'	CMer ENot GRei MGos MRav SLPl
x *stricta* 'Harold Comber'	CMer MUlv SDry
tucumanensis	CGre CPle SArc
virgata	CGre CMer CPle SDix WWat
viscosa	SSpi

EUCALYPTUS † (Myrtaceae)

acaciiformis	CArn
aggregata	CArn SArc WCel
approximans approximans	WCel
archeri	CMHG MBal WCel
¶ *caesia*	GCHN
camphora	CMHG WCel
cinerea	IOrc WCel
citriodora	CHun CTro LHol LWad SIde WCel
coccifera	CAbb CB&S CDoC CHEx CSco CTre GAri GWht IOrc MBal MFir SSpi WCel WNor WWeb
consideniana	CArn
cordata	MBal WCel
crenulata	WCel
dalrympleana	CB&S CBow CDoC CMHG CSam CSco EBre ELan ENot IOrc LBre MBal MGos MUlv SHil SPer SPla SSta WCel WDin WWeb
deanei	WCel
delegatensis	CMHG GAri IOrc WCel
divaricata	See E. *gunnii*
ficifolia	CGre CTro LRHS SLMG SLon
¶ *foecunda*	CGre
fraxinoïdes	WCel
glaucescens	CBow CMHG EBar SArc SPer WCel
globulus	CB&S CHEx GAri LHol MBal
– *bicostata*	IOrc
goniocalyx	WCel
§ *gregsoniana*	CMHG ISea WCel WWeb
§ *gunnii*	Widely available
– *divaricata*	WCel
johnstonii	GWht IOrc ISea WCel WWeb
kitsoniana	MBal WCel
kybeanensis	WCel
leucoxylon	WCel
macarthurii	WCel
mannifera ssp. *elliptica*	WCel
mitchelliana	WCel
moorei nana	IBar WNor WPat
muelleriana	CArn
neglecta	WCel
nicholii	CMHG WCel
niphophila	See E. *pauciflora n.*
nitens	CMHG GAri MBal WCel
§ *nitida*	CArn CMHG WCel WNor
¶ *nova-anglica*	CMHG
parvifolia	CB&S CDoC CLnd GAri SDry SHil WCel
pauciflora	CBow CDoC EBre GAri IBar LBre MBal MUlv SArc SPer WBod WCel WNor
– ssp. *debeuzevillei*	CMHG SArc WCel
– *nana*	See E. *gregsoniana*
§ – ssp. *niphophila*	Widely available
– – 'Pendula'	CMHG GAri WCel WWeb
perriniana	CB&S CBow CDoC CHEx CMHG ELan ENot IBlr MBal MUlv SArc SDry SPer SPla WCel WNor WWeb
pulverulenta	WCel
regnans	CGre ISea MBal
risdonii	WNor
rubida	CMHG ESis IOrc WCel
simmondsii	See E. *nitida*
stellulata	CMHG IOrc WCel
stuartiana	See E. *bridgesiana*
sturgissiana	GCHN
subcrenulata	CMHG GWht WCel
urnigera	CDoC GAri ISea SPla SSta WCel WWeb
vernicosa	WCel
viminalis	CArn CTre IOrc ISea WCel

EUCHARIS (Liliaceae/Amaryllidaceae)

§ *amazonica*	CKel CTro LAma NRog SGil
grandiflora hort.	See E. *amazonica*
x *grandiflora* Plan. & Lind.	CTro LBow SDeJ WChr

EUCODONIA (Gesneriaceae)

'Adele'	NMos
andrieuxii	NMos
– 'Naomi'	NMos WEfe
'Cornell'	NMos
'Tintacoma'	NMos
verticillata 'Frances'	NMos

EUCOMIS (Liliaceae/Hyacinthaceae)

§ *autumnalis*	CAvo CKel LAma
bicolor	CAvo CChu CHEx CKel CPar CRDP EBak LAma LBow LHil MBri NRog SChu SGil WCru WEas
– 'Alba'	LBow
– hybrids	EFou
§ *comosa*	CAvo CB&S CChu CHEx CRDP EBul LAma LBow NRog SGil WCru
– purple form	EMon
pole-evansii	CAvo CHEx
punctata	See E. *comosa*
undulata	See E. *autumnalis autumnalis*
zambesiaca	CMon EBul LBow

EUCOMMIA (Eucommiaceae)

ulmoïdes	CMCN CPle WCoo

EUCRYPHIA † (Eucryphiaceae)

'Castlewellan'	ISea
cordifolia	CB&S CGre CLan CMHG CTrw GWht ISea MBal SCog SSpi WBod
– x ***lucida***	CB&S CCla CDoC CGre IOrc ISea MBal SCog SPer WBod WDin
glutinosa	CB&S CBow CChu CCla CGre CLan CSam EHar ELan GAbr IBar ISea LHyd MBal MBri NBir SCog SHBN SHil SPer SReu SSpi SSta WAbe WBod WCoo WNor WWat
– Plena Group	ISea
x ***hillieri*** 'Winton'	CAbb CGre ISea MBal SSpi
x ***intermedia***	CBow CDoC CGre CSam ELan GAbr GGGa IDai SCog SHBN SPer SSpi WDin WWat
– 'Rostrevor'	CB&S CBow CLan CMHG CSco ELan GWht ISea LTil MBal SHil SLon SPer SReu SSta WBod
lucida	CCla CMHG GWht ISea LHyd MBal SCob SSta WBod WCoo WNor WWat
– 'Pink Cloud'	CMHG ISea LRHS
milliganii	CB&S CCla CDoC CGre CMHG ELan GWht ISea MBal MBrk MUlv SCob SCog SHBN SHil SPer SSpi SSta WAbe WBod WSHC WWat
moorei	CB&S ISea MBal SArc SSpi SSta WBod
x ***nymansensis***	CB&S CBow CPle EBre ECtt LAbb LBre MBal SArc SBar SBor SCog SReu WBod
– 'George Graham'	ISea MBal
– 'Mount Usher'	CGre IOrc ISea
– 'Nymansay'	CB&S CBra CCla CLan CMHG CSco EHar ELan GGGa GWht IDai IJoh ISea LHyd MBal MBar MBri MBrk MGos MRav SHBN SHil SLon SPer SSta WAbe WDin WMou WThu WWat
N'Penwith'	ISea MBal SSpi

EUGENIA (Myrtaceae)

¶ ***myrtifolia***	STre
¶ ***smithii***	CTro
uniflora	ESim

EUMORPHIA (Compositae)

canescens	WHer WOld
sericea	CHan CNic GAbr NNor

EUNOMIA See AETHIONEMA

EUODIA (Rutaceae)

♦***daniellii***	See TETRADIUM *d.*
♦***hupehensis***	See TETRADIUM ***daniellii*** Hupehense Group

EUONYMUS † (Celastraceae)

alatus	Widely available
– var. ***apterus***	MPla SHBN
– 'Ciliodentatus'	See E. ***a.*** 'Compactus'
§ – 'Compactus'	CChu CDoC CPMA EBre EHar EPla LBre MBlu MBri MPla MUlv WWat
bungeanus	CMCN EPla SSpi
– var. ***semipersistens***	EPla
cornutus var. ***quinquecornutus***	EPla LGre SWas WMou
europaeus	CArn CBow CBra CDoC CKin CLew CLnd CPer CSco CShe EBre ELan EPla LBre LBuc NWea SPer WCoo WDin WMou
– f. ***albus***	CChu CMCN CPMA CPle SPer WWat
– 'Atrorubens'	CPMA MPla
– 'Aucubifolius' (v)	EPla
– var. ***intermedius***	ENot EPla
– 'Red Cascade'	CB&S CBra CChu CMCN CMHG CSco EBre EGol EHar ELan ENot IJoh IOrc LBre LHop MBar MBri MWat NHol NKay SHBN SLon SPer SSpi WBod WDin WMou WPat WWat WWin
****farreri***	CLew CNic
fimbriatus	CB&S
fortunei 'Canadale Gold' (v)	CCla CDoC EPla MBri MGos NBee NFai
– 'Coloratus'	CLan ENot MBar SHBN SPer WDin
– 'Croftway	SCro
– 'Dart's Blanket'	CCla ELan ENot EPla MRav SLPl SPer WDin
– 'Emerald Cushion'	ENot NTow SPer
– Emerald Gaiety® (v)	Widely available
– 'Emerald Surprise'	MBri SHBN
– Emerald 'n' Gold® (v)	Widely available
– 'Gold Spot'	See E. ***f.*** 'Sunspot'
♦– 'Gold Tip' (v)	See E. ***f.*** Golden Prince®
¶ – 'Golden Pillar'	GWht
§ – Golden Prince® (v)	CB&S CBow CCla CPle EFol ENot EPla IJoh MBar MGos MRav NFai NHol SPer SReu SSta WStI
¶ – 'Harlequin'	ELan SHil
¶ – 'Hort's Blaze'	MGos
– 'Kewensis'	CLew CMHG CMer CPle CRiv ENot MBar MCas MPla MRav MWat NBee NTow SArc SBod SPer WCru WWat
– 'Minimus'	CDoC EGol EHal EPla ESis GAri NHol SPla WPer
– 'Sheridan Gold'	ECtt EGol EHoe EPla MPla MRav NHol NWyt SHBN SPer
– 'Silver Gem'	See E. ***f.*** 'Variegatus'
– 'Silver Pillar' (v)	EBar ENot ERav ESis
– 'Silver Queen' (v)	CB&S CCla CDec CLan CPle CSco ELan ENot IDai IJoh ISea LAbb MBal MBar MBri MGos MPla MWat NKay SHBN SPer SReu SSta WDin WPat WSHC WWat
– 'Sunshine'	CPMA CSco ELan EPla MBri MGos
§ – 'Sunspot' (v)	CBow CMHG CSco EBre ECtt EGol ELan EPla EPot ERav ESis GWht ISea LAbb LBre MBar MBri MGos MRav NFai NTow SAxl SLon SPer SPla SSta WDin WPat WStI
¶ – 'Tustin'	SLPl

§ – 'Variegatus'	CBow CMHG EFol ELan ENot MBar MCas NKay NNor SPer STre WBod WDin WPat
– 'Variegatus' EM '85	MBri
– var. ***vegetus***	EPla NNor
grandiflorus	WMou
hamiltonianus	CMCN SLon
– ssp. ***hians***	See E. ***h. sieboldianus***
§ – ssp. ***sieboldianus***	CCla CMCN CPMA EGol LHop MBal MGos WWat
– – 'Coral Charm'	EGol SHil
– – Semiexsertus Group	EHar EPla
– ***yedoensis***	See E. ***h. sieboldianus***
* ***hibarimisake***	SBla
japonicus	ENot SArc WDin
– 'Albomarginatus'	CB&S MBar MPla WSHC
– 'Aureopictus'	See E. ***j.*** 'Aureus'
– 'Aureovariegatus'	See E. ***j.*** 'Ovatus Aureus'
§ – 'Aureus' (v)	CB&S CSco ELan ENot EPla IDai IJoh LPan MBal MBri SHBN SLon WDin
– 'Duc d'Anjou' (v)	CB&S CRow EBre EFol EHoe ELan EPla LBre LPan SDry SHil SMad
§ – 'Latifolius Albomarginatus'	CCla EBre EHoe LBre SPer
– 'Luna'	See E. ***j.*** 'Aureus'
¶ – 'Macrophyllus'	GAri
– 'Macrophyllus Albus'	See E. ***j.*** 'Latifolius Albomarginatus'
♦ – 'Marieke' (v)	See E. ***j.*** 'Ovatus Aureus'
– 'Mediopictus'	MBri
– 'Microphyllus'	MBal MUlv NHol SArc
§ – 'Microphyllus Albovariegatus'	CMHG CNic ECar ECtt EFol ELan EPla ISea MBal MBar MGos MRav NHol SLon SPla WAbe WHCG WPat WThu WWat
– 'Microphyllus Aureovariegatus'	ECar WPat WThu WWin
– 'Microphyllus Aureus'	See E. ***j.*** 'Microphyllus Pulchellus'
– 'Microphyllus Gold Pillar' (v)	ESis ESma
§ – 'Microphyllus Pulchellus' (v)	CB&S CMHG CNic ECar EFol EPla EPot ESis IJoh MBar MRav SLon WHCG WWeb
– 'Microphyllus Variegatus'	See E. ***j.*** 'Microphyllus Albovariegatus'
§ – 'Ovatus Albus' (v)	CPle
§ – 'Ovatus Aureus' (v)	CFis CLan CSco EFol ELan ENot ERav ISea LPan MBal MGos MPla MRav SPer SReu WDin WPat WStI
– 'Président Gauthier' (v)	CDoC CRow EFol LHop LPan
– 'Robustus'	CDoC EPla
* – 'Silver Princess'	NHol SHBN
kiautschovicus	EPla
latifolius	CMCN WMou
– × ***hamiltonianus***	CMCN
§ ***lucidus***	CChu CGre SSpi
myrianthus	SSpi WWat
§ ***nanus***	CPle EPla ESis MBal NHol WPat WSHC WWat
– var. ***turkestanicus***	CBrd EPla ESis SPer SRms WWat
oxyphyllus	CCla CMCN SSpi WMou WThu WWat
pendulus	See E. ***lucidus***
phellomanus	CSco EBar EPla GDra LNet MBar MBlu WWat
§ ***planipes***	CCla CGre CPle CSco EBar EHar ELan ENot EPla MBri NHol SHil SPer SSpi WMou WWat
radicans	See E. ***fortunei radicans***
'Rokojo'	NHol WPat
rosmarinifolius	See E. ***nanus***
sachalinensis hort.	See E. ***planipes***
sp. B&L 12543	EPla
¶ ***velutinus***	CChu CGre
verrucosus	EPla
wilsonii	WWat
yedoensis	See E. ***hamiltonianus sieboldianus***

EUPATORIUM (Compositae)

altissima	CBot CCla CGle CHad CHan CLew CRDP EFou ELan EMon EPar GCal MHew NSal NSti SChu SPer WCHb WDav WEas WOld WWat
– 'Braunlaub'	EFou EMon WCot
altissimum JLS 88029	EMon
aromaticum	CArn CSev ECro ELan EMon SFis SSvw WCHb WPer WWye
cannabinum	CArn CKin CRDP CSam CWGN ECED EHon ELan EMFW GPoy LHol MFir MHew MSta NMir NSal NSti WGwy WNdy WOak WPer WWye
¶ – 'Album'	GCal
– 'Flore Pleno'	CCla CSev ECha ECro EFou EMon MUlv NSti WCot
fortunei	EMon
glechonophyllum	CGre CPle
¶ ***hildalgense***	CGre
§ ***ligustrinum***	CB&S CCla CDec CDoC CGle CHan CLan CPle CTre CWit ECha ELan IBar IOrc ISea LHop SDix SMrm SPer WBod WCHb WPer WSHC
maculatum	EFou EMon GCal MUlv SFis
§ – 'Atropurpureum'	CChu CCla CGre CHad CSco CSev EBre ECha EFol EFou ELan EOrc GCal LBre MBri MFir NBir NSti SMad SUsu WDav
¶ – 'Berggarten'	GCal
micranthum	See E. ***ligustrinum***
perfoliatum	CArn ECha GPoy LHol MHew NSal WWye
purpureum	CArn CChu CTom CWGN ECED ECha GPoy LHol MHew MSte MWat NDea NSal SChu SIde SMrm SPer SSvw SWat WEas WHal WHer WOak WOld WPer WRus WSHC WWye
– 'Atropurpureum'	See E. ***maculatum*** 'A.'
rugosum album	See E. ***album***
sordidum	CTro ERea MNew SLMG
triplinerve	CTom LHol MSte
weinmannianum	See E. ***ligustrinum***

EUPHORBIA † (Euphorbiaceae)

amygdaloïdes	CKin CRow WWye
– 'Purpurea'	See E. ***a.*** 'Rubra'
§ – var. ***robbiae***	Widely available
§ – 'Rubra'	Widely available
– 'Variegata'	CRDP CRow ELan EMon EOrc EPla LGre MTho NRar SMad

biglandulosa	See E. ***rigida***
****capitata***	WDav
capitulata	CLew EFol ELan EPot LHop MCas MHig MTho NMen NNrd WThu WWin
ceratocarpa	CB&S CMil EMon EPla GCal LRHS NSti NWyt SUsu
characias	CB&S CBot CBow CGle CRow CWGN ECtt ELun EMon MBri MPar NBar NNor NOak NPer NSti WByw WHoo WWat
– JCA 475.500	CMil GCal
– 'Blue Hills'	EMon GCal IBlr
¶– 'Emmer Green' (v)	SBla
¶– 'Forescate'	GCal
¶– 'Jenetta'	NCat
– 'Variegata'	CRow
– ssp. ***wulfenii***	Widely available
– – JCA 475.603	CMil GCal
– – var. ***sibthorpii***	EPla MUlv WCot WOld
– – 'Bosahan' (v)	CMHG GCal SMad
– – 'H E Bates'	NBir
– – 'Humpty Dumpty'	CRow EBre EPla LBre LRHS NPer
¶– – 'Jayne's Golden Giant'	EMon
§– – 'John Tomlinson'	CMHG EPla MUlv NSti NWyt WEas
– – Kew form	See E. ***c. w.*** 'John Tomlinson'
– – 'Lambrook Gold'	CFis CHad CMHG CRow CSam ECtt EGol ELan EMon EOrc EPar GCal MRav NPer SChu SMad SMrm SPer SSvw WHoo WRus
– – 'Lambrook Yellow'	CCla CMil EMon EPla
– – 'Margery Fish'	EFou EPla WMer
– – 'Minuet'	CHan CShe
– – 'Perry's Tangerine'	NPer
– – 'Perry's Winter Blusher'	NPer
– – 'Purpurea'	CHad NSti SAxl WRus
¶***cognata*** C&Mc 607	GCHN
coralloïdes	CArn CFis CLew CSco CTom ECha IBlr MFir NPer WCra WCru WHer
cornigera	CElw EMon GCal IBlr SAxl
cyparissias	Widely available
– Ashfield form	NRar
♦– 'Betten'	See E. ***esula***
– 'Bush Boy'	IBlr WCot
– 'Clarice Howard'	NRar
– 'Orange Man'	EMon IBlr
– 'Tall Boy'	IBlr
dulcis	CFis CGle CHal CLew CRow CTom ECha EFol EFou ELun EOrc EPla ISea LGan NBro NHol NOak NSti WByw WCot WEas WHen WOld WRus WWat
– 'Chameleon'	Widely available
epithymoïdes	See E. ***polychroma***
¶***esula***	CGle
fulgens	CBow CHal
glauca	ECou IBlr
griffithii	CBow CRow ISea LBlm NBro NWyt SBor WAbb WCru
– 'Dixter'	Widely available
– 'Fern Cottage'	SWas
– 'Fireglow'	Widely available
– 'Wickstead'	EPla GCal LHop
horrida	SLMG
hyberna	CFis CTom IBlr MFir MTho MUlv NHol NWyt SUsu
jacquemontii	CCMG CChu GCal LGan MRav SFis
x ***keysii***	MBri
lathyris	CFis CRow CSFH ERav LHol MHew NPer NRar SIng WCru WEas WWye
N***longifolia*** D Don	CLew EFou ELan EPla IBlr LHop MMil SBor SSpi SUsu WAbb
– hort.	See E. ***cornigera***
mammillaris	SLMG
x ***martinii***	Widely available
mellifera	CAbb CArn CB&S CBot CCMG CChu CDec CGle CHan CMHG CWGN ECha ELan EMon EPla GCal ISea LGre LHop NPer NSti SArc SBor SChu SMrm SSpi SUsu WCru WSHC WWat
milii	CHal EBak
– 'Koenigers Aalbäumle'	MBri
myrsinites	Widely available
nicaeënsis	CAbb CB&S CCMG CChu CCla CFis CMea EFou EMon EOrc EPla GCal LBlm LGre MRav NGar NSti SBla SChu SCro SFar SMrm SSpi SUsu WCra WWat
oblongata	CB&S CChu CMil EFou ELan EMon EPla IBlr LRHS NHol NSti
palustris	Widely available
– 'Walenburg's Glorie'	GCal
pilosa	CNat ERav NSti
– ***major***	See E. ***polychroma*** 'Major'
pithyusa	CGle ECha EPla MMil SMad SUsu
§***polychroma***	Widely available
– 'Emerald Jade'	IBlr
§– 'Major'	CFis CMHG CTom ECha GCal MUlv NCat SPer WEas
– 'Midas'	EMon SSpi
– 'Purpurea'	Widely available
– 'Sonnengold'	GCal SMad WSHC
*– 'Variegata'	EFol EPla MMil NBir NSti WPbr WSHC
portlandica	CB&S CFis ELan LGan NHol NSti NWyt WHer
§ x ***pseudovirgata***	CMil EHal EMon IBlr SAxl SUsu
pugniformis	MBri
pulcherrima	MBri
'Red Dwarf'	EOrc
♦***reflexa***	See E. ***seguieriana niciciana***
resinifera	CHal SLMG
§***rigida***	CBot CChu CFis CPar EPla ERav GCal NRar SAxl SBla SGil SMrm SSpi SWas
robbiae	See E. ***amygdaloïdes r.***
schillingii	CAbb CCMG CChu CHad CHan CMHG CRow CSam CSco EBre ECha EGol EOrc EPla GCal LBre LHop MBri SAxl SBla SDix SMad SPer SSpi SUsu SWas WWat
seguieriana	ECha EPla NCat SMrm
§– ssp. ***niciciana***	CChu CHan CMGP CMHG CMea CMil CSam CSco EBre EFol ELan ERav IBlr LBre LGre MRav NBir NCat NHol NNor NSti SBla SDix SMrm SSpi SUsu WEas
serrulata	See E. ***stricta***

sikkimensis	CBot CChu CElw CHad CHan CMHG CRow EBre ECha ELan ELun EOrc EPar LBre SAxl SBla SBor SHer SMrm SSpi WCHb WCru WEas WHal WOld WRus WWat WWin
§ ***stricta***	CNat CRow CTom IBlr NRar NSti WHil
* ***submammillaris*** 'Variegata'	MBri
uralensis	See E. x ***pseudovirgata***
§ ***virgata***	EMon
x ***waldsteinii***	See E. ***virgata***
N ***wallichii***	CChu CHad CSam CSco ECha EFou EGol ELan EOrc IBlr MBri MUlv NHol NOrc NRoo NSti NWyt SChu SMrm WAbb WHoo WRus WWat

EUPTELEA (Eupteleaceae)

franchetii	See E. ***pleiosperma***
polyandra	CCla CGre EHar SSpi WCoo

EURYA (Theaceae)

japonica K&E 3653	SSpi
– 'Variegata'	See CLEYERA ***japonica*** 'Fortunei'

EURYOPS (Compositae)

abrotanifolius	CMHG EPla WPer
§ ***acraeus***	CBot CCla CPle CShe EHar ELan EPot ESis GCHN GDra ITim LGre MBri MBro MPla NHar NHol NKay NNor NRoo SIng WDav WEas WWin
§ ***chrysanthemoïdes***	CB&S CBrk CMHG CPle CSam CSpe CTre EBar ERea IBlr LHil MSte NTow SDix WPer
evansii	See E. ***acraeus***
* ***grandiflorus***	CBot
pectinatus	Widely available
sericeus	See URSINIA ***sericea***
¶ ***tenuissimus***	CPle SMrm
tysonii	CPle
virgineus	CB&S CMHG CMer CPle CSam CTre CTro ESma IBlr

EUSTEPHIA (Liliaceae/Amaryllidaceae)

jujuyensis	LBow WChr

EUSTOMA (Gentianaceae)

§ ***grandiflorum***	MBri
russellianum	See E. ***grandiflorum***

EVOLVULUS (Convolvulaceae)

convolvuloïdes	ERea
glomeratus 'Blue Daze'	See E. ***pilosus*** 'B. D.'
§ ***pilosus*** 'Blue Daze'	ERea SSad

EWARTIA (Compositae)

nubigena	NWCA

EXACUM (Gentianceae)

affine	MBri
– 'Rococo'	MBri

EXOCHORDA (Rosaceae)

giraldii var. ***wilsonii***	CBow CCla CDoC CPMA CSam CSco EBar EHar MPla MUlv WWat
korolkowii	SHil
x ***macrantha*** 'Irish Pearl'	ERav
– 'The Bride'	Widely available
racemosa	CBow CDoC CGre CPMA EHal ISea MBal MGos NNor SEng SHBN SLon SPer SSpi WBod

FABIANA (Solanaceae)

imbricata	CBot CBra CLan CPMA CPle ECar GAbr IDai LAbb MBar SHil SLon SPer SSpi SSta WAbe WBod
– ***alba***	WThu
– 'Prostrata'	CBow CDoC CPMA CPle EBar ECar GCal MUlv SDry SHil SSpi WDin WThu WWat
– f. ***violacea***	CB&S CGre CPMA CPle LAbb MBar SHil SLon SReu SSpi SSta WBod WKif

FAGOPYRUM (Polygonaceae)

cymosum	See F. ***dibotrys***
§ ***dibotrys***	ELan

FAGUS † (Fagaceae)

crenata	CBow CMCN WCoo WNor
engleriana	CMCN CSco CTho SHil
¶ ***grandifolia***	CMCN WMou
sylvatica	CB&S CBow CDoC CKin CLnd CPer EBre ELan ENot GRei IDai IOrc ISea LBre LBuc LPan MBar MBri MGos NBee NWea SHBN SPer SReu WDin WMou WNor WStI
§ – 'Albomarginata'	EBre IOrc LBre SHil
– 'Albovariegata'	See F. ***s.*** 'Albomarginata'
– 'Ansorgei'	CMCN CTho MBri
– 'Atropunicea'	See F. ***s.*** Purpurea Group
– 'Aurea Pendula'	CMCN EHar SHil WMou
– 'Black Swan'	CMCN MBri
– 'Bornyensis'	EHar WMou
– 'Cochleata'	CMCN
¶ – 'Cockleshell'	CMCN WMou
¶ – Copper Group	WMou
– 'Cristata'	CMCN GAri
♦ – 'Cuprea'	See F. ***s.*** Copper Group
§ – 'Dawyck'	CB&S CBow CDoC CLnd CMCN COtt CSco CTho EBre EHar ELan ENot IHos IOrc ISea LBre MBal MBar NWea SPer WDin
– 'Dawyck Gold'	CAbP CDoC CMCN COtt CSco EHar IOrc ISea LPan MBar MBlu MBri SHil SMad SSpi WMou
– 'Dawyck Purple'	CAbP CBow CDoC CMCN COtt CSco EHar IOrc LPan MBlu MBri MGos SHil SMad SSpi WMou
– 'Fastigiata'	See F. ***s.*** 'Dawyck'
¶ – 'Frisio'	CMCN
– var. ***heterophylla***	CLnd CTho EHar GAri ISea
– – f. ***laciniata***	CMCN
– – 'Aspleniifolia'	CB&S CBra CDoC CMCN COtt CPMA CSco EBre EGol ELan ENot IOrc LBre LPan MBal MBri SPer WDin WMou WNor
– 'Horizontalis'	WMou
– 'Luteovariegata'	CMCN

– 'Mercedes'	CMCN
– 'Miltonensis'	WMou
¶– 'Nana'	CMCN
N– 'Pendula'	CB&S CBra CDoC CLnd CMCN CPMA CTho EBre EHar ELan ENot GRei IJoh IOrc ISea LBre MBal MBri NWea SMad SPer WAbe WDin WMou WStI
– 'Prince George of Crete'	CMCN ISea WMou
– 'Purple Fountain'	CBow CDoC CMCN COtt CSco EHar IJoh IOrc LPan MBri MGos MUlv SMad SPer
N– Purple Group	CB&S CBow CBra CDoC CKin CPMA EBre EHar ELan ENot GRei IDai IOrc LBre LBuc MBal MBar MBri MGos NBee NHol NWea SHBN SPer WCoo WDin WMou WStI
– 'Purpurea Pendula'	CBow CCla CMCN CSco CTho EHar ELan ENot GRei IJoh IOrc ISea LPan MBal MBar MGos NBee NWea SPer WStI
§ – 'Purpurea Tricolor'	CBow CDoC CMCN CSco EGol EHar IOrc LPan MGos SHBN SHil SPer WDin
¶– 'Quercifolia'	CMCN
– 'Quercina'	CMCN CTho
– 'Riversii'	CB&S CDoC CLnd CMCN CPMA CSco EBre EHar ELan ENot IDai IJoh IOrc LBre LPan MBal MBri NWea SHBN SPer SSta WAbe WDin WStI
– 'Rohan Gold'	CMCN MBri WMou
*– 'Rohan Trompenburg'	CMCN WMou
– 'Rohanii'	CAbP CB&S CDoC CLnd CMCN COtt CSco CTho CWSG EHar ELan IHos IOrc ISea LPan MBal MBlu MBri NBee SEng SHBN SHil SPer SSpi WDin WMou WNor
– 'Roseomarginata'	See F. *s.* 'Purpurea Tricolor'
– 'Rotundifolia'	CDoC EBre LBre NWea
*– 'Silver Wood'	CMCN MBri WMou
– 'Spaethiana'	MBri
– f. *tortuosa*	EHar WMou
– 'Tortuosa Purpurea'	CMCN
– 'Tricolor' (v)	CLnd COtt CPMA ELan ENot IJoh MBal MBri MUlv WDin
*– 'Trompenburg'	SSpi
– 'Zlatia'	CDoC CLnd CMCN COtt CSco CTho EHar ELan ENot IOrc MBal MBar MBri MGos NBee SEng SHBN SHil SPer WDin WMou WStI

FALLOPIA † (Polygonaceae)

aubertii	See F. ***baldschuanica***
§ ***baldschuanica***	CCla CMac CSco CShe ELan ENot GRei IDai IHos ISea MBar MGos MPla MRav MWat NEgg NHol NKay NRoo SBra SHBN SLon SPer WBod WCru
§ ***japonica***	CFis CRow ELan SAxl
§ – var. ***compacta***	CHan CRow EPla MFir MUlv
– 'Spectabilis'	CRow ECha EFol EGol ELan MUlv
– 'Variegata'	EPla IBlr SMad
sachalinensis	CRow ELan EMon

FALLUGIA (Rosaceae)

See Plant Deletions

FARFUGIUM (Compositae)

§ ***tussilagineum***	CHEx MTho
– 'Argenteum' (v)	CBos CHEx
– 'Aureomaculatum' (v)	CB&S CBos CHEx CHan CRDP MTho SAxl

FARGESIA (Gramineae(Bambuseae))

dracocephala	ISta SArc SBam SDry WJun
§ ***nitida***	CB&S CBra CDec CHEx CSco CShe EFul EHar ENot EPla ERav ETPC IOrc ISea ISta LBam MBri MGos MUlv NJap NKay SBam SCob SDry SHig SPer SReu SSpi WDin WJun
¶– 'Eisenach'	ISta
¶– 'Nymphenburg'	EPla
robusta	SBam SDry WJun
§ ***spathacea***	CCla CHEx CHan CLew EFul EHar ELan ENot EPla ISta LNet MBar MBri NBee NJap NSel SBam SCob SDry SPer WJun
*– ***dana***	WJun
– 'Simba'	CDoC EPla ISta NSel SCob WJun
– 'Variegata'	SDry
utilis	SBam SDry WJun

FARSETIA (Cruciferae)

clypeata	See FIBIGIA ***clypeata***

FASCICULARIA (Bromeliaceae)

andina	See F. ***bicolor***
§ ***bicolor***	CB&S CGre CHEx CWGN IBlr IJoh LGre LHil MTho MUlv SLMG WEas
kirchhoffiana	SLMG
pitcairniifolia	CGre CHEx CTro EBak EBul IBlr LRHS SArc SLMG

X FATSHEDERA (Araliaceae)

lizei	CB&S CBot CBow CDoC CHEx CHal CLan CRow CSam CSco EPla IBlr MBal MBri NNor NRog SArc SBra SDry SPla SReu WDin WWat
– 'Anne Mieke' (v)	MBri
¶– 'Aurea' (v)	SDry
– 'Aureopicta'	See X F. ***l.*** 'Aurea'
§ – 'Lemon and Lime' (v)	CB&S CBot CDec EPla IBlr WSHC
– ***maculata***	See X F. ***l.*** 'Lemon and Lime'
– 'Pia'	MBri
– 'Variegata'	CB&S CBow CDoC CGre CHEx CRow CSco IBlr MBal MBri SDry SGil SHer WSHC WWat

FATSIA (Araliaceae)

§ ***japonica***	CB&S CBot CBra CHEx CLan CRow CSam CSco CShe EBre ENot IJoh ISea LBre MBal MBri MGos MRav NKay SArc SDix SHBN SMad SPer SReu SSta WDin WEas
– 'Variegata'	CB&S CBot MBri MGos MUlv NPal SArc SHBN SHil SPer WDin

papyrifera	See TETRAPANAX ***papyrifer***

FAUCARIA (Aizoaceae)

tigrina	CHal MBri

FEIJOA See ACCA

FELICIA (Compositae)

§ ***amelloïdes***	CBow CCan CHal CMHG CMer CRiv CSam CSev CTro ERea ESis ESma GCal LAbb MPit NRar NTow SChu SLMG WHal WPer
– 'Astrid Thomas'	CBar CBrk CSpe
– 'Read's Blue'	CCan LGre LHil LHop
– 'Read's White'	CB&S CBrk CCan CSpe CTro EDon EMar EOrc ERav ERea ESma LHil LHop MSte NRar SMrm
§ – 'Santa Anita'	CBrk CCan CSev CSpe ECtt EDon EOrc ERea IBar LHil LHop SDix WEas WHal
¶ – 'Santa Anita' (large flowered)	LHil
– 'Santa Anita Variegated'	EMar LHop SMrm
§ – variegated	Widely available
♦ ***amethystina***	See F. 'Snowmass'
§ ***amoena***	CBrk CCla CFis CHad CHan CMer EDon ELan LHil LHop MTho NRar SChu SLon WBod WEas WHal WPer WWin
– 'Variegata'	CFis CMer EOrc LAbb MCas MPit SChu
bergeriana	WOMN
capensis	See F. ***amelloïdes***
– 'Variegata'	See F. ***amelloïdes*** variegated
drakensbergensis	NTow
echinata	WPer
♦ ***natalensis***	See F. ***rosulata***
pappei	See F. ***amoena***
§ ***petiolata***	CBrk CElw CHan CRiv ECha EMar EMon ERav ERea ESma IBlr LHil LHop MMil NSti WCru WPer WWin
* ***plena ensbergensis***	MPit
§ ***rosulata***	CMHG CWes ELan GArf GAri GDra LHop MCas MFir MHig MPit MTho NKay NMen NNrd NRoo NSti NTow SIng SSmi WHil WWin
'Snowmass'	CBot WWin
uliginosa	CPar CRiv GGar LBee MDHE MTho NBir NTow WEas WHil

FERRARIA (Iridaceae)

§ ***crispa***	CAvo CMon CTro LBow WMar
undulata	See F. ***crispa***

FERREYRANTHUS (Compositae)

¶ ***excelsus***	CB&S

FERULA (Umbelliferae)

assa-foetida	MHew NSal
* 'Cedric Morris'	ECha
communis	CSco CWes LGan LHol SDix SMrm WCot WHal WHer WWye
– 'Gigantea'	CHad ECha LGre
'Giant Bronze'	See FOENICULUM ***vulgare*** 'G.B.'

FESTUCA (Gramineae)

¶ ***alpina***	ETPC
amethystina	CLew EHoe ETPC LGan MBro NBee NHol NMir NSti WCra
– 'Aprilgrün'	EHoe
– 'Bronzeglanz'	ETPC
ampla	ETPC
arundinacea	CKin ETPC
californica	ETPC
curvula ssp. ***crassifolia***	EPla
¶ ***dalmatica***	ETPC
¶ ***dumetorum***	ETPC
¶ ***elatior*** 'Demeter'	ETPC
elegans	ETPC
¶ ***erecta***	EHoe
eskia	CPar EHoe ETPC NHol
extremiorientalis	ETPC
filiformis	EMon EPla ETPC LRHS
§ ***gautieri***	ECED ELan EPla ETPC LHil MFir MUlv NOrc SCob
– 'Pic Carlit'	ETPC
gigantea	ETPC
glacialis	EHoe EPad EPla ETPC MBal MDHE NHol NNrd NRed
glauca	Widely available
– 'Azurit'	EFou EMon EPla ETPC LRHS
– 'Blaufuchs' ('Blue Fox')	CDoC CElw EHoe ETPC MBri MSte
– 'Blauglut' ('Blue Glow')	EBlo EBre LBre NHar NMir NRoo
– 'Blausilber'	GCal
– 'Harz'	CElw EHoe EPla ETPC IBlr
– 'Meerblau' ('Sea Blue')	CElw
* – ***minima***	EFol ESis NHol NNrd
– 'Pallens'	See F. ***longifolia***
– 'Seeigel' ('Sea Urchin')	EBlo EHoe EPla ETPC LTil
♦ – 'Seven Seas'	See F. ***valesiaca*** 'Silbersee'
heterophylla	ETPC
§ ***longifolia***	EFou ETPC
mairei	EHoe ETPC IBlr SApp
ochroleuca	ETPC
¶ ***ovina***	WPer
– ssp. ***coxii***	EHoe ETPC
¶ – 'Elijah Blue'	EPla SIng
paniculata	CElw EHoe EMon EPla ETPC SApp
punctoria	CHal CLew CTom ECha EFol EHoe EPla ETPC MDHE NHol SBla SGil SIng SSmi SSpi
rubra var. ***viridis***	NHol SIng
¶ ***sclerophylla***	ETPC
scoparia	See F. ***gautieri***
tenuifolia	ETPC
valesiaca var. ***glaucantha***	WWat
§ – 'Silbersee' ('Silver Sea')	CLew CPMA EBre ECha EFol EFou EHoe EPla ETPC IBlr LBre MBar MBri MFir MSte NCat NHol NNrd SGil SHer SIng
vivipara	CPar EHoe NHol NLan
* – ***glauca***	NLan

FIBIGIA (Cruciferae)

§ *clypeata*	CRDP ECro ELan EMar ESis NBro NSti SMrm WCru WEas

FICUS † (Moraceae)

australis hort.	See F. *rubiginosa* 'Australis'
benghalensis	MBri
benjamina	MBri
– 'Exotica'	MBri
– 'Flandriana'	MBri
– 'Golden King'	MBri
– 'Golden Princess'	MBri
– 'Green Gem'	MBri
– var. *nuda*	MBri
– 'Starlight' (v)	MBri
¶ *capensis*	CTro
F *carica*	ISea MBri
F – 'Angélique'	ERea
F – 'Black Ischia'	ERea
F – 'Black Mission'	ERea
F – 'Bourjassotte Grise'	ERea
F – 'Brown Turkey'	CB&S CCla CHEx CHad CMac CSam ELan ERea ESim GBon GTwe IJoh ISea LBuc LHol MBri MRav MWat NRog SArc SDea SFam SHBN SMad WDin WHig
F – 'Brunswick'	CDoC ERea ESim GBon GTwe SFam WCot
F – 'Castle Kennedy'	ERea
F – 'Figue d'Or'	ERea
F – 'Goutte d'Or'	ERea
– 'Grise de Saint Jean'	ERea
F – 'Lisa'	ERea
F – 'Malcolm's Giant'	ERea
F – 'Malta'	ERea
F – 'Marseillaise' ('White Marseilles')	ERea ESim GTwe SDea SFam
F – 'Negro Largo'	ERea
F – 'Osborn's Prolific'	ERea
F – 'Panachée'	ERea
F – 'Rouge de Bordeaux'	ERea
F – 'Saint Johns'	ERea
F – 'San Pedro Miro'	ERea
F – 'Sugar 12'	ERea
F – 'Violette Sepor'	ERea
F – 'White Ischia'	ERea
cyathistipula	MBri
deltoidea diversifolia	CTro MBri
elastica 'Belgica'	MBri
– 'Robusta'	MBri
– 'Zulu Shield'	MBri
* *foliole*	MBri
lyrata	MBri
¶ *microcarpa*	STre
– 'Hawaii' (v)	MBri
natalensis leprieurii 'Westland'	MBri
¶ *palmata*	SMad
pumila	CB&S CHEx CHal EBak MBri NHol
– 'Minima'	ISea MCas
– 'Sonny' (v)	MBri
– 'Variegata'	CHEx CHal MBri
radicans	See F. *sagittata*
§ *rubiginosa* 'Australis'	CTro MBri
– 'Variegata'	CHal
§ *sagittata* 'Variegata'	CHal MBri
triangularis	See F. *natalensis leprieurii*

FIG See FICUS *carica*

FILBERT See CORYLUS *maxima*

FILIPENDULA (Rosaceae)

alnifolia 'Variegata'	See F. *ulmaria* 'Variegata'
digitata 'Nana'	See F. *palmata* 'Nana'
hexapetala	See F. *vulgaris*
– 'Flore Pleno'	See F. *vulgaris* 'Multiplex'
'Kahome'	EBlo EGol NHol NOrc NRoo
kamtschatica	CRow CWGN ELan NDea NMir
– *rosea*	IBlr LHop
palmata	CBre CWGN ECha WByw
¶ – 'Alba'	ECha GCal
– 'Digitata Nana'	See F. *p.* 'Nana'
§ – 'Elegantissima'	CChu CRow ECha GGar MTol
§ – 'Nana'	CChu CCla CRow ECha ECro EPla GCal MBal MBro NSti WHoo
– *purpurea*	See F. *purpurea*
– 'Rosea'	CGle NBir NCat WCHb
– 'Rubra'	CSco
§ *purpurea*	CDoC CRow CWGN EFou ELun GAbr GGar LGan MBel MUlv SBla WAbe WEas
– *alba*	CBre EGol MUlv
¶ – 'Elegans'	NFai WHil
* – *splendens*	NKay
rubra	CHan CRow CWGN ECED WCra
§ – 'Venusta'	CBow CBre CChu CCla CRow EBre ECha EFol EFou EGol ELan EPar EPla GAbr GCal LBre LGan MUlv MWat NHol NKay NSti SChu SFis SHig SMrm SPer WCot WHal WRus
– 'Venusta Magnifica'	See F. *r.* 'Venusta'
sp. CLD 360	NHol
§ *ulmaria*	CArn CFis CKin CSFH CWGN EHon EMar EPla Effi GPoy LHol MChe MHew MTho MTol NHol NLan NMir NOak NRar NSel SIde WCla WNdy WOak WPer WWye
– 'Aurea'	Widely available
– 'Flore Pleno'	CBre CPar CRDP CWGN EBre LBre LHil NHol SHer SHig
– 'Rosea'	CCla CLew CTom EPla MUlv NSel SPer
§ – 'Variegata'	Widely available
§ *vulgaris*	CBow CFis CHan CKin CWGN ECtt LGan LHol LMay MChe MHew MTol NBee NBro NLan NMir NNor NOrc NSal SIde WByw WChe WCla WNdy WPer WWye
– 'Grandiflora'	CPar EOrc NCat
§ – 'Multiplex'	CBow CCla CDoC CGle CLew CSco EBre ECha EGol ELan EOrc EPar EPla LBre LWad MBal MFir MTho MUlv NDea NHol NSti SPer WEas WHal WRus WWat
♦– 'Plena'	See F. *v.* 'Multiplex'

FINGERHUTHIA (Gramineae)

sesleriiformis SH 1	CHan

FIRMIANA (Sterculiaceae)

simplex	CHEx

FITTONIA (Acanthaceae)

verschaffeltii	CHal
– var. *argyroneura*	CHal MBri
– – *nana*	CHal MBri

FITZROYA (Cupressaceae)

cupressoïdes	CB&S CMac GAri IOrc LCon MBal MBar SBor WBod WThu

FOENICULUM (Umbelliferae)

vulgare	CArn CCor CFis CHad CHal CTom ECha EEls ELan Effi GPoy IEde LAbb LHol MChe MHew NMir NRoo NSal NSel SHer SIde WByw WOak WPer WWye
– black form	CFis
– 'Bronze'	See F. *v.* 'Purpureum'
– var. *dulce*	CArn CSev IEde MChe WWye
§ – 'Giant Bronze'	CGle CRDP CSco ELan LAbb SPer
§ – 'Purpureum'	CArn CGle CHad CHal CMea CSev ECha EEls EHoe GPoy LGan LHol MChe MFir MPit NBro NMir NOak NRoo NSal NSti SUsu WEas WHal WOak WPer WSun
– 'Smokey'	CWit EFou ESma

FOKIENIA (Cupressaceae)

hodginsii	CKen CMCN SBor

FONTINALIS (moss)

¶ *antipyretica*	SAWi

FORSYTHIA † (Oleaceae)

'Arnold Dwarf'	CBow EHal SRms WWeb
N 'Beatrix Farrand'	CCla ECtt ELan ESma MGos MPla MWat NHol NNor SHer SPer SPla WWeb
europaea	WWeb
'Fiesta' (v)	CPMA CSam EPla IJoh MBel MBri MPla NBar SFai SGly SHil WCot WHer WPat
giraldiana	SRms WBod WWeb
'Golden Nugget'	EBre ELan ESis IOrc LBre MAsh NRoo SHBN SLon SPer
x *intermedia*	CBow WWeb
– 'Arnold Giant'	CShe WBod WWeb
– 'Densiflora'	WWeb
– Goldzauber®	WWeb
– 'Karl Sax'	CBow CBra NHol SCob WWeb
– 'Lynwood'	CB&S CBra CSco CShe ELan ENot GRei IDai IJoh ISea MBal MBar MBri MGos NHol NKay NNor NRoo SDix SLon SPer SReu SSta WBod WDin WWeb
– 'Mertensiana'	WWeb
– 'Minigold'	CB&S CBow CBra ECtt EPla ESma IDai IJoh LRHS MAsh MGos MUlv MWat SHBN SPer SPla WPat WWeb
– 'Spectabilis'	CBow CDoC ELan IOrc LBuc MBar NWea SHBN SPer WBod WDin WWeb
– 'Spectabilis Variegated'	CCor ECar EFol EPla LHop MPla SDry SHer WCot WWeb
– 'Spring Glory'	ECtt ENot MBri MRav WWeb
– 'Variegata'	CPMA MUlv NHol NSti SPer SSta
– 'Vitellina'	WWeb
japonica saxatilis	WWeb
Marée d'Or ® ('Courtasol')	IJoh MBri
I 'Melissa'	WDin
'Northern Gold'	CB&S WWeb
ovata	CBow CChu EBre EPla GRei LBre
– forms	MUlv WWeb
– 'Tetragold'	CB&S CBow CSco MBal MBar MBel NHol SHBN WWeb
'Paulina'	CBow ESis GAri
* 'Spring Beauty'	EHal WWeb
suspensa	CB&S CBra CSco CShe ENot IJoh IOrc MBar MWat SHBN SPer WStI WWeb
– L 275	WWeb
– f. *atrocaulis*	CPle EMon GAri SGil WWeb
– 'Decipiens'	WBod WWeb
– var. *fortunei*	WWeb
– 'Nymans'	CBra CCla CDoC CSco MBri MUlv WWeb
– var. *sieboldii*	WWeb
§ – 'Taff's Arnold' (v)	ELan EMon
– 'Variegata'	See F. *s.* 'Taff's Arnold'
'Tremonia'	CMer EHal EHar EMon MAsh MBal MGos MPla NNor NRoo WWeb
viridissima	EHal NNor WWeb
– 'Bronxensis'	CHal CLew ECar ELan EPar EPot ESis MPla NBir SHer SIng SMad SReu SUsu WPat WWeb
– var. *koreana*	WWeb
¶ – 'Weber's Bronx'	MBar
'Week-end'	CDoC ENot

FORTUNEARIA (Hamamelidaceae)

See Plant Deletions

FORTUNELLA (Rutaceae)

F *japonica*	LPan
F – 'Meiwa'	ERea
F *margarita*	CGOG MBri WFou WHig
F – 'Nagami'	ERea WFou

FOTHERGILLA (Hamamelidaceae)

gardenii	CPMA EBlo EBre ELan IOrc LBre MBri MPla MUlv NBar SPer SPla SSpi SSta WDin WWat
– 'Blue Mist'	CAbP CPMA EBlo ELan LRHS MAsh MBri SMad SPer SReu SSpi SSta
* 'Hunstman'	CCla MUlv SReu SSta
major	CB&S CBow CBra CGre CPMA CSco EBre ECtt ELan IJoh LBre LTil MBal MBri MGos MUlv NBar NBee NTow SChu SHBN SPer SReu WDin WNor WPat WStI WWat
– Monticola Group	CBra CCla CPMA ELan ENot IBar IHos MBal MBar MBri MPla SChu SHBN SPer SPla SSpi SSta WBod

FRAGARIA † (Rosaceae)

alpina	See F. ***vesca*** 'Semperflorens'
– ***alba***	See F. ***vesca*** 'Semperflorens Alba'
F x ***ananassa*** 'Aromel'	CWSG GTwe MBri NBar SDea WHig WWeb
F – Bogota ®	GRei GTwe NBar NBee
F – 'Bounty'	GTwe SDea
¶ – 'Calypso'	CSut GTwe WHig
F – 'Cambridge Favourite'	CMac CSut CWSG ESha GRei GTwe IJoh MBri MMor NBar NElm NRog SDea WHig WWeb
F – 'Cambridge Late Pine'	CWSG GTwe
F – 'Cambridge Rival'	GTwe NEgg
F – 'Cambridge Vigour'	CDoC GTwe IJoh MMor NBar NBee NRog SDea
F – Elsanta ®	CDoC CWSG GRei GTwe NBar SDea WHig
F – Elvira ®	CSut WHig
– 'Fraise des Bois'	See F. ***vesca***
F – 'Gorella'	NBar SDea WWeb
F – 'Hapil'	GTwe
¶ – 'Harvester'	NEgg
F – 'Honeoye'	GTwe WHig
F – 'Idil'	GTwe
F – Korona ®	GTwe
F – 'Kouril'	NBar
F – 'Melody'	GTwe
F – 'Ostara'	CSut GTwe
F – 'Pandora'	GTwe SDea WWeb
F – 'Pantagruella'	GRei GTwe SDea
F – 'Pegasus'	CSut GTwe WHig
F – Rapella ®	GTwe
F – 'Redgauntlet'	NBar NRog SDea
F – 'Rhapsody'	GTwe WHig
F – 'Royal Sovereign'	CMac GTwe SDea
F – 'Talisman'	GTwe
F – 'Tamella'	GTwe SDea
F – 'Tenira'	GTwe
F – 'Totem'	GTwe
F – 'Variegata'	CCor CElw CGle CMea CMil CNic CRiv CSev CShe ECro EFol ELan EOrc EPla LHop MFir MRav NRoo SCro SIng SPer WRus WThu WWin
F 'Baron Solemacher'	EJud WHer WHig
'Bowles' Double'	See F. ***vesca*** 'Multiplex'
F ***chiloensis***	EMon
– 'Chaval'	ECha EMon
N – 'Variegata'	CAbb GCal WByw WEas
– x ***virginiana***	CArn
daltoniana	ECar NHol SIng
indica	See DUCHESNEA ***indica***
* ***japonica***	EPla
F 'Pink Panda'	EBlo EBre LBre MBel MBri NBar NBir NRoo SHer SPer
'Variegata'	See F. x ***ananassa*** 'V.'
F ***vesca***	CArn CHun CKin CRDP GPoy LHol NLan NMir NSal NSel SHer SIde WCla WNdy WOak WSun WWye
F – 'Alexandria'	MChe NHol NRog WCHb
– 'Flore Pleno'	See F. ***v.*** 'Multiplex'
F – 'Fructu Albo'	WPer
¶ – 'Mara des Bois'	GTwe WHig
F – 'Monophylla'	CElw CFis CRow CTom ELan EMon NHol SIde
§ – 'Multiplex'	CCor CFis CGle CHal CMil CRDP CRow CSev CTom ELan EMon EOrc ERav ESma MFir MPar NHol NSti SSvw WByw WCHb WHer
§ – 'Muricata'	CBos CElw CMil CPou CRDP CRow EMon NSti WHer WSun
– 'Plymouth Strawberry'	See F. ***v.*** 'Muricata'
F – 'Rügen'	CHal WHoo
F – 'Semperflorens'	IEde ILis
F – 'Semperflorens Alba'	NHol
– 'Variegata'	CRDP ECha EPar NFai NHol NMir SUsu WCru WHal WPer

FRANCOA (Saxifragaceae)

appendiculata	See F. ***sonchifolia***
§ ***ramosa***	CElw CGle CGre CHan CRDP CSam CSun ECro GAbr IBar IBlr ITim LBlm NBro NRog NRoo NSti SPer WCot WCru WHal
♦ – ***alba***	See F. ***r.***
§ ***sonchifolia***	Widely available
– Rogerson's form	CGle

FRANKENIA (Frankeniaceae)

laevis	CNic CShe GGar MBro NVic SRms WWin
thymifolia	CLew CMHG CMer CPar ELan EPot ESis GCHN IDai MBar MPla MWat NHol NKay NNrd NRed NRoo NSti SBod SIng SSmi WHoo WOld WPer WTyr WWin

FRANKLINIA (Theaceae)

alatamaha	CGre CMCN LTil SSta WNor

FRASERA (Gentianaceae)

See Plant Deletions

FRAXINUS † (Oleaceae)

americana	CMCN CSto CTho EArb EHar
– 'Autumn Purple'	SHil
¶ ***angustifolia***	CMCN
¶ – ***lentiscifolia***	CTho EHar
§ – 'Raywood'	CB&S CDoC CLnd COtt CTho EBre EHar ENot IOrc LBre MBri MGos NWea SPer SSpi WDin WMou
chinensis	CLnd CMCN CTho EArb EHar
– ssp. ***rhyncophylla***	WMou
excelsior	CB&S CBow CDoC CKin CLnd CPer EBre ENot GRei IJoh ISea LBre LBuc LPan MBar MGos NBee NWea SHBN SPer SPla STre WDin WMou WStI
¶ – 'Allgold'	SMad WMou
– 'Aurea Pendula'	LMer WMou
– 'Crispa'	EMon WMou
– f. ***diversifolia***	WMou
– 'Diversifolia Pendula'	See F. ***e.*** 'Hetrophylla Pendula'
– 'Geesink'	ENot IHos
¶ – 'Heterophylla Pendula'	WMou
– 'Jaspidea'	CB&S CDoC CLnd COtt CPMA CSco CTho EHar ENot GRei IDai IJoh IOrc MBar MBlu MBri MGos MRav SHBN SHil SPer SSpi SSta WDin WMou WStI WWat

- – 'Pendula' — CBow CDoC CLnd CPMA CSco CTho EBre EHar ELan ENot GRei IJoh IOrc LBre LPan MBri NBee SHBN SPer WDin WMou WStI
- – 'Pendula Wentworthii' — WMou
- ¶ – 'R E Davey' — CTho
- ¶ – 'Stripey' — EMon
- – 'Westhof's Glorie ' — CDoC CLnd CSco EBre ENot LBre
- ***latifolia*** — WCoo
- ***mandshurica*** — WCoo
- ***mariesii*** — See F. ***sieboldiana***
- ¶ ***nigra*** — LPan
- ***ornus*** — CBot CLnd CSco CTho CWit EBar EBre EHar ENot IOrc ISea LBre MBri SPer WCoo WDin WMou
- ¶ – 'Arie Peters' — LPan
- ¶ – 'Messek' — LPan
- ***oxycarpa*** — See F. ***angustifolia***
- ***pennsylvanica*** — EArb EHar
- ¶ – 'Aucubifolia' — CTho
- – var. ***lanceolata*** — See F. ***p. subintegerrima***
- – 'Variegata' — CLnd CTho SHil WMou
- § ***sieboldiana*** — CPMA IOrc SHil WCoo WMou
- ¶ ***sogdiana*** Potamophila Group — CMCN
- ***spaethiana*** — WMou
- ***velutina*** — CBot CSto CTho EHar ISea SHil WMou

FREESIA (Iridaceae)

- N ***alba*** — LAma NRog
- 'Diana' — LAma
- 'Fantasy' — LAma
- hybrids — CSut NRog
- 'Romany' — LAma
- 'White Swan' — LAma
- ***xanthospila*** — LBow

FREMONTODENDRON (Sterculiaceae)

- 'California Glory' — Widely available
- ***californicum*** — CAbb CBow CBra CChu CCla CGre CHEx CPMA CSun ELan IOrc ISea LAbb MBlu MBri MGos MRav MUlv SFis SHBN WAbb WBod WCru WDin WEas WNor WStI WWat WWin
- 'Ken Taylor' — ERea
- ***mexicanum*** — CBot CChu CGre MBrk
- 'Pacific Sunset' — CCla CPMA ENot LHop SMad
- 'San Gabriel' — LRHS

FREYLINIA (Scrophulariaceae)

- ***cestroïdes*** — See F. ***lanceolata***
- § ***lanceolata*** — CB&S CHan CPle CTre
- * ***rosmarinifolia*** — CB&S

FRITILLARIA † (Liliaceae/Liliaceae)

- ***acmopetala*** — CAvo CBro CMon CNic CRiv ECha ELan EPar EPot ETub EWal ITim LAma LBow MBal MHig MS&S NHar NRog SIng WAbe WChr WDav
- – ssp. ***wendelboi*** — LAma WChr
- § ***affinis*** — CBro EBul EPot EWal LAma WDav
- § – var. ***gracilis*** — LAma WChr WDav
- – 'Sunray' — NHol
- – ***tristulis*** — WChr
- ***agrestis*** — WChr
- ***alburyana*** — LRHS WChr
- ***alfredae*** ssp. ***glaucoviridis*** — WChr
- ♦ ***arabica*** — See F. ***persica***
- ***armena*** — LAma WChr
- ***assyriaca*** — ELan EPar EPot ETub EWal ITim SIng WDav
- ***aurea*** — EPot LAma WChr
- ***biflora*** — WChr
- – 'Martha Roderick' — CBro EWal NHar NHol
- § ***bithynica*** — CBro EPot LAma NMen WChr
- ***brandegeei*** — EWal LAma
- ***bucharica*** — CBro EPot NHol WChr
- ***camschatcensis*** — CAvo CBro CRDP ECha ELan EPar EPot ETub LAma LBow MPar MS&S NHar NRog SIng SSpi WAbe WChr
- ¶ – black form — NHol
- – ***multiflora*** — NHar WDav
- – yellow — LRHS
- ***carduchorum*** — See F. ***minuta***
- ***carica*** — EPot WChr
- – ssp. ***serpenticola*** — EPot LRHS
- ***caucasica*** — LAma WChr
- ***cirrhosa*** — CAvo
- ***citrina*** — See F. ***bithynica***
- § ***collina*** — NBar
- ***conica*** — LAma
- ***crassifolia*** — CRiv EPot LAma
- – ssp. ***crassifolia*** — WChr
- § – ssp. ***kurdica*** — CAvo WChr
- ***davisii*** — CBro EBul EPot ETub LAma WChr
- ***delphinensis*** — See F. ***tubiformis***
- ***drenovskyi*** — LAma
- ***eastwoodiae*** — LAma
- ***ehrhartii*** — EPot LRHS
- ***elwesii*** — CBro WChr
- ***epirotica*** — LAma LRHS
- ***glauca*** — LAma
- ***graeca*** — CBro EPot ETub
- – ssp. ***graeca*** — WChr
- – ***ionica*** — See F. ***g. thessala***
- § – ssp. ***thessala*** — LAma LRHS WChr
- § ***grayana*** — LAma WChr WDav
- ***gussichiae*** — LAma
- ***hermonis*** ssp. ***amana*** — EPot LAma WChr
- ***hispanica*** — See F. ***lusitanica***
- ***imperialis*** — CAvo CB&S CBow CHEx CNic ERav MBal MBri NRog
- – 'Argenteovariegata' — CBot
- – 'Aureomarginata' — EPar LAma LBow MBri NRog
- – 'Aurora' — CAvo CBow EPar LAma LBlo LBow NRog SIng WCru
- – 'Blom's Orange Perfection' — LBlo
- – 'Crown upon Crown' — See F. ***i.*** 'Prolifera'
- – 'Lutea Maxima' — See F. ***i.*** 'Maxima Lutea'
- – 'Maxima' — See F. ***i.*** 'Rubra Maxima'
- § – 'Maxima Lutea' — CBow CBro CCla CHEx ELan EPar ETub LAma LBlo LBow NEgg NRog SIng SMad WCru
- § – 'Prolifera' — EPar ETub LAma LBow LRHS SMad WHil

– 'Rubra'	CBow ELan EPar ETub LAma LBlo LBow NBir NRog
§ – 'Rubra Maxima'	CBro LAma SIng WCru
– 'The Premier'	EPar LAma LBow SIng SMad
involucrata	CBro LAma MS&S SIng WChr
ionica	See F. ***graeca thessala***
karadaghensis	See F. ***crassifolia kurdica***
kotschyana	LRHS WChr
lanceolata	See F. ***affinis***
latakiensis	LAma WChr
§ ***latifolia***	CAvo EPot LAma WChr
– var. ***nobilis***	See F. ***latifolia***
liliacea	CBro EPot LAma MS&S WChr WCot
§ ***lusitanica***	LAma MS&S
¶ – MS 440	CMon
lutea	See F. ***collina***
meleagris	Widely available
– ***alba***	CBro CRDP ECtt ELan EPot ETub LAma LBow MBri MBro MHig MPar MS&S NHar NRya SIng WCru
– 'Aphrodite'	CAvo EPot LBlo NHol WChr WCot
messanensis	CMon ECha LAma MBal MS&S WChr WDav
– ssp. ***gracilis***	LAma MBal
– ssp. ***messanensis***	CAvo CBro
michailovskyi	CAvo CBro CRDP ECtt ELan EPar EPot ETub EWal GCra LAma LBlo LBow MBri MPlt MTho NHar NHol NRog SIng SUsu WAbe WChr WCla WCru WHil WPat
micrantha	LAma
§ ***minuta***	LRHS
montana	WDav
nigra	See F. ***pyrenaica***
olivieri	WChr
pallidiflora	CAvo CBro EPar EPot ETub EWal GArf ITim LAma MBal NEgg NHar SUsu WAbe WChr WCru WDav
§ ***persica***	CB&S CWes ECha EPar EPot LAma LBlo MBri SUsu WCra
¶ – S&L 118	CMon
– 'Adiyaman'	CAvo CBro ELan ETub LBow NEgg NRog SIng
* – 'Senkoy'	LRHS
phaeanthera	See F. ***affinis gracilis***
pinardii	CBro EPot WChr
pontica	CAvo CBro CMon ECha EPar EPot EWal ITim LAma LBow MBal MPar MS&S NHar SBla SSpi WChr WCru WDav
– Pras 1276	LRHS
pudica	EPot ITim LAma MS&S WDav
§ ***pyrenaica***	CBro CMon EBul ECha LAma LBow MBal MPar MS&S NHar NHol SChu WChr WDav
raddeana	LAma WChr
roderickii	See F. ***grayana***
rubra major	See F. ***imperialis*** 'Rubra Maxima'
ruthenica	EBul LRHS MS&S WChr
sewerzowii	CAvo EPot LAma WChr
sibthorpiana	CBro EPot LAma SIng WChr
stenanthera	CAvo CBro EPot LAma WChr
stribrnyi	LRHS WChr
tenella	See F. ***orientalis***
thunbergii	CRiv LRHS
§ ***tubiformis***	CAvo LRHS WChr
tuntasia	LRHS
¶ – hybrids	ECha
uva-vulpis	CAvo CBro CRDP EBul LAma LBow MS&S NHar SUsu
verticillata	CAvo CBro ECha EPar EPot ETub LAma LBow NHar SPou SUsu WChr WCru
walujewii	EPot WChr
whittallii	EPot LAma WChr

FUCHSIA † (Onagraceae)

N 'A 1'	WCum
'A M Larwick'	EBak WCum
'A W Taylor'	EBak
'Abbé Farges'	CCla CLoc EBak EBly ECtt EKMF GPen LCla MSmi MWar MWhe NMGN NPor SKen SLBF SOld SPla WCum
¶ 'Abigail'	EKMF SLBF
N 'Abundance'	WCum
'Achievement'	CLoc EBly GPen LCla MJac MLab SKen SOld
'Achilles'	EGou
'Ada Perry'	ECtt EKMF MSmi WCum
'Adagio'	CLoc WCum
'Admiration'	WCum
¶ 'Adrian Young'	SLBF
'Ailsa Garnett'	EBak
'Aintree'	LCla NPor WCum
'Airedale'	MJac WCum
'Ajax'	EGou
'Alabama Improved'	MSmi SKen WCum
'Alan Ayckbourn'	EBly LCla MWar NPor
¶ 'Alan Stilwell'	NPor SLBF
'Alaska'	EBak EKMF GPen LCla MWhe SKen SOld
'Albion'	CCla
'Alde'	EBly EGou
'Alf Thornley'	EKMF MWar MWhe NPor
'Alfred Rambaud'	NMGN
'Alice Ashton'	EBak EKMF NMGN
'Alice Hoffman'	CCla CLoc CSco EBak EBly EGou EKMF GPen LCla MBar MBri MGos MJac MLab MSmi MWat MWhe NKay NMGN NPor SKen SLBF SOld SPer WCum
'Alice Mary'	EBly SLBF
¶ 'Alice Rowell'	EKMF
'Alice Topliss'	EGou
'Alice Travis'	EBak EGou
'Alison Ewart'	CLoc EBak EKMF LCla MWhe NPor SKen SOld WCum
¶ 'Alison June'	MBri
'Alison Patricia'	EKMF LCla MWhe SLBF WCum
'Alison Reynolds'	GPen LCla MBri WCum
'Alison Ryle'	EBak
'Alison Sweetman'	EKMF MJac MWhe SKen
'Allegra'	WCum
§ ***alpestris***	EBak EKMF
'Alsa Garnett'	WCum
'Altmark'	EGou
'Alton Water'	EGou EKMF
'Alwin'	LCla MWhe WCum
'Alyce Larson'	EBak ECtt GPen LCla MJac MWhe NMGN NPor
'Amanda Bridgland'	EKMF LCla SOak WCum

'Amanda Jones'	LCla MWhe WCum
'Ambassador'	EBak ECtt GPen SKen
'Amber Supreme'	SKen
'Amelie Aubin'	CLoc EBak EKMF WCum
'America'	EBak EGou
¶ 'American Dream'	MLab
'American Flaming Glory'	WCum
¶ 'American Spirit'	MLab
'Amethyst Fire'	CCla
'Amigo'	EBak WCum
'Amy Lye'	CLoc EBak EKMF GPen MSmi NMGN NPor SKen WCum
'Andenken an Heinrich Henkel'	WCum
'André Le Nostre'	EBak
¶ ***andrei***	EKMF
'Andrew'	EBak
'Andrew Carnegie'	CLoc
'Andrew George'	MJac
'Andrew Hadfield'	EBly EKMF LCla MSmi MWar SLBF WCum
'Andrew Ryle'	WCum
N 'Andromeda'	CCla
'Angela Leslie'	CLoc EBak EKMF WCum
'Angela Rippon'	GPen LCla MJac MWhe SKen SOld
'Angeline'	EGou
'Angel's Dream'	WCum
'Angel's Flight'	CLoc EBak MSmi SOld WCum
'Ann Adams'	MJac
'Ann Howard Tripp'	CLoc LCla MBri MJac MWhe NMGN NPor WCum
'Ann Lee'	CLoc EBak
'Ann Porter'	NPor WCum
'Ann Roots'	EGou
'Anna of Longleat'	CLoc EBak EBly GPen LCla SKen SLBF
'Annabel'	CLoc CSut EBak EBly EGou EKMF GPen MBri MJac MLab MSmi MWar MWhe NFai NMGN NPor SHer SKen SLBF SOak SOld WCum
'Anne Smith'	SOld
¶ 'Annie Johnson'	MLab
'Ann's Beauty'	MSmi
'Anthea Day'	CLoc
'Antigone'	LCla SLBF
¶ 'Antonia'	GPen
'Aphrodite'	CLoc EBak WCum
N 'Apollo'	SOld
'Applause'	CLoc EBak EBly ECtt EGou EKMF GPen LCla MSmi NMGN NPor SOak SOld WCum
aprica hort.	See F × ***bacillaris***
– Lundell	See F. ***microphylla aprica***
'Aquarius'	MWhe
'Arabella'	WCum
'Arabella Improved'	EGou EKMF WCum
arborea	See F. ***arborescens***
arborescens	CLoc CPle CTro EBak EGou EKMF ERea LCla NWyt SBor SLBF SOak SOld
'Arcadia'	CLoc MWar WCum
'Arcadia Gold'	ECtt EKMF GPen
'Arcadia Lady'	GPen MJac
'Arcady'	WCum
'Archie Owen'	MSmi WCum
'Ariel'	NMGN
'Ark Royal'	WCum
'Arlendon'	MWhe WCum
'Army Nurse'	CCla CLoc GPen MLab MWhe NPor SKen SLBF SOld WCum WWeb
'Art Deco'	EGou
¶ 'Art Nouveau'	MSmi
'Arthur Cope'	WCum
'Ashley and Isobel'	NPor
¶ 'Ashwell'	MLab
'Athela'	EBak
'Atlantic Star'	EBly MBri MJac NPor SOld
'Atlantis'	LCla MJac WCum
'Atomic Glow'	EBak
'Aubergine'	EGou MSmi
'Audrey Hepburn'	EKMF WCum
'Aunt Juliana'	EBak GPen WCum
'Auntie Jinks'	EBak EGou EKMF LCla MJac MSmi MWar MWhe NMGN NPor SKen SLBF SOld WCum
'Auntie Maggie'	WCum
'Aurora Superba'	CLoc EBak ECtt EKMF LCla NMGN NPor SLBF WCum
'Australia Fair'	CLoc EBak WCum
§ ***austromontana***	EBak
'Autumnale'	CLoc EBak EBly EFol EKMF LCla MBri MLab MSmi MWhe NMGN NPor SKen SLBF SOld WCum
'Avalanche'	CLoc EBak
'Avocet'	CLoc EBak GPen
'Avon Celebration'	CLoc
'Avon Gem'	CLoc WCum
ayavacensis	EKMF
'Azure Sky'	EKMF
'Baby Blue Eyes'	SLBF
¶ 'Baby Bright'	NPor SLBF
'Baby Chang'	MWhe SLBF
¶ 'Baby Neerman'	EKMF
'Baby Pink'	EBly GPen WCum
§ × ***bacillaris***	CBow CGre CMHG CRDP CSam CWit EBak GPen LCla SBor SLBF
§ – 'Cottinhamii'	ESma IMal ITim WSHC
§ – 'Oosje'	EGou EKMF
'Bagworthy Water'	CLoc
'Baker's Tri'	EBak WCum
¶ 'Balcony Queen'	WCum
'Bali Hi'	MSmi
'Balkonkönigin'	CLoc EBak GPen MSmi SKen WCum
'Ballerina'	WCum
'Ballet Girl'	CCla CLoc EBak ECtt EKMF LCla MSmi SLBF SOld WCum
'Bambini'	EBly NPor WCum
'Banstead Bell'	SLBF WCum
'Barbara'	EBak EKMF LCla MJac MWar MWhe NPor SKen SOak SOld WCum WEas
¶ 'Barbara Hallett'	MLab
'Barbara Pountain'	EBly MJac
¶ 'Barnsdale'	MLab
'Baron de Ketteler'	EKMF WCum
¶ 'Baroness van Dedem'	SLBF
'Baroque Pearl'	EKMF WCum
'Barry's Queen'	EBak SKen SOld
'Bashful'	CCla EBly LCla MBri SIng SKen SOld WWeb
'Basketfull'	SOak WCum

'Beacon'	CCla CLoc EBak EBly EGou EKMF IHos LCla MBri MLab MSmi MWhe NMGN NPor SKen SOld WCum
'Beacon Rosa'	CLoc EBly EGou EKMF LCla MBri MJac MLab MSmi MWar MWhe NPor SKen SLBF SOak SOld WCum
'Bealings'	EBly ECtt EGou LCla MJac MWar MWhe NPor SHer SOak SOld WCum
'Beatrice Burtoff'	EKMF
'Beau Nash'	CLoc
'Beauty of Bath'	CLoc EBak WCum
'Beauty of Clyffe Hall'	EBak WCum
'Beauty of Exeter'	CCla EBak EKMF SKen
'Beauty of Prussia'	CLoc ECtt GPen
'Beauty of Swanley'	EBak
'Beauty of Trowbridge'	NPor SKen WCum
'Beauty Queen'	WCum
'Bedford's Park'	LCla
'Begame Kiekeboe'	EKMF
'Bella'	CGle
'Bella Forbes'	CLoc EBak SOld
'Bella Mia'	WCum
'Bella Rosella'	MSmi
'Bellbottoms'	WCum
'Belle de Lisse'	EGou
'Belsay Beauty'	GPen MJac NPor WCum
'Belvoir Beauty'	CLoc ECtt MJac WCum
'Belvoir Elf'	ECtt
'Belvoir Lakes'	ECtt
¶ 'Ben's Ruby'	SLBF
N 'Beranger'	EBak WCum
'Berba's Coronation'	EKMF WCum
'Berba's Happiness'	EGou
'Berba's Inge Mariel'	EGou
'Bergnimf'	EGou
'Berliner Kind'	EBak GPen
'Bermuda'	EKMF WCum
'Bernadette'	WCum
'Bertha Gadsby'	EKMF
¶ 'Beryl's Choice'	WCum
'Beth Robley'	EBly NPor WCum
'Betsy Ross'	EBak
¶ 'Bette Sibley'	LCla
'Beverley'	EBak EBly GPen SLBF
'Beverley Baby'	EBly
'Bewitched'	EBak WCum
'Bianca'	SOld WCum
'Bicentennial'	CLoc EBak EBly ECtt EGou EKMF GPen LCla MJac MLab MSmi MWar MWhe NMGN NPor SKen SOak SOld WCum
'Biddy Lester'	WCum
'Big Charles'	EGou
¶ 'Bill Gilbert'	MSmi SLBF
'Bill Kennedy'	MSmi
'Billie Roe'	NMGN
'Billy Green'	CLoc EBak EBly ECtt EKMF GPen LCla MJac MSmi MWar MWhe NMGN NPor SKen SLBF SOld
'Bishop's Bells'	GPen MJac SKen
'Bits'	WCum
'Bittersweet'	WCum
'Black Beauty'	WCum
'Black Prince'	MBri MWar WCum
¶ 'Blackberry Ripple'	MLab
I 'Blanche Regina'	MJac MWhe NPor WCum
'Bland's New Striped'	EBak EKMF SLBF WCum
'Blaze'	WCum
'Blowick'	EGou LCla MLab NMGN NPor WCum
'Blue Anchor'	WCum
'Blue Beauty'	EBak WCum
'Blue Bonnet'	SOld
'Blue Boy'	WCum
'Blue Bush'	EKMF GPen MJac NMGN NPor WCum
'Blue Butterfly'	EBak
'Blue Gown'	CLoc EBak EBly EKMF GPen LCla MLab MSmi MWar SKen
'Blue Halo'	EGou
'Blue Ice'	EBly MWhe WCum
'Blue Lace'	CCla
N 'Blue Lagoon'	MLab WCum
'Blue Lake'	MLab WCum
'Blue Mink'	EBak WCum
'Blue Mirage'	EGou MLab NMGN WCum
'Blue Mist'	EBak WCum
'Blue Pearl'	EBak GPen LCla NMGN WCum
'Blue Petticoat'	CLoc
'Blue Pinwheel'	EBak WCum
'Blue Satin'	CSut MSmi WCum
'Blue Tit'	SKen SLBF
'Blue Veil'	ECtt EKMF MJac MSmi MWar NMGN NPor SKen WCum
'Blue Waves'	CLoc EBak EBly ECtt EGou EKMF GPen LCla MJac MWar MWhe NMGN NPor SLBF SOld WCum
'Blush of Dawn'	CLoc EBak EBly EGou EKMF GPen LCla MSmi NMGN SKen SLBF SOak SOld WCum
'Blythe'	EBly EGou
'Bob Armbruster'	MSmi
¶ 'Bob Brown'	NPor SLBF
'Bob Pacey'	MJac
¶ 'Bob Paisley'	MBri
'Bobby Boy'	EBak WCum
'Bobby Dazzler'	ECtt EKMF MJac WCum
'Bobby Shaftoe'	EBak EKMF MWhe WCum
'Bobby Wingrove'	EBak WCum
'Bobolink'	EBak WCum
'Bob's Best'	EBly MJac SLBF
'Bob's Choice'	WCum
'Boerhaave'	EBak WCum
¶ 'Bohémienne'	MSmi
boliviana Britton	See F. ***sanctae-rosae***
– Carriére	CTro EBak EKMF GCra MWhe
¶ – var. ***boliviana***	EGou
§ – var. ***luxurians alba***	CLoc EBak EGou EKMF LCla MWhe SLBF
♦ – ***puberulenta***	See F. ***b.***
'Bon Accorde'	CLoc EBak EBly EKMF GPen LCla NPor SKen SLBF SOld WCum
'Bon Bon'	EBak WCum
'Bonanza'	WCum
'Bonita'	MJac MSmi WCum
'Bonnie Berrycloth'	SOld
'Bonnie Doan'	MSmi
'Bonnie Lass'	EBak GPen WCum
'Bonny'	CLoc
'Bora Bora'	EBak EKMF SOak WCum
'Border Princess'	EBak LCla

'Border Queen'	CLoc EBak EBly EGou EKMF LCla MJac MLab MWhe NPor SKen SLBF WCum
'Border Reiver'	EBak LCla
'Born Free'	WCum
'Bornemanns Beste'	EBak EGou EKMF LCla NPor SKen
'Bouffant'	CLoc EBak MJac WCum
'Bountiful'	CLoc EGou EKMF MWhe NMGN NPor SKen SLBF SOak SOld WCum
'Bouquet'	EKMF SKen
'Bow Bells'	CLoc ECtt LCla MJac MWhe NMGN NPor SOak WCum
¶ 'Brain C Morrison'	EGou
'Brandt's Five Hundred Club'	CLoc EBak GPen LCla SOak WCum
¶ 'Bravo'	WCum
'Breckland'	EBak MJac SOak WCum
'Breeders' Delight'	MBri WCum
'Breeder's Dream'	EBak WCum
'Brenda'	EBak EGou LCla WCum
'Brenda Megan Hill'	EBly
'Brenda Pritchard'	ECtt WCum
'Brenda White'	EGou EKMF MWhe NMGN NPor SLBF SOld
'Brentwood'	EBak
brevilobis	EKMF
'Brian Stannard'	EGou
'Bridal Veil'	EBak
'Bridesmaid'	EBak EKMF MSmi SOld WCum
'Brigadoon'	CLoc EBak WCum
¶ 'Brightling'	MSmi
'Brighton Belle'	EBly EGou
N 'Brilliant'	CCla CLoc EBak GPen MGos MLab MPla MWat MWhe NPor SKen
'Briony Caunt'	EKMF
'British Jubilee'	EBly EKMF NMGN NPor SLBF SOak WCum
'British Sterling'	WCum
'Brodsworth'	MLab NMGN
'Brookwood Belle'	EBly MJac NPor SLBF SOak
'Brookwood Joy'	EGou GPen MJac SLBF SOak SOld WCum
'Brutus'	CCla CLoc EBak EBly EKMF ESma GPen ISea LCla MBel MSmi MWhe NPor SKen SLBF SOak SOld WCum WStI
'Bubble Hanger'	GPen MSmi SOak
'Buddha'	EBak WCum
'Buenos Aires'	EGou
'Bunny'	EBak LCla NPor WCum
'Buttercup'	CLoc EBak MWhe SKen SOld WCum
'Buttons and Bows'	NMGN WCum
'C J Howlett'	EBak
'Caballero'	EBak
'Cable Car'	WCum
'Caesar'	EBak EKMF SOld WCum
¶ 'Caetar'	WCum
'Caledonia'	EBak NMGN WCum
'Callaly Pink'	NPor
'Cambridge Louie'	EBak GPen LCla MBri MLab MWar MWhe NMGN NPor SKen SLBF SOld WCum
'Camelot'	EBak LCla
'Cameron Ryle'	WCum
¶ ***campos-portoi***	EKMF
'Candlelight'	CLoc EBak MSmi NPor WCum
'Candy Stripe'	CLoc
canescens Bentham	EBak EGou EKMF LCla
♦– Munz	See F. ***ampliata***
'Capri'	EBak WCum
'Cara Mia'	CLoc NPor SKen SOak
'Cardinal Farges'	CCla CLoc EKMF GPen LCla MBel MSte NMGN SKen SLBF SOak SOld
'Carefree'	WCum
'Carioca'	EBak WCum
¶ 'Carl Drude'	LCla
'Carl Wallace'	EKMF MJac
'Carla Johnston'	CLoc EBly ECtt EGou EKMF LCla MBri MJac MLab MWhe NPor SLBF SOak SOld
'Carmel Blue'	CLoc GPen MWhe SKen SOld WCum
'Carmen Maria'	LCla MJac SKen WCum
'Carmine Bell'	EKMF
¶ 'Carnea'	GPen
'Carnival'	EGou LCla SOld
'Carnoustie'	EBak EGou
'Carol Grase'	CLoc WCum
¶ 'Carol Nash'	CLoc
'Carol Roe'	EKMF SOld
¶ 'Carole Hardwick'	MLab
'Carole Scott'	MLab
'Caroline'	CLoc EBak EBly EKMF LCla MSmi NMGN SKen SOak SOld WCum
'Cascade'	CLoc ECtt EGou EKMF GPen LCla MBri MJac MLab MSmi MWar MWhe NMGN NPor SKen SOld WCum WEas
'Casper Hauser'	EGou EKMF NPor SLBF WCum
'Catherine Bartlett'	EKMF SLBF
'Cathie MacDougall'	EBak WCum
'Cecile'	EBly ECtt EKMF MLab MSmi SLBF WCum
'Celadore'	EKMF LCla MJac NMGN NPor SKen WCum
'Celebration'	EGou ESma WCum
'Celia Smedley'	CLoc EBak EBly EGou EKMF GPen LCla MBri MJac MWar MWhe NMGN NPor SKen SLBF SOld WCum
'Centenary'	SOld
'Centerpiece'	EBak
'Ceri'	CLoc
'Champagne Celebration'	CLoc
'Chandleri'	EKMF NPor SLBF SOld WCum
'Chang'	CLoc CMHG EBak EKMF GPen LCla MWar MWhe NMGN NPor SLBF WCum
'Chaos'	EGou
'Charisma'	LCla SOld
'Charleston'	SLBF WCum
'Charlie Gardiner'	EBak EBly ECtt EGou MWhe NMGN WCum
'Charlie Girl'	EBak
'Charming'	CCla CLoc EBak GPen LCla MJac MWhe NMGN SLBF SOld WCum
'Checkerboard'	CLoc EBak EGou EKMF GPen LCla MJac MLab MSmi MSte MWar MWhe NPor SKen SLBF SOak SOld WCum
¶ 'Checkmate'	GPen
'Cheers'	EBly EGou EKMF MSmi MSte MWar NMGN NPor SOld WCum

'Chessboard'	CLoc
'Cheviot Princess'	LCla WCum
'Chillerton Beauty'	CCla CLoc CSco ECtt EKMF GPen IDai LCla MJac MWhe SLBF SOld SPer
'China Doll'	EBak GPen MWhe SKen WCum
'China Lantern'	CLoc EBak
'Chiquita Maria'	EKMF MSmi WCum
'Christ Driessen'	EGou
'Christina Becker'	EGou
¶ 'Christine Shaffery'	EGou
'Christine Truman'	EBly
'Christine Windsor'	WCum
'Christmas Holly'	WCum
'Christmas Ribbons'	EGou MSmi
'Churchtown'	NPor
'Cicely Ann'	WCum
¶ ***cinerea***	EKMF
'Circe'	EBak EKMF WCum
'Circus'	EBak WCum
¶ 'Cissbury Gem'	LCla
'Citation'	CLoc EBak EKMF GPen LCla MJac MSmi NMGN NPor SOld WCum
'City of Adelaide'	CLoc MWhe SKen WCum
'City of Derby'	WCum
'City of Leicester'	LCla MBri MLab NPor WCum
'Claire de Lune'	EBak LCla NPor SLBF SOak WCum
'Claire Evans'	CLoc
'Classic Jean'	MWhe WCum
'Clifford Gadsby'	EBak WCum
'Cliff's Hardy'	EKMF LCla
'Cliff's Own'	GPen WCum
'Cliff's Unique'	EBly MWar NPor SOak WCum
'Clifton Beauty'	MJac WCum
'Clifton Belle'	MJac WCum
'Clifton Charm'	EBly MJac
'Cloth of Gold'	CLoc EBak LCla MJac MLab MSte MWhe NMGN NPor SKen SLBF SOld
'Clouds'	CCla
'Cloverdale Delight'	SKen
'Cloverdale Jewel'	EBak GPen MJac MLab MWhe SKen
'Cloverdale Joy'	EBak LCla WCum
'Cloverdale Pearl'	EBak EKMF ENot GPen LCla MJac MWhe NPor SKen SLBF SOld WCum
'Cloverdale Pride'	GPen WCum
'Cloverdale Star'	SKen
'Coachman'	CLoc EBak EBly EKMF LCla MLab MSmi MWar MWhe NMGN NPor SKen SLBF SOld SPla WCum
coccinea	EKMF
x ***colensoi***	CTre ECou EGou EKMF ESma
'Collingwood'	CLoc EBak GPen WCum
'Come Dancing'	ECtt MLab SKen SLBF WCum
N 'Comet'	CLoc EBak LCla WCum
'Conchilla'	EBak
'Concorde'	CLoc WCum
'Confection'	GPen MSmi NMGN WCum
'Connie'	CCla EBak
'Conspicua'	EBak EGou EKMF ELan SKen
'Constable Country'	EBak WCum
'Constance'	CCla CLoc EGou EKMF GPen LCla MJac MSmi MWar MWhe SKen SLBF SOld WCum
N 'Constellation'	CLoc EBak MWhe NPor SKen SOak SOld WCum
'Continental'	EBly EGou WCum
'Contramine'	WCum
'Cookie'	WCum
'Copycat'	WCum
'Coquet Bell'	EBak EGou NPor
'Coquet Dale'	EBak ECtt EGou EKMF LCla MJac MWhe NMGN NPor SOld WCum
'Coquet Gold'	ECtt GPen MSmi NMGN
'Coral Seas'	EBak
§ 'Coralle'	EBak EBly EGou EKMF LCla MJac MLab MSmi MWar MWhe NPor SKen SLBF SOld WCum
'Corallina'	CBra CCla CLoc CMHG EBak EKMF GPen IHos LCla MFir MWhe NMGN SKen SLBF WEas
cordifolia Bentham	CBrk CTre EBak
♦– hort.	See F. ***splendens***
'Core'ngrato'	CLoc EBak WCum
'Cornelian Fire'	CCla
'Corsage'	MSmi WCum
'Corsair'	EBak EKMF GPen MSmi NMGN SLBF WCum
§ ***corymbiflora***	EBak EGou LCla
– ***alba***	See F. ***boliviana luxurians alba***
'Cosmopolitan'	EBak WCum
'Costa Brava'	CLoc EBak
'Cotta Bella'	EGou EKMF MJac NPor WCum
'Cotta Fairy'	EKMF WCum
'Cotta Princess'	ECtt EKMF WCum
'Cottinghamii'	See F. x ***bacillaris*** 'C.'
'Cotton Candy'	CLoc EBly EGou GPen MBri MLab MWhe SLBF SOld WCum
'Countess of Aberdeen'	CLoc EBak EGou EKMF NPor SLBF SOak SOld WCum
'Countess of Maritza'	CLoc WCum
'Court Jester'	CLoc EBak
'Cover Girl'	EBak LCla MSmi MWhe WCum
¶ 'Coverdale Jewel'	ECtt
'Coxeen'	EBak
'Cracker'	WCum
'Crackerjack'	CLoc EBak MSmi WCum
¶ ***crassistipula***	EKMF
'Creampuff'	WCum
'Crescendo'	CLoc SKen
'Crinoline'	EBak WCum
'Cropwell Butler'	WCum
'Crosby Soroptimist'	EBly LCla MWar MWhe NPor SLBF
'Cross Check'	LCla MBri MJac MLab NPor SLBF WCum
'Crusader'	NMGN
'Crystal Blue'	EBak SOak WCum
'Crystal Stars'	SKen
'Cupid'	EBak
'Curly Q'	EBak EKMF GPen LCla
'Curtain Call'	CLoc EBak EGou SKen SLBF WCum
cylindracea	EKMF
'Cymon'	MWhe
'Cyndy Robyn'	WCum
'Cyril Holmes'	WCum
¶ 'Daffodil Dolly'	MLab
'Dainty'	EBak
'Dainty Lady'	EBak WCum

'Daisy Bell' CLoc EBak ECtt EGou EKMF LCla MJac MSte MWhe NPor SKen SLBF SOld WCum
'Dalton' EBak
'Dancing Flame' CLoc CSut EBly EKMF GPen LCla MJac MLab MSmi MWar MWhe NMGN NPor SKen SLBF SOak SOld WCum
'Danish Pastry' WCum
'Danny Boy' CLoc EBak MWhe NMGN SOld WCum
'Daphne Arlene' WCum
'Dark Eyes' CLoc EBak ECtt EGou EKMF LCla MJac MLab MSmi MWhe NFai NMGN SKen SLBF SOak SOld WCum
'Dark Secret' EBak WCum
¶ 'Darreen Dawn' SLBF
'David' EKMF LCla MPla SKen SLBF WCum
'David Alston' CLoc EBak
'David Lockyer' CLoc WCum
'David Ward' EGou EKMF
'Dawn' EBak LCla SKen SOld WCum
'Dawn Redfern' MJac
'Dawn Sky' EBak
'Dawn Star' EBly MJac MLab MWhe WCum
'Dawn Thunder' MSmi WCum
¶ 'Day by Day' LCla SLBF
'Day Star' EBak
'Daytime Live' EBly
'De Bono's Pride' WCum
'Debby' EBak WCum
'Deben' EGou
'Deborah' CLoc MSmi WCum
'Debra Hampson' MLab
N *decussata* CGle EBak EKMF
'Dedham Vale' EBak
'Dee Copley' EBak WCum
'Deep Purple' EGou EKMF MLab MSmi
'Delaval Lady' WCum
'Delicia' WCum
'Delilah' EKMF MJac
'Deltaschön' WCum
'Delta's Wonder' SLBF
'Denis Bolton' SLBF
§ ***denticulata*** CLoc CMHG CPle EBak EKMF IBar LCla SKen SLBF SOld
dependens See F. ***corymbiflora***
'Derby Imp' GPen MWar NMGN SKen WCum
'Devonshire Dumpling' CGre CLoc EBly ECtt EGou EKMF MBri MJac MLab MWhe NMGN SKen SLBF SOak SOld WCum
'Diablo' EBak EGou WCum
'Diamond Fire' CCla
'Diamond Wedding' SOld
'Diana' EBak WCum
'Diana Wills' GPen MSte MWhe SKen WCum
'Diane Brown' EKMF GPen MJac SLBF
'Diann Goodwin' EGou
¶ 'Dick Swinbank' SLBF
'Dilly-Dilly' MJac
'Dimples' GPen NMGN
'Dipton Dainty' CLoc EBak LCla WCum
'Dirk van Delen' WCum
'Display' CCla CLoc EBak ECtt EGou EKMF GPen IHos LCla MBel MBri MJac MLab MWar MWhe NMGN NPor SHer SKen SLBF SOld WCum WStI
'Doc' CCla EBly LCla MAsh SOld WWeb
'Docteur Topinard' CLoc EBak
'Doctor' See F. 'The Doctor'
'Doctor Brendan Freeman' GPen MJac
'Doctor Foster' CCla CLoc CMHG CSco EBak ENot EPla GPen LCla MSmi SOld WCum WEas
¶ 'Doctor Manson' LCla
'Doctor Olson' CLoc EBak
'Doctor Robert' EBly EKMF MBri MJac MWhe NPor SLBF
§ 'Dollar Princess' CCla CLoc CMHG EBak EBly ECtt EGou EKMF GPen IHos LCla MBel MBri MJac MLab MSmi MSte MWar MWhe NFai NMGN SChu SKen SLBF SOld
'Dolly Daydream' EGou EKMF SLBF WCum
'Domacin' EGou MSmi MWhe NMGN WCum
'Dominyana' CPle EBak EKMF LCla SLBF WCum
'Don Peralta' EBak WCum
'Dopy' CCla EBly LCla SOld
'Doreen Redfern' CLoc EKMF LCla MJac MWhe NPor SOld
¶ 'Doreen Stroud' SOak
¶ 'Doris Birchell' MBri
'Doris Coleman' LCla SOld
'Doris Hobbs' EKMF
'Dorothea Flower' CLoc EBak GPen
'Dorothy' SLBF
'Dorothy Day' CLoc WCum
'Dorothy M Goldsmith' EGou LCla
'Dorothy Shields' EBly MJac NPor
'Drake 400' CLoc
'Drama Girl' WCum
§ 'Drame' CCla EBak ECtt EKMF GPen LCla LHil MSmi NMGN SKen SOld WCum
'Dreamy Days' EGou
'Drum Major' EBak
'Du Barry' EBak WCum
'Duchess of Albany' CLoc EBak GPen
'Duet' MSmi WCum
N 'Duke of Wellington' CLoc
'Dulcie Elizabeth' EBak EKMF LCla MJac MWar MWhe SOld WCum
'Dusky Beauty' EKMF LCla MJac MWar NPor SLBF WCum
'Dusky Rose' CLoc EBak EGou MJac MLab MWar MWhe
'Dutch Girl' CCla
'Dutch Mill' CLoc EBak WCum
'Dutch Pearl' WCum
'Dutch Shoes' WCum
'Duyfken' WCum
¶ 'E J Goulding' SLBF
'Earl of Beaconsfield' See F. 'Laing's Hybrid'
'East Anglian' CLoc EBak
'Easter Bonnet' CLoc
'Easterling' LCla WCum
'Ebbtide' CLoc EBak
'Ecstasy' SOld
'Ed Largarde' EBak EKMF NPor WCum

'Edale'	MSmi
'Eden Lady'	CLoc LCla MWar MWhe SOld WCum
'Eden Princess'	MJac MWhe SKen
'Edith'	EKMF LCla SLBF
'Edith Emery'	WCum
'Edith Hall'	EGou EKMF
'Edith Jack'	GPen WCum
'Edith of Kimbolton'	MLab
'Edna'	MSmi
'Edna May'	MWar NPor WCum
'Edna W Smith'	ECtt
'Edwin J Goulding'	EGou EKMF
'Eelco Brinkman'	EGou
'Eileen Raffill'	EBak
'Eileen Saunders'	EBak
'El Camino'	ECtt MWhe NFai WCum
'El Cid'	CLoc EBak EKMF GPen
'Elaine Ann'	EBly MJac NPor
'Elanor Grace'	SLBF
'Eleanor Clark'	EKMF LCla NPor WCum
'Eleanor Leytham'	EBak EKMF GPen LCla NMGN SOld WCum
'Eleanor Rawlins'	EBak EKMF GPen MLab NMGN NPor SKen SOld
'Elf'	CCla
'Elfin Glade'	CLoc EBak NBir
'Elfrida'	EKMF NMGN SKen
'Elfriede Ott'	EBak EKMF MSmi MWhe SLBF SOld WCum
N 'Elizabeth'	EBak WCum
'Elizabeth Broughton'	EKMF WCum
¶ 'Elizabeth Burton'	MLab
'Elizabeth Travis'	EBak WCum
'Ellen Morgan'	EBak
'Elsa'	ECtt GPen
'Elsie Johnson'	MLab
'Elsie Mitchell'	LCla MSte MWar MWhe NMGN NPor SLBF SOak WCum
'Elsstar'	EGou
§ 'Emile de Wildeman'	EBak EGou EKMF LCla MWhe NPor WCum
'Emily Austen'	EGou EKMF SLBF
'Emma Louise'	NPor SLBF
¶ 'Emma Rowell'	EKMF
'Empress of Prussia'	CCla CLoc EBak EKMF GPen MLab SKen SLBF WCum
'Enchanted'	EBak GPen SOak WCum
encliandra	
ssp. ***encliandra***	EGou
§ 'Enfant Prodigue'	CCla CLoc EKMF EMon GPen SLBF
¶ 'Eric Cooper Taylor'	MLab
'Erica Julie'	LCla WCum
'Eric's Hardy'	SLBF
'Ernest Rankin'	EKMF
'Ernestine'	EBly EGou MWhe SOld WCum
'Ernie Bromley'	EGou
'Errol'	CLoc
'Eschott Elf'	WCum
'Esme Tabraham'	CCla
'Estelle Marie'	CLoc EBak EGou EKMF LCla MJac MWar MWhe NPor SKen SLBF SOld WCum
'Esther'	WCum
'Esther Devine'	WCum
'Eternal Flame'	EBak MBri MWhe NMGN NPor SKen WCum
N 'Ethel'	WCum
'Ethel May Lester'	SOld
'Eurydice'	CLoc
'Eusebia'	EGou EKMF MJac MSmi NMGN SLBF WCum
'Eva Boerg'	CCla CLoc CSco EBak ECtt EKMF GPen IHos LCla MBri MLab MSmi MWar MWhe NFai NMGN NPor SKen SOld WCum WKif
'Evanson's Choice'	SKen
'Evelyn Steele Little'	EBak
'Evening Sky'	EBak WCum
'Evensong'	CLoc EBak EBly GPen NMGN SOld WCum
'Excalibur'	EBak EGou WCum
excorticata	CB&S CGre CTre CTrw ECou EKMF SBor WSHC
'Exeter'	EBly EGou
'Expo '86'	MSmi WCum
¶ 'Exton Beauty'	MLab
'Fairytales'	EKMF
'Falling Stars'	CLoc EBak ECtt LCla MWhe NPor WCum
'Fan Dancer'	EBak WCum
'Fan Tan'	MSmi WCum
'Fancy Flute'	WCum
'Fancy Pants'	CLoc EBak MBri
'Fancy Sockeye'	WCum
'Fanfare'	EBak
'Fascination'	See F. 'Emile de Wildeman'
'Fashion'	EBak
'Favourite'	EBak
'Felixstowe Display'	WCum
'Feltham's Pride'	SLBF
'Fenman'	EBly EGou LCla MJac SLBF WCum
'Fergie'	LCla SOak SOld
¶ 'Festival'	GPen
'Festoon'	EBak
'Fey'	EGou EKMF WCum
'Fiery Spider'	EBak EKMF
'Filigraan' ('Filigree')	CCla GPen
'Finn'	EBly EGou
'Fiona'	CLoc EBak EGou GPen SLBF SOak WCum
'Fiona Jane'	EKMF WCum
¶ 'Fire Lady'	GPen
'Fire Mountain'	EGou MWhe NMGN NPor SKen WCum
'Firebird'	WCum
¶ 'Firefly'	CBow GPen
¶ 'Firefox'	MLab
'Firelite'	EBak
'Firenza'	MWar SLBF
'First Lady'	MSmi WCum
'First Success'	EKMF
'Fizzy Lizzy'	WCum
'Flair'	CLoc WCum
'Flame'	EBak GPen WCum
'Flash'	CCla CLoc EBak ECtt EKMF GPen LCla MJac MWhe NMGN SIng SLBF SOld WCum
'Flashlight'	ELan WCum
'Flat Jack o'Lancashire'	ECtt EKMF
'Flavia'	EBak SOld
'Flirtation Waltz'	CLoc EBak EGou EKMF GPen LCla MBri MJac MSmi MWhe NMGN NPor SKen SLBF SOak SOld WCum

'Flocon de Neige' EBak
'Floral City' CLoc EBak
'Florence Mary Abbott' EBak EBly EGou LCla MWar NMGN SLBF SOld WCum
'Florence Taylor' WCum
'Florence Turner' EBak EBly EKMF LCla MWhe NPor SKen
'Florentina' CLoc EBak EGou EKMF GPen NPor WCum
'Florrie Bambridge' WCum
'Flowerdream' MJac
'Fluffy Ruffles' WCum
'Flyaway' EBak NPor WCum
'Flying Cloud' CLoc EBak EKMF GPen MBri MWhe NMGN WCum
'Flying Scotsman' CLoc EBak EBly EGou SLBF SOld WCum
'Folies Bergères' EBak WCum
'Foline' EGou MSmi
¶ 'Fondant Cream' MLab
'Foolke' EBak LCla
N 'Forget Me Not' CLoc EBak EKMF GPen LCla MWhe SLBF WCum
'Fort Bragg' EBak MSmi SKen WCum
'Forward Look' MWhe SKen
'Fountains Abbey' GPen NPor WCum
'Foxtrot' MWar WCum
'Frank Saunders' LCla SLBF WCum
'Frank Unsworth' ECtt EKMF GPen MWar MWhe NMGN NPor SOld WCum
'Franz Veernan' SLBF WCum
'Frau Hilde Rademacher' CCla EBak EBly EKMF MPla SLBF SOak WCum
'Fred Swales' EKMF WCum
'Freefall' EBak
'Freeland Ballerina' EBly MJac
'Friendly Fire' EKMF WCum
'Frosted Flame' CLoc EBly EKMF LCla MJac MWar MWhe NPor SLBF SOld WCum
'Frühling' EBak
I 'Fuchsia Fan' EBly
'Fuchsiade '88' EBak EGou LCla MWhe SLBF SOak
'Fuchsiarama '91' EGou EKMF LCla MSmi
'Für Elise' EBak WCum
'Fuksie Foetsie' EGou EKMF
fulgens CMHG EKMF MBal MSte MWhe NWyt SOld
– ***rubra grandiflora*** See F. 'Rubra Grandiflora'
'Gala' EBak WCum
'Galadriel' EGou
'Galahad' EBak EGou
'Garden News' CCla CLoc EBly ECtt EGou EKMF GPen LCla MBel MJac MPla MSmi MWar MWhe NMGN NPor SKen SLBF SOak SOld SPla WCum
'Garden Week' MSmi MWhe SOak SOld WCum
'Gartenmeister Bonstedt' CLoc EBak EBly EKMF LCla NMGN NPor SKen SMad SOak SOld WCum WEas
'Gay Anne' EKMF
'Gay Fandango' CLoc EBak ECtt EGou GPen LCla MWar NMGN SKen SLBF SOld WCum
'Gay Future' EKMF
'Gay Parasol' CLoc EGou MSmi SOak WCum
'Gay Paree' EBak WCum
'Gay Senorita' EBak WCum
'Gay Spinner' CLoc GPen
'Gazebo' MSmi
gehrigeri EBak EKMF
'Général Monk' EBak EKMF GPen MBri MJac MPla MSmi SKen SOld WCum
'Général Voyron' MPla
'General Wavell' GPen WCum
'Genii' CCla CLoc CMHG EBak EBly ECha EGou ELan ENot LAbb LCla LHop MBal MBel MBri MLab MSmi MWar MWat MWhe NMGN SDix SKen SLBF SOld SReu WCum WEas
'Geoffrey Smith' ECtt EKMF
'Georgana' ECtt MSmi MWhe WCum
'George Barr' EKMF SKen
'George Humphrey' SOld
¶ 'George Johnson' GPen
'George Travis' EBak MBri
'George 'n' Jo' WCum
'Gerda Manthey' EKMF
'Gesneriana' CLoc EBak
'Giant Falls' CLoc MSmi
'Giant Pink Enchanted' CLoc EBak GPen WCum
'Gilda' EGou GPen LCla MJac NPor SLBF SOak WCum
'Gillian Althea' WCum
'Gilt Edge' CLoc
'Gipping' EGou
¶ 'Girls Brigade' EKMF
'Gladiator' EBak LCla SKen WCum
'Gladys Lorimer' NPor SLBF
'Gladys Miller' CLoc
'Glenby' NPor WCum
'Glitters' EBak ECtt EKMF LCla NMGN NPor WCum
'Globosa' CCla EBak SKen
'Glow' EBak LCla
'Glowing Embers' EBak WCum
Glowing Lilac ® EKMF MSmi SLBF WCum
'Glyn Jones' EKMF
'Gold Brocade' CCla SKen WCum
'Gold Crest' EBak GPen
¶ 'Gold Foil' EGou
'Golden Anniversary' CLoc EBak EBly EGou EKMF LCla MJac MSmi NMGN SOak SOld WCum
'Golden Arrow' EGou
'Golden Border Queen' CLoc WCum
'Golden Dawn' CLoc EBak ECtt LCla NPor SKen SOld WCum
'Golden Eden Lady' MWhe WCum
¶ 'Golden Jessimae' MLab
'Golden La Campanella' CLoc ECtt GPen SOld
'Golden Lena' EKMF SOld WCum
'Golden Marinka' CLoc EBak ECtt EKMF ESma GPen LCla MBri MJac MSmi MWar MWhe NMGN NPor SOak SOld
'Golden Melody' CCla
'Golden Runner' MJac NPor
'Golden Spangles' CB&S
¶ 'Golden Spring Classic' MLab
'Golden Swingtime' EGou GPen LCla MBri MLab MWar MWhe NMGN NPor SOld WCum
'Golden Tolling Bell' MLab
'Golden Treasure' CLoc CSco ECtt EKMF LCla MBri NMGN NPor

'Golden Wedding' EKMF LCla WCum
¶ 'Goldsworth Beauty' GPen LCla
'Golondrina' EBak MWhe
'Goody Goody' EBak WCum
'Gordon Thorley' EBly EKMF MWhe NPor SLBF
'Gordon's China Rose' LCla SKen
'Göttingen' EBak
'Governor 'Pat' Brown' EBak WCum
'Grace Darling' EBak MWhe
'Grace Durham' EBak EGou
gracilis See F. ***magellanica gracilis***
'Grady' WCum
'Graf Spee' EGou
'Graf Witte' CCla EGou GPen MWhe
'Grand Prix' MLab SKen SOld WCum
'Grand Slam' LCla SKen SOld
'Grandma Sinton' EBly LCla MBri MJac MWar MWhe NPor WCum
'Grandpa George' LCla SOld
'Grange Farm' EGou
'Grasmere' NPor WCum
'Gray Dawn' WCum
'Great Scott' CLoc SKen WCum
'Green 'n' Gold' EBak
'Greenpeace' EKMF SLBF WCum
'Greg Walker' WCum
'Gretna Chase' MBri MWhe WCum
'Grey Lady' SOld
'Groene Kan's Glorie' EKMF SLBF SOak WCum
'Grumpy' EBly LCla MBri NPor SKen SOld WWeb
'Gruss aus dem Bodethal' CLoc EBak EBly EKMF LCla SKen
'Guinevere' EBak WCum
'Gustave Doré' EBak WCum
'Guy Dauphine' EBak GPen WCum
'Gwen Dodge' MSmi SLBF
¶ 'Gwen Wakelin' MLab
'Gypsy Girl' SKen WCum
'Gypsy Prince' CLoc WCum
'H G Brown' EBak MWhe NPor
¶ 'Halsall Beauty' MBri
¶ 'Halsall Pride' MBri
'Hampshire Beauty' MJac SOak SOld
'Hampshire Blue' GPen SLBF SOak WCum
¶ 'Hampshire Leonora' SOak
'Hampshire Prince' SOak WCum
'Hampshire Treasure' SLBF SOak WCum
'Hanna' CCla
¶ 'Hannah Williams' MLab
'Happiness' NMGN
'Happy' CCla EBly LCla SIng SOld
'Happy Anniversary' EKMF
'Happy Fellow' CLoc EBak
'Happy Wedding Day' CCla CLoc EKMF LCla MLab MSmi MWhe SLBF SOak WCum
'Hapsburgh' EBak WCum
'Harlow Car' EKMF SLBF
N 'Harmony' EBak GPen
'Harnser's Flight' EGou
'Harriett' MSmi WCum
'Harrow Pride' SKen SLBF
'Harry Dunnett' EBak
'Harry Gray' CLoc EBak EBly ECtt EGou GPen LCla MBri MJac MLab MSmi MWar MWhe NMGN NPor SKen SLBF SOak SOld WCum
'Harry Lye' EBly EGou WCum
hartwegii EGou EKMF LCla
'Harvest Glow' EBak
'Hathersage' EBak
'Hathor' EGou WCum
'Hatschbachii' EKMF
'Haute Cuisine' EGou EKMF MSmi SLBF
'Hawaiian Night' WCum
¶ 'Hawaiian Princess' ECtt
'Hawkshead' CCla CDec EGou EKMF ELan GPen LCla LGre LHil MBel MJac MWhe NPor SAxl SChu SLBF SMrm SOak SOld WCru
'Hay Wain' EBak WCum
'Hazel' EKMF MSmi MWhe SOak WCum
'Heart Throb' EBak MBri WCum
¶ 'Heathfield' GPen
'Hebe' EBak MWhe WCum
'Heidi Ann' CLoc EBak EBly EGou EKMF IHos LCla MBri MJac MLab MSmi MWar MWhe NMGN NPor SKen SLBF SOak SOld WCum
'Heidi Weiss' GPen NMGN SKen SOld
'Heinrich Henkel' CLoc EBak LCla MWhe NMGN SOld
'Heirloom' ECtt EKMF MSmi NMGN WCum
'Helen Clare' CLoc EBak WCum
¶ 'Helen Elizabeth' MBri
¶ 'Helen Spence' MLab
'Hellan Devine' MJac
'Hello Dolly' CLoc
'Hemsleyana' See F. ***microphylla hemsleyana***
'Henri Poincaré' EBak EKMF MSmi
'Herald' EBak LCla NMGN SLBF SOld
'Herbe de Jacques' EBly GPen SKen
'Heritage' CLoc EBak
'Hermiena' CLoc EGou EKMF SLBF
'Hermione' NPor
'Heron' EBak EKMF NMGN SKen
'Hessett Festival' EBak EBly EGou WCum
'Heston Blue' EKMF LCla MWhe NMGN WCum
'Heydon' WCum
'Hi Jinks' EBak MSmi WCum
hidalgensis See F. ***microphylla hidalgensis***
'Hidcote Beauty' CLoc EBak EKMF LCla MWar MWhe NPor SKen SLBF SOak WCum
¶ 'Hidden Beauty' MLab
'Highland Beauty' WCum
'Highland Pipes' EGou EKMF MSmi
'Hilda May Salmon' EGou
'Hindu Belle' EBak EKMF MSmi
'Hinnerike' EGou SLBF
'His Excellency' EBak
'Hobson's Choice' LCla MWar SLBF SOak SOld WCum
'Hollywood Park' EBak
'Honnepon' EGou
'Horatio' MJac
'Howlett's Hardy' CLoc EBak ECtt EKMF GPen MBal MBri MSmi NMGN NPor WCum
'Hula Girl' EBak ECtt EGou EKMF LCla MJac MLab MWar MWhe NMGN NPor SKen SLBF SOak WCum
'Humboldt Holiday' ECtt EKMF GPen MLab MSmi NMGN

¶ 'Hungarton' MLab
'Ian Brazewell' CLoc
'Ian Leedham' EBak EKMF NPor WCum
'Ice Cream Soda' EBak
'Ice Festival' WCum
'Iceberg' EBak EBly WCum
'Icecap' EKMF LCla
'Iced Champagne' CLoc EBak MJac MWar NPor SKen SOak WCum
'Ichiban' CLoc SLBF
C 'Ida' EBak
'Igloo Maid' CLoc EBak EBly EKMF GPen MJac MLab MWar MWhe NPor SKen SOak SOld WCum
¶ 'Imagination' MLab
'Imperial Fantasy' MSmi SLBF WCum
'Improved Hanna' WCum
'Impudence' CLoc EBak GPen NMGN
'Impulse' ECtt EKMF SKen SLBF WCum
'Independence' NPor WCum
'Indian Maid' EBak EBly ECtt EKMF GPen MBri MJac NMGN SKen SOld WCum
'Indian Princess' WCum
'Inferno' EKMF MSmi SOak
'Ingleore' EKMF
'Insulinde' EGou
'Intercity' EKMF
'Interlude' EBak
'Iolanthe' EGou
¶ 'Irene L Peartree' EGou
'Iris Amer' CLoc EBak MWar NPor SLBF WCum
'Isabel Ryan' CCla
'Isis' CCla EKMF SKen
'Isle of Mull' EGou GPen LCla SKen WCum
'Isle of Purbeck' MJac WCum
'Italiano' MJac NPor WCum
'Jack Acland' ECtt EGou GPen NPor SKen WCum
'Jack Coast' SOld
'Jack Shahan' CLoc EBak EBly EKMF GPen IHos LCla MBri MJac MSmi MWhe NFai NMGN SKen SLBF SOld WCum
'Jack Stanway' CCla EGou
'Jackie Bull' EBak WCum
'Jackpot' EBak
'Jackqueline' EGou EKMF SOld
'Jam Roll' WCum
'Jamboree' EBak WCum
'James Lye' EBak SKen
'James Travis' EBak LCla NPor SKen
'Jandel' MSmi WCum
'Jane Humber' EKMF LCla WCum
'Jane Lye' EBak WCum
¶ 'Janet Goodwin' MLab
'Janice Revell' MJac
'Janie' MAsh
'Janneke' WCum
¶ 'Jaunty' CTre
'Jayne Rowell' NPor SKen
'Jean' EKMF WCum
'Jean Campbell' EBak WCum
'Jean Clark' SLBF
'Jean Dawes' EBly EGou
¶ 'Jean Muir' MLab
'Jennie Rachael' NMGN

'Jenny Sorensen' EBly EKMF LCla NPor SLBF
'Jess' LCla SLBF
'Jessimae' WCum
N 'Jester' CLoc
'Jet Fire' EBak WCum
'Jezebel' MSmi WCum
'Jill Whitworth' NMGN
'Jim Coleman' EBly LCla MWhe NPor SLBF SOld
'Jim Dowers' EGou
'Jim Muncaster' EKMF
¶ ***jimenezii*** EKMF
'Jimmy Carr' EKMF NPor
'Joan Barnes' LCla WCum
'Joan Cooper' CCla CLoc EBak EKMF GPen NPor
'Joan Gilbert' WCum
'Joan Goy' EBly EKMF MJac NPor
'Joan Leach' CCla
'Joan Pacey' EBak SKen
'Joan Smith' EBak NPor
'Joe Browning' CCla
'Joe Kusber' EBak EKMF NMGN SKen SOld WCum
'John Baker' WCum
'John Lockyer' CLoc EBak GPen WCum
'John Maynard Scales' EBly EGou MJac MWhe
'John Suckley' EBak
'John Yardell' MJac
'Johnny' CLoc WCum
'Jomam' EBly LCla MWhe NPor
'Jon Oram' CLoc
'Jose's Joan' LCla MLab MWhe NMGN WCum
'Joy Bielby' EGou EKMF MWhe NPor WCum
'Joy Patmore' CLoc EBak EBly EKMF LCla MJac MWhe NPor SKen SLBF SOld WCum
'Joy White' CCla
'Joyce Sinton' EKMF MBri NPor SLBF WCum
¶ 'Jo-Anne Fisher' EBly
'Jubie-Lin' WCum
'Judi Spiers' EBly
'Judith Alison Castle' WCum
'Judith Coupland' NPor SLBF
¶ 'Judith Mitchell' MLab
'Jules Daloges' EBak
'Julia' EKMF
'Julia Ditrich' WCum
'Julie Marie' EBly LCla MJac SLBF
'June Gardner' EKMF
N 'Juno' EBak MSmi WCum
'Jupiter Seventy' EBak
'Justin's Pride' EKMF MLab NMGN
'Kaboutertje' EKMF
'Kaleidoscope' EBak MSmi SLBF WCum
'Karen Bielby' EKMF
'Karen Louise' CLoc
'Karin de Groot' EKMF MSmi
'Kathleen Colville' CLoc
'Kathleen Muncaster' EKMF MWar WCum
¶ 'Kathleen Saunders' LCla
'Kathleen Smith' ECtt EKMF WCum
'Kathryn Maidment' EKMF
'Kathy's Prince' ECtt EKMF
'Kathy's Sparkler' EKMF WCum
'Katrina' CLoc EBak WCum
¶ 'Katrina Thompson' EKMF NPor SLBF

Cultivar	Suppliers
¶ 'Kay Louise'	GPen
'Keepsake'	CLoc EBak WCum
'Kegworth Carnival'	LCla MJac MLab NPor SKen SOak SOld WCum
'Kegworth Clown'	WCum
'Kegworth Delight'	LCla NPor WCum
'Kegworth Supreme'	MJac MWhe
'Ken Goldsmith'	EBly EGou
'Ken Jennings'	MJac NPor
'Ken Sharp'	MJac
'Kenny Dalglish'	EKMF
'Kernan Robson'	CLoc EBak EGou SOak
'Kerry Anne'	EBly EKMF MWar
'Keystone'	EBak
'Khada'	EKMF LCla MWhe WCum
¶ 'Kiekeboe'	SLBF
'Kim Wright'	MWhe WCum
'Kimberly'	EBak
'King of Bath'	EBak
'King of Hearts'	EBak
'King's Ransom'	CLoc EBak LCla MWhe NMGN NPor SKen SLBF SOld WCum
'Kiss 'n' Tell'	MJac
'Kit Oxtoby'	EKMF LCla
'Kiwi'	EBak GPen NMGN SKen SLBF WCum
'Knight Errant'	SLBF
'Knockout'	EGou EKMF MSmi NPor SLBF SOak WCum
'Kolding Perle'	LCla SOld WCum
'Kon-Tiki'	EKMF NMGN WCum
'Koralle'	See F. 'Coralle'
'Kwintet'	EBak LCla MJac NPor SKen WCum
'Kyoto'	EKMF
'La Apache'	EBak
'La Bianca'	EBak
'La Campanella'	CLoc EBak EBly ECtt EGou EKMF GPen LCla MBri MJac MLab MSmi MSte MWar MWhe NFai NMGN NPor SKen SLBF SOld WCum
'La Fiesta'	EBak GPen MSmi NMGN WCum
'La France'	EBak
N 'La Neige'	EBak MSmi SKen SOld WCum
'La Porte'	CLoc
'La Rosita'	EBak MSmi SLBF WCum
N 'La Traviata'	EBak WCum
'Lace Petticoats'	CLoc EBak EKMF MSmi
'Lady Beth'	WCum
'Lady Boothby'	CBow CCla CHEx CPle EBak EKMF MBel NMGN NPor SKen SOld SPla
'Lady in Grey'	EKMF
'Lady Isobel Barnett'	CLoc EBak EBly EKMF GPen IHos LCla MBri MJac MSmi MWar MWhe NPor SKen SLBF SOld WCum
'Lady Kathleen Spence'	EBak EGou EKMF GPen MJac MWhe NMGN NPor SKen SOak SOld WCum
¶ 'Lady Love'	MBri
'Lady Patricia Mountbatten'	EBly ECtt EKMF LCla MBri MJac MLab MWar MWhe NPor SOld
'Lady Ramsey'	EBak EGou LCla MJac NMGN WCum
'Lady Rebecca'	CLoc

Cultivar	Suppliers
'Lady Thumb'	CCla CLoc CMHG CSco CShe EBak EBly EKMF GPen LCla MBal MBar MBel MBri MJac MLab MPla MSmi MWar MWat MWhe NKay NMGN SKen SLBF SOak SOld SPer WCum
'Lady's Smock'	EKMF SLBF
§ 'Laing's Hybrid'	CLoc EGou
'Lakeland Princess'	EBak
'Lakeside'	CLoc EBak
'Lancashire Lass'	MBri NPor WCum
'Lancelot'	EBak EBly EGou LCla NMGN SKen WCum
¶ 'Land van Beveren'	MSmi
'Lark'	EBly EGou
'Larksfield Skylark'	EGou
'L'Arlésienne'	CLoc EBly
'Lassie'	CLoc EBak MJac MSmi WCum
N 'Laura'	EKMF MSmi MWhe NMGN SLBF
'Laura Amanda'	EBly
'Laurie'	SOld WCum
'Lavender Blue'	CCla
'Lavender Kate'	CLoc EBak MJac
'Lavender Lady'	WCum
'Lazy Lady'	EBak
'Le Berger'	EKMF
'Lechlade Apache'	EGou LCla
¶ 'Lechlade Chinaman'	EKMF
'Lechlade Debutante'	EGou
'Lechlade Fire-Eater'	EGou LCla
'Lechlade Gorgon'	EKMF LCla
¶ 'Lechlade Magician'	EKMF
'Lechlade Marchioness'	EGou EKMF
'Lechlade Rocket'	EKMF
'Lechlade Tinkerbell'	EGou
¶ 'Lechlade Violet'	EKMF
¶ 'Leica'	EKMF
'Leicestershire Silver'	MJac
'Lemacto'	EBak
'Len Bielby'	EKMF MWar
'Lena'	CCla CLoc CMHG EBak EBly EGou EKMF GPen LCla MBal MBri MJac MLab MPla MSmi MWhe NFai NMGN NPor SKen SOak SOld SPer WCum WEas
'Lena Dalton'	CLoc EBak EKMF IHos LCla MBri MJac MSmi MWar MWhe SKen SOld
'Leonora'	CLoc EBak EBly EKMF LCla MBri MLab MSmi MWar MWhe NPor SKen SLBF SOld WCum
'Letty Lye'	EBak
'Lett's Delight'	EBly
'Leverhulme'	See F. 'Leverkusen'
§ 'Leverkusen'	CLoc EBak ECtt EKMF LCla MJac MWhe SKen SOld WCum
'Libra'	MSmi
N 'Liebesträume'	EBak
'Liebriez'	EBak EBly EKMF LCla SOak SOld
'Lilac'	EBak WCum
¶ 'Lilac Dainty'	GPen
'Lilac Lady'	MJac
'Lilac Lustre'	CLoc EBak EKMF MBri
'Lilac Princess'	MJac SKen WCum
'Lilac Queen'	EBak
'Lillibet'	CLoc EBak SKen WCum
'Lillydale'	MSmi WCum
'Linda Copley'	WCum

'Linda Goulding'	EBak EBly EGou LCla MWhe NMGN SOld
'Lindisfarne'	EBak EGou EKMF GPen LCla MJac MWar NPor SKen SOld WCum
'Lindy'	WCum
'Linet'	EBak
'Lisa'	EBly MSmi
¶ 'Lisi'	EKMF
'Little Beauty'	EKMF MLab MWhe NPor
'Little Gene'	EBak
'Little Jewel'	SKen SLBF WCum
'Little Ouse'	EGou LCla
'Little Ronnie'	MWhe
'Little Witch'	EKMF
'Liz'	EBak SOld WCum
'Lochinvar'	MJac MWar MWhe
'Loeky'	EBak LCla NPor SLBF SOld WCum
'Logan Garden'	SLBF
'Lolita'	EBak SKen
'Lonely Ballerina'	CLoc WCum
'Long Wings'	EKMF NMGN SLBF
'Loni Jane'	WCum
'Lord Byron'	CLoc EBak LCla SOld
'Lord Lonsdale'	EBak EBly GPen LCla MWhe NMGN SKen SOak SOld WCum WEas
'Lord Roberts'	CLoc SKen WCum
'Lorna Swinbank'	SLBF
'Lorraine's Delight'	WCum
'Lottie Hobby'	CDec CLoc CMGP EBly ECtt EKMF GPen ISea SBar SKen WBod WThu
'Louise Emershaw'	EBak GPen MJac NMGN WCum
'Lovable'	EBak
'Love Knot'	MSmi
'Loveliness'	CLoc EBak EKMF GPen MWhe WCum
'Love's Reward'	EBly LCla MJac MWar NPor SLBF
N *loxensis*	LCla
I 'Loxensis'	EBak EKMF LCla SKen SOld
'Loxhore Calypso'	EKMF
'Loxhore Cancan'	EKMF
'Lucerowe'	WCum
'Lucinda'	EGou SLBF WCum
'Lucky Strike'	CLoc EBak SKen
'Lumière'	EGou
'Lunter's Glorie'	WCum
'Lunter's Roehm'	WCum
'Lunter's Trots'	WCum
'Luscious'	WCum
'Lustre'	EBak NPor
lycioïdes Andrews	EBak EGou EKMF
– hort.	See F. 'Lycioïdes'
'Lye's Excelsior'	EBak LCla WCum
'Lye's Favourite'	NMGN
'Lye's Own'	EBak GPen LCla NMGN SLBF
'Lye's Unique'	CLoc EBak EBly EGou EKMF LCla MJac MWar MWhe NMGN NPor SKen SLBF SOld WCum
'Lylac Sunsa'	EKMF
'Lynette'	CLoc
'Lynn Ellen'	EBak WCum
'Lynne Marshall'	CCla
'Mabel Greaves'	LCla NPor WCum
'Machu Picchu'	EBly EKMF LCla MSmi WCum
macrophylla	WEas
'Madame Butterfly'	CLoc
'Madame Cornelissen'	CCla CLoc CSco EBak EBly EKMF ENot EPla GPen IJoh MBar MBri MJac MLab MWhe NKay NMGN NPor SOld SPer SPla SReu WCum
'Madame Eva Boye'	EBak
'Madame van der Strasse'	WCum
¶ 'Madelaine Sweeney'	MBri
'Maes-y-Groes'	EKMF
magellanica	CFis CGle CMHG EKMF LCla LHil NNor NPer SKen SReu WBod WCru WWat
– 'Alba'	See F. ***m. molinae***
I – 'Alba Aureovariegata'	CBow EPla LHop MBel SApp WCru
– 'Alba Variegata'	CMHG WEas
§ – var. ***gracilis***	CCla CLoc EKMF ESma SLon
– – 'Aurea'	CBot CCla CGle CMHG CTre EGol EGou EHar EHoe EKMF ELan ENot ERav GCHN GPen ISea LCla MWat MWhe NPor SIng SKen SLBF SPer SPla WCru WWat
§ – – 'Tricolor' (v)	LCla SLBF
– – 'Variegata'	CCla CGle CLew CMHG CSco CTre EBak ECha EGou EKMF ENot EPla ERav GPen MBal MGos MLab NKay NMGN SChu SDix SIng SKen SOld SPer SUsu WEas WWat
– var. ***macrostema*** 'Variegata'	EGou SOak
§ – var. ***molinae***	CB&S CBow CCla CGle CMHG CNic CSco EBak EKMF ELan EPla ERav ISea MWhe NFai NMGN NNor NPer NPor NRoo SIng SKen SPer WBod WCru WEas
§ – – 'Sharpitor' (v)	CB&S CCla CFis CLew CTre ECha EKMF ELan EMon LHop MPla NSti SDix SMrm SPer SPla WCru WSHC
– var. ***pumila***	CRDP GCal NPor SChu SIng
– 'Riccartonii'	See F. 'Riccartonii'
§ – 'Versicolor' (v)	Widely available
'Magenta Flush'	MJac MSmi
¶ 'Maggie Little'	GPen
'Magic Flute'	CLoc GPen LCla MJac MWhe SOld
'Maharaja'	EBak WCum
'Major Heaphy'	CCla EBak LCla MWhe NMGN NPor WCum
'Malibu Mist'	EGou EKMF LCla MSmi SOak WCum
'Mama Bleuss'	EBak
'Mancunian'	ECtt EGou SOak WCum
N 'Mandarin'	EBak
'Mantilla'	CLoc EBak EKMF LCla MJac MLab MSmi MWhe NMGN SOld
'Maori Pipes'	EGou
'Marbled Sky'	MJac
'Marcus Graham'	CLoc EGou EKMF MSmi SLBF WCum
'Marcus Hanton'	ECtt EKMF LCla MWar NPor SLBF WCum
'Mardale'	MLab
'Mardi Gras'	EBak GPen WCum

'Margaret'	CLoc CSco EBak EGou EKMF ENot GPen ISea LCla MBal MWhe NMGN SChu SKen SLBF SLon SOld WCum
'Margaret Brown'	CCla CLoc EBak EKMF GPen LCla MPla MSte MWhe NMGN NPor SKen SLBF WCum
¶ 'Margaret Davidson'	CLoc
'Margaret Pilkington'	EKMF LCla MLab MWar NPor SLBF WCum
'Margaret Roe'	EBak EKMF LCla MJac MWar MWhe NPor SKen SOld WCum
'Margaret Rose'	LCla MJac
'Margaret Susan'	EBak WCum
'Margaret Swales'	WCum
¶ 'Margaret Tebbit'	NPor SLBF
'Margarita'	CCla
'Margery Blake'	CCla EBak
'Margharitte'	WCum
'Maria Landy'	EKMF SLBF
'Maria Merrills'	EKMF WCum
'Marilyn Olsen'	EBly EKMF LCla MWar NPor SLBF SOak WCum
'Marin Belle'	EBak LCla
'Marin Glow'	CLoc EBak EKMF LCla MBri NMGN NPor SLBF SOld WCum
'Marinka'	CLoc EBak EBly ECtt EGou EKMF IHos LCla MBri MJac MLab MSmi MWar MWhe NFai NMGN NPor SKen SLBF SOld WCum
'Mark Kirby'	EKMF WCum
'Marlene Gilbee'	ECtt WCum
'Marlies'	WCum
'Marshside'	LCla NPor
¶ 'Martha Brown'	MLab
'Martin Hayward'	SKen
'Martin's Midnight'	NMGN
¶ 'Marton Smith'	MWhe
'Marty'	EBak
'Mary'	CLoc EBly EGou EKMF LCla MSmi MWar MWhe NPor SKen SLBF SOld
'Mary Fairclo'	MSmi
'Mary Joan'	EKMF NMGN
'Mary Kipling'	WCum
'Mary Lockyer'	CLoc EBak WCum
'Mary Poppins'	SLBF
'Mary Reynolds'	MWar
'Mary Rose'	EKMF
'Mary Thorne'	EBak
'Mary Wright'	MWhe
¶ 'Maryn'	SOak
'Masquerade'	EBak EKMF MWhe
¶ ***mathewsii***	EKMF
'Maureen Munro'	NMGN
'Maureen Ward'	EKMF
'Mauve Beauty'	EGou EKMF LCla WCum
'Mauve Lace'	CCla
'Mauve Wisp'	SOld WWeb
'Mayblossom'	EBly ECtt EGou LCla SLBF WCum
'Mayfayre'	CLoc
'Mayfield'	MJac MWhe SKen WCum
'Mazda'	MWhe WCum
'Meadowlark'	EBak ECtt EKMF WCum
'Medalist'	NMGN WCum
'Meditation'	CLoc
'Meike Meursing'	NMGN SKen

'Melody'	EBak GPen MWhe SKen WCum
'Melody Ann'	EBak
'Melting Moments'	EKMF
'Mendocino Mini'	EGou EKMF
'Meols Cop'	MWhe NPor WCum
'Merry Mary'	EBak EKMF NPor WCum
'Mexicali Rose'	CLoc WCum
'Michael'	EBly
'Michele Wallace'	EBly
'Micky Goult'	CLoc EBly EKMF LCla MJac MWar MWhe NMGN NPor SLBF SOld WCum
¶ 'Microchip'	SLBF
microphylla	CB&S CCla CElw CGle CLoc CMHG CTre EBak EBar EKMF ERav ERea GRei LCla MBel SFar SLBF SLon WCru WCum WEas
– ssp. ***aprica***	CGre EGou EKMF LCla WCum
§ – ssp. ***hemsleyana***	CCla EKMF LCla MLab MWhe SKen SLBF SOld WCum
§ – ssp. ***hidalgensis***	EGou EKMF SLBF
– ssp. ***microphylla***	EGou
'Midas'	LCla MBri MSmi NPor SLBF
'Midnight Sun'	EBak EBly GPen SKen WCum
'Mieke Meursing'	CLoc EBak ECtt EKMF LCla MJac MWar MWhe NPor SLBF SOld WCum
'Miep Alhuizen'	EGou
N 'Mikado'	EGou
'Mike Oxtoby'	EKMF
¶ 'Millrace'	EGou
'Ming'	CLoc
'Mini Skirt'	SLBF WCum
N ***minimiflora***	GAri SRms
'Minirose'	EKMF LCla MWar MWhe NPor SKen SLBF WCum
'Minnesota'	EBak
'Minx'	WCum
'Mipan'	LCla SLBF WCum
'Mischief'	CCla WWeb
'Miss California'	CLoc EBak EBly EKMF GPen LCla MBri MLab MSmi MWar NMGN SKen SOld WCum
'Miss Great Britain'	MSmi SOld
'Miss Leucadia'	WCum
'Miss Vallejo'	EBak
'Mission Bells'	CCla CLoc EBak EKMF MJac MSmi MWhe NMGN SKen SLBF SOld WCum
'Misty Blue'	EKMF WCum
'Misty Morn'	EBly EGou SLBF
'Misty Pink'	EKMF MSmi
'Molesworth'	EBak MJac MLab MWhe NPor SKen SOld
'Mollie Beulah'	EBly ECtt EKMF
'Money Spinner'	CLoc EBak MSmi WCum
'Monsieur Thibaut'	CCla ENot LCla SKen SOld SPer
'Monte Rosa'	CLoc SKen
'Monterey'	MWhe
'Montevideo'	EGou
'Montezuma'	MSmi SOld WCum
'Montrose Village'	MSmi MWhe WCum
'Monument'	WCum
'Mood Indigo'	EGou NPor SLBF WCum
'Moonbeam'	CLoc EBly MLab MWhe NPor WCum
'Moonlight Sonata'	CLoc EBak GPen MJac MSmi SKen
'Moonraker'	ECtt WCum

'Moonshot'	NMGN SKen WCum
¶ 'Morcott'	MLab
'Mordred'	EBak WCum
'Morning Glow'	WCum
'Morning Light'	CLoc EBak GPen MSmi NPor SOak WCum
'Morning Mist'	EBak
¶ 'Morning Star'	MBri
'Morrells'	EBak
'Moth Blue'	EBak NPor WCum
¶ 'Mounbatten'	MWhe
'Mount Stewart'	CCla
'Mountain Mist'	EKMF MJac NPor WCum
'Moyra'	EKMF
'Mr A Huggett'	CLoc EBly EGou GPen LCla MWhe NPor SLBF SOak SOld
'Mr P D Lee'	MWhe
'Mr W Rundle'	EBak EBly
'Mrs Churchill'	CLoc
'Mrs Lawrence Lyon'	EBak WCum
'Mrs Lovell Swisher'	EBak EKMF LCla MBri MJac MWar MWhe NPor SKen SLBF SOld WCum
'Mrs Marshall'	EBak MWar SLBF SOld WCum
'Mrs Minnie Pugh'	CLoc
'Mrs Popple'	Widely available
'Mrs Susan Brookfield'	NPor SLBF
'Mrs W Castle'	NPor
'Mrs W P Wood'	CLoc LCla
'Mrs W Rundle'	CLoc EBak EBly EKMF GPen MWhe NPor SLBF
'Muirfield'	EGou
'Muriel'	CLoc EBak ECtt EKMF GPen MWhe SKen WCum
'My Beauty'	MSmi
'My Dear'	CLoc
'My Fair Lady'	CLoc EBak WCum
¶ 'My Honey'	GPen
'Nancy Lou'	CLoc EBly EGou EKMF GPen LCla MJac MSmi MWar MWhe NMGN NPor SKen SLBF SOld WCum
¶ 'Nanny Ed'	MBri
'Natalie Jones'	EGou
'Natasha Sinton'	MBri SLBF
'Native Dancer'	EBak
'Nautilus'	EBak
'Navy Blue'	CCla WCum
'Neapolitan'	EGou EKMF MWhe SKen SLBF
'Neil Clyne'	MWhe
'Nell Gwyn'	CLoc EBak NPor
'Nellie Nuttall'	CLoc EBak EBly EGou EKMF GPen LCla MBri MJac MSte MWar MWhe NMGN NPor SLBF SOak SOld WCum
'Neopolitan'	CCla NPor
'Neue Welt'	EBak
'New Fascination'	EBak SKen
'Nice 'n' Easy'	MBri MWhe WCum
'Nicholas Hughes'	NPor
'Nickis Findling'	EGou EKMF MSmi
'Nicola'	EBak
N 'Nicola Claire'	EGou NPor
'Nicola Jane'	CCla EBak EBly EKMF GPen LCla MBel MBri MJac MSmi NMGN NPor SLBF SOak
'Nicolette'	MJac
'Nightingale'	CLoc EBak WCum
§ ***nigricans***	EGou EKMF

– x ***gehrigeri***	EKMF
'Nikki'	SKen WCum
'Nimue'	EBak EGou WCum
'Nina Wills'	EBak
'Niobe'	EBak
'No Name'	EBak
'Noblesse'	WCum
'Norah Henderson'	GPen MLab
'Norfolk Belle'	EBly
¶ 'Norma Nield'	LCla
¶ 'Norman Greenhill'	SLBF
'Normandy Bell'	EBak MSmi
'Northern Pride'	NMGN SOld
'Northumbrian Belle'	EBak MJac SOld
'Northway'	CLoc LCla MJac MWhe NPor SKen SLBF WCum
'Norvell Gillespie'	EBak
'Novato'	EBak GPen WCum
'Novella'	EBak MSmi NPor WCum
¶ 'Nunthorpe Gem'	WCum
¶ 'O Sole Mio'	SKen
¶ 'Oakham'	MLab
'Obergärtner Koch'	EBly SKen SOld WCum
'Ocean Beach'	EBly GPen MSmi
'Oetnang'	WCum
'Old Rose'	WCum
'Old Somerset'	SOld
'Oldbury'	SOld
'Oldbury Delight'	SOld
'Oldbury Galore'	LCla SOld
'Oldbury Gem'	SOld
'Oldbury Pearl'	SOld
'Olive Moon'	EBly SLBF
'Olive Smith'	EBly LCla MJac MLab NMGN SLBF
'Olympic Lass'	EBak
'Omeomy'	NPor WCum
'Oosje'	See F. x ***bacillaris*** 'Oosje'
'Opalescent'	CLoc WCum
'Orange Bell'	NMGN
'Orange Crush'	CLoc EBak MSmi MWar MWhe SLBF
'Orange Crystal'	EBak EKMF GPen IHos LCla MBri MJac MLab MWhe NFai NMGN SKen SOld WCum
'Orange Drops'	CLoc EBak EBly ECtt EKMF MWhe NPor SKen SOak SOld WCum
'Orange Flame'	WCum
'Orange Flare'	CLoc EBak EKMF GPen LCla MJac MSmi MWar MWhe NMGN SLBF SOak SOld WCum
'Orange Flash'	SOld
'Orange King'	EGou NMGN WCum
'Orange Mirage'	CLoc EBak EBly LCla MBri MLab MSmi SKen SLBF SOld WCum
¶ 'Orange Pip'	MLab
'Orangeblossom'	LCla SLBF
'Orangy'	WCum
'Oranje Boven'	EKMF
'Oranje van Os'	MJac MWhe NPor
'Orient Express'	EGou EKMF LCla MWhe WCum
Oriental Flame ®	EKMF MSmi WCum
'Oriental Lace'	WCum
'Oriental Sunrise'	MSmi MWhe NPor SKen
'Orientalis'	EKMF
'Ornamental Pearl'	CLoc EBak ECtt LCla SKen SLBF SOld

'Ortenburger Festival'	SLBF WCum
'Orwell'	EGou
'Other Fellow'	EBak EBly EKMF LCla MLab NMGN NPor SKen SLBF SOld WCum
'Our Darling'	EBly MWhe NPor
'Our Ted'	SOld
'Ovation'	MSmi
'Overbecks'	See F. ***magellanica molinae*** 'Sharpitor'
'Overbecks Ruby'	EMon
'Pacific Grove'	EBak WCum
'Pacific Queen'	CLoc EBak EKMF
'Pacquesa'	EBak EBly EKMF GPen IHos LCla MJac MLab MWar MWhe NMGN NPor SKen SLBF SOld WCum
'Padre Pio'	MJac
'Pale Flame'	MSmi MWhe WCum
'Palford'	EBak
¶ ***pallescens***	EKMF
'Pamela Knights '	EBak EGou
'Pan America'	EBak
paniculata	CBot EBak EGou EKMF LCla LHop
'Pantaloons'	EBak WCum
'Papa Bleuss'	CLoc EBak NMGN SOld WCum
'Papoose'	CCla EBak EKMF GPen MBel MPla NMGN SLBF SOld WCum
'Party Frock'	CLoc EBak LCla MSmi NMGN SOld
♦***parviflora*** hort.	See F. x ***bacillaris***
– Lindley	EBak
'Passing Cloud'	SKen
'Pastel'	EBak
'Pat Meara'	CLoc EBak
'Pathetique'	CLoc
'Patience'	EBak EBly EGou EKMF LCla NMGN SLBF SOld WCum
¶ 'Patio Party'	MBri SLBF
'Patio Princess'	LCla MBri MWhe NPor SLBF
N 'Patricia'	EBak GPen WCum
'Patricia Ann'	EKMF MWar
'Patty Evans'	EBak MBri
¶ 'Patty Sue'	MBri
'Paul Cambon'	EBak EKMF
'Paul Roe'	MJac NPor
'Paula Jane'	LCla MWar MWhe SLBF SOld WCum
'Paula Johnson'	MJac
'Pauline Rawlins'	CLoc EBak
¶ 'Pa's Princess'	MLab
'Peace'	EBak
'Peachy Keen'	EBak
'Peacock'	CLoc
'Pearl Farmer'	WCum
¶ 'Pebble Mill'	MLab
'Pee Wee Rose'	EBak EKMF MSmi
'Peggy King'	EBak LCla
'Peloria'	CLoc EBak SKen WCum
'Pennine'	MBri MWar WCum
'Peper Harow'	EBak
'Pepi'	CLoc EBak SOld WCum
'Peppermint Candy'	MSmi
'Peppermint Stick'	CLoc EBak EBly EKMF GPen LCla MBri MJac MSmi MWhe NMGN NPor SKen SOak SOld WCum
¶ 'Perestroika'	MSmi
'Perky Pink'	EBak EBly LCla MLab MWhe NMGN SKen SOld WCum
'Perry Park'	EBak MBri MJac
¶ 'Perry's Jumbo'	NPer
perscandens	ECou EGou EKMF ISea LCla SLBF
'Personality'	EBak MSmi WCum
'Peter Bielby'	EGou EKMF MWar SLBF WCum
'Peter Crookes'	EGou EKMF LCla NPor WCum
'Peter Pan'	EBly SIng SPer
¶ 'Peter Sanderson'	EKMF LCla
¶ ***petiolaris***	EKMF
'Petite'	EBak
'Petronella'	MWar SLBF SOld WCum
'Pharaoh'	CLoc WCum
'Phénoménal'	EBak EBly EKMF GPen SKen SOld WCum
'Phyllis'	CCla CLoc EBak EBly EGou EKMF GPen LCla MBal MJac MSmi NFai NMGN SChu SKen SLBF SOld SPla WCum
'Phyrne'	EBak
¶ 'Piet Hein'	MSmi
'Pinch Me'	EBak EKMF MWar NMGN NPor SKen SOak SOld WCum
'Pink Aurora'	CLoc WCum
'Pink Ballet Girl'	CLoc EBak
'Pink Bon Accord'	CLoc WCum
'Pink Bouquet'	MJac WCum
¶ 'Pink Campanella'	MLab
'Pink Chiffon'	EKMF MSmi
'Pink Claws'	CCla
'Pink Cloud'	CLoc EBak
'Pink Darling'	CLoc EBak MWhe SKen WCum
'Pink Dessert'	EBak SKen
'Pink Fairy'	EBak NMGN NPor
'Pink Fandango'	CLoc
'Pink Fantasia'	EBak EBly EGou EKMF LCla MJac MWar MWhe NPor
'Pink Flamingo'	CLoc EBak NMGN SKen
'Pink Galaxy'	MJac
'Pink Galore'	CLoc EBak EBly EGou EKMF GPen IHos LCla MBri MJac MSmi MWhe NFai NMGN NPor SKen SLBF SOak SOld WCum
'Pink Goon'	EKMF LCla SLBF WCum
'Pink Jade'	EBak LCla NPor
'Pink La Campanella'	EKMF MJac NMGN NPor
'Pink Lace'	CCla SOld
N 'Pink Lady'	MWhe NPor
'Pink Marshmallow'	CLoc CSut EBak EBly EGou EKMF LCla MJac MSmi MWar MWhe NPor SKen SLBF SOak SOld WCum
'Pink Most'	EKMF
'Pink Panther'	ECtt EKMF LCla
N 'Pink Pearl'	EBak EKMF SLBF
'Pink Picotee'	MJac
¶ 'Pink Pineapple'	MLab
'Pink Profusion'	EBak
'Pink Quartet'	CLoc EBak LCla NMGN SOld
'Pink Rain'	EGou EKMF SLBF
'Pink Ruffles'	WCum
'Pink Spangles'	IHos MBri WCum
¶ 'Pink Surprise'	WCum
'Pink Temptation'	CLoc EBak LCla SOld WCum
¶ 'Pinkmost'	ECtt
'Pinto'	WCum
'Pinwheel'	CLoc EBak WCum

'Piper'	MWar WCum
'Piper's Vale'	EGou EKMF SLBF
'Pirbright'	EKMF LCla SLBF WCum
'Pixie'	CCla CLoc EBak EGou EKMF GPen MJac NMGN SKen SLBF SOld WCum
¶ 'Pixie Bells'	CMHG
'Playford'	EBak WCum
'Plenty'	CLoc EBak LCla MWar NPor WCum
¶ 'Ploughman'	EGou
'Plumb-bob'	EGou
'Pluto'	CCla
'Pop Whitlock'	CCla EKMF LCla SKen WCum
'Poppet'	SOld WCum
'Port Arthur'	EBak ECtt
'Postiljon'	EBak EKMF SLBF WCum
N 'Powder Puff'	CLoc EBly ECtt EKMF MBri MSmi NMGN SKen SOld WWeb
N 'Prelude'	CLoc EBak
'President'	EBak SKen
'President B W Rawlins'	EBak
§ 'President Elliot'	MWhe
'President Leo Boullemier'	EBak ECtt EKMF LCla MJac SKen WCum
'President Margaret Slater'	EBak GPen LCla MJac MLab MSte MWar MWhe SLBF WCum
'President Norman Hobbs'	EKMF
'President Roosevelt'	EBly ECtt GPen
'President Stanley Wilson'	EBak EBly ECtt LCla
'President Wilf Sharp'	SKen WCum
'Preston Guild'	CLoc EBak EKMF LCla MWhe NMGN NPer NPor SKen SLBF SOak SOld WCum
'Pretty Belinda'	WCum
'Pretty Grandpa'	WCum
'Pride of the West'	EBak
¶ 'Priest Land'	WCum
'Prince of Orange'	CLoc EBak LCla NPor SOld WCum
'Prince of Peace'	GPen MSmi NMGN WCum
'Princess Dollar'	See F. 'Dollar Princess'
'Princess of Bath'	CLoc
'Princess Pamela'	SLBF
'Princess Pat'	EKMF
'Princessita'	EBak ECtt EKMF GPen LCla MBri MJac MLab MSmi MWar MWhe SKen SLBF SOak WCum
procumbens	CLoc CRDP EBak ECou EGou EKMF ELan EPot ERea ESis GCHN IDai IReg LCla MHig MTho MWhe NWCA SIng SKen SLBF SLon SOld WBod WOMN WPer WThu
'Prodigy'	See F. 'Enfant Prodigue'
'Prosperity'	CLoc EBak EBly EGou EKMF GPen LCla MBel MJac MLab MSmi MWar MWhe NMGN SLon SOak SOld
N 'Pumila'	CCla EGou EKMF ELan GPen LCla MBal MBel MPla SLBF
'Purper Klokje'	EBak EKMF SLBF
'Purple Ann'	NMGN
'Purple Emperor'	CLoc
'Purple Heart'	CLoc EBak NMGN SKen
'Purple Lace'	CCla

¶ 'Purple Pride'	MBri
'Purple Rain'	EKMF MSmi
'Purple Showers'	WCum
'Purple Splendour'	CSco ELan SOak
'Pussy Cat'	CLoc EBak EKMF NMGN SKen WCum
putumayensis	EBak LCla
'Put's Folly'	EBak GPen LCla MJac SKen WCum
'Quaser'	EKMF NMGN SLBF SOak SOld
'Queen Mabs'	EBak
'Queen Mary'	CLoc EBak EKMF WCum
'Queen of Bath'	EBak
'Queen of Derby'	SOak WCum
'Queen of Hearts'	WCum
'Queen's Park'	EBak
'Query'	EBak GPen SKen
'R A F'	CLoc EBak EBly ECtt EKMF GPen LCla MJac MWar SKen SLBF SOak SOld WCum
¶ 'Rachel Sinton'	MBri
'Radcliffe Beauty'	MWhe WCum
'Radcliffe Bedder'	EKMF NMGN SKen
'Rading's Inge'	EGou
'Rading's Karin'	EGou
'Rahnee'	MJac NPor WCum
'Rainbow'	EGou
'Rambling Rose'	CLoc EBak EGou LCla MJac MLab SKen SLBF SOld WCum
'Rams Royal'	MJac MLab SLBF
'Raspberry'	CLoc EBak GPen LCla MSmi MWar NMGN SKen WCum
'Ratatouille'	EGou EKMF MSmi SLBF WCum
ravenii	EGou EKMF
'Ravenslaw'	EKMF
'Ray Redfern'	MJac
'Razzle Dazzle'	EBak
'Reading Show'	EBly SLBF
'Rebecca Williamson'	EGou MJac NMGN NPor SLBF WCum
¶ 'Rebekah Sinton'	MBri
'Red Imp'	CCla NPor WWeb
'Red Jacket'	CLoc EBak
¶ 'Red Petticoat'	GPen
'Red Ribbons'	EBak
'Red Shadows'	CLoc EBak EBly MBri MJac MWhe NMGN SLBF WCum
'Red Spider'	CLoc EBak EGou EKMF GPen MLab MSmi MWar MWhe NMGN NPor SKen SLBF SOak SOld WCum
'Red Wing'	CLoc
'Reg Dickenson'	MJac MWhe
'Reg Gubler'	SLBF WCum
'Regal'	CLoc
'Regal Robe'	WCum
regia alpestris	See F. ***alpestris***
– var. ***regia***	EKMF
– ssp. ***reitzii***	EGou EKMF
– ssp. ***serrae***	EKMF
'Remus'	EKMF LCla MBri
'Requiem'	CLoc IHos
'Reverend Doctor Brown'	EBak WCum
'Reverend Elliott'	See F. 'President Elliot'
N 'Rhapsody'	CLoc
'Ri Mia'	EGou

§ 'Riccartonii'	CB&S CCla CLoc CSco EBak EKMF ELan ENot GPen IDai IJoh ISea LCla MBar MBel MBri MLab NMGN NPer NWea SIng SMrm WBod WCru WCum WEas WStI
'Richard Livesy'	WCum
'Ridestar'	CLoc EBak LCla MJac MSmi MWhe NMGN SLBF
'Rika'	WCum
¶ 'Rina Felix'	EGou
'Ringwood Gold'	SOld
'Ringwood Market'	EBly ECtt EKMF LCla MWhe NMGN SKen SOld
'River Plate'	EGou
'Robbie'	EKMF NMGN SLBF WCum
'Robert Bruce'	EKMF WCum
'Robin'	MSmi
'Rolla'	EBak
'Roman City'	CLoc
'Romance'	EKMF NMGN WCum
'Ron Ewart'	EKMF MWhe NPor WCum
¶ 'Ron Holmes'	LCla
'Ronald L Lockerbie'	CLoc EKMF GPen MSmi MWhe WCum
'Rosamunda'	CLoc
'Rose Aylett'	EBak
'Rose Bower'	NMGN
'Rose Bradwardine'	EBak
'Rose Churchill'	EKMF LCla MBri MJac MSmi SOak
'Rose Marie'	CLoc
'Rose of Castile'	CCla CLoc EBak EKMF GPen MJac MWhe NMGN WCum
'Rose of Castile Improved'	CCla EBak EBly EKMF GPen LCla MJac MWar NPor SKen SOld
'Rose of Denmark'	EBak LCla MJac MLab MSmi MWar MWhe SLBF SOak SOld WCum
'Rose Reverie'	EBak
'Rose Winston'	MWhe
'Rosebud'	EBak WCum
'Rosecroft Beauty'	EBak EBly GPen LCla MWhe SKen SOld
'Rosemary Day'	CLoc WCum
'Rosy Frills'	EGou EKMF LCla MJac MSmi MWhe NMGN NPor SOld
'Rosy Morn'	CLoc EBak
Rosy Ruffles ®	EKMF MSmi
'Rough Silk'	CLoc EBak LCla SOld WCum
'Roy Walker'	CLoc EGou EKMF LCla MJac MLab MWar MWhe NMGN NPor SKen SOak SOld
'Royal and Ancient'	EGou
'Royal Orchid'	EBak
'Royal Purple'	EBak EKMF MBri
'Royal Touch'	EBak WCum
'Royal Velvet'	CLoc EBak EBly EGou EKMF GPen LCla MJac MLab MSmi MWar MWhe NMGN NPor SKen SLBF SOak SOld WCum
'Royal Wedding'	WCum
'Rubens'	MWar
§ 'Rubra Grandiflora'	EBak EKMF LCla SLBF
'Ruby'	LCla SOld
¶ 'Ruby Wedding'	SLBF
'Ruddigore'	EBly EGou ESma SLBF SOld WCum
'Ruffles'	EBak MSmi WCum
§ 'Rufus'	CCla CLoc CMHG EBak EBly EKMF EPla GPen LCla MBel MJac MWar MWhe NMGN SKen SLBF WCum
'Rufus the Red'	See F. 'Rufus'
'Ruth Brazewell'	CLoc
'Ruth King'	EBak ECtt NMGN NPor SKen SOak SOld WCum
'Ruthie'	WCum
'Sacramento Bells'	MSmi
'Sahara'	NMGN
'Sally Ann'	NPor WCum
¶ 'Sally Gunell'	MLab
'Salmon Cascade'	EBak EKMF MJac SLBF
'Salmon Glow'	GPen MJac MWhe
'Sampson's Delight'	WCum
'Samson'	EBak WCum
¶ 'Sam's Song'	MJac
'San Diego'	MSmi WCum
'San Francisco'	EBak WCum
'San Leandro'	EBak NMGN
'San Mateo'	EBak
'San Pasqual'	WCum
§ ***sanctae-rosae***	EGou EKMF SUsu
'Sandboy'	EBak SLBF SOld WCum
'Sangria'	SLBF
'Sanrina'	EKMF
'Santa Barbara'	NMGN
'Santa Cruz'	CCla EBak EGou EKMF LCla MWhe SOak SOld WCum
'Santa Lucia'	CLoc EBak WCum
'Santa Monica'	EBak
'Sapphire'	EBak MSmi
'Sara Helen'	CLoc EBak NPor WCum
'Sarah Ann'	MWar
'Sarah Greensmith'	EKMF
'Sarah Jayne'	EBak LCla WCum
'Sarah Louise'	EKMF
'Sarina'	EGou
'Sarong'	EBak MSmi WCum
'Saskia'	EKMF
'Satchmo'	EGou
'Satellite'	CLoc EBak EKMF GPen MJac MSmi WCum
'Saturnus'	EBak LCla SOld
¶ 'Saxondale Sue'	WCum
scandens	See F. ***decussata***
'Scarborough Rosette'	EGou
'Scarcity'	EBak SKen
'Schnabel'	WCum
'Schneeball'	EBak EKMF SOak
'Schneewittchen'	EBak EKMF WCum
'Schneewittcher'	EBly
'Schönbrunner Schuljubiläum	EBak SLBF
'Scotch Heather'	GPen MSmi WCum
'Sea Shell'	EBak WCum
'Seaforth'	EBak
'Sealand Prince'	CCla ECtt GPen WCum
'Sebastopol'	CLoc ECtt EKMF MSmi NPor WCum
'Sensation'	WCum
'Serendipity'	WCum
serratifolia Hooker	See F. ***austromontana***
– Ruiz & Pavón	See F. ***denticulata***
sessilifolia	EKMF LCla
'Seventh Heaven'	CLoc EGou LCla MSmi NMGN SLBF SOak WCum

'Shady Lady' MSmi
'Shangri-La' EBak
'Sharon Allsop' MWhe WCum
'Sharon Caunt' EKMF
'Sharpitor' See F. ***magellanica molinae*** 'Sharpitor'
'Shawna Ree' EKMF
'Sheila Crooks' EBak NPor WCum
¶ 'Sheila Kirby' MJac
'Shell Pink' GPen
'Shelley Lyn' SKen WCum
'Shellford' CLoc EBak EBly EGou EKMF LCla MWar MWhe NPor SLBF WCum
'Shooting Star' EBak
'Shuna' NPor WCum
'Shuna Lindsay' WCum
'Shy Lady' MWhe SKen WCum
'Sierra Blue' CLoc EBak EKMF SKen WCum
'Silver Anniversary' EKMF LCla MSmi WCum
'Silver Dawn' EBly EKMF MWhe NMGN NPor WCum
'Silver Dollar' LCla MWar MWhe NMGN NPor SKen SLBF SOld WCum
'Silver Pink' CCla
'Silverdale' EKMF MWhe
¶ 'Simon J Rowell' EKMF LCla
simplicicaulis EBak EGou EKMF LCla SOld
'Sincerity' CLoc MWhe
'Siobhan' MJac
'Sir Alfred Ramsey' EBak EGou LCla MJac MWhe WCum
N 'Siren' EBak
'Sister Ann Haley' EBly EKMF
'Skylight' MLab
'Sleepy' CCla EBly GPen LCla MBri SKen SOld
'Sleigh Bells' CLoc EBak EKMF GPen MWhe NMGN SKen SOld WCum
'Small Pipes' EGou
'Smokey Mountain' EKMF MSmi WCum
'Smoky' EGou
'Sneezy' CCla EBly LCla SKen WWeb
'Snow Burner' MSmi
'Snow White' NMGN WCum
§ 'Snowcap' CCla CLoc CMHG EBak EBly EGou EKMF GPen IHos LCla MBel MBri MJac MLab MSmi MSte MWar MWhe NFai NMGN SKen SLBF SOld SPla WCum
'Snowdon' MWar
N 'Snowdrift' CLoc EBak MWhe NMGN WCum
'Snowfire' CLoc EBly ECtt EGou EKMF LCla MSmi MWhe NMGN SKen SLBF SOak WCum
'Snowstorm' CMHG ECtt LCla NMGN
'Snowy Summit' MSmi WCum
'So Big' EKMF WCum
Software ® MSmi
'Son of Thumb' CCla CLoc EBly EKMF ELan GPen LCla MBri MJac MWhe SKen SLBF SOld WCum
'Sonota' CLoc EBak GPen MSmi NMGN SLBF SOld WCum
'Sophie Claire' EGou EKMF
'Sophie's Surprise' EGou EKMF
'Sophisticated Lady' CLoc EBak EBly ECtt EKMF GPen LCla MJac MSmi MWar NMGN SKen SOak SOld WCum
'South Seas' EBak WCum
'Southgate' CLoc EBak EBly EGou EKMF GPen LCla NMGN NPor SLBF SOak WCum
'Southlanders' EBak
'Southwell Minster' EKMF NMGN
'Space Shuttle' EKMF LCla WCum
'Sparks' WCum
'Speciosa' CTre EBak EKMF LCla WCum
¶ 'Spellbound' MLab
'Spion Kop' EBak EKMF GPen LCla MJac MLab MWar MWhe NFai NMGN SKen SLBF SOak WCum
splendens EBak EGou EKMF LCla MFir NPer SAxl SLBF SOld SUsu
'Sportsknight' EGou LCla
¶ 'Spring Classic' MLab
'Springtime' CSco
'Squadron Leader' EBak EBly EGou SOak SOld WCum
'Square Peg' WCum
'St Andrews' EGou
'Stad Elburg' MJac
'Stanley Cash' EBly EKMF LCla MBri MJac MWar MWhe NMGN NPor SKen SLBF SOak SOld WCum
'Star of Pink' MSmi MWhe
'Star Rose' EKMF
'Stardust' EBak MJac MWhe NPor SKen SOld WCum
'Stathern Surprise' MJac NPor
'Steeley' MSmi MWhe WCum
'Stella Ann' EBak EBly EGou LCla MWhe
'Stella Marina' CLoc EBak
'Stephanie' WCum
'Stevie Doidge' WCum
'Stormy Sunset' EGou
'Strawberry Delight' CLoc CMHG EBak ECtt EGou EKMF GPen LCla MLab MWhe NPor SKen SOld WCum
'Strawberry Fizz' MSmi WCum
'Strawberry Sundae' CLoc EBak NMGN WCum
'Strawberry Supreme' EKMF LCla WCum
'String of Pearls' ECtt EKMF LCla MBri MJac NPor SKen SLBF SOld WCum
'Sugar Almond' MJac NPor
'Sugar Blues' EBak
'Sugar Plum' WCum
'Suikerbossie' ('Sugarbush') MJac
'Sunkissed' EBak LCla WCum
'Sunlight Path' EGou
'Sunningdale' EGou LCla
'Sunny' SKen WCum
'Sunny Smiles' NMGN NPor
'Sunray' CLoc EBak EFol EKMF GPen LCla LHop MSmi MWhe NMGN SKen SLBF SOld
'Sunset' CLoc EBak MWhe NPor SKen SPer WCum
'Supernova' MSmi NMGN NPor
'Superstar' EBly LCla MBri MSmi NPor SLBF WCum
'Susan' LCla
'Susan Daley' NPor
'Susan Ford' EKMF NPor SKen WCum
'Susan Green' EGou EKMF LCla MWhe NMGN NPor SLBF WCum
'Susan Jill' SLBF WCum
¶ 'Susan Joy' MLab
'Susan McMaster' CLoc

'Susan Travis'	CCla CLoc EBak EKMF EPla GPen LCla MWhe NMGN SKen SOld
'Susie Olcese'	EBak NPor WCum
'Suzy'	MSmi
'Swanland Candy'	ECtt
'Swanley Gem'	CLoc EBak EKMF GPen LCla NMGN NPor SKen SLBF WCum
'Swanley Pendula'	CLoc
'Swanley Yellow'	EBak SKen SOld WCum
'Sweet Leilani'	CLoc EBak GPen NMGN SKen WCum
'Sweet Sixteen'	CLoc
N 'Sweetheart'	EBak
'Sweetie Dear'	EGou
'Swingtime'	CLoc CMHG CSut EBak EBly EKMF GPen IHos LCla MJac MLab MSmi MWar MWhe NFai NMGN NPor SKen SLBF SOak SOld WCum
'Swiss Miss'	WCum
'S'Wonderful'	CLoc EBak MSmi WCum
sylvatica	See F. ***nigricans***
'Sylvia Barker'	EGou
'Sylvy'	LCla SLBF
'Symphony'	CLoc EBak GPen WCum
'Tabatha'	MLab
'Taddle'	EBly EKMF MJac NPor SLBF WCum
'Taffeta Bow'	CLoc EKMF MSmi SOak WCum
'Taffy'	EBak WCum
'Tahoe'	WCum
'Tam O'Shanter'	WCum
'Tamar Isobel'	WCum
'Tamworth'	CLoc EBak LCla MJac NPor WCum
'Tangerine'	CLoc EBak LCla MWhe NPor WCum
¶ 'Tania Leanne'	WCum
'Tanya'	CLoc
'Tanya Bridger'	EBak WCum
'Tarra Valley'	EGou
'Tartan'	MLab
'Task Force'	NMGN SKen
'Tausendschön'	CLoc ECtt EKMF WCum
'Ted Heath'	WCum
'Ted Perry'	ECtt MJac NMGN
'Television'	CLoc LCla
N 'Temptation'	CLoc EBak ECtt LCla MBri NPor WCum
'Tennessee Waltz'	CCla CLoc CMHG EBak EBly EGou EKMF GPen LCla MBel MJac MLab MSmi MWar MWhe NMGN NPor SChu SKen SLBF SOak SOld SPer SPla WCum WEas
'Terrysue'	EKMF
'Texas Longhorn'	CLoc EBak EBly EKMF GPen MSmi NMGN SOak SOld
'Thalia'	CLoc EBak EBly ECtt EGou EKMF ERea GPen IHos LCla MBri MJac MLab MSmi MWar MWhe NMGN NPor NWyt SKen SLBF SOak SOld SPla SUsu WCum
¶ 'Thamar'	EKMF
'Thames Valley'	EGou LCla WCum
'That's It'	EBak
'The Aristocrat'	CLoc EBak NPor
§ 'The Doctor'	CLoc EBak EKMF GPen MWhe WCum
'The Jester'	EBak
'The Madame'	EBak WCum
'The Patriot'	MWhe WCum
'The Phoenix'	WCum
¶ 'The Red Arrows'	MLab
'The Rival'	EKMF MSmi NMGN WCum
'The Speedbird'	WCum
'The Spoiler'	MSmi WCum
'The Tarns'	EBak GPen LCla MBel WCru
'Therese Dupois'	EKMF
'Théroigne de Méricourt'	EBak
'This England'	WCum
¶ 'Thistle Hill'	SLBF
'Thompsonii'	EKMF EMon GPen SKen
'Thornley's Hardy'	EKMF GPen MBri NMGN NPor SOld WCum
'Three Cheers'	CLoc EBak
'Three Counties'	EBak
'Thunderbird'	CLoc EBak EGou
thymifolia	CMil EBur ELan EMon ESis ESma GCra LHop MBal MPla NRar WKif WPer
¶ – ssp. ***minimiflora***	EKMF
'Tiara'	EBak WCum
N 'Tiffany'	EBak
tillettiana	EKMF
'Timlin Brened'	EBak LCla MWhe
'Ting-a-Ling'	CLoc EBak EBly EKMF GPen LCla MBri MSmi MWar MWhe NMGN NPor SKen SLBF SOld WCum
N 'Tinker Bell'	EBak EKMF SOld
'Tintern Abbey'	NPor
'Toby Bridger'	CLoc EBak
'Tolling Bell'	EBak EBly EKMF LCla MJac MSmi MWhe NMGN NPor SKen SOld WCum
'Tom H Oliver'	EBak
'Tom Hobson'	WCum
'Tom Knights'	EBak EGou EKMF LCla MWhe SLBF SOld WCum
'Tom Redfern'	MJac NPor SOak
'Tom Thorne'	EBak
'Tom Thumb'	Widely available
'Tom West' (v)	CLoc CMHG CRDP EBak EFol EGou EKMF GPen LCla LHil MLab MSmi MWhe NMGN NPor SKen SLBF SMrm SOld SPla SUsu WCum WEas
'Tom Woods'	LCla MLab MSmi MWhe NPor WCum
'Top Score'	NMGN
'Topaz'	CLoc EBak
'Topper'	ECtt SLBF
'Torch'	CLoc EBak EKMF MJac MSmi NMGN WCum
'Torchlight'	EBly MJac
¶ 'Tortorina'	GPen
'Torville and Dean'	CLoc EBly EGou EKMF GPen MJac MLab MSmi MWhe NMGN NPor SKen SLBF SOak WCum
'Tour Eiffel'	EGou
'Tower of London'	SKen
'Towi'	EGou
'Tracid'	CLoc
'Tracie Ann'	EKMF
'Trade Winds'	MSmi
'Trail Blazer'	CLoc EBak GPen LCla MJac MLab MWhe NPor SKen SOak
'Trailing Queen'	EBak EKMF MJac WCum

'Tranquility'	MSmi WCum
'Trase'	EBak EBly EKMF LCla MLab NMGN NPor SOak
'Traudchen Bonstedt'	CLoc EBak EBly GPen LCla MWhe NMGN SLBF SOld WCum
'Treasure'	EBak WCum
'Trewince Twilight'	MLab SLBF
'Tricolor'	See F. ***magellanica gracilis*** 'Tricolor'
'Tricolorii' (v)	EBly EKMF
'Trio'	CLoc
triphylla	EBak EKMF IReg SOld
¶ 'Trish Dewey'	MLab
'Trisha'	WCum
'Tristesse'	CLoc EBak MJac MSmi MWhe NMGN SOld
'Trixie Coleman'	MSmi
'Troika'	EBak EKMF SLBF WCum
'Troon'	EGou
'Tropic Sunset'	LCla MBri MSmi MWhe SKen WCum
'Tropicana'	CLoc EBak MSmi MWhe NPor WCum
'Troubadour'	CLoc MSmi
'Trudy'	CCla EBak EKMF GPen NMGN SKen
N 'Trumpeter'	CLoc EBak EBly EGou EKMF GPen LCla MJac MSmi MWhe NMGN NPor SKen SLBF SOld WCum
'Tsjiep'	NPor SLBF WCum
'Tuonela'	CLoc EBak EKMF MWhe NMGN NPor SKen WCum
'Tutone'	MJac WCum
'Tutti-Frutti'	CLoc MWhe
'Tutu'	EKMF WCum
'Twiggy'	WCum
'Twinkling Stars'	EKMF LCla MJac
'Two Tiers'	EKMF LCla NPor WCum
'U F O'	WCum
'Ullswater'	EBak WCum
'Ultramar'	EBak WCum
'Uncle Charley'	CLoc EBak EKMF WEas
'Uncle Steve'	EBak WCum
'Unique'	WCum
¶ 'Uppingham Lass'	MLab
'Upward Look'	EBak EKMF GPen SLBF WCum
¶ 'Vale of Belvoir'	GPen
'Valentine'	EBak WCum
'Valerie'	GPen WCum
'Valerie Ann'	EBak SKen SOld WCum
'Valiant'	EBak
'Vanessa'	CLoc
'Vanessa Jackson'	CLoc MJac MWar MWhe NPor SKen SLBF
'Vanity Fair'	CLoc EBak
vargarsiana	EKMF
'Variegated Snowcap'	CCla MWhe
'Variegated Swingtime'	EBak WCum
¶ 'Variegated Vivienne Thompson'	MBri
'Variegated White Joy'	EKMF
'Varty's Pride'	NPor
N 'Venus'	CCla
'Venus Victrix'	EBak EKMF SLBF
venusta	EBak EGou EKMF
¶ 'Vera Wilding'	LCla SLBF
'Versicolor'	See F. ***magellanica*** 'Versicolor'

'Vespa'	SOld
'Victoria Louise'	EBly
'Victorian'	GPen WCum
'Victory'	EBak WCum
'Vincent van Gogh'	EGou
I 'Violacea'	MSmi
'Violet Bassett-Burr'	CLoc EBak WCum
'Violet Gem'	CLoc WCum
'Violet Rosette'	EBak GPen SLBF WCum
'Viva Ireland'	EBak MJac
'Vivien Colville'	CLoc
¶ 'Vivienne Davis'	EGou
'Vivienne Thompson'	MWar SLBF
'Vobeglo'	EKMF SLBF
'Vogue'	EBak SOld WCum
'Voltaire'	EBak GPen
'Voodoo'	CLoc EBak EBly ECtt EKMF GPen LCla NMGN NPor SKen SLBF SOld WCum
'Vulcan'	WCum
♦ ***vulcanica***	See F. ***ampliata***
'Vyvian Miller'	MJac NPor
'Waldfee'	CCla EKMF MWhe
'Walsingham'	EBak EGou LCla MJac MWhe NMGN NPor SKen SLBF WCum
'Waltzing Matilda'	WCum
'Walz Freule'	MJac
'Walz Harp'	EGou SLBF
¶ 'Walz Knipperbol'	LCla
¶ 'Walz Lucifer'	EGou
'Walz Luit'	EGou
'Walz Mandoline'	EGou
'Walz Parasol'	EGou
'Walz Triangl'	EKMF
'Walz Waterval'	EGou WCum
¶ 'Wapenfeld's Bloei'	EGou
'War Dance'	MWhe
'War Paint'	CLoc EBak WCum
'Warton Crag'	GPen NPor WCum
¶ 'Wassernymph'	WCum
'Waternymph'	CLoc SLBF WCum
'Wave of Life'	EKMF GPen MWhe SKen SLBF
'Waveney Gem'	EBak EGou EKMF LCla MJac MWar NMGN SLBF SOak SOld
¶ 'Waveney Queen'	MJac
'Waveney Sunrise'	ECtt EGou EKMF LCla MJac MSte MWar
'Waveney Valley'	EBak LCla MJac NMGN
'Waveney Waltz'	EBak EKMF LCla MJac MWar MWhe SLBF SOak WCum
'Waxen Beauty'	WCum
'Wedding Bells'	LCla SOld
'Welsh Dragon'	CLoc EBak SLBF WCum
'Wendy'	See F. 'Snowcap'
'Wendy Atkinson'	EKMF LCla
'Wendy Harris'	MJac WCum
'Wendy Leedham'	EKMF
'Wendy's Beauty'	MSmi
'Wentworth'	EGou WCum
¶ 'Wessex Belle'	LCla
'Westgate'	ECtt EKMF WCum
'Westminster Chimes'	CLoc EKMF LCla MJac MLab MWar MWhe NMGN NPor SOld
'Whirlaway'	CLoc EBak EKMF MSmi NMGN SOld WCum
'White Ann'	CLoc LCla MBri SLBF
'White Bride'	WCum
¶ 'White Clove'	SLBF

'White Fairy'	WCum
'White Galore'	EBak EBly EKMF MSmi SKen SLBF SOld
'White Gold'	EBak WCum
¶ 'White Heidi Ann'	MLab
'White Joy'	EBak EKMF LCla MWhe SKen WCum
'White King'	CLoc EBak EKMF MSmi MWhe NMGN NPor SLBF SOld
'White Lace'	CCla
'White Loeky'	NPor
'White Marshmallow'	EBly
'White Pixie'	CCla EBly EKMF ELan LCla MJac MPla SKen SOak SOld
'White Pixie' Wagtails	EBak MWhe
N 'White Queen'	EBak MJac MWhe NPor WCum
'White Spider'	CLoc EBak EKMF MWhe SKen SOld WCum
'White Surprise'	SOld
'White Water'	WCum
'Whitehaven'	EBly
'Whiteknights Amethyst'	SKen WCum
'Whiteknights Blush'	CCla MBel SKen
'Whiteknights Cheeky'	EBak EGou EKMF LCla
'Whiteknights Goblin'	See F. ***denticulata*** 'W.G.'
'Whiteknights Pearl'	ECtt EKMF GPen SLBF
'Wicked Queen'	CCla LCla SOak
¶ 'Wickham Blue'	NPor SLBF
'Wiebe Becker'	EKMF
'Wild and Beautiful'	EKMF SLBF WCum
'Wildfire'	GPen WCum
'William Caunt'	EKMF
'Willie Lot'	EGou
¶ 'Wilson's Colours'	EBly
'Wilson's Joy'	WCum
'Wilson's Pearls'	SLBF SOld
'Wilson's Sugar Pink'	EBly LCla
'Win Oxtoby'	EKMF
'Wine and Roses'	EBak MSmi WCum
'Wingfield Sheppard'	EBly
'Wingrove's Mammoth'	GPen SLBF WCum
'Wings of Song'	EBak GPen
'Winston Churchill'	CLoc EBak EBly EKMF GPen IHos LCla MBri MJac MLab MSmi MWar MWhe NFai NMGN NPor SKen SLBF SOld WCum
¶ 'Woodside Gem'	WCum
wurdackii	EGou SLBF
'Yorkshire Rally'	MJac
'Yuletide'	EBly SKen WCum
'Zara'	MWhe NPor
'Ziegfield Girl'	EBak WCum
¶ 'Zulu Queen'	MSmi

FUMARIA (Papaveraceae)

lutea	See PSEUDOFUMARIA ***lutea***
officinalis	CKin GPoy NSal

FURCRAEA (Agavaceae)

longaeva	CHEx SArc
selloa	CHEx
– var. ***marginata***	CHEx

GAGEA (Liliaceae/Liliaceae)

lutea	EPot
pratensis	EPot

GAHNIA (Cyperaceae)

¶ ***setifolia***	GCal

GAILLARDIA (Compositae)

aristata hort.	See G. x ***grandiflora***
– PurshJCA 11449	EMon
'Burgunder'	CBow CDoC CHad CPar ECtt ELan EMar GCal MBri NBro NFai NMir NOak SHer SPer
¶ 'Croftway Yellow'	SPer
'Dazzler'	CBow EBre ECtt ELan ENot LBre LWad MBri MWat NHol NNor SHer SPer WStI
'Goldkobold' ('Yellow Goblin')	EBre EMon LBre MPit NFai
§ x ***grandiflora***	CGle CPar CSco GAri MBel NMir NOak NVic WSun
¶ 'Kahome'	CSco
Kelway's hybrids	CKel
'Kobold' ('Goblin')	CB&S CDoC CKel CPar EBlo EBre ECtt EPar LBre MBri MRav NRoo SPer WHen WHil WTyr WWin
¶ 'Mandarin'	EBlo EBre LBre SPer SRms
¶ 'Summer Sun'	NFai
'Wirral Flame'	EPar WEas

GALACTITES (Compositae)

tomentosa	CBos CPle CRow ECha ECro ELan EMon LAbb MPar NBro SMrm SUsu WEas WPer

GALANTHUS † (Liliaceae/Amaryllidaceae)

allenii	CAvo WChr
alpinus	EPot LAma WChr
x ***atkinsii***	CAvo CBro EMor EOrc EPot ERav LAma LFox MPar NGar WChr WWat
– 'Moccas'	WOld
– 'Mrs Backhouse's Spectacles'	LFox
'Augustus'	EMor
'Bitton'	CBro
bortkewitschianus	CBro
'Brenda Troyle'	CBro EPot LFox NGar SPou WChr
byzantinus	See G. ***plicatus b.***
cabardensis	See G. ***transcaucasicus***
caucasicus	CAvo CBro CMea CRDP ECha EPot ERav LAma LFox WCru
– early form	WChr
– x ***elwesii***	CBro EMor
– var. ***hiemalis***	CBro ECha EMor
corcyrensis (Spring flw)	See G. ***reginae-olgae vernalis***
– (Winter flw)	See G. ***reginae-olgae*** Winter-flowering Group
'Cordelia' (d)	LFox
'Dionysus' (d)	CBro EBul EMor LFox LRHS MPar NGar SPou WChr
elwesii	CBro CMon EMon LAma LBlo LBow MBri MPar NBir NGar NRog SIng
¶ – 'Alanya Yayla'	SPou
'Ermine Street'	EPot
fosteri	CAvo CBro EPot LAma
– PD 26830	EMor
'Galatea'	EMor MPar

Plant	Suppliers
§ ***gracilis***	CAvo CBro EBul EMor EPot MPar NGar SPou WOld WThu
– Highdown form	SWas
♦***graecus*** Boissier	See G. ***elwesii***
– hort.	See G. ***gracilis***
¶ green-tipped Greatorex	MPar
'Hill Poë' (d)	CBro ERav LFox MPar
'Hippolyta' (d)	CBro ECha EMor LAma LFox
ikariae ssp. ***ikariae***	EOrc EPot ERav LAma
§ – Latifolius Group	CAvo CBro CMea EBul EMon EMor EOrc EPot LAma LFox MPar NGar WChr WOld
– Woronowii Group	EPot LAma LRHS WChr
'Jacquenetta' (d)	CBro EMor LFox
'John Gray'	EMor LFox SPou
♦***kemulariae***	See G. ***transcaucasicus***
'Ketton'	CBro EOrc LFox
¶ ***ketzhowellii***	NGar
'Kite'	CBro
'Lady Beatrix Stanley' (d)	CBro EMon EMor EPot ERav LAma LFox MPar NGar SWas WChr
♦***lagodechanus***	See G. ***transcaucasicus***
latifolius	See G. ***ikariae*** Latifolius Group
'Lime Tree'	EMor LFox
lutescens	See G. ***nivalis*** 'Lutescens'
'Magnet'	CAvo CBro EBul EMor EPot ERav LAma LFox MPar NGar NHar SWas WChr WThu
'Maidwell L'	EMor WChr
'Merlin'	EMor EOrc LFox MPar NGar SWas
¶ 'Mighty Atom'	CMea NGar
'Mrs Backhouse'	MPar
'Neill Fraser'	LFox
'Nerissa' (d)	SPou
nivalis	CAvo CBro CKin CRiv CRow ELan EMon EMor EPar EPot ERav ETub LAma LBlo LBow LFox LHop MBar MBri NGar NLan NRog SIng WPer WShi
– ***angustifolius***	CBro EPot
– 'Boyd's Double'	EMor
– dwarf form	LFox
– 'Flore Pleno'	CAvo CBro CMon CRiv CRow EMon EPar EPot ERav ETub LAma LBlo LBow LFox NGar NRog NRya SIng WCru WHal WHen WPer
– 'Humberts Orchard'	LFox
– ssp. ***imperti***	CBro EPot LFox LRHS
– – 'Ginn's Form'	EMor
– 'Lady Elphinstone' (d)	CAvo CBro CRow EMor EPot ERav LFox MPar WChr
§ – 'Lutescens'	CBro EMor EPot LAma SWas
– Poculiformis Group 'Sandhill Gate'	CMea EMor NGar
– 'Pusey Green Tip' (d)	CBro EBul EMor EPot ERav ITim LFox MPar NGar WChr
§ – Scharlockii Group	CBro EMor EOrc EPot LAma LFox MPar NGar NHar SWas WChr
– 'Tiny'	EMor NGar NHar SIng
§ – 'Virescens'	EMor LFox
– 'Viridapicis'	CAvo CBro EBul ECha EMor EPar EPot ERav ETub LAma LBlo LBow MPar NGar SIng WChr
'Ophelia' (d)	CAvo CBro EPar ERav LAma LFox NGar WChr
'Peg Sharples'	EPot
'Pewsey Vale'	EMor
platyphyllus	See G. ***ikariae*** Latifolius Group
plicatus	CAvo CMea EBul MPar NGar WChr WOMN
§ – ssp. ***byzantinus***	CAvo CBro CMea EBul EMor EOrc EPot ERav LFox WChr
– large form	EOrc SPou
– 'Silverwells'	SPou
– 'Warham'	CBro EOrc NGar SWas WOld
reginae-olgae	CBro CMea CMon EMor EPot LAma LBow LFox MPar NGar SPou WChr
§ – ssp. ***vernalis***	EMor LFox NGar
– – AJM 75	EMor
– – CE&H 541	EMor
– Winter-flowering Group	CAvo CBro EBul EMor LAma LBow LFox SPou
rizehensis	CBro EPot MPar
'Robin Hood'	EMor LFox MPar
'S Arnott'	CAvo CBro CMea EMor EPot ERav LAma LBlo LFox MPar NBir NGar NHar SIng WChr WCot WOld WThu
'Scharlockii'	See G. ***nivalis*** Scharlockii Group
'Straffan'	CBro EMor EOrc EPot ERav LAma LFox MPar NHar SPou WOld
¶ 'Tiny Tim'	NBir NHar
¶ 'Titania' (d)	NGar
§ ***transcaucasicus***	CBro EPot ERav WChr
'Trotter's Merlin'	EMor
¶ 'Warley Belles'	EBul
¶ 'Warley Duo'	EBul
¶ 'Warley Longbow'	EBul
¶ 'Winifreda Mathias'	CBro

GALAX (Diapensiaceae)

Plant	Suppliers
aphylla	See G. ***urceolata***
§ ***urceolata***	IBlr MBal SHig SReu SSpi WThi

GALEGA (Leguminosae)

Plant	Suppliers
bicolor	CCla CWit ECro IBlr LAbb NBro SUsu WCot WHer
'Duchess of Bedford'	EMon
¶ × ***hartlandii***	IBlr
– 'Alba'	EMon GCal IBlr NBro WCot
– 'Candida'	CGle GCal SPer
* 'His Majesty'	EMon GCal LRHS
'Lady Wilson'	CGle SFis WCot WRus
officinalis	Widely available
– 'Alba'	CBot CElw CHad CHan ECED EFol EMon ERav IBlr SUsu WAbb WByw WCHb WEas WHer WHoo WRus
orientalis	CGle CHad CHan ECha ECro EFol GCal SUsu

GALEOBDOLON (Labiatae)

Plant	Suppliers
luteum	See LAMIUM ***galeobdolon***

GALIUM (Rubiaceae)

Plant	Suppliers
¶ ***arenarium***	WPer

aureum	See G. ***firmum***
cruciatum	See CRUCIATA ***laevipes***
mollugo	CArn CKin MHew NLan NSal SIde WCHb WNdy
§ *odoratum*	Widely available
palustre	CKin
perpusillum	See ASPERULA ***perpusilla***
verum	CArn CKin EJud MChe MHew NLan NMir NSal NSel SIde WCHb WGwy WNdy WOak WPer WWye

GALPHIMIA (Malpighiaceae)

¶ *glauca*	CTro

GALTONIA (Liliaceae/Hyacinthaceae)

candicans	CAvo CB&S CBro CChu CCla CKel CMHG ECha ECro ELan LAma LBow LHop MBri NFai SAxl SDeJ SDix SPer WBod WDav WEas
princeps	CAvo ECha ECro EPla MFir SAxl SDix WEas
viridiflora	CAvo CBot CKel ECha ECro ECtt ELan ESma GCHN GCal SAxl SBar SDix SIgm WCru WOMN WPer
– SH 3	CHan

GAMOLEPIS See STEIRODISCUS

GARDENIA (Rubiaceae)

§ *augusta*	CB&S CBow CTro EBak LAbb MBri MNew SLMG
– 'Prostrata Variegata'	See G. ***a.*** 'Radicans Variegata'
¶ – 'Radicans Variegata'	MNew
– 'Veitchiana'	ERea
¶ *cornuta*	CTro
florida	See G. ***augusta***
♦ *globosa*	See ROTHMANNIA ***g.***
grandiflora	See G. ***augusta***
♦ *jasminoïdes*	See G. ***augusta***
¶ *spatulifolia*	CTro
thunbergia	CTro MNew

GARRYA † (Garryaceae)

elliptica	Widely available
– 'Glasnevin Wine'	LRHS MBlu
– 'James Roof' (m)	CB&S CCla CSco EBar EBre ECtt EHar ELan IJoh IOrc LBre LNet MBal MBri MWat NHol NRar SBra SHBN SLon SPer SPla SReu SSta WAbe WDin WPat WStI WWat
fremontii	CB&S CBow CKni CMHG ELan ISea WStI
¶ × *issaquahensis*	LTil
– 'Pat Ballard' (m)	IOrc LRHS

X GAULNETTYA See GAULTHERIA

GAULTHERIA † (Ericaceae)

adenothrix	EPot GDra MBal MPlt NHar WAbe
antipoda	MBal NHar NHol
crassa	MAsh NHar NHol
cuneata	ECar ELan EPot GDra GWht IBar IDai MAsh MBal MBar MBri MGos MHig NHar SPer SReu SSta WAbe WThu
depressa	ECar GArf IBar MBal NHar
– × *crassa*	MBal
– pink form	NHol
§ *eriophylla*	CCla
forrestii	CTrw
¶ *fragrantissima*	NHar
furiens	See G. ***insana***
'Glenroy Maureen'	MBal
griffithiana BM&W 69	MBal
§ *hispida*	EBro ECar GArf GDra MAsh MBal MGos NHar NHol
hispidula	See G. ***hispida***
hookeri	IBlr MBri NHar
– B 547	MBal
humifusa	MBal
§ *insana*	LMer MBal
itoana	CMHG GArf GDra MBal MBar MGos MPlt WAbe
leucocarpa	NHol
¶ *littorallis*	MBal
macrostigma	IBar MBal NHol
miqueliana	CNic EBar ECar GArf IBar LBlm MBal MBar MDHE MGos NHar SPla SReu SSta WAbe
mucronata	CLan CMHG CPle ELan ENot IDai ISea MBal MBar NNor NWea SIng WBod
– (m)	CB&S CPMA CSco ELan GRei MBar MBri MGos MRav MUlv NKay NRoo SIng SPer SReu SRms WPat
– P&W 6273	EPot
– 'Alba' (f)	CSco GRei GWht MAsh MGos MRav SIng SPer
– 'Atrococcinea' (f)	SRms WPat
– 'Barry Lock'	WPat
– 'Bell's Seedling' (m/f)	CB&S CDoC CSco ENot GRei MBri MGos NKay SHBN SPer SReu SSta WAbe WPat
– 'Cherry Ripe' (f)	CDoC CSco IOrc MPlt NHol SHBN SPer
– 'Crimsonia' (f)	CB&S ELan MAsh MGos MPlt NHol SHBN SLon SPer SPla SReu SRms WPat
– Davis's hybrids	NRoo
– 'Indian Lake'	CDoC MPlt
– 'Lilacina' (f)	CB&S MBal MBri MGos NKay
– 'Lilian' (f)	MAsh MBri MUlv NHol SHBN SPer SPla WWeb
– 'Mulberry Wine' (f)	CDoC IOrc
– 'October Red' (f)	MPlt WWeb
– 'Parelmoer' ('Mother of Pearl') (f)	CB&S CPMA ELan ENot MBri MPlt NHol NKay SPer WPat WWeb
– 'Pink Pearl' (f)	MAsh MBri SRms
– 'Rosalind' (f)	MPlt WWeb
– 'Rosea' (f)	CB&S CSco GRei
– 'Rosie' (f)	MBri
– 'Sea Shell' (f)	IOrc MBri NHol
– 'Signaal' ('Signal') (f)	CB&S CPMA ELan ENot MAsh MBri MGos MPlt SPer SReu WPat WWeb
– 'Sneeuwwitje' ('Snow White') (f)	CB&S CPMA ENot MBri MPlt SHBN SPla SReu
– 'Stag River' (f)	GDra NHar

– 'Thymifolia' (m) GAri MAsh SHBN SPer SPla
– 'White Magic' (f) SLon
– 'White Pearl' (f) IOrc MBri NHol
– 'Wintertime' (f) ELan MAsh SRms WWeb
§ ***myrsinoïdes*** GAri GDra MBal
– 'Geoffrey Herklots' MBri
nana Colenso See G. ***parvula***
nummularioïdes GAri GTou MHig NHar NHol NMen WBod
– B 673 MBal
– TW GWht
§– ***elliptica*** SSta
– ***minor*** MBal
– 'Minuta' See G. ***n. elliptica***
ovalifolia See G. ***fragrantissima***
I ***paraguayensis*** MBal
§ ***parvula*** ECou
– 'Ohau' ECar
– 'Rough Creek' ECar
phillyreifolia SSpi SSta
poeppigii ECar WPat
– ***racemosa*** SSta
procumbens Widely available
prostrata See G. ***myrsinoïdes***
– ssp. ***pentlandii*** MBal NHar NHol
*– ***purpurea*** See G. ***myrsinoïdes***
pumila ECar ECou GAri GWht MBal MBar MBri NHar
§– C&W 5226 MBal NHol
– 'E K Balls' EPot MPlt NHar NHol WDav WThu
pyroloïdes MBal NHar NHol
– BM&W 5 MBal
rupestris GDra MAsh MBal
shallon CB&S CDoC CLan CTom ENot GRei IDai IJoh MBar MBri MGos MPla SHBN SLon SPer SPla SReu SSta WDin WFro WStI WWin
– dwarf form MBal
sinensis MBal WThi
sp. Gillanders 110 NHol
sp. P&W 6142 NHol
sp. Wr 8710 NHol
tasmanica ECou GArf GDra GWht MBal MBar
– white-berried GDra WDav
– yellow-berried MBal
– x ***pumila*** MBal
tetramera CB&S
thymifolia MBal NHol
trichophylla GArf GDra MBal NHol WAbe WDav WWin
– red form NHar
willisiana See G. ***eriophylla***
x ***wisleyensis*** CCla CLan MBal MUlv SLon SPer SSta WAbe WBod WPat
– 'Pink Pixie' CCla CMHG ECro EPla IDai MBar MBri SIng SPer SSta WAbe
– 'Wisley Pearl' ECar GDra GWht IBlr IDai MBar MBri MGos NHar SDry SIng SReu WThu
yunnanensis EPla

GAURA (Onagraceae)

lindheimeri Widely available
– 'Corrie's Gold' (v) ECha ECtt EMon EPla SMad
– 'The Bride' EFou NFai
– 'Whirling Butterflies' EMon EPla LRHS SMrm

GAYLUSSACIA (Ericaceae)

brachycera GGGa LRHS WCru

GAZANIA (Compositae)

¶ 'Aztec' LHil
¶ 'Baybreak Bronze' NRoo
¶ 'Brodick' GCal
¶ 'Christopher Lloyd' LHil
'Cookie' ELan LHil LHop SAxl SMrm WEas
'Cornish Pixie' CHal
cream LHop MRav
'Cream Beauty' CHad EOrc GCal LHil MSte NTow SAxl SChu SUsu
cream & purple CHad ELan LHop SAxl SChu SUsu WPer
crimson and green MSte
'Dorothy' LHil
¶ double yellow LHil
'Flash' WEas
'Flore Pleno' WPer
¶ 'Freddie' CBos SMrm
¶ 'Garden Sun' NRoo
'Hazel' GCal
hybrids ELan LHop SDix WPer
krebsiana WPer
****madeira*** LHop
¶ 'Magenta' SAxl
'Michael' GCal
'Mini Star White' NFai WHen
'Mini Star Yellow' WHen
'New Magic' IHos
'Northbourne' GCal
'Orange Beauty' ELan
¶ 'Red Velvet' LHil
§ ***rigens*** CB&S CSam MBri
– 'Aureovariegata' LHop SAxl
– var. ***uniflora*** CBrk EOrc GCal LHop MSte WEas
– – 'Variegata' CBot
– 'Variegata' CB&S CBrk CRiv ELan EOrc MPit NSti WPer
'Silver Beauty' CBot CHad LAbb NTow SChu
'Silverbrite' CHal
'Slate' SMrm
¶ 'Snuggle Bunny' NTow
splendens See G. ***rigens***
¶ 'Talent' NRoo
'Yellow Buttons' (d) EMon LHop

GEISSORHIZA (Iridaceae)

aspera CMon NRog
inflexa NRog
monantha NRog
radians NRog

GELASINE (Iridaceae)

♦***azurea*** See G. ***caerulea***
§ ***coerulea*** EBur WThi

GELIDOCALAMUS (Gramineae(Bambuseae))

fangianus SBam SDry

GELSEMIUM (Loganiaceae)

rankinii	CChu CMCN CPle
sempervirens	CB&S CMCN ERea IBar MNew NSal
– 'Flore Pleno'	CB&S ERea
– 'Pride of Augusta'	CMCN

GENISTA † (Leguminosae)

aetnensis	CB&S CBow CCla CLan CMHG CSam CSco EBre EHar ELan ENot IOrc LBre LHop LNet MBal MBri MWat SArc SDix SHBN SMad SPer SPla SSta WBod WDin WOMN WSHC WWat
anglica	CKin
– 'Cloth of Gold'	CNic MPla WDav
§ *canariensis*	CGre CTre ERea LAbb MBri
cinerea	CDoC CShe SPer
♦ *decumbens*	See CYTISUS ***d.***
delphinensis	See G. ***sagittalis delphinensis***
'Emerald Spreader'	See G. ***pilosa*** 'Yellow Spreader'
florida	WHCG
fragrans	See G. ***canariensis***
hispanica	CB&S CBra CSco EBre ELan ENot IDai IJoh IOrc LBre MBal MBar MGos MRav MWat NHol NNor SHBN SLon SPla SReu WAbe WDin WStI
– 'Compacta'	CLew SIng
§ *horrida*	SIng
♦ *humifusa*	See G. ***villarsii***
januensis	LRHS
lydia	Widely available
♦ *monosperma*	See RETAMA ***m.***
¶ *monspessulana*	EMon
pilosa	CKel CLan CPle ENot EPot IDai ISea LNet MBar MBro MCas MGos MPla NHar NLan NMen NNor NRoo NSal SBla SIng SPer WAbe WBod WEas WWin
– 'Goldilocks'	CBow CBra CDoC CPMA ECtt ESis LTil MAsh MBar MBri MPlt NHar SSta WBod WStI
♦– 'Lemon Spreader'	See G. ***p.*** 'Yellow Spreader'
*– *major*	MHig
– *minor*	WAbe
– 'Procumbens'	CLew CNic GDra MBal NHol WEas WPat
– 'Superba'	NNrd
– 'Vancouver Gold'	CB&S COtt EBre EHal ELan EPla ESis IHos IJoh IOrc LBre LHop MBri MGos MRav NBee NHar NHol NTow SBla SLon SMad SPer SReu WSHC WStI WWat WWeb
§ – 'Yellow Spreader'	CBow CBra CMHG CPMA EBre ECtt ESis LBre MBal MBri MPlt MRav MWat NHol NNrd SHer WBod WWat WWeb
'Porlock'	CDoC ELan
radiata	COtt
sagittalis	CHan CLew CMHG CWGN LHop MBal MBro NHol NNor NNrd SBla SPer WDin WHoo WWat
§ – ssp. *delphinensis*	CLew ELan MCas MHig NHol NKay NNrd
– *minor*	See G. ***s. delphinensis***
§ × *spachianus*	CGre MBri
tenera	SPer WHCG
– 'Golden Shower'	CDoC CSco SHil
tinctoria	CArn CGle CKin CSFH GPoy ILis MBar MChe MHew NFai NNor NSal NSel SHer SIde WDin WHer WNdy WOak WWye
– 'Flore Pleno'	EMon EPla ESis MBal MBar MPla MPlt NHar NHol NKay NMen NRar SHer SPer WBod WHil WPat
– 'Humifusa'	NHar
*– *humilis*	MHig NHol
– 'Moesiaca'	CNic ITim
– var. *prostrata*	WOak
– 'Royal Gold'	CBra CSco ECtt ENot MBri MGos MPla MRav MWat NNor SHBN SHer SPla WBod WWeb
– var. *virgata*	CHan
tournefortii	CShe MBal WPat
§ *villarsii*	EPot ITim MBro NHol NKay

GENTIANA † (Gentianaceae)

§ *acaulis*	Widely available
– *alba*	WThu
– Andorra form	GDra
– 'Belvedere'	EMNN MHig WAbe WThu
– 'Coelestina'	GAng
– 'Dinarica'	See G. ***dinarica***
– 'Gedanensis'	GAng
– 'Harlin'	NNrd
– 'Holzmannii'	EPot GAng NNrd
– 'Krumrey'	EMNN EPot GDra NNrd WThu
– 'Rannoch'	EMNN EPot NHar NMen NNrd WThu
– 'Trotter's Variety'	GAng
– 'Undulatifolia'	WDav WThu
algida	CPla
'Alpha'	See G. × ***hexafarreri*** 'A.'
alpina	GAng
andrewsii	CPla CRiv WHil
angustifolia	CNic GAng GArf NHol SIgm WAbe WThu
'Ann's Special'	ESis GAng MDHE NHar NHol NRoo
asclepiadea	CCla CGle CPla CWGN EBlo EBul ECha ELan GAng GCHN GDra IDai MBri MBro MPar MTho NEgg NHar NHol NRoo SBla SPer SSpi SUsu WHoo WOld WWat
– *alba*	CBot CCla CGle CPla CRiv EBlo ELan ELun GAng IBar MBri MBro MPar MTho NHol NRoo SApp SBla SPer SSpi SUsu WAbe WHoo WOMN
– 'Knightshayes'	GAng MBri MBro SWas WHoo WOMN WRus
– 'Nymans'	ELan SHer
– pale blue	SSpi WOMN
– 'Phyllis'	MBro MTho WHoo WRus
– 'Rosea'	CNic
'Barbara Lyle'	GAng GArf NRoo WAbe
× *bernardii*	See G. × ***stevenagensis*** 'Bernardii'
bisetaea	GTou SRms WDav
'Blauer Diamant'	GAng
'Blauer Edelstein'	GAng
'Blue Flame'	GAng GDra MSte
'Blue Heaven'	CLew GAng GArf GCHN GDra NRoo WAbe
¶ *brachyphylla*	NHar

¶ – ssp. *favratii* WDav
§ *burseri* var. *villarsii* CNic
N *cachemirica* GTou MTho NGre NRoo SIgm
¶ *calycosa* NHol
Cambrian hybrids MFos WAbe
x *caroli* GAng GAri NHar NKay NWCA SBla WAbe WPat
– 'Coronation' GArf NRoo
'Christine Jean' GAbr NHar NMen WDav
clusii CNic EPot GAng GArf WAbe
¶ – *clusii* NHar WDav
– *costei* WAbe
¶ – *rochelii* SIgm
crassicaulis CLD 424 NHol
crinita See GENTIANOPSIS *crinita*
§ *cruciata* CPla GTou MTho NHol WPer
§ *dahurica* CPla ELan GAbr GCal GDra MBro SBla WPer
decumbens CPla GCal MBro WHal WPer
dendrologi CPla NHol
depressa GArf MTho NNrd SSou WAbe WThi
'Devonhall' WAbe
§ *dinarica* GAng GDra MBro MTho NHar WAbe WDav WThu
Drake's strain GAbr GAng GDra MSte NGre
'Dumpy' WAbe
'Dusk' GAng GDra
'Eleanor' GAng NHar
'Elizabeth' GAng NHar NRed
'Excelsior' NHol
'Exploi' GAng
x *farorna* GAng NRoo
farreri NKay NWCA WAbe
'Fasta Highlands' GAng NRoo
freyniana GAng NWCA
gelida NGre NHol
– JCA 518.400 NHol
'Glendevon' GAng
§ *gracilipes* ELan MSte MWat NMir NWCA SHer SIgm SRms SSou WHoo
– 'Yuatensis' See G. *wutaiensis*
gracilis CPla
grossheimii NHol
x *hascombensis* See G. *septemfida lagodechiana* 'Hascombensis'
x *hexafarreri* GAng NHar
§ – 'Alpha' GAng GCHN
hexaphylla GAng NHar
'Ida K' GAng
'Indigo' WAbe
Inshriach hybrids ESis GDra NHar NHol NNrd
'Inverleith' ELan ESis GAng MBri MBro NHar NHol NKay NRoo SIng WPat WThu
kesselringii See G. *walujewii*
kochiana See G. *acaulis*
kurroo CPla ELan NMir NNrd SHer
– *brevidens* See G. *dahurica*
lagodechiana See G. *septemfida l.*
'Leslie Delaney' GAng
lutea CArn CBot CPar CPla ECha GDra GPoy GTou LGan MBro MSte NHar NHol NSti SDix SIng SMrm SSpi SUsu WKif WPer WWye
x *macaulayi* CLew CPla CRiv GAng MBri MHig MSte NHol NKay NRoo SIng WHil
– 'Blue Bonnets' GAng NHar
– 'Edinburgh' GAng GArf MDHE NRoo
– 'Elata' ELan MBri MDHE NHar NHol
– 'Kidbrooke Seedling' NGre NHar NHol NKay NRya WAbe
– 'Kingfisher' CLew CPla CRiv GAng GDra MHig MSte NHar NMen NNor NNrd NRoo NWCA SBla SBod SIng WHil
§ – 'Praecox' ESis GAng GCHN MBri NHar NHol
§ – 'Wells's Variety' GAbr MBri MHig NKay WAbe
macrophylla See G. *burseri villarsii*
'Magnificent' GAng
makinoi GAbr GAng GTou NGre NWCA
'Maryfield' GAng
'Midnight' GAng
'Multiflora' GAng
ochroleuca See G. *villosa*
x *oliviana* NHol
oreodoxa EPot WAbe
¶ *ornata* WDav
¶ – RH 61 WThu
pannonica GDra
– hybrids GDra
paradoxa CNic GCHN LBee MFos NGre NHar SBar
parryi CNic MBro NHar WDav
phlogifolia See G. *cruciata*
pneumonanthe CRDP CRiv LBee NHol NRoo
prolata K 214 GArf NHar
pumila SWas WAbe WDav
punctata GTou NHol
purdomii See G. *gracilipes*
¶ *purpurea* SIgm WPer
robusta CRDP ELan GAbr NWCA SMrm
'Royal Highlander' GAng MDHE NHar
saxosa CNic CRDP ECou GAng GDra GTou ITim LHop MBro MPar MSte MTho NBir NGre NHar NHol NMen NNrd NRed NRoo NTow NWCA SGil SHer SSou SWas WAbe WDav WOMN
scabra WWye
§ – var. *buergeri* LBee
– svar *saxatilis* See G. *s. buergeri*
'Sensation' GAng
septemfida CCla CPla CShe CWGN ELan EMNN EPot GAng GDra LHop MBar MBri MBro MCas MPla MTho MWat NEgg NGre NHol NKay NRoo SBla SIng WCla WDav WHoo WPat
– *lagodechiana* CCla CLew CSam NGre NRoo NVic NWCA SRms
§ – – 'Doeringiana' GCHN NMen NRoo
§ – – 'Hascombensis' CPla ELan GCHN NGre NWCA WOld
– – 'Latifolia' SSou WHil
sinoörnata CPla ELan EMNN GAng GCHN GDra IDai LHop MBar MBri MFos MHig NEgg NHar NHol NKay NNrd NRoo NWCA SBla SIng WAbe WDav WOld WPat
– *alba* CPla EPot GDra MBel NHar NHol NKay NRoo SIng WWin
– 'Angel's Wings' ELan GAng MBri NHar NHol WCru
– 'Blauer Dom' GAng
– 'Brin Form' CRiv NKay NNor NNrd NRoo SBod SIng SWas WAbe WHil

– 'Downfield'	NHar NHol
– 'Edith Sarah'	ELan EPot ESis GAng GArf MBri MHig NHar NHol NKay NNrd NRoo SBla WAbe WHil
– 'Lapis'	NHol
– 'Mary Lyle'	GAng GGar MBri MTho NHar NHol NRoo WAbe
– 'Praecox'	See G. x ***macaulayi*** 'P.'
– 'Trogg's Form'	MDHE NHar NHol
– 'White Wings'	ELan NHar NHol
– 'Woolgreaves'	EPot
sp. SBEL 220	MSte
x ***stevenagensis***	CPla CRiv EMNN GAng MBel MBri MFir MHig NHar NRoo SIng WHoo WPat WSun WThu
§ – 'Bernardii'	GAng GArf MBri SIng WAbe
– dark form	GArf NRoo WAbe
– 'Frank Barker'	GAng MBel MBri NHar WAbe
x ***stevengensis*** 'Shot Silk'	MFos WAbe
'Strathmore'	CRDP ESis GAng MBri MDHE NHar NHol NRoo WAbe
'Susan'	GAng
'Susan Jane'	GAng MSte
ternifolia	ELan EPot GAng GDra MSte NKay NRoo SIng WDav
– SBEC 1053	GGGa NHol
– 'Cangshan' ex SBEC 1053	ESis NHar WAbe
– 'Dali' ex SBEC 1053	ESis MBri NBir NHar NHol WAbe
thunbergii	NHol
'Thunersee'	GAng
tibetica	CBot CNic CPla CRiv EBar GAbr GCal GTou NHol WEas WHil
– CLD 592	NHol
trichotoma CLD 212	EMon
– CLD 429	NHol
¶ ***triflora***	SUsu
¶ – var. ***japonica***	SIng
– var. ***montana***	GArf GDra
– 'Royal Blue'	GCal
¶ ***triptosperma japonica***	CRow
veitchiorum	MBri NRoo
verna	CGle CLew CNic CSam ELan GAng GTou LGan LHop MBro MPla MTho MWat NKay NRoo WAbe WDav WOMN WPat WPer
– ***alba***	WPat
– ***angulosa***	See G. ***v. pontica***
§ – ssp. ***pontica***	CPla EPot GAng GDra MBro MCas MHig MTho NGre NHar NHol NRed SBla SHer SIng WHoo WPat
– x ***pumila***	NHar
waltonii	ELan
§ ***walujewii***	CCla
wellsii	See G. x ***macaulayi*** 'Wells's Variety'
§ ***wutaiensis***	CNic ELan GAbr GDra NRed SHer SSou
'Zauberland'	GAng

GENTIANELLA (Gentianaceae)

¶ ***moorcroftiana*** C&Mc 449	GTou

GENTIANOPSIS (Gentianaceae)

See Plant Deletions

GEOGENANTHUS (Commelinaceae)

See Plant Deletions

GERANIUM † (Geraniaceae)

aconitifolium L'Héritier	See G. ***rivulare***
albanum	CFis EMou EOrc GCHN MNFA MUlv NCat SAxl SCou SDix WByw WCra WCru
albiflorum	CCor CFis GCHN MNFA NCat SAxl
anemonifolium	See G. ***palmatum***
'Ann Folkard'	CElw CLew CSco CSev EBlo EFol ELan ELun EOrc EPla GAbr MNFA NOrc NRoo SAxl SBla SCou SMrm SUsu WByw WCot WCru WHal WHoo
¶ 'Anne Thomson'	SAxl
antrorsum	ECar WEas
argenteum	ELan MDHE SCou
– 'Purpureum'	See G. x ***lindavicum*** 'Alanah'
aristatum	CElw CFis EOrc GCHN SCou WCra
armenum	See G. ***psilostemon***
asphodeloïdes	CBre CChu CElw CFis CLew CPar EBar ECro EMou EOrc ESma GAbr GCHN NCat NSti SUsu WBon WByw WCra WCru WEas WHal WHen WNdy WRus WSun WToa
§ – ssp. ***asphodeloïdes*** white form	CFis EBre EOrc LBre MNFA SCou WRus
– forms	NCat SCou WCru WHal
– 'Prince Rupert'	GCal SAxl SCou
– 'Starlight'	GCal NCat SAxl SCou WCru
atlanticum Hooker f.	See G. ***malviflorum***
¶ 'Baby Blue'	SAxl
biuncinatum	SCou
¶ 'Black Ice'	SAxl
¶ 'Blue Pearl'	SAxl
bohemicum	CBos CFis EBar GCHN MDHE MNFA NVic SCou WCra WCru WEas WHal WHer WNdy WToa
'Brookside'	CElw EMou EOrc GCHN MNFA NBir SAxl SCou WCra WToa
brutium	CFis GCHN SCou SUsu WCra WCru WHen
'Buxton's Blue'	See G. ***wallichianum*** 'Buxton's Variety'
caffrum	CElw CFis GCHN GCal SAxl SCou WCru WEas WHal
canariense	CFis NCat SCou WCru WHal
candicans hort.	See G. ***lambertii***
§ x ***cantabrigiense***	CBos CFis CHan CPar CRiv CSun EBre ECha EGol EMon EMou EOrc GCHN GCal LBre MPar NHol NMir NPer NRar NSti SCou SUsu WBon WCra WHal WNdy WRus WToa
– 'Biokovo'	Widely available
– 'Cambridge'	CBos CDoC CElw EBlo EBre ECtt EFou ELan EPla ERav LBre MRav NCat NRoo NVic SAxl SCro SSpi WCra WPbr
– 'Carmina'	CFis EPla SAxl SCou
¶ – 'Saint Ola'	SAxl

cataractarum	CFis EMon GCHN NCat SCou SUsu WCra WCru WHal
¶ – ssp. ***pitardii***	CFis SAxl
¶ 'Chantilly'	CElw GAbr SAxl
cinereum	CGle CSev GAbr SIng WToa
– 'Apple Blossom'	See G. × ***lindavicum*** 'A.B.'
– 'Ballerina'	Widely available
– var. ***cinereum***	GCHN
– – 'Album'	MBal SCou
– 'Lawrence Flatman'	CCla CDoC CElw CFis CLew CMea CSam CSco EBre EFol EFou ELan EPla GAbr GCHN LBre NEgg NHar NRoo SBla SCou SMad WByw WCra WCru WHen WPat WThu WToa WWin
– var. ***subcaulescens***	CCla CElw CMea CShe ECha ELan EMou EPar GDra IDai LHop MBro MWat NHol NKay NNor NOrc NRoo NSti SBla SCou SIng WAbe WByw WCra WEas WHoo WOMN WToa WWin
– – 'Giuseppii'	CCla CLew CWGN EBre EFou GAbr GCHN LBre MBro MNFA NFai NRoo SAxl SCou WCra WCru WHoo WRus WToa
– – 'Splendens'	CCla CLew CRDP EBre ECha EFou GCHN LBre MBal MBri NRoo WCru WHoo WRus WToa
'Claridge Druce'	See G. × ***oxonianum*** 'Claridge Druce'
clarkei 'Kashmir Blue'	See G. ***c.*** 'Kashmir Purple'
– 'Kashmir Pink'	CMea EBre LBre NBir SAxl SBla SCro SMrm SWas WHal WToa
§ – 'Kashmir Purple'	Widely available
§ – 'Kashmir White'	Widely available
collinum	CElw CFis GCHN NCat SAxl SCou SUsu WByw WCru WHen WNdy WToa
columbinum	NCat SCou
¶ 'Coombeland White'	SAxl WCru
dalmaticum	Widely available
– 'Album'	Widely available
– Coombeland form	EPla
– × ***macrorrhizum***	See G. × ***cantabrigiense***
delavayi Franchet	CBot
'Dilys'	NCat SAxl WCru
dissectum	NSal
donianum	SCou
endressii	Widely available
– dark form	CMea NCat WCru
– 'Prestbury White'	WSun
¶ – 'Priestling's Red'	SMrm
– 'Rose'	LBlm WToa
erianthum	EMon EMou GCHN SAxl SCou SSpi WCru WNdy
¶ – 'Clam Sea'	SAxl
¶ – 'Neptune'	SAxl
§ ***eriostemon*** Fischer	CElw CFis CGle CLew CPar EMou EPla GCHN GCal LGre MNFA MTol NHol NNor NSti SAxl SCou WByw WCra WCru WHal WHen WPer
farreri	CElw CGle EBre GCHN LBre MNFA NGre NKay NTow SBla SCou SWas WEas WHal WToa
flanaganii	GCHN WCru
fremontii	CFis SAxl SCou WCru
gracile	CFis GCHN MNFA NBir NSti NVic SAxl SCou SUsu WCru WHal
– pale form	CFis SCou
grandiflorum	See G. ***himalayense***
– var. ***alpinum***	See G. ***himalayense*** 'Gravetye'
§ ***himalayense***	CCla CElw CFis CSco CSun CWGN EBar ECha ELan EMou LBlm MPar MTho NBir NBro NHol NNor NSti SMrm SUsu SWas WBon WCra WCru WHen WMer WPer
– 'Birch Double'	See G. ***h.*** 'Plenum'
§ – 'Gravetye'	Widely available
– 'Irish Blue'	CBre CElw CFis GCal SAxl SCou SCro WAbb WCru
§ – 'Plenum'	Widely available
ibericum	CBow CCla CElw CFis CHal CKel CPar CShe CSun ECED EPad EPla LBlm MBal MTol MWat NRoo SCou SPer WByw WCra WCru WEas WHen WNdy WToa WWin
– ssp. ***jubatum***	CFis GCHN MNFA
– var. ***platypetalum*** Boissier	See G. ***platypetalum***
– var. ***platypetalum*** hort.	See G. × ***magnificum***
incanum	CElw CFis CHan CMHG CSev CShe CSpe CTre EMon EOrc GCHN GCal LBlm LGre LHop NBir SAxl SBar SBor SCou SMrm WCra WCru WToa
¶ – var. ***incanum***	WCru
¶ – ***multifidum***	SAxl SUsu
'Johnson's Blue'	Widely available
'Joy'	CElw SAxl SUsu WCru
¶ 'Kashmir Blue'	SAxl
§ 'Kate'	CFis SAxl SCou WCru
'Kate Folkard'	See G. 'Kate'
kishtvariense	GCHN GCal SAxl SBla SCou WCru WHal
¶ ***koreanum***	SSpi
kotschyi	WCru
– var. ***charlesii***	GCal SCou WCru
§ ***lambertii***	CHal CTom NBir NCat SCou WEas WHal WHoo
– 'Coombland White'	SCou
– 'Swansdown'	CElw GCal SCou WCru
lanuginosum	SCou
libani	CElw CFis CHan EMou GCHN GCal MNFA NSti SAxl SCro WCot WCra WEas WHal
§ 'Lily Lovell'	Widely available
§ × ***lindavicum*** 'Apple Blossom'	CFis MNFA NRoo
¶ 'Little Gem'	SAxl
lucidum	EJud GCHN MHew NSal NSti SCou
§ ***macrorrhizum***	Widely available
– 'Album'	Widely available
– 'Bevan's Variety'	Widely available
– 'Czakor'	CBre CElw CFis CLew CPar CSun EBre EMon EMou EOrc LBlm LBre MBri MBro MTho MUlv NCat NRoo NSti SAxl SCou SCro WCra WCru WHer WHoo WToa
– 'Ingwersen's Variety'	Widely available
– 'Lohfelden'	CElw SAxl SWas WCru
¶ – ***macrorrhizum***	SRms
¶ – 'Pindus'	SAxl SWas
– 'Ridsko'	CElw GCal NCat SAxl WCru
– ***roseum***	See G. ***m.***

– 'Spessart'	CCla CDoC CElw CFis CMGP ERav GCal MBel MUlv NSti SCou SHig WCru
– 'Variegatum'	CElw CFis CGle CHan CShe ECha EFol EFou EGol EHoe ELan EPar ERav LGre LHop MBri MPar MTho NBir NRoo NSti SAxl WByw WDav WHer WNdy WOld WWat WWin
¶ – 'Velebit'	SAxl
macrostylum	CCor CElw GCHN MBro MPar WCot WCru
maculatum	CBow CChu CSev ECha ELan EMou GCHN GCal GPoy MBro MNFA MRav NSal SAxl SCou SFis SMrm SSpi SUsu WCra WCru WHal
– f. ***albiflorum***	CBow CBre GCHN GCal MNFA SAxl SCou SSpi WCra WHal WSun WToa
maderense	CHEx CPla CPle CTro ECro EMon GCHN GCal IBlr NPer SAxl SCou SDix SSpi WCra WCru WEas WHal WKif WPer
§ x ***magnificum***	Widely available
¶ – 'Wisley Variety'	GAbr
magniflorum	EMon SCou
¶ – SH 32	CHan
§ ***malviflorum***	CElw CFis CHan CMon ECha EFou ELan EMou EPla GCHN LGre LHop MBro MPar MTho SAxl SBor SCou SFis SSpi SUsu WHal WHoo WKif WOMN WOld WToa
¶ 'Mary Mottram'	WEas
molle	NSal
§ x ***monacense***	CBos CBow CBre CElw CFis CHal CHan CSam CTom EFou ELan EMar GGar MBel NFai NRoo NSti SAxl SCou SCro SUsu WByw WCra WCru WHer WNdy WPbr WSun WToa
x ***monacense anglicum***	CCor EOrc GCHN MBel MNFA NSti SAxl SCou SCro WToa
¶ x ***monacense monacense***	CElw
x ***monacense*** 'Muldoon'	CMHG CSev ECha EMon EPla GAbr GCal LHil MBri MFir MUlv NOak NRoo SPer WBon WCra WCru WNdy WPbr
– 'Variegatum'	CFis EFou EGol ELan NSti SCou WEas WRus WToa
'Mourning Widow'	See G. ***phaeum***
multisectum	CHan WCru
nepalense	CTom NCat SCou
nervosum	CFis MNFA SAxl
'Nimbus'	CElw EOrc MNFA SAxl WToa
nodosum	Widely available
– dark form	CBos CElw WCru
– pale form	CElw SCou WCru
– 'Svelte Lilac'	EMon EPla LRHS
– 'Swish Purple'	EMon
– 'Whiteleaf'	EMon
ocellatum	CBre NCat
oreganum	CCor SCou WCru
§ ***orientalitibeticum***	Widely available
x ***oxonianum***	CHal CLew EBar SAxl SCou WCru WEas
– 'A T Johnson'	Widely available
§ – 'Claridge Druce'	Widely available
– 'Hollywood'	CElw ELan EMon SAxl SCro SMrm WToa
– 'Lace Time'	SCro
– 'Lady Moore'	EBre LBre LGan SAxl SCro WToa
¶ – 'Miriam Randle'	SAxl
¶ – 'Old Rose'	SAxl WCru
¶ – pale form	EOrc
¶ – 'Prestbury White'	EMon
– 'Rose Clair'	CShe CSun EBre EFou EOrc LBlm LBre NHol SAxl SChu SCou WCru WEas WHen
¶ – 'Roselicht'	SAxl
– 'Sherwood'	CElw GCal MTho NCat SApp SAxl
– 'Southcombe Double'	CBre CElw CMil CWGN EBre EMar EMou LBre MFir MNFA MUlv NCat SAxl SChu SUsu WByw WCra WCru WHal WToa
§ – 'Southcombe Star'	EHal GCal MBel NSti SAxl SCou SMrm WCru WHal WNdy
§ – 'Thurstonianum'	CChu CCor CElw CFis CHan CMil CTom EBre EGol ELan EOrc GCHN GCal LBre MNFA NCat NFai SAxl SCou SCro SUsu WAbb WCru WEas WHal WNdy WPbr WSun WWin
– 'Wageningen'	CBre CFis EPla GCal NCat SAxl SCou WCru
– 'Walter's Gift'	CGle CHan EFou EMar EMon GCal MTho NCat SAxl SCou WCot WCru
– 'Wargrave Pink'	Widely available
– 'Winscombe'	CElw CSun EBre EFou EOrc GAbr GCHN GCal LBlm LBre MNFA MTho NCat NHol NRoo NSti SApp SAxl SCou SCro SMrm WToa
x ***oxonianum*** x ***sessiliflorum nigricans***	WToa
¶ 'Pagoda'	SAxl
§ ***palmatum***	CAbb CBos CBot CDec CElw CHad CHan CSpe EPad LHil MFir MPar NCat NFai NPer NSti SCou SCro SMrm SUsu WCru WEas WHal WHer WKif WOMN WPer WToa
palustre	CElw CFis EMou GCHN GCal MNFA NSti SAxl SCou SWas WByw WCru WHal
¶ ***papuanum***	SBla WCru
¶ 'Patricia'	SAxl
Pelargonium	See PELARGONIUM
§ ***phaeum***	Widely available
– 'Album'	Widely available
– black form	NCat SAxl
– forms	CBos EMou SCro WBon
*– ***hungaricum***	GCal MFir NCat SCou
– 'Joan Baker'	CBre CGle NCat SAxl
– 'Langthorn's Blue'	ELan SMrm
– 'Lily Lovell'	See G. 'L. L.'
– var. ***lividum***	CBre CChu CElw CGle CMea CTom EBre ECar EMou GCHN LBre MUlv NSti SChu SCou SPer SWas WByw WCra WCru WDav WHal WHen WHer WSun WWin
– – 'Majus'	CElw EBre LBre LGre MNFA NCat SAxl SCou
¶ – 'Mourning Widow'	SAxl
¶ – Mrs Gardener's Selection	SUsu
¶ – var. ***phaeum***	CBos
*– 'Taff's Jester' (v)	CHad GCal MTol NSti SCou SCro WHer

Plant	Suppliers
– 'Variegatum'	CChu CElw CFis CHad CHan CMil CRDP EBre ECro EGol ELan EMon ERav LBre MFir MRav NCat NSti SAxl WHer WNdy
¶ 'Philippe Vapelle'	CElw NBir SAxl SCou
♦ ***platyanthum***	See G. ***eriostemon***
platypetalum	CHan EBre ELan ENot GAbr GCHN LBre MNFA MPit NBir NKay SCou WCru WToa WTyr
pogonanthum	GCHN GCal MNFA NSti SAxl SCou WCra WCru WHal
polyanthes	CElw GAbr GAri GDra GTou NSti NTow SCou WCra WCru WDav WHal
¶ ***potentilloïdes***	CFis NCat WCru
pratense	CArn CBow CBre CFis CKin CWGN ECro EFou ELan EMou EOrc GCHN LHol MHew NLan NMir NSal SCou WBon WCla WCru WHil WNdy WPer WToa WWye
– f. ***albiflorum***	CBot CBow CCor CElw CGle ECED GCHN GCal MBri MHew MNFA NOrc NRoo NSal SBor SCou SSpi WByw WCra WCru WHal WHoo WNdy WPer WRus WToa WWin
– 'Bittersweet'	EMon
– 'Blue Chip'	EMon
– 'Cluden Ruby'	GCHN
– 'Cluden Sapphire'	GCHN
– 'Flore Pleno'	See G. ***p.*** 'Plenum Violaceum'
– forms	GCHN SCou
– 'Galactic'	CHan EMon LRHS NCat SAxl WNdy WOMN
– 'Mrs Kendall Clark'	Widely available
§ – 'Plenum Caeruleum'	CBos CCla CElw CFis CGle CKel COtt CPar CSco EOrc GCHN GCal MBri NNor SCou SPer WCra WCru WEas WHoo WToa
– 'Plenum Purpureum'	See G. ***p.*** 'Plenum Violaceum'
§ – 'Plenum Violaceum'	CBot CFis CKel COtt EFou ELan EMou EOrc GAbr GCHN MUlv NNor SChu SCou SSpi WCra WCru WHoo WKif WNdy WOld WRus WToa WWin
– ***rectum album***	See G. ***clarkei*** 'Kashmir White'
¶ – 'Rose Queen'	SAxl
– ***roseum***	CGle ELan EOrc NBir NHol NSti WByw WCru WHoo WToa
– 'Silver Queen'	CBre CSco ELan EOrc GCHN GGar SAxl WCra WCru WHen WToa
¶ – ssp. ***stewartianum***	SAxl WCru
– 'Striatum'	CElw CFis CMil EBre ECha EMon EMou LBre MNFA NCat NFai SAxl SCou WCra WEas WHal WHoo WKif WWin
– 'Wisley Blue'	SCou SCro
procurrens	Widely available
§ ***psilostemon***	Widely available
– 'Bressingham Flair'	COtt CSco EBre ECha ECtt EFou LBre NOrc NRoo SAxl SCou SPer WCra WCru WHal WRus
¶ – 'Gold Leaf'	WCot
pulchrum	CCor CElw EMon EOrc GCal NCat SAxl SCou WCru
punctatum hort.	See G. × ***monacense*** 'Muldoon'
– ***variegatum***	See G. × ***monacense*** 'Variegatum'
pusillum	CKin NSal
pylzowianum	CElw CLew CNic CRiv CShe EPla GDra GGar MBri MNFA NGre NHol NMen NNrd NRoo NRya NVic SAxl SBor SChu SCou SSmi WCra WCru WHal WHer WHil WToa
pyrenaicum	CBre CElw CFis CKin CRDP EOrc ESma GAbr GCHN MHew NSal NSti NVic SCou SUsu WCru WHal WHen WToa
– f. ***albiflorum***	CBre CCor CElw CFis CLew EFol EJud EOrc GCHN MTho NBir NSti NVic SAxl SUsu WCla WCra WCru WHen WToa
– 'Bill Wallis'	CLew EFol EOrc LGan MTho MUlv NCat SAxl WCot WCru
¶ ***rectum***	SAxl
– 'Album'	See G. ***clarkei*** 'Kashmir White'
¶ 'Red Dwarf'	GCHN
reflexum	CElw CFis CSev EGol GCHN MNFA NCat SAxl SCou SCro SMrm SWas WEas WToa
renardii	Widely available
– blue form	See G. ***r.*** 'Whiteknights'
§ – 'Whiteknights'	EGol EPla MNFA NBir NSti SCou SWas WCru WEas
¶ – 'Zetterland'	EBlo EBre LBre SAxl
richardsonii	GCHN GCal MNFA NBir SCou WCru
¶ × ***riversleaianum***	SCou
– 'Jean Armour'	GCHN WCru
– 'Mavis Simpson'	CCla CElw CFis CMHG EBre EMon EPla GCHN LBre MNFA SAxl SCou SCro SMrm SSpi SUsu WByw WCra WCru WHal WNdy WSun WToa
– 'Russell Prichard'	Widely available
§ ***rivulare***	CFis GCHN MNFA WCru WHer WToa
– 'Album'	CBre
'Robert Burns'	GCHN
robertianum	CFis CKin EFol LHol MChe NCat SHer SIde WHen
§ – 'Album'	CFis MPar NCat NSti NVic SCou WBon WNdy
– f. ***bernettii***	See G. ***r.*** 'Album'
– 'Celtic White'	CBre CFis CTom EFol EMon GCal NCat NHol NSti WHal
robustum	CElw CFis CGle CHan EMar EMon GCHN GCal MNFA NSti SAxl SCou SMrm SUsu WByw WCra WCru WEas WHal WHil WNdy WToa
– SH 14	CHan WCru WToa
rubescens	EMon GGar MFir NBir NCat NSti SAxl SCou WCra WCru WEas WHal WNdy WToa
rubicaule	NCat
rubifolium	SAxl SUsu WCru
ruprechtii	NCat WCru
* 'Sally'	NRar
'Salome'	CElw CRDP SAxl SBla SCou SMrm WCru
sanguineum	Widely available
¶ – 'Alan Bloom'	LRHS
– 'Album'	Widely available
¶ – 'Ankum's Pride'	CGle

– 'Cedric Morris'	CElw CFis MNFA SAxl SCou SWas WCru
– 'Elspeth'	CElw CFis SAxl SCou WCru
– 'Glenluce'	CFis EPla GCHN GCal MNFA NCat NOrc SAxl SCou SCro SRms WCra WCru WHal WToa
– 'Jubilee Pink'	SBla SCou WCru WToa
– var. ***lancastrense***	See G. ***s. striatum***
– 'Max Frei'	CElw CFis CGle CMGP CSev EBre EFou EGol ELan EPla GCal LBre MNFA NBar NFai NHol SAxl SChu SCou SSpi WCru WMer WRus WToa
– 'Minutum'	CFis SCou WCru
– 'Nanum'	EPar GCal NHol NKay NNrd WCru
– 'Nyewood'	SAxl WCru
– var. ***prostratum***	See G. ***s. striatum***
– 'Shepherd's Warning'	CCla CFis CHal CMea CSco CSev CShe EBre ECtt EPla GAbr GCHN LBre LHop MRav NEgg NRoo SCou SSpi WByw WCra WCru WHal WHoo WPat WRus WToa
§ – var. ***striatum***	Widely available
¶ – – deep pink	SCro
I – – 'Splendens'	CCla CFis CKel CLew CSco ECha EGol EHar ELan EPla GDra IDai LHop MWat NKay NNor NRoo SAxl SCou SSmi WCru WEas WOld
¶ ***schlechteri***	WCru
¶ 'Sea Fire'	CElw SAxl WCru
'Sea Pink'	GCHN SAxl WCru
¶ 'Sea Spray'	CElw CFis SAxl
sessiliflorum	ECou EPar SCou WCru WToa WWye
– ssp. ***brevicaule*** var.***glabrum***	ECar SUsu
¶ – ***novae-zelandiae*** Crûg strain	WCru
– – green form	CElw GCHN
– – 'Nigricans'	Widely available
– – 'Nigricans' x ***traversii elegans***	CBos ESis GCHN NCat SAxl WCot WCru
– – red form	CBos CElw EHoe GCHN GCal SAxl WCru
*– 'Porter's Pass	EFol MPit NBir SCou
shikokianum	SCou
sibiricum	GCHN WToa
sinense	CBre CFis CHan GCHN GCal LBlm MBro MFir MPar SCou SFar SMrm SSpi SUsu SWas WCra WCru WHal WHoo
soboliferum	NBir SAxl SCou
'Southcombe Beauty'	SMrm
'Southcombe Star'	See G. x ***oxonianum*** 'S. S.'
'Spinners'	CElw GCal NCat SAxl SCou SMrm SWas
'Stanhoe'	NSti SCou SUsu WCru
stapfianum roseum	See G. ***orientalitibeticum***
¶ ***subulatostipulatum***	WCru
¶ 'Sue Crûg'	WCru
swatense	CElw SAxl WCru WHal
– SEP 131	GCHN
sylvaticum	CBow CBre CSev EMon EMou EPad MBal MNFA NSal SCou SSpi WBon WCra WCru WHal WHen WNdy

– f. ***albiflorum***	CBot CBre CElw CHan CMil CPar CSco CSun EGol ELan EMou EPad GCHN MBro NRoo NSti SCou SUsu WCru WOld WToa WWin
– 'Album'	CCla CFis CGle CLew CMGP CTom ECha EFou EPla GAbr LBlm LHop MBel MBri NHol SApp SCro SPer WBon WCra WEas WHal WHoo
– 'Amy Doncaster'	CBos CElw SCou SWas WHal
– 'Angulatum'	SCou
– 'Baker's Pink'	CCor CElw EMou MNFA NCat SAxl SBla SWas
– 'Birch Lilac'	GCal NCat SAxl SCou
– 'Mayflower'	Widely available
– 'Meran'	SCou
– f. ***roseum***	CElw GCHN NCat SPer WCra
– 'Silva'	CGle GCal SAxl SCou
– ssp. ***sylvaticum*** var.***wanneri***	CFis CGle CSun LBlm LGre NCat SCou WCra WCru WHal WHoo
¶ ***sylvestris*** 'Birch Lilac'	SAxl
thunbergii	CHan CLew EMon EPla GAbr GCHN GCal MTol NHol NOak NSal SCou SCro WCra WCru WHal WNdy WPer WToa
– ***roseum***	WCru
thurstonianum	See G. x ***oxonianum*** 'Thurstonianum'
transbaicalicum	CElw GCHN MBri MNFA WCru WHal
traversii	CBot CCor EPot MDHE
– var. ***elegans***	CBos CCla CElw CFis CHad CHan CLew CSpe ELan GCHN GCal LGan LGre MFir MPar MTho NSti NTow SAxl SCou SMad SUsu SWas WCra WCru WEas WHal WHer WNdy WOMN
– 'Seaspray'	GCal SCou
¶ – 'Sugar Pink'	NBir
tuberosum	Widely available
¶ – M&T 4032	CMon
¶ – S&L 99	CMon
– var. ***charlesii***	See G. ***kotschyi c.***
versicolor	CBre CCor CFis CHad CRDP CShe CSun CTom EMar EMou GCal MNFA NVic SAxl SCou SCro SIng STre SUsu WByw WCra WCru WEas WHal WNdy WToa WWin
– ***album***	CElw CHan NCat SAxl WCru
¶ – 'Snow White'	SAxl
violareum	See PELARGONIUM 'Splendide'
viscosissimum	EPla GCal MFir SAxl SCou SUsu WCra
wallichianum	CFis NMir WCra WHal WNdy WToa
§ – 'Buxton's Variety'	Widely available
– pink form	CBos
– 'Syabru'	CBos SWas WCru
♦ ***wilfordii*** hort.	See G. ***thunbergii***
– Maximowicz	CFis WThi
wlassovianum	CCor CElw CFis CMil CSco EGol EMou EPla GCHN LGre MNFA MTho MTol NBir NHol SAxl SCou SPer SUsu WCra WCru WHal WHoo WNdy WToa
yesoense	GCHN NBir SCou SWas WCra WCru WHal WNdy
yunnanense	CHan GGar MFir NCat SCou

GERBERA (Compositae)

jamesonii	CB&S

GESNERIA (Gesneriaceae)

cardinalis	See SINNINGIA *c.*
x *cardosa*	See SINNINGIA x *c.*

GEUM † (Rosaceae)

¶*aleppicum* CLD 610	EMon
♦*alpinum*	See G. *montanum*
¶'Beech House Apricot'	CGle MBel SUsu
N'Borisii'	Widely available
– x *montanum*	LHop
bulgaricum	LRHS NFai NHol WByw WMer WSun
¶*canadense*	ECro
capense SH 33	CHan
§*chiloense*	EBar NHol
– P&W 6513	CHan MSte
– 'Dolly North'	CGle ECED EFou GGar MBri NBro NHol WMer
– 'Fire Opal'	CSco GCal MNFA NBir SPer WTyr
– 'Georgenberg'	Widely available
– 'Lady Stratheden'	Widely available
– 'Mrs J Bradshaw'	Widely available
– 'Prinses Juliana'	CBos EFou GCal MUlv NCat NHol
– 'Sigiswang'	CRDP MBel SWas
coccineum hort.	See G. *chiloense*
coccineum Sibthorp & Smith 'Feuermeer'	LHop MBel SAxl
– 'Prince of Orange'	CSun ECha LBlm SHer
– 'Red Wings'	WMer
– 'Werner Arends'	LRHS MBri NFai
'Coppertone'	CChu CGle ECha ECtt ELan GAbr GCal IBlr MNFA NBir SAxl SUsu SWas WAbb
elatum SEP 304	CHan
¶x *heldreichii*	WAbb
**hybrida luteum*	NSti
x *intermedium*	CBre CChu CElw CRow CTom EMon EPla SChu SCro WCot WDav
leiospermum	ECou
'Lemon Drops'	CGle ECha EGol
macrophyllum	GTou
♦*magellanicum*	See G. *parviflorum*
§*montanum*	CGle CHan CLew CPar CSam ECha ELan GDra GTou LBee MBro MCas MFir NBir NBro NHol NKay NNrd NRoo SIng SSou SWas WCla WHal WHoo WPer WWin
¶*parviflorum*	MBro WBon WDav
pentapetalum	GArf WAbe
¶*pseudochinense*	SUsu
¶*pyrenaicum*	WDav
quellyon	See G. *chiloense*
♦*reptans*	See SIEVERSIA *r.*
x *rhaeticum*	NKay NTow
'Rijnstroom'	MBel MUlv
rivale	Widely available
– 'Album'	Widely available
¶– apricot form	WHil
– 'Dingle Apricot'	EFol NBir
– 'Leonard's Variety'	Widely available
– 'Leonard's Variety Double'	CGle ECtt
– 'Lionel Cox'	CBre CChu CElw CGle CHad CLew CMea CRDP CRow CSam CSev CTom EBar ECha EGol ELan EOrc GAbr MBel MMil MNFA NBir NBro NSti SMrm SWas WByw WDav WHal WWin
– 'Marika'	CRow
¶– 'Variegatum'	WNdy
'Rubin'	EFou WRus
'Tangerine'	EPla GGar MRav NRoo
x *tirolense*	NKay
triflorum	EPla
*'Two Ladies'	NBar
urbanum	CArn CKin CSFH GPoy LHol MChe MHew NLan NSal NSel SIde SWat WCla WHer
– 'Checkmate' (v)	EMon

GEVUINA (Proteaceae)

avellana	CB&S CChu CGre CHEx CTrw ISea SArc

GIBASIS (Commelinaceae)

See Plant Deletions

GIGASPERMUM (moss)

¶*repens*	LFle

GILIA (Polemoniaceae)

aggregata	See IPOMOPSIS *a.*

GILLENIA (Rosaceae)

stipulata	EMon LGre NSal
trifoliata	CArn CCla CDoC CRow ECha EFou ELan GPoy LGre LHol MBri MUlv NSal NSti SChu SDix SPer SSpi WBon WByw WEas WMer WOld WSHC WWye

GINKGO (Ginkgoaceae)

biloba	Widely available
– 'Autumn Gold'	See G. *b.* 'Saratoga'
– 'Fairmount'	WMou
– 'Fastigiata'	WMou
– 'Heksenbezen Leiden'	WMou
– 'Horizontalis'	WMou
– 'King of Dongting'	WMou
– 'Ohazuki'	WMou
– 'Pendula'	CMCN LPan LRHS MBri WMou
– 'Princeton Sentry'	WMou
¶– 'Prostrata'	CPMA
§– 'Saratoga'	CPMA LNet LTil MBri WMou
– 'Tremonia'	MBlu SHil WMou
– 'Tubifolia'	WMou
– 'Umbrella'	WMou
– 'Variegata'	CMCN SSta WMou

GLADIOLUS † (Iridaceae)

alatus	NRog
'Alice' (Min)	LAma
'Amanda Mahy' (N)	CBro GCra LAma LBlo LBow NCat NRog
'Anitra' (P)	LAma

'Applause' (L) LAma NRog
'Apricot Queen' (L) LAma
'Atom' (P) CBro LAma NRog
'Avalanche' (B) LAma
'Bell Boy' (B) LAma
'Blackpool' (M) LAma NRog
'Blushing Bride' (N) LBlo
Butterfly hybrids LBow
byzantinus See G. ***communis byzantinus***
callianthus CRDP CWes
§ – 'Murieliae' CAvo CBro CKel CSut LAma LBow NRog SDeJ
'Cambourne' (Min) LAma NRog
cardinalis 'Imperialis' IBlr
carinatus NRog
carmineus CMon EPot LBow
carneus CAvo CBro ETub LBow NRog
'Charm' (N) CAvo CBro CKel LAma LBlo
'Charming Beauty' (Tub) NRog
'Chartres' (B) LAma
¶ 'Chiquita' (M) CSut
'Christabel' (L) LBow
'Cindy' (B) LAma
'Columbine' (P) LAma NRog
'Comet' (N) LBow NRog
communis CAvo LAma NHol
§ – ssp. ***byzantinus*** CAvo CB&S CBro CGle CHEx CHad CSam CTom ECha ELan EPar ETub LAma LBow LGan MBri MUlv NHol NRog NSti SIng WEas WHil WOMN
'Desirée' (B) CBro
'Dyanito' (B) LAma
'Edward van Beinum' (L) LAma
'Elvira' (N) LAma NRog
'Esta Bonita' (G) CSut
'Fair Lady' (Tub) NRog
'Fidelio' (L) CKel LAma
'Firebird' LAma
floribundus LBow
'Flower Song' (L) LAma
¶ ***garnieri*** CAvo CMon
'Georgette' (B) LAma
'Gillian' (L) LBow
'Good Luck' (N) CBro
grandis See G. ***liliaceus***
'Green Woodpecker' (M) LAma NRog
'Guernsey Glory' (N) LAma NRog
'Halley' CBro
'Helene' (P/B) LAma
'Her Majesty' (L) CSut LAma
¶ 'Herman van der Mark' CKel
¶ 'High Style' (L) CSut
'Holland Pearl' (B) LAma NRog
'Hunting Song' (L) LAma NRog
'Hypnose' (B) LAma
¶ ***illyricus*** CMon
'Impressive' (N) LAma NRog
'Jacksonville Gold' (L) CKel LAma
'Jessica' (L) LAma
'Joyeuse Entrée' CSut
'Lady Godiva' (P/Min) LAma NRog
'Leonore' (P) LAma
§ ***liliaceus*** LBow
Maestro ® (L) CSut
'Mandy' CSut
'Mary Housley' (L) LAma
'Mascagni' (M) LAma
'Mirella' (N) NRog
'Murieliae' See G. ***callianthus*** 'M.'
'My Love' (G) LAma
§ ***natalensis*** GCal IBlr WCot
'Nicole' LAma
'Nova Lux' (L) LAma NRog
'Nymph' (N) CAvo GCra LAma LBow NRar NRog SIng
'Obelisk' (P) LAma NRog
'Oscar' (G) LAma NRog
'Ovation' (L) CSut
papilio CAvo CChu CHad ECha EOrc GCal MPar NCat SAxl SBla SChu SMad SMrm SSpi WAbb WEas WHal WOMN
– 'Grey Ghost' WEas
§ – Purpureoauratus Group CBro CGle CSam IBlr MFir
'Passion' (L) CSut
'Peach Blossom' (N) LBlo
'Pegasus' (P/Min) LAma
'Perky' (Min) LAma
'Perseus' (P/Min) LAma
'Peter Pears' (L) LAma NRog
'Picture' (P) LAma
'Picturesque' (P) LAma NRog
'Piquant' (P) LAma
'Praha' (L) LAma NRog
primulinus See G. ***natalensis***
Primulinus hybrids LBow SDeJ
¶ 'Prince Carnival' (L) CSut
'Princess Margaret Rose' (Min) LAma
'Prins Claus' (N) CBro LAma NRog
priorii NRog
'Priscilla' CKel LAma
Promise ® (M) CSut
purpureoauratus See G. ***papilio*** Purpureoauratus Group
'Red Beauty' CSut
'Red Jewel' (B) LAma
'Richmond' (B) NRog
'Robinetta' (***recurvus*** x) LAma NRog
'Rose Supreme' (G) LAma
'Rougex' NRog
'Royal Dutch' (L) CSut
¶ 'Saxony' (P) CKel
scullyi NRog
segetum See G. ***italicus***
'Shakespeare' (L) LAma
'Spic and Span' (L) LAma
'Spitfire' (N) LBlo
'Tangerine' (P) CKel
'The Bride' (Colv.) CAvo CBos CBro CGle LAma LBlo LBow MUlv NCat NRog
'Trader Horn' (G) LAma NRog
tristis CBro CRDP ECha ELan EPot LBow NRog SDix WAbe WThi
¶ – var. ***concolor*** WHer WThu
undulatus ETub LBow NHol
Up to Date ® CSut
'Velvet Joy' (P) LAma
'Victor Borge' (L) LAma NRog
¶ 'Vidi Napoli' CSut
'Violetta' (M) LAma
'White City' (P/B) LAma
'White Friendship' (L) LAma NRog

'White Prosperity' (L)	CKel LAma
'Wind Song' (L)	LAma
¶ 'Wine and Roses' (L)	CKel CSut
¶ 'Ziegennerbaum'	CSut

GLANDULARIA (Verbenaceae)

♦ ***bipinnatifida***	See VERBENA ***b.***
♦ ***pulchella***	See VERBENA ***tenera***

GLAUCIDIUM (Paeoniaceae)

palmatum	ECha GDra MBal NHar
– 'Album'	See G. ***p. leucanthum***

GLAUCIUM (Glaucidiaceae)

§ ***corniculatum***	CGle CSpe ECro LGan LGre MPar NRar SUsu WCru WEas WHer WHoo
flavum	CGle CHan CRDP CSpe EBar ECha ECro EFol LGan NBro NHex WByw WCru WGwy WHer WOld
♦– ***aurantiacum***	See G. ***f. fulvum***
§ – f. ***fulvum***	ECha MBel MNFA
♦– orange form	See G. ***f. fulvum***
– red form	CRDP SBar
phoenicium	See G. ***corniculatum***

GLAUX (Primulaceae)

maritima	ELan SHer WPer
– dwarf form	NWCA

GLECHOMA (Labiatae)

hederacea	CArn CHal CKin GPoy IHos NBro NMir SIde WHer WWye
– 'Rosea'	EMon LRHS
§ – 'Variegata'	CNic CRow CTom ECro EFol EJud ELan ILis MBri MRav NHol SFar SIde SLMG SPla WPer
hirsuta	
AL&JS 90069YU	EMon

GLEDITSIA (Leguminosae)

caspica	CB&S SMad
japonica	WCoo
¶ ***sinensis***	EArb
triacanthos	CBow CPle EArb ENot GAri IOrc LPan NWea WDin WNor
– 'Elegantissima' (v)	EHar SPer
– 'Emerald Cascade'	SEng SSpi
– f. ***inermis***	ENot
– 'Rubylace'	CBow CBra CDoC COtt CPMA CSco CWSG EHar ELan LPan MBar MBlu MGos SEng SHBN SHer SMad SSpi SSta WDin
– 'Skyline'	LPan SEng
– 'Sunburst'	CB&S CBra CCla CLnd CSPN CSco CWSG EHar ELan ENot IDai IJoh IOrc LNet MBar MBri MGos MWat NBee NRoo SHBN SMad SPer SPla SReu SSta WDin WMou WWat

GLOBULARIA (Globulariaceae)

albiflora	WAbe
bellidifolia	See G. ***meridionalis***
¶ ***bisnagarica***	NHar NWCA SIgm WDav
cordifolia	CHal CLew CMHG CNic CRiv MBro MTho NHar NHol NTow SIng WHoo WOld WPer
¶ – NS 696	NWCA
incanescens	LBee SHer SIgm WCla WDav WPer WWin
§ ***meridionalis***	CHun ITim LBee MBro MHig MWat NHar NWCA SBla WDav WHal WOld WPer
– 'Hort's Variety'	LBee NNrd WAbe
nana	See G. ***repens***
nudicaulis	CLew MBro NHar WDav WPer
punctata	CNic LBee MBro NHol NTow NWCA SBar SHer SRms WPer
pygmaea	See G. ***meridionalis***
¶ ***repens***	MBro SIgm
trichosantha	CLew GTou LBee MHig NHol SRms WDav

GLORIOSA (Liliaceae/Colchicaceae)

caramii	LBow
carsonii	See G. ***superba***
lutea	See G. ***superba superba***
rothschildiana	See G. ***superba***
§ ***superba***	CB&S CHal CKel IBlr LAma LBow LHop MBri NRog SDeJ SLMG WChr WCru
§ – ***superba***	LAma LBow NRog

GLOXINIA (Gesneriaceae)

	See also SINNINGIA
'Chic'	NMos
perennis	NMos
sylvatica	CHal WEfe
'Tessa'	WEfe

GLYCERIA (Gramineae)

aquatica variegata	See G. ***maxima v.***
fluitans	CKin
maxima	WChe
§ – var. ***variegata***	Widely available
§ ***notata***	CKin
plicata	See G. ***notata***
spectabilis 'Variegata'	See G. ***maxima variegata***

GLYCYRRHIZA (Leguminosae)

echinata	NSal
§ ***glabra***	CArn ECro LHol MHew NSal SIde WWye
– 'Poznan'	GPoy
♦ ***glandulifera***	See G. ***glabra***
lepidota	NSal
missouriensis	NSal

GLYPTOSTROBUS (Taxodiaceae)

lineatus	See G. ***pensilis***
§ ***pensilis***	LRHS

GMELINA (Verbenaceae)

¶ ***arborea***	CTro

GNAPHALIUM (Compositae)

'Fairy Gold'	See HELICHRYSUM ***thianschanicum*** 'Goldkind'
keriense	See ANAPHALIS ***keriensis***

mackayi	NHol
subrigidum	See ANAPHALIS *subrigida*
trinerve	See ANAPHALIS *trinervis*

GODETIA See **CLARKIA**

GOMPHOCARPUS See **ASCLEPIAS**

GONIOLIMON (Plumbaginaceae)

§ *tataricum*	
var. *angustifolium*	CCla ELan NFai SRms SSvw WByw WPer

GOODENIA (Goodeniaceae)

humilis	ECou

GOODIA (Leguminosae)

¶ *lotifolia*	CHan

GOODYERA (Orchidaceae)

¶ *pubescens*	CRow MPhe

GOOSEBERRY See **RIBES** ***uva-crispa***

GOOSEBERRY, Cape See **PHYSALIS** ***peruviana***

GORDONIA (Theaceae)

axillaris	CB&S CHEx

GOSSYPIUM (Malvaceae)
See Plant Deletions

GRANADILLA See **PASSIFLORA** ***quadrangularis***

GRAPE See **VITIS** ***vinifera***

GRAPEFRUIT See **CITRUS** ***paradisi***

GRAPTOPETALUM (Crassulaceae)

¶ *bellum*	SLMG
¶ – 'Super Star'	SLMG
bellus	MBri SHer
§ *paraguayense*	CHal CNic SLMG

GRATIOLA (Scrophulariaceae)

officinalis	CArn GPoy LHol MHew NSal SIde WCru WWye

GREENOVIA (Crassulaceae)

§ *aurea*	CWil SIng WCot

GREVILLEA † (Proteaceae)

alpina	SBla SSpi WCru
– 'Olympic Flame'	CB&S CBar CDoC
* 'Apricot Queen'	CB&S
'Canberra Gem'	CGre CHan CSun ECou LBlm LHop MBal SBar SDry SIgm
'Desert Flame'	CB&S
juniperina	CHan
– f. *sulphurea*	CCla CDoC CHEx COtt CPMA CTre SHil SIgm SPer SSpi WAbe WBod WPat WSHC
robusta	MBri
rosmarinifolia	CBow CBra CCla CHEx COtt CPMA CTre CTrw CWSG MBal SArc SHil SLon SPer SSpi WAbe WBod WCru WPat WSHC
– 'Jenkinsii'	CB&S
x *semperflorens*	CGre
thelemanniana	CPle ECou
thyrsoïdes	CB&S SDry

GREWIA (Tiliaceae)

§ *biloba*	CMCN
♦ *parviflora*	See G. ***biloba***

GREYIA (Greyiaceae)

radlkoferi	CHEx
sutherlandii	CHEx

GRINDELIA (Compositae)

chiloensis	CAbb CChu CGre CHan CPle ECha SAxl SBor SDix SDry SHil WCot WPat WPer
integrifolia	NSal
lanceolata	NSal
oregana	NSal
robusta	NSal WCot
sp. G&K 4423	CGre
squarrosa	SCro WCot
stricta	CArn NSal

GRISELINIA (Griseliniaceae)

* 'Crinkles'	SDry
littoralis	CB&S CBot CBra CGre CHEx CLan CPle CSco CTre EBre ENot GRei IDai ISea LBre MBal MBri MGos NNor SArc SDix SLon SPer WAbe WBod WDin WSHC WWin
– 'Bantry Bay' (v)	CAbP CChu CDoC CGre CLan EBre ECtt EPla IMal IOrc LBre MBal SGil SMad SPer WAbe
– 'Dixon's Cream' (v)	CAbb CB&S CDec CGre SDry SGil SLon SPla
– 'Green Jewel' (v)	CB&S CDoC CTre SDry
– 'Milkmaid'	SPla
– 'Variegata'	CB&S CBot CBra CLan CPle CSco CTre CTrw EHoe ENot GRei IDai IJoh IOrc ISea MBal NKay NNor SHBN SLon SPer SPla SSta WDin WSHC WThu
lucida	CHEx MUlv
ruscifolia	CMCN ISea
scandens	WSHC

GUAVA See **PSIDIUM**

GUICHENOTIA (Sterculiaceae)
See Plant Deletions

GUNNERA (Gunneraceae)

arenaria	GAri GGar IBlr
chilensis	See G. *tinctoria*

dentata	NHol
¶***flavida***	CRow GGar
¶***fulvida***	IBlr
hamiltonii	CHEx ECha ECou IBlr NHar SWas WCru
magellanica	CCla CHEx COtt CRow CTom CWGN EBre ECha EPot ESis GWht IBar IBlr LBre MBal NDea NHar NHol NMen NNor SPer SWat WCru WHal WWat
manicata	Widely available
¶***monoica***	CRow
prorepens	CTre ECou IBlr SSpi SWas SWat WCru
scabra	See G. ***tinctoria***
§***tinctoria***	CHEx CRow CWGN ECha EFou ELun GAbr MSta SDix WStI

GUZMANIA (Bromeliaceae)

'Amaranth'	MBri
'Cherry'	MBri
'Claret'	See NEOREGELIA Claret
dissitiflora	MBri
'Exodus'	MBri
Festival	MBri
'Gran Prix'	MBri
lindenii	MBri
lingulata	CHal MBri
– 'Empire'	MBri
– var. ***minor***	MBri
Marlebeca	MBri
monostachia	MBri
'Orangeade'	MBri
sanguinea	MBri
*'Surprise'	MBri
'Vulkan'	MBri
*'Witten Lila'	MBri

GYMNOCARPIUM (Dryopteridaceae)

dryopteris	CBos EBul EPar EPot MBri NKay NLan NMar NNrd SAxl SDix WAbe WRic
– 'Plumosum'	NHar NHol NKay NMar WFib WRic
¶***jessoense***	WRic
robertianum	NKay NLan NMar SMrm WRic

GYMNOCLADUS (Leguminosae)

dioica	CB&S CChu CCla CGre EArb ELan LGre MBlu MBri NPal SHil SMad SPer SSpi WCoo WDin

GYMNOSPERMIUM (Berberidaceae)

albertii	CAvo EPot LAma

GYNANDRIRIS (Iridaceae)

¶***setifolia***	CMon WThi
sisyrinchium	CAvo ETub WThi
¶– MS 416	CMon
¶– ***purpureum*** AB&S 4447	CMon

GYNERIUM (Gramineae)

argenteum	See CORTADERIA ***selloana***

GYNURA (Compositae)

§***aurantiaca*** 'Purple Passion'	MBri
sarmentosa hort.	See G. ***aurantiaca*** 'Purple Passion'

GYPSOPHILA (Caryophyllaceae)

acutifolia	ELan EMon
altissima	CPou EMon LRHS
aretioïdes	NHol NNrd
§– 'Caucasica'	EBur EPot MHig NHol NTow SIng WDav
– ***compacta***	See G. ***a.*** 'Caucasica'
¶***briquetiana***	LBee NTow
– Mac&W 5920	EPot
cerastioïdes	CHal CMHG CMea ELan EMNN ESis GArf GTou LBee MCas MFir MHig MTol NKay NMen NNrd NRed NTow NWCA SHer WHal WHil WHoo WPbr WPer WWin
– ***farreri***	WEas
dubia	See G. ***repens*** 'Dubia'
libanotica	NRed
nana	SIng
¶– 'Compacta'	CNic
¶***oldhamiana***	SFis
'Pacific Rose'	WHil
pacifica	CBow ECro ECtt EFou NBro NOak SSvw WCot
§***paniculata***	CBow CPar MWat NMir NNor SRms WByw WEas WWin
– 'Bristol Fairy' (d)	CB&S CHad CMer CSam CSco CShe EBre EFou ELan ENot EOrc ERav IBar IDai LBre MBri NBar NFai NOrc NRoo SChu SHer SMad SPer WEas WTyr
– 'Compacta Plena'	CCla EFou ELan GCal LHop MMil NRoo SRms WPer
– 'Flamingo' (b)	CB&S CBow CSco EBre ECtt EFou EOrc IDai LBre MBri MUlv NFai SHer SPer WTyr
– 'Pink Star' (b)	CSco
– 'Schneeflocke' ('Snowflake') (b)	CBow CCla EBre ECtt ESma LBre NRoo SFis SPla SSvw WHil WHoo
– 'Snow White'	LHop LWad NOrc
petraea	WDav
repens	CBow CLew EPad IDai MHig MPla MTho MWat WPer
– ***alba***	CLew CPar EFou ELan EPad ESis GArf MPla NNor NNrd SHer WAbe WDav
– 'Dorothy Teacher'	CKel CShe EMNN MCas MHig MPar MPit NHol SIng WAbe WEas WOMN WPat
§– 'Dubia'	CMHG CShe ECha EFol ELan EMNN EPot ESis MCas MHig MPla NHol SBod SHer SIgm SIng WAbe WDav WPer WWin
– ***fratensis***	CHal ELan EMNN GArf MPla NKay NMen SHer SIng WDav
– 'Letchworth Rose'	MCas
– 'Rosa Schönheit' ('Pink Beauty')	ECha ESma MMil NRoo SHer SMrm WOMN
– 'Rose Fountain'	SFis WPat WThu

– 'Rosea'	CMHG CPar EFou EMNN ESis LAbb LWad MCas MWat NFai NHar NKay NMen NNor NOak NRed NRoo NTow NWCA SBla SFis WHal
'Rosenschleier' ('Veil of Roses')	CCla CHad CHal CLew CPar EBre ECha EFou ELan ESma LBre NBar NHol NKay NMen NNrd NRoo SFis SIgm WBod WByw WEas WHoo WOld
'Rosy Veil'	See G. 'Rosenschleier'
tenuifolia	CHal CNic ECar EPot ITim LBee MBro MCas MHig MPla MWat NGre NHol NNrd NRed NTow NVic NWCA SIng WAbe WPer WThu WWin
transsylvanica	See G. ***petraea***

HAASTIA (Compositae)
See Plant Deletions

HABENARIA (Orchidaceae)

♦*radiata*	See PECTEILIS ***r.***

HABERLEA (Gesneriaceae)

ferdinandi-coburgii	CGle EPot NHol NKay SHer SIng SPou SWas WCru
rhodopensis	CChu CNic CRiv ECar EPar IDai MBal MBro MCas MHig MSte MWat NHar NHol NNrd NTow SBla SPou SSpi WAbe WCru WOMN WOld WThu
– 'Virginalis'	CChu EPot GDra NHar NHol SWas WCru WOMN WThu

HABRANTHUS (Liliaceae/Amaryllidaceae)

andersonii	See H. ***tubispathus***
gracilifolius	CBro CMon
¶ *martinezii*	CBro
§ *robustus*	CBro CKel CMon LAma MBri NRog SDeJ WAbe
texanus	CBro CMon
§ *tubispathus*	CBro CMon ESma NWCA SWas WChr WMar WPer WThu

HACQUETIA (Umbelliferae)

§ *epipactis*	CBos CLew CMea CMil CRDP CSam ECha ELan EMar EPar EPot GArf LGre LHop MBal MTho MUlv NBro SAxl SChu SIgm SWas WAbe WCru WDav WOld WPbr WRus WWin

HAEMANTHUS (Liliaceae/Amaryllidaceae)

albiflos	CHal CMon CTro EBul SLMG
¶ *coccineus*	CMon
kalbreyeri	See SCADOXUS ***multiflorus multiflorus***
katherinae	See SCADOXUS ***multiflorus katherinae***
natalensis	See SCADOXUS ***puniceus***
sanguineus	NRog
¶ sp. SH 72	CHan

HAKEA (Proteaceae)

lissosperma	SArc SHil
sericea	CChu CHan ISea SArc SBor
suaveolens	SArc
teretifolia	ISea

HAKONECHLOA (Gramineae)

macra	EHoe SSpi
§ – 'Alboaurea'	Widely available
– 'Aureola'	CAbb CChu CElw CHan CLew CRDP EBul ECha ECtt EHoe LTil MBal MBri MPar SAxl SCob SWas WAbe WCot WEas WPat WWat
– *variegata*	See H. ***m.*** 'Alboaurea'

HALESIA (Styracaceae)

carolina	See H. ***tetraptera***
diptera var. *magniflora*	WFro
monticola	CB&S CBow CSco EBre ELan IJoh ISea LBre MBal MBri SHil SPer WFro WNor WWat
– f. *rosea*	MSta SHil
– var. *vestita*	CAbP CBra CChu CCla CMHG CPMA CSam CSco CWSG CWit IOrc LTil MBlu SHBN SHil SPer SSpi SSta WBod WHig WWat
§ *tetraptera*	CB&S CBow CCla CDoC CLnd CPMA CSam EHar ELan GWht IBar IOrc LAbb MBri MGos MUlv SPer SSpi SSta WBod WSHC WWat

X HALIMIOCISTUS (Cistaceae)

algarvensis	See HALIMIUM ***ocymoïdes***
§ 'Ingwersenii'	CB&S CFis CLew CMHG CSco ECar IDai NBro NHol NRya NSti SIng SPer WAbe WBod WDav WPer WSHC
revolii Dansereau	EBar ERav LGan WCru WKif
♦– hort.	See H. ***sahucii***
§ *sahucii*	CAbb CCla CPle CSco CShe ECha ERav GCHN LHop MBal MPla MRav MWat NBro NKay NSti SAxl SHBN SPer WCru WDav WHil WRus WSHC WWin
'Susan'	See HALIMIUM 'S.'
§ *wintonensis*	CB&S CHan CMHG CMil CSco EBre ECtt ELan EOrc EPla ERav LBre LHil LHop MBri MRav MWat NSti SAxl SHBN SPer SSpi WAbe WCru WRus WSHC WWat
§ – 'Merrist Wood Cream'	Widely available

HALIMIUM † (Cistaceae)

N*alyssoïdes*	CSam
§ *atriplicifolium*	LHop SChu WStI
§ *commutatum*	SAxl SIgm WAbe
formosum	See H. ***lasianthum***
N*halimifolium*	GCal SIgm WCru WSHC
§ *lasianthum*	CB&S CBow CDoC CHan CShe CWit ECha ELan ENot EPla LAbb LGre LTil MBal NWyt SChu SLon SPer SReu WAbe WBod WEas WWin
– f. *concolor*	LHop NTow SAxl SDry SSta WAbe WCru WDin WWin
– ssp. *formosum*	CKni EPla GCal MBri NTow SAxl SDix WCru WSHC
– 'Sandling'	ELan NTow WCru
libanotis	See H. ***commutatum***
§ *ocymoïdes*	CB&S CCla CDoC CFis CHal CSco ELan ENot LGre LTil MBal MPla MWat NKay NWyt SIgm SLon SPer SReu WCru WHil WSHC WWat
– 'Susan'	CBra CDoC CMHG EBre ELan ERav LAbb LBre LGre LHop MBri NHex NMen NNor SAxl SUsu WAbe WPbr WPer
§ *umbellatum*	CSam LGre MBri NHol NSti SPer WAbe WCru WDin WHCG WHil WKif
wintonens	See X HALIMIOCISTUS ***wintonensis***

HALIMODENDRON (Leguminosae)

halodendron	CB&S CBow CCla ELan MBlu SSpi

HALLERIA (Scrophulariaceae)

¶ *lucida*	CGre

HALOCARPUS (Podocarpaceae)

§ *bidwillii*	ECou LCon

HAMAMELIS † (Hamamelidaceae)

§ 'Brevipetala'	IOrc MAsh MBri NHol SSta
x *intermedia* 'Advent'	SSta
– 'Allgold'	SSta
– 'Arnold Promise'	CBow CDoC COtt CPMA EBre ELan IOrc LBre LTil MAsh MBal MBri NHol SPer SPla SReu SSpi SSta
– 'Aurora'	SSta WDin
– 'Barmstedt Gold'	CPMA EBre LBre LRHS MBri MGos NHol SReu SSpi SSta
– 'Boskoop'	SSta
– 'Carmine Red'	CBra SSta WNor
– 'Copper Beauty'	See H. x *i.* 'Jelena'
– 'Diane'	CB&S CBow CDoC CPMA CSco EBlo EBre EHar IOrc LBre LTil MBar MBri MBrk MGos NHol SHil SLon SMad SPer SReu SSpi SSta WBod WDin
– 'Feuerzauber' ('Magic Fire')	CPMA IOrc NBar SHer SPer SSta
– Hillier's clone	SSta
– 'Hiltingbury'	LRHS SSpi SSta
§ – 'Jelena'	Widely available
– 'Luna'	SSta
– 'Moonlight'	CAlt CPMA SSpi SSta
¶ – 'Nina'	LTil
– 'Orange Beauty'	CB&S CPMA MBal MGos NBar SReu SSta
– 'Pallida'	Widely available
¶ – 'Perfume'	LTil
– 'Primavera'	CDoC IOrc LRHS MAsh MBal MBri NHol SSpi SSta
– 'Ruby Glow'	CB&S CCla CPMA EGol ELan MBal SMad SPer SSta WDin
– 'Sunburst'	MBri SHil SSta
– 'Vezna'	CPMA MBlu MBri SSta
§ – 'Westerstede'	CPMA IOrc MAsh MGos NHol SSta WDin
– 'Winter Beauty'	SHil SSta
japonica	MBal WFro WWat
– 'Arborea'	SSta WNor
– var. *flavopurpurascens*	SSta
– 'Sulphurea'	SSta
– 'Zuccariniana'	CB&S SSpi SSta
mollis	CArn CB&S CBra CSco CShe ELan ENot GRei IDai IJoh LNet MBal MBar MBri MGos NBar NHol NKay NWea SHBN SMad SPer SReu SSta WDin WWat
– 'Brevipetala'	See H. 'Brevipetala'
– 'Coombe Wood'	CAbP SSta
– 'Goldcrest'	CBra CPMA SSpi SSta
– Henry form	SSta
– 'James Wells'	SSta
¶ – 'Jermyns Gold'	SHil
¶ – 'Nymans'	CAbP
– Renken form	SSta
– 'Select'	See H. x ***intermedia*** 'Westerstede'
– 'Superba'	SSta
– Wilson Clone	SSta
vernalis 'Carnea'	SSta
– 'Christmas Cheer'	SSta
– Compact form	SSta
– 'January Pride'	SSta
– 'Lombart's Weeping'	SSta
– 'New Year's Gold'	SSta
– 'Orange Glow'	SSta
– 'Pendula'	SSta
– 'Red Imp'	SSta
– 'Sandra'	CAbP EBlo EHar MAsh MBri NHol SPer SReu SSpi SSta WWat
– 'Squib'	SSta
– f. *tomentella*	SSta
virginiana	CB&S CTre GPoy ISea LHol WCoo WWat

HANNONIA (Liliaceae/Amaryllidaceae)

¶ *hesperidum* SF 21	CMon

HAPLOCARPHA (Compositae)

rueppellii	CTom NNrd SIng SRms WHil WPer

HAPLOPAPPUS (Compositae)

acaulis	See STENOTUS ***a.***
♦ *brandegeei*	See ERIGERON ***aureus***
♦ *coronopifolius*	See H. ***glutinosus***
¶ *foliosus*	CGre
§ *glutinosus*	CHal CHan CLew CPar CRiv EBar ECha ECtt EFol EPot LBee LHil MBro MHig MMil MTho MWat NWCA SChu SIng SSmi WEas

♦*lyallii* See TONESTUS *l.*
prunelloïdes NNrd
rehderi CCor
sp. P&W 6545 MSte
¶ *suffruticosus* CPle

HARDENBERGIA (Leguminosae)

comptoniana CGre CPle CSun LBlm
– *rosea* ERea
violacea CAbb CSun ELan EMil ERea IBlr IReg LAbb WBod
♦– 'Alba' See H. *v.* 'White Crystal'
– 'Happy Wanderer' CB&S EMil ERea
§ – 'White Crystal' CGre ERea

HARRIMANELLA See CASSIOPE

HAWORTHIA (Liliaceae/Aloëaceae)

x *cuspidata* SLMG
reinwardtii CHal

HAYNALDIA See DASYPYRUM

HEBE † (Scrophulariaceae)

See also PARAHEBE
albicans CCla CLan CSco CShe ECou EFol ELan ENot ESis GIsl IJoh MBal MBar MBel MBri MGos MWat NNor NRed NSti SHBN SPer SSmi STre WBod WEas WWin
– 'Cobb' ECou
– 'Cranleigh Gem' ECou GIsl NFai SSmi
– 'Pewter Dome' See H. 'P.D.'
– prostrate form See H. *a.* 'Snow Cover'
– 'Red Edge' See H. 'R.E.'
§ – 'Snow Cover' ECou GIsl
– 'Snow Mound' ECou
§ – 'Sussex Carpet' ECou EPla ESis MFir
§ 'Alicia Amherst' CLan CSam ECou ECtt ENot IBar LHop NHol SGil WAbe WBod
allanii ECou GDra GIsl MBro NNor NTow SIng
'Amanda Cook' (v) EBre ECar ECou EHoe EMon EPla ESis LBre LHop MPla MUlv NPer SDry
amplexicaulis CNic GIsl
§ 'Amy' Widely available
x *andersonii*
'Argenteovariegata' See H. x *a.* 'Variegata'
– 'Aureovariegata' CFis ECou SDry
¶ x *andersonii compacta* GIsl
* x *andersonii* 'Heida' MBri
§ – 'Variegata' CB&S CHal CMer CPle CTrw ECou IDai IOrc MBri MSte NSti NTow SDry WEas
* – 'White Summer' MBri
'Anne Pimm' (v) WSHC
anomala hort. See H. 'Imposter'
♦– (J B Armstr.) Ckn. See H. *odora*
'Aoira' See H. *recurva* 'A.'
* 'April Joy' MUlv
§ *armstrongii* CBot CMHG ECou EHoe ELan ENot GAbr IDai IJoh LAbb MBar NNor SHer SPer WDin WEas WPer WStI
'Autumn Blush' MPla
'Autumn Glory' CB&S CMHG CSco CShe CTre EBre ECou ELan ENot ERav GCHN GIsl IJoh LBre LGro MBar MGos NNor NSti SBod SHBN SPer SReu SSta WAbe WBod WDin WRus WSHC
'Autumn Joy' EBar MPla SHer
* 'Autumn Queen' NNor
'Azurea' ELan MBri MRav SMrm WPer
'Baby Marie' CAbP CMHG ECou ELan EPla ESis GIsl NFai NPer SGil SHer SSta WPer
barkeri ECou
'Beatrice' ECou
x *bishopiana* ECou
¶ 'Blonde' NNor
'Blue Clouds' CElw ECou EHal EPla MFir SIgm SPla WEas WPat WRus
'Blue Diamond' WEas
* 'Blue Streak' ELan
'Blue Wand' MBal
'Bluebell' ECou
'Blush Wand' CAbb GIsl WAbe
bollonsoi ECou GIsl MSte NHol
'Bowles's Hybrid' CElw CMHG CNic CSco CShe ECou GIsl IJoh LHil MGos MPla MRav NBee NFai NGre NNor SChu SGil SPla WAbe WEas
brachysiphon CFis ECou ENot ISea MGos MPla SLon SPer WDin
breviracemosa ECou
'Brill Blue' CHal CMHG ECtt EMNN ESis NMen NRed NTow WWin
brockiei ECou GIsl MFir SIng
buchananii ECou EMNN ESis GAbr GDra GIsl GTou MFir MGos MTho NFai NHol NNor WBod WPer
– 'Christchurch' ECou
– 'Minima' CDoC MBar MNFA
– 'Minor' CLew ECou EPot GAbr MBar MBri MFir MHig MRav NBir NHar NHol NMen NNrd SChu SIng WOMN
– 'Nana' See H. *b.* 'Minor'
– 'Ohau' ECou
– 'Otago' ECou
§ – 'Sir George Fenwick' ECou
– 'Wanaka' ECou
buxifolia hort. See H. *odora*
– (Benth.) Ckn.&Allan CFis CMHG CSco EBre ELan ENot GAbr GCHN GIsl IHos IJoh LBre LHil MBal NNrd NSti NWea SHer WDin WHil WStI
– 'Nana' CSam CSco EHar EPad EPla ESis GIsl MBri MHig
* – *patens* MGos
N 'C P Raffill' ECou GIsl MUlv
§ 'Caledonia' CDec CLew CMHG CNic CShe ECou EPad ERav ESis GAbr GIsl MBri MFir MGos MHig MSte NFai NHol NNrd NPer NTow SBla SChu SPer WEas WHoo WOMN WPat WSHC
'Candy' ECou
§ *canterburiensis* ECou EHal GIsl
N 'Carl Teschner' See H. 'Youngii'
'Carnea' CElw
'Carnea Variegata' CAbb ECou LHop SBod SHil
carnosula CMHG ECou EHoe EPla IJoh MFir MGos NNor SPer WPer
¶ 'Cassinioïdes' ESis

catarractae	See PARAHEBE ***catarractae***
chathamica	CLew CMHG CNic ECou EMNN ESis GAbr GCal MBal MCas MPla MPlt NRed NTow SDry SIng
cheesemanii	ECou GDra GIsl MHig
'Christabel'	ECou GIsl SIgm
'Christensenii'	ECou GIsl
ciliolata	ECou
coarctata	CNic ECou GIsl
cockayneana	ECou GIsl
colensoi	ECou
– 'Glauca'	See H. 'Leonard Cockayne'
'Colwall'	ESis LHop SHer WAbe WHen
'Cookiana'	See H. ***stricta macroura*** 'C.'
corrigana	ECou
¶ ***corstorphinensis***	GIsl
'County Park'	CNic ECar ECou ECtt EMNN ESis ESma GAbr MBal MGos MHig MUlv NNrd NTow SBod SIng WAbe WSHC
¶ 'Craigpark'	GIsl
'Cranleighensis'	EBar ECou ELan SBod SFai
¶ 'Cressit'	GIsl
'Cupins'	CLew CNic
cupressoïdes	CMHG CSco ECou ELan GIsl IDai LHil MBal MBar MFir MGos NNor WDin WWat
– 'Boughton Dome'	CNic ECar ECha ECou EHoe EMNN ESis GAbr GTou LAbb LTil MBri MBro MGos MHig MPla MPlt MTho NMen NTow SDix SIng WEas WHoo WOld WPer
– 'Golden Dome'	CB&S EPla ESis NHol
– 'Nana'	ECou SPer
– 'Neil's Choice'	ECar
darwiniana	See H. ***glaucophylla***
'Debbie'	ECou
decumbens	CNic ECou ESis GDra GIsl
¶ 'Diana'	CAbb CNic
dieffenbachii	ECou GIsl SDry
diosmifolia	CBot CDoC CLan CNic ECou ESis GIsl ISea LTil MAsh
– 'Marie'	ECou ESis GIsl
divaricata	ECou
x ***divergens***	CLan
♦ 'Dorothy Peach'	See H. 'Watson's Pink'
¶ 'Douglasii'	GIsl
'E A Bowles'	ECou
'E B Anderson'	See H. 'Caledonia'
'Edinensis'	CFis CMHG CMer CNic ECou ELan ESma GAbr GIsl NNor WPer WSHC WTyr WWin
'Edington'	CElw CNic ECou MFir
elliptica	ECou GIsl IBlr SFis
– 'Anatoki'	ECou
– 'Bleaker'	ECou
– 'Charleston'	ECou
– 'Kapiti'	ECou
– 'Variegata'	See H. x ***franciscana*** 'Variegata'
'Emerald Dome'	GAbr NMen WPer
'Emerald Gem'	See H. 'Emerald Green'
§ 'Emerald Green'	CMHG CNic CRiv CSam EBlo ECou EGol ELan ESis GAbr GIsl IJoh LHop MBar MBri MBro MGos MPla MWat NHol NSti SIng WPat WPer
epacridea	ECou GAbr GDra GIsl MHig NHol NMen NNrd WAbe
§ 'Eveline'	CAbb CPle CSco LAbb MBal NBir SChu WEas WSHC
¶ 'Evelyn'	GIsl
evenosa	ECou GIsl
'Eversley Seedling'	See H. 'Bowles' Hybrid'
'Fairfieldii'	CNic CPle IBlr IDai SDry WSHC
'Fairlane'	CNic ECou
formosa	LBlm
'Fragrant Jewel'	CChu CPle CSco EBre ELan LBre SFai SMrm WRus
x ***franciscana***	ECou WTyr
– 'Blue Gem'	CLan CSco EHal ENot ESis GIsl IDai IJoh NBir NFai NPer SPer WBod
– 'Jura'	ECou
¶ – 'Red Gem'	GIsl
– 'Tresco Magenta'	ECou
§ – 'Variegata'	CB&S CMer CSco EBre ECou ELan ENot ERav GIsl GRei IDai IJoh LBre MBal MGos MRav NFai NHol NPer NSti SHBN SLon SPer WAbe WBod WStI
¶ – 'White Gem'	GIsl
'Franjo'	ECou SSmi
'Gauntlettii'	See H. 'Eveline'
gibbsii	ECou
'Gibby'	ECou
¶ ***glaucophylla***	GIsl SBod
– 'Clarence'	ECou
N 'Glaucophylla'	CSco ECou
'Glaucophylla Variegata'	CAbb CFis CHal CNic ECou GAbr GIsl MBel MHig NFai NHol NRoo NSti SBod SMad SPer WCru WHer WKif WRus WSHC
'Glengarriff'	CChu NHol
'Gloriosa'	CAbb CSam IOrc WBod
'Gnome'	ECou GIsl
¶ 'Godefroyana'	CNic GIsl
gracillima	CMHG ECou GCal GIsl
'Gran's Favourite'	ECou ECtt
'Great Orme'	CB&S CBot CSam CSco CShe EBre ECou ECtt ELan ENot GIsl LBre LHop MBal MRav NFai NHol NPer NRoo NTow SBod SFis SHBN SPer WAbe WDin WStI
'Green Globe'	See H. 'Emerald Green'
'Greensleeves'	CMHG CSam ECou EPla GAbr GIsl MGos
¶ 'Gruninard's Seedling'	GIsl
haastii	ECou GDra GIsl MHig NHol NNor NNrd
'Hagley Park'	CPle CSam ECou EOrc ERav ESis LGre LHil MPla SGil SMrm SUsu WEas WKif WPat WSHC
'Havering Green'	ECou MHig NTow
¶ 'Headfortii'	IDai SGil
hectorii	CSco EMNN EPla GIsl IJoh MBal MFir MHig NBee
– var. ***demissa***	ECou GIsl
¶ 'Hidcote'	WTyr
¶ 'Hielan Lassie'	GIsl
'Highdownensis'	CPle ECou GIsl
'Hinerua'	ECou
hookeriana	See PARAHEBE ***h.***
hulkeana	CBot CPle CSam ECou ELan LGre LTil MBel MHig MPla MUlv NBir NTow SBla SGil SHil SMad SMrm SSpi SUsu WAbe WEas WKif WPer WSHC WWat

– 'Averil'	ECou
– 'Lilac Hint'	ECou
– 'Sally Blunt'	ECou
§ 'Imposter'	ECou NFai SRms
'Inspiration'	ECou
insularis	ECou SFis
'Jack's Surprise'	ECou
'James Platt'	ECou WAbe
'James Stirling'	See H. ***ochracea*** 'James Stirling'
'Jane Holden'	CDoC CSco SBla SFar WSHC
'Jasper'	ECou ESis
'Joan Lewis'	ECou
'Johny Day'	ECou
'Joyce Parker'	ECou
'June Small'	CNic
'Killiney Variety'	CLan ECou IMal MBal
'Kirkii'	ECou MUlv SGil SPer
'Knightshayes'	See H. 'Caledonia'
§ 'La Séduisante'	CB&S CSco EBar ECou ENot IDai IOrc NRoo SChu SHBN SPer WBod WSHC
'Lady Ardilaun'	See H. 'Amy'
♦***laevis***	See H. ***venustula***
laingii	ECou GIsl
lapidosa	See H. ***rupicola***
****latifolia***	NNor
lavaudiana	ECou ESis WWat
¶ 'Lavender Queen'	CAbb
¶ ***leiophylla***	CAbb GIsl
§ 'Leonard Cockayne'	CDoC CGre GIsl IBar NSti WSHC
ligustrifolia	ECou
'Lilac Wand'	CMer GIsl
'Lindsayi'	CNic CPle ECou IDai MUlv SIng
'Loganioïdes'	CLew CRiv ECou EMNN ESis GAbr MBal MPlt NMen NNor SBod SIng SSmi WPer
'Long Acre Variety'	ECou
'Lopen' (v)	ECou GIsl
lyallii	See PARAHEBE ***lyallii***
lycopodioïdes	CMHG ECou WThu
♦– 'Aurea'	See H. ***armstrongii***
– var. ***patula***	ECou
– 'Peter Pan'	ECou GAbr SRms WPat
§ 'Macewanii'	CMHG ECou EPla ESis GIsl
mackenii	See H. 'Emerald Green'
macrantha	CShe ECou ERav ESis GAbr GRei ITim MBal MHig MPla NHol NNor SBla SGil SIng SPer WAbe WBod WOMN WSHC WWin
– var. ***brachyphylla***	ECou
macrocarpa	ECou
– var. ***brevifolia***	ECou
– var. ***latisepala***	ECou GIsl
'Margery Fish'	See H. 'Primley Gem'
'Margret'	EBar EBlo EBre GRei LBre MAsh MGos SMrm SPer
'Marjorie'	CChu CMHG CPle CSco ECou ENot EOrc GAbr GIsl LAbb MBal MBel MGos MPla MRav NFai NNor NPer NRoo SBod SLon SPer WDin
matthewsii	CMHG ECou NNor
'Mauvena'	SPer
'McEwanii'	See H. 'Macewanii'
'McKean'	ECou
¶ 'Megan'	ECou
¶ 'Menzies Bay'	GIsl
'Mercury'	ECou
'Midsummer Beauty'	CSco EBre ECou ELan ENot GIsl IOrc ISea LBre LGro MFir MGos MRav MWat NFai NNor NTow SBod SDix SHBN SPer SPla WAbe WDin WStI
'Milmont Emerald'	See H. 'Emerald Green'
'Mini'	ECou
'Miss E Fittall'	CFis ECou
'Mist Maiden'	CNic ESis
'Monica'	CNic ECou GCHN NHol
* 'Moppets Hardy'	SPer
'Morning Clouds'	ECou NHol
'Mrs E Tennant'	CSco
§ 'Mrs Winder'	Widely available
x ***myrtifolia***	NNrd SHer
'Mystery'	ECou
'Neil's Choice'	ECou GIsl MSte SHer
'Netta Dick'	ECou
'Nicola's Blush'	CAbb CElw CNic CSam EBar ECou EFol ESis GIsl LAbb LHop MBel MPla MRav MWat NFai SFai SHer SIng SMrm SSta WRus
¶ 'Northumbria Beauty'	NNor
¶ 'Northumbria Gem'	NNor
obtusata	ECou
§ ***ochracea***	ECou LAbb MGos NSti SLon SPer STre
§ – 'James Stirling'	CSco EBlo EBre ECou EHoe ELan ENot ESis GIsl IJoh IOrc LBre LHop MBal MBar MBri MGos MPla MTho NBir NHol NNor SBar SBla SHBN SReu SSta WDin WEas WWat
§ ***odora***	CDoC ECou ENot EPla GIsl MFir NNor
– 'New Zealand Gold'	CMHG CNic CSam ECou EGol SLon
– prostrate form	ECou GIsl
– 'Stewart'	ECou
¶ – 'Wintergreen'	GIsl
¶ 'Otari Delight'	CMHG
'Pageboy'	ECou
♦***parviflora*** hort.	See H. 'Bowles's Hybrid'
– var. ***angustifolia***	ECou EPla IDai WMar
– 'Christine Eggins'	WMar
– 'Palmerstone'	ECou
'Pauciflora'	EFol EMNN MPlt NHol SBod SFis
pauciramosa	ECou EPla GIsl NTow SRms
'Penny Day'	ECou
♦***perfoliata***	See DERWENTIA ***p.***
'Perryhill Lilac'	SPer
'Perryhill White'	SPer
'Perry's Bluey'	NPer
'Petra's Pink'	ECou ESis MFir WEas
§ 'Pewter Dome'	Widely available
'Pimeba'	NHol SIng
pimeleoïdes	CNic ECou EPad ESma MFir NCat NNor SFis
– 'Glauca'	GIsl SHBN WWin
– 'Glaucocaerulea'	ECou EGol GIsl LTil MBar MFir MPla SHil SIng SPer WAbe
– var. ***minor***	ECou ESis GDra NHol WDav WPer
– – 'Elf'	ECou
– – 'Imp'	ECou
– 'Quicksilver'	Widely available
– var. ***rupestris***	ECou ESis GIsl
pinguifolia	ECou GIsl
– 'Godefroyana'	ECou

– 'Hutt'	ECou
– 'Mount Dobson'	CNic ECou GIsl
– 'Pagei'	Widely available
– 'Sutherlandii'	CDoC CNic CSco ECou ESma GDra GIsl IJoh MBri MFir NSti SLon
*'Pink Payne'	LHop
'Pink Wand'	CB&S IJoh
'Polly Moore'	CLew CNic MBal MFir NNrd NTow WAbe
poppelwellii	ITim
'Porlock Purple'	See PARAHEBE ***catarractae*** 'Delight'
§ 'Primley Gem'	CFis CLan CNic EBar MFir NNor SHer WAbe WSHC
'Princess'	ECou
propinqua	ECou ESis ESma
§ – 'Aurea'	MBal
¶ – 'Minor'	GIsl
'Prostrata'	ECou
****pulchella***	CSam
'Purple Picture'	ECar ECou ECtt NFai SDry SGil
¶ 'Purple Princess'	GIsl
♦'Purple Queen'	See H. 'Amy'
'Purple Tips'	See H. ***speciosa*** 'Tricolor'
rakaiensis	CElw CMHG CSco ECou EFol EHoe ELan ENot GAbr GIsl GWht IJoh ISea LHop MBar MBri MGos MWat NBir NNor SLon SPer STre WAbe WBod WDin WEas WRus WWin
¶ ***ramosissima***	GIsl
raoulii	CShe ECou LBee MCas MFir WDav WHoo
– var. ***maccaskillii***	ECou ESis
– var. ***pentasepala***	ECou ESis
§ ***recurva***	CChu CHal CMHG CNic CPle ECou EFol EPla ESis GAbr LAbb LHop MBri MFir NBee NNor SPla WAbe WBod WDin WRus
§ – 'Aoira'	ECou NTow SPer
*– 'Boughton Silver'	SDry
– 'White Torrent'	ECou
§ 'Red Edge'	Widely available
'Red Ruth'	See H. 'Eveline'
rigidula	ECou ESis GIsl
'Ronda'	ECou SGil
'Royal Purple'	See H. 'Alicia Amherst'
salicifolia	CCla CFis CMer CPle ECou ELan ENot GAbr GCHN GIsl LAbb LGro MFir NNor SArc SHBN SPer WDav
– 'Snow Wreath' (v)	ECou IBlr WThu
– 'Variegata'	CNic CPle
salicornioïdes	ECou
– 'Aurea'	See H. ***propinqua*** 'A.'
'Sapphire'	CDoC ECou ESis GIsl MGos NTow SPla
'Sarana'	ECou
'Silver Gilt'	CBot
¶ 'Silver Wings'	NFai
'Simon Delaux'	CB&S CChu CDec CSam CSco ECou EPad GAbr GIsl LHop MBal NTow SHBN SHer SPer WAbe WBod WEas WRus
speciosa 'Dial Rocks'	ECou
– 'Rangatira'	ECou
– 'Ruddigore'	See H. 'La Séduisante'
– 'Tricolor' (v)	CHal ECou EHoe IBlr IDai LAbb NHol NPer NSti SDry SHer WEas WWin
'Spender's Seedling'	CDoC CLan CMer ECou GIsl NSti SPer WRus
stricta	ECou
– ***cookiana***	See H. ***s. macroura*** 'C.'
– var. ***macroura***	ECou GIsl IBar SDry
subalpina	CDoC CFis CLan CPle CShe EBre ECou LBre NWea
subsimilis var. ***astonii***	ESis MHig WThi
'Sussex Carpet'	See H. ***albicans*** 'Sussex Carpet'
tetrasticha	WAbe
'Tiny Tot'	ECou ESma MTho NHol
'Tom Marshall'	See H. ***canterburiensis***
topiaria	CAbP CElw CNic COtt EBre ECou EGol EPla ESis ESma GIsl LBre LHop MPlt NHol NNor SFai SGil SMrm SPer SPla SSpi SSta WAbe
'Torlesse'	ECou
townsonii	ECou
traversii	ECou GAbr GIsl MSte SPla SRms
– 'Mason'	ECou
– 'Woodside'	ECou
'Tricolor'	See H. ***speciosa*** 'Tricolor'
'Trixie'	CNic ECou MUlv
tumida	ECou
urvilleana	ECou GIsl
'Veitchii'	See H. 'Alicia Amherst'
§ ***venustula***	CMHG ECou MBel
– 'Blue Skies'	ECou WPer
– 'Patricia Davies'	ECou
vernicosa	CElw CLew CMHG CMer CNic ECou EGol EPla ESis GDra GIsl GRei LHop MBar MBri MCas MHig NHol NNor NTow SFis SIgm SIng SPer WAbe WHil
¶ 'Violet Queen'	CAbb
¶ 'Violet Wand'	GIsl
♦'Waikiki'	See H. 'Mrs Winder'
'Walter Buccleugh'	CNic ECou GIsl LBee MFir NNrd WOMN WSHC
'Wardiensis'	CMHG CSco ECou MBar SIng
'Warleyensis'	See H. 'Mrs Winder'
§ 'Watson's Pink'	CNic ECou ESma GAbr MBel SChu SPer SUsu WAbe WKif
'White Gem'	CMer ECou ECtt ESis ESma GRei MBal MGos NNor NPer WStI
'White Wand'	CB&S NFai
'Willcoxii'	See H. ***buchananii*** 'Sir George Fenwick'
'Wingletye'	CAbP CElw CLew CMHG CNic EBlo EBre ECar ECou ECtt EHoe EPla ESma GAbr GIsl LBre LHop MBal MBri MCas MGos NTow SGil SMrm WAbe WPat WPer
'Winter Glow'	CMHG ECou SPla
*'Wootten'	WPer
§ 'Youngii'	Widely available

HEBENSTRETIA (Scrophulariaceea)

dentata	ECro

HECTORELLA (Hectorellaceae)

See Plant Deletions

HEDEOMA (Labiatae)

pulegioïdes	NSal

HEDERA † (Araliaceae)

§ ***algeriensis***	CHEx CSco SArc SHil WFib
– 'Argyle Street'	EWhi WFib
§ – 'Gloire de Marengo'	Widely available
– 'Marginomaculata'	EPla EWhi MUlv WFib
– 'Montgomery'	WFib
– 'Ravensholst'	CB&S CMac EWhi WFib
azorica	EWhi WCot WFib WWat
– 'Pico'	EWhi WFib
§ – 'Saõ Miguel'	EWhi WFib
– typica	See H. ***a.*** 'Saõ Miguel'
– 'Variegata'	EWhi
canariensis hort.	See H. ***algeriensis***
– Willdenow	CDoC EWhi WFib
– 'Algeriensis'	See H. ***algeriensis***
– 'Cantabrian'	See H. ***maroccana***
– 'Gloire de Marengo' (v)	See H. ***algeriensis*** 'G. de M.'
– 'Variegata'	See H. ***algeriensis*** 'Gloire de Marengo'
chinensis typica	See H. ***nepalensis sinensis***
colchica	CBow CHEx CRow CTom ENot SPer WDin WFib
– 'Dentata'	CHEx EPla EWhi LBuc LPri MBal NKay SHil WFib
– 'Dentata Aurea'	See H. ***c.*** 'Dentata Variegata'
§ – 'Dentata Variegata'	CB&S CMac CSco ELan ENot EPla GRei IDai IJoh LGro MBal MBar MBri MFir MWat SBra SDix SHBN SLon SPer SSta STre WFib WPat WWat
– 'Paddy's Pride'	See H. ***c.*** 'Sulphur Heart'
§ – 'Sulphur Heart' (v)	CB&S CCla CHEx CMHG CMac CSco EHoe ELan ENot IHos IJoh LPri MBal MBar MBri MFir MGos MWat NKay SBra SHBN SMad SPer SSta WDin WEas WFib WWat
– ***variegata***	See H. ***c.*** 'Dentata Variegata'
cristata	See H. ***helix helix*** 'Parsley Crested'
¶ ***cypria***	EPla EWhi
helix 'Hispanica'	See H. ***maderensis iberica*** 'Alcala los Barrios'
– 'Pallida'	See H. ***hibernica*** 'Hibernica Variegata'
– 'Poetica'	See H. ***h. poetarum***
helix f. ***caucasigena***	EWhi WFib
* – – 'Telavi'	EWhi
– ssp. ***helix***	CKin CRow EWhi MBar MGos NWea WFib WHer
– – '238th Street'	EWhi
– – 'Abundance'	EWhi
– – 'Adam' (v)	CFis EMon ESis MBri MGos MTho SGil STre WByw WFib WWat WWeb
– – 'Ahorn'	EWhi WFib
– – 'Alpha'	EWhi
– – 'Alt Heidelberg'	EWhi WFib
– – 'Alten Brucken'	EWhi WFib
– – 'Ambrosia' (v)	EWhi WFib
– – 'Anchor'	EWhi
– – 'Angularis'	EWhi
– – 'Angularis Aurea'	CSco EFol EHoe EPla EWhi MPla NBir SHBN WFib
♦ – – 'Anne Borch'	See H. ***hibernica*** 'Anne Marie'
♦ – – 'Annette'	See H. ***h. h.*** 'California'
– – 'Apaloosa'	EWhi WFib
– – 'Aran'	EPla EWhi WFib
– – 'Arapahoe'	EWhi WFib
– – 'Arborescens'	EPla SArc
– – 'Arborescens Variegata'	EPla
– – 'Ardingly' (v)	EMon EWhi LTil SPer WFib
– – 'Asterisk'	EPla EWhi WFib
– – 'Astin'	EWhi WFib
– – 'Atropurpurea'	EPla EWhi MBar WFib
– – 'Aurea Variegata'	CMac EWhi WFib
– – 'Avon' (v)	EWhi WFib
– – 'Baby Face'	EWhi
– – 'Baccifer'	EWhi WFib
– – 'Baden-Baden'	EWhi WFib
– – 'Baltica'	EWhi WFib
– – 'Bates'	EWhi
– – 'Big Deal'	EWhi
– – 'Bill Archer'	EPla EWhi WFib
– – 'Bird's Foot'	See H. ***h. h.*** 'Pedata'
– – 'Blarney'	EWhi
– – 'Blodwen'	WFib
– – 'Bodil' (v)	EWhi WFib
– – 'Boskoop'	EPla EWhi WFib
– – 'Bowles Ox Heart'	EWhi WFib
– – 'Brigette'	EWhi MBri
– – 'Brightstone'	EWhi WFib
– – 'Brokamp'	EWhi MMil SLPl WFib
– – 'Bulgaria'	EWhi
– – 'Buttercup'	CBra CCla CFis CMac CRow CSco ECha ELan EPla GDra LHop MBal MBar MBri MGos MPla MTho NNor SBra SHBN SIng SLon SPer WEas WFib WWat
§ – – 'Caecilia' (v)	COtt EFol EHar ELan EPla ESis EWhi LHop MGos NSti WFib WHal
– – 'Caenwoodiana'	WFib
– – 'Caenwoodiana Aurea'	EPla EWhi
§ – – 'Calico' (v)	EHal EWhi WFib
§ – – 'California'	EWhi MBri WFib
– – 'California Fan'	EWhi SGil
– – 'California Gold' (v)	EBre ESis EWhi LBre WFib
– – 'Carolina Crinkle'	EPla EWhi WFib
– – 'Cascade'	EWhi WFib
– – 'Cathedral Wall'	EWhi WFib
§ – – 'Cavendishii' (v)	EPla EWhi MPla WFib
– – 'Ceridiwen'	CRDP EWhi WFib
– – 'Chester' (v)	EWhi MBri WFib WWat
– – 'Chicago'	WFib
– – 'Chicago Variegata'	WFib
– – 'Christian'	EWhi
– – 'Chrysanna'	EWhi WFib
– – 'Chrysophylla'	EPla WFib
– – 'Clotted Cream'	See H. ***h. h.*** 'Caecilia'
– – 'Clouded Gold'	SPer WDin
– – 'Cockle Shell'	EWhi
– – 'Compacta'	EWhi
– – 'Congesta'	CFis CPar EPla EWhi GCal GDra MBal MPlt MTho SBar SSmi STre WEas WFib
– – 'Conglomerata'	CLew CSam ELan EPla EWhi ISea MBal MBar MBri NBir NNor SMad SPer SSmi WDin WEas WFib WHil WPat
– – 'Conglomerata Erecta'	WFib
– – 'Corrugata'	EWhi
– – 'Crenata'	EWhi

-- 'Crispa'	EWhi NNor
-- 'Cristata'	See H. ***h. h.*** 'Parsley Crested'
-- 'Cristata Melanie'	See H. ***h. h.*** 'Melanie'
-- 'Curleylocks'	See H. ***h. h.*** 'Manda's Crested'
-- 'Curley-Q'	EMon
-- 'Curvaceous' (v)	EWhi
-- 'Cyprus'	See H. ***cypria***
-- 'Dark Knight'	EWhi
¶-- 'Denmark'	WFib
-- 'Denticulata'	EWhi WFib
-- 'Diana'	EWhi
-- 'Dicke von Stauss'	EWhi
-- 'Digitata-Hesse'	EWhi
-- 'Direktor Badke'	EWhi WFib
-- 'Discolor' (v)	See H. ***h. h.*** 'Minor Marmorata'
-- 'Domino' (v)	EFol EPla EWhi WFib
§-- 'Donerailensis'	EWhi GAri WFib
-- 'Dorado' (v)	EWhi
-- 'Dragon Claw'	EPla EWhi SMad WCot WCru WFib
-- 'Duckfoot'	CLew EWhi IReg MNFA MTho NSti WFib
-- 'Edison'	EWhi
-- 'Elegance'	EWhi WFib
-- 'Elfenbein' (v)	EWhi WFib
-- 'Emerald Gem'	CSco EWhi
-- 'Emerald Globe'	EPla EWhi WFib
-- 'Emerald Jewel'	EWhi
-- 'Erecta'	CMac EPla ESis GAri LTil MBar MBri MTho NHol SIng SPer WFib WHil WPat WThu
-- 'Erin'	EWhi
-- 'Ester' (v)	CDoC EWhi MBri WFib
-- 'Eugen Hahn' (v)	EPla EWhi WCot WFib WHer
-- 'Eva' (v)	CFis CMac EWhi MBal MBri MGos WFib WWeb
-- 'Evesham'	WFib
-- 'F C Coates'	EWhi
¶-- 'Fallen Angel'	WFib
-- 'Fan'	EWhi
-- 'Fantasia' (v)	CMac EWhi
-- 'Feenfinger'	EWhi
-- 'Ferney'	EWhi WFib
-- 'Fiesta'	EWhi WFib
-- 'Filigran'	EPla EWhi SMad WFib WHer
-- 'Flamenco'	EWhi WFib
-- 'Flava'	EWhi
-- 'Fleur de Lis'	EWhi WFib
-- 'Fluffy Ruffles'	EPla EWhi
*-- 'Francis'	MBri
-- 'Fringette'	EWhi MTho WFib
-- 'Frosty' (v)	EWhi
-- 'Galaxy'	EWhi
-- 'Garland'	EWhi
-- 'Gavotte'	EPla EWhi MTho WFib
-- 'Geranium'	EWhi
-- 'Gertrude Stauss' (v)	EWhi MBri
-- 'Glache' (v)	EWhi WFib
-- 'Glacier' (v)	CBra CFis CMac CRow CSam CSco EBre EHoe ELan ESis IHos LBre LPri MBal MBar MBri MGos NKay NNor NSti SHBN SLon SPer WBod WFib
-- 'Glacier Improved' (v)	EWhi
-- 'Gladiator' (v)	EWhi
§-- 'Glymii'	EPla EWhi WFib
-- 'Gold Dust'	EWhi
§-- 'Gold Harald'	MBri
-- 'Gold Knight'	EFol EWhi
-- 'Goldchild' (v)	CB&S CBos CSam EBre EPla EWhi LBre LTil MBar MBri MGos MTho NCat WByw WFib
-- 'Goldcraft' (v)	EPla EWhi
-- 'Golden Ann'	MBri
¶-- 'Golden Arrow'	LTil
-- 'Golden Emblem'	EWhi
-- 'Golden Envoy'	EWhi
-- 'Golden Ester'	CHal EWhi MBri
-- 'Golden Fleece'	EWhi
¶-- 'Golden Gate'	MBri
-- 'Golden Ingot'	ELan EWhi MGos WFib
-- 'Golden Kolibri'	MBri
-- 'Golden Medal'	EWhi WFib
-- 'Golden Pittsburgh'	EWhi
-- 'Golden Shamrock'	SGil
-- 'Golden Snow'	EWhi MBri
-- 'Goldfinger' (v)	EWhi WFib
-- 'Goldheart' (v)	See H. ***h. h.*** 'Oro di Bogliasco'
-- 'Goldstern' (v)	EWhi LHop NGar WFib
-- 'Goldtobler' (v)	EWhi
-- 'Goldwolke' (v)	EWhi
-- 'Good's'	EWhi
§-- 'Green Feather'	ESis EWhi WFib WHer
-- 'Green Finger'	EWhi
-- 'Green Heart'	EWhi
-- 'Green Ripple'	CHal CMac CSam CSco IJoh IOrc MBar MFir NCat NNor SPer SSta WAbe WFib
-- 'Green Spear'	WFib
-- 'Green Survival'	EWhi
-- 'Guinevere'	EWhi
-- 'Hahn Variegated'	EWhi
-- 'Hahn's Green Ripple'	See H. ***h. h.*** 'Green Ripple'
-- 'Hamilton'	See H. ***hibernica*** 'H.'
*-- 'Harald' (v)	CHal EBar EWhi MBal MBri SGil WEas WFib WPat WWeb
¶-- 'Harlequin'	WFib
-- 'Hazel' (v)	EWhi WFib
-- 'Hebron'	EWhi
-- 'Heise' (v)	EWhi WFib
♦-- 'Helvig'	See H. ***h. h.*** 'White Knight'
-- 'Heron'	ELan EMon WFib
-- 'Hite's Miniature'	EWhi
-- 'Holly'	EWhi
-- 'Humpty Dumpty'	CDoC MBar
-- 'Ideal'	EWhi
-- 'Imp'	EWhi
♦-- 'Ingelise'	See H. ***h. h.*** 'Sagittifolia Variegata'
-- 'Ingrid' (v)	See H. ***h. h.*** 'Hamilton'
-- 'Irish Lace'	EWhi
-- 'Itsy Bitsy'	EWhi
-- 'Ivalace'	CB&S CHal CTom ECha EFol ELan EPla ESis MBal MGos MNFA MRav NSti SGil WAbe WEas WFib
-- 'Jack Frost' (v)	EWhi WFib
*-- 'Jane's Findling'	CNat
¶-- 'Jasper'	WFib
-- 'Jersey Doris' (v)	EWhi
*-- 'Jerusalem'	LTil WFib

– – 'Jubilee' (v)	CSco ELan EWhi MNFA WFib
– – 'Knobby Eight'	EWhi
– – 'Knulch'	EPla EWhi WFib
– – 'Kobold'	EWhi
– – 'Königers Auslese'	EPla EWhi SLPl WFib
– – 'Kolibri' (v)	CDoC CHal CSam EHar EWhi MBri WFib
– – 'Konsforth'	EWhi
– – 'Kurios'	EWhi
– – 'La Plata'	EWhi
– – 'Lady Kay'	See H. ***h. h.*** 'Lucy Kay'
– – 'Lalla Rookh'	CRDP EWhi WFib
– – 'Laubfrosch'	EWhi
– – 'Lee's Silver' (v)	EWhi
– – 'Lemon Swirl' (v)	EWhi WFib
– – 'Leo Swicegood'	EPla EWhi WFib
– – 'Light Fingers'	SPer WFib
¶ – – 'Limelight'	NRar
– – 'Lise' (v)	EWhi
– – 'Little Diamond' (v)	CFis CSam EHoe EPla LTil MBar MBri MGos SHBN WFib WThu WWat
– – 'Little Gem'	EWhi WFib
– – 'Little Luzii' (v)	EFol EHal WFib
– – 'Little Picture'	ESis EWhi WFib
– – 'Liz' (v)	EWhi WFib
– – 'Lucida Aurea'	EWhi
§ – – 'Lucy Kay'	EWhi WFib
§ – – 'Luzii' (v)	CFis CHal EFol EHoe EPla EWhi MBar MGos NNor NSti SGil SHBN SPer WByw WFib
– – 'Maculata'	See H. ***h. h.*** 'Minor Marmorata'
§ – – 'Manda's Crested'	CFis ELan ESis MBal SLon WFib WWeb
– – 'Manda's Fan'	WFib
– – 'Manda's Star'	EWhi
– – 'Maple Leaf'	EPla EWhi WFib
– – 'Maple Queen'	EWhi MBri
– – 'Marginata'	SRms
♦ – – 'Marginata Elegantissima'	See H. ***h. h.*** 'Tricolor'
– – 'Marginata Major'	WFib
– – 'Marginata Minor'	See H. ***h. h.*** 'Cavendishii'
– – 'Marie Luise'	EWhi
– – 'Marmorata'	See H. ***h. h.*** 'Luzii'
– – 'Masquerade' (v)	CCla EWhi
¶ – – 'Mathilde'	WFib
– – 'Meagheri'	See H. ***h. h.*** 'Green Feather'
♦ – – 'Mein Herz'	See H. ***hibernica*** 'Deltoidea'
§ – – 'Melanie'	ECha ELan EWhi WFib
– – 'Merion Beauty'	CFis EPla EWhi GAri WFib
– – 'Microphylla Picta' (v)	EWhi
– – 'Midas Touch' (v)	EFol EPla EWhi LHop LPri
– – 'Midget'	EWhi WEas WFib
– – 'Milford'	EWhi
– – 'Mini Ester' (v)	EWhi MBri
– – 'Mini Heron'	MBri
– – 'Miniature Knight'	EWhi
– – 'Minigreen'	EWhi
– – 'Minima'	See H. ***h. h.*** 'Donerailensis'
§ – – 'Minor Marmorata' (v)	CHal EHal EPla EWhi MBal MTho WEas WFib
– – 'Mint Kolibri'	EFol MBri
– – 'Miss Maroc'	EWhi WFib
– – 'Misty'	EWhi WFib
– – 'Modern Times'	EWhi
– – 'Mount Vernon'	EWhi
– – 'Mrs Pollock' (v)	EWhi WFib
– – 'Mrs Ulin'	EWhi
– – 'Nebulosa'	EWhi
– – 'Needlepoint'	EWhi IOrc
– – 'Neilson'	EWhi SPer STre WFib
– – 'Neptune'	EWhi
– – 'New Ripples'	EHal EWhi WFib
– – 'Nigra'	EWhi
– – 'Nigra Aurea'	EWhi WFib
– – 'Northington Gold'	EWhi WFib
– – 'Obscura'	EWhi
– – 'Old English'	EWhi
– – 'Old Lace'	EWhi
– – 'Olive Rose'	EPla EWhi MTho WCot WFib
§ – – 'Oro di Bogliasco' (v)	CFis CMac CRow CSam ELan ENot ISea LGro LPri MBal MBar MBri NKay NNor NSti NWea SBra SIng SLon SPer WAbe WEas WFib WPat WThu WWat
♦ – – 'Pallida'	See H. ***hibernica*** 'Hibernica Variegata'
– – 'Paper Doll' (v)	EWhi
– – 'Parasol' (v)	EPla EWhi WFib
§ – – 'Parsley Crested'	CRow ECha ELan ESis MBal MBar MGos NKay NSti SPer WEas WFib WTyr
– – 'Pedata'	CHal ELan ENot EPla EWhi MAsh MFir WFib
– – 'Pedata Heron'	WFib
– – 'Pencil Point'	EWhi
– – 'Pennsylvanian'	EWhi
– – 'Peppermint'	EWhi
– – 'Perfection'	EWhi
– – 'Perkeo'	CHal EPla EWhi WFib
– – 'Perle' (v)	EPla EWhi NBir WFib
– – 'Permanent Wave'	EWhi
– – 'Persian Carpet'	EWhi LMer WFib
– – 'Peter' (v)	EFol EPla EWhi WFib
– – 'Pin Oak'	CHal EPla EWhi ISea MNFA SIng
* – – 'Pink 'n' Curley'	WCot
– – 'Pirouette'	EWhi WFib
§ – – 'Pittsburgh'	EWhi WFib
– – 'Pixie'	EWhi WFib
– – 'Plattensee'	EWhi
– – 'Plimpton'	EWhi
– – 'Plume d'Or'	CSam EPla EWhi MTho WFib
– – 'Preston Tiny'	EWhi NBir
– – 'Professor H Tobler'	EPla EWhi WFib
– – 'Quatermas'	EWhi WFib
– – 'Ralf'	EPla EWhi WFib
– – 'Rambler'	EWhi NBir
– – 'Rauschgold'	EWhi
– – 'Ray's Supreme'	See H. ***h. h.*** 'Pittsburgh'
– – 'Reef Shell' (v)	EWhi WFib
– – 'Regency'	EWhi
– – 'Ritterkreutz'	EWhi WFib
– – 'Rochester'	EWhi
– – 'Romanze' (v)	EWhi WFib
– – 'Rubaiyat'	EWhi
– – 'Rumania'	EWhi
– – 'Rusche'	EPla EWhi WFib
– – 'Russell's Gold'	EWhi WFib
– – 'Sagittifolia'	CHal CMac CNic CRow CSco ELan EPla LTil MBal NNor SPer WAbe WEas WFib

§-- 'Sagittifolia Variegata' CHal CMac EBre EFol EHal EHoe EPla ESis EWhi LBre LTil MBri SIng SPer WAbe WFib
-- 'Sally' (v) EPla EWhi
-- 'Salt and Pepper' See H. ***h. h.*** 'Minor Marmorata'
-- 'Schafer Four' (v) EWhi
-- 'Schafer One' (v) EWhi MMil WFib
-- 'Schafer Three' See H. ***h. h.*** 'Calico'
-- 'Schafer Two' (v) EWhi WFib
-- 'Scutifolia' See H. ***h. h.*** 'Glymii'
-- 'Serenade' (v) EPla EWhi
-- 'Shamrock' EPla LTil MBri MNFA SPer WCot WFib
-- 'Shannon' EWhi
-- 'Silver Emblem' (v) EWhi
-- 'Silver King' (v) EPla EWhi LTil NBir WFib
-- 'Silver Kolibri' (v) EWhi
-- 'Silver Queen' See H. ***h. h.*** 'Tricolor'
¶-- 'Sinclair Silverleaf' WFib
-- 'Small Deal' EWhi
-- 'Spear Point' EWhi
¶-- 'Spectabilis Aurea' EWhi WFib
-- 'Spectre' (v) CNat EFol ELan EPla EWhi MTho WFib WHer
-- 'Spetchley' CHal CLew CNic EFol EMon EPla EWhi MNFA MTho NHar
-- 'Spinosa' EPla EWhi WFib
-- 'Staghorn' EPla EWhi
-- 'Star' EWhi
-- 'Star Dust' (v) EWhi
-- 'Sterntaler' EWhi
-- 'Stift Neuberg' (v) EWhi WFib
-- 'Stiftpark' EWhi
-- 'Student Prince' (v) EWhi
-- 'Stuttgart' EWhi WFib
-- 'Succinata' EPla
-- 'Sulphurea' (v) EWhi WFib
-- 'Suzanne' See H. ***nepalensis nepalensis*** 'S.'
-- 'Sylvanian' EWhi WFib
-- 'Tango' EWhi MNFA WFib
-- 'Telecurl' EPla EWhi WFib
-- 'Tenerife' ELan EWhi
-- 'Thorndale' EWhi
-- 'Tiger Eye' EPla EWhi
-- 'Tomboy' EWhi
-- 'Transit Road' EWhi
-- 'Très Coupé' ISea MBal MGos MNFA MTho NHol SPer WDin WFib
-- 'Tribairn' EWhi
§-- 'Tricolor' (v) CB&S CDoC CMac CSco EHoe ELan EPla EWhi IDai ISea SBra SHBN SHil SPer SReu
-- 'Triloba' EWhi
-- 'Trinity' (v) EWhi NHol WByw WFib
-- 'Tristram' EWhi WFib
-- 'Triton' EPla EWhi MBal MTho WFib WHer
-- 'Trustee' EWhi
-- 'Tussie Mussie' EWhi WFib
-- 'Ustler' EWhi
-- 'Walthamensis' EWhi WFib
-- 'Welsomii' EWhi
§-- 'White Knight' (v) EPla EWhi MBri WFib
¶-- 'White Kolibri' MBri
-- 'Wichtel' EWhi
-- 'William Kennedy' (v) EWhi LTil WEas WFib
-- 'Wilson' EWhi
-- 'Wingertsberg' EWhi
-- 'Wlliamsiana' (v) EWhi WFib
-- 'Woener' EWhi WFib
-- 'Woodsii' EWhi
-- 'Yalta' EWhi
-- 'Zebra' (v) EWhi WFib
- ssp. ***hibernica*** See H. ***hibernica***
§ - ssp. ***poetarum*** EPla EWhi IOrc WFib
-- 'Poetica Arborea' ECha SDix WFib
§ ***hibernica*** CB&S ELan LBuc MBar MBri MRav NNor SBra SPer WFib WStI WWat
- 'Albany' EWhi WFib
§ - 'Anne Marie' (v) CMac ESis EWhi LTil MBri WEas WFib WWin
- 'Cuspidata Major' EWhi WFib
¶ - 'Cuspidata Minor' EWhi WFib
¶ - 'Dealbata' CMac EWhi WFib
¶ - 'Deltoidea' EPla MBal MBri NHol WCot WFib
- 'Digitata' EPla WFib
¶ - 'Gracilis' EWhi WFib
¶ - 'Hamilton' ESis EWhi WFib
- 'Helena' EPla EWhi WFib
¶ - 'Helford River' EWhi WFib
¶ - 'Hibernica Variegata' WFib
¶ - 'Lobata Major' EWhi SRms WFib
- 'Maculata' (v) EPla EWhi
- 'Palmata' EWhi WFib
- 'Rona' EWhi WFib
¶ - 'Rottingdean' EWhi WFib
- 'Sark' EWhi WFib
¶ - 'Tess' EPla EWhi
- 'Variegata' EWhi WFib
maderensis ssp. ***iberica*** 'Alcala los Barrios' WFib
§ ***maroccana*** EWhi WFib
nepalensis ISea MBal MBlu WFib
¶ - var. ***nepalensis*** 'Suzanne' EWhi WFib
§ - var. ***sinensis*** EWhi WFib
pastuchovii EMon EWhi WFib
♦- 'Cyprus Taxon Troodos' See H. ***cypria***
rhombea EWhi WCot WFib
- 'Japonica' See H. ***r. rhombea***
§ - var. ***rhombea*** EWhi
-- 'Variegata' EWhi WFib

HEDYCHIUM † (Zingiberaceae)

aurantiacum EBul NRog SLMG
chrysoleucum LAma NRog
coccineum CB&S LAma LBow MUlv NRog SLMG
- var. ***aurantiacum*** LAma LBow MNew
- 'Tara' CChu SLMG SSpi
coronarium CAvo CTro EHal LBow MNew MSte NFai SLMG SMrm WPer
densiflorum CChu CTre CTro EBul GCal SDix SSpi
- 'Assam Orange' CB&S CChu CHEx GCal LTil MNew SSpi
ellipticum LAma LBow NRog
flavescens CTro LAma MNew NRog
forrestii CChu CHEx CTre SSpi

gardnerianum	CGre CHEx CTro ERea LAma LBow MNew NRog SArc SDix SLMG
greenei	CGle CHEx LBow NRog SLMG
longicornutum	MNew
spicatum	CHEx CHan CMon LHil NRog SLMG SSpi
villosum	LAma LBow NRog

HEDYOTIS (Rubiaceae)

–	See also HOUSTONIA

HEDYSARUM (Leguminosae)

coronarium	CArn CGle CHan CPle CSpe EBar ELan GCra SUsu WCot WCra WEas WHil WOMN WWin
– 'Album'	CBot
multijugum	CB&S CDoC CSco ENot SDry SHil
– var. ***apiculatum***	ELan

HEDYSCEPE (Palmae)

§ ***canterburyana***	NPal

HEIMERLIODENDRON See **PISONIA**

HEIMIA (Lythraceae)

salicifolia	CArn CGre CHan CPle CSam ELan NSal NSti SAxl

HELENIUM † (Compositae)

autumnale	CLew EBar EHal MBel MPit NMir NSal SHer SSvw
'Baudirektor Linne'	CKel CSam ECED
bigelovii	WByw WDav
'Blütentisch'	EFou
'Bressingham Gold'	EBlo
'Bruno'	CB&S SPer WCra
'Butterpat'	CMGP CSco ECED EFou SChu SHer SMrm SPer
¶ 'Chipperfield Orange'	LRHS SGil SHer
'Coppelia'	CKel CSam CShe EBlo ECED MUlv
'Crimson Beauty'	ELan MBri MRav NBar NFai NRoo WMer
'Croftway Variety'	SCro
¶ 'Dunkelpracht' ('Dark Beauty')	LRHS
'Feuersiegel'	EFou
'Gold Fox'	CKel CSam WMer
'Goldene Jugend' ('Golden Youth')	EFou ELan NRoo WEas
'Goldrausch'	EFou
'Helena'	EFou
hoopesii	CBow CHal CPar CShe EBar EFou EMon GCal LWad MFir NBro NOak NSti SCro SHer SPla SSvw WCra WDav WPer
'July Sun'	CB&S
'Königstiger'	EFou
'Kupfersprudel' ('Copper Spray')	MRav
¶ 'Kupferzwerg'	EFou
'Mahogany'	CSco
'Margot'	EFou
'Moerheim Beauty'	Widely available
'Pumilum Magnificum'	CDoC CKel CMGP CSam CSco EPar MBri MWat NKay NRoo SCro SPer WByw
'Riverton Gem'	ECtt
'Rotgold' ('Red and Gold')	CBow CDoC ECtt NOak WFro WPer
'Sonnenwunder'	ECha EFou
'Sunshine'	CPar GCHN
'The Bishop'	CBow CMGP CSam CSco EFou MBri MRav NBar WMer
'Waldtraut'	CKel CMGP EFou ELan MUlv NBar NCat NOak SCro SGil SHer SPer WMer
'Wyndley'	COtt CSam CSco ECED EFou MRav NRoo WCra WMer
'Zimbelstern'	ECha EFou

HELIAMPHORA (Sarraceniaceae)

nutans	EFEx MSte WMEx

HELIANTHELLA (Compositae)

§ ***quinquenervis***	GCal MSte

HELIANTHEMUM † (Cistaceae)

'Alice Howarth'	CShe EPot ESis MDHE SIng WHCG WHoo WPer
alpestre serpyllifolium	See H. ***nummularium glabrum***
amabile 'Plenum' (d)	EBar GDra SIgm
¶ 'Amabile Plenum'	GCal
'Amy Baring'	EBre EMNN GAbr GAri GDra LBee LBre LHop MHig MPlt NCat NKay NMen NRoo SBod SIng SMrm WPer WSHC
'Annabel'	CCla CElw CPar CRiv EFol EOrc GCHN MFir MPit MPla NEgg NRoo NSti SAxl SChu SGil SHer WHCG WPer
apenninum	MBro NLan WCla WPer
– var. ***roseum***	WCla
¶ 'Apricot'	SBod SHer
'Baby Buttercup'	CRiv WPat
'Beech Park Red'	CHal CRiv CShe ESis GAbr LBee LBuc MBro MDHE MWat SAsh SChu SIgm WHoo WKif
'Ben Afflick'	CRiv EBar GAbr IDai LHil MBro NKay NSty SBod SGil SHer SIgm SIng
'Ben Alder'	MDHE NSty
'Ben Attow'	NKay
'Ben Dearg'	CHal ECtt EMNN ESis GAbr MPlt NHol NKay NSty SBod SIng
'Ben Fhada'	CMHG CMea CRiv ELan EMNN GAbr GDra LBee MBal MBro MFir MHig NHol NKay NSti NSty SBod SHer SSvw WAbe WEas WPer WWin
'Ben Heckla'	CHad CKel CMHG CRiv CSam GAbr GCHN MPlt MSte NEgg NMen NRoo SAxl SMrm WEas WPer
'Ben Hope'	EBar EMNN GAbr GDra MBal NHol NKay NMen NRoo NSty SChu SHer SIng WPer WWin
'Ben Lawers'	NHol
'Ben Ledi'	CMea CRiv EFol ELan EMNN ESis GCHN GDra LBee MBal MBro MPlt NKay NSty SBod SHer WAbe WHoo WPer WWin
'Ben Lomond'	CRiv MBal

'Ben Macdui'	GAbr LBee
'Ben More'	CB&S CRiv ELan EMNN EPot ESis GAbr GDra IDai IHos LBee MBal MCas MFir MPla MWat NKay NMen NNrd NSti SBod SIng WHil WPat WWin
'Ben Nevis'	CBow CRiv CShe ECha ELan EPot GAbr GDra LHop MBro MDHE SHer WHoo WWin
'Ben Vane'	CHal CRiv EMNN NHol NKay SIng
'Bishopsthorpe'	CShe
'Boughton Double Primrose' (d)	CGle ELan GAbr LAbb LBee LHop NHol NSti SChu SIgm SSvw SWas WEas WSHC
'Brilliant'	CPar
'Broughty Beacon'	GAbr GDra
'Broughty Sunset'	MBro MDHE NBir SIgm WHoo
'Brown Gold' (d)	EOrc
¶ 'Butter and Eggs' (d)	SRms
'Butterball' (d)	MDHE NKay SIng
canum	WPer
*– ***balcanicum***	NTow
– ssp. ***pilosselloïdes***	WWin
'Captivation'	EFol WDav
'Cerise Queen' (d)	CHal CKel CPar CRiv EBre ECha EPot GAbr LBre LHop MBel MCas MPla NKay SAxl SDix SGil SHer SIgm SIng WCla WHoo WPer
chamaecistus	See H. ***nummularium***
'Cheviot'	MDHE NHol WEas WHoo WPer WWat
'Chocolate Blotch'	CHal CNic ECtt ELan EMNN GAbr LBuc MTho NMen NSty SChu SFis SIng WPer
'Coppernob'	SRms
'Cornish Cream'	SIng
croceum	NTow
cupreum	EFou NHol
'Doctor Phillips'	CShe WHCG WPer WSun
double apricot	CHal CRiv CShe GAbr NHol WHil
double cream	CMea CNic ECha ECtt EMNN EOrc ESis MBel MDHE MFir NSti SGil SHer SIng WPer
'Double Orange'	EBar LHop MWat WPer
double pink	ECha GAbr
¶ 'Double Primrose'	SIng
double red	ECha MPla
double yellow	ECha MPla NSti
'Etna'	STre
§ 'Fire Dragon'	CCla CKel CSam EBre ECtt ELan ESma GAbr GAri GCHN LBee LBre LBuc NRoo SChu SIgm SIng WAbe
'Fireball' (d)	See H. 'Mrs C W Earle'
'Firefly'	CHal
'Firegold'	WAbe
'Gaiety'	CRiv GAbr WPer
'Georgeham'	CHal CMHG CRiv CShe ELan LHop MDHE SIng WDav WEas WHCG WPer
globulariifolium	See TUBERARIA ***globulariifolia***
'Gloiriette'	SIng
§ 'Golden Queen'	ECtt NHol NMen NSty SChu SGil SIng WCla WPer
'Henfield Brilliant'	CCla CHad CMHG CRiv CShe EBre EPot GAbr GDra LAbb LBee LBre LHil LHop MBro MCas MPit NHol NRoo SIng SSmi WDav WEas WHoo WPer WSHC WWat
'Highdown'	GAbr MCas SRms WAbe
'Honeymoon'	SAxl
'John Lanyon'	LBee SIng
'Jubilee' (d)	Widely available
I 'Jubilee Variegatum'	MPla SIgm
'Kathleen Druce' (d)	MCas MWat SIng
ledifolium	WPer
'Lucy Elizabeth'	GAbr
lunulatum	CLew EMon ESis MBro MCas MPla NHol NKay NMen NTow SIgm SIng WPat
'Magnificum'	MWat
'Moonbeam'	WWin
§ 'Mrs C W Earle' (d)	CHal CMHG CRiv ELan EMNN EOrc GAbr IDai LAbb LHop MPlt MWat NKay NNrd NRoo NSti NSty SBod SDix SIng STre WAbe WHil WPer WSun WWin
'Mrs C W Earle Variegated' (d)	EFol ELan LHop WWin
'Mrs Clay'	See H. 'Fire Dragon'
'Mrs Jenkinson'	CMHG LAbb
'Mrs Lake'	EMNN NSty
¶ 'Mrs Moules'	SRms
'Mrs Mountstewart Jenkinson'	LHop MBro
mutabile	EMar WPer
§ ***nummularium***	CKin GPoy MHew NLan NMir NSal NWCA SHer WCla WNdy WPat
§ – ssp. ***glabrum***	CLew CMHG EMNN GAbr MBro NHol NKay NRoo NTow SIng WHoo WPat WPer
– ssp. ***grandiflorum*** 'Variegatum'	MWat
§ – ssp. ***tomentosum***	MWat
oblongatum	MBro
oelandicum ssp. ***alpestre***	MBro NKay SRms SSmi WPer
– – 'Baby Buttercup'	CMea MPla
¶ – ***pilosselloïdes***	MHig
'Old Gold'	CRiv EBre EPot LBee LBre MHig NHol NRoo SIgm WAbe WPer
'Orange Surprise'	CHal NRed
ovatum	See H. ***nummularium obscurum***
'Pink Beauty'	CHal
¶ 'Pink Glow'	WPer
'Pink Perfection'	CMHG CSam
'Praecox'	CKel CMea CPar EMNN ESis LBee MBal MCas MPla NRoo NSty SIng STre WHoo WPer
¶ 'Prostrate Orange'	SRms
'Raspberry Ripple'	CCla CRDP CShe EBre EFol ELan EOrc ESis GCHN ITim LBre LHop MPla MRav MSte MTho NEgg NHol NRoo SAxl SChu SFis SIng WHoo WPat WPer WRus WWin
'Red Orient'	See H. 'Supreme'
§ 'Rhodanthe Carneum'	Widely available
'Rosa Königin' ('Rose Queen')	EMNN LBee LBuc MDHE NKay NMen NRed NSty WAbe

'Rose of Leeswood' (d)	CHal CMea CShe ELan EOrc LBuc LHil LHop MBro NKay NRed NRya SIgm SIng SMrm SSvw WEas WHCG WHil WHoo WKif WSHC WWin
¶ 'Roxburgh Gold'	SRms
'Rushfield's White'	WHCG WRus
'Saint John's College Yellow'	CMHG CSam EBar EHal WHCG WPer
'Salmon Bee'	CShe
'Salmon Queen'	CMHG CRiv EMNN ESis ITim LBee MCas NCat NKay NRoo SIng WPer WWin
* *scardicum*	MBro NHol
serpyllifolium	See H. ***nummularium glabrum***
'Shot Silk'	NRoo SIng
'Silvery Salmon'	WAbe
'Snow Queen'	See H. 'The Bride'
'Snowball'	EMon
'Southmead'	EMNN
'Sterntaler'	GAbr GDra NHol SIng SRms WDav
'Sudbury Gem'	CRiv EBre ECha GAri LBre LHop NRoo WDav WSHC
x *sulphureum*	GCal NLan
'Sunbeam'	CRiv CSam EMNN EPot GAbr ITim MCas NSty SRms
§ 'Supreme'	CRiv CShe ELan IDai LHop MWat NKay SChu SDix SIgm SIng SSvw WPer
§ 'The Bride'	CElw CHal CMea EBre ECha EFou ELan EOrc ESis GCHN LBre LBuc LHil LHop MSte MWat NMen NSty SChu SDix SHer SIng SSvw WAbe WPer WSHC
'Tigrinum Plenum' (d)	ESis LBee MDHE NRed NRoo WPer WWin
'Tomato Red'	ECha SMrm
umbellatum	See HALIMIUM ***umbellatum***
'Venustum Plenum' (d)	MBro WEas
'Voltaire'	EMNN ESma GAbr MDHE NHol NKay NRoo SIng WWin
'Watergate Rose'	CHal CNic MWat NBir NKay SIng
'Westfield Wonder'	CBot
'White Queen'	MBro WPer
¶ 'Windermere'	SIgm
♦ 'Wisley Pink'	See H. 'Rhodanthe Carneum'
'Wisley Primrose'	Widely available
'Wisley White'	CPar CRiv CSam ECha EPot GAbr GCal LHop MBal MBro NRoo SAxl SIgm SIng WHoo WPer WRus
'Yellow Queen'	See H. 'Golden Queen'

HELIANTHUS † (Compositae)

atrorubens	CBow CDoC MBri
– 'Monarch'	CBre CKel ECED MFir WOld
'Capenoch Star'	CBow EFou MUlv SDix WByw
¶ *decapetalus* 'Maximus'	SRms
– 'Morning Sun'	CBre CPar EMon
– 'Soleil d'Or'	ECtt
– 'Triomphe de Gand'	CBre EMon MWat WOld
'Gullick's Variety'	EMon NBro
¶ x *kellermanii*	EMon
§ x *laetiflorus*	ELan EMon NOrc WCot
'Lemon Queen'	CBre CShe ECha ECtt EFou EHal EMon EPar WCot WOld
§ 'Loddon Gold'	CKel CSco ECED ECtt EFou ELan ENot EPla NVic SFis WCot WWye
¶ *nuttallii*	EMon
orgyalis	See H. ***salicifolius***
quinquenervis	See HELIANTHELLA ***q.***
rigidus	See H. x ***laetiflorus***
§ *salicifolius*	CBre EBlo ECED ECha ELan EMon EPla MBri MSte MUlv SDix SFis SMad WHer WOld
scaberrimus	See H. ***laetiflorus***
tuberosus	NRog

HELICHRYSUM † (Compositae)

♦ *acuminata*	See BRACTEANTHA ***subundulata***
§ *aggregatum*	ECou
alveolatum	See H. ***splendidum***
ambiguum	CFis MPla NNor NOak WDav
amorginum	WPer
angustifolium	See H. ***italicum***
– Cretan Form	See H. ***italicum microphyllum***
arenarium	SSmi WHil
§ *argyrophyllum*	CBrk GCal SIng
§ *arwae*	EPot ESis ITim LHop MHig NTow SBla
asperum	See OZOTHAMNUS ***purpurascens***
¶ *basalticum*	SIng
bellidioïdes	CGle CLew CNic CShe ECar ECha ECou ELan GAbr IDai MBal MHig MTho NGre NKay NNrd NTow WCru WOMN
¶ – large form	SIgm
bellum	LHop
♦ *bracteatum*	See BRACTEANTHA ***bracteata***
chionophyllum	NTow
* 'Coco'	IHos
confertum	ITim MHig NTow
coralloïdes	GArf MHig NWCA SIng WEas WOMN
'County Park Silver'	CRiv CSam ECou EPot NHar NHol NNrd NTow SIng WDav
¶ *dasyanthum*	MHig
depressum	ECou
doerfleri	MHig WDav
'Elmstead'	See H. ***stoechas*** 'White Barn'
* *emelinii*	CHan LBlm
ericifolium	See OZOTHAMUS ***purpurascens***
ericoïdes	See DOLICOTHRIX ***ericoïdes***
foetidum	CHan
fontanesii	CFis LHil NKay NSti SPer
frigidum	EPot GArf ITim MHig NMen NNrd NTow NWCA SBla SIng WOMN
glomeratum	See H. ***aggregratum***
gunnii	CSco
hookeri	ECou ITim SChu SIng
§ *italicum*	CArn CB&S CFis CGle CHan CShe ECha EHoe ENot ERav Effi GAbr GCHN GPoy IEde LGro LHol MBri MPla NHol NKay NSel NSti SDry WDin WEas WWin
§ – ssp. *microphyllum*	CGle CSam ECha EFol ELan SChu SIde SIgm WEas

– 'Nanum'	See H. *i. microphyllum*
§ – ssp. ***serotinum***	CDoC COtt GPoy ITim LHop NRar SPer SPla WAbe WPer WWeb
lanatum	See H. ***thianschanicum***
ledifolium	See OZOTHAMNUS ***ledifolius***
lobbii	ELan NGre SPou
marginatum	See H. ***milfordiae***
microphyllum	See PLECOSTACHYS ***serpyllifolia***
§ ***milfordiae***	EBur EPot IDai ITim MBal MHig MWat NHar NHol NKay NNor NNrd NWCA SBla SGil SIng WAbe WMar WOld WPat WThu
'Mo's Gold'	See H. ***argyrophyllum***
orientale	CHan NHol NKay NTow SIng WSun WThu
pagophilum	EPot
§ ***petiolare***	CB&S CBow CCla CFis CHad CHal CTre EBak ECtt IHos LAbb MRav NRoo SDix SIng WEas WHal
– 'Aureum'	See H. ***p.*** 'Limelight'
¶ – 'Goring Silver'	CBrk LHil
§ – 'Limelight'	CB&S CBow CBrk CCla CFis CHal CTre ECtt ESma IHos LAbb MRav MUlv NRoo SDix SIng SLon WEas WHal WWye
– 'Roundabout' (v)	CBrk ESma LHil LHop MRav WEas
– 'Variegatum'	CB&S CCla CFis CHal CTre ECtt ERav ESma IHos LAbb MRav NRoo SDix SIng WEas WHal
petiolatum	See H. ***petiolare***
plicatum	CFis EBar LHol
plumeum	GArf ITim MHig NWCA
populifolium	CBrk CKni CTre EMon
praecurrens	ITim NHol
rosmarinifolium	See OZOTHAMNUS ***rosmarinifolius***
'Schweffellicht' ('Sulphur Light')	CFis CGle CHad CKel CSam CSco CShe CTom ECED ECha EFol EFou EOrc EPla ERav MBri MRav NFai NHol NRoo SPer SPla WDav WEas WHal WSHC
scorpioïdes	ECou NWCA
selago	See OZOTHAMNUS ***s.***
serotinum	See H. ***italicum serotinum***
serpyllifolium	See PLECOSTACHYS ***serpyllifolia***
sessile	See H. ***sessilioïdes***
sessilioïdes	EPot ITim MHig NHol NTow NWCA SBla SIng WDav
§ ***sibthorpii***	EPot ITim MHig NTow SIng WAbe
siculum	See H. ***stoechas barrelieri***
'Silver Princess'	ECar
'Silver Streams'	ECar
§ ***splendidum***	CFis CGle CHan CSco CShe ECha EOrc GAbr GCHN LHil LHol NHol NNor NSti SDix SPer SUsu WDin WEas WHer WHil WPer
sp. from Drakensburg Mountains	CLew CRDP CRiv GAbr NHol NKay
stoechas	IDai
§ – ssp. ***barrelieri***	CFis CNic
§ – 'White Barn'	ECha
'Sussex Silver'	EPla
§ ***thianschanicum***	NHol
§ – 'Goldkind' ('Golden Baby')	LHil NBir NMen SFis SPla WHil
thyrsoideum	See OZOTHAMNUS ***thyrsoideus***
trilineatum	See H. ***splendidum***
tumidum	See OZOTHAMNUS ***s. t.***
virgineum	See H. ***sibthorpii***
woodii	See H. ***arwae***

HELICHRYSUM X RAOULIA (Compositae)

'Rivulet'	ECou
'Silver Streams'	ECou

HELICODICEROS (Araceae)

¶ ***muscivorus***	CMon

HELICONIA (Heliconiaceae)

¶ ***bihai***	CTro
mariae	MNew
rostrata	MNew
stricta 'Dwarf Jamaican'	MNew

HELICTOTRICHON (Gramineae)

¶ ***filifolium***	ETPC
pratense	EFou EMon EPla ETPC
§ ***sempervirens***	Widely available
– var. ***pendulum***	EMon EPla

HELIOPHILA (Cruciferae)

longifolia	ELan

HELIOPSIS † (Compositae)

helianthoïdes 'Gigantea'	WCot
– var. ***scabra*** 'Ballerina'	NBee
– – 'Desert King	EBlo
– – 'Goldgefieder' ('Golden Plume')	CKel EBre LBre LRHS
– – 'Goldgrünherz'	ECED EPla LRHS WCot
– – 'Incomparabilis'	CKel
– – 'Light of Loddon'	MWat
– – 'Sommersonne' ('Summer Sun')	CBow CMGP CSco EBlo EBre ECtt EFou EHal LBre LHop LWad MFir NFai NMir SCro SHer SPer SPla SSvw WPer WWin
¶ – 'Sonnenglut'	MBri

HELIOTROPIUM (Boraginaceae)

¶ ***amplexicaule***	SWas
♦ ***anchusifolium***	See H. ***amplexicaule***
§ ***arborescens***	CArn CKni CSev MPit WCru
'Chatsworth'	CBar CBrk CCla CHad CPle ERea LHil SAxl SHer SIde SSad SUsu WCru WEas
europaeum	WHer
'Gatton Park'	ERea LHil SMrm SSad
'Lord Roberts'	ERea SMrm
¶ 'Netherhall White'	ERea
'P K Lowther'	CBrk ERea WEas
peruvianum	See H. ***arborescens***
'Princess Marina'	CBrk ERea LHil SSad WEas
¶ 'The Speaker'	CBrk
'W H Lowther'	MNew
'White Lady'	CBrk ERea SSad

HELIPTERUM (Compositae)

albicans ssp. *albicans*
incanum GDra
– ssp. *alpinum* GTou NTow
anthemoïdes CSun ECou

HELLEBORUS † (Ranunculaceae)

§ *argutifolius* Widely available
¶ – JCA 559.800 CLCN
– x *sternii* LHil
atrorubens hort. See H. ***orientalis abchasicus*** Early Purple Group
¶ – Waldst. & Kit. SWas WStI
– WM 9028/9101/9261 MPhe
colchicus See H. ***orientalis abchasicus***
corsicus See H. ***argutifolius***
cyclophyllus NRoo SBla SPou SSpi
dumetorum Croatia WM 9025 MPhe
¶ – Hungary WM 9209 MPhe
¶ – Slovenya WM 9214 MPhe
§ x *ericsmithii* SBla
foetidus Widely available
– Bowles' form CBro
– 'Chedglow' CNat
– 'Green Giant' WCru
– Italian form WRus
– 'Sopron' MPhe NSti WCru
– Wester Flisk Group CAvo CBot CBro CChu CSco ELan EPla ERav LGre MBri MFir MPar MPhe NHol NRar NSti SBla SSpi WAbb WAbe WCru WFib WHoo WOMN WRus WWat
lividus CAvo CBos CBot CBow CBro CChu CGle CHan CLCN ELan MUlv NHar SAxl SBla SHer WAbb WOMN
– *corsicus* See H. ***argutifolius***
– dwarf SPou
¶ *multifidus* NBir
– ssp. *bocconei* SBla WOMN
– ssp. *hercegovinus* WM 9011/9105 MPhe
– ssp. *istriacus* CBro SBla SWas
– – WM 9002/9222 MPhe
– ssp. *multifidus* SBla
– – WM 9010/9104 MPhe
niger Widely available
– Blackthorn Group SWas
– Harvington hybrids LRHS
– 'Higham's Variety' CGle
– 'Louis Cobbett' CBro
– ssp. *macranthus* NHol
– – WM 9030 WCru
¶ – 'Madame Fourcade' MBri
– *major* See H. ***n. macranthus***
– 'Potter's Wheel' CBro CChu CCla CPMA EPad GCal MHig MUlv NRar SApp SBla SHer SPer SSpi WCru WWat
– 'Saint Brigid' NRar
– Sunset Group WM 9113 MPhe
– 'White Magic' CPMA GDra NHol SBla SWas
¶ x *nigercors* SBla
♦ x *nigristern* See H. x ***ericsmithii***
odorus EBar GCal SBla SSpi
– WM 9016/9103 MPhe
¶ – WM 9202 MPhe
♦ – *laxus* See H. ***multifidus istriacus***
N *orientalis* hort. Widely available
– 'Agnes Brook' WFib
¶ – 'Albin Otto' EBre LBre
– Anderson's Red Hybrids CLCN
¶ – 'Angela Tandy' WFib
– 'Baby Black' LRHS
– Ballard's Group NRar WRus
– black seedlings CGle ERav GDra MPar WCru
– 'Carlton Hall' WFib
– 'Cheerful' NBir
– 'Christmas Lantern' LRHS
– Draco strain CLCN
¶ – 'Dusk' WBal
– 'Elizabeth Coburn' WFib
– 'Eric's Best' ECha
¶ – 'Fred Whitsey' WFib
– Galaxy Group SHig
– 'Gertrude Raithby' WFib
¶ – 'Gladys Burrow' WFib
– 'Greencups' WBal
– ssp. *guttatus* CAvo CChu CLCN COtt ELun MUlv SBla SHig SSpi WCot WCru
– – cream ECha
– – pink ECha WCru
¶ – 'Hades' NBir WBal
– Hadspen hybrids CHad
¶ – 'Helen Ballard' WBal
– 'Hercules' MUlv
– 'Ian Raithby' WFib
– ivory CLCN
– 'John Raithby' WFib
– Kochii Group COtt ECha ELun MUlv NRoo WCru WRus
¶ – 'Lady Charlotte Bonham-Carter' WFib
¶ – 'Lavinia Ward' WFib
– 'Leo' MUlv
¶ – 'Limelight' ECha
– 'Little Black' ELan WAbe WFib
– 'Mary Petit' WFib
– 'Maureen Key' WFib
– Midnight Sky Group WWat
¶ – 'Mystery' WBal
¶ – 'Nancy Ballard' WBal
¶ – Party Dress Group (d) SBla
¶ – 'Patchwork' WBal
– 'Pebworth White' WFib
¶ – 'Philip Ballard' WBal
– pink CLCN CPMA WCru
– 'Plum Stippled' ECha
– purple CLCN CRDP ECha MPar WCru
¶ – 'Sirius' SHig
– 'Sunny' WBal
– 'Trotter's Spotted' GDra MPar
– 'Ushba' LRHS WBal
¶ – 'Victoria Raithby' WFib
– white CGle ECha MBal MPar WCru
– Zodiac Group CLCN SHig
orientalis Lamarck MPhe SPou SWas
¶ – JCA 562.402 CLCN
§ – *abchasicus* CAvo MBri NRoo WCru
§ – – Early Purple Group CBow CLCN CSco ELun IDai SHig
– *olympicus* See H. ***o. orientalis***

– *orientalis purpurascens*	SFis SPou WWat
	CBow CHad ECha LWad NBir SPou SWas WSHC
¶ – Hungary WM 9208/9211	MPhe
x *sternii*	CBot CBow CChu CCla CLCN CPMA CPar EGol ELan GCal MBal MFir NBar NHar NRoo SBla SFis SMad SWas WAbe WHal WRus WWat
– Blackthorn strain	CChu CPMA EHar MBri MUlv SBla SWas WCru WWat
– 'Boughton Beauty'	CAvo CB&S CBro CChu LGre MTho SFar WCot WOMN
– Boughton Group	CBot MUlv WCru
torquatus	CBro SPou SSpi WCot
– BM 5279	SPou
– Bosnia WM 9003/9111	MPhe
– hybrids	SBla WCru
– Montenegro WM 9106	MPhe
viridis	ECha GCal LWad SBla SRms SSpi WCru WStI
– ssp. *occidentalis*	CAvo CBro MPhe SBla

HELONIOPSIS (Liliaceae/Melanthiaceae)

japonica	See H. ***orientalis***
§ *orientalis*	EPot WCru
§ – var. *breviscapa*	SWas WThi
– var. *yakusimensis*	See H. ***o. breviscapa***

HELWINGIA (Helwingiaceae)

himalaica	EMon
japonica	CBot GWht LGre WWat

HELXINE See SOLEIROLIA

HEMEROCALLIS † (Liliaceae/Hemerocallidaceae)

¶ 'Added Dimensions'	SApp
'Admiral'	MAus
'Adoration'	SPer
'Alan'	CKel CMGP SCro SHig
¶ 'Amadeus'	SApp
'Ambassador'	CKel
'Amber Star'	LMay
'Angel Flight'	MAus
'Anne Welch'	EPla
'Anzac'	CPar ECha ECtt EPla ERou GAri MBlu MSta NBee NHol NMir WCot
¶ 'Apple Court Damson'	SApp
'Apricot Beauty'	SFis WHil
'Artistic Gold'	EGol
¶ 'Atalanta Bouquet'	SApp
aurantiaca	CB&S
'Aurora'	WAbe
¶ 'Autumn Red'	CBow ERou NCat NFai
'Back Bay'	MAus
¶ 'Ballet Dancer'	ERou
'Baroni'	ECha
'Battle Hymn'	MAus
'Beauty Bright'	MAus
'Bejewelled'	EGol EPla MSta
'Beloved Returns'	MAus
'Bess Ross'	MAus
'Bess Vestale'	ERou NHol
'Bibury'	SCro
'Black Falcon'	CKel
'Black Knight'	SRms
'Black Magic'	CBro CGle CHad CMGP CPar CSev EBre ECED EGol ELan EPla ERou LBre MAus MBri MRav NHol SHer SPer WHal
¶ 'Black Prince'	CBow CKel
'Blushing Belle'	WWin
'Bold Courtier'	CKel MAus
'Bonanza'	CB&S CBro CCla CKel CMGP CSco CTom EBlo EBre ECha EHon ELan EPla ERou LBre MAus MBri MRav NBee NBro NCat NHol SChu SHig SPer WAbe
'Bourbon King'	EBre EGol EPla ERou LBre
'Brass Cup'	MAus
¶ 'Bright Banner'	MAus
'Burlesque'	CKel
'Burning Daylight'	CKel CMGP CSco EBre EPla ERou LBre MAus MBel NBar NHol NVic SPer WOld
'Buttons'	CShe
'Buzz Bomb'	EBlo SHig SPer
'By Jove'	MAus
¶ 'Canary Glow'	EBlo EBre LBre NCat WWat
'Captured Heart'	MAus
'Caramea'	WHil
'Cartwheels'	CKel CRiv ECha MAus MMil NFai SApp SPer
¶ 'Catherine Wheel'	NBir
'Catherine Woodbery'	CCla CKel CLew COtt CSev EBlo EBre ECtt EGol ELan EPla LBre MRav MSta NBar NCat NFai NRoo SApp SAxl SMad SPer WCot WCra
'Chartreuse Magic'	CRiv EGol EPla NHol SPer
'Cherry Cheeks'	CKel EBlo EBre ECtt EGol ELan EPla ERou LBre MAus MRav SFis WCot WCra
¶ 'Cherry Smoke'	SApp
'Chic Bonnet'	SPer
¶ 'Chicago Apache'	SApp
'Chicago Petticoats'	EGol
¶ 'Chicago Picotee Queen'	LRHS MBri
'Chicago Royal Robe'	EBlo EGol EPla MBel MSta MUlv WCot WWin
'Chicago Sunrise'	EGol EPla LWad MSta NHol NOrc WMer
'Chief Sarcoxie'	MAus
'Children's Festival'	CB&S CHad CWes EBlo ECtt EGol LWad NHol WAbe WHil WRus
'Chinese Coral'	CKel
'Chloe's Child'	SCro
'Christmas Candles'	MAus
citrina	CCla ELan EMon SPla
'Classic Simplicity'	MAus
'Colonial Dame'	CKel
'Conspicua'	CShe CWGN SFis
'Constitutional Island'	MAus
'Contessa'	CBro ELan SCro SPer
'Corky'	EBul ECha GCal SAxl SChu SDix SPer SSpi SWas
¶ 'Cosmic Flash'	SApp
'Countess Zora'	MAus
'Cream Drop'	CB&S CBow CHad CWes EBlo ECtt EFou EGol LWad NHol NOrc WAbe WMer WRus
¶ 'Crimson Pirate'	ERou
'Croesus'	MAus NHol SCro SRms
¶ 'Croftway'	SCro

'Corky' EBul ECha GCal SAxl SChu SDix SPer SSpi SWas
¶ 'Cosmic Flash' SApp
'Countess Zora' MAus
'Cream Drop' CB&S CBow CHad CWes EBlo ECtt EFou EGol LWad NHol NOrc WAbe WMer WRus
¶ 'Crimson Pirate' ERou
'Croesus' MAus NHol SCro SRms
¶ 'Croftway' SCro
¶ 'Crumpet' SApp
'Dark Elf' SApp
'Dawn Play' CKel
'Decatur Imp' EGol
'Devon Cream' SPer
'Diamond Dust' CRiv SPer
'Dido' CSco ERou
¶ 'Dominic' SApp
'Dorcas' MAus
'Dorothy McDade' EGol
¶ 'Double Cutie' SApp
'Down Town' MAus
'Dresden Doll' SPer
'Dresden Gleam' CRiv
§ 'Dubloon' CKel CMGP EBre EBul ERou GAbr LBre MAus NHol
dumortieri CAvo CBot CBro CChu CCla CDec EBlo EBre EBul ECha EFou EGol ELan EOrc EPla LBre MAus MUlv MWat NHol NSti NVic SHig SPer SSpi
¶ 'Edna Spalding' SApp
'Eenie Weenie' CB&S CBro CWes ECtt EGol LWad MAus NHol NOrc SApp WMer WRus
¶ 'Elaine Strutt' WCot
'Esther Walker' CKel
'Evelyn Claar' CKel SCro
'Fairy Wings' SAxl SPer
'Fandango' SPer
¶ 'Feelings' SApp
'Fire Dance' SCro
'First Formal' SPer
¶ 'Flaming Sword' CB&S
flava See H. ***lilioasphodelus***
'Folklore' MAus
'Frances Fay' SApp
'Frans Hals' CBre COtt EPla ERou MBri MRav NFai SPer SPla WHal WHil WHoo
¶ 'Fresh Air' SApp
'Full Reward' MAus
fulva CRow CWGN ELan EPla NCat NHol SChu SHig
N– 'Flore Pleno' CAvo CHan CKel CRDP CRow CWGN EFou EGol EHon ELan EMon EOrc EPla GAbr LGan MAus MFir NSti SAxl SFis SHig SPer SSvw WEas WHil WHoo WWin
N– 'Green Kwanso' EMon
N– 'Kwanzo Variegata' CBot CChu CGle ELan MTho NBir WCot
'Garnet Garland' CKel
'Gateway' MAus
* 'Gay Nineteen' CKel
'Gay Rapture' SPer
'Gay Troubadour' CKel
¶ 'Gentle Shepherd' CKel
'George Cunningham' CGle CMGP CRiv CSev EBre ECtt EGol ELan EPla ERou LBre MAus MBri NRoo SChu SGil WAbb
'Giant Moon' EBre EGol ELan EPla ERou LBre MBri MUlv SAxl SPer WHal WRus
¶ 'Gingerbread Man' SApp
'Glowing Gold' MAus
'Gold Imperial' CB&S CBow CShe
'Golden Bell' NHol SChu
'Golden Chance' CCla MAus
'Golden Chimes' Widely available
'Golden Gate' SHig
¶ 'Golden Ginko' LRHS MBri
'Golden Orchid' See H. 'Dubloon'
¶ 'Golden Peace' SApp
'Golden Prize' EBre EPla LBre SApp
¶ 'Graceful Eye' SApp
¶ 'Green Chartreuse' ECha
'Green Drop' WHil
¶ 'Green Flutter' CSev NBir
'Green Magic' EGol EPla MAus NSti
'Grumbly' ELan
'Gusto' MAus
'Halo Light' CKel SPer
'Heartthrob' MAus
'Heaven Knows' MAus
'Heirloom Lace' MAus
'Helios' CSco SHig
'Her Majesty' CKel
'Holiday Mood' ELan ERou SGil
'Home Run' MAus
'Hornby Castle' CBro CKel EBre LBre NHol NVic
'Hyperion' CB&S CCla CMGP CShe EBre ECED ECtt EGol GAri LBre MAus MRav NBar NHol NRoo SApp SChu SPer WOld
¶ 'Ice Castles' SApp
¶ 'Ice Cool' SApp
'Imperator' CWGN EPla LMay NHol
'Iron Gate Glacier' EPla SApp
'Jo Jo' MAus
'Joan Senior' EGol EPla MBel SApp
¶ 'Judah' SApp
'Kelway's Gold' CKel
N 'Kwanso Flore Pleno' See H. ***fulva*** 'Green Kwanso'
N 'Kwanso Flore Pleno Variegata' See H. ***fulva*** 'Kwanzo Variegata'
'Lady Inora Cubiles' MAus
¶ 'Lady Limelight' SApp
¶ 'Ladykin' SApp
¶ 'Lark Song' COtt EGol
'Lavender Bonanza' MAus
¶ 'Lemon Bells' SApp
¶ 'Liitle Deeke' SApp
'Lilac Wine' ECha NHol WMer
§ ***lilioasphodelus*** CAvo CBre CGle CHad CHan CTom EBul ECha ELan EPla GCal LGan MBro MFir NHol NSti NTow SApp SAxl SDix SHig SMad SPer SPla SSpi SSvw SUsu WHal WHil WHoo
'Linda' CMGP ERou MAus NHol
¶ 'Little Beige Magic' EGol
'Little Cameo' EGol
¶ 'Little Cranberry Cove' EGol

¶ 'Little Fat Dazzler'	SApp
'Little Grapette'	SApp
¶ 'Little Greenie'	SApp
¶ 'Little Gypsy Vagabond'	SApp
¶ 'Little Lavender Princess'	EGol
'Little Maggie'	SApp
'Little Men'	MAus
'Little Sally'	EGol
'Little Wart'	EGol
'Little Wine Cup'	CB&S EBlo ECtt EFou EGol LWad MAus NHol NOrc SApp WHil
'Lively Set'	MAus
'Lotus Land'	CKel
¶ 'Lowenstine'	SApp
'Lullaby Baby'	EGol SApp
'Luxury Lace'	CDec COtt EBlo EBre EFol EFou EGol ELan EOrc EPla LBre MAus MSta MUlv SAxl
'Lynn Hall'	EGol
'Mabel Fuller'	SCro SPer
'Magic Dawn'	CKel
'Mallard'	COtt EBre ECtt EGol EPla LBre MBri MRav MUlv SApp WCot WCra WMer
'Marion Vaughn'	CCla CMGP EBre EGol EPla LBre LHop MAus MMil MUlv NSti SChu SDix WCot
'Mary Todd'	EGol
'Mavoureen Nesmith'	SCro
'May Colven'	EGol
'Meadow Sprite'	SApp
'Melody Lane'	EGol
'Meno'	EGol
middendorffii	EBul EMon GDra MAus
¶ – var. ***esculenta***	WDav
¶ 'Mini Pearl'	EGol
¶ 'Mini Stella'	CBro EPla SApp
Miniature hybrids	SRms WPer
minor	CBro CCla CPar EGol SApp SPla SRms
¶ 'Misty'	MAus
'Morocco Red'	CCla CKel COtt CWGN EFol ELan GGar MAus WAbe WWat
'Mount Joy'	SPer
¶ 'Mountain Laurel'	LRHS MBri
'Mrs David Hall'	CKel SCro
'Mrs Hugh Johnson'	CHad CMGP EHon NHol
'Mrs John J Tigert'	CSco ERou
'Mrs Lester'	CKel
multiflora	CCla NHol SHig
¶ 'My Happy Valentine'	SApp
'Nashville'	CBro CKel CPar ELan ERou SGil
¶ 'New Swirls'	SApp
'Neyron Rose'	EBre EGol EPla ERou LBre SPer
¶ 'Night Raider'	SApp
'Nigrette'	LMay MUlv MWat NHol
¶ 'Nina Winegar'	SApp
'Nob Hill'	EGol
'Olive Bailey Langdon'	EGol
¶ 'Open Hearth'	SApp
'Orangeman'	CBow CDoC
'Orford'	WWin
'Ozark Lass'	MAus
'Paige Parker'	EGol
'Painted Lady'	CKel
¶ 'Pandora's Box'	SApp
'Paradise Prince'	EGol
¶ 'Pardon Me'	EGol SApp
'Party Partner'	MAus
¶ 'Pastel Accent'	SApp
'Patricia Fay'	CKel
'Peaceful'	MAus
'Persian Princess'	CKel
'Persian Shrine'	EGol
'Pink Charm'	CCla CGle CMGP CWGN LHop LMay MAus MBal MWat NHol NOrc WCra WHil WTyr
'Pink Damask'	Widely available
'Pink Dream'	NHol
'Pink Heaven'	EGol
'Pink Lady'	CSco ERou SPer SRms
'Pink Prelude'	CKel NHol
¶ 'Pink Snowflake'	MAus
'Pink Sundae'	ECha
¶ 'Pixie Pipestone'	SApp
¶ 'Pogo'	EGol
¶ 'Pony'	SApp
¶ 'Prairie Bells'	NFai WHoo
'Prairie Blue Eyes'	EGol
'Prairie Sunset'	MAus
'Precious Treasure'	CKel
'Premier'	MAus
'Prima Donna'	CKel SCro
'Primrose Mascotte'	NBir WCot
¶ 'Rajah'	NBro NCat
¶ 'Red Joy'	SApp
'Red Precious'	EGol MBel SAsh
'Red Torch'	CKel CSco SPer
'Revolute'	MAus
¶ 'Right On'	SApp
'Romany'	LMay
'Royal Ruby'	CSco
'Royalty'	CKel EBul
'Ruffled Pinafore'	CCla
¶ 'Russell Prichard'	ERou
¶ 'Saladin'	EBul
'Salmon Sheen'	CKel
'Sammy Russell'	CB&S CGle CWGN EGol EOrc EPla LHop MAus MBal MBro NBro NFai NHol WCra WHer
'Sandra Walker'	EGol
¶ 'Scarlet Flame'	ECha
¶ 'Scarlet Tanager'	LRHS MUlv WMer
¶ 'Screech Owl'	LRHS WMer
'Shooting Star'	CKel EGol SPla
¶ 'Silent World'	MAus
'Silken Fairy'	EGol
'Siloam Baby Talk'	EGol SApp
¶ 'Siloam Bo Peep'	EGol
¶ 'Siloam Button Box'	EGol
¶ 'Siloam Byelo'	EGol
¶ 'Siloam Fairy Tale'	EGol
¶ 'Siloam Pink Glow'	EGol
'Siloam Pocket Size'	SApp
¶ 'Siloam Prissy'	SApp
'Siloam Purple Plum'	EGol
¶ 'Siloam Sugar Time'	EGol
'Siloam Tiny Mite'	EGol SApp
¶ 'Siloam Tom Thumb'	EGol
'Siloam Uri Winniford'	EGol SApp
¶ 'Siloam Virginia Henson'	EGol
'Sirius'	MWat NHol
¶ 'Snow Elf'	SApp

'Solid Scarlet'	CSco
'Song Sparrow'	CBro SApp
'Sound of Music'	MAus
'Spanish Gold'	CSco
'Stafford'	CKel CSco EBlo EBre ECED ECtt EFou ELan EPla ERou LBre LGro LHop MAus MBri NHol NOrc SApp SAxl SChu SGil SHig SPer WCra
'Starling'	EGol
'Stella de Oro'	CBro CChu CKel CTom EBar EBlo EBre ECha ECtt EGol ELan EOrc EPla ERou LBre MAus MBri MRav MTho MUlv NMir NRoo SApp SAxl SPer SPla SSpi WHoo WMer WRus
'Summer Interlude'	MAus
¶ 'Summer Wine'	CMGP EPla LRHS NFai WCot WCra WHoo
¶ 'Sun Pixie'	SApp
¶ 'Sure Thing'	SApp
'Sweet Refrain'	CBot
'Tasmania'	SPer
'Tejas'	CSco
'Telstar'	CSco
'Thelma Perry'	CHad
'Thumbelina'	ECha
§ ***thunbergii***	EBul EPla SSpi
¶ 'Tom Collins'	SApp
'Towhead'	EGol LRHS MAus MUlv WMer
¶ 'Toyland'	LRHS
'Triple Treat'	CCla MAus
¶ 'Turkish Turban'	SApp
'Twenty Third Psalm'	WHal
'Varsity'	CCla COtt EBlo EBre EGol LBre SApp SPer
vespertina	See H. ***thunbergii***
'Vicountess Byng'	SFis SHig
¶ 'Victoria Aden'	CBro
'Virgin's Blush'	SPer
¶ 'Wally Nance'	LRHS
¶ 'Walt Disney'	CB&S
'Water Witch'	EGol
'Waxwing'	CKel
'Whichford'	CBro CKel EBlo EBre ECtt EGol ELan LBre NHol SChu SGil SHig SSpi WWin
'Wild Welcome'	MAus
'Windsor Tan'	MAus
'Winnetka'	MAus
'Winnie the Pooh'	MAus SApp
'Wishing Well'	SChu WCot
'Woodbury'	WRus
'World of Peace'	MAus
'Yellow Rain'	WCot
'Young Countess'	MAus
'Zara'	CRiv SPer

HEMIPHRAGMA (Scrophulariaceae)

¶ ***heterophyllum***	GTou

HEPATICA † (Ranunculaceae)

acutiloba	CBro EPar LAma NGar NHol NKay WChr
americana	CArn CBro CRDP LAma NGar NHol WChr WCru
angulosa	See H. ***transsilvanica***
x ***media*** 'Ballardii'	IBlr NBir NGar
§ ***nobilis***	CAvo CBro CCla CNic CRiv EBre ECha EPot GArf IBlr LBre LHop MBri MTho MWat NBar NHar NTow SHer SIgm SUsu SWas WCru WHal WSHC
– blue	MS&S NGar SBla SPou SRms SWas
– double pink	See H. ***n.*** 'Rubra Plena'
– var. ***japonica***	CBro CRDP EPar LAma NGar NHol NRya SHer SSpi WChr WHil WOMN WWat
– lilac	SWas
¶ – 'Little Abington'	NGar
– pink	ELan MS&S NGar SBla SPou SWas
– red	ECha
§ – 'Rubra Plena'	MBri NBir NGar NHol
– white	CAvo CNic ELan MHig MS&S NGar NHol SBla SPou
§ ***transsilvanica***	CAvo CBro CCMG CHad CRDP EBre ECar ELan EPar EPot GDra LBee LBre LHop MBri MBro NHar NHol NKay SPou WChr WCru
– ***alba***	SPou
¶ – 'Elison Spence'	NGar
¶ – 'Lilacina'	NGar
¶ – 'Loddon Blue'	NGar
¶ – 'Nivea'	NGar
¶ – pink	SPou
triloba	See H. ***nobilis***

X HEPPIMENES (Gesneriaceae)

I 'Purple Queen '	NMos

HEPTACODIUM (Caprifoliaceae)

jasminoïdes	CAbb CBot CChu CPle ERav SMad SSpi

HEPTAPLEURUM See SCHEFFLERA

HERACLEUM (Umbelliferae)

antasiaticum	EMon LRHS
mantegazzianum	CRow EMon MFir WOak
minimum roseum	ELan MTho NGre WBon WEas WOMN WPat

HERBERTIA (Iridaceae)

¶ ***lahue***	WThi
¶ ***pulchella***	WPer WThi

HERMANNIA (Sterculiaceae)

♦ ***candicans***	See H. ***incana***
erodioïdes SH 12	CHan
¶ ***incana***	CBrk
verticillata	LHop SSad

HERMODACTYLUS (Iridaceae)

§ ***tuberosus***	CAvo CBro CChu CCla CHan CMea CMil CMon ECha ELan ERav LAma LBlo LBow NRog SCro SIng SUsu WHil
¶ – MS 976/762	CMon

HERNIARIA (Illecebraceae)

glabra	CLew EPar GPoy LHol MHew NCat NHol NSal NSel WHer WWye

HERPOLIRION (Liliaceae/Anthericaceae)

novae-zealandiae	ECar

HERTIA See **OTHONNA**

HESPERALOË (Agavaceae)

parviflora 'Rubra'	SArc

HESPERANTHA (Iridaceae)

♦*buhrii*	See H. *cucullata* 'Rubra'
§ *cucullata* 'Rubra'	ECar NWCA SUsu
huttonii	GCal MFir
moysii	WHal

HESPERIS † (Cruciferae)

lutea	See SISYMBRIUM *luteum*
matronalis	CArn CCMG CCla CGle CKin CLew CRow CSFH CSev EEls EFou ELan LAbb LHol MHew NBee NBro NSal SIde SSvw WBon WCla WHer WOak WPer WWye
– *alba*	CBot CCMG CCla EFou EMar EPad MFir SPer SSvw
– 'Alba Plena'	SMrm WDav WRus
– double form	MBri NHol
– 'Lilacina Flore Pleno'	CBos CBot CBre CGle CHad CMil CSco EMon LBlm MBel NBir NPer NSti SSvw

HETEROCENTRON (Melastomataceae)

§ *elegans*	CTre LTil

HETEROMELES See **PHOTINIA**

HETEROPAPPUS (Compositae)

altaicus	WPer

HETEROTHECA (Compositae)

villosa	CRDP ECha EMon LRHS

HEUCHERA † (Saxifragaceae)

§ *americana*	CRDP CRow CShe ECha EFol EOrc EPar LHil MNFA MUlv NSal SAxl SCro SHer WDav WEas WHal WThu WWat
'Apple Blossom'	CSco
¶ 'Baby's Breath'	CRDP
'Bressingham Blaze'	CDoC EBlo EBre LBre MBel WPbr
Bressingham hybrids	CBow CMGP CPar EBlo EBre EFou GDra LBre LHil LWad MBri MUlv NHol NMir NOak SCro SFis SHer SPer SPla WHoo WPer WWin
× *brizoïdes* 'Gracillima'	CGle
¶ 'Charles Bloom'	EBlo
¶ 'Cherry Red'	ECha
chlorantha	NHol
Coral Bells	See H. *sanguinea*
'Coral Cloud'	CB&S CKel EBre ENot GCHN IDai LBre
cylindrica	CChu CSun EBar GCHN LBlm MBel MSte
– var. *alpina*	NGre NHol
¶ – 'Chartreuse'	CGle
– 'Greenfinch'	Widely available
– 'Hyperion'	CSco EBre LBre MBal MNFA MUlv
'Dennis Davidson'	CGle ECha EPla SMad
'Dingle Mint Chocolate'	EFol
'Firebird'	CKel CSco ELan MBal MNFA NVic
'Firefly'	CPar ECha EFou EPla ESis ESma MFir MRav NBar NFai NMir NOrc NRoo SCro SFis SPer SPla WHoo WPer
glauca	See H. *americana*
'Green Ivory'	CCla CGle CMil CWGN EBre EFou EGol ELan ELun GCHN LBre MBal MBel MBri MNFA MRav MUlv NCat NSti SHer SPer
grossulariifolia	MTho NHar SGil WPer
hispida	ESis LRHS MSte SMad WBon WCra
'Huntsman'	ELan
'Ibis'	NSti
* *maritima*	SIng
'Mary Rose'	CSco
* *micans*	NHar SUsu WDav WThi WThu
micrantha	CSun CTom ECar ELan LBlm SRms
– JLS 86275CLOR	EMon
– var. *diversifolia*	NHol
N– 'Palace Purple'	Widely available
* 'Moondrops'	CRow
¶ 'Mother of Pearl'	ECha EFol
parvifolia	GCal
¶ 'Pewter Moon'	COtt CSco EBlo ESma LRHS MSta NHol NOrc SMad SPla SWas WCot
pilosissima	MPlt WCot
'Pluie de Feu'	CDoC EHal GCal WTyr
'Pretty Polly'	ENot
¶ *pringlei*	WPer
pubescens	GCHN LBee LRHS
– 'Alba'	WCot WHoo WSun WThi
pulchella	ESis LGre NRed SBla
– JCA 9508	CRDP NHol SWas
¶ 'Rachel'	CAbP CGle CMGP COtt EBlo EBre EFou EGol EPla GCal LBre LGan LRHS MMil MUlv NHol SMad SMrm WWat
'Red Spangles'	CBow CGle CKel EBre EPla GCHN LBre NBir SRms
richardsonii	ECED
¶ 'Rosemary Bloom'	EBlo
rubescens	GArf MTho NHar WWin
¶ 'Ruffles'	CRow
§ *sanguinea*	CGle CHal CMea GCHN MBal NBar NNor NRoo SPla WByw WHal WPer WWye
'Schneewittchen' (v)	ECha EFou EPla WMer
'Scintillation'	CB&S CKel CSco EBre ECED GCHN LBre SRms
¶ 'Silver Veil'	CRow
'Snow Storm' (v)	Widely available
'Sparkler' (v)	CKel
'Taff's Joy' (v)	CElw CLew CRow EFol LGre LHil LHop MBel MTho WCot
versicolor	CCor CPar GCal LGre

villosa	CElw ECha GCHN MRav
'Widar'	NHol SAxl

X HEUCHERELLA (Saxifragaceae)

alba 'Bridget Bloom'	Widely available
– 'Rosalie'	CGle SWas
tiarelloïdes	CMGP EBar EFol ELan MNFA NCat NFai NNor NSti SAxl SPer

X HIBANOBAMBUSA (Gramineae(Bambuseae))

tranquillans	EFul SDry WJun
– 'Shiroshima' (v)	EPla ISta SDry WJun

HIBBERTIA (Dilleniaceae)

aspera	CGre CPle CSun LBlm
cuneiformis	CGre CPle ERea
dentata	SLMG
procumbens	ITim SBla
§ *scandens*	CB&S CGre CHEx CPle CSpe CSun CTre CTro ERea LAbb LBlm WBod
♦ *tetrandra*	See H. ***cuneiformis***
volubilis	See H. ***scandens***

HIBISCUS † (Malvaceae)

¶ *coccineus*	MSte
¶ *fallax*	CTro
geranioïdes	CSun LBlm
huegelii	See ALYOGYNE ***h.***
¶ *leopoldii*	SRms
militaris	CSun
* *moesiana*	MBri
¶ 'Morning Glory'	MNew
moscheutos	CArn CHan CSun MSte
purpureus 'Variegatus'	SGly
rosa-sinensis	EBak MBri SLMG
– 'Casablanca'	CHal MBri
– 'Cooperi'	CHal MNew
¶ – 'El Capitolio'	MNew
¶ – 'Full Moon'	MNew
– 'Helene'	MBri
¶ – 'Herm Geller'	MNew
– 'Holiday'	MBri
– 'Kardinal'	MBri
– 'Koeniger'	CHal MBri
– 'Rose of China'	CHal MBri
– 'Tivoli'	MBri
– 'Weekend'	MBri MNew
rubis	ELan
schizopetalus	CTro MNew SLMG
sinosyriacus 'Autumn Surprise'	SHil
– 'Lilac Queen'	SHil
* – 'Red Centre'	CBot
– 'Ruby Glow'	MGos
syriacus	CHEx
¶ – 'Admiral Dewey'	CCla
– 'Ardens' (d)	ELan MRav SGil
– 'Blue Bird'	See H. ***s.*** 'Oiseau Bleu'
– 'Coelestis'	SPer
– 'Diana'	CSco EPla
– 'Dorothy Crane'	ENot
– 'Duc de Brabant' (d)	CBow SHBN SRms
– 'Elegantissimus'	See H. ***s.*** 'Lady Stanley'
– 'Hamabo'	CBow CBra CCla CDoC ELan ENot IHos MBri MGos MRav MWat SGil SHBN SPer SReu WStI
– 'Jeanne d'Arc' (d)	CBot
§ – 'Lady Stanley' (d)	CCla ECtt MPla NWyt SGil SPer SPla
– 'Meehanii'	EGol LGre SGly
– 'Monstrosus'	IOrc
§ – 'Oiseau Bleu' ('Blue Bird')	CB&S CBow CBra CCla CDoC CSco CShe EBlo ELan ENot EPla IHos IOrc MBri MGos MWat NBee NWyt SGil SHBN SHer SPer SPla SReu SSpi WDin WStI WTyr
– Pink Giant ®	CB&S CBow CCla EBlo ELan NWyt SGil SHer SPer WDin
– 'Red Heart'	CBow CCla CDoC CSco ECtt ELan MPla MRav MWat SHer SPer WDin WStI WWeb
– 'Russian Violet'	CBow CBra CCla CDoC CSco ELan MRav NWyt SGil SHer WWeb
– 'Speciosus'	SPer
* – 'Variegatus'	CBot MBri
– 'William R Smith'	CCla EBlo ELan ENot EPla SHBN SPer WWeb
– 'Woodbridge'	CB&S CBow CBra CCla CSco CShe ELan ENot IHos MBri MGos MRav MWat SHBN SHer SPer SPla SReu SSpi WStI
trionum	CArn CHad ECou LHop SLMG
– 'Spirits Bay'	ECou
– 'Sunny Day'	ELan WEas

HIERACIUM (Compositae)

alpinum	CTom
♦ *aurantiacum*	See PILOSELLA ***aurantiaca***
♦ *bombycinum*	See H. ***mixtum***
brunneocroceum	See PILOSELLA ***aurantiaca carpathicola***
candidum	LHil
* *glabrum*	WPer
§ *glaucum*	CFis CRiv MTol NHol WByw WEas WWin
§ *lanatum*	CCor CGle CMea CNic EBar ECro EHal NBir NBro NHol NWCA SUsu WCru WEas WHal WPer WWin
maculatum	CRow ECro EFol EHoe ELan EMar EPar EPla GGar LWad MFir MUlv MWat NCat NFai NSti SIng WCru WDav WOak WPer WWye
§ *mixtum*	NWCA
murorum	NWCA
pannosum NS 399	NWCA
♦ *pilosella*	See PILOSELLA ***officinarum***
♦ *praecox*	See H. ***glaucum***
scotostictum	EMon LRHS
sp. from Afghanistan	NKay
x *stoloniflorum*	See PILOSELLA ***stoloniflora***
variegatum	See HYPOCHAERIS ***variegata***
villosum	CChu CNic CRow CSam EFol EFou EHoe MSte NBro NNor SIng WCru WDav WEas WHer WPer WWin
waldsteinii	CHal MPar NHol NNor
welwitschii	See H. ***lanatum***

HIEROCHLOË (Gramineae)

odorata ETPC
redolens ETPC GAbr

HILDABERRY See RUBUS 'Hildaberry'

HIMALAYACALAMUS (Gramineae(Bambuseae))

§*falconeri* EFul EPla ISta LBam SBam SCob

HIPPEASTRUM (Liliaceae/Amaryllidaceae)

'Apple Blossom' LAma NRog
'Beautiful Lady' LAma
'Bestseller' LAma
♦*bifidum* See RHODOPHIALA *bifida*
'Bouquet' LAma
'Byjou' NRog
'Dutch Belle' LAma
'Fantastica' LAma
'Fire Dance' LAma
gracile 'Donau' ETub
– 'Pamela' ETub
'King of the Stripes' LAma
¶ 'Lady Jane' ETub
'Lucky Strike' LAma
'Ludwig's Goliath' LAma
'Maria Goretti' LAma
'Oskar' LAma NRog
papilio LAma NRog WChr
'Papillon' LAma
phycelloïdes CHan
'Picotee' LAma
♦*roseum* See RHODOPHIALA *rosea*
'Striped Vlammenspel' LAma
'United Nations' LAma
'Vera' LAma
'White Dazzler' LAma
'Wonderland' LAma
'Yellow Pioneer' LAma

HIPPOBROMA See LAURENTIA

HIPPOCREPIS (Leguminosae)

comosa CKin MWil WGwy
– 'E R Janes' EFol MPla
§ *emerus* CHan CMHG CPle CSco ECro EHal ELan ERea MBal SHil WAbe WKif

HIPPOLYTIA (Compositae)

§ *herderi* CFis EFol EMon LHop MPar NBro SAxl SChu SGil

HIPPOPHAË (Elaeagnaceae)

rhamnoïdes CB&S CBow CBra CKin CLnd CSco EBre ELan ENot GPoy GRei IHos IOrc LBre LBuc MBar MWat NWea SPer WDin WHCG WStI WWat
– 'Leikora' (f) EPla MGos
– 'Pollmix' (m) MGos
¶ *salicifolia* CLnd CPle SSpi

HIPPURIS (Hippuridaceae)

vulgaris CBen CRDP EHon EMFW SAWi WHol WWye

HIRPICIUM (Compositae)

armerioïdes SH 6 CHan

HISTIOPTERIS (Dennstaedtiaceae)

incisa EBul SSpi

HOHERIA (Malvaceae)

§ *angustifolia* CB&S CBot CChu CCla CHan SSpi WBod WSHC
glabrata CB&S CBot CSco ECou ISea MBal MBar SHil SPer SSpi
'Glory of Amlwch' CChu CGre CMHG CSam GCal MRav SSpi WSHC
§ *lyallii* CB&S CBow CChu CCla CDoC CMHG CSam CWSG ECou ELan GAbr IDai IOrc ISea SHBN SPer SReu SSpi SSta WBod WDin
microphylla See H. *angustifolia*
populnea CBot WBod
sexstylosa CBot CBow CCla CDoC CPle EHar ELan IOrc ISea LTil MUlv NNor NTow SHil SPer SSta
– var. *crataegifolia* CGre
*– *pendula* CB&S
– 'Stardust' SPla SSpi

HOLBOELLIA (Lardizabalaceae)

coriacea CBot CChu MGos SArc SBor SBra SHil WSHC
latifolia CGre CSam SArc SSpi

HOLCUS (Gramineae)

lanatus MWil
mollis 'Albovariegatus' CElw CLew CRow CShe ECha EHoe ELan EMon EPar ETPC GCHN MBar MFir NBro NHol NNrd NRed NSti SCob SPer SUsu WBon WEas WHil WWat

HOLODISCUS (Rosaceae)

discolor CBow CCla CDoC CPle EBar ELan EPla GCal MBlu SHBN SHil SLon SPla SSta WDin WHCG WSHC
dumosus CCor

HOMALOCLADIUM (Polygonaceae)

§ *platycladum* CHal

HOMERIA (Iridaceae)

♦*breyniana* See H. *collina*
– var. *aurantiaca* See H. *flaccida*
§ *collina* EPot WThi
comptonii EPot
§ *flaccida* LAma LBow NRog
¶ *marlothii* CMon
ochroleuca EPot LAma LBow NRog

HOMOGLOSSUM See GLADIOLUS

HOMOGYNE (Compositae)
See Plant Deletions

HOOKERIA (moss)
¶ *lucens* LFle

HORDEUM (Gramineae)
jubatum EHoe ETPC NSti
murinum CKin

HORMINUM (Labiatae)
pyrenaicum CPar CRiv ELan GDra MBro MFir MHig MTho NGre NHol NSti SBla SIng SSmi SSou WAbe WCla WHil WOMN WPat WPer WThu WWin
– pale blue MSte WDav

HOSTA † (Liliaceae/Hostaceae)
aequinoctiiantha EBul EGol
'Aksarben' EMic
♦ 'Alba' (*sieboldiana*) See H. 'Elegans Alba'
albomarginata See H. *sieboldii*
'Albomarginata' (*fortunei*) CB&S CRDP CWGN EBul EGol EMic EPGN GKit MBar NFai SHer WCru WHoo
'Allan P McConnell' (v) CBdn EGol EMic
'Alpine Aire' EMic
'Amanuma' EGol EMic
'Antioch' (*fortunei*) (v) CBdn EGol EMic
'Aoki' (*fortunei*) EMic EPGN NHol
¶ 'Aphrodite' (*plantaginea*) (d) EGol
'Apple Green' EMic
'Argentea Variegata' (*undulata*) See H. *undulata undulata*
'Aspen Gold' (*tokudama* x) EMic
'August Moon' CBdn CBro CHan CMHG CSam CWGN EBre EGol ELan EMic EOrc EPGN GKit LBre MBar MBri MUlv NBar NBee NFai NHol NJap NOrc SApp SMad SPla WCra WRus
'Aurea' (*sieboldii*) See H. *sieboldii subcrocea*
aureafolia See H. 'Starker Yellow Leaf'
'Aureoalba' (*fortunei*) See H. 'Spinners'
'Aureomaculata' (*fortunei*) See H. *fortunei albopicta*
§ 'Aureomarginata' (*montana*) CBdn CBow EGol EHoe EMic EPGN SApp SSpi WRus
– (*rohdeifolia*) See H. *rohdeifolia aureomarginata*
§ – (*ventricosa*) CBdn CHad EBre ECha EGol EMic EPGN ERav LBre NHol NRoo NSti SDix SHig SPer WRus
'Banyai's Dancing Girl' EMic
¶ 'Barbara White' EGol
♦ *bella* See H. *fortunei obscura*
'Bennie McRae' EGol
'Betsy King' CBdn EPGN GKit
'Big Daddy' (*sieboldiana*) CBow CBro COtt CRDP EBlo EBre ECtt EGol ELan EMic EOrc EPGN EPla ERav ESma GKit LBre MBri NBir NFai NHol NSti SApp SMad SPer WAbe WCra WCru WRus
¶ 'Big John' (*sieboldiana*) EGol
'Big Mama' (*sieboldiana* x) EGol EMic LRHS
§ 'Birchwood Parky's Gold' CBdn CBos CHad CHan CRiv CTom ECar EGol EMic EPGN GKit NHol SApp SAxl SSpi WCru
'Birchwood Ruffled Queen' EGol EMic
§ 'Blonde Elf' EGol EMic
'Blue Angel' (*sieboldiana*) CBdn CCMG ECha EGol EHoe ELan EMic EOrc EPGN MBal MTol MWat NHol NOrc SApp SFis WHoo
'Blue Belle' (x *tardiana*) ECha EGol EMic
'Blue Blush' (x *tardiana*) EGol
'Blue Boy' CHad EGol EMic EPGN NHol
'Blue Cadet' CBdn CHad ECha EGol EMic MBar WStI
'Blue Danube' (x *tardiana*) ECha EGol EMic
'Blue Diamond' (x *tardiana*) CHad EGol EMic NFai
'Blue Dimples' (x *tardiana*) EGol EMic LRHS
¶ 'Blue Edger' ECha
¶ 'Blue Heart' (*sieboldiana elegans*) ECha EMic
¶ 'Blue Lake' SGil
¶ 'Blue Mammoth' (*sieboldiana*) EMic
'Blue Moon' (x *tardiana*) CB&S CBro CChu CHad CMHG EBar EBlo EBre EFou EGol ELan EMic EOrc EPGN ESma LBre LGre LWad MBri NFai NHol SApp SHer SMad SSpi WCru WEas
'Blue Seer' (*sieboldiana*) EGol
'Blue Skies' (x *tardiana*) ECar EGol ELan EMic EPGN
'Blue Umbrellas' (*sieboldiana* x) EGol ELan EMic EOrc EPGN EPla GKit NHol NJap SPer
¶ 'Blue Vision' EPGN
'Blue Wedgwood' (x *tardiana*) CBow CBro CMHG CRow EGol ELan EMic EOrc EPla GKit MTol NHol SApp WCru WRus
'Bold Ribbons' (v) EGol EMic
'Bold Ruffles' (*sieboldiana*) EGol EMic GKit LRHS
'Bonanza' (*fortunei*) EMic
'Bountiful' EMic
'Bouquet' EGol
'Bressingham Blue' CWGN EBlo EBre ECtt EGol EMic EPla LBre NDea NMir SApp SAxl SHig SPer
'Bright Glow' (x *tardiana*) EGol EMic
'Bright Lights' (*tokudama*) (v) EGol EPGN
'Brim Cup' (v) CBdn EGol
'Brooke' EMic

Plant	Suppliers
¶ 'Brother Ronald' (x ***tardiana***)	EGol
¶ 'Bruces Blue'	EGol
'Buckshaw Blue'	CBdn EGol EMic EPGN MBal NBir SApp SAxl SDix WCot
'Butter Rim' (***sieboldii***) (v)	EGol
'Camelot' (x ***tardiana***)	EGol EMic
'Candy Hearts'	CBdn CHan ECar EGol EMic EPGN GKit
capitata	EBul EMic
caput-avis	See H. ***kikutii c-a.***
'Carol' (***fortunei***) (v)	CBdn EMic
'Carrie' (***sieboldii***) (v)	EMic
'Celebration' (v)	EGol ELan EMic EPGN SApp
'Challenger'	EMic
'Change of Tradition' (v)	EMic
'Chartreuse Wiggles' (***sieboldii***)	EGol
'Chinese Sunrise' (***cathayana***) (v)	CBdn EGol EMic EPGN NHol
¶ 'Chiquita'	EGol
'Christmas Tree' (v)	CBdn EGol EMic GKit LRHS
clausa	EMic
– var. ***normalis***	EGol EMic GCal SApp
'Color Glory' (***sieboldiana***) (v)	EGol
'Colossal'	EGol EMic LRHS
¶ 'County Park'	EGol
'Cream Delight' (***undulata***)	See H. ***undulata undulata***
'Crested Reef'	EGol EMic
§ ***crispula*** (v)	CB&S CBdn CHad CRow CSco CShe EBre EGol EHon EMic EOrc EPGN EPar LBre MBal NFai NHol SHig SSpi WTyr
¶ 'Crown Jewel'	EMic
'Crown Prince'	EMic
§ 'Crowned Imperial' (***fortunei***) (v)	CBdn EMic NHol
'Curlew' (x ***tardiana***)	ECha EMic
'Dawn'	EGol SApp
'Daybreak'	EGol
decorata (v)	EGol EMic LGro WPat
'Devon Blue' (x ***tardiana***)	CBdn CHad EGol EMic
¶ 'Devon Cream'	CBdn
¶ 'Devon Tor'	CBdn
'Diamond Tiara' (v)	EGol
¶ 'Dimple'	ECha
'Dorothy'	EMic
'Dorset Blue' (x ***tardiana***)	EMic SApp
'Dorset Charm' (x ***tardiana***)	EGol EMic MBal
'Dorset Flair' (x ***tardiana***)	EMic
'Drummer Boy'	EMic
elata	CBos EMic MUlv WWat
'Eldorado'	See H. 'Frances Williams'
'Elegans'	See H. ***sieboldiana elegans***
§ 'Elegans Alba' (***sieboldiana***)	EGol
'Elfin Power' (***sieboldii***) (v)	EMic
'Elizabeth Campbell' (***fortunei***) (v)	CBdn SApp
'Ellen'	EMic
'Ellerbroek' (***fortunei***) (v)	EMic
'Emerald Carpet'	EMic
'Emerald Skies'	EGol
'Emerald Tiara'	EGol LRHS
'Eric Smith' (x ***tardiana***)	EGol EMic GKit MUlv
'Eunice Choice'	EMic
'Evening Magic' (v)	EGol EMic
'Excitation'	EGol EMic GKit
¶ 'Fall Bouquet' (***longipes hypoglauca***)	EGol
'Fall Emerald'	EMic
'Feather Boa'	EMic
* 'Fenman's Fascination'	EMic
'Floradora'	CBdn EGol EMic
¶ 'Flower Power'	EGol
fluctuans	EMic NHol
– variegated	CBdn EGol EMic LRHS SApp
♦ 'Fortis'	See H. ***lancifolia***
fortunei	CBdn CBow CCla CHad CMHG CPar CRow CShe CWGN EGol EMic EOrc EPGN GKit MBal NDea NGre NHol SChu SHig SPer WCru WEas
§ – var. ***albopicta***	Widely available
§ – – f.***aurea***	CBdn CCla CHad CKel CRow ECha EGol EHoe ELan EMic EPGN EPla LHyd MBal SChu SHig SPer SPla SSpi WRus
– – f.***viridis***	GKit
– f. ***aurea***	See H. ***fortunei albopicta aurea***
§ – var. ***aureomarginata***	Widely available
♦– var. ***gigantea***	See H. ***montana***
§ – var. ***hyacinthina***	CBdn CCla CGle CHad CSco CTom EGol EMic EOrc EPGN EPla GGar GKit MBal MBar NBar NDea NSti SSpi WCru WRus WWin
– – variegated	See H. 'Crowned Imperial'
§ – var. ***obscura***	CShe EGol EMic LHyd WCru
– var. ***rugosa***	CHad EMic
'Fountain'	EMic NHol
'Fragrant Gold'	EGol EMic
'Francee' (***fortunei***) (v)	Widely available
§ 'Frances Williams' (***sieboldiana***) (v)	Widely available
'Frances Williams Improved' (***sieboldiana***) (v)	EGol
¶ 'Fresh' (v)	EGol
'Fringe Benefit' (v)	EBre EGol EMic EPGN LBre NHar NHol SApp
'Frosted Jade' (v)	CBdn EGol EMic GKit LRHS SApp
'Geisha' (v)	EGol
¶ 'Gene's Joy'	EPGN
'Gilt Edge' (***sieboldiana***) (v)	EMic
'Gingee'	EMic
'Ginko Craig' (v)	Widely available
glauca	See H. ***sieboldiana elegans***
'Gloriosa' (***fortunei***) (v)	EGol EMic
'Gold Drop'	CBdn EGol EMic
'Gold Edger'	Widely available
'Gold Flush' (***ventricosa***)	EMic
§ 'Gold Haze' (***fortunei***)	CHad EGol EMic EOrc EPGN NHol WCru
'Gold Leaf' (***fortunei***)	EGol

'Gold Regal'	CBdn EGol EMic
'Gold Standard' (*fortunei*) (v)	CBdn EBlo ECha EGol ELan EMic EPGN EPla GKit MNFA MWat NFai SApp SGil SWas WRus
'Goldbrook' (*fortunei*) (v)	EGol
¶ 'Goldbrook Genie'	EGol
'Goldbrook Glimmer' (x *tardiana*) (v)	EGol
¶ 'Goldbrook Gold'	EGol
'Goldbrook Grace'	EGol
♦ 'Golden' (*nakaiana*)	See H. 'Birchwood Parky's Gold'
'Golden Age'	See H. 'Gold Haze'
'Golden Bullion' (*tokudama*)	EMic
'Golden Circles'	See H. 'Frances Williams'
¶ 'Golden Isle'	EGol
'Golden Medallion' (*tokudama*)	CB&S CBdn CBow CBro EBar EBre EGol ELan EMic EOrc EPGN LBre MNFA NFai NHol NJap NSti SApp SMad SSpi
'Golden Nakaiana'	See H. 'Birchwood Parky's Gold'
'Golden Prayers' (*tokudama*)	CAbb CBdn CBow CBro CCMG CHad CRDP EGol ELan EMic EOrc EPGN LGre MBri NBar NBee NFai NHol NOrc SApp SChu SHer SIng SPer SPla SSpi WAbe WRus
'Golden Scepter' (*nakaiana*)	CBdn EGol EMic GKit SApp
'Golden Sculpture' (*sieboldiana*)	EGol
'Golden Spider'	EMic
'Golden Sunburst' (*sieboldiana*)	CBdn CHad CSco ECha EGol ELan EMic EPGN GGar MBal MBri NBar NHol NJap NRoo SApp SGil WCru WRus
'Golden Tiara' (v)	CBdn CHan EGol ELan EMic EPGN GKit LWad MNFA NFai NHar NHol NJap NSti SApp SSpi SWas WCru WRus
¶ 'Goldsmith'	EGol
'Good as Gold'	EMic
gracillima	CRow EBul EPGN EPar GKit LHyd MNFA NHar NHol NKay
¶ 'Grand Master'	EGol EPGN
'Great Expectations' (*sieboldiana*) (v)	EGol EPGN
'Green Acres' (*montana*)	EMic
'Green Fountain' (*kikutii*)	CBdn EGol EMic EPla
'Green Gold' (*fortunei*) (v)	CBdn EMic
'Green Piecrust'	EGol EMic LRHS
'Green Sheen'	EGol EMic GKit LRHS
'Green Smash'	EMic
'Greenwood'	EMic
'Ground Master' (v)	CBdn CBow CBro COtt EBre ECha ECtt EGol ELan EMic EOrc EPGN ESma GKit LBre LWad MBri MRav NBee NFai NHol NJap NOrc NSti SApp WAbe WCru WRus
'Ground Sulphur'	EGol EMic
'Gum Drop'	CBdn EMic
'Hadspen Blue' (x *tardiana*)	CCla CDoC CHad CMHG EBar EBre ECha EGol EMic EOrc EPGN EPla LBre NBro NHol NJap NSti SApp WRus
'Hadspen Blue Jay' (x *tardiana*)	CBro
'Hadspen Heron' (x *tardiana*)	CBdn CHad ECha EGol EMic EPGN GKit MBal
'Hadspen Samphire'	CHad CHan EGol EMic EPGN
'Hadspen Seersucker'	CHad
'Hadspen White' (*fortunei*)	EPGN
'Hakujima' (*sieboldii*)	EGol
§ 'Halcyon' (x *tardiana*)	Widely available
'Happiness' (x *tardiana*)	CBdn ECha EHoe EMic EPGN WCot
¶ 'Happy Hearts'	EGol
'Harmony' (x *tardiana*)	EGol EMic
'Harrison'	EMic
'Harvest Glow'	EGol LRHS
¶ 'Harvest Moon'	SApp
'Hazel'	EMic
'Heartleaf'	EMic
'Helen Doriot' (*sieboldiana*)	EGol EMic LRHS
helonioïdes f. ***albopicta*** hort.	See H. ***rohdeifolia***
'Herifu' (v)	EGol
'Hoarfrost'	EMic
'Holstein'	See H. 'Halcyon'
§ 'Honeybells'	Widely available
'Hydon Gleam'	EPGN
'Hydon Sunset' (*nakaiana*)	CBdn CCMG CHan CMHG EBar EGol EMic EOrc EPGN GKit LHyd MBal MBri NFai NHol NOrc NSti SApp SIng SSpi WAbe WWat
hypoleuca	EGol LRHS
§ 'Inaho'	EGol EMic EPGN
'Invincible'	CBdn EGol EMic EPGN SApp
'Iona' (*fortunei*)	EGol
'Jade Scepter' (*nakaiana*)	EGol EMic
'Janet' (*fortunei*) (v)	EGol EMic EOrc NHol
'Japan Boy'	See H. 'Montreal'
'Japan Girl'	See H. 'Mount Royal'
'Julie Morss'	EGol EMic
'Jumbo' (*sieboldiana*)	EMic
¶ 'June' (x *tardiana*) (v)	CBdn EGol EPGN SApp SMad
'Kabitan'	See H. ***sieboldii kabitan***
'Kath's Gold'	CBdn EMic
¶ 'Kelly'	SApp
'Kelsey'	EMic
kikutii	EGol EMic
– var. ***caput-avis***	EGol EMic
– var. ***polyneuron***	EBul
– var. ***pruinosa***	EGol LRHS
– var. ***yakusimensis***	EGol EMic GDra GKit
¶ 'Kirishima'	NKay
kiyosumiensis	CRow EBul NHol
'Klopping Variegated' (*fortunei*)	EMic
'Krinkled Joy'	EMic
'Krossa Regal'	Widely available
'Lady Helen'	EMic

Plant	Suppliers
§ *lancifolia*	Widely available
'Leather Sheen'	EGol EMic LRHS
'Lemon Lime'	CRiv CWGN EGol EMic SApp
¶ 'Leola Fraim' (v)	EGol
* *lilacina*	SCro
'Little Aurora'	EGol EMic MBal
'Little Blue' (*ventricosa*)	CBdn EGol EMic
'Little Razor'	EGol EMic
'Little White Lines' (v)	EGol EMic
longipes	EGol SApp
– var. *longipes*	EBul
longissima	EBul EGol EPla LHyd NHol WCru WWin
– var. *longissima*	EMic LHyd
'Louisa' (*sieboldii*) (v)	ECha EGol EPGN MSte NHol NNrd
'Love Pat' (*tokudana*)	CBdn EGol EMic
'Lucky Charm'	EMic
'Lunar Eclipse' (v)	EGol EMic GKit LRHS SApp SSpi
'Maculata'	EMic
¶ 'Maculata Aurea'	SCro
'Maekawa'	EGol
'Maple Leaf'	GKit
N 'Marginata Alba' (*fortunei*)	CBdn CBot CHad CKel ECha LMay NDea SPer SPla WAbe WWin
'Marilyn'	EGol EMic
'Mary Jo'	EMic
'Mary Marie Ann' (*fortunei*) (v)	EMic
'Mediovariegata' (*undulata*)	See H. ***undulata undulata***
'Mentor Gold'	EMic
'Midas Touch' (*tokudama* x)	EGol EMic EPGN EPla ESma GKit NBar NFai NHol NJap NVic SApp WRus
'Middle Ridge'	EMic
'Mildred Seaver'	CBdn EGol LRHS
'Minnie Klopping'	EMic SApp
§ *minor*	CBro CTom EGol ELan EMic EPot GDra NHol NTow SPou WBon WWin
– f. *alba* hort.	See H. ***sieboldii alba***
'Misty Waters' (*sieboldiana*)	EMic
'Moerheim' (*fortunei*) (v)	EGol EPGN EPar MBri NHol SApp WCru
N *montana*	CHad ECha EGol EMic NHol SApp
'Montreal'	EMic
'Moon Glow' (v)	EGol EMic EPGN LRHS
'Moonlight' (*fortunei*) (v)	EGol EMic
'Mount Kirishima' (*sieboldii*)	See H. 'Kirishima'
'Mount Royal' (*sieboldii*)	EMic
'Mountain Snow' (*montana*) (v)	EGol EMic
nakaiana	EMic NHol SIng WCru
'Nakaimo'	EMic NHol WCru
'Nameoki'	NHol
'Nana' (*ventricosa*)	See H. ***minor***
§ 'Nancy Lindsay' (*fortunei*) (v)	EMic SApp
'Neat Splash Rim' (v)	EMic
'New Wave'	EMic
'Nicola' (x *tardiana*)	EGol EMic EPGN WCot
nigrescens	EGol EMic GCal LRHS
'Nokogiryama'	EMic
'North Hills' (*fortunei*) (v)	EMic NBir
'Northern Halo' (*sieboldiana*) (v)	EGol ELan EMic SApp
'Northern Lights' (*sieboldiana*)	EGol LRHS
'Northern Sunray' (*sieboldiana*) (v)	EMic
'Obscura Marginata' (*fortunei*)	See H. ***f. aureomarginata***
'Olga's Shiny Leaf'	EGol EMic
¶ 'On Stage' (*montana*) (v)	CBdn
'Oriana' (*fortunei*)	CBdn EGol EMic
'Osprey' (x *tardiana*)	EGol
'Oxheart'	EMic
pachyscapa	EMic
¶ 'Pacific Blue Edge'	SApp
¶ 'Parker Jervis Blue'	NFai
'Pastures New'	CBdn EGol EMic EPGN NHol SApp
'Paul's Glory' (v)	EGol EMic
'Pearl Lake'	CBdn EGol EMic GKit NHol SApp SSpi
'Pelham Blue Tump'	EGol SApp
'Perry's True Blue'	EMic
'Peter Pan'	EMic
♦ 'Phyllis Campbell' (*fortunei*)	See H. 'Sharmon'
'Picta' (*fortunei*)	See H. ***f. albopicta***
'Piedmont Gold'	CBdn EBre EGol EMic EPGN EPla GKit LBre
'Pineapple Poll'	EMic EPGN
'Pizzazz' (v)	EGol EPGN
plantaginea	CBdn CBrd CWGN EGol EMic ERav MPar SApp SAxl
§ – var. *japonica*	CBot CGle CHan CSco ECha EMic EPar SApp SSpi WPat WWat
'Purple Dwarf'	GKit NHar NHol WCra
'Purple Profusion'	EMic
rectifolia	CMHG EMic NHol WKif
'Regal Splendor' (v)	EGol EMic
'Resonance' (v)	EMic SApp
'Reversed' (v)	EMic EPGN NHol
'Richland Gold' (*fortunei*)	CBdn EGol EMic LRHS
'Rippling Waves'	EMic
'Robusta' (*fortunei*)	See H. ***sieboldiana elegans***
§ *rohdeifolia* (v)	EGol EMic MPar
§ – f. *albopicta*	CBdn EGol ELan EPGN EPar MPar NHol
'Rosanne'	EMic
'Royal Standard'	CBdn CBro CCla CHad CPar CRow CSco EBlo ECha EGol ELan EMic ENot EPGN EPla GKit LHyd MBal MPar NHol NJap SDix SPer SPla WAbe WRus WTyr
¶ 'Royalty'	EGol
rupifraga	EMic GKit
¶ 'Russell's Form' (*ventricosa*)	EMic
'Ryan's Big One'	EMic LRHS
§ 'Saishu Jima' (*sieboldii spathulata*)	ECar EGol NHol WCru
'Samual Blue'	EMic
'Samurai' (*sieboldiana*) (v)	CBdn EMic

'Sazanami' (***crispula***)	See H. ***crispula***
'Sea Dream' (v)	EGol LRHS
'Sea Drift'	EGol EMic
¶ 'Sea Fire'	EGol
'Sea Gold Star'	EGol EMic LRHS
'Sea Lotus Leaf'	EGol LRHS
'Sea Monster'	EGol LRHS
'Sea Octopus'	EGol EMic
¶ 'Sea Sapphire'	EGol
'Sea Yellow Sunrise'	CBdn EGol EMic LRHS
'See Saw' (***undulata***)	EGol EMic
'September Sun' (v)	EGol
'Serendipity'	CBdn EGol EMic
'Shade Fanfare' (v)	CBdn CBro COtt EBlo EBre ECar ECha EGol ELan EMic EOrc EPGN GKit LBre MBal MBri MNFA MRav MWat NFai NHar NJap NRoo SApp SCro SPer WHoo
'Shade Master'	EMic NHol
'Sharmon' (***fortunei***) (v)	EMic EPla GKit NHol WCru
'Sherbourne Profusion' (x ***tardiana***)	EMic
'Sherbourne Songbird' (x ***tardiana***)	EMic
'Sherbourne Swan' (x ***tardiana***)	EMic
'Sherbourne Swift' (x ***tardiana***)	CBdn EMic GKit
'Shining Tot'	CBdn EGol
¶ 'Shogun' (v)	EGol
sieboldiana	CHad CHan CKel CMHG CRow CShe EGol ELan EMic EOrc EPot GKit IBar IDai LHyd MBal NBar NHol NNor SHig SPer WAbe WHil WWat
§ – var. ***elegans***	Widely available
§ ***sieboldii*** (v)	CMGP EBre EBul ECha EGol EMic EPGN GKit IDai LBre LHyd MBal MFir MRav NKay SApp SBla SFis WPer WRus
§ – var. ***alba***	CBdn CBos CCla CHad CHan CMGP CRiv EGol ELan EMic NHar SSpi
– f. ***kabitan*** (v)	CBdn EGol EMic EPGN LRHS
– f. ***shiro-kabitan*** (v)	EGol EMic EPGN
– var. ***thunbergiana***	See H. ***sieboldii spathulata***
'Silver Lance' (v)	EGol EMic
'Snow Cap' (v)	EGol
'Snow Crust' (***elata***) (v)	EMic
'Snowden'	CBdn CHad CMHG COtt EBre ECha EGol EMic EPGN LBre MBal NHol SApp SSpi WRus
'Snowflakes' (***sieboldii***)	EGol EPGN GCal MBri NHol
'So Sweet'	CBdn EGol EMic
'Special Gift'	EMic
§ 'Spinners' (***fortunei***) (v)	CBdn CHad ECha EGol EMic SApp SSpi
'Spritzer' (v)	EGol EPGN
¶ 'Squiggles' (v)	EGol
'Starker Yellow Leaf'	EMic
'Stenantha Aureomarginata' (***fortunei***)	EMic
'Sugar and Cream' (v)	CBdn EGol EMic EPGN GKit SApp SGil
'Sugar Plum Fairy' (***gracillima***)	EGol EMic
'Sum and Substance'	CBdn EBre EGol EMic EPGN ESma LBre MUlv NHol SApp
'Summer Fragrance'	EGol EMic GKit LRHS
'Sun Glow'	EMic
'Sun Power'	CBdn CBro EGol EMic EPGN GKit MWat NJap SApp SPer WRus
'Sundance' (***fortunei***) (v)	CBdn EGol EMic
¶ 'Super Bowl'	EGol
'Suzuki Thumbnail'	EMic
'Sweet Susan'	EMic GKit MUlv SPer
'Sweetheart'	EMic
'Tall Boy'	CBdn CMHG ECha EGol EMic EPGN GCal NHol SPer SSpi
'Tall Twister'	EMic
x ***tardiana***	CBro CCla CMGP CRiv CShe EBre EGol ELan EPla LBre MBal NHol SHig SPer SSpi WAbe WKif
tardiflora	CBos CSco EGol EMic EPla MBal NHol NKay SPer
tardiva 'Aureostriata'	See H. 'Inaho'
'The Twister'	EMic GKit
'Thomas Hogg'	See H. ***undulata albomarginata***
tibae	EMic
'Tiny Tears' (***venusta***)	EGol EMic LRHS
tokudama	CBdn CChu CHad EGol ELan EPGN ERav IHos MBri NBar NFai NHar NHol NSti SApp SChu SPer SPla SSpi WAbe WCru WKif WRus WWat
§ – f. ***aureonebulosa***	CBdn EGol EMic EPGN GKit MPar
– f. ***flavocircinalis*** (v)	ECha EGol EMic
'Tot Tot'	EMic
'Trail's End'	EMic
'True Blue'	CBdn EMic EPGN
'Twinkle Toes'	EMic
undulata (v)	CBow CMGP EMic NDea SApp
§ – var. ***albomarginata***	Widely available
– var. ***erromena***	CBdn CBow CCla CHad CHan CWGN EHon EMic EPGN EPla GKit LMay MNFA MPlt NHol NKay SChu SPer WAbe
§ – var. ***undulata*** (v)	Widely available
– var. ***univittata*** (v)	CRow ECha EGol EMic EPGN EPla GKit LHyd NFai SApp SPla WKif
'Valentine Lace'	EGol EMic
'Vanilla Cream' (***cathayana***)	EGol EMic
'Variegata' (***gracillima***)	See H. 'Shirofukurin'
– (***tokudama***)	See H. ***tokudama aureonebulosa***
– (***undulata***)	See H. ***undulata undulata***
– (***ventricosa***)	See H. 'Aureomarginata' (*ventricosa*)
ventricosa	CB&S CBdn CBro CHad CKel CSco CTom EBre EGol EMic EPGN ERav GDra LBre LHyd LMay NHar NHol SDix SHig WWat
– var. ***aureomaculata***	CCla CHad EGol EMic EPGN SPla WCru WRus
– ***minor***	See H. ***minor***
I 'Venucosa'	EMic
venusta	Widely available
¶ – dwarf form	LGre
¶ – x ***sieboldiana***	CHan
– ***yakusimensis***	See H. ***kikutii y.***
N 'Venusta Variegated'	EGol
♦ 'Vera Verde' (v)	See H. 'Shirofukurin'
'Vilmoriniana'	EMic

'Viridis Marginata'	See H. ***sieboldii kabitan***
'Wagtail' (x ***tardiana***)	EMic
'Wayside Blue'	EMic
'Wayside Perfection'	See H. 'Royal Standard'
'Weihenstephan' (***sieboldii***)	GKit
¶ 'White Gold'	EGol
'Wide Brim' (v)	CBdn CBow CCla CDoC EBlo ECtt EGol EHoe ELan EMic EOrc EPGN EPla ESma GKit LWad MBal MBri MWat NBro NFai NHol NJap SApp WAbe WCru WRus
¶ 'Wind River Gold'	SApp
'Windsor Gold'	See H. 'Nancy Lindsay'
'Wogon' (***sieboldii***)	CRDP CRow ECha EFou EGol EMic EPGN EPar EPla GKit NHar NHol SApp WCru
'Wogon Giboshi'	See H. 'Wogon'
'Wrinkles and Crinkles'	LRHS
'Yellow Boa'	EMic
'Yellow Edge' (***fortunei***)	See H. ***f. aureomarginata***
– (***sieboldiana***)	See H. 'Frances Williams'
'Yellow River' (***montana***) (v)	EGol LRHS
'Yellow Splash' (v)	ECha EPGN SApp
'Yellow Splash Rim' (v)	EGol EMic
'Zager Blue'	EMic
'Zager Green'	EMic
'Zounds'	CDoC CHad CMHG EBre EFou EGol EHoe ELan EMic EOrc EPGN GKit IHos LBre MBri NBee NFai NHol NJap NOrc NSti SApp SCro SGil SMad WAbe WRus WWat

HOTTONIA (Primulaceae)

palustris	CBen CWGN EHon ELan EMFW LMay MSta NDea SAWi SWat

HOUSTONIA (Rubiceae)

caerulea Hort.	See H. ***michauxii***
– Linnaeus	CLew CRiv CSam EBar ELan GGar MPit MPla NGre NMen WAbe WOld WWin
– ***alba***	CLew NHol NTow WPer
'Fred Millard'	EPot NHol SIng WHoo

HOUTTUYNIA (Saururaceae)

cordata	CBow CFis CHal CHan CTom IBlr MUlv SWat
– 'Chameleon' (v)	Widely available
– 'Flore Pleno'	Widely available
– 'Tricolor' (v)	See H. ***c.*** 'Chameleon'
– ***variegata***	IBar IBlr MPit NDea NVic WByw WChe WHol

HOVENIA (Rhamnaceae)

acerba	CMCN
dulcis	CB&S CMCN CPle ELan

HOWEA (Palmae)

forsteriana	LPal MBri

HOYA † (Asclepiadaceae)

¶ ***angustifolia***	MNew
¶ ***archboldiana***	MNew
¶ ***arnottiana***	SLMG
§ ***australis***	CTro MNew SLMG
bandaensis	CTro SLMG
¶ ***bilobata***	MNew
carnosa	CB&S CHal CMer CTro EBak ERea LAbb MNew NRog SHer SLMG
– 'Compacta'	CB&S MBri SLMG
– 'Exotica'	SLMG
*– 'Jungle Garden'	SLMG
– 'Krinkle Eight'	SLMG
– 'Nana'	CHal
¶ – 'Prolifica'	SLMG
– 'Red Princess'	MBri
– 'Rubra'	SLMG
– 'Variegata'	CB&S CHal MBri SLMG
¶ ***crassicaulis***	MNew
¶ ***cumingiana***	MNew
¶ ***curtisii***	MNew
♦ ***darwinii*** hort.	See H. ***australis***
engleriana	SLMG
fusca 'Silver Knight'	SLMG
♦ ***fuscomarginata***	See H. ***pottsii***
imperialis	MNew SLMG
¶ ***ischnopus***	MNew
¶ ***kenejiana***	MNew
¶ ***kerrii***	MNew
¶ ***lacunosa***	MNew
lanceolata ssp. ***bella***	CB&S CHal ERea LAbb MBri NRog SLMG
linearis	MNew
longifolia	MNew
¶ ***macgillivrayi***	MNew
¶ ***meredithii***	MNew
motoskei	CTro MNew
multiflora	CTro MBri MNew
* ***neocaledonica***	CTro LAbb SLMG
¶ ***nicholsoniae***	MNew
¶ ***obovata***	MNew
¶ ***parasitica*** var. ***citrina***	MNew
¶ ***pauciflora***	MNew
polyneura	CTro MNew SLMG
¶ ***pottsii***	MNew
pubicalyx 'Red Buttons'	CHal CTro MNew SLMG
¶ ***purpureofusca***	CTro
¶ ***serpens***	MNew
shepherdii	MNew
'Shibata'	MNew
¶ ***uncinata***	MNew

HUGUENINIA (Cruciferae)

alpina	See H. ***tanacetifolia***

HUMATA See DAVALLIA

HUMEA (Compositae)

elegans	See CALOMERIA ***amaranthoïdes***

HUMULUS (Cannabaceae)

japonicus	ISea NHex NSal
lupulus	CArn CB&S CBow CRDP CSFH GAri GPoy ILis LHol MHew NSal SIde WHer WWye
– 'Aureus'	Widely available
– 'Fuggle'	GPoy

- 'Hip-Hop' EMon
- 'Wye Challenger' GPoy

HUTCHINSIA See THLASPI

HYACINTHELLA (Liliaceae/Hyacinthaceae)

acutiloba EPot LAma WChr
heldreichii WChr
lineata LRHS WChr
¶– M&T 5048 CMon
millingenii WChr
¶***pallens*** ETub

HYACINTHOÏDES (Liliaceae/Hyacinthaceae)

§***hispanica*** CAvo CBro IBlr MBri NHol SIng
¶– ***algeriensis*** AB&S 4337 CMon
– 'Azalea' LBlo
– 'Danube' ('Donau') LBow
– 'Excelsior' ETub
– 'La Grandesse' CBro
– 'Mount Everest' LBlo
– 'Myosotis' LBlo
– 'Queen of the Pinks' LBow
– 'Rosabella' CBro
– 'White City' LBow
¶***italica*** CMon
– ***vicentina alba*** WChr
§***non-scripta*** CAvo CBro CKin EPar ERav ETub GDra IBlr LAma LBlo LBow LFox MBri NLan NMir NRog NSel SIng WCla WShi
– pink bell LBlo
– white bell LBlo

HYACINTHUS † (Liliaceae/Hyacinthaceae)

amethystinus See BRIMEURA ***amethystina***
azureus See MUSCARI ***azureum***
comosus 'Plumosus' See MUSCARI ***comosum*** 'Plumosum'
orientalis 'Amethyst' LAma NRog
– 'Amsterdam' ETub LAma NRog
– 'Anna Liza' NRog
– 'Anna Marie' CBro ETub LAma LBlo MBri NRog
– 'Apollo' LBlo
– 'Ben Nevis' (d) LAma MBri NRog
– 'Bismarck' LAma NRog
– 'Blue Giant' LAma NRog
– 'Blue Jacket' CBro ETub LAma LBlo NRog
– 'Blue Magic' LAma LBlo NRog
– 'Blue Orchid' (d) LAma
– 'Blue Star' LAma
– 'Blushing Dolly' LBlo
– 'Borah' LAma NRog
– 'Carnegie' CBro ETub LAma LBlo NRog
– 'Cherry Blossom' LBlo
– 'Chestnut Flower' (d) ETub
– 'City of Haarlem' CBro ETub LAma LBlo NRog
– 'Colosseum' LAma
– 'Concorde' LAma LBlo
– 'Debutante' LBlo
– 'Delft Blue' CBro ETub LAma LBlo MBri NRog
– 'Distinction' LAma LBlo
– 'Edelweiss' LAma
– 'Fireball' LBlo
– 'Fondant' LAma
– 'Gipsy Queen' LAma LBlo MBri NRog
– 'Grace Darling' LBlo
– 'Hollyhock' (d) ETub LAma LBlo MBri NRog
– 'Indian Prince' LBlo
– 'Jan Bos' ETub LAma LBlo NRog
– 'King Codro' (d) LAma MBri NRog
– 'King of the Blues' LAma NRog
– 'La Victoire' LAma NRog
– 'Lady Derby' LAma LBlo
– 'Lord Balfour' LAma LBlo
– 'L'Innocence' CBro LAma LBlo NRog
– 'Madame Krüger' LAma
– 'Marconi' (d) LAma NRog
– 'Marie' LAma NRog
– 'Maryon' LBlo
– 'Morning Star' LBlo
– 'Mulberry Rose' LAma NRog
– 'Myosotis' LAma
– 'Orange Queen' LBlo
– 'Oranje Boven' ETub LAma LBlo
– 'Ostara' CBro ETub LAma LBlo MBri NRog
– 'Paul Hermann' LBlo
– 'Peter Stuyvesant' NRog
– 'Pink Pearl' CBro ETub LAma LBlo NRog
– 'Pink Royal' (d) LAma NRog
¶– 'Pink Surprise' ETub
– 'Princess Margaret' LAma
– 'Princess Victoria' LBlo
– 'Prins Hendrik' LAma
– 'Queen of the Pinks' LAma NRog
– 'Queen of the Violets' NRog
– 'Rosalie' NRog
– 'Rosette' (d) LAma NRog
– 'Salmonetta' See H. ***o.*** 'Oranje Boven'
– 'Sky Jacket' LBlo
– 'Sneeuwwitje' ('Snow White') LAma LBlo NRog
– 'Violet Pearl' CBro ETub LAma LBlo NRog
– 'Vuurbaak' LAma
– 'White Pearl' LAma NRog

HYDRANGEA † (Hydrangeaceae)

anomala CChu
§– ssp. ***petiolaris*** Widely available
§– – ***cordifolia*** CChu CHan EBar EPla SReu SSta WWeb
– – ***tiliifolia*** MBlu SSpi WSHC
– – dwarf form See H. ***a. p. cordifolia***
§***arborescens*** CArn NNor WWeb
– 'Annabelle' CAbb CB&S CBow CCla COtt ELan ENot EPla ERav IJoh IOrc ISea LHop MBri MGos MPla NHar NHol NSti SBod SHBN SMad SPer SPla SSpi SSta WDin WPat
– ssp. ***discolor*** 'Sterilis' EPla SGil SPla SSpi
– 'Grandiflora' CB&S CBot CBow CCla ELan IJoh SBod SPer SReu SSpi WBod WDin WSHC WWin
– 'Hills of Snow' SSpi
– ssp. ***radiata*** CHan ELan MAsh NHlc SSpi WCru WWat
aspera CBow CGre CSco IOrc MBar SChu SDry SPer SSpi SSta WCru

– Kawakamii Group	EPla LRHS
– var. ***macrophylla***	CBow CCla EPla MBri NRar SSpi WBod
– 'Mauvette'	CBow MBlu SSpi SSta
– ssp. ***robusta***	EPla GAri SDry WCru
– 'Rocklon'	SSpi
§ – ssp. ***sargentiana***	CAbP CB&S CBot CBow CCla CHEx COtt CSco EHar ELan LTil MBal MBlu MBri SArc SBor SHBN SHil SMad SPer SSpi SSta WBod WCru WDin WKif WWat
– ssp. ***strigosa***	CDoC
– 'Taiwan'	NHlc SSpi
§ – Villosa Group	Widely available
§ 'Blue Deckle' (L)	CCla CMHG CSco EBar EPla NHlc SPla SSpi
cinerea	See H. ***arborescens discolor***
§ 'Grant's Choice' (L)	NHlc SSpi
heteromalla	CBot CCla SMrm SPer
– Bretschneideri Group	CB&S CChu CMCN EHal GAri NHlc SPer SSta WBod WWat
– 'Snowcap'	EArb EHar NHlc SHil
– f. ***xanthoneura***	CBot GAri WSHC
– 'Yelung Ridge'	NHlc
hirta	CPle
integerrima	See H. ***serratifolia***
involucrata	CBow CCla MBal MPla NHlc SDry SHil SSpi SSta WCru
– 'Hortensis' (d)	CBow CHan CPle IOrc SHer SHil SSpi WBod WKif WSHC
macrophylla 'Aduarda'	SSpi
– 'Alpenglühen' ('Alpen Glow') (H)	ELan ENot ESis IOrc NHar NHlc SBod SHBN SHer SPla WBod
– 'Altona' (H)	CB&S CSco EPla GAri IOrc ISea MBal MGos MRav NHlc NKay NRoo SBod SPer SReu
– 'Amethyst' (H/d)	SSpi
– 'Ami Pasquier' (H)	CB&S CSco EPla IOrc NHlc SHer SSpi
– 'Aureovariegata'	SMad
– 'Ayesha' (H)	CAbb CB&S CBot CBra CChu CCla CDec CGre CHan CMHG CPle CSco CTrw EBre EPla LBre MRav SBod SChu SDix SHBN SMad SPer SPla SSpi WBod WHil
– 'Beauté Vendômoise' (H)	SSpi
– 'Belzonii' (L)	NHlc
– 'Benelux' (H)	CB&S IJoh WAbe
– 'Beni-gaku'	SSpi
– 'Blauer Prinz' ('Blue Prince') (H)	CB&S EBre IJoh IOrc LBre NHlc SHBN
– 'Blaumeise' (L)	NHlc
– 'Blue Bonnet' (H)	MAsh MGos SPer
– 'Blue Wave' (L)	See H. ***m.*** 'Mariesii Perfecta'
– 'Bodensee' (H)	ELan MRav SBod SHer SPla WStI WWeb
– 'Bouquet Rose' (H)	CSco ECtt EHal MGos
♦– 'Cordata'	See H. ***arborescens***
– 'Deutschland' (H)	IOrc
¶ – 'Domotoi' (H)	EPla
*– 'Dwaag Pink'	WWeb
– 'Enziandom' ('Gentian Dome') (H)	CB&S EPla SPla SSpi WAbe
– 'Europa' (H)	CB&S CTrw IOrc MGos MRav NHlc SBod SGil WStI
– 'Forever Pink'	EPla MAsh
¶ – 'Frillibet' (H)	EPla
– 'Générale Vicomtesse de Vibraye' (H)	CB&S CBot CMHG IDai ISea MBal MBar MBri NHlc SHBN SLon SPer SReu SSpi WAbe WBod WWin
– 'Geoffrey Chadbund' (L)	CB&S CBow CCla CSco ECtt EPla IHos MBri NHlc SAxl SBod SChu SDix SHer SMad SPer SSpi SSta WWeb
– 'Glowing Embers'	SSpi
– 'Goliath' (H)	MBri SSpi
– 'Hamburg' (H)	CB&S CSco ECtt ENot IDai IOrc MGos MPla NBee NHlc NKay SDix SLon WAbe WStI
– 'Harry's Pink Topper' (H)	MAsh
– 'Hatfield Rose' (H)	CB&S CDoC
– 'Heinrich Seidel' (H)	CB&S CDoC NHlc
– 'Holstein' (H)	COtt IDai MAsh NBee NRoo SPla
– 'Intermezzo'	WWeb
♦– 'James Grant'	See H. 'Grant's Choice'
– 'Joseph Banks' (H)	See H. ***m.*** 'Otaksa'
*– 'Khudnert'	WWeb
– 'King George' (H)	CB&S CSco EBre ENot IDai IOrc LBre MBar MGos MRav NHlc SPer WStI WWeb
– 'Kluis Superba' (H)	CB&S CPle CSco IOrc MRav NHlc WAbe
– 'Koningin Wilhelmina' ('Queen Wilhelmina') (H)	CDoC SSpi
– 'La France' (H)	EHal MBar SGil WWeb
– 'Lanarth White' (L)	CB&S CCla CSco MPla MRav NHlc SDix SHBN SLon SPer SReu SSpi WBod WWeb
§ – 'Le Cygne' (H)	MBri MGos WBod
§ – 'Libelle' (L)	CB&S CCla MBri MPla NBar NHlc NSti SPer SSpi WKif
– 'Lilacina' (L)	CCla CGre EPla NHlc SPer SSpi
§ – 'Maculata' (L)	EFol ELan EPla IOrc LAbb LHop MPla NKay WWat
¶ – 'Madame A Riverain'	COtt SBod
– 'Madame Emile Mouillère' (H)	CB&S CBot CCla CHan CSco ENot IDai IOrc MBri MPla NHlc SAxl SBod SChu SDix SGil SHBN SHer SLon SMad SPer SSta WBod
*– 'Magic Light'	MBri
– 'Maréchal Foch' (H)	IOrc
– 'Mariesii' (L)	CBot CCla CMHG ELan ENot IDai ISea MBal NBee NHlc NKay SAxl SDix SHil SLon SPer SSpi WKif WStI WWat
§ – 'Mariesii Perfecta' (L)	CBot CMHG CPle CSco ELan ENot IDai IJoh ISea MBri MGos MRav NKay SAxl SDix SPer WBod WStI
– 'Mariesii Variegata' (L)	WAbe
– 'Masja' (H)	COtt IHos IOrc MBri MGos SHBN WBod
– 'Mathilda Gutges' (H)	MPla SSpi WAbe WStI WWeb
– 'Miss Belgium' (H)	IDai IOrc MBal MBri MUlv SBod
– 'Miss Hepburn'	COtt LRHS SPer
– 'Niedersachsen' (H)	CDoC EPla MRav SSpi
– 'Nigra' (H)	CChu CCla CGre CHan CPle CTre ELan EPla IOrc ISea MBal SChu SDix SHBN SLon SPer SPla SSpi SSta WAbe WStI
– 'Nikko Blue'	CB&S SSpi
– var. ***normalis***	NHlc

– 'Regula' (H)	CTrw SPla
– 'Rheinland' (H)	WBod
– 'Rosita' (H)	MAsh
– 'Rotdressel'	SSpi
– 'Rotsawana'	SSpi
¶ – 'Saint Claire'	CB&S
– 'Sea Foam' (L)	EPla IJoh IOrc NHlc
– 'Seascape'	NHlc
– 'Sibylla' (H)	CB&S MPla NHlc WAbe
– 'Sir Joseph Banks'	See H. ***m.*** 'Otaksa'
– 'Soeur Thérèse' ('Sister Therese') (H)	CB&S CPle GAri IOrc MAsh MGos WBod WStI WWeb
– 'Souvenir du Président Paul Doumer' (H)	CB&S CSco
¶ – 'Taube'	CB&S
*– 'Teller's Blue'	MBri NHlc WDin
*– 'Teller's Red'	IHos MBri WDin
♦– 'Teller's Variegated'	See H. ***m.*** 'Tricolor'
♦– 'Teller's White'	See H. ***m.*** 'Libelle'
– 'Tokyo Delight'	CBrd IOrc NHlc SBla SSpi
– 'Tovelit'	EPla GAri MBri SMad
§ – 'Tricolor' (L/v)	CB&S CBot CBow CBra CCla CRDP EPla ERav ISea MAsh MBri MGos MTho SBod SChu SLon SPer SReu SSpi WCru WKif
– 'Variegata'	See H. ***m.*** 'Maculata'
– 'Veitchii' (L)	CBot CCla CGre CHan CMHG CSco ENot IJoh LTil MBri SAxl SBod SDix SSpi WBod WWat
– 'Vicomte de Vibraye'	See H. ***macrophylla*** 'Générale Vicomtesse de Vibraye'
– 'Westfalen' (H)	NHlc SDix SPla SSpi
– 'White Lace' (L)	ELan
♦– 'White Swan' (H)	See H. ***m.*** 'Le Cygne'
– 'White Wave' (L)	CCla CPle CSco ENot MBar SBod SHBN SPer SPla SSpi WDin WStI
– 'Wryneck' (H)	NHlc
paniculata	CMCN CPle CTrw SLon
– 'Brussels Lace'	CKni MAsh SPla SSpi
– 'Floribunda'	CCla SPer SSpi
– 'Grandiflora'	CBot CCla CSco ELan ENot GRei IOrc MBal MBar MBri MGos MWat NHlc NKay NNor NRoo SBod SHBN SLon SMad SPer SReu SSta WAbe WBod WDin
– 'Kyushu'	CAbb CB&S CCla COtt CPMA CSco EBlo EBre ECtt ELan EPla ERav GCHN IOrc LBre LTil MBlu MBri MGos NBee NHar NHlc NRoo SPer SPla SSpi SSta WPat WWat
– 'Pink Diamond'	EBlo EBre EHar LBre LRHS MAsh SMad
– 'Praecox'	CCla CSco ENot IDai NKay SDix SPer SSpi WWin
– 'Tardiva'	CB&S CBot CBow CCla CSam CSco EHar EPla MRav NHlc SDix SHil SPer SPla SSpi WBod WPat
– 'Touchard'	CSco
– 'Unique'	CB&S CBow CDoC CPMA EHar EPla IJoh LHop LTil MBri NHlc SPla SSpi
– 'Vera'	ENot
– 'White Moth'	CKni EHar MAsh MBri MUlv SMad SSpi
petiolaris	See H. ***anomala p.***
'Preziosa'	Widely available
quelpartensis	CB&S CChu CHan CPle CTre
quercifolia	Widely available
– 'Flore Pleno'	See H. ***q.*** 'Snowflake'
– 'Harmony'	SSpi
– Snow Flake ® (d)	CB&S CBow CChu CPMA CSPN ELan EPla ERav LGre MBri MUlv NBar SMad SPer SSpi SSta WWat
– Snow Queen ®	CDoC CPMA MAsh MBal MBri WWat
sargentiana	See H. ***aspera s.***
scandens	CGre SSpi
¶ – ssp. ***chinensis***	SPer SSpi
seemannii	CB&S CBot CBow CChu CHEx CMac CPle CSam CTrw EPla ISea NHlc SSpi SSta WCru WSHC WWat
serrata	CBow CDoC CTrw NHlc
– 'Acuminata'	See H. ***s.*** 'Bluebird'
– 'Amagyana'	SSpi
– 'Belle Deckle'	See H. 'Blue Deckle'
§ – 'Bluebird'	CBot CBra CCla EBre ELan ISea LBre MBal MBri MGos NBee NHlc NKay SBod SDix SHBN SMad SPer SSta WStI
– ***chinensis***	NHlc
– 'Diadem'	CBrd CPle ECar EPla MAsh NHlc SBod SDix SHBN SSpi WHil
– 'Grayswood'	CBot CCla CGre CHig CPle CSam CSco ENot LHop MBal NHlc NKay SDix SPer SSpi WKif WWat
– 'Intermedia'	CCla ENot
– 'Macrosepala'	SSpi
– 'Miranda' (L)	CBrd CMHG EPla NHlc SSpi
– 'Preziosa'	See H. 'P.'
– 'Rosalba'	CCla MRav SChu SPer SPla SSpi WHCr WSHC
– var. ***thunbergii***	CB&S CMHG
§ ***serratifolia***	CBot CChu EPla LHop SArc SHil SSpi WCru WSHC
sinensis	See H. ***scandens chinensis***
tiliifolia	See H. ***anomala petiolaris***
♦ ***umbellata***	See H. ***scandens chinensis***
villosa	See H. ***aspera*** Villosa Group

HYDRASTIS (Ranunculaceae)

canadensis	GPoy NSal

HYDROCHARIS (Hydrocharitaceae)

morsus-ranae	CBen CRDP CWGN EHon EMFW LMay MSta NDea SAWi SWat WChe

HYDROCLEYS (Limnocharitaceae)

See Plant Deletions

HYDROCOTYLE (Umbelliferae)

§ ***americana***	NHol
asiatica	See CENTELLA ***a.***
moschata	CRiv GAri NHol WPer WWin
ranunculoïdes	See H. ***americanum***
vulgaris	MSta WChe WHol

HYDROPHYLLUM (Hydrophyllaceae)

appendiculatum	NSal
canadense	EMon
virginianum	NSal WEas

HYDROCLEYS (Limnocharitaceae)
See Plant Deletions

HYDROCOTYLE (Umbelliferae)
§ *americana* NHol
asiatica See CENTELLA *a.*
moschata CRiv GAri NHol WPer WWin
ranunculoïdes See H. *americanum*
vulgaris MSta WChe WHol

HYDROPHYLLUM (Hydrophyllaceae)
appendiculatum NSal
canadense EMon
virginianum NSal WEas

HYLOMECON (Papaveraceae)
japonica CHun CLew CRDP EBar EPar MBri MSte MTho MTol MUlv NBro NKay WCru WOMN WPer

HYLOTELEPHIUM See SEDUM

HYMENANTHERA See MELICYTUS

HYMENOCALLIS (Liliaceae/Amaryllidaceae)
'Advance' LAma LBow
amancaes WChr
§ *caroliniana* LAma
x *festalis* CAvo CMon CSut ERea LAma LBow MBri NRog SDeJ SLMG WChr WHil
¶ – 'Zwanenburg' CKel
harrisiana CKel LBow WChr
littoralis NRog
longipetala LBow WChr
narcissiflora WChr
occidentalis See H. *caroliniana*
'Sulphur Queen' LBow NRog SDeJ SLMG WChr

HYMENOSPORUM (Pittosporaceae)
flavum CGre CPle

HYMENOXYS (Compositae)
See also TETRANEURIS
subintegra CNic WDav WPer

HYOPHORBE (Palmae)
§ *lagenicaulis* LPal

HYOSCYAMUS (Solanaceae)
albus LHol WWye
niger CArn CSFH GPoy LHol MChe NSal NSel WHer WWye

HYPERICUM † (Guttiferae)
acmosepalum EPla
– SBEC 93 CChu
addingtonii EPla
adenotrichum GCHN SMrm
aegypticum CHal CRiv CSam ELan EPad EPot ESis GCHN MHig NHol NMen NTow NWCA SGil SHer SIng WAbe WPat WPer
¶ *amblycalyx* SIgm
androsaemum CArn CFis CKin ECha ELan ENot MFir NMir NRoo NSal SLon WDin WHil WNdy
*– 'Autumn Blaze' MBal MBel
¶ – 'Dart's Golden Penny' SLPl
§ – 'Gladys Brabazon' (v) EFol EMon EPla MUlv
– 'Orange Flair' CDoC MGos
– 'Variegatum' See H. *a.* 'Gladys Brabazon'
§ *annulatum* EFol ELan EMon
¶ *armenum* WDav
athoum GCHN LHop MBro MHig MPla NHol NTow SIng WPer
augustinii CChu CPle CTre
balearicum CHan EBur EPad EPla MCas MFir MPla MTho SBar SChu SDry SIgm SSta WHil WPer WSHC
beanii CChu EBar EMon LRHS
bellum GCal
– ssp. *latisepalum* CChu EBar
buckleyi GCHN MDHE MHig
calycinum CB&S CKel CLan CPle CSco ELan ENot IDai ISea LBuc LGro MBal MBar MFir MGos MWat NNor NRoo NWea SHBN SLon SPer SReu STre WDin
– *aureum* WWin
§ *cerastioïdes* CLew CMHG CSam ESis GCHN MBro MPla NTow SChu SIgm SIng SUsu WAbe WHil WHoo WPer WWin
choisyanum B&L 12469 CChu
coris CLew CNic CSam CShe ECha EPot ESis LHil MBro MCas MFir MTho MWat NMen NTow SIng WCla WHoo
cuneatum See H. *pallens*
x *cyathiflorum* 'Gold Cup' CTre MBal
delphicum SIng
x *dummeri* 'Peter Dummer' CChu CCla WWat
elatum See H. x *inodorum*
¶ *elodeoïdes* MSta SRms
elongatum EMon ESis SAxl SMrm
empetrifolium CLew MCas MHig
§ – ssp. *oliganthum* ECha ESis ESma GCHN NHar SIgm WOMN WPer
– 'Prostatum' See H. *e. oliganthum*
ericoïdes SIgm WDav
§ *forrestii* CBot CCla CLan EHar ELan ENot EPla MBal MGos WWat
N*fragile* hort. See H. *olympicum minus*
frondosum WPat
¶ – 'Buttercup' EMil
– Sunburst ® EPla MBri MGos
'Gold Penny' See H. *androsaemum* 'Dart's Golden Penny'
grandiflorum See H. *kouytchense*
henryi L 753 CChu
'Hidcote' Widely available
'Hidcote Variegated' CMHG CMer COtt CPle EBre EHar ELan EMon GCHN IJoh LBre MBal MUlv NWyt SPer WCru WWeb
hircinum
ssp. *cambessedesii* EMon LRHS
– ssp. *majus* EMon
hirsutum CKin

hookerianum	CLan GWht
humifusum	WCla
hyssopifolium	SIgm
¶ x ***inodorum***	SHer
– 'Albury Purple'	EFol EPla LMer SHer WDin
– 'Elstead'	CB&S CLan CShe ELan IDai LHop MBal MBar MBel MGos MWat NKay NNor NRoo SHBN SHer SPer WDin WEas WWin
– 'Summergold'	CBos EHal ENot IBar NHol SUsu
– 'Ysella'	CMer CRow ECha ECtt EFol ELan SDry
kalmianum	CBot CDoC EHar
kamtschaticum	CChu
kelleri	CLew GCHN NHol
§ ***kouytchense***	CGle CLan CSco EMon IBar MBri SDry WKif WPat WWeb
lagarocladum	CChu ELan
lancasteri	EMon LRHS
– L 750	CChu
N ***leschenaultii***	CLan
¶ ***linarioïdes***	WDav
maclarenii L 863	CChu
manolatum	See H. ***annulatum***
¶ ***montanum***	NSal
x ***moserianum***	CB&S CLan CMHG CSco CShe EBre ENot IDai IJoh LBre MBal MBar MBri NNor NRoo SHBN SHer SPer WAbe WStI
§ – 'Tricolor' (v)	Widely available
– 'Variegatum'	See H. x ***m.*** 'Tricolor'
'Mrs Brabazon'	See H. ***androsaemum*** 'Gladys Brabazon'
nummularium	NWCA
olympicum	CArn CHal CMea CShe ECha ELan EPot GCHN GDra IDai MFir MPla MPlt MWat NMen NNor SBla SIng SLon SPer SPla SSmi
– 'Edith'	CLew NCat NHol SAsh WPat
– 'Grandiflorum'	See H. ***o. uniflorum***
§ – f. ***minus***	CPar ECha ECtt ELan EMNN ESis GArf GCHN GDra IDai LBee MCas MPlt MRav NHol NKay NRoo SGil SIgm SIng STre WHil WPer WStI WWin
§ – – 'Sulphureum'	CBot CChu CRiv ESis MRav NRoo SGil SPer SUsu WSHC WWin
§ – – 'Variegatum'	CDec CHal CRDP EFol ELan MHig SIng WPat
§ – f. ***uniflorum***	EBar EBre GAri LBre MBal MBar MBro NBro NHol NRoo NVic WAbe WCla WHoo
– – 'Citrinum'	CLew CMea CNic ECha EFol EPot GCHN LHop MBal MWat NKay NRoo SBar SBla SIgm WAbe WCla WEas WOMN WWat
orientale	CHal CLew CMHG CNic EMNN GCHN MBro MPla MPlt NNrd NRoo NWCA SChu WCla WPer
patulum var. ***forrestii***	See H. ***forrestii***
– var. ***henryi***	See H. ***pseudohenryi***
– 'Variegatum'	CMHG EFol EPla LHop MUlv SPer
perforatum	CArn CHal CKin CSFH Effi GPoy LHol MChe MHew NLan NMir NSel SIde WCla WHer WNdy WOak WPbr WWye
¶ 'Peter Dummer'	MBri
polyphyllum	See H. ***olympicum minus***
– ***citrinum***	See H. ***olympicum minus*** 'Sulphureum'
– 'Grandiflorum'	See H. ***olympicum uniflorum***
– 'Sulphureum'	See H. ***olympicum minus*** 'Sulphureum'
– 'Variegatum'	See H. ***olympicum minus*** 'Variegatum'
prolificum	CChu CCla CSco ECtt EHal EPla GCHN SChu WPat
§ ***pseudohenryi***	EBar EMon EPla
– B&L 12009	CChu
– L 1029	CChu
pseudopetiolatum	GTou WPer
– var. ***yakusimense***	See H. ***y.***
pulchrum	CKin WHil
♦ ***quadrangulum*** Linnaeus	See H. ***tetrapterum***
reptans	See H. ***olympicum minus***
rhodoppeum	See H. ***cerastioïdes meuselianum***
'Rowallane'	CB&S CBot CLan CPle CSco CTre CTrw EPla IDai ISea MBri SDix SHBN SHer SPer SSpi WAbe WBod
stellatum	CGre EPla SLon WWat
subsessile	ELan EMon EPla
♦ 'Sungold'	See H. ***kouytchense***
tenuicaule KR 743	ISea
§ ***tetrapterum***	CKin CRDP EHal MHew MWil NLan NSal
tomentosum	GCHN WPer
trichocaulon	CHal CLew CMea ELan EMNN EPot ESis GCHN LBee MBro MPit NHol NRoo SHer SIng WAbe WCru WOMN WPat WPer WThu
uralum	EPla MBal
wilsonii	CChu
yakusimense	GCHN MBar MFir MTho NGre NTow NWCA WCla

HYPOCHAERIS (Compositae)

radicata	CKin NMir
¶ ***uniflora***	CNic

HYPOCYRTA See NEMATANTHUS

HYPOËSTES (Acanthaceae)

phyllostachya (v)	CHal MBri
– 'Bettina' (v)	MBri
– 'Carmina' (v)	MBri
– 'Purpuriana' (v)	MBri
– 'Wit' (v)	CHal MBri
sanguinolenta	See H. ***phyllostachya***

HYPOLEPIS (Dennstaedtiaceae)

millefolium	CRDP GAri
¶ ***punctata beddomei***	WRic

HYPOXIS (Liliaceae/Hypoxidaceae)

* ***crebbsii***	LHil
hygrometrica	CRDP ECou NHol WAbe WPer WThu

HYPOXIS X RHODOHYPOXIS (Liliaceae/Hypoxidaceae)

¶ H. ***parvula*** x R. ***baurii***	EPot NHar SBla

HYPSELA (Campanulaceae)

longiflora	See H. ***reniformis***
§ ***reniformis***	CHal CNic CPar EBre ELan EMNN EPar EPot LBre MCas MHig MPar MPit NGre NHar NMen NNrd NOak NRed NRoo NWCA SSmi SSou WHal WPer WWin
– 'Greencourt White'	CNic GGar MCas NHar WPer

HYSSOPUS (Labiatae)

officinalis	CArn CBow CHal CHan CHun CRDP CSFH CSev ECha ELan Effi GPoy IEde LAbb LHol MBri MChe MHew NRoo NSel SChu SIde WCHb WEas WHer WHil WOak WPer WSun WWye
– f. ***albus***	CHun CSFH ECED ECha EMon GPoy MChe NNor SChu SIde SUsu WCHb WHer WMar WPer WSun WWin WWye
– ssp. *angustifolius*	See H. ***o. officinalis***
– ssp. ***aristatus***	CHal CLew CSFH CSco EBre EMon ESis GPoy LBre LHol MChe MPlt NRoo SHer SIde SPla SUsu WCHb WEas WPer WWin WWye
– ***decussatus***	MBar
§ – ***purpurascens***	ECha
– ***roseus***	CRDP CSFH EMon GPoy LAbb MChe NNor NSti SChu SIde SUsu WCHb WHer WKif WMar WPer WSHC WSun WWin WWye
– f. *ruber*	See H. ***o. purpurascens***
seravshanicus	EMon WPer

HYSTRIX (Gramineae)

patula	EHoe EMon EPla ETPC GAbr GCal NBro NCat SMad WHal

IBERIS (Cruciferae)

amara	CFis GPoy
candolleana	See I. ***pruitii***
commutata	See I. ***sempervirens***
* ***correvoniana***	WEas
gibraltarica	CLew CRiv ELan NNor NTow SRms WPer
jordanii	See I. ***pruitii***
§ ***pruitii***	CRiv EBur MBal NKay WCla
saxatilis	MBro WPat
– *candolleana*	See I. ***pruitii***
¶ ***semperflorens***	NGar
§ ***sempervirens***	CB&S CFis CKel CMHG CNic CRiv ELan LAbb LGro LHil MBal MPit MWat NBro NGre NNor NOrc WHil WPer WTyr
– 'Little Gem'	See I. *s.* 'Weisser Zwerg'
¶ – pink	SIgm
– 'Pygmaea'	CHal EMNN GArf ITim MWat NHar NHol NMen WDav
– 'Schneeflocke' ('Snowflake')	CHal CShe ENot GAri IDai MBri MCas MFir SHer SIng SPer WHoo
– 'Variegata'	EMon
§ – 'Weisser Zwerg'	CHal CLew CMea CShe EBre ECha EFou ELan EMNN EPla LBee LBre MBro MCas MHig MPla MTho NGre NHar NHol NKay NMen NTow SBla SHer SIng WHoo WOld WWin

IDESIA (Flacourtiaceae)

polycarpa	CMCN EHar SHil SSpi WCoo WWat

ILEX † (Aquifoliaceae)

x ***altaclerensis***	
'Atkinsonii' (m)	CRos
N– 'Belgica Aurea' (f/v)	CB&S CMHG CRos CSam EHar ELan EPla LNet MBal MBar MBri MWat SGil SHBN SHil SSpi
– 'Camelliifolia' (f)	CChu CMCN CMHG ELan GWht MMea MRav MUlv MWat SBod SGil SHil SMad SPer SSpi WWat
– 'Camelliifolia Variegata' (f)	CChu
– 'Golden King' (f/v)	Widely available
– 'Hendersonii' (f)	NWea SBod
– 'Hodginsii' (m)	CDoC CRos IOrc IReg MBar NWea
– 'Lady Valerie' (f/v)	IReg
– 'Lawsoniana' (f/v)	CB&S CBow CDec CMHG CPMA CPle CRos CSam EBre EHoe ELan LAbb LBre LNet MBal MBar MBri MGos MMea MWat NHol NWea SBod SGil SHil SLon SMad SPer WPat WThu
– 'Maderensis Variegata'	See I. ***aquifolium*** 'M.V.'
– 'Nigrescens' (m)	MWat
– 'Ripley Gold' (f)	SSpi
– 'Silver Sentinel'	See I. x ***a.*** 'Belgica Aurea'
– 'Wilsonii' (f)	CMHG IOrc IReg LTil MMea MWat NWea SBod SMad
aquifolium	CB&S CBow CKin CPer CSam CSco GRei LNet MBar MBri MGos MWat SHBN SLon WDin WMou WPat WStI
– 'Alaska' (f)	CDoC CMCN CRos EBre IHos LBre LBuc MBal MMea MWat WMou
– 'Alcicornis' (m)	CMCN
– 'Amber' (f)	COtt NWea SHil SMad SPer
– 'Angustifolia' (m or f)	CB&S EHar GAri IOrc MBar MWat SArc WThu WWeb
§ – 'Argentea Marginata' (f)	CB&S CBow CBra CSam CSco CShe EBre ECtt ENot ISea LBre LPan MBri MGos MMea MRav NWea SPer SReu WAbe WDin WPat WStI
§ – 'Argentea Marginata Pendula' (f)	CPMA CSco CShe EHar LPan MBal MBri NHol SBod SHil SLon SPer SReu SSpi WPat WWat WWeb
– 'Argentea Pendula' (f)	See I. ***a.*** 'Argentea Marginata Pendula'
– 'Argentea Variegata' (f)	See I. ***a.*** 'Argentea Marginata'
– 'Atlas' (m)	CB&S CDoC CRos LBuc
– 'Aurea Marginata' (f)	CMHG CPMA ECtt EHoe LPan MMea SBod SHBN WAbe WPat
– 'Aurea Marginata Pendula' (f)	CRos WPat
– 'Aurea Ovata'	See I. ***a.*** 'Ovata Aurea'
– 'Aurea Regina'	See I. ***a.*** 'Golden Queen'
– 'Aureomarginata Pendula'	CDoC EBre LBre NHol
– 'Aurifodina' (f)	IReg
§ – 'Bacciflava' (f)	CPle CSam ECtt EHar ELan EPla GCHN IOrc IReg ISea MBal MBlu MGos MMea MRav MWat NBee NHol SPer WDin WMou

– 'Crassifolia' (m)	EPla
– 'Crispa' (m)	CRos EPla ISea MBal NHol
– 'Donningtonensis' (m)	CRos
– 'Ferox' (m)	CBra CLan CPMA EHal EHar ELan LPan MBal
– 'Ferox Argentea' (m/v)	CCla CMHG CPMA CRos EBre ECtt EHar ELan IJoh IOrc ISea LBre LNet LTil MBal MBar MBri MMea MRav MWat NHol NKay NRoo SHBN SPer SPla SReu WPat WSHC
– 'Ferox Aurea' (m/v)	CBra CCla CMHG CPMA EHar ELan EPla LTil MWat NBee NHol SGil SPer WPat
– 'Flavescens' (f)	CBot EHar EPla SHil
– 'Fructu Luteo'	See I. *a.* 'Bacciflava'
– 'Gold Flash' (f/v)	ECtt EMil MBri NBee NHol
– 'Golden Milkboy' (m/v)	CB&S CCla CLan CRos ECtt EHoe ENot IHos LNet MBal MWat NHol SPla WPat
– 'Golden Milkmaid' (f/v)	CRos ELan IOrc
§ – 'Golden Queen' (m/v)	CB&S CBow CRos CShe ELan ENot IJoh LNet MBal SHil SPer SReu
*– 'Golden Tears'	LRHS
– 'Golden van Tol' (f/v)	CB&S CBra CRos CSco EBre ECtt ENot IJoh IOrc ISea LBre LHol LNet MBal MBar MBri SGil SHBN SPer
– 'Green Pillar' (f)	MMea SPer WMou
– 'Handsworth New Silver' (f/v)	Widely available
– 'Harpune' (m)	CRos
§ – 'Hascombensis'	CBow CLew CRos GDra LGre MBal MGos MPla NHar NHol SAxl WOMN WWat
– 'Hastata' (m)	CMHG CRos EPla SMad
– 'Ingramii' (m/v)	CRos EHar SMad
– 'J C van Tol' (f)	CSco EBre ECtt ELan ENot IDai IJoh IOrc LBre MBal MBar MBri MGos MWat NBee NHol NRoo NWea SBod SHBN SMad SPer SReu SSta WDin WMou WStI WWat
¶ – 'Lichtenthalii' (f)	LTil
– 'Madame Briot' (f/v)	CBow CDoC CMHG CRos CSco EHar ELan ENot EPla IOrc LHol MBal MBar MBri MMea NHol NRoo SBod SGil SHer SPer SPla SReu SSpi WAbe WDin
– 'Monstrosa' (m)	EPla
– 'Moonlight'	See I. *a.* 'Flavescens'
– 'Myrtifolia' (m)	CBow CDoC CSam ELan EPla GAri IBar MBar MBri NHol SGil
– 'Myrtifolia Aureomaculata' (m/v)	CDoC CLan CMHG CRos EBar EBre EHar EHoe LBre LNet MBal MBri NHol NWea SChu SMad WPat
§ – 'Ovata Aurea' (m/v)	CBra CRos SSta
– 'Pendula' (f)	CDoC CRos MBri SBod WMou
– 'Pendula Medio Picta'	See I. *a.* 'Weeping Golden Milkmaid'
§ – 'Pyramidalis' (f)	CBow CRos CSco EBre ELan ENot EPla GCHN GRei IHos LBre MBar MBri NBee NHol NWea SPer SPla SReu WAbe WDin WMou
– 'Pyramidalis Aureomarginata'	CDoC
– 'Pyramidalis Fructu Luteo' (f)	CSco MBar
– 'Recurva ' (m)	EPla MWat WWeb
– 'Rubricaulis Aurea Variegata' (f)	CRos MBal
– 'Scotica' (f)	CRos
– 'Silver King'	See I. *a.* 'Silver Queen'
– 'Silver Milkboy' (f/v)	See I. *a.* 'Silver Milkmaid'
§ – 'Silver Milkmaid' (f/v)	CB&S CMHG EHoe ELan IJoh LTil MBal MBar MBri MRav MWat NRoo SHBN SHer SPer SSta
§ – 'Silver Queen' (m/v)	CB&S CLan CSco EBre GRei IDai IJoh ISea LBre LHol MBal MBar MBri MGos MMea MWat NHol NRoo NWea SPer SPla WStI
– 'Silver Sentinel'	See I. x ***altaclerensis*** 'Belgica Aurea'
– 'Silver van Tol' (f)	EHar MBri WAbe
§ – 'Watereriana' (m/v)	CLan ISea MAsh MBal SBod SGil
– 'Waterer's Gold'	See I. *a.* 'Watereriana'
x ***attenuata***	CRos
– x ***opaca***	CRos
– 'Sunny Foster' (f)	CRos EPla
¶ ***bioritsensis***	MMea
cassine	IReg
– var. ***angustifolia*** (f)	CRos
– yellow berry	CMCN
ciliospinosa	CMCN CRos GWht SMad
'Clusterberry' (f)	CRos
colchica	CRos
cornuta	CLan CLew CMCN CRos EPla GAri
*– 'Aurea'	LTil
– 'Burfordii' (f)	CRos SHil
– 'O'Spring' (f/v)	CMHG EPla LTil MBri
¶ – 'Rotunda'	EPla
crenata	CBow CMCN LHol MGos SArc SReu STre WBod WCru WWat
– 'Aureovariegata'	See I. *c.* 'Luteovariegata'
– 'Compacta'	CMHG
*– 'Congesta'	CRos
– 'Convexa' (f)	CB&S CDoC CRos ENot GDra GWht MBal MBar MBri NWea WPat WWat
*– 'David Ellis'	LTil
¶ – 'Dwarf Pagoda'	LTil
– 'Fastigiata'	LRHS
– 'Fukarin'	See I. *c.* 'Shiro-fukurin'
– 'Golden Gem' (f)	Widely available
– 'Green Island' (m)	EPla
– 'Green Lustre' (f)	CRos
– 'Helleri' (f)	CRos ECar MBar NHol WPat
– 'Ivory Hall' (f)	CRos EPla
¶ – 'Ivory Tower' (f)	LTil
§ – 'Luteovariegata'	CChu CDoC CMHG CRos CSam EBre ECar ELan EPla GAri LBre MBar
– 'Mariesii' (f)	CRos ECar GWht MHig MPla NHol SIng WPat
– f. ***microphylla***	CMHG
¶ – 'Mount Halla' (f)	CMCN
– 'Piccolo' (f)	CRos
¶ – 'Pyramidalis' (f)	NHar
¶ – 'Rotundifolia'	EPla
– 'Sentinel' (f)	CLew CMHG CRos CSam
§ – 'Shiro-fukurin' (f/v)	CMCN CMHG EPla LGre NHar NHol WPat
♦– 'Snowflake'	See I. *c.* 'Shiro-fukurin'
– 'Stokes' (m)	CRos GAri NHol WPat
– 'Twiggy' (f)	CLew CRos
– upright form	CMCN

♦– 'Variegata'	See I. *c.* 'Luteovariegata'
– ***watanabeana*** (f)	CRos
decidua	CMCN
¶ – 'Warren's Red' (f)	CMCN
dimorphophylla	CChu LGre SGil
– 'Somerset Pixie'	SSpi
¶ 'Doctor Kassab' (f)	CMCN
'Drace' (f)	ELan EPla
¶ 'Dragon Lady' (f)	SGil
fargesii	CRos
ficoidea	CMCN
georgei	CRos
glabra	CRos
– 'Ivory Queen' (f)	CRos
¶ – 'Snow White' (f)	MBal
'Good Taste' (f)	CRos
hascombensis	See I. ***aquifolium*** 'Hascombensis'
hookeri	CMHG
'Indian Chief' (f)	CMHG CRos CSam MBri SMad WWat
insignis	See I. ***kingiana***
* 'Jim'	LRHS
'John T Morris' (m)	CRos MBal
§ ***kingiana***	CB&S CRos SHil WWat
x ***koehneana***	CBot CRos
– 'Chestnut Leaf' (m&f)	CCla CMCN CMHG EHar EPla LTil MMea MRav SHil SMad
§ ***kunsanoi***	CMCN CRos
latifolia	CHEx CMCN CRos SArc SHil SMad
¶ ***longipes***	CMCN
'Lydia Morris' (f)	CMHG CSam EPla WWat
macropoda	CMCN
x ***makinoi***	CMCN
x ***meserveae*** Blue Angel ® (f)	CBow COtt CSam ECtt EHoe ENot EPla IOrc MBal MBri MMea MWat NHol NNor SHer SPer SReu SSta WDin WPat WStI
– 'Blue Boy' (m)	CRos
– 'Blue Girl' (f)	CRos
– 'Blue Prince' (m)	CB&S CBow CMHG COtt CRos EHoe IOrc MBal MBar MMea NBee NHol SHBN SHer SPer WDin WStI
– Blue Princess® (f)	CB&S CDec CMHG COtt CRos ENot LPan MBal MBar MMea NHol SHBN SPer SReu SSta WDin WStI
*– 'Glenroy Purple'	MBal
– 'Goliath' (f)	CRos
*– 'Red Darling' (f)	COtt
muchagara	CMCN CRos
¶ ***myrtifolia***	CMCN NHar SPer
– yellow berry form	CMCN
'Nellie R Stevens' (f)	CRos ENot IHos
nothofagifolia C&H 424	GAri GGGa ISea
opaca	CMCN CRos EArb
– 'Villanova' (f)	CRos
pedunculosa	CMCN CRos LTil
perado latifolia	See I. *p.* ***platyphylla***
§ – ssp. ***platyphylla***	CB&S CHEx CMCN CRos
pernyi	CB&S CRos IOrc IReg MBal MBri NHol SHil SLon SMad SPla WThu WWat WWeb
– var. ***veitchii***	CRos EPla NWea
♦ ***poneantha***	See I. ***kusanoi***
¶ ***pringlei***	CMCN
'Pyramidalis'	See I. ***aquifolium*** 'Pyramidalis'
rotunda	CMCN
rugosa	CMCN
'September Gem' (f)	CMCN CRos
serrata	CMCN IReg
'Shin Nien' (m)	CRos
'Sparkleberry' (f)	CRos
¶ ***verticillata***	NHol
– (f)	CRos ELan GAri
– (m)	ELan GAri
¶ – 'Afterglow' (f)	MBlu
¶ – ***aurantiaca*** (f)	MBlu
¶ – 'Christmas Cheer' (f)	SHil
¶ – dwarf male	MBlu
¶ – early male	MBlu
§ – 'Nana' (f)	MBlu
♦– 'Red Sprite'	See I. *v.* 'Nana'
¶ – 'Winter Red'	MBlu
x ***wandoensis***	CMCN CRos
'Washington' (f)	EPla NHol WPat
yunnanensis	CMCN CRos GAri GWht

ILIAMNA See SPHAERALCEA

ILLICIUM (Illiciaceae)

anisatum	CArn CChu CCla CPle CTre EPla NHol SBor SHil SSpi SSta WPat WSHC WWat WWye
– ***laurifolium***	SSta
floridanum	CBow CChu CCla MBal SSpi SSta WBod WCoo WSHC WWat
henryi	SHil WSHC
verum	NSal

ILYSANTHES (Scrophulariaceae)

* ***floribunda***	CSpe

IMPATIENS (Balsaminaceae)

auricoma	EBak
¶ ***burtonii***	CGre
¶ ***capensis***	CRDP
congolensis	CPle
¶ 'Dan White'	CSut
¶ 'Danbee'	CSut
¶ 'Dandin'	CSut
¶ 'Danova'	CSut
¶ 'Danrose'	CSut
¶ 'Danshir'	CSut
¶ 'Dansky'	CSut
double flowered forms	CRDP EBak
glandulifera 'Candida'	EMon
hawkeri	EBak
¶ 'Lambada'	CSut
New Guinea hybrids	CHal EBak MBri
niamniamensis	CHal EBak ERea GCra
¶ – 'Congo Cockatoo'	CTro
pseudoviola	CSpe
¶ 'Samba'	CSut
tinctoria	CChu CGre CRDP CTre EMon LHil SBor
walleriana	EBak MBri

IMPERATA (Gramineae)

cylindrica	EPar EPla GCal WCot
– 'Red Baron'	See I. *c.* 'Rubra'

§ – 'Rubra' — CAbb CDec CDoC CLew CPMA CRDP ECha EFol EHoe ELan EPla ETPC MBri SApp SBar SBla SChu SFar SHer SSpi SWas WPat WPbr WRus WWat

INCARVILLEA (Bignoniaceae)

arguta — CBot CChu CHad CHan ECro EMon GCal GCra GTou SAxl SMrm SSpi SUsu WHil WOMN WPer WThi WTyr WWin
– C&Mc 117 — GCHN
brevipes — See I. ***mairei***
compacta — WHil WHoo
delavayi — Widely available
emodi — SBla
§ ***mairei*** — ECro ESma GDra GTou MTho NHol SBar WDav WPer
– 'Bees' Pink' — CAvo CKel ELan GCra NSti
– 'Frank Ludlow' — GDra
– var. ***grandiflora*** — ECar ELan MTho SBla WHoo
– 'Nyoto Sama' — GDra SBla
olgae — CChu CSam ELan SMrm WHoo WOMN
sinensis — WPer
¶ – 'Alba' — SUsu WCru
¶ sp. CLD 0233 — NHol

INDIGOFERA (Leguminosae)

amblyantha — CBow CChu CPle EHar ESma GCal SDry SSpi WCru WKif WSHC
dielsiana — CChu CPle ESma GCal SSpi WSHC
gerardiana — See I. ***heterantha***
hebepetala — WBod WDin WSHC
§ ***heterantha*** — Widely available
kirilowii — CGre
potaninii — CDoC CSco SHBN SHil
pseudotinctoria — CChu GCal SRms SSpi

INDOCALAMUS (Gramineae(Bambuseae))

¶ ***hamadae*** — EPla SDry
latifolius — EPla SBam SDry WJun
longiauritus — SBam SDry
solidus — EPla SBam SDry WJun

INULA † (Compositae)

acaulis — MTho
conyzae — CKin MHew NSal
crithmoïdes — WHer
ensifolia — CHan CLew CSam ECro ELan EPla IBlr LHop MPit MRav MTho NDea NHol SFis SSvw WEas WHal WHoo WMer
– 'Compacta' — MBri
– 'Gold Star' — CBow CMGP EBar ECtt ESma LHil NBir NNor NOak NRoo NVic WPer WRus WTyr
glandulosa — See I. ***orientalis***
'Golden Beauty' — See BUPHTHALMUM ***salicifolium*** 'G.B.'
helenium — CArn CFis CHun CKin CSFH CSev ECro Effi GPoy ILis LHol MChe MFir MHew NMir NSal SIde WByw WHal WHer WOak WPer WWye
hookeri — CBos CBre CMea CSev EBar ECha ELan EMar EMon EPla IBlr LAbb LHil MBri MFir MSte NDea NHol NSti WAbb WByw WEas WHal WOld WTyr
magnifica — CHan CLew CSam EBre ECha ECro EFol ELan EMon ESma GGar LBre MBri MBro MFir MRav MUlv NDea NHol NRar SFis SMrm SSvw WHal WHoo WMer WOld WWye
* 'Mediterranean Sun' — NNrd WHil
§ ***orientalis*** — CDoC CKel CSco ECro EFou ESma GAbr GCra MBri MBro NCat NMir NNor NRoo WHoo WOld
racemosa — ECha ECro EMon ESma GCal MSte NHol SRms
¶ – C&Mc 620 — GCHN
rhizocephala — CSam
royleana — CSam ECha EPla GCal GCra MBri MBro MSte NSti SIgm SUsu WHoo WPer
¶ sp. CLD 658 — EMon
verbascifolia — GCal NHol
viscosa — WHer

IOCHROMA (Solanaceae)

¶ ***coccinea*** — CTro
cyanea — CGre CPle CTro
grandiflora — CHEx SLMG
¶ ***violacea*** — CPle LHil
¶ ***warscewiczii*** — CTro

IPHEION (Liliaceae/Alliaceae)

¶ 'Alberto Castello' — CBro
¶ ***dialystemon*** — CMon
§ 'Rolf Fiedler' — CAvo CBro CMon EBul ELan EPar EPot MTho NHol SBla SPou WChr WThu
uniflorum — CAvo CBro CNic CRiv ECha EFol ETub LAma MBri MBro NMen NRog NWCA SApp SIng WAbb WCla WHoo WPer
– ***album*** — CAvo CBro CMon EBul ECha ELan EPar EPot GDra MTho SBla SIng SPou WChr
– 'Froyle Mill' — CAvo CBro CRiv EPar EPot GDra LBow MTho NHol SBla SIng SPou WChr WOMN
– 'Wisley Blue' — CAvo CBro CMea CNic CRiv ECha ELan EPar EPot ETub LAma LBlo LBow LHil LTil MPlt MTho NHol SApp SBla SIng SUsu WChr WCru WHil WWat

IPOMOEA (Convolvulaceae)

acuminata — See I. ***indica***
§ ***cairica*** — ECou
¶ ***carnea*** — MNew
§ ***indica*** — CB&S CHEx CHal CKni CMer CRDP CSun CTro ERea GCal LAbb MNew SLMG
♦ ***learii*** — See I. ***indica***
§ ***lobata*** — SMad
♦ ***palmata*** — See I. ***cairica***
¶ ***purpurea*** — WHer
quamoclit — CHEx
tuberosa — See MERREMIA ***t.***

IPOMOPSIS (Polemoniaceae)

¶ ***rubra***	WPer

IRESINE (Amaranthaceae)

herbstii	CHal EBak IBlr NWyt SLMG
– 'Aureoreticulata'	CHal SLMG
¶– 'Brilliantissima'	CBrk
lindenii	CBrk CHal SLMG

IRIS † (Iridaceae)

'A W Tait' (***spuria***)	GCal
'Abracadabra' (SDB)	LBro MRob MS&S
'Abridged Version' (MTB)	NZep
'Acapulco Gold' (TB)	SCro
'Ace of Clubs' (SDB)	NZep
'Action Front' (TB)	CKel ERou NFai SFis SGil SHer WTyr
'Actress' (TB)	EFou
acutiloba	EPot LAma
'Adobe Sunset' (Spuria)	LBro MS&S
'Adrienne Taylor' (MDB)	LBro MAus WWin
¶ 'Ain't She Sweet' (IB)	NZep SCro
¶ ***aitchisonii chrysantha***	NHol
'Alastor' (TB)	CKel MS&S
'Alba' (***sibirica***)	CRDP CRow ECha EWav GDra MAus MNFA NKay SBla
'Albatross' (TB)	CKel
albicans	MAus
¶ 'Alenette' (TB)	MAus
'Alien' (IB)	LBro
¶ 'All Right' (IB)	NZep
'Allegiance' (TB)	MAus WEas
'Alpine Lake' (MDB)	NZep
'Alsterquelle' (SDB)	NZep
¶ 'Amadora' (TB)	LBro
'Amaranth Gem' (SDB)	LBro
¶ 'Amas' (***germanica***)	MAus
'Amazon Princess' (SDB)	MAus NZep
¶ 'Ambassadeur' (TB)	ERou
'Amber Blaze' (SDB)	NZep
'Amber Queen' (DB)	CMGP ECtt ELan LHil SChu SPer
'American Heritage' (TB)	NZep
'Amethyst Crystal' (CH)	LBro
'Amethyst Flame' (TB)	CKel EBre ERou LBre LHil MAus MS&S
'Amethyst Sunset' (MTB)	LBro
'Amigo' (TB)	SCro
'Amphora' (SDB)	CBro NNrd
'Ancilla' (Aril)	CMon EPot
'Angel Eyes' (MDB)	LBlo
'Angel Unawares' (TB)	MAus
'Angelic' (SDB)	LBro MAus
'Angel's Kiss' (SDB)	NZep
'Angel's Tears'	See I. ***histrioïdes*** 'Angel's Eye'
anglica	See I. ***latifolia***
'Ann Dasch' (***sibirica***)	EFou LBro
¶ 'Anna Belle Babson' (TB)	SCro
'Annabel Jane' (TB)	LBro MAus SCro
'Anne Elizabeth' (SDB)	CBro
'Annemarie Troeger' (***sibirica***)	LBro
'Annikins' (IB)	NZep
'Anniversary' (***sibirica***)	LBro MAus SCro
'Antarctic' (TB)	CKel CMGP
¶ 'Apache Warrior' (IB)	LBro
aphylla	MAus NOrc WThu
'Appledore' (SDB)	CBro MRob
'April Accent' (MDB)	MRob
'April Ballet' (MDB)	NZep
'April Sweetheart' (SDB)	NZep
'Apropos' (TB)	MAus
'Arabi Pasha' (TB)	MAus
'Arabi Treasure' (IB)	LBro
'Arabic Night' (IB)	MAus
'Archie Owen' (Spuria)	LBro MAus
¶ 'Arctic Fancy' (IB)	LBro SCro
'Arctic Star' (TB)	CKel CShe
'Arctic Tern' (TB)	LBro
'Arctic Wine' (TB)	MAus
¶ 'Arden' (BB)	LBro
arenaria	See I. ***humilis***
'Arnold Sunrise' (CH)	LBro
'Arnold Velvet' (SDB)	LBro MRob
'Art Gallery' (IB)	NZep
'Ask Alma' (IB)	LBro NZep
§ ***attica***	CBro CMon EPot LAma LBee MHig WDav WThu
¶– S&L 486	CMon
'Auburn Valley' (SDB)	NZep
§ ***aucheri***	CBro EPot LAma WChr
'Audacious' (BB)	NZep
'Aunt Martha' (BB)	MAus
'Austrian Sky' (SDB)	CBot CHad CSam EGol ELan LBro LGre MAus MBro MMil MRob
'Autumn Leaves' (TB)	MAus MMil
'Avanelle' (IB)	EFou ERou LBro
'Az Ap' (IB)	NZep SCro
'Aztec Star' (SDB)	LBro
¶ 'Azure Excho' (IB)	LBro
'Babe' (SDB)	NZep
'Baby Blessed' (SDB)	CBro NSti NZep
'Baby Face' (TB)	MMil
'Baccarat' (TB)	MAus
'Baked Alaska' (TB)	MMil
bakeriana	LAma LRHS
¶ 'Ballerina Blue'	ERou
'Ballyhoo' (TB)	MAus
'Banbury Beauty' (CH)	LBro NSti
'Banbury Fair' (CH)	LBro
'Banbury Melody' (CH)	LBro
'Banbury Ruffles' (SDB)	MAus NSti WHil
¶ 'Banbury Welcome'	IBlr
'Bang' (TB)	CKel
'Barbara's Kiss' (Spuria)	LBro
'Barbushka' (SDB)	LBro
'Baria' (SDB)	CBot EPot LBro
'Barletta' (TB)	MAus
barnumae polakii (Oncocyclus)	See I. ***polakii***
'Baroque Prelude' (TB)	MMil
¶ 'Basso' (IB)	SCro
¶ 'Batik' (BB)	SCro
'Batsford' (SDB)	CBro
'Baxteri' (***sibirica***)	CRow
'Bay Ruffles' (SDB)	NZep
'Be Dazzled' (SDB)	EFou LBro
'Beauty Mark' (SDB)	NSti NZep
'Bedtime Story' (IB)	LBro
'Bee Wings' (MDB)	MRob NZep WEas

'Belise' (Spuria) LBro
'Benton Arundel' (TB) SCro
'Benton Cordelia' (TB) SCro
'Benton Dierdre' (TB) SCro SRms
'Benton Lorna' (TB) SCro
'Benton Nigel' (TB) MAus
'Benton Sheila' (TB) SCro
'Berkeley Gold' (TB) CMGP CPar CSco EBlo ECtt ERav LHil NOrc SPer
¶ 'Berry Rich' (BB) SCro
'Betsey Boo' (SDB) MRob NZep
'Betty Chatten' (TB) MHig NMen NNrd
'Betty Cooper' (Spuria) LBro MS&S
'Betty Wood' (SDB) LBro
¶ 'Beverly Sills' (TB) EFou
¶ 'Beyond' (TB) SCro
'Bibury' (SDB) LBro MAus MMil
'Big Day' (TB) CKel
'Big Wheel' (CH) LBro
biliottii CBro
¶ 'Black Dragon' (TB) SCro
'Black Hills' (TB) LRHS MAus MUlv
'Black Ink' (TB) CKel
'Black Lady' (MTB) LBro
'Black Star' (SDB) NZep
'Black Swan' (TB) EBlo EBre ECtt ELan GCHN LBre MAus MRav MRob SPer
'Black Watch' (IB) NZep
¶ 'Blackberry Brandy' (BB) LBro
* 'Blackfoot' ESma
'Blazing Saddles' (TB) NZep
¶ 'Blenheim Royal' (TB) SCro
'Blitz' (SDB) NZep
'Blockley' (SDB) MAus
'Blood Dance' (SDB) NZep
'Blue Admiral' (TB) CKel
'Blue Asterisk' (IB) LBro
'Blue Ballerina' (CH) LBro
'Blue Denim' (SDB) CBro CPar CSco EBre ECtt EGol ENot GCHN LBre LBro LHil MRob MS&S SUsu WCra WMar WMer
'Blue Doll' (MDB) MRob MS&S NZep
'Blue Duchess' (TB) CKel LHil
'Blue Elegance' (Dutch) LAma
¶ 'Blue Eyed Blond' (IB) SCro
'Blue Eyed Brunette' (TB) LHil MAus
'Blue Hendred' (SDB) LBro MAus NBir
'Blue Icing' (IB) NZep
'Blue King' (***sibirica***) CKel
'Blue Line' (SDB) NZep
'Blue Luster' (TB) LBro SCro
'Blue Magic' (Dutch) LAma NRog
¶ 'Blue Mascara' (SDB) SCro
'Blue Mere' (***sibirica***) LBro
¶ 'Blue Moss' (SDB) LBro
'Blue Neon' (SDB) NZep
'Blue Owl' (TB) CKel MS&S
'Blue Pigmy' (SDB) CGle CMGP CSco EBre LBre NBar NMen SCro SPer
'Blue Pools' (SDB) EFou LBro NZep SCro
'Blue Reflections' (TB) MMil
'Blue Rhythm' (TB) CKel CMGP CSco ERou MAus MS&S NFai SCro SPer
'Blue Sapphire' (TB) MAus
'Blue Shimmer' (TB) CKel CPar EBre ELan ENot LBre MAus MRav NFai SCro SPer
'Blue Smoke' (TB) CKel
'Blue Sparks' (SDB) LBro
¶ 'Blue Staccato' (TB) SCro
'Blue Zephyr' (Spuria) LBro
'Bluebird in Flight' (IB) LBro
¶ 'Bluebird Wine' (TB) MAus
¶ 'Blushes' (IB) SCro
¶ 'Blushing Pink' (TB) SCro
¶ 'Bodderlecker' (SDB) EFou
'Bold Lassie' (SDB) LRHS WHer
'Bold Print' (IB) NZep SCro
'Bonny' CBro
'Boo' (SDB) LRHS MAus NZep
'Born Graceful' SSpi
'Bracknell' (***sibirica***) CWGN
bracteata EBul EPot MHig
'Braithwaite' (TB) CKel ELan ERou LHil LRHS MAus SRms WPer
brandzae See I. ***sintenisii b.***
'Brannigan' (SDB) CBro EGol LBro LHil MMil MRob NBir NNrd
'Brass Tacks' (SDB) LBro MAus NZep
'Brassie' (SDB) CBro CRiv LBro LHil MRob NNrd SIng
¶ 'Bridal Crown' (TB) SCro
¶ 'Bride' (DB) LHil SPla
'Bride's Halo' (TB) SCro
'Bright Chic' (SDB) NZep
'Bright Moment' (SDB) LBro NZep
'Bright Vision' (SDB) MRob NZep
'Bright White' (MDB) CBro EPot LBro MRob NNrd WHil
'Bright Yellow' (DB) EBre GCHN LBre MRav
'Brighteyes' (IB) CCor CPar CSco EBre ECar ELan ENot ESis LBre LBro LHil MHig MMil MRob MS&S MTho SChu SCro
'Brilliant Excuse' (TB) NZep
¶ 'Brindisi' (TB) SCro
¶ 'Bristo Magic' (TB) SCro
¶ 'Bristol Gem' (TB) SCro
'Broad Grin' (SDB) LBro NZep
'Broadleigh Ann' (CH) CBro
'Broadleigh Dorothy' (CH) CBro
'Broadleigh Elizabeth' (CH) CBro
'Broadleigh Emily' (CH) CBro
'Broadleigh Florence' (CH) CBro
'Broadleigh Joan' (CH) CBro
'Broadleigh Lavinia' (CH) CBro
'Broadleigh Mitre' (CH) CBro
'Broadleigh Nancy' (CH) CBro
'Broadleigh Peacock' (CH) CBro
'Broadleigh Rose' (CH) CBos CBro EOrc LGre SMrm
'Broadleigh Sybil' (CH) CBro SBar WCru
'Broadleigh Victoria' (CH) CBro WCru
'Broadway' (TB) NZep SCro
'Bromyard' (SDB) CBro MAus
'Bronze Beauty' (***hoogiana*** x) EPot
'Bronze Bird' (TB) CKel CSco

'Bronze Cloud' (TB)	CKel
'Bronze Perfection' (Dutch)	LAma
'Bronze Queen' (Dutch)	LAma LBlo
'Broseley' (TB)	LBro
'Brown Chocolate'	MAus
'Brown Lasso' (BB)	EFou LBro SCro
'Brown Trout' (TB)	CKel
'Brummit's Mauve'	MAus
¶ 'Bubbling Over' (TB)	SCro
'Bubbly Blue' (IB)	NZep
bucharica Foster	CAvo CBro CMon EPar EPot ETub GCra LAma LBow MBro NHar NRog SIng WChr WHil WThu
– hort.	See I. ***orchioïdes***
– x ***aucheri***	EPot
'Buckeye Blue' (SDB)	NZep
¶ ***bulleyana***	SRms SWas
'Bumblebee Deelite' (MTB)	NZep
'Bunny Hop' (SDB)	NZep
'Burgundy Brown' (TB)	NZep
¶ 'Butter and Sugar' (*sibirica*)	NFai NSti
'Butter Pecan' (IB)	NZep SCro
'Buttercup Bower' (TB)	MAus
'Buttercup Charm' (MDB)	NZep
'Buttered Chocolate' (Spuria)	LBro
¶ 'Buttermere' (TB)	SRms
'Buttermilk'	LGre
'Butterpat' (IB)	NZep
'Butterscotch Kiss' (TB)	EBre ELan ERou LBre
'Buttertubs' (TB)	CKel
'Button Box' (SDB)	NZep
'Byword' (SDB)	LBro
caerulea	See I. ***albomarginata***
'Caesar' (*sibirica*)	CKel CSco LBro MNFA WCot
'Caesar's Brother' (*sibirica*)	CMGP IBlr MAus MSta MUlv SPer WWin
'Caliente' (TB)	MAus
'California Style' (IB)	NZep
§ Californian hybrids	CChu CGle CWGN ELan EMon EOrc GAbr LHil MBal NSti SChu SMrm SSpi WBon
¶ 'Calypso Mood' (TB)	SCro
'Cambridge' (*sibirica*)	EFou MAus NHol
'Cambridge Blue' (Spuria)	MAus
'Camelot Rose' (TB)	MAus
'Campbellii'	See I. ***lutescens*** 'C.'
'Canary Bird' (TB)	CKel LHil
¶ 'Cannington Bluebird' (TB)	LBro
'Cantab' (Reticulata)	CAvo CBro ELan EPar EPot ETub LAma LBlo LBow NHar NRog SIng WHil WPer
'Can't Stop' (SDB)	NZep
¶ 'Capricious' (TB)	SCro
'Captain Gallant' (TB)	MAus
'Captive Heart' (SDB)	NZep
'Caramba' (TB)	NZep SCro
'Caress' (SDB)	MRob
'Carilla' (SDB)	LBro
'Carnaby' (TB)	EFou LBro MAus
'Carnival Glass' (BB)	LBro
'Carnival Time' (TB)	EFou
'Carnton' (TB)	CKel MAus WEas
¶ 'Carolina Gold' (TB)	SCro
'Carolyn Rose' (MTB)	LBro MS&S NZep
¶ 'Casbah' (TB)	SCro
¶ 'Cascading Skies'	ERou
¶ 'Catalyst' (TB)	SCro
caucasica	EPot
'Cayenne Capers' (TB)	MMil
'Celestial Glory' (TB)	LRHS MAus
'Centre Court' (TB)	NZep SCro
'Centrepiece' (SDB)	LBro
chamaeiris	See I. ***lutescens***
'Champagne Music' (TB)	MAus
¶ 'Change of Pace' (TB)	SCro
'Chantilly' (TB)	ELan NOrc SCro SGil SHer
'Chapeau' (TB)	MAus NSti
'Chapel Hill' (SDB)	LBro
'Char True' (Spuria)	MAus
'Charm Song' (IB)	LBro
'Charming' (TB)	CKel
¶ 'Chartreuse Ruffles' (TB)	SCro
'Cheers' (IB)	LBro NZep
'Cherry Falls' (TB)	LBro
'Cherry Garden' (SDB)	CBro CPar EBlo EBre ECtt EFol EGol GCHN LBre LGre LHil MRav MRob MS&S NHar NNrd WCra WHil
'Cherry Orchard' (TB)	NNor
¶ 'Cherry Pop' (SDB)	NZep
¶ 'Cherry Smoke' (TB)	SCro
'Cherub Tears' (SDB)	MRob NZep
¶ 'Cherub's Smile' (TB)	SCro
'Chickee' (MTB)	NZep
'Chicken Little'	CBro
'Chief Chickasaw' (TB)	LBro
'Chief Moses' (TB)	MAus
¶ 'Chief Quinaby' (TB)	SCro
¶ 'Chief Waukesha' (TB)	SCro
'Chieftain' (TB)	CKel MAus NSti
'Chinese Coral' (TB)	MAus
'Chippendale' (TB)	NZep
'Chivalry' (TB)	MAus SCro
'Christmas Angel' (TB)	ECtt ERou MAus
'Christmas Time' (TB)	NZep
Chrysofor Group	NHol
chrysographes	CCla CGle CHad EBar ELan ELun LBro MBal MTho NHol NNor SIng SUsu WWin
– B&L 12617	EMon
– ***alba***	NBir
– 'Black Beauty'	NHol
– black form	CHan CMil CPar CRDP CRow CSam CWGN EFou ELun EPot GAbr GCal GDra MBal MBro MFir NHar NHol NMen NRar SBla SChu SPer WCru WDav WHal WHoo WRus WSun
– 'Black Knight'	CBot ECha EFol ELan GCal LHop NNor NOrc NSti SPer WWin
– 'Black Velvet'	ECha
– crimson form	NCat NHol SIng
– 'Inshriach'	NHol
– 'Inshriach'	GDra
– 'Mandarin Purple'	CWGN GCal NCat SPer WThi

– 'Margot Holmes' (Cal-Sib)	GCal GDra IBlr SChu
¶ – purple form	CRDP
– red form	CRDP MBal SHer
– 'Rob'	GCal
– 'Rubella'	CRow GDra LGre
– 'Rubella'	NHol SCro
– 'Rubens'	SChu
¶ ***chrysophylla***	EPot
'Chubby Cheeks' (SDB)	NZep
¶ 'Church Stoke' (SDB)	MAus SCro
'Cider Haze' (TB)	CKel
'Circus Stripes' (TB)	NZep
'Cirrus'	LHil
'City Girl' (SDB)	NZep
¶ 'City of David' (TB)	SCro
'Clairette' (Reticulata)	CAvo CBro EPar LAma SIng
'Clap Hands' (SDB)	LBro NZep
'Clarke Cosgrove' (Spuria)	LBro
clarkei	CHan ELan GAbr LGan NNrd NSti NTow NWCA
'Classy Babe' (SDB)	NZep
'Clay's Caper' (SDB)	EFou LBro MS&S
'Cleo' (TB)	CKel NBir
'Cliffs of Dover' (TB)	CKel LBro MS&S SRms
'Climbing Gold'	WHil
'Closed Circuit' (TB)	NZep
¶ 'Clotted Cream'	ECha
¶ 'Cloud Cap' (TB)	SRms
'Cloud Fluff' (IB)	LBro
¶ 'Cloudless Sunrise'	ERou
'Colonial Gold' (TB)	MAus
¶ 'Color Brite' (BB)	SCro
¶ 'Color Splash' (TB)	SCro
¶ 'Columbia Blue' (TB)	SCro
'Colwall' (TB)	LBro
'Comma' (SDB)	NZep
'Concord Touch' (SDB)	NZep
¶ 'Condottiere' (TB)	SCro
'Confederate Soldier' (IB)	LBro
confusa	CGle CHEx CHan CRDP GCal LHil MTho MUlv SArc
'Connoisseur' (Spuria)	LBro
'Consummation' (MTB)	NZep
'Cool Spring' (***sibirica***)	WThi
'Copper Classic' (TB)	NZep SCro
'Copper Pot' (TB)	CKel
'Coquette Doll' (SDB)	NZep
¶ 'Coral Chalice'	ERou
'Coral Strand' (TB)	MAus
¶ 'Coral Wings' (SDB)	NZep
'Corn Harvest' (TB)	MMil NZep
'Cotaty' (BB)	LBro
¶ 'Cote d'Or' (TB)	SCro
'Cotton Blossom' (SDB)	EGol LBro NZep
'Court Magician' (SDB)	NZep
¶ 'Cozy Calico' (TB)	SCro
'Cracklin Burgundy' (TB)	SCro
¶ 'Cranberry Ice' (TB)	SCro
¶ 'Creative Stitchery' (TB)	SCro
crenata 'Lady Gem'	ECar
cretensis	See I. ***unguicularis*** Cretensis
'Cricket Lane' (SDB)	NZep
'Crimson Velvet' (SDB)	MAus
'Crispen Rouge' (TB)	CKel
'Crispin' (SDB)	NZep
cristata	CBro ECha ITim LAma SBar SIng SSou SSpi WCru
– ***albs***	CBro CRDP LBee MBal MDHE SCro SIng SWas WAbe
– x ***lacustris***	CHan GArf
♦ ***croatica***	See I. ***germanica***
crocea	SCro WDav
'Crocus' (MDB)	NZep
'Croftway Lemon' (TB)	SCro
'Cross Stitch' (TB)	MMil NZep
¶ 'Crown Sterling' (TB)	SCro
'Crushed Velvet' (TB)	MAus
¶ 'Cum Laude' (IB)	SCro
'Cup Race' (TB)	MAus NSti NZep
¶ 'Curio' (MDB)	LBro
'Curlew' (IB)	LBro SCro
'Cutie' (IB)	NZep
'Cyanea' (DB)	CKel
'Cycles' (TB)	NZep
cycloglossa	LRHS WChr
'Daisy Fresh' (MDB)	LBro
'Dale Dennis' (DB)	LBro
'Dame Judy' (TB)	CKel
'Dancer's Veil' (TB)	CKel EBre ECtt EFou ELan ERou LBre LBro MAus NVic SCro SPer
'Dancing Eyes' (SDB)	LBro
'Dancing Gold' (MTB)	NZep
'Dancin'' (IB)	NZep
danfordiae	CAvo CB&S CBro EPar EPot ETub LAma LBlo LBow MBri NRog SIng WHil WPer
'Dante' (TB)	CKel LHil
'Dappled Pony' (MTB)	NZep
'Dardanus' (Aril)	EPot
'Daring Eyes' (MDB)	NZep
'Dark Blizzard' (IB)	NZep
¶ 'Dark Bury' (TB)	LBro
'Dark Rosaleen' (TB)	LBro
'Dark Spark' (SDB)	MAus NSti
'Dark Vader' (SDB)	NZep
'Darkover' (SDB)	LBro MAus
¶ 'Darkside' (TB)	SCro
'Dash Away' (SDB)	NZep
'Dawn Candle' (Spuria)	LBro
'Dawn Favour' (SDB)	LBro
¶ 'Dawn Glory' (TB)	SCro
¶ 'Dazzling Gold' (TB)	SCro
§ ***decora***	CBro MAus WDav
'Deep Black' (TB)	CHad CMGP CSco MAus SCro
¶ 'Deep Fire' (TB)	SCro
'Deep Pacific' (TB)	MAus
'Deep Space' (TB)	LHil MAus
'Deft Touch' (TB)	MAus
delavayi	CKel SIng SWas
– 'Didcot'	LBro
'Delicate Air' (SDB)	EGol LBro MS&S
¶ 'Delphi' (TB)	SCro
'Demon' (SDB)	EFou LBro
'Deputé Nomblot' (TB)	CShe LHil
'Derring Do' (SDB)	LBro MS&S
'Derry Down' (SDB)	LBro
'Derwentwater' (TB)	CKel CWes MAus SRms
'Desert Dream' (AB)	GDra
'Desert Echo' (TB)	EFou
'Desert Quail' (MTB)	LBro

'Desert Song' (TB)	CKel SGil
¶ 'Designer Gown'	ERou
'Dew Point' (IB)	LBro SCro
'Die Braut' (DB)	See I. 'Bride'
'Diligence' (SDB)	NZep
'Disco Jewel' (MTB)	NZep
¶ 'Discretion' (TB)	SCro
'Ditto' (MDB)	NZep
'Dixie Pixie' (SDB)	NZep
'Doll Dear' (SDB)	LBro NZep
'Doll Ribbons' (MTB)	NZep
'Doll Type' (IB)	EFou LBro
¶ 'DoSiDo' (SDB)	SCro
'Dotted Doll' (MTB)	NZep
'Double Lament' (SDB)	CBro LBro MMil MRob SCro
'Douglas 402' (TB)	SCro
douglasiana	CBre EBul EPar EPla EPot GArf GDra IBlr LBro LGan SSpi WChe WDav
¶ – pale pink form	MS&S
'Doxa' (IB)	LBro SCro
'Dragonfly' (***sibirica***)	MAus
'Dream Builder' (TB)	NZep
'Dreamcastle' (TB)	CKel
'Dreaming Spires' (***sibirica***)	MAus
'Dreaming Yellow' (***sibirica***)	CTom EBre LBre MUlv NBro NRoo SCro SPer WRus
'Dresden Candleglow' (IB)	CHad CWGN MAus
'Dresden China'	CRow
'Dumpling' (MDB)	NZep
¶ 'Dundee' (TB)	SCro
'Dunlin' (MDB)	CBro LHil MRob NRar
'Dusky Challenger' (TB)	SCro
'Dusky Dancer' (TB)	MAus
'Dutch Lament' (SDB)	MMil
dykesii	CRow
'Eagle's Flight' (TB)	NZep
¶ 'Eardisland' (IB)	LBro
'Earl' (TB)	MMil
'Earl of Essex' (TB)	MAus MMil
'Early Edition' (IB)	LBro LHil
'Early Light' (TB)	LBro
'Early Snowbird' (TB)	NZep
'East Indies' (TB)	MAus
'Easy Grace' (TB)	MAus
'Easy Strolling' (SDB)	LBro NZep
'Eccentric' (SDB)	NZep
'Echo Pond' (MTB)	NZep
¶ 'Edith Wolford' (TB)	SCro
'Edward' (Reticulata)	LAma WPer
'Edward of Windsor' (TB)	CHad ELan ERou NOrc SCro
'Ego' (***sibirica***)	CDoC ECha ELun GCal LBro LWad MBri MUlv NHol WHal WThi
'Eleanor's Pride' (TB)	CKel MAus
'Elegans' (TB)	LHil
'Elegante' (***laevigata*** x)	CRow CWGN EGol
elegantissima	See I. ***iberica e.***
'Elixir' (Spuria)	LBro
'Elizabeth Arden' (TB)	CKel
'Elizabeth Poldark' (TB)	LBro
'Ellesmere' (***sibirica***)	GCal
'Elvinhall'	CBro

'Emperor' (***sibirica***)	CB&S CBre CKel CRow EHon ERou LMay MNFA MS&S NHol
'Emphasis' (TB)	NZep
'Empress of India' (TB)	LWad MAus SFis
¶ 'Encanto' (SDB)	MAus
'Enchanted Blue' (SDB)	LBro MRob NZep
'Enchanted Gold' (SDB)	NZep
'English Cottage' (TB)	GCal LHil MMil SCro
¶ 'Ennerdale' (TB)	MAus SRms
§ ***ensata***	CB&S CBen CCla CCor CKel CMHG CRDP CWGN ELan EPot LBro LHil LMay LWad MAus MBri MSta NBro NRoo SHig SWat WDav WHol WWin
– 'Alba'	CBot CGle CWGN ECha
– 'Aoigata'	WThi
– 'Apollo'	CRow
– 'Benokohji'	EHon
– 'Blue Peter'	CRow
– 'Chitose-no-tomo'	CRow
¶ – 'Dancing Waves'	CRow
¶ – 'Enchanting Melody'	CRow
¶ – 'Freckled Geisha'	CRow
– 'Galatea'	CRow CWGN EHon
– 'Gei-sho-ui'	CWGN
– 'Gipsey'	CRiv
¶ – 'Glitter and Gaiety'	CRow
– 'Hakug-yokuro'	CRow
– 'Hana-aoi'	CRow IBlr WThi
– 'Hatsu-shimo'	CRow IBlr
– 'Hercule'	CRow CWGN
– Higo hybrids	CGle CRow IBlr LHop MSta SCro SPer WThi
– 'Hokkaido'	CGle CRow CWGN EHon
– 'Komo-no-obi'	CRiv
– 'Kuma-funjin'	CWGN
– 'Laced'	SPer
– 'Landscape at Dawn'	EHon
¶ – 'Magic Opal'	CRow
– 'Mandarin'	CRow EHon
¶ – 'Midsummer Reverie'	CRow
§ – 'Moonlight Waves'	CCla CDoC CRow CWGN EGol EHon ELan GCal GCra MAus MFir NRoo SApp SCro WRus
– 'Narihiri'	CRow
– 'Oku-banri'	CWGN
– pale mauve	SPer
– 'Pink Frost'	CHad
– purple	SPer
– 'Purple East'	CDoC CKni CRow CWGN
– 'Rampo'	CRow
¶ – 'Red Dawn'	EHon
§ – 'Rose Queen'	CCla CRDP CRow CSco CWGN EBre ECha EHon ELan ELun EMFW EPar ERou EWav GCal LBre LMay MSta NKay NRoo SChu WChe WRus
– 'Rowden'	CRow
¶ – 'Royal Crown'	CRow
– 'Royal Purple'	CGle NHol
– 'Ruby King'	CRiv
¶ – 'Shihainami'	IBlr
¶ – 'Springtime Showers'	CRow
¶ – 'Tago-sode'	CRow
¶ – 'Umi-botaro'	CRow
¶ – 'Valiant Prince'	CRow

Plant	Suppliers
– 'Variegata'	CBen CElw CMil CRDP CRow CTom CWGN ECha EGol EHon IBlr LMay MSta MUlv WByw WHol WRus
– 'Waka-muasaki'	WRus
¶ – 'Worley Park'	CRow
– 'Yako-no-tami'	CRow
¶ – 'Yusho'	CRow
¶ 'Erleen Richeson' (TB)	SCro
'Essay' (Spuria)	LBro
'Etched Apricot' (TB)	MAus
¶ 'Eveneing Magic' (TB)	SCro
'Evening Pond' (MTB)	NZep
¶ 'Everything Plus'	ERou
ewbankiana	EPot
'Ewen' (***sibirica***)	EFou LBro SCro
'Excelsior' (DB)	CSco CShe
'Exotic Gem' (TB)	MAus
'Exotic Isle' (TB)	NZep
'Exotic Shadow' (SDB)	LBro
'Eye Shadow' (SDB)	MAus
'Eyebright' (SDB)	CBro EFou LHil MAus MMil WThi
'Fairy Time' (IB)	LBro
'Fall Primrose' (TB)	LBro
'Fancy Capers' (IB)	MAus
'Fancy Tales' (TB)	NZep
'Fantasy World' (IB)	LBro
'Farolito' (Spuria)	LBro
'Fashion Fling' (TB)	MAus
'Fashion Lady'	CBro NNrd WThi
'Favorite Angel' (SDB)	NZep
'Feminine Charm' (TB)	MAus
¶ 'Feminist' (TB)	SCro
¶ ***fernaldii***	EPot
'Festive Skirt' (TB)	MAus
'Fiery Song' (TB)	CKel
'Fiji Dancer' (TB)	MMil
filifolia	CBro
¶ – MS 437	CMon
¶ – var. ***latifolia*** SF 332	CMon
'Fire and Flame' (TB)	NBir
'Fire One' (SDB)	LBro
'Fire Siren' (TB)	MMil
'Firecracker' (TB)	EBre ERou LBre MAus MRav SCro SPer
¶ 'First Interstate' (TB)	SCro
'First Lilac' (IB)	LBro
'First Step' (SDB)	NZep
'First Violet' (TB)	MAus
¶ 'Five Star Admiral' (TB)	SCro
'Flamingo' (TB)	CKel
'Flareup' (TB)	MAus
'Flashing Beacon' (MTB)	NZep
flavescens	MAus NSti
'Flea Circus' (MDB)	MRob NZep
'Flight of Butterflies' (***sibirica***)	CRDP CRow CTom EBre EGol ELan ERou LBre MNFA MRav NCat NRar SPer SWas WRus
¶ 'Flight of Cavalry' (IB)	CGle
'Florentina' (IB)	CArn CBro CMil CRow EBre ECha EFou ERav Effi GAbr GPoy IBlr LBre LBro LHil LHol MChe MRav SCro SIde WSun WWye
'Focus' (TB)	NZep SCro
§ ***foetidissima***	Widely available
¶ – ***aurea*** MS 902	CMon
– 'Aurea'	CMon WDav
– ***chinensis***	See I. *f. citrina*
§ – var. ***citrina***	CChu CFis CMea CRDP CRow EBul ECha EGol EPla GAbr GCal LBro MBal MBro MNFA NSti SChu SSpi SUsu WAbe WOMN WRus WWin
– 'Fructu Albo'	CRow EGol
– var. ***lutescens***	EMon
¶ – 'Moonshy Seedling'	EGol
– 'Variegata'	CAvo CBro CChu CGle CRDP CRow CSam EFol EGol ELan EOrc EPar EPla ERav MBri NDea NHol NPer NRar NRoo NRya NSti SBla SPla WAbe WEas WRus WThu WWat
¶ – yellow seeded	EFou
'Forest Hill' (TB)	CKel
'Forest Light' (SDB)	CBro LBro MRob
formosana	CHEx
'Forncett Moon' (***sibirica***)	EFou
forrestii	CHan CNic CRDP CRow CSun CWGN EFol ELan EOrc EPar ESis GArf GCal GDra LHop LMay MBri MPlt NBro NHol SSpi SUsu WCla WHer WHil WHol
– L 1696	SSpi
– x ***chrysographes***	GDra NBir
¶ – hybrids	NHol
¶ 'Fort Apache' (TB)	SCro
'Fort Regent' (TB)	LBro
'Forte' (SDB)	NZep
'Foxfire' (TB)	MAus
'Fracas' (SDB)	NZep
'Frank Elder' (Reticulata)	CBro LAma MTho
'French Gown' (TB)	EFou MAus
'Fresno Flash' (TB)	NZep SCro
'Friendly Welcome' (***sibirica***)	LBro
'From the Heart' (IB)	NZep
'Frost and Flame' (TB)	CMGP CPar EBlo EBre ECtt ELan ERav ERou LBre MAus MMil MRav MRob NOrc SChu SCro SPer
'Frosty Crown' (SDB)	NZep
¶ 'Full Tide' (TB)	SCro
'Full Time'	MAus
fulva	CRDP GCal MNFA MUlv NSti WChe WEas
x ***fulvala***	CCor CHan CRDP GCal MAus NSti WChe WRus WWat
'Fun Time' (SDB)	MAus
'Funny Face' (MDB)	NZep
'Furnaceman' (SDB)	CBro
¶ 'Fuzzy' (MDB)	LBro
'Gala Gown' (TB)	MAus
§ ***galatica***	EPot LAma
'Galleon Gold' (SDB)	NZep
'Garden Gnome' (MDB)	NZep
gatesii	EPot LAma
'Gatineau' (***sibirica***)	GDra WThi
'Gay Prince' (TB)	CKel MS&S
'Gay Trip' (TB)	CKel
'George' (Reticulata)	CAvo CBro EPar EPot ETub LBow SIng
'George Barr' (***stolonifera***)	ETub

'Gerald Darby' (x *robusta*)	CBro CCor CFis CRDP CRow CWGN ECha EFol EGol ELun EPar GCal IBlr MAus MUlv NSti SCro SHig SSpi SUsu WChe WEas WRus
germanica	LBro MAus NNor SPla
'Gibson Girl'	MMil
'Gigglepot' (SDB)	LBro MRob
'Gilston Gulf' (TB)	MAus
¶ 'Ginger Swirl' (TB)	SCro
'Gingerbread Man' (SDB)	CBro EFou LBro LGre LHil MRob MS&S
'Glad Rags' (TB)	NZep
¶ 'Glebe Mantel'	NSti
'Glee Club' (IB)	NZep
'Glen' (TB)	CKel
¶ 'Godfrey Owen'	MAus
'Going My Way' (TB)	MAus NZep SCro
'Gold Burst' (TB)	NZep SCro
¶ 'Gold Canary' (MDB)	NZep
'Gold Flake' (TB)	CKel
'Gold Galore' (TB)	NZep SCro
'Gold Intensity' (BB)	LBro
'Golden Alps' (TB)	ENot MAus
'Golden Dewdrops' (SDB)	LBro
'Golden Emperor' (Dutch)	LBlo
'Golden Encore' (TB)	MAus
'Golden Eyelet' (MDB)	NZep
'Golden Fair' (SDB)	LHil NBir SIng
'Golden Forest' (TB)	MAus
'Golden Harvest' (Dutch)	CB&S LAma
'Golden Lady' (Spuria)	LBro
'Golden Muffin' (IB)	LBro NZep
'Golden Planet' (TB)	CKel
'Golden Ruby' (SDB)	LBro MRob
'Golden Spice' (TB)	LBro
'Golden Starlet' (SDB)	LBro
'Golden Veil' (TB)	CKel
'Golden Waves' (Cal-Sib)	LBro
'Goldilocks' (TB)	CKel
¶ 'Good and True' (IB)	SCro
'Good Morning America' (TB)	NZep
'Good Nature' (Spuria)	LBro
'Gordon' (Reticulata)	EPot LAma LBow
'Goring Ace' (CH)	LBro
gormanii	See I. ***tenax***
'Gossamer Steel' (TB)	MAus
gracilipes	CRiv GArf MBal
– 'Alba'	CRDP
'Graclac'	SIng
graeberiana	EPot
graminea	CAvo CBro CCor CFis CHan CMon CPar CRDP CRow CSco ECha EFou EGol ELan EPar LBro MAus NHol NNrd NSti SAxl SIng SPer SUsu WOMN WRus WWat
– 'Hort's Variety'	GCal NHol
¶ – var. ***pseudocyperus***	CMon
¶ 'Granada Gold' (TB)	SRms
'Grand Baroque'	MMil
¶ 'Grand Waltz' (TB)	SCro
'Grandpa's Girl' (MTB)	LBro NZep
'Grape Orbit' (SDB)	NZep
'Grapelet' (MDB)	LBro NZep
'Grapesicle' (SDB)	NZep
'Graphic Arts' (TB)	NZep
¶ 'Grecian Skies' (TB)	SCro
'Green Halo' (DB)	EGol LBro
'Green Ice' (TB)	CKel MS&S
'Green Jungle' (TB)	LBro
'Green Spot' (IB)	Widely available
'Greenstuff' (SDB)	LBro MMil
'Gypsy Boy' (SDB)	NZep
'H C van Vliet' (Dutch)	LAma NRog
'Hagar's Helmet' (IB)	LBro
'Hallowed Thoughts' (TB)	MMil
halophila	See I. ***spuria h.***
'Happening' (SDB)	NZep
'Happy Choice' (Spuria)	LBro
'Happy Mood' (IB)	LBro
¶ 'Happy Song' (BB)	LBro
'Happy Thought' (IB)	CKel
'Harbor Blue' (TB)	LRHS MAus MWat
¶ 'Harleqinade' (BB)	LBro
'Harlow Gold' (IB)	NZep
'Harmony' (Reticulata)	CAvo CBro EPot ETub LAma LBlo LBow MBri NHar NRog SIng
hartwegii	EPot WDav
'Harvest Festival' (SDB)	LBro
'Hazy Skies' (MTB)	LBro
'Headlines' (TB)	CKel
'Heather Hawk'	MAus
'Heavenly Blue' (***sibirica***)	CKel CSco EHon LMay
¶ 'Heavenly Days'	MAus
'Hedge'	CDoC
'Helen Astor' (***sibirica***)	CCla CPar CRow CSco CWGN GAbr GDra
¶ 'Helen Boehm' (TB)	SCro
'Helen McGregor' (TB)	CKel
'Helen Proctor' (IB)	NZep SCro
'Helge'	LWad NFai SFis
'Hellcat' (IB)	NZep
¶ 'Hell's Fire' (TB)	SCro
'Hercules' (Reticulata)	LAma
¶ 'Hers' (IB)	SCro
'High Barbaree' (TB)	MAus
'High Command' (TB)	CKel LHil SCro
'Highland Cascade' (TB)	MAus
'Hildegarde' (Dutch)	LAma
'Hills of Lafayette' (IB)	NZep
¶ 'His' (IB)	SCro
histrio ssp. ***aintabensis***	LAma MPar
§ ***histrioïdes*** 'Angel's Eye'	EPot
– 'Angel's Tears'	See I. ***h.*** 'Angel's Eye'
– 'Major'	CBro LAma LBlo LBow MBal MBri NRog
¶ – 'Sheila Ann Germaney'	EPot
– var. ***sophenensis***	LRHS WChr
'Hocus Pocus' (SDB)	EFou LBro
'Holden Clough'	CAvo CBot CGle CHad CRDP CWGN ELan ELun EMFW EOrc GCal LBro MAus MFir MMil MUlv NHol NSti SHig SSpi SUsu WAbb WChe WEas WRus WWin
'Holiday Flame' (IB)	NZep
'Honey Glazed' (IB)	EFou LBro MAus NZep
'Honington' (SDB)	LRHS MAus MMil
'Honorabile' (MTB)	MAus

'Hoodwink' (SDB) LBro NZep
hoogiana EPot ETub LAma LBow MTho WChr WThu
– 'Alba' EPot ETub
– 'Purpurea' LRHS WChr
¶ 'Hopscotch' (BB) SCro
'Hot Fudge' (IB) NZep
'Hot Spice' (IB) NZep
¶ 'Hubbard' (IB) SCro
¶ 'Hubbub' (TB) SCro
'Hugh Miller' (TB) MAus
'Hula Doll' (MDB) LBro MRob
§ ***humilis*** EPot WHil WThu
hyrcana CBro LAma LBow
'I Do' (TB) NZep
§ ***iberica*** EPot
§ – ssp. ***elegantissima*** EPot
'Ice Chip' (SDB) LBro NZep
'Ida' (Reticulata) LAma
'Ideal' (Dutch) LAma
illyrica JCA 589.800 See I. ***pallida***
¶ ***imbricata*** MAus
'Imperator' (Dutch) CB&S LBlo
'Imperial Bronze' (Spuria) MAus
'Imperial Sun' (Spuria) LBro
'Impetuous' (BB) LBro
'Indeed' (IB) LBro NZep
'Indian Chief' (TB) ENot LBro LRHS
'Indian Jewel' (SDB) LBro
'Indian Pow Wow' (SDB) LBro
¶ 'Indigo Flight' (IB) EFou LBro
¶ 'Infinite Grace' (TB) SCro
'Ingenuity' (SDB) LBro
¶ 'Innocent Heart' (TB) MAus
innominata CCla CGle CMea CRDP CRow CSam EBar ECha EPot GAbr LBee MFir MHig MTho NHar NMen NNrd NSti NTow SIng SMrm SSou SUsu WCla WEas WOMN
– 'Doctor Riddle's Form' CGle CRDP EPla GDra MBal NHol
– rose form CNic
– 'Spinners' SAxl SWas WDav
'Inscription' (SDB) LBro NZep
'Interpol' (TB) MAus
'Irish Doll' (MDB) LBro LHil MAus MRob
¶ 'Irish Tune' (TB) SCro
'Ishmael' (SDB) LBro
'Ivor Knowles' (CH) LBro
'Ivory Gown' (TB) MAus
'J S Dijt' (Reticulata) CAvo CBro EPar EPot LAma LBlo LBow MBri NRog SIng WHil WPer
'Jack o' Hearts' (SDB) LBro
'Jade Mist' (SDB) LBro
'Jan Reagan' (SDB) NZep
'Jana White' (MTB) MAus
'Jane Phillips' (TB) CHad CKel CMGP CSco CShe EBlo ECtt ELan ENot ERou LBro LGre MAus MMil MRav NOrc SChu SCro SPer SWat
'Jane Taylor' (SDB) CBro NNrd
'Janice Chesnik' (Spuria) LBro MS&S
'Janice Ruth' (TB) MAus
¶ ***japonica*** LHil NPer SCro
¶ – L 638 SCro
– 'Ledger's Variety' CAvo CBro CHad CHan CMon CRDP CRow CSco ECha ELan EPar GCal LGan MAus MBro MUlv NHol SCro SIng SSpi SUsu WEas WHoo WWat
– 'Rudolph Spring' GCal
– 'Variegata' CBot CHan CMon CRDP CRow ECha EFol EPar GCal LBro LHop MBal MPar MUlv NHol NOrc NPer SArc SBla SCro WHer WWin
'Jasper Gem' (MDB) LBro MMil MRob MS&S
¶ 'Java Charm' (TB) MMil
¶ 'Jazzebel' (TB) SCro
'Jean Guymer' (TB) LBro MMil NBir
'Jeannine (Reticulata) LAma LRHS
'Jeremy Brian' (SDB) MAus NZep
'Jersey Lilli' (SDB) EFol LRHS MAus NSti
'Jesse's Song' (TB) NZep SCro
'Jewel Baby' (SDB) CBro NZep
¶ 'Jewel Bright' (SDB) EFou MAus
¶ 'Jillaroo' (SDB) SCro
¶ 'Jillian Mason' MAus
'Joan Lay' (TB) CSco
'Joanna Taylor' (MDB) CBro MAus NZep WMar
'Joette' (MTB) LBro
¶ 'John' (IB) SCro
'Jolly Fellow' (SDB) LBro WThi
¶ ***jordana*** S&L 38 CMon
'Joyce' (Reticulata) CAvo CBro ELan EPar EPot LAma MBri NRog SIng WPer
'Joyful' (SDB) LBro NZep
'Joyous Isle' (SDB) LBro NZep
'Jubilee Gem' (TB) CKel
'Juliet' (TB) CKel
¶ ***juncea*** CMon
'June Prom' (TB) SCro
'Jungle Fires' (TB) MAus
'Jungle Shadows' (BB) MAus
'Jungle Warrior' (SDB) NZep
'Just Jennifer' (BB) LBro MAus
kaempferi See I. ***ensata***
¶ 'Karen Christine' (TB) SCro
'Karen Maddock' (TB) LBro
'Kashmir White' EGol LAma
'Kate Izzard' LHil
'Katharine Hodgkin' (Reticulata) CAvo CBro CRDP EPot GArf LAma LBow MTho NHar NRog SIng WAbe WChr WCru
'Katinka' (CH) LBro
'Katy Petts' (SDB) EFou LRHS MAus NZep
'Kayo' (SDB) CHad EFou LBro MAus MRob MS&S NSti NZep
kemaonensis GDra WDav
'Kent Pride' (TB) CMGP CSco EFou ERou LBro MRav SGil SHer SPer
'Kentucky Bluegrass' (SDB) EFou LBro MMil MRob NZep WWin
¶ 'Kentucky Derby' (TB) SCro
¶ 'Kermit' (IB) SCro
kerneriana CBro CRiv ELan EPot SWas WEas
¶ 'Keyhaven' (SDB) LBro
'Kharput' EGol LBro
'Kildonan' (TB) MAus
¶ 'Kilt Lilt' (TB) SCro
'Kirkstone' (TB) MAus
¶ ***kirkwoodii*** EPot

'Kissing Circle' (BB) LBro
'Kista' (SDB) LRHS MAus
'Kiwi Capers' (SDB) NZep
klattii See I. *spuria musulmanica*
'Knick Knack' (MDB) CBro CCor CGle CMGP ECar ELan LGre LHil MAus MHig MRob NMen NNrd SChu SGil SHer SIng
'Knotty Pine' (SDB) MAus
'Kochii' See I. *germanica* 'K.'
kolpakowskiana EPot
kopetdagensis EPot
¶ *korolkowii* CMon
– f. *violacea* WChr
kuschakewiczii EPot
'La Nina Rosa' (BB) MAus
¶ 'Laced Cotton' (TB) SCro
'Laced Lemonade' (SDB) EFou LBro
lactea SCro WThi
lacustris CRDP CRiv EPot GArf MBro MHig NCat NHar NKay NTow NWCA SMrm WOMN WPat
– x *gracilipes* CRDP EPla GDra LGre SAxl SWas WAbe WOMN
'Lady Bell' (MTB) LBro
¶ 'Lady Friend' ERou SCro
'Lady Ilse' MAus
¶ 'Lady Madonna' (TB) SCro
'Lady Mohr' (AB) CKel MAus
'Lady of Nepal' (IB) LBro
'Lady River' (TB) CKel
§ *laevigata* CBen CRDP CRow EBre ECha EGol EHon ELan LBre LHil LMay MSta NBar NBro NDea SHig SWat WChe WDav WHol
– 'Alba' CBen CRDP CRow CWGN EGol LMay WChe
– 'Atropurpurea' CRDP CRow EGol IBlr LMay MSta SBar
– 'Colchesterensis' CBen CRDP CRow CWGN EBre EGol EHon LBre LMay MSta SCro SWat WChe
– 'Dorothy' CWGN CWes MSta SCro WChe
– 'Midnight' CBen CRow CWGN EGol EHon SCro SWat
– 'Mottled Beauty' CBen CRow MSta
– 'Richard Greany' CRow
– 'Rose Queen' See I. *ensata* 'R.Q.'
– 'Snowdrift' See I. 'Snowdrift'
– 'Variegata' CBot CChu CRDP CWGN ECha EGol EHon EWav LMay MSta NDea SCro SSpi SWat WChe WHol WWat
– 'Violet Garth' CRow
– 'Weymouth' CRDP CRow CWGN EGol SCro
¶ 'Lake Placid' (TB) SCro
¶ 'Land o' Lakes' (TB) SCro
'Langport Carnival' (IB) CKel
'Langport Chapter' (IB) CKel
'Langport Chief' (IB) CKel MS&S
'Langport Chimes' (IB) CKel
'Langport Duchess' (IB) CKel
'Langport Fairy' (IB) CKel
'Langport Fashion' (IB) CKel
'Langport Finch' (IB) CKel NZep
'Langport Flame' (IB) CKel MMil
'Langport Flash' (IB) CKel
'Langport Flush' (IB) CKel SCro
'Langport Girl' (IB) CKel
'Langport Honey' (IB) CKel
'Langport Jane' (IB) CKel
'Langport Judy' (IB) CKel
'Langport Lady' (IB) CKel LHil
'Langport Magic' (IB) CKel
'Langport Minstrel' (IB) CKel NZep
'Langport Pagan' (IB) CKel
'Langport Pansy' (IB) CKel
'Langport Pearl' (IB) CKel
'Langport Pinnacle' (IB) CKel
'Langport Prince' (IB) CKel
'Langport Robin' (IB) CKel
'Langport Romance' (IB) CKel
'Langport Secret' (IB) CKel
'Langport Smoke' (IB) CKel
'Langport Snow' (IB) CKel
'Langport Song' (IB) CKel MMil
'Langport Star' (IB) CKel
'Langport Storm' (IB) CKel EFou
'Langport Sultan' (IB) CKel
'Langport Sun' (IB) CKel LHil
'Langport Tartan' (IB) CKel MS&S
'Langport Vale' (IB) CKel
'Langport Violet' (IB) CKel
'Langport Vista' (IB) CKel
'Langport Warrior' (IB) CKel MS&S
'Langport Wren' (IB) CBro CKel LGre LHil MMil
'Langthorn's Pink' (*sibirica*) CRDP ELan
¶ 'Las Olas' (CH) LBro
§ *latifolia* WDav
– *alba* ELan
¶ 'Latin Rock' (TB) SCro
'Laurenbuhl' (*sibirica*) SCro
'Lavendula Plicatee' MRob
§ *lazica* CAvo CBro CMon EPla EPot IBlr MAus MUlv NSti SChu SCro SPou SWas WCot WEas WRus
¶ 'Leda's Lover' (TB) SCro
'Lemon Blossom' (SDB) NZep
'Lemon Brocade' (TB) MAus
'Lemon Drop' (TB) CKel
'Lemon Flare' (SDB) CMGP EBlo EBre ECtt EGol LBre LBro MAus MS&S NHar NRoo
'Lemon Flurry' (IB) LBro
'Lemon Glitter' (TB) EFou
'Lemon Ice' (TB) MMil
'Lemon Lark' (SDB) NZep
'Lemon Mist' (TB) MMil
'Lemon Puff' (MDB) CBro LBro MRob
'Lemon Queen' (Dutch) LBlo
'Lemon Reflection' (TB) MMil
'Lemon Tree' (TB) MAus
'Lena' SHer WCot WCra WHil
'Letitia' WThu
¶ 'Libation' (MDB) LBro
'Licorice Stick' (TB) MAus
'Light Cavalry' (IB) NZep
¶ 'Light Laughter' (IB) LBro
¶ 'Lighted Window' (TB) SCro
'Lilac and Lavender' (SDB) MMil NZep
'Lilac Lulu' (SDB) NZep
'Lilac Mist' (TB) MAus
'Lilli-White' (SDB) CHad EBlo EBre EFol EGol ESma LBre LBro MAus MRob NHar WCra

'Lime Grove' (SDB) SCro
'Limeheart' (*sibirica*) CRDP ELan ERou LBro NHol NRoo NSti SPer WHal
¶ 'Limelight' (*sibirica*) SRms
¶ 'Limpid Pools' (SDB) SCro
'Liquid Smoke' (TB) EFou
'Listowell' (IB) LBro
'Little Amigo' (SDB) NZep
'Little Annie' (SDB) NZep
'Little Bill' (SDB) EFou WThi
'Little Bishop' (SDB) NZep
'Little Black Belt' (SDB) EFou LBro MRob MS&S NZep
'Little Blackfoot' (SDB) CHad LRHS MAus WWin
¶ 'Little Blue' (TB) SCro
'Little Chestnut' (SDB) LBro MAus
'Little Cottage' (IB) SCro
'Little Dandy' (SDB) MAus
'Little Dogie' (SDB) LBro
'Little Dream' (SDB) NZep
'Little Episode' (SDB) NZep
¶ 'Little Miss' (BB) SCro
'Little Paul' (MTB) LBro
'Little Pearl' (MDB) NZep
'Little Rosy Wings' (SDB) CBro LBro LGre MMil SCro
'Little Shadow' (IB) CKel CSco EBre ECtt LBre LBro MRav MRob NHar SHer WCra
'Little Sir Echo' (BB) MAus
'Little Snow Lemon' (IB) EFou NZep
¶ 'Little Suki' (SDB) EFou
'Little Vanessa' (SDB) MAus NSti
'Live Jazz' (SDB) MRob NZep
'Lively Rose' (MTB) LBro
'Llanthony' (SDB) MAus NZep
'Lodestar' (TB) LBro MS&S
'Lodore' (TB) CKel MAus SRms
'Logo' (IB) NZep
'Lollipop' (SDB) NZep
longipetala NBir
'Lookin' Good' (IB) NZep
¶ 'Lord Baltimore' (TB) SCro
'Lord Warden' (TB) EFou
'Lord Wolsely' (Spuria) LBro
¶ 'Lorilee' (TB) SCro
'Lorna Lee' (TB) MAus
¶ ***lortetii*** SIng
'Lothario' (TB) CKel MS&S
'Loud Mouth' (AB) LBro
'Loud Music' (TB) MAus
'Louise Hopper' (MTB) NZep
'Love Lisa' (SDB) NZep
¶ 'Loveday' (TB) LBro
'Lovely Again' (TB) MAus
¶ 'Lovely Kay' (TB) SCro
'Lovely Light' (TB) MAus
'Lovely Me' (SDB) NZep
'Loveshine' (SDB) NZep
'Love's Allure' (TB) NZep
¶ 'Love's Tune' (IB) SCro
'Low Snow' (SDB) NZep
'Lucinda' (TB) CKel
'Lucky Charm' (MTB) LBro
'Lucky Duck' (SDB) NZep
'Lugano' (TB) MMil
'Lunar Fire' (TB) MAus
'Luscious One' (SDB) LBro
lutescens LBro LHil MAus WChr
§ – 'Campbellii' CBro EBre ECar EGol LBre LGre MBro MHig NBar NNrd SIng WMar
– ***cyanea*** NKay
– 'Jackanapes' NKay
¶ – ***lutescens*** CMon
'Lydia Jane' (Spuria) LBro
'Lynn Hall' (TB) CKel
¶ 'Lynwood Gold' (IB) EFou
macrosiphon EPot WDav
'Madeira Belle' (TB) MAus
'Maestro' (TB) CKel
'Magenta and Peach' MAus
'Magic Carpet' (TB) CKel
'Magic Flute' (MDB) LBro MRob
'Magic Hills' (TB) CKel
'Magic Man' (TB) LBro
magnifica EPot ETub WChr WThu
'Mahogany Snow' (SDB) NZep
¶ 'Maiden's Blush' LHil
¶ 'Mama Hoohoo' (IB) SCro
'Mandarin' (TB) GDra
maracandica EPot
'Marcus Perry' (*sibirica*) CRow MSte
'Marhaba' (MDB) CBro
'Maritima' (Spuria) CCor
'Marmalade Skies' (BB) LBro NZep
¶ 'Marmot' (MDB) MAus
'Maroon Caper' (IB) MAus
'Marshlander' (TB) EFou SCro
'Marty' (IB) LBro
'Mary Frances' (TB) LBro MAus SCro
'Mary McIlroy' (SDB) CBro LBro
'Mary Randall' (TB) MAus MS&S
¶ 'Master Touch' (TB) SCro
'Matchpoint' (TB) LBro
'Maui Moonlight' (IB) NZep
'May Melody' (TB) MAus
'Meadow Court' (SDB) CBro CHad MAus MRob WMer
'Meadow Moss' (SDB) EGol
'Media Luz' (Spuria) CHad LBro
'Melbreak' (TB) CKel EBre LBre MAus
¶ 'Melissa Sue' (TB) SCro
mellita See I. ***suaveolens***
– ***rubromarginata*** See I. ***suaveolens***
'Melon Honey' (SDB) LBro MAus MRob NZep WWin
'Memphis Delight' (TB) MAus
¶ 'Menton' (SDB) LBro
'Merry Day' (IB) CKel
'Merseyside' (SDB) LBro LHil
'Metaphor' (TB) MAus MMil
'Michael Paul' (SDB) LBro NZep
'Midas Kiss' (IB) LBro
¶ 'Midnight Fire' ERou
'Midnight Madness' (SDB) NZep
milesii CHan NBir SCro WPer
'Mini Dynamo' (SDB) NZep
'Minnie Colquitt' (TB) CKel MS&S SCro
'Mirror Image' (TB) NZep
'Miss Banbury' (TB) CKel
¶ 'Miss Carla' (IB) LBro
'Mission Sunset' (TB) EBlo MAus
'Missouri Gal' (Spuria) LBro
missouriensis CRow ESma
¶ – ***arizonica*** WDav
'Mister Roberts' (SDB) LBro NZep

'Mockingbird' (MTB)	MS&S
'Monaco' (TB)	EFou
monnieri	CMil CMon SDix
Monspur Group (Spuria)	GCal
'Moon Shadows' (SDB)	MAus
'Moonlight' (TB)	EGol EPot ESma LBro MAus MRav NNor
'Moonlight Waves'	See I. ***ensata*** 'M.W.'
¶ 'Morning Hymn' (TB)	SCro
¶ 'Morning Show' (IB)	SCro
¶ 'Morocco' (TB)	SCro
¶ 'Morwenna' (TB)	LBro MAus
'Mrs Nate Rudolph' (SDB)	EFou LBro LHil WThi
'Mrs Rowe' (***sibirica***)	CBre CRow EFou LBro MAus MNFA
'Mrs Saunders' (***sibirica***)	CBre CRow
'Mulberry Rose' (TB)	CKel
¶ ***munzii***	EPot
'Muriel Neville' (TB)	MAus
'Music Box' (SDB)	NZep
'Music Caper' (SDB)	LBro
'Music Maker' (TB)	MS&S
'My Honeycomb' (TB)	MAus
'My Mary' (TB)	CKel MS&S
'my seedling' (DB)	CBro
'My Smoky' (TB)	CKel
'Myra's Child' (SDB)	MAus
¶ 'Mystique' (TB)	SCro
'Nambe' (MTB)	LBro
'Nampara' (TB)	LBro
'Nancy Hardy ' (MDB)	CBro
'Nancy Lindsay'	See I. ***lutescens*** 'N.L.'
¶ 'Naranja'	LHil
'Narnia' (SDB)	NZep
'Nashborough' (TB)	CKel MS&S
'Natascha' (Reticulata)	EPot ETub LAma LBlo SIng WHil
¶ 'Navajo Blanket' (TB)	SCro
'Navy Doll' (MDB)	NZep
'Nectar' (TB)	CKel MS&S
'Needlecraft' (TB)	MMil
¶ 'Needlepoint' (TB)	SCro
'Neon Pixie' (SDB)	NZep
'Neophyte' (Spuria)	LBro
nepalensis	See I. ***decora***
nertschinskia	See I. ***sanguinea***
'New Idea' (MTB)	LBro MAus MS&S
'New Snow' (TB)	CKel CWes ENot MAus
'New Wave' (MTB)	NZep
'Nice 'n' Nifty' (IB)	NZep
nicolaii	EPot LRHS WChr
¶ 'Niebelungen' (TB)	NFai
¶ 'Night Owl' (TB)	LHil SCro
'Night Shift' (IB)	NZep
'Nightfall'	SFis
¶ ***nigricans*** S&L 148	CMon
'Nineveh' (AB)	MAus NSti
¶ 'Nora Distin'	MAus
'Normandie' (TB)	MAus
'Norton Sunlight' (Spuria)	LBro
'Nottingham Lace' (***sibirica***)	LBro
¶ 'No-name'	NSti
'Nuggets' (MDB)	NZep
nusairiensis	EPot LRHS WChr
'Nylon Ruffles' (SDB)	EGol LBro
¶ 'Ochraurea'	GCal
ochroleuca	See I. ***orientalis***
'Offenham' (TB)	LBro
'Oh Jay' (SDB)	NZep
'Ohio Belle' (SDB)	NZep
'Oklahoma Bandit' (IB)	LBro
'Ola Kala' (TB)	CSco ERou MAus SCro SFis
'Old Flame' (TB)	NZep
'Oliver' (SDB)	LBro MAus MS&S
'Olympic Torch' (TB)	LHil MAus
'On Fire' (SDB)	MRob NZep
¶ 'One Accord' (SDB)	SCro
'One Desire' (TB)	NZep
'Open Sky' (SDB)	NZep
'Orange Blaze' (SDB)	CBro
'Orange Caper' (SDB)	EBlo NHar NZep
'Orange Dawn' (TB)	LBro
'Orange Maid' (Spuria)	LBro
'Orange Plaza'	WHil
'Orange Tiger' (SDB)	NZep
'Orchardist' (TB)	CKel
¶ 'Orchid Flare' (MDB)	LHil
'Oregold' (SDB)	NZep
¶ 'Oregon Skles' (TB)	SCro
'Oriental Blush' (SDB)	LBro
'Oriental Glory' (TB)	MAus
§ ***orientalis***	CBot CCor CHan CMil CRiv CRow ELan LBro LMay MAus MBal MBro NSti SChu SCro SDix SHig WWat WWin
– 'Alba'	See I. ***sanguinea*** 'A.'
¶ 'Oritam' (TB)	SCro
'Ornament' (SDB)	LBro MS&S NZep
'Oroville' (Spuria)	LBro
'Orville Fay' (***sibirica***)	EFou GCal LBro SAxl SCro
'Ottawa' (***sibirica***)	CCla CHad CKel CRiv CRow CWGN ELan ERou EWav MS&S NRoo SChu SCro
'Ouija' (BB)	LBro
'Out Yonder' (TB)	MAus
'Outstep' (SDB)	NZep
¶ 'Ovation' (TB)	SCro
'Owlet' (SDB)	MAus
'Pacer' (IB)	NZep
'Pacific Coast Hyb'	See I. Californian hybrids
¶ 'Pacific Mist' (TB)	SCro
'Pagan Princess' (TB)	MAus
'Painted Rose' (MTB)	LBro
'Pale Primrose' (TB)	MAus WEas
'Pale Suede' (SDB)	LBro
§ ***pallida***	CMGP EFou LHol MAus NSti
– 'Argentea Variegata'	CCla CGle CHad CKel CRDP EFol ERav LHop MUlv NRoo NSti SCro SSpi WHoo WRus
– 'Aurea'	See I. ***p.*** 'Variegata'
– 'Aurea Variegata'	See I. ***p.*** 'Variegata'
¶ – ssp. ***cengialtii***	CMon
– var. ***dalmatica***	See I. ***pallida pallida***
§ – ssp. ***pallida***	CBot CCla EBre ECha EGol ELan LBre LBro LHil MBri MUlv NSti SCro SDix SPer
– x ***tectorum***	MPar
N– 'Variegata'	Widely available
'Palomino' (TB)	MAus
'Paltec'	LGre
¶ 'Pandora's Purple' (TB)	SCro
¶ 'Papil' (***sibirica***)	NCat

'Papillon' (***sibirica***) CCla CHad CMGP EBre ELan ERou LBre LHop MAus MBro MUlv NHol NRoo NSti SPer WRus WSun
'Paradise' (TB) LBro SCro
'Paradise Bird' (TB) LBro
'Paradise Pink' (TB) CSco
paradoxa EPot
'Parakeet' (MTB) LBro
'Paricutin' (SDB) CBro NNrd
'Party Dress' (TB) CKel CMGP EBre ECtt ELan ENot EPla ERou LBre LBro MRav MRob MS&S NOrc SChu SPer WTyr
'Passport' (BB) MAus MS&S
¶ 'Pastel Delight' (SDB) NZep
'Patacake' (SDB) NZep
'Path of Gold' (DB) CBro CKel LBro MRob NNrd WHil
'Patterdale' (TB) MAus MS&S NBar NVic
'Pauline' (Reticulata) CAvo CBro EPot LAma NRog SIng WPer
'Peach ala Mode' (BB) MAus
¶ 'Peach Band' ERou
'Peach Eyes' (SDB) LBro
'Peach Float' (TB) MAus
'Peach Petals' (BB) LBro NZep
¶ 'Peach Picotee' (TB) SCro
'Peach Spot' (TB) MAus
'Peaches 'n' Topping' (BB) LBro
'Peachy Face' (IB) LBro NZep
'Peacock' ECha LGre SUsu WSHC
'Pearly Dawn' (TB) CCla CMGP EBlo EBre ECtt GCHN LBre MS&S NVic SGil SHer SPer
'Pecan Spot' (SDB) NZep
'Pegasus' (TB) SCro
'Peggy Chambers' (IB) EFou LBro
¶ 'Peking Summer' (TB) SCro
'Pennies' (MDB) NZep
'Penny Bunker' (Spuria) LBro
'Penny Candy' (MDB) NZep
¶ 'Pennywort' (IB) SCro
¶ 'People Pleaser' (SDB) SCro
'Peppermint Twist' (SDB) NZep
'Perry Hill' (TB) CKel
'Perry's Blue' (***sibirica***) CB&S CCla CKel CPar CWGN EBre EFou EPar ERou ESma GAbr GDra LBre MNFA NFai NKay NPer SCro SPer SUsu WHal WRus WSun WWat
'Perry's Favourite' (***sibirica***) CBre CRow
'Perry's Pygmy' (***sibirica***) CRow
'Persian Doll' (MDB) NZep
'Persian Fancy' (TB) CKel
'Persian Romance' (TB) CKel
persica LAma
¶ 'Persimmon' (***sibirica***) EBre ERou LBre
'Pet' (SDB) NSti NZep
'Picadee' MMil NNrd
¶ 'Pied Pretty' (SDB) SCro
'Pigmy Gold' (IB) LBro
'Pinewood Amethyst' (CH) LBro
¶ 'Pink Angel' (TB) SCro
'Pink Bubbles' (BB) LBro NZep
'Pink Clover' (TB) LBro
¶ 'Pink Confetti' (TB) SCro
¶ 'Pink Haze' (TB) SCro
'Pink Kitten' (IB) NZep
'Pink Lamb' (BB) LBro
'Pink Lavender' (TB) SCro
'Pink Pleasure' (TB) NZep
'Pink Pussycat' MAus
'Pink Randall' (TB) SCro
'Pink Ruffles' (IB) CKel
¶ 'Pink Taffeta' (TB) SCro
¶ 'Pink 'n'Mint' (TB) SCro
'Pinnacle' (TB) CKel MAus
'Piper's Tune' (IB) NZep
'Pipes of Pan' (TB) MAus
'Pippi Longstockings' (SDB) NZep
'Pirate Prince' (***sibirica***) LBro NPer
'Pixie' (DB) CKel
'Pixie Flirt' (MDB) LBro
'Pixie Plum' (SDB) MAus
'Pixie Princess' (SDB) MAus
planifolia EBul
¶ – AB&S 4609 CMon
¶ – S&L 301 CMon
¶ 'Pledge Allegiance' (TB) SCro
plicata MAus
¶ 'Plum Perfect' (SDB) ECha SCro
'Poet' (TB) NZep
¶ 'Poet Time' (TB) SCro
'Pogo' (SDB) EBlo EBre ECtt EGol ELan ENot LBre MMil MRav NHar NNrd NZep SCro WCra
'Pogo Doll' (AB) LBro
'Polly Dodge' (***sibirica***) LBro
'Pony' (IB) LBro MS&S
'Popinjay' (CH) LBro
'Port of Call' (Spuria) LBro
'Pot Luck' (IB) LBro MS&S
'Powder Pink' (TB) CKel
'Powder Rock' (TB) CKel
'Prairie Sunset' (TB) CKel
¶ 'Prairie Warbler' CRow
'Praise the Lord' (TB) LBro
¶ 'Prancing Pony' (TB) SCro
'Pretender' (TB) MAus
¶ 'Prettie Print' (TB) SCro
¶ 'Pride of Ireland' (TB) SCro
'Prince' (SDB) EFou LBro
'Princess Beatrice' See I. ***pallida pallida***
prismatica CBre CMon CSun EPla EPot SIng
¶ – ***alba*** GAbr
'Privileged Character' (SDB) NZep
¶ 'Prodigy' (MDB) LBro
'Professor Blaauw' (Dutch) LAma
¶ 'Prophetic Message' (AB) LBro
'Protégé' (Spuria) LBro
'Proud Land' MAus
¶ 'Proud Tradition' (TB) SCro
pseudacorus CKin CPar CRDP CRow CSco CTom CWGN EBre EHon ELan EWav GPoy LBre LMay MAus MChe MSta MUlv NDea NLan NNor NSel SWat WChe WHer WHol WShi WWin

¶– 'Alba' GCal
– var. ***bastardii*** CChu CRDP CRow CWGN ECha EGol EMFW MS&S MUlv SPer WChe
– cream form EGol MUlv NBir
– dwarf form NSti
– 'Ecru' CRow
– 'Flore Pleno' CRow EMFW
– 'Golden Fleece' SPer
– 'Golden Queen' CRow MSta MUlv
– 'Ivory' CRow
¶– 'Turnispeed' GCal
– 'Variegata' Widely available
¶– x ***versicolor*** SCro
pseudopumila WThu
¶– MS 986/975 CMon
pumila CChu CMon CRDP EPla MAus MBro NKay NNor NWCA SPla WAbe WCla WDav
– ***aequiloba*** EPot
– ***atroviolacea*** MBro MCas MNFA NTow
– ssp. ***attica*** See I. ***attica***
– ***aurea*** CBow MBro MCas MNFA NTow SPla
– ***lutea*** WHil
– 'Violacea' MBro SCro SPer
'Pumpkin Center' (SDB) NZep
'Puppet' (SDB) EGol LBro NZep
'Puppet Baby' (MDB) NZep
'Puppy Love' (MTB) NZep
¶***purdyi*** EPot NSti
'Purple Cloak' (***sibirica***) LBro MSte SMad
'Purple Dream' (CH) LBro
'Purple Gem' (Reticulata) CBro EPot LAma
'Purple Mere' (***sibirica***) CPar LBro
'Purple Sensation' (Dutch) CB&S LAma
'Purple Song' (TB) CKel MS&S
¶'Purple Streaker' (TB) SCro
purpurea See I. ***galatica***
'Pussytoes' (MDB) NZep
'Queechee' (TB) ERou MRav MS&S SCro
'Queen in Calico' (TB) SCro
¶'Queen of Hearts' (TB) SCro
'Queen's Ivory' (SDB) MAus
'Queen's Pawn' (SDB) LBro NZep
'Quiet Lagoon' (SDB) NZep
'Quiet Thought' (TB) LBro
'Quintana' (CH) LBro
'Quip' (MDB) NZep
¶'R C Dardanus' ETub
'Rabbit's Foot' (SDB) NZep
¶'Radiant Summer' (TB) SCro
'Rain Dance' (SDB) MAus NZep
'Rainbow Sherbet' (SDB) NZep
'Rainbow Trout' (TB) LBro
'Raindance Kid' (IB) NZep
'Rajah' (TB) CMGP EBre ERou LBre LBro LHil NOrc WHer
¶'Rancho Rose' (TB) SCro
'Ranger' (TB) CKel LHil
'Rare Edition' (IB) EFou LBro MRob MS&S NZep SCro
'Rare Treat' (TB) NZep
'Raspberry Acres' (IB) MAus MS&S
'Raspberry Blush' (IB) NZep
'Raspberry Jam' (SDB) EFou LBro MS&S NZep
'Raspberry Rose' (IB) NZep
'Raspberry Sundae' (BB) LBro NZep
'Rathe Primrose' (IB) SCro
'Raven Hill' (TB) MAus
'Real Jazzy' (MTB) NZep
'Red Flag' (***sibirica***) NHol
'Red Flare' (***sibirica***) ELan LBro LHop MS&S
'Red Flash' (TB) CKel
'Red Heart' (SDB) ECtt MRav NHar
'Red Lion' (TB) NZep
'Red Oak' (Spuria) MAus
'Red Orchid' (IB) CBow CDoC CKel
'Red Revival' (TB) MAus
'Red Rum' (TB) CKel
'Red Tempest' (IB) NZep
¶'Red Zinger' (IB) SCro
¶'Reddy Maid' (***sibirica***) LBro SCro
'Redwing' (TB) CKel MWat
'Redwood Supreme' (Spuria) LBro MS&S
'Regards' (SDB) CBro LBro MRob
¶'Reginae' MAus
¶***reichenbachii*** LBee
– Balkana Group SIng
'Reluctant Dragon' (SDB) NZep
¶'Repartee' (TB) SCro
§ ***reticulata*** CB&S CBro CMon EPar EPot ERav ETub LBlo MPlt NRog SIng
– cvs. See under cultivar name
'Reward' CSco
'Riches' (SDB) NZep
'Rickshaw' (SDB) LBro
'Right Royal' (TB) MAus
¶'Rime Frost' (TB) MAus
¶'Rimouski' (***sibirica***) LBro
'Ringo' (TB) NZep SCro
'Rio Tulare' LBro
'Ripple Chip' (SDB) NZep
¶'Rising Moon' (TB) SCro
¶'River Hawk' (TB) SCro
'River Patrol' (TB) EFou
'Robert Graves' (TB) MAus
§ 'Rocket' (TB) CKel CMGP NBir SCro SPer
'Roger Perry' (***sibirica***) CRow
'Roman Emperor' (TB) EFou
¶'Romance' (TB) ERou
¶'Ron' (TB) SCro
'Rose Queen' See I. ***ensata*** 'R.Q.'
'Rose Violet' (TB) MAus
¶'Roselene' (TB) SCro
'Rosemary's Dream' (MTB) NZep
rosenbachiana WChr
'Rosie Lulu' (SDB) NZep
'Rosy Air' (SDB) NZep
'Rosy Wings' (TB) EGol
'Roustabout' (SDB) EFou LBro
'Roy Elliott' NHol
'Royal Ascot' (TB) LBro
'Royal Blue' (Reticulata) LAma LBow
– (***sibirica***) ECha SBla
'Royal Contrast' (SDB) LBro NZep
'Royal Elf' (SDB) NZep
'Royal Eyelash' (SDB) NZep
¶'Royal Intrigue' (TB) SCro
¶'Royal Midget' (SDB) LBro
¶'Royal Regency' (TB) SCro

'Royal Ruffles' (TB) MAus
'Royal Sparks' (SDB) NZep
'Royal Toss' (TB) CKel
'Royal Touch' (TB) EFou
'Royal Velours' LHil
'Royal Yellow' (Dutch) LAma NRog
'Ruby Chimes' (IB) CHad MAus MS&S
'Ruby Contrast' (TB) MAus MS&S
'Ruby Gem' (TB) CKel
'Ruby Locket' (SDB) LBro NZep
'Ruby Mine' (TB) MAus
rudskyi See I. ***variegata***
¶ 'Ruffled Ballet' (TB) SCro
¶ 'Ruffled Surprise' (TB) SCro
'Ruffled Velvet' (***sibirica***) LBro WTyr
¶ 'Ruffles and Lace' (TB) SCro
'Rushing Stream' (TB) MAus
'Rustam' (TB) CKel
'Rustic Jewel' (TB) CKel
'Rusty Dusty' (SDB) NZep
'Ruth Couffer' (BB) LBro MS&S
'Ruth Nies Cabeen' (Spuria) LBro
ruthenica ECar GArf NKay NNrd SIng WOMN
'Sable' (TB) CHad CPar CSco EBre LBre MAus NOrc SPer
'Sable Night' (TB) CKel ERou MAus
'Saffron Charm' (AB) MAus
'Saint Crispin' (TB) CHad CMGP CSco EBre ERou LBre MRav MUlv MWat SChu SPer
¶ 'Salonique' (TB) NFai
'Saltwood' (SDB) CBro
'Sam' (SDB) NZep
¶ 'Sam Carne' MAus
¶ 'Samurai Warrior' (TB) SCro
'San Jose' (TB) NZep
¶ 'Sand and Sea' (TB) LBro
'Sand Princess' (MTB) EFou
'Sandy Caper' (IB) MAus
§ ***sanguinea*** CAvo SSpi
§ – 'Alba' CRow WThi
¶ – x ***laevigata*** SCro
¶ 'Santana' (TB) SCro
'Sapphire Beauty' (Dutch) LAma NRog
¶ 'Sapphire Hills' (TB) SCro
'Sapphire Jewel' (SDB) NZep
'Sarah Taylor' (SDB) CBro EFou MAus
sari EPot LAma WChr
'Sass with Class' (SDB) NZep
'Satin Gown' (TB) MAus
'Saturnus' (Dutch) LAma SCro
'Saucy Peach' (BB) LBro
'Savoir Faire' (***sibirica***) CRDP CWGN ECha LBro
'Saxon Princess' (TB) LBro
schachtii WChr
¶ 'Schortman's Garnet Ruffles' (TB) SCro
'Scintilla' (IB) MMil SCro
¶ 'Scintillation' (TB) SCro
'Scribe' (MDB) CBro LHil LRHS MAus NZep
'Scrimmage' (SDB) NZep
'Sea Fret' (SDB) CBro
¶ 'Sea Horse' (***sibirica***) NCat
'Sea of Joy' (TB) SCro
'Sea Shadows' (***sibirica***) MAus NBir
'Sea Urchin' (SDB) NZep
'Seawolf' (TB) NZep
serbica See I. ***reichenbachii***
'Serena' (TB) CKel
'Serenity Prayer' (SDB) NZep
setosa CBro CCla CCor CMea CRDP CRiv CRow ECha EGol EMNN GAbr ITim LGan LHil MHig MSta NKay NNrd SIng WCru WHil
– ***alba*** CRow LGan
§ – var. ***arctica*** CCla CNic CRDP CRow CTom ELan ELun EPot ESis GDra LBee LGre MBal MBro NHol NTow NWCA SBla SCro SHer SPer WAbe WDav WHoo WOMN WPer
¶ – ssp. ***canadensis*** ESis
– dwarf form See I. ***s. arctica***
– 'Hookeri' See I. ***s. canadensis***
*– ***major*** SIng
– ***nana*** See I. ***s. arctica***
¶ 'Shaft of Gold' (TB) SCro
'Shampoo' (IB) EFou NZep
'Sheer Class' (SDB) NZep
¶ 'Sheik' (AB) SCro
'Shelford Giant' (Spuria) LBro
'Shepherd's Delight' (TB) MAus
'Short Distance' (IB) LBro
'Show Me Yellow' (SDB) NZep
'Showcase' (TB) NZep
'Showdown' (***sibirica***) CB&S CDoC ECtt LBro LWad MBri MUlv NHar NHol WHal
¶ 'Showman' ERou
'Shrawley' (***sibirica***) MAus
'Shrinking Violet' (MTB) LBro
'Shy Violet' (SDB) NZep
sibirica CFis CMHG CMea CRDP CShe CTom CWGN EHon LAma LHil MBro MFir MWat NDea NNor NSel SMad WCru WEas WHer WHol WHoo WWin
¶ – cream form WCot
'Sierra Nevada' (Spuria) EFou LBro
'Sigh' (SDB) NZep
'Silent Strings' (IB) LBro
'Silver Edge' (***sibirica***) MAus NFai SAxl SCro WTyr
'Silver Tide' WEas
'Silvery Moon' (TB) SCro
sindjarensis See I. ***aucheri***
'Sindpers' (Juno) SWas
'Sing Again' (IB) CWes MAus
sintenisii CBro CHan CSun EPar SIng
¶ – ssp. ***brandzae*** CRDP
'Siva Siva' (TB) EBre ERou LBre MAus WHer
¶ 'Skating Party' (TB) SCro
¶ 'Skier's Delight' (TB) SCro
'Skip Stitch' (SDB) LBro MAus
'Sky and Snow' (SDB) NZep
'Sky Bolt' (SDB) MAus
¶ 'Sky Hooks' (TB) SCro
'Sky Wings' (***sibirica***) CWGN ECha
¶ 'Skyfire' (TB) SCro
'Slap Bang' (SDB) NZep
'Sleepy Time' (MDB) NZep
'Slim Jim' (MTB) LBro
'Small Sky' (SDB) CBro LBro MRob
'Small Wonder' (SDB) LBro
'Smart Girl' (TB) CKel

'Smarty Pants' (MTB) LBro
'Smell the Roses' (SDB) NZep
¶ 'Smoke Rings' (TB) SCro
'Smokey Dream' (TB) CKel
'Smoky Valley' (BB) LBro MS&S
'Smooth Orange' (TB) MAus
'Snappie' (IB) NZep
'Sneak Preview' (TB) NZep
'Snow Crest' (*sibirica*) CCla NHol SMad
'Snow Elf' (SDB) LBro
'Snow Festival' (IB) NZep
'Snow Fiddler' (MTB) NZep
'Snow Gambit' (MTB) NZep
¶ 'Snow Jo' NCat
¶ 'Snow Mound' (TB) SCro
'Snow Queen' (*sibirica*) CCla CHad CKel CRow CSco CWGN EHon ELan EPot ERou EWav LGan LMay MAus MBro NSti SCro SPer
'Snow Troll' (SDB) LRHS MAus WHer
'Snowcone' (IB) NZep
'Snowcrest' (*sibirica*) MAus
§ 'Snowdrift' (*laevigata* x) CRow CWGN EGol EHon EMFW EWav LMay MSta NDea SCro SHig WChe WHol
'Snowshill' (TB) LBro
'Snowy Owl' (TB) MAus
'Snowy River' (MDB) NZep
'Snowy Wonderland' (TB) NZep
'Soaring Kite' (TB) LBro MAus
'Soft Blue' (sibirica) LBro
'Soft Breeze' (SDB) NZep
¶ 'Solar Song' (SDB) NZep SCro
'Solid Gold' (TB) CKel
'Solid Mahogany' (TB) MAus MUlv
'Somerset Girl' (TB) CKel
'Somerset Vale' (TB) CKel MS&S
'Something Special' (BB) NZep
'Song of Norway' (TB) NZep SCro
¶ 'Soul Power' ERou
'Sounder' (BB) LBro
'Southcombe White' (*sibirica*) CRow GCal SWas
'Southern Clipper' (SDB) LRHS
'Space Odyssey' (TB) NZep
'Spanish Coins' (MTB) LBro NZep
'Sparkling Cloud' (SDB) MAus
'Sparkling Rosé' (*sibirica*) CB&S CBot CDoC EBlo EBre ECtt EFou EGol LBre LBro LWad MAus MBri NHar NHol NOrc WHal WRus
'Spartan' See I. ***germanica*** 'S.'
'Specify' (TB) CKel
'Speckled Bird' (AB) MAus
'Spirit of Memphis' (TB) MMil
'Splash of Red' (SDB) LBro NZep
'Spring Bells' (SDB) EFou
¶ 'Spring Dancer' (IB) SCro
'Spring Festival' (TB) CKel MAus
'Spring Signal' (TB) LBro
'Spring Wine' (IB) LBro
'Springtime' (Reticulata) CAvo EPot LAma LBow NRog SIng WCru
spuria ELan WDav
¶ – ssp. ***carthaliniae*** WPer
– ssp. ***demetrii*** ESma
– ssp. ***halophila*** CMon LBro MAus
– ssp. ***maritima*** NNrd SIng
§ – ssp. ***musulmanica*** CPar LBro
– ***ochroleuca*** See I. ***orientalis***
¶ sp. AGSJ 431 WDav
¶ sp. CLD 0495 NHol
¶ sp. CLD 0566 NHol
sp. CLD 1399 NHol
sp. CLD 1541 NHol
x ***squalens*** MAus
'Squeaky Clean' (SDB) NZep
'Stability' (Spuria) LBro
'Stapleford' (SDB) CBro
¶ 'Starcrest' (TB) SCro
'Stardate' (SDB) NZep
'Starlight Waltz' (SDB) NZep
'Starlit River' (TB) EFou
'Starry Eyed' (SDB) LBro
'Starshine' (TB) CKel MAus
¶ 'Startler' (TB) SCro
'Staten Island' (TB) CKel ELan ENot LHil MAus MS&S SRms
'Stella Polaris' (TB) SCro
§ ***stenophylla*** EPot
'Stepping Little' (BB) NZep
'Stepping Out' (TB) EBlo EBre EFou LBre MAus SCro
'Stitch in Time' (TB) SCro
'Stockholm' (SDB) LBro NZep
stolonifera CMon EPot
¶ – 'Bronze Beauty' CMon
¶ 'Stop the Music' (TB) SCro
'Storrington' (TB) SCro
'Strange Child' (SDB) NZep
'Strawberry Love' (IB) MAus NZep
'Strawberry Sensation' (TB) NZep
'Striking Gold' (MTB) NZep
'Strum' (IB) NZep
'Stylish' (DB) CKel
stylosa See I. ***unguicularis***
¶ 'Suave' (TB) SCro
§ ***suaveolens*** CBro ELan EPot SIng WDav WMar
subbiflora CCor WDav
'Sudeley' (SDB) SCro
'Sugar' (IB) CHad MAus NSti
'Sugar Candy' (CH) LBro
'Sugar Please' (SDB) NZep
'Sullom Voe' (TB) LBro
'Summer Luxury' (TB) NZep
'Summer Pearl' (TB) CKel
¶ 'Sumptuous' (TB) SCro
¶ 'Sun Dappled' ERou
'Sun Doll' (SDB) NZep
'Sun King' (TB) MAus
'Sun Miracle' (TB) MAus
'Sun Symbol' (SDB) MRob
'Sunbrella' (SDB) NZep
¶ 'Sunday Chimes' (TB) SCro
'Sunlit Sea' (Spuria) LBro
'Sunlit Trail' (SDB) MAus
'Sunny Dawn' (IB) LBro NZep
'Sunny Day' (Spuria) LBro
'Sunny Heart' (SDB) NZep
'Sunny Honey' (IB) NZep SCro
'Sunnyside' (Spuria) LBro
¶ 'Sunshine Isle' (SDB) NZep

'Superlation' (TB) SCro
¶ 'Superstition' (TB) SCro
'Surprise Blue' (MTB) NZep
'Surprise Orange' (MDB) NZep
'Susan Bliss' (TB) ELan NFai
susiana ETub LAma SIng
'Suspense' (Spuria) LBro
'Svelte' (IB) LBro
¶ 'Swahili' (TB) MAus
'Swank' (***sibirica***) LBro
¶ 'Swazi Princess' (TB) SCro
¶ 'Sweet and Neat' (SDB) SCro
'Sweet Lavender' (TB) SCro
¶ 'Sweet Musette' (TB) SCro
'Sweet Treat' (SDB) NZep
'Swizzle' (IB) LBro MS&S
'Syllable' (SDB) NZep
'Sylvia Murray' (TB) MAus
¶ 'Syncopation' (TB) LBro
'Tall Chief' (TB) CWes EBre LBre MAus NSti SCro
¶ 'Tanex' MAus
¶ 'Tangerine Sky' (TB) SCro
¶ 'Tangerine Sunrise' (TB) LBro
'Tantara' (SDB) MRob NZep SCro
'Tarheel Elf' (SDB) LBro
'Tarn Hows' (TB) CKel MAus SRms
'Taupkin' (SDB) LBro
tauri See I. ***stenophylla***
'Tease' (SDB) LBro
tectorum CMon CRDP LGre MPar SCro WOMN
– 'Alba' CMea SCro WThi WThu
– Burma form WThi
– 'Variegata' GAbr MBri SPer WAbe WHal
'Tell Fibs' (SDB) NZep
'Ten' (SDB) NZep SCro
tenax CMil CNic EBul EPot LBee MBal MHig WChe
– 'Alba' EPot
tenuis MHig NNrd
'Tequila Sunrise' (TB) CKel
'The Bride' See I. 'Bride'
'The Citadel' (TB) CKel SCro
'The Desert' (TB) CKel
'The Monarch' (TB) CKel
'The Rocket' See I. 'Rocket'
'Theatre' (TB) NZep SCro
¶ 'Theda Clark' (IB) SCro
'Theseus' (Aril) EPot
'Third Charm' (SDB) CBro
'Third World' (SDB) CBro
'Thor' (Aril) EPot
'Three Cherries' (MDB) CBro
'Threepio' (SDB) NZep
'Thrice Blessed' (SDB) NZep
'Thriller' (TB) NZep
thunbergii See I. ***sanguinea***
'Thundercloud' (TB) MAus
'Tic Tac' (MDB) NZep
'Tidbit' (DB) LBro
'Tiddle de Winks' (BB) LBro
¶ 'Tide's In' (TB) ERou SCro
'Tillamook' (TB) MAus
'Time for Love' (TB) NZep
¶ 'Timeless Moment' (TB) SCro
'Timmie Too' (BB) LBro
tingitana CMil
– var. ***fontanesii*** SPou
¶ – – AB&S 4452 CMon
'Tinkerbell' (SDB) CKel EBlo EGol LBro LGre MRob NRoo SChu SHer WCra
'Tiny Freckles' (MDB) NZep
'Titan's Glory' (TB) LBro SCro WCot
'Toasty' (SDB) NZep
'Tom Tit' (TB) MAus
'Tomingo' (SDB) LRHS MAus MFir
¶ 'Tomorrow's Child' (TB) SCro
'Toni Lynn' (MDB) NNrd
'Toots' (SDB) LBro
'Top Flight' (TB) CHad CMGP ENot ERou SHer SPer
'Topolino' (TB) CKel
'Topsy Turvy' (MTB) LBro NZep
'Torchlight' (TB) CKel MS&S
'Torchy' (SDB) NZep
¶ 'Total Eclipse' SRms
'Touch of Spring' (TB) MMil
'Toy Boat' (SDB) NZep
'Transcribe' (SDB) NZep
'Treasure' (TB) MAus
¶ 'Treveance Coce' (TB) LBro
'Tricks' (SDB) NZep
'Triplicata' (IB) LGre
trojana CMon MAus WDav
'Tropic Night' (***sibirica***) CCla CRiv CSco CWGN EBre EFou ERou GAbr LAbb LBre MRav MSta NHol NRoo NRya SCro SMad SPer WRus WWat
¶ 'Trout River' GArf
'Truly' (SDB) MAus
'Tu Tu Turquoise' (SDB) NZep
tuberosa See HERMODACTYLUS ***tuberosus***
'Tumbleweeds' (SDB) NZep
'Tupelo Honey' (TB) NZep
'Tuscan' (TB) CKel NZep
¶ 'Tut's Gold' (TB) SCro
'Twist of Fate' (TB) SCro
'Twist of Lemon' (MDB) NZep
¶ 'Two Rubies' (SDB) NZep
'Tycoon' (***sibirica***) CWGN NHol SAxl SPer
'Tyke' (MTB) NZep
§ ***unguicularis*** CAvo CB&S CBow CBro CCla CFis CKel CPar CShe EBre EFou ELan EPar EPot ERav IBlr IHos LBre LBro NRoo NSti NWCA SCro SDix SHer SIng SPou WEas WHal WHoo
– 'Abington Purple' CAvo CBro
– ***alba*** CAvo CBro ECha
¶ – f. ***angustifolia*** CAvo IBlr
– 'Bob Thompson' CAvo
– broken form WCot
§ – ssp. ***cretensis*** ECha MSte NHol SPou
¶ – 'Francis Wormsley' ECha
– var. ***lazica*** See I. ***lazica***
¶ – 'Marginata' LBro
– 'Mary Barnard' CAvo CBro CHan CMon CRiv CSam CSco EBre ECha LBre LBro MUlv SChu SCro SPer SPou WAbe WDav WRus WSun
– 'Oxford Dwarf' CBro SPou
– 'Walter Butt' CAvo ECha GCal NBir SChu SSpi SWas WDav
urmiensis See I. ***barnumae u.***
¶ ***uromovii*** CMil WHoo

'Ursula Vahl' (TB) LBro
'Valimar' (TB) MAus
'Vanity' (TB) NZep SCro
¶ 'Vanity's Child' ERou
§ ***variegata*** EPar MAus MPar NHol SWas
– ***alba*** EPar
*– ***pontica*** SCro
'Vegas Showgirl' (SDB) NZep
¶ 'Velvet Bouquet' (MTB) LBro
'Velvet Robe' (TB) SRms
'Vera' (Aril) EPot ETub WChr
verna CGle CNic NHol WThi
versicolor CBow CCla CRow CSun CWGN EGol EHon EMFW EPar EPot EWav LGan LMay MAus MSta NDea NRoo NSal SIng WHol
– 'Blue Light' CBow WChe
¶ – 'Dottie's Double' CRow
– 'Goldbrook' EGol
– 'Kermesina' CRDP CRow CWGN ECha EGol EHon ELan EMFW EPar GCal GGar MSta SHig WChe WRus
– purple form CRow
– ***rosea*** CRow
¶ – 'Version' CRow
'Vi Luihn' (***sibirica***) LBro
¶ 'Victor Herbert' (TB) SCro
'Victoria' (CH) LBro
'Victoria Falls' (TB) NZep SCro
'Vim' (SDB) LBro
'Vintage Year' (Spuria) LBro
violacea See I. ***spuria musulmanica***
'Violet Beauty' (Reticulata) EPot LAma LBow SIng WPer
'Violet Classic' (TB) EFou MAus MMil
'Violet Lass' (SDB) NZep
'Violet Lulu' (SDB) NZep
'Violet Miracle' (TB) MMil
'Violet Zephyr' (Spuria) LBro
¶ 'Violetmere' (***sibirica***) LBro
'Violetta' (DB) CKel
virginica var. ***shrevei*** MAus
'Virtue' (IB) MAus
viscaria EPot
¶ 'Visual Arts' (TB) SCro
¶ 'Vitality' (IB) SCro
¶ 'Vivien' (TB) SCro
'Voila' (IB) EFou LBro NZep
'Wabash' (TB) CKel CSco EBre ERou LBre LBro MAus
'Wake Up' (SDB) NZep
'Walter Butt' See I. ***unguicularis*** 'W.B.'
¶ 'Wampum' (IB) SCro
¶ 'War Sails' (TB) SCro
'Warlsind' (Juno) EPot
'Waterboy' (SDB) NZep
'Watercolor' (SDB) NZep
wattii CHEx
'Webelos' (SDB) LBro LGre LHil
'Wedding Candles' (TB) SCro
'Wee Doll' (MDB) NZep
¶ 'Well Endowed' (TB) SCro
'Well Suited' (SDB) NZep
'Wenlock' (IB) MAus
'Westar' (SDB) LBro NZep
'Westwell' (SDB) LRHS MAus
¶ 'What Again' (SDB) SCro
'Whisky' (MDB) NZep
'White Bridge' (Dutch) LAma NRog
'White Canary' (MTB) LBro MAus
'White City' (TB) CMGP CSco ERav LBro LHil MAus MBro MMil NPer SCro SRms SWat
'White Excelsior' (Dutch) CB&S LAma LBlo
'White Gem' (SDB) NZep WWin
'White Heron' (Spuria) LBro
'White Knight' (TB) CBow ELan SCro
'White Queen' (***sibirica***) LBro
* 'White Sails' (***sibirica***) WRus
'White Swirl' (***sibirica***) CBot CCla CPar CRDP EBar EBlo EBre ECtt EGol EPla ERou LBre MBro MUlv MWat NBro NRoo SAxl SCro SPer WHoo WWat WWin
'White van Vliet' (Dutch) NRog
'White Wedgwood' (Dutch) LAma
¶ 'Whiteladies' (IB) LBro LHil
'Whoop 'em Up' (BB) LBro NZep
'Why Not' (IB) LBro NZep
'Widecombe Fair' (SDB) EPar MMil
'Widget' (MTB) LBro
'Wild Echo' (TB) CKel
willmottiana 'Alba' EPot WChr
'Willow Mist' (SDB) NZep
¶ 'Willow Ware' (IB) SCro
wilsonii 'Gelb Mantel' NBir
¶ 'Windsor Rose' (TB) SCro
winogradowii GArf SDix WChr
'Winter Olympics' (TB) EFou
'Wisley White' (***sibirica***) CSco LBro NFai WTyr
'Wisteria Sachet' (IB) MAus
'Witch of Endor' MMil
'Wizard of Id' (SDB) LBro NZep
'Woodling' (SDB) NZep
¶ 'World Beyond' MAus
¶ 'World News' (TB) SCro
'Wow' (SDB) LBro MRob
'Wrights Pink' (SDB) MAus
* 'Xamagito' (CH) LBro
xiphioïdes See I. ***latifolia***
xiphium WThi
¶ 'Yellow Apricot' CRow
¶ 'Yellow Court' CRow
'Yellow Girl' (SDB) NZep
'Yo-Yo' (SDB) NZep
'Zantha' (TB) CKel
¶ 'Zeeland' (BB) LBro
¶ 'Zink Pink' (BB) SCro
'Zipper' (MDB) NZep
'Zowie' (SDB) NZep
'Zua' (IB) MUlv

ISATIS (Cruciferae)

tinctoria	CArn CHad CSFH ELan GPoy IEde ILis LHol MChe MHew MTol NSal NSel SHer SIde SSvw WHer WNdy WOak WPer WWye

ISCHYROLEPIS (Restionaceae)

§ ***subverticillata***	CHEx

ISMENE See **HYMENOCALLIS**

ISOCOMA (Compositae)
See Plant Deletions

ISOLEPIS (Cyperaceae)

§ ***cernua***	CHal MBri

ISOLOMA See **KOHLERIA**

ISOPLEXIS (Scrophulariaceae)

canariensis	CHEx WEas
sceptrum	CBot

ISOPOGON (Proteaceae)
See Plant Deletions

ISOPYRUM (Ranunculaceae)

affine-stoloniferum	EPot
§ ***nipponicum***	
var. ***sarmentosum***	NTow
ohwianum	See I. ***nipponicum sarmentosum***
thalictroïdes	SPou

ISOTOMA See **SOLENOPSIS**, LAURENTIA

ITEA (Escalloniaceae)

ilicifolia	Widely available
japonica 'Beppu'	MGos NHol SLPl
virginica	CCla CDoC CPle CWit ECro ELan LHop MBal MGos MUlv SEng SPer SReu SSpi SSta WBod WDin WSHC WWat
– Swarthmore form	LMer
yunnanensis	CGre IOrc

IVESIA (Rosaceae)

gordonii	WDav WPer

IXIA (Iridaceae)

'Blue Bird'	LAma LBow
conferta	EPot
flexuosa	NRog
'Hogarth'	LAma
'Hubert'	LBow
hybrids	CRDP SDeJ
'Mabel'	ETub NRog
maculata	NRog
'Marquette'	NRog
paniculata	ETub LBow NRog
'Paradijsvogel' ('Bird of Paradise')	LAma
polystachya	NRog
rapunculoïdes	EPot
'Rose Emperor'	ETub LAma LBow NRog
'Uranus'	LBow
'Venus'	LAma LBow
viridiflora	NRog

IXIOLIRION (Liliaceae/Ixioliriaceae)

pallasii	See I. ***tataricum***
§ ***tataricum***	ETub LAma LBlo MBri NRog WCru
– Ledebourii Group	CAvo LAma

JABOROSA (Solanaceae)

integrifolia	ELan EMon GCal WCru

JACARANDA (Bignoniaceae)

acutifolia HBK	MBri
– hort.	See J. ***mimosifolia***
mimosifolia	CB&S CPle SLMG

JACOBINIA See **JUSTICIA**

JAMESIA (Hydrangeaceae)

americana	CCla WSHC

JASIONE (Campanulaceae)

§ ***crispa***	ECro
– ssp. ***crispa***	NRed
§ ***heldreichii***	CHan CLew CRiv CSun GDra LBlm LGan MHig NKay NMir NNrd NRoo SBla SChu SFar SIng WCra WHoo WWin
humilis	See J. ***crispa***
jankae	See J. ***heldreichii***
§ ***laevis***	CBow EBre EHal ELan LBre LGan MUlv NBro NMir SRms WHal WWin
– 'Blaulicht' ('Blue Light')	CFis EBar ECha ESis MBri MRav NOak NRed SUsu WHil WPer
montana	CKin CSam MChe WCla
perennis	See J. ***laevis***

JASMINUM † (Oleaceae)

angulare	CBow CGre CTro ERea
azoricum	CB&S CTro ERea
beesianum	CArn CB&S CBot CBra CHal CHan CPle CSco CTre GCal LHol MBea MPla MRav NEgg SBra SHBN SLon SPer SSvw STre WBod WDin WHer WSHC
floridum	IOrc
fruticans	CDoC CMac ECro ELan EPla GAri MWat NKay
grandiflorum 'De Grasse'	ERea
humile	IBlr SHer SLon WBod WKif
– B&L 12086	CBot
– KR 709	ISea
§ – 'Revolutum'	CArn CB&S CBot CBra CCla CGle CMHG CMac CMer CPle CSco EBre ELan ERav IOrc ISea LBre LHol MBal MBea MGos NKay SHBN SPer STre WAbe WEas WPat WSHC WWat
– f. ***wallichianum***	CGle EHal

§ *mesnyi*	CB&S CBot CBow CCla CDoC CGre CHan CMac CPle CSco CTro EBak ECar ELan EOvi EPad ERea GCal IOrc LAbb LHop MBea SBra SGil SHer SLMG SSta WCru WSHC
nitidum	ERea
nudiflorum	Widely available
– 'Aureum'	CDec CDoC CMer EFol EHar ELan EPla MRav NSti SApp SSpi WEas WPat WRus
– 'Nanum'	ELan
odoratissimum	ERea
officinale	Widely available
§ – f. *affine*	CB&S CPle EBre ELan ENot EPla ERea GCal IBar IDai IOrc LBre SDix SMad WCru
§ – 'Argenteovariegatum'	CArn CB&S CBot CDec CFis CGle CPle ECha EFol EHar ELan LGre LHop MBri MSta NHol NSti SApp SBra SEng SHBN SHil SMad SPer SPla SSta WPat WRus WSHC WWat
– 'Aureovariegatum'	See J. *o.* 'Aureum'
§ – 'Aureum'	CB&S CBot CCla CFis CGle CMac EBre EFol EHal EHar ELan EOvi EPla ERav IJoh LBre MBri MWat NBir NHol SApp SHBN SHil SMad SPer SSpi SSta WPat WSHC WWat
– 'Grandiflorum'	See J. *o. affine*
– 'Variegatum'	See J. *o.* 'Argenteovariegatum'
parkeri	CB&S CBot CHal ECar EPla EPot IDai MBro MCas MPla NHar NHol NKay NNrd SHBN SIng SReu WAbe WCru WPat WThu WWat
polyanthum	CArn CB&S CGle CHal CHan CPle CSco CTre CTro CTrw CWit EBak ELan ERav ERea IReg ISea LAbb LHop MBea MBri NRog NTow SGil SLon WWat
primulinum	See J. *mesnyi*
reevesii	See J. *humile* 'Revolutum'
sambac	CTro LAbb MNew SHil
– 'Maid of Orleans'	ERea
simplicifolium suavissimum	MNew SHil
x *stephanense*	CB&S CBot CBra CCla CMac CSco ELan ENot ERav IBar IHos IJoh IReg LHol LHop MBri MGos MWat SBra SEng SHBN SLon SPer SSta WEas WPat WSHC WWin
¶ – 'Variegatum'	CHan

JEFFERSONIA (Berberidaceae)

diphylla	CArn CChu CElw CGle CHEx CRDP EPar LAma LRHS MTho NBir NHar NHol NRog NRya NSal SBla WChr WCru WHil WWat
dubia	NBir NHol NRog SBla SWas WCot

JOVELLANA (Scrophulariaceae)

punctata	CHan CPle
sinclairii	CBos CGle CNic CRDP ECou GCal MRav NGre SWas WBod WCru
violacea	CAbP CB&S CGle CHan CMHG CMer CPle CSam CWit ERea GCal ISea ITim LHop MBal MPla MTho NHol SArc SDry SHil SLon SMad SSpi WBod WSHC

JOVIBARBA (Crassulaceae)

§ *allionii*	CHal CMea CWil EPad EPot GAri LBee MCas NKay NNor NNrd SIng SMit SSmi WAbe WThu
– from Estang x *hirta* from Biele	SMit
– x *hirta glabrescens* from Smeryouka	SMit
– x *hirta*	CWil NHol SSmi
– x *hirta* 'Oki'	CWil
– x *sobolifera*	SMit SSmi
§ *arenaria*	CWil ESis GCHN MDHE NKay NMen SIng SSmi
– from Murtal	CWil MDHE SSmi
– 'Opiz'	MCas
'Emerald Spring'	CWil
§ *heuffelii*	CWil MCas NBra NMen NWCA SMit
¶ – 'Almkroon'	SSmi
– 'Angel Wings'	SSmi
¶ – 'Apache'	SSmi
– 'Aquarius'	CWil SSmi
– 'Artemis'	SSmi
– 'Beacon Hill'	CWil SMit SSmi
– 'Belcore'	CWil SSmi
– 'Bermuda'	CWil SSmi
– 'Bermuda Sunset'	SSmi
– 'Brocade'	SMit
– 'Bronze Ingot'	CWil
– 'Bronze King'	CWil SMit
– 'Chocoleto'	CWil
– 'Cloverdale'	SMit
¶ – 'Copper King'	SSmi
– 'Fandango'	CWil SSmi
– 'Gento'	CWil
– 'Giuseppi Spiny'	CWil SSmi
¶ – var. *glabra*	NGre
– – *frm* Kosova x *hirta glabres. frm* Smeryouka	SMit
– – from Anabakanak	CWil SMit
– – from Anthoborio	CWil SSmi
– – from Backovo	SSmi
– – from Bansko Vihren	SSmi
– – from Galicica	SSmi
– – from Haila	CWil SMit
– – from Jakupica	CWil
– – from Kapaenianum	SSmi
– – from Koprovnik	CWil
– – from Kosovo	SSmi
– – from Ljubotin	CWil SMit SSmi
– – from Osljak	SSmi
– – from Pasina Glava	CWil
– – from Pelister	SSmi
– – from Rhodope	CWil GAri SSmi
– – from Stogovo	SSmi
– – from Treska Gorge	CWil SMit
– – from Vitse	CWil SMit
– 'Goya'	SSmi
– 'Grand Slam'	CWil SSmi
– 'Greenstone'	CWil SMit SSmi
– 'Henry Correvon'	CWil SMit SSmi

– 'Hystyle'	SMit
– 'Inferno'	CWil SMit
– 'Iole'	SSmi
¶ – 'Jade'	SSmi
– 'Kapo'	SMit SSmi
– var. ***kopaonikensis***	CWil
– 'Miller's Violet'	CWil SMit
– 'Minuta'	CWil
– 'Mystique'	CWil
¶ – 'Nobel'	SSmi
– 'Orion'	CWil SMit
– 'Pink Skies'	SSmi
– 'Prisma'	CWil SSmi
– 'Purple Haze'	CWil SSmi
– 'Springael's Choice'	SSmi
– 'Sundancer'	CWil SMit
– 'Suntan'	CWil
– 'Tan'	CWil SMit SSmi
– 'Tancredi'	SMit SSmi
– 'Torrid Zone'	CWil SMit SSmi
– 'Tuxedo'	CWil SMit SSmi
– 'Violet'	CWil SSmi
– 'Vulcan'	CWil
§ ***hirta***	CRiv CWil MCas MDHE NHol NMen SIng STre WCru
– ssp. ***borealis***	CWil MBro
– from Col d'Aubisque	SMit
¶ – ssp. ***glabrescens***	ESis
– – from Belansky Tatra	CWil GCHN NGre SSmi
¶ – – from High Tatra	MDHE
– – from Smeryouka	CWil SIng SSmi
– – var. ***neilreichii***	SIng
– 'Preissiana'	CWil NMen
¶ x ***mitchellii*** 'Sandy'	SSmi
– 'Suzan'	SSmi
x ***nixonii*** 'Jowan'	SMit SSmi
§ ***sobolifera***	CNic CRiv CWil EPot ESis GAri GCHN NGre NHol NKay SIng SMit SSmi
– 'Green Globe'	CWil MDHE NGre NNrd SSmi

JUANIA (Palmae)

See Plant Deletions

JUANULLOA (Solanaceae)

aurantiaca	See J. ***mexicana***
mexicana 'Gold Finger'	CTro MBri

JUBAEA (Palmae)

§ ***chilensis***	CHEx LPal NPal SArc
♦ ***spectabilis***	See J. ***chilensis***

JUGLANS † (Juglandaceae)

§ ***ailanthifolia***	CHEx ESim SHil SSta WCoo
¶ – ***cordiformis***	EArb
x ***bixbyi***	ESim
F ***cinerea***	EArb ESim SHil SSta WCoo
– x ***ailanthifolia***	See J. x ***bixbyi***
microcarpa	EArb
F ***nigra***	CB&S CBow CBra CLnd EHar ESim GTwe IOrc LNet NRog SDea SHBN SKee SPer SSta WCoo WDin WMou WStI
F ***regia***	Widely available
F – 'Broadview'	CDoC ESim GTwe MBri SDea SKee WHig WMou
F – 'Buccaneer'	ESim GTwe SDea SHil WMou
– 'Fords Farm'	WMou
– 'Franquette'	CDoC EHar GTwe SKee WMou
– 'Laciniata'	EHar WMou
¶ – 'Lara'	SKee
– 'Northdown Clawnut'	WMou
¶ – 'Red Leaf'	WMou
sieboldiana	See J. ***ailanthifolia***

JUNCUS (Juncaceae)

¶ ***acutus***	ETPC
articulatus	CKin
compressus	CKin
concinnus SEP 187	LBlm
conglomeratus	EHoe ETPC
§ ***decipiens*** 'Curly-Wurly'	CRDP EHoe EMon EPla ETPC GCal MFir MUlv NCat SHer SWat
– 'Spiralis'	See J. ***d.*** 'Curly-Wurly'
effusus	CKin EMFW ETPC NLan SWat WHol
– 'Aureostriatus'	EMon
§ – 'Spiralis'	CLew CRDP CRow CWGN EHoe EHon ELan EMon EPla ETPC GCal GDra IBlr LMay MBal MSta NDea NNrd SMad SSpi WChe WHol WPbr
ensifolius	CRow MSta SGil
inflexus	CKin EHon SWat
– 'Afro'	CRDP EMon EPla LRHS SApp
¶ ***pallidus***	ETPC
tenuis	ETPC
xiphioïdes JLS 86161LACA	EMon

JUNIPERUS † (Cupressaceae)

ashei	CMCN
chinensis	CFis CMac NWea SLim
– 'Aurea'	CKen CMHG CMac EBre EHar EHul EPla GPen IJoh LBre LCon LLin LNet MAsh MBal MBar MBri MGos SLim SLon WMou WThu
– 'Blue Alps'	CDoC CMHG EBre EHar EHul EPla GPen IJoh LBre LCon LNet LPan MAsh MBal MBar MBri MGos NHol SLim WStI
– 'Blue Point'	EHul MBar
– 'Densa Spartan'	See J. ***c.*** 'Spartan'
– 'Echiniformis'	CKen CMac
– 'Expansa Aureospicata'	CBra CDoC CKen CMac EBre EHar EHul ENHC LBre LCon LLin MBar SBod SLim SPla SSmi
§ – 'Expansa Variegata'	CBra CMac EBre EHar EHul GAri GPen LBre LCon LLin MBal MBar MGos MPla NHol SBod SLim SLon SSmi WAbe WDin WStI WTyr
– 'Globosa Cinerea'	MBar
– 'Iowa'	CMHG
– 'Japonica'	MBar
– 'Japonica Variegata'	EBre LBre LCon
– 'Kaizuka'	CDoC CMHG EBre EHul ENHC GAri LBre LCon MBal MBar SLim
– 'Kaizuka Variegata'	See J. ***c.*** 'Variegated Kaizuka'
– 'Keteleeri'	LCon
– 'Kuriwao Gold'	CDoC CMHG CMac EBre EHul ENHC GRei GWht LBee LBre LCon LLin LNet MBar MGos MRav MWat NHol NRoo SBod SLim SPer SPla SReu WAbe WStI

– 'Kuriwao Sunbeam'	NHol
¶– 'Mas'	MAsh
– 'Obelisk'	CDoC EBar LBee LCon MBar MGos NHol SBod SLim
– 'Oblonga'	EHul EPla LCon LLin MBar
– 'Parsonsii'	CMHG CMac EHul MBar SHBN STre
– 'Plumosa'	MBar SHil
– 'Plumosa Albovariegata'	LCon MBar
– 'Plumosa Aurea'	CDoC EHar EHul ENHC ENot EPla LCon MBar SHil WDin
– 'Plumosa Aureovariegata'	CKen LCon MAsh MBar
– 'Pyramidalis'	CDoC CMac EBar EBlo EBre EHar EHul ENHC ENot GAri GWht LBre LCon LLin MGos MWat NRoo SBod SLim SRms
– 'Pyramidalis Variegata'	See J. *c.* 'Variegata'
– 'Robusta Green'	LCon SLim
– 'San José'	CDoC EHul ESis GAri LCon LLin LPan MBar MPla SLim WWeb
– 'Shimpaku'	CKen EPla LCon MBar
§ – 'Spartan'	EHul LBee
– 'Stricta'	CKen EHul ENHC GPen IHos LBee MBal MBar MBri MPla SLim SPla WDin
– 'Stricta Variegata'	See J. *c* 'Variegata'
– 'Sulphur Spray'	CDoC CKen CMHG CMac EBlo EBre EHul ENHC EPla GPen GRei GWht IJoh LBee LBre LCon MBar MBri MGos MPla MWat NHol SLim SPer SSmi WStI
§ – 'Variegata'	CFis EHul LLin MBar MPla SLim
§ – 'Variegated Kaizuka'	EHul EPla MBar NHol
communis	CArn CKin CSev EHul GAri GPoy GRei ITim LHol MHew MPla NHex NSal NSel NWea SIde SLim SPer WMou
– 'Arnold'	LCon MGos NHol
– 'Atholl'	CKen GAbr
I – 'Aureopicta'	LCon
– 'Barton'	LLin MPla NHol
– 'Berkshire'	EPla LCon
– 'Brien'	CKen
– 'Clywd'	LBee WThu
– 'Compressa'	Widely available
– 'Constance Franklin'	EHul EPla MBar MCas
– 'Corielagen'	MBar MCas MGos MPla MWat
– 'Cracovia'	EHul
– ssp. ***depressa***	GPoy LLin MBal MBar
– 'Depressa Aurea'	Widely available
– 'Depressed Star'	CDoC MBar
– 'Gelb'	See J. *c.* 'Golden Showers'
§ – 'Gold Cone'	CDoC CKen EBre EHul EPla ESis LBee LBre LCon LLin MAsh MBar MBri MCas MPla NHol SGil SHil SLim SPla
§ – 'Golden Showers'	EBlo EBre EPla LBre NEgg SLim
¶ – 'Goldenrod'	SHil
– 'Green Carpet'	EBlo EBre EPla EPot LBre LCon LLin MBri SLim WStI
– 'Greenmantle'	SPla
– ssp. ***hemispherica***	MBar SRms
– 'Hibernica'	Widely available
– 'Hornibrookii'	CDoC CMac CSco EBar EHul ENot GDra GWht IDai LLin MBal MBar MGos MPla MWat NWea SBod SHBN SLim SLon SPla SReu SSmi STre WDin WWin
– 'Horstmann'	EBre EPla GAri LBre MBri SSmi
– 'Mayer'	SLim
§ – 'Minima'	ENHC LCon SBod
§ – var. ***montana***	EHul EPla EPot SSta
– 'Nana Prostrata'	See J. *c.* 'Minima'
– 'Pyramidalis'	LLin
– 'Repanda'	Widely available
– 'Sentinel'	CBra CDoC EBre EHul ENHC IHos IJoh LBee LBre LCon LPan MBar MBri MPla SLim WBod WWeb
– 'Silver Lining'	See J. *c.* 'Minima'
– 'Spotty Spreader'	SLim
– f. ***suecica***	EHul ENot IHos LCon LPan MBar NWea SBod
♦– 'Suecica Aurea'	See J. *c.* 'Gold Cone'
– 'Zeal'	CKen EPla
conferta	CBra CDoC EHar EHul IDai LBee LLin MBar MBri MWat SBod SLim SLon SPer
– 'Blue Pacific'	CDoC CMac EBre GAri LBre LCon MAsh MBar SLim
– 'Emerald Sea'	EHul
♦– ***maritima***	See J. ***taxifolia lutchuensis***
davurica	EHul
♦– 'Expansa'	See J. ***chinensis*** 'Parsonsii'
– 'Expansa Albopicta'	See J. ***chinensis*** 'Expansa Variegata'
¶ ***deppeana*** var. ***pachyphlaea***	GAri
– 'Silver Spire'	MBar MGos MPla SMad
horizontalis	NRar NWea SLim
– 'Alpina'	CKen
§ – 'Andorra Compact'	CKen CMac ESis LBee LCon MBar
– 'Banff'	CKen EBre LBre
– 'Bar Harbor'	CB&S CKen CMac ENHC LPan MBar MGos MPla MPlt NHol SBod SPla
§ – 'Blue Chip'	CDoC CKen CMac EBlo EBre EHar EHul ENHC ENot EPla LBee LBre MBar MBri MGos MPla NHol SBod SLim SPla SSmi
– 'Blue Moon'	See J. *h.* 'Blue Chip'
– 'Blue Rug'	See J. *h.* 'Wiltonii'
– 'Douglasii'	CMac EHul LLin MBal MBar
– 'Emerald Spreader'	CKen EBar EHul ENHC ENot LPan MBar MGos SLim SSmi
– ***glauca***	CMac EHul ENHC ENot GDra IDai LGro MBal MGos WWin
– 'Glomerata'	CKen EPla MBar
– 'Grey Pearl'	CDoC CKen EBre EHar EHul EPla ESis LBre LCon MBri NHol SBod SLim WWeb
– 'Hughes'	CDoC CKen CMac CSco EBar EBre ENot EPla IHos LBee LBre LCon LLin MAsh MBar MBri MGos MPla MRav NBee NRoo SBod SLim
– 'Jade River'	CKen LRHS MBri SLim
– ***montana***	See J. ***communis m.***
– 'Neumann'	CKen
– 'Plumosa'	GPen SSmi
– 'Plumosa Compacta'	See J. *h.* 'Andorra Compact'
– 'Prince of Wales'	CDoC CKen EBar EBlo EBre EHul GRei LBee LBre LCon MAsh MGos NHol SLim
– ***saxatalis***	See J. ***communis montana***
– 'Turquoise Spreader'	CKen EHul LCon MBar MPla
– 'Variegata'	EPla MBar
– 'Venusta'	CKen LCon
– 'Webberi'	LCon MAsh MBar SLim WWeb
– 'Wilms'	EPla

– 'Wiltonii'	CKen EHul ENot IHos LLin MBal MGos MPla MWat WThu WTyr
– 'Winter Blue'	ENHC EPla LBee SLim
– 'Youngstown'	CMac EBlo EBre LBre LCon MBar NHol SBod SPla SSta
– 'Yukon Belle'	CKen
§ ***macropoda***	LMer
x ***media*** 'Armstrongii'	EHul
– 'Blaauw'	CDoC CMac CSco EHul ENHC ENot GAri IHos LCon LLin MBar MGos SHBN SHil SLim STre WStI
– 'Blue and Gold'	CDoC CKen EPla ESis GPen MBri SHBN SLim
§ – 'Carbery Gold'	CDoC CMac EBar EHul GPen LBee LCon LLin LPan MAsh MBar MGos NHol SHer SLim
– 'Gold Coast'	CDoC CKen CMac EBlo EBre EHul ENHC ENot IHos LBee LBre LCon MBar MBri MGos MWat NBee SLim
– 'Gold Sovereign'	EBlo EBre LBre MGos NBar
– 'Golden Saucer'	LCon MAsh MBri NHol SBod
– 'Goldkissen'	MBri
– 'Milky Way'	MWat
– 'Mint Julep'	CDoC CMac CSco EBar EBre EHul ENHC ENot EPla GRei IDai IJoh LBee LBre LCon LLin LPan MBar MGos MPla MPlt NBee NHol NRoo SLim SPer WStI
– 'Mordigan Gold'	LPan
*– 'Nelson's Compact'	NHol
– 'Old Gold'	CBra CDoC CKen CMac CSco EBre EHar EHul ENHC ENot GRei LBee LBre LBuc LCon LLin MBal MBar MGos MPla MWat NHol NRoo SBod SGil SLim SPer WAbe WDin
– 'Old Gold Carbery'	See J. 'Carbery Gold'
– 'Pfitzeriana'	CBra CMac EHar EHul ENHC ENot LLin MBal MBar MBri MGos NWea SBod SLim SLon SPer SReu WDin WWin
– 'Pfitzeriana Aurea'	CB&S CDoC CMac EHar EHul ENHC ENot EPot GDra GPen IHos LBee LCon MBal MBar MBri MGos MPla MWat NWea SBod SHBN SLim SLon SPer SReu
– 'Pfitzeriana Compacta'	CDoC CMac EHul MBar SLim
– 'Pfitzeriana Glauca'	CDoC CSco EBre EHul LBre LCon LPan MWat NEgg SLim
– 'Richeson'	MBar
– 'Sea Green'	EHul
– 'Silver Cascade'	EHul
– 'Winter Surprise'	EPla LCon SLim
oxycedrus	CMHG GAri
pingii 'Glassell'	CLew LCon MBar NHol
¶ ***procera***	CGre
procumbens	MBri SLim SLon WAbe WBod
– 'Bonin Isles'	CSam MBal MBar MGos SLim SRms WAbe
– 'Nana'	CDoC CKen CLew CMac EHar EHul ISea LBee LCon LLin MBal MBri MGos MPla MWat NHar NHol NKay SHBN SLim SPla SSmi SSta
recurva	GWht SLim
– 'Castlewellan'	EBre LBre MGos
– var. ***coxii***	CBra CChu CDoC CMac EHar EHul EPla ISea LBee LCon MBri MGos MPar SIng SLim SLon SMad WThu
§ – 'Densa'	CKen EBre EHul EPla GAri LBre LCon LLin MBar NHol SHBN SLim SPla STre
– 'Embley Park'	EHul LCon MAsh MBar MBri SHil SLim
♦– 'Nana'	See J. ***r.*** 'Densa'
rigida	GAri MBar SIng
sabina	GPoy NWea SReu
– 'Arcadia'	CMac SRms
– 'Blue Danube'	CMac EHul IDai LPan MBar MGos SLim SRms
– 'Broadmoor'	SLim
– 'Buffalo'	EHul
– 'Cupressifolia'	MBar
– 'Hicksii'	CMac MBar MGos NWea
– 'Rockery Gem'	EHul LCon LTil SLim WStI
– 'Skandia'	CKen
– 'Tamariscifolia'	CB&S CBra CDoC CMac EBre EHul ENot GPen IDai LBee LBre LCon LGro MBal MBar MBri MGos MPla MWat NRoo NWea SBod SHBN SLim SLon SPer SSmi WSHC
– 'Tripartita'	MBar
– 'Variegata'	CMac EHul GWht LBee MBar SLim
sargentii	EHul GAri LCon MBal WWeb
¶ – 'Glauca'	GAri
– 'Viridis'	EHul GAri
scopulorum 'Blue Arrow'	CKen MGos MWat
– 'Blue Heaven'	CSco EBre EHar EHul ENHC ENot GAri LBre LCon MBal MBar SLim WMou
– 'Boothman'	EHul
– 'Gray Gleam'	EBre EHul ENHC LBre
– 'Moonglow'	EBre LBre MBar MBri
¶ – 'Mrs Marriage's Form'	CKen
– 'Repens'	MBar MGos SRms
– 'Silver Globe'	LCon
– 'Silver Star'	CKen EHar EHul EPla MGos
– 'Skyrocket'	Widely available
– 'Springbank'	CMac EHar ENHC LBee LCon MBar SLim
– 'Tabletop'	MBar
– 'Wichita Blue'	EBre LBre LCon
♦ ***seravshanica***	See J. ***macropoda***
squamata	NWea
– 'Blue Carpet'	Widely available
– 'Blue Spider'	CKen LCon LLin LTil MBar MBri
– 'Blue Star'	Widely available
♦– 'Blue Star Variegated'	See J. ***s.*** 'Golden Flame'
♦– 'Blue Swede'	See J. ***s.*** 'Hunnetorp'
– 'Chinese Silver'	CMHG EBre EHul LBre LCon MBar
– 'Filborna'	CDoC CKen LBee MBar MWat NHol SLim
♦– 'Glassell'	See J. ***pingii*** 'G.'
§ – 'Golden Flame'	CKen EPla
– 'Holger'	CDoC CKen CMac EBlo EBre EHul EPla ESis GAri IDai LBee LBre LCon LLin MBar MBri MGos MPla MWat NHol SBod SGil SLim
– 'Hunnetorp'	EBre EHul EPla LBre LCon LLin LPan MBar MBri MGos MPlt
– 'Loderi'	CKen EHar EHul LCon MBar NHol SSta

– 'Meyeri'	CB&S CBra CMac EHul ENHC ENot GDra GPen IDai ISea LCon LLin MBal MBar MWat NWea SBod SLim SLon SPer WStI WTyr WWin
*– 'Pygmaea'	CDoC LCon MBar MPla SLim
– 'Wilsonii'	CKen LCon MBar
§ ***taxifolia*** var. ***lutchuensis***	EHar EPot LBee LCon MBal MPla MWat
virginiana	CMCN GWht NWea WCoo
– 'Blue Cloud'	CDoC EHul LCon LLin MBar SLim
– 'Burkii'	EHar EHul LCon MBal
¶– 'Canaertii'	LPan
I – 'Compressa'	SRms
– 'Frosty Moon'	CKen EHul LCon MBar
– 'Glauca'	EHul NBee NWea SLon
¶– 'Golden Spring'	CKen
– 'Grey Owl'	CBra CDoC CMHG CMac CSco EBre EHar EHul ENot GRei ISea LBre LCon LLin MBal MBar MBri MGos MPla SLim SLon SPer SPla STre WDin WTyr
– 'Helle'	See J. ***chinensis*** 'Spartan'
– 'Hetzii'	CB&S CBra CMac EHar EHul ENHC GWht LCon LPan MBal MBar MBri MGos NWea SBod WTyr
– 'Hillii'	MBar
– 'Hillspire'	EHul
– 'Nana Compacta'	MBar
– 'Pendula'	EPla
I – 'Robusta Green'	ENHC MBar
– 'Silver Spreader'	EHul LCon LLin MGos SPer
– 'Straver'	EHul
¶ ***wallichiana***	LTil

JURINEA (Compositae)

ceratocarpa	See SAUSSUREA ***c.***

JURINELLA (Compositae)

¶ ***moschus*** ssp. ***moschus***	NWCA

JUSSIAEA See LUDWIGIA

JUSTICIA (Acanthaceae)

§ ***brandegeeana***	CHal MBri SLMG
– ***lutea***	See J. ***b.*** 'Yellow Queen'
§ – 'Yellow Queen'	CHal SLMG
§ ***carnea***	CHal CSev CTro EBak ERea MBri
♦***floribunda***	See J. ***rizzinii***
guttata	See J. ***brandegeeana***
* 'Norgard's Favourite'	MBri
pauciflora	See J. ***rizzinii***
pohliana	See J. ***carnea***
¶ ***polianthor robusta***	CTro
§ ***rizzinii***	CAbb CB&S CKni CPle CSun CTre CTro ERea IBar IBlr LBlm LHil LHop
spicigera	ERea
suberecta	See DICLIPTERA ***s.***

KADSURA (Schisandraceae)

japonica	CGre CHan CPle EMil WSHC
– 'Variegata'	EMil SSpi SSta WSHC
¶ ***suromi***	EMil

KALANCHOË (Crassulaceae)

beharensis	CHal MBri SLMG
blossfeldiana	CHal
fedtschenkoi	CHal
– 'Variegata'	CHal
manginii	CHal
marmorata	CHal SGil
pumila	IBlr SGil WEas
¶ ***synsepala***	SGil
¶ – ***laciniata***	SGil
'Tessa'	MBri SLMG
tomentosa	CHal SLMG
'Wendy'	MBri

KALIMERIS (Compositae)

§ ***incisa***	EMon SMrm
* ***intricifolia***	ECha WCot
§ ***mongolica***	MBro WPer
¶ ***yomena*** 'Shogun' (v)	ECha EFol EMon EPla NBir WCot
♦– 'Variegata'	See K. ***y.*** 'Shogun'

KALMIA † (Ericaceae)

angustifolia	CBow CLan IJoh ISea LNet MBar WDin
– f. ***candida***	GGGa
– 'Rubra'	CB&S CBow CBra CCla CDoC CMHG CSco EBlo ECar ELan GGGa GWht LAbb MBal MGos NBar NBee NHol NKay NRoo NWea SHBN SPer SReu SSpi SSta WPat WThu WWeb
¶ ***cuneata***	SSta
latifolia	CB&S CBow CBra CLan CSco ELan ENot GGGa GRei ISea LAbb LHyd LNet MBal MBar MGos NWea SPer SReu SSta WAbe WDin WStI WWat
– 'Alpine Pink'	GGGa MLea
– 'Brilliant'	GGGa
– 'Bullseye'	LNet
– 'Candy'	GGGa
¶– 'Carol'	LTil
– 'Carousel'	CAbP GGGa LMil LNet LTil MAsh MGos MLea SHBN
– 'Clementine Churchill'	SSpi
– 'Elf'	ECar GGGa LTil MAsh MLea
– 'Freckles'	GGGa LMil LNet LTil MAsh MLea
– 'Fresca'	CPMA GGGa LTil SHer
– 'Goodrich'	CB&S CPMA MGos SPer WWeb
– 'Heart of Fire'	CAbP LMil
¶– 'Hearts Desire'	LTil
– 'Minuet'	CAbP GGGa LTil MAsh MLea SHer
– f. ***myrtifolia***	SSpi
¶– 'Nancy'	LTil
– 'Nipmuck'	IBar LHyd LTil MGos MLea
– 'Olympic Fire'	ELan GGGa IBar IOrc LNet MBal MGos MLea
¶– 'Olympic Wedding'	LTil
– 'Ostbo Red'	CB&S CBra CPMA EBlo ECar EHar ELan ENot GGGa IBar IOrc LHyd LNet MBal MBri MGos MLea SHBN SHer SPer SReu SSpi SSta
– 'Pink Charm'	MAsh MBal MGos MLea SHBN
– 'Pink Frost'	CB&S CCla CPMA LMil LNet MGos MLea SHBN WWat WWeb
– 'Pink Star'	MLea SHBN
– 'Pinwheel'	GGGa LTil MLea

¶ – 'Raspberry Glow' LTil
– 'Richard Jaynes' GGGa LTil
– 'Sarah' GGGa LMil LTil MLea
– 'Shooting Star' GGGa IBar MGos
– 'Silver Dollar' ELan MAsh
¶ – 'Snowdrift' LTil
– 'Willowcrest' LMil
¶ – 'Yankee Doodle' LTil
§ ***microphylla*** ECar GGGa MBal WPat WThu
– 'Mount Shasta' GGGa
– var. ***occidentalis*** ECar GGGa
polifolia CB&S CDoC ECar GGGa MBar MRav SReu SSpi SSta WPat
¶ – ***compacta*** GArf
– 'Glauca' See K. ***microphylla***
– f. ***leucantha*** GGGa
****pygmaea*** GGGa

KALMIOPSIS (Ericaceae)

leachiana ECar EPot GArf MBal MGos SIng
– 'Glendoick' GGGa NHar NHol SReu WPat WThu
– 'La Piniec' GGGa MGos SSpi
– Umpqua Valley form EPot

X KALMIOTHAMNUS (Ericaceae)

ornithomma GGGa

KALOPANAX (Araliaceae)

♦***pictus*** See K. ***septemlobus***
§ ***septemlobus*** CBot CHEx EArb EHar ELan MBri SArc SHil
– var. ***maximowiczii*** CHEx MBlu MBri NBee SMad

KECKIELLA (Scrophulariaceae)

§ ***cordifolia*** CMHG LGre SIgm
¶ ***corymbosa*** NWCA
– JCA 11618 CMHG LGre
§ ***ternata***
JLS 86304LACA EMon

KELSEYA (Rosaceae)

uniflora WDav

KENNEDIA (Leguminosae)

¶ ***coccinea*** CTro SLMG
nigricans CTro LHop

KENTIA (Palmae)

belmoreana See HOWEA ***b.***
canterburyana See HEDYSCEPE ***c.***

KENTRANTHUS See CENTRANTHUS

KERNERA (Cruciferae)

See Plant Deletions

KERRIA (Rosaceae)

japonica CB&S CBow CChu CTrw IOrc NBee NKay SDix WDin WTyr WWin
– 'Golden Guinea' CChu CDoC CPMA EBre ECtt ELan ESma IOrc LBre LRHS MBri MRav NBar NHol SGil SPla SSpi WWat WWeb
§ – 'Picta' (v) CB&S CLan CPle CSco CShe EBre EHoe ELan ESis IJoh IOrc ISea LAbb LBre MBar MBri MGos MPla MWat NBar NKay NNor SPer WDin WEas WPbr WSHC WWat WWin
– 'Pleniflora' CB&S CBra CLan CPle CSco CShe EBre ELan ENot GRei IDai IJoh ISea LBre MBar MBri MGos MPla MRav MWat NHol NNor NRoo NWea SHBN SLon SPer STre WDin
– 'Simplex' CLan CSco ELan ENot IDai ISea MGos NWea
– 'Variegata' See K. ***j.*** 'Picta'

KICKXIA (Scrophulariaceae)

spuria MHew NSal

KIRENGESHOMA (Hydrangeaceae)

palmata CB&S CChu CCla CElw CHEx CHad CSam CSco EBre ECha ECro ELan EPar IBar IDai LBre LHop MBri MTho MUlv NBir NBro NHol NSti SBla SLon SMad SPer WEas WSHC
§ – Koreana Group CCla CRDP CSco ECha ECro ELan EPar GCra MBri SPer WAbe WMer

KITAIBELA (Malvaceae)

vitifolia CGle CHan CSam CTom ECro ELan EMar EMon LGan LHop LWad MTol NBro NSti SFis SMad WCot WDav WPer

KITCHINGIA See KALANCHOË

KIWI FRUIT See ACTINIDIA *deliciosa*

KLEINIA (Compositae)

¶ ***senecioïdes*** WEas

KNAUTIA (Dipsacaceae)

arvensis CArn CKin CRDP CRiv LHol MChe NLan NMir WCla WGwy WHer WNdy WOak
dipsacifolia WCot
§ ***macedonica*** Widely available
¶ – pink form SWas

KNIGHTIA (Proteaceae)

excelsa CHEx

KNIPHOFIA † (Liliaceae/Asphodelaceae)

¶ 'Ada' EBre ERou LBre WCot
'Alcazar' CBow CDoC CMGP EFou EPar MBri WMer
¶ 'Apple Court' SApp
¶ 'Apricot Souffle' ECha
'Atlanta' EBlo EBre EMon GCal IBlr LBre SAxl
¶ 'Bees' Lemon' IBlr
'Bees' Sunset' LAbb MBri SHig SMrm SPer WHal
'Border Ballet' CMHG ECtt LHop LWad MFir MPit NBro NFai NMir NOak WBon WByw
¶ 'Bressingham Comet' EBlo

Bressingham hybrids	COtt EBre IBlr LBre NBir NKay
¶ 'Bressingham Sunbeam'	EBlo
'Brimstone'	EFou EPla
'Buttercup'	CChu CGle CMHG CRDP EBul LGre MBri WSHC
'C M Prichard' hort.	See K. ***rooperi***
'Candlelight'	SAxl WWin
'Catherine's Orange'	EFou
caulescens	CBot CHEx CHan CSam EBre EBul EMon LBre MUlv SAxl SBla SCro SDix SHig SMrm SSpi SUsu WCot
¶ – BH 5020	ECha
¶ ***citrina***	MBal SIgm WWat
¶ 'Cobra'	COtt EBlo ERou
¶ 'Comet'	EBre LBre
'Corallina'	LRHS MBri WCot
¶ 'Cream Flame'	SApp
'Dr E M Mills'	CKni COtt SPer
'Early Buttercup'	CMGP CWGN EFou EGol EOrc MUlv SPer
¶ 'Fairyland'	WCot
'Fiery Fred'	CMHG COtt EBre EFou ELan LBre WCot
'Fireking'	LRHS MBri
galpinii Baker	CAbb CChu CGle CMGP ENot MBal NBir NSti WCot WHil WWat
– hort.	See K. ***triangularis triangularis***
'Goldelse'	CChu ECha EOrc IBlr NBir SAxl SBla
'Goldfinch'	SAxl SMrm
'Green Jade'	CChu CLew CRow ECha EFou EGol EPar LGre MUlv NBir NCat SAxl SIgm
hirsuta H&B 16444	EMon
'Ice Queen'	COtt CRDP EBre EFou EGol EOrc LBre MRav MUlv SMrm SPer WCot WRus
¶ ***ichopensis***	CHan
¶ 'Innocence'	CChu LRHS SApp
'Jenny Bloom'	SAxl SMrm SWas WCot
late orange	EBul MUlv
'Limelight'	EOrc MBri
'Little Elf'	SBla
'Little Maid'	Widely available
macowanii	See K. ***triangularis triangularis***
'Maid of Orleans'	IBlr WCot
'Mermaiden'	CMHG LRHS MBri
'Modesta'	GCal IBlr LGre SUsu SWas
¶ 'Mount Etna'	CGle
nelsonii	See K. ***triangularis triangularis***
'Nobilis'	See K. ***uvaria*** 'N.'
northiae	CBot
¶ 'Painted Lady'	WCot
'Percy's Pride'	CSam EBre EBul EOrc LBre LGre MBri MRav SApp SAxl SMrm WCot
¶ 'Pfitzeri'	SRms
'Primrose Beauty'	WMer
'Prince Igor'	CRiv EBlo ECha GAbr MBal SApp
pumila	WCot
§ ***rooperi***	CBot MBal SAxl WCot
¶ 'Royal Caste'	CBow NOrc
'Royal Standard'	CB&S CHEx CMHG ELan ENot GAbr IBlr IDai LWad MBri SBla SCro SMrm
rufa	GCal
'Samuel's Sensation'	EBlo MBri
'September Sunshine'	EFou
'Shining Sceptre'	CChu CMHG COtt EBre ECtt LBre MBri MUlv SAxl SBla SPer WMer
'Sir C K Butler'	IBlr
¶ sp. ex Ethiopia	GCal
'Star of Baden-Baden'	LRHS MBri NBir
'Strawberries and Cream'	LGre SBla
¶ 'Strawberry Split'	ECha
'Sunningdale Yellow'	ECha SChu SRms WEas
thomsonii var. ***snowdenii***	CBot CChu CHan ECha IBlr LBlm MSte NRar SApp SAxl SBla SWas WCot
¶ 'Toasted Corn'	ECha
'Toffee Nosed'	EFou ERou GCal
¶ 'Torchbearer'	WCot
triangularis	CBot CMon EPla SBla
§ – ssp. ***triangularis***	CBot CChu CGle IBlr NFai SHig SIgm SUsu WCot
'Tuckii'	CGre CSun LBlm LGan MBal SIgm WCot
uvaria	CHEx CShe LRHS NBir NCat NFai SIgm SRms WByw WHoo
§ – 'Nobilis'	EBul SDix WCot
¶ 'Vesta'	EBlo
'Wrexham Buttercup'	GCal
'Yellow Hammer'	CBot EGol GAbr GCal IBlr NCat

KNOWLTONIA (Ranunculaceae)

See Plant Deletions

KOBRESIA (Cyperaceae)

See Plant Deletions

KOELERIA (Gramineae)

glauca	CElw EBar ECha EHoe EOrc EPla ESis ETPC GAbr GCHN MBri NHol NMir NRar NSti WCot WPer
macrantha	ETPC MWil
vallesiana	EMon EPla ETPC LRHS MFir

KOELLIKERIA (Gesneriaceae)

'Red Satin'	NMos

KOELREUTERIA (Sapindaceae)

bipinnata	CHEx
paniculata	Widely available
– ***apiculata***	CMHG MBri
– 'Fastigiata'	EBre LBre MBlu MBri

KOHLERIA (Gesneriaceae)

'Clytie'	MBri
digitaliflora	CTro WEfe
eriantha	CHal CPle MBri SLMG WEfe
¶ 'Hanna Roberts'	WEfe
hirsuta	CPle
*x ***hybrida***	NMos
'Strawberry Fields'	MBri NMos

KOLKWITZIA (Caprifoliaceae)

amabilis	CB&S CFis CLan CSco CTrw ELan GRei IDai IJoh LAbb MGos MPla MWat NBee NHol NNor NWea SSta WDin WStI WWin
– 'Pink Cloud'	Widely available

KUMMEROWIA (Leguminosae)
See Plant Deletions

KUNZEA (Myrtaceae)
baxteri CHEx
§ *ericoïdes* ECar ECou

LABICHEA (Leguminosae)
See Plant Deletions

LABLAB (Leguminosae)
See Plant Deletions

+ LABURNOCYTISUS (Leguminosae)
adamii CBow CBra CDoC COtt CPMA CSco CWSG EHar ELan GAri IOrc MBri SHBN SHil SPer

LABURNUM (Leguminosae)
alpinum CBow CNic GAri NWea
– 'Pendulum' CBow CDoC CPMA EBre ELan IJoh IOrc LBre LNet MBri MGos MRav NBar NBee SHBN SMad SPer WDin
§ *anagyroïdes* GAri GRei ISea NWea WDin
– 'Pendulum' CLnd
vulgare See L. *anagyroïdes*
x *watereri* 'Alford's Weeping' MBar MGos
– 'Vossii' CB&S CLnd CSco EBre ELan ENot GRei IJoh IOrc LBre LBuc LNet MBar MBri MGos MRav NBar NBee NWea SFam SHBN SPer SReu SSta WAbe WDin

LACCOSPADIX (Palmae)
See Plant Deletions

LACHENALIA (Liliaceae/Hyacinthaceae)
§ *aloïdes* EBul EPot ETub LBow MBri WThi
– var. *aurea* CMea ETub LBow
– var. *luteola* LBow
– 'Nelsonii' LBow
– var. *quadricolor* LBow
– var. *vanzyliae* LBow
§ *bulbifera* LBow MBri NRog
– 'George' LBow
contaminata LBow
hybrid Lac. 213 LBow
mediana LBow
pallida NRog
pendula See L. *bulbifera*
pustulata NRog
reflexa WThi
rubida NRog
tricolor See L. *aloïdes*
¶ *zeyheri* EBul

LACTUCA (Compositae)
alpina See CICERBITA *alpina*
perennis CHan CLew SChu WPer

LAGAROSIPHON (Hydrocharitaceae)
§ *major* CBen CRow EHon ELan EMFW NDea SAWi SRms WChe WHol

LAGAROSTROBOS (Podocarpaceae)
§ *franklinii* CB&S LLin WBod

LAGENOPHORA (Compositae)
pinnatifida WPer
stipitata ECar

LAGERSTROEMIA (Lythraceae)
chekiangensis EArb
¶ *fauriei* LTil
indica CPle CTro SEng SLMG WSHC
¶ – 'Petite Pinkie' LTil
– 'Rosea' CB&S

LAGUNARIA (Malvaceae)
patersonii CTro MNew
¶ – 'Royal Purple' ERea

LALLEMANTIA (Labiatae)
See Plant Deletions

LAMARCKIA (Gramineae)
See Plant Deletions

LAMIASTRUM See LAMIUM

LAMIUM † (Labiatae)
album aureovariegatum See L. *a.* 'Goldflake'
– 'Friday' (v) EHoe EMon LRHS MBel MTho SApp WCHb WCot
§ – 'Goldflake' (v) EFol EMon MBel WCHb
¶ – 'Pale Peril' EMon
flexuosum EMon MBel
§ *galeobdolon* CArn CGle CHal CKin EBre EMon LBre LGro LHil MHew MWat NFai NLan NSal SPer WCru WNdy WOak
§ – 'Florentinum' CFis CGle CKel CRow CSFH CSco CShe CTom EBre ECha ECro EFol EHoe ELan ENot EPar ERav LBre MFir NHol NNor SBar SDix SIng SSvw STre WPer
– 'Hermann's Pride' CHal CMHG COtt CRDP CWit EBre ECtt EHal EMon GAbr GCal GCra LBre LHil MBel MBri MUlv NFai NMir WCru
– 'Silberteppich' ('Silver Carpet') CPar CRow ECha EFol EFou ELan EMar EMon EOrc EPla ERav GGar LHop MTho NKay NNor NSti SBla SHer SIng SMad SMrm WCru WPer WWat
– 'Silver Angel' (v) ELan EMon MBel NSti WCru
– 'Variegatum' See L. *g.* 'Florentinum'
garganicum ssp. *garganicum* CGle CHan CRDP CSev EFol EMon NSti SUsu WCru
¶ – 'Laevigatum' EMon MBel
– *pictum* See L. *g. striatum*
– *reniforme* See L. *g. striatum*
§ – ssp. *striatum* CRDP EFol ELan SHer
– – DS&T 89011T EMon
maculatum CArn CBow CFis CMer CRow CTom EMon NBee SIng WByw WCru WEas WWat WWye

– ***album***	CBow CCla CFis CGle CLew CMea CNic CPar CRow CSco EFou ELan EMon LGro MHig NHol SPer WBon WByw WCru WWat
§ – 'Aureum'	Widely available
– 'Beacon Silver'	Widely available
– 'Beedham's White'	EPla NSti SCro SUsu WRus
– 'Cannon's Gold'	ECha ECtt EFol EHoe ELan EMon EPla WCru
N– 'Chequers'	CDoC CSFH CSco EBre ELan EMon ENot EPla LBre NHol SPer
– 'Dingle Candy'	EFol
– 'Elizabeth de Haas' (v)	EHoe EMon WCot
– 'Gold Leaf'	See L. ***m.*** 'Aureum'
– 'Golden Nuggets'	LWad SFis
– 'Hatfield'	ELan EMon
– 'Immaculate'	EMon
– 'James Boyd Parselle'	EMon LRHS WCHb
¶ – 'Margery Fish'	SRms
– 'Pink Nancy'	CSpe WAbb
– 'Pink Pewter'	CBre CGle ECha ECtt EFou EMon EPla MBel NSti SCro SMrm SUsu WBon WCHb WHoo
– 'Red Nancy'	CBre EMon EPla EPot GCal
§ – ***roseum***	CBre CCla CFis CGle CLew CMea CMer CPar CRow CShe EFol EFou EGol ELan EPla ESis GCal LGro LHop MWat NFai NHol NMir NNor SIng SPer WBon WHer WHil
– 'Shell Pink'	See L. ***m. roseum***
– 'Silver Dollar'	EMon MBri
– 'Sterling Silver'	EMon
– 'White Nancy'	Widely available
– 'Wootton Pink'	WCra WEas
orvala	CBot CFis CHan EBre ECha ECro EFol EMon EPla LBre MFir NGar SIng WHal
– 'Album'	CBot CHan ECro EFol ELan EMon EPla SIng

LAMPRANTHUS (Aizoaceae)

aberdeenensis	See DELOSPERMA ***aberdeenense***
aurantiacus	CB&S CHEx
blandus	CB&S CHEx
§ ***brownii***	CB&S CHEx CRDP ELan NMen NTow SHer WCru
* 'Carn Brae'	CB&S CHal
§ ***deltoïdes***	CHEx MRav SLMG WEas
edulis	See CARPOBROTUS ***e.***
falcatus	SLMG
¶ ***falciformis***	WPer
glaucus	CB&S CHEx
haworthii	SLMG
lehmannii	See DELOSPERMA ***l.***
oscularis	See L. ***deltoïdes***
pallidus	See DELOSPERMA ***pallidum***
spectabilis	CB&S SLMG
– 'Tresco Apricot'	CB&S
– 'Tresco Brilliant'	CB&S
¶ – 'Tresco Fire'	CBrk
– 'Tresco Red'	CB&S WPer
zeyheri	CB&S

LANTANA (Verbenaceae)

camara	CPle CTro ERea ISea LAbb MBri
– 'Brasier'	ERea
– 'Feston Rose'	ERea
– 'Firebrand'	SLMG
– forms	ERea IBlr
– 'Mine d'Or'	ERea
– 'Mr Bessieres'	ERea
– 'Snow White'	ERea SLMG
'Gold Dust'	SLMG
§ ***montevidensis***	CBrk CPle CTro ERea LHop SLMG WEas
¶ – 'Boston Gold'	CBrk
'Radiation'	ERea
sellowiana	See L. ***montevidensis***

LAPAGERIA (Liliaceae/Philesiaceae)

rosea	CAbb CB&S CBow CGre CHEx CMac CTro EBak ERea MBal MNew SArc SHBN SMad SPer SReu SSpi WNor WWat
– var. ***albiflora***	CB&S MNew
– – 'White Cloud'	CGre
– 'Flesh Pink'	CB&S CGre ERav MNew
– 'Nash Court'	CB&S CBot CChu CGre CMac CSam ERav ERea IBar IOrc ISea SSpi WSHC WStI
– 'Penheale'	CB&S SSpi
¶ – 'Picotee'	CB&S

LAPEIROUSIA (Iridaceae)

cruenta	See ANOMATHECA ***laxa***
laxa	See ANOMATHECA ***laxa***

LAPIEDRA (Liliaceae/Amaryllidaceae)

¶ ***martinezii*** MS 423	CMon

LAPSANA (Compositae)

communis 'Inky'	CNat

LARDIZABALA (Lardizabalaceae)

biternata	CGre

LARIX † (Pinaceae)

decidua	CB&S CBow CDoC EHar ENHC ENot GRei IDai IHos LCon LPan MBal MBar NWea SHBN SMad SPer WDin WMou WStI
– 'Corley'	CKen EBre LBre MAsh
¶ – 'Little Bogle'	CKen
– 'Pendula'	CB&S EBre EHar LBre WMou
x ***eurolepis***	See L. x ***marschlinsii***
gmelinii	GAri ISea WThu
¶ – ***olgensis***	CMCN
§ ***kaempferi***	CBow CDoC CLnd CPer CSco CTre EHar ENHC ENot GRei IJoh LBuc LCon LNet MBar MGos NWea SLim SMad SPer WFro WMou WNor WStI
– 'Bambino'	CKen
– 'Blue Ball'	CDoC CKen LLin
– 'Blue Dwarf'	CDoC CKen EBre LBre LCon LLin LPan MAsh MBri SLim
– 'Blue Rabbit Weeping'	LPan SLim
– 'Cruwys Morchard'	CKen
– 'Dervaes'	EHar
– 'Diana'	CKen EBre GAri LBre MBlu
– 'Grant Haddow'	CKen
¶ – 'Jacobsen'	SMad
– 'Little Blue Star'	CDoC LLin

– 'Nana'	CKen EBre GAri LBre MAsh
I – *nana prostrata*	CKen
– 'Pendula'	CBra CDoC EHar IBar IJoh IOrc MBar MBlu MBri MGos MUlv SHil SLim
– 'Varley'	CKen
– 'Wolterdingen'	CKen
¶ *laricina*	GAri
¶ – 'Arethusa Bog'	CKen
leptolepis	See L. ***kaempferi***
§ x *marschlinsii*	EHar ENot GRei MBar NWea WMou
– 'Domino'	CKen LLin
– 'Gail'	CKen
– 'Julie'	CKen
¶ x *pendula* 'Pendulina'	GAri
russica	See L. ***sibirica***
§ *sibirica*	GAri LCon MBar WNor
* *sieboldii*	LCon
sukaczevii	See L. ***sibirica***

LASERPITIUM (Umbelliferae)

halier	WPer

LASIAGROSTIS See STIPA

LATHYRUS † (Leguminosae)

§ *aureus*	CBos ECha GCal GCra MPar MTho NHol NSti SBla SFar SSad SUsu WEas WOMN
♦ *azureus* hort.	See L. ***sativus***
chloranthus	SSad
¶ *cyaneus alboroseus*	MTho
¶ *davidii*	SAxl
* *fremontii*	CSpe SSad WWin
grandiflorus	CGle CSev ECha EMon LGre NSti SBla SSad WOak
¶ *heterophyllus*	WCot WHal WHil
inermis	See L. ***laxiflorus***
japonicus	CRDP MWil WGwy
latifolius	Widely available
– 'Albus'	CBot CHad CRDP ELan EMon GDra LGre LWad MSte SAxl SGil SSpi SUsu SWas WCot WEas WHal WSun
– 'Blushing Bride'	WCot
¶ – deep pink	NSti
– pale pink	CSam NSti SIng WEas WHal
– 'Red Pearl'	CDoC EBre ECro ECtt EFou GCal LBre MBri SPer SSvw
– 'Rosa Perle' ('Pink Pearl')	CDoC ECro ECtt EFou GAbr GCal LAbb LGan MBri MSte SIng SMrm SPer SSvw WRus
– 'White Pearl' ('Weisse Perle')	Widely available
§ *laxiflorus*	EOrc NCat SAxl
linifolius montanus	CKin WNdy
♦ *luteus* 'Aureus'	See L. ***aureus***
♦ *magellanicus*	See L. ***nervosus***
§ *nervosus*	CBot CHan CPla CPou CRDP CSpe EBre ECro EFou LBre MTho NRar SBla SFis SIgm SMad SSad SUsu WEas WHal WOMN WRus
neurolobus	CNic
niger	EMon
nissolia	ELan
odoratus	CGle
– 'Bicolor'	ELan
¶ – 'Painted Lady'	EJud
¶ *pannonicus*	MFir
pratensis	CKin MWil WGwy WNdy
pubescens	SIgm
rotundifolius	EPad ERav GCal GDra LGre MTho SBar SSad SUsu SWas WCot WHal WOMN
§ *sativus*	CHad CMea CSpe ELan SSad WEas WSun WWye
♦ – *azureus*	See L. ***s.***
sylvestris	CKin ECro ELan LGre MWil WGwy WNdy
tingitanus	ECro WEas WHer
tuberosus	ELan EMon MWat WOld
vernus	CBot CHad CHan CTom EFou ELan GAbr LGre MFir MPar MTho NOak NSti SSad SUsu WBon WDav WHal WKif WPer WRus WThu WWye
– 'Alboroseus'	CFis EFol EFou ELan GCal LGre MBri MNFA NHol SBla SIng SMrm SSad SUsu WCot WHoo WKif WOMN WRus WThu
– *albus*	SSad
– *aurantiacus*	See L. ***aureus***
– 'Caeruleus'	LGre
– *cyaneus*	CHad SSad WRus
– 'Flaccidus'	EMon WKif
– f. *roseus*	CRDP ECha ECro MPar MPlt NTow
– 'Spring Melody'	WCot

LAURELIA (Monimiaceae)

§ *sempervirens*	CAbb CB&S CGre CTrw SArc SBor
serrata	See L. ***sempervirens***

LAURENTIA (Campanulaceae)

§ *longiflora*	WPer

LAURUS (Lauraceae)

§ *azorica*	CB&S CTre
canariensis	See L. ***azorica***
nobilis	Widely available
– f. *angustifolia*	CPle EHar EPla LAbb LHol SArc SDry SLon
– 'Aurea'	CB&S CBow CDec CMHG CPle CSco CSev EBre EHar ELan IOrc LBre LHol LNet MChe SHil SPer WCHb WPat WWat

LAVANDULA † (Labiatae)

N 'Alba'	CArn CB&S CBot CFis CJer CSco CSev EFol EFou ELan EOrc ERav LHol MPar MPla SBla SLon SMad SPer WEas WHal WOak WPer WSHC WWye
x *allardii*	ENor NHHG
§ *angustifolia*	CArn CBow CFis CLan CSFH CShe ENot GPoy LBuc MBar MBri MChe MGos MPla MWat NHar NNor NPer NSel NWyt SHBN SLon WAbe WHil WWye
– 'Alba'	CHad EBar ENor GPoy NFai NSel WPbr
– 'Alba Nana'	See L. ***a.*** 'Nana Alba'
§ – 'Bowles' Early'	CHad CJer CSam CSco GAbr NHHG NWyt
– 'Bowles' Variety'	See L. ***a.*** 'Bowles' Early'
– 'Dwarf Blue'	EFol LHop NHHG

– 'Folgate'	CAbb CB&S CBow CDoC CHad CJer CMGP CPMA CSco EFou LHol NFai NHHG SIde
– 'Fring Favourite'	CJer NHHG
– 'Heacham Blue'	CJer
§ – 'Hidcote'	Widely available
– 'Hidcote Pink'	Widely available
– 'Imperial Gem'	CBow CCla CJer ENor ESis NFai NHHG NHar NWyt SIde
– 'Jean Davis'	CJer NHHG
– 'Loddon Blue'	CJer LHol NHHG
– 'Loddon Pink'	CBow CJer GCra IEde MChe NHHG
– 'Maillette'	CJer
– 'Munstead'	Widely available
§ – 'Nana Alba'	Widely available
– 'Nana Atropurpurea'	CJer
– No. 9	CJer NHHG
– 'Princess Blue'	CJer ENor ESis NHar NWyt SHer SIde
§ – 'Rosea'	Widely available
– 'Twickel Purple'	CDoC CJer EBar NHHG SAxl
¶ ***canariensis***	NHHG
dentata	CArn CFis CHan CJer CMHG CMer CSev ELan ENor ERav LAbb LGre LHol MChe NFai NHHG NRar NSel SDry SFis SHer WEas WHal WHer WOak WPer WSHC WWye
§ – var. ***candicans***	CGle CHal CJer EBar EOrc ESma GCal LGre LHil LHol LHop NHHG SCro SGil SIde SMrm SSad WCHb WHal WPer
– silver form	See L. ***d. candicans***
heterophylla allardii	CJer
'Hidcote Blue'	See L. ***angustifolia*** 'Hidcote'
¶ x ***intermedia*** 'Alba'	NHHG
§ – Dutch Group	CArn CFis CJer EFou ELan EMon ENot MBar MBri MChe NSel SChu SPer WEas WHer WHil WPer
– 'Grappenhall'	CAbb CArn CBow CCla CHad CHal CJer CPMA CSco CShe EBar EBre ENor EOrc GAbr IEde LBre LHol MChe NFai NHHG NSel SChu SHer SPer WOak WPer WSun WWat WWye
– 'Grey Hedge'	LHol NHHG
– 'Grosso'	CJer LHol NHHG NHex
– 'Heacham Blue'	CJer NHHG
– 'Hidcote Giant'	CJer EHal
– Old English Group	CArn CBow ELan SPla WEas WOak WWat WWeb
– 'Royal Purple'	CArn CJer CSev ENor GAbr LHol NHHG NHar NWyt SGil SIde
– 'Seal'	CArn CJer EFou LHol MChe NHHG NSel NSti SApp SGil SHer SIde SPla WPer WWat
N – 'Twickel Purple'	CArn CBow CCla CHal CMHG CPMA CSco CSev EMon ENot LHol NFai NHHG NSel SChu SFis WAbe WOak WPer WWat
'Jean Davis'	See L. ***angustifolia*** 'Rosea'
lanata	Widely available
– x ***angustifolia***	CJer NHHG
latifolia	CArn CJer LGre MHew
'Loddon Pink'	See L. ***angustifolia*** 'Rosea'
¶ 'Lullingstone Castle'	SIde
multifida	CArn CFis CJer ENor ERav ERea LHol NHHG SIde SSad WHer WPer
officinalis	See L. ***angustifolia***

pink	LGre
pinnata	CFis ENor LGre LHol SDry SSad WCHb WPer
¶ – var. ***buchii***	NHHG
pterostoechas pinnata	CJer NHHG
'Richard Gray'	EFol EMon LRHS
'Rosea'	See L. ***angustifolia*** 'Rosea'
'Sawyers'	ENor LGre NPer
spica	See L. ***angustifolia***
stoechas	Widely available
– ***albiflora***	See L. ***s. leucantha***
§ – f. ***leucantha***	Widely available
¶ – ssp. ***luisieri***	NHHG
– 'Nana'	CArn ESma WEas
– 'Papillon'	See L. ***s. pedunculata***
§ – ssp. ***pendunculata***	Widely available
– – 'James Compton'	CSev EMon LRHS NHHG NHar NSti NWyt SMad
♦ ***vera*** De Candolle	See L. ***angustifolia***
– hort.	See L. x ***i.*** Dutch Group
viridis	Widely available
– ***alba***	CHan

LAVATERA (Malvaceae)

arborea	CArn ISea WHer WWye
– 'Ile d'Hyères'	NPer
– ***rosea***	See L. 'Rosea'
– 'Variegata'	CB&S CHan ECro ELan LHop NFai NPer SGil WAbe WCru WEas WHer
assurgentiflora	EMon LHop NPer NRar
'Barnsley'	Widely available
'Barnsley Perry's Dwarf'	NFai NPer
bicolor	See L. ***maritima***
'Bredon Springs'	CB&S ECha ELan EMil EMon LHop MBri MGos NHol SAxl SFis SHer SMrm WRus WStI
* 'Bressingham Pink'	LHop SMad
'Burgundy Wine'	Widely available
¶ ***cachemiriana***	CB&S CGle CHan CSun ELan LBlm MBro NPer NSti SMad SMrm WDav WPer WRus
'Candy Floss'	Widely available
'Kew Rose'	CKni EDon EOrc LHop NPer SMad SMrm
§ ***maritima***	Widely available
– ***bicolor***	See L. ***m.***
oblongifolia	CBot SMad
N ***olbia***	CBot CGle EMon MPla MWat NFai SDix WCru
'Peppermint Ice'	See L. 'Ice Cool'
* 'Pink Frills'	CBot CCla CSam EBlo EBre EPla ERav LBre LHop SDry SFai SMad
§ 'Rosea'	Widely available
'Shorty'	CB&S EFol ELan EMon
¶ ***tauricensis***	WCot
N ***thuringiaca***	EMon
– AL&JS 90100YU	EMon
§ – 'Ice Cool'	CBot CBow CCla CDoC CMil CPMA EFol ELan EMon EOrc ERav GCal MBri NBee NPer SAxl SChu SFai SHBN SHer SMad SMrm SPer SPla SSpi SUsu WHen WHil WPbr WRus
'Variegata'	See L. 'Wembdon Variegated'
§ 'Wembdon Variegated'	CBow CPMA EDon EFol ELan EMar EMon NPer NRar SHBN SHer SMad WCot

LAWSONIA (Lythraceae)
See Plant Deletions

LEDEBOURIA (Liliaceae/Hyacinthaceae)

♦ ***adlamii***	See L. ***cooperi***
§ ***cooperi***	CMon EBul ELan ESis IBlr MPar SIng WMar WOMN
§ ***ovalifolia***	EBul
§ ***socialis***	CHEx CHal CMon IBlr NRog
♦ ***violacea***	See L. ***socialis***

X LEDODENDRON (Ericaceae)

§ 'Arctic Tern'	CBow CDoC CSam EBlo GGGa ITim LHyd LMil MBal NHar NHol SLeo SPer SReu WAbe WThu

LEDUM (Ericaceae)

columbianum	ECar GWht MBal
glandulosum	ECar GWht NHol SPer
groenlandicum	MBar NHol NTow SPer SSpi WSHC
– 'Compactum'	ECar LNet LRHS MAsh MBal
palustre	ECar EPot GPoy MBal MGos WThu
– var. ***decumbens***	NHol
§ – f. ***dilatatum***	CLew GGGa
– var. ***diversipilosum***	ECar
– ***hypoleucum***	See R. ***p. dilatatum***
– 'Minus'	GGGa

LEEA (Leeaceae)

coccinea	MBri

LEIBNITZIA (Compositae)

anandria	NWCA

LEIOPHYLLUM (Ericaceae)

buxifolium	GArf GGGa GWht MBal MHig SSpi WCru WDav WThu
– 'Nanum'	GArf
– var. ***prostratum***	WPat

LEMBOTROPIS See **CYTISUS**

LEMNA (Lemnaceae)

gibba	CBen LMay MSta SAWi
minor	CBen EMFW EWav LMay MSta SAWi SWat WHol
polyrhiza	See SPIRODELA ***polyrhiza***
trisulca	EMFW LMay MSta SAWi SWat

LEMON See **CITRUS *limon***

LEONOTIS (Labiatae)

¶ ***dysophylla***	LHil
leonurus	See L. ***ocymifolia***
§ ***ocymifolia***	CB&S CPle CTre CTro LAbb LHil LHop SAxl SLMG SMad WHer
– var. ***albiflora***	CPou
– var. ***ocymifolia***	LHil

LEONTICE (Berberidaceae)

albertii	See GYMNOSPERMIUM ***a.***

LEONTODON (Compositae)

autumnalis	CKin
hispidus	CKin MWil NMir

LEONTOPODIUM (Compositae)

alpinum	CB&S CKel CPar EBre ELan EMNN GAbr GCHN GTou IDai LAbb LBre LGan MBal MHew MPit MRav NHol NKay NMen NNor NNrd NRoo SIng WHoo WPer WWin
– 'Mignon'	CLew CRiv ELan EMNN EPad GDra MBro MCas MHig NHol NKay NMen NRoo NRya NVic SHer SIng SSmi WHil WPer
– ssp. ***nivale***	GDra
¶ ***hayachinense***	WDav
– ***miyabeanum***	WHoo
himalayanum	CLew
¶ – EMAK 605	NHol
§ ***ochroleucum***	
var. ***campestre***	WPer
♦ ***palibinianum***	See L. ***ochroleucum campestre***
sibiricum	See L. ***leontopodioïdes***
¶ ***souliei***	WHil
tataricum	See L. ***discolor***
¶ ***wilsonii***	ECha

LEONURUS (Labiatae)

cardiaca	CArn CSev EFol EMon Effi GPoy LHol MChe MHew NSal NSel SIde WHer WOak WWye
sibiricus	MHew NSal

LEOPOLDIA (Liliaceae/Hyacinthaceae)

¶ ***brevipedicellata***	CMon
comosa	See MUSCARI ***comosum***
spreitzenhofera	See MUSCARI ***s.***
tenuiflora	See MUSCARI ***tenuiflorum***

LEPECHINIA (Labiatae)

floribunda	CGre

LEPIDIUM (Cruciferae)

¶ ***nanum***	NWCA WDav

LEPIDOTHAMNUS (Podocarpaceae)

§ ***laxifolius***	SIng WThu

LEPIDOZAMIA (Zamiaceae)

hopei	LPal
peroffskyana	LPal

LEPTINELLA (Compositae)

§ ***atrata***	NMen
– ssp. ***luteola***	ECar GDra MCas MHig NGre NMen NNrd
§ ***dendyi***	ECou ESis NHol SIng
– forms	ECou
maniototo	ECou
§ ***pectinata***	ECou NGre WCru
– var. ***sericea***	See L. ***albida***
perpusilla	See COTULA ***p.***

§ ***potentillina***	EBar ECha EHoe ELan EMon ERav ESis MMil NKay NMir NNrd NRya SChu SIng WCru WPer WWin
pyrethrifolia	CNic
– var. ***linearifolia***	CLew ELan ESis ESma SFar SIng
reptans	See L. ***scariosa***
§ ***rotundata***	CKni ECou NCat WCru WPer
§ ***scariosa***	ECou LHop
serrulata	NHol WCru
§ ***squalida***	CLew CNic CRiv ECha ECou EMar ESis IBlr MBar MCas NCat NHol NMir NNrd NRya NVic SIng SSmi WByw WPer

LEPTODACTYLON (Polemoniaceae)

See Plant Deletions

LEPTOSPERMUM † (Myrtaceae)

citratum	See L. ***petersonii***
cunninghamii	See L. ***lanigerum***
ericoïdes	See KUNZEA ***ericoïdes***
N***flavescens***	See L. ***polygalifolium***
§ ***grandiflorum***	CHan CPle ELan ISea SSpi WSHC
humifusum	See L. ***rupestre***
juniperinum	CPle
laevigatum	ISea
§ ***lanigerum***	CB&S CMHG CPle ECou IOrc ISea NHol SLon SPer WBod WSHC WWin
– 'Citratum'	ECou
§ – 'Cunninghamii'	CAbb CBow CChu CCla CDoC CPMA CSco CTre ECou IBar LGre SDry SPla SSpi SSta WPat
– 'Silver Sheen'	See L. *l.* 'Cunninghamii'
– 'Wellington'	ECou
liversidgei	CPle CTre GAri SSta
macrocarpum	ISea
¶ ***minutifolium*** × ***scoparium*** 'Green Eyes'	ECou
¶ – × ***scoparium*** 'Pink Surprise'	ECou
nitidum	CSun ECou
obovatum	CMHG
§ ***petersonii***	CPle ECou
phylicoïdes	See KUNZEA ***ericoïdes***
¶ ***polygalifolium***	SRms
prostratum	See L. ***rupestre***
pubescens	See L. ***lanigerum***
rodwayanum	See L. ***grandiflorum***
§ ***rupestre***	CB&S CChu CCla CMHG CPle CTre ECou EPot IBar IDai ISea MBal MBar MGos NHar SDry WBod WCru WDav WPat WSHC WWat
scoparium	CDoC CLan CPle ECou GAri GWht IOrc SBar WDin
– 'Album'	WPat
– 'Autumn Glory'	CPle CTre WStI
¶ – 'Avocet'	ECou
– 'Blossom'	CB&S ECou
– 'Bunting'	ECou
– 'Burgundy Queen'	CB&S ECou
– 'Chapmanii'	CMHG
– 'Charmer'	CB&S
– 'Cherry Brandy'	CB&S ELan
– 'Chiff Chaff'	ECou
– 'Elizabeth Jane'	CB&S CDoC SHer
– 'Fascination'	CB&S CGre
– 'Firecrest'	ECou
– 'Gaiety Girl' (d)	CGre
– 'Grandiflorum'	CTrw
– 'Jubilee'	CB&S
– 'Keatleyi'	CGre ECou LAbb WBod
– 'Leonard Wilson'	CSun ECou LBlm
– 'Lyndon'	ECou
– 'Martinii'	CB&S CTre
– 'McLean'	ECou
– ***nanum***	CRiv NHol SBod SHBN SIng WPat WThu
– – 'Huia'	CB&S CDoC CTre ECou ENot IOrc
– – 'Kea'	CLew ECou ELan EPot ESis MHig NHol WPat WThu
– – 'Kiwi'	CB&S CTre ECou ELan ENot EPot IOrc ITim SHer SLon WPat
– – 'Kotoku'	ELan EPot
– – 'Tui'	CDoC CTre
– 'Nichollsii'	CB&S CGre CMHG CSco CTre ENot EPot ITim SIng SLon WAbe WSHC
– 'Nichollsii Grandiflorum'	IDai
¶ – 'Nichollsii Nanum'	MHig
– 'Pink Cascade'	CB&S MBal
– 'Pink Champagne'	ECou LAbb
♦ – var. ***prostratum***	See L. ***rupestre***
– 'Red Damask' (d)	CB&S CCla CGre CLan CPle CSam CSco ELan ENot ESis IBar IDai IOrc LAbb MRav SBod SHBN SHer SIgm SPla WAbe WDin WSHC WStI
– 'Red Ensign'	ENot SBod
– 'Red Falls'	ECou
– 'Redpoll'	ECou
– 'Redstart'	ECou
– 'Robin'	ECou
– 'Ruby Glow' (d)	WBod
– 'Snow Flurry'	CB&S CDoC CGre CTre ENot SHer SIgm WDin
– 'Sunraysia'	CDoC CSam CSun CTrw LBlm
– 'Winter Cheer'	CB&S

LESPEDEZA (Leguminosae)

bicolor	CB&S CBow CCla CPMA CWit ECro EHal ESma LAbb SLPl SSpi WDin
buergeri	ELan LRHS
davurica	CBow
floribunda	CCla CPle WSHC
♦ ***hedysaroïdes***	See L. ***juncea***
thunbergii	CBow CCla CGre CPMA CSam CSco EHar ELan LHop MBlu MBri MGos MPla SBla SHil SMad SPer SReu SSpi SSta WBod WCru WDin
– 'Albiflora'	WSHC WThi
tiliifolia	See DESMODIUM ***elegans***
yakushima	MPla

LESQUERELLA (Cruciferae)

¶ ***alpina***	NWCA
¶ ***arizonica***	WHil
fendleri	NTow WDav

LEUCADENDRON (Proteaceae)

argenteum	CHEx

discolor CSun
sessile CSun
tinctum CSun

LEUCAENA (Leguminosae)

§ ***latisiliqua*** CPle
leucocephala See L. ***latisiliqua***

LEUCANTHEMELLA (Compositae)

§ ***serotina*** CBre CGle CHan CLew ECha EJud ELan MSte NSti SApp SPer SPla WEas WWin

LEUCANTHEMOPSIS (Compositae)

§ ***alpina*** MDHE WPer
hosmariensis See PYRETHROPSIS ***hosmariensis***
¶ ***radicans*** SMrm SWas

LEUCANTHEMUM † (Compositae)

discoïdeum EMon
'Fringe Benefit' EMon
hosmariense See PYRETHROPSIS ***hosmariensis***
mawii See PYRETHOPSIS ***gayana***
§ ***maximum*** ERav GCHN NNor NPer SApp SPla WByw WEas WOak WWin
– ***uliginosum*** See LEUCANTHEMELLA ***serotina***
nipponicum See NIPPONANTHEMUM ***nipponicum***
'Sonnenschein' ECha EMon WCot
x ***superbum*** 'Aglaia' (d) LRHS MBri MUlv SFis WHal
– 'Alaska' CDoC CMGP NFai NOak SMrm SPer
– 'Antwerp Star' MFir
– 'Beauté Nivelloise' CBre CKel CMil ECha
– 'Bishopstone' CDec ELan LHil MUlv WEas
¶ – 'Christine Hagemann' MBri
– 'Cobham Gold' (d) EMon ERea NOrc
– 'Esther Read' (d) CGle CKel ECED ELan ERea NNor NRoo SChu SFis SHer SPla WByw
¶ – 'Everest' NOak
– 'Fiona Coghill' CSco WCot
– 'H Seibert' CKel CSam ECED SMrm
– 'Horace Read' ECED ECha EFol ELan EMon EPla ERea LHil SChu SPla WEas
– 'John Murray' LRHS MBri MUlv
¶ – 'Little Miss Muffet' MBri
– 'Little Princess' See L. x ***s.*** 'Silberprinzesschen'
– 'Manhattan' EMon LRHS
– 'Mount Everest' LHil SRms WCot
– 'Phyllis Smith' CGle CHan CSco ECha EJud EPla MBri NCat NFai SFis SMrm WAbb WDav WHal
– 'Polaris' NFai NOak
– 'Shaggy' NCat WSHC
§ – 'Silberprinzesschen' CDoC CShe EJud LHil MFir NHol NMir NOak NRoo SHer WCot WHal WHen
– 'Snow Lady' GCHN LAbb MPit NMir NRoo WHen
– 'Snowcap' CCla CPar ECha ENot EPla GAri MBri NBar SApp SMrm SPer SPla
– 'Starburst' (d) EFou GCra MBri NMir NRoo WHen
¶ – 'Sunshine' LRHS SMrm
– 'T E Killin' (d) CGle CSco ECha EJud EMon EPla
– 'Wirral Pride' LHil
§ – 'Wirral Supreme' (d) CCla CKel CPar CRDP CShe ECED EFou ELan ENot EOrc EPla IDai LHil MBro MFir MWat NFai NNor NWyt SApp SFis SHer SPer SPla WByw WEas
§ ***vulgare*** CArn CKin NLan NMir WCla WEas WHen WHer WOak WWye
¶ – 'Corinne Tremaine' WHer
– 'Hullavington' CNat
– 'Maikönigin' ('May Queen') CBre EMon GCal
– 'Maistern' EMon
– 'Woodpecker's' WCot
'Tizi-n-Test' See PYRETHROPSIS

LEUCOCORYNE (Liliaceae/Alliaceae)

ixioïdes LBow

LEUCOGENES (Compositae)

¶ ***aclandii*** EPot
grandiceps GArf ITim NHar SBla WAbe
leontopodium GArf GGar ITim MHig NHar NRoo WAbe

LEUCOJUM † (Liliaceae/Amaryllidaceae)

aestivum CB&S CBro ELun EOrc LAma LBlo LBow MBri NEgg NLan NRog WCla WCru WGwy WShi
– 'Gravetye Giant' CAvo CBro CHad ECha ELan EMar EPar EPot ERav ETub LAma LBlo LBow LFox MBro MPar NEgg NRog SIng WThu
autumnale CAvo CBos CBro CNic CRDP CTom ELan ITim LAma LBee LBow MHig MPit MPlt NGar NMen SAxl SPou SSpi SWas WChr WCru WOMN WThu
*– ***aportense*** NHar
– 'Cobb's Variety' LHop
– var. ***oporanthum*** CAvo CMon EPot NRog
– var. ***pulchellum*** CBro CMon CRiv EPot
longifolium CMon EBul
nicaeënse CAvo CBro EBul EPot GArf LBow LHop MHig NGar SWas WChr WOMN WThu
roseum CAvo CRDP EBur LAma LBow SPou SWas WChr WDav
¶ ***tingitanum*** CMon
trichophyllum CBro CMon WChr
– ***purpurascens*** EPot WChr
valentinum CAvo CBro WChr
vernum CBro CMea ELan EPar EPot ERav ETub GDra LAma LBow MBri MHig SGil SHer SIng SSpi WAbe WHil WShi
– var. ***carpathicum*** EBul EPot LAma WChr
– var. ***vagneri*** EBul LFox MPar WChr

LEUCOPOGON (Epacridaceae)

ericoïdes MBar
§ ***fasciculatus*** ECou
§ ***fraseri*** ECar ECou GArf IBar
♦ ***parviflorus*** See CYATHODES ***parviflora***

X LEUCORAOULIA (Compositae)

§ ***loganii*** EPot GArf GDra ITim MHig NHar NWCA WDav
§ R. ***hectorii*** x L. ***grandiceps*** EPot MHig NHol NMen NMir

LEUCOSPERMUM (Proteaceae)
See Plant Deletions

LEUCOTHOË (Ericaceae)

axillaris	LBlm SSta
davisiae	GGGa MBal NHar SSta WAbe
fontanesiana	CCla EArb GWht MBal MGos SPer SReu WStI WWat
– 'Lovita'	GCal MBri MRav MUlv SSpi SSta
– 'Nana'	SPer
– 'Rainbow'	CAbb CB&S CBra CLan CPle CSco CTrw EHar ELan ENot GRei IBar IDai IJoh IOrc LHop LNet MBal MBar MGos NHol SHBN SLon SPer SReu SSta WBod WDin WThu
– 'Rollissonii'	GWht MBal MBar NHol SPer SPla SReu SSta WBod
grayana	MBal NHol SSpi
keiskei	NHol SSpi
¶– 'Royal Ruby'	WDin
populifolia	See AGARISTA ***p.***
'Scarletta'	CB&S CBow CChu CCla CKni CMHG COtt CPMA CSam IBar IJoh LBuc MAsh MBal MBar MBri MGos MUlv NHol SHer SPer SPla SReu SSpi SSta WDin WWeb

LEUZEA (Compositae)

§ ***centauroïdes***	MFir
conifera macrocephala	WOMN

LEVISTICUM (Umbelliferae)

officinale	CArn CCor CHal CSFH CSev ECha EJud ELan Effi GPoy LHol MBar MChe MHew NSel SDix SFar SHer SIde SWat WHal WHer WOak WPer WWye

LEWISIA † (Portulacaceae)

¶ 'Archangel'	NRya
'Ashwood Pearl'	MAsh NNrd
'Ben Chace'	MAsh
Birch strain	CB&S ELan EPad SIng
brachycalyx	ECar EPot GArf GDra MAsh MBal MTho NGre NHar SSou WDav
cantelovii	ESis MAsh NGre NNrd WThu
columbiana	CNic CPla ESis GArf MAsh NGre NHar NNrd NRed NTow SIng WHal WHil
– 'Alba'	GDra MAsh
– 'Rosea'	CLew ESis MAsh MHig NGre WAbe WMar WThu
– ssp. ***rupicola***	CNic EPot ESis MAsh NGre NMen NNrd NWCA
– ssp. ***wallowensis***	CLew CNic EPot MAsh NMen NNrd NRed WThu
congdonii	NGre
cotyledon	CNic CPla ESis GArf MAsh MFir NEgg NNrd NWCA SRms WHil WPat WTyr
– f. ***alba***	CPla ESis GAbr GDra GTou LHop MAsh MBro NGre NHol NTow SHer WAbe WCla WDav WHoo WThu
– Ashwood Ruby Group	MAsh NHar
– Ashwood strain	EBre ESis LBee LBlm LBre MAsh MBri NRoo NRya SIng WAbe WHoo
– 'Harold Judd'	CRiv
– var. ***heckneri***	CRDP ESis GDra MAsh
– var. ***howellii***	CPla ELan SHer SRms WPer
– hybrids	CCla CMHG CMea CNic EMNN EPad EPot GDra GTou ITim LGan MBro MFos MHig NGre NHar NHol NMen NRed WAbe WDav WThu WWin
– 'John's Special'	GDra
– magenta strain	MAsh NHol
– 'Rose Splendour'	ELan EPad EPar EPot MAsh SHer
– 'Sundance'	GDra MAsh
– Sunset Group	CSam ECar ELan GAbr GCHN GDra LAbb MBal MBri NGre NHar NHol NKay NTow SBla SHer WCla WDav WPer
¶– 'White Splendour'	MAsh
'George Henley'	CRiv EBre ECar ESis LBre MAsh NHar NNrd NRya SHer SIng WAbe WDav WThu
* 'L W Brown'	SIng
leeana	CNic MAsh WThu
longifolia	See L. ***cotyledon cotyledon***
§ ***longipetala***	EBar ESis GDra GTou MAsh MHig NGre NNrd NRed NTow NWCA WAbe WHal WThu
*– ***arizonica***	GArf
* ***longiscapa***	ESis MAsh NGre
§ ***nevadensis***	Widely available
♦– ***bernardina***	See L. ***n.***
oppositifolia	LBee MAsh NWCA
'Oxstalls Lane'	WThu
'Paula'	CNic SIng
'Phyllellia '	MAsh
'Pinkie'	CRiv EPot MAsh MCas SIng
pygmaea	CNic CRiv ECar EPot ESis GCHN GTou ITim LBee LGan MAsh MBri MBro MFos NBir NGre NHar NHol NNrd NRed NRoo NWCA SSou WAbe WHil WThu
– ssp. ***longipetala***	See L. ***longipetala***
rediviva	GDra GTou ITim MAsh MBro MFos NGre NHar NHol NWCA SIng WAbe WDav
– Jolon strain	MAsh
– white form	MAsh NGre NHol
¶ 'Regensbergen'	WPer
serrata	MAsh WHil
sierrae	EPot MAsh NGre NNrd NRed WThu
'Trevosia'	CRiv EPot MAsh MHig SIng WThu
triphylla	MAsh NGre NWCA SIng
tweedyi	CMea EBre EPad EPot ESis GDra GTou LBre MAsh NGre NHar NWCA SIng
– 'Alba'	GDra MAsh NGre
– 'Elliott's Variety'	ESis MAsh
– 'Rosea'	ESis GDra MAsh NGre NNrd NTow WThu

LEYCESTERIA (Caprifoliaceae)

crocothyrsos	CAbb CGre CPle MFir
formosa	Widely available

LEYMUS (Gramineae)

§ ***arenarius***	CElw CHad CHan CRDP CWGN ECha EFol EHoe ELan EOrc EPla ETPC GCal LHil MUlv NBro NFai NOrc NSti SApp SPla WEas WRus WWat

hispidus	See ELYMUS *hispidus*
¶ *racemosus*	ETPC

LHOTZKYA See CALYTRIX

LIATRIS (Compositae)

aspera	ECro NHol
pycnostachya	EBar ECro MWil NMir WWin
scariosa 'Magnifica'	CB&S CCla
§ *spicata*	Widely available
– 'Alba'	CCla CRDP ECha ECro EFol EFou EGol ELan EOrc GGar LAma LHol LHop NBar NFai SDeJ SPer WCra WHal WHoo WPer
– *callilepis*	See L. *s.*
– 'Floristan Violett'	CBow CSam GAbr NRoo WHil
– 'Floristan Weiss'	CBow CSam EBre ECro EMar EPla GAbr GCHN LBre LGan MRav NBro NOak NRoo SApp WAbe WHil
– 'Kobold' ('Goblin')	CB&S CShe EBre ECED ECtt ENot EOrc EPla IDai LBre MBri MRav NRoo SPla WCra WHoo WMer

LIBERTIA † (Iridaceae)

¶ 'Amazing Grace'	SAxl
caerulescens	CHan CPou EBul ECro IBlr MFir NCat
chilensis	See L. *formosa*
elegans	CGre WCot
§ *formosa*	CCla CDoC CElw CGle CHan CRDP CWGN EBre EGol ESis GCHN LBre LGan MBal MBri MUlv NBro NHol NSti SArc SChu SPer WCra WEas WHer WOld WPer WWin
– form	GCal IBlr
grandiflora	CAvo CB&S CDoC CHEx CHan CTom ECha ECro ELan EPar EPla ESma GCHN GCal IBlr ISea MBel MFir NCat NFai SPer SSpi WAbe WBod WCru WHal WPer
ixioïdea 'Tricolor'	See L. *i.*
ixioïdes	CAvo CCla CHan CSam ECou ESis GGar IBar IBlr NHol WHoo
'Nelson Dwarf'	ECou
paniculata	CHan EGol IBlr
peregrinans	CChu CCla CDoC CHan CRDP ECha GCal IBlr LTil MFir SChu SDix SMad SPer WAbe WHal WPat WThi
¶ – East Cape form	IBlr
– 'Gold Leaf'	CB&S LRHS WCot
* *procera*	CGre WCot
pulchella	CGle
sp. ex New Zealand	EPla GCal
stolonifera	NHol

LIBOCEDRUS (Cupressaceae)

chilensis	See AUSTROCEDRUS *c.*
decurrens	See CALOCEDRUS *decurrens*

LIBONIA See JUSTICIA

LICUALA (Palmae)

grandis	LPal MBri

LIGULARIA (Compositae)

amplexicaulis	CRow
¶ *calthifolia*	CRow
clivorum	See L. *dentata*
§ *dentata*	CHEx CHan CRDP CRow ELun LWad MFir NBro SPla SWat WCru WOld
– 'Desdemona'	Widely available
– 'Orange Princess'	CSco
– 'Othello'	CCla CRow CSco EPla MBal MBri NFai NKay SCro SWat WCot WCra WMer
– 'Rubrifolia'	GDra
*– 'Sonnengold'	EBlo ECha
¶ *glabrescens*	CRow
§ 'Gregynog Gold'	CDoC CHad CHan CRow CSco EBre ECha EGol ELun ENot LBre MBri MRav NBro NDea NKay NMir NOrc SCro SPer WCru WHoo WMer
x *hessei*	CHan CRow ECha SWat
hodgsonii	CSam CSco MBri NHol NSti WMer WPer
¶ *jacquemoniana*	CRow
japonica	CRow CSco
macrophylla	CHan CRow ECro
¶ *moorcroftiana*	CRow
♦ *oblongata*	See CREMANTHODIUM *oblongatum*
x *palmatiloba*	EBlo ECha EPla GCal LRHS WCot
§ *przewalskii*	CArn CDoC CGle CHEx EBre EFol EFou ELun EPar EPla GCal LBre LMay LWad MBal MBri MBro MFir MWat NDea NKay NNor NOak NTow SMad SPla WCru WHal WHoo WOld
♦ *reniformis*	See CREMANTHODIUM *reniforme*
smithii	See SENECIO *smithii*
stenocephala	CHEx CRow EGol NBro NDea
– 'Weihenstephan'	LRHS MBri WMer
♦ *tangutica*	See SINACALIA *tangutica*
'The Rocket'	Widely available
tussilaginea	See FARFUGIUM *tussilagineum*
veitchiana	CCla CHan CRow CSco EOrc GCal GDra LGan MSte NDea SApp SFis SWat WCru
wilsoniana	CHan CRow EPla SFis

LIGUSTICUM (Umbelliferae)

¶ *ferulaceum*	LGre
¶ *porteri*	NSal
scoticum	GPoy ILis MHew NSal

LIGUSTRUM † (Oleaceae)

chenaultii	WWat
delavayanum	GAri WWat
x *ibolium* 'Midas'	CMHG
japonicum	EHar ENot ISea WBod WDin WWat
– 'Coriaceum'	See L. *j.* 'Rotundifolium'
§ – 'Rotundifolium'	CCla CDec CDoC EHar GAri LNet MUlv SDry SGil SHil SReu
– 'Texanum'	CDec SEng
lucidum	CBow CBra CChu CCla CCor CDoC CMCN CPle CShe EHar ELan ENot MBar MGos MUlv SArc SMad SPer SSpi WDin WMou WWat

– 'Aureovariegatum'	EHar
– 'Excelsum Superbum' (v)	CAbP CBow CDoC CPMA CSco ECtt EHar ELan LPan MBar MBri MMea SHil SPer SSpi
– 'Golden Wax'	LRHS MUlv
– 'Latifolium'	MUlv SHil
– 'Tricolor' (v)	CBow CLan CPMA CSco EHar ELan IOrc MBal MBri SChu SHBN SPer SSpi WWat
¶ ***obtusifolium*** 'Dart's Elite'	SLPl
– var. ***regelianum***	CDoC
ovalifolium	CB&S CBra CDoC CLnd CSco EBre GRei IDai ISea LAbb LBre LBuc LPan MBar MBri MGos NBee NNor NWea SPer WDin WMou
§ – 'Argenteum' (v)	CB&S CBra CDoC CFis CGle CLan CSco EFol EHoe EPla ERav ISea MBar MBri NBee NHol SGil SLon SPer SPla SReu WEas WPat WWin
– 'Aureomarginatum'	See L. *o.* 'Aureum'
§ – 'Aureum' (v)	Widely available
* – 'Lemon and Lime' (v)	SPla
– 'Variegatum'	See L. *o.* 'Argenteum'
quihoui	CCla CDoC CHan EHar ELan EPla MGos SDix SHil SSpi SSta WHCG WPat WWat
§ ***sempervirens***	CCla SSta
sinense	CHan CMCN CMHG WWat
– 'Pendulum'	EHar EPla NHol
– 'Variegatum'	CMHG CRow EBar EHar EPla IDai WWat
– 'Wimbei'	CPMA EPla ESis SSpi WWat
strongylophyllum	SArc
¶ ***tschonoskii***	SLPl
'Vicaryi'	EBre EHar ELan EPla ERav LBre NHol SPer WPat WWat
vulgare	CKin CPer EBre GRei LBre LBuc WDin WHer WMou WNdy

LILAEOPSIS (Umbelliferae)

macloviana	NHol

LILIUM (Liliaceae/Liliaceae)

African Queen (VIa)	CKel LAma LBlo NRog SDeJ SRms
'Alliance' (VII)	CB&S
amabile (IX)	LBlo
¶ 'Angela North' (Ic)	EBul
'Apeldoorn' (Ie)	LAma
'Apollo' (Ia)	CKel ETub GCra LRHS MBri SDeJ WCru
* ***argenteum***	CHEx
'Aristo'	See L. 'Orange Aristo'
Asiatic hybrids (VI/VII)	LAma LBlo SDeJ
'Attila' (Ib)	SDeJ
auratum (IX)	CB&S CBro CKel LAma LBow SDeJ
– 'Cinnabar' (IX)	CKel
– 'Crimson Beauty' (IX)	LAma SDeJ
– var. ***platyphyllum*** (IX)	CB&S
'Avignon' (Ia)	LAma
'Ballade' (Ia)	LBlo
'Barcelona' (Ia)	CB&S ETub WCru WHil
Bellingham hybrids (IV)	EBul LBlo
'Bellona' (Ia)	NRog
¶ 'Black Beauty' (VIId)	EBul
'Black Dragon' (VIa)	LAma LBlo
Black Magic (VIa)	SDeJ
'Bonfire' (VIIb)	SDeJ
'Brandywine' (Ib)	SRms
'Bright Star' (VIb)	CBro ETub LAma LBlo SDeJ SRms
¶ 'Bronwen North' (Ic)	EBul
¶ ***bulbiferum*** (IX)	CKel
– var. ***croceum*** (IX)	LBlo
Bullwood hybrids (IV)	EBul
§ ***canadense*** (IX)	CRDP EBul LAma MBal MS&S NRog SDeJ WChr WCru
– var. ***editorum***	LAma
– ***flavum***	See L. ***canadense***
'Canasta' (Ia)	LBlo
candidum (IX)	CArn CAvo CB&S CBro CHEx ECha ECtt ELan EMon ETub GAbr LAma LBlo LBow MBri MBro NRog SDeJ SUsu
– 'Plenum'	EMon
'Capitol' (VII)	CB&S
'Carla Luppi' (Ia)	LBlo
'Carmen' (VIIc)	CB&S
'Casa Blanca' (VIIb)	CB&S CKel ETub LAma LBlo NRog SDeJ
cernuum (IX)	LBlo SDeJ
chalcedonicum (IX)	MPar MS&S WChr
'Charisma' (Ia)	LRHS MBri
'Cherrywood' (IV)	EBul
'Chinook' (Ia)	LAma NRog
Citronella (Ic)	CBro LAma LBlo MS&S NRog SRms SUsu
'Coachella' (IV)	EBul
'Cocktail' (Ia)	LBlo
concolor var. ***partheneion*** (IX)	EPot
'Concorde' (Ia)	SDeJ
'Connecticut King' (Ia)	CAvo CB&S CBro CKel ETub LAma LBlo LBow NRog SDeJ WCru
'Corina' (Ia)	MBri SDeJ
'Corsage' (Ib)	CAvo CKel LBlo NRog
'Côte d'Azur' (Ia)	CKel ETub LAma SDeJ WCru WHil
§ x ***dalhansonii*** (II)	LAma MPar
dauricum	CNic
§ ***davidii*** var. ***willmottiae*** (IX)	LAma MS&S SRms
'Destiny' (Ia)	CKel LAma NRog SRms
'Discovery' (Ic)	LBlo MS&S
'Dominique' (VII)	LAma NRog
'Dream' (Ia)	CSut
¶ 'Dreamland' (Ia)	EBul
duchartrei (IX)	CBro MPar
* 'Elvin's Son'	CB&S ETub LAma LRHS WCru WHil
'Enchantment' (Ia)	CB&S CBro CKel LAma LBlo LBow MBri NEgg NRog SDeJ
'Exception' (Ib)	LAma
'Festival' (Ia)	CB&S LAma MS&S
¶ 'Feuerzauber' (Ia)	WCru WHil
'Fire King' (Ib)	ETub LAma LBlo NRog SDeJ SRms WCru
§ 'Firebrand' (I)	LAma
'Firecracker' (Ia)	LAma
'Flamenco' (Ib)	MS&S
formosanum (IX)	CHun EBul SHer WHal

– var. ***pricei*** (IX)	CMea CNic COtt CRDP CRiv CSam EBul ELan EPar EPot ITim LBee LGre LHop MBal MBri MCas MFir MHig MTho NHol NMen NNrd NWCA SBla SWas WAbe WHoo WPer
– 'Snow Queen' (IX)	CKel
'Fresco' (VII)	CB&S
'Friendship' (VII)	CB&S
'Fuga' (Ic)	SDeJ
'Furore' (VIIc)	CB&S
'Geisha' (VII)	CB&S
Golden Splendor (VIa)	LAma LBlo NRog SRms
'Gran Cru' (Ia)	CB&S
'Gran Paradiso' (Ia)	CB&S EBul LAma
'Grand Cru'	SDeJ
grayi (IX)	EBul
'Green Dragon' (VIa)	CAvo CBro CKel LAma LBlo
Green Magic (VIa)	LAma
'Hannah North' (Ic)	EBul LGre
hansonii (IX)	CKel LAma LBlo NRog SUsu
Harlequin hybrids (Ic)	CKel SDeJ
'Harvest' (Ia)	ETub
henryi (IX)	CAvo CKel LAma LBlo LBow NRog SDeJ
'Hornback's Gold' (Ic)	EBul
Imperial Gold (VIIc)	LAma LBlo SDeJ
Imperial Silver (VIIc)	LAma SDeJ
'Iona' (Ic)	EBul
§ 'Jacques S Dijt' (II)	LAma LBlo
Jamboree (VIId)	SDeJ
'Jetfire' (Ia)	CB&S LAma SDeJ
'Journey's End' (VIId)	CB&S CKel ETub LAma NRog SDeJ
§ 'Joy' (VIIb)	CB&S CKel LAma
'Karen North' (Ic)	EBul
'King Pete' (Ib)	SDeJ WCru
'Lady Ann' (VIb)	LBlo SDeJ
'Lady Bowes Lyon' (Ic)	EBul
'Ladykiller' (Ia)	LAma NRog
'Lake Tahoe' (IV)	EBul
'Lake Tulare' (IV)	EBul
§ ***lancifolium*** (IX)	LAma LBow SDeJ SRms
– var. ***flaviflorum***	SRms
– 'Flore Pleno' (IX)	CAvo CRDP EMon WCot
§ – var. ***splendens*** (IX)	CBro EMon ETub LAma LBow MPar SDeJ
'Laura' (VII)	CB&S
'Le Rêve'	See L. 'Joy'
¶ ***leichtlinii*** 'Delta' (IX)	CKel
'Levant' (Ic)	LAma
'Liberation' (I)	LAma LBlo NBir
¶ 'Lilliput' (Ia)	LRHS
'Limelight' (VIa)	CAvo CKel LAma LBlo
'Little Snow White' (v)	MPar NOak
longiflorum (IX)	CAvo CB&S LAma NRog SUsu WCot WCru WHal
– 'Gelria' (IX)	SDeJ
– 'White American' (IX)	LBlo MBri
¶ 'Lotus' (VI)	LRHS
'Luxor' (Ib)	CB&S CSut NBir
mackliniae (IX)	ECha GGGa IBlr MBal NBir NHol WAbe
♦ ***maculatum davuricum***	See L. ***dauricum***
'Marhan' (II)	See L. x ***dalhansonii***
x ***marhan*** 'J S Dijt'	See L. 'Jacques S Dijt'
'Maria Callas' (Ia)	CSut
'Marie North' (Ic)	EBul
martagon (IX)	CAvo CBro CKel ECha EFou ELan ELun EMon ETub GAbr LAma LBlo LBow MBal MS&S NBir NRog SDeJ SUsu WWat
– var. ***album*** (IX)	CAvo CBro ECha EFou ETub LAma LBlo LBow MPar MS&S MTho SDeJ WChr
– var. ***cattaniae*** (IX)	EMon
¶ – 'Netherhall Pink' (IX)	EMon
¶ – 'Netherhall White' (IX)	EMon
– var. ***pilosiusculum*** (IX)	MPar
¶ – 'Plenum' (IX)	EMon
'Massa'	LRHS
'Medaillon' (Ia)	LAma NRog
'Mona Lisa' (VIIb/d)	CB&S LRHS MBri
§ ***monadelphum*** (IX)	CBro LAma LBlo LBow MPar NRog NTow SSpi SUsu
'Mont Blanc' (Ia)	CB&S CBro CKel LAma NBir SDeJ
¶ 'Monte Negro' (Ia)	WCru
'Monte Rosa' (Ic)	SDeJ
'Montreux' (Ia)	CB&S EBul LAma
'Moonflower' (Ia)	CB&S
Moonlight (VIa)	LBlo SDeJ
'Moulin Rouge' (Ib)	NRog
'Mrs R O Backhouse' (II)	LAma LRHS
§ ***nanum*** (IX)	CAvo GGGa NHar NHol NRog NTow
– deep purple (IX)	NKay
– 'Len's Lilac' (IX)	GDra NHol NKay
– McBeath's form (IX)	NHar NKay
nepalense (IX)	LAma NRog SDeJ WCot WCru
'New Yellow'	LRHS MBri
'Nivea' (I)	CKel
'Olivia' (Ia)	CSut ETub LAma SDeJ SUsu
Olympic Hybrids (VIa)	CKel LAma SDeJ
'Omega' (VII)	CB&S GCra LAma SDeJ WHil
§ 'Orange Aristo' (Ia)	LBlo LRHS MBri
'Orange Pixie' (Ia)	CBro LRHS MBri
* 'Orange Sensation'	LBlo
'Orange Triumph' (Ia)	LAma SRms
'Orange Wattle ' (Ic)	EBul
'Orchid Beauty' (Ia)	MBri
* Oriental Superb	LBlo
oxypetalum (IX)	CAvo CBro GGGa NHol
– var. ***insigne*** (IX)	GDra GGGa NHar NHol
¶ Paisley hybrids (II)	CBro
'Pandora' (Ia)	CB&S
'Paprika' (Ib)	LBlo
pardalinum (IX)	CAvo CBro CGle ECha ELan MPar
– var. ***giganteum*** (IX)	CBro CKel EBul NCat
'Peachblush' (Ia)	CB&S LAma WHil
'Peggy North' (Ic)	EBul
¶ 'Perugia' (VIId)	CKel
philippinense (IX)	ESma WHil
'Pink Beauty' (VIIc)	CBro
* 'Pink Panther'	LBlo
Pink Perfection (VIa)	CAvo CB&S CBro CKel LAma LBlo NRog SDeJ
'Pink Sunburst'	SDeJ
'Pirate' (Ia)	LAma MS&S SRms
¶ ***pomponium*** (IX)	MS&S
'Prominence'	See L. 'Firebrand'
§ ***pumilum*** (IX)	CAvo CBro CCla ETub LAma LBlo LHop MTho NBir SDeJ SUsu WCru
pyrenaicum (IX)	ELan GDra LHop MS&S SPla WByw WChr WCot
– var. ***aureum***	See L. ***p. pyrenaicum***

§ – var. ***pyrenaicum*** (IX)	LBlo
'Rangoon' (Ia)	EBul
'Red Carpet' (Ia)	CBro CKel ETub MBri NBir
Red Jewels (Ic)	LAma
'Red Lion' (Ia)	CKel CSut SDeJ
* 'Red Marvel'	LBlo
'Red Night' (I)	NRog
'Redstart' (Ib)	MPar
regale (IX)	CArn CAvo CB&S CBro CCla CHad CKel CSam CSut EBul EFol EFou ETub LAma LBlo LBow LGre LHop MBal MS&S NEgg NRog SDeJ WBod WCru WEas WHal WPbr WWat
– Album Group (IX)	CAvo CKel EFou LAma LBlo LBow NRog SDeJ WCru
§ – Royal Gold (IX)	CB&S CKel LAma LBlo NEgg SDeJ SRms
'Roma' (Ia)	EBul ETub LAma NBir WCru WHil
'Rosefire' (Ia)	LAma
'Rosemary North' (I)	EBul
'Rosita' (Ia)	LAma MBri NRog
Royal Gold strain	See L. ***regale*** Royal Gold
'Sans Pareil' (Ia)	SDeJ
'Sans Souci' (VIId)	LBlo LRHS MBri
'Scentwood' (IV)	EBul
♦ ***shastense***	See L. ***kelleyanum***
¶ 'Shuksan' (IV)	CBro
'Simoen' (Ia)	SDeJ
'Snow Princess'	LAma
'Snow Trumpet' (v)	CSam
'Sorrento' (Ia)	CSut
speciosum var. ***album*** (IX)	CBro CKel LAma LBlo NBir SDeJ
– 'Grand Commander' (IX)	LAma LBlo SDeJ
– 'Ida Uchida' (IX)	LBlo
– 'Rosemede' (IX)	LBlo
– var. ***roseum*** (IX)	LAma LBlo SDeJ
– var. ***rubrum*** (IX)	CAvo CB&S CBro CKel ECha LAma LBlo LBow NBir NRog SDeJ WCot WCru
– 'Uchida' (IX)	LAma SDeJ
'Star Gazer' (VIIc)	CB&S CBro CKel CSut LAma LBlo NRog SDeJ WCru WHil
¶ 'Stardrift' (VIId)	CSut
¶ 'Starfish' (I)	SRms
* 'Sterling Silver'	LAma
'Sterling Star' (Ia)	CB&S ETub LAma LBlo NCat NRog SDeJ
'Sun Ray' (Ia)	LAma LRHS NRog
superbum (IX)	LAma NRog SUsu WChr
szovitsianum	See L. ***monadelphum***
'Tabasco' (Ia)	MS&S
'Tamara' (Ib)	CSut LAma MBri MS&S NRog
tenuifolium	See L. ***pumilum***
x ***testaceum*** (IX)	CAvo ETub LAma LBlo LBow MPar NRog SDeJ
'Tiger White' (Ic)	LBlo
tigrinum	See L. ***lancifolium***
'Trance' (VIIb)	CB&S LBlo LRHS MBri
'Troubadour' (VIIc)	LBlo
¶ 'Uchida Kanoka'	CSut
wallichianum (IX)	CBro LAma NRog SDeJ
¶ 'Walter Bentley' (Ic)	SRms
'Wattle Bird' (Ia)	EBul
'White Happiness' (Ia)	LAma
'White Journey's End' (VIId)	CB&S
'White Lady' (VIa)	CBro CKel
'White Mountain' (VIIc)	SDeJ
willmottiae	See L. ***davidii willmottiae***
Yellow Blaze (Ia)	LAma NRog SDeJ
'Yellow Giant'	See L. 'Joanna'
'Yellow Present'	SDeJ
* 'Yellowhammer'	LBlo

LIME See CITRUS *aurantiifolia*

LIMNANTHES (Limnanthaceae)

douglasii	CDoC CKni CMea CRiv ELan IBlr LHil MPit SHer SIng WBod WCra WEas WHal WHer

LIMONIUM (Plumbaginaceae)

bellidifolium	CLew CRDP CShe EBre ECha ELan ESis GDra LBre MHig NHol NMen NTow SBla SHer SSou WCla WEas WPer
cosyrense	CHal CLew CMea LBlm NHol NMen SIng SRms WPer
§ ***dregeanum***	WThu
dumosum	See GONIOLIMON ***tataricum angustifolium***
globulariifolium	See L. ***ramosissimum***
gmelinii	SSvw WPer
– 'Perestrojka'	NMir WSun
gougetianum	MCas NTow
latifolium	See L. ***platyphyllum***
minutum	CElw ELan MHig SHer WPer
paradoxum	CLew ELan SHer
§ ***platyphyllum***	CBow CCla CGle CSco EGol IDai LHil MFir MTol MWat NBee NMir NRar NWyt SCro SDix SPer SSvw WEas WHoo WOld WPer WSun
– 'Grandiflorum'	CKel
– 'Robert Butler'	EOrc MMil MRav
¶ – 'True Blue'	LRHS
– 'Violetta'	CBot CDoC CKel CSco EBre ECha EFol ELan LBre MBri MRav MUlv SMrm SPer WHoo WSun
§ ***ramosissimum***	NTow WThu
tataricum	See GONIOLIMON ***t.***
tetragonum	See L. ***dregeanum***
¶ ***vulgare***	WGwy

LINANTHASTRUM See LINANTHUS

LINANTHUS (Polemoniaceae)

See Plant Deletions

LINARIA (Scrophulariaceae)

aeruginea var. ***nevadensis***	NMir WCla WHil
alpina	CMea CRiv CTom ECro ELan EMNN GDra LBee MBro MPit MTho NKay NMen NOak NWCA SHer SIng SSou SUsu WCla WPer WWin
– 'Rosea'	NKay WCla WCru
* 'Blue Pygmy'	CHun MPit
cymbalaria	See CYMBALARIA ***muralis***

dalmatica	CDec CGle CHan CPar CSev CSun CTom ECha ELan EMon GCal LAbb LBlm LGan MFir MTol NBro NCat NSti NWCA SAxl SChu SMrm SSou SSvw WKif WPer WRus
x ***dominii*** 'Carnforth'	EMar EMon ERav LRHS NSti
– 'Yuppie Surprise'	ELan EMon LRHS NBir NPer
genistifolia	GAbr GDra NCat SFis
hepaticifolia	See CYMBALARIA ***h.***
*****lobata alba***	SHer
origanifolia	See CHAENORHINUM ***origanifolium***
pallida	See CYMBALARIA ***pallida***
'Parham Variety'	CPar
pilosa	See CYMBALARIA ***pilosa***
purpurea	CDec CGle CKin CPar CRiv CWGN ECro EFou ELan LHol MChe MFir MHew NBro NCat NFai NMir NNor NPer WCla WCra WHal WPer WWin
– 'Alba'	See L. ***p.*** 'Springside White'
– 'Canon Went'	Widely available
¶ – 'Dwarf Canon Went'	WCot
– 'Radcliffe Innocence'	See L. ***p.*** 'Springside White'
§ – 'Springside White'	ECha ECro EMon LGre LRHS
repens	CCor CKin WCot WHer
supina	EMNN MWat NKay WCla WHer WPer
triornithophora	CBrd CDec CElw CGle ECha ECro EMar ERav LGan MFir MNFA NBro SFis SMrm SUsu WCot WHil WWin
– pink form	CBot CGle CHan WEas WPer
– purple form	CHan CSun ELan
tristis 'Toubkal'	MPar WOMN WWin
vulgaris	CKin CNat CRiv EJud GCal LHol MChe MHew NLan NMir NSel SIde WHer WNdy
– peloric form	CNat

LINDELOFIA (Boraginaceae)

♦***anchusoïdes*** hort.	See L. ***longiflora***
§ – Lehmann	CHan EBar ECro GCal LBlm MBro NSti WCru WDav
longiflora	GCal SAxl WCru WPer

LINDERA (Lauraceae)

benzoin	CB&S SHil SSpi
erythrocarpa	CMCN SSta WCoo
¶ ***megaphylla***	CB&S
obtusiloba	SHil SSta WCoo
umbellata	WCoo

LINNAEA (Caprifoliaceae)

borealis	CRDP GAri GDra MBal NGre NNrd WAbe WOMN
– var. ***americana***	CLew CNic ECar NHar NMen NNrd NWCA

LINUM † (Linaceae)

arboreum	ECha MBro MPla NHol NMen NSti SBla SIng SUsu SWas WDav WOMN WPat WThu WWat
bienne	CKin
capitatum	MHig NTow WAbe WOMN
flavum	CBow CGle EPot MBro NMen SHer SSvw WHoo WPbr WPer
– 'Compactum'	CCla CDoC CKel CNic ECha EFou ELan GDra LAbb LGan MPit MRav NKay NMen NRoo SBla SPer SSvw WHal WHil WMer WOld WWin
'Gemmell's Hybrid'	CLew CRDP CShe EPot LBee MBro MHig NHar NHol NWCA SBla SIng SWas WAbe WDav WPat WThu
leonii	ELan EMon LRHS SWas
mongolicum	MBro WPer
monogynum	ECou LGre NTow NWCA SBla SChu SFar SFis WDav
§ – ***diffusum***	ECou NHol
– dwarf form	CLew MTho
– 'Nelson'	See L. ***m. diffusum***
¶ ***mucronatum armenum***	WDav
narbonense	CKel CPar CSam CShe ECha ELan LAbb LGre LGro MBri MBro MFir MPar MRav MUlv NBro NHol NNrd NOak SIgm SMrm WCra WHoo WKif WMer WOld WPer
– 'Heavenly Blue'	ELan EPla LHop SUsu WEas WHen WPer
perenne	CArn CHan CMea CPar ECha EFol ELan EPla GCal LAbb LHol MBri MChe MHew MPit MPla NMir NNor SHer SIde SPer SSvw WEas WHer WPer WTyr WWin WWye
– ***album***	CDoC CGle CHad CSco ECha EFou ELan EPla GCal LHol MBro NSel SGil SHer SPer SUsu WHer WPer WRus
– ssp. ***alpinum***	LGre MBro WPer
– – 'Alice Blue'	NHar SBla WDav
– ssp. ***anglicum***	CNat NMir NSel SSvw
– 'Blau Saphir' ('Blue Sapphire')	CBow CDoC CSam EFou EOrc ESis MPit NFai NHol NOrc NRoo SSvw WPbr
– 'Diamant'	CBow MRav NFai NRoo WPbr
– ***lewisii***	LGre MHig NBir NHol NTow NWCA
– 'White Diamond'	ESis LGre WCot
¶ ***rubrum***	MChe
sibiricum	See L. ***perenne***
suffruticosum ssp. ***salsoloïdes*** 'Nanum'	MBro NTow SIng WThu
– – 'Prostratum'	ECha SIgm
tenuifolium	WPer
viscosum	WPer

LIPPIA (Verbenaceae)

canescens	See PHYLA ***c.***
chamaedrifolia	See VERBENA ***peruviana***
citriodora	See ALOYSIA ***triphylla***
nodiflora	See PHYLA ***nodiflora***
repens	See PHYLA ***nodiflora***

LIQUIDAMBAR (Hamamelidaceae)

formosana	CGre CMCN ELan GAri GWht MBlu MBri SSpi SSta WCoo WNor
– Monticola Group	SHil SSta
orientalis	CMCN LMer MGos SSta
styraciflua	Widely available
*– ***acalycina***	SSta
– 'Aurea'	CLnd IOrc NHol SSta WPat
– 'Burgundy'	COtt CPMA WPat

*– *festeri* SSta
– 'Golden Treasure' (v) CBow CPMA CSco SMad SSpi SSta
– 'Gumball' EHar SSta
¶ – 'Kia' CPMA
– 'Lane Roberts' CCla CDoC CPMA CSco EHar LPan MUlv NHol SHil SReu SSpi SSta WDin WPat
– 'Moonbeam' (v) EBre LBre SSta WPat
– 'Moraine' SSta
– 'Palo Alto' LPan SSta WPat
– 'Pendula' CPMA SSta
– 'Silver King' CPMA
– 'Variegata' CPMA SEng SSpi SSta WPat
– 'Worplesdon' CCla CDoC COtt CSco EBre EHar ELan ENot ESma IHos LBre LMer MBri SMad SPer SReu SSpi SSta WAbe WWat

LIRIODENDRON † (Magnoliaceae)

chinense CAbP CChu CGre CMCN CPle EArb EHar ELan ISea MBlu MBri SSpi WCoo WWat
tulipiferum Widely available
– 'Aureomarginatum' Widely available
– 'Fastigiatum' COtt CSco CTho EBre EHar ELan ENot LBre LPan MBri SHil SPer SSpi SSta WMou
– 'Mediopictum' ELan MBlu SMad

LIRIOPE † (Liliaceae/Convallariaceae)

exiliflora
'Ariaka-janshige' ('Silvery Sunproof') (v) WCot WThu
¶ – 'Silvery Sunproof' MUlv
gigantea SApp
graminifolia See LL. ***spicata, muscari***
hyacinthifolia See REINECKEA ***carnea***
minor SApp
§ *muscari* Widely available
♦– *alba* See L. ***m.*** 'Monroe White'
¶ – 'Curley Twist' SApp
– 'Gold-banded' GCal NOrc WCot
– 'John Burch' (v) NOrc WCot
¶ – 'Majestic' GCal SApp SPla WCot
§ – 'Monroe White' GCal NOrc SApp SLMG SPer WCot
¶ – 'Purple Bouquet' SApp
¶ – 'Royal Purple' NOrc WCot
¶ – 'Silvery Midget' WCot
– 'Superba' WCot
– *variegata* CAvo CBos CRow ELan EPla NOrc WCot
¶ – variegated white bloom WCot
¶ – 'Webster Wideleaf' WCot
platyphylla ECro SApp SSpi
§ *spicata* CElw NOrc SSpi WHoo
– 'Alba' CCla CHad CRow EBre ECro EGol EPla GCal LBre MRav MTho MUlv SAxl SMad
– 'Silver Dragon' (v) WCot

LITHOCARPUS † (Fagaceae)

densiflorus WCoo
edulis CHEx SArc
§ *glaber* CHEx
¶ *pachyphyllus* CB&S

LITHODORA (Boraginaceae)

§ *diffusa* CNic MPit NKay SBla SSpi
– 'Alba' CB&S CCla CLew CMHG EPot GAri GWht LBee MBri MBro MPla NEgg NHar NHol NMen NRoo SHer SIng SUsu WAbe
– 'Cambridge Blue' LAbb LHop MPla WSHC
– 'Compacta' LHop SAxl
– 'Grace Ward' CCla CGle EPot IDai MPla NHar NHol NRoo SBod SIng SMrm WAbe WPat WThu
– 'Heavenly Blue' Widely available
– 'Inverleith' LBee LHop LRHS SAxl
– 'Picos' GArf NHar SIgm WDav
graminifolia See MOLTKIA ***suffruticosa***
hispidula ELan NMen SHer WCru
x *intermedia* See MOLTKIA x ***i.***
§ *oleifolia* CShe ELan EPot MBro MHig MTho MWat NHar NHol NKay NMen SIng WCru WDav WPat
rosmarinifolia CSpe ELan
zahnii ELan EPad LHop NTow SHer SIgm SIng WAbe WHil

LITHOPHRAGMA (Saxifragaceae)

bulbiferum See L. ***glabrum***
¶ *glabrum* JCA 10514 CNic
parviflora EPot GArf GDra MHig MTho NBir NHol NMen SBar WOMN

LITHOSPERMUM (Boraginaceae)

arvense NSal
diffusum See LITHODORA ***diffusa***
doerfleri See MOLTKIA ***doerfleri***
officinale GPoy MHew NSal WCla WHer
oleifolium See LITHODORA ***oleifolia***
purpureocaeruleum See BUGLOSSOIDES ***purpurocaerulea***

LITSEA (Lauraceae)

japonica CHEx

LITTONIA (Liliaceae/Colchicaceae)

modesta CGre CMon CTro LBow SLMG

LIVISTONA (Palmae)

australis CHEx LPal NPal
chinensis LPal
decipiens NPal

LOASA (Loasaceae)

♦ *lateritia* See CAIOPHORA ***l.***
¶ *triphylla volcanica* GCal

LOBELIA † (Campanulaceae)

anatina ESma GCal SGil WHil
N *angulata* ECar MTho NGre NHar NHol NMen SSmi WAbe
– 'Jack's Pass' CHun GAri MTho NHar NRya
¶ – 'Messenger' ECou
– 'Ohau' ECou EPla ESis WOMN
– 'Tim Rees' ELan MTho SBla SIng SMrm WCru WPer
– 'Woodside' ECou
'Bees' Flame' CB&S CRow EBre LBre MTho
'Brightness' CRow EBre ELan LBre SAxl

¶ 'Butterfly Blue'	CAbb CB&S GCal SMad
¶ 'Butterfly Rose'	CAbb CB&S GCal SBla SFis SMad
cardinalis	CArn CHad CKel CNic CPar CRDP CRow CSun CWGN EHon EPot EWav GCHN GCal LHol LMay MSta MSte NDea NSal SChu SSpi SUsu WChe WCru WHol WMer WOld WWin WWye
– JLS 88010WI	EMon
¶ – ***multiflora***	GCal
'Cherry Ripe'	CChu CGle CRDP CRiv CWGN ELan MSte MTho SAxl SBla SChu SHer SUsu WCHb
'Cinnabar Rose'	CAbb CChu SRms WCot WHil WPer
'Complexion'	ESma GCHN MTol SMad
'Compliment Scarlet'	CBow CRow EBar EBre GCHN LBre NBro NPer WHil
'Dark Crusader'	CB&S CChu CHad CMHG CRDP CRiv CRow CWGN ECha ECtt EFou ELan GCal LHil MBri MTho NBro NDea NHol NOrc NSti SAxl SChu SMrm WEas
erinus 'Kathleen Mallard' (d)	CElw CGle CRDP CRow CSev CSpe ELan ERav GCal SFis SHer WOMN
'Eulalia Berridge'	CGle CRDP SMrm SWas
excelsa	CHEx
'Fan Deep Red'	CHad GCHN WHil
'Flamingo'	See L. 'Pink Flamingo'
fulgens	CHad CWGN IBlr SCro SMrm SSpi WByw WCot WEas
'Galen'	CRow
x ***gerardii***	NHol
– 'Eastgrove Pink'	WEas
§ – 'Vedrariensis'	Widely available
gibberoa	CHEx
'Hadspen Royal Purple'	CHad
inflata	CArn NSal SIde WWye
'Jack McMaster'	CChu CWGN LHop MBel MSte MTho
laxiflora	CBot CWGN MTho SMrm
– var. ***angustifolia***	CChu CGre CHEx CMHG CRDP ELan EPla ERea GCal IBlr LHil LHop MSte SUsu WAbb WHal WMar WPer WWye
lindblomii	CRDP CRiv CTom LBee NCat NHar WHal WHil WPer
linnaeoïdes	EPot GCHN LBee MTho NGre NHar NMen NTow WEas WOMN WPer
macrodon	NGre SIng
¶ ***minorescens***	CElw
§ ***oligodon***	GAri GGar NKay
pedunculata	CHan CMHG CMea CPar CRDP CRow CWGN ECha ECou EFol ELan EPot ESis GCHN LBee LHop MBar NGre NKay NRya SBla SIng SSmi WAbe WHil WWin
– 'Blue Stars'	ECou WThi
– 'Clear Skies'	ECou
– 'County Park'	CHal CHun CLew CMea CRDP CRiv CSpe ECha ECou ELan ELun EPot ESis LBee LRHS NGre NHar NHol NWCA SBla SIng SSmi WHal WPat WPer WThi
– 'Kinsey'	ECou
– 'Tom Stone'	EBar ECar ECou EPot NHar
¶ ***pendunculata*** 'Klandra'	ECou
perpusilla	ECou
– 'Fragrant Carpet'	ECou
– 'Summer Meadows'	CLew ECou WPer
¶ 'Pink Elephant'	SWas
§ 'Pink Flamingo'	Widely available
'Queen Victoria'	Widely available
repens	ECou
richardsonii	CBrk LHil SDix SFis WEas
'Rowden Magenta'	CRow
¶ 'Royal Robe'	CRow
N 'Russian Princess'	CChu CGle CRow CSam CSco CWGN GCra LHil LHop MBri MTho NBee NHol NOrc NSti SAxl SChu SMad WMer
sessilifolia	CPar GDra MBel NGre SBla SMrm SRms WChe WPer
– B&L 12396	EMon
siphilitica	Widely available
– ***alba***	CB&S CBrd CBre CRow ECro GCal LGan LHil NSti WByw WCra WEas WHoo WPer
– 'Nana'	GCal
¶ 'Sonia'	CGle
x ***speciosa***	CRow WPer
– dark form	CRow SMrm
sp. CLD 1007	NHol
surrepens	ECou
'Tania'	CB&S CChu CGle CRDP CRow EFou IBlr MSte MUlv SAxl SChu SCro SHig SMad WByw
treadwellii	CMea CRDP ECha EPla ESis LBee MHig MPar MTho NMen NMir SUsu WAbe WHal WHen WPer WWin
tupa	Widely available
– G&K 4253	CCla
¶ – dark orange form	GCal
valida	CHad ELan GCal NBro SMrm WPer
vedrariensis	See L. x ***gerardii*** 'Vedrariensis'
'Will Scarlet'	CChu EBre LBre MTho SAxl SBla
¶ 'Zinnoberrosa'	SMad

LOGANBERRY See **RUBUS**

LOISELEURIA (Ericaceae)
See Plant Deletions

LOMANDRA (Lomandraceae)

longifolia	ECou GWht

LOMARIA See **BLECHNUM**

LOMATIA (Proteaceae)

dentata	CB&S ISea
ferruginea	CAbb CHEx CLan IBar ISea MBal SArc WBod
longifolia	See L. ***myricoïdes***
§ ***myricoïdes***	CAbb CCla CHEx CLan CTre CTrw ELan LAbb SArc SDry SHil SSpi WBod WWat
silaifolia	CTre SArc SDry SHil
tinctoria	CHEx CLan CPle CTre CTrw SArc SSpi

LOMATIUM (Umbelliferae)

utriculatum	NSal

LONICERA † (Caprifoliaceae)

albertii	CCor WHCG
alseuosmoïdes	CChu SBra SLon WWeb
altmannii	CPle
N× ***americana*** hort.	See L. × ***italica***
¶ – (Miller) K. Koch	CSPN SBra SHil SReu SSta WCru
¶ ***arizonica***	SBra
× ***brownii***	CMac IDai
– 'Dropmore Scarlet'	See L. ***sempervirens*** 'D.S.'
– 'Fuchsioides'	CBow CCla ELan EOvi ERav NSti SBra SPer WPat WSHC WWat WWeb
caerulea	CPle EHal
– var. ***edulis***	ESim
caprifolium	CDoC CSco CShe EBre ELan EPla LBre LGre LHol LPri MBar MBri SBra SHBN SPer WWat
– 'Anna Fletcher'	EBar SBra WEas WWeb
– f. ***pauciflora***	See L. × ***italica***
chaetocarpa	CBot CMHG WPat
chrysantha	CMCN CPle
ciliosa	CGre SBra
'Clavey's Dwarf'	IOrc MPla NHol SPer
¶ ***dioica***	SBra
'Early Cream'	See L. ***caprifolium***
etrusca	CHan CSco CWit EHal EPla LHol LPri MBri SBra SHil WWeb
– 'Donald Waterer'	CCor SBra SPer SSpi
– 'Michael Rosse'	CCor SBra
– 'Superba'	EBre ECtt ELan ESma GCal LBre MUlv NSti SBla SBra SSpi WCru WSHC WWat
flexuosa	See L. ***japonica repens***
fragrantissima	Widely available
giraldii hort.	See L. ***acuminata***
– Rehder	CB&S CBot CChu CHan EBre LBre LPri SBra WSHC
glabrata	SBra WWat
¶ ***glaucescens***	SBra
glaucohirta	See L. ***periclymenum g.***
grata	See L. × ***americana*** (Miller) K. Koch
× ***heckrottii***	CDoC CMHG CMac CMer CMil ECtt ISea LPri MBar NBar NKay NRoo SPer WDin WStI WWat
– 'Gold Flame'	CB&S CSco EBlo EBre ELan EPla GAri IDai LBre MBal MBea MBri MGos NHol SBra SHBN WAbe WSHC WStI WWat
§ ***henryi***	CB&S CChu CCla CHan CMac CSco EBre EGol ELan EPla IOrc LBre LHop LPri MBar MBri MWat NHol SBra SHBN SLon SPer SSpi WBod WDin WSHC
– var. ***subcoriacea***	See L. ***henryi***
*'Hidcote'	CMac
hildebrandtiana	CGre CHEx
hirsuta	SBra
hispida	CPle
¶ ***hispidula***	SBra
implexa	EFol ELan EPla LGre SBra
insularis	CMCN CPle
involucrata	CChu CCla CCor CHan CMCN CMHG CPle EBar LHil LHop MBar MBel MRav SPer WBod WDin WHal
– var. ***ledebourii***	CHan CSPN ELan EPla GRei MWat NHol WHCG WPat WTyr
§ × ***italica***	Widely available
japonica	WWat
§ – 'Aureoreticulata'	Widely available

¶ – 'Dart's Acumen'	SLPl
– 'Dart's World'	SBra SLPl
– 'Halliana'	Widely available
– 'Hall's Prolific'	ECtt MAsh MBri MGos SBra WWeb
– 'Peter Adams'	LHop MGos
§ – var. ***repens***	CDoC CMac CSco CShe CTre EBar EBre ECtt ELan ENot EPla IHos LBre LPri MBri MPla SBra SHBN SPer SPla WCru WWat WWeb
¶ – 'Soja'	SBra
♦– 'Variegata'	See L. ***j.*** 'Aureoreticulata'
korolkowii	CBow CChu CCla CMCN CPle CSam MBel MWat NBir
– var. ***zabelii***	EFol ELan
maackii	CHan CMCN WHCG
× ***muscaviensis***	CPle
nigra	EPla
nitida	CB&S CKin CLan CSco EBre ELan EMar ESma ISea LBre MRav NBee NNor SHBN SLon SPer WDin WHen WMou WStI
– 'Baggesen's Gold'	Widely available
– 'Elegant'	CDoC ELan IOrc LBuc
– 'Ernest Wilson'	MBar SRms
– 'Fertilis'	SPer SRms
– 'Maigrün' ('Maygreen')	EPla MBri
¶ – 'Silver Beauty'	MGos
periclymenum	CArn CBow CKin EPla GPoy NMir NNor NWea WDin WMou WOak WWin
N– 'Belgica'	Widely available
¶ – ***clarkii***	SBra
– 'Cornish Cream'	EBre EGol LBre
– 'Florida'	See L. ***p.*** 'Serotina'
¶ – ***glaucohirta***	SBra
– 'Graham Thomas'	CB&S CBot CCla CHad CSam EBre ECtt EFol ELan EPla ERav IHos ISea LBre LHop LPri MBri MGos MRav MUlv NSti SBra SLPl SMad SPer SSpi WPat WSHC WWat WWeb
– 'Harlequin' (v)	CCla EMil ENot MGos NSti SMad SPer
¶ – 'Heaven Scent'	EMil
– 'La Gasnérie'	EPla GAri
– 'Liden'	SBra
¶ – 'Munster'	SBra
*– 'Red Gables'	NHol WPat
N– 'Serotina'	Widely available
§ – 'Serotina' EM '85	MBri
– 'Serpentine'	SBra
– ***sulphurea***	EPla
– yellow form	SPer
pileata	CB&S CCla CFis CLan CMer CSco CShe EBre EGol ELan EMar ENot GRei IJoh LBre LBuc MBar MBel MGos NBee NHol NNor SLon SPer SPla SUsu WDin WStI WWat WWin
– 'Moss Green'	CDoC SLPl
¶ – 'Stockholm'	SLPl
¶ ***pilosa***	SBra
¶ – CD&R 1216	CHan
praeflorens	CChu
× ***purpusii***	CBow CBra CHan CPle CSam CSco EBre LAbb LBre MBar MBel MPla WBod WCru WEas WHal WSHC WWin

– 'Winter Beauty'	CBow CCla CDoC CPMA CSam CSco EBre ECtt ELan LBre MBlu MBri MBrk MPla MRav NSti SLon SPer SPla SSpi SSta WWat
pyrenaica	CPle LGre SHil WSHC
quinquelocularis	CPle EHal
reflexa	EHar LHop
§ ***rupicola*** var. ***syringantha***	CBra CChu CCla CCor CHan CMHG COtt CPle CRDP CSam EFol EHar ELan LGre MBel MGos MWat NHol SHBN SLon SPer SPla SSpi SUsu WKif WSHC WWat WWin
– – 'Grandiflora'	MPla WAbe
ruprechtiana	CCor CPle
segreziensis	CPle
sempervirens	CBot CBow EGol GAri LPri MRav MWat SBra SHil SSpi
– 'Dropmore Scarlet'	Widely available
N– f. ***sulphurea***	CMCN SBra WWeb
setifera	CBot SHil
similis var. ***delavayi***	CBot CDoC CSPN SBra SWas WSHC
¶ 'Simonet'	SBra
splendida	CBot CSam SBra SSpi WEas
standishii	CB&S CPle LHol MBea MBel MGos MRav MUlv SPer WDin WRus WThu WWat WWin WWye
syringantha	See L. ***rupicola s.***
tatarica	CBow CMCN LPri WHCG
– 'Arnold's Red'	CB&S CBot CBow CDoC CPle CSco EHal ELan MBal MBlu MPla SMrm WAbe
– 'Hack's Red'	CB&S CBow CBra CCla CPMA MPla NKay SPer STre WHCG
– f. ***sibirica***	EHal SPer
– 'Zabelii'	CChu CCor MGos SMrm
x ***tellmanniana***	Widely available
¶– 'Joan Sayer'	CCor EPla
thibetica	CPle
tragophylla	CB&S CChu CCla CMac EBlo EBre EHar ELan EOvi ERav IOrc LBre MBri NSti SBla SBra SHil SPer SReu SSpi SSta WBod WCru WDin WSHC WWat
webbiana	ELan
x ***xylosteoïdes*** 'Clavey's Dwarf'	MBel MGos SLPl
– 'Miniglobe'	EPla
xylosteum	WBod

LOPHOMYRTUS (Myrtaceae)

§ ***bullata***	CChu CGre CPle CTre ECou WCHb
'Gloriosa'	CB&S CDoC CGre WCHb
§ ***obcordata***	CGre CTre WWat
§ x ***ralphii***	CTre WCHb WWat
§ – 'Kathryn'	CB&S CHan CPle ERea GAri ISea WCHb WSHC
– 'Lilliput'	CB&S
– 'Pixie'	CB&S
§ – 'Traversii'	CGre CTrw
– 'Variegata'	EBre ERea LBre
'Tricolor'	CTre GAri
'Versicolor'	CB&S CDoC CMer CSun LAbb

LOQUAT See ERIOBOTRYA *japonica*

LOROPETALUM (Hamamelidaceae)

chinense	CCla CMCN CPle

LOTUS (Leguminosae)

berthelotii	CB&S CBar CBrk CGle CHEx CSev CSun CTro ELan ERav ERea IHos LAbb LHil MUlv SAxl SChu SIgm SLMG SSpi SUsu WEas WHal WKif WPer
– Kew form	CBrk GCal LHil LHop
– x ***maculatus***	CBar CSpe ERav LHil SAxl SMrm WPer
corniculatus	CArn CKin GAbr NLan
– 'Plenus'	CHal CLew CMer CMil CRiv ELan EPot GCal IBlr LAbb NHol SFis WPer
'Gold Flash'	IHos
§ ***hirsutus***	CBot CChu CCla CFis CGle CHad CHan CMea CSam CSco CSev CShe CSun ELan ENot LAbb LGre LHop MPar NSti SAxl SDix SFis SPer WEas WOld WSHC WWat WWin
jacobaeus	CHad LGre LHil SMrm
maculatus	CBar CBrk CGle CSpe CSun CTro ESma LBlm LHil LHop SIgm
maritimus	NGre NSal NWCA
♦***mascaensis*** hort.	See L. ***sessilifolius***
pedunculatus	See L. ***uliginosus***
§ ***sessilifolius***	ERea LHil SIgm SUsu
suffruticosus	See L. ***pentaphyllus pentaphyllus***
¶ ***uliginosus***	NMir

LUCULIA (Rubiaceae)

gratissima	CB&S CBot CHEx CHan LHop SHil

LUDWIGIA (Onagraceae)

¶ ***grandiflora***	CRow
¶ ***palustris***	SAWi

LUETKEA (Rosaceae)

pectinata	CLew GCHN GDra MHig NHol NMen SIng WAbe WDav WThu

LUMA (Myrtaceae)

§ ***apiculata***	CAbb CHan CLan CMHG CPle CSam CTre CTrw EBre ISea LBre LHol MBal SArc SDix SHil SPer SSpi STre WBod WCHb WSHC WWat
§ – 'Glanleam Gold' (v)	Widely available
– 'Penwith' (v)	CPMA
– 'Variegata'	CMHG ISea NHol WWat
§ ***chequen***	CChu CPle CTre GAri LHol WCHb WWat

LUNARIA (Cruciferae)

§ ***annua***	NCat SHer WByw WEas WHer WOak
– ***alba***	CCMG ECro EFol NBir NCat SIde WHer WOak
I – 'Alba Variegata'	CRDP CSpe EMon SUsu WByw WCru
– 'Croftacre Purple Pod'	ECro
*– 'Ken Aslet'	NHol
*– 'Stella'	ECro GCal WHen
– ***variegata***	CCMG CSFH CTom EFol GCal IBlr MPar MTho NBir WEas WHal WHer WHil WOMN WOld
– violet	NBir
biennis	See L. ***annua***

rediviva CRDP ECha ECro EJud EMon GAri GCHN GCra GGar IBlr NBro NRar NSti SAxl SSpi SUsu WCot WCru WEas WHer

LUPINUS † (Leguminosae)

¶ 'Alan Titchmarsh' MWoo
albifrons LGre SIgm SMrm SUsu
– var. *douglasii* LGre
¶ – var. *emineus* CNic
'Ann Gregg' MWoo
arboreus Widely available
¶ – cream form SMad
– 'Golden Spire' GWht NBee SMad WDin
– 'Mauve Queen' CB&S NBee
– 'Snow Queen' CB&S CCla WDin
argenteus ELan
'Band of Nobles' ECtt GAbr LAbb NVic
'Barnsdale' MWoo
'Beryl, Viscountess Cowdray' EMon
'Blushing Bride' CSco EMon
'Boningale Lass' CSco
'Catherine of York' CSco
chamissonis LHop MTho NTow SAxl SDry SMrm
'Chandelier' CBow CHad CSco EBre ECtt EFou ELan GAbr GAri GCHN LBre LWad MBri NBar NMir NRoo SCro SHer SPer SPla WHil WPer WTyr
'Chelsea Pensioner' MWoo
'Clifford Star' MWoo
'Deborah Woodfield' MWoo
Dwarf Gallery hybrids LAbb NOak
'Dwarf Lulu' See L. 'Lulu'
'Esmerelder' MWoo
'Fred Yule' CSco
Gallery series CBow NRoo
'Gold Dust' CSco
'Helen Sharman' MWoo
'Household Brigade' MWoo
'Judith Chalmers' MWoo
'Kayleigh Ann Savage' MWoo
'Lady Fayre' CSco
¶ *lepidus utahensis* WDav
'Little Eugenie' MWoo
littoralis CMea CPar GDra NCat
'Loveliness' CSco
§ 'Lulu' CBow EBre ECtt ELan LBre MPit MRav NMir NOak SFis SHer SPer WPer
Minarette Group CBow ECtt MBri SPla SRms
'Misty' MWoo
'Moonraker' MWoo
'My Castle' CBow CSco EBre ECtt EFou ELan GAbr GAri GCHN LBre LWad MBri MRav NBar NMir NOak NRoo SCro SHer SPer SPla WHil WPer WTyr
'Nellie B Allen' CSco
'Noble Maiden' CBow EBre ECtt EFou ELan GAbr GAri GCHN LBre MBri NBar NMir NOak NRoo SCro SPer WHen WHil WPer WTyr
nootkatensis WPat
'Olive Tolley' MWoo
¶ *oreophilus* F&W 7353 SIgm
'Party Dress' MWoo
perennis CGle EMon
♦ *pilosus* See L. *varius orientalis*
'Pope John Paul' MWoo
princei ELan
'Royal Parade' CSco
'Royal Wedding' MWoo
Russell hybrids CB&S CBow CKel CPar CSco ELan NMir NRoo SGil SHer WHer
sericatus SIgm
¶ sp. F&W 7366 SIgm
'Sunset' MWoo
'Sunshine' CGle CSco
'The Chatelaine' CHad CSco EBre ECtt EFou ELan GAbr GAri GCHN LBre LWad MBri MRav NBar NMir NRoo SHer SPer SPla WHen WPer
'The Governor' CBow CSco EBre ECtt ELan GAbr GAri GCHN LBre LWad MBri MRav NBar NMir NRoo SCro SHer SPer SPla WHil WPer WTyr
'The Page' CBow CDoC EBre EFou ELan GAbr GAri LAbb LBre LWad MBri MRav NBar NMir NRoo SCro SHer SPer SPla WHil WPer
'Thundercloud' CHad
'Troop the Colour' MWoo
¶ *varius* ssp. *orientalis* WCot
'Walton Lad' MWoo
¶ 'Yellow Boy' CB&S

LUZULA (Juncaceae)

alopecurus ECou
¶ *alpinopilosa* ssp. *candollei* ETPC
x *borreri* 'Botany Bay' (v) EHoe EMon EPla ETPC
campestris CKin
celata ECou
¶ *forsteri* ETPC
lactea ETPC
luzuloïdes 'Schneehäschen' EMon EPla ETPC
maxima See L. *sylvatica*
multiflora EHoe
* *nivalis* CHan
nivea CBre ECha EFol EFou EHoe EOrc EPla ETPC GAbr GCal LGan MBri MFir NCat NHar NHol NSti SAxl SFar SGil SSpi WByw WDav WOMN WWye
pilosa ERav GCal IBlr
plumosa ETPC SSpi
pumila ECou
purpureosplendens ETPC
rufa ECou
¶ *sibirica* ETPC
§ *sylvatica* CKin CRow EFou EPla ETPC MFir NBro NLan NOrc SSpi
– 'A Rutherford' CRow
– 'Anerlese' ETPC
– 'Aurea' ECha EMon EPla ETPC GAbr SApp WCot
– 'Hohe Tatra' CElw EFol EHoe
– 'Marginata' CB&S CBre CElw CHEx CKel CRow ECha EFol EGol EHoe EMon EPla ETPC GAbr LGan MBal NBro NNrd NSti SApp SSpi WByw WRus WWat WWin
– 'Tauernpass' EHoe EMon EPla ETPC WRus
ulophylla ECar ECou EHoe NHol

LUZURIAGA (Liliaceae/Philesiaceae)

radicans WCru WSHC

X LYCENE (Caryophyllaceae)

See Plant Deletions

LYCHNIS † (Caryophyllaceae)

alpina CRDP ECro ELan GDra GTou LAbb NGre NKay NMen NMir NNor NRoo SHer WCla WHil WPer WWin
– 'Alba' CNic NBir
– *americana* NTow
– *rosea* CHan SIng SRms
x *arkwrightii* CBow CGle CKel CPar CRDP CRow CSun EBre ECha EFou EHoe ELan LBre LGan MBri MPit NBro NGre NMen NOak NSti SIng SPer WCla WHoo WOMN WOld WWin
– 'Vesuvius' CB&S CBow CDoC CGle CHad EBre ESma GGar LAbb LBlm LBre NBar NBir NRoo SFis WCot WHoo WMer WPbr WPer WTyr
chalcedonica Widely available
– 'Alba' CCor CSam ECha ECro EFou ELan EMon ERav IBlr LGan MBri MFir NBro NCat NFai NOak NSti SFis SHer SPer SUsu WDav WEas WHen WHoo WPer WTyr
– 'Carnea' GCal NCat
– 'Flore Pleno' CPar ECha GCal MUlv NSti SFis SSvw WOld WPer
– 'Rosea' CGle CHad CLew CTom ECro EFou EHal MUlv NFai NHol NMir SPer SUsu WAbb WByw WHen
§ *coronaria* Widely available
– 'Abbotswood Rose' See L. x *walkeri* 'A.R.'
– Alba Group CBro CGle CHan CRDP CRow CSco EBar ECha EFou EGol EHoe ELan EPar GCHN LGan MBri MHew MMil NFai NHol NNor NOak NSti SPer SUsu WCla WEas WHer WMer WWin
– 'Angel's Blush' ECro GCHN NMir WPbr
– Atrosanguinea Group CBow CBre ECro EFou EPad EPla GCHN IBlr LHil NFai NHol SCro SPla WPer
¶ – 'Cerise' ESma
– Oculata Group CBro CChu CCor CGle CHad CHan CLew CMHG CMil ELan EMar EMon ESma GCHN IBlr LHop MFir MMil MTho NFai NOak NSti SSvw SUsu WDav WEas WHen WHer WHoo
§ *coronata* var. *sieboldii* WPer
dioica See SILENE *dioica*
flos-cuculi Widely available
– *albiflora* CBre CRDP CRow CSFH CSam CTom ECro EMon EPar LGan NBro NSel NSti SIde SUsu WCla WHer
– 'Nana' ELan EMon EPla GArf GGar LHop MBro MFir MTol NMir WCla WOMN WPat WPer
flos-jovis CGle CLew CSco ECha ECro ELan EMon LHop MFir MPlt NOak SHer WByw WEas WPat WPer WSun
– 'Alba' MRav
– 'Hort's Variety' CDec CHal CKel CMil CPar EFou EJud MBel MHig MUlv NSti NTow SBla SPer WCla
– 'Minor' See L. *f-j.* 'Nana'
§ – 'Nana' CRow ECro GCHN LHop MCas MNFA MTol NFai NRed SAxl SIng WHoo WOMN
x *haageana* CMil CSun CTom EOrc LBlm LHil LWad MBri NMir NWCA SIng WHil WPer
kubotae See X LYCENE *k.*
lagascae See PETROCOPTIS *glaucifolia*
miqueliana CChu CNic CPou EBar EMon LGan MFir NBro NGre SFis WCot WThi
¶ 'Molten Lava' NOrc WPer
nutans MHew NSal
sp. Andes WOMN
§ *viscaria* CBow CGle CKin ECha ECro MHew NGre NLan NNor NNrd NSal WCla
– *alba* ECha ECro GCal NBro
– *alpina* See L. *a.*
– ssp. *atropurpurea* GCal
– 'Firebird' EFou
– 'Plena' CDoC CSco EFou NCat NSti SFis WHil WOld WPbr
– 'Snowbird' EFou
– 'Splendens Plena' CGle CLew CShe ECha EFol ELan EMar EMon EPla IDai MBal MBri NBro NKay NVic WEas
§ x *walkeri* 'Abbotswood Rose' EMon ESma NBar NCat
wilfordii CBot CPou EBar NGre NRed SUsu
yunnanensis CCor CRDP ECro GCHN LGan MFir MSte NHol NOak WGwy WPer

LYCIANTHES (Solanaceae)

§ *rantonnetii* CB&S CBar CBrk CHad CHan CKel CSpe CSun ERea LBlm LHop WKif

LYCIUM (Solanaceae)

barbarum ELan WWye

LYCOPODIUM (Lycopodiaceae)

clavatum GPoy

LYCOPSIS See ANCHUSA

LYCOPUS (Labiatae)

europaeus CArn CHal CSFH GPoy MChe MHew NSal WChe WHer WNdy WWye
sp. JLS 88040 EMon

LYCORIS (Liliaceae/Amaryllidaceae)

albiflora CKel SDeJ
aurea CKel SDeJ

LYGODIUM (Schizaeaceae)

japonicum NMar

LYONIA (Ericaceae)

ligustrina CCla ELan SSpi

LYONOTHAMNUS (Rosaceae)

floribundus
- ssp. *aspleniifolius* — CAbb CChu CGre CMHG SArc SHil SSpi

LYSICHITON (Araceae)

americanus — CB&S CBen CCla CHEx CHad CPar CRow CWGN ECha EHon ELan EMFW EPar EWav GDra IBar LMay MRav MSta MUlv NDea NHar SPer SSpi SWat WBod WChe WHol WWat
camtschatcensis — CB&S CBen CCMG CCla CHEx CRDP CRiv CRow CWGN ECha EHon ELan EMFW EPar LMay MSta NDea SPer SSpi SWat WChe WHol WWat

LYSIMACHIA † (Primulaceae)

atropurpurea — SFis SSvw WCot
barystachys — MRav WCot
ciliata — CBos CBre CChu CGle CMHG CMea CRDP CRow ECar ECha EFol EGol EHoe ELan LHil MBri MFir NDea NMir SChu SFis SUsu WDav WEas WHal WHoo WOld WRus WWin
¶– 'Firecracker' — SFis
– 'Purpurea' — WPer
clethroïdes — Widely available
ephemerum — Widely available
fortunei — EMon WCot
henryi — CRDP GCal LHil WCru WEas
japonica 'Minutissima' — GCHN MBro MTho NGre NKay NRya WAbe WCru WHil WPer WWin
lanceolata — WCot
lichiangensis
- B&L 12317 — CGle EMon
– B&L 12464 — CRow EMon NSti WCot WThi
¶ *lyssii* — LHil
mauritiana — WCot
minoricensis — CBot CHan CRDP CRow GCra NCat NGre NRar SCro SFis SMad SUsu SWat WBon WCot WDav WPer
nemorum — CKin WCot WPer
nummularia — CBen CMea CRDP CSFH CShe CWGN EBre ECtt EHon EJud GPoy LBre LHol LMay MBar MBri MFir NBro NDea NHol NNor NNrd SWat WByw WChe WCru WHol WOak WTyr WWye
– 'Aurea' — Widely available
*– *nana* — MPit
ovata — NHol
pseudohenryi — LHop WCot
punctata — Widely available
– *verticillata* — See L. ***verticillaris***
thyrsiflora — CBen CRDP CRow EBre EHon LBre MSta NDea SWat WChe WCot WHer
¶ *verticillaris* — WCot
vulgaris — CArn CWGN EHon MHew NSal NSel SIde WChe WCru WGwy WHil WWye
¶– var. *davurica* — WCot

LYSIONOTUS (Gesneriaceae)

¶ *pauciflora* — NTow WCru

LYTHRUM (Lythraceae)

'Croftway' — CDoC
salicaria — CArn CGle CKin CRDP CRow CWGN EHon GCHN LAbb MChe MFir MHew NBee NBro NLan NMir NNor NSal NSel SUsu SWat WByw WChe WCla WHer WHil WPbr WWye
– 'Brightness' — CSco NCat NHol
– 'Feuerkerze' ('Firecandle') — CKel CMGP EBre EFou EHal ELan EPad LBre MBel MRav MUlv NCat NFai NHol SHer SMrm SPer
– 'Florarose' — EFou
– 'Happy' — GCal
– 'Lady Sackville' — EFou GCal SAxl SFis WAbe
– 'Morden's Pink' — CDoC EFou MBri
– 'Robert' — CDoC CMGP CSco CShe EBre ECha ELan EPar LBre MWat NHol NOak SChu SPer WChe WEas
– 'Rose' — ELan
– 'The Beacon' — CDoC CGle CRow LWad NSti SFis SRms WCot
– Ulverscroft form — MUlv
virgatum 'Dropmore Purple' — MBri NSti SMad
– 'Rose Queen' — ECha EFol GCal SPer
– 'Rosy Gem' — CBow CRow ECtt EMar EPad MFir NOak NTow SFis SPla SSvw WHal WHoo WPer
– 'The Rocket'' — CMGP CPar CSco EBre LBre NCat NHol SHer SPer WWin

LYTOCARYUM (Palmae)

§ *weddellianum* — MBri NPal

MAACKIA (Leguminosae)

amurensis — CB&S CChu CCla EHar ELan WCoo

MACFADYENA (Bignoniaceae)

§ *unguis-cati* — CGre CTro

MACHAERANTHERA (Compositae)

¶ *glabriuscula* — CNic
pattersonii — See M. ***bigelovii***

MACHILUS See PERSEA

MACKAYA (Acanthaceae)

§ *bella* — CTro ERea LHop

MACLEAYA (Papaveraceae)

N*cordata* — CArn CBow CHEx CWGN EFou ELan EPar ESma LAbb MRav MTol MWat NOrc SFis SPer WEas WHal WHoo WKif WWin
– 'Flamingo' — EBre ECha EFou GCHN GCal LBre MRav MUlv SGil
¶ x *kewensis* — ERav WHoo
microcarpa — EHal EPla ESma SUsu WHer
– 'Kelway's Coral Plume' — CB&S CGle CHEx CHad CKel CShe CWGN EBre ECha EFol EFou ELan EOrc LBre LHil MBri NBar NBro NSti SGil SPer WEas WOld WWat

MACLURA (Moraceae)

pomifera	CB&S CLnd CPle EArb EHar NSal WDin

MACRODIERVILLA See WEIGELA

MACROPIPER (Piperaceae)

crocatum	See PIPER *ornatum*
excelsum	CHEx ECou
– 'Aureopictum'	CHEx

MACROZAMIA (Zamiaceae)

communis	LPal WNor
miquelii	LPal
moorei	LPal
reidlei	LPal WNor

MAGNOLIA † (Magnoliaceae)

acuminata	CMCN GCal MBal SHil SSpi
¶ – 'Kobandori'	LTil
§ – var. *subcordata*	LRHS SHil SSpi
¶ – – 'Miss Honeybee'	ELan LRHS LTil SSpi
¶ 'Albatross'	LTil
'Ann'	CTrh SSpi
'Anne Rosse'	LTil SSpi
'Apollo'	CB&S CBow CPMA LTil SSpi
'Athene'	CB&S CBow CPMA LTil SSpi
'Atlas'	CB&S CPMA LTil SSpi
'Betty'	CB&S CTrh LNet LTil MGos SReu SSpi SSta WBod WDin WStI
biondii	LTil
x *brooklynensis* 'Woodsman'	CB&S CPMA LTil SSpi
¶ 'Butterflies'	LTil
'Caerhays Belle'	CB&S CPMA
¶ 'Caerhays Surprise'	LTil SSpi
campbellii	CB&S CBow CMCN CSam ELan SPer SSpi
– var. *alba*	CB&S CPMA LTil SSpi SSta
– ssp. *mollicomata*	CB&S CBow CDoC CTrh CTrw IBar SHil SSpi
– – 'Lanarth'	CB&S CBow CPMA SSpi
campbellii Raffillii Group 'Charles Raffill'	CB&S CBow CPMA EHar IBar MUlv SSpi
– 'Kew's Surprise'	CGre SSpi
¶ 'Cecil Nice'	LTil
'Charles Coates'	CBow CCla CLan LHyd SSpi
cordata	See M. *acuminata subcordata*
cylindrica	CB&S CMCN LTil SSpi SSta
dawsoniana	CB&S CMCN SHil
¶ – 'Clarke'	LTil
– 'Ruby Rose'	SSpi
delavayi	CB&S CHEx CTre LRHS LTil SArc SHil SSpi WBod
§ *denudata*	CB&S CCla CMCN CTrh CTrw EHar LPan LTil MBal SEng SHil SPer SReu SSpi SSta WBod WNor WWat
– 'Forrest's Pink'	SSpi
– late form	SSpi
– var. *purpurascens*	See M. *sprengeri diva*
'Elizabeth'	ELan LTil SSpi
'Emma Cook'	SSpi
'Eva Maria'	LTil SSpi
¶ 'Fourteen Carat'	SSpi
¶ 'Frank Gladney'	LTil
fraseri	WCoo
'Galaxy'	CB&S CPMA LTil SSpi
'George Henry Kern'	CMHG COtt EB&P LTil MGos SEng SSpi WBod WDin
globosa	CB&S CMCN LTil SSpi WWat
grandiflora	CBow CHEx CMCN EBre IJoh ISea LBre MRav MWat SArc SLon SSpi SSta WDin WNor WWat
– 'Charles Dickens'	SSpi
– 'Exmouth'	CB&S CBot CBow CBra CChu CGre CLan CMCN CSco CTrh ECtt EHar ELan ENot IOrc ISea LNet MBal MBri SHBN SMad SPer SPla SReu SSta WBod WStI WWat
– 'Ferruginea'	CLan
– 'Galissonière'	CDoC ISea LPan LTil SEng
¶ – 'Galissonière Nana'	LPan
– 'Goliath'	CB&S CBow CHEx CLan EHar ELan IOrc ISea LNet MBal SArc SHil SPer SSpi SSta WBod
– 'Little Gem'	CBow CPMA LTil SSpi
– 'Russet'	CPMA LNet SSpi
– 'Saint George'	WSHC
– 'Saint Mary'	CBow CPMA LRHS
– 'Samuel Sommer'	CMCN CPMA LNet LRHS LTil SSpi
– 'Victoria'	ELan LRHS LTil SSpi
¶ 'Hattie Cartham'	SSpi
'Heaven Scent'	CAbP CB&S CBow CMCN COtt CTre EHar IDai IOrc LPan LTil MBal MBar MBri MGos SPer SSpi SSta
heptapeta	See M. *denudata*
hypoleuca	CB&S CBow CDoC CHEx SPer SReu SSpi SSta WThu
'Iolanthe'	CB&S CMCN CPMA EHar LTil MBri SPer SSpi
'Jane'	CDoC COtt CTrh EBre LBre LTil MBri MGos NHol SPer SSpi SSta WBod
¶ 'Jon-Jon'	SSpi
'Judy'	CTrh
x *kewensis* 'Kewensis'	CB&S SHil
– 'Wada's Memory'	CB&S CBow CCla CMCN CMHG CSco CTrh LHyd LRHS LTil MBri SHil SPer SSpi SSta WBod WWeb
* 'Koban Dori'	SSpi
kobus	CB&S CBot CBow CBra CGre CMCN EHar ISea LHyd LPan SEng SHBN SLeo SPer WBod WNor WWat
¶ 'Ko-1'	LTil
'Lilenny'	SSpi WBod
§ *liliiflora*	CSco CTrh CTrw MAsh MBar
– 'Doris'	SSpi
¶ – 'Mini Mouse'	LTil
§ – 'Nigra'	CB&S CBow CGre CLan CMHG EBre ELan ENot IJoh ISea LBre LPan MGos MRav MWat NBar SDix SHBN SPer SPla SReu SSpi WBod WDin WStI WWat
x *loebneri*	CB&S CBow CLan CTrh EHal ELan LHyd
– 'Ballerina'	CMCN LTil MBri SSpi
– 'Leonard Messel'	Widely available

– 'Merrill'	CB&S CBow CCla CMCN CMHG CSam CSco CTrh EBre ECtt EHar ESma IOrc ISea LBre LPan MBal MBri SPer SReu SSta WBod WDin WWat
¶ – 'Neil McEacharn'	LTil
– 'Snowdrift'	CMCN LTil
¶ – 'Spring Snow'	LTil
– 'Star Bright'	CLan CMCN
macrophylla	CMCN SArc SHil SSpi
– 'Sara Gladney'	CHEx
¶ 'Mag's Pirouette'	LTil
'Manchu Fan'	LRHS LTil MBri SSpi
'Mark Jury'	CB&S CMCN CPMA LTil SSpi
'Maryland'	CPMA SSpi
'Milky Way'	CB&S CBow CPMA LTil
¶ 'Mossman's Giant'	LTil
N ***obovata***	CTre WBod
officinalis	SSpi
– var. ***biloba***	LTil
'Peppermint Stick'	LRHS LTil MGos SSpi SSta
'Peter Smithers'	SSpi
'Pickard's Coral'	MBal SSta WWeb
'Pickard's Firefly'	WWeb
'Pickard's Garnet'	WWeb
'Pickard's Glow'	WWeb
¶ 'Pickard's Ruby'	LTil
'Pickard's Schmetterling'	See M. 'Schmetterling'
¶ 'Pickard's Stardust'	LTil
'Pinkie'	LTil MAsh MBri SSpi
x ***proctoriana***	CDec SReu
– 'Proctoriana'	EBre LBre LHyd SLeo SPer SPla
quinquepeta	See M. ***liliiflora***
¶ 'Randy'	LTil
'Raspberry Ice'	LRHS MBal SSpi SSta WBod
'Ricki'	CMCN COtt CTrh EB&P LRHS LTil MBri MGos SSpi
'Rouged Alabaster'	SSpi
'Royal Crown'	CKni EHar MBri SSpi SSta WBod
salicifolia	ISea SHil SPer SSpi SSta
– 'Jermyns'	LHyd SLeo
sargentiana	CGre
¶ – 'Nymans'	LTil
– var. ***robusta***	CB&S CTrw EHar NHlc SPer SReu SSpi SSta
– – ***alba***	CTrw
'Sayonara'	CB&S CBow COtt CPMA IOrc SSpi
§ 'Schmetterling'	LTil SSta
'Serene'	CB&S CBow CPMA LTil SSpi
* 'Seyu'	SSpi
sieboldii	CB&S CBra CCla CGre CMCN CSco CTrh EHar ELan IOrc LTil MBal MBar MBri MGos SHBN SHil SPla SReu SSpi SSta WAbe WBod WCoo WNor
– ssp. ***sinensis***	CB&S CDoC CMCN CSam CSco ELan ISea SHil SPer SSpi WWat
¶ 'Snow White'	LTil
x ***soulangeana***	CB&S CBra CLan CSco CShe CTrh CTrw EBre ELan ENot IBar IDai IJoh ISea LBre LHyd MBal MBar MBri MGos MWat NBar SHBN SPer SReu WAbe WDin WNor WWat
– 'Alba'	See M. x *s.* 'Alba Superba'
§ – 'Alba Superba'	CB&S CBra CGre COtt CSco ENot IOrc ISea MGos SPer SReu SSpi WBod
– 'Alexandrina'	CBow CDoC CTrh ELan IOrc MBri SPer WBod WWeb
– 'Amabilis'	CDoC WBod
– 'Brozzonii'	CB&S CBow CGre CMCN CMHG CSam CTrh IOrc ISea SSpi WBod
N – 'Burgundy'	CB&S CBot EBre ISea LBre MAsh SSpi SSta WBod
– 'Coimbra'	SSpi
– 'Garnet'	SSpi
– 'Just Jean'	SSpi
– 'Lennei'	CB&S CBow CBra CMCN CMHG CSco CTrh EHar ENot GWht IOrc MGos NKay SHBN SPer SReu SSpi WBod WNor WStI
– 'Lennei Alba'	CMCN CSco ELan IOrc SSpi WBod
– 'Nigra'	See M. ***liliiflora*** 'Nigra'
– 'Picture'	CDec CDoC CGre CMCN CSco CTrh IOrc SSpi WBod
– 'Rubra'	See M. x *s.* 'Rustica Rubra'
§ – 'Rustica Rubra'	CB&S CBra CLan CMCN CSam CSco CTrh EBre ECtt EHar ELan ENot IOrc ISea LBre LNet LPan MBri SHBN SPer SReu SSpi SSta WBod
– 'San Jose'	CCla CMCN EB&P MBri SPer SSpi SSta
– 'Sundew'	CB&S CMCN EB&P IOrc ISea MBri MGos SEng SHBN SSpi WBod WWeb
– 'Verbanica'	CCla LRHS SSpi
'Spectrum'	LTil SSpi
sprengeri	CTrw SSpi
§ – var. ***diva***	CB&S CMCN SSpi
– – 'Burncoose'	CB&S SSpi
¶ – – 'Claret Cup'	SSpi
– 'Lanhydrock'	SSpi
'Star Wars'	CB&S CBow CPMA LTil
§ ***stellata***	Widely available
– 'Centennial'	LTil
– ***chrysanthemiflora***	CMCN LRHS LTil SSpi
– f. ***keiskei***	CDoC
– 'King Rose'	CB&S CTrh ISea MBlu MBri SMad SPer SPla SSta WBod
– 'Massey'	WBod
– 'Norman Gould'	CMCN LTil
– 'Rosea'	CDoC EHar ELan IOrc MGos MPla SHBN WBod
– 'Royal Star'	CB&S CBot CLan CMCN CSco CTrw EBre ECtt ENot IOrc ISea LBre LPan MBri MGos NHol SPer SPla SSpi SSta WAbe WBod WStI
– 'Waterlily'	CB&S CBot CBow CMCN CSam CSco EHar ELan IOrc ISea LTil SPer SSpi SSta WBod WWeb
'Susan'	CAbP CB&S CCla CMCN COtt EBre ELan IJoh IOrc LBre LTil MBal MBri MGos MWat NHol SEng SHBN SHer SMad SPer SPla SReu SSpi SSta WAbe WBod WDin WStI WWeb
x ***thompsoniana***	CBow CMCN WBod
'Tina Durio'	SSpi
tripetala	CB&S CGre CHEx CMCN LTil SHBN SSpi WWat
– 'Woodlawn'	SSpi
¶ 'Ursula Grau'	LTil
x ***veitchii***	CGre SSpi
– 'Isca'	WBod
– 'Peter Veitch'	CGre
virginiana	CB&S CGre CMCN SSpi WOMN
'Vulcan'	CB&S CPMA LTil SSpi

× *watsonii* — See M. × *wiesneri*
§ × *wiesneri* — CB&S ELan LTil MBlu SReu SSpi SSta WBod
wilsonii — CB&S CGre CMCN CSam CSco EHar ELan GGGa IOrc ISea MBal SAxl SHil SPer SReu SSta WCoo WDin WNor WPat WSHC WWat
¶ 'Yellow Bird' — LTil
¶ 'Yellow Fever' — SSpi
¶ *zenii* — LTil

MAGNOLIA × MICHELIA (Magnoliaceae)

¶ *Yuchelia No 1* — LTil

× MAHOBERBERIS (Berberidaceae)

aquisargentii — CAbP CBra CSam EHar ENot EPla GWht LHop MGos MPla MRav NHol SLon WPat WWat
'Dart's Treasure' — LRHS MBri
'Magic' — CBow MGos MWat WWeb
miethkeana — CBow CDoC CMHG CPMA CSam MBar SPer

MAHONIA † (Berberidaceae)

acanthifolia — See M. ***napaulensis***
§ *aquifolium* — CB&S CBow CBra CPer ELan ENot GRei IDai IJoh ISea MBal MBar MBri MGos MWat NKay NNor NRoo NWea SHBN SLon SPer SPla SReu WDin WStI WWin
– 'Apollo' — CBow CSco CShe ECtt EGol EHar ELan ENot EPla IOrc MBar MBri MGos NBee NHol SHBN SPer SReu SSpi SSta WPat WWat
– 'Atropurpurea' — CDoC CSco EHar ENot EPla IDai NKay SHBN SPer SPla WPat WWat
– 'Fascicularis' — See M. × ***wagneri*** 'Pinnacle'
– 'Green Ripple' — MBri NBar SPla
– 'Orange Flame' — LRHS
– 'Scallywag' — LRHS
– 'Smaragd' — CCla CDoC CSco EBre EPla LBre MBlu MUlv NBee NHol SEng WPat
bealei — See M. ***japonica*** Bealei Group
confusa — SSpi
eutriphylla — EPla SGil
fortunei — CBot EPla MBal SArc WSHC
fremontii — LGre
¶ *gracilipes* — LRHS
haematocarpa — LGre
japonica — CBow CHEx CSco CShe CTre CTrw EGol ELan ENot IDai IJoh ISea MBal MBri MWat NHol NKay SDix SHBN SPer SReu SSta WBod WDin WPat WSHC WThu WWat
§ – Bealei Group — CB&S CBow CCla CLan EBre ELan GRei IOrc ISea LBre MBar MGos SLon SPla WDin WStI WWeb
– 'Hiemalis' — See M. ***j.*** 'Hivernant'
§ – 'Hivernant' — CChu EBre EHar LBre MBri NHol SReu WAbe WWat
lomariifolia — CAbb CB&S CBot CBow CHEx CLan CSco ENot IHos IOrc MBal MRav MUlv SArc SDry SPer SPla SReu SSpi SSta
× *media* 'Buckland' — CAbP CB&S CBra CChu CMHG CSam CSco CTrw ECtt ENot ISea MBal MBri SGil SHer SLon SPer WBod WPat WSHC WWat
– 'Charity' — Widely available
– 'Charity's Sister' — MBri
– 'Faith' — EPla
– 'Lionel Fortescue' — CB&S CChu CMHG COtt CSam CSco CTre CTrw EHar ELan EPla ESma ISea LHop MBal MBri NHol SBla SGil SMad SPer SReu SSpi SSta WPat WWat
– 'Underway' — ELan MBri SPla WAbe
– 'Winter Sun' — CB&S CBow COtt CSco EBre EHar ELan EPla IOrc ISea LBre MBal MBlu MBri MGos MWat NHol NRoo SGil SHBN SHer SPer SSta WAbe WDin WWat
nervosa — CChu CDoC COtt CSco EPla GGGa MBlu MBri MUlv NHol SHBN SHil SPer SSpi SSta WPat WWat
pallida T&K 553 — CChu
N *pinnata* — CWit ELan ENot IOrc MBal MBar NWea SPer WDin WPat WStI
piperiana — MUlv
pumila — CBrd EPla
repens — CPle EGol EPla GCal SRms WWat
siamensis — CGre
trifoliolata — LGre
– var. *glauca* — SHil
× *wagneri* 'Fireflame' — MUlv
– 'Moseri' — CChu MUlv SPla SSpi
§ – 'Pinnacle' — CSco MBri MGos
– 'Undulata' — CSco ECtt EGol ENot IHos MUlv NHol SDix SPer

MAIANTHEMUM (Liliaceae/Convallariaceae)

bifolium — CNic CRDP CRow EBul ECar ELan ELun EMon EPar EPot MBal MCas NGar NKay WCru WDav WWat
– British form — WThu
§ – var. *kamtschaticum* — CRDP EBul ECar ECro EMon EPar
canadense — GCal NSal
dilatatum — See M. ***bifolium kamtschaticum***

MALEPHORA (Aizoaceae)

lutea — CNic MHig NMen

MALLOTUS (Euphorbiaceae)

¶ *japonicus* — CGre

MALPIGHIA (Malpighiaceae)

coccigera — CPle

MALUS † (Rosaceae)

× *adstringens* 'Almey' — SIgm
– 'Hopa' — WJas
– 'Purple Wave' — LRHS MBri SIgm WJas
– 'Simcoe' — CDoC CLnd GChr MBri
'Aldenhamensis' — See M. × ***purpurea*** 'A.'
× *atrosanguinea* — NWea
baccata — CMCN GTwe MBrk SSpi STre WMou WNor
¶ – 'Gracilis' — MBri
– 'Lady Northcliffe' — CLnd SFam

– var. ***mandshurica***	EHar
brevipes	CCor
'Butterball'	EHar MBri
'Cheal's Weeping'	MBar WStI
coronaria 'Charlottae'	CDoC CLnd COtt CSco CTho EHar ENot SHil SPer
'Crittenden'	IMal SHil
F ***domestica***	MGos SNTN
F – 'Acme' (D)	CSco SDea SKee
F – 'Adam's Pearmain' (D)	CSco GTwe SDea SFam SFru SIgm SKee SNTN WJas
F – 'Advance' (D)	CSco SKee
F – 'Akane' (D)	SDea
¶ – 'Alderman' (C)	CSco
¶ – 'Alexander' (C)	GTwe
F – 'Alford' (Cider)	SKee
¶ – 'Alfriston' (C)	CSco SKee
F – 'Alkmene' (D)	GTwe SKee
F – 'Allen's Everlasting' (D)	CSco GTwe SDea SKee
F – 'Allington Pippin' (D)	CSam CSco NRog SDea SFru SKee WJas
F – 'American Mother'	See M. *d.* 'Mother'
¶ – 'Ananas Reinette' (D)	CSco
F – 'Anna Boelens' (D)	SDea
F – 'Anne-Marie' (C)	SKee
F – 'Annie Elizabeth' (C)	CSco GTwe LBuc MMor SDea SFam SFru SKee WHig WJas
¶ – 'Api Noir' (D)	SKee
F – 'Api Rose' (D)	SKee WJas WMou
F – 'Ard Cairn Russet' (D)	CSco GTwe SDea SKee
¶ – 'Aromatic Russet' (D)	CSco
F – 'Arthur Turner' (C)	CDoC CSco EBre GTwe LBre LBuc MGos NRog SDea SFam SKee WJas
¶ – 'Arthur W Barnes' (C)	CSco
F – 'Ashmead's Kernel' (D)	CSam CSco EBre GTwe LBre LBuc MWat NRog SDea SFam SFru SIgm SKee SNTN WHig WJas WMou
F – 'Ashton Bitter'	CSam
F – 'Autumn Pearmain' (D)	CSco SDea WJas
¶ – 'Backwell Red' (Cider)	CSco
F – 'Baker's Delicious' (D)	CSco SDea SIgm SKee
F – 'Balsam'	See M. *d.* 'Green Balsam'
F – 'Barnack Beauty' (D)	CSco SKee
¶ – 'Barnack Orange' (D)	SKee
F – 'Baron Ward' (C)	SKee
F – 'Baumann's Reinette' (D)	CSco SKee
F – 'Baxter's Pearmain' (C/D)	SKee
¶ – 'Beachamwell' (D)	WJas
F – 'Beauty of Bath' (D)	CDoC CSam CSco EHar GTwe IJoh IOrc MBea NRog SFam SKee WJas
¶ – 'Beauty of Hants' (D)	SKee
F – 'Beauty of Kent' (C)	SDea SKee
¶ – 'Beauty of Moray' (C)	SKee
F – 'Beauty of Stoke' (C)	SKee
F – 'Beeley Pippin' (D)	GTwe SDea SKee
F – 'Belle de Boskoop' (C/D)	CSco SKee
¶ – 'Belle-Fille Normande' (C)	SKee
¶ – 'Bembridge Beauty'	SDea
F – 'Bess Pool' (D)	CSco SKee
F – 'Bismarck' (C)	CSco SKee
F – 'Blaze' (D)	GTwe
F – 'Blenheim Orange' (C/D)	CDoC CSam CSco EHar EWar GBon GTwe LBuc MBri MMor MWat NRog SDea SFam SFru SIgm SKee SNTN SPer WHig WJas WMou WStI
F – 'Blenheim Red'	See M. *d.* 'Red Blenheim'
F – 'Bloody Ploughman'	SKee
F – 'Blue Pearmain' (D)	SKee
F – Bolero ®/ 'Tuscan (D/Ball)	EBal MBri MGos NBar SDea WWeb
♦– 'Boston Russet'	See M. *d.* 'Roxbury Russet'
F – 'Bountiful' (C)	CDoC CSco GTwe MGos SFru SIgm WHig
¶ – 'Bow Hill Pippin' (D)	SKee
¶ – 'Box Apple' (D)	SKee
¶ – 'Braddick Nonpareil' (D)	CSco SKee
F – 'Braeburn' (D)	SDea SKee
F – 'Bramley's Seedling' (C)	Widely available
¶ – 'Bread Fruit'	SKee
¶ – 'Breakwell Seedling' (Cider)	CSco
¶ – 'Bridgwater Pippin' (C)	WJas
F – 'Broad-Eyed Pippin' (C)	SKee
F – 'Brownlees Russet' (D)	CSco GTwe NRog SDea SFam SFru SKee SNTN WJas
¶ – 'Brown's Apple' (Cider)	CSco
¶ – 'Broxwood Foxwhelp' (Cider)	CSco
¶ – 'Bulmer's Chisel Jersey' (Cider)	CSco
¶ – 'Bulmer's Crimson King' (Cider)	CSco
¶ – 'Bulmer's Fillbarrel' (Cider)	CSco
¶ – 'Bulmer's Foxwhelp' (Cider)	CSco
¶ – 'Bulmer's Norman'	CSco SKee
F – 'Bushey Grove' (C)	SDea SKee
F – 'Calagolden Elbee' (D)	SKee
F – 'Calville Blanc d'Hiver' (D)	CSco SKee WMou
F – 'Calville des Femmes' (C)	SKee
F – 'Calville Rouge d'Hiver' (C)	WMou
¶ – 'Cambusnethan Pippin' (D)	SKee
¶ – 'Carlisle Codlin' (C)	CSco
¶ – 'Caroline' (D)	WJas
¶ – 'Carswell's Orange' (D)	SKee
F – 'Catherine' (C)	SKee
F – 'Catshead' (C)	CSco SDea SKee SNTN WJas WMou
F – 'Cellini' (C)	CSco SDea SKee
F – 'Charles Eyre' (C)	CSco SKee
F – 'Charles Ross' (C/D)	CMac CSam CSco EBre EWar GBon GRei GTwe LBre MBea NRog SDea SFam SIgm SKee WJas WStI WWeb
¶ – Charlotte ® (C/Ball)	EBal MGos NBar SSpi
F – 'Cheddar Cross' (D)	CSco SKee
F – 'Chelmsford Wonder' (C)	SKee

F– 'Chivers Delight' (D) CSco GTwe MMor NBee SDea SFru SIgm SKee SNTN WHig WJas
F– 'Christmas Pearmain' (D) CSco GTwe SDea SKee WJas
F– 'Cinderella' CDoC
F– 'Claygate Pearmain' (D) CSco GTwe MJas SDea SFam SFru SIgm SKee SNTN
F– 'Cockle Pippin' (D) CSco GTwe SDea SKee
F– 'Coeur de Boeuf' (C) SKee
F– 'Colonel Vaughan' (C) SKee WMou
F– 'Cornish Aromatic' (D) CDoC CSam CSco GTwe SDea SFam SKee WJas WMou
¶– 'Cornish Crimson Queen' GTwe
F– 'Cornish Gilliflower' (D) CDoC CSco SDea SFam SKee WJas
F– 'Cornish Pine' (D) SDea SKee
F– 'Coronation' (D) SDea SKee
F– 'Cortland' (C) CSco SKee
F– 'Costard' (C) GTwe SKee
F– 'Cottenham Seedling' (C) SKee
¶– 'Coul Blush' (D) SKee
¶– 'Court of Wick' (D) CSco SKee
F– 'Court Pendu Plat' (D) CSco NRog SDea SFam SKee SNTN WJas WMou
F– 'Cox's Orange Pippin' (D) CB&S CMac CSco EBre EHar ELan EWar GTwe IJoh LBre LBuc MBea MBri MMor MWat NElm NRog SDea SFam SFru SKee SNTN SPer WHig WJas WWeb
F– 'Cox's Pomona' (C/D) CSco SDea SKee
F– 'Cox's Red Sport' (D) SKee
F– 'Cox's Rouge de Flandres' (D) SKee
F– 'Crawley Beauty' (C) CSco GTwe SDea SFam SFru SKee WJas
F– 'Crimson Bramley' (C) CSam CSco SKee
¶– 'Crimson Cox' (D) SDea
¶– 'Crimson Peasgood' (C) SKee
¶– 'Crimson Queening' (D) SKee WJas
F– 'Crispin' See M. *d.* 'Mutsu'
F– 'Crown Gold' CSco GBon SKee
F– 'Curl Tail' (D) SKee
F– 'Dabinett' (Cider) CSco SDea SKee
F– 'DArcy Spice' (D) CSco SDea SFam SFru SIgm SKee WHig
¶– 'Dawn' (D) SKee
F– 'Deacon's Blushing Beauty' (C/D) SDea
F– 'Decio' (D) SFru SKee
¶– 'Delkid' GTwe
¶– 'Devonshire Buckland' (C) WJas
F– 'Devonshire Quarrenden' (D) CSam CSco SDea SFam SKee WHig WJas
¶– 'Dewdney's Seedling' (C) GTwe
¶– 'Diamond Jubilee' (D) WJas
F– 'Discovery' (D) CB&S CSam CSco EBre EWar GBon GChr GRei GTwe IOrc LBre LBuc MBea MBri MMor MWat NBee NElm NRog SDea SFam SFru SIgm SKee SPer WHig WJas WWeb
¶– 'Doctor Hare's' (C) WJas
F– 'Doctor Harvey' (C) EHar
F– 'Doctor Kidd's Orange Red' (D) SDea
F– 'Domino' (C) SKee
¶– 'Downton Pippin' (D) SKee WJas
F– 'Duchess of Oldenburg' (C/D) CSco SKee
F– 'Duchess's Favourite' (D) CSco SKee WJas
F– 'Duke of Devonshire' (D) CSam CSco SDea SFam SKee WJas
N– 'Dumeller's Seedling' (C) GTwe SDea SFru SKee
F– 'Dunn's Seedling' (D) SDea
¶– 'Dutch Mignonne' (D) SKee
¶– 'Early Crimson' CSco
F– 'Early Julyan' (C) SKee WJas
F– 'Early Victoria' See M. *d.* 'Emneth Early'
F– 'Early Worcester' See M. *d.* 'Tydeman's E. W.'
F– 'Easter Orange' (D) CSco SKee WJas
F– 'Ecklinville' (C) SDea SKee
F– 'Edward VII' (C) CDoC CSco EBre GTwe LBre SDea SFam SFru SKee WJas
¶– 'Edwin Beckett' (D) SKee
F– 'Egremont Russet' (D) CMac CSam CSco EBre EWar GBon GChr GTwe IOrc LBre LBuc MBea MBri MMor MWat NBee NElm NRog SDea SFam SFru SIgm SKee SNTN SPer WHig WJas WMou WWeb
F– 'Ellison's Orange' (D) CSam CSco EWar GBon GTwe MBri MMor NBar NRog SDea SFam SFru SIgm SKee WJas WStI
F– 'Elstar' (D) CSco GTwe IOrc SDea SFru SIgm SKee WHig
F– 'Elton Beauty' (D) SDea
F– 'Emneth Early' (C) CSam GTwe MGos MMor NRog SDea SFam SFru SKee WJas
F– 'Empire' (D) SKee SNTN
F– 'Encore' (C) CSco SDea SFru SKee
F– 'Epicure' (D) CDoC CSam CSco GBon GTwe IOrc NElm NRog SFam SFru SIgm SKee
F– 'Ernie's Russet' (D) SDea
F– 'Evening Gold' (C) SDea
F– 'Eve's Delight' (D) SDea
F– 'Exeter Cross' (D) CSco SDea SFam SKee
F– 'Fall Russet' (D) GTwe
F– 'Falstaff' (D) CDoC CSco GTwe MGos SFru SIgm SKee
¶– 'Fameuse' (D) SKee
F– 'Fearn's Pippin' (D) CSco SFam SKee
¶– 'Feltham Beauty' (D) CSco
¶– 'Feuillemorte' (D) SKee
F– 'Fiesta' (D) CDoC CSam CSco EBre GBon GTwe LBre LBuc MBri MGos NBar SDea SFam SFru SIgm SKee WHig
¶– 'Fillbarrel' (Cider) CSco
F– 'Firmgold' (D) SDea
¶– 'First and Last' (D) CSco
F– 'Five Crowns' SKee
¶– Flamenco ® (D/Ball) EBal MGos NBar
F– 'Flower of Kent' (C) CSco SDea SFru SKee
¶– 'Flower of the Town' (D) WJas
¶– 'Folkestone' (D) SKee
F– 'Forge' (D) CSco SDea SKee
¶– 'Formosa Nonpareil' (C) WJas

Cultivar	Suppliers
F – 'Fortune' (D)	CDoC CMac CSam GChr GRei GTwe MGos NElm NRog SDea SFam SFru SIgm SKee WJas
F – 'Foxwhelp' (Cider)	WMou
¶ – 'Franklyn's Golden Pippin' (D)	CSco
¶ – 'Frederick' (Cider)	CSco
F – 'French Crab' (C)	CSco SDea
¶ – 'Freyberg' (D)	SKee
¶ – 'Friandise' (D)	CSco
¶ – 'Frogmore Prolific' (C)	CSco WJas
F – 'Fuji' (D)	SDea SKee
F – 'Gala' (D)	CSam CSco GBon GTwe MBri SDea SFam SFru SIgm SKee
F – 'Gala Royal'	SKee
F – 'Galloway Pippin' (C)	GTwe SKee
F – 'Gascoyne's Scarlet' (D)	CSco SDea SFam SKee
F – 'Gavin' (D)	GTwe SDea SKee
F – 'Genesis II' (D/C)	SDea
¶ – 'Genet Moyle' (C)	WJas
F – 'Geneva' (Crab)	SKee
¶ – 'George Carpenter' (D)	SKee
F – 'George Cave' (D)	CSco GChr GTwe NBee NRog SDea SFam SFru SIgm SKee WJas
F – 'George Neal' (C)	CSco SDea SFam SFru SIgm SKee
F – 'Gladstone' (D)	SKee WJas
F – 'Gloria Mundi' (C)	SDea SKee
¶ – 'Glory of England' (C)	WJas
F – 'Gloster '69' (D)	CSco GTwe SDea SIgm SKee
¶ – 'Gloucester Cross' (D)	SKee
F – 'Golden Delicious' (D)	CB&S CMac CSco EBre ELan EWar GBon IJoh LBre MBea MBri MMor NElm NRog SDea SKee SPer WStI WWeb
¶ – 'Golden Harvey' (D)	CSco
F – 'Golden Knob' (D)	SKee WJas
F – 'Golden Noble' (C)	CDoC CSco GTwe SDea SFam SFru SIgm SKee WJas
¶ – 'Golden Nonpareil' (D)	CSco
F – 'Golden Nugget' (D)	SIgm
F – 'Golden Pippin' (C)	CSco SKee WMou
F – 'Golden Reinette' (D)	CSco GTwe SKee
F – 'Golden Russet' (D)	CSco GTwe SDea SKee WJas
F – 'Golden Spire' (C)	CSco NRog SDea SKee
F – 'Goldilocks'	CDoC CSco GTwe
F – 'Gooseberry' (C)	CSco SKee
¶ – 'Grange's Pearmain' (C)	CSco
F – 'Granny Smith' (D)	CSco GTwe MBea MBri SDea SIgm SKee SPer WWeb
F – 'Gravenstein' (D)	SDea SFam SFru SKee
F – 'Green Balsam' (C)	NRog
F – 'Green Roland'	See M. *d.* 'Greenup's Pippin'
F – 'Greensleeves' (D)	CDoC CSam CSco EBre GTwe LBre MBea MBri MGos NBee NRog SDea SFam SFru SIgm SKee SPer WHig WJas
F – 'Greenup's Pippin' (D)	SKee
F – 'Grenadier' (C)	CDoC CSco EBre EWar GChr GRei GTwe IJoh IOrc LBre MBri MGos MMor NBee NElm NRog SDea SFru SIgm SKee SPer WHig WStI
¶ – 'Gulval Seedling'	SKee
F – 'Hambledon Deux Ans' (C)	CSco SDea SKee WJas
¶ – 'Hambling's Seedling' (C)	CSco SKee
F – 'Harry Masters Jersey' (Cider)	CSco SDea
¶ – 'Harry Master's Dove' (Cider)	CSco
¶ – 'Harry Master's Lambrook' (Cider)	CSco
¶ – 'Harry Master's Red Streak' (Cider)	CSco
F – 'Harvey ' (C)	CSco SDea SKee
F – 'Hawthornden' (C)	SKee
¶ – 'Hereford Cross' (D)	CSco SKee
F – 'Herefordshire Beefing' (C)	SKee WJas
F – 'Herring's Pippin' (D)	CSco GTwe SDea SKee SNTN
¶ – 'Heusgen's Golden Reinette' (D)	CSco SKee
¶ – 'High View Pippin' (D)	SKee
¶ – 'Hills Seedling'	SKee
F – 'Histon Favourite' (D)	SKee
F – 'Hoary Morning' (C)	SDea SKee
F – 'Holland Pippin' (C)	SKee
F – 'Holstein' (D)	CSco GTwe SDea SIgm SKee
¶ – 'Hormead Pearmain' (C)	CSco SKee
¶ – 'Horneburger Pfannkuchen' (C)	SKee
¶ – 'Houblon' (D)	SKee
F – 'Howgate Wonder' (C)	CDoC CSam CSco GBon GChr GTwe IJoh IOrc LBuc MBri MGos MMor NBee NElm NRog SDea SFam SFru SIgm SKee SPer WHig WJas
F – 'Idared' (D)	CSco GBon GTwe MGos NBar SDea SFru SKee
F – 'Improved Cockpit' (D)	NRog
F – 'Ingrid Marie' (D)	CSco SDea SIgm SKee WJas
F – 'Invicta' (D)	SKee
F – 'Irish Peach' (D)	CSco GTwe SDea SFam SFru SKee SNTN WHig WJas
F – 'Isaac Newton's Tree'	See M. *d.* 'Flower of Kent'
F – 'Isle of Wight Pippin' (D)	SDea
F – 'Isle of Wight Russet' (D)	SDea
F – 'James Grieve' (D)	CMac CSam CSco EWar GBon GChr GRei GTwe IJoh IOrc LBuc MBea MBri MMor MWat NBar NBee NElm NRog SDea SFam SFru SIgm SKee SNTN SPer WHig WJas WMou WWeb
¶ – 'James Lawson' (D)	SKee
F – 'Jerseymac' (D)	CSco SDea
F – 'Jester' (D)	CSco GTwe SDea SKee WHig
F – 'John Apple' (C)	SKee
F – 'John Broad'	CDoC
F – 'John Standish' (D)	GTwe SDea
F – 'Jonagold' (D)	CSco GTwe IJoh MBea MBri SDea SFam SIgm SKee SPer WHig WWeb
F – 'Jonagold Crowngold' (D)	GTwe
F – 'Jonagored' (D)	CSco SFru SKee
F – 'Jonared' (D)	GTwe
F – 'Jonathan' (D)	CSco SDea SKee
F – 'Jordan's Weeping'	GTwe SDea WJas
¶ – 'Josephine' (D)	SDea
F – 'Joybells' (D)	CSco SKee
F – 'Jubilee'	See M. *d.* 'Royal Jubilee'

F– 'Jupiter' (D) CDoC CSam CSco GBon GTwe IOrc LBuc MBea MBri MGos MWat NBar NRog SDea SFam SFru SIgm SKee WHig WJas WWeb
F– 'Kapai Red Jonathan' (D) SDea
F– 'Karmijn de Sonnaville' (D) SDea SFru SKee
F– 'Katja' (D) CDoC CSam CSco EBre GBon GChr GTwe IJoh IOrc LBre LBuc MBea MBri NBar NBee SDea SFam SFru SIgm SKee SPer WHig
F– 'Katy' See M. *d.* 'Katja'
F– 'Kent' (D) GTwe SDea SKee
F– 'Kentish Fillbasket' (C) SKee
F– 'Kentish Pippin' See M. *d.* 'Colonel Vaughan'
F– 'Kentish Quarrenden' (D) SKee
F– 'Kerry Pippin' (D) CSco SKee
F– 'Keswick Codling' (C) CSam CSco NRog SDea SKee SNTN WJas
F– 'Kidd's Orange Red' (D) CSco EBre GTwe LBre MMor SFam SFru SIgm SKee SNTN WHig
F– 'Kilkenny Pippin' GTwe
F– 'King Charles' Pearmain' (D) SKee
¶– 'King George V' (D) CSco SKee WJas
F– 'King Luscious' (D) SDea
F– 'King of the Pippins' (D) CSam CSco GTwe SDea SFru SKee WJas
¶– 'King of Tompkins County' (D) CSco SKee
F– 'King Russet' (D) SDea SFru
F– 'Kingston Black' (Cider) CSam CSco SDea SKee
F– 'King's Acre Bountiful' (C) CSco SKee WJas
F– 'King's Acre Pippin' (D) CSco SDea SFam SFru SKee WJas
¶– 'Lady Bacon' SKee
F– 'Lady Henniker' (D) CSco GTwe SDea SKee WJas
F– 'Lady Lambourne' (C/D) SKee
¶– 'Lady of the Wemyss' (C) SKee
F– 'Lady Stanley' (D) SDea
F– 'Lady Sudeley' (D) CSco SDea SFam SFru SKee
¶– 'Lady's Delight' (C) WJas
¶– 'Lady's Finger of Hereford' (D) WJas
F– 'Lady's Finger of Lancashire' (C/D) SKee
F– 'Lady's Finger of Offaly' (D) SDea SKee
¶– 'Lamb Abbey Pearmain' (D) SKee WJas
¶– 'Landsberger Reinette' (D) SKee
F– 'Lane's Prince Albert' (C) CSam CSco EBre EHar EWar GBon GTwe IJoh LBre MGos MWat NRog SDea SFru SIgm SKee WJas
F– 'Langley Pippin' (D) SDea SKee
¶– 'Lass o' Gowrie' (C) CSco SKee
F– 'Laxton's Fortune' See M. *d.* 'Fortune'
¶– 'Laxton's Pearmain' (D) CSco
¶– 'Laxton's Rearguard' (D) CSco SKee WJas
¶– 'Laxton's Reward' (D) CSco
F– 'Laxton's Royalty' (D) CSco SDea SFam
F– 'Laxton's Superb' (D) CB&S CSam CSco EBre EHar ELan EWar GBon GTwe IJoh IOrc LBre LBuc MBea MBri MMor NBee NElm NRog SDea SFam SFru SIgm SKee SPer WJas WWeb
F– 'Leathercoat Russet' (D) SKee WMou
¶– 'Leeder's Perfection' SKee
F– 'Lemon Pippin' (C) CSco SDea SKee SNTN WJas WMou
F– 'Lewis's Incomparable' (C) SKee
F– 'Liberty' (D) SDea
¶– 'Linda' (D) CSco
F– 'Loddington' (C) CSco SKee
¶– 'Lodgemore Nonpareil' (D) CSco
F– 'Lodi' (C) SDea SKee
F– 'Lord Burghley' (D) GTwe SDea SKee
F– 'Lord Derby' (C) CDoC CMac CSam CSco EBre GTwe LBre MBri NBar NRog SDea SKee WJas
F– 'Lord Grosvenor' (C) CSco GTwe SKee
F– 'Lord Hindlip' (D) CSco GTwe SDea SKee WJas
F– 'Lord Lambourne' (D) CDoC CSam CSco EBre EHar EWar GChr GTwe IOrc LBre MMor MWat NBee NRog SFam SFru SIgm SKee SPer WHig WJas
F– 'Lord of the Isles' CDoC
¶– 'Lord Rosebery' (D) SKee
F– 'Lord Stradbroke' (C) SKee
F– 'Lord Suffield' (C) CSco SKee WJas
F– 'Lucombe's Seedling' (D) SKee
¶– 'Mabbott's Pearmain' (D) CSco
F– 'Madresfield Court' (D) CSco SDea SKee WJas
¶– 'Maiden's Blush' (D) WJas
F– 'Maidstone Favourite' (D) SKee
¶– 'Major' (Cider) CSco
F– 'Malling Kent' (D) CSam CSco SDea SFam
F– 'Maltster' (D) SKee WJas
F– 'Manks Codlin' (C) SKee
F– 'Mannington's Pearmain' (D) SKee
F– 'Margil' (D) CSco GTwe SDea SFam SIgm SKee SNTN
F– 'Marriage-Maker' (D) SKee
F– 'May Queen' (D) CSco SDea SFam SKee WJas
F– 'Maypole' (D/Ball) CWSG EBal MBri MGos NBar SDea WWeb
F– 'McIntosh Red' (D) SKee WJas
F– 'Mead's Broading' (C) SKee
¶– 'Medina' (D) GTwe
F– 'Melba' (D) CSam SKee
F– 'Melon' (D) SDea
F– 'Melrose' (D) CSco GTwe SKee
¶– 'Mère de Ménage' (C) CSco
F– 'Merton Beauty' (D) CSco SFru
F– 'Merton Charm' (D) CSco SFam SKee
¶– 'Merton Joy' (D) CSco
F– 'Merton Knave' (D) CSco GTwe MGos SDea SFru
F– 'Merton Russet' (D) CSco SDea SKee SNTN

F– 'Merton Worcester' (D) CSco SDea SKee
F– 'Michaelmas Red' (D) CSco GTwe SKee WHig WJas
F– 'Michelin' (Cider) CSco SDea
¶– 'Miel d'Or' SKee
F– 'Miller's Seedling' (D) GTwe SKee WJas
F– 'Millicent Barnes' (D) SDea
¶– 'Mollie's Delicious' (D) GTwe
F– 'Monarch' (C) CSco GTwe MMor NRog SDea SFam SKee WJas
F– 'Morgan's Sweet' (C/Cider) CSco SDea SKee WMou
F– 'Moss's Seedling' (D) CSco GTwe SDea
F– 'Mother' (D) CDoC GTwe SDea SFam SFru SKee WJas
¶– 'Mrs Phillimore' (D) SKee
F– 'Muscadet de Dieppe' CSam
F– 'Mutsu' (D) GTwe MBri MGos MMor NRog SDea SFru SIgm SKee
¶– 'Nehou' (Cider) CSco
F– 'Nettlestone Pippin' (D) SDea
¶– 'New German' (D) WJas
F– 'Newton Wonder' (D/C) CDoC CMac CSam CSco EWar GTwe IJoh MMor NElm NRog SDea SFam SFru SIgm SKee WHig WMou WStI
F– 'Newtown Pippin' (D) SDea
¶– 'Niemans Neiburger' CSco
F– 'Nittany Red' (D) SDea
¶– 'Nobby Russet' GTwe
F– 'Nonpareil' (D) CSco SKee SNTN WMou
F– 'Norfolk Beauty' (C) CSco SKee
F– 'Norfolk Beefing' (C) CSco SKee WJas
F– 'Norfolk Royal' (D) CDoC CSco EHar GTwe MGos SDea SFam SIgm SKee WHig
¶– 'Norfolk Winter Coleman' SKee
¶– 'Norman's Pippin' (D) CSco
F– 'Northern Greening' (C) GTwe SKee
¶– 'Northwood' (Cider) CSco
¶– 'Nutmeg Pippin' (D) CSco
F– 'Old Pearmain' (D) SDea SKee WMou
¶– 'Opalescent' (D) CSco SKee
F– 'Orange Goff' (D) SKee
F– 'Orkney Apple' SKee
F– 'Orleans Reinette' (D) CSco EBre GTwe LBre LBuc MWat SDea SFam SFru SIgm SKee SNTN WHig WJas WMou
F– 'Oslin' (D) SKee
F– 'Owen Thomas' (D) CSco SKee
F– 'Paroquet' (D) SKee
F– 'Patricia' (D) SKee
F– 'Paulared' (D) SDea SKee
F– 'Peacemaker' (D) SKee
¶– 'Pearl' (D) CSco SDea
F– 'Peasgood's Nonsuch' (C) CSco GTwe SDea SFam SFru SKee WHig WJas
F– 'Peck's Pleasant' (D) SKee
F– 'Pickering's Seedling' (D) SKee
¶– 'Pine Golden Pippin ' (D) SKee
F– 'Pitmaston Pine Apple' (D) SDea SFam SFru SKee WJas WMou
¶– 'Pitmaston Pippin Nonpareil' CSco SKee
F– 'Pixie' (D) CSam CSco GTwe SFru SIgm SKee WJas
F– Polka ®/ 'Trajan (D/Ball) CWSG EBal MBri MGos NBar SDea WWeb
¶– 'Polly Prosser' (D) SKee
F– 'Polly Whitehair' SDea SKee
¶– 'Ponsford' (C) CSco SKee
¶– 'Porter Pefection' (Cider) CSco
F– 'Pott's Seedling' (C) SKee
¶– 'Powell's Russet' (D) CSco
¶– 'Priscilla' (D) GTwe
¶– 'Puckrupp Pippin' (D) WJas
F– 'Queen' (C) CSco SKee
F– 'Queen Caroline' (C) SKee
F– 'Queen Cox' (D) CSco CWSG GBon MBri MRav SDea SFam SFru SIgm SKee
¶– 'Racky Down' SKee
F– 'Red Astrachan' (D) SKee
F– 'Red Blenheim' (C/D) SKee
F– 'Red Charles Ross' (C/D) SDea SFru
F– 'Red Devil' (D) CWSG SIgm SKee WHig
F– 'Red Ellison' (D) CSco GTwe NRog SDea
¶– 'Red Fuji' SDea
F– 'Red James Grieve' (D) SDea
F– 'Red Joaneting' (D) CSco SKee WMou
¶– 'Red Melba' (D) CSco
F– 'Red Miller's Seedling' (D) CSco SDea
F– 'Red Siberian' (Crab) SDea
F– 'Red Superb' (D) SKee
¶– 'Red Victoria' (C) CSco WJas
F– 'Redfree' GTwe
F– 'Redsleeves' (C) CSco GTwe SDea SIgm WHig
¶– 'Reinette Doreé de Boediker' (D) GTwe
F– 'Reinette du Canada' (D) CSco SFru SKee
¶– 'Reinette d'Obry' (Cider) CSco
F– 'Reinette Rouge Etoilée' (D) SDea SKee
F– 'Reverend Greeves' SDea
F– 'Reverend W Wilks' (C) CDoC CSco EBre LBre LBuc NRog SFam SFru SIgm SKee WJas
F– 'Ribston Pippin' (D) CSco EBre GTwe LBre LBuc MWat SDea SFam SFru SIgm SKee SNTN WJas WMou
F– 'Rival' (D) CSco SDea SKee WJas
F– 'Robin Pippin' (D) GTwe
F– 'Rome Beauty' (D) SDea
¶– 'Rosamund' (D) SKee
F– 'Rosemary Russet' (D) CSam CSco GTwe SDea SFam SFru SIgm SKee WHig WJas
F– 'Ross Nonpareil' (D) CSco GTwe SDea SKee
F– 'Roundway Magnum Bonum' (D) CSco SDea SKee
F– 'Roxbury Russet' (D) CSco SKee
F– 'Royal Gala' See M. *d.* 'Tenroy'
F– 'Royal Jubilee' (C) SKee
F– 'Royal Russet' (C) SDea WMou
¶– 'Royal Snow' (D) SKee
F– 'Rubinette' CDoC CWSG GTwe MBri MGos NBar WHig WJas
F– 'S T Wright' (C) SKee
F– 'Saint Albans Pippin' (D) SKee

Cultivar	Suppliers
¶– 'Saint Augustine's Orange'	SKee
F– 'Saint Cecilia' (D)	CSco SDea SKee WJas
F– 'Saint Edmund's Pippin' (D)	CSam CSco LBuc SKee
F– 'Saint Edmund's Russet' (D)	GTwe SDea SFam SFru SIgm WJas
F– 'Saint Everard' (D)	CSco SFru SKee
F– 'Saint Magdalen'	SKee
¶– 'Saltcote Pippin' (D)	CSco SKee
¶– 'Sam Young' (D)	CSco SKee
F– 'Sandringham' (C)	SKee
F– 'Sanspareil' (D)	SKee
¶– 'Saw Pits'	SKee
¶– 'Scarlet Crofton' (D)	CSco SKee
¶– 'Scarlet Nonpareil' (D)	CSco SKee
F– 'Scarlet Pimpernel' (D)	CSco WJas
¶– 'Schweizer Orange' ('Swiss Orange')	CSco
F– 'Scotch Bridget' (C)	SKee WJas
F– 'Scotch Dumpling' (C)	GTwe
¶– 'Shakespeare' (D)	WJas
F– 'Sheep's Nose' (C)	SDea SKee
¶– 'Shenandoah' (C)	SKee
F– 'Shoesmith' (C)	SIgm
F– 'Sir Isaac Newton's'	See M. *d.* 'Flower of Kent'
F– 'Sir John Thornycroft' (D)	SDea
F– 'Smart's Prince Arthur' (C)	SDea
¶– 'Somerset Red Streak' (Cider)	CSco
¶– 'Sops in Wine' (C/Cider)	SKee
F– 'Spartan' (D)	CDoC CSam CSco EBre GBon GTwe LBre LBuc MBri MGos MMor MWat NBar NRog SDea SFam SFru SIgm SKee SPer WHig WJas WStI
F– 'Spur Mac' (D)	SDea
F– 'Star of Devon' (D)	SDea
F– 'Stark' (D)	SDea
F– 'Starking' (D)	SKee
¶– 'Starking Red Delicious' (D)	CSco
F– 'Starkrimson' (D)	SKee
F– 'Starkspur Golden Delicious' (D)	SKee
F– 'Stark's Earliest' (D)	SKee
¶– 'Stembridge' (Cider)	CSco
¶– 'Stembridge Jersey' (Cider)	CSco
F– 'Steyne Seedling' (D)	SDea
F– 'Stirling Castle' (C)	CSco GTwe SKee
¶– 'Stobo Castle'	SKee
F– 'Stoke Edith Pippin' (D)	SKee WJas
¶– 'Stoke Red' (Cider)	CSco
F– 'Stone's'	See M. *d.* 'Loddington'
F– 'Striped Beefing' (C)	CSco SKee
¶– 'Stub Nose'	SKee
F– 'Sturmer Pippin' (D)	CSam CSco GTwe MWat SDea SFam SFru SIgm SKee SNTN
F– 'Summer Golden Pippin' (D)	SKee
F– 'Summer Granny'	SDea
¶– 'Summergold'	CSco
F– 'Summerred' (D)	CSco CWSG SKee
F– 'Sunburn' (D)	SIgm SKee
F– 'Sunset' (D)	CDoC CMac CSam CSco CWSG GTwe LBuc MBea MBri NBee NRog SDea SFam SFru SIgm SKee SPer WHig
F– 'Suntan' (D)	CSam CSco GBon GTwe MWat SDea SFru SKee WHig
F– 'Superb'	See 'M. *d.* 'Laxton's Superb'
F– 'Surprise' (D)	GTwe
¶– 'Sweet Alford' (Cider)	CSco
¶– 'Sweet Coppin' (Cider)	CSco
¶– 'Taunton Cream'	CSco
F– 'Taylor's' (Cider)	CSco SDea
F– 'Ten Commandments' (D)	SDea WJas
F– 'Tenroy' (D)	SDea
¶– 'The Queen'	CSco
F– 'Thomas Rivers' (C)	SDea SKee
¶– 'Thorle Pippin' (D)	SKee
¶– 'Tillington Court' (C)	WJas
F– 'Tom Putt' (C)	CDoC CSam CSco CWSG GTwe SDea SKee WJas WMou
F– 'Tower of Glamis' (C)	SKee
F– 'Transparente de Croncels' (C)	SKee
F– 'Tremlett's Bitter' (Cider)	CSco SDea
F– 'Twenty Ounce' (C)	GTwe SKee WJas
¶– 'Twinings Pippin' (D)	SKee
F– 'Tydeman's Early Worcester' (D)	CSco GRei GTwe NBee NRog SDea SKee WJas
F– 'Tydeman's Late Orange' (D)	CSco GTwe MMor NRog SDea SFam SFru SKee
F– 'Tyler's Kernel' (C)	SKee
¶– 'Underleaf' (D)	CSco
F– 'Upton Pyne' (D)	CSam CSco SDea SKee
¶– 'Veitch's Scarlet'	GTwe
¶– 'Vetch's Perfection'	SKee
F– 'Vickey's Delight' (D)	SDea
¶– 'Vilberie' (Cider)	CSco
F– 'Vista-Bella' (D)	CSco GTwe NBee SDea SKee
F– 'Wagener' (D)	CSco SDea SFam SKee
F– Waltz ®/ 'Telamon (D/Ball)	CWSG EBal MBri MGos NBar SDea WWeb
F– 'Wanstall Pippin' (D)	SKee
F– 'Warner's King' (C)	CSco SDea SFru SKee WJas
F– 'Wealthy' (D)	SDea SKee
F– 'Wellington'	See M. *d.* 'Dumeller's Seedling'
F– 'Wellspur Delicious' (D)	CSco WJas
F– 'Wellspur Red Delicious'	GTwe
F– 'Welsh Russet' (D)	SDea
¶– 'White Jersey' (Cider)	CSco
F– 'White Joaneting' (D)	CSco WMou
F– 'White Melrose' (C)	CSco GTwe SDea SKee
¶– 'White Paradise' (C)	SKee
F– 'White Transparent' (C/D)	CSco GTwe SDea SKee
F– 'William Crump' (D)	SDea SFru SKee WHig WJas
F– 'Winston' (D)	CSco GTwe NRog SDea SFam SIgm SKee WJas
F– 'Winter Banana' (D)	SDea SKee
¶– 'Winter Pearmain' (D)	CSco SKee
F– 'Winter Quarrenden' (D)	SDea SKee

F – 'Winter Queening' (D/C)	SDea
¶ – 'Woolbrook Pippin' (D)	CSco
F – 'Woolbrook Russet' (C)	CSco SFru SKee
F – 'Worcester Pearmain' (D)	CSam CSco EWar GBon GChr GRei GTwe IJoh LBuc MBea MBri MMor NBar NElm NRog SDea SFam SFru SIgm SKee SNTN SPer WHig WJas WStI WWeb
F – 'Wormsley Pippin' (D)	SKee WJas
F – 'Wyken Pippin' (D)	CSco GTwe SDea SFam SKee WJas WMou
F – 'Yarlington Mill' (Cider)	CSco SDea SKee
F – 'Yellow Ingestrie' (D)	CSco SKee WJas
F – 'Yellowspur' (D)	SKee
F – 'Zabergäu Renette' (D)	SKee
'Echtermeyer'	See M. x ***gloriosa*** 'Oekonomierat Echtermeyer'
'Elk River'	WJas
'Evereste'	CBar CDoC CLnd CSco EBar EBre GChr LBre MBlu MBri WAbe WDin
florentina	WMou
floribunda	CBra CDoC CLnd CSam CSco CTho ELan ENot IDai IHos IOrc LBuc MBri MGos MRav NBee SChu SHBN SKee SPer SReu WDin WJas WMou
'Gardener's Gold'	MBri
§ x ***gloriosa*** 'Oekonomierat Echtermeyer'	CTho EBre LBre WDin
'Golden Gem'	SIgm WJas
'Golden Hornet'	See M. x ***zumi*** 'G. H.'
¶ 'Goldsworth Purple'	CTho
¶ ***halliana***	CMCN
x ***hartwigii*** 'Katherine'	COtt
'Hillieri'	See M. x ***schiedeckeri*** 'H.'
hupehensis	CB&S CBow CCla CLnd CMCN CTho EHar ENot IHos MBri SFam SHBN SIgm SPer SSpi WCoo WJas WMou WNor WWat
F 'John Downie'	Widely available
'Kaido'	See M. x ***micromalus***
kansuensis	CLnd WMou
x ***magdeburgensis***	CLnd NWea SIgm WJas
'Makamik'	WJas
§ x ***micromalus***	CLnd GAri
x ***moerlandsii***	CLnd
– 'Liset'	CBra CLnd EBar EBre ECtt ENot GChr LBre NBar SPer WStI
– 'Profusion'	CBra CLnd CSco CTho EBar EBre ELan ENot GRei IDai IOrc LBre MBar MBri MGos NBee NWea SFam SHBN SIgm SPer SPla SReu WAbe WDin WJas WStI
¶ ***orthocarpa***	CLnd
'Pink Perfection'	CLnd ENot SHBN SHil SPer
'Pom-Zai'	MAsh
'Prince Georges'	SHil
prunifolia 'Cheal's Crimson'	NRog
¶ – 'Pendula'	GAri
pumila 'Cowichan'	LRHS MBri SPer WJas
– 'Dartmouth'	CLnd CSco CTho NRog SFam SKee SPer
– 'Montreal Beauty'	MBri SFam
– 'Niedzwetzkyana'	CLnd
– 'Veitch's Scarlet'	CLnd CTho NRog SFam SIgm WJas
x ***purpurea*** 'Aldenhamensis'	CBra CLnd MGos SDea WDin
– 'Eleyi'	CLnd EBar ENot MGos NWea WDin
– 'Lemoinei'	CTho GRei IOrc SDea WJas
– 'Neville Copeman'	CAbP CDoC CLnd
– 'Pendula'	See M. x ***gloriosa*** 'Oekonomierat Echtermeyer'
'Red Glow'	CDoC CLnd COtt CSco MBri WJas
x ***robusta***	CDoC CLnd EBre GTwe LBre MBal NWea SNTN SPla WJas
– 'Red Sentinel'	CDoC CLnd COtt CSco EBre ELan ENot LBre LNet MBar MBri NBee SFam SIgm SPer WJas
– 'Red Siberian'	SHBN SHil SPer
– 'Yellow Siberian'	CLnd SHil
'Royal Beauty'	CBar COtt CSco EBre GTwe LBre MBri
'Royalty'	CB&S CBra CDoC CLnd CSco CTho EBar EBre ELan ENot GRei GTwe IHos LBre LBuc LNet MBar MBri MGos MRav SFam SHBN SIgm SPer SPla SSta WJas WStI
'Rudolph'	ENot
sargentii	See M. ***toringo s.***
x ***schiedeckeri*** 'Exzellenz Thiel'	SIgm
– 'Hillieri'	CLnd CTho EBar EBre IDai LBre SFam
– 'Red Jade'	CLnd CSco EBre ECtt ELan ENot GTwe IJoh IOrc LBre LBuc MBar MBri MGos MRav NBee SFam SHBN SPer SPla WAbe WDin WJas WStI
sieboldii	See M. ***toringo***
– 'Gorgeous'	CLnd COtt CSco MBri SIgm
'Snowcloud'	CLnd ENot MBri SHBN SHil SPer
¶ ***spectabilis***	CLnd
sp. CLD 417	EMon
'Strathmore'	WJas
sylvestris	CKin CLnd CPer EBre GAri GChr LBre LBuc NRog NWea SKee WDin
§ ***toringo***	CSto
§ – ssp. ***sargentii***	ECtt ENot MBri MGos SFam SIgm SPer WJas WNor WThu WWat
– 'Wintergold	CDoC CLnd CSam ECtt MRav SFam SKee WStI
toringoïdes	CLnd CMCN CTho MBri SFam SHBN SIgm SPer SSpi WMou WNor WWat
transitoria	CLnd CTho SHil SSpi WCoo WWat
¶ – 'R J Fulcher'	CTho
trilobata	CLnd SHil WMou
tschonoskii	CBra CDoC CLnd CTho EBar EBre ELan ENot GTwe IOrc LBre MBal MBri MGos MRav NBar NBee NWea SHBN SIgm SKee SPer SSta WAbe WDin WJas WStI WWat
'Van Eseltine'	CBar CBra CLnd EBre ENot GChr GTwe LBre MBri SReu
'Wisley'	CLnd GChr GTwe LRHS SDea SFam SKee
x ***zumi*** 'Golden Hornet'	Widely available
¶ – 'Professor Sprenger'	CLnd

MALVA (Malvaceae)

alcea	CShe CSun LBlm NBee
– var. *fastigiata*	CArn CGle CHan EBre ECED ECro ELan EMon LBre LGan LHil MBri MNFA MRav NBro NCat NHol NPer NRoo NVic SPer WHal WPer WRus
bicolor	See LAVATERA ***maritima***
crispa	See M. ***verticillata***
hispida	CNat
moschata	CArn CB&S CElw CGle CKin CPar CSev CShe CSun ELan EOrc GCHN LHol LHop MChe NBro NLan NMir NOak SIde SPer SWat WCla WHer WNdy WOak WPer
– *alba*	Widely available
– – 'Pirouette'	WHen WPbr
– 'Romney Marsh'	GCal MRav MTol SAxl SGil WSHC
– *rosea*	CHun ECha ESma NBee NNor NPer SFis WByw WPbr
pyramidalis	CSco
sylvestris	CGle CKin CLew CPar CTom EMon GCHN MChe MPit NBro NLan NOak NRoo NSti SMad SWat WEas WHer WPer WWin
– 'Brave Heart'	CB&S EMon LRHS NPer
– 'Cottenham Blue'	ELan EMon LRHS WPbr
– *mauritiana*	CSun ECro ELan EMar EPad LBlm LHop MFir MPit NFai NNor NPer SFis SHer SMrm WHer WPbr WRus
– 'Primley Blue'	CB&S CBot CElw CFis CGle CHad CHan ECha EFol ERav LAbb LGre LHop MTho NFai NPer SHer SMad SMrm SUsu WHal WOld WPer WWin
– 'Zebrina'	ECro EJud EMar LHil NFai NPer SMad SMrm WBon WHil WPbr
§ *verticillata*	ELan
– 'Crispa'	EMon MChe

MALVASTRUM (Malvaceae)

x *hypomandarum*	See ANISODONTEA x ***hypomandarum***
lateritium	Widely available
– 'Eastgrove Silver' (v)	LGan LHil WCot
– 'Hopley's Variegated'	LHop SUsu
– 'Variegatum'	WPer
* *latifolium*	SPer WByw

MALVAVISCUS (Malvaceae)

arboreus var. *mexicanus* CSun

MANDARIN See CITRUS *reticulata* Mandarin Group

MANDEVILLA (Apocynaceae)

x *amoena* 'Alice du Pont'	CB&S CBar CHEx CTro EMil ERea IHos IOrc MNew SHil SLMG
boliviensis	MNew
§ *laxa*	CAbb CB&S CBot CChu CHEx CPle CSPN CSam CTro ERea GCal IHos IOrc LBlm MNew NPal SBra SHil SMad SSpi WBod WOMN WSHC
sanderi	CB&S EMil MBri
splendens	CGre CHEx EBak LHil SLMG
suaveolens	See M. ***laxa***

MANDRAGORA (Solanaceae)

¶ *arborescens*	SMrm
autumnalis	GPoy NSal WThi
§ *officinarum*	CRDP GPoy LGre NSal WWye

MANETTIA (Rubiaceae)

♦ *inflata*	See M. ***luteorubra***
§ *luteorubra*	CTro LHop SLMG

MANGLIETIA (Magnoliaceae)

¶ *insignis*	CTre

MARANTA (Marantaceae)

bicolor	EBak
leuconeura var. *erythroneura*	MBri
– var. *kerchoveana*	CHal MBri

MARCHANTIA (liverwort)

¶ *calcarea*	LFle
¶ *palmatoïdes*	LFle
¶ sp. from Tristan da Cunha	LFle

MARGYRICARPUS (Rosaceae)

§ *pinnatus*	CElw CLew CRiv ECar ELan ESis GCal MCas NMen NWCA SFar SHer WAbe WHil WPer WTyr
setosus	See M. ***pinnatus***

MARISCUS See CYPERUS

MARKHAMIA (Bignoniaceae)

lutea	CPle
♦ *platycalyx*	See M. ***lutea***

MARRUBIUM (Labiatae)

candidissimum	See M. ***incanum***
¶ *catariifolium*	EMon
cylleneum	ECha ECro EFol EMar EMon SAxl WPer WWin
* – 'Velvetissimum'	CHad CMGP EMar EOrc ESma LHil LHop SChu SCro SFis
'Gold Leaf'	EBar ECha EFol ESma NSti
§ *incanum*	CGle CHan CSun EHal EMon LBlm LHil NSti NTow SFis WEas WHal
libanoticum	EMon WPer
supinum	GCal NSti WDav
velutinum	CGle EMar EMon
vulgare	CArn CHal CSev EEls EJud EMar Effi GPoy IEde LHol MChe MHew NMir NSal NSel SHer SIde WHer WOak WPer WWye
– variegated	NRar

MARSDENIA (Asclepiadaceae)

erecta	See CIONURA ***e.***

MASCARENA See **HYOPHORBE**

MATELEA (Asclepiadaceae)
See Plant Deletions

MATRICARIA (Compositae)

chamomilla	See M. *recutita*
parthenium	See TANACETUM *parthenium*
§ *recutita*	EJud GPoy IEde LHol MChe MHew NSel SIde

MATTEUCCIA (Dryopteridaceae)

orientalis	NHar NMar NOrc SPla
¶ *pensylvanica*	NHar
struthiopteris	CBar CBot CBow CRow CWGN ECha EGol EHon ELan EMar EPar MBri MPar NBar NDea NEgg NHol NMar NOrc SAxl SCob SHig SPer SSpi SWat WFib WHal WHoo WWat

MATTHIOLA (Cruciferae)

fruticulosa ssp. *perennis*	EMon NSti NWCA WHil
incana	WRus
'Les Merriennes' (d)	WOMN
pink perennial	WRus
sinuata	CNat
thessala	SPou
white perennial	CGle CHad CHan CMil CRDP CSpe MPar NPer NTow SSvw WEas WSun

MAURANDYA (Scrophulariaceae)

§ *barclayana*	CBot CHEx CSam CSpe GCra LWad MBri SLMG SUsu WCru WEas
– *alba*	CBot
§ *erubescens*	CBot CHEx CHal CSam CSun CWes LHop MSte NSti SLMG WCru WHil WOMN WOld WPer
§ *lophantha*	WOMN
§ *lophospermum*	CSun LBlm
¶ 'Pink Ice'	SLMG
scandens	CPle ELan LWad SLMG WPer
¶ 'Victoria Falls'	SLMG

MAYTENUS (Celastraceae)

boaria	CBot CGre CMCN EHar SArc SHil WWat
– 'Worplesdon Fastigiate'	LMer

MAZUS (Scrophulariaceae)

pumilio	EBur ECar ECou NKay
radicans	CRiv ECou NKay SIng WByw WCru WThi
reptans	CHal CNic CRDP CRow CTom ELan EPar EPot ESis LGan MBar MPit NMen NNrd NRoo NWCA SBla SSou WHer WHoo WOld WPer
– 'Albus'	CHal CMer CNic CRDP CRiv CRow CTom ECha ELan LGan NNrd SBla SHer SSou WHoo WMar WPer

MECONOPSIS † (Papaveraceae)

aculeata	GCra GTou NTow
baileyi	See M. *betonicifolia*
x *beamishii*	CNic GGar NHar NRoo
§ *betonicifolia*	Widely available
– *alba*	CB&S CCla CSam EBre EFou ELan EPot GArf GCra LBre MBal MBri NHar NHol NLin NRoo SBla SPer SSpi
– 'Glacier Blue'	NHol
cambrica	CCla CGle CKin CMea CNic CRDP CRow EBar EJud ELan EMar GTou MPar MPit NCat NGre NHol NLan NMir SIng WAbe WBon WCru WHal WHer WPer
– var. *aurantiaca*	ELan EMon NBir WBon WPer
– *flore-pleno*	CGle CRDP CRow ECha EMon EPar ESma MFir MTho NBro NCat NVic WBon WOMN
¶ – 'Frances Perry'	CRDP ESma IBlr WCru
chelidoniifolia	EBre LBre NHol SSpi WCru
dhwojii	CB&S GCra NBir NHar NTow WDav
¶ – C&Mc 531	GTou
grandis	CB&S CCla CElw CGle CMea CNic EPot ESma GArf GCra MBri NHar NLin NRoo SBla SIgm SSpi WCru WEas
– GS 600	NBir NWCA
– PS&W 5423	GDra
horridula	CNic CSam ELan EPot GAbr GCra MBri MTho NKay WCot
– CLD 1070	NHol
– CLD 1202	NHol
integrifolia	GCra GDra
¶ Kingsbarns hybrids	GArf
napaulensis	CB&S CNic CRiv ELan EPot GArf GDra MBal MBri NCat NHar NKay NRoo NVic WCru WHal WThu WWin
– C&Mc 282	WDav
– forms	GArf NHar WDav
– red form	CRiv NBir NWCA WDav
¶ – Wallich's form	GCra NHar
nudicaulis	See PAPAVER *nudicaule*
paniculata	GDra NBir NLin
– C&Mc 127	GTou WDav
– C&Mc 296	WDav
quintuplinervia	CBos EBre GArf GDra LBre NBir NRoo NRya SBla WHal
regia	CB&S CBot ELan GAbr GArf GCra NHar NHol NRoo SIgm WDav WPer
¶ – hybrids	CAbP
x *sarsonsii*	CNic GAbr NBir NRoo
x *sheldonii*	MFir NBir NHar NLin NRoo NVic SSpi WOld
– 'Branklyn'	GAbr IBlr
– Crewdson hybrids	EPot GArf GDra MBri WEas
– 'Ormswell'	GArf NKay SRms
– 'Slieve Donard'	EBre GDra GGar IBlr LBre MUlv NHar
simplicifolia	NGre
sp. CLD 704	NHol
superba	CB&S GCra MBal NHar NRoo SIgm
villosa	CSam GArf GTou IBlr NBir SIgm

MEDEOLA (Liliaceae/Convallariaceae)

virginica	CRDP LAma WChr WCru WThi

MEDICAGO (Leguminosae)
arborea CPle ELan IBlr WHer
echinus See M. ***intertexta***
sativa CKin WHer
– ssp. *sativa* IBlr

MEDINILLA (Melastomataceae)
magnifica MBri

MEDLAR See **MESPILUS** ***germanica***

MEEHANIA (Labiatae)
urticifolia EMon MBel MPar WCot

MEGACARPAEA (Cruciferae)
polyandra GDra

MELALEUCA (Myrtaceae)
¶ *acuminata* CB&S
armillaris CPle CTre
capitata ISea
decussata ECou
erubescens See M. ***diosmatifolia***
gibbosa CB&S CPle CTre GCal
hypericifolia CGre CMer ECou GWht
pauciflora See M. ***biconvexa***
pulchella CSun LBlm WThi
¶ *pustulata* ECou
¶ *rosmarinifolia* ECou
squamea ECou GWht
squarrosa GWht
¶ *thymifolia* CB&S
viridiflora CB&S

MELANDRIUM See **SILENE**

MELANOSELINUM (Umbelliferae)
decipiens CHEx

MELANTHIUM (Liliaceae/Melanthiaceae)
virginicum NSal

MELASPHAERULA (Iridaceae)
graminea See M. ***ramosa***
§ *ramosa* CAvo CMon ELan NRog WThi

MELIA (Meliaceae)
§ *azedarach* CB&S CPle SLMG
– var. *japonica* See M. ***azedarach***

MELIANTHUS (Melianthaceae)
major CB&S CBot CChu CCla CHEx CHad CHan CTro ECha ECro EFou EHoe EPla ERav LAbb LGre LHil NWyt SArc SBla SChu SDix SMad SPer SSpi WHal
minor CHEx SChu SMad

MELICA (Gramineae)
altissima ETPC
– 'Atropurpurea' CDec CElw CHan CSun ECha EHoe EMon EPla ESis ETPC LBlm MPar NSti WCot WPer
ciliata CElw CSam EHoe EMon EPla ETPC GCHN WPer
¶ – bronze form ETPC
¶ – ssp. *magnolii* ETPC
¶ – *taurica* ETPC
macra EHoe ETPC
* *minima* ETPC
nutans CElw EHoe EMon EPla ETPC NLan WHal
picta ETPC
subulata ETPC
transsilvanica EHoe ETPC
¶ – 'Atropurpurea' ETPC
uniflora CKin
– f. *albida* EMon EPla ETPC
– 'Variegata' CBre EHoe EMon EPla ETPC SApp SSpi WCot

MELICOPE (Rutaceae)
ternata ECou

MELICYTUS (Violaceae)
alpinus ECou MFos
angustifolius ECou MHig SDry
crassifolius CBot CChu CPle CTre ECou EMon NHol WHCG WSHC
obovatus ECou
ramiflorus CPle ECou

MELILOTUS (Leguminosae)
¶ *altissima* NMir
officinalis CArn CKin CSFH Effi GPoy LHol MChe MHew SIde WHer WNdy
¶ – *albus* MHew

MELINIS (Gramineae)
repens EHoe

MELIOSMA (Meliosmaceae)
§ *dilleniifolia* ssp. *flexuosa* WBod
– ssp. *tenuis* WCoo
myriantha WCoo
pendens See M. ***dilleniifolia flexuosa***
veitchiorum CB&S CHEx

MELISSA (Labiatae)
officinalis CArn CBow CHal CSFH CTom EJud Effi GPoy LHol MBal MBar MBri MChe MHew MPar MPit NSel SIde WEas WOak WPer WWye
– 'All Gold' CHal CLew CMea CRiv CSev ECha EFou EHoe EJud ELan EMon LHol MBri MChe NFai NHol NRoo NSti SHer SSpi WEas WWye
§ – 'Aurea' (v) Widely available
N– 'Variegata' See M. ***o.*** 'Aurea'

MELITTIS (Labiatae)
melissophyllum ECha MHew SIng SRms SSpi
– ssp. *albida* SSpi
– pink form EMon

MENISPERMUM (Menispermaceae)
¶ *canadense* GPoy LAbb SHBN

MENTHA † (Labiatae)	
aquatica	CBen CKin CRDP CRow CWGN EBre EHon EJud EWav GAbr GPoy LBre LMay MChe MSta NSal NSel SHer SWat WChe WHer WHol WOak
arvensis	CArn CKin MHew NSal SIde WHer
asiatica	SIde
¶***cervina***	MSta WChe
citrata	See M. x ***piperata c.***
cordifolia	See M. x ***villosa***
****corsica***	CTom
'Eau de Cologne'	See M. x ***piperita citrata***
♦x ***gentilis***	See M. x ***gracilis***
§ x ***gracilis***	CArn CBow CHun EOrc Effi LHol MChe NDea NOak NSel SHer SIde WOak WSun WWye
– 'Aurea'	See M. x ***g.*** **'Variegata'**
§ – 'Variegata'	CDec CFis CGle CHal CPar CSFH CSev CTom CWGN ECha EHoe ELan EPar ESma GPoy ILis MBal MFir NFai NNor NRar NRoo NSal NSti WEas WHal WHer WOak WPer
Lavender Mint	CBre NFai
§ ***longifolia***	CCor CFis CGle CHal CHun ECha ELan EMar EOrc ESma LHop NSti SAxl WEas WHer WOak WPer WWye
¶ – Buddleia Mint Group	GAbr
*– 'Variegata'	NCat NSti
§ x ***piperita citrata***	CArn CBre CFis CGle CHal CSFH ECha Effi GAbr GPoy LHol MBri MChe MFir NFai NSal NSel NSti SIde WEas WOak WPer
– 'Lemon'	GAbr MBri SIde WPer
x ***piperita***	CArn CRiv CSFH CSev ECha EHoe EJud Effi GPoy ILis MBri MChe MHew MPit NNor NOak NRoo NSal NSel WHal WOak WPer WWye
pulegium	CArn CRDP CRiv CRow CSFH CSev CWGN EBar ECha EJud EPar Effi GPoy LHol MChe MHew MPit NOak NSal SHer SIde WHer WOak WPer WWye
¶ – Greek form	WHer
– 'Upright'	MWil WPer
requienii	Widely available
rotundifolia hort.	See M. ***suaveolens***
– 'Bowles'	See M. x ***villosa alopecuroïdes***
rubra raripila	See M. x ***smithiana***
§ x ***smithiana***	CArn CHal CHun EJud GAbr GPoy ILis MChe NFai SIde WChe WHer WPer WWye
– 'Capel Ulo'	WHer
§ ***spicata***	CArn CHal CRDP CSFH CSev CTom ELan Effi GPoy ILis LHol MBal MBri MChe MHew MPit NFai NNor NRoo NSel SHer WEas WHal WHer WOak WWye
– 'Crispa'	CBre EMon GAbr NFai NSel
– 'Moroccan'	CArn CHun CSev GAbr SHer SIde WHer WOak WPer WWye
sp. Nile Valley Mint	CArn
§ ***suaveolens***	CArn CFis CHal CRDP CSFH CWGN EJud ESma Effi GPoy ILis LHol MBal MBri MFir MPar MPit NRoo NSel SHer WHal WHer WOak WPer WWye
§ – 'Variegata'	CArn CDec CGle CNic CRow CSFH CShe CWGN EBar ECha EFol EHoe EOrc EPar Effi GAbr MBal MBri MChe NFai NNor NSel SIng WEas WHer WOak WPer
sylvestris	See M. ***longifolia***
§ x ***villosa alopcuroïdes*** Bowles' Mint	CBre CHal GPoy ILis LHol MChe NFai NRar SHer SIde WEas WHer WOak WPer
– 'Cae Rhos Lligwy' (v)	WHer
viridis	See M. ***spicata***

MENYANTHES (Menyanthaceae)	
trifoliata	CBen CNic CRDP CRiv CRow CWGN EBre ECha EHon EMFW EWav GPoy LBre LMay MSta NDea SLon WChe WHol WOak WWye

MENZIESIA (Ericaceae)	
alba	See DABOECIA ***cantabrica alba***
ciliicalyx	MBlu
– dwarf form	CNic ECar
– ***lasiophylla***	See M. ***c. purpurea***
– var. ***multiflora***	GDra GGGa MBal NHar WThu
§ – var. ***purpurea***	GDra GGGa MBal SHil WBod
ferruginea	MBal
polifolia	See DABOECIA ***cantabrica***

MERCURIALIS (Euphorbiaceae)	
perennis	CKin CNat GPoy

MERENDERA (Liliaceae/Colchicaceae)	
attica	LBow WChr
¶ – S&L 451	CMon
eichleri	See M. ***trigyna***
¶***filifolia*** AB&S 4665	CMon
hissarica	WChr
kurdica	EPot LAma
montana	WMar
¶ – MS 900/913	CMon
¶ – SF 221	CMon
nivalis	WChr
♦***raddeana***	See M. ***trigyna***
sobolifera	EPot WChr WThu
¶ – BSBE 806	CMon
§ ***trigyna***	EPot LAma WChr

MERREMIA (Convolvulaceae)	
§ ***tuberosa***	MNew

MERTENSIA (Boraginaceae)	
ciliata	CHan EBre EFol ELan EOrc LBre MRav MTol SPer
echioïdes	NTow SRms WCru
franciscana	GCal
maritima	EPad GPoy NTow NWCA WCru WOMN WWin
♦– ssp. ***asiatica***	See M. ***simplicissima***
primuloïdes	CHad CRDP WCru
♦***pterocarpa***	See M. ***sibirica***
§ ***pulmonarioïdes***	CBot CBro CGle CHad CPar CRDP CRiv EFol ELan EPot GDra LAma LHop MTho NHol WByw WCru WWat

§ ***sibirica*** CCMG CRDP EPot GArf GCal LGre NKay SAxl
¶ ***simplicissima*** CBos CBot CCMG CHad CHan COtt CRDP CSun EBre ELan GCal LAbb LBee LBre LGre MMil MPit MTho NBir NGre NWCA SBla SMad SMrm SPer SWas WAbe WCru WHoo WOMN
virginica See M. ***pulmonarioïdes***

MERYTA (Araliaceae)
sinclairii CHEx
§ – 'Moonlight' (v) CHEx
– 'Variegata' See M. *s.* 'Moonlight'

MESEMBRYANTHEMUM (Aizoaceae)
'Basutoland' See DELOSPERMA ***nubigenum***
brownii See LAMPRANTHUS ***brownii***
ornatulum See DELOSPERMA ***ornatulum***
putterilii See RUSCHIA ***p.***

MESPILUS (Rosaceae)
F ***germanica*** CB&S CBow CBra CDoC CLnd ELan IJoh IOrc LHol MWat SHBN WDin WMou
F – 'Autumn Blaze' SFru
¶ – 'Breda Giant' GTwe
F – 'Dutch' SDea SKee
F – 'Large Russian' ERea ESim SKee
F – 'Monstrous' GTwe SDea
F – 'Nottingham' CBow CDoC CWSG EHar ERea ESim EWar GChr GTwe LBuc MBea MMor NBee SDea SFru SHil SKee SPer WHig WMou
F – 'Royal' SFru
F – 'Westerveld' CMac

METAPANAX See **PSEUDOPANAX**

METASEQUOIA (Taxodiaceae)
glyptostroboïdes Widely available
– 'Fastigiata' See M. *g.* 'National'
* – 'Green Mantle' EHul
§ – 'National' CSam
– 'Sheridan Spire' CB&S LNet SSpi
– 'Waasland' WMou

METROSIDEROS (Myrtaceae)
carmineus CHEx
– 'Carousel' ERea
– 'Ferris Wheel' ERea
excelsus CAbb CB&S CHEx ECou
– 'Aureus' ECou
– 'Scarlet Pimpernel' SLon
fulgens ECou
'Goldfinger' ERea
kermadecensis CTro ECou
– 'Variegatus' CSun CTro ECou ERea LGre LHop
lucidus See M. ***umbellatus***
'Mistral' CB&S
robustus CHEx ISea
§ ***umbellatus*** CGre CHEx ECou

MEUM (Umbelliferae)
athamanticum CLew COtt CRDP EBre EFou EGol EPla GCal GPoy LBre LHop MHew MTho MUlv NRoo SMrm WPer

MIBORA (Gramineae)
mimima SIng

MICHAUXIA (Campanulaceae)
campanuloïdes EPad ESma LRHS SMrm SUsu
laevigata EPad
tchihatchewii CBot CPou ECro EPad ESma SMrm

MICHELIA (Magnoliaceae)
¶ ***compressa*** CGre
¶ ***crassipes*** LTil
doltsopa CB&S CGre CHEx SHil SSpi WBod
– 'Silver Cloud' CB&S
figo CB&S CBow CGre ERea
¶ 'Touch of Pink' LTil

MICRANTHUS (Iridaceae)
alopecuroïdes NRog

MICROBIOTA (Cupressaceae)
decussata CDoC CKen CMHG CMac CSut EBar EBre EHar EHul ENHC EPla EPot ESis GRei IBar LBee LBre LCon LLin MBar MBri MGos MWat NHol SIng SLon SSmi WBod WWat
¶ – 'Trompenburg' CKen

MICROCACHRYS (Podocarpaceae)
tetragona ECar ECou EPla ESis LCon SIng

MICROCOELUM See **LYTOCARYUM**

MICROGLOSSA (Compositae)
albescens See ASTER ***albescens***

MICROLEPIA (Dennstaedtiaceae)
speluncae MBri

MICROMERIA (Labiatae)
corsica See ACINOS ***corsicus***
rupestris See M. ***thymifolia***
§ ***thymifolia*** MPla
varia ELan MCas

MICROSERIS (Compositae)
¶ ***rigens*** CRDP EBre LBre
¶ ***ringens*** 'Girandale' WPer

MICROSORUM (Polypodiaceae)
diversifolium CHEx EBul SArc

MICROSTROBOS (Podocarpaceae)
fitzgeraldii CKen
niphophilus WThu

MIKANIA (Compositae)

dentata	MBri
scandens	NSal
ternata	See M. *dentata*

MILIUM (Gramineae)

effusum	CKin NNrd
– 'Aureum'	Widely available

MILLIGANIA (Liliaceae/Asteliaceae)

See Plant Deletions

MIMOSA (Leguminosae)

See Plant Deletions

MIMULUS (Scrophulariaceae)

'A T Johnson'	CKel GCHN MBel NVic SIng
§ 'Andean Nymph' (ex Mac&W 5257)	CMea CPar EBre EFol ELan EPot ESis GCHN GTou LBre MBal MFir MFos MSte NKay NNrd NRed SHer SIng WAbe WCla WOMN
'Andean Nymph' forms	CGle CRDP NTow
§ *aurantiacus*	Widely available
§ – var. *puniceus*	CBot CBrk CCla CGre CHal CPle CRDP CTro LHil LHop NNrd SDry SIng SLMG SMrm SUsu WEas WOMN WPer
x *bartonianus*	CCla CRow ELun NVic
'Bees' Scarlet'	NFai WPer
bifidus	CRDP LGre LHop SMrm SWas
¶ – 'Verity Buff'	LHil
boydii	NKay WPer
'Burgess'	CBen
x *burnetii*	CGle CKel CNic CRow LMay MFir NVic SRms
¶ *californicus*	CHan
Calypso hybrids	NNrd SRms
cardinalis	CDoC CHal CPar CRDP CRow CWGN EHon ELan LHop MFir MNFA MTho NCat NDea NHol NNor SIng SPer WPer
cupreus	CRow MBal
– 'Minor'	LBee
– 'Whitecroft Scarlet'	CBen CWGN EBre ECha ELan EPot GDra GTou LBre LMay NGre NHar NNrd SBod SHer WPer WWin
'Doreen's Delight'	SIng
glutinosus	See M. *aurantiacus*
– *atrosanguineus*	See M. *aurantiacus puniceus*
– *luteus*	See M. *aurantiacus*
§ *guttatus*	CBen CKin CRDP CRow EBre GAbr LBre MFir NHol NKay NRar SIng WChe WPer
¶ – variegated	WCot
'Highland Orange'	CBow GCHN MBel NHar NMen WPer
'Highland Pink'	ECtt ESis LBee NHar NNrd NRoo SBod WPer
'Highland Red'	CGle CHun ECtt ESis GCHN GDra LBee MBar MBel MPit NHol NMen NNrd NRed SHer WHal WPat WPer WWin
'Highland Yellow'	CGle CRiv ECtt GCHN LBee MPit NMen NRoo SBod SHer WHal WPat WPer
hose in hose	CMer CRow ECha GCal LGan MTho NCat NDea NFai WHer WPer
'Inshriach Crimson'	GAri GCHN GDra
langsdorffii	See M. *guttatus*
lewisii	CNic CRDP CRiv CSun ELan GDra GTou LGan MSte MTho NHol NOak NWCA SFis SMrm WHal WHoo WOMN WPer
longiflorus	CBot LGre LHil WCot
luteus	CBen CMer CRiv CRow CWGN ECha EHon LMay MBal MSta NDea NFai NNor WByw WChe WCru WHal
'Magnifique'	SIng WHal
* 'Major Bees'	CDoC GCal
'Malibu'	NFai NNor NNrd NRoo
'Malibu Ivory'	NFai NRoo
¶ 'Malibu Red'	CBow
'Mandarin'	EBre LBre NNrd
moschatus	CHal CRDP CRiv CRow CSam NCat NKay NMen WCla WCru WEas WHal
'Old Rose'	CMGP ECha
'Orange Glow'	WHal
'Plymtree'	CGle CNic NKay NNrd WPer
primuloïdes	CRDP ELan EPot GCHN LBee MBar MFos MPit MTho NGre NHar NHol NMen NTow NWCA SBod SFis SHer SIng WAbe WHal WOMN WPer WWin
¶ 'Puck'	GCal LBee
'Quetzalcoatl'	LGre SMrm
ringens	CBen CDoC CRDP CRiv CRow CWGN EBar EBre EHon EMFW LBre LMay MSta NDea NHol SWas WBon WChe WHal WHol WPer
'Roter Kaiser' ('Red Emperor')	SRms WHil
sp. CW 5233	NTow
sp. JCA 64	NNrd
sp. Mac&W 5257	See M. 'Andean Nymph'
tilingii	CHal SMrm
– var. *caespitosus*	NGre NTow
¶ Verity hybrids	ERea
¶ 'Western Hills'	NRar WCru
'Wisley Red'	CKel CPar ECha ELan SFis SHer SIng

MINA See IPOMOEA

MINUARTIA (Caryophyllaceae)

biflora	NHol
§ *circassica*	ESis MDHE MHig NTow NWCA WCru WDav WPer
juniperina NS 270	NWCA
¶ *obtusiloba*	WDav
parnassica	See M. *stellata*
§ *stellata*	EPot NHol NMen NNrd NTow SIng
§ *verna*	CLew EMNN MCas NHar NHol NMen NNrd WOMN WPer
– ssp. *caespitosa* 'Aurea'	See SAGINA *subulata* 'A.'
– ssp. *gerardii*	See M. *verna verna*
¶ – ssp. *verna*	SIng

MIRABILIS (Nyctaginaceae)

jalapa	CArn ECro LAbb LAma MBri NRog SLMG WCru

MISCANTHUS (Gramineae)

floridulus	EHoe SAxl SDix SMad WCot
oligostachyus	CElw
sacchariflorus	CB&S CHEx CRow CWGN EBre ECha ELan EPla LBre LMay MUlv NHol NJap NVic SCob SHig SPer SSpi WBod WWat WWye
sinensis	CHEx
– 'Cabaret' (v)	SApp
– var. *condensatus*	EFou ETPC
– dwarf form	MUlv
– 'Ferne Osten'	ECha EPla
– 'Goldfeder' (v)	EBre LBre
– 'Goliath'	EFou
– 'Gracillimus'	CB&S CDoC CHEx CRow CWGN EBre ECha EFou ELan ENot EPla ETPC LBre MBal MBri MRav NBro NHol SAxl SCob SDix SPer SSpi WHer
– 'Graziella'	EFou EPla SApp
– 'Grosse Fontäne'	ECha EFou EPla WCot
– 'Hercules'	EFou
– 'Kascade'	EPla
– 'Kleine Fontäne'	EBre EPla LBre SApp SWas
– 'Kleine Silberspinne'	CRow EFou EHoe EPla ETPC SApp SAxl
– 'Malepartus'	CRow EBre ECha EPla LBre SAxl
– 'Morning Light' (v)	EBre EPla ETPC LBre SApp
– 'Nippon'	EFou EHoe EPla SApp
– 'Punktchen' (v)	EPla
– var. *purpurascens*	CRDP EBlo EBre ECha EGol EHoe EPla ETPC GAri LBre MUlv SCob SSpi WHal
– 'Rotsilber' (v)	ECha EFou EHoe EPla
– 'Silberfeder' ('Silver Feather')	CCla CDoC CRow EBlo EBre ECha EFou EHoe ELan EPla ETPC LBre MBri MUlv NHol NVic SAxl SCob SDix SMad SPer SSpi SWat WCot WHal WWat
– 'Silberpfeil' (v)	EPla ETPC SMad
– 'Silberspinne'	EFou EPla ETPC SApp
– 'Sirene'	SMad
– 'Slavopour'	EPla
– 'Spatgrun'	EPla
– 'Strictus' (v)	ECha EPla MBri SDix WCot
– 'Undine'	ECha EHoe EPla ETPC
– 'Variegatus'	CHEx CHad CRow EBlo EBre ECha EFou EGol EHoe ENot ETPC GCal LBre LHil MBal MSta MUlv NBee NHol NJap NMir NRoo SApp SAxl SCob SDix SMad SPer WWat
– 'Zebrinus' (v)	Widely available
sp. ex Yakushima	EPla
* *tinctorius* 'Nanus Variegatus'	CRow EHoe EPla SApp
yakushimensis	CLew ECha EHoe EPla ETPC SApp

MISOPATES (Scrophulariaceae)

orontium	WCla

MITCHELLA (Rubiaceae)

repens	ECar MHig NSal WCru WWat

MITELLA (Saxifragaceae)

breweri	CGle CHal CLew CNic CRDP CTom CWGN ECha ECro EFol ELan ELun ESis GCal MFir MSte NHol NKay NSti SSpi SUsu WByw WCru WEas WOMN WPer WWat WWin
caulescens	ECar ECha ECro EFol NCat NHol NSti SFis
diphylla	LGro
stauropetala	MFir NCat

MITRARIA (Gesneriaceae)

coccinea	Widely available
¶ – 'Lake Caburgua'	GCal
– Lake Puye form	CGre CHan GCal LHil LHop SSpi WCru

MITRIOSTIGMA (Rubiaceae)

¶ *axillare*	MNew

MNIUM See PLAGIOMNIUM

MOEHRINGIA (Caryophyllaceae)

¶ *glaucovirens*	MHig

MOLINIA (Gramineae)

altissima	See M. ***caerulea arundinacea***
caerulea	CLew
§ – ssp. *arundinacea*	ECha EFou EPla ETPC SPer
– – 'Bergfreund'	EMon EPla ETPC GCal
– – 'Fontäne'	ETPC GCal
– – 'Karl Foerster'	EFou EHoe EPla GCal
– – 'Strahlenquelle'	EMon EPla ETPC GCal
– – 'Transparent'	ETPC GCal
– – 'Windspiel '	ECha EHoe EPla ETPC GCal NHol WCot
¶ – – 'Zuneigung'	ETPC
¶ – ssp. *caerulea* 'Edith Dudszus'	EMon
– – 'Heidebraut' (v)	ECha EHoe EMon EPla ETPC NHol
– – 'Moorhexe'	ECha EHoe EMon EPla GCal
– – 'Variegata'	Widely available
– 'Carmarthen'	CNat
¶ – 'Claerwen'	GCal
– 'Edith Dudszus'	ETPC
♦ *litoralis*	See M. ***caerulea arundinacea***

MOLOPOSPERMUM (Umbelliferae)

¶ *peloponnesiacum*	LGre

MOLTKIA (Boraginaceae)

§ *doerfleri*	CPle CSco
graminifolia	See M. ***suffruticosa***
§ x *intermedia*	CNic ELan MWat NKay SIgm WOld WWin
petraea	ECha MWat SIgm WHil
§ *suffruticosa*	LBee WHil

MONADENIUM (Euphorbiaceae)

lugardae	MBri
¶ *ritchiei*	SGil
'Variegatum'	MBri

MONARDA † (Labiatae)

'Adam' CDoC CSco ECED EFol GAbr GCal MBri MSte NTow
'Aquarius' CGle ECha EFou EMon LRHS MNFA WCHb
'Beauty of Cobham' CCla CGle CHad CHan ECha EFou EOrc MBri MRav MSte MUlv MWat NFai NHol NOak NRoo NSti SChu SHer SMrm SPer WMer WRus
'Blaukranz' EFou
'Blaustrumpf' ('Blue Stocking') CAbb CElw CSco EBre EFou LBre MSte NHol NOrc SHer SMrm SPer WMer WSun
bradburyana EMon LRHS SFis
'Cambridge Scarlet' Widely available
'Capricorn' CGle EFou EMon LRHS WCHb
¶ 'Cherokee' EFou EMon
citriodora CArn CRDP EEls EMon GPoy LHol MChe MWat NSal SHer SIde WPer WWye
¶ 'Commanche' EMon
'Croftway Pink' Widely available
'Dark Ponticum' EMon LRHS
didyma CArn CHan CSFH Effi IEde LHol MChe MFir NBee NSal NSel SIde WGwy WHoo WOak WOld WSun WTyr
– 'Alba' EOrc GAbr LGan WDav WWat
¶ – 'Duddiscombe' CSam
'Elsie's Lavender' EFou EMon
'Feuernschopf' ('Firecrown') CGle EBre EFou LBre MSte
fistulosa CArn ECro EJud GPoy LHol MChe NSal SIde WHer WPer WWye
'Hartswood Wine' CSun LBlm
'Kardinal' CGle ECha EFou SMrm
'Libra' EMon LRHS WCHb
'Loddon Crown' CBre CRDP EFou EMon LRHS
'Mahogany' CDoC CMGP CSam EFou EMon LHop MMil NHol NSti SPer
'Maiden's Pride' EMon
'Meerswogen' SAxl
I 'Melissa' CGle EFou MMil
¶ ***menthifolia*** GCal LGre
¶ 'Mohawk' EFou EMon SMrm
'Morgenröte' ECha SAxl
'Mrs Perry' EFou
'Ou Charm' EMon LRHS WCHb
'Pale Ponticum' EMon LRHS
'Panorama' CFis ECtt GAbr GCra LGan MBal NFai NRoo NSal SGil WPer WTyr
¶ 'Pawnee' EMon
'Pink Tourmalin' MBri SMad
'Pisces' ('Fishes') CGle ECha EFol EFou EHal EMon GCal MNFA MSte SMrm WCHb
'Poyntzfield Pink' GPoy SChu
'Präriebrand' SUsu
'Prärienacht' ('Prairie Night') CBre CGle CPar CSam CSev EBre ECha EFol ELan Effi LBre MBri MFir MRav MWat NHol NKay NRoo NVic SChu SGil SPer WEas WHil WMer WOld WPer WRus WWin
punctata CArn CGle CHad CRDP ECro ELan EMon LGan LGre LHil NSal SIde WCHb WCot WWye
'Sagittarius' ('Bowman') EMon LRHS WCHb
§ 'Schneewittchen' ('Snow White') CCla CSev EBre ECED ECha ECtt EGol ELan EMon EOrc LBre LHop MRav NFai NHol NOrc NRoo NSti SChu SMrm SPer WEas WMer WPer WRus WWin
'Scorpio' ('Scorpion') CGle EFou EMon LRHS MSte WCHb
¶ 'Sioux' EMon
'Snow Maiden' See M. 'Schneewittchen'
¶ 'Snow Queen' EFou
'Squaw' CGle CHan ECha EFou EMon SUsu WCot
stipitatoglandulosa ECro
'Talud' CGle EFou EMon
'Thundercloud' EMon
¶ 'Twins' SAxl WMer
'Vintage Wine' ECtt ELan EMon SMad

MONARDELLA (Labiatae)

macrantha LGre LRHS MTho SMrm
villosa LGan
– 'Sheltonii' EOrc WPer

MONOTOCA (Epacridaceae)

¶ ***glauca*** GWht

MONSONIA (Geraniaceae)

emarginata GCHN
¶ ***speciosa*** CMon MHul

MONSTERA (Araceae)

deliciosa CHal MBri SRms
– 'Variegata' MBri SRms

MONTBRETIA See CROCOSMIA, TRITONIA

MONTIA (Portulacaceae)

australasica See NEOPAXIA ***a.***
californica ELan EMar
parvifolia See CLAYTONIA ***parvifolia***
perfoliata See CLAYTONIA ***p.***
sibirica See CLAYTONIA ***s.***

MORAEA (Iridaceae)

§ ***aristata*** LBow NRog
§ ***bellendenii*** LBow
¶ ***fugax*** CMon
gawleri CMon WThi
glaucopsis See M. ***aristata***
¶ ***huttonii*** CHan
iridioïdes See DIETES ***i.***
loubseri CMon NRog
¶ ***natalensis*** ESma
¶ ***papilionacea*** WThi
pavonia var. ***lutea*** See M. ***bellendenii***
polystachya NRog WThi
ramosissima CGre LBow WThi
robusta CD&R 269 SWas
spathacea See M. ***spathulata***
§ ***spathulata*** CBro CCla CGre CHan CMon GAbr GCal MFir MHig SBla
¶ sp. SH 53 CHan
¶ ***stricta*** WThi
¶ ***tripetala*** WThi

vegeta	WThi
villosa	LBow NRog

MORINA (Morinaceae)

alba	See ACANTHOCALYX ***a.***
longifolia	CBot CChu CCla CDec CFis CGle CPar ECha ELan EOrc LGan LGre MBri MFir NHol NTow SAxl SFis SHig SIgm SSpi SUsu WDav WEas WOld WPer WRus WWye
persica	CChu ECro

MORISIA (Cruciferae)

hypogaea	See M. ***monanthos***
§ *monanthos*	CLew EPad LBee MCas MFir MFos MHig NMen NNrd NTow NWCA
– 'Fred Hemingway'	EBre ECar EPot LBee LBre NHar NHol NMen NNrd SBla SHer SUsu WAbe

MORUS (Moraceae)

§ *alba*	CB&S CBow CBra CChu CHEx CLnd EHal EHar ELan ERea GTwe IOrc LTil SHBN SPer WCoo WDin WMou WWat
¶ – 'Black Tabor'	LPan
– 'Globosa'	See M. ***a.*** 'Nana'
¶ – 'Laciniata'	WMou
¶ – 'Macrophylla'	WMou
– var. ***multicaulis***	ERea
– 'Pendula'	CBow CDoC CSco ELan ERea GTwe LHol LNet LPan MBri MWat NBee SEng SHBN SHil SPer WDin
♦ ***bombycis***	See M. ***alba***
F ***nigra***	Widely available
F – 'Chelsea'	EHar ERea
¶ – 'King James'	GTwe WHig
F – 'Wellington'	CDoC LPan WDin
platanifolia	MBri SEng
rubra	CBow
– x ***alba*** 'Illinois Everbearing'	ESim

MUEHLENBECKIA (Polygonaceae)

astonii	ECou ISea LGre
§ *axillaris*	CPle ECou EFol EPla GAri IBar MUlv NCat NHol NTow SDry SHil WCru
complexa	CB&S CDoC CGre CHEx CHal CHan CPle CSun ECou EFol EPla ESis ESma IBlr ISea LBlm MUlv NFai NRar SArc SBra SDry SMad WCru WSHC WWat WWye
– 'Nana'	See M. ***axillaris***
– var. ***trilobata***	GCal IBlr
ephedroïdes	ECou
– 'Clarence Pass'	ECou
– prostrate form	ECou
gunnii	ECou
♦ ***platyclada***	See HOMALOCLADIUM ***platycladum***

MUHLENBERGIA (Gramineae)

japonica 'Cream Delight' (v)	EHoe

MUKDENIA (Saxifragaceae)

§ *rossii*	CChu CRDP ECar ECro EPla SSpi WCot WOld WSHC

MULBERRY See **MORUS *nigra***

MUNDULEA (Leguminosae)

¶ *sericea*	CTro

MURBECKIELLA (Cruciferae)

pinnatifida	MPlt

MURRAYA (Rutaceae)

paniculata	MNew

MUSA (Musaceae)

F ***acuminata***	LPal MBri
basjoo	CB&S CHEx SArc
cavendishii	See M. ***acuminata*** (AAA Group) 'Dwarf Cavendish'
ensete	See ENSETE ***ventricosum***
nana	See M. ***acuminata***

MUSCARI † (Liliaceae/Hyacinthaceae)

ambrosiacum	See M. ***muscarimi***
armeniacum	CBro EPar ETub LBow LRHS MBri NRog WPer
– 'Argael Album'	CAvo LAma NEgg
– 'Blue Pearl'	LBlo
– 'Blue Spike'	CBro EPar LAma LBlo LBow MBri NEgg NRog SIng WBod WPer
– 'Early Giant'	LAma SIng
– 'Heavenly Blue'	LAma LBlo
¶ – 'New Creation'	ETub SGil
– 'Saffier'	ETub LAma
§ *aucheri*	CAvo CBro CNic LAma LBlo NRog SIng WThu
§ *azureum*	CAvo CBro CNic CRDP ELan LAma LBlo NRog WAbe WHil
– 'Album'	CAvo CBro EPar ETub LAma NRog WAbe
¶ – 'Amphibolis'	ETub
botryoïdes	LAma NRog
– 'Album'	CAvo CBro ELan ETub LAma LBlo LBow MBri NRog SIng
caucasicum	WChr
chalusicum BSBE	See M. ***pseudomuscari*** BSBE
§ *comosum*	CAvo CBro EPar LBow WPer
– 'Monstrosum'	See M. ***c.*** 'Plumosum'
§ – 'Plumosum'	CAvo CBro CRDP ELan EMon EPar ETub LAma LBow MBri SIng SUsu
'Dark Eyes'	WChr
¶ ***grandifolium populeum*** AB&S 5357	CMon
¶ ***inconstrictum*** S&L 19/20	CMon
latifolium	CAvo CBow CBro CMon ETub LAma NRog SUsu WPer
§ *macrocarpum*	CAvo CBro EPot LAma LBow SPou WChr WThu
moschatum	See M. ***muscarimi***
§ *muscarimi*	CAvo CBro EPar ETub LAma LBow NHol SIng WChr
♦ – ***flavum***	See M. ***macrocarpum***
– 'Major'	LBow

§ *neglectum* ELan ETub LAma SIng WShi
¶ – B&S 349 CMon
¶ *pallens* CMon
paradoxum See BELLEVALIA ***pycnantha***
§ *pseudomuscari* BSBE CMon WChr
racemosum See M. ***neglectum***
'Sky Blue' WChr
¶ *spreitzenhoferi* MS 712 CMon
¶ *tenuiflorum* S&L 91 CMon
tubergenianum See M. ***aucheri***
'White Beauty' WChr

MUSCARIMIA (Liliaceae/Hyacinthaceae)

ambrosiacum See MUSCARI ***muscarimi***
macrocarpum See MUSCARI ***macrocarpum***

MUSSCHIA (Campanulaceae)

aurea CHEx
wollastonii CHEx SIgm

MUTISIA (Compositae)

clematis CGre
coccinea EOvi
decurrens CB&S CHEx EOvi
ilicifolia CBow CMac EOvi IBlr SDry WMar WSHC
oligodon CGre CHEx CHan EOvi IBlr SBla
retusa See M. ***spinosa pulchella***
¶ *spinosa* CGre
§ – *pulchella* EOvi

MYOPORUM (Myoporaceae)

♦ *acuminatum* See M. ***tenuifolium***
debile ECou
laetum CHEx CPle CTre ECou
§ *tenuifolium* CPle

MYOSOTIDIUM (Boraginaceae)

§ *hortensia* CB&S CBos CHEx CPla CRDP IBlr LHop SHer SIgm WCru
nobile See M. ***hortensia***

MYOSOTIS (Boraginaceae)

alpestris 'Ruth Fischer' NMen NNrd
australis GGar NHol NMen NNrd WEas
colensoi ECou ELan EMon EPot MHig MTho NHol NKay NNrd NWCA SCro WAbe
elderi CBot
explanata NMen NNrd NTow SHer WEas
palustris See M. ***scorpioïdes***
'Popsy' ECar ECou
rakiura EMar WCla WPer
rehsteineri SIng
rupicola See M. ***alpestris***
§ *scorpioïdes* CBen CBre CRDP CRow CWGN EHon ELan EPar EWav LMay MSta NDea SHig SWat WChe WEas WHol
– 'Mermaid' CBen CMGP CNic CRiv CRow EBre ECha EFol ILis LBre LHop MFir MSta NCat NHol NNrd NSti SDix SWat WCru WPer WWin
– 'Pinkie' CBre CRDP CRow SWat
secunda CKin
sylvatica alba CRow WBon

MYOSURUS (Ranunculaceae)

See Plant Deletions

MYRCEUGENIA (Myrtaceae)

See Plant Deletions

MYRICA (Myricaceae)

californica EPla GAri SLon SSta
gale CDoC GAri GPoy LHol MGos MUlv SIde SWat WDin WWye
pensylvanica CCla LHol MBal

MYRICARIA (Tamaricaceae)

See Plant Deletions

MYRIOPHYLLUM (Haloragaceae)

§ *aquaticum* CHEx CRDP CRiv CRow CWGN EBre EHon ELan EMFW LBre LMay MSta NDea SHig SWat WChe
brasiliense See M. ***aquaticum***
proserpinacoïdes See M. ***aquaticum***
spicatum CBen EHon EMFW NMir SAWi WChe
verticillatum CBen EHon

MYRRHIS (Umbelliferae)

odorata Widely available
¶ – 'Forncett Chevron' EFou

MYRSINE (Myrsinaceae)

africana CTre SArc WCru WWat
nummularia ECou

MYRTEOLA (Myrtaceae)

§ *nummularia* GAbr GArf GAri GDra ITim MBal MHig NHar SIng

MYRTUS (Myrtaceae)

apiculata See LUMA ***apiculata***
bullata See LOPHOMYRTUS ***bullata***
chequen See LUMA ***chequen***
communis Widely available
* – *citrifolia* SArc
– 'Flore Pleno' CDoC CSco EPla LHol MPla
– 'Jenny Reitenbach' See M. ***c. tarentina***
– 'Microphylla' See M. ***c. tarentina***
– 'Nana' See M. ***c. tarentina***
§ – ssp. *tarentina* CB&S CHan CLan CMHG CSco CShe CTre ELan ENot ERav ISea LHol LHop MBal MBri MPar SArc SLMG SLon SPer SReu STre WEas WOak WSHC WWat
– – 'Compacta' WWye
§ – – 'Microphylla Variegata' CHan CMHG CPle EJud ELan EPla ERav LGre LHol LHop MBal MPla SArc SLMG SPer WHal WOak WSHC WWat
– 'Tricolor' See M. ***c.*** 'Variegata'
– 'Variegata' CArn CBot CFis CHun CMCN CTre CWit ECtt ERav LHop SDry SHBN SHer SLMG SLon SPer SPla WStI WWat WWye

'Glanleam Gold'	See LUMA *apiculata* 'Glanleam Gold'
♦*lechleriana*	See AMOMYRTUS *luma*
luma	See LUMA *apiculata*
nummularia	See MYRTEOLA *n.*
obcordata	See LOPHOMYRTUS *o.*
x *ralphii*	See LOPHOMYRTUS x *r.*
'Traversii'	See LOPHOMYRTUS x *ralphii* 'Traversii'
ugni	See UGNI *molinae*

NANDINA (Berberidaceae)

domestica	CB&S CBar CBot CBow CDoC CPle CSam CTre ELan GWht IOrc ISea LAbb LHop LPan MBri MUlv NKay NRog SMad SPla SReu SSpi SSta WBod WDin WSHC WStI WWat
– 'Firepower'	CB&S CBow CDoC EBlo EBre ECtt ELan ENot EPla GAri IBar IHos IOrc LBre LHop LNet MGos MUlv NHol SHBN SHer SPer SSta WHig WWat
– 'Harbor Dwarf'	EPla LRHS
– 'Nana'	See N. *d.* 'Pygmaea'
– 'Nana Purpurea'	EPla
§ – 'Pygmaea'	CBra CSam GAri WDin
– 'Richmond'	CB&S CDoC EBre ELan EPla LBre MBlu MGos MMea MUlv SPer SPla SSpi
– 'Wood's Dwarf'	CB&S GAri

NANNORRHOPS (Palmae)

ritchieana	LPal

NARCISSUS † (Liliaceae/Amaryllidaceae)

'Abalone' (2)	EWal
'Accent' (2)	ICar
'Acclamation' (4)	EWal
'Accolade' (3)	ECop
'Achduart' (3)	ECop GEve ICar IDun
'Achentoul' (4)	ICar
'Achnasheen' (3)	GEve ICar
'Acropolis' (4)	ECop EWal ICar LAma LBlo
'Actaea' (9)	ETub LBlo MBri NRog SIng
'Advocat' (3)	IDun
'Affable' (4)	ICar
'Aflame' (3)	LAma MBri
'Aircastle' (3)	IBal ICar
'Akala' (1)	IDun
'Alba Pax' (2)	ECop
'Albus Plenus Odoratus '	See N. *poeticus* 'Plenus'
'Algarve' (2)	IDun
'Alice's Pink' (2)	ICar
'Alliance' (1)	EWal
alpestris	See N. *pseudonarcissus moschatus*
¶ – MS 571	CMon
'Alpha' (9)	EWal
'Altruist' (3)	ECop EWal IDun
'Amber Light' (2)	EWal
'Ambercastle' (2)	ECop ICar IDun
'Ambergate' (2)	EWal GEve LAma
'Amberglow' (2)	EWal LBlo
'Amboseli' (3)	IDun
'Amor' (3)	EWal
'Andalusia' (6)	ECop SIng
'Androcles' (4)	IDun
Angel's Tears	See N. *triandrus triandrus*
'Angkor' (4)	ICar
'Ann Abbott' (2)	EWal
'Annalong' (3)	IBal
'Anniversary' (2)	EWal
'Anthea' (2)	EWal
'Apotheose' (4)	EWal
'Apricot' (1)	CBro
'Apricot Sundae' (4)	ICar
'April Charm' (2)	ICar
'April Love' (1)	ECop IBal ICar
'April Snow' (2)	CBro
'April Tears' (5)	CBro CCla EWal LAma LBlo NRog SIng
'Aranjuez' (2)	LAma
'Arbar' (2)	EWal
'Arcady' (2)	EWal
'Arctic Char' (2)	ICar IDun
'Arctic Gold' (1)	ECop ICar LBlo
'Ardbane' (2)	ICar
'Ardglass' (3)	GEve IBal ICar
'Ardour' (3)	ICar
'Ardress' (2)	IDun
'Arie Hoek' (2)	LBlo
'Arish Mell' (5)	ECop EWal ICar IDun
'Arkle' (1)	ECop GEve ICar LBlo
'Armagh' (1)	ICar
'Armynel' (2)	EWal
'Arndilly' (2)	ECop
'Arpege' (2)	ECop
'Artillery' (3)	EWal
'Ashmore' (2)	ICar IDun
'Aslan' (4)	ICar
'Aspasia' (8)	CBro
§ *assoanus*	CBro EPar LAma
¶ – MS 582/581/511	CMon
¶ – var. *praelongus* MS 656	CMon
§ *asturiensis*	CBro CRDP CSam ELan EPar EPot IBlr LAma LBow MBal NHar SIng WChr WCru WHil
– 'Fuente De'	WChr
*– 'Giant'	ETub
'Atholl Palace' (4)	IDun
atlanticus	SPou WChr
'Attrus' (2)	EWal
'Audubon' (3)	EWal
'Aurum' (1)	ICar
'Avalanche' (8)	EWal GEve IDun
'Avenger' (2)	ECop ICar
'Ayston' (2)	ECop
'Baby Doll' (6)	EWal
'Baby Moon' (7)	CCla ELan EPar EPot ETub LAma MBri NRog SIng SUsu WPat
'Baccarat' (11)	EWal LAma MBri
'Badanloch' (3)	IDun
'Badbury Rings' (3)	ECop IDun
baeticus	See N. *assoanus praelongus*
'Bailey' (2)	ICar
'Ballintoy' (2)	ICar
'Ballyarnett' (1)	ICar
'Ballycastle' (3)	ICar
'Ballyfrema' (1)	ICar
'Ballygarvey' (1)	EWal
'Ballynichol' (3)	IBal
'Ballyrobert' (1)	ECop
'Ballytrim' (2)	ICar

¶ 'Baltic Shore' (3) IBal
'Balvenie' (2) ECop
¶ 'Balvraid Lass' (2) GEve
'Bambi' (1) CBro NRog
'Banbridge' (1) ECop IBal ICar
'Bandleader' (2) EWal
'Bantam' (2) CBro EWal
'Barley Cove' (2) ICar
'Barley Sugar' (3) ICar
'Barleygold' (2) IBal
'Barleythorpe' (1) EWal
'Barnsdale Wood' (2) ECop
'Barnwell Alice' (2) ICar
'Baronscourt' (1) ICar
'Barrett Browning' (3) ETub LBlo MBri NRog
'Bartley' (6) EWal
'Bastion' (1) EWal
'Beauticol' (11) IDun
'Beauvallon' (4) ECop IDun
'Bebop' (7) CBro
'Beefeater' (2) EWal
'Beersheba' (1) MBri
'Beige Beauty' (3) EWal ICar
'Belisana' (2) LAma
'Bell Song' (7) CBro ETub EWal WShi
'Beltrim' (2) ICar
'Ben Bhraggie' (2) GEve
'Ben Loyal' (2) GEve
'Ben Vorlich' (2) ICar
'Benvarden' (3) ICar
'Bergerac' (11) IDun
'Berkeley Court' (4) IDun
'Bermuda' (2) EWal
'Berry Gorse' (3) ECop
¶ ***bertolonii*** CMon
'Beryl' (6) CBro EWal ICar LAma LBow
'Best of Luck' (3) IBal
'Bethany' (2) EWal ICar
¶ ***bicolor*** B&S 448 CMon
'Big John' (1) IDun
'Bilbo' (6) IDun
'Binkie' (2) CBro EWal LAma MBri
'Birdsong' (3) ICar
'Birichen' (2) GEve
'Birkdale' (2) IDun
'Birma' (3) EWal LAma MBri
'Birthday Girl' (2) IDun
'Birthright' (1) EWal
'Biscayne' (1) EWal
'Bishopstone' (1) ICar
'Bit o'Gold' (2) ICar
'Bithynia' (3) EWal
'Bittern' (2) ICar
'Bizerta' (2) EWal
'Blarney' (3) EWal
'Blessing' (2) EWal
'Blue Bird' (2) EWal
'Bob Minor' (1) EWal
'Bobbysoxer' (7) CBro EWal ICar LAma
'Bodilly' (2) EWal
'Bonamargy' (2) ICar
'Border Chief' (2) ICar
'Borrobol' (2) ECop
'Bossa Nova' (3) IDun
'Boudoir' (1) ICar
'Bovagh' (2) ICar
'Bowles' Early Sulphur' (1) CRow MPar
'Bracken Hill' (2) ICar
'Braddock' (3) IBal
'Brandaris' (11) GEve
'Brave Journey' (2) ICar
'Bravoure' (1) EWal LBlo
'Breakthrough' (2) EWal
'Bridal Crown' (4) EWal LAma
'Bridesmaid' (2) IBal
'Brigton' (1) LAma
'Broadland' (2) ECop
'Broadway Rose' (2) IDun
'Broadway Star' (11) EWal LAma
'Brookdale' (1) IDun
'Brookfield' (2) ICar
'Broomhill' (2) ECop
'Broughshane' (1) ICar
¶ ***broussonetii*** SF 269 CMon
'Brunswick' (2) EWal LAma WShi
'Bryanston' (2) ECop IDun
'Bryher' (3) ICar
'Buffawn' (7) EWal
'Bulbarrow' (2) IDun
bulbocodium CBro CRiv ETub LBow NHol SBla WCla WPer
– ssp. ***bulbocodium*** CBro WChr
– – var. ***citrinus*** MS&S
– – var. ***conspicuus*** CAvo CBro CRDP CSam EPar EPot LAma LBlo MBal MBri MS&S NRog NRya SIng WChr WCru WShi
¶ – – ***graellsii*** MS 567/408 CMon
¶ – – var. ***nivalis*** SPou
– – var. ***tenuifolius*** CMon CRDP LAma MS&S SIng SPou
¶ – – var. ***tenuifolius*** S&B 189 CMon
*– ***filifolius*** CBro
¶ – ssp. ***genuinus*** SF 177/180 CMon
¶ – ssp. ***mairei*** SF 181 CMon
– var. ***mesatlanticus*** See N. ***romieuxii m.***
– ssp. ***praecox*** var. ***paucinervis*** WChr
– ***tananicus*** See N. ***tananicus***
¶ – ssp. ***viriditubus*** MS 453 CMon
'Bullseye' (3) EWal
'Bunclody' (2) ECop ICar IDun
'Buncrana' (2) ECop ICar
'Bunting' (7) ICar IDun
'Burgemeester Gouverneur' (1) LAma
'Burma Star' (2) ICar
'Burning Heart' (11) EWal
'Burning Torch' (2) ICar
'Burntollet' (1) IDun
'Bushmills' (3) ICar
'Buster' (2) EWal
'Buttercup' (7) CBro
'By Jove' (1) EWal
'Cabra' (1) ICar
'Cadence' (3) ICar
'Cairn Toul' (3) ECop
'Cairndhu' (2) ICar
'Calabar' (2) EWal
¶ ***calcicola*** B&S 413 CMon

Name	Suppliers
¶ – MS 450	CMon
'Callaway' (3)	ICar
'Camelot' (2)	EWal ICar
'Campion' (9)	GEve IDun
canaliculatus	See N. ***tazetta lacticolor***
'Canaliculatus' (8)	CBro CMon EPar ETub LAma LBlo LBow MBri SIng WPer
'Canarybird' (8)	CBro
'Canby' (2)	ICar
'Candida' (4)	EWal
'Canisp' (2)	ECop GEve ICar
'Cantabile' (9)	ECop IBal SIng
cantabricus ssp. ***cantabricus***	CRiv WChr
¶ – – SF 396	CMon
– – var. ***foliosus***	CAvo EPot LBow SPou WChr
¶ – – var. ***foliosus*** SF 284/2	CMon
– – var. ***petunioïdes***	LAma
¶ – ssp. ***monophyllus*** var. ***laciniatus***	CMon
'Cantatrice' (1)	LBlo
'Canticle' (9)	IBal
'Cape Cool' (2)	ICar
'Capisco' (3)	IBal
'Carbineer' (2)	LAma LBlo
'Carlton' (2)	ETub LAma LBlo MBri NRog
¶ 'Carnearny' (3)	ICar
'Caro Nome' (2)	EWal
'Carrickbeg' (1)	LBlo
'Carrigeen' (2)	ICar
'Caruso' (2)	LAma
'Cassata' (11)	EWal LAma LBlo NBir NRog
'Casterbridge' (2)	IDun
'Castle Dobbs' (4)	ICar
'Castlehill' (3)	IBal
'Cavoda' (1) or (2)	ICar
'Cedric Morris' (10)	CBro ECop SWas
'Celtic Song' (2)	ECop
'Cernuus Plenus' (4)	ICar
'Ceylon' (2)	EWal LAma
'Chablis' (11)	GEve
'Chagall' (2)	ICar
'Chania' (1)	ICar
'Chanterelle' (11)	EWal LAma NRog
'Chapeau' (2)	ICar
'Charade' (2)	ICar
'Charity May' (6)	CBro EWal IBal ICar LAma MBri NRog SIng
'Charleston' (2)	IDun
'Charter' (2)	EWal
'Chat' (7)	ICar
'Cha-Cha' (6)	IDun
'Checkmate' (2)	ICar
'Cheer Leader' (3)	IDun
'Cheerfulness' (4)	ETub EWal LAma LBlo MBri NRog SIng
'Chelsea Derby' (2)	ICar
'Chérie' (7)	CBro
'Cherrygardens' (2)	ECop
'Chesterton' (9)	IDun
'Chickerell' (3)	IDun
'Chief Inspector' (1)	IDun
'Chig' (2)	EWal
'Chinchilla' (2)	IDun
'Chinese Sacred Lily' (8)	ETub
'Chinese White' (3)	ICar
'Chinita' (8)	CBro EWal
'Chit Chat'	CBro IDun
'Chivalry' (1)	EWal
'Chungking' (3)	ICar
'Church Bay' (2)	ICar
'Churchfield' (2)	ICar
'Churchman' (2)	IBal ICar
¶ ***citrinus*** ssp. ***belinensis*** MS 579	CMon
'Clady Cottage' (2)	ICar
'Clare' (7)	CBro
'Clare Park' (2)	ICar
'Clashmore' (2)	GEve
'Clockface' (3)	EWal
'Cloud Nine' (2)	EWal ICar
'Cloudcap' (2)	ICar
'Cloud's Hill' (4)	IDun
'Cloyfin' (2)	ICar
'Collector's Choice' (3)	ICar
'Colloggett' (2)	ECop
'Colorama' (11)	IDun
'Coloratura' (3)	ICar
'Colour Sergeant' (2)	IBal
'Colston Bassett' (3)	IBal
'Columbus' (2)	ICar
'Comal' (1)	IDun
¶ 'Como' (9)	GEve
♦ ***compressus***	See N. × ***intermedius***
§ ***concolor***	CBro EPot MBal MS&S SIng
'Conestoga' (2)	IBal
'Congress' (11)	EWal
'Connor' (2)	ICar
'Cool Autumn' (2)	ICar
'Cool Crystal' (3)	ECop ICar IDun
'Coolattin' (2)	ICar
'Cophetua' (1)	ICar
¶ 'Copper Nob' (2)	IBal
'Cora Ann' (7)	CBro
'Coral Fair' (2)	IBal
'Coral Light' (2)	ICar
'Coralline' (6)	IDun
'Corbridge' (2)	EWal
cordubensis	WChr
¶ – MS 434	CMon
'Corinthian' (1)	LAma
'Cornerstone' (2)	EWal
'Coromandel' (2)	IDun
'Country Morning' (3)	ICar
'Coverack Perfection' (2)	EWal
'Crackington' (4)	IDun
'Cragford' (8)	EWal LAma
'Craigdun' (2)	ICar
'Craigtara' (2)	ICar
'Craigywarren' (2)	EWal
'Cranborne' (2)	IDun
'Creagh Dubh' (2)	IDun
'Crenelet' (2)	IDun
'Crimson Chalice' (3)	IDun
'Crinoline' (2)	EWal
'Cristobal' (1)	ECop LBlo
'Crock of Gold' (2)	EWal
'Croila' (2)	ECop
'Crown Royalist' (2)	IBal
'Cryptic' (2)	IDun
'Crystal River' (3)	EWal
cuatrecasasii	CMon WChr
¶ – MS 429	CMon

¶ – var. ***segimonensis*** MS 559	CMon
'Cushendall' (3)	EWal ICar
cyclamineus	CBro CNic EPot LAma NRog SBla SIng SWas WChr
'Cyros' (1)	IDun
'Dailmanach' (2)	ECop IDun LBlo
'Dalliance' (2)	ICar
'Dancer' (2)	EWal
'Dancing Partner' (2)	EWal
'Danes Balk' (2)	ICar
* 'Darlow Dale' (2)	ECop
'Dateline' (3)	IDun
'Davlyn' (2)	EWal
¶ 'Davochfin Lass' (1)	GEve
'Dawn' (5)	CBro ICar
'Dawn Mist' (2)	EWal
'Daydream' (2)	ECop EWal ICar IDun LAma LBlo
'Debrett' (2)	IDun
'Debutante' (2)	LBlo
'Decoy' (2)	ICar
'Delamont' (2)	ICar
'Delia' (6)	IDun
'Delibes' (2)	LAma LBlo
'Delnashaugh' (4)	ICar IDun
'Delos' (3)	IDun
'Delphin Hill' (4)	IBal
'Delta Wings' (6)	IDun
'Derg Valley' (1)	IDun
¶ 'Derryboy' (3)	IBal
'Descanso' (1)	ECop EWal
'Desdemona' (2)	EWal NRog
'Desert Orchid' (2)	IBal
'Desert Rose' (2)	ICar
'Diane' (6)	IDun
'Dick Wilden' (4)	ETub EWal LAma
'Dickcissel' (7)	ICar
'Dilemma' (3)	IDun
'Dinkie' (3)	CBro
'Diversion' (3)	ICar
'Divertimento' (7)	ICar
'Doctor Alexander Fleming' (2)	EWal
'Doctor Hugh' (3)	EWal IDun
'Dolly Mollinger' (11)	EWal LAma LBlo
'Don Carlos' (2)	ICar LBlo
'Double Blush' (4)	ICar
'Double Event' (4)	ICar LBlo
¶ 'Double Fashion' (4)	EWal
'Doubtful' (3)	ECop ICar
'Dove of Peace' (6)	IBal
'Dove Wings' (6)	CBro EWal IBal LAma SIng
'Dovekie' (12)	ICar
'Dover Cliffs' (2)	ECop
'Downhill' (3)	ICar
'Downpatrick' (1)	ECop ICar
'Dramatis' (9)	IDun
'Dream Castle' (3)	EWal ICar
'Drenagh' (2)	ICar
'Drumadarragh' (1)	ICar
'Drumadoon' (2)	ICar
'Drumawillan' (2)	ICar
'Drumnabreeze' (2)	ICar
'Drumnasole' (3)	ICar
'Drumragh' (1)	IDun
'Drumrunie' (2)	ICar
'Drumtullagh' (2)	ICar
¶ ***dubius*** var. ***dubius*** MS 512	CMon
'Duet' (4)	EWal
'Duke of Windsor' (2)	LBlo
'Dundarave' (2)	ICar
'Dunskey' (3)	IDun
'Durango' (6)	IDun
'Dutch Master' (1)	ETub EWal LAma LBow MBri NRog
'Dynamite' (2)	EWal
'Early Blossom' (1)	IBal
'Early Splendour' (8)	LAma
'Easter Bonnet' (2)	LAma
'Easter Moon' (2)	ICar
'Eaton Park' (3)	IDun
'Eaton Song' (12)	ECop
'Edge Grove' (2)	ICar
'Edwalton' (2)	ECop
'Edward Buxton' (3)	LAma LBlo MBri
'Egard' (11)	EWal
'Egg Nog' (4)	ICar
'Eland' (7)	IDun
¶ 'Eleanor Rose' (2)	IBal
¶ ***elegans*** var. ***elegans*** SF 316	CMon
¶ – var. ***fallax*** S&L 324	CMon
¶ 'Elf' (2)	CBro
'Elfin Gold' (6)	IDun
'Elizabeth Ann' (6)	IDun
¶ 'Elka' (1)	IBal
'Elphin' (4)	ICar
'Elrond' (6)	IDun
'Elvira' (8)	CBro
'Elwing' (6)	IDun
'Elysian Fields' (2)	EWal
'Embo' (2)	GEve
'Emily' (2)	IBal ICar
'Eminent' (3)	EWal
'Empress of Ireland' (1)	ECop EWal IBal IDun LBlo
¶ 'Englander' (6)	EPot
'Entrancement' (1)	EWal
¶ 'Eribol' (2)	GEve
'Eriskay' (4)	GEve
'Ernevale' (3)	IDun
'Eskylane' (2)	ICar
'Estio Pinza' (2)	EWal
'Estrella' (3)	ECop
'Estremadura' (2)	IDun
'Euphony' (2)	ICar
'Evelix' (2)	GEve
'Evendine' (2)	EWal
'Exception' (1)	LBlo
'Exemplar' (1)	EWal
'Eyecatcher' (3)	ICar
'Eystettensis' (4)	CBos CBro ECha
'Fair Head' (9)	IBal
'Fair Prospect' (2)	ICar IDun LBlo
'Fairgreen' (3)	ICar
'Fairlight Glen' (2)	ECop

'Fairlight Glen' (2)	ECop
'Fairmile' (3)	ICar LAma
'Fairsel' (3)	IBal
'Fairy Footsteps' (3)	IBal ICar
'Fairy Island' (3)	ICar
¶ 'Fairy Spell' (3)	IBal
'Falconet' (8)	IDun
'Falstaff' (2)	EWal ICar
'Fanad Head' (9)	IBal
'Far Country' (2)	GEve ICar
'Faraway' (3)	IBal ICar
'Faro' (1)	IBal
'Farranfad' (2)	IBal
'Favor Royal' (3)	IBal
'Favourite' (2)	EWal
'February Gold' (6)	CAvo CBro EPar ETub EWal IBal LAma LBlo LBow MBri NRog SIng SUsu WPer WShi
'February Silver' (6)	CAvo CBro EPar ETub EWal LAma LBow NRog SIng
'Feeling Lucky' (2)	EWal
'Felindre' (9)	EWal IBal
'Fellowship' (2)	GEve IDun
'Fergie' (2)	EWal
fernandesii (10)	CBro CMon SPou WChr
'Ferndown' (3)	ECop IDun
'Festivity' (2)	ECop EWal ICar
'Fiji' (4)	ECop ICar
'Filly' (2)	EWal
'Finchcocks' (2)	ECop
'Fionn' (2)	GEve ICar
'Fire Flash' (2)	ICar IDun
'Fire Raiser' (2)	ICar
'Firestorm' (2)	IBal
'Firgrove' (3)	ICar
'First Date' (3)	ICar
'Flaming Meteor' (2)	ICar
'Flirt ' (6)	ICar
'Flomay' (7)	CBro
'Florida Manor' (3)	IBal
'Flower Carpet' (1)	LAma
'Flower Drift' (4)	LAma
'Flower Record' (2)	ETub LAma
* 'Flowerdream'	LAma
'Fly Half' (2)	IDun
'Flycatcher' (7)	IDun
'Flying Saucer' (2)	EWal
'Fool's Gold' (4)	ICar
'Foray' (2)	EWal
'Foresight' (1)	ICar LAma LBlo WShi
'Forge Mill' (2)	ICar
'Fort Knox' (1)	EWal
'Fortune' (2)	EWal LAma LBlo NRog
'Foundling' (6)	CBro ECop EWal IBal ICar IDun SIng
'Fount' (2)	ICar
'Foxfire' (2)	ICar
¶ 'Fragrant Breeze'	EWal
'Fragrant Rose' (2)	EWal ICar IDun
'Frank's Fancy' (9)	IBal
'Frigid' (3)	IBal ICar
'Frolic' (2)	EWal
'Front Royal' (2)	ECop ICar
'Frou-Frou' (4)	ICar
'Fuego' (2)	ICar
'Fulwell' (4)	IDun
'Gabriël Kleiberg' (11)	IDun
gaditanus (10)	CBro CMon
¶ – MS 526/633	CMon
'Gainsborough' (2)	ICar
'Galway' (2)	EWal
'Ganaway' (3)	IBal
'Garden News' (3)	IDun
'Garden Princess' (6)	CBro LAma
'Gay Challenger' (4)	LBlo
'Gay Kybo' (4)	ECop IDun
'Gay Mood' (2)	EWal
'Gay Song' (4)	ICar
'Gay Time' (4)	EWal
'George's Pink' (2)	ICar
'Georgie Girl' (6)	IDun
'Geranium' (8)	CBro ETub EWal LAma LBlo MBri NRog SIng
'Gettysburg' (2)	IDun
'Gigantic Star' (2)	EWal LAma MBri
'Gilda' (2)	IBal
'Gilford' (3)	ICar
'Gimli' (6)	IDun
'Gin and Lime' (1)	ICar IDun
'Gipsy Moth' (2)	ICar
'Gipsy Queen' (1)	ICar
'Glacier' (1)	LBlo
'Glad Day' (2)	ICar
'Glaston' (2)	ICar
'Glen Clova' (2)	LBlo
'Glenamoy' (1)	ICar
'Glencraig' (2)	ICar
'Glendermott' (2)	ICar
'Glenfarclas' (1/2)	GEve ICar LBlo
¶ 'Glenganagh' (4)	ICar
'Glorious' (8)	IBal
¶ 'Glory of Lisse' (9)	CBro
'Glowing Embers' (2)	ICar
'Gold Bullion' (1)	ICar
'Gold Convention' (2)	IDun
'Gold Medal' (1)	EWal LAma
¶ 'Gold Medallion' (1)	IBal
'Gold Mine' (2)	IBal
'Gold Phantom' (1)	ICar
'Gold Quest' (1)	IDun
'Gold Strike' (1)	ICar
'Golden Amber' (2)	IBal ICar
'Golden Aura' (2)	ECop EWal IBal ICar
'Golden Ducat' (4)	EWal LAma LBlo MBri NRog
'Golden Halo' (2)	IBal
'Golden Harvest' (1)	ETub LAma LBlo MBri NRog
'Golden Jewel' (2)	ECop GEve IDun
'Golden Joy' (2)	ICar IDun
'Golden Orchid' (11)	LAma
'Golden Perfection' (7)	LAma
'Golden Radiance' (1)	IBal
'Golden Ranger' (2)	IDun
'Golden Rapture' (1)	LBlo
'Golden Riot' (1)	EWal
'Golden Sheen' (2)	IDun
'Golden Showers' (1)	IBal
'Golden Sovereign' (1)	IBal
'Golden Strand' (2)	IBal
'Golden Topaz' (2)	IBal
'Golden Vale' (1)	ECop IDun
'Golden Wings' (6)	IBal
'Goldfinger' (1)	IDun

'Golly' (4) EWal
'Good Measure' (2) EWal
'Goose Green' (3) IBal
'Gossamer' (3) EWal
¶ 'Gouache' EWal
'Gourmet' (1) LAma
gracilis See N. x *tenuior*
'Gracious Lady' (2) IDun
'Grand Prospect' (2) IBal IDun
'Grand Soleil d'Or' (8) ETub LAma NRog
'Gransha' (3) IBal
'Grapillon' (11) GEve
'Great Expectations' (2) IBal
'Green Glens' (2) ICar
'Green Gold' (2) EWal
'Green Howard' (3) ECop
'Green Ice' (2) IDun
*'Green Orchid' LAma
'Green Rival' (2) EWal
'Greenfinch' (3) ICar
'Greenholm' (2) IDun
'Greenpark' (9) IBal
'Greenstar' (4) EWal
'Greenvale' (2) IDun
'Greeting' (2) ECop
'Gresham' (4) IDun
'Grey Lady' (3) ICar
'Grosvenor' (4) IDun
'Halley's Comet' (3) ECop
'Halolight' (2) EWal
'Halstock' (2) IDun
¶ 'Halvose' (8) CBro
'Hambledon' (2) ECop IDun
'Hammoon' (3) EWal
'Happy Face' (2) ICar
'Hawaii' (4) IBal
'Hawera' (5) CAvo CBro CCla EPar EPot ETub EWal LAma LBow MBri MBro NHar NRog SIng WHil WOMN WPat
'Hazel Rutherford' (2) GEve
'Hazel Winslow' (2) IDun
'Heart Throb' (2) IDun
'Heart's Desire' (4) EWal
'Heat Haze' (2) ICar
¶ ***hedraeanthus*** MS 543/419 CMon
henriquesii See N. *jonquilla h.*
'Hero' (1) EWal IDun
'Hesla' (7) ICar
'High Note' (7) EWal
'High Society' (2) EWal IDun
'Highfield Beauty' (8) ECop EWal IDun
'Highland Wedding' (2) ICar
'Highway Song' (2) ICar
'Hilford' (2) IBal
'Hill Head' (9) IBal
¶ 'Hilltown' (2) IBal
'Holbeck' (4) IDun
'Holiday Fashion' (2) EWal
'Holland Sensation' (1) LAma
'Holly Berry' (2) ICar
'Hollypark' (3) IBal
'Homage' (2) EWal
'Home Fires' (2) ETub LBlo
'Honeybird' (1) ECop EWal ICar
'Hoodsport' (11) LBlo
'Hoopoe' (8) ICar
'Hope' (4) EWal
'Horace' (9) ICar
'Hors d'Oeuvre' (8) CBro
'Hot Toddy' (4) ICar
'Hotspur' (2) ICar
'Howard's Way' (3) IBal IDun
****humilis humilis*** AB&S 4301 CMon
*– ***mauretanicus*** SF 260 CMon
'Ibberton' (3) ECop
'Ibis' (6) CBro
'Ice Follies' (2) ETub EWal LAma LBlo LBow MBri NRog
'Ice King' (4) EWal
'Ice Wings' (5) CBro EWal IDun SIng
'Indian Maid' (7) ICar
'Inglescombe' (4) LAma
'Initiation' (1) ICar
'Innis Beg' (2) ICar
'Innisfree' (3) ICar
'Inniswood' (1) ICar
'Interim' (2) EWal ICar
¶ x ***intermedius*** CBro
'Interval' (2) IBal
'Intrigue' (7) ICar IDun
'Inverpolly' (2) GEve ICar
'Ireland's Eye' (9) IBal
'Irene Copeland' (4) EWal LBlo
'Irish Light' (2) ICar
'Irish Linen' (3) ICar
'Irish Luck' (1) EWal LAma
'Irish Mist' (2) ECop ICar
'Irish Nymph' (3) ICar
'Irish Ranger' (3) ICar
'Irish Splendour' (3) ICar
'Islandhill' (3) IBal
'Itzim' (6) CBro
'It's True' (1) EWal
'Ivy League' (1) ICar
¶ ***jacetanus*** MS 580 CMon
'Jack Snipe' (6) CAvo CBro CCla CNic EPot ETub EWal LAma LBlo LBow MBri NRog SIng SUsu WHil
'Jambo' (2) IDun
'Jamestown' (3) IBal
¶ 'Jane Frances' (1) GEve
'Jane MacLennan' (4) GEve
¶ 'Jane van Kralingen' (3) GEve
'Janis Babson' (2) ICar
'Jeannine Hoog' (1) LRHS
'Jenny' (6) CAvo CBro EPar EPot ETub EWal IBal ICar LAma LBlo NRog SIng SUsu
'Jessamy' (12) SPou
'Jetfire' (6) CBro ECop EPot ETub EWal IDun LAma
'Jewel Song' (2) ICar
'Jezebel' (3) CBro GEve
¶ 'Johanna' (5) CBro
'John Ballance' (4) IBal
'John of Salisbury' (2) EWal
§ 'Jolity' (2) EWal
'Jolly Roger' (2) ICar
Jonquil Single LBlo
jonquilla CAvo CBro EPar EPot LAma LBow NEgg NRog SIng WPer WShi

§ – var. ***henriquesii*** CBro
¶ – – MS 455 CMon
¶ – var. ***jonquilla*** B&S 420 CMon
¶ – var. ***stellaris*** MS 466 CMon
'Joseph Macleod' (1) EWal
'Joy' See N. 'Jolity'
'Joy Bishop' See N. ***romieuxii*** 'J. B.'
'Jubilation' (2) EWal
'Jules Verne' LAma
'Julia Jane' See N. ***romieuxii*** 'J. J.'
'Jumblie' (6) CAvo CBro CCla CMea EPot EWal LAma MBri NEgg NRog SUsu WPer
'Jumbo Gold' (1) IDun
juncifolius See N. ***assoanus***
'Kamau' (9) IDun
'Kanchenjunga' (1) ICar
'Karachi' (2) ICar
'Karamudli' (1) ICar
'Kathleen Munro' (2) GEve
'Kaydee' IDun
¶ 'Keats' (9) CBro
'Kehelland' (4) CBro
'Kelanne' (2) IDun
'Kenbane Head' (9) IBal
¶ 'Kenellis' (12) CBro
'Kildavin' (2) ICar
'Kildrum' (3) EWal ICar
'Kilkenny' (1) EWal
'Killeen' (2) IBal
'Kilmood' (2) IBal
'Kilmorack' (2) ICar
'Kiltonga' (2) IBal
'Kilworth' (2) EWal LAma LBlo
'Kimmeridge' (3) ECop IDun
'Kindled' (2) ICar
'King Alfred' (1) LAma LBlo WShi
'King Size' (11) GEve
'Kinglet' (7) ICar
'Kingscourt' (1) ECop
'King's Bridge' (1) IDun
'King's Grove' (1) IDun
'King's Stag' (1) ECop IDun
'Kirkinriola' (3) ICar
'Kirklington' (2) IBal
'Kissproof' (2) LAma LBlo
'Kitten' (6) EWal
'Klamath' (2) EWal
'Knockstacken' (1) ICar
'Krakatoa' (2) EWal
'La Riante' (3) LAma
'Lady Emily' (2) IBal
'Ladybank' (1) IDun
'LAmour' See N. 'Madelaine'
'Lanarth' (7) CBro
'Lancaster' (3) IBal ICar
'Landmark' (2) EWal
'Langford Grove' (3) ECop
'Larkelly' (6) CBro ICar
'Larkfield' (2) ICar
¶ 'Last Promise' (1) ICar
'Last Word' (3) EWal
'Late Call' (3) IBal
'Lavender Lass' (6) ECop ICar IDun
'Lemnos' (2) EWal
'Lemon Beauty' (11) EWal
¶ 'Lemon Candy' (2) ECop
'Lemon Cloud' (1) EWal
'Lemon Drops' (5) IDun
'Lemon Express' (1) IDun
'Lemon Heart' (5) CBro ICar
'Lemon Meringue' (1) ICar
'Lemon Sherbet' (2) ICar
'Lemonade' (3) ECop ICar
'Lennymore' (2) IDun
'Leonaine' (2) EWal
'Leslie Hill' (1) ICar
'Liberty Bells' (5) CBro EWal LAma MBri NRog SIng
'Lichfield' (3) EWal
'Lighthouse' (3) GEve IDun
'Lilac Charm' (6) IDun
'Lilac Hue' (6) IDun
¶ 'Lillande' (4) ICar
'Limbo' (2) EWal IDun
'Limeade' (2) ICar
'Limegrove' (3) IDun
'Limehurst' (2) IDun
'Limelight' (1) EWal
'Limerick' (3) EWal ICar
'Lintie' (7) CBro EWal LAma MBri NRog SIng
'Lionheart' (4) EWal
'Lisanore' (2) ICar
'Lisbarnett' (3) IBal
'Lisnamulligan' (3) IBal
'Lisrenny' (1) ICar
'Little Beauty' (1) CBro EPot ETub LAma
'Little Dancer' (1) CBro
'Little Gem' (1) CBro EPot LAma NRog
'Little Princess' (6) ICar
'Little Sentry' (7) CBro
¶ 'Little Spell' (1) CBro
'Little Witch' (6) CAvo CBro CCla EPot EWal LAma LBow MBri NRog SIng SUsu
'Lizard Light' (2) EWal
lobularis See N. ***pseudonarcissus*** 'Lobularis'
'Loch Assynt' (3) ECop GEve ICar
'Loch Carron' (2) IDun
'Loch Fada' (2) ICar
'Loch Garvie' (2) ICar
'Loch Hope' (2) ECop GEve ICar IDun
'Loch Loyal' (2) IDun
'Loch Lundie' (2) ICar IDun
'Loch Naver' (2) GEve IDun
'Loch Owskeich' (2) ECop
'Loch Stac' (2) ECop ICar
¶ 'Loch Tarbert' (2) GEve
¶ ***longispathus*** MS 546 CMon
'Loth Lorien' (3) IDun
'Lothario' (2) LAma MBri NRog
'Lough Bawn' (2) GEve ICar
'Lough Cuan' (1) IBal
'Lough Ryan' (1) IBal
'Loughanisland' (1) IBal
'Loughanmore' (1) ICar
'Lovable' (3) EWal
'Lunar Sea' (1) EWal
'Lurgain' (1) EWal
'Lusky Mills' (3) IBal
'Lydwells' (2) ECop
'Lyles' (2) ECop

'Lynwood' (1) ICar
'Lyric' (9) IDun
§ 'Madelaine' (2) EWal
'Madrigal' (2) EWal
'Magic Flute' (2) ICar
'Magic Maiden' (2) IDun
'Magna Carta' (2) IDun
'Magnet' (1) LAma MBri
'Magnificence' (1) LAma
'Mahmoud' (3) ICar
'Maiden Over' (2) ECop
¶ 'Mairead' (2) GEve
'Majestic Star' (1) IDun
'Manchu' (2) EWal
'Manly' (4) EWal LBlo
'Mantle' (2) IDun
'Marabou' (4) IDun
'Maraval' (1) EWal ICar
'March Madness' (2) ICar
'March Sunshine' (6) CBro EPot EWal ICar LAma
'Marcola' (2) ICar
'Marie-José' (11) ETub LAma
'Marshfire' (2) ICar
'Martha Washington' (8) CBro
marvieri See N. ***rupicola m.***
'Mary Bohannon' (2) EWal
'Mary Copeland' (4) EWal LAma MBri
'Mary Kate' (6) IDun
'Mary Lou' (6) IDun
'Mary Sumner' (1) ICar
'Mary's Pink' (2) ICar
'Masai Mara' (2) IDun
'Mayan Gold' (1) IBal
'Medalist' (2) ICar
¶ x ***medioluteus*** CMon
'Megalith' (2) IDun
'Melancholy' (1) IDun
'Melbury' (2) ECop IDun
¶ 'Meldrum' (1) ECop
'Mellon Park' (3) IDun
'Melody Lane' (2) EWal
'Mentor' (2) IDun
'Menucha' (2) ICar
'Mercato' (2) LAma
'Merlin' (3) ECop GEve IBal LBlo
'Merlin's Castle' ICar
'Mermaid's Spell' (2) ICar
'Merry Bells' (5) ICar
'Merrymaker' (4) EWal
'Mexico City' (2) IBal
'Midas Touch' (1) IDun
'Midget' CAvo CBro EPot
'Millennium' (1) CBro
'Millgreen' (1) EWal
¶ 'Minicycla' (6) CAvo CBro
'Minikin' (3) ICar
minimus See N. ***asturiensis***
'Minnow' (8) CAvo CBro CCla CMea EPot ETub EWal LAma LBlo MBri NHar NRog SIng SUsu WHil WPat
§ ***minor*** CBro LAma LBlo MPar
– 'Cedric Morris' ECha
§ – var. ***pumilus*** WPer
– – ***plenus*** See N. 'Rip van Winkle'
'Mint Cup' (3) GEve ICar
¶ ***minutiflorus*** B&S 412 CMon
'Missouri' (2) EWal
'Misty Dawn' (3) IBal
'Misty Glen' (2) ECop GEve ICar
'Misty Moon' (3) ICar
'Mockingbird' (7) IDun
¶ 'Modern Art' (2) ETub
'Moina' (3) ICar
'Mol's Hobby' (11) EWal LAma
'Mondaine' (2) EWal
¶ 'Mondragon' (11) EWal
'Moneymore' (2) ICar
¶ 'Monk Silver' (3) ECop
'Montalto' (2) ICar
'Montego' (3) ECop
'Monterrico' (4) IDun
'Monument' (2) ICar
'Monza' (4) IDun
'Moon Goddess' (1) IBal
'Moon Jade' (3) IBal
'Moon Orbit' (2) ETub LBlo
'Moon Ranger' (3) IBal
'Moon Rhythm' (4) IBal
'Moon Tide' (3) IBal
'Moon Valley' (2) IDun
'Moonshine' (5) CBro
'Moonshot' (1) EWal
'Moonspell' (2) IBal ICar
'Morag MacDonald' (2) GEve
'Moralee' (4) IDun
'Mother Catherine Grullemans' LAma
'Mount Angel' (3) IDun
'Mount Fuji' (2) IDun
'Mount Hood' (1) ETub EWal LAma LBlo MBri NBir WShi
'Mount Ida' (2) IBal
¶ 'Mount Oriel' (2) IBal
'Mount Vernon' (2) ICar
'Mountjoy' (7) EWal
'Mountpleasant' (2) IBal
¶ 'Mourneview' (1) IBal
'Moyle' (9) IBal
'Moyola' (2) ICar
'Mrs R O Backhouse' (2) LAma MBri WShi
'Mrs William Copeland' (4) EWal
'Muirfield' (1) IDun
'Mulatto' (1) EWal
'Murlough' (9) IBal
'Murrayfield' (3) IDun
'My Lady' (2) EWal
'My My' (2) EWal
'My Word' (2) ICar
'Naivasha' (2) IDun
'Nampa' (1) EWal
'Namraj' (2) IDun
'Nancegollan' (7) CBro
nanus See N. ***minor***
'Narok' (4) IDun
'Nether Barr' (2) IDun
¶ ***nevadensis*** CMon
'Nevta' (2) IDun
'New Generation' (1) IDun
'New Song' (2) EWal
'New Star' (2) EWal
'New World' (2) EWal
'Newcastle' (1) ECop IDun
'Nirvana' (7) CBro

'Niveth' (5) ICar
¶ ***nobilis*** var. ***nobilis*** MS 486 CMon
¶ – var. ***primagenius*** MS 593 CMon
'Northern Light' (2) ICar
'Northern Sceptre' (2) IBal ICar
¶ 'Nor-Nor' (2) CBro
'Notable' (3) IBal
'Nouvelle' (3) IBal
'Noweta' (3) ICar
'Nuage' (2) EWal
'Nylon' (12) CBro SPou WChr
'Nymphette' (6) IDun
'Oadby' (1) ECop
'Oakwood' (3) EWal
'Obelisk' (11) IDun
obesus WChr
¶ – MS 451 CMon
'Obsession' (2) IDun
obvallaris See N. ***pseudonarcissus o.***
¶ – MS 560 CMon
x ***odorus*** 'Campernelli Plenus' LAma SIng
– 'Rugulosus' (10) CAvo CBro EPar LAma NRog
'Odyssey' (4) ICar
Old Pheasant's Eye See N. ***poeticus recurvus***
'Old Satin' (2) ICar
'Omaha' (3) IBal
'Oneonta' (2) ICar
'Orange Beacon' (2) ICar
'Orange Lodge' (2) IDun
'Orange Queen' (3) IDun
'Orange Sherbet' (2) ICar
'Orangery' (11) ETub LAma LBlo MBri NRog
¶ 'Orator' (2) ECop
'Oratorio' (2) EWal
'Oryx' (7) IDun
'Osmington' (3) ECop IDun
'Ottoman Gold' (2) IBal
'Owen Roe' (1) IBal
'Oykel' (3) GEve ICar
'Pacific Princess' (3) IBal
'Painted Desert' (3) ECop ICar
'Pale Sunlight' (2) ICar
'Palmares' (11) EWal
'Palmyra' (3) ICar
'Panache' (1) ECop EWal GEve ICar
panizzianus CMon EPot
'Pankot' (2) ICar
'Paolo Veronese' (2) EWal
'Paper White' See N. ***papyraceus***
'Papillon Blanc' (11) EWal LAma
§ ***papyraceus*** (8) ETub EWal LAma LBow MBri NRog
¶ – ***papyraceus*** AB&S 4399 CMon
'Parcpat' (7) CBro
'Parfait' (4) ICar
'Paricutin' (2) EWal
'Parisienne' (11) LAma NRog
'Park Springs' (3) ECop IBal ICar IDun
'Parterre' (2) IDun
'Parthenon' (4) ICar
'Passionale' (2) ECop EWal IBal ICar LAma LBlo LBow WShi
'Pastorale' (2) EWal
'Patabundy' (2) IDun
¶ ***patulus*** CMon
'Paula Cottell' (3) CBro
'Pay Day' (1) ICar
'Peacock' (2) ICar IDun
'Pearl Wedding' (4) IBal
'Pearlax' (11) EWal IDun
'Peeping Tom' (6) CAvo CBro EPar ETub LAma LBlo LBow MBri NRog SIng
'Pencrebar' (7) CAvo CBro LAma LBlo MBri WHil WShi
'Pennine Way' (1) ECop
¶ 'Pennyghael' (2) GEve
'Penpol' (7) CBro
'Penvose' (2) EWal
'Pepper' (2) CBro
'Perimeter' (3) ECop IBal ICar
'Perseus' (1) GEve ICar
'Pet Finch' (7) EWal
'Petit Four' (4) ETub EWal LAma LBlo NRog
'Petrel' (5) CAvo CBro ETub ICar
'Petsamo' (1) ICar
'Picasso' (3) ICar
'Pick Up' (11) ICar
'Pinafore' (2) EWal
'Pink Angel' (7) ICar
'Pink Champagne' (4) ECop
'Pink Charm' (2) ETub EWal
'Pink Gin' (4) EWal
'Pink Mink' (2) IDun
'Pink Monarch' (2) EWal
'Pink Pageant' (4) EWal IDun
'Pink Panther' (2) ICar
'Pink Paradise' (4) IDun
'Pink Silhouette' (2) IDun
'Pink Whispers' (2) IBal
'Pinza' (2) ICar LBlo
'Pipe Major' (2) EWal IBal
'Piper's Barn' (7) CBro
'Pipit' (7) CAvo CBro ETub EWal ICar IDun LAma SIng
'Piraeus' (4) IDun
'Pismo Beach' (2) ECop ICar IDun
'Pitchroy' (2) ECop
'Playboy' (2) ICar
'Playschool' (3) ICar
poeticus CAvo LAma
– var. ***hellenicus*** EWal
– Old Pheasant's Eye See N. ***poeticus recurvus***
§ – 'Plenus' CBro
¶ – 'Praecox' (9) CBro
§ – var. ***recurvus*** CBro CGle ETub EWal ICar LAma LBlo LBow NBir SIng WShi
'Poet's Way' (9) ECop
'Polar Circle' (2) ICar
'Polar Imp' (3) ICar
'Polglass' (3) CBro
'Polindra' (2) EWal
'Polnesk' (7) CBro
'Pomona' (3) LAma
'Pontresina' (2) ICar LBlo
'Pops Legacy' (1) IBal
'Port Patrick' (3) IBal
¶ 'Port William' (3) IBal
'Portavo' (2) ICar
'Porthchapel' (7) ECop

'Portnagolan' (2)	ICar
'Portrush' (3)	EWal
'Portstewart' (3)	IBal
'Post House' (4)	IDun
'Prairie Fire'	IDun
'Preamble' (1)	ECop IBal ICar LBlo
'Premiere' (2)	IDun
'President Carter' (1)	LAma
'Pretty Polly' (2)	ICar
'Pride of Cornwall' (8)	CBro
¶ 'Primrose Beauty' (4)	CBro
'Prince of Brunswick' (2)	IBal
¶ 'Printal' (11)	ETub
'Professor Einstein' (2)	ETub LAma LBlo LBow NRog
'Prologue' (1)	EWal
'Prophet' (1)	EWal
'Proska' (2)	IDun
pseudonarcissus	CBro CGle CRDP CRow LAma LBow SIng WChr WShi
– ssp. ***gayi***	CBro
§ – 'Lobularis'	CAvo CBro LBlo NLan NRog SIng
§ – ssp. ***moschatus***	CBro CMon
– ssp. ***nevadensis***	WOMN
§ – ssp. ***obvallaris***	CAvo CBro EPot ETub LBow NLan NRog SIng WCla WShi
'Pueblo' (7)	ICar
x ***pulchellus***	SIng
pumilus	See N. ***minor pumilus***
'Puppet' (5)	ICar
'Puppy' (6)	EWal
'Purbeck' (3)	ECop EWal IDun
§ 'Pzaz' (3)	IDun
'Quail' (7)	CAvo CBro EWal ICar LAma NRog
'Quasar' (2)	ICar IDun
'Queen Anne's Double'	See N. 'Eystettensis'
'Queen of Bicolors' (1)	LAma
'Queenscourt' (1)	ECop ICar
'Quetzal' (9)	ICar
'Quick Step' (7)	EWal
'Quiet Day' (2)	ICar
'Quince' (6)	CAvo CBro
'Quirinus' (2)	ETub LAma
'Radiation' (2)	EWal
'Radical' (6)	EWal
'Rainbow' (2)	ECop EWal ICar LBlo
'Rame Head' (1)	ECop
'Rameses' (2)	ECop
'Rarkmoyle' (2)	ICar
'Rathgar' (2)	ICar
'Ravenhill' (3)	IDun
¶ ***readinganorum*** B&S 434	CMon
'Reckless' (3)	ICar
'Red Arrow' (1)	IBal
'Red Bay' (2)	ICar
'Red Cameo' (2)	IDun
'Red Cottage' (2)	ICar
'Red Devil' (2)	ICar
'Red Devon' (2)	LBlo
'Red Ember' (3/2)	IDun
'Red Goblet' (2)	LAma
'Red Hall' (3)	ICar
'Red Haze' (2)	IDun
'Red Hugh' (9)	IBal
'Red Mission' (2)	IDun
'Red Rascal' (2)	LBlo
'Red Spartan' (2)	IDun
'Redlands' (2)	ICar
'Redman' (2)	IBal
'Redstart' (3)	EWal
'Regal Bliss' (2)	IDun
'Reggae' (6)	ICar IDun
'Reliance' (2)	EWal
'Rembrandt' (1)	LAma LBlo MBri
'Replete' (4)	ICar IDun
requienii	See N. ***assoanus***
'Resplendent' (2)	ICar
'Revival' (4)	EWal
'Riding Mill' (3)	EWal
'Rijnveld's Early Sensation' (1)	CBro ECop EWal
'Rima' (1)	ECop
'Rimmon' (3)	IDun
'Ringhaddy' (3)	IBal
'Ringleader' (2)	EWal ICar IDun
'Ringmaster' (2)	ICar
'Ringmer' (3)	ECop
'Rio Bravo' (2)	IBal
'Rio Gusto' (2)	IBal
'Rio Rouge' (2)	IBal ICar
§ 'Rip van Winkle' (4)	CAvo CBro EPar EPot ETub LAma LBlo LBow MBri NRog WHil WShi
'Rippling Waters' (5)	CBro ECop LAma LBlo WHil
'Riptide' (1)	ICar
'Rivendell' (3)	ICar IDun
'Rob Roy' (3)	EWal
'Rockall' (3)	ECop ICar LBlo
'Rockport' (2)	ICar
'Rococo' (2)	EWal
'Roger' (6)	CBro ICar
'Roman Tile' (2)	EWal
'Romance' (2)	EWal LAma LBlo
'Romany Red' (3)	IDun
romieuxii	CAvo CBro EPot LBow SBla SIng SPou
¶ – AB&S 4384	EPot NHar
– JCA 805	EPot NHar NHol WChr
¶ – SF 370	CMon
– ssp. ***albidus***	WChr
¶ – – SF 110	CMon
– – var. ***zaianicus***	WChr
¶ – 'Atlas Gold'	EPot
– 'Joy Bishop' (10)	EPot SPou WChr
§ – 'Julia Jane' (10)	EPot
§ – ssp. ***romieuxii*** var. ***mesatlanticus***	CAvo CMon CRiv EPot SBla SWas
¶ – 'Treble Chance'	EPot
'Rosapenna' (2)	ICar
'Roscarrick' (6)	ECop
'Rose Gold' (1)	IDun
'Rose Royale' (2)	IBal ICar
'Roseate Tern' (2)	IDun
'Rosedew' (2)	LBlo
'Rosedown' (5)	CBro
'Roseworthy' (2)	LAma LBlo
'Rossferry' (2)	IBal
'Rosy Sunrise' (2)	LAma
'Rosy Trumpet' (1)	CBro
'Rosy Wonder' (2)	EWal
'Rotarian' (3)	IDun
'Roulette' (2)	LBlo
'Round Robin' (2)	ICar

'Rousillon' (11) IDun
'Royal Ballet' (2) IDun
'Royal Coachman' ICar
'Royal Command' (2) See N. 'Royal Decree'
§ 'Royal Decree' (2) EWal
'Royal Dornoch' (1) GEve
'Royal Orange' (2) EWal
'Royal Princess' (3) ECop IBal
'Royal Regiment' (2) ICar
'Royal Viking' (3) IBal
'Royal Wedding' (2) ICar
'Rubh Mor' (2) ECop
'Ruby Tail' (2) EWal
'Rubyat' (6) IBal
rupicola CMon CRDP EPot LAma LBow MS&S NHar SIng
¶ – MS 567/455 CMon
§ – ssp. ***marvieri*** WChr
¶ – – AB&S 4414 CMon
¶ – – SF 126 CMon
'Rushlight' (2) EWal
'Rushmore' (2) IDun
'Ruth Haller' (5) ICar
'Ryan Son' (3) IBal
'Saberwing' (5) ICar
'Sabine Hay' (3) EWal ICar IDun
'Sacajawea' (2) EWal
¶ 'Sacramento' (3) ECop
'Safari' (2) ICar
¶ 'Saint Duthus' (1) GEve
'Saint Keverne' (2) EWal IBal LAma NRog
'Saint Patrick's Day' (2) EWal LAma
'Salmon Leap' (2) ICar
'Salmon Spray' (2) LBlo
'Salmon Trout' (2) ECop EWal LAma
'Salomé' (2) EWal LAma LBlo MBri NRog
'Samantha' (4) ECop ICar
'Samaria' (3) CBro
'Samite' (1) EWal
'Sammy Boy' (2) ECop
'Sarah' (2) EWal
'Sateen' (2) EWal
'Satellite' (6) EWal ICar
'Satin Pink' (2) ETub EWal MBri
'Saturn' (3) ICar
scaberulus CBro CMon LAma LBow SIng WChr WCru WPer
¶ – S&B 208 CMon
'Scarlet Elegance' (2) LAma
'Scarlet Gem' (8) ETub EWal LAma SIng
'Scarlett O'Hara' (2) LAma
'Scoreline' (1) IDun
'Scotney Castle' (1) ECop
'Sea Gift' (7) CBro
'Sea Green' (9) ECop
'Sealing Wax' (2) ECop EWal
'Segovia' (3) CBro IDun
'Sempre Avanti' (2) LAma LBlo MBri NRog
'Sennocke' (5) CBro
serotinus CMon WThi
¶ – SF 298/285 CMon
'Sextant' (6) EWal IDun
'Shandon' (2) IDun
'Shanes Castle' (1) ICar
'She' (2) EWal
'Sheerline' (2) IDun
'Sheik' (2) ICar
'Sherborne' (4) IDun
'Sherpa' (1) IDun
'Shining Light' (2) ECop ICar
'Shot Silk' (5) LAma
'Showboat' (2) ICar
'Shuttlecock' (6) IDun
'Shy Face' (2) ICar
'Sidley' (3) IDun
'Sigrid Undset' (3) LAma
'Silent Valley' (1) ICar IDun
'Silk Cut' (2) IDun
'Silken Sails' (3) ICar
'Silver Bells' (5) IDun
'Silver Blaze' (2) IDun
'Silver Chimes' (8) CAvo CBro ETub EWal LAma LBlo NRog SIng
'Silver Crystal' (3) IDun
'Silver Princess' (3) EWal
'Silver Shell' (11) IDun
'Silver Standard' (2) EWal
'Silver Surf' (2) IDun
'Silvermere' (2) IDun
'Silverwood' (3) IDun
¶ 'Sinopel' (3) ETub
'Sir Winston Churchill' (4) EWal LAma LBlo NRog
¶ 'Skerry' (2) ICar
'Slaney' (3) ICar
'Slowcoach' (3) IDun
'Small Fry' (1) EWal
'Smokey Bear' (4) IDun
'Snoopie' (6) IDun
'Snow Dream' (2) EWal ICar
'Snow Gleam' (1) IDun
'Snowcrest' (3) IDun
'Snowfire' (4) ICar
'Snowshill' (2) ICar LBlo
'Solar Tan' (3) IDun
'Soldier Brave' (2) EWal
'Soledad' (2) ICar
'Soleil d'Or' (8) EWal MBri
'Solferique' (2) IDun
'Sorcerer' (3) ICar
'Southease' (2) ECop
'Sovereign' (11) IDun
'Space Age' (2) ICar
'Spanish Moon' (1) EWal
'Sparkling Eye' (8) IBal
'Spellbinder' (1) EWal LAma LBlo MBri
'Spey Bay' (3) IDun
'Sportsman' (2) IDun
'Spring Valley' (3) ICar
'Springston Charm' (2) ICar
'Springwood' (2) IDun
'Sputnik' (6) IDun
sp. ABS 4450 SPou
sp. ABS 4656 SPou
sp. C M Stocken (10) CBro
'Stadium' (2) EWal
'Stainless' (2) IBal
'Standard Value' (1) LAma
'Starfire' (7) ICar
'Starship' (2) IDun
'State Express' (2) IDun
'Statue' (2) EWal
'Stint' (6) IDun

'Stoke Charity' (2) ICar
'Stormy Weather' (1) ECop
¶ 'Stourbridge' (2) ECop
'Strangford' (3) IBal
'Strathkanaird' (1) GEve ICar
'Stratosphere' (7) ECop ICar IDun
'Strephon' (1) ICar
'Strines' (2) ECop EWal
'Stromboli' (2) EWal
'Suda Bay' (2) ICar
'Sugarbush' (7) CBro LAma LBlo MBri NRog SIng
'Suilven' (3) GEve ICar
'Sun Chariot' (2) LBlo
'Sun Disc' (7) CBro EPot EWal MBri SIng WHil WPat
'Sun Salver' (2) IBal
'Sunbather' (2) ICar
'Sundial' (7) CAvo CBro EPot ETub EWal ICar LAma LBlo
'Sundisc' (7) LAma
'Suntory' (3) IDun
¶ 'Super Star' (2) ETub
'Surrey' (2) IDun
'Susan Pearson' (7) ICar
'Suzy' (7) CBro EWal ICar LAma LBlo MBri NRog SIng
¶ 'Svenska Bojan' (2) GEve
'Swallowcliffe' (6) IDun
'Swallownest' (1) ECop
'Swansdown' (4) EWal ICar
¶ 'Sweet Charity' (2) EWal
'Sweet Pepper' (7) CBro ECop GEve ICar
'Sweetness' (7) CAvo CBro EWal IBal IDun LAma NRog
'Swing Wing' (6) IDun
'Sydling' (5) IDun
'Sylvan Hill' (1) IBal
'Symphonette' (2) GEve ICar
'Syracuse' (3) ECop ICar
'Taffeta' (12) CBro SPou WChr
'Tahiti' (4) ECop EWal IDun LAma LBlo MBri NRog
'Tamar Fire' (4) ECop
§ ***tananicus*** WChr
¶ – SF 44 CMon
'Tanera' (2) ICar
'Tangent' (2) EWal ICar
'Tardree' (1) ICar
'Tarlatan' (12) CBro SPou
¶ ***tazetta*** ssp. ***lacticolor*** MS 517 CMon
¶ – – MS 519 CMon
'Tedstone' (1) EWal
'Tekapo' (2) ICar
§ 'Telamonius Plenus' (4) CBro LAma LRHS WShi
§ x ***tenuior*** CAvo
'Testament' (2) EWal
'Tête-à-Tête' (12) CAvo CBro EPar EPot ETub EWal IBal IDun LAma LBlo LBow MBri SIng WHil WPer
'Texas' (4) ETub LAma MBri
'Thalia' (5) CAvo CBro ETub EWal ICar LAma LBow MBri NRog SIng SUsu
¶ 'The Little Gentleman' (6) CBro
'Theano' (2) ICar
'Thoughtful' (5) CBro EWal
¶ 'Three Trees' (1) ICar
'Thunderbolt' (1) EWal
'Tibet' (2) EWal IBal
'Tiger Moth' (6) IDun
'Timolin' (3) ICar
'Tiri Tomba' (11) EWal IDun LBlo
'Tittle Tattle' (7) CBro EWal IBal ICar LAma
'Toby' (2) EWal
'Tonga' (4) ECop ICar
'Top Gallant' (3) IBal
'Top Notch' (2) ICar
'Top of the Hill' (3) IBal ICar
'Topkapi' (2) IBal
'Topolino' (1) CAvo CBro ETub LAma NRog
'Torcross' (3) IDun
'Torr Head' (9) IBal
'Torridon' (2) ECop ICar IDun
'Torrish' (3) ICar
¶ ***tortifolius*** MS 540 CMon
'Tranquil Morn' (3) EWal
'Trena' (6) IDun
'Tresamble' (5) CBro EWal ICar LAma SIng
'Trevithian' (7) CBro EWal IBal LAma LBlo NRog SIng SUsu
'Trewirgie' (6) CBro
triandrus WChr
– var. ***albus*** See N. ***triandrus triandrus***
– var. ***concolor*** See N. ***concolor***
– var. ***pulchellus*** LAma
'Trillick' (3) IDun
'Trilune' (11) IDun
'Tripartite' (11) ECop EWal ICar IDun NZep
'Tristram' (2) ICar
'Tropic Isle' (4) ICar
'Trousseau' (1) EWal LAma LBlo
'Tudor Grove' (2) IDun
'Tudor Minstrel' (2) EWal
'Tudor Rose' (2) ECop
'Tuesday's Child' (5) ECop ETub EWal ICar IDun
'Tullybeg' (3) IBal
'Tullycore' (2) ICar
'Tullygirvan' (2) ICar
'Tullyglass' (2) ICar
'Tullynakill' (2) IBal
'Tullynog' (4) ICar
'Tullyroyal' (2) IBal
'Turncoat' (6) IDun
'Tutankhamun' (2) ECop
'Twicer' (2) IDun
'Tynan' (2) ICar
'Tyneham' (3) IDun
'Tyrone Gold' (2) IDun
¶ 'Ufo' (3) EWal
'Ulster Bank' (3) IDun
'Ulster Bullion' (2) IBal
'Ulster Prince' (1) ICar
'Ultimus' (2) EWal
'Una Bremner' (2) GEve
'Uncle Ben' (1) IBal
'Uncle Remus' (1) EWal
'Undertone' (2) IDun
'Unique' (4) ECop EWal ICar IDun LAma LBlo
'Unsurpassable' (1) LAma LBlo
'Upper Broughton' (2) IDun

♦'Urchin' See N. 'Pzaz'
'Vahu' (2) IDun
'Val d'Incles' (3) IDun
'Valdrome' (11) MBri
'Valediction' (3) IDun
'Valinor' (2) IDun
'Van Dyck' (1) IDun
'Van Sion' See N. 'Telamonius Plenus'
'Vantage' (2) ICar
'Verdant' (1) IDun
'Verdin' (7) GEve ICar IDun
'Verger' (3) LAma LBlo MBri
'Vernal Prince' (3) IDun
'Verona' (3) ECop ICar IDun LBlo
'Vers Libre' (9) IDun
'Verwood' (3) IDun
'Victory' (2) EWal
'Vigilante' (1) GEve IDun
'Viking' (1) ECop GEve LBlo
'Vilna' (2) EWal
'Violetta' (2) EWal ICar IDun
'Vireo' (7) ICar
'Virgil' (9) EWal
viridiflorus WThi
¶– MS 500 CMon
¶– SF 323 CMon
'Vital' (2) IDun
'Vivarino' (11) EWal
'Vocation' (2) IDun
'Voltage' (2) IDun
'Vulcan' (2) EWal LBlo
'W P Milner' (1) CAvo CBro LAma MBri NRog SIng WOMN
'Wahkeena' (2) ICar
'Waldorf Astoria' (4) IDun
'Waterperry' (7) CBro LAma NRog SIng SUsu
watieri CAvo CBro CMon EPot NHar NHol SPou WChr
¶– AB&S 4518 CMon
'Waxwing' (5) IDun
'Webster' (9) IDun
'Wee Bee' (1) EWal
'Welvan' (3) ICar
'Wendy Walsh' (2) ICar
'Westholme' (2) IDun
'Westward' (4) EWal
'Wetherby' (3) IDun
'Whang-hi' (6) ECop
'Whisper' (5) EWal
'Whitbourne' (3) EWal
'White Butterfly' (2) EWal
¶'White Cross' (2) IBal
'White Empress' (1) IBal ICar
'White Ermine' (2) IDun
'White Hill' (2) IBal
'White Lion' (4) ETub EWal LAma LBlo NRog
'White Majesty' (1) IBal
'White Marvel' (4) CBro EWal LAma NRog
'White Phantom' (1) ICar
'White Plume' (2) EWal
'White Spray' (2) ICar
'White Star' (1) ICar IDun
'Whiteabbey' (2) IBal
'Widgeon' (2) EWal
willkommii SPou
'Winchester' (2) EWal
'Windjammer' (1) EWal
'Winfrith' (2) EWal
'Witch Doctor' (3) IBal
'Woodcock' (6) CBro
'Woodgreen' (2) EWal
'Woodland Prince' (3) ECop ICar
'Woodland Star' (3) ECop
'Woolsthorpe' (2) IBal
'Worcester' (2) EWal
'Xanthin Gold' (1) IDun
'Xit' (3) SPou WChr
'Yellow Cheerfulness' (4) ETub EWal LAma LBlo MBri NRog SIng
'Yellow Standard' (2) LAma
'Yellow Sun' (3) LAma
¶'Yellow Tresamble' (5) CBro
'Yes Please' (2) EWal
'Young Blood' (2) IDun
'Young Idea' (7) EWal
****zaianicus albus*** MS 168 CMon
*– ***lutescens*** SF 374 CMon NHar
'Zeus' (2) ICar

NARDOPHYLLUM (Compositae)
bryoïdes ITim MHig

NARTHECIUM (Liliaceae/Melanthiaceae)
ossifragum WGwy

NASSELLA (Gramineae)
trichotoma EMon EPla ETPC LRHS SApp

NASTURTIUM (R. Brown) (Cruciferae)
officinale CBen SWat WEas WHer WHol

NASTURTIUM (hort.) (Cruciferae)
See **TROPAEOLUM**

NECTARBERRY See **RUBUS**

NECTARINE See **PRUNUS *persica nectarina***

NECTAROSCORDUM (Liliaceae/Alliaceae)
§ ***siculum*** CAvo CBro CFis CGle CHan CMea CNic ECro ELan EOrc EPar ERav MBal NBir NEgg SUsu WDav
§ – ssp. ***bulgaricum*** CBro CHad CRDP ECha EFou EPar EPot ETub IBlr LBow SIng

NEILLIA (Rosaceae)
affinis CCla CDec CDoC EFol EHal MBal MUlv WHCG
longiracemosa See N. ***thibetica***
sinensis CMCN CPle EGol LAbb MRav
§ ***thibetica*** CB&S CCla CLan CPle ELan ENot IOrc ISea LAbb MBri SHil SPer SPla SSta WAbe WBod WPat WWin
thyrsiflora ERav

NELUMBO (Nelumbonaceae)
'Kermesina' MSta
lutea 'Flavescens' MSta
nucifera MSta

- – 'Alba Grandiflora' MSta
- – 'Alba Striata' MSta
- – 'Pekinensis Rubra' MSta
- – 'Rosea' MSta
- – 'Rosea Plena' MSta
- 'Osiris' MSta
- 'Pulchra' MSta

NEMASTYLIS (Iridaceae)

- ***tenuis*** ssp. ***pringlei*** WPer

NEMATANTHUS (Gesneriaceae)

- 'Black Gold' CHal
- 'Black Magic' MBri WEfe
- 'Christmas Holly' WEfe
- 'Freckles' WEfe
- * ***glabra*** MBri
- § ***gregarius*** CHal MBri WEfe
- § – 'Golden West' (v) CHal MBri WEfe
- ♦– 'Variegatus' See N. *g.* 'Golden West'
- 'Jungle Lights' WEfe
- ***radicans*** See N. ***gregarius***
- ***strigillosus*** MBri
- 'Tropicana' MBri WEfe

NEMESIA (Scrophulariaceae)

- ***denticulata*** EOrc
- ***foetens*** See N. ***fruticans***
- § ***fruticans*** CBrk CDoC CSam CTro LHil MTho NPer NTow SDix SUsu WKif WOMN WPer WWin
- N– 'lilac/blue' CBrk CGle CMHG CRiv CSam CTro EMon EOrc GCal LHil LHop MBro MFir NPer SAxl SUsu WEas WOMN WPer WRus
- 'Hermione' EMon
- ***umbonata*** hort. See N. ***fruticans*** 'lilac/blue'

NEMOPANTHUS (Aquifoliaceae)

See Plant Deletions

NEODYPSIS (Palmae)

- ***decaryi*** LPal

NEOLITSEA (Lauraceae)

- ***glauca*** See N. ***sericea***
- § ***sericea*** CHEx SArc

NEOMARICA (Iridaceae)

- ¶ ***gracilis*** CTro
- ¶ ***northiana*** SLMG

NEOPANAX See **PSEUDOPANAX**

NEOPAXIA (Portulacaceae)

- § ***australasica*** CMHG ECar ECou EPot ESis MHig NGre NHar NTow WCru WPer
- – blue leaved form See N. *a.* 'Koscuisko'
- – bronze form See N. *a.* 'Ohau'
- § – 'Great Lake' ECou
- – green form See N. *a.* 'Great Lake'
- – grey form See N. *a.* 'Kosciusko'
- § – 'Kosciusko ' ECar GDra NBir NHol
- – 'Lakeside' ECou
- – 'Lyndon' ECou
- § – 'Ohau' ECou EPla GGar

NEOREGELIA (Bromeliaceae)

- ***carolinae*** MBri
- § – Meyendorffii Group 'Flandria' MBri
- – Meyendorffii Group 'Meyendorffii' MBri
- – f. ***tricolor*** (v) CHal MBri
- § Claret MBri

NEPENTHES (Nepenthaceae)

- ***alata*** WMEx
- x ***coccinea*** MBri WMEx
- ***khasiana*** WMEx

NEPETA † (Labiatae)

- ***argolica*** See N. ***sibthorpii***
- 'Blue Beauty' See N. ***sibirica*** 'Souvenir d'André Chaudron'
- ***camphorata*** CPou EJud SHer SIde WPer WWye
- ***cataria*** CArn CFis CHal CSFH CSev EJud Effi GPoy LHol MChe MHew NSal NSel SHer SIde WHer WOak WPer WWye
- – 'Citriodora' CArn EHal EMon GCal GPoy LHol NSal SChu SMrm WCHb
- ***clarkei*** CCor CHan EFou GCal MSte SUsu
- x ***faassenii*** CCla CGle CHad EBre EMon LBre LBuc MTol NKay NMir NVic SChu SCro SIng SPla WHil
- – 'Little Titch' EFou GCal MSte SChu SMrm WSHC WSun
- – 'Snowflake' CCla CGle CMGP CMea CSam CSco EFou EHal ELan EMon GCal MSte NBir NCat NSel SChu SCro SMrm SPer SSvw SUsu WPbr WSun
- § – 'Superba' EFou ELan EMon
- – 'Walker's Low' EFou GCal SMrm WSun
- x ***gigantea*** CFis
- ***glechoma*** 'Variegata' See GLECHOMA ***hederacea*** 'Variegata'
- ***govaniana*** CChu CCla CHad CHan CPar CSam ECha EFou EGol ELan EOrc GCal LGre MBel MMil NBro NSti NTow SAxl SPer SSpi SUsu WHal WPbr WPer WWin
- ***grandiflora*** NFai SIde
- ***hederacea*** 'Variegata' See GLECHOMA ***hederacea*** 'Variegata'
- ***lanceolata*** See N. ***nepetalla***
- ***longiflora*** WPer
- * ***longipes*** CHan EMon SChu SCro
- ***macrantha*** See N. ***sibirica***
- ***melissifolia*** EHal EMon WCHb WPer
- ***mussinii*** See N. ***racemosa***
- § ***nepetella*** CSam EHal EMon LGre LRHS WPer
- ¶ – ssp. ***amethystina*** EMon
- ***nervosa*** CArn CChu CCla CDec CSam EBre ECED ECha EFol EFou ELan EMar EMon LBre LGan LGre MFir MSte NFai NOak NSti NTow SDix SHer WHer WHoo WPer WRus

§ ***nuda*** ECha EFol EHal ELan EMon LRHS NHol WCot
– ssp. ***albiflora*** EMon LRHS
¶ – ssp. ***nuda*** CHan LRHS
pannonica See N. ***nuda***
parnassica CDB 13073 EMon
§ ***phyllochlamys*** CBot CFis EMon LHil MSte SBla SSad
– Mac&W 5882 WOMN
'Pool Bank' EFou EHal EMon MBel WPer
'Porzellan' EFou EHal EMon
§ ***prattii*** CSco EHal GCal
§ ***racemosa*** Widely available
¶ – 'Blue Ice' EMon
♦ ***reichenbachiana*** See N. ***racemosa***
§ ***sibirica*** CGle ECha EFou EJud LHil MBri NBro NSal SChu SCro SIgm SUsu WCot WEas WHal WMer WPer WWye
§ – 'Souvenir d'André Chaudron' CDoC CGle CLew CMHG CRDP CSam CSco EBre EFou EGol EMon GCal LBre LGan MBri SCro SMrm SPer SUsu WEas WHer WOld WPer WSun
§ ***sibthorpii*** WPer
sintenisii EMon
'Six Hills Giant' Widely available
¶ sp. DS&T 09054T MBel
sp. DS&T 89048T EMon
sp. DS&T 89054T EMon
stewartiana CLD 551 EMon
subsessilis CHan CRDP EMar SAxl SBla SMrm SWas WBon WPer WWye
¶ – forms WBon WCot
¶ – var. ***yesoensis*** CHan
teydea EMon WPer
'Thornbury' CShe
tuberosa CSam EHal LGan NSti SChu
ucranica NHex

NEPHROLEPIS (Nephrolepidaceae)

cordifolia MBri NMar
exaltata 'Bostoniensis' MBri SRms
– 'Rooseveltii' MBri
– 'Smithii' MBri
– 'Smithii Linda' MBri
– 'Teddy Junior' MBri
– 'Todeoïdes' NMar

NEPHROPHYLLIDIUM (Menyanthaceae)

See Plant Deletions

NERINE † (Liliaceae/Amaryllidaceae)

¶ 'Baghdad' CMon
bowdenii Widely available
– 'Alba' EBre ECha LBre
– 'Mark Fenwick' CB&S ECha EPot ERav WCot
– 'Pink Triumph' CAvo CB&S CKel CRDP LAma LBlo LBow NHol NRog SDeJ WAbe
¶ – 'Variegata' SHBN
¶ – 'Wellsii' CMon WCot
¶ 'Brocade' CMon
corusca major See N. ***sarniensis corusca***
crispa See N. ***undulata***
¶ ***filamentosa*** CMon
filifolia CAvo CBro EPot GArf GCal
flexuosa CMon SLMG
– 'Alba' CAvo CBro CMon EBre LAma LBre LGre SDeJ SGil
¶ – pink CMon
¶ ***fothergillii*** 'Queen Mary' CMon
¶ 'Gaby Deslys' CMon
¶ 'Grisle' CMon
¶ ***humilis*** CMon
¶ – Breachiae Group CMon
¶ – Tulbaghensis Group CMon
¶ 'Mansellii' CMon
¶ 'Marnie Rogerson' CGle LGre
masoniorum MTho WOMN WThu
pudica LHop SHer
¶ 'Rose Camellia' CMon
sarniensis CKel CMon ECha NRog SLMG WThi
§ – var. ***corusca*** LAma
¶ – – 'Major' LBow
– ***fothergillii*** CMon WCot
¶ Smee No. 11 CMon
§ ***undulata*** CAvo CBro CMon ECha LAma LBow MBri NHol NRog WCot
¶ 'Zeal Giant' CMon

NERIUM (Apocynaceae)

oleander CHEx CPle EBak LAbb SEng WOMN
– 'Alsace' CSun LBlm
*– 'Avalanche' CB&S
– 'Belle Hélène' CSun
– 'Cardinal' CB&S
*– 'Clare' ERea
– double apricot CSun
– double white CBot
– 'Emile Sahut' CSun
– 'Emilie' CSun ERea
– forms CTro MNew SLMG
– 'Géant des Batailles' CSun ERea LBlm
– 'Hardy Red' ERea
– 'Isle of Capri' ERea
– 'Italia' ERea
– 'Luteum Plenum' CSun ERea
– 'Madame Allen' CSun
– 'Madame Léon Brun' CSun LBlm
– 'Magaly' CSun ERea
– 'Margaritha' ERea
– 'Marie Gambetta' CSun
– 'Mont Blanc' CSun
– 'Papa Gambetta' CSun
*– 'Peach Blossom' LAbb
– 'Petite Salmon' CSun LBlm
– 'Professeur Granel' CSun ERea
– 'Provence' CSun ERea
– 'Rosario' CSun
– 'Rosée du Ventoux' ERea
– 'Roseum' SLMG
– 'Roseum Plenum' CB&S CSun SLMG
– 'Sealy Pink' CB&S
*– 'Snowflake' ERea
– 'Soeur Agnès' CSun ERea
– 'Soleil Levant' ERea
– 'Souvenir des Iles Canaries' CSun
– 'Souvenir d'Emma Schneider' CSun

– 'Splendens' ERea
– 'Tito Poggi' CSun
– 'Variegatum' CBot ERea LAbb LHop NHex SLMG WCot
– 'Ville de Carpentras' ERea
– 'Yellow Queen' CB&S

NERTERA (Rubiaceae)
♦*depressa* See N. ***granadensis***
§ ***granadensis*** ECou MBri NTow

NEVIUSIA (Rosaceae)
alabamensis CHan SPla

NICANDRA (Solanaceae)
physalodes CArn CRDP CRiv EJud ELan NBir NHex SIde WWye
– ***alba*** NBir

NICOTIANA (Solanaceae)
glauca CB&S CGle CGre CPle CTro LHil SLMG SMrm WEas WHal
langsdorffii CB&S CBrk CGre CHad CHal CHan CMea CTom ECro LHil MPlt NBro NRar NSti SLMG SMrm SUsu WEas WHal WRus
noctiflora EBar
rustica ECro NSal NSti
suaveolens WEas WRus
sylvestris CBrk CGre CHEx CHad CHal CHan EBar GCal LHil SMrm SUsu WEas WHal WRus WSun
tabacum CHEx CPle EJud WWye

NIDULARIUM (Bromeliaceae)
flandria See NEOREGELIA ***carolinae*** Meyendorfii Group 'Flandria'

NIEREMBERGIA (Solanaceae)
§ ***caerulea*** ECha WThi
frutescens CGle CHad CHan EMon ESma ITim LGre LHop MTho WRus
hippomanica See N. ***caerulea***
§ ***repens*** CKel CMHG CPar CRDP CRiv ELan ELun EPot MCas MPit NMen NRed NRoo SIng WHal WHil WOMN WPer WTyr WWin
– 'Violet Queen' ELan MTho
rivularis See N. ***repens***

NIPHAEA (Gesneriaceae)
oblonga NMos

X NIPHIMENES (Gesneriaceae)
'Lemonade' NMos

NIPPONANTHEMUM (Compositae)
§ ***nipponicum*** CFis CHan CLew CNic CRiv CSam CSco CSev ECha EMon GCal MFir MTho NRoo SApp WBon WEas

NOCCAEA See **THLASPI**

NOLANA (Solanaceae)
See Plant Deletions

NOLINA (Dracaenaceae)
¶ ***beldingii*** SIgm
¶ ***brevifolia*** SIgm
¶ ***greenii*** SIgm
humilis SArc
longifolia SArc
¶ ***palmeri*** SIgm
¶ ***texana*** SIgm

NOMOCHARIS (Liliaceae/Liliaceae)
aperta CAvo CBro CNic EBre GCHN GDra LBre NHol NRog WCru
farreri CAvo CNic GArf NHol
mairei See N. ***pardanthina***
nana See LILIUM ***nanum***
§ ***pardanthina*** CAvo GArf NHar NRog
– f. ***punctulata*** CAvo GDra NHar NRog
saluenensis GDra NHol NRog

NONEA (Boraginaceae)
¶ ***lutea*** WAbb WByw

NOTELAEA (Oleaceae)
ligustrina GWht

NOTHOFAGUS † (Fagaceae)
alessandrii CGre GAri ISea SSpi
§ ***alpina*** CBra CDoC CGre CLnd CPer GAri GRei IOrc ISea MBal NWea SPer WDin WFro WMou WNor
antarctica CB&S CCla CDoC CGre CLnd CMHG EHar ELan IOrc LPan LTil MBal MBar MBri MGos NBar NBee NWea SEng SPer SSpi WBod WCoo WDin WNor WSHC
– 'Prostrata' See N. ***a.*** 'Benmore'
betuloïdes GAri
cunninghamii CB&S CGre GAri ISea LTil SSpi WNor
dombeyi CGre GAri IOrc SArc SPer WMou WNor
fusca CB&S WNor
menziesii CB&S CGre CLnd CMHG GAri SArc SSpi WCoo WNor
obliqua CDoC CGre CLnd CSam GAri IOrc ISea MBal NWea SSpi WDin WFro WMou WNor
procera See N. ***alpina***
pumilio CGre GAri ISea WNor WWat
solanderi SArc WNor
– var. ***cliffortioïdes*** CAbb CB&S CGre CLnd GAri MBal SSpi WCoo WNor
truncata SSpi WNor

NOTHOLIRION (Liliaceae/Liliaceae)
bulbuliferum CAvo CRDP ECro ITim NHol
macrophyllum CAvo CRDP EBul NHol WCru
thomsonianum EBul ETub

NOTHOPANAX See PSEUDOPANAX

NOTHOSCORDUM (Liliaceae/Alliaceae)

bivalve NSal
¶ *bonariense* WDav
¶ *gracile* CHan
inodorum CBro
¶ – *macrostemon* CL 7/76 CMon
neriniflorum See CALOSCORDUM *n.*

NOTOSPARTIUM (Leguminosae)

carmichaeliae CHan ECou
glabrescens ECou
torulosum ECou

NOTOTRICHE (Malvaceae)

compacta MTho

NUPHAR (Nymphaeaceae)

japonica var. *variegata* CRow
lutea CBen CRDP CRow EHon EMFW LMay SWat WChe WHol
– *variegata* See N. *variegata*
pumila variegata MSta
§ *variegata* WChe

NUT, Cob See CORYLUS *avellana*

NUT, Filbert See CORYLUS *maxima*

NYMPHAEA † (Nymphaeaceae)

'Afterglow' (T/D) MSta
alba (H) CBen CBow CRow CWGN EHon EMFW EWav LMay MSta SAWi SWat WChe WHol WStI
– ssp. *occidentalis* (H) MSta
– 'Plenissima' (H) MSta
'Albatros' (H) CBen EHon EMFW LMay MSta SLon SWat
'Amabilis' (H) CBen CRiv CRow EMFW LMay MSta SHig
'American Star' MSta
'Andreana' (H) CBen EMFW LMay MSta
¶ 'Anna Epple' EMFW
'Arc-en-ciel' (H) EMFW MSta
'Atropurpurea' (H) CBen EMFW EWav LMay MSta
'Attraction' (H) CBen CRiv CRow CWGN EHon EMFW EWav LMay MSta SHig SWat WChe WHol WStI
'August Koch' (T/D) MSta
'Aurora' (H) CBen EMFW EWav LMay MSta
'Blue Beauty' (T/D) CBen
'Brackleyi Rosea' (H) CBen EMFW LMay MSta
candida (H) CBen EHon EMFW LMay MSta
'Candidissima' (H) MSta
'Candidissima Rosea' (H) MSta
capensis (T/D) MSta
caroliniana 'Rosea' (H) CRiv MSta
'Caroliniana Nivea' (H) CBen CRDP EMFW MSta
'Caroliniana Perfecta' (H) CBen LMay MSta
§ 'Charlene Strawn' EMFW MSta
'Charles de Meurville' (H) CBen CRow EMFW EWav LMay MSta SLon
'Chrysantha' (H) EMFW MSta
'Colonel A J Welch' (H) CBen CRow EHon EMFW EWav LMay MSta SAWi SWat WChe
'Colonel Lindbergh' (T/D) MSta
colorata (T/D) CBen MSta
'Colossea' (H) CBen EHon EMFW EWav LMay MSta WHol
'Comanche' (H) CBen EMFW MSta SWat
'Conqueror' (H) EMFW LMay MSta SAWi SHig SLon SWat
¶ 'Darwin' (H) MSta
x *daubenyana* (T/D) MSta
'Director George T Moore' (T/D) MSta
'Ellisiana' (H) CBen CRDP EMFW LMay MSta
'Escarboucle' (H) CBen CRow CWGN EMFW EWav LMay MSta SAWi SHig SLon SWat WHol
'Evelyn Randig' (T/D) CBen MSta
'Exquisita' (H) MSta
'Fabiola' (H) EMFW LMay
'Firecrest' (H) CBen CBow EHon EMFW EWav LMay MSta SLon
'Froebelii' (H) CBen CRiv CRow CWGN EHon EMFW EWav LMay MSta SHig SLon SWat WChe WHol
'Fulva' (H) MSta
'Galatée' (H) MSta
'General Pershing' (T/D) MSta
'Gladstoneana' (H) CBen CRow CWGN EHon EMFW EWav LMay MSta SAWi SHig SWat WHol
'Gloire de Temple-sur-Lot' (H) CBen EMFW MSta
'Gloriosa' (H) CBen EMFW LMay MSta
'Gonnère' (H) CBen CRow CWGN EMFW EWav LMay MSta SHig SWat
'Graziella' (H) CBen CWGN EMFW LMay MSta
'Green Smoke' (T/D) MSta
¶ 'Hal Miller' (H) EMFW
¶ 'Helen Fowler' (H) EMFW
x *helvola* (H) CBen CRow CWGN EHon EMFW EWav LMay MSta SAWi SHig SWat WHol
'Hermine' (H) EMFW MSta SWat
'Hollandia' CBen EMFW SWat
'Indiana' (H) CBen CWGN EMFW LMay MSta SLon SWat
'James Brydon' (H) CBen CRiv CRow CWGN EHon EMFW EWav LMay MSta SAWi SHig SLon SWat WHol
'James Hudson' (H) MSta
'Julian Decelle' MSta
¶ 'Juliana' EMFW
'Laydekeri Fulgens' (H) CBen EMFW LMay MSta
'Laydekeri Lilacea' (H) CBen CRow EMFW EWav LMay MSta SHig SWat
'Laydekeri Purpurata' (H) EMFW LMay MSta SWat
'Laydekeri Rosea' (H) CBen EMFW LMay
¶ 'Luciana' (H) EMFW
'Lucida' (H) CBen EMFW LMay MSta
'Lusitania' (H) MSta
'Madame Wilfon Gonnère' (H) CBen EHon EMFW EWav LMay MSta SWat

'Marliacea Albida' (H)	CBen CRiv CWGN EHon EMFW EWav LMay MSta SWat WChe WHol
'Marliacea Carnea' (H)	CBen CRiv CRow CWGN EHon EMFW EWav LMay MSta SWat WHol
'Marliacea Chromatella' (H)	CBen CRDP CRiv CRow CWGN EHon EMFW EWav LMay MSta SAWi SHig SLon SWat WChe WHol
'Marliacea Flammea' (H)	MSta
'Marliacea Ignea' (H)	EMFW MSta
'Marliacea Rosea' (H)	EMFW EWav MSta SHig
'Marliacea Rubra Punctata' (H)	MSta
'Martin E Randig'	MSta
'Masaniello' (H)	CBen CRow CWGN EHon EMFW EWav LMay MSta SLon SWat
¶ 'Maurice Laydeker' (H)	EMFW
'Maxima' (H)	MSta
mexicana (T/D)	MSta
'Moorei' (H)	CBen CWGN EHon EMFW LMay MSta SHig WHol
'Mrs C W Ward' (T/D)	MSta
'Mrs Richmond' (H)	CBen CRow EHon EMFW EWav LMay MSta SAWi SHig SWat WHol
'Neptune' (H)	MSta
'Newton' (H)	EMFW MSta
¶ 'Nigel'	MSta
'Norma Gedye' (H)	CBen MSta SWat
'Odalisque' (H)	EMFW MSta
§ ***odorata*** (H)	CBen CRow CWGN LMay MSta SHig
– var. ***pumila*** (H)	MSta
– var. ***rosea*** (H)	EMFW MSta SAWi
– var. ***rubra*** (H)	MSta
'Odorata Alba' (H)	See N. ***odorata***
'Odorata Eugène de Land' (H)	MSta
'Odorata Gigantea' (H)	MSta
'Odorata Juliana' (H)	MSta
'Odorata Minor' (H)	CBen CRow CWGN EMFW LMay MSta
'Odorata Sulphurea Grandiflora' (H)	CBen CRow CWGN EHon EMFW EWav LMay MSta SAWi
'Odorata Turicensis' (H)	CBen EMFW LMay MSta
'Odorata William B Shaw' (H)	CBen CWGN EHon EMFW LMay MSta SLon SWat
'Pamela' (T/D)	CBen MSta
'Paul Hariot'	CBen CWGN EHon EMFW EWav LMay MSta SLon SWat
Pearl of the Pool ® (H)	MSta
'Pennsylvania' (T/D)	MSta
'Perry's Pink'	MSta
'Peter Slocum'	MSta
'Phoebus' (H)	MSta
'Picciola' (H)	EMFW MSta
'Pink Opal' (H)	CBen EMFW LMay MSta
'Pink Platter' (T/D)	CBen
'Pink Sensation' (H)	CBen EMFW MSta
'Princess Elizabeth' (H)	CBen EMFW LMay MSta
¶ 'Pumila Rubis'	MSta
'Pygmaea Alba' (H)	See N. ***tetragona***
'Pygmaea Rubis' (H)	CRow EHon EWav LMay MSta SWat WHol
¶ 'Pygmaea Rubra' (H)	CBen EMFW
'Ray Davies'	MSta
'Red Cup'	MSta
'Red Flare' (T/N)	MSta
'Rembrandt' (H)	EMFW
'René Gérard' (H)	CBen EHon EMFW EWav LMay MSta SAWi SHig SWat
'Robinsoniana' (H)	EMFW MSta
'Rose Arey' (H)	CBen CRow CWGN EHon EMFW EWav LMay MSta SLon SWat WHol
'Rose Magnolia' (H)	CRiv EMFW SWat
'Rosennymphe' (H)	CBen LMay
¶ 'Rosy Morn' (H)	EMFW
'Sanguinea' (H)	EMFW MSta
¶ 'Seignourettii' (H)	EMFW
'Sioux' (H)	CBen CWGN EHon EMFW LMay MSta SHig SWat
'Sir Galahad' (T/N)	MSta
'Sirius' (H)	EMFW MSta
'Solfatare' (H)	EMFW EWav MSta
¶ 'Somptuosa' (H)	EMFW
'Souvenir de Fridolfing' (H)	MSta
'Suavissima' (H)	MSta
¶ 'Sultan'	EMFW MSta
'Sunrise' (H)	CRDP EMFW EWav LMay MSta SWat
§ ***tetragona*** (H)	CBen CRDP CRow EMFW LMay MSta WHol
¶ – 'Johann Pring' (H)	EMFW
¶ 'Texas Dawn'	EMFW
tuberosa (H)	CBen LMay
– 'Alba' (H)	MSta
– 'Richardsonii' (H)	CWGN EHon EMFW MSta
– 'Rosea' (H)	CBen CWGN EMFW LMay MSta WHol
¶ 'Venusta' (H)	MSta
¶ 'Vésuve' (H)	EMFW
¶ 'Virginalis' (H)	EMFW
¶ 'Virginia' (H)	EMFW
¶ 'William Doogue' (H)	EMFW
'William Falconer' (H)	CBen CWGN EMFW EWav LMay MSta SAWi SLon
'Yellow Dazzler' (T/D)	MSta
¶ 'Yul Ling'	EMFW

NYMPHOÏDES (Menyanthaceae)

peltata	CRDP CRiv EMFW SWat WChe WHol
§ – 'Bennettii'	CBen CWGN EBre EHon EWav IBlr LBre LMay MSta

NYSSA (Cornaceae)

¶ ***ogeche***	CGre
sinensis	CAbP CB&S CBow CChu CCla CDoC CGre CMCN CPMA CPle CSam EHar LTil MBri MUlv SHil SPer SReu SSpi SSta WCoo WWat
sylvatica	CB&S CCla CLnd CMCN CMHG CSco CWSG EHar ELan IBar IJoh MBal MBar MBri MBrk MMea MRav MUlv SHBN SPer SPla SReu SSpi SSta WBod WCoo WDin WFro WWat
– 'Jermyns Flame'	SHil SSpi
– 'Windsor'	SSpi

OAKESIELLA See UVULARIA

OCHAGAVIA (Bromeliaceae)

rosea	CHEx

OCHNA (Ochnaceae)

serrulata	CPle CSun

OCIMUM (Labiatae)

§ *americanum*	WHer
– 'Meng Luk'	WPer
basilicum	CArn CHun CSFH CSev EEls EJud GPoy IEde LHol MBri MChe MPit NSal NSel SHer SIde SWat WHal WHer WPer WWye
– 'Anise'	CSev MChe WPer
– 'Cinnamon'	CSev MChe NSal SHer SWat WHer WPer WWye
– var. *citriodorum*	CArn MChe NOak NSal SHer SIde SWat WOak WPer
– 'Dark Opal'	SWat
– 'Genovese'	NSel
*– *glycyrrhiza*	NSal
– 'Green Ruffles'	MChe SWat
♦– 'Holy'	See O. ***tenuiflorum***
– var. *minimum*	CArn CHun CSFH CSev EEls EJud LHol MBri MChe NSal SHer SIde WHer WOak WPer
*– *neapolitanum*	MChe SIde SWat WPer
– 'Purple Ruffles'	MChe SHer SIde SWat WPer
– var. *purpurascens*	CArn CHun CSev EEls GPoy LHol MBri MChe NSal NSel SIde WHer WPer WWye
canum	See O. ***americanum***
'Horapha'	WPer
sanctum	See O. ***tenuiflorum***
'Spice'	MChe
§ *tenuiflorum*	CArn CSev GPoy MChe NOak NSal SIde SWat WPer

OEMLERIA (Rosaceae)

§ *cerasiformis*	CB&S CCla CHan ELan WCot WEas WWat

OENANTHE (Umbelliferae)

japonica	See O. ***javanica***
javanica 'Flamingo'	CGle CMil CRDP CRow CSpe EBar ECar ECha EFol EHal ELan EMar EMon EPla LWad MBel MBri SUsu WCru WHer
pimpinelloïdes	WOak

OENOTHERA † (Onagraceae)

§ *acaulis*	CBot CChu CLew CNic EPad LHil LHop MCas MPar SChu SMrm SUsu WPer WThu
¶– BC&W 4110	MFos
§ – 'Aurea'	MFir NRed NTow NWCA SUsu WCla WPer
– *lutea* hort.	See O. ***a.*** 'Aurea'
♦ *berlandieri*	See O. ***speciosa*** 'Rosea'
§ *biennis*	CHal CKin CRDP CRow CTom EBre ECha EHoe GPoy LBre LHol MChe MHew NBro NSel SHer SIde SIng WEas WHal WHer WOak WPer WWye
caespitosa	EPad MTho WOld
¶ *californica*	EMon
childsii	See O. ***speciosa*** 'Rosea'
cinaeus	See O. ***fruticosa glauca***
¶ *elata hirsutissima*	CHan
§ – ssp. *hookeri*	WCla WHer WPer
erythrosepala	See O. ***glaziouana***
flava	CNic MTho NNrd
¶ *fruticosa*	EBre GCal LBre NBro
– cream form	LGan WCot WHoo
¶ – ssp. *fruticosa*	CHan
– 'Fyrverkeri' ('Fireworks')	CBow CDoC CGle CKel CSam CSco CShe EBre ECED ECro EFou ELan ENot EPla GAbr LBre LHop NHol NKay SPer SUsu WRus WWin
§ – *glauca*	CBow CElw CHan CMGP CRDP EBar EBre EMon GAbr IDai LBre LGan LHol LWad MTho NBro NCat NHol NTow SIng WEas WHoo WPat WPer
¶– – 'Erica Robin' (v)	EMon
– 'Lady Brookborough'	LHop MRav MUlv
– var. *riparia*	CHal ELan EPad IDai LHop NKay SMrm SUsu WRus
– 'Yellow River'	CB&S CSco ECED EOrc ESma MBri
glabra hort.	NSti
– Miller	See O. ***biennis***
§ *glaziouana*	CRDP EMon IBlr IEde NBir WPbr WWye
* 'Hollow Meadows'	EPot NMen
hookeri	See O. ***elata h.***
kunthiana	CTom EPad NWCA WAbe WHil WPer
¶ *laciniata*	SChu
lamarckiana	See O. ***glaziouana***
♦ *linearis*	See O. ***fruticosa***
§ *macrocarpa*	Widely available
– *alba*	CRiv
– 'Greencourt Lemon'	EMon LRHS
♦ *mexicana*	See O. ***laciniata***
♦ *missouriensis*	See O. ***macrocarpa***
nuttallii	NHol
odorata Jacquin	CArn CDoC CRDP CRiv CSev CSpe EFol ESma GCal IBlr LAbb LHil MPar NOrc SSvw WCru WEas WHil
– 'Sulphurea'	See O. ***stricta*** 'S.'
pallida	CRiv ELan IBlr NFai
¶ – 'Innocence'	WPer
– ssp. *trichocalyx*	LHol
¶ – 'Wedding Bells'	NPer
¶ 'Penelope Hobhouse'	SUsu
§ *perennis*	CHal CLew CNic CPar CRiv CTom EBre EPla LBre MCas MTho NMen NNrd SFis WCla WEas WPat WPer WThu WWin
pumila	See O. ***perennis***
rosea	GCra MBel NPer SIde SMrm SUsu WOMN
speciosa	CCor CHan CLew CMGP EMon LHil NPer NWyt SAxl SMad SMrm SUsu WByw WCot WCra WHal WPbr WPer WRus WTyr
– var. *childsii*	See O. ***speciosa*** 'Rosea'
¶ – 'Pink Petticoats'	NFai
§ – 'Rosea'	CGle CLew CNic EMon SAxl SUsu WCra WPer WWin
¶ sp. CD&R 1140	CHan

stricta	CHal CKin CSpe EPad MNFA SUsu WPat WWye
§ – 'Sulphurea'	CHad CHan CMil CSun CTom ELan EMon GCal IBlr LBlm LRHS MBel MNFA NPer SChu SMrm WAbb WPer
taraxacifolia	See O. ***acaulis***
♦ *tetragona*	See O. ***fruticosa glauca***
♦ – var. *fraseri*	See O. ***fruticosa glauca***
¶ *tetraptera*	NWCA
texensis	EPla
– 'Early Rise'	ELan EMon LHop NSti WEas

OLEA (Oleaceae)

europaea	ERea GAri LHol LPan SArc SSpi STre WNor
¶ – var. *europaea* 'Cipressino'	ERea
– – 'El Greco'	CB&S ERea GAri
– – 'Picholine'	ERea
♦ – – 'Pyramidalis'	See O. ***e. e.*** 'Cipressino'

OLEARIA † (Compositae)

albida	CB&S CTre EPla WWat
– x *paniculata*	CPle
arborescens	IBar
argophylla	ECou
avicenniifolia	CMHG CPle ECou EPla WBod WSHC
– 'White Confusion'	WWat
capillaris	CMHG CPle ECou EPla GAbr ISea SDry SLon WWat
chathamica	GCal IDai
§ *cheesemanii*	CCla CMHG CPle WSHC
floribunda	CPle CTre
frostii	WSHC
furfuracea	CB&S CHEx
glandulosa	ECou
gunniana	See O. ***phlogopappa***
x *haastii*	Widely available
– 'McKenzie'	ECou
§ 'Henry Travers'	CAbb CB&S CDoC CGre CPle GCal IBar IBlr IDai ISea LAbb MBal SGil WBod
ilicifolia	CBow CCla CPMA CPle SDry SSpi
insignis	WCru
¶ *lacunosa*	SDry
lepidophylla	ECou NHol WThi
– green form	ECou
– silver form	ECou
lirata	ECou
x *macrodonta*	Widely available
– 'Major'	SHBN
– 'Minor'	CChu
x *mollis* hort.	See O. ***ilicifolia***
– (Kirk) Ckn.	CB&S CBow CPMA CPle CTre EPla NNor SLon SPer SSpi WSHC WWat
– 'Zennorensis'	CAbb CB&S CBow CGre CLan CMHG CPMA CPle IBar ISea NNor NTow SDry SSpi WSHC
moschata	ECou SLon SSpi WSHC
myrsinoïdes	CCla CMHG CPle
§ *nummulariifolia*	CLew CMHG CPle CSco ECou EPla ISea MBal NNor NWyt SArc SBor SDry SIng SPer WBod WSHC WStI
– var. *cymbifolia*	ECou
– hybrids	ECou
odorata	CPle ECou SGil WBod
♦ *oleifolia*	See O. 'Waikariensis'
paniculata	CAbb CB&S CDoC CGre CMHG CPle CTre IDai ISea SDry
§ *phlogopappa*	CHan CMHG ECou GWht IBar IJoh ISea NPer NTow SBar
– 'Comber's Blue'	CB&S CBow CCla CDoC CGre CPMA CTre EBar IBar IBlr ISea NPer SSta
§ – 'Comber's Pink'	CB&S CDoC CGre CPMA CTre EBar IBar IBlr ISea SPer SSta WBod
– 'Rosea'	See O. ***p.*** 'Comber's Pink'
– Splendens Group	CAbb CLew NRar SHil
– var. *subrepanda*	CB&S CGre EBar WBod
* *pleniflora*	CLew
§ *ramulosa*	CB&S CGre CLew CPle CTre WCot WWat
– blue form	See O. ***ramulosa***
– *ramulosa*	ECou
♦ *rani* hort.	See O. ***cheesemanii***
x *scilloniensis* hort.	See O. ***stellulata***
– Dorrien-Smith 'Master Michael'	CBow CCla CPMA CPle CTrw NFai SBor SPer WBod WStI
semidentata	See O. 'Henry Travers'
solandri	CBra CHan CMHG CMer CPle CSam EBre ECou EMon EPla GAbr IDai IJoh LAbb LBre MRav NFai SDix SDry SLon SPer
– 'Aurea'	CB&S
§ *stellulata* De Candolle	CBot CGre CMHG CMer CPle CSco CTre CTrw CWit EBar ECou ELan ENot IBar IHos ISea LAbb MWat NTow SBor SDix SLon SPer SPla SSta WStI WWin
♦ – hort.	See O. ***phlogopappa***
traversii	CAbb CDoC CMHG CPle CTre IOrc LTil WDin WSHC
§ – 'Tweedledum' (v)	CPle ECou
♦ – 'Variegata'	See O. ***t.*** 'Tweedledum'
virgata	CMHG CPle ECou ELan ISea
– 'Laxifolia'	CTre
– var. *lineata*	CMer WDin WSHC
¶ – – 'Dartonii'	SLPl
§ 'Waikariensis'	CBot CBow CMHG CPMA CPle CSam CTre ECou SChu SLon SSpi WBod WDin WSHC WWat

OLSYNIUM (Iridaceae)

§ *biflorus*	NHol
douglasii	CBro CNic CRDP EBur EPot GArf GDra NGar NHar NTow SIng SPou WAbe WDav WThu
¶ – JCA 11132	CNic
– *album*	EBur EPot GAbr GDra NHar NHol SPou WThu

OLYSNIUM

filifolium	WPer
– ssp. *junceum* JCA 12289	CNic MTho

OMPHALODES (Boraginaceae)

cappadocica	CBos CCla CElw CFis CGle CHad CRow EBre ECha EFol ELan EOrc EPot GAbr IDai LBre MBro MHig NBro NKay NNor NPer SDix WCru WEas WHoo WOMN WPbr WWat
– 'Alba'	EBre LBre SRms WEas
– 'Anthea Bloom'	IBlr NTow
– 'Cherry Ingram'	MUlv NBir NCat SAxl SBla SMrm SUsu SWas WCot WCru
– 'Starry Eyes'	EMon IBlr SWas WCru
§ *linifolia*	CHad CTom EJud LHil MPar SBor SUsu WCru WEas WHil WWin
– *alba*	See O. *linifolia*
luciliae	WHoo
verna	Widely available
– 'Alba'	Widely available

OMPHALOGRAMMA (Primulaceae)

¶ *elwesianum* EMAK 663	GArf

ONIXOTIS (Liliaceae/Colchicaceae)

¶ *triquetra*	LAbb

ONOBRYCHIS (Leguminosae)

viciifolia	CKin CPar ECro ELan MHew NSal

ONOCLEA (Dryopteridaceae)

sensibilis	CBar CHan CPar CRow CWGN ECha EGol EHon ELan EPar IOrc MBri NBir NDea NHar NHol NKay NMar NNrd SAxl SCob SHig SPer SSpi SWat WEas WFib WHal WRic
– copper form	NKay WRic

ONONIS (Leguminosae)

cenisia	See O. *cristata*
¶ *cristata*	NTow
natrix	EMon
repens	CArn CKin CRDP MHew MWil NMir NSal WGwy
rotundifolia	CNic EMon MHew NSal NTow WOMN WPer WWin
spinosa	CKin CNic CRDP MHew NSal WGwy WNdy WPer
– 'Alba'	EMon

ONOPORDUM (Compositae)

acanthium	CArn CBow CCla CKin EBre ECha ECro ELan EMon GCra LBre LHol MPar SFis SIde WHer WWye
arabicum	See O. *nervosum*
bracteatum	WPer
§ *nervosum*	CFis CSpe ECro GCra LHil NBro NSti NVic SFis SMad SMrm WEas
salteri	ECro

ONOSMA (Boraginaceae)

alborosea	CMea CNic ECha EFol ELan EOrc GCal LHop MFir NTow SChu SMrm SUsu WCru WEas WOMN WOld WPat WPer
armena	WDav
echioïdes	EPad MHig
helvetica	WAbb WPat
montana	NTow
nana	NTow WDav
– Mac&W 5785	CLew WOMN
stellulata	CLew CNic WOld
taurica	CHan EBar EFol NBir NHol WCru WOMN WOld WWin

ONYCHIUM (Adiantaceae)

¶ *contiguum*	SMrm
japonicum	CRDP NMar SBla SSpi SWas WRic
¶ – L 1649	SBla

OPHIOPOGON † (Liliaceae/Convallariaceae)

'Black Dragon'	See O. *planiscapus* 'Nigrescens'
bodinieri B&L 12505	EMon
graminifolius	See LIRIOPE *muscari*
intermedius	EMon EPla MSte SApp WCot
– *parviflorus*	EBul NSti
§ *jaburan*	CHan CMGP EBul EPla LAma MSte MUlv NHol SBar WPbr WWat
– 'Variegatus'	See O. *j.* 'Vittatus'
§ – 'Vittatus' (v)	CHEx EBul WCot
japonicus	CBro CElw CRiv CRow EBul EPla NSti SApp
– 'Albus'	EPla
– 'Compactus'	WCot
¶ – 'Nippon'	EGol
* – Tamaryu No 2	NHar
¶ 'Kigimafukiduma'	WCot
planiscapus	CHan EBul EPad EPar EPla GCal MBel MSte MTho MWat NGar NHar SApp SSpi WAbe
– *leucanthus*	CRow WCot
§ – 'Nigrescens'	Widely available
sp. DF 617	EBul
* *tamaryu*	WThi
* *wallichianus*	SApp SSpi WCot

OPITHANDRA (Gesneriaceae)

See Plant Deletions

OPLISMENUS (Gramineae)

§ *africanus* 'Variegatus'	CHal
hirtellus	See O. *africanus*

OPUNTIA (Cactaceae)

lindheimeri	CHEx
♦ *linguiformis*	See O. *lindheimeri*
¶ *phaeacantha*	CHEx

ORANGE, Sour or Seville See CITRUS *aurantium*

ORANGE, Sweet See CITRUS *sinensis*

ORCHIS (Orchidaceae)

elata	See DACTYLORHIZA *e.*
foliosa	See DACTYLORHIZA *f.*
fuchsii	See DACTYLORHIZA *f.*

maculata	See DACTYLORHIZA ***m.***
maderensis	See DACTYLORHIZA ***foliosa***
majalis	See DACTYLORHIZA ***m.***
¶ *mascula*	SWes WChe

OREOBOLUS (Cyperaceae)
See Plant Deletions

OREOPANAX (Araliaceae)

epremesnilianus	CHEx

ORIGANUM † (Labiatae)

acutidens	WCHb
– JCA 735.000	EMon WDav
amanum	ELan EPot MBro NTow SBla SChu SHer SPou SSou SUsu SWas WOMN WPat WThu
– *album*	SWas
'Barbara Tingey'	CElw CSev ECha ECou EFol ELan ESma LBee LBlm LHop MFir MHig MTho SBla SChu SHer SPou SUsu SWas WCru WPat
*'Bristol Cross'	SIng
'Buckland'	CGle NRar SBla SPou
**caespitosum*	NCat
§ *calcaratum*	CLew CShe ELan ESma LBee SBla SHer SPou SWas WByw WOld
dictamnus	EEls ELan EPot GPoy NHol NTow SGil SPou SUsu SWas WOMN WPer
'Dingle Fairy'	EFol NBir
'Emma Stanley'	SPou
'Erntedank'	EFou EMon
heracleoticum hort.	See O. x ***applei***
– Linnaeus	See O. ***vulgare hirtum***
x *hybridinum*	EGol LHop MBro SBla SChu SPou WDav WPat WWat WWin
'Kent Beauty'	CDec CMHG CRDP CSun ECha ELan EPot LBee LGre SBla SChu SGil SHer SSou SUsu SWas WOMN
kopatdaghense	See O. ***vulgare gracile***
laevigatum	CArn CElw CGle CHan CMea CPar CShe CTom EFol EGol ELan EPot MBro MHig NBro NMir NSti SBla SHig SUsu WAbe WByw WDav WEas WHal WHoo WPer WRus WWat WWin
– 'Dingle'	EFol
– 'Herrenhausen'	Widely available
– 'Hopleys'	Widely available
majorana	CArn CSFH CSev ELan Effi GPoy LHol MChe NSal NSel SHer SIde WOak WPer WWye
microphyllum	CArn CBot CGle CShe EMon ESis ITim LBee MTho NTow SBla SChu SUsu WCru WHil WHoo WOMN WThu WWye
'Norton Gold'	ECha EFol EFou EMon LRHS WCHb
'Nymphenburg'	CLew LHop SUsu SWas WPer
onites	CArn CHal CSFH EEls Effi GPoy ILis LHol MChe NRoo NSal SBla SHer SIde WHer WOMN WOak WPer WWye
pulchellum	EFol SPou
'Rosenkuppel'	CGle ECha GCal SUsu SWas WSun
rotundifolium	CArn CBos CElw CGle CLew CRDP CSev ECha EFol ELan ESma LGre LHop MBro NBir SBla SChu SUsu SWas WCru WKif WMer WRus WThu
scabrum	CArn
sp. Mac&W 5882	See NEPETA ***phyllochlamys***
tournefortii	See O. ***calcaratum***
**villosum*	CBot
vulgare	CArn CFis CHal CKin CSev CTom EJud Effi GPoy LHol MChe MHew NBro NFai NLan NMir NRoo NSel SHer SIde SSvw WByw WEas WHal WHer WOak WWye
– var. *album*	CElw WHer
– 'Aureum'	Widely available
– 'Aureum Album'	EMar WHer
– 'Aureum Crispum'	CHun EOrc ILis NFai NSti SIde WSun
– 'Compactum'	CArn CHal CNic CRDP CSFH CSev EFol GPoy ILis LGan LHol MHig NHol NRar SBla SIde SPou WCHb WPer WWye
¶ – 'Compactum Album'	MHig
§ – 'Gold Tip' (v)	CArn CElw CHal CMea CMer CSev EFol EHoe EJud EMar EOrc ILis NFai NRoo NSel NSti SHer WCHb WHal WHer WPer WRus WWye
¶ – 'Golden Shine'	NRoo
§ – ssp. *gracile*	NHol
§ – ssp. *hirtum*	EEls GPoy LAbb NSal WPer
– 'Nanum'	LHop WCla
¶ – 'Polyphant' (v)	CBre
– 'Thumble's Variety'	EHoe
– 'Tracy's Yellow'	CCor
– 'Variegatum'	See O. ***v.*** 'Gold Tip'

ORIXA (Rutaceae)

japonica	CBot CCla CMCN GWht SSpi WDin

ORNITHOGALUM (Liliaceae/Hyacinthaceae)

arabicum	CAvo CGle LAma LBow MBri NRog SDeJ SGil
¶ *arcuatum*	CMon
♦ *balansae*	See O. ***oligophyllum***
♦ *caudatum*	See O. ***longibracteatum***
¶ *chionophyllum*	CMon
¶ *concinnum* MS 452	CMon
¶ *exscapum*	CMon
¶ *fimbriatum*	EPot
lanceolatum	CAvo
§ *longibracteatum*	CHEx ELan SLMG WHer
magnum	LRHS
¶ *montanum* BSBE 2360	CMon
nanum	See O. ***sigmoideum***
narbonense	CBro ETub
nutans	CAvo CBro CMea CMon EPar EPot ETub LAma LBlo LBow MBro MTho NHol NLan NMen NNrd NRog SIng WHal WPer
§ *oligophyllum*	CBro EPot ETub WCot
pyramidale	EPot
pyrenaicum	CArn CAvo ECha
¶ – AB&S 4600	CMon

¶ – Flavescens Group CMon
reverchonii CMon MPar
saundersiae LBow
¶ *sessiliflorum* AB&S 4619 CMon
sibthorpii See O. ***sigmoideum***
¶ *spicatum* MS 585 CMon
¶ *tenuifolium* CMon EPot
thyrsoïdes CKel LAma LBow MBri NRog SDeJ SRms WCru
umbellatum CAvo CBro CCla CMea CRiv ELan EPar ETub GPoy LAma LBlo LBow MBri MFir NLan NRog SIng WHil WOMN WPer WShi WWye
¶ *unifolium* MS 435 CMon
¶ *woronowii* EPot

ORONTIUM (Araceae)

aquaticum CBen CHEx CWGN EBre EHon EMFW EWav LBre LMay MSta NDea SHig SWat WChe WHol

OROSTACHYS (Crassulaceae)

§ *aggregata* NGre
chanetii NBra NMen
iwarenge ESis NTow
malacophylla See O. ***aggregata***
§ *spinosa* CRow NGre NMen NNrd NTow WDav WOMN WThu

ORPHIUM (Gentianaceae)

frutescens CTro

ORTHROSANTHUS (Iridaceae)

chimboracensis WPer
laxus NHol
multiflorus CHan
polystachyus CHan

ORYZOPSIS (Gramineae)

lessoniana ETPC
miliacea ETPC

OSBECKIA (Melastomataceae)

stellata CGre

OSCULARIA (Aizoaceae)

deltoïdes See LAMPRANTHUS ***d.***

OSMANTHUS (Oleaceae)

armatus CHan NNor SArc SHil SPla WWat
§ x *burkwoodii* Widely available
§ *decorus* CB&S CDoC CGre EGol ELan ENot MGos MRav MUlv SHil SLon SPer SSpi WBod WWat
– 'Angustifolius' SLon
delavayi Widely available
x *fortunei* CDoC CGre
– 'Variegatus' See O. ***heterophyllus*** 'Latifolius Variegatus'
fragrans CBot CGre
§ *heterophyllus* CB&S CBow CGre CLan CPle CSco EHar ELan ENot LPan LTil MBar MUlv NNor SCob SPer SReu SSpi SSta WDin WStI WTyr WWat
– 'Argenteomarginatus' See O. ***h.*** 'Variegatus'
§ – 'Aureomarginatus' CB&S CDoC CGre CPMA CPle CSco EHoe ELan EPla IOrc LTil MBal MPla SGil SHBN SPer
– 'Aureus' See O. ***h.*** 'Aureomarginatus'
¶ – 'Dodd and Zinger's Variegated' LTil
– 'Goshiki' ('Tricolor') (v) CAbP CB&S CBow CDoC CPMA CSco EHar ELan EPla IJoh IOrc LHop MAsh MBal MBar MBri MGos MPla MUlv SCob SDry SGil SHBN SPer SSta WStI
– 'Gulftide' ELan MAsh MGos MUlv SCob SSpi
§ – 'Latifolius Variegatus' SBla
– 'Purple Shaft' LRHS
– 'Purpureus' CAbP CB&S CBow CMHG EGol EHar ELan IBar MBal MBri MRav SDry SSpi SSta WStI
– 'Rotundifolius' MBri
§ – 'Variegatus' CB&S CBot CBra CCla CSco EBre EGol EHar ELan ENot IBar IDai IJoh IOrc LBre MBal MBar MPla MRav MWat NKay SChu SCob SHBN SLon SPer SPla SSta WDin
ilicifolius See O. ***heterophyllus***
serrulatus CBot EPla GWht SHil
¶ *suavis* LTil
yunnanensis MBlu SArc SSpi WWat

X OSMAREA (Oleaceae)

burkwoodii See OSMANTHUS x ***burkwoodii***

OSMARONIA See OEMLERIA

OSMORHIZA (Umbelliferae)

claytonii NSal

OSMUNDA † (Osmundaceae)

cinnamomea NHar NKay SPer
claytoniana NKay
regalis Widely available
– 'Crispa' NMar
– Cristata Group CRDP EBre ELan LBre MBri SMad WFib WRic
– *purpurascens* CRDP CRow EBre ELan IOrc LBre MBri NBro NHol NMar NOrc SCob SSpi SWat WFib WRic
– *undulata* ELan NHar NHol SMad
¶ – Undulata Group WRic

OSTEOMELES (Rosaceae)

schweriniae B&L 12360 EMon
¶ *subrotunda* LRHS

OSTEOSPERMUM † (Compositae)

'African Queen' See O. 'Tresco Purple'
'Ballyrogan Pink' IBlr
barberae hort. See O. ***jucundum***
¶ 'Blackthorn seedling' MBri WKif

'Bloemhoff Belle'	CMHG GCal MBri MSte SBor WEas
'Blue Streak'	CB&S CCan CFis CGre CMHG CSpe CTre ECtt ELan EMar ERav GAbr LAbb NBro SAxl SMrm WHal WHil WRus
'Bodegas Pink'	CBrk CElw EFol ELan EMon EOrc ERav GCal MBri MSte NRar SChu SMrm
'Brickell's Hybrid'	CCan CHal CMHG CMea CSam CSev CTre EBar EMar EOrc ESma GCal MSte NRoo SAxl WHal WHil WPer
'Buttermilk'	Widely available
'Cannington John'	CB&S CCan CMHG EOrc LAbb LHop NPer
'Cannington Joyce'	CCan CSpe EDon LHop SAxl
'Cannington Katrina'	CCan
'Cannington Roy'	CB&S CBar CCan CGle CGre CMHG CSam CSpe CTre CTrw EBar EBre ECtt EDon ELan EMar GAbr GCal LBre LHil LHop MBri NHar NPer SMrm WRus
'Cannington Vernon'	CCan
¶ 'Catriona'	GCal
caulescens	See O. ***ecklonis prostratum***
¶ 'Coconut Ice'	CElw
'Croftway Blush'	SCro
'Croftway Coconut Ice'	SCro WRus
'Croftway Eveningstar'	SCro
'Croftway Goldback'	SCro
'Croftway Hall'	SCro
'Croftway Halo'	SCro
'Croftway Humbug'	SCro
'Croftway Silverspoons'	SCro WRus
'Croftway Snow'	SCro WRus
'Croftway Tufty'	SCro
'Croftway Velvetspoons'	SCro
'Croftway Wonderwhirls'	SCro
¶ 'Dennis Weston'	ECtt
ecklonii	CB&S CCla CFis CGle CHEx CHad CMHG CRiv CSam CShe CTre IDai ISea LAbb MTho NBro NHol NRar SBla SBor SCro SMrm SPer WPer WWin
*– deep pink form	MBri NRar
– 'Giant'	CCan CHan
§ – ***prostratum***	CBrk CCan CHan CMHG CMea CTre EFol EFou ELan GAbr GCal IBlr LHop MBri NRar NSti SAxl SChu SCro SDix SLMG SMad SPla SUsu SWas WRus
– 'Starshine'	EOrc
'Edna Bond'	WEas
'Falmouth'	CFis
'Gold Sparkler' (v)	EOrc
'Gweek Variegated'	CB&S CBot CBrk CSpe ERav LHil NRar
'Hampton Court Purple'	LHop SAxl
'Hopley's'	CCan CTre EBar EOrc WCru
¶ 'James Elliman'	CB&S CCan CMHG MSte NHar
§ ***jucundum***	CBrk CCan CCla CFis CGle CHad CMHG CMea CPar CShe CTre ECha ELan ENot EOrc GAbr MWat NHol NSti SBla SBor SChu SDix SFis SIng SUsu WHil WMar
– 'Blackthorn Seedling'	ECha SBla SFai WCru
– var. ***compactum***	CMea ECha ELan GCal LBlm MHig MSte SBla SMrm WDav WHil WMar WRus
'Killerton Pink'	CCan CGle CMHG EOrc SCro WPer WRus
'Kriti'	EOrc
'La Mortola'	CHad LAbb
§ 'Lady Leitrim'	CCan CHEx CMHG CSam CTre EBar ECha EFol EOrc LBlm LHop MBri NSti SAxl SBla SChu SSvw WAbe WRus
'Langtrees'	CCan ECtt EDon EFol GAbr LHop NRar SMrm
'Molly's Choice'	SMrm
'Nairobi'	See O. 'Tresco Purple'
'Pale Face'	See O. 'Lady Leitrim'
'Peggyi'	See O. 'Tresco Purple'
'Penny Pink'	CCan ECtt EMar EOrc LHop NSti
¶ 'Perhill Purple'	WPer
¶ 'Perhill White'	WPer
'Pink Whirls'	Widely available
¶ 'Port Wine'	CB&S NRoo SFis
prostratum	See O. ***ecklonis prostratum***
'Silver Sparkler' (v)	Widely available
'Sparkler'	CB&S CCla CHEx EBre EOrc LAbb LBre LHil MSte
¶ 'Stardust'	COtt NPer
'Starshine'	NBro
'Sunny Boy'	CB&S EBar LHil
¶ 'Sunny Girl'	ECtt LHil SUsu
'Tauranga'	See O. 'Whirligig'
'Tresco Pink'	CB&S IBlr
§ 'Tresco Purple'	CB&S CBot CBrk CCan CGle CHEx CMea CMer CRiv CShe CTre EBar EBre EDon EOrc GAbr GCal LAbb LBre LHil MBri NHar NSti SBor WAbe WEas WHal WOMN WPer WRus
'Tresco Sally'	CFis WEas
'Weetwood'	CGle CMHG EBar ECtt EDon GAbr GCal LHop MBri MSte NPer NRar SChu SIng SMrm SWas WAbe WCru WPer WRus
§ 'Whirligig'	Widely available
* 'White Pim'	LHil
'Wine Purple'	See O. 'Tresco Purple'
Wisley hybrids	CHal CSpe LAbb WEas WRus

OSTROWSKIA (Campanulaceae)

See Plant Deletions

OSTRYA (Corylaceae)

carpinifolia	CB&S CDoC CLnd CMCN CPle EArb EHar ELan IOrc MBar SHil SSpi WCoo WMou WNor
virginiana	CDoC CMCN EArb EHar SSpi WNor

OTANTHUS (Compositae)

See Plant Deletions

OTHONNA (Compositae)

capensis	CHal
cheirifolia	CBot CFis CHan CLew CPle CSam EBar ECha EFou ELan EMon EOrc GCal LGre MBel NNor NSti NTow SDry SIgm SLon SPer SUsu WCru WEas WHal WOMN WPer WRus

OTHONNOPSIS See OTHONNA

OURISIA † (Scrophulariaceae)

caespitosa ECou ELan EPot GGar NMen
– var. *gracilis* GArf GAri GGar IBlr ITim
coccinea CBot CGle CNic GArf GCra GDra IBar MTho NRya WCru WDav
¶ *crosbyi* IBlr
¶ *elegans* NBir
'Loch Ewe' CChu CLew CNic GAbr GCal GDra GGar IBlr MUlv NHar NKay SAxl WCru
macrophylla CNic GAbr GDra GGar IBlr NHar NRoo WBon
microphylla EPot WAbe WThu
– Wr 8819 NGre
'Snowflake' EPot GArf GDra GGar IBlr MTho NBir NHar NMen NTow SBla WAbe
¶ *vulcanica* WCru

OXALIS † (Oxalidaceae)

acetosella CKin CRow NGre NLan NMir NSal SIde SIng SSou WBon WHer WNdy
– ***subpurpurascens*** EMon
adenophylla Widely available
– dark form GDra MHig
§ *articulata* CRiv CTom LGro MFir MTho MTol NEgg NPer WCot WWin
'Beatrice Anderson' GDra MDHE MTho NHar NHol NNrd WAbe
bowiei EPot NGre
'Bowles' White' WHil WThu
brasiliensis EPot LHil MTho
chrysantha CHal CRDP CRow ELan GAbr SHer SIng WAbe
corniculata
var. *atropurpurea* MTho
deppei See O. ***tetraphylla***
§ *depressa* CNic CRow ELan EPot GAbr MCas MPlt MTho NBir NGre NHol NMen NNrd NRya SHer SIng
§ *drummondii* GCal
enneaphylla ECou EPar EPot GArf IDai MCas MTho WThu
♦– x *adenophylla* See O. 'Matthew Forrest'
– 'Alba' EPot GArf MDHE MHig NHol NNrd
– 'Minutifolia' EPot GArf MHig MTho NGre NHol NKay NNrd SSmi SWas WAbe
– 'Rosea' CBro EPot GAbr GDra MBal MTho NGre NHol SIng
– 'Rubra' GAbr GDra NHar NKay WAbe
flava NNrd
floribunda See O. ***articulata***
¶ *glabra* CMon
hedysaroïdes GCra
hirta CAvo CBro CMon CRiv LBow LHil MCas MTho NGre NHol NNrd SIng WAbe WHil
– 'Gothenburg' EPot MTho
inops See O. ***depressa***
'Ione Hecker' CRiv EPot GAbr GArf LBee MHig MTho NGre NHar NHol NNrd NTow SIng SSou SWas WAbe
japonica 'Picta' WThu
laciniata EPot GAbr GArf GDra MTho NHar NHol NNrd SBla SIng WAbe WOMN
lactea double form See O. ***magellanica*** 'Nelson'
lasiandra CAvo
lobata CAvo CBro CLew CRow ELan EPot LBow MFos MTho NHol NTow SHer SUsu SWas WOMN
magellanica CHal CMHG CNic CRiv CSam CTom ECar ELan ESis GAbr GCHN LRHS MTho NHol NMen NNrd SHer SIng SSou WCru WDav WHil WPer WTyr
– 'Flore Pleno' See O. ***m.*** 'Nelson'
§ – 'Nelson' (d) CElw CGle CHal CLew CMil CRDP CRiv CRow CSpe ECar ESis GCHN MBro MTho NBir NHar NHol NNrd SHer SUsu WCru WHil WPer
– 'Old Man Range' ECou
¶ 'Matthew Forrest' GDra NGre WAbe
melanosticta LBow
obtusa CMon CRiv ECha ELan EPot ESis MCas MFir MHig MTho NCat NTow SHer SIng SSad WOMN
oregana CAvo CGle CNic CRDP CRiv CRow ECha SBar SFis WBon WCru
ortgiesii SLMG
palmifrons CMon EPot MTho
patagonica MDHE MHig NHol NKay NNrd WHil
§ *purpurea* LBee LHop MPlt NGre NHol NPer WAbe WCru
– 'Ken Aslet' CAvo CBro CMon CRow EPot MCas MFos MTho NGre NHol NNrd NTow SBla SIng SSou SWas WAbe WOMN WThu
♦ *regnellii* See O. ***triangularis papilionacea***
¶ *rosea* 'Aureoreticulata' MTho
¶ 'Royal Velvet' NBir
speciosa See O. ***purpurea***
¶ *stipularis* CMon WThu
§ *tetraphylla* CRiv CRow CSam EPar LAma MBri MTho NCat NOrc NPer NRog SDeJ SIng SLMG
¶ – *alba* WCru
– 'Iron Cross' CAvo CRow ELan LAma NBir SAxl SUsu WCot WEas WHal WHil
triangularis LAma NPer SMad
¶ – 'Cupido' EOrc
§ – ssp. *papilionacea* CMon CRow NRog WHal
¶ – – *rosea* CMon
¶ – – 'Atropurpurea' WCot
tuberosa GPoy WCru WHer
versicolor CRiv EPot MCas MTho NNrd SBla SIng SSad WThu
♦ *vespertilionis* Torey & A Gray See O. ***drummondii***
♦– Zuccarini See O. ***latifolia***
vulcanicola WCru

OXYCOCCUS See VACCINIUM

OXYDENDRUM (Ericaceae)

arboreum CB&S CCla CWSG ECar EHar ELan IBar MBal MBri MGos SHil SPer SReu SSpi SSta WDin WFro WWat

OXYLOBIUM (Leguminosae)
¶ *lancelolatum* CHan

OXYPETALUM (Asclepiadaceae)
caeruleum See TWEEDIA ***caerulea***

OXYRIA (Polygonaceae)
digyna GCHN GGar NWCA WCru WGwy

OXYTROPIS (Leguminosae)
¶ *campestris* var. ***gracilis*** WPer
halleri GTou NTow
¶ *jacquinii* WDav
¶ *podocarpa* MFos NWCA
williamsii NWCA

OZOTHAMNUS (Compositae)
§ *ledifolius* CCla CElw CMHG CPle CSam ECha ELan EPla IBar IJoh LHop MBri MBrk MPla NNor SBla SChu SIgm SLon SPer SSpi WHCG WKif WMar WPat WSHC WWat
microphyllus ITim
§ *purpurascens* CFis
§ *rosmarinifolius* CB&S CCla CDoC CMHG CPar CPle CWit ELan EPla ERea GWht IBar IDai IOrc ISea LAbb NNor SChu SHer SLon SPer WHCG WSHC WStI WWat
– 'Purpureus' CMHG ESma
– 'Silver Jubilee' CB&S CCla CDoC CHan CLan CMHG CSam CTre ELan EPla IJoh ISea LBlm NNor NSti NTow SBla SHBN SLon SMad SPer WAbe WHCG WSHC WWat
scutellifolius ECou
§ *selago* CHal ESis ITim MWat SBla
¶ 'Threave Seedling' SPer
§ *thyrsoïdeus* CB&S CTre WWat

PACHYLAENA (Compositae)
¶ *atriplicifolia* JCA 12522 CNic

PACHYPHRAGMA (Cruciferae)
§ *macrophyllum* ECar ECha EFol ELan EMon IBlr MNFA NSti WCru WEas

PACHYPODIUM (Apocynaceae)
lamerei MBri

PACHYSANDRA (Buxaceae)
stylosa EPla
terminalis Widely available
– 'Green Carpet' CCla CDoC CPMA EFou EGol EPla MBar MBri MGos SPla WWat
– 'Variegata' Widely available

PACHYSTACHYS (Acanthaceae)
lutea CHal MBri

PACHYSTEGIA See **OLEARIA**

PACHYSTEMA See **PAXISTIMA**

PACKERA (Compositae)
§ *werneriifolius* NHol

PAEDERIA (Rubiaceae)
scandens WCru WSHC

PAEDEROTA (Scrophulariaceae)
§ *bonarota* CLew

PAEONIA † (Paeoniaceae)
albiflora See P. ***lactiflora***
anomala EPot NHol SCou
arietina See P. ***mascula a.***
'Avant Garde' WKif
bakeri MAus
'Ballerina' CKel
banatica See P. ***officinalis b.***
'Baroness Schröder' CKel ELan MAus MPhe
broteroi MPar SCou SSpi
¶ 'Buckeye Belle' MAus
* 'Byzantine' CKel
cambessedesii CMon EPot LGre MPar SBla SCou SSpi WAbe WKif
'Carol' MAus
caucasica See P. ***mascula mascula***
¶ 'Chocolate Soldier' MUlv
'Claire de Lune' CKel
'Coral Fay' MAus
corallina See P. ***mascula mascula***
daurica See P. ***mascula triternata***
'Daystar' CKel
decora See P. ***peregrina***
delavayi (S) CB&S CCMG CCla CGre CKel COtt CSam EOrc GCal IBlr MBal MBri MPar SCou SMad SMrm SPer SSpi WBod WEas WHal WSHC WWat
§ – var. ***ludlowii*** (S) CB&S CCMG CCla CGle CKel CLan COtt CSco EHar ELan ISea MBal NHol SBla SMad SPer SSpi WEas WHoo WOMN WWat
§ – var. ***lutea*** (S) CCla CHad CRiv ELan LGan MPar NRoo SBar SHBN STre WEas WWat
– 'Mrs Sarson' CCla
§ – Potaninii Group (S) MPar WWat
– Trollioïdes Group (S) EPla
– 'Yellow Queen' NBar
¶ 'Ellen Cowley' MAus
emodi SCou
¶ 'Friendship' MAus
¶ 'Horizon' MAus
humilis See P. ***officinalis h.***
¶ 'Illini Belle' MAus
'Illini Warrior' MAus
japonica See P. ***lactiflora***
kevachensis See P. ***mascula mascula***
'Kinkaku' See P. x ***lemoinei*** 'Souvenir de Maxime Cornu'
'Kinko' See P. x ***lemoinei*** 'Alice Harding'

'Kinshi' (S)	See P. × ***lemoinei*** 'Chromatella'
'Kintei'	See P. × ***lemoinei*** 'L'Esperance'
§ *lactiflora*	ECha SCou WCot
– 'Adolphe Rousseau'	LRHS MAus MBri
*– 'Afterglow'	CKel
– 'Agida'	COtt EBre ECtt ELan GCHN LBre MAus MRav
– 'Albert Crousse'	CKel CMGP IDai MAus
– 'Alexander Fleming'	CMGP CSco LWad MUlv NBar SCro
– 'Alice Harding'	CKel MAus
– 'Arabian Prince'	CKel
– 'Argentine'	CKel
– 'Auguste Dessert'	CKel
– 'Augustin d'Hour'	CKel LWad
– 'Aureolin'	CKel
¶– 'Balliol'	COtt
– 'Barrymore'	CKel
– 'Beersheba'	CKel
– 'Belle Center'	MAus
– 'Blush Queen'	EBre ELan LBre MAus
– 'Border Gem'	COtt EBre ELan GCHN LBre MRav
– 'Bowl of Beauty'	CBow CCMG CCla CKel CSco EBre ECtt ELan EOrc LBre MAus MBri MUlv NBar NKay NRoo NVic SMad SPer SPla WEas WKif
¶– 'Bowl of Cream'	MAus
– 'Bridal Gown'	MAus
– 'Bridal Veil'	CKel
– 'Bright Knight'	MAus
– 'British Beauty'	CKel
– 'Bunker Hill'	CDoC CKel CShe MAus NHol
¶– 'Butch'	MAus
– 'Butter Ball'	MAus
– 'Calypso'	CKel
– 'Captivation'	CKel
– 'Carmen'	CKel
– 'Carnival'	CKel
¶– 'Charm'	MAus
– 'Cherry Hill'	MAus
– 'Chestine Gowdy'	CKel
– 'Chocolate Soldier'	CKel MPhe
¶– 'Claire Dubois'	EBre LBre MAus
– 'Colonel Heneage'	CKel SPer
– 'Cornelia Shaylor'	CKel EBre ELan LBre
– 'Countess of Altamont'	CKel
– 'Country Girl'	CKel
– 'Couronne d'Or'	EBre LBre
– 'Crimson Glory'	CKel
– 'Dayspring'	CKel
– 'Dinner Plate'	MAus
– 'Docteur H Barnsby'	CKel
– 'Dominion'	CKel
– 'Doreen'	MAus
– 'Dresden'	CKel
– 'Duchess of Kent'	CKel
– 'Duchess of Marlborough'	CBow CCMG CKel
– 'Duchesse de Nemours'	CCla CKel COtt CSco EBre ECtt EFou ELan LBre MAus MBri MUlv NBar NBro NCat NRoo SPer
– 'Duke of Devonshire'	CKel
– 'Edith Cavell'	CKel MAus
– 'Edulis Superba'	COtt EBre ELan LBre MAus SPer SPla
– 'Elsa Sass'	MAus
– 'Emperor of India'	CKel
– 'Eugénie Verdier'	MUlv
– 'Eva'	SHig
– 'Evening World'	CKel MPhe MUlv
– 'Fairy's Petticoat'	MAus
– 'Fedora'	MPhe
– 'Félix Crousse'	CBow CKel CMGP COtt CShe EBre ECtt ELan LBre MBri NCat NHol NRoo NVic SCro SPer
– 'Festiva Maxima'	CBow CCla CKel COtt EBre ECtt ELan LBre MBri NKay SCro SPer SRms
– 'Flamingo'	CKel
– 'France'	CKel
¶– 'François Ortegat'	MAus
– 'Gay Ladye'	CKel
– 'Gay Paree'	EBre LBre MAus
– 'Gayborder June'	EBre LBre
– 'Général MacMahon'	See P. *l.* 'Augustin d'Hour'
– 'Gilbert Barthelot'	MAus
– 'Gleam of Light'	CKel
– 'Globe of Light'	CKel
– 'Glory of Somerset'	CKel
– 'Great Sport'	CKel
– 'Heirloom'	CKel
– 'Helen Hayes'	MAus
– 'Her Majesty'	CKel
¶– 'Hiawatha'	MAus
– 'Hyperion'	CKel
– 'Inspecteur Lavergne'	CDoC CKel COtt CSco EBre EFou LBre LWad MRav MUlv NBar NBee SPer
– 'Instituteur Doriat'	CKel CSco MPhe
¶– 'Jan van Leeuwen'	LRHS MBri
– 'Jeanne d'Arc'	CKel
¶– 'John Howard Wigell'	MAus
– 'June Rose'	MAus
– 'Kansas'	CCla ELan
– 'Karl Rosenfield'	CCla CKel CMGP COtt CSco IDai LWad MBri NBar NBee WAbe
– 'Kelway's Brilliant'	CKel
¶– 'Kelway's Glorious'	LWad
– 'Kelway's Gorgeous'	CKel
– 'Kelway's Majestic'	CKel
¶– 'Kelway's Perfection'	MPhe
– 'Kelway's Supreme'	CKel MUlv
– 'Kelway's Unique'	CKel
– 'King Arthur'	CKel
– 'King George VI'	CKel
– 'King of England'	CKel
– 'Knighthood'	CKel
¶– 'Krinkled White'	MAus
– 'La Lorraine'	CKel
– 'Lady Alexandra Duff'	CDoC CMGP MAus NBar
¶– 'Lady Orchid'	MAus
– 'Laura Dessert'	CKel
¶– 'Le Cygne'	EBre LBre
– 'Lois Kelsey'	MAus
¶– 'Lora Dexheimer'	MAus
– 'Lord Kitchener'	CKel MPhe SPer
¶– 'Lotus Queen'	MAus
– 'Lowell Thomas'	MAus
– 'L'Eclatante'	CKel
– 'Madame Calot'	CKel LWad MRav SRms

– 'Madame Claude Tain'	LRHS
– 'Madame Ducel'	CKel
– 'Madame Emile Debatène'	CKel MAus
– 'Madelon'	CKel
– 'Magic Orb'	CKel
– 'Marie Lemoine'	MAus SPla
¶ – 'Mischief'	MAus
¶ – 'Miss America'	MAus
– 'Miss Eckhart'	CCla CKel CSco
¶ – 'Mister Ed'	MAus
– 'Mistral'	CKel LRHS
– 'Monsieur Jules Elie'	CKel CSco EFou LWad MBri MPhe SPer
¶ – 'Monsieur Martin Cahuzac'	EBre LBre
– 'Mr G F Hemerik	CSco ECtt LRHS MBri SHig
– 'Mrs Franklin D Roosevelt'	ELan
– 'Ornament'	CKel
– 'Orpen'	CKel
– 'Paul M Wild'	MAus
– 'Peregrine'	CKel
¶ – 'Persier'	SCro
– 'Peter Brand'	LRHS
– 'Philomèle'	MAus
– 'Pink Dawn'	MAus
– 'Pink Giant'	LRHS MAus MBri
¶ – 'Pink Lemonade'	EBre LBre
¶ – 'Pink Parfait'	MAus
– 'Poetic'	CKel
– 'President Franklin D Roosevelt'	EBre ECtt ELan GCHN LBre MRav NRoo
– 'Président Poincaré'	CCla CKel COtt EBre LBre SPer
– 'President Taft'	See P. *l.* 'Reine Hortense'
– 'Primevere'	CKel LRHS MBri MPhe
– 'Queen of Sheba'	MAus
– 'Raspberry Sundae'	ECtt MAus MRav
– 'Red Flag'	CKel
§ – 'Reine Hortense'	CKel MAus
¶ – 'Richard Carvel'	MAus
– 'Rose of Delight'	CKel MPhe MUlv
– 'Sante Fe'	MAus
– 'Sarah Bernhardt'	CBow CCMG CCla CHad CKel CMGP CShe EBre ELan GCHN IDai IHos LBre MAus MBri MPhe MRav MUlv NBar NBee NBro NHol NRoo NVic SCro SPer SPla WAbe WEas
– 'Shimmering Velvet'	CKel
– 'Shirley Temple'	CKel EFou ELan LWad MAus MBri
– 'Silver Flare'	CKel
– 'Sir Edward Elgar'	CKel
– 'Snow Cloud'	IDai
– 'Solange'	EBre LBre
– 'Strephon'	CKel
– 'Surugu'	ELan MBri
– 'Sweet Sixteen'	MAus
¶ – 'Thura Hires'	MAus
– 'Top Brass'	EBre LBre MAus
– 'Torpilleur'	CKel
– 'Victoire de la Marne'	COtt EBre LBre NBar
– 'Vogue'	CKel MAus
– 'Westerner'	MAus
– 'White Wings'	CKel COtt EBre ELan LBre MAus MBri NRoo NSti SPer
¶ – 'Whitleyi Major'	MBri
– 'Wiesbaden'	MAus
¶ 'Late Windflower'	ECha
§ x ***lemoinei*** 'Chromatella' (S)	CKel LAma
§ – 'L'Espérance'	LAma
§ – 'Souvenir de Maxime Cornu' (S)	CKel LAma
lobata 'Fire King'	See P. ***perigrina***
lutea	See P. ***delavayi lutea***
– var. ***ludlowii***	See P. ***delavayi ludlowii***
'Mai Fleuri'	SHig
§ ***mascula***	CKel
§ – ssp. ***arietina***	ESma LGre MPhe SCou WKif
¶ – – JCA 746.800	SBla
– – 'Northern Glory'	CKel MAus MBri SHig SPer WCot
– – 'Purple Emperor'	CKel
– 'Immaculata'	EFou GCal
§ – ssp. ***mascula***	EPot NHol SCou
§ – ssp. ***russii***	MPar SCou
§ – ssp. ***triternata***	MPar NTow SCou WHoo
mlokosewitschii	CCMG CCla CHad EBre ECha EPot LBre LGre MBal MPar NTow SApp SChu SSpi WDav WEas WHoo WThu
mollis	CKel ELan
¶ 'Montezuma'	MAus
obovata	SCou
– var. ***alba***	MPar WAbb WAbe WEas
– 'Grandiflora'	ELan SPer
officinalis	EBre LBre WEas
– 'Alba Plena'	CCMG CKel CSco MAus MBri SPer
– 'Anemoniflora Rosea'	MAus MBri SHig
– ssp. ***banatica***	MAus MPhe
– 'China Rose'	ELan
§ – ssp. ***humilis***	ESma MAus SCou
– 'James Crawford Weguelin'	CKel CSco
– 'Lize van Veen'	ELan SPer
– 'Mutabilis Plena'	IBlr
– 'Rosea Plena'	CCMG CCla CKel LRHS NBar SPer
– 'Rosea Superba Plena'	COtt CSco EBre LBre MAus NKay NRoo
– 'Rubra Plena'	CAvo CCMG CCla CKel CSco EBre ECtt LBre MAus MBri NKay NRoo SPer WHoo
'Paladin'	CKel
paradoxa	See P. ***officinalis humilis***
'Paula Fay'	MAus
§ ***peregrina***	MAus NHar SCou
– 'Fire King'	CKel NBar
§ – 'Otto Froebel'	CKel COtt EBre ELan LBre MBri NKay NRoo SHig SPer
– 'Sunshine'	See P. ***p.*** 'Otto Froebel'
'Polindra'	CKel
¶ 'Postilion'	MAus
potaninii	See P. ***delavayi*** Potaninii Group
romanica	See P. ***peregrina***
'Rose Gem'	CKel
'Roselette'	MAus
russii	See P. ***mascula r.***
'Scarlett O'Hara'	MAus
sinensis	See P. ***lactiflora***
¶ 'Smouthii'	MBri
sp. ex Stern	MPar

suffruticosa (S) CSco ELan MGos WStI
– 'Cardinal Vaughan' (S) CKel
– 'Duchess of Kent' (S) CKel
– 'Duchess of Marlborough' (S) CKel
– 'Gessekai' ('Moon World') (S) MAus
– 'Godaishu' (S) LAma
– 'Hakuojisi' ('King of White Lions') (S) MAus
– 'Hana-daigin' ('Magnificent Flower') (S) LAma MAus
– 'Hana-kisoi' ('Floral Rivalry') (S) LAma MAus
– 'Higurashi' ('Twilight') (S) LAma
– 'Howki' ('Charming Age') (S) MAus
– 'Kamada-fuji' ('Wisteria at Kamada') (S) LAma
– 'Kamada-nishiki' ('Kamada Brocade') (S) MAus
– 'Kaow' ('King of Flowers') (S) MAus
– 'Kokuryu-nishiki' ('Black Dragon Brocade') (S) LAma
– 'Lord Selbourne' (S) CKel
– 'Montrose' (S) CKel
– 'Mrs William Kelway' (S) CKel
– 'Naniwa-nishiki' ('Brocade of the Naniwa') (S) MAus
– 'Raphael' (S) CKel
– 'Renkaku' ('Flight of Cranes') (S) MAus
– 'Rimpo' ('Bird of Rimpo') (S) LAma
– 'Shugyo-kuden' ('Palace of Gems') (S) MAus
– 'Sitifukujin' ('Seven Gods of Fortune') (S) MAus
– 'Superb' (S) CKel
– 'Taisho-no-hokori' ('Pride of Taisho') (S) MAus
– 'Taiyo' ('The Sun') (S) LAma
– 'Tama-fuyo' ('Jewel in the Lotus') (S) LAma
– 'Tama-sudare' ('Jewelled Screen') (S) MAus
– 'Yachiyo-tsubaki' ('Eternal Camellias') (S) LAma MAus
– 'Yae-zakura' ('Double Cherry') (S) LAma MAus
'Sunshine' See P. ***peregrina*** 'Otto Froebel'
'Tango' MAus
tenuifolia EPot NHol
veitchii LGre MBal MPhe SCou WAbb
¶ – 'Alba' MAus
– var. ***woodwardii*** GDra LGre MAus NHar NHol SCou WCot WHoo
¶ 'Walter Mains' MAus
wittmanniana MPhe

PAESIA (Dennstaedtiaceae)
scaberula GCal NMar SSpi WAbe

PALISOTA (Commelinaceae)
¶ ***barteri*** CTro

PALIURUS (Rhamnaceae)
See Plant Deletions

PALLENSIS (Compositae)
spinosus See ASTERISCUS ***s.***

PANAX (Araliaceae)
quinquefolius GPoy NSal

PANCRATIUM (Liliaceae/Amaryllidaceae)
¶ ***foetidum*** S&L 354 CMon
maritimum CAvo

PANDANUS (Pandanaceae)
See Plant Deletions

PANDOREA (Bignoniaceae)
jasminoïdes EBak IBlr MNew SLMG
– 'Alba' EMil ERea SFai
¶ – 'Charisma' (v) CB&S EMil
– 'Lady Di' CB&S MNew
– 'Rosea Superba' CB&S CTro EMil ERea MNew SFai
– 'Variegata' MNew
lindleyana See CLYTOSTOMA ***callistegioïdes***
pandorana CB&S CSam ERea LRHS SLMG

PANICUM (Gramineae)
bulbosum CHan ETPC
clandestinum EMon EPla ETPC
coloratum 'Bambatsi' ETPC
miliaceum EFou EPla ETPC
– 'Violaceum' EHoe WPer
virgatum ECha EMon EPla MSte
– 'Hänse Herms' EFou EPla ETPC
– 'Pathfinder' ETPC
– 'Rehbraun' CDec EFou ETPC NEgg
– 'Rubrum' CCla CGle CMGP LBre ECha EHoe ELan EPla LBre MSte MTol NSti SApp SDix SPer
– 'Strictum' EHoe ETPC

PAPAVER † (Papaveraceae)
alboroseum GCHN GTou
§ ***alpinum*** Linnaeus EMNN ESis GCHN GDra GTou MBal MWat NGre NKay NOak SHer SIng SPla WByw WEas WOMN WPer WWin
– ***album*** ECro
– 'Flore Pleno' NBir
§ ***atlanticum*** CNic EMar GCHN NBro NOak SWas WCru
– ***flore-pleno*** MRav NBro NFai NSti WCot WCra WOld
bracteatum See P. ***orientale b.***

§ ***commutatum***	ELan EMon LHol SMrm SUsu WEas
– 'Ladybird'	See P. ***commutatum***
degenii	GCHN
§ 'Fireball'	CBos CMHG CRow EBre ECha ELan GCal LBre LHop MWat NCat WAbb WCru
* 'French Grey'	MPar
heldreichii	See P. ***spicatum***
x ***hybridum*** 'Flore Pleno'	EMon
kerneri	WCru
lateritium JCA 752.100	NSti
– 'Flore Pleno'	NSti
§ ***miyabeanum***	CGle CMea CNic ECro EFol ELan EPot GCHN GDra GTou LGan LHop NKay NMen NTow NWCA SHer WEas WHal WOMN WPer WWin
– ***album***	ELan SHer
– ***tatewakii***	See P. ***miyabeanum***
nanum 'Flore Pleno'	See P. 'Fireball'
nudicaule	ELan WPer
¶ – 'Champagne Bubbles'	NFai SRms
– 'Constance Finnis'	EMon LRHS
– Gartenzwerg Group (Garden Gnome)	CDoC MBri MPit WPbr
§ – Oregon Rainbow Group	ECro
– 'Pacino'	MPit WPer
– Wonderland hybrids	NRoo
orientale	CB&S LHil NBee WBod WPer
– 'Allegro'	CBow CMGP CMil CSam CSco CShe EBar EBre ECro ECtt EFou LAbb LBre MBri MPit NFai NRoo SHer SPer SSvw WByw WCra WPbr
– 'Avebury Crimson'	MWat
§ – 'Beauty of Livermere'	CBow CFis CGle CHad CHan CKel EFou ELan LWad MUlv NBro NOak NVic SDix SPer SSvw SUsu WEas WHoo WRus
– 'Beauty Queen'	CMGP CTom EBre EOrc LBre MBri NBar NCat NRoo SMrm WPbr
– 'Black and White'	CCla CGle CHad CKel CMGP CSco CSev CShe EBlo EBre ECha EFou ELan GCHN LAbb LBre MRav MUlv NRoo NWyt SChu SCro SPer WPbr WRus
– 'Blue Moon'	CHad CMGP EBre LBre NBir SMrm
– 'Bonfire Red'	ELan
§ – ***bracteatum***	ECha EMon GCHN GDra NBir
– 'Brilliant'	NFai
– ***carneum***	ECro
– 'Cedar Hill'	EFou WMer
¶ – 'Cedric Morris'	CHad NFai
– 'Cedric's Pink'	ECha MUlv
– 'Charming'	LGre
– 'Curlilocks'	CMGP EBlo EBre EFou ELan LBre MBri MUlv NCat NKay NRoo SGil SMrm SPer
– 'Doubloon'	CDoC EBlo EBre LBre NRoo WCot
– 'Dwarf Allegro'	CPar MFir NNor NOak
¶ – 'Elam Pink'	ECha
– 'Flore Pleno'	EFou EMon
– 'Garden Gnome'	CBow NOak
– 'Glowing Embers'	COtt EBre LBre WCot
* – 'Goldie'	ELan
– 'Goliath'	See P. ***o.*** 'Beauty of Livermere'
¶ – 'Grave Witwe'	ECha NFai
– 'Harvest Moon'	CShe EBre ECro LBre MBri MRav NBar WCot
– 'Helen Elisabeth'	COtt EBre ECtt EFou LBre MRav MUlv NRoo WCot WMer
– 'Indian Chief'	WMer
– 'Juliane'	ECha NFai
– 'Karine'	ECha NFai
– 'King George'	MWat NCat WEas
¶ – 'Lady Moore'	WMer
– 'Ladybird'	COtt EBre ELan LBre NRoo WCot
¶ – 'Lilac Girl'	ECha
– 'Marcus Perry'	CBow CDoC CMGP COtt CSco GGar LWad NCat SCro WMer
– 'Midnight'	EBre LBre NBar WCot
§ – 'Mrs Marrow's Plum'	CBos CHad CRDP
– 'Mrs Perry'	CBow CKel CMGP CSam CSco CSev CShe EBre ECtt EFou ELan EOrc LAbb LBre LHop LWad MBri MFir MUlv MWat NFai NKay NRoo NSti SChu SHer SPer WHal WHoo
– 'Nanum Flore Pleno'	See P. 'Fireball'
– 'Orange Glow'	WMer
– 'Oriana'	MBri MMil NCat SMrm
– 'Patty's Plum'	See P. ***o.*** 'Mrs Marrow's Plum'
– 'Perry's White'	Widely available
– 'Picotée'	CKel CSco CShe EBre ECro ECtt EFou ELan EMon EOrc LBre MRav MUlv MWat NOak NRoo SGil SPer WByw WCot WRus WTyr
– 'Pink Chiffon'	CGle
– 'Pinnacle'	NFai WCra
– 'Prinzessin Victoria Louise'	CDoC EFol EFou LRHS LWad MMil SSvw WMer
– 'Raspberry Queen'	ELan WMer
– 'Redizelle'	EBre LBre WCot
¶ – 'Rembrandt'	CMGP MMil WMer
– 'Salmon Glow'	CBow CSco NFai WMer WPbr
– 'Scarlet King'	MBri MMil WTyr
– 'Showgirl'	CBow WRus
¶ – 'Sindbad'	EFou
– 'Sultana'	ECha NOak
N – 'Türkenlouis'	CCla CMGP CSco EBlo EBre EFol EFou ELan EMon EOrc GCHN LBre LWad MBri MMil MRav NBar NBir NBro SChu SPer WByw WPbr WRus
– 'Turkish Delight'	See P. ***o.*** 'Türkenlouis'
pilosum	CLew NCat SRms
rhaeticum	ELan GTou SHer
– JCA 752.500	CNic
rhoeas	CArn CSFH EFol GPoy LHol
– 'Mother of Pearl'	ECro
– 'Valerie Finnis'	ELan
rupifragum	CGle ECha ESis GCHN GCra MFir SUsu WEas WHer WPer WWin
– 'Flore Pleno'	SSvw WCru WHer
somniferum	CArn CSFH GPoy ILis LHol NSel SIde
– 'Pink Chiffon'	WEas
§ ***spicatum***	CNic CSam ECha ECro LHop MTol NBir SUsu WCot WEas
triniifolium	EFol GCra LGan SMrm

PARABENZOIN See **LINDERA**

PARADISEA † (Liliaceae/Asphodelaceae)

liliastrum	CGle MNFA SSpi
– 'Major'	MPar WPer
lusitanica	CMHG NSti

PARAHEBE † (Scrophulariaceae)

x *bidwillii*	CHal CLew CMHG CRiv ECou EMNN GGar MHig MPlt NMen SBod WWat
– 'Gillian'	CNic ECou GGar MCas MFir MPlt NMen SFis SPla
– 'Kea'	CMea CNic EBur ECou ECtt ELan EMNN ESis GCHN GCal LBee MHig MPlt NHar SBla SHer WPer
canescens	ECou
§ *catarractae*	CCla CFis CHal CHan CMHG CMer CShe ECou ELan EMNN GWht MCas MFir MPla MPlt NMen NNor NRar NTow SAxl SBod SPer SPla SReu WPer WWin
– blue form	GIsl SPer WSun WWat
§ – 'Delight'	CGre ECou ESis ESma GCHN GCal GGar LHop SDix SLon WEas WHen WHoo
– ssp. *diffusa*	CMHG ECou EMNN IOrc MCas MPlt NHar NMen NVic
– – 'Annie'	ECou
– – 'Pinkie'	ECou
– garden form	ECha SBla WAbe
– ssp. *martinii*	ECou
– 'Miss Willmott'	CLew CNic CShe GIsl LGan NNrd NRar NVic SIng WBod WPer
– 'Porlock Purple '	See P. *c.* 'Delight'
– 'Rosea'	CMea CNic ESma LGan NHol NNor NRed SBla WWat
– 'Tinycat'	ESma
– white form	CBot CCla CHan ECha ELan EMNN ESis GCHN GIsl IBlr MBro MFir MPlt NCat NMen SAxl SPla WEas WPer WSun
decora	ECou EMNN GAbr GAri GCHN MPlt NHol NTow SGil WHil
¶ *derwentiana*	ECou EMon
formosa	CPle ECou
– erect form	ECou
– lax form	ECou
– white	ECou
'Greencourt'	See P. *catarractae* 'Delight'
§ *hookeriana*	CFis CNic CShe ESma GAbr GGar LGre NMen NTow SMrm WHoo WWat
'Joy'	ECou ESma
linifolia	CLew EMNN MCas MHig NMen NNrd SGil
– 'Blue Skies'	CNic ECou GAbr GIsl
§ *lyallii*	CBot CMer CPar ECou ELan EMNN EMon ERav ESis GAbr GIsl LHop MCas MPit MPla MPlt MRav NHol NMen NNor NNrd NOrc NRar NWCA SBor SIng SSmi WAbe WWin
– 'Clarence'	ECou
– 'Engel's Blue'	LGan
– 'Glacier'	ECou
– 'Julie-Anne'	ECou GCal
– 'Rosea'	GGar MBal WHoo WPer WTyr
'Mervyn'	CNic ECou ECtt GCHN GGar LGre LHop MCas MPlt NHol NMen NRed SFis SPla WAbe WHen WPer
olsenii	ECou GGar NHol
¶ *peltata*	NHol
¶ *perfoliata*	Widely available
– dark blue form	EMon GCal GWht NCat
spathulata	ECar

PARAJUBAEA (Palmae)

cocoïdes	LPal

PARAQUILEGIA (Ranunculaceae)

adoxoïdes	See SEMIAQUILEGIA ***adoxoïdes***
§ *anemonoïdes*	NHar WDav
grandiflora	See P. ***anemonoïdes***

PARASERIANTHES (Leguminosae)

§ *distachya*	CHEx CTre ISea WNor

PARASYRINGA See **LIGUSTRUM**

X PARDANCANDA (Iridaceae)

norrisii	WHil WPer

PARDANTHOPSIS (Iridaceae)

dichotoma	ECro

PARIETARIA (Urticaceae)

§ *judaica*	GPoy MHew NSal WHer
¶ – 'Corinne Tremaine'	WHer
officinalis	See P. ***judaica***

PARIS (Liliaceae/Trilliaceae)

incompleta	MPlt SPou
polyphylla	See DAISWA ***p.***
quadrifolia	GPoy NSal SPou WCru WHer

PARNASSIA (Parnassiaceae)

cabulica	GDra
nubicola	GDra LGan MBal
palustris	MTol SIng WBon

PAROCHETUS (Leguminosae)

communis	CB&S CBre CGle CGre CLew CMer CNic CRDP CRiv ELan GDra LAbb LHil NBro NHar NKay NWCA SIng WAbe WCru WEas WHal WOMN WPer WThu WWat
– *africanus*	GCal WCru
– dark form	GCal
– Himalayan form	IBlr WCru

PARONYCHIA (Illechebraceae)

argentea	EPot LHil MBro WPer
¶ *argyroloba*	WDav
§ *capitata*	CHal CLew CNic CRiv ELan EMNN NHol NKay NMen NNrd WPat WPer WWin
§ *kapela*	MCas NHol NTow WPer
nivea	See P. ***capitata***

serpyllifolia	See P. ***kapela***

PARROTIA (Hamamelidaceae)

persica	CB&S CBow CBra CCla CPMA CSco EHar ELan ENot IDai IJoh LPan MBal MBri MGos NBar NHol SHBN SMad SPer SPla SSpi SSta WBod WDin WWat
– 'Pendula'	CBow CDoC CPMA EHar IOrc MBal SHBN SPer SSpi WBod
¶ – 'Vanessa'	SSpi WMou

PARROTIOPSIS (Hamamelidaceae)

jacquemontiana	CB&S CCla CCor MBri MUlv SSpi SSta

PARRYA (Cruciferae)

menziesii	See PHOENICAULIS ***cheiranthoides***

PARSONSIA (Apocynaceae)

capsularis	ECou LWad
heterophylla	ERea

PARTHENIUM (Compositae)

integrifolium	NSal

PARTHENOCISSUS † (Vitaceae)

§ *henryana*	Widely available
himalayana	ECtt
– var. *rubrifolia*	CMac WWat
§ *quinquefolia*	CArn CLan CMac CSco EBre EHar ELan ENot GRei IHos IJoh ISea LBre MBal MBri MWat NKay NNor NRoo NWea SBra SHBN SPer SReu SSta WBod WDin WWat
– var. *engelmannii*	CDoC MGos SPer WAbe
semicordata	CHEx
striata	See CISSUS ***s.***
♦ *thomsonii*	See CAYRATIA ***t.***
tricuspidata	CBow CHEx CShe ECtt MBal MGos NNor SPer SReu WBod WDin
– 'Beverley Brook'	CBow CDoC CMac CSco CShe EBre LBre MBri SBra SPer SPla WAbe WBod
– 'Green Spring'	CDoC CSco EHal IHos IJoh MBri MGos SBra
– 'Lowii'	CDoC CMac EBre EHal EPla LBre MGos SPer
§ – 'Veitchii'	CBra CMac EBre ECtt EHar ELan ENot IDai IHos IJoh LBre MBar MGos MRav MWat NKay NWea SBra SHBN SLon SPer SSta WDin WPat WWat

PASSIFLORA † (Passifloraceae)

¶ *actinia*	CGrh
¶ *adenopoda*	CGrh
¶ *adulterina*	CGrh
alata	CGrh ERea SLMG
× *alatocaerulea*	See P. × ***belotii***
¶ *allantophylla*	CGrh
allardii	CGre CGrh CTro SHil
¶ *ambigua*	CGrh
¶ 'Amethyst'	CGrh
amethystina	CB&S CDoC CTro ERea MAsh SLMG WWeb
¶ *ampullacea*	CGrh
¶ *anfracta*	CGrh
antioquiensis	CB&S CBot CGre CGrh CHEx CTro ERea IBlr ISea LBlm MNew SLMG
¶ *atomaria*	CGrh
§ *aurantia*	CGrh ERea
¶ *auriculata*	CGrh
banksii	See P. ***aurantia***
§ × *belotii*	CGrh CSPN CTro ERea MNew NRar WDin
– 'Impératrice Eugénie'	See P. × ***b.***
biflora	CGrh
¶ *brevipes*	CGrh
§ *caerulea*	Widely available
– 'Constance Elliott'	CB&S CBot CBow CCla CGre CGrh CMac CSco EBlo EBre ELan GCal LBre LHop LPri SBra SHer SLMG SPer SPla SReu SSta WCru WWeb
– forms	SLMG
– *rubra*	ECtt WPat
× *caeruleoracemosa*	CB&S CCla CGrh CKni ERea ISea SPla
– 'Eynsford Gem'	CGrh IOrc
– 'Lilac Lady'	SFai
× *caponii*	ERea
capsularis	CGrh CTro SLMG
¶ – *quinquadrangularis*	CGrh
chinensis	See P. ***caerulea***
¶ *citrina*	CGrh ERea
coccinea	CGrh
× *colvillei*	CGrh
coriacea	CGrh
costaricensis	CGrh
edulis	CGrh CTro EBak LAbb SHil SLMG
– 'Crackerjack'	CB&S CHEx COtt ERea
F – f. *edulis*	CB&S
F – f. *flavicarpa*	CGrh
– 'Supreme'	CB&S
eichleriana	CGrh
'Empress Eugenie'	See P. × ***belotii***
× *exoniensis*	CBot CGre CGrh CTro LAbb LPri SHil
foetida	CGrh
glandulosa	CGrh
gracilis	CGrh
¶ *guatemalensis*	CGrh
herbertiana	CGrh SLMG
holosericea	CGrh
incana	See P. ***seemannii***
incarnata	CArn CGrh ESim NSal
'Incense'	CGrh MNew
× *innesii*	See P. × ***decaisneana*** 'Innesii'
* *iralda*	CGrh
¶ *jorullensis*	CGrh
× *kewensis*	CGrh
laurifolia	CGrh
'Lavender Lady'	CGrh EBlo ELan IOrc LPri MAsh SFai
ligularis	CGrh CTro
¶ *lowei*	CGrh
¶ 'Lucia'	CGrh
lutea	CGrh
maliformis	CGrh

manicata	CGrh
¶ 'Mavis Mastics'	CGrh
mayana	See P. ***caerulea***
menispermifolia	See P. ***pilosa***
misera	CGrh
mixta	ERea
– x *antioquiensis*	CGrh
mollissima	CAbb CB&S CBot CGre CGrh CSun CTro ELan ERea LBlm LHop SHil SLMG
morifolia	CGrh CTro
¶ *naviculata*	CGrh
¶ *nelsonii*	CGrh
nitida	CGrh
oerstedii	CGrh
onychina	See P. ***amethystina***
¶ *pallens*	CGrh
¶ *perfoliata*	CGrh
§ *pilosa*	CGrh
¶ *pinnatistipula*	CGrh
platyloba	CGrh
¶ *punctata*	CGrh
'Purple Passion'	See P. ***edulis edulis***
quadrangularis	CB&S CBot CGrh CTro ERea SHil
racemosa	CGrh CTro ELan ERea IBlr SHil
rubra	CGrh CMac ELan LPri MAsh WStI WWeb
¶ 'Saint Rule'	CGrh
sanguinolenta	CGrh CTro ERea
§ *seemannii*	CArn
¶ *serratifolia*	CGrh
¶ *sexflora*	CGrh
'Star of Bristol'	CGrh
'Star of Clevedon'	CGrh
'Star of Kingston'	CGrh
suberosa	CGrh
subpeltata	CGrh
¶ 'Sunburst'	CGrh
§ *tetrandra*	CGre CGrh ECou
trifasciata	CGrh
tuberosa	CGrh
umbilicata	CBot CGrh SHil
¶ *urbaniana*	CGrh
¶ *vespertilio*	CGrh
violacea	CGrh CTro ERea MBri
¶ *viridiflora*	CGrh
vitifolia	CB&S CGrh ERea MNew
¶ *yucatanensis*	CGrh
¶ *zamorana*	CGrh

PASSION FRUIT, Purple See **PASSIFLORA *edulis edulis***

PASSION FRUIT, Yellow See **PASSIFLORA *edulis flavicarpa***

PASTINACA (Umbelliferae)

sativa	CKin

PATRINIA (Valerianaceae)

gibbosa	ECro GCHN LGan MHig NHol
scabiosifolia	CLew ECha ECro MPlt SSvw WDav WWin
triloba	CRDP ECha NHol
– var. *palmata*	CShe NKay SHer
– var. *triloba*	CGle CLew GCal MCas MHig MPar NNrd NTow SSpi WWin

PAULOWNIA (Scrophulariaceae)

coreana	CGre
fargesii Franchet	CBow CChu CGre CHEx CLnd CWSG EHar SMad SSpi
– Osborn	See P. ***tomentosa*** 'Lilacina'
¶ *fortunei*	CChu CWSG SSpi
tomentosa	CB&S CBot CBow CBra CGre CHEx CLnd CPle EHar ELan ENot IOrc LPan MBri MRav MUlv SEng SHBN SHil SMad SPer SSpi SSta WAbe WNor
§ – 'Lilacina'	CGre GWht WCoo

PAVONIA (Malvaceae)

¶ x *gledhillii*	CTro
♦ x *intermedia*	See P. x ***gledhillii***
praemorsa	CBot

PAW PAW See **CARICA *papaya***

PAXISTIMA (Celastraceae)

canbyi	EPla MUlv WThu WWin
myrsinites	See P. ***myrtifolia***
myrtifolia	CPle WWat

PEACH See **PRUNUS *persica***

PEAR See **PYRUS *communis***

PEAR, Asian See **PYRUS *pyrifolia***

PECAN See **CARYA *illinoinensis***

PECTEILIS (Orchidaceae)
See Plant Deletions

PEDICULARIS (Scrophulariaceae)

canadensis	NSal
¶ *verticillata*	NWCA

PEGANUM (Zygophyllaceae)

harmala	NSal

PELARGONIUM † (Geraniaceae)

♦ 'A Happy Thought'	See P. 'Happy Thought'
'A M Mayne' (Z/d)	SDen WFib
'Abel Carrière' (I/d)	SDen SKen WFib
abrotanifolium (Sc)	MHul NWyt SKen WFib WWye
¶ – broad-leaved	SDen
acerifolium hort.	See P. ***vitifolium***
– L'Héritier	See P. ***cucullatum stringifolium***
acetosum	CSpe GCHN GCal LGre MHul SMrm SUsu
¶ *acraeum*	MHul WFib
¶ Action ® (Z/d)	WFib
'Ada Sutterby' (Dw/d)	SBro SKen WFib
'Adagio' (Dw)	ESul
'Adam's Quilt' (Z/C)	SKen SOld
'Adele' (Min/d)	ESul SBro WFib
'Aerosol' (Min)	ESul

'Aerosol Improved' (Min) CSpe
'Ailsa' (Min/d) ESul MBri SBro
'Ainsdale Angel' (A) LDea
'Ainsdale Claret' (Z) WFib
'Akela' (Min) ESul SBro
'Alan West' (Z/St) SDen
'Albert Sheppard' (Z/C/d) WFib
'Alberta' (Z) NWyt SKen WFib
'Albert's Choice' (R) WFib
¶ ***album*** MHul
¶ ***alchemilloïdes*** MHul WFib
'Alcyone' (Dw/d) ESul IHos SBro SDen SKen SOak
'Alde' (Min) ESul MWhe SBro SDen SKen
'Aldham' (Min) SBro
¶ 'Aldwyck' (R) LDea
'Alex' (Z) SKen SOak
'Algenon' (Min/d) ESul SBro WFib
'Alice Crousse' (I/d) SKen WFib
'Alison' (Dw) ESul SBro
¶ 'Alison Wheeler' (Min/d) MWhe
'All My Love' (R) LDea WFib
'Alma' (Min/C) ESul SBro
I 'Aloe' (Z) WEas
'Alpine Glow' (Z/d) IHos MSmi MWhe NWyt SDen SKen SOld
¶ 'Alpine Orange' (Z/d) SDen
'Alta Bell' (R) WFib
'Altair' (Min/d) MWhe SBro
¶ ***alternans*** MHul
'Ambrose' (Dw/d) ESul SBro WFib
'Amelia' (Min) SBro
'Amethyst' (I/d) ECtt IHos LDea MWhe SOak WFib
– (R) LDea MBri MSmi MWhe SDen SKen SOak WFib
'Ami' (R) WFib
'Anabell Stephenson' (Dw/d) WFib
'Andersonii' (Sc) CHun WFib
'Andrew Salvidge' (R) LDea WFib
I 'Andromeda' (Min) SBro WFib
'Ange Davey' (Z/d) WFib
'Angela' (Min) SBro
'Angela Mitchell' (Z/C/d) SBro
'Angela Read' (Dw) ESul SBro
'Angelique' (Dw/d) SBro
'Anglia' (Dw) ESul SBro
'Ann Hoysted' (R) WFib
'Ann Redington' (R) LDea SDen WFib
'Anna' (Dw) ESul SBro
¶ ***antidysentericum*** MHul
'Antigua' (R) LDea WFib
'Antoinette' (Min) ESul SBro
'Apache' (Z/d) CHal WFib
'Aphrodite' (Z) ECtt WEas WFib
appendiculatum GCHN
'Apple Blossom Rosebud' (Z/d) CHal ECtt MBri MWhe NRar NWyt SDen SKen SMrm SOak SOld SUsu WEas WFib
¶ 'Appledram' (R) LDea
'Apricot' (Z/St/d) ESul SDen SKen
'Apricot Queen' (I/d) LDea SOak
§ 'Arctic Star' (Z/St) CSpe ESul SOak SOld WEas
'Arcturus' (Min) SBro
¶ × ***ardens*** MHul WEas
¶ ***aridum*** MHul
'Aries' (Min/C) ESul MWhe SBro
'Arizona' (Min/d) ESul NWyt SBro SDen SKen WFib
'Arthings Slam' (R) LDea SKen
'Arthur Biggin' (Z) MWhe SKen
¶ ***articulatum*** MHul
'Ashdown Forest' (Dw) SBro
'Ashfield Blaze' (Z/d) WFib
'Ashfield Jubilee' (Z/C) SKen
'Ashfield Monarch' (Z/d) MWhe WFib
'Ashfield Serenade' (Z) SKen WFib
'Ashley Stephenson' (R) WFib
'Askham Fringed Aztec' (R) LDea
¶ 'Askham Slam' (R) LDea
asperum Ehr. ex Willd. See P. 'Graveolens'
'Astrakan' (Z/d) SDen
'Athabasca' (Min) ESul SBro
'Atomic Snowflake' (Sc/v) CArn CHun ESul LHil NWyt SDen SIde WCHb WFib
'Attar of Roses' (Sc) CArn CHal CHun ESul IHos LHil MWhe NHHG NSty NWyt SDen SHer SIde SKen SOak WCHb WEas WFib
'Attraction' (Z/St/d) WFib
'Aubusson' (R) WFib
'Audrey' (Z/d) WFib
'Audrey Clifton' (I/d) ECtt SDen WEas WFib
'Augusta' LHop SMrm
¶ Auralia ® (Z/d) WFib
¶ ***auritum*** MHul
'Aurora' (Z/d) CHal MWhe
'Aurore' (U) See P. 'Unique Aurore'
australe EPad GCHN IHos MHul MSte WFib WHer WThi
– from Tasmania SSpi
'Autumn' (Z/d) IHos MWhe
'Autumn Colours' (Min) ESul SBro
'Autumn Festival' (R) WFib
'Autumn Mist' (R) WFib
'Avalon' (Dw/d) WFib
'Aztec' (R) LDea SKen WFib
'Baby Birds Egg' (Min) CSpe ESul SBro SDen
'Baby Brocade' (Min/d) ESul NWyt SBro SOak
'Baby Clare' (Min) SBro
'Baby Doll' (Min/d) SBro
'Baby Helen' (Min) ESul SBro
'Baby James' (Min) SBro SKen
'Babylon' (R) WFib
'Badley' (Dw) ESul SBro
Balcon Imperial ® See P. 'Roi des Balcons Impérial'
'Balcon Royale' (I) See P. 'Roi des Balcons Impérial'
'Ballerina' (Dw/d) LDea MWhe WFib
'Ballet Dancer' (Min/d) ESul SBro
'Bantam' (Min/d) ESul SBro WFib
§ 'Barbe Bleu' (I/d) ECtt LDea MSmi MWhe SDen SKen SOak WFib
¶ 'Barbecue' (Z/d) NWyt
'Barcelona' (R) SKen
'Barham' (Min/d) ESul SBro
'Barking' (Min) ESul SBro
¶ ***barklyi*** MHul WFib
'Baron de Layres' (Z/d) WFib
'Baronne A. de Rothschild' (Z/d) WFib
'Bashful' (Min) ESul SBro

'Bath Beauty' (Dw) SBro SDen SKen WEas
'Baylham' (Min) ESul SBro
'Beacon Hill' (Min) SBro
'Beatrice Cottington' (I/d) SKen
'Beatrix' (Z/d) ESul SBro SKen
¶ 'Beatrix Little' (Dw) NWyt
'Beauty of Bath' (R) WFib
'Beauty of Calderdale' (Z/C) WFib
'Beauty of Coldwell' (Z/C) MWhe
N 'Beauty of Eastbourne' See P. 'Lachskönigin'
'Beauty of El Segundo' (Z/d) SKen WFib
'Beauty of Jersey' (I/d) WFib
'Beckwith's Pink' (Z) SDen SKen
'Belinda Adams' (Min/d) ESul MWhe SBro
¶ 'Belladonna' (I/d) ECtt
Belladonna ® IHos NWyt
'Belstead' (Min) ESul SBro
'Bembridge' SDen
'Ben Franklin' (Z/v) IHos MWhe
'Ben Nevis' (Dw/d) ESul SBro SDen
'Benedict' (Min) SBro
'Bentley' (Dw) ESul SBro
¶ Bergpalais ® (Z/d) WFib
'Berliner Balkon' (I) SDen SKen
¶ 'Bernado' CSut
'Beronmunster' (Dec) LDea LHil SOld WFib
'Bert Pearce' (R) LDea
'Beryl Gibbons' (Z/d) MWhe
'Beryl Read' (Dw) ERea SBro
'Beryl Reid' (R) LDea SOak
'Berylette' (Min/d) SBro
'Bess' (Z/d) SBro SDen SKen
'Beta' (Min/C) ESul SBro
'Betsy Trotwood' (Dw) SBro
'Bette Shellard' (Z/d) MWhe
'Betty Dollery' (Z/d) SDen
'Betty Hulsman' (A) ESul SBro
'Betty Read' (Dw) ESul SBro
'Betty West' (Min/d) SBro SDen
betulinum GCHN MHul WFib
'Bewerley Park' (Z/C/d) SKen WFib
'Bianca' (Min/d) ESul SBro
'Biedermeier' (R) SOak
¶ ***bijugum*** MHul
'Bildeston' (Z/C) ESul SBro
'Bill West' (I) SDen
'Billie Read' (Dw/d) ERea ESul SBro
'Bingo' (Min) ESul SBro
'Bird Dancer' (Dw/St) CSpe ERav ESul LHil MWhe NWyt SBro SDen SKen SOak SOld WEas WFib WPer
¶ 'Birthday' (Z/D) SDen
'Birthday Girl' (R) WFib
'Bi-Coloured Startel' (Z/St/d) CBot MWhe
'Black Butterfly' (R) See F. 'Brown's Butterfly'
'Black Knight' (R) CSpe MSte
'Black Magic' (R) WFib
'Black Pearl' (Z/d) NWyt
'Black Velvet' (R) LDea
'Black Vesuvius' See P. 'Red Black Vesuvius'
'Blakesdorf' (Dw) CSpe ESul MWhe SBro
'Blanchland Cerise' (Dw) SBro
'Blanchland Dazzler' (Min) SBro
§ 'Blandfordianum' (Sc) MHul WHer
§ 'Blauer Frühling' (I/d) IHos LDea MWhe SDen SKen WFib
'Blaze Away' SDen
'Blazonry' (Z/v) CBrk MWhe SDen
'Blisworth Mrs Mappin' (Z/v) MWhe
'Blooming Gem' (Min/I/d) LDea SBro
'Blue Beard' (I) See P. 'Barbe Bleu'
'Blue Peter' (I/d) SKen
'Blue Spring' See P. 'Blauer Frühling'
§ Blues ® (Z/d) IHos NWyt
'Blush Mariquita' (R) WFib
'Blush Petit Pierre' (Min) ESul SBro
'Blushing Bride' (I/d) IHos LDea SKen
'Bob Legge' (Z/d) WFib
¶ 'Bold Appleblossom' (Z) SOak
¶ 'Bold Sunset' (Z/d) SOak
'Bolero' (U) IHos
'Bonanza' (Z/d) SBro
'Bosham' (R) LDea
'Botley Beauty' (R) LDea
'Boudoir' (Z/C/d) SBro
¶ ***bowkeri*** MHul
'Brackenwood' (Min/d) SBro
'Bramford' (Dw) ESul SBro
'Braque' (R) LDea WFib
'Bravo' (Z/d) MWhe
'Break o' Day' (R) LDea SDen SKen WEas
'Bredon' (R) WFib
'Brenda' (Min/d) ESul SBro
'Brenda Hyatt' (Dw/d) ESul SBro
'Brenda Kitson' (Z/d) MWhe WFib
'Brett' (Min) SBro
'Brettenham' (Min) ESul SBro
'Bridal Veil' (Min/C) SBro
'Bridesmaid' (Dw/C/d) ESul SBro SDen SOld WFib
'Brightwell' (Min/d) ESul SBro WFib
'Britannia' (R) LDea
'Brixworth Boquet' (Min/C/d) MWhe
'Brixworth Charmer' (Z/v) MWhe
'Brixworth Gold' (Min/C/d) MWhe
'Brixworth Melody' (Z/v) MWhe
'Brixworth Pearl' (Z) MWhe
'Brixworth Rhapsody' (Z/v) MWhe
'Brixworth Serenade' (Min/C/d) MWhe
'Brixworth Starlight' (I/v) MWhe
'Brocade' (Z/d) IHos NWyt WFib
'Bronze Corinne' (Z/C/d) SDen SKen
'Bronze Queen' (Z/C) MWhe NWyt
'Bronze Velvet' (R) WFib
'Brookside Flamenco' (Min/d) SBro
'Brookside Primrose' (Min/C/d) MWhe SBro
'Brook's Purple' See P. 'Royal Purple'
'Brownie' (Min) SBro
§ 'Brown's Butterfly' (R) LDea LHop SMrm SUsu WFib
'Brunii' (Z/d) IHos MWhe WFib

'Brunswick' (Sc)	NWyt SDen
'Brutus' (Z)	SDen
'Bucklesham' (Dw)	ESul SBro
'Bumblebee' (Dw)	ESul SBro
'Burgenlandmädel' (Z/d)	NWyt SKen SOak WFib
'Burgundy' (R)	LDea WFib
'Burstall' (Min/d)	ESul SBro SDen
'Butley' (Min)	ESul SBro
'Butterfly' (Min/v)	ECtt
Butterfly ®	IHos
'C Z' (Ca)	ESul
Cabaret ® (Z/d)	IHos MBri
¶ *caffrum*	MHul
'Cal' (Z/d)	See P. 'Salmon Irene'
'Caledonia' (Z)	NWyt SDen SKen
'Caligula' (Min/d)	SBro WFib
'Cally' (Min/d)	SBro
'Cameo' (Dw/d)	MWhe NWyt SBro WFib
'Camilla' (Dw)	SBro SDen
'Camphor Rose' (Sc)	ESul
candicans	GCHN MHul WFib
'Candy' (Min/d)	ESul SBro
'Candy Kisses' (D)	SBro
canescens	See P. 'Blandfordianum'
'Can-Can' (I/d)	WFib
'Capel' (Dw/d)	ESul SBro
'Capella' (Min)	SBro
¶ Capen ® (Z/d)	WFib
capitatum (Sc)	CHun GCHN MHul SDen WCHb WFib
'Caprice' (R)	SKen WFib
'Capricorn' (Min/d)	ESul SBro
'Captain Starlight' (A)	ESul LDea SBro SOak
'Cardinal' (Z/d)	See P. 'Kardinal'
'Cariboo Gold' (Min/C)	SKen
'Carisbrooke' (R)	LDea SDen SKen WEas WFib
'Carnival' (R)	See P. 'Marie Vogel'
– (Z)	WFib
¶ *carnosum*	MHul
'Carol'	SOld
'Carol Gibbons' (Z/d)	MWhe SOak
'Carol Plumridge' (Dw/C)	WFib
'Caroline Schmidt' (Z/d/v)	CBrk CHal MBri MWhe NWyt SDen SKen SOak WFib WPer
'Carolyn' (Min)	SBro
Casino ® (Z/d)	IHos NWyt
'Cassio' (Min/d)	SBro
'Catford Belle' (A)	CSpe ESul LDea LHil MWhe SBro SDen SKen SOld WEas WFib
¶ *caucalifolium* ssp. *caucalifolium*	MHul
¶ – ssp. *convolvulifolium*	MHul WFib
¶ *caylae*	MHul
'Cayucas' (I/d)	SKen
'Celebration' (Z/d)	ESul SBro
'Celia' (Min)	ESul SBro SDen
¶ *ceratophyllum*	MHul
'Cerise' (I/d)	MWhe
'Cézanne' (R)	IHos LDea SDen SKen SMrm SOak SUsu WFib
'Chantilly Lace' (R)	LDea
§ 'Charles Gounod' (Z/d)	SDen
Charleston ® (Z)	IHos
'Charlie Boy' (R)	LDea SDen WFib
'Charlotte Read' (Dw)	ERea SBro
'Charm' (Min)	ESul
'Charmer' (R)	LDea
'Chattisham' (Min)	ESul SBro
'Chelmondiston' (Min/d)	ESul MWhe SBro
§ 'Chelsea Gem' (Z/d/v)	CBrk SDen SKen SOak SOld WFib
'Chelsworth' (Min/d)	ESul NWyt SBro
'Chelvey' (R)	WFib
'Cherie' (Min)	ESul SBro WFib
– (R)	LDea WFib
'Cherie Maid' (Z/v)	CSpe
'Cherie Mitchell' (Min)	SBro
'Cherie Salmon'	WEas
'Cherry' (Min)	SBro WFib
– (Z/d)	WFib
'Cherry Blossom' (Z/d)	SKen
'Cherry Cocktail' (Z/v)	MWhe
'Cherry Galilee' (I/d)	SKen
'Cherry Hazel Ruffles' (R)	LDea
'Cherry Orchard' (R)	LDea SKen SMrm WFib
'Cherry Sundae' (Z/d/v)	ESul
¶ 'Cherryade' (Dw)	SDen
'Chew Magna' (R)	WFib
'Chieko' (Min/d)	ESul MWhe NWyt SBro SDen SOak WFib
'Chiltern Beacon' (Min/d)	SBro
'Chime' (Min/d)	SBro
'China Doll' (Dw/d)	WFib
'Chiquita' (R)	LDea WFib
'Chi-Chi' (Min)	ESul SBro
'Chocolate Blotch' (Z/C)	SBro SMrm
§ 'Chocolate Peppermint' (Sc)	CHal CHun CSev CSpe ESul IHos MWhe NHHG NWyt SDen SHer SKen WCHb WEas WFib WHer WPer
'Chocolate Tomentosum'	See P. 'Chocolate Peppermint'
'Choice Cerise' (R)	LDea
'Chorus Girl' (R)	SDen WEas
'Christine Read' (Dw)	ESul
'Christopher Ley' (Z)	SDen SKen
'Christopher Mitchell' (Min)	SBro
'Cindy' (Dw/d)	ESul NWyt SBro
'Circus Day' (R)	WFib
'Citriodorum' (Sc)	CArn NHHG NWyt WCHb WFib WPer
'Citronella' (Sc)	NHHG SHer WCHb WFib
citronellum (Sc)	MHul NSty SDen SKen WFib WHer WPer
'Clair' (Min)	WFib
'Clara Read' (Dw)	ESul SBro
'Clare' (Min)	SBro
'Claret Rock Unique' (U)	NWyt SDen SKen SMrm WFib
'Clarissa' (Min)	ESul
'Claude Read' (Dw)	ERea ESul SBro
'Claudette' (Min)	SBro
'Claudius' (Min)	ESul SBro SDen WFib
'Claydon' (Dw/d)	CSpe ESul SBro
'Clorinda' (U/Sc)	CHal CHun CSev ESul LHil NWyt SHer SIde SKen WCHb WFib WHer
'Clorinda Variegated'	See P. 'Variegated Clorinda'
Coco-Rico ® (I)	NWyt
'Coddenham' (Dw/d)	ESul SBro WFib

§ 'Colonel Baden-Powell' (I/d)	LDea WFib
'Colour Sergeant' (Min)	SBro
Columbia ® (Z/Sc)	IHos
¶ ***columbinum***	MHul
'Concolor Lace' (Sc)	SKen
¶ 'Constancy' (Z/d)	NWyt
'Contrast' (Z/d/C/v)	MWhe NWyt SDen SKen SOak WFib
'Copdock' (Min/d)	ESul SBro
'Copthorne' (Sc)	CSpe WFib WHer
'Coral Frills' (Dw)	SBro
¶ 'Coral Reef' (Z/d)	NWyt
'Coralglow' (Z/d)	IHos SOak
¶ ***cordifolium***	MHul WFib
coriandrifolium	See P. ***myrrhifolium***
'Cornell' (I/d)	ECtt IHos MBri MWhe
'Corsair' (Z/d)	MWhe WFib
¶ ***cortusifolium***	MHul
'Cotswold Queen' (Z/d)	WFib
'Cotton Candy' (Dw/d)	ESul SBro
'Cottontail' (Min/d)	ESul SBro
cotyledonis	GCHN MHul WFib
'Countess Mariza'	See P. 'Gräfin Mariza'
'Countess of Scarborough'	See P. 'Lady Scarborough'
'Country Girl' (R)	IHos
'Cover Girl' (Z/d)	WFib
'Cramdon Red' (Dw)	SKen SOld
'Crampel's Master' (Z)	SKen
¶ 'Cransley Blends' (R)	LDea
'Cransley Star' (A)	LDea
¶ ***crassicaule***	MHul
crassipes	GCHN
'Creamery' (Z/d)	SKen WFib
§ 'Creamy Nutmeg'	CHal MWhe
'Creeting St Mary' (Min)	ESul SBro
'Creeting St Peter ' (Min)	ESul SBro
¶ 'Crescendo' (I/d)	ECtt
'Crestfield Pink' (Min)	SBro
'Crimson Fire' (Z/d)	MBri MWhe SKen
'Crimson Glow' (Dw/d)	SBro
¶ 'Crimson Nosegay'	NWyt
'Crimson Unique' (U)	LHil SKen WFib
crispum (Sc)	NHHG SDen SHer SIde WCHb WEas WFib WWye
– 'Major' (Sc)	ESul GPoy NSty SDen SKen WFib WHer WPer
– 'Peach Cream' (Sc/v)	CHal MWhe SIde
– 'Variegatum' (Sc/v)	CHal CHun CSev CSpe GCHN IHos LDea LHil MWhe NRoo NSty NWyt SBro SDen SHer SKen SOak SOld WCHb WEas WFib WHer WPer WWye
crithmifolium	CTro GCHN
'Crocketta' (I/d)	SOak
'Crocodile'	See P. 'The Crocodile'
'Crowfield' (Min/d)	ESul SBro
'Crystal Palace Gem' (Z/v)	MWhe SDen SKen
cucullatum	MHul WFib
– ssp. ***strigifolium***	GCHN MHul WHer
'Culpho' (Min/C/d)	ESul SBro
'Cupid' (Min/Dw/d)	ESul SBro WFib
'Cynthia' (Min)	ESul SBro
'Cyril Read' (Dw)	ERea ESul SBro
'Czar'	See P. 'Maréchal MacMahon'

'Dainty Lassie' (Dw/v)	ESul
'Dale Queen' (Z)	WFib
'Dancer' (Dw)	ESul SBro
¶ 'Danny West'	SDen
'Dark Red Irene' (Z/d)	MWhe WFib
'Dark Secret' (R)	CSpe LDea SDen SKen WFib
'Dark Venus' (R)	LDea SOak
'Darmsden' (A)	ESul SBro SOak
¶ ***dasyphyllum***	MHul
'David John' (Dw/d)	NWyt SBro SDen
'David Mitchell' (Min/Ca/C/d)	SBro
'Davina' (Min/d)	ESul MWhe SBro WFib
¶ 'Dawn Bonanza' (R)	SOak
¶ 'Daydream' (Z/C/d)	NWyt
'Deacon Arlon' (Z/d)	ESul MWhe SKen
'Deacon Barbecue' (Z/d)	ESul MWhe SBro SDen
'Deacon Birthday' (Z/d)	ESul MWhe SBro
'Deacon Bonanza' (Z/d)	ESul MWhe SDen SKen SOak WFib
'Deacon Clarion' (Z/d)	ESul SBro SKen
'Deacon Constancy' (Z/d)	ESul MWhe SBro SDen
'Deacon Coral Reef' (Z/d)	ESul MWhe SBro SKen SOld
'Deacon Finale' (Z/d)	ESul SBro SDen
'Deacon Fireball' (Z/d)	ESul MWhe SDen SKen SOld
'Deacon Flamingo' (Z/d)	ESul MWhe SDen
'Deacon Gala' (Z/d)	ESul MWhe SBro SDen
'Deacon Golden Bonanza' (Z/C/d)	ESul SBro
'Deacon Golden Gala' (Z/C/d)	ESul SBro
'Deacon Golden Lilac Mist' (Z/C/d)	ESul SDen
'Deacon Jubilant' (Z/d)	ESul MWhe SBro SDen SKen
'Deacon Lilac Mist' (Z/d)	CHal ESul MWhe SBro SDen SKen SOak SOld
'Deacon Mandarin' (Z/d)	ESul MWhe SBro SKen
'Deacon Minuet' (Z/C/d)	ESul MWhe SBro SDen SKen SOak
'Deacon Moonlight' (Z/d)	ESul MWhe SBro
'Deacon Peacock' (Z/C/d)	ESul MWhe SBro SDen SKen SOak
'Deacon Picotee' (Z/d)	CHal ESul IHos MBri SBro SDen SKen
'Deacon Regalia' (Z/d)	ESul MWhe SDen SKen
'Deacon Romance' (Z/d)	ESul MWhe SBro SKen
'Deacon Summertime' (Z/d)	ESul MWhe SBro
'Deacon Sunburst' (Z/d)	CHal ESul MWhe SBro SKen SOld
'Deacon Suntan' (Z/d)	ESul MWhe SBro SKen
'Deacon Trousseau' (Z/d)	ESul SBro SDen
'Decora Impérial' (I)	SKen
§ 'Decora Lilas' (I)	ECtt SKen WFib
'Decora Mauve' (I)	See P. 'Decora Lilas'
§ 'Decora Rose' (I)	ECtt IHos SKen
§ 'Decora Rouge' (I)	CSpe ECtt NWyt SKen WFib
'Degas' (R)	WFib
'Delilah' (R)	LDea SDen
'Della' (Min/d)	SBro
'Delta' (Min/d)	SBro
'Denebola' (Min/d)	ESul SBro WFib
Denticulatum Group (Sc)	CHal MHul NHHG NWyt SDen SHer SIde SKen WCHb WFib

Name	Suppliers
§ – 'Filicifolium' (Sc)	CHal CSev CSpe GCHN IHos LHil NHHG NWyt SDen SKen WFib WHer WPer
¶ ***desertorum***	MHul
'Destiny' (R)	WFib
'Dewit's' (Dw)	NWyt SBro
'Di' (Min/d)	SBro
'Diadem' (R)	SKen WFib
'Diane' (Min/d)	ESul SBro SDen WFib
dichondrifolium	MHul SSad WFib
'Dick's White' (Dw/d)	SBro
'Didden's Improved Picardy' (Z/d)	MWhe
'Diddi-Di' (Min/d)	SBro
'Didi' (Min)	SBro
'Dinky' (Min/d)	SBro
¶ ***dipetalum***	MHul
§ Disco ® (Z/d)	IHos NWyt
'Distinction' (Z)	CBrk IHos MWhe NWyt SDen SKen WFib
'Doctor A Chipault' (I/d)	LDea WFib
'Dodd's Super Double' (Z/d)	CHal IHos
'Dollar Bute' (R)	LDea
'Dollar Princess' (Z/C)	SKen
¶ 'Dolly Daydream' (C)	SDen
¶ 'Dolly Moon' (C)	SDen
'Dolly Read' (Dw)	ERea ESul SBro WFib
'Dolly Varden' (Z/v)	IHos LHop MBri MWhe NWyt SDen SKen WFib
dolomiticum	GCHN MHul WFib
'Dolphin' (Min)	NWyt SBro WFib
¶ 'Don Quixote' (A)	LDea
'Dondo' (Dw/d)	SBro
'Dopey' (Min)	ESul SBro
'Doreen Featherby' (R)	SDen
'Doris Brook' (Z/d)	WFib
'Doris Frith' (R)	LDea SKen WFib
'Doris Hancock' (R)	WFib
'Doris Shaw' (R)	WFib
¶ 'Double Bird's Egg' (Z/d)	NWyt
'Double Grace Wells' (Min/d)	ESul SBro
'Double Jacoby' (Z/d)	WFib
'Double Lilac White' (I/d)	IHos MWhe
'Double New Life' (Z/d)	CHal
'Double Orange' (Z/d)	SKen
'Double Pink Bird's Egg' (Z/d)	SKen
'Dove' (Z)	NWyt WFib
'Dovedale' (Dw/C)	NWyt SBro SOak
'Downlands' (Z/d)	SDen
'Dream' (Z)	WFib
'Dresden China' (R)	LDea
'Dresden Pink' (Dw)	SBro WFib
'Dresden White' (Dw)	CSpe SBro
'Drummer Boy' (Z)	SKen
drummondii	GCHN
'Dryden' (Z)	CHal NWyt SDen SKen
'Dubonnet' (R)	SOak WFib
'Duchess' (I)	CSpe
'Duchess of Devonshire' (Z)	SKen
'Duke of Buckingham' (Z/d)	NWyt SDen
'Duke of Edinburgh'	See P. 'Hederinum Variegatum'
'Dulcie' (Min)	ESul SBro
'Dunkery Beacon' (R)	LDea WFib
'Dusty Rose' (Min)	SBro
'Dutch Vermillion' (Min)	SBro
§ 'Dwarf Miriam Baisey' (Min)	SBro SDen SOak WFib
'Dwarf Miriam Read'	See P. 'Dwarf Miriam Baisey'
'E Dabner' (Z/d)	SKen WFib
'Earleana' (Dec)	CSpe ESul LDea SBro SKen
'Eastbourne Beauty' (I/d)	WFib
'Easter Greeting'	See P. 'Ostergruss'
¶ 'Easter Moon'	NWyt
echinatum	CSpe GCHN MHul SSad
¶ – 'Alba'	SSad
– 'Miss Stapleton'	SSad
'Eclipse' (Min/d)	MWhe NWyt SBro SDen SKen
'Eden Gem' (Min/d)	ESul SBro SDen
'Edith Steane' (Dw/d)	SBro
'Edmond Lachenal' (Z/d)	WFib
'Edward Humphris' (Z)	SDen SKen
'Edwin Clarke' (Dw/Min)	SBro
'Eileen Postle' (R)	WFib
'Eleanor' (Z/d)	SDen
'Electra' (Z/d)	SDen WFib
¶ ***elegans***	MHul
'Elfin Rapture' (R)	WFib
'Elgar' (R)	WFib
'Elizabeth Angus' (Z)	SDen SKen WFib
'Elizabeth Cartwright' (Z)	WFib
'Elizabeth Read' (Dw)	ERea ESul NWyt SBro
¶ 'Elmscfi' (Dw)	NWyt
'Elmsett' (Z/C/d)	ESul SBro
'Elna' (Min)	ESul SBro
elongatum	GCHN MHul
'Els' (Min/St)	ESul LHil SBro SKen
'Elsi' (I/d/v)	SDen WFib
'Elsie' (Z/C/d)	SBro
'Elsie Hickman' (R)	LDea SDen SKen WFib
'Elsie Portas' (Z/C/d)	ESul SKen
'Embassy' (Dw)	ESul SBro WFib
'Emerald' (I)	MSmi SDen SKen
'Emma' (Min/C/d)	SBro
'Emma Hössle'	See P. 'Frau Emma Hössle'
'Emma Jane Read' (Dw/d)	ERea ESul MWhe SBro WFib
'Emma Louise' (Z)	SKen
¶ 'Emperor Nicholas' (Z/d)	NWyt
'Empress' (Z)	SKen
'Ena' (Min)	ESul SBro
'Enchantress' (I)	CHal MBri MWhe SDen
endlicherianum	CMon GCHN MHul SApp SAxl SPou SSpi
'Endora' (Min)	SBro SDen
'Endsleigh' (Sc)	SDen
'Enid Blackaby' (R)	WFib
'Enid Read' (Dw)	ERea ESul SBro
'Eric Ellis' (Dw/d)	WFib
'Erwarton' (Min/d)	ESul SBro SDen
'Escapade' (Dw/d)	ESul SBro
'Etna' (Min)	SBro
'Evesham Wonder' (Z/d)	SDen WFib
¶ ***exhibens***	MHul
¶ ***exstipulatum***	MHul WFib

'Fair Dinkum' (Z/v) MWhe
§ 'Fair Ellen' (Sc) ESul SIde SKen WFib WPer
¶ 'Fairlee' (DwI) SDen
'Fairy Orchid' (A) LDea SBro
'Fairy Princess' (Min) SBro
– (R) LDea
'Fairy Tales' (Dw) ESul SBro
'Falkenham' (Min) ESul SBro
'Falklands Hero' (Z/v) MWhe SBro SKen SOak WFib
'Fanny Eden' (R) WFib
'Fantasie' (Dw/d) ESul MWhe SBro WFib
'Fareham' (R) LDea
'Fascination' (Z/Ca) WFib
'Feneela' (Dw/d) SBro
¶ 'Fenton Farm' (Z/C) SOak
'Festal' (Min/d) ESul SBro
'Feu d'Amour' (I/d) SOak WEas
'Fiat' (Z/d) SKen
'Fiat Queen' (Z/d) SKen WFib
'Fiat Supreme' (Z/d) SKen WFib
§ Fidelio ® (Z/d) IHos NWyt
'Fiery Sunrise' (R) LDea
'Fiesta' (Z) LDea
'Fifth Avenue' (R) CSpe SDen
'Filicifolium' See P. Denticulatum Group 'Filicifolium'
'Filigree' (Dw/v) IHos SBro
'Finger' SBro
'Finito' (Dw/d) ERea SBro
'Fire Dragon' (Z/St/d) CHal MWhe SKen WFib
'Fireball' NWyt SBro
'Firefly' (Min/d) ESul SBro WFib
'Fireglow' (Z/d) ESul
'First Blush' (R) WFib
¶ ***fissifolium*** MHul
'Flakey' (I/C/d) CSpe ESul LDea MWhe NWyt SBro SDen SKen
'Flame' (Z) WFib
'Flamingo Dancer' (Z/Ca) SBro
'Flash' (Min) SBro
'Fleur d'Amour' (R) WFib
'Fleurette' (Dw/d) CHal ESul MWhe NWyt SBro SDen SKen SOld WFib
§ Flirt ® (Min) ESul MBri NWyt
'Floral Cascade' (Fr/d) NWyt WFib
'Florence Storey' (Z/C/d) WFib
'Flower of Spring' (Z/v) CHal CSpe MWhe NWyt SDen SKen WFib
'Flowerfield' (Z) SDen
'Flowton' (Dw/d) ESul SBro
'Flynn' (Min) ESul
Fox ® (Z/d) WFib
'Foxhall' (Dw) ESul SBro
Fragrans Group (Sc) CHal CHun CMil CSev ERav ESul GCHN GPoy MWhe NHHG NSty NWyt SDen SHer SKen WFib WHer WPer WWye
– 'Creamy Nutmeg' (Sc/v) See P. 'C.N.'
§ – 'Fragrans Variegatum' (Sc/v) CHal CHun CMil CSev CSpe ERav ESul LHil LHop MHul MWhe NSty NWyt SDen SHer SKen SOak WCHb WFib WPer
– 'Snowy Nutmeg' See P. Fragrans Group 'Fragrans Variegatum'
¶ 'Francis James' (Z) NWyt
'Francis Parrett' (Min/d) ESul MWhe NWyt SBro WFib
'Francis Read' (Dw/d) ERea ESul SBro
'Frank Headley' (Z/v) CBrk CHal CSpe ESul IHos LHil MSte MWhe NWyt SBro SDen SKen SMrm SOak SOld WEas WFib WSun
'Frank Parrett' (Min/d) ESul SBro
§ 'Frau Emma Hössle' (Dw/d) ESul MWhe NWyt WFib
'Frau Käthe Neubronner' (Z/d) SDen
'Freak of Nature' (Z/v) CHal ESul IHos MWhe SDen SKen WEas WFib
'Frensham' (Sc) ESul IHos
'Freston' (Dw) ESul
'Freya' (Min) SBro
'Friary Wood' (Z/C/d) ESul NWyt SKen SOak WFib
'Friesdorf' (Dw) ESul LHil MWhe NWyt SBro SDen SKen WEas WFib
'Frills' (Min/d) ESul MWhe NWyt SBro SKen SOak WFib
'Fringed Aztec' (R) LDea SDen SOak SOld
¶ 'Fringed Rouletta' (I) LDea
'Frosty' (Min/v) SBro
fruticosum MHul WFib WHer
fulgidum GCHN MHul WFib
'Fynn' (Dw) SBro
'Galilee' (I/d) IHos LDea SDen SKen SOak WFib
'Galway Star' (Sc/v) CSpe MWhe NWyt SDen SIde WFib
'Gama' (Min) SBro
¶ 'Garda' (I/d) ECtt
'Garibaldi' (Z/d) NWyt WFib
'Garland' (Dw/d) ESul SBro
– (R) SKen
'Garnet' (Z/d) WFib
'Garnet Rosebud' (Min/d) ESul SBro
'Garnet Wings' (R) WFib
¶ 'Gary Salvidge' (R) LDea
'Gauguin' (I/d) IHos
'Gay Baby' (DwI) ESul LDea MWhe NWyt SBro SDen SKen
'Gay Baby Supreme' (DwI) ESul SDen SKen
'Gazelle' (Z) SDen SKen
'Gemini' (Z/St/d) SKen SOak
Gemini ® (Z/St) IHos
'Gemma' (Min/C) SKen
– (R) LDea
¶ 'Gemma Jewel' (R) SOak
¶ 'Gemma Pride' (R) SOak
¶ 'Gemma Rose' (R) SOak
'Genetrix' (Z/d) WFib
'Genie' (Z/d) MWhe SDen WFib
'Geoff May' (Dw) ESul SBro SDen WFib
'Geoffrey Horsman' (R) WFib
'Georgia Peach' (R) SDen WFib
'Geo's Pink' (Z/v) MWhe
'Gerald Portas' (Dw/C) SBro
'Gerald Wells' (Min) SBro
'Geraldine' (Min) ESul SBro
'Geratus' (Min/Ca/d) SBro
'Gess Portas' (Z/v) ESul SKen
¶ 'Giant Butterfly' (R) SOak
gibbosum CTro GCHN MHul WFib
'Gilbert West' (Z) SKen
'Gilda' (R) LDea SKen
'Gill' (Min/Ca) ESul SBro
'Gillian Clifford' (Z/d) SDen
'Gina' (Min) SBro

'Glacier Claret' (Z) IHos
¶ Glacis ® (Z/d) WFib
'Gladys Evelyn' (Z/d) WFib
'Gladys Stevens' (Min/d) ESul SBro
glaucum See P. ***lanceolatum***
'Glenn Barker' (Z/d) WFib
'Glenshree' (R) LDea SKen
Gloria ® (Z/d) NWyt
'Gloria Pearce' (R) LDea WFib
'Glory' (Z/d) WFib
'Glowing Embers' (R) LDea WFib
§ ***glutinosum*** CSev MHul
'Goblin' (Min/d) ESul IHos NWyt SBro SDen SKen SOak WFib
¶ 'Golden Baby' (DwI/C) MWhe
'Golden Bonanza' SBro
'Golden Brilliantissimum' (Z/C) ESul MWhe NWyt SKen WFib
'Golden Butterfly' (Z/C) SBro
'Golden Chalice' (Min/v) MWhe SBro SDen SKen SOak
'Golden Clorinda' (U/Sc/C) CHal SDen WEas
'Golden Crest' (Z/C) NWyt SDen SKen SMrm SOak
'Golden Ears' (Dw/St/C) ESul MWhe NWyt SBro SKen SOak SOld WFib
'Golden Everaarts' (Dw/C) ESul SBro
'Golden Fleece' (Min/C/d) ESul SDen SKen
'Golden Gala' (D/C) SBro SDen
'Golden Gates' (Z/C) ESul SBro SDen SKen
'Golden Gleam' (Z/C) SDen
'Golden Harry Hieover' (Z/C) CBrk ESul SDen SKen WEas
'Golden Lilac Mist' NWyt SBro
'Golden Orange' (Dw/C) SBro
'Golden Orfe' (Dw/C) SBro WFib
'Golden Oriole' (Dw/C) SKen
'Golden Petit Pierre' (Min/C) ESul SBro
'Golden Princess' (Min/C) ESul SBro WFib
– (R) LDea
'Golden Roc' (Min/C) ESul SBro
'Golden Staphs' (St/C) ESul NWyt SBro SDen
'Golden Tears' (MinI/C/d) ESul SDen
'Goldie' (R) WFib
'Goldilocks' (A) LDea
'Gordano Midnight' (R) WFib
'Gordino Pixie' (R) LDea
'Gosbeck' (A) ESul MWhe SBro
¶ 'Gosport Girl' (R) LDea
'Grace Read' (Min) SBro
'Grace Wells' (Min) ESul WFib
§ 'Gräfin Mariza' (Z/d) IHos NWyt SDen SKen WFib
'Granada' (R) IHos
'Grand Slam' (R) IHos LDea SKen SOak SOld WFib
grandiflorum GCHN MHul WFib
'Grandma Fischer' See P. 'Grossmutter Fischer'
¶ 'Grandma Ross' (R) LDea
'Granny Hewitt' (Min/d) ESul MWhe SBro
§ 'Graveolens' (Sc) CHal CSev GCHN GPoy LHil MHul MWhe NSty NWyt SDen SHer SKen SOak WFib
'Great Bricett' (Min/d) ESul SBro
'Green Eyes' (I/d) LDea SDen
'Green Goddess' (I/d) SKen
'Green Woodpecker' (R) LDea SDen
§ 'Greengold Kleine Liebling' (Min/C/v) NWyt SBro SKen
'Greengold Petit Pierre' See P. 'Greengold Kleine Liebling'
¶ Gregor ® (Z/d) WFib
'Grenada' (R) SKen
§ 'Grenadier' (Z/St/d) NWyt SDen
'Grey Lady Plymouth' (Sc/v) CHun WFib
'Grey Sprite' (Min/v) ESul SBro WFib
¶ ***griseum*** MHul WFib
§ 'Grossmutter Fischer' (R) LDea WEas WFib
grossularioïdes CHal MHul NSty
'Grozser Garten' (Dw) ESul
'Grozser Garten Weiss' (Dw) ESul
'Gustav Emich' (Z/d) SDen SKen WFib
'Gwen' (Min/v) SBro
'H Guinier' See P. 'Charles Gounod'
'Hadleigh' (Dw) ESul SBro
'Haidee' (Min) SBro
¶ 'Hamble Lass' (R) LDea
§ 'Hannaford Star' (Z/St) ESul SDen
§ 'Happy Thought' (Z/v) CHal IHos MBri MWhe NWyt SDen SKen
'Happy Valley' (R) WFib
'Harbour Lights' (R) LDea
'Harewood Slam' (R) LDea SMrm SOak WFib
'Harkstead' (Min) ESul NWyt SBro
'Harlequin Alpine Glow' (I) LDea MWhe SDen SOak WFib
'Harlequin Mahogany' (I/d) IHos LDea MBri MWhe SDen SKen SOak SOld WFib
§ 'Harlequin Miss Liver Bird' (I) LDea MSmi MWhe SDen SKen SOak SOld
'Harlequin My Love' (I) SKen
'Harlequin Picotee' (I/d) LDea MWhe SDen SOak
'Harlequin Pretty Girl' (I) IHos MWhe SDen SKen SOak WFib
'Harlequin Rosie O'Day' (I) LDea MWhe SDen SKen SOak WFib
'Harlequin Ted Day' (I) LDea
'Harold Headley' (Z/v) WFib
'Harriet Le Hair' (Z) SKen
¶ 'Harvard' (I) SDen
'Harvey' (Z) MWhe
'Hayley Charlotte' (Z/v) MWhe
'Hazel' (R) CHal SDen SKen WFib
¶ 'Hazel Anson' (R) LDea
'Hazel Birkby' (R) LDea
¶ 'Hazel Burgundy' (R) LDea
¶ 'Hazel Burtoff' (R) LDea
¶ 'Hazel Carey' (R) LDea
'Hazel Cherry' (R) LDea SOak WFib
¶ 'Hazel Chick' (R) LDea
¶ 'Hazel Choice' (R) LDea
¶ 'Hazel Frances' (R) LDea
¶ 'Hazel Frills' (R) LDea
'Hazel Gipsy' (R) LDea SOak
'Hazel Glory' (R) LDea
¶ 'Hazel Harmony' (R) LDea
¶ 'Hazel Heather' (R) LDea
¶ 'Hazel Henderson' (R) LDea
'Hazel Herald' (R) LDea SDen SOak

¶ 'Hazel Mist' (R) LDea
¶ 'Hazel Perfection' (R) SOak
'Hazel Satin' (R) LDea
¶ 'Hazel Star' (R) LDea
¶ 'Hazel Wright' (R) LDea
§ 'Hederinum' (I) IHos MWhe SDen SKen WEas WFib
§ 'Hederinum Variegatum' (I/v) CSpe LDea MWhe SKen WFib
'Heidi' (Min/d) ESul SBro SDen SKen WFib
'Helena' (I/d) LDea MWhe SDen SKen
'Hemingstone' (A) ESul LDea SBro
'Henhurst Gleam' (Dw/C/d) WFib
'Henley' (Min/d) ESul
'Henry Jacoby' (Z) WEas
¶ 'Hermine' (Z/d) WFib
'Hermione' (Z/d) CHal MWhe NWyt
'High Tor' (Dw/C/d) ESul NWyt SKen
'Highfields Always' (Z/d) IHos WFib
'Highfields Appleblossom' (Z/d) IHos SKen
'Highfields Attracta' (Z/d) SDen SKen
'Highfields Choice' (Z) SKen
'Highfields Comet' (Z) SKen
'Highfields Contessa' (Z/d) SDen SKen
'Highfields Fancy' (Z/d) IHos SKen
'Highfields Fantasy' (Z) SKen
'Highfields Festival' (Z/d) CHal MWhe SDen SOak
'Highfields Joy' (Z/d) SDen WFib
'Highfields Melody' (Z/d) SDen
'Highfields Paramount' (Z) MWhe SDen SKen
'Highfields Prestige' (Z) SKen
'Highfields Pride' (Z) SKen
'Highfields Prima Donna' (Z/d) MWhe SKen
'Highfields Promise' (Z) SDen SKen
'Highfields Snowdrift' (Z) SKen
'Highfields Sugar Candy' (Z/d) ECtt IHos NWyt SDen SKen SOak
'Hildegard' (Z/d) CHal SKen SOak WFib
'Hills of Snow' (Z/v) CHal SDen SKen
'Hillscheider Amethyst' (I/d) See P. 'Amethyst'
'Hindoo' (R) WFib
'Hintlesham' (Min) ESul SBro
hirtum GCHN MHul
¶ ***hispidum*** MHul
'Hitcham' (Min/d) ESul SBro
¶ 'Hi-Jinks' (Z/v) MWhe
'Holbrook' (Min/C/d) ESul SBro
'Hollywood Star' (Z) MWhe
'Honeywood Lindy' (R) LDea SDen
'Honeywood Matthew' (Dw) SBro
'Honeywood Suzanne' (Min/Fr) ESul SBro
'Honne Früling' (Z) SKen WFib
'Honneas' (Min) ESul
'Honnestolz' (Min) ESul SBro SKen
'Hope' (Z) WFib
'Hope Valley' (Dw/C/d) ESul MWhe SBro SDen SKen
'Horace Parsons' (R) WFib
'Horace Read' (Dw) ERea ESul SBro
'House and Garden' (R) WFib
'Howard Stanton' (R) WFib
'Howard's Orange' (R) LDea SKen
'Hugo de Vries' (Z/d) WFib
'Hunter's Moon' (Z/C) ESul SBro SKen SOak
'Hurdy-Gurdy' (Z/d/v) ESul WFib
HWD Corelli ® IHos
HWD Gabrieli ® IHos
HWD Monteverdi ® IHos
HWD Onyx ® IHos
HWD Romanze ® IHos
HWD Vivaldi ® IHos
¶ ***hystrix*** MHul
'Ian Read' (Min/d) ERea ESul SBro WFib
'Ice Cap' (Min) SBro
'Icing Sugar' (I/d) LDea MWhe NWyt SOak
'Immaculatum' (Z) WFib
'Imperial Butterfly' (A) LDea SBro SOak
'Improved Petit Pierre' (Min) ESul
'Improved Ricard' (Z/d) WFib
¶ Ina ® (Z/d) WFib
'Inca' (R) LDea SDen SOak
incrassatum GCHN MHul
'Ingres' (I/d) ECtt IHos
inquinans GCHN MHul WFib
¶ ***iocastum*** MHul
¶ ***ionidiflorum*** MHul
'Ipswich Town' (Dw/d) ESul
'Irene' (Z/d) NWyt WFib
'Irene Cal' (Z/d) SKen
'Irene Corsair' (Z/d) SKen
'Irene La Jolle' (Z/d) SKen
'Irene Lollipop' (Z/d) SKen
'Irene Toyon' NWyt
'Isaac Read' (Dw) SBro
'Isidel' (I/d) MSmi SKen WFib
'Isobel Gamble' (Z/d) SKen
Isobell ® (Z/d) WFib
'Italian Gem' (I) SKen
'Ivalo' (Z/d) IHos MWhe SKen WFib
'Ivory Snow' (Z/d/v) NWyt SKen
'Jacey' (Z/d) SDen SKen
'Jack Read' (Dw) ERea ESul SBro
'Jackie's Gem' (I/d) MWhe
'Jacky Gauld' (I/d) IHos LDea MBri MWhe SKen
'Jacqueline' (Z/d) SKen
'Jan Portas' (Min/C) MWhe
¶ Jana ® (Z/d) WFib
'Jane Biggin' (Dw/C/d) ESul MWhe SBro SKen SOld
'Jane Shoulder' (Min) SBro
'Janet Kerrigan' (Min/d) ESul MWhe SBro WEas WFib
¶ 'Janna Whelan' (Dw/d) SDen
'Jasmine' (R) LDea
'Jaunty' (Min/d) ESul NWyt SBro SDen
'Jay' (Dw) SBro
'Jayne' (Min/d) CAbP SBro
'Jayne Eyre' (Min/d) CHal ESul MWhe NWyt SBro SDen SOak WFib
Jazz ® IHos
'Jean Oberle' (Z/d) SDen SKen
§ 'Jeanne d'Arc' (I/d) SKen WFib
'Jenifer' (Min) ESul SBro

'Jenifer Read' (Dw) ERea ESul SBro
¶ 'Jennifer Strange' (R) SOak
'Jessel's Unique' (U) SDen
¶ Jessika ® (Z/d) WFib
'Jewel' (Z/d) NWyt SDen
'Jeweltone' (Z/d) WFib
'Jill Portas' (Z/C) SKen
'Jim Field' (R) WFib
'Jimmy Read' (Min) ERea ESul SBro
'Joan Cashmore' (Z/d) SDen
'Joan Fairman' (R) WFib
'Joan Hayward' (Min) ESul SBro
'Joan Morf' (R) LDea LHop SDen SKen SOak WFib
'Joan of Arc' (I/d) See P. 'Jeanne d'Arc'
'Joan Shearman' (Min) ESul SBro
'Joanna Pearce' (R) LDea SKen
'John West' SDen
¶ 'Joseph Haydon' (R) LDea
'Joseph Paul' (R) SDen
'Joseph Warren' (I/d) LDea
'Joy' (R) WFib
'Joy Lucille' (Sc) CSev ESul SDen SOak WCHb WFib
'Joyce Delamere' (Z/C/d) NWyt WFib
'Joyce Headley' (Dw/C) SBro
'Joyful' (Min) SBro
'Jubel Parr' (Z/d) SDen
¶ 'Jubilant' NWyt
'Judy Read' (Dw) SBro
'Julia' (R) LDea
'Julie' (A) ESul LDea SBro SKen
'Julie Smith' (R) LDea WFib
¶ 'Junney Reeves' (R) LDea
'Jupiter' (Min/d) SBro WFib
¶ – (R) LDea
'Just William' (Min/C/d) SBro
'Kamahl' (R) WFib
'Kardinal' (Z/d) IHos
'Karen' (Dw/C) SBro
'Karl Hagele' (Z/d) SKen WFib
¶ *karooicum* MHul
karrooense 'Graham Rice' See P. 'Grollie's Cream'
'Kathleen Gamble' (Z) SKen
'Kathleen Mott' (Z/C) WFib
'Kathryn' (Min) ESul
'Kathryn Portas' (Z/v) ESul SKen
'Kayleigh West' (Min) SDen
'Keepsake' (Dw/d) ESul SBro WFib
'Kelvedon Beauty' (Min) SBro WEas
'Ken Salmon' (Dw/d) SBro
'Kerensa' (Min/d) ESul SBro SKen
'Kershy' (Min) ESul SBro
'Kesgrave' (Min/d) ESul SBro
'Kettle Baston' (A) ESul LDea MWhe SBro SOak
'Kewense' (Z) CSpe NWyt
¶ 'Kimono' (R) LDea
'King Edmund' (R) LDea SDen
'King of Balcon' See P. 'Hederinum'
'King of Denmark' (Z/d) CHal SKen WFib
¶ 'Kingsmill' (R) LDea
'Kingswood' (Z) SDen
'Kirton' (Min/d) ESul SBro
§ 'Kleine Liebling' (Min) CSev LHop MWhe NWyt SBro SKen
'Koora' (Min/d) SBro
'Kosset' (Min/d) SBro
'Krista' (Min/d) ESul NWyt SBro SDen WFib
'Kyra' (Min/d) ESul SBro WFib
'L E Wharton' (Z) SDen SKen
'La France' (I/d) LDea MBri MSmi MWhe SDen SKen SOak SOld WEas WFib
'La Jolla' (Z/d) SDen
'La Paloma' (R) LDea SKen WEas
¶ 'Laced Belle Notte' NWyt
¶ 'Laced Red Mini Cascade' (I) SDen
¶ 'Laced Sugar Baby' (DwI) NWyt SDen
¶ Lachsball ® (Z/d) WFib
§ 'Lachskönigin' (I/d) IHos LDea MSmi MWhe NWyt SKen WFib
'Lady Churchill' WFib
'Lady Cullum' (Z/C/v) MWhe
'Lady Ilchester' (Z/d) NWyt SDen SKen WFib
'Lady Lexington' (I) SKen
'Lady Mary' (Sc) SDen SOak WFib
'Lady Plymouth' (Sc/v) CHal CHun CMil CSpe ESul IHos LHop MWhe NHHG NRoo NSty NWyt SDen SHer SKen SOak SOld WEas WFib WHer WPer
§ 'Lady Scarborough' (Sc) CArn SKen WFib
¶ *laevigatum* MHul
'Lakeland' (I) SBro
¶ 'Lakis' (R) LDea
'Lamorna' (R) LDea SDen SKen
¶ *lanceolatum* MHul WFib
'Langley' (R) LDea SDen
'Lanham Lane' (I) LDea
'Lark' (Min/d) ESul SBro
N 'Lass o'Gowrie' (Z/v) MWhe NWyt SDen SKen WFib
– (American)(Z/v) WFib
Laura ® (Z/d) WFib
'Lauripen' (Z/d) WFib
¶ 'Lavender Frills' (R) LDea
'Lavender Grand Slam' (R) IHos LDea SDen SKen SOak SOld WFib
'Lavender Harewood Slam' (R) LDea SOak
'Lavender Mini Cascade' See P. 'Lila Mini Cascade
'Lavender Sensation' (R) WFib
¶ *laxum* MHul
'Layham' (Dw/d) ESul SBro
'Layton's White' (Z/d) SKen
'Le Lutin' (Z/d) WFib
'L'Elégante' (I/v) CHal CSpe IHos LDea MBri MSmi MWhe SDen SKen SOak SOld WEas WFib
'Lemon Fancy' (Sc) IHos MWhe NWyt SDen WFib
'Lemore' (Min/d) SBro
'Len Chandler' (Min) ESul SBro
'L'Enfer' (Min/C) See P. 'Mephistopheles'
'Lenore' (Min) ESul
'Leo' (Min) ESul SBro
'Leonie Holbrow' (Min) ESul SBro
'Leopard' (I/d) SKen
'Leslie Judd' (R) SOak WFib
'Leslie Salmon' (Min/C) ESul MWhe SBro
'Lethas' (R) LDea
'Letita' (A) ESul LHil
'Leucht-Cascade' See P. 'Decora Rouge'
Leucht-Cascade ® See P. 'Decora Rouge'
'Levington' (Min/d) SBro

Lila Compakt-Cascade ®	See P. 'Decora Lilas'
§ 'Lila Mini Cascade' (I)	ESul MWhe
'Lilac Cascade'	See P. 'Roi des Balcons Lilas'
'Lilac Domino'	See P. 'Telston's Prima'
'Lilac Gem' (Min/I/d)	IHos LDea MWhe NWyt SDen SKen SOak SOld WFib
'Lilac Mini Cascade' (I)	LDea SBro SOak
¶ 'Lilac Mist' (Dw/d)	NWyt
'Lilac Ricard' (Z/d)	WFib
'Lili Marlene' (I)	NWyt SKen
'Lilian' (Dw)	SBro
'Lilian Pottinger' (Sc)	CArn CHal SDen SIde SKen WFib WHer
'Limoneum' (Sc)	NWyt SDen SKen SOak WEas WFib WPer
'Lin Davis' (Z/C)	WFib
'Linda' (R)	LDea
¶ Linda ® (Z/d)	WFib
'Lindsey' (Min)	ESul
'Lindy Portas' (I/d)	SKen
'Lisa' (Min/C)	ESul SBro
'Little Alice' (Dw/d)	ESul MWhe SBro WFib
'Little Blakenham' (A)	ESul LDea SBro SOak
'Little Fe Fine' (Min)	ESul SBro
'Little Gem' (Sc)	SDen
'Little John' (Min/d)	SBro
'Little Love' (A)	LDea SBro SKen
'Little Margaret' (Min/v)	ESul SBro SDen
'Little Primular' (Min)	ESul SBro
'Little Trot' (Z/v)	SBro WFib
'Little Vectis' (D)	SDen
'Lively Lady' (Dw/C)	ESul SBro SDen
'Liverbird' (I)	See P. 'Harlequin Miss Liver Bird'
lobatum	GCHN MHul
'Lolette' (Min)	ESul
'Lollipop' (Z/d)	SDen WFib
¶ ***longifolium***	MHul
'Lord Baden-Powell' (I/d)	See P. 'Colonel Baden-Powell'
'Lord Bute' (R)	ERav LDea SIde SMrm SUsu WEas
'Lord de Ramsey'	See P. 'Tip Top Duet'
'Lorelei' (Z/d)	SOak WFib
'Loretta' (Dw)	ESul
'Lorna' (Dw/d)	ESul
'Lorraine' (Dw)	ESul SBro
'Louise' (Min)	ESul SBro
¶ 'Love Song' (R)	LDea
'Love Story'	ESul SBro
* 'Loverly' (Min/d)	ESul SBro
Lovesong ® (Z/d)	WFib
'Lowood' (R)	WFib
'Lucilla' (Min)	ESul SDen
'Lucinda' (Min)	ESul SBro
'Lucy' (Min)	ESul SBro
'Lucy Gunnet' (Z/d/v)	MWhe
'Lucy Jane' (R)	LDea SOak
¶ ***luridum***	MHul
'Luscious' (Min)	ESul
'Lustre' (R)	WFib
¶ ***luteolum***	MHul
'Luz del Dio' (R)	WFib
¶ 'Lyewood Bonanza' (R)	LDea SOak
'Lyric' (Min/d)	ESul SBro WFib
I 'M A F F' (Min)	SBro
'M J Cole' (I/d)	WFib
'Mabel Grey' (Sc)	CHal CHun CSev CSpe ESul IHos LHil MWhe NHHG NWyt SDen SKen SOak WEas WFib WHer
¶ ***madagascariense***	NWyt
'Madame Butterfly' (Z/C/d)	ESul MWhe SDen SKen SOld
'Madame Crousse' (I/d)	NWyt SDen WEas WFib
'Madame Dubarry' (Z)	WFib
'Madame Fournier' (Min/C)	ESul SBro
'Madame Guinier'	See P. 'Charles Gounod'
'Madame Hibbault' (Z)	SDen SKen
'Madame Kingsbury'	SDen
'Madame Layal' (A)	CSpe ESul LDea SBro SDen SKen SOak WFib
'Madame Margot'	See P. 'Hederinum Variegatum'
§ 'Madame Nonin' (Sc)	CHal LHil SDen SMrm WFib
'Madame Recamier' (Z/d)	WFib
'Madame Salleron' (Min/v)	CBrk LDea LHil NWyt SKen
'Madame Thibaut' (Z/d)	CSpe LDea WFib
'Madge Hill' (Min)	ESul NWyt SBro WFib
'Magaluf' (I/C/d)	LDea SOak WFib
'Magda' (Z/d)	NWyt
¶ ***magenteum***	MHul
'Magic Lantern' (Z/C)	IHos MWhe SKen
'Magic Moments' (R)	WFib
'Magnum' (R)	WFib
'Mahogany' (I/d)	ECtt MSmi
'Maid of Honour' (Min)	ESul SBro SDen
'Mairi' (A)	ESul LDea SBro SKen
'Maloja' (Z)	NWyt SDen SKen
'Mamie' (Z/d)	SDen SKen
'Mangles' Variegated' (Z/v)	SDen
'Manta' (Min)	SBro
'Mantilla' (Min)	SBro SKen
'Manx Maid' (A)	ESul LDea SBro SKen WFib
'Marble Sunset'	See P. 'Wood's Surprise'
§ 'Maréchal MacMahon' (Z/C)	CBrk SKen SOak WFib
'Margaret Bryan' (Z/C)	SKen
'Margaret Pearce' (R)	LDea SDen WFib
'Margaret Salvidge' (R)	LDea WFib
¶ 'Margaret Soley' (R)	LDea
'Margery Stimpson' (Min/d)	ESul LDea SBro SDen WFib
'Maria Wilkes' (Z/d)	WFib
'Marie Rober' (R)	SKen WFib
§ 'Marie Vogel' (R)	WFib
'Marion' (Min)	ESul SBro
'Mariquita' (R)	SOak WFib
'Market Day' (R)	SDen SOak
'Marktbeherrscher' (Z/d)	WFib
'Marmalade' (Dw/d)	ESul MWhe SBro SDen SOak WFib
Mars ® (Z/d)	NWyt
'Martin Parrett' (Min/d)	ESul SBro
'Martin's Splendour' (Min)	ESul
'Mary Ellen Tanner' (Min/d)	ESul SBro
'Mary Godwin' (Z)	WFib
'Mary Read' (Min)	ERea ESul SBro

'Mary Webster' (Min)	ESul SBro
'Masquerade' (R)	LDea SBro
'Masterpiece' (Z/C/d)	ESul SDen SKen
'Mataranka' (Min/d/C/v)	MWhe
'Maureen' (Min)	SBro
'Mauve Beauty' (I/d)	IHos SKen WFib
'Mauve Duet' (A)	ESul SBro
'Maxime Kovalevski' (Z)	WFib
¶ 'May Day' (R)	LDea
'May Magic' (R)	WFib
'Medallion' (Z/C)	ESul SKen WFib
'Meditation' (Dw)	ESul SBro
'Medley' (Min/d)	ESul MWhe SBro WFib
'Melanie' (Min/d)	ESul LDea SBro
I 'Melissa' (Min)	CSpe ESul SBro WEas
¶ Melody ® (Z/d)	WFib
'Memento' (Min/d)	SBro SKen
'Mendip' (R)	SKen SOak WFib
¶ 'Meon Maid' (R)	LDea
§ 'Mephistopheles' (Min/C)	ESul IHos SBro
¶ 'Mercia Glory' (R)	LDea
¶ Mercutio ® (Z/d)	WFib
'Mere Greeting' (Z/d)	MWhe
'Merry-Go-Round' (Z/C/v)	ESul WFib
'Meshed Pink Gay Baby' (DwI)	See P 'Laced Sugar Baby'
'Mexican Beauty' (I)	CHal MWhe NWyt SDen SKen WFib
'Mexicanerin'	See P. 'Rouletta'
'Mia' (Min/d)	SBro
'Michelle' (Min/C)	SBro WFib
'Michelle West' (Min)	SDen
'Milden' (Z/C)	ESul SBro
'Milkmaid' (Min)	SBro WFib
'Mill Purple' (I)	MWhe
'Millbern Clover' (Min/d)	MWhe
'Millbern Engagement' (Min/d)	MWhe
'Millbern Sharna' (Min/d)	MWhe
'Millfield Gem' (I/d)	CHal LDea NWyt SDen SKen SOak WFib
'Millfield Rose' (I/d)	IHos MWhe NWyt SDen SKen
'Millie' (Z/d)	WFib
'Mimi' (Min/C/d)	ESul SBro
¶ ***minimum***	MHul
Minipel Karminrot ® (Dw)	SBro
Minipel Orange ® (Dw)	SBro
* Minipel Red ® (Dw)	SBro
Minipel Rosa ® (Dw)	SBro
Minipel Scharlach ® (Dw)	ESul SBro
'Mini-Czech' (Min/St)	SBro WEas
'Minstrel Boy' (R)	LDea SDen WFib
¶ 'Minuet' (Dw/C/d)	NWyt
'Minx' (Min/d)	SBro WFib
'Miranda' (Dw)	ESul SBro
'Miriam Basey'	See P. 'Dwarf Miriam Baisey'
'Miss Australia' (R/v)	LDea SKen WFib
'Miss Burdett Coutts' (Z/v)	ESul IHos MWhe
¶ 'Miss Liverbird' (I/d)	ECtt
'Miss Muffett' (Min/d)	ESul SBro
'Miss Prim' (Min)	SBro
§ 'Miss Stapleton'	MHul
'Miss Wackles' (Min/d)	ESul NWyt SBro SDen WFib
¶ 'Mission Dubonnet' (R)	LDea
'Misty' (Z)	ESul SBro
'Mitzi' (Min)	SBro
'Mixed Blessings' (Min/C)	SBro
'Modesty' (Z/d)	NWyt SDen WFib
'Modigliani' (R)	SDen SKen
¶ ***mollicomum***	MHul
'Mollie' (R)	LDea WFib
¶ 'Momo'	CSut
'Monarch' (Dw/v)	SBro
'Monica Bennett' (Dw)	ESul SBro SDen SKen SOak WEas
¶ 'Monkwood Beacon' (R)	SOak
¶ 'Monkwood Bonanza' (R)	SOak
¶ 'Monkwood Charm' (R)	LDea SOak
'Monkwood Delight' (R)	SDen SOak
¶ 'Monkwood Dream' (R)	LDea SOak
¶ 'Monkwood Jester' (Z/d)	SOak
'Monkwood Rhapsody' (R)	SDen SOak SOld
¶ 'Monkwood Sprite' (R)	LDea SOak
'Monsal Dale' (Dw/C/d)	ESul SKen
'Monsieur Ninon' (U)	NWyt
'Mont Blanc' (Z/v)	CHal MWhe SBro WFib
'Monty' (I/d)	WFib
'Moon Maiden' (A)	ESul LDea SBro WFib
'Moor' (Min/d)	ESul SBro
'Moppet' (Min/d)	SBro
'More Mischief' (Dw/Ca/d)	ESul
'Morello' (R)	SDen WFib
'Morning Cloud' (Min/d)	SBro
'Morning Sunrise' (Min/v)	ESul SBro
'Morval' (Dw/C)	ESul MWhe NWyt SBro SKen SOak SOld WFib
'Morwenna' (R)	LDea SMrm SOak WFib
'Mountie' (Dw)	ESul SBro
'Mozart' (R)	LDea
'Mr Everaarts' (Dw/d)	ESul MWhe NWyt WEas WFib
'Mr Henry Cox' (Z/v)	CBrk IHos MWhe NWyt SOak SOld WFib
'Mr Pickwick' (Dw)	SBro
'Mr Ritson' (Min)	ESul SBro
'Mr Wren' (Z)	CHal IHos LHop MWhe SDen SKen SMrm WFib
¶ 'Mrs Brock' (Z)	SOak
'Mrs Cannell' (Z)	SKen
'Mrs Dumbrill' (A)	CHal ESul LDea SDen
'Mrs Farren' (Z/v)	SKen WFib
'Mrs G H Smith' (A)	CSpe ESul LDea MSte MWhe SBro SDen SKen SOak SOld
'Mrs G More' (R)	SOak WFib
'Mrs J C Mappin' (Z/v)	NWyt SDen SKen
'Mrs Kingsbury' (U)	LHil SKen WEas
¶ 'Mrs Kingsley' (Z/v)	WPer
¶ 'Mrs Langtry' (R)	LDea
'Mrs Lawrence' (Z/d)	SDen SKen WFib
'Mrs Martin' (I)	NWyt WFib
¶ 'Mrs Morf' (R)	LDea
'Mrs Parker' (Z/v)	IHos MWhe NWyt SDen SKen WFib
'Mrs Pat' (Min/St/C)	ESul MWhe SBro
'Mrs Pollock' (Z/v)	CBrk MWhe NRoo NWyt SDen SKen SOak WFib

'Mrs Quilter' (Z/C) MWhe NWyt SDen SKen SMrm WFib WPer
'Mrs Salter Bevis' (Z/Ca/d) CHal ESul NWyt SDen WFib
'Mrs Strang' (Z/d/v) SKen SOak SOld WEas
'Mrs Tarrant' (Z/d) CHal NWyt WFib
'Mrs W A R Clifton' (I/d) LDea SKen WFib
¶ 'Müttertag' (R) SOak
¶ ***multibracteatum*** MHul
multicaule MHul
– ssp. ***multicaule*** GCHN
'Music Man' (R) WFib
'Mustang' IHos
¶ ***mutans*** MHul
¶ 'My Love' (I/d) LDea
myrrhifolium var. ***coriandrifolium*** GCHN WHer
'Nacton' (Min) ESul SBro
'Nadine' (Dw/C/d) ESul SBro WFib
¶ Nadja ® (Z/d) WFib
'Nan Greeves' (Z/v) SDen
'Nancy Grey' (Min) ESul SBro WFib
'Nancy Hiden' (R) WFib
'Naomi' (R) LDea
'Naughton' (Min) ESul SBro
'Naunton Velvet' (R) WFib
'Naunton Windmill' (R) WFib
'Nedging Tye' (A) ESul LDea SBro
'Needham Market' (A) CSpe ESul LDea SBro
'Neene' (Dw) ESul MWhe SBro
'Nella' (Min) SBro
'Nellie' (R) LDea
'Neon Fiat' (Z/d) WFib
'Nervosum' (Sc) ESul
¶ 'Neville West' SDen
'New Life' (Z) ESul MWhe NWyt SDen SKen SOak
'Nicholas Purple' (R) LDea
'Nicor Star' (Min) ESul SBro
'Night and Day' (Dw) SBro
'Nimrod' (R) LDea
'Nina West' (Z) SDen
'Noche' (R) LDea WFib
'Noel' (Z/Ca/d) WFib
'Noele Gordon' (Z/d) WFib
¶ 'Noir' (R) LDea
'Nono' (I) LDea WFib
'North Star' (Dw) ESul
¶ 'Northern Lights' (R) LDea
'Notting Hill Beauty' (Z) SKen
'Nuhulunbuy' (R) WFib
'Obergarten' (Z/d) WFib
¶ ***oblongatum*** MHul
'Occold Embers' (Dw/C/d) ESul NWyt SBro SOld
'Occold Lagoon' (Dw/d) ESul SBro SDen SKen
'Occold Orange Tip' (Min/d) ESul SBro SOak
'Occold Profusion' (Min/d) ESul SBro
'Occold Ruby' (Dw/C) SBro
'Occold Shield' (Dw/C/d) ESul SBro
'Occold Surprise' (Min/d) ESul SBro
'Occold Tangerine' (Dw) ESul SBro
'Occold Volcano' (Dw/d) ESul SBro
¶ ***ochroleucum*** MHul

odoratissimum (Sc) CHal CHun GPoy IHos MHul MWhe NHHG NSty SDen SHer SIde SKen SMrm SOak WCHb WEas WFib WWye
– 'Variegatum' (Sc) WEas
¶ ***oenothera*** MHul
'Offton' (Dw) ESul SBro
'Old Spice' (Sc/v) SOak WFib
'Olga' (R) IHos LDea
¶ 'Olive West' SDen
'Olympia' (Z/d) WFib
'Onnalee' (Dw) ESul SBro
'Orange Glow' (Dw/d) SBro
'Orange Imp' (Dw/d) ESul SBro
'Orange Ricard' (Z/d) CHal MWhe SDen SKen SOak SOld WFib
'Orange River' (Dw/d) ESul MWhe SBro SKen
'Orangeade' (Dw/d) ESul SKen
'Orangesonne' (Z/d) SDen WFib
'Orchid Paloma' (Dw/d) ESul SBro
¶ ***oreophilum*** MHul
'Orion' (Min/d) ESul MWhe NWyt SBro SDen SKen SOak WFib
'Orwell' (Min) SBro
'Otley' (Min) SBro
¶ ***ovale*** ssp. ***hyalinum*** MHul
¶ – ssp. ***ovale*** MHul WFib
'Oyster Maid' (Min) SBro
PAC cultivars See under cv. name
'Paddie' (Min) ESul NWyt SBro
'Pagoda' (Z/St/d) ESul NWyt SBro SDen SKen
Palais ® (Z/d) SKen SOak WFib
'Pamela Underwood' (R) WFib
panduriforme GCHN MHul WFib
papilionaceum CHEx CTro MHul
'Paradise Moon' (Min/d) SBro
'Parasol' (R) WFib
'Parisienne' (R) LDea SDen
'Party Dress' (Z/d) MWhe NWyt SDen WFib
'Pascal' (Z) SKen
'Patience' (Z/d) IHos SKen WFib
'Paton's Unique' (U/Sc) IHos LHop NWyt SDen SKen SOak SOld WEas WFib
'Patricia Andrea' (T) NWyt SDen SOld
'Patricia Read' (Min) ERea ESul SBro
'Patsy 'Q'' (Z/C) IHos SKen
patulum GCHN
'Paul Crampel' (Z) CBrk CHal NWyt WFib
'Paul Gotz' (Z) SKen
'Paul Gunnett' (Min) MWhe
'Paul Humphries' (Z/d) NWyt WFib
'Paul West' (Min/d) SBro SDen
'Pauline' (Min/d) ESul MWhe SBro
'Pavilion' (Min) SBro
¶ 'Pax' (R) LDea
'Peace' (Min/C) ESul SBro WFib
'Peace Palace' (Dw) ESul SBro
'Pearl Brocade' (R) WFib
'Pearl Eclipse' (I) SDen SKen
'Pearly Queen' (Min/d) SBro
'Pegasus' (Min) SBro
'Peggy Franklin' (Min) SBro
'Peggy Sue' (R) LDea
'Peggy West' (Min/C/d) SBro SDen
PELFI cultivars See under cv. name
peltatum MHul NWyt SDen WFib
¶ – 'Lateripes' MHul

'Penny' (Z/d) MWhe SDen WFib
'Penny Serenade' (Dw/C) ESul SKen
¶ Penve ® (Z/d) WFib
'Percival' (Dw/d) SBro SDen SOak SOld
'Perfect' (Z) SDen SKen
¶ Perlenkette Orange ®
(Z/d) WFib
¶ Perlenkette Weiss ® (Z/d) WFib
¶ 'Persian King' (R) LDea
'Persian Queen' (R) WFib
'Petals' (Z/v) SKen
¶ 'Peter Godwin' (R) LDea
'Peter Read' (Dw/d) ERea ESul SBro
¶ 'Peter's Choice' (R) LDea
'Petit Pierre' (Dw) See P. 'Kleine Liebling'
'Petite Blanche' (Dw/d) SBro WFib
'Philomel' (I/d) SKen WFib
¶ 'Philomel Rose' (I/d) LDea SOak
'Phlox New Life' (Z) ESul SBro
¶ 'Phyllis Brooks' (R) SOak
'Phyllis Mary' (R) WFib
'Phyllis Read' (Min) ERea ESul MWhe SBro WFib
'Phyllis Richardson'
(R/d) LDea SDen SOak WFib
Picasso ® IHos
'Pickaninny' (Min) ESul SBro
¶ 'Pico' CSut
'Pin Mill' (Min/d) ESul SBro
¶ 'Pink Aztec' (R) LDea
'Pink Bonanza' (R) LDea SOak SOld WFib
'Pink Bouquet' (R) WFib
– (Z/d) IHos
'Pink Carnation' (I/d) IHos LDea SKen
'Pink Cascade' (I) See P. 'Hederinum'
'Pink Champagne' (Sc) ESul SDen WFib WHer
'Pink Countess Mariza'
(Z) SKen
¶ 'Pink Flamingo' (R) LDea
'Pink Fondant' (Min/d) ESul SBro
'Pink Gay Baby' (I) See P. 'Sugar Baby'
'Pink Golden Ears'
(Dw/St/C) SBro
'Pink Golden Harry
Hieover' (Z/C) ESul SBro
'Pink Grace Wells' (Min) ESul SBro
'Pink Happy Thought'
(Z/v) SKen WFib
'Pink Ice' (Min/d) ESul NWyt SBro
'Pink Kewense' (Min) SBro
'Pink Lively Lady'
(Dw/C) SBro
'Pink Margaret Pearce'
(R) SDen
'Pink Mini Cascade' See P. 'Rose Mini Cascade'
'Pink Moon' MSmi
¶ 'Pink Nosegay' NWyt
'Pink Rambler' (Z/d) MWhe SKen SOld WFib
'Pink Raspail' (Z/d) WFib
'Pink Rosebud' (Z/d) IHos NWyt SDen SKen WFib
'Pink Satisfaction' (Z) IHos
'Pink Slam' (R) WFib
'Pink Snow' (Min/d) SBro SOak
¶ 'Pink Snowdrift' (I/d) SOak
'Pink Splash' (Min/d) SBro SDen
'Pink Splendour' (Min/d) SBro
¶ ***pinnatum*** MHul

'Pixie' (Dw) ESul SBro
'Platinum' (Z/v) SBro
'Playboy Blush' (Dw) SBro
'Playboy Candy' (Dw) SBro
'Playboy Cerise' (Dw) SBro
'Playboy Coral' (Dw) SBro
'Playboy Coral Orange'
(Dw) SBro
'Playboy Mauve' (Dw) SBro
'Playboy Powder Pink'
(Dw) SBro
'Playboy Salmon' (Dw) SBro
'Playboy Salmon Eyed'
(Dw) SBro
'Playboy Scarlet' (Dw) SBro
'Playboy White' (Dw) SBro
'Playford' (Dw) ESul SBro
'Playmate' (Min/St) SBro SKen
'Plenty' (Z/d) SOak WFib
'Plum Rambler' (Z/d) CHal SKen WFib
¶ 'Poetesse' (A) LDea
'Polaris' (Min) SBro
'Pompeii' (R) LDea SMrm SOak WEas WFib
¶ 'Posey' (Min/d) NWyt
'Potpourri' (Min) SBro SKen
¶ ***praemorsum*** MHul
'Presto' (Min) CSpe ESul SBro
'Preston Park' (Z/C) SKen SMrm WFib
¶ 'Pretty Girl' (I) LDea
'Pride of the West' (Z) SKen
'Prim' (Min/d) ESul
'Primavera' (R) LDea
'Prince Harry' (I) SKen
'Prince of Orange' (Sc) CArn CHun CSev GPoy IHos NHHG NSty NWyt SDen SKen SOak WCHb WEas WFib WHer WPer
'Prince of Wales' (Z) NWyt WFib
'Princess Alexandra' (R) CHal NWyt WFib
– (Z/d/v) MWhe SDen SKen WFib
'Princess Anne' (Z) CSpe
'Princess Josephine' (R) WFib
'Princess Margaretha' (Z) MWhe
'Princess of Balcon' (I) See P. 'Roi des Balcons Lilas'
'Princess of Wales' (R) SDen
'Princess Pink' (Z) SKen
'Princess Virginia' (R/v) CSpe LDea
'Professor Eckman' (R) WFib
'Promenade' (Z/d) WFib
¶ 'Prospect' (Z/d) MWhe
'Prudence' (Min) SBro SKen
pseudoglutinosum WFib
¶ ***pulchellum*** MHul
pulverulentum GCHN
punctatum GCHN
'Purple Emperor' (R) LDea WFib
'Purple Gem' (Min) ESul
'Purple Light' See P. 'Purple Gem'
'Purple Orchid' (R) LDea
'Purple Pat' (Min/d) SBro
'Purple Rambler' (Z/d) MWhe
¶ 'Purple Rogue' (R) SOak
'Purple Unique' (U/Sc) IHos SDen SKen SMrm WCHb WFib
¶ Purple Wonder ® (Z/d) WFib
Purpurball ® (Z/d) SKen SOak SOld

'Pygmalion' (Z/d/v)	SDen WFib
'Quakeress' (R)	LDea
'Quakermaid' (Min)	ESul SBro
'Quantock' (R)	WFib
'Queen Ingrid' (Z)	IHos
'Queen of Denmark' (Z/d)	CHal NWyt SDen SKen WFib
'Queen of Hearts' (I/d)	NWyt WFib
N *quercifolium* (Sc)	CHal CHun CSev ESul GPoy MHul NHHG NSty NWyt SHer SKen SMrm WCHb WEas WFib WWye
– 'Fair Ellen'	See P. 'Fair Ellen'
quinquelobatum	GCHN MHul
'Rachel' (Min)	ESul SBro
'Rachel Fisher' (Z)	NWyt WFib
radens (Sc)	MHul NHHG SIde WFib
'Radiance' (Z/d)	WFib
'Radiant' (Z/d)	WFib
Radula Group (Sc)	CCla CHun ESul GCHN LHil MWhe NWyt SDen SKen WCHb WFib WPer
¶ 'Radula Roseum'	LHil
¶ *radulifolium*	MHul
'Rager's Pink' (Dw/d)	ESul SBro
'Rager's Star' (Min)	SBro
¶ 'Ragtime' (St)	NWyt
¶ *ranunculophyllum*	MHul
rapaceum	GCHN MHul
'Rapture' (R)	LDea WEas WFib
'Raspberry Parfait' (R)	LDea SDen
'Raspberry Ripple' (A)	LDea SBro
'Raspberry Sundae' (R)	LDea
'Raviro' (I)	MSmi WFib
'Ray Coughlin' (Z/C/d)	WFib
'Raydon' (Min)	ESul SBro
'Rebecca' (Min/d)	ESul SBro
'Red Admiral' (Min/d/v)	ESul SBro SKen
¶ 'Red Beauty' (Z/d)	SOak
§ 'Red Black Vesuvius' (Min/C)	CHal CSpe ESul MWhe NWyt SDen SKen WEas WFib
'Red Brooks Barnes' (Dw/C)	SBro
'Red Cascade' (I)	MWhe SKen
'Red Comet' (Min)	SBro
'Red Dwarf' (Min/d)	SBro
'Red Fox' (Min)	SBro SDen
'Red Galilee' (I/d)	MWhe SKen
'Red Gem' (Min)	ESul
'Red Glow' (Min)	ESul
'Red Ice' (Min/d)	MWhe NWyt SBro
'Red Light' (Z/d)	WFib
'Red Magic Lantern' (Z/C)	SKen
'Red Mini Cascade' (I)	See P. 'Rote Mini-Cascade'
'Red Pandora' (T)	NWyt
'Red Pearl' (Min)	SBro
'Red Rambler' (Z/d)	CHal MWhe NWyt SDen SKen WFib
'Red Satisfaction' (Z)	IHos
'Red Spider' (Min/Ca/d)	CSpe ESul SBro
'Red Startel' (Z/d)	MWhe SKen
'Red Streak' (Min/Ca)	SBro
¶ 'Red Susan Pearce' (R)	LDea
'Red Tiny Tim' (Min)	SBro
'Red Velvet' (R)	WFib
'Red Witch' (Dw/St)	CSpe ESul SBro
'Redondo' (Min/d)	CSpe ESul MWhe NWyt SBro SDen WEas WFib
'Reg "Q"' (Z/C)	SBro
'Regal Perchance'	SDen
'Regi' (I/d)	IHos
'Regina' (Z/d)	NWyt SDen SKen SOak SOld WEas WFib
'Rembrandt' (R)	LDea SDen SKen SOak WEas WFib
¶ Remo ® (Z/d)	WFib
'Renee Ross' (I/d)	SOak WFib
¶ *reniforme*	MHul WFib
'Rhineland' (I)	SKen
'Rhodamant' (I/d)	WFib
'Rhodamine' (R)	LDea SKen
'Rhodo' (R)	WFib
ribifolium	MHul
¶ Rica ® (Z/d)	WFib
'Richard Key' (Z/d/v)	NWyt WFib
'Richard West' (I/d)	SDen
'Rietje van der Lee' (A)	ESul SBro
'Rigel' (Min/d)	ESul MWhe SBro SKen WFib
'Rigi' (I)	ECtt LDea MBri MSmi NWyt SDen SKen
'Rigoletta' (I)	LDea MWhe NWyt
'Rimfire' (R)	WFib
'Ringo Rose' (Z)	SKen
'Rio' (Z)	NWyt
'Rio Grande' (I/d)	CSpe LDea MWhe NWyt SDen SKen SOak SOld WEas WFib
'Rita Brook' (Z/d)	WFib
'Rita Coughlin' (R)	WFib
'Rita Scheen' (A)	ESul LDea MWhe SBro WFib
'Robbie Hare' (R)	WFib
¶ Robe ® (Z/d)	WFib
'Robert Fish' (Z/C)	ESul SBro SDen
'Rober's Lavender' (Dw)	ESul SBro
'Rober's Lemon Rose' (Sc)	CHun ESul NHHG SDen SHer SIde SMrm WCHb WFib WHer
'Rober's Salmon Coral' (Dw/d)	SBro
'Robin' (R)	LDea
'Robinson Crusoe' (Dw/C)	WFib
rogersianum	See P. ***worcesterae***
'Rogue' (R)	LDea WFib
'Roi des Balcons' (I)	See P. 'Hederinum'
§ 'Roi des Balcons Impérial' (I)	IHos MWhe
§ 'Roi des Balcons Lilas' (I)	IHos MWhe SKen WFib
'Roi des Balcons Rose'	See P. 'Hederinum'
Rokoko ® (Z)	IHos
'Roller's Echo' (A)	LDea SBro SOak
'Roller's Pathfinder' (I/v)	LDea
'Roller's Pioneer' (I/v)	NWyt SKen
'Rollisson's Unique' (U)	NWyt SDen SKen WFib
'Romance'	SBro
'Rosaleen' (Min)	SBro
'Rosalie' (Min)	ESul SBro
'Rosamunda' (Z/d)	WFib
'Roscobie' (Z/d)	SKen
'Rose Bengal' (A)	CMil ESul LDea NSty SKen SMrm WEas WFib WPer
'Rose Crousse' (I/d)	MWhe
'Rose Irene' (Z/d)	MWhe NWyt SDen WFib

'Rose Mini Cascade' (I) ESul MWhe SBro SDen SOak SOld
'Rose of Amsterdam' (Min/d) SBro
'Rose Silver Cascade' (I) LDea
'Rose Slam' (R) LDea
'Rosebud' (Z/d) NRar
'Rosee Normande' (Z/d) WFib
'Rosemarie' (Z/d) MWhe
'Rosenpen' (Z/d) SOak
'Rosette' (Dw) SBro SKen WFib
'Rosina Read' (Dw) ERea ESul SBro
'Rosita' (Dw/d) SBro SDen
*'Rosmaroy' (R) LDea SOak
¶ Rospen ® (Z/d) WFib
*'Rosseau' (Min) SBro
'Rosy Dawn' (Min/d) SBro
§ 'Rote Mini-Cascade' (I) IHos LDea MWhe NWyt SBro SDen SKen WFib
Rote Mini-Cascade ® See P. 'Rote Mini-Cascade'
¶ 'Rotherfield' (I/d) LDea
'Rotlieb' (Z/d) WFib
§ 'Rouletta' (I) CHal ECtt IHos LDea MSmi MWhe NWyt SDen SKen SOak SOld WEas WFib
'Rousillon' (R) WFib
'Royal Ascot' (A) LDea
'Royal Blaze' (Z/v) SKen
'Royal Carpet' (Min/d) ESul SBro
'Royal Fiat' (Z/d) WFib
'Royal Norfolk' (Min/d) ESul MWhe SBro SKen SOak SOld WFib
'Royal Oak' (Sc) CSev ESul LHil MWhe NWyt WFib WHer WPer
§ 'Royal Purple' (Z/d) CHal WFib
'Royal Surprise' (R) LDea
'Royal Wedding' (R) LDea SOak
'Rubella' (Z/d) WFib
¶ 'Ruben' (Z/d) SOak
'Ruby' (Min/d) ESul SBro WFib
¶ 'Ruffled Velvet' (R) SDen
'Rushmere' (Dw/d) ESul
'Rusty' (Dw/C/d) ESul SBro
¶ 'Ruth Karmen' (I/d) LDea
'Ryan Dollery' (Z) SDen
'Ryecroft Pride' (Z/d) WFib
'Sally Anne' (R) LDea WEas
'Sally Munroe' (R) LDea SOak
'Sally Read' (Dw/d) ERea ESul SBro
'Salmon Beauty' (Min/d) SBro WFib
'Salmon Black Vesuvius' (Min/C) ESul SBro
'Salmon Comet' (Min) ESul SBro
'Salmon Grozser Garten' (Dw) ESul
§ 'Salmon Irene' (Z/d) MWhe SOak WFib
¶ 'Salmon Nosegay' NWyt
'Salmon Queen' See P. 'Lachskönigin'
'Salmon Slam' (R) SDen WFib
'Salmon Startel' (Z/St/d) MWhe
'Saltford' (R) WFib
¶ 'Samantha' (R) LDea
'Sancho Panza' (Dec) CSpe ESul LDea MSte SBro SKen SOak SOld WFib
§ x ***sanguineum*** MHul
'Santa Maria' (Z/d) NWyt SDen SKen WFib
'Santa Marie' (R) LDea
'Santa Paula' (I/d) CHal ECtt LDea MWhe SDen SKen
'Sante Fe' (Z/C) SDen
'Sarah Mitchell' (Min) SBro
'Sasha' (Min) SBro WFib
¶ Sassa ® (Z/d) WFib
Satellite ® (Z/St) IHos
'Saxifragoïdes' GCHN SBro
¶ ***scabroïde*** MHul
scabrum WFib
'Scarlet Breakway' (Z) MWhe
'Scarlet Crousse' (I/C) WFib
¶ 'Scarlet Gem' (St) NWyt
¶ 'Scarlet Nosegay' NWyt
'Scarlet Pet' (U) ESul MWhe
'Scarlet Pimpernel' (Z/C/d) ESul SBro WFib
'Scarlet Rambler' (Z/d) NWyt SKen SOak SOld WFib
'Scarlet Unique' (U) NWyt SDen SKen WCHb WFib
'Scarlett O'Hara' (Min) SBro
¶ ***schizopetalum*** MHul
§ 'Schneekönigin' ('Snow Queen') (I/d) CSpe ECtt IHos LDea MSte WEas
x ***schottii*** See P. x ***sanguineum***
¶ 'Seaview Star' (Z/St) SDen
'Seeley's Pansy' (A) CSpe ESul LDea SBro
'Sefton' (R) LDea SKen
'Selby' (Z/C/d) NWyt WFib
'Selina' SBro
'Semer' (Min) ESul SBro SKen
senecioïdes GCHN MHul
'Sensation' (Z) SKen
'Serena' (Min) ESul SBro
¶ ***sericifolium*** MHul
'Shalimar' (St) CSpe SDen
¶ 'Shanks' SDen
'Sharon' (Min/d) ESul SBro
'Sharon Louise' (Min) SDen
'Sharon West' SDen
'Shaun Jacobs' (Min/d) SBro SDen
'Shaunough' (Min) ESul SBro
'Sheila' (Dw) ESul SBro
'Sheila Thorp' (Dw/d) SBro
'Shelley' (Dw) ESul NWyt SBro
'Shenandoah' (Min) WFib
'Sheraton' (Min/d) ESul MWhe SBro
'Shimmer' (Z/d) IHos MWhe SKen SOak SOld WFib
'Shiraz' (R) SKen
'Shirley Anne' (Dw/d) SBro SDen
'Shirley Ash' (A) ESul SBro
¶ 'Shirley Maureen' (R) LDea
'Shocking' (Z/d) NWyt
'Shotley' (Min) ESul SBro
'Shottesham Pet' (Sc) SIde
'Shrubland Pet' (U/Sc) CHal NWyt SDen SKen
¶ ***sidoïdes*** MHul
'Sienna' (R) LDea
'Silas Marner' (Dw) SBro
'Silberlachs' (Z/d) SDen WFib
¶ Silepen ® (Z/d) WFib
'Silver Kewense' (Dw/v) ESul IHos SBro SKen SOld WFib
'Silver Wings' (Z/v) MWhe SDen
'Simon Read' (Dw) ERea ESul SBro
'Sir Arthur Hort' (I) WFib
'Sister Teresa' (Z/d) IHos SKen
'Skelly's Pride' (Z) NWyt SDen SKen WEas

'Skies of Italy' (Z/C/d) SDen SOak
'Sleuring's Robin' (Min/d) SBro
'Small Fortune' (Dw) SBro SKen
'Smuggler' (R) LDea
'Sneezy' (Min) ESul SBro
'Snow Queen' (I) See P. 'Schneekönigin'
'Snow White' (Min) SBro
¶ 'Snowbaby' (Min/d) NWyt SOak
'Snowball' (Z/d) SDen
'Snowdon' (Min) SBro
'Snowdrift' (I/d) NWyt SOak WFib
'Snowflake' (Min) ESul SBro SDen SIde WPer
'Snowmass' (Z/d) CHal MWhe SDen SKen SOak
'Snowstorm' (Z) SKen WFib
'Snowy Baby' (Min/d) ESul SBro SDen WFib
'Sofie' See P. 'Deacora Rose'
'Solano' (R) WFib
'Solent Star' SDen
'Solent Sunrise' (Z/C) SDen
¶ 'Solent Waves' (R) LDea
'Solferino' (A) ESul LDea SBro SKen
Solidor ® (I/d) NWyt
'Somersham' (Min) ESul SBro
'Something Special' (Z/d) MWhe SOak SOld
'Sonata' (Dw/d) SBro
'Sophie Dumaresque' (Z/v) MWhe SDen SKen SOld
'Sophie Koniger' (Z/d) WFib
'Sorcery' (Dw/C) ESul IHos MWhe NWyt SBro SKen
'South American Bronze' (R) LDea SDen SKen SMrm WFib
'Southern Belle' (Z/d) WFib
'Souvenir' (R) CHal LDea SDen
'Spanish Angel' (A) LDea
'Sparkle' (Dw) SBro
'Speckled Egg' (Dw) SBro
'Speckled Hen' (Dw) SBro
'Speckled Orange' (Dw) SBro
'Speckles' (Z) MWhe SBro
'Spellbound' (R) WFib
'Spitfire' (Z/Ca/v) ESul NWyt WFib
¶ 'Spithead Cherry' (R) LDea
§ 'Splendide' LGre SMrm SSad WEas
'Sporwen' (Min) SBro
'Spot-on-Bonanza' (R) LDea SOak SOld
¶ 'Spring Bride' (R) LDea
'Spring Park' (A) CHal ESul SBro SDen
'Springfield Black' (R) LDea
'Springfield Lilac' (R) LDea
'Springfield Pearl' (R) LDea
'Springfield Rose' (R) LDea
'Springfield Unique' (R) LDea
'Springtime' (Z/d) MWhe SDen SOak WFib
'Sprite' (Min/v) SBro
'Sproughton' (Dw) ESul
'St Helen's Favourite' (Min) ESul SBro
¶ 'Stacey' (R) LDea
'Stadt Bern' (Z/C) CHal IHos MBri MWhe SKen WEas WFib
'Stanton Drew' (Z/d) WFib
'Staplegrove Fancy' (Z) NWyt SDen SKen
x ***stapletonae*** See P. 'Miss Stapleton'
'Starry Eyed' (Dw) ESul SBro
'Stella Read' (Dw/d) ERea ESul SBro
'Stellar Arctic Star' (Z/St/d) See P. 'Arctic Star'
'Stellar Cathay' (Z/St/d) ERav WFib
'Stellar Dawn Star' (Z/St) CHal SOld WEas WFib
'Stellar Grenadier' (Z/St/d) See P. 'Grenadier'
'Stellar Hannaford Star' (Z/St/d) See P. 'Hannaford Star'
'Stellar Ragtime' (Z/St/d) SDen
stenopetalum GCHN MHul
'Stephen Read' (Min) ERea ESul SBro
'Stewart Read' (Dw) ERea ESul SBro
¶ ***stipulaceum*** MHul
'Strawberry Sundae' (R) LDea SDen WFib
'Stutton' (Min) ESul SBro
sublignosum GCHN MHul
¶ ***suburbanum***
ssp. ***bipinnatifidum*** MHul
'Suffolk Gold' (Min/C) SDen
§ 'Sugar Baby' (DwI) CHal ECtt ESul IHos LDea MBri MSmi MWhe NWyt SBro SDen SKen SOak SOld WEas WFib
'Summer Cloud' (Z/d) NWyt SKen WFib
'Summertime' (R) SDen
'Sun Rocket' (Dw) ESul MWhe SBro WFib
'Sunbeam' (Dw/d) SBro
'Sunburst' NWyt SDen
'Sunrise' (R) LDea SKen SOak SOld WEas WFib
'Sunset Snow' (R) WFib
'Sunspot Petit Pierre' (Min/v) SBro SKen
'Sunstar' (Min/d) ESul SBro SOak WFib
'Super Rose' (I) MBri MSmi NWyt SDen SKen SOak
'Supernova' (Min/d) ESul
– (Z/St/d) NWyt SBro
'Surcouf' (I) LDea WFib
'Susan' (Dw) SBro WFib
'Susan Baldwin' See P. 'Salmon Kovalevski'
'Susan Payne' (Dw/d) ESul SBro
'Susan Pearce' (R) LDea SKen SOak
'Susan Read' (Dw) ERea ESul SBro
'Susie 'Q'' (Z/C) ESul MWhe SBro SDen SKen SOak
'Sussex Beauty' (Dw/C/d) ESul SBro SOak
'Sussex Delight' (Min) ESul SBro SKen
'Sussex Gem' (Min) SBro SKen
'Sussex Jewel' (Min) SBro SKen
'Sussex Lace' See P. 'White Mesh'
'Sussex Surprise' (Dw/v) SBro
'Swedish Angel' (A) LDea SBro SKen
'Sweet Mimosa' (Sc) LHil NWyt SDen SKen WEas WFib
'Sweet Sue' (Min) ESul SBro
'Swilland' (A) ESul LDea MWhe SBro
'Sybil Bradshaw' (R) LDea WFib
'Sybil Holmes' (I/d) ECtt IHos MBri MSmi MWhe NWyt SKen SOak SOld WFib
'Sylvia' (R) LDea
'Sylvia Gale' (R) WFib
'Sylvia Marie' (Dw/d) MWhe SKen
'Sylvia Mariza' IHos
'Tami' (Min) SBro
'Tamie' (Dw/d) MWhe SBro
'Tamie D' (Min) SKen
'Tammy' (Dw/d) ESul MWhe NWyt SBro WFib
'Tangerine' (Min/Ca/d) CHal ESul SDen WFib

Tango ® (Z/d)	IHos
'Tanya' (Min)	SBro
'Tanzy' (Min)	ESul SBro
'Tapestry' (Min/v)	LDea WEas
'Tashmal' (R)	LDea
'Tattingstone' (Min)	ESul SBro
'Tattoo' (Min)	ESul SBro
'Tavira' (I/d)	IHos LDea MSmi SDen SKen SOak SOld WFib
'Ted Brooke' (Z/d)	WFib
'Ted Dutton' (R)	SDen WFib
'Telstar' (Min/d)	ESul SBro WFib
§ 'Telston's Prima' (R)	WFib
¶ 'Ten of Hearts' (I)	NWyt
'Tenderly' (Dw/d)	SBro
'Tenerife Magic' (MinI/d)	SBro
tenuicaule	WFib
'Terence Read' (Min)	ERea ESul SBro
¶ ***ternatum***	MHul
tetragonum	EPad GCHN MHul NWyt WFib
¶ 'The Barle' (A)	LDea
'The Boar' (Fr)	CSpe NRar WEas WPer
§ 'The Crocodile' (I/C/d)	ECtt IHos MWhe SDen SKen WEas WFib
'The Czar'	See P. 'Maréchal MacMahon'
¶ 'The Lynn' (A)	LDea
'The Prince' (Min)	ESul SBro
'The Speaker' (Z/d)	SDen SKen WFib
¶ 'The Tone' (A)	LDea
'Thomas Gerald' (Min/C)	ESul SKen
'Tiberias' (I/d)	WFib
'Tilly' (Min)	CHal ESul SBro
'Tim' (Min)	ESul SBro
'Timmy Griffin' (Min)	SBro
'Timothy Clifford' (Min/d)	ESul MWhe NWyt SBro SDen WFib
'Tiny Tim'	SBro
§ 'Tip Top Duet' (A)	ESul LDea LHil MWhe SBro SDen SKen WEas WFib WPer
'Token' (Z)	IHos
'Tom Portas' (Dw/d)	ESul
'Tom Tit' (Dw)	SBro
¶ Tomcat ® (Z/d)	WFib
tomentosum (Sc)	CHEx CHal CHun CSev CSpe ERav GCHN GPoy LHop MHul MWhe NHHG NSty NWyt SDen SKen SOak WEas WFib WWye
– 'Chocolate'	See P. 'Chocolate Peppermint'
¶ 'Tommays Delight' (R)	LDea
tongaense	GCHN MHul WEas WFib
'Toni' (Min)	SBro
'Tony' (Min)	ESul SBro
'Topscore' (Z/d)	WFib
'Torento' (Sc)	ESul SDen
¶ 'Tornado' (R)	LDea
'Tortoise Shell' (R)	WFib
'Toyon' (Z/d)	WFib
'Tracy' (Min/d)	SBro
¶ ***tragacanthoïdes***	MHul
¶ ***transvaalense***	MHul WFib
'Trautlieb' (Z/d)	WFib
'Treasure Chest' (Z/d)	SDen
¶ ***tricolor***	MHul SOak
– hort.	See P. 'Splendide'
trifidum	GCHN MHul WFib
'Trimley' (Dw/d)	ESul SBro
'Trinket' (Min/d)	IHos SBro SKen
'Triomphe de Nancy' (Z/d)	NWyt WFib
triste	CBre CTro GCHN MHul WFib
'Trudie' (Dw)	CSpe ESul SBro SKen WFib
'Trulls Hatch' (Z/d)	MWhe NWyt SKen
'Trumps' (Min)	SBro
'Tu Tone' (Dw/d)	ESul
'Tuddenham' (Min/d)	ESul SBro
'Tuesday's Child' (Dw/C)	SKen
'Tunias Perfecta' (R)	WFib
'Turkish Delight' (Dw/v)	ESul MWhe SOak SOld
'Turtle's Surprise' (Z/d/v)	NWyt SKen
'Turtle's White' (R)	LDea SKen
Tutti Frutti ® (Z)	IHos
'Tweedle-Dum' (Dw)	ESul MWhe
'Twinkle' (Min/d)	ESul SBro WFib
'Tyabb Princess' (R)	WFib
§ 'Unique Aurore' (U)	CHun SKen SMrm WEas WFib
'Urchin' (Min)	CSpe ESul SBro
'Ursula Key' (Z/v)	SKen WFib
'Vagabond' (R)	WFib
'Valanza' (A)	ESul LDea SBro
'Valcandia' (Dw)	ESul SBro
'Valencia' (R)	WEas
'Valenciana' (R)	LDea WFib
'Valentin' (R)	LDea
'Valentina' (Dw/d)	ESul SBro
'Valley Court' (I)	LDea
'Vancouver Centennial' (Dw/St/C)	ERav MWhe NWyt SBro SDen SOld
§ 'Variegated Clorinda' (Sc/v)	WCHb WHer
'Variegated Fragrans'	See P. 'Fragrans Variegatum'
§ 'Variegated Kleine Liebling' (Min/v)	CHal CSpe ESul SKen SOak
'Variegated Madame Layal' (A/v)	LDea SBro
'Variegated Petit Pierre'	See P. 'Variegated Kleine Liebling'
'Vasco da Gama' (Dw/d)	ESul SBro
'Vectis Cascade'	SDen
'Velvet' (Z)	IHos
'Velvet Duet' (A)	ESul LDea SBro SDen SKen
'Venus' (Dw/d)	SBro
'Vera Dillon' (Z)	NWyt SKen WFib
'Verona' (Z/C)	CHal SDen SKen
'Veronica' (Z)	MWhe SKen
* 'Vesuvius' (Min)	SBro WPer
'Vicky Claire' (R)	LDea SDen SKen
'Vicky Town' (R)	LDea SOak SOld WFib
'Victoria Regina' (R)	LDea WFib
'Vida' (Min)	ESul SBro
'Video Blush' (Min)	CSpe SBro
'Video Red' (Min)	SBro
'Video Rose' (Min)	SBro
'Video Salmon' (Min)	SBro
'Viking' (Min/d)	SBro SKen
'Viking Red' (Z)	MWhe
'Village Hill Oak' (Sc)	ESul
'Ville de Paris' (I)	See P. 'Hederinum'
'Vina' (Dw/C/d)	MWhe SKen SOak WFib
'Vincent Gerris' (A)	LDea SDen
violareum hort.	See P. 'Splendide'
'Violet Lambton' (Z/v)	NWyt WFib

'Violetta' (R)	CHal LDea
– (Z/d)	WFib
'Virginia' (R)	IHos LDea
'Virginia Ley' (Z)	SKen
'Viscossisima'	NWyt WCHb
viscosum	See P. ***glutinosum***
§ ***vitifolium***	GCHN MHul
'Vivat Regina' (Z/d)	WFib
'Voodoo' (U)	CSpe SSad
Vulcan ® (Z/d)	IHos
'W H Heytman' (R)	WFib
'Wallis Friesdorf' (Dw/C/d)	MWhe SBro SOld
'Waltz' (Z)	IHos
'Wantirna' (Z/v)	ECtt SDen
'Warrior' (Z/d)	WFib
'Washbrook' (Min/d)	ESul SBro
¶ 'Watersmeet' (R)	LDea
¶ 'Wattisham' (R)	LDea
'Waveney' (Min)	ESul SBro
'Wayward Angel' (A)	ESul LDea SBro SKen
'Wedding Gown' (R)	LDea
¶ Weisse Perle ® (Z/d)	WFib
'Wellington' (R)	LDea SOak WFib
'Wendy' (Min)	SBro
¶ 'Wendy Hawley' (R)	LDea
'Wendy Read' (Dw/d)	ERea ESul MWhe SBro
'Wensum' (Min/d)	ESul SBro WFib
'Westerfield' (Min)	SBro
'Wherstead' (Min)	ESul SBro
'Whisper' (R)	CSpe
'White Bird's Egg' (Z)	WFib
'White Boar' (Fr)	NWyt
'White Bonanza' (R)	LDea SOak SOld
¶ 'White Charm' (R)	LDea
'White Chiffon' (R)	CSpe LDea
'White Eggshell' (Min)	ESul SBro
'White Gem' (Min)	SBro
'White Glory' (R)	LDea SOak WFib
'White Lively Lady' (Dw/C)	SBro
§ 'White Mesh' (I/v)	ECtt MBri MWhe NWyt SDen SKen SOak WEas WFib
¶ 'White Nosegay'	NWyt
'White Pearl Necklace' (Z/d)	WFib
¶ 'White Queen' (Z/d)	CSut
'White Roc' (Min/d)	SBro
'White Unique' (U)	CHal NSty NWyt SDen SKen WFib
¶ 'White Wooded Ivy'	NWyt
¶ 'Wico'	CSut
'Wilf Vernon' (Min/d)	SBro
'William Sutton' (R)	WFib
'Winnie Read' (Dw/d)	ERea ESul SBro
'Winston Churchill' (R)	LDea
'Witnesham' (Min/d)	ESul SBro
§ 'Wood's Surprise' (MinI/d)	LDea MWhe SBro SDen SKen SOak WFib
'Wookey' (R)	WFib
worcesterae	GCHN MHul
'Wrington' (R)	WFib
'Wyck Beacon' (I/d)	SKen
'Wycombe Maid' (Min/d)	CHal SBro WFib
'Xenia Field' (Z)	CHal NWyt SDen SKen
¶ ***xerophyton***	MHul WFib
'Yale' (I/d)	CHal CSpe IHos LDea MBri MSte MWhe NWyt SDen SKen SOak SOld WEas WFib
'Yhu' (R)	LDea
'Yolanda' (Min/C)	ESul SBro
'York Minster' (Dw/v)	SBro SKen
'Yours Truly' (Z)	CHal MWhe SKen
'Yvonne' (Z)	SKen
'Zinc' (Z/d)	NWyt WFib
'Zoe' (D)	SDen
¶ ***zonale***	MHul WFib

PELLAEA (Adiantaceae)

falcata	MBri
rotundifolia	CHal MBri NMar
sagittata	NMar

PELLIONIA See **ELATOSTEMA**

PELTANDRA (Araceae)

§ ***undulata***	CBen CRDP CRow CWGN EHon LMay MSta NDea SRms SWat
virginica	See P. ***undulata***

PELTIPHYLLUM (Saxifragaceae)

peltatum	See DARMERA ***peltata***

PELTOBOYKINIA (Saxifragaceae)

§ ***tellimoïdes***	EBre ECro LBre

PENNANTIA (Icacinaceae)

corymbosa	ECou

PENNISETUM (Gramineae)

§ ***alopecuroïdes***	CKel COtt EGol EPla ETPC GCal NHol SApp SCob SPer SSpi SUsu WWat
– 'Hameln'	ECha EFou EMon EPla ETPC LHop MBri MSte SGil
– f. ***viridescens***	ELan ETPC GAbr WCot WWat
– 'Woodside'	EBre EGol EHoe EPla LBre NRoo WHal
¶ ***americanum***	GCal
compressum	See P. ***alopecuroïdes***
flaccidum	EPla
imcomptum purple form	ETPC
longistylum	See P. ***villosum***
macrourum	CHan EHoe ETPC
orientale	CHEx EBre ECha EPla ETPC LBre MMil NBir NHol SUsu WCot WOMN
ruppelii	See P. ***setaceum***
§ ***setaceum***	EOrc ETPC
¶ – 'Rubrum'	ECha
§ ***villosum***	EBar ECha EHoe EMon EPla GCal NBro SApp SAxl SMad SPla SUsu WCot

PENSTEMON † (Scrophulariaceae)

'Alice Hindley'	Widely available
'Alice Howarth'	NHol
alpinus	GCra GTou NOak NTow WAbe WHil WThi
– ***brandegeei***	See P. ***b.***
ambiguus	SSvw WPer

Name	Suppliers
§ 'Andenken an Friedrich Hahn'	Widely available
§ ***angustifolius***	ECro MHew NSal WPer
antirrhinoïdes	See KECKIELLA ***a.***
N 'Apple Blossom'	Widely available
¶ ***aridus***	WDav
arizonicus	See P. ***whippleanus***
¶ ***arkansanus***	GTou
attenuatus	SCou WPer
¶ ***australis***	MHig
azureus	SCou WPer
baccharifolius	LGre
'Barbara Barker'	See P. 'Beech Park'
§ ***barbatus***	CBot CBow CGle CPar CSco CSun ECha ECro EFol EGol ELan EMar ERav IBar LGre MBel MFir NMir SBor SCou SIgm SPer SSvw SUsu WAbe WEas WHCG WHil WPbr WSpr
– 'Coccineus'	MBri NOak SCou SCro WPer WSpr WTyr
¶ – Limoges form	GCal
– 'Praecox'	WPer
– 'Praecox Nanus'	GCHN GCal MSte SRms WRus WSpr
barrettiae	CNic GCHN NRoo WSpr
§ 'Beech Park'	CChu CElw CMil ELan EMar ESma LHil LHop SAga SAxl SChu SCou SPer WPer WRus WSpr
♦ 'Bisham Seedling'	See P. 'White Bedder'
'Blackbird'	Widely available
'Blue Eye'	WEas WPer
'Blue King'	SCro
'Blue Spring'	CBot CBow CRDP CSun MBri SFis SUsu
'Bodnant'	WPer WSpr
brandegeei	CNic WDav
'Breitenbrush Blue'	LHop SAga
bridgesii	SCou
'Bridget's White'	CSam
¶ Broken Tops Mountain Form	WPer
'Burford Seedling'	See P. 'Burgundy'
'Burford White'	See P. 'White Bedder'
§ 'Burgundy'	CDec CDoC CElw CMHG CSam ECha EDon EOrc GCHN GCal IHos LHil MBri NFai NHol NSti SAxl SBor SChu SCou SPer WAbe WBod WHCG WPer WRus
caeruleus	See P. ***angustifolius***
caespitosus	SCou
§ ***campanulatus***	CHan CMea CPar CRiv CSam EMNN EPot LGre LHil LHop LRHS MBro MPit MTho NHar NHol NMen NNrd NRed NTow SAga SCou SFis WAbe WDav WPer WRus WSpr
– ***chihuahuensis***	SAga
– ***pulchellus***	See P. ***campanulatus***
– ***roseus***	WEas
¶ 'Candy Pink'	WEas
cardwellii	ECha ECtt ESma LGan LGre SAga WPer
'Castle Forbes'	CElw CGle WEas WPer WSpr
'Catherine de la Mare'	CGle CHan CKel COtt CPar EBar ECtt EDon EFou ELan ERav GCHN LGre LHil NVic SAga SAxl SChu SCro SPer WPer WSpr
§ 'Charles Rudd'	CElw CGle CHan CRDP GCal LGre NFai NRar NVic SAga SAxl SBor SChu SCou SMrm WPer
'Cherry Ripe'	CChu EBar EPla LHil SCou WDav WHCG WHal WHoo WKif WPer WRus WSpr
§ 'Chester Scarlet'	CChu CElw CFis CGle CHan EOrc EPla GCHN GCal GGar LBlm MBel MBri NFai NHol SAga WEas WHCG WPer WRus WSpr
clutei	SMrm
confertus	CHal CMHG EBar ECar ECtt ELan EMNN MCas MFir MHig MPla MPlt NGre NMen NNrd NRed NRoo NSti NTow WAbe WHal WHil WPbr WPer
cordifolius	See KECKIELLA ***cordifolia***
crandallii	
ssp. ***glabrescens***	LGre NHar SAga SUsu WDav
§ – – var. ***taosensis***	EOrc ESma LGre LHop SChu SGil SMrm WAbe WCot
cristatus	See P. ***eriantherus***
davidsonii	CMHG EMNN LGre MHig WAbe WDav WPat
§ – var. ***menziesii***	CSam MFir NHar NRar SBla WEas WPer
– – 'Microphyllus'	CMea CPar LBee MBro NHar NMen SChu SMrm SWas WDav WMar
– ***praeteritus***	CNic WDav
'Dazzler'	CGre WPer
deustus	MBel
'Devonshire Cream'	WHCG
¶ 'Diane'	WMer
diffusus	See P. ***serrulatus***
digitalis	CGle CHal CHan CMil CNic ECha EPad ERav GCra LGan LGre LHop MBel MNFA MRav NHol SCro SSvw WAbb WKif WPer
§ – 'Huskers Red'	EBre ECro EFol LBre NBir NHol SAga SBla SCro SFis SUsu WByw WCot WEas
♦ – ***purpureus***	See P. ***d.*** 'Husker's Red'
discolor	CCor LGre
§ 'Drinkstone'	CChu CGle CMGP CRiv CSam ECha EPla ESma LGre LHop SAga SAxl SDix SGil SMrm WPer WSpr
♦ 'Drinkwater Red'	See P. 'Drinkstone'
eatonii	CHan LGre SBla
'Edithiae'	EFol EOrc MBal MPlt SChu WAbb WDav WEas WMar WPer
¶ ***ellipticus***	WDav
§ ***eriantherus***	EBar MHig SBla WDav WPer
§ 'Evelyn'	Widely available
fendleri	See P. ***nitidus***
'Firebird'	See P. 'Schoenholzeri'
'Flame'	CGle EMar ESma NHol WPer
'Flamingo'	WHoo WOld
¶ ***frutescens***	GTou
fruticosus	CNic NWCA WDav WHil WPbr WSpr
§ – var. ***scouleri***	CNic CShe ITim MBel NRed NSti SCou WPat WPer
– – f. ***albus***	CBot CHan CNic ELan EMon GArf GDra LBee LGre LHop MBro SAga SBla SChu WAbe WEas WMar WOMN WPer
– – f. ***ruber***	WOMN
– – 'Hopleys'	LHop WPer

*'Gaff's Pink' EOrc SChu
gairdneri ssp. *oreganus* NWCA
'Garden Red' See P. 'Windsor Red'
'Garnet' See P. 'Andenken an Friedrich Hahn'
gentianoïdes WCot WRus
§ 'George Home' CGle ECtt LHil LRHS SAxl SCou WByw WSpr
glaber CElw CHal CMHG CRiv CSev EDon EGol ESma LGan LGre LHil LHop MBro MRav NBro NRed SAga SCou SMrm SSvw WCru WEas WKif WPer WRus WSpr
¶ 'Gletsjer' SPla
¶ *gormanii* MHig
gracilis CNic GCHN WPer
hallii LBlm LGre NTow WDav
hartwegii CGre EOrc LHil LHop NCat NRar SAga SChu SMrm WAbe WCru WKif WPer WRus WSpr
– *albus* CGle CRiv EOrc LGan LGre LRHS NNor SChu WRus
§ *heterophyllus* Widely available
– *australis* See P. *australis*
– 'Blue Gem' EBre EOrc IDai LBre MBro NRoo SIng SMrm WHoo WPer WSpr
– 'Blue Springs' CGle CSam EBar EOrc NHol SAga SBla SChu SMrm SPla SUsu WAbe WEas WRus WSpr
– 'Heavenly Blue' ECtt EHal LHop NRar SFis SLon WRus
¶ – 'Perhill Purple' WPer
– ssp. *purdyi* SMrm
– 'True Blue' See P. *heterophyllus*
– 'Züriblau' CChu CHan SAga WWat
'Hewell Pink Bedder' CGle CMGP EBar EBre ECro EFou EGol LBre LHil NRar NRoo SChu SCou SCro WHCG WHal WPer WRus WSpr
'Heythrop Park' WHCG WSpr
§ 'Hidcote Pink' Widely available
'Hidcote Purple' CElw CHan LHil SChu
*'Hidcote White' CBot EBar EOrc WAbe WRus WWin
§ *hirsutus* CGle CSun EBar LBlm LHil MNFA MPlt SCou WOMN WThi
– bronze leaf form WThi
– 'Minimus' NTow WHil WThi
– 'Pygmaeus' CGle CMil CNic CRDP CSun CWGN ELan LBlm MBro MHig MPar MPit MPla NHar NHol NRed NTow NWCA SBla SFis SIng SSou WAbe WDav WHoo WOMN WThi WThu WWin
'Hopleys Variegated' CRDP ECtt EFol EHal EMon EOrc EPla NBir NRar NSti SMrm WHil
humilis NTow
– JCA 11499 WPer
– 'Pulchellus' LGre
'Hyacinth' ELan
isophyllus CBrk CGle CHan SChu SCou WCot WEas WHCG WOld WPer WSpr
jamesii CGle CHan SBla SWas WDav WPer
'Jeannie' NHol
¶ 'John Booth' WEas
'John Nash' CElw CFis CHan CMil CRiv EBar LHil SIgm SMrm WSpr
'Joy' CChu WHoo WPer WSpr
♦ 'June' See P. 'Hidcote Pink'
'King George' CFis CGre CHan CKel CSam EBar EBre ECtt EFou EPla IHos LBre LHil MBri NRoo SAxl SBor SChu SCou SCro SFis SPer WEas WHCG WOld WPer WRus WSpr
¶ 'Knightwick' WPer
kunthii See P. *campanulatus*
laetus ssp. *roezlii* EFol ESma GDra MBar MBro MPla NHar NHol NMen SIng SMrm WAbe WDav WHil WPer WSHC WWin
linarioïdes JCA 9694 SIgm WDav
– ssp. *taosensis* See P. *crandallii glabrescens t.*
¶ 'Little Whitley' WPer
'Lord Home' See P. 'George Home'
lyallii ELan EMar EMon ERav LHil MNFA SIgm
*'Lynette' WMar WOld WPer
'Macpenny's Pink' EBar SAxl
'Madame Golding' CGle LGre LHil MMil SAga WCru
'Margery Fish' CHan EBar ESis MMil NFai WOld WPer WSpr
¶ *mensarum* WDav
menziesii See P. *davidsonii m.*
'Midnight' CChu CGle CHad EOrc LAbb LGre LHil MMil NCat SAga SChu SIgm SMrm WByw WCot WCru WEas WMar WMer WOld WPer WRus WSpr WWin
'Modesty' CChu CHan LGre LRHS WSpr
montanus GCHN GTou
'Mother of Pearl' CChu CElw CFis CHan EBar ECtt EFou EOrc GCal IBar LGre LHil LHop MBel NFai NRoo NSti SAga SAxl SChu SIgm SMrm SPer SUsu WHCG WHal WPer WRus WSpr
*'Mountain Wine' LRHS SChu WThi
'Mrs Golding' WPer
♦ 'Mrs Morse' See P. 'Chester Scarlet'
'Myddelton Gem' CGle EMon MWat NFai SAxl SCou WHCG WRus WSpr
newberryi CGle CNic ELan LBee LGre MBro MFos MHig NBir NMen NRar NRoo NTow SChu WKif WMar WPat WPer WWin
– f. *humilior* EPad
¶ – *sonomensis* MHig
'Oaklea Red' EDon LHil NRar
* old candy pink EOrc WPer WRus WSpr
oliganthus WDav
'Osprey' CElw CGle CHan EBar EPla LGre LHil WCot WEas WHal WOld WPer WRus
ovatus CHan ELan ESma GCal LGan MFir MNFA MPar MTol NCat SAga SFar SFis SMrm WDav WKif WPer WSun WWat
palmeri LGre
'Papal Purple' CChu CMHG EBar EDon LHil NCat NRar NSti SAga SChu SUsu SWas WByw WEas WHCG WOld WPer WRus WSpr
'Park Garden' WPer
'Peace' LRHS SCou
¶ *peckii* WPer

'Pennington Gem'	CChu CGle CSam CWit ECtt ELan EOrc ESma LGre LHil LHop MSte SAga SCou SPer WCru WEas WMar WMer WOld WPer WRus WSpr
'Phare'	WPer
'Phyllis'	See P. 'Evelyn'
pinifolius	Widely available
– 'Mersea Yellow'	Widely available
¶– 'Wisley Flame'	SIgm
pink and cream	CHan
'Pink Dragon'	EOrc GCHN GDra LGre MBal MHig MPla NHol SAga WPat WRus
§ 'Pink Endurance'	CChu CElw CMea ELan EMar EOrc ESis LGan MMil NRar SChu SCou WEas WHCG WHal WHoo WPat WPer WSpr
¶ 'Pink Ice'	WHil
¶ 'Pink Profusion'	SIgm SUsu
'Plum Beauty'	EDon
'Port Wine'	CChu CGle CSam CSco ESma GCHN LHil NCat NHol SCou SPla WOld
'Powis Castle'	WPer
'Prairie Fire'	EMar GCal
¶ 'Primrose Thomas'	CKel
'Priory Purple'	WHCG WPer
procerus	SCou WPer WSpr
– ***formosus***	CNic
– ssp. ***tolmiei***	CSev EPot GCHN GCal LGre NTow NWCA SMrm SSvw WCla WDav
¶ ***procurrens***	SIng
pubescens	See P. ***hirsutus***
pulchellus	See P. ***campanulatus***
'Purple and White'	See P. 'Charles Rudd'
'Purple Bedder'	CChu CGle CGre MWat SFis
'Purple Dragon'	MPla SBla
'Purple Gem'	GDra WMar
♦ 'Purpureus Albus'	See P. 'Charles Rudd'
¶ 'Purpurglocken'	NSti
purpusii	LGre WCru
rameleyi	WDav
'Raven'	CChu LHil MBel NBro WAbb WCot WEas WHCG WHal WHoo WMer WOld WPer WRus WSpr
'Razzle Dazzle'	WPer
'Red Emperor'	CMHG EDon NFai SFis WMer WPer WSpr
'Rich Ruby'	CBrk CChu CElw CGle CHan CMGP CSun EDon ELan LAbb LGre LHil LHop NOak SAga SAxl SChu SMrm SUsu WCot WPer WRus WSpr
richardsonii	LHop WOMN WPer
roezlii	See P. ***lactus r.***
* ***roseocampanulatus***	GCal LGre NRar SIgm SMrm WAbe WMar
rostriflorus	ESma WPer
¶– JJA 9548	SBla
* 'Roy Davidson'	CElw CNic WPer
♦ 'Royal White'	See P. 'White Bedder'
'Rubicundus'	CChu CElw CGle CHan CRiv EBar EDon ESma LHil LHop NRar NSti SAga SCou SMrm WAbe WCot WHoo WMer WOld WPer WRus
'Ruby'	See P. 'Schoenholzeri'
'Ruby Field'	WHCG WOld
rupicola	GDra GTou MBro MFir MPla NWCA SIgm WAbe WOMN WPer
– 'Albus'	LGre
– 'Diamond Lake'	WDav
– mauve hybrid	GDra LGre
'Russian River'	CKel EDon LHil SChu SMrm WSpr
rydbergii	WDav WPer
¶ ***sanguineus***	WHil
'Scarlet Queen'	LRHS WSpr
'Scarlet 'n' White'	WAbe
§ 'Schoenholzeri'	Widely available
scouleri	See P. ***fruticosus s.***
§ ***serrulatus***	ECha LRHS MSte SCou WEas
– 'Albus'	LHil NRed WPer
¶ 'Shell Pink'	WPer
'Sissinghurst Pink'	See P. 'Evelyn'
'Six Hills'	CLew CRiv MBro MHig MPla NRoo SAga WDav WMar WPat WPer WSHC
* 'Skyline'	EBar ECtt NMir WHil
smallii	EHal EPot WPer
'Snow Storm'	See P. 'White Bedder'
'Snowflake'	See P. 'White Bedder'
'Sour Grapes'	SWas
♦– misapplied	See P. 'Stapleford Gem'
'Southgate Gem'	MWat SCro
'Souvenir d'Adrian Regnier'	WOld
♦ 'Souvenir d'André Torres'	See P. 'Chester Scarlet'
spectabilis	WPer
§ 'Stapleford Gem'	Widely available
strictus	EBar ECro EHal LBlm LGre SSvw WAbe WPer WSpr
taosensis	See P. ***crandallii glabrescens t.***
ternatus	See KECKIELLA ***ternata***
teucrioïdes	EPot NMen WThi
'Thorn'	CGle EFou LRHS MBel SCou SUsu WPer WRus WSpr
'Threave Pink'	See P. 'Pink Endurance'
* 'Threave White'	CHan CMil LBlm
'Torquay Gem'	CElw WHCG WOld WPer WRus
utahensis	EBre LBre LGre MNFA SUsu WCot WPer WTyr
venustus	CCor CSam EBar GCal SIgm WPer
virens	CElw CNic EFol EMar MBro MHig NRoo SAxl WSpr
¶– R/Mr 7890	WPer
– ***albus***	GCHN MPla NHol SFis WDav WWin
virgatus ssp. ***arizonicus***	WPer
watsonii	LHop SAga SCou SIng SMrm WCot WPbr WPer
§ ***whippleanus***	CBot CElw CGle CHan ECro GCal LGan LGre MBel MNFA MSte NRar SAga WCla WPer
– JCA 9504	LBlm
§ 'White Bedder'	Widely available
'Whitethroat'	CGre WCot WMer WPer WSpr
'Windsor Red'	CChu CMer ESma LHil NTow WCot WSpr
wislizenii	LGre

PENTAGLOTTIS (Boraginaceae)

§ *sempervirens*	CArn CKin Effi MHew NSal NSel WHen WOak WWye

PENTAPTERYGIUM See AGAPETES

PENTAS (Rubiaceae)

lanceolata	CHal ERea LAbb MBri

PENTASCHISTIS (Gramineae)

sp. SH 44	CHan

PEPEROMIA (Piperaceae)

§ *argyreia*	MBri
arifolia	CHal
caperata	MBri
– 'Little Fantasy'	CHal
– 'Variegata'	CHal
clusiifolia 'Variegata'	CHal
glabella	CHal
griseoargentea	CHal
magnoliifolia	See P. ***obtusifolia*** Magnoliifolia Group
obtusifolia 'Jamaica'	MBri
– 'Tricolor'	MBri
obtusifolia Magnoliifolia Group 'Golden Gate'	MBri
– 'Greengold'	CHal MBri
– 'USA'	MBri
I *orba* 'Pixie Variegata'	MBri
– 'Pixie '	MBri
pulchella	See P. ***verticillata***
resediflora	See P. ***fraseri***
sandersii	See P. ***argyreia***
scandens	MBri
– 'Variegata'	CHal MBri
§ *verticillata*	CHal

PERESKIA (Cactaceae)

* *aculeata* 'Variegata'	CHal

PEREZIA (Compositae)

recurvata	EPot MCas NTow WAbe

PERICALLIS (Compositae)

¶ *appendiculata*	NGar
§ *lanata*	CB&S CBrk CFis CHan CMer CPle CSev CTro ELan EOrc ERav LGre LHil LHop SMad SMrm SUsu

PERILLA (Labiatae)

♦*frutescens crispa*	See P. ***f. nankinensis***
§ – var. *nankinensis*	CArn
– *rubra*	CArn

PERIPLOCA (Asclepiadaceae)

graeca	CB&S CMac CPle SBra SPer WCru

PERISTROPHE (Acanthaceae)

speciosa	ERea SLMG

PERNETTYA See GAULTHERIA

PEROVSKIA (Labiatae)

atriplicifolia	CArn CBot CHan CPle CShe GPoy LGre LHol MBri NNor SIde SPer WBod WHal WOld WPer WWye
'Blue Spire'	CB&S CCla CFis CSco EBre EFou ELan ENot GCal IJoh IOrc LBre LHop MBar MPla NSti SBla SHBN SLon SPer SReu SSpi SSta SUsu WEas WHil WPat WSHC WWat WWin
'Superba'	WWeb

PERROTTETIA (Celastraceae)

¶ *racemosa*	CMCN

PERSEA (Lauraceae)

ichangensis	CTre SArc
lingue	CGre

PERSICARIA (Polygonaceae)

§ *affinis*	CB&S CFis CHal CPar CShe CTom CWGN ECha EFol MBar MTho NBro NKay NSel NSti SAxl WEas WHal WOld WWat WWin
– 'Darjeeling Red'	CB&S CCla CGle CRDP CRow CSco ECED ELan ENot EPla GCal IDai LGro LWad MBal MBri NBar NBir NFai NMir SChu WAbe WHen
– 'Dimity'	See P. ***a.*** 'Superba'
– 'Donald Lowndes'	CGle CKel CRow CSco CShe ECha EFol EGol ELan ENot EOrc EPla MBal MSta MTho MWat NDea NKay NMir NNor NRoo SPer SPla WAbe WHoo WOld
– 'Hartswood'	EMon LRHS
– 'Ron McBeath'	EFou EMon LRHS
§ – 'Superba'	CCla CLew CRow EBre EFou EGol EMon EPla ERav LBre MBri MFir NBar NBro NHol NRoo SFis SMrm SSpi WHoo WPer WRus
alata	CRow EPla ESma NHol SMad
alpina	CRow
amphibia	CRDP CRow
§ *amplexicaulis*	CBre CFis CPar CRow CShe EBre ELan ELun EMar ERav LBre LGro MBal NDea NNor NOrc SChu SCro SUsu WBon WHoo
– 'Alba'	CRow ECha EPla
– 'Arun Gem'	See P. ***a. pendula***
– 'Atrosanguinea'	CKel CNic CRow CSco EBre ECED ECha EPla LBre MFir NBir NFai NHol NKay NRar NTow NVic SFis SHig SMrm SPer WOld WWin
– 'Firetail'	CCla CDec CHan CLew CRow CTom EBre ECED ECha ECtt EFou EPla LBre NHol NRoo NSti SMrm WHal WOld WRus
– 'Inverleith'	CBre CHan CRow EBre ECha ECtt EFou EGol EPla LBre NCat NRoo WWye
§ – var. *pendula*	CHan COtt CRow CShe EBre EGol GAri LBre NBir NRoo
– 'Rosea'	CFis CRow ECha ELan
¶ – 'Taurus'	LRHS

§ ***bistorta***	CArn CKin CRow CSFH CShe Effi GPoy LHol MChe NLan NSal SIde WBon WNdy WWye
– ssp. ***carnea***	CRow ECha EFol ELan EMon NBir
– 'Superba'	Widely available
campanulata	CFis COtt CRow CSco ECha EFol ELan EMar EOrc EPar ISea LHop NBro NKay NNor NRoo SCro SPer SPla WPer WThu WWat WWin
– Alba Group	CFis CGle CRow CTom ELan EMar EMon EOrc GCal NBro NCat NSti SChu WWat
– pale pink form	GCal
– 'Rosenrot'	CBre CRow EGol ELan EMon EOrc GCal IBlr NHol SCro WOld
– 'Southcombe White'	CRow
capitata	CGle CHal CNic CRDP CRiv CRow CWGN EFol ELan MFir SIng SMrm SUsu WEas WPer
elata	GGar
emodi	CRow WWat
♦***filiformis***	See P. ***virginiana***
§ ***macrophylla***	CRow EBre LBre
microcephala	CRow LGre
milletii	CGle CRDP CRiv CRow ECha GAri GDra LGan MBri MFir MTho NOak WCru WMer WRus
runcinata	CRow EHal LHop NBro NFai SChu WCru WEas WHer WOld WPer
scoparia	See POLYGONUM ***scoparium***
sphaerostachya Meissner	See P. ***macrophylla***
tenuicaulis	CGle CHal CLew CRiv CRow CTom EBre EMon EPar EPla LBee LBre MBal NHol NKay SIng
vacciniifolia	Widely available
§ ***virginiana***	EPla MFir
§ – 'Painter's Palette' (v)	Widely available
§ – Variegata Group	CBot CHan CRow ECha EFol EPla GCal LHop WOld
vivipara	CRow NLan
§ ***wallichii***	CRow IBlr
weyrichii	GCal NBir WCot

PETAMENES See GLADIOLUS

PETASITES (Compositae)

albus	EMon GPoy LRHS NSal NSti
fragrans	CHEx CNat ELan EMon EPar MUlv SHer SWat WHal
hybridus	CKin EMFW MSta WHer
japonicus var. ***giganteus***	CHEx CHad CRDP CWGN ECha EGol ELan EMon EPar MBri MTol MUlv NDea NVic WCra WCru
– – 'Variegatus'	CRDP EMon EPla IBlr MUlv WCot
kablikianus	
AL&JS 90170YU	EMon
¶ ***palmatus***	CRDP
– JLS 86317CLOR	EMon
paradoxus	EMon SApp

PETREA (Verbenaceae)

volubilis	MNew

PETROCALLIS (Cruciferae)

lagascae	See P. ***pyrenaica***
§ ***pyrenaica***	LBee MHig NTow NWCA WDav WPer

PETROCOPTIS (Caryophyllaceae)

§ ***glaucifolia***	EBar ESis MCas MFir MPla NBir NCat NGre NMen NRed NWCA WPer WWin
pyrenaica	NGre SRms WOMN

PETROCOSMEA (Gesneriaceae)

See Plant Deletions

PETROMARULA (Campanulaceae)

See Plant Deletions

PETROPHYTUM (Rosaceae)

caespitosum	GArf NHar WDav
§ ***hendersonii***	EPot GArf NHol NKay WDav WOMN

PETRORHAGIA (Caryophyllaceae)

nanteuilii	CNat
§ ***saxifraga***	CNic CPar EBur MHew MNFA MPit NCat NGre NKay NMen NSal NVic SIng WHil WPer WThu WTyr
§ – 'Rosette'	ECha GCal MTho WAbe WWin

PETROSELINUM (Umbelliferae)

§ ***crispum***	CArn CSFH CSev EJud Effi GPoy IEde ILis LHol MChe SIde WHal WPer

PETTERIA (Leguminosae)

ramentacea	CB&S EHal MPla SSpi

PEUMUS (Monimiaceae)

¶ ***boldus***	CGre

PHACELIA (Hydrophyllaceae)

sericea	MFos
¶ – ssp. ***ciliosa***	MFos
¶ ***tanacetifolia***	WWye

PHAEDRANASSA (Liliaceae/Amaryllidaceae)

¶ ***dubia***	CMon

PHAEDRANTHUS See DISTICTIS

PHAENOSPERMA (Gramineae)

globosa	EMon EPla SPla

PHAGNALON (Compositae)

¶ ***helichrysoïdes***	SIng

PHAIOPHLEPS (Iridaceae)

♦***biflora***	See OLSYNIUM ***biflorum***
nigricans	See SISYRINCHIUM ***striatum***

PHALARIS (Gramineae)

¶ ***aquatica*** ETPC
arundinacea CKin CWGN EHal ETPC SWat
– 'Elegantissima' See P. ***a. picta*** 'Picta'
– var. ***picta***
'Aureovariegata' CB&S CKel CRow SWat WHol
– – 'Feesey' (v) CElw CRow ECha EHoe EMon EPla ETPC IBlr SMad
– – 'Luteopicta' EHoe EPla WCot
§ – – 'Picta' (v) CRow CSco EBre EHoe EHon ELan EPla EPot ETPC GCHN IBlr LBre LGro MBal MBar MFir NHol NNor NSti SCob SPer SWat WChe WDav WEas WWin
– – 'Tricolor' (v) EHoe EMon EPla ETPC LRHS
– 'Streamlined' (v) EMon EPla ETPC WCot
canariensis EHoe
♦ ***tuberosa stenoptera*** See P. ***aquatica***

PHANEROPHLEBIA See POLYSTICHUM

PHARBITIS See IPOMOEA

PHASEOLUS (Leguminosae)

♦ ***caracalla*** See VIGNA ***c.***

PHEGOPTERIS (Thelypteridaceae)

§ ***connectilis*** EBul MBal NKay NLan NMar SRms WRic
decursive-pinnata NMar WRic

PHELLODENDRON (Rutaceae)

amurense CB&S CCla EArb EHar ELan SEng SHil SSpi WDin WFro
– var. ***sachalinense*** WCoo
chinense WCoo
¶ ***japonicum*** EArb

PHILADELPHUS † (Hydrangeaceae)

'Albâtre' CB&S
'Avalanche' CMHG EBre ELan ISea LAbb LBre SPer WDin WHCG
'Beauclerk' CB&S CBow CDoC CLan CMHG CMil CSco CShe EBre ENot LBre MBri MGos NBee NHol NKay SHer SLon SPer SPla SReu SSpi WBod WWat WWin
'Belle Etoile' Widely available
'Boule d'Argent' CMHG WEas
'Bouquet Blanc' IDai MBri SRms WKif
brachybotrys IOrc
'Buckley's Quill' MUlv
'Burfordensis' CCla MAsh SLon SPer WBod WWat WWeb
coronarius CDec CSco EHar LAbb LBuc MWat NNor SHBN SPer WDin
– 'Aureus' Widely available
– 'Bowles' Variety' (v) See P. ***c.*** 'Variegatus'
– 'Gold Mound' MGos
§ – 'Variegatus' Widely available
'Coupe d'Argent' MRav
delavayi SSpi
– var. ***calvescens*** See P. ***purpurascens***
'Enchantment' SDix
'Erectus' CSco EFol ENot ISea MBal MRav NWea WHCG
'Frosty Morn' CB&S CCla CDoC EHal IJoh MBri NHol SPer
'Galahad' LRHS
incanus CMCN
§ 'Innocence' (v) CBot CCla CDec CDoC CPMA CPle CSco ECtt EFol EHoe ELan EPla IJoh LHop MBri MPla MUlv NWyt SDry SFis SGil SMad SPer SPla SReu SSpi SSta WHCG WPat WRus
'Innocence Variegatus' See P. 'Innocence'
§ ***insignis*** WBod
x ***lemoinei*** CMer IDai IJoh MGos NNor NWyt SHBN SLon WStI
lewisii EHal WHCr WWat
'Manteau d'Hermine' Widely available
¶ 'Marjorie' CHan GCal
¶ ***mexicanus*** CBow
microphyllus CBot CCla CHan CMHG CSco CShe EHar ELan EPla ERav ESis IDai LAbb LGre MPla NHol SDry SLon SPer SReu SSpi WHCG WKif WPat WSHC WWat
'Minnesota Snowflake' ECtt
'Mrs E L Robinson' ECtt EPla
'Natchez' ECtt
'Perryhill' SPer
'Rosace' SPer
'Silberregen' ('Silver Showers') CBow CCla CPle CSco ECtt IJoh IOrc ISea MBal MBar MGos MUlv NHol SHBN WAbe WDin WPat WWat
'Silver Slipper' ISea
¶ 'Snowflake' MBal NHol
'Souvenir de Billiard' See P. ***insignis***
¶ ***subcanus*** CMCN
'Sybille' CBow CCla CMHG COtt CSco ENot IDai ISea MBri MRav SPer SSpi SSta WAbe WHCG WSHC WWat
tomentosus WHCG
'Virginal' CB&S CBra CCla CDec CPle CSco CShe CTrw EBre ELan ENot GRei IDai IJoh ISea LBre MBal MBar MBri MGos MWat NKay NNor NRoo NWea SHBN SPer SReu WDin WWin
– LA '82 MBal MUlv
¶ 'White Rock' MBal

PHILESIA (Liliaceae/Philesiaceae)

buxifolia See P. ***magellanica***
§ ***magellanica*** CB&S CBow CCla CTrw GGGa IBar IDai MBal SArc SPer SSpi WBod

PHILLYREA (Oleaceae)

angustifolia CCla CHan SSpi
decora See OSMANTHUS ***decorus***
§ ***latifolia*** CBot CHan SArc SHBN SHil SSpi WCoo WWat
media See P. ***latifolia***

PHILODENDRON (Araceae)

§ ***angustisectum*** MBri
§ ***bipennifolium*** MBri
elegans See P. ***angustisectum***
'Emerald Queen' MBri

epipremnum	See EPIPREMNUM ***pinnatum***
erubescens	CHal MBri
– 'Burgundy'	MBri SGil
– 'Imperial Red'	MBri
– 'Red Emerald'	EBak MBri
– 'Valeria'	MBri
melanochrysum	MBri
'New Red'	MBri
panduriforme	See P. ***bipennifolium***
pedatum	MBri
'Purple Queen'	MBri
radiatum	MBri
scandens	CHal
sodiroi	See P. ***ornatum***
tuxtlanum 'Royal Queen'	MBri
– 'Tuxtla'	MBri

PHLEBODIUM See POLYPODIUM

PHLEUM (Gramineae)

hirsutum	ETPC
montanum	ETPC
pratense	CKin EHoe

PHLOMIS † (Labiatae)

****anatolica***	CHan CKni ELan WCru
*– 'Lloyd's Variety'	CAbP CChu CKni ELan EMon EPla GCal LHop SGil WCru WSHC WWat
betonicoïdes B&L 12600	EMon
bovei ssp. ***maroccana***	CBot CChu CHan EMon GCal LGan SFis WCru WWat
cashmeriana	CAbb CBot CChu CDec CGle CHan CPle CPou SSpi SWas WSHC
chrysophylla	CB&S CBot CBow CChu CFis CGre CHan CMil CPle CSam ECar ELan EPla GCal SDix SDry SLon SPer SUsu WCru WWat
crinita	LGre
§ 'Edward Bowles'	CDoC CSco GCal LHop NRar SDry WCot WCru
fruticosa	Widely available
grandiflora	CBot CChu ELan
herba-venti ssp. ***pungens***	WCru
italica	CB&S CBot CCla CElw CFis CHan CMer CSco EFou ELan GCHN GCal LGre LHop NSti SChu SLon SMad SPer SSpi SUsu WCru WEas WHer WPbr WSHC WWat WWin
lanata	CChu CFis CHan CMHG CMer CPou ELan EMon EPla LGre LHop SBla SDry SPer SUsu WCru WDav WHer WSHC WWat
leucophracta	CKni
longifolia	CBot CHan WCru WWye
– var. ***bailanica***	CChu CKni CPle EMon EPla WWat
lycia	CCla CKni EMon EPla LGre
*'Nova'	CBot
purpurea	CBow CHan ELan NBir WCru WSHC
– ***alba***	CBot CHan LHop WCru
¶ – dark form	WCru
§ ***russeliana***	Widely available
samia Boissier	See P. ***russeliana***
tuberosa	CBot CHan CPou EMon GCal WCru WDav
– 'Amazone'	ECha EPla
viscosa hort.	See P. ***russeliana***

PHLOX † (Polemoniaceae)

adsurgens	ITim MHig SBla WPer
– 'Alba'	SBla
– 'Red Buttes'	CGle EPot LGre NHar NHol SBla SMrm
– 'Wagon Wheel'	CGle CRDP CRiv EBre ECha EPad EPot ITim LBre LHop MHig NGre NHar NHol NMen SIng SMrm SUsu WEas WPat WPer WThu WWin
amoena hort.	See P. x ***procumbens***
x ***arendsii*** 'Anja'	WCot
¶ – 'Hilda'	EMon WCot
– 'Lisbeth'	WCot
austromontana	EPot
bifida	ITim MBro MHig SWas WHil WThi WThu WWin
– 'Alba'	CNic
– blue form	ELan LBee LRHS SHer SWas
– 'Colvin's White'	LBee LHop MCas WPer
– 'Minima Colvin'	ECtt
– 'Petticoat'	SBla SWas
– 'Starbrite'	EPot ITim LBee MBro NMen WHoo WPat WPer WThi
– 'Starcleft'	CNic
*– 'The Fi'	WPer
'Black Buttes'	EPot WThi
borealis	CShe ELan GDra ITim NRed NTow WThi
****caerulea*** x ***aleutica***	NHar
caespitosa	EMNN EPot ITim LBee NMen NTow SGil
– ssp. ***pulvinata***	ITim
canadensis laphamii	See P. ***divaricata laphamii***
carolina 'Bill Baker'	CChu CGle CHan CSam ECha EMon LGan MBel MSte SCro SMrm SWas WOMN
– 'Miss Lingard'	EFou EMon GCal LRHS MMil SBla SDix WCot
'Charles Ricardo'	CRDP ERav NTow SMrm WOMN
'Chattahoochee'	CBot CHad CMea CRiv EBre ELan EMNN EPot LBre LGre LHop MBro MCas MHig NHar NHol NSti SBla SGil SIng WBon WMar WOMN WOld WPat WSHC WThu WWin
¶ ***condensata***	NWCA
'Daniel's Cushion'	See P. ***subulata*** 'McDaniel's Cushion'
divaricata	MRav NKay WPer WWin
– ***alba***	ELan
– 'Blue Dreams'	SMrm SWas
– 'Dirigo Ice'	CHad CNic CRDP ERav LBee LGre SBla SFar WPer
§ – ssp. ***laphamii***	CNic MBro MPar NVic SBar SBla WCru WKif WPer WRus WThi
– 'May Breeze'	ECha SMrm SWas
douglasii	EBar NHol NWCA SRms SUsu
– 'Apollo'	ELan EMNN GAbr GDra MBro MHig NGre NHol NMen NNrd SHer WAbe WDav WPer WWin
– 'Blue Mist'	NHol

- 'Boothman's Variety' CGle CHal CShe ECha ELan EMNN EPar EPot ESma LBee MHig MPar MPit MPla MWat NHol NKay NMen SBod SGil SHer SIng WEas WHil WPer WWin
- 'Concorde' GDra NHar
- 'Crackerjack' CHal CSam CShe CTom ELan EMNN EPot GAbr GDra ITim LBee MCas MHig MPla MWat NGre NHar NKay NMen NNrd NRed NRoo SBod SIng WAbe WDav
- 'Eva' CHal CNic EBre ELan EMNN EPot GTou LAbb LBee LBre MHig MRav NBir NGre NHar NHol NKay NNrd NRoo SBod SGil SHer SIng WAbe WPer WThi WWin
- 'Galaxy' ESis GDra NHar NHol
- 'Holden Variety' NHol
- 'Ice Mountain' CNic IHos SHer WPer
- 'Iceberg' EPot ESis GDra ITim MBro NHar NHol NRed SGil WDav WWin
- 'J A Hibberson' EPot ESis LRHS MHig NHar WThi
- 'Lilac Cloud' NHol
- 'Lilakönigin' ('Lilac Queen') WHil
- 'Millstream Laura' CNic
- x ***nana depressa*** EPot MBro NHol WDav
- 'Pink Chintz' CNic
- 'Red Admiral' CHal CMHG CShe EBre EMNN EPot GCHN GDra IHos LBre MCas MHig NHar NHol NMen NNrd NRoo SBod SChu SGil SHer
- 'Rose Cushion' CNic ESis GDra LRHS MPla NHol SGil SHer
- 'Rose Queen' CMHG CPar ESis GDra NHol
- 'Rosea' EBre ELan EMNN EPad EPar ESis LBee LBre MBal MCas MRav NGre NKay NNrd NRed NRoo SBod SHer SIng SSmi WAbe

¶ - 'Sprite' SRms
- 'Tycoon' ESis GDra GTou NMen WAbe
- 'Violet Queen' EMNN EPot GDra NHar NHol SGil SHer
- 'Waterloo' CTom EBre EPot GAri ITim LBre LHop MRav NHar NHol NMen SChu SUsu WAbe WWin
- 'White Drift' WThu

drummondii NRar
hoodii EPot LBee
'Kelly's Eye' CMHG CSam ECha ECtt EMNN EPot GAbr ITim LBee LHop MHig MMil NHar NMen NRoo SBod SIng SMrm SWas WPer
kelseyi 'Rosette' CPar ESis LBee MCas MHig NGre NHar NMen WAbe WHil WPer
maculata NOrc WPer
- 'Alpha' CGle CHan CSco EBre ECha EFou GCHN GCal LBre LGan MBri MBro MRav MUlv NHol NOrc NRoo NSti NVic SBla SChu SCro SMrm SPer SSvw WByw WOld WRus
- 'Delta' EBre LBre NSti

¶ - 'Good White' SMrm
- 'Omega' CHad CHan CSco EFou EOrc GCHN GCal LGan MBri MBro MRav MTho MUlv NHol NRoo NSti SChu SMrm SPer SSpi WByw WOld WRus
- 'Rosalinde' EBre EFou LBre MBel SAxl

mesoleuca See P. ***nana ensifolia***
Mexican hybrids See P. ***nana***
'Millstream' See P. x ***procumbens*** 'M.'
'Minima Colvin' SHer
'Mrs Campbell' See P. ***paniculata*** 'Elizabeth Campbell'

§ ***nana*** EPad
- 'Arroya' NHar SBla
- 'Chameleon' ECar NHar
- 'Denver Sunset' WThi

§ - ssp. ***ensifolia*** EPad EPot WThu
- ***lutea*** NHar
- 'Manjana' ECar NHar NHol SBla WThu
- 'Mary Maslin' NHar SBla WThi WThu
- 'Paul Maslin' ECar NHar NHol WThi
- 'Tangelo' NHar
- 'Vanilla Cream' ECar NHar NHol SBla WThi WThu

nivalis NHar
- 'Camla' EPot ITim LBee LHop WAbe WDav WThi
- 'Jill Alexander' NHol
- 'Nivea' ITim LBee NGre NTow SIng WPer

paniculata CHad CShe NNor SChu SDix SMrm SSpi WEas WOld

¶ - 'A E Amos' EFou ERou
- 'Aida' CB&S CKel ERou MWat
- ***alba*** GCal SDix WCot
- 'Alba Grandiflora' WEas
- 'Albert Leo Schlageter' CShe ERou SRms WMer

§ - 'Amethyst' CBla CCla CDoC CKel CPar CRiv CSam EBlo EBre EOrc ERou LBre MBel MRav NBir NRoo SChu SFis SPer WCra WOld WPer
- 'Annie Laurie' SRms
- 'Balmoral' CBow CDoC CGle CMGP EBre ECtt LBre NCat NMir
- 'Barnwell' ELan NBar WMer
- 'Betty Symons-Jeune' ERou SFis
- 'Bill Green' EBre LBre MRav
- 'Blue Boy' CMGP EFou ERou LWad WPer
- 'Blue Ice' CMGP EBlo EBre EFou ELan LBre MBro NCat NRoo WCra

¶ - 'Blushing Bride' SRms

¶ - 'Bonny Maid' CBla
- 'Border Gem' CB&S CBow CHad EBre EFou EMon ENot LBre NRoo SChu WCot

¶ - 'Boy Blue' NFai

¶ - 'Branklyn' CKel EBre LBre SBla
- 'Brigadier' CDoC CHal CKel CSam CSco EBre ELan ENot LBre LWad MFir MWat NBar NKay NVic SApp SPer WCra
- 'Bright Eyes' CBla CHal EBre LBre

¶ - 'Caroline van den Berg' ERou SRms

¶ - 'Cecil Hanbury' ERou NFai SRms
- 'Charmaine' CBla

¶ - 'Cherry Pink' EBre LBre
- 'Chintz' SRms
- 'Cinderella' ERou WMer
- 'Cool of the Evening' CBla CHal WCot

– 'Dodo Hanbury Forbes' CBla CKel
– 'Dresden China' ERou MUlv
– 'Düsterlohe' NBar
– 'Elizabeth Arden' EFou ERou NBar WMer
§ – 'Elizabeth Campbell' ECtt
¶ – 'Endurance' ERou
– 'Europe' CB&S CGle CMGP EFou ELan ERou MFir NFai WHil WMer
– 'Eva Cullum' EBre EFou EPad LBre NRoo WCot
– 'Eventide' CBow CDoC CSco EBre ECED ECtt EFou EHal ENot ERou LBre LWad NMir SChu SMrm SPer
– 'Excelsior' CPar EBre LBre MRav
– 'Fairy's Petticoat' MWat SPer WCot WEas
– 'Firefly' CKel ENot SFis
– 'Flamingo' NBar
– 'Franz Schubert' EBlo EBre EFou LBre NRoo SApp SMrm WCot WCra
§ – 'Frau A von Mauthner' NKay SRms
§ – 'Fujiyama' CBos CCla CHad CKel CPar CSam EBre ECha EFou EMon EOrc EPad LBre NBir NSti SApp SChu SMrm WAbb WCot WEas WThi
– 'Gaiety' CSco
– 'Glamis' MWat
– 'Graf Zeppelin' CBla CHal ELan MWat SRms
– 'Hampton Court' CKel
– 'Harewood' ERou
– 'Harlequin' (v) CChu EBre LBre NVic SSpi WCot
– 'Iceberg' MFir
¶ – 'Iris' SRms
– 'Juliglut' ('July Glow') EBre ELan LBre MWat WCot
– 'Kelway's Cherub' CKel
– 'Kirmesländler' CB&S CBow CKel ERou
¶ – 'Lady Clare' SRms
♦– 'Latest Red' See P. *p.* 'Spätrot'
– 'Le Mahdi' ELan MWat SRms
– 'Lilac Time' CSco MWat
¶ – 'Look Again' ERou
– 'Marlborough' NRoo
– 'Mary Fox' CSam ERou NRoo
– 'Mia Ruys' EFou ERou LWad NVic
– 'Mies Copijn' CDoC CSco CShe NBar NBee WCra
– 'Mother of Pearl' CGle CHad CMGP CSco EFou ELan MWat NVic SPer
– 'Mount Fujiyama' See P. *p.* 'Fujiyama'
¶ – 'Mrs A E Jeans' SRms
– 'Mrs Fincham' SFis
¶ – 'Newbird' ERou SRms
– 'Norah Leigh' (v) Widely available
– 'Orange Perfection' CB&S EFou EMon
¶ – 'Othello' CBla
– 'Otley Choice' EFou MWat NCat NVic
– 'Pastorale' MWat WCot
¶ – 'Pax' EMon
– 'Pike' WCot
– 'Prince of Orange' CBla CCla CGle CKel CPar CSam EBre EFou ELan ERou LBre MRav MUlv MWat NKay NRoo SApp SPer WCot
♦– 'Prospero' See P. 'Amethyst'
¶ – 'Purpurkuppel' SRms
– 'Rapture' MWat
– 'Red Indian' CKel EBre ERou LBre MWat
– 'Rembrandt' CSco CShe ERou MUlv WCot
– 'Rheinländer' WPer
– 'Rijnstroom' CB&S CMGP EFou ERou LAbb MBel NCat NFai WCot WHil
¶ – 'Rougham Supreme' ERou
– 'Russian Violet' CSco MWat
– 'San Antonio' CSco WCot
– 'Sandringham' CBow CCla CKel CSam EBre ELan ENot LBre LHop MUlv NBar NBir NCat NKay NMir NRoo NVic SChu SPer
– 'Shenstone' MWat
– 'Sir John Falstaff' CSco SFis WMer
¶ – 'Sir Malcolm Campbell' ERou
– 'Skylight' CShe NKay SFis
¶ – 'Snowdrift' ERou
§ – 'Spätrot' EFou WMer
– 'Spitfire' See P. *p.* 'Frau A von Mauthner'
– 'Starfire' CB&S CBla CBow CGle CKel CMil CSam CSco EBlo EBre EFou ELan ENot ERou LBre MFir NBar NBee NKay NRoo NSti SChu SFis SPer WCot WMer
– 'Sternhimmel' ERou
– 'Tenor' CBow EFou LWad NFai NMir
– 'Toits de Paris' MWat
– 'Vintage Wine' CHal CKel SPer
– 'White Admiral' CB&S CBla CCla CGle CHad CHal CKel CMil EBlo EBre ELan ENot EOrc LBre LHop LWad MBel MRav MUlv MWat NBee NKay NRoo SPer WEas WHil WMer WPer
– 'William Ramsay' ELan
– 'Windsor' CBla CHal CMGP EBre EFou ERou LBre LWad MBel NBar NBee NMir SFis WPer

pilosa CMGP ECha NSti SMrm SUsu
* 'Pleu de Pervanche' CSco
§ × ***procumbens*** CPar WHil
§ – 'Millstream' ECha ELan EPad ITim LBee SBla SMrm WPer WThi WWin
– 'Variegata' CBot CPar CRDP ECha EFol ELan EMNN ESis LGro MHig MPla MTho NEgg NGre NHol NNor NRoo NSti SBla WAbe WDav WHil WPat WThi WThu WWin
× ***rugellii*** CNic ECha NHol SRms WPer WWin
stolonifera CCla CHan CNic EPar LBee MTho WMer WPbr WPer
– 'Ariane' CMGP CNic CRDP CRiv ECha EPar LBee LHop MFir NVic SBla SWas WMar WPbr WPer WThu WWin
– 'Blue Ridge' CRDP ECha EPar LBee LHop NVic SBla SMrm WWin
– 'Mary Belle Frey' CBos CNic ECha MFir SBla SMrm SWas WDav WMar WPer WTyr WWin
– 'Violet Vere' EMon SBla SMrm SUsu SWas WKif
¶ ***subulata*** NWCA
– 'Alexander's Surprise' CGle CMea CNic CRiv CSam CShe EBre ECtt EPot ESis GCHN LBee LBre LHop MBal MCas MFir MPit NBir NGre NHol NKay NMen
– 'Amazing Grace' CGle CHal CNic ECtt EPad EPot ESis ITim NHol NMen SHer SIng WAbe WEas WPer WThi WWin
– 'Apple Blossom' GAbr GDra NHol SChu

– 'Atropurpurea'	EBre GCHN LBre NKay NNor WWin
– 'Beauty of Ronsdorf'	See P. *s.* 'Ronsdorfer Schöne'
– 'Betty'	ECtt EMNN MDHE NMen NNrd NRoo WHil WPer
– 'Blue Eyes'	See P. *s.* 'Oakington Blue Eyes'
– 'Blue Saucer'	EPot MBro NHol NNrd
– 'Bonita'	EMNN GAbr GAri LBee MRav NMen NRoo SChu SMrm SWas
– 'Bressingham Blue Eyes'	See P. *s.* 'Oakington Blue Eyes'
– 'Brightness'	CNic CRiv GCHN GTou LRHS MCas MRav NKay SChu
– ssp. ***brittonii*** 'Rosea'	EBar EPot ITim MBro NHol WOMN WPer
¶ – 'Daisy Hill'	NHol
– 'Drumm'	LBee LRHS
– 'Emerald Cushion Blue'	CNic CRiv EBre EPad LBee LBre MBal MCas MRav NHol NNrd NRoo SBod SHer WAbe WPer WSun WThi
– 'Fairy'	WPer WSun
– 'G F Wilson'	CHal CMea CNic CShe CTom ECha ECtt ELan EPad IDai LBee LGro MBal MCas MFir MHig MWat NGre NHol NKay NMen NNor NNrd NRoo SChu WAbe WDav WPer WWin
– 'Greencourt Purple'	NCat NHol
¶ – 'Jupiter'	SChu
– 'Lavinia'	NHol
§ – 'Maischnee' ('May Snow')	CB&S EBre ECtt ELan EMNN EPot ITim LBee LBre LGro MBal MCas MHig MPla MWat NGre NHol NNor NRoo WEas WHil WPer WWin
– 'Marjorie'	CHal ECtt ELan EMNN LBee MBal MCas NKay NMen SChu SHer WDav WEas WPer WTyr
§ – 'McDaniel's Cushion'	CGle CMHG CPar CShe EBre ECha ELan EMNN EPad EPot ITim LBee LBre MCas MHig MMil NHol NNor NRoo SBla SHer SIng WPer WWin
– 'Model'	LGro MWat
– 'Moonlight'	CNic ECtt WPer
– 'Nelsonii'	CShe
§ – 'Oakington Blue Eyes'	CHal CMHG CPar EBre EPar ESma GAbr GCHN GDra LBee LBre NHol NRoo WPer
– 'Red Wings'	CHal EBre ECtt GCHN LBee LBre MBal MCas MPit MRav NHol NKay NMen NNor NRar NRoo SSvw STre WHil
§ – 'Ronsdorfer Schöne'	EPad EPot NNrd WDav
– 'Rose Mabel'	NVic
– 'Samson'	CNic ELan GAbr IDai LBee NHol NKay SBod SHer SSvw STre WPer WThi WWin
¶ – 'Sarah'	WHil
– 'Scarlet Flame'	CB&S CNic CTom EBre ECha ECtt ELan EMNN EPot GDra LBee LBre LGro MBal MCas MPit MRav MWat NHol NKay SBod WHil WPer WTyr WWin
– 'Schneewitchen'	NHol
¶ – 'Sensation'	SRms
– 'Snow Queen'	See P. *s.* 'Maischnee'
– 'Starglow'	LRHS NHar NHol WPer
– 'Tamaongalei'	SBla SChu SUsu SWas
– 'Temiskaming'	CB&S CGle CHal CKel CMHG CNic CPar EBre ECha EMNN GCHN GDra IDai LAbb LBre LGro MCas MFir NHol NKay NMen NRoo SChu WAbe WEas
– violet seedling	NHol NKay
– 'White Delight'	CPar CRiv EBre ECha ECtt ELan EMNN EPad GCHN GTou LBre MCas MFir MHig NHol NKay NMen NRoo SBod SChu SHer WDav WPer
– 'White Swan'	WThi
– 'Winifred'	LMer
– 'Woodside'	SIng
'Vivid'	EPad WAbe
¶ x ***weseli***	EPot

PHOEBE (Lauraceae)

sheareri	CMCN

PHOENICAULIS (Cruciferae)

§ ***cheiranthoïdes***	WOMN

PHOENIX (Palmae)

canariensis	CGre CHEx LPal MBri NPal SMad WNor
F ***dactylifera***	LPal
¶ ***paludosa***	LPal
roebelenii	LPal MBri
sylvestris	LPal
theophrasti	LPal

PHORMIUM † (Agavaceae/Phormiaceae)

'Apricot Queen' (v)	CAbb CB&S IBlr IJoh LNet MBal
'Bronze Baby'	CAbb CB&S CBar CBow CSam CSco ECtt MBal MSte MWat SApp SBla SHBN WStI
colensoi	See P. ***cookianum***
§ ***cookianum***	CHEx CHan CTrw IBlr MBal MGos NTow SArc WWat
– 'Alpinum Purpureum'	See P. ***tenax*** 'Nanum Purpureum'
– ssp. ***hookeri*** 'Cream Delight' (v)	CAbb CB&S CSco EBre ELan ENot IJoh IOrc LBre LTil MBal MGos SHBN SLon SPer SSpi WCot
– – 'Tricolor'	CB&S CBra CHEx EBre ELan ENot IBar IBlr IJoh LBre MBal SArc SHBN SSpi WCot WWye
'Dark Delight'	CB&S CDoC LNet
'Dazzler' (v)	ENot IOrc LNet MBal
'Duet' (v)	COtt LNet
'Dusky Chief'	COtt
'Gold Spike'	CB&S
'Guardsman' (v)	CB&S
'Jack Spratt' (v)	COtt ECou IBlr
¶ 'Jester'	CB&S COtt
§ 'Maori Chief' (v)	CB&S EGol IJoh SHBN SSpi
'Maori Maiden' (v)	CB&S CDoC MBal SSpi
'Maori Queen' (v)	CB&S SSpi
'Maori Sunrise' (v)	CB&S ENot GWht IJoh LNet MSte SLon WCot WWye
'Pink Panther' (v)	CAbb CDoC MGos
'Rainbow Chief'	See P. 'Maori Chief'
Rainbow Hybrids	CSpe IJoh LTil MBal SHer

'Smiling Morn' (v) LNet WDin
'Sundowner' (v) CB&S CBar CBow CSco CTro EBre EGol ELan ENot IBar IBlr IJoh IOrc LBre LHop LNet MBal MGos SHBN SPer
'Sunset' (v) CB&S
'Surfer' (v) COtt
tenax CB&S CBra CHEx CSco CTro ELan ENot IBar ISea MBal MFir MWat NBro NNor SArc SBla SLon SMad SPer SPla SReu WBod WCot WDin
§ – 'Nanum Purpureum' EHoe SWas
– Purpureum Group CB&S CBot CBow CBra CFis CGre CHEx CHad CSco EBre EGol ELan ENot ERav IBar IJoh IOrc LBre MBal SLon SMad SPer SSpi WDin
– 'Radiance' (v) MBal SBla
– 'Variegatum' CBow CHEx IBlr MBal SArc SEng SRms
'Thumbelina' CB&S MFir MSte NHar
'Yellow Wave' (v) CAbb CB&S CBar CDoC CHEx CSco EBre EHoe ELan IBlr IJoh IOrc LBre LHop MBal SHer SSpi WCot

PHOTINIA † (Rosaceae)

§ ***arbutifolia*** CPle
beauverdiana CB&S CDoC CPle EHar SHil WWat
§ ***davidiana*** CCla CMCN CPle CSco CShe CTrw ELan GRei GWht IDai LHop MBal MBar MBri MGos MRav MWat SPer SReu WBod WHCG WNor WTyr WWat
– 'Palette' (v) CB&S CBow CCla CMHG CPle CSco CTrw EFol EGol EHar EHoe ELan ERav IJoh LHop MBal MBar MBri MGos MPla MRav NHol SPer SReu SSta WPat WSHC WStI
– var. ***undulata*** CMCN MRav
– – 'Fructu Luteo' CBow CCla CMHG CTrw EHar EPla MBri MRav SReu WWat
– – 'Prostrata' CCla EHar ELan LHil MBar MBri WSHC WWat
× ***fraseri*** IDai ISea WDin
– 'Birmingham' CChu CLan CMHG EHar LAbb MBal NBee SHBN WDin WSHC WWeb
– 'Red Robin' Widely available
– 'Robusta' CMHG MBal WWat
– 'Rubens' CChu CDoC CPMA EHar ELan MBri NTow SDry SPer SPla SSpi SSta WPat WWat
§ ***glabra*** 'Parfait' (v) CSco ELan LHop MBal MUlv SDry SHBN SPer WAbe WPat
– 'Pink Lady' (v) See P. ***g.*** 'Parfait'
– 'Rubens' See P. × ***fraseri*** 'R.'
♦– 'Variegata' See P. ***g.*** 'Parfait'
glomerata CHEx CMHG
lasiogyna CMCN EPla
¶ ***lindleyana*** LTil
§ 'Redstart' EHar MGos MUlv SHil SLon SPer SSpi SSta WWat
§ ***serratifolia*** CBot CChu CDoC CHEx CPle EHar EPla MBal SDry SHil SMad WBod WPat WWat
serrulata See P. ***serratifolia***
villosa CAbP CChu CCla CDoC CSco EHar GAri IDai IOrc MBal MBar SPer SSpi WBod WDin
¶ – var. ***laevis*** CB&S
– f. ***maximowicziana*** CCla

PHRAGMITES (Gramineae)

§ ***australis*** CBen LMay NDea SWat WHol
– ***giganteus*** See P. ***a. altissimus***
– ***pseudodonax*** GCal
– 'Variegatus' CBen EHoe EMFW EMon GCal MUlv WChe WCot WHal
communis See P. ***australis***
¶ ***karka*** 'Variegatus' WChe

PHUOPSIS (Rubiaceae)

§ ***stylosa*** CBre CElw CFis CGle CLew CMea CMer CRiv ECha EFol EFou ELan ESis LGan MFir NBar NBro NHol NRoo NSti NWCA SChu SSvw SUsu WAbb WHal WPbr WPer WWin WWye
– 'Purpurea' CRDP EBre ECha EFol ELan EMon ESis LBre NCat SChu WByw WHal

PHYGELIUS (Scrophulariaceae)

aequalis CBot CCla CGle CMHG CMer CSev CTre ELan EOrc MFir MPla NNor SAxl SBor SChu SDix SLon SUsu WSHC WWat
– ***albus*** See P. ***a.*** 'Yellow Trumpet'
¶ – 'Apricot Trumpet' SPer
– 'Aureus' See P. ***a.*** 'Yellow Trumpet'
– 'Cream Trumpet' See P. ***a.*** 'Yellow Trumpet'
– 'Indian Chief' See P. × ***rectus*** 'African Queen'
*– 'Pink Trumpet' CB&S EFou ERav NNor SMrm
§ – 'Yellow Trumpet' Widely available
capensis CBot CFis CGle CHan CMea CPar CPle CShe EBar ELan ENot EOrc ERav NBro NNor NRoo SBor SLon SPer WAbe WEas WHil WOld WPer
– × ***aequalis*** See P. × ***rectus***
– ***albus*** CGle
– ***coccineus*** CAbb CB&S CHEx CSco CSun CTrw EOrc IDai IJoh LAbb LWad MBal MPla SMad WBod
– orange form EPla
– ***roseus*** CTrw
§ × ***rectus*** EPla
§ – 'African Queen' CBow CGle CPMA CSun EBre ECtt EFou EGol ELan EOrc EPla LBre LHil LHop MBri MBro MPla MRav NBir NHol NKay NSti NTow SUsu WMer WOld WPer WRus WTyr WWin
– 'Devil's Tears' CCla CHal CMHG CTre EBar EOrc EPla ERav NFai SHil SLon WHoo WMer WPer WRus
– 'Moonraker' CCla CMHG EBar ECtt EFol ELan EOrc EPla ERav ESma MBri SHil SMad WHoo WMer WSun
– 'Pink Elf' ELan EOrc ERav ESis
– 'Salmon Leap' CMHG EBar EOrc EPla ESma LHil NBro NTow SHil WPer
§ – 'Winchester Fanfare' CAbb CFis CMHG CRDP EBre EOrc EPla ERav ESis LAbb LBre MBro SChu SCro SFis SHil SLon SPer WEas WHal WHoo WMer WOld WPer WRus WSHC WSun WWat

– 'Winton Fanfare'	See P. x *r.* 'Winchester Fanfare'
'Trewidden Pink'	LHop MBel

PHYLA (Verbenaceae)

§ ***canescens***	CLew EFol NHol WCru WHal
§ ***nodiflora***	CMer CRow ECha SMrm WHil WPer WTyr

PHYLICA (Rhamnaceae)

See Plant Deletions

X PHYLLIOPSIS (Ericaceae)

hillieri	GArf
– 'Coppelia'	CNic ECar GArf GGGa MAsh MBal NHar SSta WAbe WPat WThu
– 'Hobgoblin'	ECar GArf MBal SSta
¶ – 'Mermaid'	SSta
– 'Pinocchio'	ECar EPot GDra GGGa MAsh MBal MBri SHil SSpi SSta WAbe WPat WThu
– 'Puck'	ECar SSta
– 'Sprite'	ECar SSta WPat

PHYLLITIS See ASPLENIUM

PHYLLOCLADUS (Phyllocladaceae)

aspleniifolius var. ***alpinus***	CKen

PHYLLODOCE † (Ericaceae)

aleutica	CRiv EPot GAbr GArf GGGa MBal MBar MHig NHar WBod WPat WThu
§ – ssp. ***glanduliflora***	GArf GDra GWht MBal NHol WThu
§ – – 'Flora Slack'	GGGa MBal MHig WThu
– – white form	See P. ***a. g.*** 'Flora Slack'
x ***alpina***	GDra NHar
breweri	GArf GDra GGGa GWht
caerulea	GAbr GArf GDra GGGa GWht MBal MHig NHar WAbe
– ***japonica***	See P. ***nipponica***
empetriformis	CRiv GArf GDra GGGa GWht MBal MBar MBri MGos MHig NHar NHol WAbe WBod WPat WThu
glanduliflora	See P. ***aleutica g.***
x ***intermedia***	ECar GArf GDra MBal WDav
– 'Drummondii'	GArf GGGa GWht
– 'Fred Stoker'	GArf GGGa GWht MHig NHol SSta
§ ***nipponica***	GDra GWht MBal NHar NHol

PHYLLOSTACHYS † (Gramineae(Bambuseae))

angusta	SBam SDry WJun
arcana	EPla SBam SDry WJun
¶ – 'Luteosulcata'	SDry
§ ***atrovaginata***	SBam SDry
aurea	CHEx EFul EPla GAri ISta LBam LPan LTil SArc SBam SCob SDry SHil WJun WWat
– 'Albovariegata'	WJun
– 'Flavescens Inversa'	ISta SBam SDry WJun
– ***formosana***	WJun
– 'Holochrysa'	EFul EPla ISta SBam SDry WJun
– 'Koi'	SBam SDry WJun
– 'Variegata'	EFul EPla SBam SDry
aureosulcata	EFul EPla NJap SBam SDry WJun
¶ – f. ***alata***	SDry
– 'Aureocaulis'	SBam SDry WJun
¶ – 'Harbin'	SDry
– 'Spectabilis'	EFul EPla SBam SDry WJun
bambusoïdes	ISta LBam NJap SBam SDry SHil WJun
§ – 'Allgold' ('Holochrysa')	SBam SDry
– 'Castillonis'	EFul EPla ISta SArc SBam SDry WJun
– 'Castillonis Inversa'	SBam SDry WJun
– 'Katashibo'	WJun
¶ – 'Kawadana'	SDry WJun
– 'Slender Crookstem'	WJun
– ***subvariegata***	SBam SDry
– 'Sulphurea'	See P. ***b.*** 'Allgold'
¶ – 'Tanakae'	SDry
bissettii	EPla ISta LBam SBam SDry WJun
congesta hort.	See P. ***atrovaginata***
decora	SBam SDry WJun
dulcis	SBam WJun
§ ***edulis***	CGre EPla GAri ISta MBal NJap SArc SBam SDry WJun
– 'Bicolor'	SBam SDry WJun
– ***heterocycla***	SBam SDry
– ***pubescens***	See P. ***e.***
flexuosa	EFul EPla ISta LBam SBam SCob SDry SHil WJun
fulva	WJun
¶ ***glauca***	EPla
– 'Yunzhu'	SDry WJun
§ ***heteroclada***	SBam SDry WJun
– 'Solid Stem'	SBam SDry WJun
– 'Straight Stem'	EPla SBam SDry WJun
heterocycla	See P. ***edulis h.***
humilis	EPla SBam SDry WJun
¶ ***iridescens***	SDry
¶ ***lithophila***	WJun
¶ ***makinoi***	WJun
mannii	SBam SDry WJun
meyeri	EPla SBam SDry WJun
nidularia	ISta SBam SDry WJun
– Smooth Sheath	WJun
nigra	CHEx EFul EPla LBam LPan SBam SCob SDry WJun
– 'Boryana'	EPla ISta LBam MUlv SBam SDry WJun
– 'Han-chiku'	WJun
– var. ***henonis***	EPla ISta LBam SArc SBam SDry WJun
– 'Megurochiku'	EPla SBam SDry WJun
– f. ***punctata***	EPla ISta SBam SDry WJun
nuda	EPla SBam SDry
– ***localis***	SBam SDry
propinqua	SBam WJun
purpurata	See P. ***heteroclada***
rubicunda	WJun
rubromarginata	EPla SBam SDry
¶ ***stimulosa***	WJun
sulphurea 'Houzeau'	SBam SDry
– 'Robert Young'	ISta SBam SDry WJun
– 'Sulphurea'	See P. ***bambusoïdes*** 'Allgold'
– var. ***viridis***	EFul SBam SDry

-- 'Mitis' ISta SBam SCob
violascens EPla ISta SBam SDry WJun
viridiglaucescens CGre CHEx EFul EPla ISta LBam SArc SBam SCob SDry WJun
vivax EPla SBam SDry WJun
¶- 'Aureocaulis' SDry

X PHYLLOTHAMNUS (Ericaceae)

erectus ECar EPot GDra GGGa MHig NHar WAbe WPat

PHYMOSIA (Malvaceae)

§ *umbellata* CBot CGre

PHYODINA See CALLISIA

PHYSALIS (Solanaceae)

alkekengi WOak
- var. *franchetii* CB&S CKel CPar CSco ECED ELan ENot EPla LAbb LWad MBri MFir NBar NBro NFai NRoo SHer SPer WHal WHil WPer WTyr WWin WWye
-- 'Gigantea' CSco NNor
-- 'Variegata' IBlr MUlv

PHYSARIA (Cruciferae)

¶*alpestris* MFos
¶*floribunda* WDav

PHYSOCARPUS (Rosaceae)

capitatus EMon
opulifolius EBre EGol LBre NSal
- 'Dart's Gold' CCla CSco EBre EFol EGol EHoe ENot IJoh IOrc LBre MBar MBri MWat NBar NNor SPer SPla SSpi SSta WAbe WDin WSHC WWin
§- 'Luteus' CB&S CBot CPle CSam ELan ENot ISea MBar MGos MRav NHol NNor NRoo SLon SPer WBod WDin WRus WSHC
ribesifolius 'Aureus' See P. ***opulifolius*** 'Luteus'

PHYSOCHLAINA (Solanaceae)

orientalis NSal

PHYSOPLEXIS (Campanulaceae)

§ *comosa* EPad GArf MCas NHol SIng SPou WDav WHoo

PHYSOSTEGIA (Labiatae)

angustifolia ECro
§ *virginiana* CTom EBar ECro GCHN LGan NRoo NSal SSvw WByw
- 'Alba' CChu CGle CRiv CSam EBre ECro LBre MSte NOrc NRoo WEas WHil
*- 'Crown of Snow' CBow CHal CPar EBar ECro ECtt ESma LWad NHol NMir SPla WCot WHil WPer
¶- dwarf form ECha
- 'Galadriel' EMon LRHS
- pale pink form EFou LGan
- 'Red Beauty' CBow WRus
- 'Rosea' CB&S CBow MBel WPer
*- 'Snow Queen' MWat NVic
- ssp. *speciosa* EMon
-- 'Bouquet Rose' ('Rose Bouquet') CBow CHan CPar EBre ECED ECha EMar LBre MBri MFir MRav MSte NCat NKay NMir SChu SFis WHal WHoo WRus
§-- 'Variegata' Widely available
- 'Summer Snow' CB&S CCla CKel CSco ECha EFou EGol ELan ENot EOrc LHop MBel MBri MFir NHol SHer SPer WHal WHoo WOld WRus WWin
- 'Summer Spire' CKel ECha ECro ELan EPla MSte NHol NKay SPer
- 'Vivid' CGle CMGP CRDP CSam CSco EBre ECED ECha ECro EFou ELan LBre MBro MRav MWat NHol NOak SChu SDix SHer SPer SUsu WEas WHoo WWin

PHYTEUMA (Campanulaceae)

balbisii See P. ***cordatum***
betonicifolium ESma WPer
charmelii WPer WThi
comosum See PHYSOPLEXIS ***comosa***
§ *cordatum* EBar NBir
halleri See P. ***ovatum***
hemisphaericum MTho WPer
humile NNrd NWCA SHer
nigrum CLew CRiv NCat SHer WCru WHoo WPer WThi
orbiculare ECar MBro WCru WDav WHoo WPer
scheuchzeri CNic CRDP CRiv ECar ECha EFol ELan ESis LGan MBro NCat NHol NKay SBla SFis SHer WCru WDav WPer WThi
sieberi GDra NBir
spicatum WPer WWye
¶- *caeruleum* WPer
tenerum CKin GAbr

PHYTOLACCA (Phytolaccaceae)

acinosa EBar IBlr NSal SFis
§ *americana* CArn CCla CHEx CRDP CSev EBar ECha ELan EMar GPoy IBlr LHol MChe NSal SIde SSpi WByw WEas WOld WPer WWye
clavigera See P. ***polyandra***
decandra See P. ***americana***
§ *polyandra* ECha GCHN GWht LHol NBro NHex SAxl WWye

PICEA † (Pinaceae)

§ *abies* CPer EHar EHul ENot GRei IDai ISea LBuc MBar MBri MGos NBee NRoo NWea SLim WDin WMou WThu
- 'Acrocona' CDoC EBre EHar EHul LBre LCon LPan MBar MBri MGos MPla NHol SHil SLim SSta
- 'Argenteospica' (v) EBre LBre LCon MAsh NHol
- 'Aurea' LLin LPan SLim
- 'Aurea Magnifica' LCon
- 'Capitata' CKen GAri LCon MBar
*- 'Cinderella' MBri
- 'Clanbrassiliana' CKen LCon MBar
¶- 'Columnaris' EBre GAri LBre
- 'Compacta' LBee
*- 'Congesta' CKen

Plant	Suppliers
– 'Crippsii'	CKen
– 'Cruenta'	CKen
– 'Cupressina'	CKen
– 'Diffusa'	CKen LCon MBar WAbe
– 'Dumosa'	WAbe
– 'Elegans'	LCon MBar
– 'Ellwangeriana'	LCon
– 'Excelsa'	See P. ***abies***
– 'Finedonensis'	LCon NHol
– 'Formanek'	CKen EBre EPot LBre LLin
¶ – 'Four Winds'	CAbP
– 'Frohburg'	CDoC ENHC GAri IBar LCon MBar MBri MGos NHol SLim
I – 'Frohburg Prostrata'	LCon
– 'Globosa'	LCon MBar WStI
– 'Globosa Nana'	MGos
– 'Gregoryana'	CDoC CKen LCon MBar MBri MPla MWat NHar NHol WAbe
¶ – 'Gregoryana Veitchii'	LCon
– 'Inversa'	CDoC EHul ENHC GAri IJoh IOrc LCon LPan MBar SHil SLim
– 'Kamon'	LCon
– 'Little Gem'	CDoC CKen CMac EHul ENHC LBee LCon LLin MBar MBri MGos MPla MWat NHar NHol SLim WAbe WThu
– 'Maxwellii'	CMHG EHul LCon MBar MGos NHar
– 'Merkii'	GAri WAbe
– 'Nana'	LCon MBar
– 'Nana Compacta'	CKen EHul ESis MBar SLim WAbe
– 'Nidiformis'	CDoC CKen CMac EBre EHul ENHC ENot GRei IJoh IOrc LBre LCon LLin MBal MBar MBri MGos MPla MWat NHar NRoo NWea SHBN SLim SLon SPer SPla WDin WStI
– 'Norrkoping'	CKen
– 'Ohlendorffii'	CKen EHul ENHC LCon MBar MBri MPla MWat NHar NHol NRoo SHBN SLim WDin WStI
– 'Pachyphylla'	CKen
– 'Pendula Major'	SHBN
– 'Procumbens'	LCon MBar
– 'Pseudomaxwellii'	LCon NHol
– 'Pumila'	IDai
– 'Pumila Nigra'	CMac EHul LCon LLin MBar MGos MPla NHar SLim WAbe
– 'Pygmaea'	CKen GDra LCon MBar MGos MPla NHol SLim WAbe
– 'Pyramidata'	MBar
– 'Reflexa'	EHul LLin WThu
– 'Remontii'	LPan NWea
– 'Repens'	LCon MBar MBlu MGos NBee
¶ – 'Rydal'	LCon
– 'Saint James'	CKen NHol
– 'Saint Mary's Broom'	CKen
– 'Tabuliformis'	MBar
– 'Veitchii'	See P. ***a.*** 'Gregoryana Veitchii'
– 'Waugh'	LCon MBar
– 'Wills Zwerg' ('Will's Dwarf')	MBri
§ ***alcockiana***	LCon MBri
– 'Prostrata'	LCon MBal MBar NHol
asperata	LCon
* – 'Blue Sky'	LCon
balfouriana	MBri NHol
bicolor	See P. ***alcockiana***

Plant	Suppliers
brachytyla	LCon WCoo
breweriana	Widely available
engelmannii	EBre LBre MBar NWea
– f. ***glauca***	EHar EHul LCon SSta
glauca	NWea
– 'Alberta Globe'	CDoC CSco EBar EBre EHul ENHC EPot GRei IJoh LBee LBre LCon LLin MBar MBri MGos MPla NBee NHar NHol NRoo SLim WAbe WDin
– var. ***albertiana*** 'Conica'	Widely available
– 'Caerulea'	LCon MBar
– 'Echiniformis'	CKen EHul EPot GAri IJoh LBee LCon LLin MBal MBar MBri MWat NHar WDin
– 'Gnome'	CKen LCon
– 'Laurin'	CDoC CKen EBre LBee LBre LCon LLin MAsh MBri NHar SSta WAbe
– 'Lilliput'	EPot LCon MBar MBri SIng WAbe
– 'Nana'	CKen
– 'Piccolo'	CDoC CKen LLin SLim
– 'Sander's Blue'	CKen
– 'Tiny'	CKen EHul LCon MBar WAbe
– 'Zuckerhut'	LCon
glehnii 'Sasanosei'	CKen
– 'Shimezusei'	CKen
– 'Yatsubusa'	LCon
jezoensis	GAri LCon MBri MGos
– var. ***hondoensis***	EHar WNor
– – 'Mrs Cesarini'	CKen
koraiensis	See P. ***koyamae***
kosteri 'Glauca'	See P. ***pungens*** 'Koster'
§ ***koyamae***	CGre CLnd LCon STre WHCr WThu
likiangensis	CGre LCon MBal WWat
– var. ***balfouriana***	See P. ***b.***
– var. ***purpurea***	See P. ***p.***
mariana	LCon NWea WCoo
¶ – 'Aureovariegata'	LCon
– 'Doumetii'	LCon
– 'Ericoides'	GAri LCon MPla NHol
– 'Fastigiata'	CKen
– 'Nana'	CBra CKen CMHG CMac CSco EBlo EHar EHul ENHC ESis GDra IDai LCon LLin LNet MBar MBri MGos MPla MWat NHol SIng SLim SPer SSta WDin WThu
x ***mariorika***	MBar
– 'Machala'	CDoC
meyeri	EArb
omorika	CDoC CMCN CSco EHar ENHC ENot GRei IDai IJoh LBuc LCon LNet MBal MBar MBri MGos NWea SMad SPer SReu WCoo WDin WMou
– 'Nana'	CMac EHar ENHC GAri LBee LCon LNet MBar MBri NHol SEng SHil SLim
– 'Pendula'	EHar EHul IOrc LCon MBar MBri SHBN SHil SSta
– 'Pimoko'	CKen LCon MBri
– 'Treblitzsch'	CKen
orientalis	CMCN LCon MBal NWea SHil WCoo
§ – 'Aurea'	CBra CDoC CMac EHar EHul ELan ENHC IJoh IOrc LCon LLin LPan MBar MBri NHol SHBN SLim WThu
– 'Aureospicata'	See P. ***o.*** 'Aurea'

¶– 'Bergman's Gem'	CKen
– 'Early Gold'	EBre LBre NHol SSta
– 'Gowdy'	MBar NHol
– 'Gracilis'	LCon
– Hatch's WB No.2	CKen
– 'Kenwith'	CKen
– 'Pendula'	MGos
– 'Skylands'	CKen LCon MGos SLim
*– 'Wittbold'	EBlo LCon MAsh
pungens	MBar NWea WDin WNor
– 'Endtz'	CKen EBre LBre LLin
– 'Erich Frahm'	CDoC EBre EHar ENHC GAri LBee LBre LCon MAsh MBri SLim
¶– 'Fat Albert'	MBrk
– 'Glauca Globosa'	See P. ***p.*** 'Globosa'
– Glauca Group	CBra CDoC CSam EHul GRei IBar LBee LPan MBal MBar NBee NWea SReu WDin WMou WStI
N– 'Glauca Pendula'	NBee
– 'Glauca Procumbens'	EHar LNet NHol
§– 'Glauca Prostrata'	CKen CMac EBre EHul LBre MAsh MBal SLim SSta
– 'Globe'	CKen NHol
§– 'Globosa'	Widely available
I – 'Globosa Viridis'	EHul
– 'Gloria'	CKen LCon
– 'Hoopsii'	Widely available
– 'Hoto'	CMac EBre EHul ENHC IOrc LBee LBre LCon MBar SSta
¶– 'Hunneywelliana'	LLin MAsh
– 'Iseli Fastigiate'	MAsh
§– 'Koster'	CBra CDoC CMac CPMA EBre EHar EHul ENHC ENot GRei IJoh IOrc LBre LCon LLin LNet LPan MBar MGos NWea SLim SMad SPer SReu SSta WDin WStI
– 'Koster Prostrate'	MBal NHol
– 'Lucky Strike'	CKen EBre LBre LCon MAsh MGos
– 'Moerheimii'	CBra CMac EBre EHul LBre LCon LNet MBar MGos
– 'Montgomery'	CKen LCon LLin MBar NHol
– 'Procumbens'	EBre LBre LCon SHil SRms
– 'Prostrata'	See P. ***p.*** 'Glauca Prostrata'
– 'Saint Mary's Broom'	CKen
– 'Thomsen'	CKen LCon MAsh MBal MBri SLim
– 'Thuem'	LCon LLin
purpurea	CMCN LCon MBri
rubens	GAri WCoo
schrenkiana	CMCN LCon
sitchensis	CPer EBre GRei IDai LBre LBuc LCon MGos NWea WMou
♦– 'Papoose'	See P. ***s.*** 'Tenas'
– 'Strypemonde'	CKen
§– 'Tenas'	EBlo EBre LBre LCon MAsh NHol
smithiana	EHar GAri IBar ISea LCon MBal MBar MBri SLim WCoo

PICRASMA (Simaroubaceae)

§ ***ailanthoïdes***	CMCN SHil
♦***quassioïdes***	See P. ***ailanthoïdes***

PICRIS (Compositae)

echioïdes	CKin

PIERIS † (Ericaceae)

'Bert Chandler'	CCla CTrh ELan SPer SSpi
'Brouwer's Beauty'	SSpi
'Flaming Silver' (v)	CB&S CBra CHig CKni COtt CPMA CSam EBre ECar EHoe ELan GGGa IHos IJoh IOrc LBre MBar MBri MGos NHol SEng SExb SHBN SMad SReu WAbe WBod WPat WWeb
floribunda	IDai IOrc MBal MBar SPer
'Forest Flame'	Widely available
formosa	CHig CTrh
– var. ***forrestii***	CDoC CSco CTre CTrw ENot GRei IBar IJoh ISea MPlt NWea SExb WAbe WWeb
– – 'Charles Michael'	CB&S CLan
– – 'Fota Pink'	WSHC
– – 'Jermyns'	CB&S GWht IOrc MBal SExb SHBN SSpi
– – 'Wakehurst'	CB&S CBra CCla CHig CLan CTrh EBre ECar ERav IBar IOrc LBre LHyd MBal MRav NKay SArc SExb SLon SPer SReu SSpi WBod WPat WWeb
'Havila'	CPMA IOrc LTil MBal MBri MGos NHol SGil SHer
japonica	CB&S CHig CLan CTrh CTrw GGGa MBal MBar MGos NHol NWea SArc SExb SReu WBod WDin WWeb
– 'Bisbee Dwarf'	CTrh GGGa MAsh NHol WPat WThu
– 'Blush'	CCla CHig NHol SHBN WSHC
– 'Cavatine'	CMHG GWht
§– 'Christmas Cheer'	CCla CTrh IOrc MBal MGos NHol NKay NWyt SHer WDin
– 'Coleman'	CMHG
– 'Compact Crimson'	GGGa LRHS MBal
– 'Compacta'	NHol
– 'Cupido'	MBar MGos
– 'Daisen'	CLan CTrw NHol SPer
¶– 'Daisy Hill'	IDai
§– 'Debutante'	CHig ELan GGGa MAsh MPla SExb SPer SSpi WStI WWat
– 'Don'	EPla
– 'Dorothy Wyckoff'	CB&S CDoC CMHG CTrw EBre IDai LBre NHol SHBN SHer SPer SSta
– 'Firecrest'	CB&S CBra CCla CHig CMHG CTrh ECar EGol IDai IOrc LAbb MBal MBri MPlt NHol NRoo SGil SHer SSpi WAbe WWeb
– 'Flaming Star'	SPer
– 'Flamingo'	CB&S CBra CCla CHig CPMA CTrw LTil MBal MBar MGos NHol SHil SPer SReu SSta WAbe WPat
¶– 'Glenroy Pink Plenty'	MBal
– 'Grayswood'	CGre CMHG CSam EBre IBar IOrc LBre LTil MBri MPlt SSpi
– 'Green Pillar'	LRHS
– 'Hino Crimson'	CB&S CHig
– 'Kakashima'	WSHC
– 'Little Heath' (v)	CBra CCla CHig CMHG CRiv CTrh EBar EBre ECar EHoe EPla GCHN GGGa IOrc LBre LTil MBar MBri MGos MHig NHol SExb SPer SReu SSpi SSta WAbe WBod WPat WWeb
– 'Little Heath Green'	CGre CHig CMHG CTrh EBre ECar EPla GAri GGGa LBre LHyd MBar MBri NHar NHol SEng SPer SSta

– 'Minor' EPla MAsh NHol WPat WThu
– 'Mountain Fire' CB&S CBra CMHG CPMA CSco CTrh EBre ECar GCHN GRei IBar IDai IOrc LBre LTil MBal MBar MBri MGos NHol NJap SExb SHBN SReu SSta WPat WWeb
– 'Pink Delight' CAbP CB&S CBra IBar LTil MBal MBar MGos MPla MRav NHol NKay SHBN SHer SPer SSpi WPat WThu
– pink form NHol SExb
– 'Prelude' GCHN MAsh MBri MRav MUlv NHol WPat WThu
– 'Purity' CB&S CHig CMHG CTrh GWht IDai IOrc MBal MBar MGos MPlt NHol NJap NTow SExb SPer SReu SSta WBod WDin WPat WStI
– 'Pygmaea' CTrh GDra IDai MBal NHol WPat WSHC WThu
– 'Red Mill' CAbP CDoC CSco GGGa MAsh NHol SExb SPer SSpi
– 'Robinswood' SSpi SSta
¶ – 'Rosamund' IDai
– 'Rosea' LHyd
– 'Sarabande' GGGa MAsh MBri MGos NHol SHer WPat
– 'Scarlett O'Hara' CB&S IBar MGos SExb SSta
– 'Select' IDai MGos
¶ – 'Silver Sword' CSco
– 'Snowdrift' CGre GCHN MSta SPer
– 'Spring Candy' CB&S MGos
– Taiwanensis Group CCla CHig CMHG CSco CTre ENot GCHN GRei IDai IOrc LHyd MBal MBar MPlt MRav NWea SLon SPer SSta WAbe WPat WWat WWeb
– 'Tickled Pink' CB&S
– 'Tilford' CCla CHig MBal MBri NHar NHol SHer SSta WWeb
– 'Valley Rose' CBra CDoC CSam CTrh ECar ENot GCHN IDai MAsh MBal MGos NHol SExb SSpi WStI
– 'Valley Valentine' COtt ECar LRHS MBal MBri MGos SHer SReu SSpi SSta
§ – 'Variegata' Widely available
– 'Wada's Pink' See P. *j.* 'Christmas Cheer'
– 'Weeping Bride' LRHS
– 'Weeping Groom' LRHS
– 'White Caps' CHig CTrh MBal
– 'White Cascade' CTrh WWat
– 'White Pearl' CAbP IDai IJoh LTil MBal MBri MGos SHer SSta
– 'White Rim' See P. *j.* 'Variegata'
– 'William Buchanan' ECar MAsh MHig MUlv NHol WPat WThu
nana GArf GAri MBal MBar WThu
– 'Redshank' MBal
ryukuensis 'Temple Bells' CB&S IBar
yakushimensis CMHG

PILEA (Urticaceae)

* 'Anette' CHal MBri
cadierei MBri SLMG
– 'Minima' CHal SLMG
depressa CHal
involucrata 'Norfolk' CHal
microphylla CHal
nummulariifolia MBri
peperomioïdes CSev EPad
repens MBri
'Silver Tree' CHal

PILEOSTEGIA (Hydrangeaceae)

viburnoïdes CB&S CChu CCla CGre CHEx CLan CMac CTrw EHar ELan IDai LHop SArc SBra SDix SHBN SHil SLon SPer SSpi SSta WBod WPat WSHC WWat

PILGERODENDRON (Cupressaceae)

See Plant Deletions

PILOSELLA (Compositae)

§ ***aurantiaca*** CCor CFis CNic CRiv CRow CTom CWGN EBar EFol ELan MFir MHew NLan NOrc NRya NSal NSti SIng SSmi WCla WEas WHer WNdy WPer
§ – ssp. ***carpathicola*** MWil
§ ***officinarum*** CKin CRow MWil WGwy WNdy WPer
§ ***stoloniflora*** CRow

PILULARIA (Marsileaceae)

globulifera CNat

PIMELEA (Thymelaeaceae)

arenaria ECou WCru
¶ ***argentea*** LGre
coarctata See P. ***prostrata***
filiformis ECou WCru
§ ***prostrata*** CNic ECou GArf MBar MFir MHig NHar NHol SHer SIng WAbe WCru WHil WOMN WPat WPer WThu
– f. ***parvifolia*** ECou WCru
suteri ECou WCru

PIMPINELLA (Umbelliferae)

anisum CArn GPoy IEde LHol MChe MHew NSal SIde WPer
¶ ***flahaultii*** CBos
major 'Rosea' CHan CRDP ECha EFol EMon MPar NSti SAxl SPla SUsu WCot WEas
minima rosea SBar
saxifraga LHol

PINELLIA (Araceae)

cordata EPot SPou
pedatisecta CRDP MRav SAxl
§ ***pinnatisecta*** CMon
ternata CMon CRDP EPar EPot SIng WCru WOld WThu WWye
tripartita See P. ***pinnatisecta***

PINGUICULA † (Lentibulariaceae)

agnata EFEx WMEx
¶ ***alpina*** EFEx
caerulea WMEx
cyclosecta MSte WMEx
ehlersiae EFEx MSte
esseriana EFEx WMEx

grandiflora	CPar CRDP CRiv EFEx EPot NHar NKay NMen NRya NWCA WMEx WThu
gypsicola	WMEx
ionantha	WMEx
'Kewensis'	EFEx WMEx
laueana	EFEx WMEx
¶ *lusitanica*	WMEx
lutea	WMEx
macrophylla	EFEx WMEx
moranensis alba	EFEx WMEx
– var. *caudata*	EFEx MSte WMEx
– *flos-mulionis*	WMEx
– var. *mexicana*	EFEx WMEx
¶ – *moreana*	EFEx
– *morelia*	EFEx WMEx
¶ – *superba*	EFEx
¶ *oblongiloba*	EFEx
¶ *orchidioïdes*	EFEx
planifolia	WMEx
primulifolia	EFEx
¶ *rosea*	WMEx
¶ *rotundifolia*	EFEx
'Sargent'	WMEx
'Sethos'	EFEx WMEx
vulgaris	EFEx WMEx
'Weser'	EFEx WMEx
¶ *zecheri*	EFEx

PINUS † (Pinaceae)

albicaulis 'Nana'	See P. *a.* 'Noble's Dwarf'
§ – 'Noble's Dwarf'	CKen
N *aristata*	CAbP CDoC CKen CMCN EBre EHar EHul IBar LBre LCon LLin LTil MAsh MBal MBar MBri MGos NHol SEng SHil SReu SSta STre WCoo WMou WThu
– 'Cecilia'	CKen
– 'Sherwood's Compact'	CKen LCon
armandii	CChu CGre LCon WCoo
austriaca	See P. ***nigra nigra***
N *ayacahuite*	SLim
– var. *veitchii*	LCon
banksiana	EHul LCon MBal STre
– 'Chippewa'	CKen
I – 'Compacta'	CKen
– 'Manomet'	CKen
– 'Neponset'	CKen LCon
– 'Wisconsin'	CKen
brutia	LCon WCoo
bungeana	CAbb CGre CKen CLnd CMCN EHar EHul LCon LLin LTil MBal MBlu SHil WFro
canariensis	EHul
cembra	CDoC EHar EHul ENHC LBee LCon MBal MBar NWea
– 'Aurea'	See P. *c.* 'Aureovariegata'
§ – 'Aureovariegata'	CKen EHar LCon
– 'Barnhourie'	CKen
– 'Blue Mound'	CKen
– 'Chalet'	CKen
– 'Compacta Glauca'	LCon
– 'Glauca'	NHol
* – 'Griffithii'	WDin
– 'Inverleith'	CBra CKen EBre LBre MBri
– 'Jermyns'	CKen
– 'King's Dwarf'	CKen
– *nana*	See P. ***pumila*** 'Nana'
– 'Roughills'	CKen
– *sibirica*	LCon
– 'Stricta'	CKen
– Witches' broom	CKen
cembroïdes	EHar
contorta	CB&S CDoC CPer EBre GRei LBre LCon MBal MBar MGos NWea SEng STre WDin WMou
¶ – 'Asher'	CKen
¶ – 'Frisian Gold'	EBre LBre
– ssp. *latifolia*	CLnd MBal
– 'Spaan's Dwarf'	CKen EBre LBre LCon LLin MBar MBri MGos NHol SLim
corsicana	See P. ***nigra maritima***
coulteri	CAbb CMCN EHar LCon MBal SHil SMad WCoo WNor
densiflora	CDoC CMCN EHul ENHC GAri LCon MBal WNor
– 'Alice Verkade'	LCon LLin MBri SLim
– 'Aurea'	LCon MBar MGos SLim
– 'Jane Kluis'	CKen MBri
– 'Oculus Draconis'	CDoC LCon MBar SHil SLim
– 'Pendula'	CKen LLin MBal SLim
¶ – 'Pygmy'	CKen
– 'Umbraculifera'	CDoC EBre EHul IOrc LBre LCon LLin MBar MBri MGos NHar NHol SLim SSta
edulis	LCon
flexilis	LCon MBal
– 'Firmament'	LCon LLin MBri
– 'Glenmore Dwarf'	CKen
– 'Nana'	CKen
¶ – 'Pendula'	MAsh
– WB No. 2	CKen
gerardiana	EHar LCon MBal
griffithii	See P. ***wallichiana***
¶ *hartwegii*	LCon MUlv
heldreichii 'Aureospicata'	LCon MBar
– 'Compact Gem'	CDoC CKen EBre IOrc LBre LCon LLin MBar MBri MGos NHar SLim SSta
¶ – 'Groen'	CKen
§ – var. *leucodermis*	CMac COtt EHar LCon LNet LPan MBal MBar WDin
¶ – 'Malinki'	CKen
– 'Pygmy'	CKen
– 'Satellit'	CDoC CSco EBre ENHC IOrc LBee LBre LCon LLin MBri SEng SLim
– 'Schmidtii'	CKen EBlo LCon LLin MAsh MBar MBri SHil SLim
jeffreyi	CLnd EHar ISea LCon MBal MBar WFro
¶ – 'Joppi'	CKen
koraiensis	CMCN LCon MBal NWea WNor
– 'Bergman'	CKen
– 'Compacta Glauca'	SHil
– 'Dragon Eye'	CKen
– 'Jim Corbit'	CKen
– 'Shibamichi'	CKen
– 'Silver Lining'	LCon MAsh
– 'Silveray'	CKen
– 'Winton'	CKen
lambertiana	LCon
leucodermis	See P. ***heldreichii leucodermis***
magnifica	See P. ***montezumae***
monophylla	CKen EHar MBal SEng

Plant	Suppliers
§ ***montezumae***	CAbb CB&S CChu CGre CHEx CMCN ESma IOrc ISea LCon LLin MUlv NWyt SArc SHil SLim WBod WCoo
monticola	CLnd LCon NWea
– 'Pendula'	MBar
♦– 'Pygmy'	See P. *m.* 'Raraflora'
§ – 'Raraflora'	CKen
– 'Skyline'	MBar MBri
¶ – 'Windsor Dwarf'	CKen
mugo	CB&S CBra EHul ENot GRei MBal MBar MBri MGos WDin WStI
– 'Brownie'	LCon
– 'Carsten's Wintergold'	See P. *m.* 'Winter Gold'
– 'Corley's Mat'	CKen EBre LBre LCon LLin MAsh SLim SSta
– 'Gnom'	CKen CMac EHul IJoh LCon LLin MBar MBri NBar NBee SLim WDin WWat
– 'Humpy'	CKen EBlo EBre ENHC GAri LBee LBre LCon LLin MAsh MBri NHar SLim
– 'Jacobsen'	CKen
– 'Kissen'	CKen LCon MAsh NHol
– 'Knapenburg'	LCon
– 'Kobold'	LCon NHol
¶ – 'Krauskopj'	CKen
¶ – 'Laarheide'	NHar
– 'March'	CKen LCon NHol
– 'Minikin'	MAsh
– 'Mops'	CDoC CMac CSco EBre EHar EHul ENHC IDai IHos LBee LBre LCon LLin LPan MBar MBri MGos NHar NHol SLim SPer SSta
¶ – var. ***mughus***	LPan
– var. ***mugo***	GRei LCon MBar
¶ – 'Mumpitz'	CKen
– 'Ophir'	CKen CSco EBlo EBre EHar EHul ENHC IOrc LBee LBre LCon LLin LNet MBar MBri MGos NHar NHol SEng SLim SSta WDin
– 'Pal Maleter'	LCon MAsh MBri
– var. ***prostrata***	See P. ***m. uncinata***
– var. ***pumilio***	CDoC CMac EHul ENot GRei IOrc LCon LLin MBar MBro MGos NWea SHBN SPer STre WNor
– 'Spaan'	CKen
§ – var. ***uncinata***	CLnd GRei LCon NWea
¶ – 'White Tip'	CKen
§ – 'Winter Gold'	CKen EBre EHul IOrc LBee LBre LCon MAsh NHar SSta
– 'Zundert'	CKen LCon MBar MBri MGos NHar
muricata	CAbP CDoC CLnd LCon MBal MGos WCoo
nigra	CB&S CDoC CKin CSco ENHC ENot GRei IJoh LBuc LCon LNet MBar MGos NWea SHBN SPer WMou
– var. ***austriaca***	See P. ***nigra nigra***
– 'Black Prince'	CKen LLin SLim
– 'Bright Eyes'	CKen EHul LCon LLin NHar SLim
N– 'Cebennensis Nana'	CKen
– ***corsicana***	See P. ***n. maritima***
– 'Géant de Suisse'	WMou
– 'Hornibrookiana'	CKen EBre LBre MAsh NHol SHil SSta
– ssp. ***laricio***	See P. ***n. maritima***
§ – var. ***maritima***	CDoC CKen CKin CPer CSco ENot GRei IHos LBuc MBri NWea SMad WMou
– – 'Aurea'	WMou
¶ – – 'Bobby McGregor'	CKen LLin
– – 'Globosa Viridis'	GAri NHol
¶ – – 'Goldfinger'	CKen
§ – – 'Moseri'	CKen GAri LCon MAsh MBri NHar SHil SLim SSta
¶ – – 'Pygmaea'	CKen SLim
– – 'Spingarn'	CKen
– – 'Talland Bay'	CKen
– – 'Wurstle'	CKen
– 'Nana'	MBri
§ – var. ***nigra***	LPan MBri NWea WStI
– – 'Bright Eyes'	CKen
– – 'Helga'	CKen
– – 'Schovenhorst'	CKen
– – 'Strypemonde'	CKen
– – 'Yaffle Hill'	CKen
I – 'Semeriana'	LCon
palustris	LCon LLin MAsh WCoo
parviflora	GAri LCon NWea STre WCoo WDin WNor
– 'Adcock's Dwarf'	CKen GAri LCon MAsh NHol SLim
– 'Al Fordham'	CKen
– 'Aoi'	CKen
– 'Azuma-goyo'	CKen
I – 'Baasch's Form'	CKen
– 'Bergman'	LCon MAsh MBar
– 'Bonny Bergman'	CKen
– 'Brevifolia'	GAri
– 'Daiho'	CKen
– 'Daisetsuzan'	CKen
– 'Fukai Seedling'	CKen
– 'Fukushima-goyo'	CKen
¶ – 'Fuku-ju'	CKen
– 'Gimborn's Pyramid'	NHol
– 'Glauca'	CDoC CMac EHul ENHC GAri IHos IOrc LCon LLin MBar MBri WDin
– 'Goykusen Seedling'	CKen
– 'Goyokusui'	CKen
¶ – 'Go-ko-haku'	CKen
– 'Gyokkesen'	CKen
– 'Gyokuei'	CKen
– 'Gyokukan'	CKen
– 'Hagaromo Seedling'	CKen
– 'Hakko'	CKen
– 'Ibokan'	CKen
– 'Ichinose'	CKen
– 'Irifune'	CKen
– 'Janome'	CKen
¶ – 'Kanzan'	CKen
– 'Kiyomatsu'	CKen
– 'Kobe'	CKen
– 'Kokonde'	CKen
– 'Kokonoe'	CKen
– 'Kokuho'	CKen NHol
– 'Koraku'	CKen
– 'Meiko'	CKen MAsh
– 'Michi-noku'	CKen
¶ – 'Nasu'	CKen
– 'Negishi'	CKen GAri LCon MAsh MBal MBlu MBri
– 'Ogonjanome'	CKen
– 'Ryokuho'	CKen

– 'Ryuju'	CKen
¶ – 'Sanbo'	CKen
– 'Saphir'	LCon
– 'Setsugekka'	CKen
– 'Shikishima'	CKen
– 'Shizakagoten'	CKen
¶ – 'Shure'	CKen
– 'Tempelhof'	ENHC GAri LNet MBri SLim
patula	CAbb CGre CSam CTre GAri ISea LCon MBal MBlu SArc SHil SIgm WCoo WWat
peuce	LCon MBar NWea STre WFro
– 'Arnold Dwarf'	CKen
pinaster	CB&S CDoC CLnd EHul LCon MBal
¶ – 'Hamiltonii'	SIng
pinea	CHEx CKen CMac EHar IOrc LCon LPan MGos SArc WNor
– 'Queensway'	CKen
ponderosa	EHar ISea LCon LPan NWea SIgm WCoo
¶ ***pseudostrobus***	CGre MBal
pumila 'Buchanan'	CKen
– 'Draijer's Dwarf'	SLim
– 'Dwarf Blue'	See P. *p.* 'Glauca'
§ – 'Glauca'	CKen IDai LCon LLin LNet MBri NHar NHol
– 'Globe'	MAsh MBar MBri
– 'Knightshayes'	CKen
– 'Säntis'	CDoC CKen EBre LBre LCon
– 'Saphir'	CKen EBre LBre MBri
radiata	CB&S CDoC CGre CHEx CPer CSco CTre CTrw EBre ENot IHos IOrc ISea LBre MBal SArc SHBN SLim WDin
– 'Aurea'	CKen EBre LBre LCon MAsh SLim
– 'Marshwood'	CKen
resinosa 'Joel's Broom'	CKen
– 'Nobska'	CKen
– 'Quinobequin'	CKen
– 'Watnong'	CKen
rigida	EHul LCon
roxburghii	CMCN ISea
¶ ***sabineana***	LCon
x ***schwerinii***	CDoC LCon
sibirica	See P. ***cembra s.***
strobiformis	LCon
strobus	CCor CDoC CSco EHul GAri GRei IOrc ISea LCon MBar NWea STre
§ – 'Alba'	NHol SHil
– 'Amelia's Dwarf'	CKen
¶ – 'Anna Fiele'	CKen
– 'Bergman's Mini'	CKen
I – 'Bergman's Sport of Prostrata '	CKen
– 'Blue Shag'	CKen LLin MBri MGos SLim
– 'Contorta'	SMad
– 'Densa'	CKen EBre LBre LCon
¶ – 'Dove's Dwarf'	CKen
– 'Fastigiata'	CKen LLin
– 'Hillside Gem'	CKen EBre LBre
– 'Horsford'	CKen
– 'Jericho'	CKen EBre LBre
– 'Krügers Liliput'	CKen EBre LBre LCon MAsh MBri SLim
– 'Merrimack'	CKen
– 'Minima'	CDoC CKen LCon MAsh MBar MBlu MBri NHar NHol SLim
– 'Minuta'	CKen
– 'Nana'	See P. *s.* 'Radiata'
– 'Nivea'	See P. *s.* 'Alba'
– 'Northway Broom'	CKen LLin
§ – 'Radiata'	EBre EHul ENHC IHos IOrc LBee LBre LCon LLin LNet MBri NBee NHar NHol SLim
I – 'Radiata Aurea'	LCon
– 'Reinshaus'	CKen EBre LBre MAsh
– 'Sea Urchin'	CKen
– 'Uncatena'	CKen
– 'Verkade's Broom'	CKen
sylvestris	CB&S CBra CDoC CKin CPer CSco EHar EHul ENot GRei IHos LBuc LCon MBal MBar MBri MGos NBee NWea SHBN SPer SReu WDin WMou WNor WStI
– 'Andorra'	CKen
§ – 'Argentea'	EHar LNet SHil
– 'Aurea'	CKen CMac CSco EBlo EBre EHar EHul IOrc LBre LCon LLin LNet MBal MBar NHol SHBN SHil SLim SSta
– 'Beuvronensis'	CKen CMac EHar GAri LCon LLin LNet MBlu MBri MGos NHol SLim SSta
– 'Bonna'	LCon
– 'Brevifolia'	LCon MBar NHol
¶ – 'Buchanans Gold'	CKen
– 'Burghfield'	CKen LCon
– 'Chantry Blue'	LCon LLin MAsh MBar NHar NHol SLim
– 'Compressa'	GAri
– 'Dereham'	CKen
– 'Doone Valley'	CKen
♦– 'Edwin Hillier'	See P. *s.* 'Argentea'
– 'Fastigiata'	CDoC CKen EBlo EHar LCon LLin MAsh MBar MBri NHar SLim SSta
– 'Frensham'	CKen LCon LLin MAsh
– 'Gold Coin'	CBra CKen LCon LLin MBar MBri MGos SLim
¶ – 'Gold Medal '	CKen
¶ – 'Goldfinger'	LLin
¶ – 'Grand Rapids'	CKen
– 'Green Flare'	CKen
– 'Hibernia'	ENHC
– 'Hillside Creeper'	CKen SLim
– 'Inverleith'	GAri LCon LLin MAsh MBar MGos NHol SLim
– 'Jade'	See P. *s.* 'Iceni'
– 'Jeremy'	CKen LLin
¶ – 'Kelpie'	CKen
– 'Kenwith'	CKen
– 'Little Brolly'	CKen
– 'Lodge Hill'	CKen LCon MAsh MBar SLim
¶ – 'Longmoor'	CKen
– 'Martham'	CKen
♦– 'Moseri'	See P. ***nigra maritima*** 'M.'
– 'Nana'	See P. *s.* 'Watereri'
– 'Pixie'	CKen LCon
– 'Repens'	CKen
– 'Sandringham'	LCon NHol
– 'Saxatilis'	LCon NHol
*– 'Sei'	LRHS
– 'Sentinel'	CKen
I – 'Skjak I'	CKen
I – 'Skjak II'	CKen

– 'Spaan's Slow Column'	CKen
– 'Tabuliformis'	CMCN
– 'Tage'	CKen
– 'Treasure'	CKen LCon
– 'Variegata'	NHol
§ – 'Watereri'	CDoC CMac EHul ENHC ENot IDai IHos IOrc LBee LCon LLin LNet LPan MBar MBri MGos NBar NHar NHol SLim SPer SSta WDin
tabuliformis	CLnd EHul LCon
taeda	WCoo
thunbergii	CDoC CGre EHar EHul LCon LLin MBal MBar MGos STre WCoo WFro WNor
¶ – 'Akame'	CKen
– 'Banshoho'	CKen
¶ – 'Dainagon'	CKen
¶ – 'Iwai'	CKen
– 'Kotobuki'	CKen
¶ – 'Ko-yo-sho'	CKen
– 'Kujaku'	CKen
¶ – 'Nishiki-nee'	CKen
§ – 'Sayonara'	CKen EBre GAri LBre LCon MAsh NHol
– 'Senryu'	CKen
– 'Shio-guro'	CKen
– 'Sunsho'	CKen
¶ – 'Taihei'	CKen
– 'Yatsubusa'	See P. ***t.*** 'Sayonara'
uncinata	See P. ***mugo u.***
¶ – 'Paradekissen'	CKen
virginiana	MBal
– 'Wate's Golden'	CKen
§ ***wallichiana***	CAbP CChu CDoC CKen CMCN CSco EHar EHul ENHC GRei IBar IOrc LCon LLin MBal MBar MGos NBee NHol SEng SLim WCoo WMou
– 'Nana'	CKen MBar SHil
– 'Umbraculifera'	MBal SLim
– 'Zebrina' (v)	LCon MAsh MBar
yunnanensis	LCon

PIPER (Piperaceae)

See Plant Deletions

PIPTANTHUS (Leguminosae)

♦***forrestii***	See P. ***nepalensis***
laburnifolius	See P. ***nepalensis***
§ ***nepalensis***	Widely available
¶ ***tomentosus***	SDry

PISONIA (Nyctaginaceae)

brunoniana	See P. ***umbellifera***
§ ***umbellifera***	CHEx
– 'Variegata'	CHEx

PISTACIA (Anacardiaceae)

chinensis	CB&S EHar ELan

PISTIA (Araceae)

stratiotes	CBen MSta

PITTOSPORUM † (Pittosporaceae)

anomalum	ECou SDry
bicolor	ECar ECou
colensoi	WHCr
crassifolium	CB&S ECou SHil
– x ***tenuifolium***	ECou
– 'Variegatum'	CGre LHop SHil
dallii	CHEx SArc SHil
divaricatum	ECou
eugenioïdes	CB&S CGre MFir
– 'Variegatum'	CB&S CGre EBre IOrc LBre SHil
'Garnettii' (v)	CB&S CBot CBra CCla CDec CLan CMHG CPle CSco CShe CTrw EBre EHoe ELan ENot IBlr IJoh IOrc LBre MBal SLon SPer WAbe WBod WDin WSHC WWat
'Limelight' (v)	CB&S CGre
§ 'Margaret Turnbull' (v)	CB&S COtt ECou IReg LHop
michiei	ECou
* ***molvocata***	CHan
obcordatum var. ***kaitaiaense***	ECou
omeiense	SArc
patulum	SArc
phillyreoïdes	CPle
pimeleoïdes	ECou
ralphii	ECou IBlr
– 'Green Globe'	ECar ECou
– 'Variegatum'	SLon SSpi
'Saundersii' (v)	CGre CKni CMHG ENot MBal
tenuifolium	CB&S CBar CBra CPle CSco CShe EBre ECou ELan ENot IDai ISea LBre LHop MBal MBri MUlv NTow SChu SDix SLon SReu WAbe WDin WOMN WStI WWat
– 'Abbotsbury Gold' (v)	CAbb CBot CCla CDoC CSam EBre ELan LBre NRoo SDry SHBN SHer SPer WSHC WStI WWeb
– 'Arundel Green'	LRHS SDry
– 'Atropurpureum'	CB&S CSco
– 'County Park Dwarf'	ECou
– 'Deborah' (v)	CB&S CBra EBre LBre LHop
– 'Dixie'	CMHG ECou
§ – 'Eila Keightley' (v)	CDoC CMHG IOrc MBal
¶ – 'Gold Star'	CB&S
– 'Golden King'	CB&S CDoC CMHG IJoh MBal MRav MUlv
– 'Irene Paterson' (v)	CAbb CB&S CCla CGre CMHG CSam CSco EBre ELan IJoh IOrc LBre LHop MBal MGos MRav MUlv SDry SHer SLon SPer SSta WAbe
– 'James Stirling'	CDoC IOrc SLon
– 'John Flanagan'	See P. 'Margaret Turnbull'
– 'Marjory Channon' (v)	CB&S MUlv
– 'Nigricans'	CB&S CLan CMHG GWht
¶ – 'Nutty's Leprechaun'	IMal
– 'Purpureum'	CBot CBra CMHG CPle CSam CTrw ELan IJoh IOrc ISea MBal MRav SDry SHBN SHer SPer SPla WDin WSHC
* – 'Silver Dollar'	MBri
– 'Silver Magic'	CB&S
§ – 'Silver Queen' (v)	CB&S CBar CBra CCla CDoC CGre CLan CMHG CSam CSco CTrw EBre EPla GWht IBar IDai IJoh IOrc LBre MBal MRav NKay NTow SHBN SPer SPla WBod WKif WSHC WStI
– 'Stirling Gold' (v)	CB&S
– 'Sunburst'	See P. ***t.*** 'Eila Keightley'

¶– 'Tiki'	CB&S
– 'Tom Thumb'	CB&S CMHG CTrw EBre ECou ECtt EHoe IBar IJoh IOrc IReg LBre LHop MBal MPla MUlv NRoo SDry SHBN SPer SPla SSta WAbe WStI WWat
♦– 'Tresederi'	See P. *t.* 'Silver Queen'
– 'Warnham Gold'	CB&S CDoC CMHG COtt CSco CTrw EBre EPla IOrc ISea LBre MUlv SDry SSpi WAbe WDin WWat
– 'Wendle Channon' (v)	CB&S CBra CCla CDoC CMHG CSam EBre IJoh LBre MBal MUlv SHer SPer WStI WWeb
– 'Winter Sunshine'	SSta
'Tenuifolium Variegatum'	CB&S
tobira	CB&S CBot CCla CHEx CHan CMCN CMHG CPle CTro IJoh MGos MNew SArc SBor SEng SHBN SHil SPer SSpi SSta WEas
– 'Nanum'	CB&S ERea MUlv WSHC
– 'Variegatum'	CB&S CBot CDoC CGre CHEx CPle ERea LHop MBri SEng SHil SPer SSta
undulatum	CAbb CB&S CHEx CPle
– 'Variegatum'	CGre

PITYROGRAMMA (Adiantaceae)

See Plant Deletions

PLAGIANTHUS (Malvaceae)

betulinus	See P. ***regius***
lyallii	See HOHERIA ***lyallii***
§ *regius*	ECou ISea SHil
– var. *chathamicus*	IReg

PLAGIOMNIUM (moss)

¶ *affine*	LFle

PLANERA (Ulmaceae)

See Plant Deletions

PLANTAGO (Plantaginaceae)

asiatica 'Variegata'	EHoe ELan EMon NSti WByw WHer
coronopus	CKin
cynops	EMon LRHS MTho WCot
lanceolata 'Streaker' (v)	CRow
major B&L 12649	EMon GPoy
¶– B&L 12649	CRDP
– 'Atropurpurea'	See P. *m.* 'Rubrifolia'
§ – 'Rosularis'	CArn CFis CGle CHal CRDP CRiv CRow CTom CWGN ECha ECro ELan EMon LHol MFir MTho NBro NFai NMir NSti WBon WHal WHer WHil WRus WWye
§ – 'Rubrifolia'	CFis CGle CRDP CRiv CRow CSFH CTom EBar ECha EHoe ELan EMar EMon GAbr LHol MFir MPar NBro NFai NHar NMir NRed NSti SFis WHal WHer
– 'Variegata'	CRDP CRiv CRow ECro EFol LHol NRoo
maritima	CKin
media	CKin WNdy
nivalis	CLew EPot MFir NMir WDav WHer WThu
psyllium	NSal
raoulii	NHol
rosea	See P. ***major*** 'Rosularis'
sempervirens	ECro WHer

PLATANUS † (Platanaceae)

× *acerifolia*	See P. × ***hispanica***
§ × *hispanica*	CB&S CDoC CGre CKin CLnd CSco CTho EHar ENot IDai IJoh LBuc LPan MGos NWea SHBN SPer WDin WMou
¶– 'Bloodgood'	WMou
¶– 'Liberty'	WMou
– 'Suttneri' (v)	CDoC CTho SHil SMad WMou
occidentalis	WCoo
orientalis	CBow CLnd CMCN CSto EBre EHar IOrc LBre SMad SSpi WCoo WMou
¶– 'Autumn Glory'	WMou
§ – f. *digitata*	CLnd CTho SHil SMad SSpi
– var. *insularis*	EHar
– 'Laciniata'	See P. ***o. digitata***
– 'Mirkovec'	CDoC IJoh MBri SFai WMou
wrightii	WCoo

PLATYCARYA (Juglandaceae)

strobilacea	CB&S CGre CMCN EArb WMou
– MSF 804	SSpi

PLATYCERIUM (Polypodiaceae)

alcicorne hort.	See P. ***bifurcatum***
§ *bifurcatum*	MBri
grande hort.	See P. ***superbum***

PLATYCLADUS (Cupressaceae)

orientalis	See THUJA ***o.***

PLATYCODON † (Campanulaceae)

grandiflorus	CGle CNic CSco CWGN ECha EPad LHop MFir MHew NBee NBro NFai NKay NNor NOrc NSal NWyt SAxl SFis SUsu WCla WCru WDav WHoo WOld WWye
– *albus*	CBow CCla CSco CSun ECro EFou ELan EPad LAbb LWad MBri MBro NFai NOak NTow SPer SSvw WHoo WPer WWin
– *apoyama*	CNic EPad ESma MBro MCas MHig NKay SWas WAbe WHoo WPer
– – *albus*	ECro LGre SAxl SWas WCru WEas
– 'Baby Blue'	ECro
– blue	CBow ECro LAbb
– 'Blue Pearl'	WHoo
– 'Blue Surf'	SFis SSvw WPer
– double blue	ECro
– 'Flore Pleno'	CNic
– 'Florist Rose'	EPad MWil NOak
– 'Florist Snow'	LGan NOak
– 'Fuji Pink'	NHol WDav WHil
– 'Fuji White'	NHol WHil
– 'Hakone'	ECro LHop WHil
– 'Mammoth Blue'	ECro
– 'Mammoth White'	ECro

– ***mariesii***	CCla CGle CHad CKel CNic CPar EBre ECtt EFou ELan EMar ENot EPad LBre MBal MBro MFir MHig NHol SDix SFis SGil SPer SSvw WEas WHoo WOMN WPer WTyr WWin
– – ***albus***	CNic GCal MBro WOMN
– 'Misato Purple'	NHol
– 'Park's Double Blue'	LGan NOak SMrm WHer WHoo
– 'Perlmutterschale' ('Mother of Pearl')	CGle EBre ECro ELan EPad LBre MBri NSti
– ***pumilus***	GArf NWCA WMar
– ***roseus***	CSun ECro EFou WHoo
– 'Zwerg'	LGre

PLECOSTACHYS (Compositae)

§ ***serpyllifolia***	CCla CFis CHal CSun IHos LAbb LBlm SDix

PLECTOCOLEA (liverwort)

¶ ***hyalina***	LFle

PLECTRANTHUS (Labiatae)

australis	CHal SLMG
♦***behrii***	See P. ***fruticosus***
♦***coleoïdes*** 'Marginatus'	See P. ***forsteri*** 'M.'
♦– 'Variegatus'	See P. ***madagascariensis*** 'Variegated Mintleaf'
§ ***forsteri*** 'Marginatus'	CBar CHal ERea ESma LHil MRav NFai SIde SLMG WHal
§ ***fruticosus***	SLMG
¶ ***madagascariensis*** 'Variegated Mintleaf'	CHal
oertendahlii	CHal EBak SLMG
§ ***thyrsoideus***	CHal

PLEIOBLASTUS † (Gramineae(Bambuseae))

akebono	SBam SDry
§ ***auricomus***	Widely available
– 'Bracken Hill'	EPla ISta SBam SDry WJun
– f. ***chrysophyllus***	EPla SBam SDry WJun
§ ***chino***	EPla IJoh ISta LBam SBam SDry WJun
§ – f. ***angustifolius***	EPla ISta LBam SBam SDry
– 'Aureostriatus' (v)	EPla ISta SBam SDry
– ***chrysanthus***	See SASA ***chrysantha***
– f. ***elegantissimus***	EPla SBam SDry WJun
¶ – 'Kimmei'	SDry
– 'Murakamianus'	SBam SDry
fortunei	See P. ***variegatus***
'Gauntlettii'	See P. ***humilis pumilus***
glaber 'Albostriata' (v)	See SASAELLA ***masamuneana*** 'Albostriata'
gramineus	EPla ISta SBam SDry WJun
§ ***hindsii*** hort.	EPla ISta SArc SBam SDry SHil WJun
§ ***humilis***	ELan SBam SHil
§ – var. ***pumilus***	CRow CSco CTom EHoe ELan EPar EPla ISea ISta LBam MBlu MBri NHol NSel SArc SBam SCob SDry SHil WJun WNor WPat
kongosanensis 'Aureostriatus' (v)	EPla SBam SDry
linearis	EPla ISta SBam SDry WJun
¶ ***oleosus***	SDry WJun
§ ***pygmaeus***	CB&S CBar CCla CLew CRow CWit EFul EHoe ELan EPla IOrc ISea ISta MBar MBri MGos NSel SBam SCob SDry SHil SIng SPer WJun
§ – var. ***distichus***	EFul EPla ISta LBam SArc SBam SCob SDry WJun
§ – 'Mirrezuzume'	EPla SBam WWat
shibuyanus 'Tsuboi'	EPla SDry
§ ***simonii***	CHEx EFul ISta LBam SBam SCob SDry SHil
– var. ***heterophyllus***	See P. ***s. variegatus***
§ – ***variegatus***	EPla ISta LBam MBlu SBam SDry SPer WJun
§ ***variegatus***	CB&S CBra CElw CKel ECha EFul EGol EHoe ELan ENot EPar EPla ETPC GCal LBam LHop MBal MBri MGos NJap NNrd NSel SArc SBam SCob SDry WCot WJun WPat WRus
– var. ***viridis***	SDry
viridistriatus	See P. ***auricomus***

PLEIONE † (Orchidaceae)

§ ***albiflora***	WChr
¶ Alishan	SWes
¶ 'Asama'	SWes
aurita	WChr
¶ 'Berapi'	SWes
§ ***bulbocodioïdes***	IBlr NHol
– 'Yunnan'	CRDP
bulbocodioïdes Limprichtii Group	CBro CRiv EFEx NTow SWes WAbe
– – 'Primrose Peach'	CBro SWes
bulbocodioïdes Pricei Group	See P. ***formosana***
x ***confusa***	WChr
¶ Danan	SWes
Eiger	CBro
¶ El Pico	SWes
¶ Erebus	SWes
Etna	SWes WAbe
§ ***formosana***	CAvo CBro CNic CRDP CRiv EFEx ELan IBlr LAma MBri NHar NHol NTow SDeJ SHer SIng WAbe WChr
I – 'Alba'	CAvo CBro IBlr NWCA
– 'Avalanche'	CBro
– 'Cairngorm'	CBro
– 'Clare'	CAvo CBro WAbe
I – 'Iris'	NNrd WAbe
– 'Lilac Beauty'	SWes WAbe
– 'Lilac Jubilee'	CBro
¶ – 'Oriental Grace'	EFEx NHol SWes
– 'Oriental Jewel'	CBro SWes
– 'Oriental Splendour'	SIng SWes WAbe
– 'Polar Star'	WAbe
– Pricei Group	CNic MCas NTow
¶ – 'Ruby Throat'	CNic
– 'Serenity'	WAbe
– 'Snow Cap'	EFEx NHol SWes
– 'Snow White'	WAbe
forrestii	CRDP EFEx LAma NHol SWes WChr
Fuego	SWes
Hekla	SWes
humilis	SDeJ
Jorullo	SWes

¶ Katla	SWes
¶ *maculata*	SWes
¶ 'Myosin'	SWes
pinkepankii	See P. ***albiflora***
pogonioïdes hort.	See P. ***speciosa***
♦– Rolfe	See P. ***bulbocodioïdes***
praecox	SWes
¶ Shantung 'Piton'	LAma
– 'Ridgeway'	CAvo WAbe
§ *speciosa*	CAvo SWes
Tarawera	SWes WAbe
Tolima	SWes
Versailles	CBro EFEx LAma SWes
– 'Bucklebury'	SWes WAbe
– 'Muriel Turner'	CBro LAma SWes WAbe
Vesuvius	CBro
yunnanensis hort.	See P. ***bulbocodioïdes*** 'Yunnan'
– Rolfe	LAma NHol NTow SWes

PLEOMELE See DRACAENA

PLEUROCHAETE (moss)

¶ *luteoalba*	LFle

PLEUROSPERMUM (Umbelliferae)

brunonis	CBos WHal

PLUM See PRUNUS *domestica*

PLUMBAGO (Plumbaginaceae)

§ *auriculata*	CB&S CHal CPle CSun CTre CTro EBak EEls ELan ERav ERea LAbb LBlm LHol LHop MBri MNew MRav NEgg NPal NRog SIde SLMG SLon WBod WEas
– var. *alba*	CB&S CBot CBow CHal CSun CTro EBak ELan ERav ERea IBlr LAbb LBlm LHol MNew SHer SLMG
capensis	See P. ***auriculata***
indica	CPle SLMG
– *rosea*	CHal CTro LAbb MNew
larpentiae	See CERATOSTIGMA ***plumbaginoïdes***
zeylanica	CPle

PLUMERIA (Apocynaceae)

forms	MNew
§ *obtusa*	MNew
rubra	CTro MNew SLMG
'Singapore'	See P. ***obtusa***

PNEUMATOPTERIS See CYCLOSORUS

POA (Gramineae)

acicularifolia	NHol
alpina	NLan
araratica	ETPC
badensis 'Ingelkissen'	ETPC
buchananii	EHoe
¶ *bulbosa*	ETPC
chaixii	CElw EHoe EMon EPla ETPC
colensoi	EHoe ETPC WDav
¶ *glauca*	ETPC
imbecilla	ETPC
x *jemtlandica*	NHol
nemoralis	ETPC

PODALYRIA (Leguminosae)

¶ *calyptrata*	CTro

PODANTHUS (Compositae)

¶ *ovatifolius* G&K 4386	CGre

PODOCARPUS (Podocarpaceae)

acutifolius	ECou GWht STre
andinus	See PRUMNOPITYS ***andina***
chilinus	See P. ***salignus***
cunninghamii	See P. ***hallii***
dacrydioïdes	See DACRYCARPUS ***d.***
ferrugineus	See PRUMNOPITYS ***ferruginea***
'Golden Dwarf'	See PRUMNOPITYS ***ferruginea*** 'G.D.'
§ *hallii*	ECou IBar WBod WThu
¶ – x *nivalis*	ECou
¶ – 'Roro' (m)	ECou
lawrencei (f)	ECou MBar MGos MPla SSmi WWat
¶ – 'Alpine Lass' (f)	ECou
¶ – x ***acutifolius*** 'Autumn Shades'	ECou
lawrencei alpinus	CDoC EHul GAri IOrc MBar SBor
– – 'Blue Gem' (f)	MAsh MBri MGos WWat
– – 'Bluey'	CDoC LLin SLim
¶ – x ***nivalis*** 'Blaze'	ECou
¶ – – 'Spring Sunshine'	ECou
¶ – – 'Young Rusty' (f)	ECou
macrophyllus	CGre CMCN SArc SMad WWat
– 'Angustifolius'	CHEx
nivalis (f)	CHal CMHG CMac CSco ECou EHar EPla GWht MBar MHig MPla SBor SLon SPer SSmi WThu WWat
– bronze	EPla MBri
– 'Clarence' (m)	ECou
– 'Green Queen' (f)	ECou
– 'Jack's Pass' (m)	ECou
– 'Little Lady' (f)	ECou
¶ – 'Livingstone' (f)	ECou
¶ – 'Lodestone' (m)	ECou
¶ – 'Moffatt' (f)	ECou
– 'Otari' (m)	ECou
– 'Park Cover'	ECou
– 'Princess' (f)	ECou
¶ – 'Ruapehu'	ECou
§ *salignus*	CB&S CChu CDoC CGre CHEx CLan CMer CPle IOrc ISea SArc WWat
spicatus	See PRUMNOPITYS ***taxifolia***
totara	CHEx CHan ECou STre
– 'Aureus'	CB&S ECou EPla MBal MBar MUlv SHBN WSHC
– 'Pendulus'	ECou

PODOLEPIS (Compositae)

¶ *jaceoïdes*	MHig

PODOPHYLLUM (Berberidaceae)

emodi	See P. ***hexandrum***
– var. ***chinense***	See P. ***hexandrum c***
§ ***hexandrum***	CChu CCla CHEx CRDP CRow ECha EFou ESis GAbr GCal GDra GPoy MBal MBri MHig MPar NHar NSal NSti SAxl SSpi WDav WPer
§ – var. ***chinensis***	LGre WCru WWat
– 'Majus'	NHol SHig
peltatum	EBre EBul ECro GPoy LAma LBre MBri NSal SSpi WChr WWat
versipelle	ECro

PODRANEA (Bignoniaceae)

§ ***ricasoliana***	CTro EMil ERea LHop LRHS MNew SLMG

POGONATHERUM (Gramineae)

paniceum	See P. ***saccharoideum***
saccharoïdeum	MBri

POGOSTEMON (Labiatae)

See Plant Deletions

POINSETTIA See EUPHORBIA *pulcherrima*

POLEMONIUM † (Polemoniaceae)

¶ ***acutifolium*** var. ***nipponicum***	WPer
¶ – – ***album***	WHil
'Apricot Beauty'	CChu ECro EMar ESma GAbr NBir NFai NOak WCot WThi
¶ 'Apricot Delight'	CBre ESis WHil
archibaldii	WCot
boreale	ECro GTou
brandegeei	ECro MHig NRed WDav WPer
¶ – JCA 9501	CNic
– ***mellitum***	GCHN
caeruleum	Widely available
– ***album***	CBre CChu CCla CFis CGle CHad CSco CShe EBar ECha EFol EFou ELan EOrc EPar GAbr LHop MPar NBro NNor NOak NSel SFis SPer SUsu WBon WCla WEas WWin
– ssp. ***amygdalinum*** 'Album'	NHol
– 'Blue Bell'	CGle NMir NNrd
– dwarf form	CNic
– Himalayan	GCra WPer
– 'Hopleys'	CHan ECha GCal LHop WByw WCot
¶ – 'Humile'	EMon LRHS
carneum	CChu CGle EBre ECha EMon EOrc LBre LHop LWad MNFA MPar MTho NHar SHer SUsu WOMN WPer WWin
cashmerianum	CChu CHan ECro EMon ESma GAbr GCHN NOak SFis SHer WEas WHen WHoo
'Churchills'	CBre CChu
♦ ***confertum***	See P. ***viscosum***
delicatum	MTho NHar NWCA
flavum	See P. ***foliosissimum flavum***
foliosissimum	CBot CCla CGle CHan CKel CSco EBre ECha EJud LBre MPar SCro WHen WKif WPer
– 'Album'	See P. ***f. alpinum***
§ – var. ***alpinum***	CMea ECro NBir
– ***flavum***	CHan GAbr MHig NBro SCro WHil
¶ 'Glebe Cottage Lilac'	CGle
x ***jacobaea***	WCot
pauciflorum	CCor CGle CMea CPar EFol ELan EOrc ESma LHop LWad MPar MTho NBir NOak SSvw SUsu WAbe WCla WEas WHal WHer WHil WOMN WPer WRus WWin
pulcherrimum	CBre CTom EBre ECro ELan EPla EPot ESma GAbr GCal LBre LHil NBro NHar NHol NRed WHen WHil WPer
– ssp. ***pulcherrimum***	NHol
– 'Tricolor'	NFai SFis WDav WPer
reptans	CArn CFis GPoy LHol MHew MTho NHar NSal WEas WPer WWye
– 'Blue Pearl'	CBow CBre CFis CGle CMGP CMea CPar CSco ECro EFol GAri NCat NRoo SIng SPer SUsu WByw WHen
– 'Dawn Flight'	EBre LBre NCat
– 'Lambrook Manor'	See P. ***r.*** 'Lambrook Mauve'
§ – 'Lambrook Mauve'	CBre CChu CGle CHan EBre ECha EFol EOrc GAbr GCal LBre MBro MNFA MSte MTho MUlv NTow SUsu SWas WDav WHoo WRus WSun
– 'Pink Beauty'	CMGP EFou ELan EMon GCal LRHS MTol NFai SChu SPer
x ***richardsonii***	CBow CMil NKay WEas
'Sapphire'	CBre CSco EFol ELan EMon MBel NNor
scopulinum	NHol WPer
¶ 'Sonia's Bluebell'	CGle
§ ***viscosum***	ESma GCHN LHil
yezoense	CCor CFis WGwy

POLIANTHES (Agavaceae)

geminiflora	LAma LBow
tuberosa	CB&S CKel NRog
– 'The Pearl' (d)	LAma SHer SLMG

POLIOTHYRSIS (Flacourtiaceae)

sinensis	CAbP CChu CMCN CPle SMad SSpi WWat

POLYGALA (Polygalaceae)

calcarea	MHig NHar NKay WOMN WPat
¶ – Bulley's form	LBee SIng
– 'Lillet'	ELan EPot LMer MCas MTho NHar SBar SIng SWas WPat WWin
chamaebuxus	CNic EBre ECar GDra GGGa LBre MBal MBro MHig MPla NHar NHol NKay NNrd SHer WDav WThu
– ***alba***	WAbe
§ – var. ***grandiflora***	CB&S CNic ELan EPar EPot GArf GDra GGGa LBee MBal MBar MBro MGos MHig MPla NHar NHol NKay NMen NWCA SBla SHBN SHil SIng WAbe WPat WSHC WThu WWin
– 'Kamniski'	CMHG EPot GGGa

– 'Loibl'	EPot GGGa MAsh MPlt SBla
– 'Purpurea'	See P. ***c. grandiflora***
– 'Rhodoptera'	See P. ***c. grandiflora***
§ x ***dalmaisiana***	CAbb CB&S CBar CDoC CSun ERea GAri SBla
'Dolomite'	GGGa
myrtifolia	CFis CPle CTre CTro IBlr LBlm SChu SMrm SUsu
– 'Grandiflora'	See P. x ***dalmaisiana***
virgata	CArn WBod
vulgaris	CKin IOrc

POLYGONATUM (Liliaceae/Convallariaceae)

§ ***biflorum***	CBro CChu CCla CPou EBre ELan GCHN LBre LWad NRoo NSal SMad WDav WHer
– dwarf form	WChr WCot
canaliculatum	See P. ***biflorum***
¶ ***cirrhifolium***	WCru
commutatum	See P. ***biflorum***
¶ ***curvistylum***	CRDP SWas
cyrtonema	See DISPOROPSIS ***pernyi***
§ ***falcatum***	CHan CPar CRDP CRiv CRow EBre EBul ECar ELan EMon ERav LBre MBal NOak SIng WAbe WThu WWin
– 'Variegatum'	CBos CChu CDoC CHad CMil CRDP ECha EFou ELan EPar LGre MBri NDea NHol NSti SBla SCro SSpi WRus
'Falcon'	See P. ***humile***
¶ ***geminiflorum***	SWas
giganteum	See P. ***biflorum***
graminifolium	EPot
§ ***hirtum***	EBul EMon EPla
hookeri	CBro CChu CCor CMea COtt CRDP EBul ECha EPla EPot GArf LGre MBal MCas MFir MHig MTho NGar NHar NHol NKay NNrd NRya NWCA SIng SWas WDav WEas WHil
§ ***humile***	CGle CRDP EPot MBel WCot WHal WRus
§ x ***hybridum***	Widely available
§ – 'Striatum' (v)	CAvo CBos CBot CCor CPou CRow EBre ECha EFol EPla IDai LBre MBal MBel MBri MHig MPar MRav MUlv NBar NFai NHar NOak NOrc NRoo SBla SGil SHer SSpi WHal
– 'Variegatum'	See P. x ***h.*** 'Striatum'
latifolium	See P. ***hirtum***
multiflorum hort.	See P. x ***hybridum***
– Linnaeus	EBul NHol WHil
– ***giganteum***	See P. ***biflorum***
§ ***odoratum***	CBro CRow EBul ECar EPar EPla EPot MPar NRya NSal SPou SSpi
– 'Flore Pleno'	MCas SPou
– 'Grace Barker'	See P. x ***hybridum*** 'Striatum'
¶ – Kew form	EPot
* – ***pluriflorum***	SSpi
* – 'Silver Wings' (v)	MPar SPou
N – 'Variegatum'	CBro CChu CCla CRDP EBul ECar EFol EGol ELun EOrc EPla LGan LGre MBal MCas MPar NRar NRoo NRya SPer SPla WCru WRus WWat WWin
officinale	See P. ***odoratum***
pumilum	See P. ***falcatum***
roseum	CRDP MPar WThu
sp. Ewlat	SPou
¶ sp. Himalaya	WCru
¶ sp. SS&W	CRDP
stewartianum	EBul
verticillatum	ECha EPla EPot MBal NHol WWat
– ***rubrum***	CArn EPla MSte MUlv SPou

POLYGONUM † (Polygonaceae)

	See also PERSICARIA
affine	See PERSICARIA ***affinis***
amplexicaule	See PERSICARIA ***amplexicaulis***
aubertii	See FALLOPIA ***baldschuanica***
baldschuanicum	See FALLOPIA ***baldschuanica***
bistorta	See PERSICARIA ***bistorta***
cuspidatum	See FALLOPIA ***japonica***
equisetiforme hort.	See P. ***scoparium***
polystachyum	See PERSICARIA ***wallichii***
reynoutria	See FALLOPIA ***japonica compacta***
§ ***scoparium***	CPar CRow EPla LHil MUlv NFai NSti SDry

POLYMNIA (Compositae)

See Plant Deletions

POLYPODIUM † (Polypodiaceae)

¶ 'Addison'	WHil
¶ ***aureum*** ruffled form	NMar
australe	See P. ***cambricum***
§ ***cambricum***	NHar NKay NMar SApp WCot WFib WRic
§ – 'Barrowii'	NKay NMar WRic
¶ – 'Cristatum'	WRic
– 'Oakley'	WAbe
¶ – 'Prestonii'	WRic
– 'Wilharris'	NKay WRic
¶ x ***font-queri***	WRic
glycyrrhiza 'Longicaudatum'	NMar
interjectum	NMar WFib WRic WWat
¶ ***malhattense***	NHar
x ***mantoniae***	NKay WRic
¶ ***scouleri***	NBro WRic
x ***shivasiae***	NKay WRic
vulgare	CBar CKin CWGN GPoy MBal NBro NEgg NHol NKay NMar NNrd NOrc SCob SPer WFib WRic
– 'Acutum'	NMar
– 'Bifidocristatum'	NHar NHol NKay NNrd SIng WFib WWat
– 'Bifidograndiceps'	NMar
§ – 'Congestum Cristatum'	NHar NKay SApp
– 'Cornubiense'	CBos CWGN ECha EMon EPla GCal NBir NBro NHar NHol NKay NMar NVic SPer SSpi WAbe WFib
– 'Cornubiense Multifidum'	NHar NKay
– 'Crispum Cristatum'	See P. ***v.*** 'Congestum Cristatum'
– Cristatum Group 'Forster'	NKay
– 'Elegantissimum'	NNrd

– 'Jean Taylor' See P. *v.* 'Congestum Cristatum'
– 'Longicaudatum' WFib
– 'Omnilacerum Oxford' WRic
– Pulcherrimum Addison' WRic
– Pulcherrimum Group EGol EPla NHar NKay
– Pulcherrimum Group 'Pulchritudine' WRic
– 'Pulcherrimum May' WRic
– Ramosum Group NMar
– 'Semilacerum Falcatum O'Kelly' NMar WRic
– Semilacerum Group WRic
– 'Semilacerum Jubilee' NMar WRic
– 'Semilacerum Robustum' WRic

POLYPOGON (Gramineae)

viridis ETPC

POLYSCIAS (Araliaceae)

'Elegans' MBri
fruticosa MBri
scutellaria 'Pennockii' (v) MBri

POLYSTICHUM † (Dryopteridaceae)

acrostichoïdes IOrc NMar
aculeatum CBar EBre EBul ECha EHon ELan IOrc LBre LWad MBri NHar NHol NKay SCob SRms SSpi WFib WRic
– Grandiceps Group NMar WFib
andersonii NHar NHol
braunii CB&S EGol WRic
caryotideum NMar WRic
§ ***falcatum*** CHEx CMil CRDP MBri NKay NOrc SSpi WOMN WRic WWat
– 'Rochfordianum' CRow WFib
falcinellum NKay
¶ ***fallax*** WRic
fortunei EBul EFou IOrc NHol NMar SApp SBla SIng SSpi WCot WFib WRic
¶ ***imbricans*** NHar
lonchitis NKay
makinoi NHol WCot
munitum IOrc NHar NHol NOrc WFib
polyblepharum CBar EBre ELan IOrc LBre MBri NHar NHol NMar SApp SBla SIng SRms SSpi WCot WFib WHal
proliferum hort. See P. ***setiferum*** Acutilobum Group
– (R.Br.) C. Presl. SApp
rigens NHar NHol NMar NNrd SMad WRic
§ ***setiferum*** CBar CKin CPar CSam CWGN EBre EFou EGol ELan IOrc LBre LWad MBri NEgg NHol NOrc SApp SArc SBla SCob SPer SSpi WBon WEas WFib WStI
§ – Acutilobum Group CB&S CRDP EBul ECha EPot GAri LWad MBal MPar NHar NKay SApp SCob SDix SMad SSpi WAbe WCot
– ***angulare*** See P. ***setiferum***
*– ***bulbosum*** SApp
– Congestum Group CRDP EPla IOrc MBri NHar NHol NKay NMar SApp SAxl SRms WFib WRic
– ***cristatogracile*** See P. ***s.*** Percristatum Group
– Cristatum Group SApp
– Dahlem Group ELan SCob
– Divisilobum Group CWGN EBre ELan EPar LBre MBri MBro NHol NKay NMar SMad SPer SPla SRms WBon WEas WFib WHoo WRic
– Divisilobum Group 'Divisilobum Densum' MBal MPar NMar NOrc
¶ – Divisilobum Group 'Divisilobum Grandiceps' WRic
– Divisilobum Group 'Divisilobum Iveryanum' NHol NMar SRms WFib
– Divisilobum Group 'Herrenhausen' EBre ELan LBre MBri NMar NOrc
– Divisilobum Group 'Mrs Goffy' NMar
– 'Foliosum' NKay
– 'Imbricatum' NKay
– Lineare Group NKay SApp
¶ – Multilobum Group WRic
§ – Percristatum Group NMar
– Perserratum Group NKay
– Plumosodivisilobum Group CMil EGol NHar SApp SDix SPla WAbe WCru
– Plumosodivisilobum Group 'Baldwinii' NMar
– Plumosum Group CBar CNic CSam CWGN NOrc WFib WStI
– ***proliferum*** See P. ***s.*** Acutilobum Group
– 'Pulcherrimum Bevis' NKay WRic
*– ***ramopinnatum*** NMar
*– ***ramulosum*** NMar
¶ – Revolvens Group WRic
¶ – 'Rotundatum' CRDP
N– 'Wollaston' NBar
¶ ***stenophyllum*** WRic
tsussimense CMil CRDP EFou MBri NHol NMar SIng SMad SMrm SRms WFib WRic
¶ ***yunnanense*** WRic

POLYXENA (Liliaceae/Hyacinthaceae)

♦ ***ensifolia*** See P. ***pygmaea***
odorata LBow
§ ***pygmaea*** LBow

POMADERRIS (Rhamnaceae)

¶ ***kumeraho*** LAbb

POMEGRANATE See PUNICA *granatum*

PONCIRUS (Rutaceae)

§ ***trifoliata*** CB&S CBra CChu CDoC CLan CMCN CTro ECtt EHar ELan ENot ERea IBar SArc SHil SMad SPer SSpi SSta STre WCru WDin WNor WPat WWat

PONTEDERIA (Pontederiaceae)

cordata	CBen CRDP CRiv CRow CWGN EBre ECha ECtt EHon ELan EMFW EWav LBre LMay MSta NDea SHig SWat WChe WHol
– *alba*	CRow EMFW NDea
§ – var. *lancifolia*	CRiv CRow EMFW MSta SRms SWat
¶ *dilatata*	CRDP SRms
lanceolata	See P. *cordata lancifolia*

POPULUS † (Salicaceae)

alba	CDoC CKin CLnd CPer EBre ENot GRei IDai LBre LBuc MBar MRav NWea SHBN SPer WDin WMou WStI WWin
– 'Bolleana'	See P. *a.* 'Pyramidalis'
§ – 'Pyramidalis'	CB&S CCor WMou
– 'Raket' ('Rocket')	CLnd CSco CTho EHar ELan ENot MGos SPer
– 'Richardii'	CBot CCla CGre CSco CTho CWit EBlo EBre ECtt EFol EHar EPla LBre MBar MUlv SHil SMad SPer SSpi WMou
§ 'Balsam Spire' (f)	CDoC CLnd ENot GRei LBuc NWea WMou
§ *balsamifera*	CDoC ELan ENot MGos NWea SHBN SPer SPla WDin
x *berolinensis*	CDoC
x *canadensis* 'Aurea' (v)	CDoC CLnd CSco ENot MRav SPer WDin WMou
– 'Eugenei' (m)	ENot WMou
– 'Robusta' (m)	CDoC CKin CLnd ENot LBuc NWea WDin WMou
– 'Serotina' (m)	CDoC CTho EHar GRei NWea WDin WMou
x *candicans*	WDin
– 'Aurora'	CB&S CCla CCor CKin CPle CSco CTre CTrw EBre EHar EHoe ELan ENot GRei IDai IJoh ISea LBre LBuc MBar MBri NBar NWea SHBN SMad SPer SReu SSta WDin
x *canescens*	CDoC ELan WDin WMou
– 'De Moffart' (m)	ENot
deltoïdes 'Cordata' (f)	CCor
x *euroamericana*	See P. x *canadensis*
lasiocarpa	EHar ELan ENot SHil SMad SPer
§ – var. *tibetica*	EHar WMou
nigra	EHar ELan ENot WDin WMou
– var. *betulifolia*	CKin CTho MGos
N– var. *italica*	CB&S CDoC CLnd CMHG CTho EBre ELan ENot LBre LBuc MBri MGos NWea SHBN SPer WDin
– 'Italica Aurea'	See P. 'Lombardy Gold'
§ – 'Lombardy Gold' (m)	ELan GRei LMer SMad SSpi WMou
– 'Pyramidalis'	See P. *n. italica*
¶ *simonii*	CTho
– 'Fastigiata'	CB&S
tacamahaca	See P. *balsamifera*
'Tacatricho 32'	See P. 'Balsam Spire'
tremula	CKin CLnd CPer EBre EHar ELan ENot GRei LBre LBuc MBar MBri NBee NWea SHBN SPer WDin WMou
§ – 'Erecta'	CLnd EHar WMou
– 'Fastigiata'	See P. *t.* 'Erecta'
– 'Pendula' (m)	CLnd EHar SHil WDin WMou
trichocarpa	EHar GRei SPer
– 'Fritzi Pauley' (f)	WMou
violascens	See P. *lasiocarpa tibetica*
wilsonii	WMou
yunnanensis	WMou

PORTULACA (Portulacaceae)

grandiflora	MBri
oleracea	CArn GPoy MChe SIde WHer WOMN WWye
¶ – *aurea*	MChe

POTAMOGETON (Potamogetonaceae)

crispus	CBen EHon EMFW SAWi SRms
¶ *pectinatus*	EHon SAWi

POTATO See SEED Supplier's Index

POTENTILLA † (Rosaceae)

alba	CGle CMil CNic CShe EBar ECha EFou ELan EMar GCHN ISea LGro MCas MNFA MRav MTho NHol NRoo NSti SAxl SCro SPer SUsu WByw WCra WPer WTyr
alchimilloïdes	CLew CTom MHig
¶ *alpicola*	WPer
ambigua	See P. *cuneata*
anserina	CArn CKin WHer
– 'Ortie'	CNat
I – 'Variegata'	WHer
¶ *anserinoïdes*	GCal
arbuscula D Don	See P. *fruticosa a.*
– hort.	See P. *fruticosa* 'Elizabeth'
argentea	EBar WCla WCru WPer
– 'Calabre'	EFol GAbr
– *glabra*	SIgm WWin
argyrophylla	See P. *atrosanguinea a.*
atrosanguinea	Widely available
§ – var. *argyrophylla*	CGle CHan CMHG ECro ELan GAbr GCal GTou LGan NBir NBro NFai NMir NOak NRed SCro SIng SUsu WAbe WByw WHal WHil WPer WTyr
– – SS&W 7768	GAbr GDra MPla MSte NGre
– var. *leucochroa*	See P. *a. argyrophylla*
aurea	CBow CLew ECtt ELan EMNN MBri MTho NMen NMir NOrc NWCA SHer SIng SSmi WWin
– 'Aurantiaca'	GCHN MRav NNrd NRoo SBod SHer SUsu
§ – ssp. *chrysocraspeda*	NHol NKay NMen NNrd NRoo
§ – 'Goldklumpen'	EFou EPla GAbr NBar SCro
– 'Plena'	CNic EMNN GCHN GDra GTou MRav NHar SBod SHer WWin
'Blazeaway'	CB&S MBri NCat
calabra	ECha EMar WByw WPer
§ *cinerea*	CLew CPar CRiv CShe CSpe CTom ELan MCas NHar NMen NNrd SIgm SSmi WAbe WDav
§ *crantzii*	CCor CMea CSun CTom ESis GCHN LBee LBlm MBar MCas MHig NMen NNrd NTow SIng WCla WPer WThu
– *nana*	WPer
– 'Pygmaea'	ECtt MPlt NHar
§ *cuneata*	CLew CNic CRiv CTom ELan EMNN ESis GDra GTou MHig MPla MTho NHar NKay NMen NWCA SIng SSmi WPer WWin
*– *aurea*	ECro
delavayi	MBro NHol

¶ ***detommasii*** WPer
dickinsii NTow
dombeyi GCHN NHol
* 'Emilie' GCal
§ ***erecta*** CArn CKin GPoy MChe MHew NSal
eriocarpa CNic EMNN ESis GCHN GDra LHil MBro MFir MHig MNFA MPla MWat NGre NHar NKay NMen NNrd NRed NRoo SBod SHer SSmi WAbe WCla WDav
'Etna' CElw CHad CHal CSco ECtt EJud ELan EMon GAbr GCal GCra GTou LGre NFai NNor WByw WDav WMer WPer
'Everest' See P. ***fruticosa*** 'Mount Everest'
'Fireflame' ECha
fissa CSun LBlm MBri
¶ 'Flambeau' WRus
'Flamenco' CB&S CHal CSam CSco ELan MBri MRav NCat NRoo WByw WCru WHoo WOld WTyr
fragiformis See P. ***megalantha***
fruticosa LAbb LBuc NHar NMen
– 'Abbotswood' CB&S CBot CMHG CMer CSco EBlo EGol EHar ENot GRei IDai IJoh LHop MBal MBar MBri MGos NHol NNor NRoo SPer WBod WDin WHCG WSHC WWat WWeb
– 'Abbotswood Silver' CB&S CBow CDoC CHal CMHG CPle CSco ECtt EFol ELan MRav NHol NMen SHer SPla WHCG WSHC WWat WWeb
– 'Annette' CDoC CSco WHCG
– var. ***arbuscula*** hort. See P. *f.* 'Elizabeth'
– – KW 5774 WWeb
– 'Argentea Nana' See P. *f.* 'Beesii'
– 'Barnbarroch' SIng
– 'Beanii' NHol SPer WWeb
§ – 'Beesii' CBot CBow CDoC CSco CShe EHar ELan EPla ESis IDai MBar MBri MPla NHol NKay NRoo SIng SPer WAbe WDin WHCG WPer WWat WWeb WWin
– 'Beverley Surprise' SPer WAbe WWeb
– 'Buttercup' WHCG WWeb
– 'Cascade' LHop
*– 'Chelsea Star' WHCG
– 'Clotted Cream' MBar
– 'Dart's Cream' MBri
– 'Dart's Golddigger' CB&S ECtt MBal NHol NRoo SLPl WHCG WWeb
– 'Dart's Nugget' WHCG
– var. ***davurica*** WHCG
– – 'Farrer's White' CSam
– – 'Hersii' See P. *f.* 'Snowflake'
– – 'Rhodocalyx' EMNN EPla MGos WHCG WWat
– 'Daydawn' Widely available
*– 'Donard Orange' NNor
– 'Eastleigh Cream' CCla SPer
§ – 'Elizabeth' Widely available
– 'Farreri' See P. *f.* 'Goldkugel'
– 'Floppy Disc' CBow CDoC ECtt ELan MGos SHBN
– 'Frances Lady Daresbury' ISea MPla WWeb
– 'Friedrichsenii' WWeb
– 'Glenroy Pinkie' EPla MBal WAbe WHCG
¶ – 'Glenroy Seashell' MBal
– 'Goldcharm' NKay
¶ – 'Golddigger' NSti
¶ – 'Golden Spreader' EBlo
– 'Goldfinger' CBow CDoC CMer EBre ELan ENot GRei IOrc LBre LHop MBri MGos MRav MWat SPla STre WAbe WDin WHCG WStI WWeb
§ – 'Goldkugel' ('Gold Drop') ENot NHol NNor SPla WHCG WStI WWeb
¶ – 'Goldrush' CSco
– 'Goldstar' CBot CDoC CMHG EBlo EBre EPla GAri GCHN IOrc LBre MBri MGos SIng SSta WHCG WPat WWeb
– 'Goldteppich' MBar NBar SHBN
– 'Goscote' MGos
– 'Hachmann's Gigant' WWeb
– 'Honey' WHCG
– 'Hopleys Little Joker' CMHG EMNN WPat WWin
– 'Hopleys Orange' CB&S CBow CDoC CSco EBlo EPla GAri GCHN LHop MBri SHer WHCG WPat WWin
– 'Hurstbourne' WWeb
– 'Jackman's Variety' CDoC CSam CSco ECtt ENot SPer WBod WDin WWeb
– 'Judith' WWeb
– 'Katherine Dykes' CBow CDoC CPle CSco ELan ENot GDra IDai MBal MBar NHol SLon SPer SReu WBod WDin WHCG WStI WWeb
– 'Klondike' CB&S CDoC CLan CSco ELan IDai MBar NNor NRoo NWea WAbe WBod WDin WWeb
– 'Knap Hill' ENot WWeb
*– 'Knap Hill Buttercup' ELan EPar GDra GRei MPit NNor SHer WWeb
– 'Kobold' MBar WWeb
– 'Logan' WWeb
– 'London Town' CMHG SLon
– 'Longacre Variety' CSco GDra GRei ISea MBar NWea SLPl SLon WBod WWat WWeb
– 'Maanelys' ('Moonlight') CPle CSco CTrw ECtt ELan MBal MWat NWea SPer WDin WHCG WWeb
§ – var. ***mandshurica*** 'Manchu' CCla CLew CMHG ELan ENot EPar GDra IDai MBar MBri MPla MRav NHol NNor SChu SHBN SIng SLon SPer SPla SSta WEas WPat WSHC WWat WWeb WWin
*– 'Medicine Wheel Mountain' EHal ELan NTow WHCG WPat WWeb
– 'Milkmaid' WWeb
§ – 'Mount Everest' CDoC CHal ELan MPla MWat NHol NWea WBod WHCG WWeb
– 'Nana Argentea' See P. ***fruticosa*** 'Beesii'
– 'Northman' WWeb
– 'Nugget' WWeb
– 'Ochroleuca' WWeb
– 'Orange Star' MPla NHol WWeb
– 'Orange Stripe' WWeb
– var. ***parvifolia*** EPla
– 'Pastel Pink' LHop
– 'Peaches and Cream' EPla WEas WWeb
– 'Perryhill' SPer
– 'Pink Glow' GDra
– 'Pink Pearl' EBlo EBre LBre NSti WWin

– 'Pretty Polly'	CBow CDoC CMHG COtt CSco EBre ELan IOrc LBre LHop MBar MBlu MBri MGos MPla MRav NHar NRoo SHBN SLon SPer SPla SSta WDin WPat WSHC WStI WWeb
– 'Primrose Beauty'	CBow CLan CPle CSco CShe CTre ELan ENot ISea MBal MBar MBri MGos MPla NNor NRoo SLon SMad WBod WDin WHCG WStI WWat WWeb
§ – 'Princess' ('Blink')	CBow CCla EBlo EBre EHar ELan GRei IJoh LBre MBal MBar MBri MGos MWat NHar NHol NRoo SMad SPer SReu WBod WDin WHCG WRus WStI WWat WWeb
– 'Prostrate Copper'	GAbr NHol
– *pumila* CC 312	GTou
¶ – 'Pumila'	MBro NHar WDav
– 'Red Ace'	CBra CMer CPle CSco EBlo EBre EHar ELan ENot GRei IJoh ISea LBre LHop MBar MBri MGos MWat NHar NHol NRoo SMad SPer SReu WBod WDin WHCG WWeb
– 'Red Robin'	EBlo EBre GCHN GRei LBre MBri MGos NBar SPer
– 'Royal Flush'	CBra CCla CPle GAri LHop MBar MBri SPer WHCG WStI
– 'Ruth'	SHil WWeb
– 'Sandved'	IDai WWeb
– 'Silver Schilling'	LHop
¶ – 'Snowbird'	EBlo
§ – 'Snowflake'	CB&S NHar WHCG WWeb
– 'Sophie's Blush'	CBow IBar ISea MBal NHol NRoo WSHC WWeb
– 'Sunset'	CB&S CBow CDoC CSam CSco ELan EMNN ENot GDra MBal MBar MBri MGos MPla MPlt NKay NNor NWea SPer SReu SSta WStI WWeb
– 'Tangerine'	CB&S CBow CBra CLan CPle CTre CTrw ELan ENot GRei IDai IJoh ISea MBal MBar MWat NHol NKay NRoo NWea SIng SLon SPer STre WAbe WDin WHCG WWat WWeb WWin
– 'Tilford Cream'	CBow CMHG CSco EBre ELan ENot GDra IJoh LBre MBar MBri MPla MRav MWat NHol NRoo SHBN SHer SPer SPla SReu WDin WHCG WStI WWat WWeb
– 'Tom Conway'	MUlv SMrm WHCG WPat
§ – 'Veitchii'	CBow CCla CDoC CPle CSco NHol SHBN SPer WHCG WStI WWeb
– 'Vilmoriniana'	CBow CHad CSco EFol ELan IDai NNor SChu SHil SIng SLon SMad SPer SSpi WAbe WHCG WSHC WWat WWeb
– 'Walton Park'	MBal WWeb
– 'Wessex Silver'	CDoC WHCG
– 'Whirlygig'	CPle WHCG
– 'White Rain'	CMer GDra NNor WWeb
– 'William Purdom'	WHCG WWeb
– 'Yellow Giant'	WWeb
– 'Yellow Star'	LHop
fulgens	EMon
gelida	See P. ***crantzii ternata***
'Gibson's Scarlet'	CBow CBre CCla CHad CKel CSam CSco ECha ECtt EFou ELan ELun GCal IDai MBri MFir NHar NHol NRoo SAxl SCro SPer WEas WHil WMer WRus WSHC WTyr WWat
¶ ***glandulosa***	MFir WPer
'Gloire de Nancy'	CBos ELan MRav NBir SPer
'Gold Clogs'	See P. ***aurea*** 'Goldklumpen'
¶ 'Grace Darling'	CWit
gracilis	CCor NNrd
– var. ***pulcherrima***	NHol
'Helen Jane'	CDoC CGle ESma NFai NHol WMer WPer
x ***hopwoodiana***	CBos CGle CHad MUlv NBir SWas WByw
hyparctica nana	LBee NHol WDav WPat
¶ ***lignosa***	WDav
* 'Limelight'	CKni ELan MAsh
'Mandshurica'	See P. ***fruticosa mandshurica*** 'Manchu'
¶ 'Master Floris'	GCal
§ ***megalantha***	Widely available
'Melton'	CBre CSco EFou EJud NBir NMir NOak WHen WHil
'Monsieur Rouillard'	CGle EBar GAbr MUlv MWat NHol NNor SUsu WByw WCru WHoo
montana	CTom GCHN NHol WHer WPer
nepalensis	CHan CNic CRDP CShe ECha ECro GAbr LAbb MFir NNor NSti SSvw WCru WHoo WWat
– 'Flammenspiel'	EFou
¶ – 'Kirsten'	MHig
§ – 'Miss Willmott'	Widely available
– 'Roxana'	CGle CKel CPar CSco CShe EBar ELan EOrc MFir MPar MRav NBro NFai SUsu WByw WCra WCru WOld
§ ***neumanniana***	MWat NTow WAbe WHil
¶ – ***aurea***	SRms
– 'Goldrausch'	ECha MBri
§ – 'Nana'	CHal CKel CLew CNic CSam ECro EMNN ESis GArf LHop MCas MHig MPla MWat NHar NHol NKay NMen NMir NNrd NRed NRoo SBla SIng WDav WEas WPer WWin
nevadensis	ESis NHol WPer WThu
nitida	NHar NHol NKay NMen SHer WDav
¶ – 'Alba'	EPot GArf
– 'Rubra'	CShe EFol EPot NBir NRoo NTow NWCA SBla SSmi WAbe WPat WWin
¶ ***nivalis***	GTou
nivea	NHol
* 'Olympic Mountains'	WPer
palustris	CRDP MSta WCla WGwy
¶ ***peduncularis***	EMon SUsu
¶ – C&Mc 532	GCHN
'Pink Panther'	See P. ***fruticosa*** 'Princess'
'Pyrenaica'	See P. ***fruticosa*** 'Farreri Prostrata'
recta	CHad CHan ELan GTou MHew MRav SIgm WDav WHil
¶ – 'Alba'	WPer
– 'Citrina'	See P. ***recta pallida***
– 'Macrantha'	See P. ***r.*** 'Warrenii'

§ – *pallida* CFis CGle CMil CSam EBar EPad ERav LHop MFir MUlv NCat NFai NSti SIgm SIng SSvw SUsu WBon WCra WHal WHoo WPer
– var. *sulphurea* See P. *r. pallida*
§ – 'Warrenii' CBow CPar CSam EBar ECro EPad GAbr LGan LHil MFir MPar MRav MWat NFai NMir NOrc NSti SIng SPer SSvw WCru WHal WHoo
reptans CKin
– 'Pleniflora' EMon
rupestris CCor CGle CNat ECha EMon MFir MNFA NHol NLan NRed NRoo NSti SSvw WByw WCla WDav WHal WHil WPer WSHC WWin
¶ *salesoviana* MFos
speciosa EPad LGre SUsu WDav WOMN
– var. *speciosa* MFir NRed NWCA
sterilis CKin ELan
– 'Turncoat' (v) EMon
'Sungold' ESis WHCG WThi
tabernaemontani See P. *neumanniana*
ternata See P. *aurea chrysocraspeda*
thurberi EPad LGre SAsh SAxl SMrm WKif
tommasiniana See P. *cinerea*
x *tonguei* CHad CKel CPar CShe ECha ECtt EFou ELan EMNN ESis GCHN GDra LHop MBal MBri MCas MRav NFai NHar NHol NKay NNrd NRoo SBla SIng SSmi WMer WWat WWin
tormentilla See P. *erecta*
tridentata See SIBBALDIOPSIS *tridentata*
verna See P. *neumanniana*
– *pygmaea* See P. *neumanniana nana*
'Versicolor Plena' GCal WCru
villosa See P. *crantzii*
* 'White Beauty' CKni
'Wickwar Trailer' CShe EPot MPla WHCG WSHC
'William Rollison' CB&S CKel CRDP CSam EBar ECro EFou ELan GAbr LHil MBri MRav NFai NHol NOrc NSti SChu SCro SPer SRms WCru WHil WRus WSHC
willmottiae See P. *nepalensis* 'Miss Willmott'
'Yellow Queen' CB&S CKel CPar CSco ELan LHil MRav NHol NRoo SCro SPer WMer WSun WTyr

POTERIUM See SANGUISORBA

PRATIA See LOBELIA

PRESLIA See MENTHA

PRIMULA † (Primulaceae)

acaulis See P. *vulgaris*
'Alan Robb' (D.Prim) EBre ECtt EFol EMNN GAbr LBre MBri MYat NHol NRoo SIng SPer WHal WHil WPbr
algida (11) CNic CPla NGre
allionii (2) EMNN EPot ITim LFox MBro MCas MHig NCra NHar NHol NNrd NRya SHer SIng WAbe WDav WHil WOMN WWin
– JCA 4161.21/2/3(2) EPot
¶ – KRW 61.404(2) WDav
– KW 1952/324(2) WDav
– W 1971(2) WDav
¶ – 'A K Wells' (2) EPot
– 'Adrian Jones' (2) NNrd
– var. *alba* (2) MCas MHig SIng WHil
– 'Anna Griffith' (2) EPot ITim MCas MHig NHol NNrd WAbe WThu
– 'Anne' (2) WDav
¶ – 'Apple Blossom' (2) NNrd WThu
– 'Austen' (2) EPot LFox MHig NHol SIng
– 'Avalanche' (2) EPot ITim LFox MBro MHig NHar NHol WAbe WDav
– 'Bill Martin' (2) EPot
¶ – Burnley form (2) EPot
– 'Crowsley Variety' (2) EPot MCas MHig NHol NMen NNrd NRya WAbe WDav WThu
¶ – 'E K Balls' (2) WDav
§ – 'Edinburgh' (2) EPot ITim MHig
– 'Edrom' (2) ITim
♦ – 'Elliott's Variety' See P. *a.* 'Edinburgh'
¶ – 'Fanfare' (2) WDav
– 'Frank Barker' (2) EPot NHol
– 'Hartside' (2) EPot NHol NNrd
– 'Hemswell Ember' (2) NHar
¶ – Ingwersen's form (2) NHol SIng
♦ – 'K R W' (2) See P. *a.* 'Ken's Seedling'
§ – 'Ken's Seedling' (2) EPot NHar NHol SIng WAbe WDav WHil WThu
¶ – 'Lindisfarne' (2) WDav
¶ – Lismore P45/16 (2) WDav
– 'Lismore Treasure' (2) WDav
– 'Margaret Earle' (2) NHol
– 'Marion' (2) EPot ITim LFox
– 'Martin' (2) EPot MBro MHig MYat NNrd WDav
– 'Mary Berry' (2) EPot MHig NHar NHol WDav
– 'Mrs Dyas' (2) NHol WAbe WDav
– 'Peggy Wilson' (2) EPot
– 'Pennine Pink' (2) EPot NHol NNrd WDav
– 'Picton's Variety' (2) EPot
¶ – 'Pinkie' (2) WDav
– 'Praecox' (2) EPot MCas NHol NNrd
– R C E form (2) WAbe
– 'Raymond Wooster' (2) EPot
– 'Scimitar' (2) NHar
– 'Snowflake' (2) EPot MCas NHar NHol WDav WThu
¶ – Stanton's form (2) NHol
– 'Stradbrook Charmer' (2) EPot
¶ – 'Stradbrook Dream' (2) WDav
– 'Tranquillity' (2) NHar NHol NNrd
¶ – 'Travellers' (2) EPot
¶ – 'Viscountess Byng' (2) WDav
– 'Wharfedale Ling' (2) EPot NHar
– 'William Earle' (2) EPot NHar NHol SIng WAbe WDav WThu
♦ – x *auricula* See P. x *loiseleurii*
♦ – – *hirsuta* (2) See P. x *pubescens*
– – *marginata* (2) EBre LBre NHar
– – *pubescens* (2) MYat
alpicola (26) CBot CBre CCla COtt CRow CWGN EBre ELun GAbr GDra LBre LMay MBal MBro MFie NBro NCra NHol NKay NLin SPer WAbe WDav WWat

– var. ***alba*** (26) CNic CPla CRow ESma GCra MBal NGre NRoo
– hybrids (26) NHol
¶– ***luna*** (26) CNic
– var. ***violacea*** (26) CPla CRow ELun GAbr GDra MBal MBri MFie NHol WHil
altaica grandiflora See P. ***elatior meyeri***
'Altaica' See P. ***elatior meyeri***
amoena See P. ***elatior meyeri***
angustifolia (20) WDav
anisodora (4) CBre CNic CPla ELan GCra MBal MFie NHol NKay SHig
'April Rose' (D.Prim) CGle EBre ECtt EMNN ESis GAbr LBre NEgg NHar NHol SHer SIng WCla WHil WPbr
x ***arctotis*** (2) See P. x ***pubescens***
aurantiaca (4) CPla EHon GAbr GTou MSta NGre SIng SPer SRms WChe
aureata (21) GArf NCra
¶– 'R B Cooke' (21) NRya
§ ***auricula*** hort. (2) CArn CPar ELan EPar ESis GDra GTou LAbb MBal MRav MTho NBro NCra NHar NHol NRoo NWCA SPer SSmi WCla WDav WHil WThu
¶– 'A B Spring' (A) MFie
¶– 'Admiral' NSel
– 'Adrian' (A) EDon MCas MFie NCra NJap NSel SHya
¶– 'Alan Ravenscroft' (A) MFie
– 'Albury' (D) EDon MFie
– 'Alfred Niblett' (S) MFie NNrd SHya
¶– 'Alice' (D) MFie
– 'Alice Haysom' (S) MFie NNrd SHya WHil
¶– 'Alien' (S) MFie
– 'Alison Jane' (A) EDon MFie NCra SHya
– 'Almondbury' (S) SHya
– ***alpina*** See P. ***a.*** hort.
– Alpine mixed (A) CNic GCra GDra NCra SRms
– 'Amethyst' (S) SHya
– 'Andrea Julie' (A) EDon MCas MFie NCra NHol NJap NRed NSel SHya WHil WSun
– 'Ann Hill' (S) SHya
– 'Ann Taylor' (A) MFie NCra
– 'Antoc' (S) MFie NCra
¶– 'Anwar Sadat' (A) MFie
– 'Applecross' (A) ESis LFox MCas MFie NCra NJap NNrd NRed NSel SHya
– 'Argus' (A) CNic EDon ELan EMNN ESis LFox MCas MFie NCra NJap NMen NNrd NRed NRya NSel SHya WHil WRus
– 'Arundel Stripe' (S) SHya
– 'Astolat' (S) MFie NCra SHya
¶– 'Athur Delbridge' (A) MFie
– 'Aurora' (A) MCas MFie SHya
– 'Aviemore' (A) MFie NNrd
¶– 'Avocet' (S) MFie
¶– 'Avril Hunter' (A) MFie
¶– 'Bacchus' (A) MFie
¶– 'Balbithan' (B) MFie
– 'Ballet' (S) MFie SHya
– 'Banana Split' CGle
¶– 'Barbarella' (S) MFie
¶– 'Bartle's Cross' (S) MFie
– 'Basuto' (A) MFie SHya
– 'Baupaume' (S) NCra
– 'Beatrice' (A) GAbr LFox MCas MFie NCra NNrd
– 'Beauty of Bath' (S) MFie SHya
¶– 'Beckjay' (S) MFie
– 'Beechen Green' (S) MFie SHya
¶– 'Ben Lawers' (S) MFie
– 'Ben Wyves' (S) SHya
– 'Betty Sheriff' (B) SHya
– 'Big Ben' (S) SHya
– 'Bilton' (S) EDon MFie NCra NSel
¶– 'Blackfield' (S) MFie
¶– 'Blackhill' (S) MFie
– 'Blairside Yellow' (B) LFox NHar NMen WAbe WDav WThu WWin
– 'Blakeney' (D) SHya
– 'Blossom' (A) EDon LFox MFie NCra NJap NSel SHya
– 'Blue Garden' MCas
– 'Blue Jean' (S) CGle EDon LFox MFie NCra NHar NJap NRed NSel
¶– 'Blue Mist' (B) MFie
– 'Blue Nile' (S) EDon MFie NCra NHar SHya
– 'Blue Steel' (S) SHya
– 'Blue Velvet' (B) MCas MFie SHya WHil
– 'Blue Wave' (D) NNrd
– 'Bluebird' (S) SHya
¶– 'Bob Lancashire' (S) MFie NHar
– 'Bookham Firefly' (A) ECar ESis GAbr LFox MCas MFie NCra NHar NJap NNrd NSel
– 'Bookham Star' (S) SHya
¶– 'Border Stripe' (B) MFie
– 'Bramshill' (S) SHya
– 'Brazil' (S) EDon ESis LFox MCas MFie NCra NHol NRed NSel WHil
– 'Brenda's Choice' (A) MFie SHya
¶– 'Bright Eyes' (A) MFie
– 'Broadwell Gold' (B) LFox MCas MFie SHya WHil
– 'Brookfield' (S) EDon MFie
– 'Broughton' (S) MFie SHya
– 'Brown Bess' (A) MCas MFie NCra
– 'Bunty' (A) MFie
– 'Butterwick' (A) EDon MFie
– 'C G Haysom' (S) CNic EDon ELan LFox MCas MFie NCra NJap NRed NSel SHya
– 'C W Needham' (A) CNic EDon MFie NCra NJap NNrd NRed NRya NSel SHya
– 'Café au Lait' (A) MFie
– 'Camelot' (D) EDon ELan MCas MFie NCra NHol NJap NNrd NRed NSel SHya WAbe
– 'Camilla' (A) MFie
– 'Carole' (A) MFie NNrd SHya
– 'Catherine' (D) EDon ELan MFie NCra NJap NRed NSel
– 'Chaffinch' (S) LFox MFie SHya
– 'Cherry' (S) LFox MFie NCra SHya
¶– 'Cheyenne' (S) MFie
– 'Chirichua' (S) NCra
– 'Chloe' (S) NJap SHya
– 'Chloris' (S) NRya
– 'Chorister' (S) EDon ELan EPot ESis GAbr LFox MBro MCas MFie NCra NNrd NRed NRya NSel SHya WDav
¶– 'Cindy' (A) MFie
– 'Clare' (S) MPar
– 'Claudia Taylor' SHya
– 'Clunie' (S) EDon
¶– 'Coffee' (S) MFie
– 'Colbury' (S) LFox MFie NCra
– 'Coll' (A) SHya
– 'Colonel Champney' (S) MFie SHya

- – 'Comet' (S) MCas MFie
- – 'Commander' (A) SHya
- ¶ – 'Connie' (S) MFie
- – 'Conservative' (S) MFie SHya
- – 'Consett' (S) MFie NCra SHya
- – 'Coppernob' (S) SHya
- – 'Coral' (S) MCas MFie NCra SHya
- – 'Cortina' (S) EDon LFox MCas NCra NJap NNrd
- – 'County Park' (B) SHya
- – 'County Park Cream' (B) SHya
- – 'County Park Red' (B) ECou SHya
- – 'Crackley Tagetes' (D) SHya
- – 'Craig Vaughan' (A) MFie NCra NNrd NRya
- – 'Creenagh Stripe' (A) MFie
- – 'Crimson Cavalier' CGle
- – 'Daftie Green' (S) SHya
- – 'Dakota' (S) MFie NCra
- – 'Daphnis' (S) LFox
- – 'Delilah' (D) EDon MFie
- – 'Devon Cream' (D) CGle CPla EDon ELan ESis MCas MFie NCra NHol NJap NNrd NRed NRya NSel SHer WRus
- – 'Diane' MFie NCra NRed WDav
- ¶ – 'Doctor Duthrie' (S) MFie
- ¶ – 'Doctor Lennon's White' (B) MFie
- – 'Donhead' (A) EDon MCas MFie SHya
- ¶ – 'Donna Claney' (S) MFie SHya
- – 'Doublet' (D) EDon EMNN MCas MFie NCra NNrd SHya WDav WHil WPbr
- – 'Douglas Black' (S) SHya
- – 'Douglas Blue' (S) SHya
- – 'Douglas Green' (S) MFie SHya
- – 'Douglas Rose' (S) SHya
- – 'Douglas Salmon' (S) SHya
- – 'Douglas White' (S) MFie
- – 'Dowager' (A) MFie SHya
- – 'Durness' (S) SHya
- – 'Dusky Yellow' CNic MCas MPar
- – 'E' NNrd
- – E82 (S) MFie
- ¶ – 'Ed Spivey' (A) MFie
- – 'Elegance' (S) MFie SHya
- – 'Elizabeth Ann' (A) GAbr MFie NCra SHya
- – 'Ellen Thompson' (A) MFie NNrd SHya
- – 'Elsie' (A) MFie SHya
- – 'Elsie May' (A) CNic EDon MFie NCra NRed NSel SHya WRus
- – 'Elsinore' (S) MFie SHya
- – 'Embley' (S) MFie NCra SHya
- – 'Emerald' (S) SHya
- – 'Emery Down' (S) MFie NNrd SHya
- ¶ – 'Erica' (A) MFie
- – 'Esso Blue' (S) SHya
- – 'Ettrick' (S) SHya
- ¶ – 'Eve Guest' (A) MFie
- ¶ – 'Eventide' (S) MFie
- – 'Everest Blue' (S) EDon MFie SHya
- – 'Fairy' (A) SHya
- – 'Falcon' (S) SHya
- – 'Fanciful' (S) EDon MFie SHya WHil
- – 'Fanny Meerbeck' (S) CGle CRiv EDon LFox MCas MFie NCra NJap NRed NSel WHil
- ¶ – 'Faro' (S) MFie
- – 'Fawsley's Favourite' (S) SHya
- – 'Finchfield' (A) MFie SHya
- – 'Flamingo' (S) MFie SHya
- – 'Fleminghouse' (S) CGle EDon ELan MFie NJap NRed SHya
- ¶ – 'Forsinard' (S) MFie
- – 'Frank Crosland' (A) MFie NCra NNrd NRya SHya WHil
- – 'Freda' (S) SHya
- – 'Frittenden Yellow' (B) LFox
- ¶ – 'Fuller's Red' (S) MCas MFie
- – 'G Douglas' (A) NCra
- – 'G Swinford' (B) SHya
- – 'Galen' (A) EDon MFie NCra NNrd SHya
- ¶ – 'Gay Crusader' (A) MFie
- ¶ – 'Gee Cross' (A) MFie
- – 'Gem' (A) SHya
- – 'George Edge' (B) SHya
- – 'George Harrison' (B) SHya
- – 'George Swinnerton's Leathercoat' CGle
- – 'Geronimo' (S) MFie SHya
- – 'Gilda Green' (S) MFie NHar SHya
- – 'Gizabroon' ELan LFox MCas MFie NCra NRed
- – 'Gleam' (S) MFie NHar NNrd SHya
- – 'Glencoe' (S) SHya
- ¶ – 'Gleneagles' (S) SHya
- ¶ – 'Glenelg' (S) MFie SHya
- – 'Glenluce' (S) SHya
- – 'Gold Blaze' (S) SHya
- – 'Goldcrest' (S) MFie SHya
- – 'Golden Chartreuse' (S) WPbr
- – 'Golden Gleam' (A) WHil
- – 'Golden Lilliput' (S) SHya
- – 'Gooseberries and Cream' CGle
- – 'Gordon Douglas' (A) EDon MFie NRya SHya
- – 'Grace Ellen' (S) SHya
- – 'Green Isle' (S) MFie SHya
- – 'Green Jacket' (S) SHya WHil
- ¶ – 'Green Mansions' (S) SHya
- – 'Green Mouse' (S) MFie SHya
- – 'Green Parrot' (S) LFox MFie NHar SHya WHil
- – 'Green Shank' (S) MFie SHya
- – 'Greenfinger' (S) SHya
- – 'Greenheart' (S) EDon SHya
- – 'Greensleeves' (S) SHya
- – 'Greta' (S) EDon ELan NHar NNrd SHya
- – 'Gretna Green' MFie SHya
- – 'Grey Bonnet ' (S) LFox
- ¶ – 'Grey Friar' (S) MFie
- – 'Grey Lag' MFie NNrd
- – 'Grey Monarch' (S) MFie SHya
- ¶ – 'Grey Shrike' (S) MFie
- ¶ – 'Grey Yellow' (S) MFie
- ¶ – 'Grizedale' (S) MFie NHar
- – 'Guildersome Green' (S) LFox MCas MFie NNrd SHya
- – 'Guinea' (S) EDon LFox MCas MFie NCra NNrd NRya SHya
- ¶ – 'Gwen Baker' (D) EDon
- – 'Hardley' (S) NCra
- ¶ – 'Harmony' (B) MFie
- – 'Harrison Weir' (S) SHya
- – 'Harry 'O'' (S) MFie SHya
- ¶ – 'Harvest Moon' (S) MFie
- ¶ – 'Haughmond' (A) MFie

– 'Hawkwood' (S)	LFox NCra NHar NNrd NRya
– 'Hawkwood Fancy' (S)	MCas MFie SHya
– 'Hazel' (A)	ESis MFie NCra
– 'Headdress' (S)	LFox MFie
– 'Helen' (S)	SHya
– 'Helen Barter' (S)	SHya
– 'Helena' (S)	LFox MFie NHar NNrd SHya
¶ – 'Hew Dalrymple' (S)	SHya
¶ – 'Hinton Fields' (S)	MFie
– 'Holyrood' (S)	MFie SHya
¶ – 'Hopley's Double Mauve' (D)	MFie
– 'Hurstwood Majesty' (S)	NNrd
– 'Hyacinth' (S)	NJap NSel NWCA WDav WRus
– 'Ibis' (S)	MFie
– 'Idmiston' (S)	SHya
– 'Jack Dean' (A)	MFie SHya
– 'James Arnot' (S)	LFox MFie NCra NHar SHya
¶ – 'Jane Myers' (D)	MFie
– 'Jeannie Telford' (A)	NCra SHya
– 'Jenny' (A)	ECar GArf MFie MYat NHar NRya SHya WHil
– 'Jezebel' (B)	ECar SHya
– 'Joan Elliott' (A)	MFie MYat WHil
– 'Joanne' (A)	SHya
¶ – 'Johann Bach' (B)	MFie
– 'John' (S)	SHya
¶ – 'John Gledhill' (A)	CNic
¶ – 'John Stewart' (A)	MFie
¶ – 'John Wayne' (A)	MFie
– 'Joy' (A)	EDon ELan MCas MFie NCra NNrd NRed NSel SHer SHya
– 'Joyce'	MFie NRya
– 'Jungfrau' (D)	EDon
¶ – 'Jupiter' (S)	MFie
– 'Kath Dryden'	WHil
– 'Kathy' (A)	SHya
– 'Kelso' (A)	MFie SHya
– 'Kercup' (A)	MFie NCra NNrd SHya
– 'Kim' (A)	MFie NCra SHya
¶ – 'Kincraig' (S)	SHya
– 'Kingcup' (A)	MFie NCra SHya
– 'Kinloch' (A)	SHya
¶ – 'Kiowa' (S)	MFie
– 'Kirklands' (D)	EDon MFie
– 'Lady Croft' (S)	SHya
– 'Lady Daresbury' (A)	MFie NCra
¶ – 'Lady Emma Monson' (S)	SHya
– 'Lady Joyful' (S)	EDon
– 'Lady Zoë' (S)	MFie NCra
¶ – 'Lamplugh'	MFie NNrd
¶ – 'Langley Park' (A)	MFie
¶ – 'Laverock Fancy' (S)	MFie
– 'Lechistan' (S)	MCas MFie NHol NJap NNrd NRed NSel
– 'Lee' (A)	NCra
– 'Lee Paul' (A)	EDon MFie NCra SHya
– 'Lemon Drop' (S)	SHya
¶ – 'Lemon Sherbert' (B)	MFie
¶ – 'Lemon White Eye' (B)	MFie
– 'Lilac Domino' (S)	MFie SHya
– 'Lime 'n' Lemon'	CGle
– 'Lindley' (S)	NCra
– 'Lindsey Moreno' (S)	SHya
– 'Ling' (A)	MFie NCra SHya
– 'Lisa' (A)	EDon EMNN GAbr MBal MCas MFie NCra NRed NSel SHya
– 'Lisa's Red' (S)	SHya
– 'Lisa's Smile' (S)	LFox MFie NCra NNrd SHya
– 'Little Rosetta' (D)	EDon WHil
¶ – 'Lochlands' (S)	SHya
¶ – 'Lockyer's Gem' (B)	MFie
¶ – 'Louisa' (D)	MFie
– 'Lovebird' (S)	EDon LFox MCas MFie NCra NHar NJap NRed NSel SHya SUsu
¶ – 'Madame Gina' (S)	MFie
¶ – 'Magnolia' (B)	MFie
¶ – 'Magpie' (S)	MFie
– 'Maid Marion' (D)	EDon SHya
– 'Mandan' (S)	SHya
– 'Manka' (S)	EDon MFie NCra SHya
– 'Mansell's Green'	MFie NNrd
– 'Margaret Faulkner' (A)	LFox MCas MFie NCra SHya
– 'Margot' (S)	SHya
– 'Marigold' (D)	EDon MFie NCra NJap NRed NSel
– 'Mark' (A)	MFie NCra NHol NJap SHya
– 'Marmion' (S)	SHya
– 'Marsco' (S)	LFox
¶ – 'Martin Luther King' (S)	MFie
– 'Martin's Red'	MPar
– 'Mary' (D)	EDon MFie SHya
– 'Matley' (S)	MFie
– 'Matthew Yates' (D)	EDon MFie NCra
– 'Maureen Millward'	MCas MFie
– 'Mermaid'	CPla EDon MFie NCra NNrd NRed
– 'Merridale' (A)	EDon MCas MFie NCra SHya
– 'Midnight' (S)	CBot CGle ELan NCra NHar NHol NSel
– 'Mikado' (S)	EDon MFie SHya
¶ – 'Millicent' (A)	MFie
– 'Mink' (A)	MFie SHya WHil
– 'Minley' (S)	EDon LFox MFie SHya
– 'Minsmere' (S)	SHya
– 'Mipsie Miranda' (D)	MFie
– 'Mojave' (S)	LFox MBro MFie NCra NHar NNrd WAbe WDav
– 'Moneymoon' (S)	MFie SHya
¶ – 'Monica' (A)	MFie
– 'Monk' (A)	MFie
¶ – 'Moonbeam' (S)	MFie
– 'Moonglow' (S)	CGle EDon ELan MFie NCra NJap NSel SHya
¶ – 'Moonrise' (S)	MFie
– 'Moonstone' (D)	EDon MFie
¶ – 'Moscow' (S)	MFie
– 'Mr 'A'' (S)	SHya WHil
– 'Mrs L Hearne' (A)	EDon MFie NCra NNrd NRed SHya
– 'Mrs R Bolton' (A)	SHya
– 'Natham Silver' (A)	MFie
– 'Neat and Tidy' (S)	CNic EDon ESis LFox MCas MFie MHig NCra NJap NRed NRya NSel SHya WAbe
¶ – 'Neville Telford' (S)	MFie
– 'New Baby' (A)	SHya
– 'Nigel' (D)	EDon
– 'Night and Day' (S)	MFie NCra
– 'Night Heron' (S)	SHya
– 'Nocturne' (S)	CGle ELan LFox MCas MFie NCra NHol NRed NSel SHya
– 'Norah' (A)	SHya
– 'Norma' (A)	MFie NNrd

¶ – 'Nubian' (S) MFie
– 'Oake's Blue' (S) MFie NCra
¶ – 'Oban' (S) SHya
¶ – 'Old Double Green' (D) MFie
¶ – 'Old England' (S) SHya
– 'Old Gold' (S) LFox SHya
– 'Old Gold Dusty Miller' (B) ECha MFie SHer
– 'Old Irish Blue' (B) CNic MCas MFie NHol SHya
¶ – 'Old Lilac' (B) MFie
– 'Old Pink Lace' CGle
– 'Old Red Dusty Miller' (B) CRiv ECha GAbr LFox MCas MFie MHig MYat NBir NHar SHer SHya WDav
– 'Old Suffolk Bronze' (B) LFox MFie SHya
¶ – 'Old Tawny' (B) MFie
– 'Old Wine' (A) MCas MFie
– 'Old Yellow Dusty Miller' (B) GAbr LFox MBro MCas MFie MHig MPar NHol SHya WDav WHil
¶ – 'Olton' (A) MFie
– 'Orb' (S) EDon LFox MCas MFie NJap NNrd NRed NRya NSel SHya
¶ – 'Osbourne Green' (B) MFie
– 'Ower' (A) MFie
– 'Paradise Yellow' (B) EPar GAbr LFox MFie NMen SHya
¶ – 'Paris' (S) MFie
– 'Party Dress' (S) SHya
– 'Party Time' (S) SHya
¶ – 'Pastiche' (A) MFie
– 'Pat' (S) EDon LFox MFie NCra SHya
– 'Patience' (S) MFie SHya
¶ – 'Pauline' (A) MFie
– 'Peggy' (A) EDon EPot MCas MFie NCra NNrd NWCA
– 'Phyllis Douglas' (A) LFox MFie NCra SHya
¶ – 'Pierot' (A) MFie
– 'Pink Lady' (A) MFie SHya
– 'Pioneer Stripe' (S) EDon MFie
¶ – 'Pioner Stripe' (B) MFie
– 'Pippin' (A) MFie SHya
– 'Pixie' (A) NCra
– 'Plush Royal' (S) MFie SHya
¶ – 'Portree' (S) SHya
– 'Pot of Gold' (S) EDon LFox MFie NCra NHar SHya
– 'Prague' (S) EDon MFie SHya
– 'Prince Charming' (S) EDon MFie
– 'Prince John' (A) EDon LFox MCas MFie NCra NJap NNrd NRya NSel SHya
– 'Proctor's Yellow' (B) SHya
– 'Prospero' (A) SHya
– 'Purple Emperor' (A) SHya
– 'Purple Frills' CGle
– 'Purple Mermaid' (D) EDon MFie
¶ – 'Purple Sage' (S) MFie
– 'Purple Velvet' (S) MFie NHol SHya
– 'Queen Bee' (S) MFie
– 'Queen of Sheba' (S) NCra
– 'Rabley Heath' (A) EDon LFox MFie SHya
¶ – 'Radient' (A) MFie
– 'Rajah' (S) CGle EDon ELan MCas MFie NCra NHar NJap NRed NSel SHya WHil
– 'Red Beret' (S) LFox MFie NCra NJap WHil
– 'Red Gauntlet' (S) EDon ELan LFox MCas MFie NCra NHar NJap NNrd NRed NSel SHya
¶ – 'Red Mark' (A) MFie
– 'Red Rum' (S) MFie NCra SHya
– 'Remus' (S) EDon LFox MCas MFie NCra NHar NNrd NRed NRya NWCA SHya WHil
¶ – 'Renata' (S) MFie
– 'Riatty' (D) MFie
¶ – 'Richard Shaw' (A) MFie NNrd
– 'Roberto' (S) SHya
– 'Rock Sand' (S) MFie NHar NNrd
– 'Rodeo' (A) EDon MFie NCra SHya
– 'Rolts' (S) EDon LFox MCas MFie NCra NHar NNrd NRya SHya
– 'Rosalie Edwards' (S) LFox MFie NCra NNrd SHya
– 'Rosamund' (D) SHya
– 'Rosanna' (S) MFie SHya
– 'Rose Kaye' (A) SHya
– 'Rosebud' (S) MFie
¶ – 'Rosemary' (S) MFie NHar
– 'Rossiter's Grey' (S) SHya
– 'Rover Stripe' (S) EDon
– 'Rowena' (A) EDon GAbr MCas MFie NCra NHol NJap NNrd NSel SHya
– 'Roxburgh' (A) SHya
– 'Royal Purple' (S) NNrd SHya
– 'Royalty' (S) MFie SHya
¶ – 'Ruby Hyde' (B) MFie
¶ – 'Ruth Hyde' (B) MCas
– 'Ruth Steed' (S) SHya
– 'Sailor Boy' (S) LFox MFie SHya
– 'Saint Boswells' (S) MFie SHya
– 'Saint Elmo' (D) MFie
– 'Saint Gerrans' White' (B) MFie
¶ – 'Salad' (S) MFie
– 'Salome' (A) SHya
– 'Sandhills' (A) SHya
– 'Sandmartin' (S) MFie SHya
– 'Sandra' (A) ECar ESis GAbr LFox MFie NNrd SHya
– 'Sandwood Bay' (A) CNic EDon LFox MCas MFie NCra NHar NMen NNrd NRed NSel SHya WRus WSun
– 'Sarah Lodge' (D) MFie SHya
– 'Serenity' (S) LFox MFie SHya
– 'Shalford' (D) EDon MFie SHya
– 'Sheila' (S) EDon LFox MFie NHar NNrd NRed SHya WAbe
– 'Shere' (S) EDon LFox MFie NCra SHya
– 'Sherwood' MCas MFie NHar
– 'Shotley' (A) MFie
– 'Sir Robert Ewbank' (D) MCas NCra
– 'Sirius' (A) EDon LFox MFie NCra NHol SHya
– 'Slioch' (S) MFie NHar SHya
– 'Snooty Fox' CGle CNic MFie NNrd
¶ – 'Snowy Owl' MFie NHar
– 'Sonya' (A) EMNN NHol NNrd
– 'South Barrow' (D) MFie
– 'Sphinx' (A) SHya
– 'Spinney Lane' (A) SHya
– 'Spring Meadows' (S) EDon ELan MFie NCra SHya
– SS TY 72 (S) MFie
– 'Standish' (D) EDon MCas MFie NCra NHol NJap NNrd NSel

– 'Stant's Blue' (S)	EDon LFox MCas MFie NCra NHol NJap NSel SHya
¶– 'Starry' (S)	MFie
– 'Stella' (S)	EDon LFox MFie SHya
– 'Stonnal' (A)	MFie SHya
– 'Stubb's Tartan' (S)	MCas SHya
– 'Sue' (A)	MFie
– 'Summer Sky' (A)	SHya
– 'Sunflower' (S)	LFox MFie
¶– 'Sunsal' (S)	MFie
¶– 'Sunstar' (S)	MFie
– 'Super Para' (S)	MFie NHar SHya
– 'Superb' (S)	SHya
– 'Susan' (A)	LFox MFie SHya
– 'Susannah' (D)	EDon MFie SHya
– 'Swale' (A)	SHya
– 'Sweet Pastures' (S)	EDon MCas MFie NCra NHol NJap NSel SHya
¶– 'Swift' (S)	MFie
– 'Symphony' (A)	SHya
¶– 'Tall Purple Dusty Miller' (B)	MFie
– 'Tally-ho' (A)	SHya
– 'Tarantella' (A)	MCas MFie NCra NJap NNrd NSel
– 'Tavistock' (S)	SHya
– 'Ted Roberts' (A)	EDon MCas MFie NCra SHya
– 'Teem' (S)	MFie NCra NJap NNrd SHya
– 'Tenby Grey' (S)	MFie SHya
– 'The Baron' (S)	CGle LFox MCas MFie NJap NRed
– 'The Bishop' (S)	MFie NCra
– 'The Bride' (S)	EDon MCas NCra NJap SHya
– 'The Cardinal' (D)	EDon SAsh SHya
– 'The Czar' (A)	SHya
– 'The Maverick' (S)	SHya
¶– 'The Raven' (S)	MFie
– 'The Snods' (S)	MFie NCra
– 'Thetis' (A)	MFie NCra SHya
– 'Thirlmere' (D)	MFie SHya
– 'Tinkerbell' (S)	MFie NJap NNrd
¶– 'Tomboy' (S)	MFie
¶– 'Tomdown' (S)	SHya
¶– 'Tosca' (S)	SHya
– 'Trojan' (S)	SHya
– 'Trouble' (D)	EDon MFie NCra NHol
– 'Trudy' (S)	MCas MFie NCra SHya
– 'True Briton' (S)	MFie SHya
¶– 'Trumpet Blue' (S)	MFie
¶– 'Tumbledown' (A)	MFie
– 'Tye Lea' (S)	EDon MFie
– 'Typhoon' (A)	MFie SHya
– 'Valerie' (A)	EDon MCas MFie NCra NNrd SHya
– 'Vee Too' (A)	MFie SHya
¶– 'Vera' (A)	MFie
– 'Verdi' (A)	MFie NCra NJap NSel
¶– 'Victoria' (S)	MFie
¶– 'Victoria de Wemyss'	MFie
– 'Vivien' (S)	SHya
– 'Vulcan' (A)	EDon MCas MFie NCra NNrd SHya
– 'Waincliffe Red' (S)	MFie
– 'Walhampton' (S)	MFie NHar SHya
– 'Walton' (A)	MFie SHya
– 'Walton Heath' (D)	EDon MFie SHya
¶– 'Warwick' (S)	EDon
– 'Watt's Purple' (D)	EDon MCas MFie
¶– 'Wedding Day' (S)	MFie
– 'Westcott Pride' (D)	EDon MFie
– 'White Ensign' (S)	MFie SHya
– 'White Wings' (S)	MFie NCra NHar SHya
¶– 'Wide Awake' (A)	MFie
¶– 'Wincha' (S)	MFie
¶– 'Windways Mystery' (B)	MFie
– 'Winifrid' (A)	ECar EDon MCas MFie NCra NHol SHya WHil WRus
¶– 'Woodstock' (S)	MFie
¶– 'Wor Jackie' (S)	MFie
¶– 'Y I Hinney' (A)	MFie
– 'Yorkshire Grey' (S)	EDon MFie
– 'Zambia' (D)	EDon MFie SHya WHil
auricula Linnaeus ssp. ***bauhinii*** (2)	MBro NHol
¶– ***auricula***	NHol
¶***auriculata*** (11)	WDav
'Barbara Barker' (2)	ITim
*'Barnard's Crimson' (Prim)	CCot
Barnhaven Blues Group (Prim)	CDec GAbr
Barnhaven doubles (D.Poly)	MFie WBon WPbr
Barnhaven Reds (Prim)	See P. Tartan Reds Group
¶ Barnhaven Traditional Group (Poly)	MFie
'Beatrice Wooster' (2)	CNic EPot LFox MBro MCas MYat NHar NMen NNrd NRed NRya SGil SIng SSmi WAbe WDav WHil WThu
beesiana (4)	CArn CMea CPar CRow EBar EHon ELan GCHN GTou LMay MBri MFie MSta MSte NHar NKay NOak NRoo NSti NWCA SHer SHig SPer WChe WDav WHil WWat
'Belle Watling' (D.Prim)	GAbr NHar NHol
bellidifolia (17)	CPla NGre
beluensis	See P. × ***pubescens*** 'Freedom'
§ × ***berninae*** 'Windrush' (2)	MPar NHar NNrd WAbe WDav
'Betty Green' (Prim)	MBri NHol
'Bewerley White'	See P. ***pubescens*** 'Bewerley White'
♦***bhutanica***	See P. ***whitei*** 'Sherriff's Variety'
'Big Red Giant' (D.Prim)	NHar NHol SIng
bileckii	See P. × ***forsteri*** 'Bileckii'
'Blue Rhapsody'	NHar
'Blue Riband' (Prim)	CCot CGle COtt ECar EPot LFox MHig NCat NHar NHol SPer WCru
'Blue Sapphire' (30)	CBot EDon NEgg NHol NRoo SIng
¶ Blue Striped Victorians Group (Poly)	GAbr
'Blutenkissen' (Prim)	ELun EPot LFox NNrd
'Bon Accord Elegance' (D.Poly)	CGle
'Bon Accord Gem' (D.Poly)	CCot CGle
'Bon Accord Purple' (D.Poly)	CCot CGle EJud
'Bonfire' (4)	GDra
– (Poly)	ELun

Name	Suppliers
Bootheosa Group (21)	NHar
boothii (21)	GArf NHar
bracteosa (21)	ITim
'Brimstone' (Poly)	CGle
'Buckland Enchantress'	CRow
'Buckland Wine' (Prim)	CCot CRow
x ***bulleesiana*** (4)	NHol NKay
– Asthore hybrids (4)	EHon
bulleyana (4)	Widely available
¶ – CLD 920(4)	MFie NHol
burmanica (4)	CPar CPla CWGN ELun GDra GGar LBee MBal MFie MSta NCra NHar NHol NKay SIng WDav
'Butterscotch' (Prim)	CGle
'Caerhays Ruby' (Prim)	CB&S
'Caerulea Plena' (D.Prim)	GCal
calderiana (21)	GDra NHar
Candelabra hybrids (4)	CBro EMNN LFox MTho NCra NLin SHer
Candy Pinks Group (Prim)	GAbr NHol
capitata (5)	CArn CBot CGle CMea CNic CPla GAbr GDra GTou MBal MBri MFie MFir MSte NCra NGre NHar NLin NSti WCla WDav WHal
¶ – CLD 497/274(5)	MFie
– ssp. ***capitata*** (5)	EPot
– ssp. ***crispata*** AGS/ES 407(5)	GCra
¶ – dark forms (5)	MFie
– ssp. ***mooreana*** (5)	CWGN LMay NVic WCla WHoo
– ssp. ***sphaerocephala***	GCra NWCA
'Captain Blood' (D.Prim)	CBot CDec CGle ECar ECtt EOrc ESis GAbr NEgg NHar NHol SIng WHil WPbr
'Carmen' (Prim)	LFox
'Carnation' (Poly)	GAbr MFie NJap
¶ ***carniolica*** (2)	NHar
¶ 'Casquet'	GAbr
cernua (17)	CPla GDra MFie NGre NHar
'Charlene (D.Prim)	GAbr NHar SRms
Chartreuse Group (Poly)	CGle EDon GAbr MFie NJap
'Cherry' (Prim)	CCot
'Chevithorne Pink' (Poly)	CGle EMNN
chionantha (18)	CBot CCla CGle CMea CPla CRow CWGN ELan ELun EMNN ESis GDra MBal MBri MFie NCra NGre NHar NHol NJap NKay NMen NNor SPer WDav WHil WWat
§ – Sinopurpurea Group (18)	CGle CNic CPla CRow ELun EMNN GDra MBal MBro NCra NKay NLin
'Chocolate Soldier' (D.Prim)	CBot CGle ECtt ELan GGar MBal MYat NHol NJap SIng WHil WPbr
chungensis (4)	CCla CGle CMea CRDP ELan GCal GTou MBri MSta NHar NKay NLin WBon WDav WHal
§ – x ***pulverulenta*** (4)	EBre LBre NHol
x ***chunglenta***	See P. ***chungensis*** x ***pulverulenta***
clarkei (11)	EPot GArf MFir MHig NCra NHar NWCA SGil SHer WOMN
'Cluny'	GArf
clusiana (2)	GDra MBal NGre NHol WDav
– 'Murray-Lyon' (2)	NHar
cockburniana (4)	CPar CRow GAbr GDra GGar GTou MBal MBri MFie NCra NGre NHar NLin
concholoba (17)	CPla CRow EBar ELan GAbr GCra GGar GTou MBro MFie NGre NHar NLin NMen WDav
'Corporal Baxter' (D.Prim)	CGle EDon ELan ELun EMNN EOrc MCas MYat NEgg NHol SHer SIng WHil WPbr WSun
cortusoïdes (7)	CPla MBro NCra SRms
¶ Cottage Mixed (Prim)	NCat
Cowichan (Poly)	CCot CDec CWGN GAbr LFox MBri MBro NCra NJap WHoo
Cowichan Amethyst Group (Poly)	EDon GAbr
Cowichan Blue Group (Poly)	EDon GAbr WSun
Cowichan Garnet Group (Poly)	EDon GAbr WSun
Cowichan Red Group (Poly)	NHar
Cowichan Venetian Group (Poly)	EDon GAbr
Cowichan Yellow Group (Poly)	EDon GAbr
'Craven Gem' (Poly)	CFis MHig NKay NRoo
'Crescendo' (Poly)	GAbr MPit NRoo
'Crimson Cushion'	NNrd
¶ 'Crimson Queen' (Prim)	LSur
'Crimson Velvet' (2)	GAbr NNrd WDav
crispa	See P. ***glomerata***
¶ ***daonensis*** (2)	MFie NMen
darialica (11)	CGle CPla ELan GAbr GDra MYat NCra NHol NMen NMir
'David Valentine'	CCor
'Dawn Ansell' (D.Prim)	CB&S CBot CBre CGle CRow EBre ECtt EDon EFol ELan ELun EMNN EOrc ESis GAbr GGar LBre LHop MBal MBri MRav NEgg NHar NRoo NSti SAxl SIng SPer WHil WRus
¶ Daybreak Group (Poly)	MFie
denticulata (9)	Widely available
– ***alba*** (9)	CB&S CCla CGle CMil CRDP CSco EBre ECha EGol ELan EMNN EPar EPot ERav GAbr GTou LBre MBal MBri MFie MWat NCra NHar NHol NJap NOrc NRoo SHer SIng WPbr
¶ – 'Bressingham Beauty' (9)	EBre LBre MUlv
– ***cashmeriana*** (9)	CNic ELan MUlv WCla WPbr
– 'Glenroy Crimson' (9)	MBal
– 'Inshriach Carmine' (9)	GDra
– lilac (9)	EHon GTou MFie NJap
– purple (9)	EMNN GAbr IBlr NRoo
– red (9)	CB&S CRow EMNN EPar NOrc
– 'Robinson's Red' (9)	EPot
– rose (9)	MFie NHar
– 'Rubinball' (9)	EBre GAri LBre NHol NRoo
– ruby (9)	CSco EHon GAbr GTou MBri MFie NJap NOak SIng WHen WHoo WPbr
– 'Snowball' (9)	MBro MFir NOak WHen WHoo
x ***deschmannii***	See P. x ***vochinensis***
'Desert Sunset' (Poly)	EDon MFie
'Dianne'	See P. x ***forsteri*** 'D.'
'Dorothy' (Prim)	CBro LSur SIng

'Double Lilac' (D.Prim)	See P. ***vulgaris*** 'Lilacina Plena'
'Duckyls Red' (Prim)	CRDP GAbr SRms
'Dusky Lady'	MBri WPbr
'Easter Bonnet'	NHar
edelbergii (12)	EPot NHar
edgeworthii (21)	GArf NHol WAbe
elatior (30)	CGle CKin CNic CPla CRow CSev CShe EHon ELun ESis GAbr GDra LFox NCra NHol NJap NMir NOrc NRoo NSal NSel NSti SPer SUsu WCla WEas WHil
– JCA 785.150(30)	WDav
– ssp. ***intricata*** (30)	CNic
– ssp. ***leucophylla*** (30)	ELun EPad MHig
§ – ssp. ***meyeri*** (30)	CFis CShe LRHS LSur MFos NHol
¶ – ssp. ***pallasii*** (30)	NSti
ellisiae (21)	NHol
'Erin's Gem' (Poly)	CGle CRow
¶ ***erythra*** (26)	NHol
'Ethel Barker' (2)	EPot ITim LFox MCas MHig NGre NHar NMen NNrd SIng WAbe WDav WThu
'Ethel M Dell' (D.Prim)	EOrc NHar NHol SIng SRms WCla WHal
'Eugénie' (D.Prim)	CBot CGle EFol ELan GAbr MYat NHar SIng SPer WPbr
farinosa (11)	CArn CNic CPla CRDP ELun GAbr LGan MBal MBri MBro NCra NGre NHar NKay NMen NSal SIng WCla WDav
'Fire Dance' (Poly)	EDon GAbr MFie
Firefly Group (Poly)	GAbr LFox
firmipes (26)	EPot NHol
§ ***flaccida*** (28)	ELan GCra GDra MBal MFie NCra NHar NHol NMen WAbe WDav
♦ x ***flagellicaulis***	See P. x ***polyantha***
Flamingo Group (Poly)	EDon GAbr MFie NJap
§ x ***floerkeana*** (2)	NHar WAbe
florindae (26)	Widely available
– hybrids (26)	CBre CRDP LFox MFie NHol WDav WHal
– orange form (26)	IBlr
– red form (26)	CRDP MSta NHar NHol NKay NOak
Footlight Parade Group (Prim)	NCat
forrestii (3)	CNic EPot MFie NGre NHar SGil
¶ – CLD 1242(3)	MFie
– CLD 738(3)	MFie
§ x ***forsteri*** (2)	CShe ITim MHig NHar NHol NKay NMen WAbe
§ – 'Bileckii' (2)	ECar ELun MBal MBro MHig MYat NHar NHol NKay NNrd SGil SWas WAbe WDav WHil
§ – 'Dianne' (2)	CNic EPot GAbr MBro MCas MHig MYat NHar NHol NNrd NRed NRya SGil SIng WAbe WThu
'Freckles' (D.Prim)	ELan GGar NHar NHol SIng WCla WHil WPbr
'Freedom'	See P. x ***pubescens*** 'F.'
frondosa (11)	CGle CMea CPla CShe EMNN ESis GAbr LFox MBal MBri MBro MPar MPit NCra NHar NHol NJap NKay NMen NWCA WAbe WEas WHil WHoo WThu
'Frühlingszauber' (Prim)	NHol
Fuchsia Victorians Group (Poly)	GAbr MFie NJap
Galligaskins Group (Poly)	CCot
¶ 'Garnet' (D.Prim)	MFie
'Garryard Guinevere'	See P. 'Guinevere'
¶ ***gaubaeana*** (12)	NHar
geraniifolia (7)	GDra MFie
§ 'Ghia'	EDon MFie
'Gigha' (Prim)	NHol
glaucescens (2)	CNic MFie NHol WDav
– JCA 786.900(2)	NHol
¶ 'Glebe Grey' (Prim)	CGle
§ ***glomerata*** (5)	GAbr MBro NKay WDav
– BM&W 35(5)	NHol
'Gloriosa' (Prim)	CCot LSur SIng
'Glowing Embers' (4)	ELun NBir NLin NSti
glutinosa (2)	ITim WDav
Gold Laced Group (Poly)	CBre CCot CDec CGle CPla CRDP CRow EDon ELan ELun EPar GAbr GCal LAbb LFox MBri MCas NCra NHar NHol NMen NSti NWCA SUsu WEas WHer WHoo WPbr
¶ 'Gordon'	NGar
gracilipes (21)	CGle EPar GArf NHar NKay SRms
– L&S 1(21)	NHar NHol
– L&S 1166(21)	NHar NHol
– early form (21)	NHar
– 'Heathpool' (21)	NHar NHol
– late form (21)	NHar NHol
¶ – mid form (21)	NHol
– 'Minor'	See P. ***petiolaris***
– 'Winter Jewel' (21)	NHar NHol
¶ 'Graham'	NGar
Grand Canyon Group (Poly)	GAbr MFie NJap
'Granny Graham' (Prim)	CBot NHar NHol SIng SRms WCla WHil WPbr
griffithii (21)	NHar
'Groeneken's Glory' (Prim)	CGle CNic CRiv ELun MBri NCra NHol SIng SPer WPbr
§ 'Guinevere' (Poly)	CCot CGle CHad EBre ECha ELan ELun EPar EPot ITim LBre LFox LSur MBal MBri MCas MHig NCra NHar NKay NSti SAxl SBla WAbe WEas WPbr WRus WWat WWin
'Hall Barn Blue'	NHar
'Hall Barn White'	NHar
§ ***halleri*** (11)	CNic CPla GAbr MBal NCra NHar NNor NRed NWCA WCla WOMN WPat
– 'Longiflora'	See P. ***h.***
Harbinger Group (Prim)	CDec CGle GAbr LSur NHol NNrd
'Harbour Lights'	GAbr MFie
Harlow Carr hybrids (4)	NHol NRoo NSti WDav WHil
Harvest Yellows Group (Poly)	EDon GAbr MFie
x ***heeri*** (2)	EPot
helodoxa	See P. ***prolifera***
¶ 'Herbert Beresford'	NMen
heucherifolia (7)	CBot CCla CPar CPla CRDP CSam GAbr LFox MFie NHar NLin WHil
hirsuta (2)	CNic MFie MPar NWCA
– 'Dyke's Variety'	LRHS
Hose in Hose (Poly)	CCot CGle LFox NCra NRoo WRus

*'Husky'	MPit NRoo
hyacinthina (17)	GArf NGre
Indian Reds Group (Poly)	EDon GAbr MFie NJap
'Ingram's Blue' (Prim)	CRow
Inshriach hybrids (4)	CMHG CNic ELun GAbr GDra GGar MBri MFie MSte NHol WDav WHal
x ***intermedia*** (2)	MHig
'Inverewe' (4)	CBro CKel CRiv GDra GGar NHar
involucrata (11)	CBot CCla CGle CRiv NHar NKay NMen NTow WPat
– ssp. ***yargongensis*** (11)	CGle CPla CRow MBal MBri MFie NGre NHar NWCA WHil
ioessa (26)	CPla EBre LBre MBal MBri NHar NHol NJap NTow WOMN
– hybrids	MFie NHar
'Iris Mainwaring' (Prim)	EPot NCra NNrd SIng WHil WPbr
¶ 'Ivy Agnee'	NGar
Jack in the Green Group (Poly)	CCla CCot CDec CGle CNic GAbr LFox NBar NCra NNrd SHer WHer WHil WRus
japonica (4)	CCla CGle CMHG CMea CRDP CRow CWGN ECha ELun EPot GTou LMay MFir MPlt NBro NCra NHar NMen NNor SBla SSpi SUsu WChe WCla WEas WHil
– 'Alba' (4)	WDav WHil
– 'Fuji' (4)	ELun ESis GDra MBal MBri MSta NHar NJap WHal
– 'Glowing Embers' (4)	CGle MBri NJap
– 'Miller's Crimson' (4)	CB&S CGle CKel CPar CPla CRow CSco CTrw CWGN EBre ECha EHon ELan GAbr GDra LBre MBal MBri MFie NHar NHol NRed SBla SPer WBod WFro WHil WRus WWat
– 'Oriental Sunrise' (4)	NJap SPer
– 'Postford White' (4)	Widely available
– red shades (4)	NJap NSti WAbe
– 'Valley Red' (4)	GGar
jesoana (7)	NHar NTow
¶ 'Jill'	GAbr
'Johanna' (11)	EBre EPot GAbr GArf LBre NHar NRya
¶ 'Jo-Jo' (2)	MCas
juliae (30)	CGle CPla CRDP CRiv NGre NHar NHol NKay NNrd WEas
– white form (30)	CGle
'Julian'	NNrd
x ***juribella*** (2)	NHar
'Ken Dearman' (D.Prim)	CBot CGle ECtt EDon EFol ELan ESis GAbr GGar MBal MRav MYat NEgg NHol NSti SIng SPer WHal WPbr
kewensis	NWCA
'Kinlough Beauty' (Poly)	CCot CDec CFis CRow CShe ELun EMNN EPar GAbr LFox LSur NCra NHol NRoo NSti SIng SWas WCru WEas WHil
kisoana (7)	CPla WCru
– ***alba*** (7)	CBre CPla CRDP WCru
'Lady Greer' (Poly)	Widely available
'Lambrook Lilac' (Poly)	CRow
'Lambrook Yellow' (Poly)	CGle
§ ***latifolia*** (2)	CShe NCra NHar
– 'Crimson Velvet' (2)	EPot MHig SRms WThu
laurentiana	See P. ***mistassinica macropoda***
'Lilian Harvey' (D.Prim)	CBot CGle CMea EBre ECtt ELan LBre MCas MRav NEgg NHol NRed NRoo NSti SPer WHal WHil WPbr
Limelight Group (Poly)	CGle GAbr MFie
'Lingwood Beauty' (Prim)	LSur NKay
'Linnet ' (21)	ITim NHol NRya
'Lismore Yellow' (2)	CNic ITim MHig NHol WAbe WDav
¶ Lissadel hybrids (4)	MFie NHol
'Little Egypt' (Poly)	CGle EDon GAbr
littoniana	See P. ***vialii***
'Lizzie Green' (Prim)	NCra NHol
§ x ***loiseleurii*** (2)	EBre LBre
'Lopen Red' (Poly)	CFis
macrophylla (18)	MBal
– H 78(18)	GDra MSte NGre WDav
'Madame Pompadour' (D.Poly)	CGle
magellanica (11)	NGre
malacoïdes (3)	MBri
marginata (2)	CGle CRiv ECar ELun EPar EPot GAbr GDra LFox LHop MYat NCra NGre NHar NHol NNrd NRed NRya SSmi WAbe WHil WOMN
– ***alba*** (2)	ECar EPot GAbr MBro MHig MYat NCra NGar NHar NKay NNrd SIng SSmi WAbe WDav WThu
¶ – 'Alpbach'	NGar
¶ – 'Amethyst'	EPot MFie
– 'Arthur Branch' (2)	EPot WAbe
¶ – 'Baldock's Mauve'	NGar
¶ – 'Barbara Clough'	NGar
– 'Beamish' (2)	EPot NGar NRya SPou WDav
– 'Beatrice Lascaris' (2)	CRiv ECar EPot ITim MBro MCas MHig MYat NGar NHol NMen NNrd NRya SPou WAbe WDav WHil WThu
– 'Caerulea' (2)	EPot GArf ITim MHig MYat NGar NHol WAbe WThu
– 'Clear's Variety' (2)	EPot MCas MHig MYat NMen NNrd WDav
– 'Correvon's Variety' (2)	NCra NGar
– cut-leaved (2)	NHar WDav
– 'Doctor Jenkins' (2)	WDav
– 'Drake's Form' (2)	EMNN EPot ITim MCas MHig MPar NHol SIng SPou
– 'Earl L Bolton' (2)	EPot NGar NHol NNrd SPou WAbe WDav
– 'Elizabeth Fry' (2)	LFox MCas MPar NNrd SPou
– 'F W Millard' (2)	WDav
– 'Gold Plate' (2)	NHar
– 'Grandiflora' (2)	NGar NHar NHol NNrd WDav
– 'Highland Twilight' (2)	NNrd SPou
– 'Holden Variety' (2)	CNic MBal MBro MCas MHig NGar NHar NHol NMen NNrd SIng WDav
– 'Hyacinthia' (2)	CShe EPot NHol SPou WAbe
– 'Ivy Agea' (2)	EPot
– 'Janet' (2)	MHig WDav
– 'Jenkins Variety' (2)	EPot SIng
– 'Kesselring's Variety' (2)	ECar ELan EPot MBro MCas MHig MYat NGar NHar NHol NRed SSmi WAbe WDav WHil WWin
¶ – 'Laciniata'	NGar
– 'Lilac' (2)	GDra LFox NGar NNrd

– 'Linda Pope' (2)	CGle CNic CShe ECar EPot ITim LBee MPar NCra NHar NHol NRed SPou WAbe WDav
– 'Marven' (2)	EPot MBro MCas NCra NGar NNrd SPou WDav
– 'Millard's Variety' (2)	NGar NMen
¶ – 'Miss Savory'	NGar
¶ – 'Mrs Carter Walmsley'	NGar
– 'Prichard's Variety' (2)	CGle CShe ECar ELan ELun EMNN EPot GArf GDra ITim LFox MBro MCas MYat NCra NGar NHar NHol NKay NMen NNrd NRed NRya SSmi WAbe WCla WDav WEas WHil WOMN
– 'Rheniana' (2)	EPot NGar SPou WDav
– 'Rosea' (2)	EPot
¶ – 'Sheila Denby'	NGar
¶ – 'Shipton'	NGar
¶ – small flowered form	NGar
– 'Violet Form' (2)	GDra MBro NHar WDav
– 'Waithman's Variety' (2)	EPot
'Marianne Davey' (D.Prim)	CB&S CGle EDon EFol ELan EMNN EOrc MBri MRav MYat NEgg NHar NHol NRed NRoo NSti SHer SPer WHil WPbr
'Marie Crousse' (D.Prim)	CFis CGle EBre ECar EDon EFol GTou LBre MBal MBro MYat NHol NRed SHer SSpi WHal
Marine Blues Group (Poly)	GAbr MFie NCat WSun
'Mary Anne'	CTom
¶ Mauve Victorian Group (Poly)	EDon MFie
'McWatt's Claret' (Poly)	CCot EPot GAbr NCra
'McWatt's Cream' (Poly)	CRiv GAbr LSur NCra NMen NRya SIng
¶ ***megaseifolia*** (6)	NHar
melanops (18)	CGle CPla ELan GAbr NGre NHar NWCA
¶ 'Mexico'	MFie
Midnight Group (Poly)	GAbr MFie
'Miniera' (2)	EPot
minima (2)	ECar GArf MHig NGre NHar NHol NRed NWCA SGil
– – (2)	GArf NHar NHol
♦– x ***glutinosa*** (2)	See P. x ***floerkeana***
♦– – ***hirsuta*** (2)	See P. x ***forsteri***
♦– – ***villosa*** (2)	See P. x ***truncata***
– – ***wulfeniana*** (2)	See P. x ***vochinensis***
'Miss Indigo' (D.Prim)	CB&S CGle CSam CWGN EBre ECtt EDon EFol ELan ELun EMNN EOrc LBre MBri MCas MRav MYat NEgg NHar NHol NRed SIng SPer WCla WHal WHil WPbr
§ ***mistassinica*** var. ***macropoda*** (11)	CNic GAbr MSte NWCA
modesta (11)	CNic EMNN
– var. ***faurieae*** (11)	MBro MFie WHoo
*– ***saximontana*** (11)	NGre
¶ ***mollis*** (7)	SIng
'Morton'	NGre
'Mrs McGillivray' (Prim)	NNrd
muscarioïdes (17)	CGle CPla GCra GTou MFie NHar NLin
¶ Muted Victorian Group (Poly)	MFie
nepalensis	See P. ***tanneri n.***
New Pinks Group (Poly)	EDon GAbr MFie NCat
nivalis (18)	CPla
nutans Delavay	See P. ***flaccida***
– Georgi (25)	GCra GDra NCra NHar
obconica (19)	MBri
'Old Port' (Poly)	CDec CFis NHar WPat
'Old Rose' (Poly)	GAbr MFie
'Olive Wyatt' (D.Prim)	CB&S CGle EMNN EOrc MPit MYat NHar NHol SIng WHal WHil
'Oriental Sunrise' (4)	LAbb MBri NHol
Osiered Amber Group (Prim)	CRow GAbr NHol
'Our Pat' (D.Poly)	CDec GCal IBlr NCat WCot
Pagoda hybrids (4)	MBri MFie NHol NJap
palinuri (2)	MFie
'Paris '90' (Poly)	EDon MFie
parryi (20)	CNic EMNN MBro NCra NHar NHol NMen
pedemontana (2)	MSte NGre NHar NHol WDav
'Perle von Bottrop' (Prim)	LSur MHig
'Peter Klein' (11)	CRiv ECar GDra ITim MBal MBro MCas NHar SGil WCru WHoo WOMN
'Peter's Red'	NHar
'Peter's Violet'	NHar
§ ***petiolaris*** (21)	EMNN EPar GArf ITim MPit NCra NHar NHol
– LS&H 19856(21)	EPot GArf NHar
'Petticoat'	NHar NHol SIng
pinnatifida (17)	GDra
– CLD 1092(17)	NHol
poissonii (4)	CBot CGle CPla CRDP CTom CWGN EMon IBlr LGan LMay MBal NGre NHar NHol NJap NKay NLin
¶ – CLD 485(4)	MFie
§ x ***polyantha*** (30)	NHol WHil
Polyanthus (30)	ENot GDra NCra NKay
polyneura (7)	CBot CNic CPla GTou MBal MBro MFie MHig NHol NMen NTow NWCA WDav WEas WWat
praenitens	See P. ***sinensis***
'Prince Silverwings' (D.Poly)	WEas
§ ***prolifera*** (4)	CBre CMHG CTrw EBul ECha LGan LMay MFie MFir NHar NHol NLin NSti SBla SHig SPer SSpi WHal WWat
x ***pruhonicensis***	See under ***cultivar name***
pseudosikkimensis	See P. ***sikkimensis***
§ x ***pubescens*** (2)	EMNN EPot GDra LFox MBro MYat NHol NRed NRya SGil SHer SSmi WDav
– 'Apple Blossom' (2)	EPot MFie NHol SGil SIng
– 'Balfouriana' (2)	CNic LFox MBro MPar WDav
§ – 'Bewerley White' (2)	CNic CRiv ELun EPot ESis ITim MBal MBro MCas MFie NCra NMen NNrd NRed NRya SSmi WEas WHil WRus WThu WWin
¶ – 'Blue Wave' (2)	MFie
§ – 'Boothman's Variety' (2)	CNic ECar EMNN EPot ESis ITim MBro MCas MFie MHig MPlt MYat NCra NGar NGre NKay NMen NNrd NRed SBla SGil SSmi WAbe WCla WDav WHil WPat WRus WThu WWin
♦– 'Carmen' (2)	See P. x ***p.*** 'Boothman's Variety'
¶ – 'Chamois' (2)	MFie

– 'Christine' (2)	CNic ECar EPot GArf MBro MFie MHig MYat NCra NNrd NRed WDav WHil WOMN WThu
– 'Cream Viscosa' (2)	CRiv EMNN MCas MFie MPlt NMen NNrd SGil WHil
¶ – 'Crimson Velvet' (2)	MFie
¶ – 'Deep Mrs Wilson' (2)	MFie
¶ – 'Ellen Page' (2)	MFie
– 'Elphenor' (2)	CRiv
– 'Faldonside' (2)	CNic CRiv ECar EPot ESis GCHN MBro MCas MFie MHig MYat NCra NKay NMen NNrd NRed NRya SHer WAbe WHil WThu
§ – 'Freedom' (2)	CNic ECar ELan EMNN EPot GArf ITim MBro MCas MFie MHig MPlt MYat NCra NHar NNrd NRya SHer SSmi WDav WHil WPat WThu WWin
¶ – 'George Harrison' (2)	MFie
– 'Gnome' (2)	SPou WThu
– 'Harlow Car' (2)	EPot ESis ITim LFox MFie MHig MYat NHar NHol NMen NNrd SBla WAbe WDav WHil WThu
– 'Henry Hall' (2)	ELun MFie SGil SHer WDav
¶ – 'Joan Danger' (2)	MFie
– 'Joan Gibbs' (2)	CNic EPot MFie MHig NCra NHar NNrd SGil WDav
¶ – 'Kath Dryden' (2)	MFie
– 'Mrs J H Wilson' (2)	CNic CRiv ITim MBal MFie MHig NCra NKay NMen NNrd NRed SSmi WDav WHil WRus
– 'Nivea' (2)	MPar
– 'Pat Barwick' (2)	ECar EPot LFox MFie NMen NRed WDav WHil
¶ – 'Paul' (2)	NRya
¶ – 'Peggy Fell' (2)	MFie
– 'Rufus' (2)	CRiv ITim MBal MFie MHig NCra SBla SGil SPou WHil WOld WThu
¶ – 'S E Matthews' (2)	NNrd
¶ – 'Sonya' (2)	MFie
– 'The General' (2)	GAbr MCas MFie MHig NCra NNrd SGil WDav WHil
– 'Wharfedale Gem' (2)	NNrd
x ***pubescens*** x ***allionii*** (2)	NNrd
x ***pubescens*** yellow form (2)	CCor
pulchra (21)	NHar
pulverulenta (4)	CB&S CCla CMea CPar CRow CSco CTrw CWGN EBul EHon ELun ENot EPar GDra GTou LMay MBal MBri MFie NHar NHol NKay NWCA SBla SMad SPer WChe WHil WWat
– Bartley hybrids (4)	CBot CGle CRDP ELun GAbr NCat NKay WHal
– 'Bartley Pink' (4)	CPla LRHS NHol NSti
'Purpurkissen' (Prim)	NHol
'Quaker's Bonnet'	See P. ***vulgaris*** 'Lilacina Plena'
¶ 'Ramona' (Poly)	EDon MFie
¶ 'Raven'	NMen
♦ 'Ravenglass Vermilion' (4)	See P. 'Inverewe'
'Red Paddy' (D.Prim/Poly)	MPit
'Red Sunset' (4)	GDra
'Red Velvet' (D.Prim)	LHop NHar NHol SIng
reidii (28)	MBri MFie NCra NHar
– var. ***williamsii*** (28)	CPla EBre GDra GTou LBre MBal MBri NGre WAbe
– – ***alba*** (28)	GDra MBal MBri NGre
reptans (16)	NHar
'Reverie' (Poly)	EDon GAbr MFie
'Rhubarb and Custard' (Poly)	CGle
'Romeo' (Prim)	NCra
'Rose O'Day' (D.Prim)	CB&S CGle ELan EOrc MBal NEgg NHol NRoo NSti SIng WHil
rosea (11)	CBot CPar CPla CRDP CRow CTom ELun GDra GTou LHop MBal MHig NCra NGre NHar NJap NKay NSti NVic SBla SIng SSpi WChe WEas WRus
¶ – C&Mc 367(11)	GCHN
– 'Delight'	See P. ***r.*** 'Micia Visser-de Geer'
– var. ***elegans*** (11)	GDra
– 'Gigas' (11)	MSta
– 'Grandiflora' (11)	CGle CNic CWGN ECar EHon ELan EMNN EPar GAbr LMay MBri MCas MPit MPlt NHol NLin NMen NNrd NRed NRoo NTow SCro SSou WHil WPer
§ – 'Micia Visser-de Geer' (11)	CKel NKay SPer
* – ***splendens*** (11)	IDai WDav
rotundifolia	See P. ***roxburghii***
'Rowallane Rose' (4)	CBro
'Roy Cope' (D.Prim)	EBre ECar EDon GGar LBre MBal MPit NHar SIng
rubra	See P. ***erythra***
rusbyi (20)	NHar NHol NMen WDav
Rustic Reds Group (Poly)	MFie NJap
'Sandy's Form' (21)	EPot NHol
saxatilis (7)	MCas MFie NHar SIng WHil
¶ ***scandinavica*** (11)	GTou
x ***scapeosa*** (21)	GArf MBal NHar
scapigera (21)	NHar NHol
– DF 614(21)	EBul
§ 'Schneekissen' (Prim)	CCot CElw CTom EBre ELun EOrc EPla GAbr LBre SIng WHer WRus
scotica (11)	CNic EMNN GArf LFox MBal NCra NHar NMir NRed NTow NWCA WAbe WCla WThu
'Sea Way' (Prim)	LGre MRav
secundiflora (26)	CB&S CCla CGle CNic CPar CPla CWGN ELan EMNN GDra GTou MBal NCra NHar NKay NMen NRed SPer SUsu WAbe WDav
¶ – CLD 363/488(26)	MFie
♦ x ***serrata*** (2)	See P. x ***vochinensis***
serratifolia (4)	SBla
♦ ***sibirica***	See P. ***nutans*** Georgi
sibthorpii	See P. ***vulgaris sibthorpii***
sieboldii (7)	CBre CGle CHan CRiv CRow CShe EGol ELun EMNN LAbb LFox MBal MBri NCra NHar NRya NVic NWCA SAxl SBar SIng SSpi WEas WHal WHil
¶ – ***alba*** (7)	SWas
– 'Carefree' (7)	CGle NHol
– 'Cherubim' (7)	EBre ECtt GCHN LBre NHar NNrd
– 'Colin' (7)	EDon
– 'Dancing Ladies' (7)	CGle CNic ELan GAbr MFie NHol NJap NRed WSun
– 'Galaxy' (7)	GAbr NHol NRed
– 'Geisha Girl' (7)	CTom EBre ECtt GCHN LBre MRav NHar

Name	Suppliers
– 'Joan Jervis' (7)	EDon
– 'Lilac Sunbonnet' (7)	CGle NNrd
– 'Manankoora' (7)	CDec CGle ELan MFie NHol NJap NRed
– 'Mikado' (7)	EBre ECtt GCHN LBre MFie MRav NHar NNrd
– 'Pago-Pago' (7)	CGle CNic ELun MFie NHol NJap NRed
*– 'Seraphim' (7)	EBre LBre NHar
– 'Snowflake' (7)	CGle CSco EBre EDon GCHN LBre NHar NRed
– 'Tah-ni' (7)	CNic ELan NHol NJap NNrd NRed
– 'Winter Dreams' (7)	CGle CNic ELun MFie NJap
– 'Wrangle Blush' (7)	EDon
– 'Wrangle Snowflake' (7)	EDon
– 'Wrangle White' (7)	EDon
§ ***sikkimensis*** (26)	CBot CGle CMea CPar CRDP CWGN EBre EMNN ENot EPar EPot GCHN LBre LMay MBal MBri MBro MSta NBro NCra NGre NHar NHol NKay NLin NWCA SIng SPer WChe WDav
– BM&W 40(26)	NHol
– crimson and gold (26)	GAbr MFie NHol
¶– var. ***hopeana*** (26)	MFie
*– 'Phokphey' (26)	NHar
– var. ***pudibunda*** (26)	MPlt
– 'Tilman Number 2' (26)	ELun GAbr GDra MFie NHol WDav
silver-laced (Poly)	CDec CGle CRDP ELan EPar WEas WHer
§ ***sinensis*** (27)	MBri
sinoplantaginea (18)	CPla GAbr
sinopurpurea	See P. ***chionantha*** Sinopurpurea Group
'Sir Bedivere' (Prim)	GAbr
smithiana	See P. ***prolifera***
*'Snow Carpet' (Prim)	CB&S
'Snow Cushion' (Prim)	See P. 'Schneekissen'
soldanelloïdes (28)	NCra
sonchifolia (21)	GArf GDra NHar
spectabilis (2)	CArn CNic NHar NHol NMen WAbe WHoo
specuicola JCA 8926(11)	CNic
Spice Shades Group (Poly)	CDec EDon GAbr MFie NHol
¶ Springtime Group (Prim)	NCat
¶ sp. CLD 1173	MFie
sp. CLD 183	EMon
sp. CLD 222 (26)	NHol
sp. CLD 351 (7)	NHol
¶ sp. CLD 487 (4)	MFie
sp. CLD 586 (26)	NHol
¶ sp. CLD 708	MFie
– (7)	NHol
x ***steinii***	See P. x ***forsteri***
¶ 'Stradbrook Gem'	NGar
¶ 'Strawberries and Cream'	CRow
¶ Striped Victorian Group	CMil MFie NHol
'Sue Jervis' (D.Prim)	CTom EBre EDon ELun GCal LBre MBri NHar WEas WHer WPbr WRus
suffrutescens (8)	NMen WThu
¶ 'Sunrise'	WDav
Sunset Group	CNat WFro
'Sunshine Susie' (D.Prim)	CGle EBre ECtt EDon ELan ELun GAbr LBre MBri MRav MYat NCat NEgg NHol NSti SHer SIng WHal WHil WPbr
'Sylvia' (Prim)	NHol
takedana (24)	NHar
tanneri ssp. ***nepalensis*** (21)	ITim NHar NHol
'Tantallon' (21)	EPot
'Tawny Port' (Poly)	CBrd CCot CGle CRiv CRow EPot GAbr LSur NCra WRus
'Techley Red' (Prim)	EPot NNrd
'The Grail' (Prim)	LSur NKay
'Tipperary Purple' (Prim)	GAbr LSur
'Tomato Red' (Prim)	CBrd CRow GAbr NCra NKay
'Torchlight' (Prim)	LHop
¶ ***tosaensis*** (24)	NMen
¶ x ***truncata*** (2)	NHal WDav
'Tyrian Purple' (D.Poly)	CGle
uralensis	See P. ***veris macrocalyx***
'Val Horncastle' (D.Prim)	CB&S ECar ECtt EFol EOrc GAbr MRav MYat NEgg NHar NHol NRoo NSti SHer SPla WCla WHal WHil WPbr
Valentine Victorians (Poly)	GAbr MFie
x ***variabilis***	See P. x ***polyantha***
veris (30)	Widely available
– ssp. ***columnae*** (30)	NHol
¶– hybrids (30)	NHol
§– ssp. ***macrocalyx*** (30)	WHil
¶– red form (30)	CRDP
vernalis	See P. ***vulgaris***
¶ ***verticillata*** (12)	MFie
§ ***vialii*** (17)	Widely available
Victorian shades (Poly)	NCat
§ ***villosa*** (2)	NHol
– var. ***cottica*** (2)	See P. ***villosa***
Violet Victorians (Poly)	MFie WSun
viscosa Allioni	See P. ***latifolia***
§ x ***vochinensis*** (2)	CRiv MBro MHig MSte MYat NHar NHol NKay NNrd NWCA SIng WAbe WDav
§ ***vulgaris*** (30)	Widely available
– ***alba*** (30)	CGle CRow ECha LGre MHig NNrd WDav
– 'Alba Plena' (30)	CGle CRow GAbr GGar IBlr SHer SRms WBon WEas
– Ballyrogan cream edge (30)	CRow IBlr
– 'Brendon Hills' (30)	CRow
– Cornish pink (30)	GAbr
¶– 'Double Sulphur' (30)	CRDP CRow ELan
– green flowered (30)	See P. *v.* 'Viridis'
§– 'Lilacina Plena' (30)	CBot CDec CFis CGle CRow CSam EFol GAbr IBlr MYat NHol NSti SHer SIng SSvw WCla WEas WHal WHer WHil
¶– 'Lutea' (30)	SPla
§– ssp. ***sibthorpii*** (30)	CBro CElw CGle CNic COtt EJud ELun EPla GAbr GTou LFox LSur NBro NCra NHol NNrd NRya SBla SIng WAbe WCra WDav
¶– 'Viridis' (30)	CRow IBlr WCot
waltonii (26)	CBot CNic CPla CWGN GCra MBal MHig WCru WHal
'Wanda' (Prim)	CB&S CBro CCot CFis CGle CKel CRDP CRow CShe CWGN EFou ELan ELun EPar GAbr LSur MPit NGre NHol NSti SBla SIng SPer WEas WPbr
'Wanda Hose in Hose' (Prim)	CGle CTom GAbr NHol SRms WHer

¶ 'Wanda Jack in the Green' (Prim) — CRow
♦ *wardii* — See P. ***involucrata***
warshenewskiana (11) — CBre CNic CPla EMNN EPot GAbr GDra MBal MCas MHig NCra NGre NHar NMen NNrd NRed NRya NTow SBod WEas WOMN WThu
'Wharfedale Ling' (2) — NGar WAbe WDav
'Wharfedale Superb' (2) — NGar NHar WAbe WDav
'Wharfedale Village' (2) — NGar NHar
¶ 'White Lady' — NGar
¶ 'White Linda Pope' (2) — WDav
'White Wanda' (Prim) — CRow LGre LSur SHer WCru
whitei (21) — CBrd MBal NHar SBar SHer
¶ – 'Arduaine' (21) — NHar NRya
§ – 'Sherriff's Variety' (21) — GArf IBlr NCra NHar
'William Gender' (Poly) — CBro LSur WRus
wilsonii (4) — CPla GAbr GArf GCra NHol
'Windrush' — See P. x ***berninae*** 'W.'
♦ 'Winter White' (Poly) — See P. 'Ghia'
'Wisley Red' (Prim) — CTom
wulfeniana (2) — CRiv NMen
yargongensis — See P. ***involucrata yargongensis***
yuparensis (11) — GAbr GTou MFie NHar NMen
¶ 'Zenobia' — NGar

PRINSEPIA (Rosaceae)
See Plant Deletions

PRITCHARDIA (Palmae)
See Plant Deletions

PROSOPIS (Leguminosae)
♦ *chilensis* — See P. ***glandulosa***
¶ *pubescens* — CGre

PROSTANTHERA (Labiatae)
cuneata — Widely available
– 'Alpine Gold' — CMHG GCal
¶ – 'Fastigiata' — GCal
lasianthos — CAbb CHan CPle CTro ECou LGre WPer WWye
melissifolia — CSun LBlm
– var. *parvifolia* — CB&S CTrw GCal WBod WHer WSHC
nivea — CPle CTre CTro
ovalifolia — ECou
'Poorinda Ballerina' — LHop
'Poorinda Pixie' — CBot WBod
rotundifolia — CArn CB&S CGre CHan CPle CSun CTre CTro ERea ISea LAbb SHil SIgm SLMG WBod WWye
– *alba* — CBot
♦ – 'Chelsea Girl' — See P. ***r. rosea***
§ – *rosea* — CB&S CGre CPle CSev CSun CTre ERea GCal LHop SLMG WWye
sieberi — CBow CTre CTrw
walteri — CMHG CPle ECou LGre SAxl SChu SIgm SMrm SUsu

PROTEA (Proteaceae)
compacta — CSun SIgm
cynaroïdes — CHEx SIgm
eximia — CSun

PRUMNOPITYS (Podocarpaceae)
§ *andina* — SLon WWat
elegans — See P. ***andina***
§ *ferruginea* — ECou SBor
§ – 'Golden Dwarf' — CMer
§ *taxifolia* — ECou

PRUNELLA (Labiatae)
§ *grandiflora* — CBow CFis CLew CRow CSco MWat NBee NGre NKay SIng SRms WCHb WHoo WWye
– *alba* — CBow CDoC CHal CPle EPla NKay SChu WCHb
– 'Blue Loveliness' — CNic ELan GDra SPla WCHb
– 'Little Red Riding Hood' — See P. ***g.*** 'Rotkäppchen'
– 'Loveliness' — CBow CDoC CGle CSco CTom EBre ECha ECtt ELan EOrc EPar LBre MRav NBro NMir NNrd SPer WHal WWin
– 'Pagoda' — CPar EHal LAbb NOak WCHb
– 'Pink Loveliness' — CBos CBow CFis CGle CHal CKel CNic CPar CRow CSco EBre ECha EGol EOrc EPar GCHN GDra LBre MBal SIng SPer WByw WEas WPer WWin
– *rosea* — CPle NSel
§ – 'Rotkäppchen' — CGle CTom EBre ECtt GCHN LBre MRav SPer WCHb
– 'White Loveliness' — CGle CRow CTom EBre ECha EGol EOrc EPar EPla GCHN GDra GGar LBre SPer SPla WEas WPer WRus WWin
incisa — See P. ***vulgaris***
* 'Inshriach Ruby' — NBir SPla WCHb
laciniata — WCHb WHer
§ *vulgaris* — CArn CKin CSFH EJud ELan Effi GPoy IEde LHol MChe NLan NMir NSal NSti SIde WCHb WCla WHer WOak WWye
– *alba* — WHer WNdy
– *lilacina* — CHal LBlm
♦ x *webbiana* — See P. ***grandiflora***

PRUNUS † (Rosaceae)
'Accolade' — CAbP CDoC CLnd COtt CSam CSco CTho EBre ECtt ENot GRei IOrc LBre MBri NWea SFam SHBN SIgm SPer SSta WDin WStI
§ 'Amanogawa' — CB&S CBra CLnd CSam CSco EBre EHar ELan ENot GRei IDai IJoh LBre LBuc LNet MBal MBar MBri MGos NBar NWea SFam SHBN SIgm SPer SPla SReu
* – 'Baggesen's Variety' — CLnd
x *amygdalopersica* 'Pollardii' — ELan ENot NWea
– 'Spring Glow' — CDoC
amygdalus — See P. ***dulcis***
F *armeniaca* 'Alfred' — CSco EHar GTwe MBri SDea SFru SPer
F – 'Bredase' — SDea
– 'De Nancy' — See P. ***a.*** 'Gros Pêche'
F – 'Early Moor Park' — CDoC EWar GBon GRei GTwe MBea NElm SDea SFam SFru SIgm WWeb
F – 'Farmingdale' — SDea SFru SKee
F – 'Goldcot' — SDea
F – 'Gros Pêche' — CMac
F – 'Hongaarse' — SDea

Plant	Suppliers
F – 'Moor Park'	CSco EHar ERea GTwe IJoh LBuc MGos NRog SDea SFru SKee WHig WStI
F – 'New Large Early'	CSco GTwe SDea SFru SKee
F – 'Royal'	CMac
F – 'Tross Orange'	SDea
♦ 'Asano'	See P. 'Geraldinae'
avium	CB&S CBra CKin CLnd CPer EBre EHar ENot GRei ISea LBre LBuc MBar MBri MGos MRav NBee NRoo NWea SHBN SPer WDin WMou
F – 'Amber Heart'	SDea SKee
F – 'Bigarreau Gaucher'	CSco SDea SFru SKee
F – 'Bigarreau Napoléon'	CSco GTwe MGos NElm SDea SFru SKee
F – 'Black Heart'	SKee
F – 'Black Tartarian'	SKee
F – 'Bradbourne Black'	CSco SFru SKee
– 'Cherokee'	See P. *a.* 'Lapins'
F – 'Circassian Black'	SKee
F – 'Colney'	SFru
F – 'Early Rivers'	CSco EWar GTwe IJoh SDea SFru SKee
F – 'Elton Heart'	SKee
F – 'Emperor Francis'	SKee
F – 'Florence'	CSco SKee
¶ – 'Frogmore Early' F	CSco
F – 'Governor Wood'	CSco GTwe NElm SKee
F – 'Hertford'	SFru
F – 'Inga'	MBea
F – 'Ironsides'	SKee
F – 'Kassins Frühe Herz'	SKee
¶ – 'Kent Bigarreau'	CSco
¶ – 'Kentish Red'	CSco
F – 'Lapins'	CSco GTwe SDea SFru SKee SNTN WHig
– 'May Duke'	See P. x ***gondouinii*** 'M.D.'
F – 'Merchant'	CDoC GTwe SFru SKee
F – 'Mermat'	GTwe
F – 'Merpet'	GTwe
F – 'Merton Bigarreau'	CMac CSco SDea SFru
F – 'Merton Bounty'	CMac CSco
¶ – 'Merton Crane'	CSco
F – 'Merton Favourite'	CSco SFru SKee
F – 'Merton Glory'	CDoC CSco EHar EWar GChr GTwe MGos SDea SFru SKee
F – 'Merton Heart'	CMac GSco SDea SKee
¶ – 'Merton Late'	CSco
F – 'Merton Marvel'	CSco SKee
¶ – 'Merton Premier'	CSco
F – 'Merton Reward'	CSco SKee
¶ – 'Nabella'	CSco
– 'Napoléon'	See P. *a.* 'Bigarreau Napoléon'
F – 'Newstar'	SFru
F – 'Noble'	SKee
F – 'Noir de Guben'	GChr GTwe SFru SKee
F – 'Nutberry Black'	SKee
F – 'Plena'	CB&S CLnd CTho ELan ENot GRei IOrc LBuc LPan MBal MGos NBee NWea SPer WDin
F – 'Roundel'	CSco SDea SFru SKee
¶ – 'Sasha'	GTwe
¶ – 'Starkrimson'	GTwe
F – 'Stella'	CMac CSam CSco EBre EHar EWar GBon GChr GRei GTwe IJoh LBre LBuc MBea MBri MGos NBar NBee NElm NRog SDea SFru SIgm SKee SPer WHig WWeb
F – 'Stella Compact'	CSco GTwe LBuc MBri SKee WHig
¶ – 'Summit'	SFru
F – 'Sunburst'	CSco GTwe LBuc MBri SDea SFru SKee SNTN WHig
F – 'Turkish Black'	SKee
F – 'Van'	CDoC CSco EHar GTwe SFru SIgm SKee
F – 'Waterloo'	SFru SKee
F – 'White Heart'	NElm SKee
besseyi	CCor EPla MGos
* 'Birch Bark'	GRei
x ***blireana***	CBra CDoC CLnd CSco CTho ECtt IDai MBar MBri MRav NBee SPer SReu
'Blushing Bride'	See P. 'Shôgetsu'
capuli	See P. ***salicifolia***
cerasifera	CSco GAri LBuc NWea WDin WMou
F – 'Cherry Plum'	SKee
– 'Crimson Dwarf'	CDoC SPer
– 'Hessei'	CDoC MRav WPat
F – 'Kentish Red'	SKee
F – Myrobalan Group	CKin CSco SDea SFru SKee
N – 'Nigra'	CBra CDoC CLnd CSam CSco EHar ELan IDai IOrc LBuc LNet LPan MBri MGos NBar NBee SDea SHBN SPer SPla WAbe WDin WStI
– 'Pendula'	WMou
§ – 'Pissardii'	CBra CSco EBre GRei LAbb LBre LBuc MBar MRav NNor NWea SIgm SPer
– 'Rosea'	SHil
F ***cerasus*** 'Montmorency'	SDea SFru SKee
F – 'Morello'	CMac CSam CSco EBre EHar EWar GBon GChr GRei GTwe IJoh LBre LBuc MBea MBri NBar NBee NElm NRog SDea SFru SIgm SKee SPer WHig WWeb
F – 'Nabella'	EWar
– 'Rhexii'	EHar MGos SHil SPer WAbe
F – 'Wye Morello'	SKee
♦ 'Cheal's Weeping'	See P. 'Kiku-shidare'
§ 'Chôshû-hizakura'	CDoC CLnd EBar ECtt GRei IOrc LNet SDea SHil SPer WAbe
§ x ***cistena***	CB&S CBot CPMA CPle CSco CShe EBre EFol ELan ENot IJoh IOrc LBre MBar MBri MGos MPla MWat NBee NKay NRoo SHBN SPer SPla WAbe WDin WPat WStI WTyr
– 'Crimson Dwarf'	See P. x *c.*
¶ 'Collingwood Ingram'	SHil
♦ ***conradinae***	See P. ***hirtipes***
F ***domestica*** 'Angelina Burdett' (D)	CSco GTwe NRog SKee SNTN
F – 'Anna Späth' (C/D)	SKee
F – 'Ariel' (C/D)	SDea SKee
F – 'Autumn Compote' (C)	SKee
F – 'Avalon'	GTwe SFru SKee WHig
F – 'Belgian Purple' (C)	SKee
F – 'Belle de Louvain' (C)	CSco GTwe NRog SDea SFru SKee
¶ – 'Black Prince' (C)	CSco
¶ – 'Blaisdon Red' (C)	CSco

F – 'Blue Imperatrice' (C/D) SKee
F – 'Blue Tit' (C/D) SKee
F – 'Bonne de Bry' (D) CSco SKee
¶ – 'Bountiful' (C) CSco
F – 'Brandy Gage' (C/D) CSco SKee
F – 'Bryanston Gage' (D) CSco SKee SNTN
F – 'Burbank' (C/D) SDea
F – 'Bush' (C) SKee
F – 'Cambridge Gage' (D) CDoC CSam CSco EBre EHar ERea GBon GTwe LBre LBuc MBri MGos MWat NRog SDea SFam SFru SIgm SKee SPer WHig WStI WWeb
F – 'Coe's Golden Drop' (D) CSco GTwe MBri MGos SDea SFam SFru SIgm SKee SNTN
F – 'Count Althann's Gage' (D) EHar GTwe NRog SDea SFru SIgm SKee
¶ – 'Cox's Emperor' (C) CSco
F – 'Crimson Drop' (D) SKee
– 'Cropper' See P. *d.* 'Laxton's Cropper'
F – 'Curlew' (C) SDea
F – 'Czar' (C) CDoC CSam CSco EBre EHar EWar GChr GTwe IJoh IOrc LBre LBuc MBea MGos NBar NElm NRog SDea SFru SIgm SKee SPer WWeb
– 'Delicious ' See P. *d.* 'Laxton's Delicious'
– 'Denniston's Superb' See P. *d.* 'Imperial Gage'
F – 'Diamond' (C) SKee
F – 'Dittisham Ploughman' (C) SKee
F – 'Early Laxton' (C/D) CSco GTwe SDea SFam SKee
♦– 'Early Orleans' See P. *d.* 'Monsieur Hâtif'
– 'Early Prolific' See P. *d.* 'Rivers's Early Prolific'
– 'Early Rivers' See P. *d.* 'Rivers's Early Prolific'
F – 'Early Transparent Gage' (C/D) CSco GTwe SDea SFam SFru SIgm SNTN
F – 'Edwards' (C/D) CSco EWar GTwe MBri NBee SDea SFam SFru SIgm SKee WHig
F – 'Excalibur' GTwe SFru
F – German Prune Group (C) SKee
F – 'Giant Prune' (C) CSco GTwe NRog SKee
F – 'Godshill Blue' (C) SDea
F – 'Golden Transparent' (D) CSco GTwe NRog SFam SFru
F – 'Goldfinch' (D) CSco GTwe NRog SFam SKee
F – Green Gage Group (C/D) EHar GTwe MBea NElm NRog SDea SFam SKee SPer
F – Green Gage Group 'Old Green Gage' (D/C) SFru SIgm SNTN
F – 'Grove's Late Victoria' (C/D) CSco SKee
F – 'Guthrie's Late Green' (D) SKee
F – 'Herman' (C/D) CSam GTwe
F – 'Imperial Gage' (C/D) CMac GRei GTwe LBuc MBri SDea SFam SFru SIgm SKee WHig
– ssp. *institia* See P. *institia*
F – 'Jefferson' (D) CSco GTwe NRog SDea SFam SFru SIgm SKee
F – 'Kirke's' (D) CSco CWSG GTwe MBri SDea SFam SFru SIgm SKee
¶ – 'Late Muscatelle' (D) SKee
¶ – 'Late Transparent Gage' (D) CSco
– 'Laxton's Bountiful' See P. *d.* 'Bountiful'
F – 'Laxton's Cropper' (C) CSco GTwe NRog SKee
¶ – 'Laxton's Delicious' (D) CSco GTwe SKee
F – 'Laxton's Delight' (D) CSco GTwe
F – 'Laxton's Gage' (D) CSco SDea SKee
¶ – 'Laxton's Supreme' (C/D) CSco
F – 'Marjorie's Seedling' (C) CDoC CSco EBre EHar GBon GTwe LBre LBuc MGos MWat NBee NElm SDea SFam SFru SIgm SKee SPer WHig
F – 'McLaughlin' (D) SKee
F – 'Merton Gem' (C/D) CSco GTwe SFam SFru SKee
F – 'Monarch' (C) CSco GTwe SKee
F – 'Monsieur Hâtif' (C) SKee
F – 'Ontario' (C/D) CSco GTwe SKee
F – 'Opal' (D) CDoC CSco EWar GTwe IJoh IOrc MGos MWat NElm SDea SIgm SKee WHig
F – 'Orleans' (C) SKee
F – 'Ouillins Gage' (C/D) CMac CSam CSco EHar ERea EWar GBon GChr GTwe IJoh LBuc MBri MWat NElm NRog SDea SFam SIgm SKee SNTN SPer
F – 'Peach Plum' (D) SKee
¶ – 'Pershore' (C) CSco
F – 'Pond's Seedling' (C) SDea SKee
F – 'President' (C/D) SDea SKee
F – 'Prince Englebert' (C) SKee
F – 'Priory Plum' (D) SDea
F – 'Purple Pershore' (C) CSco CWSG GTwe NRog SDea SKee
– 'Quetsche d'Alsace' See P. *d.* German Prune Group
F – 'Reeves' (C) CSco GTwe SFru SIgm SKee
F – 'Reine Claude de Bavais' (D) CSco GTwe NRog SFam SKee
– 'Reine Claude Dorée' See P. *d.* Green Gage Group
F – 'Reine Claude Violette' (D) SKee
F – 'Rivers's Early Prolific' (C) CSco GTwe MBri MWat NRog SDea SFru SIgm SKee
F – 'Royale de Vilvoorde' (D) SKee
F – 'Ruth Gerstetter' (C) SKee
F – 'Sanctus Hubertus' (D) CSco EWar GTwe LBuc SDea SIgm SKee
F – 'Severn Cross' (D) GTwe SKee
F – 'Stint' (C/D) SKee
¶ – 'Thames Cross' (D) CSco
F – 'Transparent Gage' (D) CSco SFru SKee
F – 'Utility' (D) SKee
F – 'Victoria' (C/D) CMac CSam CSco EBre EHar EWar GBon GChr GRei GTwe IJoh IOrc LBre LBuc MBea MBri MWat NBar NBee NElm NRog SDea SFam SFru SIgm SKee SNTN SPer WHig WWeb

Plant	Suppliers
F– 'Warwickshire Drooper' (C)	CSam CSco EWar GBon GTwe SDea SFru SKee SPer
F– 'Washington' (D)	CSco SKee
F– 'White Magnum Bonum' (C)	SDea
F– 'Wyedale' (C)	CSco GTwe
F– 'Yellow Egg' (C)	GTwe SDea SFam
F– 'Yellow Pershore' (C)	MBea NRog SKee
§ ***dulcis***	CLnd CSco ENot MBar NWea SDea SKee WDin
F– 'Macrocarpa'	EHar ESim SFam SHil
fruticosa 'Globosa'	CDoC MBri
'Fudan-zakura'	SHil
§ 'Geraldinae'	CLnd EBar ENot SHil
glandulosa 'Alba Plena'	CB&S CBot CBow CCla CDec CSco CTre EGol EHar ELan ENot ESis MBal MBar MGos MPla MWat NHol SHBN SHil SPer SPla SSpi WDin WPat WSHC
♦– 'Rosea Plena'	See P. *g.* 'Sinensis'
§ – 'Sinensis' (d)	CBot CBow CCla CDec CPMA EGol EHar ELan ENot EPla ESis LHop MBal MGos MPla MPlt NHol SHBN SHil SPer SPla SSpi SSta WPat WSHC
F× ***gondouinii*** 'May Duke'	SKee
'Hally Jolivette'	CChu COtt CShe ELan MBri WAbe
'Hillieri'	EBre LBre MBar MGos
'Hillieri Spire'	See P. 'Spire'
¶ ***hirtipes***	CTho
'Hisakura'	See P. 'Chôshû-hizakura'
♦ 'Hokusai'	See P. Uzu-zakura
Hollywood ®	See P. 'Trailblazer'
'Ichiyo'	See P. 'Chôshû-hizakura'
¶ 'Imose'	EBar
incisa	GAri IOrc SPer
¶– 'Beniomi'	EBlo
– 'February Pink'	MBri
– 'Fujima'	WPat WWat
– 'Kojo-no-mai'	EBlo EBre EPla GAri LBre MAsh MBri
– 'Oshidori'	MBri WPat
¶– 'Pendula'	MBri
– 'Praecox'	LRHS MBri SHil
F ***institia***	EHar SFru
F– 'Black Bullace'	SKee
F– 'Blue Violet Damson'	SKee
F– 'Bradley's King Damson'	CSco SKee
F– 'Farleigh Damson' (C)	CSco GTwe NBee SDea SFru SIgm SKee SPer
F– 'Godshill Damson' (C)	SDea
– 'Golden Bullace'	See P. *i.* 'White Bullace'
– 'King of Damsons'	See P. *i.* 'Bradley's King Damson'
¶– 'Langley Bullace'	CSco SKee
F– 'Merryweather Damson' (C)	CDoC CMac CSco EBre EHar ERea GBon GChr GRei GTwe LBre LBuc MBea MBri NBar NBee NRog SDea SFam SFru SKee WStI
¶– 'Mirabelle de Metz' (C)	CSco SFru
F– Mirabelle de Nancy (C)	GTwe SDea SKee
F– 'Mirabelle de Nancy (Red)' (C)	SDea
♦– 'Mirabelle Petite'	See P. *i.* 'Mirabelle de Metz'
F– 'Prune Damson'	CSam CSco EHar EWar GBon GTwe LBuc MBri MGos MWat NRog SDea SFam SFru SIgm SKee WHig
¶– 'Shepherd's Bullace'	SKee
– 'Shropshire Damson'	See P. *i.* 'Prune Damson'
F– 'Small Bullace'	SKee
F– 'White Bullace'	CSco SKee
F– 'Yellow Apricot'	SKee
§ ***jamasakura***	GAri SHil
'Jô-nioi'	CLnd SHil
'Kanzan'	CB&S CBra CLnd CSco EBre EHar ELan GRei IDai IJoh LBre LBuc LPan MBal MBar MBri MGos NWea SDea SFam SHBN SPer SReu SSta WAbe
§ 'Kiku-shidare-zakura'	CB&S CBra CLnd CSam CSco EBre ECtt ELan GRei IDai IJoh LBre LBuc LNet MBal MBar MBri MGos MRav NBar NBee NWea SFam SHBN SIgm SPer SReu WAbe WDin WStI
Korean Hill Cherry	See P. ***serrulata pubescens***
♦ ***kurilensis***	See P. ***nipponica k.***
'Kursar'	CBar COtt EHar IOrc LNet LRHS MBri SEng SHil
laurocerasus	CB&S CBow CBra CKin CSco ELan GRei IDai LNet MRav MWat NNor NWea SArc SPer SReu WAbe WMou WStI WWin
– 'Aureovariegata'	See P. *l.* 'Taff's Golden Gleam'
– 'Camelliifolia'	CChu CFis EPla ISea SMad WHCG
N– 'Castlewellan' (v)	CB&S CBot CChu COtt CPle CTrw EFol EGol ELan EMon EPla IBar IJoh IOrc ISea MBar MBri MGos MPar NHol SLon SPer SPla SSta WDin WPat
– 'Caucasica'	EMon IDai WWeb
– 'Cherry Brandy'	ENot SFai SGil SPer
– 'Dart's Low Green'	ENot
¶– 'Golden Splash'	EMon
– 'Green Marble' (v)	CBow CPMA EMon MUlv SFai WSHC
– 'Grünerteppich' ('Green Carpet')	COtt EMil
– 'Herbergii'	CDoC
§ – 'Latifolia'	CBow CHEx EMon EPla SArc
♦– 'Magnoliifolia'	See P. *l.* 'Latifolia'
– 'Marbled White'	See P. *l.* 'Castlewellan'
– 'Mischeana'	ENot MBri MUlv
– 'Mount Vernon'	MBar MBri MGos NBee SFai WDin
– 'Otto Luyken'	Widely available
– 'Reynvaanii'	CBow CPMA MBri MGos
– 'Rotundifolia'	CDoC EBar ELan ENot LBuc MBar MBri WDin
– 'Rudolf Billeter'	EPla
– 'Schipkaensis'	CSco NNor SPer
§ – 'Taff's Golden Gleam' (v)	CBow CCla CPMA SMad
– 'Van Nes'	EMil IOrc MUlv WStI WWeb
N– 'Variegata'	EMon MGos
– 'Zabeliana'	CDoC CLan CMHG CSco ENot MBar NRoo SHBN SLon SPer SReu WCru WDin WPat WWin
lusitanica	CB&S CKin CLan CMHG CSco EBre EHar ELan ENot GRei IDai ISea LBre LNet MBal MBar MBri MGos NNor NWea SLon SPer SSta WCoo WDin WMou WWat

– ssp. ***azorica***	EPla SHil SLon SMad SPer WMou WWat
– 'Myrtifolia'	EHar EPla MUlv SMad
– 'Variegata'	CB&S CBot CBra CCla CMHG CSco EBre EHar EHoe ELan ENot IJoh IOrc ISea LBre MBal MBri MWat SDix SHBN SLon SPer SSta WDin WPat WWat
maackii	CTho EHar LPan SSpi WWat
– 'Amber Beauty'	CBow CPMA LTil SSpi
¶ ***mahaleb***	CTho
mandshurica	WCoo
♦ 'Mount Fuji'	See P. 'Shirotae'
mume	CDoC WNor
– 'Alboplena'	GAri SHil
– 'Alphandii'	GAri SHil
– 'Beni-chidori'	EBre ELan GAri LBre LPan LRHS MBri SHil SIgm SSpi
– 'Beni-shidori'	See P. ***m.*** 'Beni-chidori'
§ – 'Omoi-no-mama'	GAri LRHS MBri SSpi
– 'Omoi-no-wac'	See P. ***mume*** 'Omoi-no-mama'
– 'Pendula'	CLnd MBri
myrobalana	See P. ***cerasifera*** Myrobalan Group
x ***nigrella*** 'Muckle'	WPat
¶ ***nipponica*** var. ***kurilensis***	WPat
– – 'Ruby'	COtt LRHS MGos
'Okame'	CLnd CSam CTho EBre EHar LBre MBri MGos NWea SHil SPer
§ 'Okumiyako'	CB&S
¶ 'Opal'	LBuc
padus	CDoC CKin CLnd CPer EHar IDai IOrc LBuc LNet MBri MGos NBee NRoo NWea WDin WMou WStI
– 'Albertii'	CTho SEng SHil
– 'Colorata'	CDoC CMHG CTho ELan IOrc LNet MBri SHBN SPer SSpi WDin
– 'Dropmore'	SPer
– 'Grandiflora'	See P. ***p.*** 'Watereri'
– 'Purple Queen'	CTho ENot MGos
§ – 'Watereri'	CB&S CDoC CLnd CTho EHar ELan ENot IDai IOrc MBri SHBN SPer SPla SReu SSta WDin
'Pandora'	CBar CDoC CLnd EBre ECtt ENot LBre MBal NWea SFam SHBN SPer WAbe
pendula var. ***ascendens*** 'Rosea'	CLnd SReu
§ – 'Pendula Rosea'	CB&S CDoC ECtt ENot MBar MBri SIgm SPer
§ – 'Pendula Rubra'	CDoC COtt ENot LNet MBri MGos SFam SHBN SPer
§ – 'Stellata'	SHil
F ***persica*** 'Amsden June'	ELan ERea GTwe SDea SFam
F – 'Bellegarde'	ERea GTwe SDea SFam SFru SKee
F – 'Bonanza'	CDoC ELan ERea SFru
F – 'Doctor Hogg'	SDea
F – 'Duke of York'	ERea EWar GTwe SDea SFam SFru SKee WWeb
F – 'Early Alexander'	GTwe
F – 'Early Rivers'	CDoC CMac EHar GTwe NRog SDea
F – 'Francis Miriam'	SKee
F – 'Garden Anny'	ELan ERea MBri
F – 'Garden Lady'	ERea GTwe WHig
F – 'Hale's Early'	ERea GTwe MBri SDea SFam SKee
F – var. ***nectarina*** Crimson Gold®	SDea
F – – 'Early Gem'	SDea
F – – 'Elruge'	ERea GTwe SFam SFru
F – – 'Fantasia'	SDea
F – – 'Fire Gold'	SDea
F – – 'Fuzalode'	SDea
F – – 'Humboldt'	GTwe SFam SFru
F – – 'John Rivers'	ERea GTwe SFam SFru
F – – 'Lord Napier'	CDoC CWSG EHar ERea IJoh LBuc MBea MGos SDea SFam SFru SIgm SKee SPer WHig WStI
F – – 'Nectared'	GTwe SKee
F – – 'Nectarella'	CDoC ERea GTwe SFru WHig
F – – 'Pineapple'	CDoC EHar ERea GTwe NElm SDea SFam SFru SKee WHig
F – – 'Red Haven'	CDoC GTwe SFam SKee
F – – 'Rivers Prolific'	SDea
F – – 'Ruby Gold'	SDea
– 'Nemarquard'	CDoC
F – 'Peregrine'	CMac CWSG EHar ERea EWar GBon GRei GTwe IJoh LBuc MBea MBri MGos NBee NElm NRog SDea SFam SFru SIgm SKee SPer WHig WWeb
– 'Red Peachy'	NBar
F – 'Reliance'	SDea
F – 'Robin Redbreast'	SDea
F – 'Rochester'	CWSG EHar ERea EWar GBon GTwe MBea MBri NElm SDea SFam SIgm SKee WHig WStI
F – 'Royal George'	GTwe NRog SFam SFru SKee
– 'Rubira'	EPla
F – 'Saturne'	WHig
– 'Spring Glow'	MBri
F – 'Springtime'	SDea
– 'White Peachy'	NBar
– 'Windle Weeping' (d)	CB&S
'Pink Perfection'	CB&S CLnd CSco EBre GRei LBre LPan MBri SFam SHBN SPer SPla SReu WAbe
'Pink Shell'	CLnd CTho MBri SFam SHil WStI
pissardii	See P. ***cerasifera*** 'Pissardii'
'Pissardii Nigra'	See P. ***cerasifera*** 'Nigra'
prostrata	CLew WThu
¶ ***pumila***	SIng
– var. ***depressa***	CBow CLew CPMA EGol GAri LHop MBar MPla MRav SHil SPla SSpi
'Red Cascade'	SDea
'Rhexlicer'	CDoC
sargentii	CBra CDoC CLnd CTho EBar EBre EHar ELan ENot IDai IHos IJoh IOrc LBre LPan MBri MGos NWea SFam SHBN SPer SPla SReu SSta STre WAbe WDin WMou
– Rancho ®	CLnd ENot MBri SPer
x ***schmittii***	CLnd CTho SHil SPer
'Sekiyama'	See P. 'Kanzan'
serotina	NWea WMou
§ ***serrula***	CBar CBra CDoC CLnd CTho EHar ELan ENot IDai IOrc LPan MBal MBar MBri MGos NBar NBee NBir NWea SEng SKee SMad SPer SPla SSta WAbe WDin WMou WWat
– var. ***tibetica***	See P. ***serrula***
serrulata	WNor
– 'Erecta'	See P. 'Amanogawa'
– 'Grandiflora'	See P. 'Ukon'

– 'Grandiflora'	See P. 'Ukon'
– 'Longipes'	See P. 'Okumiyako'
♦– 'Miyako	See P. 'Okumiyako'
N– ***pubescens***	See P. x ***verecunda***
– 'Rosea'	See P. 'Kiku-shidare-zakura'
– var. ***spontanea***	See P. ***jamasakura***
'Shidare-zakura'	See P. 'Kiku-shidare-zakura'
'Shimizu-zakura'	See P. 'Okumiyako'
'Shirofugen'	CB&S CBra CDoC CLnd EBre ECtt EHar IDai IOrc LBre LPan MBri SDea SFam SPer WDin
§ 'Shirotae'	CDoC CLnd CSam CTho ELan ENot IDai IOrc MBal MGos MRav NWea SPer SPla SReu
§ 'Shôgetsu'	CLnd CSco EBar ELan ENot GRei IOrc MBal MBri SFam SHBN SHil SPer
'Shosar'	CLnd CSco MBri SEng SPer WAbe
'Snow Goose'	MBri
spinosa	CDoC CKin CPer LBuc MBri NNor NWea SPer STre WDin WMou WNor
– 'Purpurea'	CSco SHil WPat
§ 'Spire'	CBra CDoC CLnd CSco CTho EHar ENot GRei IOrc LPan SFam SPer WAbe WWat
x ***subhirtella***	WNor
x ***subhirtella ascendens***	See P. ***pendula a.***
x ***subhirtella*** 'Autumnalis'	CB&S CBra CLnd CSco CTho EBre EGol EHar ELan ENot IDai IHos IJoh ISea LBre MBal MBar MBri NBee NWea SDea SFam SHBN SIgm SPer SReu SSta WDin WWat
– 'Autumnalis Rosea'	CB&S CSam CTho EHar ELan ENot GRei IJoh LBuc LNet MBar MBri MGos NBar NBee NWea SHBN SIgm SPer SPla SReu WAbe WDin WWat
– 'Fukubana'	CLnd COtt CTho ELan MBri SHil WDin
– 'Pendula' hort.	See P. ***pendula*** 'Pendula Rosea'
♦– 'Pendula Rubra'	See P. ***pendula*** 'Pendula Rubra'
N– 'Rosea'	CLnd SReu
♦– 'Stellata'	See P. ***pendula*** 'Stellata'
'Taihaku'	CB&S CDoC CLnd CSam CSco CTho EBre EHar ELan ENot IOrc LBre LNet LPan MBri MGos NWea SFam SHBN SPer SReu WAbe WDin WStI
'Taoyame'	CLnd
tenella	CB&S CBow CBra CCla CSco ECtt ELan MBri MGos NBee SDix SEng SHer SIng WStI WWat
– 'Fire Hill'	CBow CCla CDoC CPMA CSco CShe EBre EHar ELan IJoh LAbb LBre LNet LTil MBar MGos MPla NHar SHBN SHil SPer SSpi SWas WDin WPat
tibetica	See P. ***serrula***
tomentosa	EPla ESim WAbe
F 'Trailblazer' (C/D)	CLnd CSco IOrc LPan MGos NWea SKee
triloba	CB&S CBow CBra CLnd CSco ECtt IJoh LAbb LBuc LPan MBar MBri MGos MPla SHBN SIgm SPer SSpi WDin WTyr
– 'Multiplex'	EBre EGol ENot IHos LBre SRms
– 'Rosenmund'	MBri
§ 'Ukon'	CB&S CDoC CLnd CSco CTho EBar EHar ENot IOrc LNet MBal MBar MBri NWea SFam SPer SReu WAbe WDin WStI
'Umineko'	CDoC CLnd ENot IOrc MGos SPer
§ x ***verecunda***	CDoC CLnd EBar NWea SPer
– 'Autumn Glory'	EBre LBre SHil SPer
virginiana 'Shubert'	CDoC CLnd CTho EHar ELan ENot EPla IOrc MBri SEng SSpi SSta
'Wood's Variety'	See P. ***cerasifera*** 'Woodii'
x ***yedoensis***	CBra CLnd CTho ENot SFam SPer WDin WWat
– 'Ivensii'	CDoC ECtt SHBN WStI
x ***yedoensis pendula***	See P. x ***y.*** 'Shidare-yoshino'
x ***yedoensis*** 'Perpendens'	See P. x ***y.*** 'Shidare-yoshino'
§ – 'Shidare-yoshino'	CDoC CLnd CSco EBar ECtt LNet MBar MBri MRav SPer WWat
¶ – 'Tsubame'	MBri

PSEUDOCYDONIA (Rosaceae)

§ ***sinensis***	LNet

PSEUDOFUMARIA (Papaveraceae)

§ ***alba***	CMil CRow EPot ESis MTho SSou WBon
§ ***lutea***	CHad CNic ECro EHal EMar IBlr LGro MPit MTol MUlv NFai WBon WCot

PSEUDOLARIX (Pinaceae)

§ ***amabilis***	CAbP CDoC CGre CMCN CMHG EBre EHar EHul LBre LCon LNet LTil MBal MBar MBri NHol SHil SMad SSpi STre WCoo WNor WWat
kaempferi	See P. ***amabilis***

PSEUDOMERTENSIA (Boraginaceae)

sp. SEP 234	WDav

PSEUDOMUSCARI See MUSCARI

PSEUDOPANAX † (Araliaceae)

Adiantifolius Group 'Adiantifolius'	CB&S CHEx IBar
– 'Cyril Watson'	CB&S
arboreus	CHEx
chathamicus	CHEx
crassifolius	CB&S CBot CHEx ECou IBar SArc
ferox	CHEx
laetus	CB&S CHEx
lessonii	CB&S CHEx ECou
– 'Gold Splash' (v)	CB&S CTro NPal
– hybrids	CHEx
– 'Purpureus'	CB&S
'Sabre'	SMad

PSEUDOPHEGOPTERIS (Thelypteridaceae)

levingei	CRDP EMon LRHS

PSEUDOPHOENIX (Palmae)
* *nativo* MBri

PSEUDOSASA (Gramineae(Bambuseae))
§ *amabilis* ISta SBam SCob SDry
♦– hort. See ARUNDINARIA *tecta*
§ *japonica* CHEx EFul ELan ERav IDai ISta LBam MBal NJap NSel SBam SCob SDry SHil SMad SPer SReu WDin WJun
– 'Tsutsumiana' LBam SBam SDry WJun
– 'Variegata' EFul EPla SBam SDry
¶ *owatarii* SDry
pleioblastoïdes EPla SBam SDry
¶ *usawai* WJun

PSEUDOTSUGA (Pinaceae)
§ *menziesii* CDoC CPer EHar IDai IOrc LBuc LCon MBar NWea WMou
¶– 'Blue Wonder' CKen MAsh
– 'Densa' CKen
– 'Fastigiata' CKen
– 'Fletcheri' CKen LCon MAsh MBar MBri SLim
– var. *glauca* EHar IBar LCon MBar STre
– 'Glauca Pendula' EHar MBar MGos
I – 'Gotelli's Pendula' CKen
– 'Graceful Grace' CKen
¶– 'Julie' CKen
¶– 'Little Jamie' CKen
– 'Little Jon' LCon MBar SLim
– 'Nana' CKen
– Pendula Group LCon MAsh MBri
– 'Stairii' CKen
– 'Templehof Compact' SLim
– 'Viridis' GRei
taxifolia See P. *menziesii*

PSEUDOWINTERA (Winteraceae)
§ *colorata* CB&S CDec CDoC CLan CTrw IBar IDai IJoh IOrc ISea NHol SDry SHil WBod WPat

PSIDIUM (Myrtaceae)
♦ *cattleianum* See P. *littorale longipes*
F *littorale* ERea ESim
– var. *littorale* ESim
§ – var. *longipes* CTro
– var. *lucidum* See P. *l. littorale*

PSILOSTROPHE (Compositae)
See Plant Deletions

PSORALEA (Leguminosae)
affinis CHEx
¶ *pinnata* CTro

PSYCHOTRIA (Rubiaceae)
capensis SLMG

PTELEA (Rutaceae)
trifoliata CB&S CBow CBra CChu CCla CLnd CMHG CSco EHar GWht LHol SHil SPer SSpi WBod WCoo WNor WOMN
– 'Aurea' CAbP CBot CBow CCla CPMA CSco EHar ELan GWht LTil MBri MGos MUlv SHBN SHil SPer SSpi WHig WPat

PTERACANTHUS See **STROBILANTHES**

PTERIDIUM (Dennstaedtiaceae)
aquilinum Percristatum Group IOrc NKay

PTERIDOPHYLLUM (Papaveraceae)
racemosum EPot

PTERIS (Adiantaceae)
argyraea MBri NMar
cretica CHal MBri SApp SArc
– *albolineata* MBri NMar SRms
– *cristata* CHal MBri
– 'Gautheri' MBri
– 'Parkeri' MBri
– 'Rivertoniana' MBri
– 'Rowei' MBri
– 'Wimsettii' MBri
ensiformis MBri NMar
– 'Arguta' MBri
– 'Victoriae' MBri
tremula CHal MBri NMar
umbrosa MBri
¶ *wallichiana* WRic

PTEROCARYA (Juglandaceae)
fraxinifolia CAbb CB&S CDoC CLnd CMCN CSam EArb EHar ENot IBar IOrc MBlu SHil SPer WDin WMou
¶– var. *dumosa* WMou
x *rehderiana* WMou
rhoifolia CCor CMCN EHar WCoo WMou
stenoptera CB&S CLnd CMCN EArb EHar WMou
– 'Fern Leaf' WMou

PTEROCELTIS (Ulmaceae)
See Plant Deletions

PTEROCEPHALUS (Dipsacaceae)
parnassi See P. *perennis perennis*
§ *perennis* CShe EFol ESis LHil MPit NBir NKay NRar WAbe WHil WPat WPer
§ – ssp. *perennis* CHal CLew CNic EPot GCHN LBee MBro MCas MFos MHig NTow SBla SIng SPla WEas WHoo WOMN WOld WWin

PTEROSTYLIS (Orchidaceae)
¶ *curta* CRDP NHar

PTEROSTYRAX (Styracaceae)
corymbosa CChu CMCN GWht LRHS SSpi
hispida CB&S CChu CCla CMCN CPle ELan LTil MRav SHil SReu SSpi SSta WBod WCoo WWat

PTILOSTEMON (Compositae)

See Plant Deletions

PTILOTRICHUM See ALYSSUM

PTYCHOSPERMA (Palmae)

See Plant Deletions

PULICARIA (Compositae)

dysenterica — CArn CKin IEde MChe NMir NSal WCHb WGwy WNdy WOak WWye

PULMONARIA † (Boraginaceae)

affinis — EMon
angustifolia — CFis CHEx CHad CRow CSam EFol GDra MFir MNFA MPlt MWat NHol NOrc NSal NSel SChu SSpi WBon WEas WPer WRus WWin
– ssp. *azurea* — CBow CBro CElw CLew CMil CRow CWGN EBre EFou EGol ELan ELun EPla ERav IDai LBre MBri NBro NKay NRar NRoo NSti NTow SPer SPla SSpi SSvw WCru WTyr
– 'Beth's Blue' — ECha EOrc LRHS MBri MUlv
– 'Beth's Pink' — ECha LRHS NCat NSti
– 'Blaues Meer' — SAxl SSpi WThi
– 'Blue Ensign' — ECha EFou EPla LRHS
– 'Munstead Blue' — CBre CChu CElw CGle CKel CRDP CShe EBre ECar ECha EGol EHal ENot EPar EPla LBre MTho NCat NRya SCro WCru
– 'Rubra' — CLew ELun MWat NSel SRms SSvw
¶ 'Barfield Regalia' — EMon
¶ 'Botanic Hybrid' — NCat
¶ 'Chintz' — SWas
'Cleeton Red' — NSti
'Fiona' — LHil
'Glacier' — CGle CRDP ECha EMon EPla LRHS NSti SAxl
'Highdown' — See P. 'Lewis Palmer'
§ 'Lewis Palmer' — Widely available
longifolia — CBot CBro CGle CHan CMHG CRow EFol EGol ELan EPar EPla GCal LGan LHil MBri MUlv NCat NSal NSti NVic SChu SMad WByw WCHb WCru WEas WRus
– 'Bertram Anderson' — CGle CHad CRDP CWGN EMon MUlv SBla SUsu SWas WCHb WCot
¶ – ssp. *cebennensis* — EMon
– 'Dordogne' — CGle CRDP SUsu SWas
'Mary Mottram' — CCot MBel MUlv NBir NSti SWas WCru
'Mawson's Blue' — CRDP CTom EBlo ECar ECha EMon EPla MBri MWat WAbe WCru WPbr WSun WWat
¶ 'Merlin' — EMon
mollis — CBot CHan EMar EOrc EPla GCal NCat NSti SFar
– 'Royal Blue' — EFou EGol GCHN MRav NRoo WRus
'Mournful Purple' — CGle CRDP CRow ECar EPla ERav MUlv NCat NSti WAbb WCru
¶ 'Mrs Kittle' — SWas
'Nürnberg' — CRDP EMon EPla LRHS
obscura — EMon
officinalis — CArn CBro CFis CGle CRow CSFH EOrc EPar Effi GPoy LHol MBel MChe MFir NBar NKay NSel SIde WCru WEas WHal WOak WRus
– *alba* — EHal NCat WByw
§ – 'Bowles' Blue' — CChu CGle CRow EBre ECha LBre LGre NCat NSti SAxl WAbb WCru WPbr WRus WThi
– 'Cambridge Blue' — CBos CBre CBro CElw CHan CMea CRDP EFol EFou EGol EMon EOrc EPla ERav NHol NSti SAxl WBon WByw WEas WHal
– *rubra* — EOrc EPla NBir WByw WCHb
– 'Sissinghurst White' — Widely available
– 'White Wings' — CHan CRDP CSco EPla NHol SChu SSpi WBon WCHb WCra WEas WSun
¶ 'Oxford Blue' — CCot
'Patrick Bates' — NSti
¶ 'Prestbury Pink' — WEas
'Roy Davidson' — CBos CGle CHad CRDP EBre LBre SWas
rubra — CElw CFis CGle CHan CRDP CSam CShe ECha ELan EMar EPar LWad MFir NHol NOak NOrc NRar NSti SChu SFis SHer SSpi SUsu WBon WCru WHoo
– *albocorollata* — CRDP ECha EFol EMon EPla LRHS MUlv NCat NSti SAxl
– 'Barfield Pink' — CElw CMil CRow ECtt EFol ELan EMar EMon EPla GCal MBri MBro MNFA MUlv NSti SAxl SChu SSpi SUsu WDav WRus
¶ – 'Barfield Ruby' — EMon EPla LRHS
– 'Bowles' Red' — CBot CBre CBro CCla CMea CPar CSco EBre ECtt EFol EJud ENot ERav GAbr LBre LHop MNFA NHol NRoo NSti SCro SPer WCra WHal WRus
– 'David Ward' (v) — CElw CRow ECha ECtt EFol EOrc EPla LGre MBel MUlv NBir SMad WCot WCru WEas
¶ – 'Largeren' — CRDP
¶ – 'Prestbury' — EMon
– 'Redstart' — Widely available
§ *saccharata* — CBow CBre CElw CHEx CMea CRDP CRow CShe CSun ECha ELan EPad LAbb LGro MFir NBee NSel SChu SCro SSvw WBon WCHb WCru WEas WHoo WPbr WPer WWat WWin
– 'Alba' — CBro CRow ECha EFol LBlm NNrd NOak SRms WCru
– Argentea Group — CBro CGle CPar CRow CWGN EBlo ECha EFol EGol ELan EMar EOrc EPla ERav ESma GAbr LBlm MPit MTho NBro NHol SPer SSpi SUsu WBon WCru
– 'Blauhimmel' — CCot NSti
♦– 'Blue Mist' — See P. *officinalis* 'Bowles' Blue'
– 'Brentor' — CRow
– 'Dora Bielefeld' — CRDP ECha EFou EPla NSti SAxl SWas
– 'Frühlingshimmel' — CGle ECha EOrc EPla MUlv NCat NSti SAxl SBla SWas WCHb
¶ – 'Highdown' — EBlo
– 'Lady Lou's Pink' — WCru
– 'Leopard' — CGle EBlo EBre ECtt ELun EPla LBre MUlv NCat SSpi WRus

– 'Mrs Moon' CBow CDoC ECtt EFou ELun ENot LHil LWad NBro NFai NMir NOrc NSti SChu SFis SPer WCHb WCru WSun WTyr
– 'Picta' See P. *s.*
– 'Pink Dawn' CDoC CSco EOrc EPla MBri MUlv NCat SPer WAbe WDav WPbr
– 'Reginald Kaye' CRow ECha NSti
– 'Snow Queen' NHol
* 'Salmon Glow' MTho
'Skylight' LHil
'Tim's Silver' ECha EPla
vallarsae 'Margery Fish' CBro CChu CGle CKel COtt CRDP EBre EGol EOrc EPla LBre LHil MBri MUlv NBro NRoo SAxl SMad SPer WAbe WByw WCru WEas WMer WPbr WRus WSun
'Weetwood Blue' CChu MSte

PULSATILLA (Ranunculaceae)

alba CBro
albana CBro SPou
– 'Lutea' SPou
¶ – white form SWas
alpina CBot NRoo SRms WDav
§ – ssp. ***apiifolia*** CBot CNic ELan GArf GDra NHar NHol NRoo WAbe WHoo WOMN
– ssp. ***sulphurea*** See P. ***a. apiifolia***
ambigua NHol
¶ ***caucasica*** SSou
¶ ***dahurica*** MFos SPou
¶ ***halleri*** SIng
– ssp. ***grandis*** EBar NHol NTow SPou
– ssp. ***rhodopaea*** EPot
– ssp. ***slavica*** CBro CSun SPou
– ssp. ***styriaca*** SPou
– ssp. ***taurica*** SPou
¶ ***koreana*** CBro
montana CNic LGre
occidentalis NMen WOMN
patens WDav WHoo
pratensis GTou MTho NRoo
– ssp. ***hungarica*** WHil
– ssp. ***nigricans*** CBro CRDP LRHS
¶ ***sibirica*** SPou
sp. JH 908145 NHol
§ ***vernalis*** EPot GArf GDra NHar NHol NTow WAbe WDav WHoo
§ ***vulgaris*** Widely available
– ***alba*** CAvo CCla CGle CMea EFou ELan EPar GTou LGan LHop MBri MBro NHar NHol NNrd NOak NRoo SBla SPer SSpi WAbe WHal WPat WPer WRus WThu
– 'Eva Constance' CBro EBre LBre LHop LRHS SWas
– 'Flore Pleno' CNic
– 'Gotlandica' GDra
– 'Röde Klokke' ('Rote Glocke') LGan MBro MUlv NHol SPou WDav WHil
– ***rubra*** CArn CAvo CBro CCla CGle CShe EFol EFou ELan EOrc EPar LHop MBal MBri MBro MHig NHar NHol NKay NNrd NRed NRoo SBla SIng SSpi SUsu WHoo

¶ – 'Weisse Schwan' ('White Swan') MBro WHil

PUMMELO See CITRUS *grandis*

PUNICA (Lythraceae)

granatum ERea GAri STre WSHC
¶ – 'Flore Pleno Lutea' GAri
¶ – 'Flore Pleno Rubra' GAri
– ***nana*** CArn CHal CPle ERea GAri LAbb MPla SHil SMad SMrm WPat WWat
– 'Plena' CB&S

PURSHIA (Rosaceae)

tridentata CPle

PUSCHKINIA (Liliaceae/Hyacinthaceae)

¶ ***scilloïdes*** Polunin 5238 CMon
§ – var. ***libanotica*** CAvo CBro CCla EPar EPot ETub LAma LBlo MBal NEgg NRog SIng SUsu WPer
– – 'Alba' CAvo EPar EPot LAma NRog SIng WCot

PUTORIA (Rubiaceae)

calabrica WOMN

PUYA (Bromeliaceae)

alpestris CHEx SArc
berteroniana CHEx LHil
chilensis CAbb CB&S CHEx ESma MUlv NBro SArc WCot
coerulea CHEx SIgm
– var. ***violacea*** CGre
conquimbensis GCal SSpi
laxa CHEx
mirabilis CHEx CTro GCra NBro
raimondii CHEx
¶ sp. G&P 5036 CGre
venusta CGre CHEx
weberbaueri CHEx

PYCNANTHEMUM (Labiatae)

pilosum CArn CHal CSev GPoy NSal SIde WGwy WPer WWye

PYCNOSTACHYS (Labiatae)

See Plant Deletions

PYGMAEA See CHIONOHEBE

PYRACANTHA † (Rosaceae)

'Alexander' CBow CSco EHal ENot EPla GAri LHop MGos MRav SLon WStI WWat
'Alexander Pendula' See P. 'Alexander'
angustifolia CB&S CMac CSco ELan WWat
– B&L 12387 EMon
§ ***atalantioïdes*** CB&S CBra CDoC CMac CPle CSam CSco CShe IDai MRav MWat SLon SPer SPla WBod WDin WPat WWat
§ – 'Aurea' CSco EBre LBre SLon WWin
– 'Nana' MRav

'Brilliant'	CB&S CBra
'Buttercup'	EPla GAri
coccinea	CTrw
§ – 'Kasan'	MWat
§ – 'Lalandei'	CBra CMac CSam LRHS MGos NNor SPer WBod WDin
– 'Red Column'	CBow CMac CMer EBre ECtt ELan GRei IJoh LBre LBuc MBar MGos MRav NBee WDin WPat WTyr
– 'Red Cushion'	EBre ENot IHos LBre LRHS SRms
– 'Telstar'	CB&S SPer
'Dart's Red'	NRoo
gibbsii	See P. ***atalantioïdes***
– 'Flava'	See P. ***atalantioïdes*** 'Aurea'
'Golden Charmer'	CBow CDoC CSco EBre ECtt ELan IJoh LBre MBal MGos NKay NRoo NTow NWyt SHBN SPer WAbe WBod WDin WTyr
'Golden Dome'	CBra
'Golden Sun'	See P. 'Soleil d'Or'
'Harlequin' (v)	CB&S CBow CMac CPMA EBre ECtt EFol ELan EMar EPla IJoh LBre MBal MBar MGos MRav SHBN SReu WSHC
'John Steadman'	MAsh
'Mohave'	CB&S CMac CSco EBre ELan ENot GRei IJoh LBre MBal MBar MGos MRav MWat NKay NNor NRoo SHBN SLon SPer SReu WAbe WBod WDin WStI
'Mohave Silver' (v)	CBow CPMA CSam EPla LRHS MBar MGos NNor SPer WPat WStI
♦'Monrovia'	See P. ***coccinea*** 'Lalandei'
*'Mozart'	MBri WWeb
'Navajo'	CBow CDoC CSco EBre LBre MPla MRav NWyt SDry SReu WAbe WBod
'Orange Cadence'	IJoh
N'Orange Charmer'	CBow CDoC CPle CSco CShe ELan ENot IJoh MBal MBar MBri MGos SHBN SPer WAbe
'Orange Giant'	See P. ***coccinea*** 'Kasan'
'Orange Glow'	CMac CSco CShe EBlo EBre ECtt ENot GRei IDai IHos IJoh LBre LBuc MBar MBri MGos MRav NKay NNor NTow NWea SLon SPer WBod WDin WPat WStI
*'Orange Sun'	CMer
'Red Delight'	MPla
'Red Pillar'	CBow CDoC CSco MBri
'Renault d'Or'	SLPl
rogersiana	CBra ENot IJoh MPla NNor
– f. ***flava***	CBra ENot IDai LHop MBal MBar MGos NNor WBod
'Shawnee'	CB&S CMac MAsh MBri MRav MWat WDin WWeb
§ 'Soleil d'Or'	CBow CDoC CMac CPle CSam CSco CShe EBlo EBre ECtt ELan ENot IHos LAbb LBre MBar MBri MPla MRav NBee NNor NRoo SPer SReu WDin WPat WStI WTyr
'Sparkler' (v)	CBra CMac CPMA EBar EBre EFol EHoe LBre LHop NHol NNor SDry SEng SMad SPer SPla WRus WStI
¶ 'Steadman's Seedling'	WPat
'Teton'	CBow CBra CDec CMHG CMac CSco ELan ENot ESis MBar MBri MGos MRav NHol NRoo SLon SPer SPla WAbe WBod WDin WPat WStI
'Watereri'	NWea SPer
'Yellow Sun'	See P. 'Soleil d'Or'

X PYRACOMELES (Rosaceae)

See Plant Deletions

PYRETHROPSIS (Compositae)

atlanticum	NHol NTow SIng
catananche	ELan EPad EPot LBee LHop MHig NTow SIng SMrm SUsu
§ ***gayanum***	CCan CMHG CSam CSpe EBar EDon ELan IHos LHil NRar NSty NTow SAxl SChu SCro SIng WKif WOMN WPer WRus WSun
§ ***hosmariense***	Widely available
¶ 'Tizi-n-Test'	SBla SWas
*'Tizi-n-Tichka'	CRiv ECar LRHS NBir SBla SUsu WDav

PYRETHRUM See TANACETUM

PYROLA (Ericaceae)

See Plant Deletions

PYROSTEGIA (Bignoniaceae)

venusta	CTro MNew WSHC

PYRROSIA (Polypodiaceae)

serpens	EBul

PYRUS † (Rosaceae)

betulifolia	CMCN SHil
¶ ***calleryana*** 'Bradford'	CLnd CTho
– 'Chanticleer'	CDoC CLnd CTho ECtt EHar ENot IOrc NBee SHBN SPer WDin WWat
caucasica	WCoo
F ***communis***	CKin MBlu SKee SPer WMou
F – 'Abbe Fétel' (D)	SKee
F – 'Admiral Gervais'	SFru SKee
F – 'Alexandrina Bivort' (D)	CSco
F – 'Autumn Bergamot' (D)	SKee
F – 'Barland' (Perry)	CSco WMou
F – 'Baronne de Mello' (D)	CSco SFam SKee
– 'Beech Hill'	CLnd CSco CTho EHar ENot
F – 'Belle Guérendais'	SKee
F – 'Belle Julie' (D)	SFru SKee
F – 'Bellissime d'Hiver' (C)	SFru
F – 'Bergamotte d'Automne' (D)	CSco SKee
F – 'Bergamotte Esperen' (D)	SKee SNTN
F – 'Beth' (D)	CDoC CSco CWSG EBre EWar GBon GChr GTwe LBre LBuc MBea MBri MGos NBar NBee NElm NRog SDea SFam SFru SIgm SKee SPer WHig WWeb
F – 'Beurré Alexandre Lucas' (D)	CSco SKee
F – 'Beurré Bachelier' (D)	CSco

Cultivar	Suppliers
F– 'Beurré Bedford' (D)	CSco NRog SIgm SKee
F– 'Beurré Bosc' (D)	CSco SKee
F– 'Beurré Clairgeau' (C/D)	SKee
F– 'Beurré de Jonghe' (D)	SKee
F– 'Beurré de Naghin' (C/D)	SKee
F– 'Beurré Diel' (D)	CSco
F– 'Beurré Dumont' (D)	CSco SFam SFru
F– 'Beurré d'Amanlis' (D)	CSco SKee
F– 'Beurré Giffard' (D)	SFru
F– 'Beurré Hardy' (D)	CDoC CSco ERea GTwe IJoh LBuc MBri MWat NRog SDea SFam SFru SIgm SKee
F– 'Beurré Mortillet' (D)	SKee
F– 'Beurré Six' (D)	CSco SKee
F– 'Beurré Superfin' (D)	CSco GTwe SFam SFru SKee SNTN
F– 'Bianchettone'	SKee
F– 'Black Worcester' (C)	CSco GTwe SKee WMou
F– 'Blakeney Red' (Perry)	CSco SDea WMou
F– 'Blickling'	SKee
F– 'Bonne de Beugny'	SKee
F– 'Brandy' (Perry)	CSco SDea WMou
F– 'Bristol Cross' (D)	CSco GTwe SIgm SKee
F– 'Buckland'	CSco
F– 'Butt' (Perry)	CSco
F– 'Catillac' (C)	CSco GTwe NRog SFam SFru SKee
– 'Chalk'	See P. *c.* 'Crawford'
F– 'Charles Ernest'	CSco
F– 'Chaumontel' (D)	SKee
F– 'Clapp's Favourite' (D)	CSco GTwe IOrc SIgm SKee
F– 'Comte de Lamy' (D)	SFam SFru SKee
F– 'Concorde' (D)	CDoC CSam CSco CWSG EHar EWar GTwe LBuc MBri MGos NBee NElm SDea SFru SIgm SKee WHig
F– 'Conference' (D)	Widely available
F– 'Crawford' (D)	SKee
F– 'Deacon's Pear' (D)	SDea
F– 'Docteur Jules Guyot' (D)	CSco SKee
F– 'Double de Guerre' (C)	SFru SKee
F– 'Doyenné du Comice' (D)	CDoC CMac CSam CSco CWSG EBre EHar ERea EWar GBon IOrc LBre MBea MBri MWat NBar NRog SDea SFam SFru SIgm SKee SNTN SPer WHig WWeb
F– 'Doyenné d'Eté' (D)	CSco SFam SKee
F– 'Doyenné Georges Boucher'	SKee
F– 'Duchesse de Bordeaux' (D)	SFru SKee
F– 'Duchesse d'Angoulême' (D)	CSco SFam SKee
F– 'Durondeau' (D)	CSco GTwe NRog SFru SIgm SKee
F– 'Easter Beurré' (D)	CSco SFru
F– 'Emile d'Heyst' (D)	CSco GTwe SIgm SKee
F– 'Eva Baltet'	SKee
F– 'Fertility' (D)	CSco
– 'Fertility Improved'	See P. *c.* 'Improved Fertility'
F– 'Fondant d'Automne' (D)	CSco SFru SKee
F– 'Forelle' (D)	SKee SNTN
F– 'Gin' (Perry)	CSco WMou
F– 'Glou Morceau' (D)	CSco GBon GTwe MWat NRog SDea SFam SFru SIgm SKee SNTN
F– 'Glow Red Williams' (D)	SFam
F– 'Gorham' (D)	CSco GTwe NBee SFam SKee
F– 'Green Horse' (Perry)	CSco
F– 'Hacon's Imcomparable' (D)	SKee
F– 'Hellens Early' (Perry)	CSco
F– 'Hendre Huffcap' (Perry)	CSco WMou
F– 'Hessle' (D)	CSco NRog SDea SFam SKee
F– 'Highland'	SKee
F– 'Improved Fertility' (D)	CDoC GBon GTwe SDea SKee
F– 'Jargonelle' (D)	CSco GTwe NRog SDea SFam SFru SKee SNTN
F– 'Jeanne d'Arc'	SNTN
F– 'Joséphine de Malines' (D)	CSco GTwe SDea SFam SFru SIgm SKee SNTN
F– 'Judge Amphlett' (Perry)	CSco WMou
F– 'Laxton's Early Market' (D)	CSco
F– 'Laxton's Foremost' (D)	CSco SKee
F– 'Laxton's Satisfaction'	CSco SFam SKee
F– 'Louise Bonne of Jersey' (D)	CDoC CSco EWar GTwe MBri NRog SDea SFam SFru SIgm SKee
F– 'Louise Marillat'	CSco
F– 'Madame Treyve' (D)	SFru
F– 'Marguérite Marillat'	GTwe SKee
F– 'Marie Louise d'Uccle' (D)	SKee
F– 'Marie-Louise' (D)	CSco SFam SKee SNTN
F– 'Merton Pride' (D)	CSco GTwe MWat SDea SFam SFru SIgm SKee
F– 'Moorcroft' (Perry)	CSco WMou
F– 'Muirfield Egg' (D)	SKee
F– 'Nouveau Poiteau' (C)	CSco GTwe SFru SKee
F– 'Nouvelle Fulvie' (D)	CSco SKee
F– 'Oldfield' (Perry)	CSco WMou
F– 'Olivier de Serres' (D)	CSco SFam SFru SKee SNTN
F– 'Onward' (D)	CSco GChr GTwe MGos NBee NRog SDea SFam SFru SIgm SKee
F– 'Ovid'	CSco
F– 'Packham's Triumph' (D)	CDoC CSco GBon GTwe NRog SFru SKee
F– 'Parsonage' (Perry)	CSco
F– 'Passe Crassane' (D)	CSco SKee
F– 'Pear Apple' (D)	SDea
F– 'Pitmaston Duchess' (C/D)	CSco CWSG GTwe SDea SFru SIgm SKee
F– 'Red Comice' (C)	GTwe SIgm SKee
F– 'Red Pear' (Perry)	CSco
F– 'Robin' (C/D)	CSco ERea SDea SKee
F– 'Roosevelt'	SKee
F– 'Santa Claus'	CSco SDea SFam SFru SKee
F– 'Seckle' (D)	CSco SFam SFru SKee
F– 'Souvenir du Congrès' (D)	CSco NRog
F– 'Starkrimson' (D)	SFru
F– 'Sweet Huffcap'	See P. *c.* 'Hellens Early'
F– 'Taynton Squash' (Perry)	CSco

F– 'Thompson's' (D)	CSco GTwe SFam SFru SKee SNTN
F– 'Thorn' (Perry)	CSco WMou
F– 'Triomphe de Vienne' (D)	CSco SFam SKee
F– 'Triumph'	See 'P. *c.* 'Packham's Triumph'
F– 'Uvedale's St Germain' (C)	SKee
F– 'Vicar of Winkfield' (D)	CSco GTwe SDea SKee
F– 'Williams Red' (D)	CSam GTwe SKee WHig
F– 'Williams' Bon Chrétien' (D)	CMac CSco CWSG EBre EHar ERea EWar GBon GChr GRei IOrc LBre LBuc MBea MBri MGos MWat NBar NElm NRog SDea SFam SFru SIgm SKee SNTN SPer WWeb
F– 'Winnal's Longdon' (Perry)	CSco
F– 'Winter Nelis' (D)	CSco EHar GTwe SDea SFam SFru SKee SNTN
F– 'Yellow Huffcap' (Perry)	CSco WMou
cordata	CNat CTho SKee
nivalis	CLnd CSco CTho EHar ENot SHBN SHil SPer SSpi
pashia	EHal
– CLD 114	EPla
pyraster	CPer EHar
pyrifolia	WHig
– '20th Century'	See P. *p.* 'Nijusseiki'
F– 'Chojura'	IOrc SKee WHig
F– 'Hosui'	SNTN
F– 'Kumoi'	ESim LBuc MGos NBar SDea WHig
F– 'Nijusseiki'	IOrc SKee SNTN
F– 'Shinko'	IOrc SNTN
F– 'Shinseiki'	CWSG SDea SKee WHig
F– 'Shinsui'	SDea SKee WHig
F– 'Yakumo'	SNTN
salicifolia 'Pendula'	CB&S CBra CCla CLnd CSco EBre EGol EHar ELan ENot GRei IDai IJoh LBre LNet MBal MBar MBri MGos NKay NWea SHBN SMad SPer SReu SSta WAbe WDin WThu WWat

QUERCUS † (Fagaceae)

acuta	CHEx CMCN SArc
acutissima	CMCN EArb SSpi WCoo WNor
– ssp. ***chenii***	CB&S CMCN
aegilops	See Q. ***macrolepis***
agrifolia	CB&S CMCN EArb WCoo
alba	CMCN EArb WCoo
aliena	WCoo
alnifolia	CMCN
¶ ***arkansana***	CMCN
bicolor	CMCN IOrc WCoo
borealis	See Q. ***rubra***
canariensis	CMCN SHil WMou
castaneifolia	CMCN WMou
– 'Greenspire'	CDoC CMCN EHar MBri SHil WMou
cerris	CB&S CDoC CKin CLnd CMCN CSco EHar ENot IOrc NWea SPer SSta STre WCoo WDin WFro WMou
§ – 'Argentoariegata'	CMCN CTho EHar SHil SSpi WMou
♦– 'Variegata'	See Q. *c.* 'Argenteovariegata'
¶ – 'Wodan'	WMou
chrysolepis	CMCN WCoo
coccifera	CMCN WCoo
coccinea	CAbP CB&S CBra CChu CMCN CWSG EArb EHar ELan IBar IOrc SEng SPer WCoo WNor
– 'Splendens'	CDoC CMCN COtt CSco EHar ELan IOrc MBlu SHBN SHil SPer SSpi WDin
dentata	CMCN SMad WCoo
¶ – 'Pinnatifida'	CMCN
douglasii	CMCN EArb WCoo
dumosa	CMCN EArb WCoo
durifolia	CMCN
ellipsoidalis	CAbP CDoC CGre CMCN WCoo WWat
engelmannii	CMCN
falcata	CLnd CMCN EArb
¶ – var. ***pagodifolia***	CMCN EArb
frainetto	CLnd CMCN CTho EHar IOrc MBri SMad SPer SSpi WCoo WDin WMou WWat
¶ – 'Trump'	WMou
§ ***fruticosa***	CMCN
gambelii	CMCN
garryana	CMCN
georgiana	CMCN
glabra	See LITHOCARPUS ***glaber***
glandulifera	CMCN WCoo
glauca	CMCN
graciliformis	WCoo
¶ ***hemisphaerica***	CMCN
¶ x ***hickelii*** 'Gieszelhorst'	WMou
x ***hispanica*** 'Diversifolia'	WMou
– 'Lucombeana'	CMCN CTho EHar MBri SHil SPer WDin WMou
¶ – 'Suberosa'	CTho
– 'Wageningen'	WMou
ilex	CB&S CBra CCla CGre CKin CLnd CMCN CSam CSco CTrw EHar ELan GRei IBar IJoh IOrc ISea LPan MBri SArc SHBN SPer SReu SSta STre WCoo WDin WMou WNor
ilicifolia	CMCN WWat
imbricaria	CMCN EArb
incana Bartram	CMCN EArb
♦– Roxburgh	See Q. ***leucotrichophora***
kelloggii	CMCN EArb
x ***kewensis***	SHil WMou
¶ ***laurifolia***	CMCN EArb
¶ ***leucotrichophora***	CMCN
x ***libanerris*** 'Rotterdam'	CMCN WCoo
libani	CMCN WCoo WMou
lobata	CMCN EArb
x ***ludoviciana***	SArc SHil SSpi WMou
lusitanica	See Q. ***fruticosa***
¶ ***lyrata***	CMCN
macranthera	CMCN WMou
macrocarpa	CMCN EArb WCoo WMou WNor
§ ***macrolepis***	CMCN WCoo
marilandica	CMCN SHil
¶ ***mexicana***	CMCN
michauxii	CMCN
mongolica	WCoo
– var. ***grosseserrata***	CMCN

muehlenbergii CMCN WCoo
myrsinifolia CB&S CBow CMCN SArc SSpi WCoo
nigra CMCN CMHG EArb SHil WCoo
¶ ***nuttallii*** CMCN EArb
palustris CDoC CGre CLnd CMCN EArb EHar IJoh IOrc LPan MBal SMad SPer SSpi WDin WNor WWat
– 'Pendula' CMCN EHar
pedunculata See Q. ***robur***
§ ***petraea*** CDoC CKin CLnd CPer EHar GRei IOrc LBuc MBal NWea SPer WDin WFro WMou
– 'Columna' CTho
§ – 'Insecata' CMCN SSpi WMou
– 'Laciniata' See Q. ***p.*** 'Insecata '
¶ – 'Mespilifolia' WMou
– 'Purpurea' CMCN SHil WMou
§ ***phellos*** CLnd CMCN EArb ISea SHil SSpi WDin WNor
– ***latifolia*** IOrc MBlu
phillyreoïdes CB&S CMCN EArb SBor SSpi WCoo WWat
¶ 'Pondaim' LTil
§ ***prinus*** CMCN WCoo
pubescens WCoo
pumila Michaux See Q. ***prinus***
– Walt. See Q. ***phellos***
¶ ***pungens*** WMou
pyrenaica CMCN CTho
*– 'Argenteomarginata' CMCN
– 'Pendula' CMCN EHar
§ ***robur*** CB&S CBow CBra CDoC CKin CLnd CMCN CPer CSco EBre ENot GRei IJoh IOrc LBre LBuc LPan MBar MBri MGos NBee NWea SHBN SPer SPla WCoo WDin WMou WStI
¶ – 'Albomarmorata' CTho
¶ – 'Argenteomarginata' WMou
– 'Atropurpurea' SHil SPer WMou
¶ – 'Aureobicolor' (v) WMou
– 'Concordia' CB&S CMCN COtt CTho EHar ELan MBlu MBri SHil SMad SSpi WMou
– 'Cristata' CMCN
– 'Cucullata' CMCN
– f. ***fastigiata*** CDoC CLnd CSco CTho EHar ENot IOrc LPan MBar MBri NBee NWea SPer WMou
– 'Fastigiata Kassel' CSco
– 'Fastigiata Koster' CMCN COtt
– 'Fastigiata Purpurea' CMCN IOrc
– 'Hungaria' MBri
– f. ***pendula*** CMCN CTho SMad SSpi WMou
– 'Salicifolia Fastigiata' CTho WMou
– 'Strypemonde' CMCN WMou
x ***rosacea*** 'Filicifolia' WMou
§ ***rubra*** CB&S CBra CCla CKin CLnd CMCN CPer CSco EBre EHar ELan ENot GRei IJoh IOrc LBre LBuc MBal MBar MBri MGos NWea SHBN SPer SSta WCoo WDin WMou WNor
– 'Aurea' CMCN MBlu WMou
rugosa CMCN
sadleriana CMCN
x ***saulii*** CMCN
x ***schochiana*** SHil
serrata See Q. ***acutissima***
sessiliflora See Q. ***petraea***
shumardii CMCN EArb SHil
¶ ***stellata*** EArb
suber CB&S CBow CMCN EArb EHar GAri ISea SArc SHil SSpi WMou
trojana CMCN
x ***turneri*** CDoC CLnd CMCN CTho EHar MBri SHil WMou
¶ – 'Pseudoturneri' CB&S
vacciniifolia MBal
variabilis CMCN WCoo
velutina CGre CLnd CMCN EArb SSpi WWat
– 'Rubrifolia' CMCN SHil
virginiana CMCN EArb ISea
wislizenii CMCN IOrc

QUESNELIA (Bromeliaceae)
See Plant Deletions

QUILLAJA (Rosaceae)
saponaria CGre CPle

QUINCE See CYDONIA *oblonga*

QUIONGZHUEA (Gramineae(Bambuseae))
tumidinoda See CHIMONOBAMBUSA ***tumidissinoda***

RACOPILUM (moss)
¶ ***robustum*** LFle

RACOSPERMA See ACACIA

RAMONDA (Gesneriaceae)
§ ***myconi*** CRDP CRiv CShe EPot GDra MBro MCas NHar NKay NMen NTow SBla SIng SPou SSpi WCru WThu
– 'Rosea' NKay SPou
nathaliae CNic WCru
pyrenaica See R. ***myconi***
serbica CNic GDra NTow

RANUNCULUS † (Ranunculaceae)
abnormis SWas WThi
aconitifolius CGle CRDP EBre ECha LBre NSti
– 'Flore Pleno' CRow EBre ECha IBlr LBre LGre MUlv NBir NRya NTow WByw
acris 'Farrer's Yellow' CRow
– 'Flore Pleno' CAvo CBre CElw CGle CPar CRDP CRow CSco ECha EMon EPar GAbr MNFA NBro NFai NHol NRya WByw WHal
– 'Sulphureus' CBre CLew EMon NRed
alpestris NKay NMen SRms
amplexicaulis CMon GDra NHar SIng SWas WDav
aquatilis CBen EHon EMFW NDea SAWi SWat WChe
¶ ***arendsii*** GArf
asiaticus CMon
– Accolade NNrd WStI
– red form WChr
*– Tecolote hybrids LAma LBlo
auricomus CKin

bilobus	NHar
bulbosus	CKin MWil
– 'F M Burton'	CBos CElw EMon MPar MTho SAxl SWas WCot
¶ – ***farreri***	SBla
– 'Speciosus Plenus'	See R. ***constantinopolitanus*** 'Plenus'
calandrinioïdes	CAvo CMon SPou
¶ – SF 37	CMon
§ ***constantinopolitanus*** 'Plenus'	CBos CGle CRow ECha GCal GGar MBri NBro NRya NTow SUsu
crenatus	ELan EPot GArf ITim MBal MHig NHar NHol NMen NNrd NRya NTow SBla WAbe WHal
creticus	MPar
ficaria	CArn CKin CNat CRow CSFH GCal MChe MHew NNrd NSal SIde WHer WOak WShi WWye
– ***albus***	CBre CGle CLew CMon CRow NGre NHol SIng WByw
– anemone centred	See R. ***f.*** 'Collarette'
– ***aurantiacus***	See R. ***f.*** 'Cupreus'
– 'Brazen Hussy'	Widely available
¶ – 'Button Eye'	CMon
§ – 'Collarette' (d)	CBre CGle CMil CRDP CRow ECar ECha EMon EPar EPot GAbr GGar MTho NNrd NRya SIng WCot WHil
¶ – 'Coppernob'	CBos
§ – 'Cupreus'	CBos CBre CLew CMil CMon CNic CRow ECha EMon EPar EPot GDra MBro MPar NGre NMen NRya SBla SIng WCru WHil
– double bronze	EMon NGre
– double cream	CBre SBla SIng WCot
– double green eye	CRow
– 'Double Mud'	EMon
– 'E A Bowles' (d)	NGre SBla SIng WAbe WCla WCot
– ***flore-pleno***	CBro CGle CMil CMon CNic CRDP CSFH ECar ECha ELan EMon EPar GAbr GDra MPar NDea NGre NHol NNrd SIng WCot
– 'Green Petal'	CMil EMon MTho NGre NHol NNrd SIng
– 'Lemon Queen'	NHol SIng WCot
– 'Major'	CBre CRDP CRow EPot NGre SIng WCot WCru
– 'Mobled Jade'	CNat
– 'Picton's Double'	CGle CRDP CRow
– 'Primrose'	CBre EMon GGar MTho NGre NHol
– 'Randall's White'	CGle MTho NRya NTow WCot
¶ – 'Rowden Magna'	NGre
– 'Salmon's White'	CAvo CBos ECar EPot NGre NNrd SBla WHil
¶ – 'Single Cream'	EMon
– 'Wisley Double Yellow'	CLew
– 'Yaffle'	CBre
¶ × ***flahautii***	GArf
flammula	CArn CBen CKin CRDP CRow EHon EMFW LMay MSta NDea SWat WChe WHol
¶ ***glacialis***	GTou
gouanii	CRDP EPot MFir NBro NGre NHol NKay WHoo
gramineus	CDec CLew CMea CPar EFou ELan EPad EPot ESis GAbr LGan MBro MPar MTho NGre NHol NNrd NRya SAxl SChu SHer SIgm SIng WByw WCot WDav WHoo WThu
– 'Pardal'	SPou
illyricus	CRDP EMar EMon
kochii	EPot NHol NNrd
¶ ***lanuginosus***	WCot
lingua	CKin CRDP EMFW WChe WNdy
– 'Grandiflorus'	CBen CRiv CRow CWGN EHon LMay MSta NDea SWat WHol WOak WWye
lyallii	CPla CRow
millefoliatus	NNrd NRya SIng WHil
montanus	MBal
– 'Molten Gold'	CMea ELan EPad EPot MHig MRav MTho NHar NHol NKay NMen NNrd NRya NTow SIng
¶ ***nivicola***	NTow
ophioglossifolius	CNat
parnassiifolius	GTou NGre NHar NNrd WDav WOMN
platanifolius	LGre
pyrenaeus	MBal
repens	CKin
– 'Joe's Golden'	CElw CRDP EFol EHoe EMon
– var. ***pleniflorus***	CBre CDec CElw CGle CRow ECha ELan EMon GCal NSti WEas
rupestris	CRDP WOMN
sceleratus	CKin
seguieri	NHar
speciosus 'Flore Pleno'	See R. ***constantinopolitanus*** 'Plenus'

RANZANIA (Berberidaceae)

See Plant Deletions

RAOULIA (Compositae)

australis Hooker	ECar ECou EHoe ELan EMNN EPot GAbr GCHN GDra ITim MBal MBar MCas MHig MWat NGre NHol NKay NNrd NSti NWCA SGil SIng WAbe WHoo WThu
– hort.	See R. ***hookeri***
– 'Calf'	ITim NHol SHer
§ – Lutescens Group	ECha EPot GAbr GAri ITim MHig NHol NTow SGil WAbe
– 'Saxon Pass'	ESma GCHN NHol SGil
glabra	ECou EPot GAbr ITim NHol NKay NTow
haastii	ECou GArf GDra NHol
§ ***hookeri***	CLew CPar EBre ECar ECha ECou ELan EMNN EPot GCHN ITim LBee LBre MBro MCas NHol NMen NNrd NTow NWCA SBla SBod SGil SIng WAbe WDav WOMN WPat WPer WThu
– var. ***apice-nigra***	GArf NHol
– var. ***hookeri***	NHol
× ***loganii***	See X LEUCORAOULIA ***loganii***
lutescens	See R. ***australis*** Lutescens Group
monroi	ECou ELan EPot GCHN ITim NHol NTow WMar
* ***nova***	EPot GDra NKay
parkii	GDra

x *petrimia* 'Margaret Pringle'	MHig WAbe WDav
subsericea	ECou MHig NGre NHol NMen WHil
tenuicaulis	ECar ECha ECou GAbr NHol WHil WHoo

RAOULIA X LEUCOGENES See **X LEUCORAOULIA**

RASPBERRY See **RUBUS *idaeus***

RATIBIDA (Compositae)
See Plant Deletions

RAVENALA (Strelitziaceae)

madagascariensis	LPal

RAVENEA (Palmae)

rivularis	LPal

RECHSTEINERIA See **SINNINGIA**

REEVESIA (Sterculiaceae)
See Plant Deletions

REGELIA (Myrtaceae)
See Plant Deletions

REHDERODENDRON (Stryracaceae)

macrocarpum	CB&S

REHMANNIA (Scrophulariaceae)

angulata	See R. ***elata***
§ *elata*	CBot CCla CDec CGre CHad CRDP CSev ECro EGol NRar SFis SMrm WCot WCra WCru WHal WHil WPer WWye
glutinosa	WOMN

REINECKEA (Liliaceae/Convallariaceae)

§ *carnea*	CElw CFis CRDP EBul ECha ELan EPar EPla GCal LGan MPar MTho MUlv NNrd NRar NSti SFis WBon WCru WHal

REINWARDTIA (Linaceae)

§ *indica*	CPle CTro
trigyna	See R. ***indica***

RESEDA (Resedaceae)

lutea	CKin MChe NSal NSel SHer SIde
luteola	CKin CSFH GPoy LHol MChe MHew NSal SIde WCHb WHer WWye

RESTIO (Restionaceae)

subverticillatus	See ISCHYROLEPIS ***subverticillata***
tetraphyllus	ECou

RETAMA (Leguminosae)

§ *monosperma*	CPle
sphaerocarpa	CCor

REYNOUTRIA See **FALLOPIA**

RHABDOTHAMNUS (Gesneriaceae)

solandri	ECou WCru

RHAGODIA (Chenopodiaceae)

triandra	ECou

RHAMNUS (Rhamnaceae)

§ *alaternus* 'Argenteovariegatus'	CB&S CCla CHan CMHG CPle CSam CSco CShe EBar EBre EHar ELan ENot IBar LBre LHop NSti SApp SArc SHBN SLon SPer SPla SSta STre WDin WPat WThu WWat
– *variegatus*	See R. ***a.*** 'Argenteovariegatus'
catharticus	CKin EBre LBre LBuc WDin WMou
frangula	CArn CDoC CKin CPer CSam EBre ENot GPoy LBre LBuc STre WDin WMou
¶ x *hybridus* 'Billardii'	ESis
imeretinus	SHil

RHAPHIOLEPIS (Rosaceae)

x *delacourii*	IJoh SPer WBod
– 'Coates' Crimson'	CBow CCla MUlv SHBN SSpi WSHC
– 'Enchantress'	CB&S CGre EBre IBlr LBre
– 'Spring Song'	SHil
indica	CHEx CPle
ovata	See R. ***umbellata***
§ *umbellata*	CB&S CBot CChu CCla CDoC CHEx CMCN CPle CSam MNew MUlv NTow SHil WAbe WBod WCru WHCG

RHAPHITHAMNUS (Verbenaceae)

cyanocarpus	See R. ***spinosus***
§ *spinosus*	CGre CHan CPle EPla ERea IBar SArc WBod

RHAPIDOPHYLLUM (Palmae)

hystrix	LPal

RHAPIS (Palmae)

§ *excelsa*	LPal
¶ *humilis*	LPal

RHAZYA (Apocynaceae)

orientalis	See AMSONIA ***o.***

RHEKTOPHYLLUM See **CERCESTIS**

RHEUM † (Polygonaceae)

§ 'Ace of Hearts'	CBot CHad CRow CWit ECha ECtt EFol EGol ELan EPar EPla MBri MUlv NDea WCot

'Ace of Spades'	See R. 'Ace of Hearts'
acuminatum	CRow
alexandrae	CRow EBlo EBre GAri LBre MUlv NNor SPer WCot
§ ***australe***	CArn CChu CCla CRow LWad WCot WHer WHoo
¶ ***compactum***	CRow
x ***cultorum***	See R. x ***hybridum***
delavayi	EMon LRHS
emodi	See R. ***australe***
Nx ***hybridum*** 'Cawood Delight'	GTwe
– 'Champagne'	GTwe
– 'Early Champagne'	GTwe
– 'Fenton's Special'	GTwe WHig
¶ – 'Hammond's Early'	GTwe
– 'Harbinger'	GTwe
¶ – 'Hawke's Champagne'	GTwe
– 'Mac Red'	GTwe
– 'Prince Albert'	GTwe
– 'Reed's Early Superb'	GTwe
– 'Stockbridge Arrow'	GTwe
– 'The Sutton'	GTwe LBuc
– 'Timperley Early'	CDoC CMac CSam ECtt GChr GTwe LBuc MBea MMor NElm NFai SDea WHig
– 'Victoria'	GChr GTwe
kialense	ECha WCot
nobile	CHEx
officinale	CHEx MBri
palmatum	CB&S CBow CCMG CCla CHEx ECha EHal MRav NDea NNor NSti SHig SPer WHal WHoo WPbr WRus WStI
– 'Atropurpureum'	See R. ***p.*** 'Atrosanguineum'
§ – 'Atrosanguineum'	CBot CHEx CRow CSco CShe CWes EBre ECha ECtt EGol ELan EPar LBre NBro NNor WCru WWin
– 'Bowles' Crimson'	CHad LRHS MBri
– 'Hadspen Crimson'	CHad
– ***rubrum***	CCla CDoC COtt CWGN EFou GCHN SPer WCot
– 'Saville'	LRHS
– var. ***tanguticum***	CRow CWit ECha ELun EOrc LWad MSta MUlv WCot
¶ ***spiciforme***	GTou WCot
sp. CLD 1408	EMon
¶ ***undulatum***	CRow

RHEXIA (Melastomataceae)

See Plant Deletions

RHINANTHUS (Scrophulariaceae)

¶ ***minor***	CRDP

RHINEPHYLLUM (Aizoaceae)

broomii	NGre

RHIPSALIS (Cactaceae)

¶ ***baccifera***	CTro
cassytha	See R. ***baccifera***

RHODIOLA (Crassulaceae)

♦ ***crassipes***	See R. ***wallichiana***
fastigiata	GCal NGre
– x ***kirilovii***	NGre
§ ***heterodonta***	ECha ESis NGre
himalensis	CNic NGre SSmi
kirilovii var. ***rubra***	NGre SSmi
pachyclados	See SEDUM ***p.***
pamiroalaica	NGre
primuloïdes	See SEDUM ***p.***
rhodantha	NGre
§ ***rosea***	CKel CSco ECha ECro EFou EGol ELan EPla MBal MFir NGre NNor NRoo NSti SCro SSmi STre WEas
§ – ssp. ***integrifolia***	NGre
sp. CLD 1196	NHol
sp. C&Mc 158	GCHN
¶ sp. JJH 392	WDav
trollii	NGre
§ ***wallichiana***	LHil NGre NTow WCot
¶ ***yunnanense***	EMon

RHODOCHITON (Scrophulariaceae)

§ ***atrosanguineus***	CB&S CChu CDoC CGle CHEx CMac CTro ECtt ELan ERea LAbb LHop LWad NEgg NFai NTow SMad SUsu WAbe WCru WEas WHal WHil WPer
volubilis	See R. ***atrosanguineus***

RHODODENDRON † (Ericaceae)

aberconwayi	CWal GWht IOrc ISea LMil MBal SLeo SReu
– dwarf form	GGGa
– 'His Lordship'	GGGa LHyd
adenogynum	CWal GGGa SLeo
¶ – CLD 795	LMil
§ – Adenophorum Group	CWal SLeo
– – F 20444	SLeo
adenophorum	See R. ***adenogynum*** Adenophorum Group
adenopodum	CWal GGGa SLeo
adenosum	LMil
– R 18228	GGGa
– Kuluense Group	SLeo
adroserum R/USDA 59201	See R. ***lukiangense*** R 11275
♦ ***aeruginosum***	See R. ***campanulatum a.***
aganniphum	GGGa SLeo
– var. ***aganniphum*** Doshongense Group	CWal GGGa SLeo
– – Glaucopeplum Group	GGGa
– – Schizopeplum Group	GGGa
– var. ***flavorufum***	GGGa SLeo
agapetum	See R. ***kyawii*** Agapetum Group
agastum	SLeo
albertsenianum	SLeo
albrechtii (A)	GGGa LHyd SReu
alutaceum var. ***alutaceum***	GGGa
– – Globigerum Group R 11100	GGGa SLeo
– var. ***iodes***	GGGa LMil

– var. ***iodes***	GGGa LMil
– var. ***russotinctum***	GGGa SLeo
– – Triplonaevium Group R/USDA59442/R10923	GGGa
– – Tritifolium Group	GGGa
amagianum (A)	LMil LTil SSpi
– ***x reticulatum*** (A)	SSta
ambiguum	CDoC CHig CWal ISea LMil SLeo SReu
– dwarf form	GGGa
– 'Jane Banks'	LMil
– 'Keillour Castle'	GGGa
amesiae	CWal SLeo
annae	GGGa LMil SLeo
– Hardingii Group	CWal
anthopogon	GWht LMil SLeo
– 'Annapurna'	GGGa
– 'Betty Graham'	LMil
§ – ssp. ***hypenanthum***	CWal LMil LTil
anthosphaerum	GGGa
– F 26432	SLeo
– Eritimum Group	CWal
anwheiense	See R. ***maculiferum a.***
aperantum	GGGa
– F 26933	SLeo
araiophyllum	SLeo
§ ***arborescens*** (A)	GGGa LKna LMil SLeo
arboreum	CB&S CWal GGGa GWht IOrc ISea LMil SLeo SReu
– B 708	MBal
– BM&W 172	MBal
– Sch 1111	CWal
– 'Blood Red'	CWal GWht
– ssp. ***cinnamomeum***	CBow CWal GGGa SLeo SReu
¶ – – var. ***roseum***	CWal GGGa
– – Campbelliae Group	SLeo
– ssp. ***delavayi***	GGGa SLeo
– 'Goat Fell'	CWal
* – ***nigrescens***	SLeo
§ – 'Sir Charles Lemon'	CWal MLea SLeo SPer SReu SSta
– 'Tony Schilling'	CWal LHyd SLeo
– ssp. ***zeylanicum***	SLeo
x ***arbutifolium***	See R. Hybrid Arbutifolium
§ ***argipeplum***	CWal SLeo
– Bhutan form	GGGa
– Eastern form	GGGa
argyrophyllum	CWal SLeo
– KR 184	GGGa
– 'Chinese Silver'	CWal LHyd LMil SLeo SSpi
§ – ssp. ***hypoglaucum***	GGGa SLeo
– – 'Heane Wood'	GGGa
– ssp. ***nankingense***	GGGa IOrc LMil
– 'Sichuan'	GGGa
arizelum	See R. ***rex arizelum***
atlanticum (A)	CCla CWal GAri GGGa SLeo
– 'Seaboard' (A)	LMil
augustinii	CB&S CTrw EBre GGGa IOrc ISea LBre LHyd LMil MBal MLea SCog SExb SLeo SPer SSpi SSta WBod
– ssp. ***augustinii*** Vilmorinianum Group	CWal
– ssp. ***chasmanthum***	CWal GGGa LMil
– Dartington Form	CWal
§ – Electra (g.&cl.)	CBow CWal GGGa LHyd LMil SCog SExb SLeo
– Exbury best form	SReu
§ – ssp. ***hardyi***	CWal GGGa LHyd SLeo
– Reuthe's dark form	SReu
– ssp. ***rubrum***	GGGa LMil
§ – – 'Papillon'	CWal
¶ – 'Werrington'	MUlv
aureum	GGGa LMil SLeo WDav
auriculatum	CGre CWal GGGa LHyd LMil MBal MLea SLeo SReu SSta
– Reuthe's form	SReu
auritum	CWal GGGa
§ ***austrinum*** (A)	GGGa LMil
Azalea 'Abbot' (E)	CTrh
– 'Addy Wery' (E)	CBow CHig CMac CSco CTrh CWal IDai IOrc LHyd LKna LTil MBal MBar MGos SBod SCog SLeo SPer SReu WBod WStI
– 'Adonis' (E/d)	CMac IOrc MBar SCog SDeJ SPer SReu SSta
– 'Adorable' (E)	CTrh IOrc
– 'Advance' (O)	CTrh LTil MPlt SExb SGil SLeo WAbe WPat
– 'Ageeth' (E)	LRHS
– 'Aida' (R/d)	GGGa SReu
– 'Aladdin' (E)	IJoh IOrc MAsh
– 'Alexander' (E)	CB&S CTrh IOrc LMil MBri MGos MPlt SBod SSta
– 'Alice' (E)	CBow CMac IHos LHyd LKna WBod
– 'Ambrosia' (E)	CTrh
§ – 'Amethystinum' (E)	LKna
– 'Amoenum' (E/d)	CB&S CMHG CMac CTrw GWht LHyd LKna MBar MGos NHol SCog SExb SLeo WBod
– 'Amoenum Coccineum' (E/d)	CBow ECar GWht SCog
– 'Anchorite' (E)	CTrh LMil LTil
– 'Andrew Elphinstone' (E)	CBow LMil
– 'Angelus' (E)	SExb
– 'Annabella' (K)	CWal LHyd MBri MMor NBar SExb SReu
– 'Anne Frank' (E)	NBar WBod
– 'Anne Rothwell'	LHyd
– 'Anneke' (K)	GGGa MBar MBri MMor NBar SSta
– 'Anny' (E)	CMac LKna
§ – 'Antilope' (Vs)	LKna LMil MMor SSpi SSta
– 'Aphrodite' (E)	LMil
N – 'Appleblossom' (E)	See R. A. 'Ho-o'
– 'Apricot Surprise'	CDoC GGGa
– 'Arabesque'	MBri MMor
– 'Arborescens'	See R. ***arborescens***
– 'Arcadia' (E)	CSco LKna
– 'Arctic Regent' (K)	SExb
§ – 'Arpege' (Vs)	CDoC LKna LMil MBal SPer SReu SSpi WWat
– 'Asa-gasumi' (E)	LHyd
– 'Atalanta' (E)	SExb
– 'Audrey Wynniatt' (E)	MAsh SExb
– 'Aurora' (K)	SExb
– 'Azuma-kagami' (E)	CB&S LHyd LKna SCog WBod
– 'Babeuff' (M)	CB&S
– 'Baby Scarlet'	SSta
– 'Ballerina' (K)	CWal MBal SExb
– 'Balzac' (K)	CSam CWal IJoh IOrc MBri MGos SExb SReu

Azalea 'Banzai' (E)	CWal SLeo
– 'Barbara Coates'	LHyd
– 'Barbecue' (K)	LMil SExb
– 'Basilisk' (K)	CWal SExb
– 'Beaulieu' (K)	LMil SExb SPer
¶– 'Beaulieu Manor'	SExb
– 'Beethoven' (E)	LHyd LKna MBal MBar SBod SExb SLeo SReu WBod
– 'Ben Morrison' (E)	LTil SSta
– 'Bengal Beauty' (E)	LMil
– 'Bengal Fire' (E)	CMac SExb
§– 'Benifude' (E)	WBod
– 'Benigasa' (E)	CTrh SReu WPat
– 'Beni-giri' (E)	CMac
– 'Berryrose' (K)	CSco CWal EBlo EBre GWht IDai IJoh IOrc LBre LHyd LKna LMil LTil MAsh MBal MBar MBri MMor MRav NBar SDeJ SExb SPer SReu WAbe
– 'Betty' (E)	LHyd SReu SRms
– 'Betty Anne Voss' (E)	LHyd LRHS SExb
– 'Betty Kelly' (K)	LKna
– 'Bijou de Ledeberg' (E)	SSta
– 'Blaauw's Pink' (E)	CBow CHig CMac CSco CWal GWht IDai IJoh IOrc ISea LHyd LKna LMil MBar MBri MGos NKay SBod SCog SDeJ SExb SLeo SPer SReu WBod
– 'Black Hawk' (E)	CB&S
– 'Blaue Donau' ('Blue Danube') (E)	Widely available
– 'Blazecheck'	LRHS NBar NHol
– 'Blizzard' (E)	CTrh
– 'Blue Monday'	MBri WBod
– 'Bob White' (E)	SExb
– 'Bouquet de Flore' (G)	CDoC CSco LMil MAsh MBar MBri SReu
– 'Bravo' (E)	CTrh
– 'Brazier' (E)	LHyd MAsh SLeo
– 'Brazil' (K)	CWal LKna SExb SReu
– 'Breslau' (E)	SSta
– 'Bridesmaid' (O)	GWht SExb
– 'Bridesmaid White'	NKay
¶– 'Bride's Bouquet' (E/d)	LRHS
– 'Bright Forecast' (K)	LMil MBri SExb
– 'Brilliant' (E)	NBar
*– 'Brilliant Crimson'	SSta
*– 'Brilliant Pink'	MAsh SSta
– 'Buccaneer' (E)	CSco CTrh CWal LHyd LKna LTil MBal SBod SExb SPer SReu
– 'Bungo-nishiki' (E/d)	CMac CWal SReu SRms WPat WThu
– 'Buttercup' (K)	SExb
– 'Buzzard' (K)	LKna LMil
– 'Caerhays Lavender'	CB&S IOrc
§– 'Campfire' (E)	NKay
– 'Canby' (K)	LMil
– 'Cannon's Double' (K)	GGGa LMil
¶– 'Canzonetta' (E)	NBar
– 'Carat'	CDoC MBri SReu
– 'Carnival' (E)	CTrh
¶– 'Cassley' (Vs)	LMil
– 'Cayenne' (E)	SExb
– 'Cecile' (K)	CB&S CSam CSco CWal GGGa GWht IJoh ISea LHyd LKna LMil MAsh MBal MBri MGos MMor NBar SDeJ SExb SPer SReu
– 'Celestial' (E)	CMac CTrh
– 'Centennial'	See R. A. 'Washington State Centennial'
– 'Chaffinch' (K)	LKna
– 'Chameleon' (E)	LKna
– 'Chanel' (Vs)	MMor SSta
– 'Chanticleer' (E)	LRHS LTil SExb SPer
– 'Charlemagne' (G)	LKna
– 'Charlotte de Rothschild'	SExb
– 'Cheerful Giant' (K)	GGGa
*– 'Chelsea Manor'	SExb
– 'Chelsea Reach' (K)	LKna
– 'Chenille' (K)	LKna
– 'Chetco' (K)	GGGa
– 'Chicago' (M)	LKna
– 'Chippewa' (E)	CDoC GGGa LMil MBri NKay SReu WAbe
– 'Chocolate Ice' (K)	LKna
– 'Chopin' (E)	WBod
– 'Chorister' (K)	LKna
– 'Christina' (E/d)	CMac MBri MMor NKay SPer WBod
– 'Christmas Cheer' (E)	See R. A. 'Ima-shojo'
§– 'Christopher Wren' (K)	CSco ELan MBal NBar
¶– 'Citroen'	SExb
– 'Coccineum Speciosum' (G)	CBow CSco CWal GGGa IDai IOrc LHyd LMil LTil MBar MGos SReu SSta
– 'Cockade' (E)	LKna
– 'Cockatoo' (K)	LKna
– 'Colin Kenrick' (K)	LKna
– 'Colyer' (E)	LHyd LMil
– 'Commodore' (E)	SExb WAbe
– 'Congo'	See R. A. 'Robin Hill Congo'
– 'Cora Grant' (E)	SExb
¶– 'Coral Beauty'	CSut
– 'Coral Redwing' (E)	CTrh
– 'Coral Wing' (E)	CTrh
– 'Corneille' (G/d)	LKna SReu
– 'Coronation Lady' (K)	LKna MBri MMor
¶– 'Corot'	SExb
– 'Corringe' (K)	GWht SExb
– 'Crimson Glory'	See R. A. 'Natalie Coe Vitetti'
– 'Crinoline' (K)	LTil SPer SSta WWeb
¶– 'Crown Supreme'	SExb
– 'Cumberlandense'	See R. ***calendulaceum***
– 'Cytherea' (E)	ISea
– 'Daimio' (E)	CMHG LHyd SPer
– 'Daisetsuzan'	CTrh
– 'Darkness' (E)	CTrh SExb
– 'Daviesii' (G)	CB&S CSam GGGa LHyd LKna LMil LTil MAsh MBal MBri MLea MMor MRav SDeJ SExb SPer SPla SReu WWat WWeb
– 'Dawn's Glory'	SExb
N– 'Daybreak' (K)	See R. A. 'Kirin'
N– 'Debutante'	GRei GWht IHos ISea MMor NBar
– 'Delectable' (K)	LMil SExb
– 'Delicatissimum' (O)	LMil LRHS SExb
– 'Desert Pink' (K)	LKna
– 'Diabolo' (K)	LKna SExb
– 'Diamant'	CDoC GAri GGGa
– Diamant Group (lilac) (E)	GGGa MBri

Azalea Diamant Group (pink) (E)	GGGa MGos
– Diamant Group (rosy-red) (E)	COtt GAri GGGa MBri
– 'Diamant Purpur' ('Purple Diamond') (E)	CTrh MGos
– 'Diamant Rot' ('Red Diamond') (E)	CTrh
– 'Diorama' (Vs)	CDoC MBar MBri MMor SReu SSta
– 'Doctor M Oosthoek' (M)	CSco LHyd LTil MMor NBar SReu
– 'Dorothy Corston' (K)	LKna
¶ – 'Dorothy Gish' (E/d)	LTil
– 'Dorothy Hayden' (E)	LHyd
– 'Double Beauty' (E/d)	CTrh ECar LKna MMor SBod SCog SPer SReu SSta
– 'Double Damask' (K)	LHyd LKna
– 'Double Delight' (K/d)	CBow GGGa
– 'Driven Snow' (E)	LTil SBod SExb
¶ – 'Drury Lane'	SExb
– 'Early Beni' (E)	LHyd
– 'Eastern Fire' (E)	CTrh
– 'Eddisbury' (K)	MMor
– 'Eddy' (E)	LKna SExb SLeo
– 'Edna Bee' (E)	LMil
N – 'Elizabeth' (E)	CBow CTrh ISea MGos MPlt SCog SExb SGil WAbe
– 'Elizabeth Gable' (E)	NKay
– 'Elsie Lee' (E)	ECar GGGa SBod SReu SSta
– 'Elsie Pratt' (K)	MBar MBri MMor NBar SSta
N – 'Esmeralda'	CMac SBod
– 'Eunice Updike' (E)	LHyd
– 'Eva Goude' (K)	LKna
N – 'Evening Glow'	SExb
– 'Evensong' (E)	LKna SDeJ
– 'Everest' (E)	CBow CWal LHyd MBar MBri WAbe WBod
– 'Everest White'	NKay
– 'Exbury White' (K)	GWht LTil SExb
– 'Exquisitum' (O)	LKna LMil MBri SReu
– 'Fanny'	See R. A. 'Pucella'
– 'Favorite' (E)	CMac CTrw LKna MBar MBri MMor SExb SLeo SPer SSta
¶ – 'Fawley' (K)	SExb
– 'Fedora' (E)	CB&S CTre CTrh LHyd LKna MRav SDeJ SPer SReu
– 'Fénelon' (G)	GGGa
¶ – 'Fiesta' (E/d)	LTil
– 'Fireball' (K)	CB&S CBow CMHG CSco GGGa GRei GWht IJoh ISea LHyd LMil MAsh MBri MLea NKay SExb WWeb
– 'Firefly' (E)	See R. A. 'Hexe'
– 'Firefly' (K)	LMil SExb WBod
– 'Fireglow'	MBri
– 'Flaming June' (K)	LKna
– 'Floradora' (M)	SReu
– 'Florida' (E/d)	CMac CSco CTrh GWht LKna MRav SBod SCog SExb SPer SSta WAbe WBod
– 'Frans van der Bom' (M)	IDai
– 'Fraseri' (M)	CBow GGGa
¶ – 'Fridoline' (E)	NBar
– 'Frieda' (E)	LKna
– 'Frills' (K/d)	CWal SExb
¶ – 'Frilly Lemon' (K/d)	LMil
– 'Frome' (K)	LKna
– 'Fudetsukasi'	SLeo
– 'Fuko-hiko' (E)	CWal SLeo
– 'Gabriele' (E)	SExb SSpi
– 'Gaiety' (E)	GGGa GWht LMil MAsh SCog
– 'Galathea' (E)	GGGa LTil
– 'Gallipoli' (K)	SExb SPer
¶ – 'Garden State Glow' (E/d)	SBod
– 'Gauche'	SExb
*– 'Geisha Lilac' (E)	MBri
*– 'Geisha Orange' (E)	CBow GGGa MBar MBri MGos
*– 'Geisha Purple' (E)	MBar
*– 'Geisha Red' (E)	MBar MBri
– 'Gekkeikan' (E)	CB&S
– 'General Wavell' (E)	CMac CTrh CWal GAri LKna SExb
– 'Georg Arends'	CDoC ECar IJoh NBar
– 'George Reynolds' (K)	CWal SExb
– 'Getsutoku' (E)	CTrh LTil
– 'Gibraltar' (K)	Widely available
– 'Gilbert Mullier'	MBri
– 'Ginger' (K)	CWal GWht LMil MBal SExb
§ – 'Girard's Hot Shot' (E)	GGGa SBod SGil SReu SSta
– 'Girard's Pink' (E)	SReu
– 'Girard's Scarlet' (E)	SReu
– 'Glamora' (E)	LHyd
– 'Glencora' (E)	LHyd
– 'Glockenspiel' (K)	LKna
¶ – 'Glon Komachi' (EA)	LTil
– 'Gloria Mundi' (G)	SReu WAbe
– 'Glowing Embers' (K)	CMHG CSam GAri GRei GWht ISea LTil MAsh MBal MBri MLea MMor NBar NKay SDeJ SExb SPer SReu WWeb
– 'Gog' (K)	CSam CWal LHyd LKna MBal
– 'Gold Crest' (K)	LKna
– 'Goldball'	See R. A. 'Christopher Wren'
– 'Golden Eagle' (K)	CB&S CDoC COtt LKna MAsh MBri MGos SDeJ
– 'Golden Eye' (K)	LKna
– 'Golden Flare' (K)	CB&S CMHG ISea MAsh MBri WWeb
– 'Golden Horn' (K)	CWal
– 'Golden Lights'	LMil
– 'Golden Oriole' (K)	LKna SReu
– 'Golden Sunlight' (M)	See R. A. 'Directeur Moerlands'
– 'Golden Sunset' (K)	CSco IJoh LKna LMil MBri MMor NBar SDeJ WStI
– 'Goldfinch' (K)	LKna
– 'Goldtopas' (K)	GGGa
¶ – 'Gorbella'	NHol
– 'Graciosum' (O)	LKna
– 'Greenway' (E)	CB&S CGre CTre SPer
– 'Greta' (E)	LHyd
§ – 'Gumpo' (E)	CMac CTrh EPot SCog SPer WAbe WThu
– 'Gumpo Pink' (E)	ECar SReu SSta WBod
– 'Gumpo White' (E)	ECar SBod SSta WAbe WBod
– 'Gumpo' x ***nakaharae***	SSta
– 'Gwenda' (E)	LHyd
¶ – 'Gyokushin' (E)	MBal
– 'Gypsy' (E)	SExb
¶ – 'H H Hume' (E)	MBal SGil
– 'H O Carre' (E)	CMac SExb

Azalea 'Hachmann's Rokoko' (E) GGGa
– 'Hamlet' (M) LMil
¶– 'Hanah-fubuki' (E) LTil
– 'Hana-asobi' (E) CB&S EPot LHyd SExb WBod
– 'Harbinger' (E) SBod SExb SLeo
– 'Hardy Gardenia' (E/d) ECar SCog SSta
– 'Harkwood Red' LMil LRHS
– 'Harumiji' (E) CWal SLeo
– 'Haru-no-hikari' (E) CTrh
– 'Haru-no-sono' (E) CTrh
– 'Harvest Moon' (K) IHos LTil NBar SReu
– 'Hatsugiri' (E) CHig CMac ECar IJoh IOrc LHyd LKna LTil MBar MBri MMor SBod SCog SDeJ SReu SSta WBod WPat
– 'Heather Macleod' (E) LHyd
– 'Heiwa-no-kagami' (E) CTrh GAri
– 'Helen Close' (E) LRHS
– 'Helen Curtis' (E) SReu
¶– 'Helena' (E) SExb
– 'Herbert' (E) CMac
¶– 'Hexe' (E/d) SExb WBod
– 'Hiawatha' (K) LKna
– 'Higasa' (E) CTrh GAri
– 'Hinode-giri' (E) CB&S CHig CMac CTrw CWal LHyd LKna SBod SExb SLeo SReu WBod
– 'Hinode-no-kumo' (E) CWal SLeo
– 'Hino-crimson' (E) CBow CGre CMac CSco CSut CWal GWht IDai IJoh IOrc LKna LMil MBar MBri MGos MMor NHol NJap NKay SPer SReu SSta WPat WStI
– 'Hino-mayo' (E) CB&S CCla CMHG CMac CSco CTre CWal EBre GRei IOrc LBre LHyd LKna LMil MBri MRav NKay SCog SDeJ SExb SLeo SPer SReu SSta WBod WStI
– 'Hino-Red' (E) GGGa
– 'Hino-Scarlet' See R. A. 'Campfire'
– 'Hino-tsukasa' (E) CWal SLeo
– 'Hojo-no-odorikarako' (E) SLeo
– 'Homebush' (R/d) CB&S CCla CMHG CWal GGGa GWht IJoh IOrc ISea LHyd LKna LMil LTil MAsh MBal MBri SPer SReu SSta WWeb
– 'Honeysuckle' (K) IOrc MBar MMor NBar SExb
– 'Hortulanus H Witte' (M) MMor SReu
– 'Hot Shot' See R. A. 'Girard's Hot Shot'
– Hotspur Group (K) ELan GGGa WWeb
¶– 'Hotspur Orange' (K) SExb
– 'Hotspur Red' (K) CWal LKna LMil MBri SReu
– 'Hotspur Yellow' (K) CWal LHyd SReu
§– 'Ho-o' (E) CB&S CGre CMac SCog SExb
– 'Hyde and Seek' SExb
– 'Hyde Park' (K) LMil SExb
– 'Ightham Pink' SReu
– 'Il Tasso' (R/d) LKna SRms
§– 'Ilam Melford Lemon' LMil
§– 'Ilam Ming' LMil
– 'Imago' (K) LKna
§– 'Ima-shojo' (E/d) CB&S CMac GAri IHos LHyd MAsh SExb SPer WBod
– 'Impala' (K) LKna
– 'Indicum' See R. ***indicum***
– 'Irene Koster' (O) CMHG CWal ELan GGGa GWht ISea LHyd LKna LMil MAsh MBri SExb SPer SReu WWeb
– 'Iroha-yama' (E) CBow CMac CTrw LHyd LKna LMil SCog SReu SSta WBod
– 'Ishiyama' (E) SCog
– 'Issho-no-haru' (E) CTrh
– 'Ivette' (E) CMac LHyd LKna LMil LTil SExb
– 'Iwato-kagami' (E) CWal SLeo
– 'Izayoi' (E) WBod
– 'J Jennings' (K) WAbe
– 'James Gable' (E) MAsh
– 'Jean Read' LHyd
– 'Jeanette' (E) LKna LMil
– 'Jock Brydon' (0) GGGa
– 'Jock Coutts' LKna
– 'Johann Sebastian Bach' (E) WBod WWeb
– 'Johann Strauss' (E) WBod
– 'Johanna' (E) CDoC CMac GGGa LMil MAsh MBri MMor MRav NHol SPer WBod
– 'John Cairns' (E) CMac CWal ECar LHyd LKna LMil MBal MBar SCog SPer SReu WBod
– 'Jolie Madame' (Vs) CDoC MBri SReu
– 'Joseph Haydn' (E) WBod
– 'Joseph Hill' (E) LMil SSpi
– 'June Fire' GGGa
¶– 'Kaho-no-hikari' (E) GAri
– 'Kakiemon' (E) LHyd SPer
– 'Kasane-kagaribi' (E) SExb
N– 'Kathleen' CWal GWht IOrc LHyd LKna MBar MMor SCog SExb
– 'Katinka' (E) MBal MGos
– 'Katisha' (E) LHyd
– 'Katsura-no-hana ' (E) WBod
*– 'Keija' SCog
– 'Keinohana' (E) CWal SLeo
– 'Kentucky Minstrel' (K) LKna
– 'Kermesinum' (E) CDoC COtt GGGa MBar MBri MPlt NBar SDeJ SReu WPat
– 'Kermesinum Album' (E) GGGa MBar MBri NBar WThu
– 'Keston Rose' SReu SSta
– 'Kijei' CB&S
– 'Kilauea' (K) LKna
– 'Killarney' (E) CTrh
– 'Kimigayo' (E) LHyd SExb
– 'King's Red' (K) LMil
§– 'Kirin' (E/d) CGre CMac CSut CTrh CTrw CWal IOrc LHyd LKna MBri SBod SCog SDeJ SExb WBod WPat
– 'Kirishima' (E) CHig LKna SReu SRms
– 'Kiritsubo' (E) GAri LHyd WBod
– 'Kiusianum' See R. ***kiusianum***
– 'Klondyke' (K) CB&S CSam CSco EBre ELan GGGa IOrc LBre LKna LMil MAsh MBri MGos NBar SExb SPer SReu
– 'Knap Hill Apricot' (K) LKna LMil
– 'Knap Hill Red' (K) LKna LMil
– 'Kobold' (E) ECar SLeo SSta
¶– 'Kojo-no-hikari' (E) LTil
– 'Komurasaki' (E) CWal SLeo
– 'Koningin Emma' ('Queen Emma') (M) LMil MBri

Azalea 'Koningin Wilhelmina' (E) SExb WBod
– 'Koster's Brilliant Red' (M) CSco MBal MBar SReu
¶ – 'Kozan' (E) MBal
§ – 'Kure-no-yuki' (E/d) CBow CHig CMac CWal LHyd LKna SBod SCog SExb SReu SSta WBod
– 'Kusudama' (E) CTrh GAri
– 'Lady Elphinstone' (E) LHyd
– 'Lady Rosebery' (K) LKna SReu
– 'Langmans' LKna
– 'Lapwing' (K) CBow GAri GGGa LKna
– 'Late Love' (E) ECar IJoh MGos SExb SSpi
– late pink Inverewe WBod
– 'Laura Morland' (E) LHyd
*– 'Lavender Brilliant' CTrh
– 'Ledifolium' See R. ***mucronatum***
– 'Ledifolium Album' See R. ***mucronatum***
– 'Leibnitz' (G/d) GGGa
– 'Lemonora' (M) ELan MAsh MBri SDeJ
– 'Lemur' (E) EPot GGGa LTil MAsh MBri MGos WPat WThu
– 'Leo' (E) CBow CWal LHyd LKna LMil SBod SCog SLeo SPer SReu WAbe WWeb
– 'Lilac Time' (E) MBar WBod
– 'Lilacinum' SCog
– 'Lillie Maude' (E) CTrh
– 'Lilliput' (E) SBod SPer
– 'Lily Marleen' (E) CDoC CSut CWal MMor SReu
– 'Linearifolium' See R. ***macrosepalum*** 'L.'
– 'Linnet' LKna
– 'Lobster Pot' (K) LMil SExb
– 'Lorna' (E) CSco LMil LTil MAsh MGos
– 'Lotte' (E) SReu
– 'Louis B Williams' GGGa
– 'Louisa' (E) SExb SSpi
– 'Louise Dowdle' (E) CDoC CTrh LMil MMor SExb SGil SPer
– 'Lullaby' (E) LKna
I – 'Mac Ovata' CMac
– 'Macranthum' See R. ***indicum***
– 'Macranthum Roseum' (E) MAsh SBod
– 'Macrosepalum' See R. ***macrosepalum***
– 'Macrostemon' See R. ***obtusum*** 'Macrostemon'
– 'Madame van Hecke' (E) COtt MAsh MBri NBar SReu
¶ – 'Madrigal' (E) LTil
N– 'Magnificum' CBow LMil MBri SCog
– 'Malvaticum' (E) SExb WBod
– 'Margaret George' (E) LHyd
– 'Marie' (E) CMac SCog
– 'Marilee' (E) MGos
¶ – 'Marina' (K) SExb
– 'Marion Merriman' (K) LKna
– 'Marionette' CTrh
– 'Martha Hitchcock' (E) LKna MPlt SExb SGil SRms WAbe
– 'Martine' See R. Azaleodendron 'M.'
– 'Mary Helen' (E) CDoC LHyd LRHS SExb SReu WBod
– 'Mary Meredith' (E) LHyd
*– 'Mary Poppins' CDoC GRei
– 'Master of Elphinstone' (E) SCog
– 'Matsuyo' (E) SExb
– 'Mauna Loa' (K) LKna
– 'Maxwellii' (E) CMac SCog SExb WBod
– 'Mazurka' (K) LKna
– 'Megan' (E) GGGa GWht MAsh
– 'Meicho' (E) CTrh GAri LTil
– 'Melford Lemon' See R. A. 'Ilam Melford Lemon'
– 'Mephistopheles' (K) LKna
N– 'Merlin' (E) LMil MBal WWeb
– 'Michael Hill' (E) CB&S CBow CTrh MAsh MPlt SPer SSpi WWeb
– 'Midori' (E) SExb
– 'Mikado' (E) CMHG CWal ECar LTil SBod SPer SReu SSta
– 'Mimi' (E) CMac LHyd MBri
– 'Ming' See R. A. 'Ilam Ming'
– 'Misomogiri' CHig
– 'Miss Muffet' (E) SExb
– 'Mizu-no-yamabuki' (E) CWal SLeo
*– 'Moidart' (Vs) LMil
– 'Moira Salmon' (E) LHyd
– Mollis orange SRms
– Mollis pink GGGa SRms
– Mollis red SRms
– Mollis salmon (M) GGGa
– Mollis yellow SRms
– 'Moon Maiden' (E) MMor
– 'Motet' LKna
– 'Mother's Day' (E) CBow CGre CMac CSco CSut CWal EBre GRei GWht IJoh LBre LHyd LKna LMil MBal MBar MBri MGos MMor MRav NBar NKay SBod SDeJ SExb SLeo SReu SSta WBod WPat
– 'Mount Rainier' (K) LMil
– 'Mount Saint Helens' CBow GGGa LHyd LMil
– 'Mozart' (E) SBod WBod
– 'Mrs Anthony Waterer' (O) LKna
– 'Mrs Doorenbos' CMac
– 'Mrs Emil Hager' (E) LHyd
– 'Mrs Peter Koster' (M) IJoh
– 'Mucronatum' (E) See R. ***mucronatum***
– 'Mucronatum Amethystinum' See R. A. 'Amethystinum'
– 'Multiflorum' NBar
– ***nakaharae*** x 'Kin-no-zai' SSta
– 'Nakahari Orange' See R. ***nakaharae*** Orange form
– 'Nakahari-mariko' See R. ***nakaharae*** 'Mariko'
– 'Nancy Buchanan' (K) MAsh SExb
– 'Nancy of Robinhill' (E) LHyd
– 'Nancy Waterer' (G) CSco GGGa MBri NBar SReu
– 'Nanki Poo' (E) LHyd SPer
– 'Naomi' (E) GWht IOrc LHyd LKna LMil SCog SExb SPer SPla SReu
– 'Narcissiflorum' (G/d) CDoC CSco CWal IOrc LHyd LKna LMil MBri SDeJ SExb SReu
– 'Nettie' (E) SCog
– 'Niagara' (E) CTrh LHyd MBal SCog WBod
– 'Nichola' (E) MAsh SBod
– 'Nico' CDoC CMac MAsh MBri MRav SPer WBod WPat
– 'Nihon-no-hana' (E) CHig CTrh
– 'Nishiki' (E) CMac
N– 'Norma' (G) LMil SExb SReu

Azalea 'Northlight' MBri
¶ – 'Nuccio's Allegro' (E/d) LTil
– 'Nuccio's Bit o' Sunshine' (E) CTrh
¶ – 'Nuccio's Carnival' (E) LTil
¶ – 'Nuccio's Carnival Blaze' (E) LTil
¶ – 'Nuccio's Carnival Candy' (E) LTil
¶ – 'Nuccio's Carnival Clown' (E) LTil
¶ – 'Nuccio's Carnival Jackpot' (E) LTil
¶ – 'Nuccio's Carnival Magic' (E) LTil
¶ – 'Nuccio's Dew Drop' (E) LTil
¶ – 'Nuccio's Dream Clouds' (E/d) LTil
¶ – 'Nuccio's Feathery Touch' (E) LTil
¶ – 'Nuccio's Garden Party' (E/d) LTil
¶ – 'Nuccio's Happy Days' (E/d) LTil
¶ – 'Nuccio's Harvest Moon' (E) LTil
¶ – 'Nuccio's High Society' (E) LTil
¶ – 'Nuccio's Magnificence' (E/d) LTil
¶ – 'Nuccio's Mama Mia' (E) LTil
¶ – 'Nuccio's Masterpiece' (E/d) LTil
¶ – 'Nuccio's Melody Lane' (E) LTil
¶ – 'Nuccio's Mexicali Rose' (E) LTil
¶ – 'Nuccio's Misty Moon' (E) LTil
¶ – 'Nuccio's Pink Bubbles' (E/d) LTil
¶ – 'Nuccio's Pink Champagne' (E/d) LTil
¶ – 'Nuccio's Pink Snow' (E) LTil
¶ – 'Nuccio's Pink Tiger' (E) LTil
¶ – 'Nuccio's Polka' (E) LTil
¶ – 'Nuccio's Primavera' (E) LTil
¶ – 'Nuccio's Rain Drops' (E) LTil
¶ – 'Nuccio's Snow Storm' (E) LTil
¶ – 'Nuccio's Spring Triumph' (E) LTil
¶ – 'Nuccio's Sunburst' (E/d) LTil
¶ – 'Nuccio's Wild Cherry' (E) LTil
– 'Oi-no-mezame' (E) LHyd
– 'Old Gold' (K) SReu
N – 'Ophelia' CBow
– 'Optima' (E) SCog
– 'Orange Beauty' (E) CMac CSco CSut CTrh CWal ECar GGGa IDai IJoh LHyd LKna LMil MBal MBar MGos MMor SBod SCog SExb SLeo SPer SReu SSta WAbe WBod
– 'Orange King' (E) MBar WStI
– 'Orangeade' (K) GGGa LTil
¶ – 'Orchid Lights' EBlo
– 'Orient' (K) SExb
– 'Oryx' (O) LKna
¶ – 'Otome Zakura' (E) LTil
– 'Ouchiyama' LKna
– 'Oxydol' (K) CWal GGGa LHyd LKna SExb
– 'Palestrina' (E) CB&S CMac CSco CWal EPot GWht IDai IOrc LHyd LKna MBal MBar MMor SBod SCog SExb SLeo SPer SReu SSta WBod WPat WStI
– 'Pallas' (G) CSco MBri SReu
– 'Pamela Miles' LHyd
– 'Pancake' CMac
– 'Panda' (E) CDoC CMac EBlo EBre GGGa LBre LHyd LMil MBri SReu
– 'Paramount' (K) LKna
– 'Pavane' (K) LKna
– 'Peach Blossom' (E) See R. A. 'Saotome'
– 'Peach Blow' (E) ISea
– 'Peach Glow' (K) GGGa
– 'Pearl Bradford' (E) LMil SExb
– 'Peep-Bo' (E) LHyd LMil SPer
– 'Perfect' MBal SPer
¶ – 'Perfection' (E) SDeJ
– 'Persil' (K) CB&S CSco CWal ELan GRei IDai IJoh ISea LHyd LKna MAsh MBar MBri MGos MMor NBar SDeJ SReu WBod
¶ – 'Peter Berg' NBar
– 'Petrouchka' (K) LKna MAsh MBri
– 'Pettychaps' (E) SReu
– 'Phoebe' SReu
– 'Piccolo' (K) LKna
– 'Pink Beauty' SExb
N – 'Pink Delight' LHyd LKna SExb WBod
– 'Pink Pancake' (E) CB&S CTrh IJoh LMil MAsh MGos SGil SSpi WWeb
N – 'Pink Ruffles' WBod
– 'Pippa' (E) CMac SRms
– 'Polar Bear' (E) IJoh MBal
– 'Polar Haven' (E) LKna
– 'Polar Sea' (E) CTrh SBod SExb
– 'Polonaise' (E) LKna
– ***ponticum*** See R. ***luteum***
– 'Pooh-Bah' (E) LHyd
– 'Port Knap' (E) LKna
– 'Port Wine' (E) LKna
– 'Princess Ida' (E) LHyd
I – 'Princess Margaret of Windsor' (K) SExb
– 'Prins Bernhard' (E) LKna MAsh SExb
– 'Prinses Juliana' (E) CDoC MMor SExb SGil SHer SReu WAbe WBod
§ – 'Pucella' (G) MLea NBar
– purple Glenn Dale (E) SExb
– 'Purple Queen' (E/d) MAsh
– 'Purple Splendor' (E) CMac CWal EBre IOrc LBre LKna MGos NHol
– 'Purple Triumph' (E) CB&S CHig CWal EBre IJoh LBre LKna LMil SLeo SReu SSta WBod

Azalea 'Queen Louise' (K)	MAsh SExb
– 'Raphael de Smet' (G/d)	LKna SReu
– 'Rashomon' (E)	LHyd LKna SLeo WBod
– 'Raspberry Delight' (K/d)	LMil
– 'Red Bird' (E)	CMac
– 'Red Fountain' (E)	COtt
– 'Red Red'	GGGa
– red selected (K)	GGGa
– 'Red Sunset' (E/d)	LMil
– 'Redmond' (E)	LHyd SExb
– 'Redwing' (E)	LMil LRHS SPer
– 'Rennie' (E)	SExb
– 'Rêve d'Amour' (Vs)	MMor SSta
– 'Rex' (E)	CWal MBar SPer
– 'Robin Hill Frosty' (E)	LHyd SExb
– 'Robin Hill Gillie' (E)	LHyd
– 'Rosalinda' (E)	GGGa
– 'Rosata' (Vs)	CDoC GGGa MBri MMor SReu SSta
– 'Rose Glow'	MMor
– 'Rose Greeley' (E)	CDoC CHig CSco CTrh ECar LTil SBod SExb SHer SReu
– 'Rose Haze'	MMor
– 'Rose Plenum' (G)	GGGa
¶ – 'Rose Queen'	LTil
– 'Rose Ruffles' (K)	GGGa LMil
– 'Rose Torch'	MMor
– 'Rosebud' (E/d)	CB&S CHig CMac CSco CTrh CTrw CWal GGGa GWht ISea LHyd LKna MBar MGos MMor NKay SBod SCog SDeJ SExb SLeo SPer SReu WBod
– 'Rosiflorum'	See R. ***indicum*** 'Balsaminiflorum'
– 'Rosy Lights'	EBlo LMil
– 'Royal Command' (K)	CSco GAri GRei MBar MMor NBar SDeJ SExb
– 'Royal Lodge' (K)	CWal GGGa GWht SExb
– 'Royal Ruby' (K)	LMil MMor
– 'Rozanne Waterer'	LKna
– 'Rubinetta' (E)	CDoC
– 'Rumba' (K)	LKna
– 'Sabina'	NBar
– 'Sahara' (K)	LKna
– 'Sakata Red' (E)	CGre CMac IOrc SExb WBod
– 'Sakon' (E)	CWal SLeo
¶ – 'Sakuragata' (E)	LTil
– 'Salmon King' (E)	MBar
– 'Salmon Sander' (E)	LKna SExb
– 'Samuel Taylor Coleridge' (M)	MMor
– 'Sang de Gentbrugge' (G)	SReu
– 'Santa Maria'	COtt EBre IDai LBre NHol SGil SHer SReu SSta
§ – 'Saotome' (E)	CMac LHyd
– 'Saroi' (E)	CWal SLeo
– 'Saskia' (K)	LKna
– 'Satan' (K)	CB&S CWal ELan GAri GGGa GWht LKna MBri MMor NBar SReu
– 'Satsuki' (E)	CGre IJoh LNet MAsh SExb SSta WWeb
– 'Saturnus' (M)	ELan
– 'Scarlatti' (K)	LKna
– 'Scarlet Pimpernel' (K)	CWal GWht NKay SExb
– 'Schubert' (E)	MGos WAbe WBod
– 'Shanty' (K)	LKna
– 'Shiho' (E)	CTrh
– 'Shiko' (E)	CTrh LTil SReu
¶ – 'Shiko-no-kagami' (E)	LTil
– 'Shin Seikai' (E/d)	CB&S
– 'Shinimiagagnoo' (E)	CWal SLeo
¶ – 'Shinnyo-no-hikari'	GAri
¶ – 'Shinsei' (E)	GAri
– 'Shintoki-no-hagasane' (E)	LHyd WBod
– 'Shintsune' (E)	CWal SLeo
¶ – 'Shinyomo-no-haru' (E)	LTil
¶ – 'Shira-fuji' (E/v)	LTil
– 'Shi-no-noe' (E)	SBod SLeo
– 'Shukishima' (E)	CWal SLeo
¶ – 'Shuku-fuku' (E)	GAri
– 'Silver Glow' (E)	CMac
– 'Silver Moon' (E)	CTrh ECar IOrc SBod SCog SExb SLeo SPer
– 'Silver Slipper' (K)	CWal GAri GWht LHyd LKna LMil MBal MBar MBri MLea MMor NBar SReu SSta
– 'Silverwood' (K)	LMil
– 'Silvester' (E)	COtt MBri MMor WAbe WPat
– 'Sir William Lawrence' (E)	LKna SReu
– 'Snow' (E)	CMac COtt ECar IJoh MAsh
– 'Snow Hill' (E)	LHyd LMil
– 'Snowbird'	GGGa
– 'Snowflake'	See R. A. 'Kure-no-yuki'
– 'Soft Lips' (K)	GWht
– 'Soho' (E)	CTrh GAri LNet SExb
– 'Soir de Paris' (Vs)	MAsh MBar MBri MMor SSta
¶ – 'Solway' (Vs)	LMil
– 'Sophie Hedges'	LKna
– 'Souvenir du Président Carnot' (G)	LKna
– 'Spek's Orange' (M)	CWal LHyd MGos SReu
– 'Spicy Lights'	LMil
– 'Spoonbill'	LKna
– 'Spring Beauty' (E)	CBow CMac SExb
– 'Squirrel' (E)	CDoC CMac EBlo EBre ECar GGGa GRei LBre LHyd LMil MAsh MBal MBri MGos SCog SGil SReu SSta WBod WPat
¶ – 'Star of Zaffelare'	NHol
– 'Stewartstonian' (E)	CMac CTrh CWal ECar IJoh IOrc LHyd LMil LTil MBal MBar MBri MMor SBod SDeJ SSta
– 'Stour' (K)	GGGa
– 'Stranraer'	MBri
– 'Strawberry Ice' (K)	CBow CMHG CSco CWal GGGa GWht IJoh IOrc ISea LKna LMil MBri MGos SExb SPer SReu
– 'Sugared Almond' (K)	CWal MBal
– 'Sugi-no-ito'	See R. A. 'Kumo-no-ito'
– 'Summer Fragrance' (O)	NBar SReu SSta
– 'Sun Chariot' (K)	CB&S CSam CWal EBlo GRei ISea LHyd LKna LMil MBri SDeJ SPer SReu
¶ – 'Sun Charm'	NHol
– 'Sunbeam'	See R. Azalea 'Benifude'
– 'Sunset Pink' (K)	CDoC ISea LHyd LMil SExb WWeb
– 'Sunte Nectarine' (K)	GWht LMil SExb

Azalea 'Surprise' (E)	CDoC CTrh EBre ISea LBre MAsh SCog SExb SLeo SPer SReu SSta WWeb
– 'Susannah Hill' (E)	CB&S CTrh LMil MBri SBod SExb SGil SPer SSta
– 'Swansong' (E)	CMac CSut SCog
– 'Sword of State' (K)	LMil SExb
– 'Sylphides' (K)	GAri LKna MBri
– 'Sylvester'	CDoC MGos NHol SReu
– 'Takasago' (E/d)	LMil SCog SExb
– 'Tanager' (E)	CTrh LKna
– 'Tangiers' (K)	SExb
– 'Tender Heart' (K)	LMil SExb
– 'Terra-cotta Beauty' (E)	WPat WThu
– 'Tinsmith' (K)	LMil SExb
– 'Tit Willow' (E)	CWal GRei LHyd
– 'Titipu' (E)	CWal LHyd
– 'Tonkonatsu' (E)	CWal SLeo
*– 'Top of the Rockery'	MAsh
– 'Toreador' (E)	CMac LKna SExb
¶– 'Torridon' (Vs)	LMil
– 'Totally Awesome' (K)	CBow GGGa
– 'Toucan' (K)	CMHG LKna
– 'Tower Beauty' (C)	LHyd
– 'Tower Dainty' (C)	LHyd
– 'Tower Daring' (C)	LHyd
– 'Tower Dexter' (C)	LHyd
– 'Tower Dragon' (C)	LHyd
– 'Trent' (K)	SReu
– 'Troll' (E)	SReu
– 'Troupial' (K)	LKna
– 'Tsuta-momiji' (E)	LHyd SExb
– 'Tunis' (K)	CWal MBri MLea
N– 'Twilight'	MBri
*– 'Twilight Sky'	SExb
– 'Ukamuse' (E/d)	LHyd
– 'Umpqua Queen' (K)	GGGa ISea
– 'Unique' (G)	LKna SReu
*– 'Uta-maru'	LTil
– 'Van Heka'	CDoC NHol
– 'Velvet Gown' (E)	LRHS MBri
– 'Venetia' (K)	MBri MMor
– 'Vespers' (E)	CTrh MAsh
– 'Vida Brown' (E/d)	CMac GWht LKna MAsh MBri SBod SCog SPer SReu SSta WPat WThu
– 'Viking' (E)	LHyd
– 'Violet Longhurst'	LHyd
– 'Violetta' (E)	GGGa ISea NBar SExb WAbe
– 'Vuyk's Rosyred' (E)	Widely available
– 'Vuyk's Scarlet' (E)	CB&S CCla CMac CSco CTrh EPot GGGa GWht IDai IJoh ISea LHyd LKna LMil MBar MBri MGos MMor MRav NHol NKay SCog SExb SLeo SPer SReu SSta WBod
– 'W E Gumbleton' (M)	SReu
– 'Wallowa Red' (K)	LMil MAsh
– 'Ward's Ruby' (E)	CSut CTrh CTrw LTil SReu
– 'Washington State Centennial'	GGGa
– 'Waxwing'	LKna
– 'Westminster' (O)	LKna LMil
¶– 'White Frills' (E)	MBal
– 'White Lady' (E)	IJoh LKna SExb SRms
– 'White Lights'	CBow EBlo GGGa LMil LRHS
¶– 'White Prince' (E/d)	LTil
– 'White Swan' (K)	ISea
– 'Whitethroat' (K/d)	IOrc LKna MBri SExb SReu
– 'Willy' (E)	CBow GGGa LHyd LKna MBri SPer SReu
– 'Windsor Apple Blossom' (K)	LMil
– 'Windsor Peach Glow' (K)	LMil
– 'Windsor Sunbeam' (K)	LMil
– 'Winston Churchill' (M)	MBar MMor NBar
– 'Wintergreen' (E)	CB&S CTrh SSta WWeb
– 'Wombat' (E)	CDoC EBlo ECar GGGa GRei LHyd LMil LTil MAsh MBal MBar MBri MGos NHol SCog SReu SSta WPat
– 'Wryneck' (K)	LHyd LMil MBri SReu
– 'Yamato-no-hikari'	CTrh
– 'Yoga' (K)	LKna
– 'Yo-zakura' (E)	CWal SLeo
Azaleodendron 'Broughtonii Aureum'	SReu
– 'Cameronian'	LKna
– 'Galloper Light'	LKna
– 'Glory of Littleworth'	LKna
– 'Govenianum'	CLan LKna
– 'Hammondii'	LKna
§ – 'Hardijzer Beauty'	CB&S LKna MBal
– 'Joy's Delight'	LKna
– 'Martha Isaacson'	MBal MGos SBar
– 'Martine'	LHyd LKna MBri MGos SLeo WBod
– 'Ria Hardijzer'	LKna MBri SSta
– 'Wilsonii'	LKna
baileyi	CWal GGGa LHyd LMil
bainbridgeanum R/USDA 59184/R 11190	CWal SLeo
♦ ***bakeri*** (A)	See R. ***calendulaceum***
balfourianum	GGGa
– Aganniphoïdes Group	CWal LMil
barbatum	CBow CWal GGGa GWht LHyd LMil SLeo SReu SSpi
– BB 152	MBal
– DF 525	MBal
§ ***basilicum***	CWal LMil SLeo
bathyphyllum	SLeo
beanianum	CWal GGGa LMil SLeo
– compact form	See R. ***piercei***
beesianum	GGGa SLeo
bergii 'Papillon'	See R. ***augustinii rubrum*** 'Papillon'
bhutanense EGM 077	GGGa LMil
¶– KR 1753	LMil
bodinieri	LMil
brachyanthum	CWal GGGa SLeo
§ – L&S 2764	GGGa LMil
– ssp. ***hypolepidotum***	CWal GGGa LMil MBal SLeo
brachycarpum	CWal GGGa MBal SLeo
– ssp. ***fauriei***	CWal SLeo
– pink form	SLeo
¶– 'Roseum Dwarf'	GGGa
brachysiphon	See R. ***maddenii maddenii***
bracteatum CH&M 2586	GGGa
bullatum	See R. ***edgeworthii***
bureaui	CAbP CBow CWal GGGa GWht IOrc LHyd MBal MBlu SBar SLeo SReu SSpi SSta
¶– EGM 141	LMil

– 'Ardrishaig'	GGGa
burmanicum	CWal LMil SBor SLeo
caesium	GGGa
§ ***calendulaceum*** (A)	GGGa LHyd LMil MBal SLeo
¶ – yellow form	LMil
callimorphum	CWal GGGa LMil
– var. ***myiagrum***	CWal
– – F 21821A	SLeo
calophytum	CHEx CWal GGGa LHyd LMil SLeo
calostrotum	CWal LMil MBlu MPlt WAbe
– R18453	GGGa
– 'Gigha'	CSam CWal EPot GGGa LHyd LMil MAsh MBri NHar NHol
§ – ssp. ***keleticum***	GAbr GAri GDra GWht LHyd LTil MBal MBar MGos NKay SBod SReu WAbe WBod WThu
– – F 19915	NHol
– – F 21756	CWal SLeo
– – R 58	NHol
§ – – Radicans Group	CWal ECar EPot GAbr GWht LHyd LMil MAsh MBar MLea MPlt NHol SPla WAbe WBod WPat WThu
– – Radicans Group mound form	MAsh NHol
– – Radicans Group R 59182	MLea
– ssp. ***ripariöides***	LMil
– ssp. ***riparium***	CWal GAbr MBal
– – Calciphilum Group	GAbr GGGa MBar MLea WBod
– – Calciphilum Group Yu 19754	GGGa
§ – – Nitens Group	GGGa LMil
– – Rock's form R 178	GGGa GWht MAsh NHol
caloxanthum	See R. ***campylocarpum caloxanthum***
calvescens F 25036*	GGGa
camelliiflorum	CWal GGGa
campanulatum	GWht IOrc LHyd LKna LMil SLeo SReu
– B 643	MBal
– DF 563	MBal
– SS&W 9107	CWal GGGa SLeo
– TSS 11	SLeo
– TSS 7	SLeo
§ – ssp. ***aeruginosum***	CWal GGGa LMil SReu
¶ – – EGM 068	LMil
– ***album***	CWal SLeo
– 'Knap Hill'	CWal LHyd SReu
– 'Waxen Bell'	LHyd SLeo
campylocarpum	CHig CWal GGGa GWht LHyd LMil SCog SLeo SReu
– BM&W 150	MBal
– DF 558	MBal
§ – ssp. ***caloxanthum***	CWal GGGa IOrc LHyd
– – forms	SLeo
§ – – Telopeum Group KW 5718B	SLeo
– ***campylocarpum*** Elatum Group	CWal
campylogynum	CB&S CMHG CTrw CWal GGGa GWht IOrc LMil NHar NKay SLeo SReu
– KW 21481	NHol
– 'Album'	See R. ***c. leucanthum***
– apricot form	LMil
– 'Beryl Taylor'	GGGa LMil
– 'Bodnant Red'	EPot GAbr GGGa LHyd LMil LTil MAsh NHar SLeo WBod
– Castle Hill form	LMil
– Celsum Group	LMil
– Charopoeum Group	CWal GGGa LMil MAsh MBal MGos MLea MPlt NHar WAbe WBod
– Charopoeum Group 'Patricia'	GGGa MBal WAbe WBod WThu
– claret form	GGGa LMil MBal MLea WAbe WBod
– copper	SReu
§ – Cremastum Group	CWal GGGa LHyd LMil NHol SLeo
§ – var. ***leucanthum***	GGGa LMil
– Myrtilloides Group	CWal EPot GAri GGGa GWht LHyd LMil MBal MBri NHar SExb SLeo WAbe WBod WCru
– Myrtilloides Group Farrer 1046	GGGa NHar NHol
– pink form	MBar
– 'Plum Brandy'	GGGa
– salmon pink	CWal GGGa LTil MBal MLea NBar NHar NHol WAbe WBod
– yellow form	MBar
camtschaticum	ECar GArf GAri GDra GGGa MBal MLea SReu
– ***album***	GGGa
– red forms	GGGa
canadense (A)	GGGa MBal NHol SLeo
– f. ***albiflorum*** (A)	GGGa
x ***candelabrum***	SLeo
canescens (A)	CWal
capitatum	GGGa
carneum	GGGa LMil
carolinianum	See R. ***minus minus*** Carolinianum Group
catacosmum	GGGa SLeo
– R 11185	SLeo
catawbiense	CHig LHyd SLeo
– 'Powell Glass'	CWal
caucasicum	CWal MBal
– ex AC&H	GGGa SLeo
cephalanthum	EPot GGGa
– SBEC 0751	GGGa
– ssp. ***cephalanthum***	MBal
– – Crebreflorum Group	GAri GGGa
– – Crebreflorum Group Week's form	GDra
cerasinum	GGGa LMil SLeo
– KW 5830	SLeo
– KW 6923	CWal
– 'Cherry Brandy'	CWal LHyd
– 'Coals of Fire'	CWal SLeo
– deep pink	SLeo
– x ***forrestii forrestii***	MBal
chamaethomsonii	CSam CWal GGGa GWht LMil MBal NHar SLeo
– var. ***chamaethauma*** F 21768	LMil
– – KW 5847	LMil
– var. ***chamaethomsonii*** Exbury form L&S	GGGa
– – pink forms L&S	GGGa
– – Rock form	GGGa
chameunum	See R. ***saluenense c.***
championiae	GGGa

charitopes	CWal GGGa LMil MBal MBri SLeo
§ – ssp. ***tsangpoense***	CWal GGGa LMil SExb
¶ – – KW 5844	NHol
chasmanthum	See R. ***augustinii c.***
chlorops	SLeo
chrysodoron	CWal GGGa LMil
chrysomanicum	See R. Hydrid 'Chrysomanicum'
ciliatum	CB&S CHig CWal EPot GGGa GWht IOrc LHyd MBal SBor
¶ – BL&M 324	NHol
– 'Multiflorum'	See R. Hybrid 'Multiflorum'
ciliicalyx	CWal
– ***lyi***	See R. ***lyi***
cinnabarinum	CBow CWal LMil MBal SLeo SReu
– B 652	MBal
– BL&M 234	GWht LMil
– Caerhays John	CWal
– 'Caerhays Lawrence'	CWal MBal SLeo
– 'Caerhays Philip'	CWal MBal
– ***cinnabarinum*** 'Aestivale'	LMil
– – Blandfordiiflorum Group	LMil MBal SLeo
§ – – 'Mount Everest'	CWal LHyd LKna LMil SExb SLeo SReu SSta
– – 'Nepal'	CWal LHyd LMil SLeo
– – Roylei Group	CWal GGGa LHyd LMil MBal MBlu MLea SLeo SReu
– – 'Vin Rosé'	CWal LMil
§ – 'Conroy'	GGGa LHyd LMil MBal WAbe
– ssp. ***tamaense***	GGGa LMil SLeo
§ – ssp. ***xanthocodon***	CHig CWal GWht LMil MBal SCog SExb SLeo SReu
– – EGM 088	GGGa LMil
– – KW 6026	WThu
– – Concatenans Group	CSam CWal EPot GGGa LHyd SExb SLeo SSta WBod
– – Concatenans Group KW 5874	LMil LRHS
– – Concatenans Group LS&T 6560	SLeo
– – Concatenans Group mustard form	SLeo
– – 'Daffodilly'	CWal LHyd SLeo
– – forms	CWal SLeo
– – Purpurellum Group	CWal GGGa LHyd LMil SLeo
citriniflorum	CWal SReu
– R 108	GGGa
– var. ***horaeum*** F 21850	GGGa LMil
– – F 25901	GGGa LMil
clementinae	GGGa SLeo
– F 25705	SLeo
¶ – F 25917	LMil
coelicum	CWal
– F 21830	SLeo
¶ ***coeloneuron***	GGGa
¶ – EGM 108	LMil
collettianum H&W 8975	GGGa
complexum F 15392	GGGa
concatenans	See R. ***cinnabarinum xanthocodon*** Concatenans Group
concinnum	CHig CTrw CWal LHyd LMil MBal SLeo
– Pseudoyanthinum Group	CWal GGGa SLeo
coriaceum	CBow CWal GGGa LMil SLeo
coryanum	CWal GGGa SLeo
¶ – 'Chelsea Chimes' ex KW 6311	LMil
¶ ***cowanianum***	GGGa
coxianum C&H 475B	GGGa
crassum	See R. ***maddenii crassum***
cremastum	See R. ***campylogynum*** Cremastum Group
crinigerum	CWal GGGa LMil SLeo
¶ ***crutwellii***	GGGa
cubittii	See R. ***veitchianum*** Cubittii Group
¶ ***cumberlandense*** (A)	LMil
cuneatum	CWal GGGa
– F 27119 *	SLeo
cyanocarpum	CWal GGGa LMil SLeo
dalhousieae	CWal GGGa SLeo
§ – var. ***rhabdotum***	GGGa SLeo
dasypetalum	GGGa MBal MBar MLea NBar
dauricum	EPot LMil MBal MBlu MPlt SExb SLeo WBod WThu
– ***album***	See R. ***d.*** 'Hokkaido'
¶ – 'Arctic Pearl'	GGGa
¶ – dwarf	GAri
§ – 'Hokkaido'	GAri GGGa LHyd
– 'Midwinter'	CWal GGGa LHyd LMil SLeo
– 'Nanum'	MBal
– 'Suzuki'	SLeo
– × ***formosum***	SSta
davidsonianum	CB&S CBow CTrw CWal GGGa GWht IOrc ISea LHyd LMil MBal MBlu MMor SExb SLeo SSpi SSta WBod
* – 'Bodnant'	LMil
– 'Caerhays Pink'	GGGa
– 'Ruth Lyons'	LMil
– 'Serenade'	LMil
decorum	CWal IOrc LHyd LMil LTil SLeo SReu
– 'Cox's Uranium Green'	SReu
– forms	GGGa
degronianum	GGGa
§ – ssp. ***degronianum***	CWal SLeo
– – 'Gerald Loder'	CWal GGGa LHyd
§ – ssp. ***heptamerum***	CWal GGGa SLeo
¶ – – 'Ho Emma'	LMil
– 'Metternianum'	See R. ***d.*** Kyomaruense Group
delavayi peramoenum	See R. ***arboreum d. p.***
¶ ***dendricola*** KW 20981	GGGa
– Taronense Group	CWal
¶ ***dendrocharis***	GGGa
¶ ***denudatum*** Cox 5090	GGGa
desquamatum	See R. ***rubiginosum*** Desquamatum Group
× ***detonsum***	CWal SLeo
diaprepes	IOrc LHyd
– Farrer 979	SLeo
– 'Gargantua'	CWal SLeo SReu
dichroanthum	CWal GGGa IOrc LHyd MBal SLeo SReu
– SBEC 0545	GGGa
– SBEC 0601	GGGa
– ssp. ***apodectum***	CWal GGGa LMil SLeo
– ssp. ***scyphocalyx***	CWal GWht LMil MBal SLeo

– ssp. ***septentrionale***	GGGa
didymum	See R. ***sanguineum didymum***
dilatatum leucanthum (A)	GGGa
diphrocalyx	CWal
drumonium	See R. ***telmateium***
dryophyllum	See R. ***phaeochrysum levistratum***
– Balfour & Forrest	See R, ***phaeochrysum phaeochrysum***
eclecteum	CWal SLeo
– var. ***bellatulum***	CWal
edgarianum	CWal LMil
§ ***edgeworthii***	CTrw CWal GGGa LHyd MBal SLeo WBod
– Yu 17431*	LMil
– forms	GGGa
elegantulum	CWal GGGa LMil SLeo
elliottii	GGGa SLeo
erosum	SLeo
erubescens	See R. ***oreodoxa fargesii*** Erubescens Group
§ x ***erythrocalyx*** Panteumorphum Group	SLeo
euchaïtes	See R. ***neriiflorum neriiflorum*** Euch. Group
eudoxum	GGGa LMil
eurysiphon	CWal
exasperatum	CWal SLeo
– KW 8250	GGGa
eximium	See R. ***falconeri e.***
§ ***faberi***	CBow CWal GGGa SLeo
¶ – EGM 111	LMil
– ssp. ***prattii***	CWal GGGa SLeo
¶ – – EGM 147	LMil
facetum	GGGa SLeo
falconeri	CBow CHEx CWal GGGa IOrc LMil SLeo SReu
– BM&W 66	MBal
– DF 526	MBal
– EGM 055	LMil
§ – ssp. ***eximium***	GGGa LMil SSpi
fargesii	See R. ***oreodoxa f.***
fastigiatum	CWal EPot GAbr GDra LMil MBal MBar MLea SLeo WBod
– SBEC 0804/4869	GGGa WThu
– 'Blue Steel'	GGGa LMil
– 'Harry White'	LMil
– pink form	GGGa
faucium	GGGa SLeo
fauriei	See R. ***hyperythrum f.***
ferrugineum	COtt CSco CWal GGGa LKna LMil MBal MBar MGos MPlt NBar SLeo SReu WAbe
– f. ***album***	CWal
– Atrococcineum Group	GWht
– 'Glenarn'	NHol
fictolacteum	See R. ***rex fictolacteum***
fimbriatum	See R. ***hippophaëoïdes hipp.*** Fimbriatum Group
flavidum	CWal GGGa MBal SExb SSta
– 'Album'	CWal LMil SBod SExb
¶ ***fletcherianum***	MBal
– R 22302	CWal SLeo
– 'Yellow Bunting'	GGGa
§ ***flinckii***	GGGa LMil

floccigerum	CWal GGGa LMil SLeo
– F 20305	SLeo
floribundum	SLeo
¶ – Cox 5090	GGGa
formosum	CB&S CGre CWal ERea GGGa LMil
§ – formosum Iteaphyllum Group	CWal GGGa SLeo
– var. ***inaequale*** C&H 301	GGGa GWht
– 'Khasia'	GGGa
forrestii	GAbr GGGa
– ssp. ***forrestii*** Repens Group	CWal GAbr GGGa LMil MBal NHar SLeo WAbe WBod
– – Tumescens Group	CWal GGGa SLeo
fortunei	GGGa IOrc LHyd LMil SLeo SSpi
– McLaren S146	CWal
– ssp. ***discolor***	CWal GGGa LHyd LMil SLeo
§ – – Houlstonii Group	CWal LMil SLeo
– 'Foxy'	SLeo
♦ – 'Mrs Butler'	See R. ***f.*** 'Sir Charles Butler'
§ – 'Sir Charles Butler'	CWal LMil
fulgens	CWal GGGa LHyd LMil SLeo
– DF 543	MBal
fulvum	CWal GGGa IOrc LHyd LMil SLeo SReu SSta
– F 24110	SLeo
galactinum	CWal GGGa SLeo
¶ – CC&H 4023	GGGa
genestierianum	CWal
x ***geraldii***	SLeo
glaucophyllum	CWal GGGa LHyd LMil SLeo SReu
– L&S 2764	See R. ***brachyanthum*** L&S 2764
– BH form	LMil
– 'Branklyn'	GGGa
– 'Glenarn'	GGGa
§ – var. ***tubiforme***	CWal GWht SCog SLeo
– white	GGGa
glischrum	GGGa SExb SLeo
– ssp. ***glischroïdes***	LMil SLeo
– ssp. ***glischrum***	GGGa
§ – ssp. ***rude***	GGGa SLeo
glomerulatum	See R. ***yungningense*** Glomerulatum Group
grande	CGre CWal GGGa IOrc
– DF 524	MBal
– EGM 058	LMil
griersonianum	CWal GGGa IOrc ISea LHyd LTil MBal SLeo
griffithianum	CWal GGGa SLeo
¶ – EGM 101	LMil
gymnocarpum	See R. ***microgynum*** Gymnocarpum Group
habrotrichum	CWal GGGa SLeo
haematodes	CWal GGGa MBal MBri SLeo
¶ – CLD 1282	LMil
– F 6773	SLeo
– McLaren S124A	SLeo
– ssp. ***chaetomallum***	GGGa
– – KW 21077	SLeo
– – KW 5431	CWal
– – R 18359	SLeo
hanceanum	CHig NKay SLeo
– 'Canton Consul'	EPot GGGa LHyd SSta
– Nanum Group	CB&S CWal EPot GAbr GGGa MBal WAbe WBod WThu

hardyi	See R. ***augustinii h.***
headfortianum	See R. ***taggianum*** Headfortianum Group
heliolepis	CWal IOrc LMil MBal SLeo
– var. ***brevistylum***	CWal
§– – Pholidotum Group F 6762	SLeo
x ***hemigynum***	SLeo
hemitrichotum	LMil
hemsleyanum	CWal GGGa IOrc SLeo
hippophaëoïdes	CHig CSco CWal LKna LMil MAsh MBri SExb SLeo SSta
– F 22197A	SLeo
– Yu 13845	GGGa
– 'Bei-ma-shan'	GGGa
¶– 'Habashan'	WThu
§– ***hippophaëoïdes*** Fimbriatum Group	CWal
hirsutum	CWal GGGa GWht MBal SReu SSpi WBod
– f. ***albiflorum***	GGGa
– 'Flore Pleno'	EPot GGGa MBal MBar NKay WAbe
hirtipes	GGGa
– KW 5659	GGGa SLeo
– KW 6223	SLeo
hodgsonii	CBow GGGa IOrc LMil SLeo
– B 653	MBal
– DF 532	MBal
– EGM 081	LMil
hongkongense	SLeo
hookeri	SLeo
– Tigh-na-Rudha form	GGGa
horlickianum	CBow GGGa LMil SLeo
houlstonii	See R. ***fortunei discolor*** Houlstonii Group
hunnewellianum	CWal GGGa SExb
NHybrid 'A Bedford'	GGGa LHyd LKna
– 'A J Ivens'	See R. H. 'Arthur J Ivens'
– 'Abegail'	MGos SLeo
– 'Abendrot'	SSta
– 'Achilles'	CWal SLeo
– 'Actress'	CWal ISea LHyd SLeo
– 'Adamant'	CWal
– Adelaide (g.&cl.)	CWal SExb
– 'Admiral Piet Hein'	SReu
– 'Adriaan Koster'	CWal
*– 'Ahren's Favourite'	SSta
– 'Airy Fairy'	GGGa LHyd
¶– 'Akbar' (g.&cl.)	SExb
– 'Aksel Olsen'	CDoC MBal MBar MPlt NHol WBod
– Albatross (g.&cl.)	LHyd LKna LMil MBlu SExb SLeo SReu SSta
– 'Albatross Townhill Pink'	LMil
– 'Albert Schweitzer'	CWal IJoh LMil MBal MBar SLeo SReu SSta WStI
– 'Alice'	CBow CWal LHyd LKna MMor SCog SExb SLeo SPer SReu
*– 'Alice Gilbert'	CWal
– 'Alice Street'	SExb SLeo
– Alison Johnstone (g.&cl.)	CB&S CBow COtt CSam CTrw CWal GGGa GWht LHyd LMil MBal MLea NHol SCog SExb SLeo SPer SSta WBod WThu
– 'Aloha'	CAbP CBow GGGa LMil MAsh MBar MLea MMor SHBN WWeb
¶– 'Alpine Dew'	GGGa
– Alpine Gem	GGGa MAsh NHol
– 'Alpine Glow'	CWal SLeo
– Amalfi (g.&cl.)	CWal
– Amaura	WBod
– 'America'	CB&S IJoh MAsh MBal MBar MGos SExb SLeo
– 'Amethyst'	CWal LHyd
– Amor (g.&cl.)	LHyd SLeo SReu
– 'Anah Kruschke'	GGGa SExb
– 'Analin'	See R. H. 'Anuschka '
– 'Anchorage'	SExb
– 'Andre'	MBri SLeo SReu SSta
– Angelo	LHyd LMil MMor SCog SReu
¶– 'Angelo Solent Queen'	SExb
¶– 'Anilin'	GGGa
– Anita	CWal SLeo
– 'Anita Dunstan'	LMil
– 'Anna Baldsiefen'	CSam GGGa LMil LTil MAsh MBri NHar NHol SSta
– 'Anna H Hall'	GGGa LMil MAsh WWeb
– 'Anna Rose Whitney'	CB&S GGGa GRei LHyd LKna LMil MBar MBri MGos MLea SExb SHBN SLeo SPer SReu SSta WBod
– 'Annapurna'	SReu
– 'Anne George'	LHyd
– 'Anne's Delight'	GGGa
– 'Antje'	LRHS
– Antonio (g.&cl.)	CWal SCog SExb
– 'Antoon van Welie'	SSta
§– 'Anuschka'	GGGa LRHS MAsh MGos
– 'Apotrophia'	CWal
– 'Apple Blossom'	CWal LKna
– 'Apricot Fantasy'	LMil
– 'Apricot Lady Chamberlain'	GGGa
¶– 'April Chimes'	WThu
¶– 'April Gem'	GGGa
§– 'April Glow'	GWht LHyd NKay SLeo
– 'April Showers'	See R. H. 'April Glow'
¶– 'April White'	GGGa
– Arbcalo	SLeo
– Arblact	CWal
– 'Arborfield'	LMil SLeo
– Arbsutch	SLeo
§– Arbutifolium	NHol
♦– 'Arctic Tern'	See X LEDODENDRON 'A.T.'
– Argosy	CWal LMil SReu
– Ariel	SLeo
¶– 'Arkle'	LHyd
– 'Armantine'	LKna
– Armia	CWal
– 'Arthur Bedford'	LRHS MBri SExb SLeo SReu
– 'Arthur J Ivens'	CWal
– 'Arthur Osborn'	CHig CWal SLeo SSpi
– 'Arthur Stevens'	CWal SLeo
– 'Arthur Warren'	LKna
– 'Ascot Brilliant'	SLeo
– Atroflo	GGGa
– Augfast	CB&S CTrw CWal EPot IJoh IOrc ISea MBal SBod SReu WBod
– Aurora (g.&cl.)	SExb SLeo
– 'Autumn Gold'	CDoC GGGa LMil MBal NHol SExb
– Avalanche (g.&cl.)	CWal SReu
– Avocet	CWal

Hybrid 'Award'	GGGa
¶– Ayesha	SExb
¶– 'Ayton'	SExb
– Azor (g.&cl.)	CWal GGGa LHyd LMil SLeo SReu SSta
*– 'Azorazie'	SLeo
– 'Azurika'	GGGa LMil
– 'Azurro'	GGGa LMil SBar
– 'Azurwolke'	GGGa
¶– 'B de Bruin'	SExb
– 'Bad Eilsen'	NWea SSta
– 'Baden-Baden'	CSco CWal EBre ELan EPot GCHN GGGa GRei GWht IJoh ISea LBre LHyd LKna MBal MBar MBri MGos MMor NBar NHol NKay SBod SCog SExb SHBN SPer SSta WAbe WBod
– 'Bagshot Ruby'	LKna SBod SExb SReu
– 'Bali'	LMil
– 'Balsaminiflorum'	See R. ***indicum*** 'Balsaminiflorum'
– 'Bambi'	CWal LHyd MBri SCog SLeo SPla SReu
– 'Bambino'	CAbP CBow EBlo LMil LNet MAsh MLea SBar SLeo
*– 'Bandoola'	SReu
– 'Barbara Reuthe'	SReu
– 'Barclayi Helen Fox'	CWal
– 'Barclayi Robert Fox'	CWal SLeo
– 'Barmstedt'	GGGa SBar SExb
*– 'Barnaby Sunset'	CSam GAri GGGa MAsh NHol
– Baron Phillipe de Rothschild (g.&cl.)	SExb
– 'Bashful'	CB&S CWal ELan GGGa GRei GWht ISea LHyd MBal MBlu MBri MGos MMor SCog SLeo SReu
– 'Bastion'	SExb
– Bauble	SExb
– 'Beatrice Keir'	CWal LHyd SLeo SReu
– Beau Brummel (g.&cl.)	LMil
– 'Beautiful Day'	GGGa
– 'Beauty of Littleworth'	CWal ISea LHyd LKna LMil SExb SLeo SPer SReu
– 'Belle Heller'	CSam GGGa LMil LRHS MBal MBri
– 'Belle of Tremeer'	CWal
¶– Bellerophon	SExb
– 'Ben Moseley'	GGGa SSta
– 'Bengal'	CDoC GGGa ISea MBal MBar MLea MPlt NBar NHol SCog SReu
– 'Bernard Shaw'	SReu
– 'Bernstein'	GGGa LMil
– Berryrose (g.&cl.)	CWal SExb
– 'Bert's Own'	CWal
– 'Betty Arrington'	GGGa
*– 'Betty Robertson'	NKay
– 'Betty Stewart'	SLeo
– 'Betty Wormald'	CBow CHig CSco CWal GGGa IHos LHyd LKna LMil MGos NBar SCog SExb SHBN SLeo SPer SReu SSta
– Bibiani (g.&cl.)	SExb
– 'Billy Budd'	LHyd SCog
– 'Binfield'	SLeo
– 'Birthday Greeting'	SExb
– 'Biscuit Box'	SLeo
– Biskra (g.&cl.)	CWal GGGa
– 'Black Magic'	GGGa LMil
¶– 'Black Satin'	GGGa
– 'Blanc-mange' (g.&cl.)	SExb
– 'Blewbury'	CWal LHyd LMil MAsh SCog SExb SPer SSta
– 'Blitz'	LRHS MBri SLeo
– 'Blue Bell'	LKna
– 'Blue Boy'	LMil MBlu
– 'Blue Chip'	LHyd LMil SLeo
– 'Blue Danube'	CWal LKna
– Blue Diamond (g.&cl.)	CB&S CMHG CSco CTrw CWal EPot GAbr GGGa GRei GWht IDai IJoh LHyd LKna MBal MBar MGos NHol SBod SCog SExb SHBN SIng SLeo SPla SReu WBod WThu
– 'Blue Ensign'	CWal GGGa LRHS SExb
*– 'Blue Gown'	LKna
– 'Blue Haze'	LHyd
– 'Blue Jay'	MBlu NKay SReu
– 'Blue Mountain'	GDra MBal WThu
¶– 'Blue Pacific'	SBod
– 'Blue Peter'	CB&S CHig CSco CWal GGGa GWht IHos IOrc LKna MBar MBri MGos MMor SExb SHBN SLeo SPer SReu SSta WStI
– 'Blue Pool'	LMil MBal MBar MLea WBod
– Blue Ribbon	CB&S CTrw ISea
– 'Blue Silver'	GGGa MAsh NHol
– 'Blue Star'	CMHG CWal GGGa LHyd LMil SPer
– 'Blue Steel'	See R. ***impeditum*** 'Blue Steel'
– Blue Tit	CB&S CSam CTre CWal ELan GDra GGGa IJoh ITim LHyd LKna MBal MBar MMor NHol NKay SExb SHBN SLeo SPla SReu SSta STre WBod
– Bluebird (g.&cl.)	CBow CWal IOrc LKna MBal MBar MGos MMor NBar SExb WBod
– Bluestone	MBar MMor SExb
– 'Bluette'	GWht ISea LMil MBal SLeo
– 'Bluretta'	GGGa
– Boadicea	CWal
– 'Bob's Blue'	ISea SReu
– 'Boddaertianum'	CWal LHyd
– 'Bodnant Yellow'	CSam CWal LMil
– 'Bonfire'	CWal GGGa SReu
– Bonito (g.&cl.)	SCog
– 'Borderer'	SCog SLeo
– 'Boule de Neige'	GWht SBod SLeo
– 'Bounty'	GGGa
– Bow Bells (g.&cl.)	CBow CSam CSco CWal EBlo EBre ELan GWht IOrc ISea LBre LHyd LKna LMil LTil MBal MBar MBri MGos MLea MMor NKay SBod SExb SHBN SPla SReu SSpi WBod
– 'Bow Street'	LHyd
– Bo-peep (g.&cl.)	CB&S CBow CHig CSam CWal GWht LHyd LMil MBal MLea NKay SExb SLeo SPla SReu
– Break of Day (g.&cl.)	CWal SLeo
– 'Bremen'	SExb
– 'Brentor'	SLeo
– 'Brets Own'	SLeo
– Bric-a-Brac (g.&cl.)	CB&S CTrw CWal LHyd MBal NHol SExb SLeo SReu WThu
– 'Brigitte'	GGGa MAsh

Hybrid 'Brilliant'	GGGa MAsh NHol
– 'Brinny'	GGGa
– 'Britannia'	CB&S CSam CSco EBre ECar GGGa GWht IJoh LBre LHyd LKna LNet MBal MBar MBlu MBri MGos MMor NWea SBod SExb SHBN SLeo SPer SReu SSta
– Brocade	CWal GWht LHyd LKna LMil SCog SExb SLeo SPer
– 'Brookside'	CWal
– 'Broughtonii'	SExb SLeo
– 'Brown Eyes'	GGGa
– 'Bruce Brechtbill'	CSco GGGa LRHS MAsh MBal MLea NHol SSta
– 'Bud Flanagan'	MBlu SExb
– 'Buketta'	GGGa
– Burning Bush	CWal
– Bustard	SExb SLeo
– 'Butter Yellow'	SLeo
*– 'Buttered Popcorn'	LMil
– 'Butterfly'	LKna LRHS SLeo
– 'Buttermint'	CSam GAri GGGa ISea LMil MBal MBri MLea NBar SBar SExb SHBN SLeo SPer SPla SReu SSta
– 'Buttersteep'	SLeo
– 'C B van Nes'	CWal
– 'C I S'	GGGa MBlu SLeo
– 'Cadis'	GGGa
– 'Caerhays'	See R. ***cinnabarinum*** 'C.'
– Calfort (g.&cl.)	CWal
– Calstocker	SLeo
– Calsutch	SLeo
– 'Canadian Beauty'	GGGa SExb
– 'Canary'	GGGa LKna MBal SLeo SReu
– 'Captain Jack'	GGGa
– 'Caractacus'	MBar SLeo
– Cardinal (g.&cl.)	CWal
– Carex (g.&cl.)	SCog
– Carita	CWal LKna SExb SReu
– 'Carita Golden Dream'	CWal LKna LMil SExb SLeo
– 'Carita Inchmery'	CWal LHyd LKna SCog SExb SLeo
– Carmen	CSam CWal EPot GDra GGGa GRei GWht ISea LHyd LKna LMil MBal MBar MBri MGos MLea MMor NHar NHol NWea SBod SExb SHBN SLeo SReu WBod
– 'Caroline'	LMil
– 'Caroline Allbrook'	CBow CHig CMHG CSam CWal GGGa ISea LHyd LMil NHol SCog SLeo SReu SSta WWeb
– 'Caroline de Zoete'	LHyd
– 'Cary Ann'	CDoC CSco GCHN GRei ISea MBal MLea SLeo SSta
– 'Castle of Mey'	SExb
– 'Catawbiense Grandiflorum'	IJoh LRHS
– 'Catherine Hopwood'	SLeo
– Cauapo	CWal
– 'Caucasicum Pictum'	GGGa LMil MBri
– 'Cavalcade'	CWal
– Cavalier	GWht
– 'Centennial Celebration'	GGGa
– 'Cetewayo'	SLeo SReu
§– 'Champagne'	CWal LHyd LMil MGos SCog SExb SLeo
– 'Charlotte Currie'	SLeo
– 'Charlotte de Rothschild'	CWal LMil SExb
– Charmaine (g.&cl.)	CSam EPot GGGa MBal MBri NHol WBod
– 'Cheer'	GGGa GWht IJoh IOrc MBal MBar MBri SSta
– 'Chelsea Seventy'	CWal ELan IHos MAsh MBal NHol SCog SLeo SReu
– 'Cherry Pink'	ISea
– 'Chevalier Felix de Sauvage'	CWal LMil MGos SBod SExb SLeo SReu SSta
– 'Cheyenne'	CWal SLeo
– 'Chiffchaff'	EPot LHyd SLeo WAbe
– 'Chikor'	CMHG CSam CWal EPot GDra GGGa GWht LKna LMil MBal MBar MBlu MBri MGos MLea MMor NHar NHol NKay NRoo SCog SExb SLeo SReu SSta WBod WSHC WThu
– China (g.&cl.)	CDoC CWal LKna SReu
– 'China A'	LKna
– 'Chink'	CB&S CSam CWal ECar LHyd MBal MBar MPlt NBar SCog SExb SLeo SPer WBod WThu
– 'Chinmar'	GGGa
– 'Chionoïdes'	CWal GGGa GWht ISea LKna
– 'Choremia'	CTrw GWht ISea SCog SExb WBod
– 'Christmas Cheer'	CBow CDoC CHig CWal ELan GGGa GWht IOrc ISea LHyd LKna LMil MBlu MBri NKay SBar SExb SLeo SReu
– 'Christobel Maude'	LHyd
§– Chrysomanicum (g.&cl.)	CWal LMil SLeo
– Cilpinense	CB&S CBow CSam CWal ELan GGGa GWht IJoh IOrc LHyd LKna LMil LTil MBal MBar NHol SCog SExb SLeo SPer SReu SSta WAbe WBod WThu
– Cinnkeys (g.&cl.)	CWal GGGa LMil SReu
– Cinzan	LHyd LMil SReu
– 'Circus'	GGGa
– 'Cliff Garland'	LMil
– Clio	CWal SLeo
– 'Colonel Coen'	LMil MBal SHBN
– Colonel Rogers	CWal LHyd SLeo SReu
– Comely	CWal LHyd SLeo
– 'Comte de Gomer'	CB&S
¶– 'Concerto'	SExb
– 'Concessum'	LKna
– 'Concorde'	LHyd MBar MMor NBar SCog
♦– 'Conroy'	See R. ***cinnabarinum*** 'C.'
– 'Constable'	CWal LHyd SExb SLeo
– 'Constant Nymph'	LKna
– 'Contina'	GGGa
– Conyan	LHyd
– 'Coral Reef'	SLeo SReu
– 'Cornish Cracker'	SLeo
– Cornish Cross	CWal LHyd SCog SExb SLeo SReu
– Cornish Early Red	See R. H. Smithii Group
– 'Cornish Red'	See R. H. Smithii Group
– Cornsutch	CWal
– Cornubia	CWal SLeo
– 'Corona'	CWal LKna SCog SReu
– 'Coronation Day'	SReu
¶– Coronet	SExb

Hybrid 'Corry Koster' LKna SExb
– 'Cosmopolitan' CDoC GGGa IJoh MGos NBar SExb SSta
– 'Costa del Sol' SLeo
– 'Cotton Candy' LMil SExb
– 'Countess of Athlone' CWal LKna
– 'Countess of Derby' ISea SReu
– 'Countess of Haddington' CB&S CTre ERea ISea LMil SLeo
– 'County of York' See R. H. 'Catalode'
– Cowslip CSam ELan IJoh LHyd LKna LMil MBal MBar MBri MGos NHol SCog SExb SHBN SLeo SReu WBod
– 'Cranbourne' SReu
– 'Crater Lake' GWht
– 'Cream Crest' ISea LTil SHBN SLeo SPer
– 'Cream Glory' LHyd LMil LTil SReu WWeb
– 'Creamy Chiffon' CSam GCHN GGGa LHyd LMil MAsh MBal MLea SLeo SReu SSpi SSta
§ – 'Creeping Jenny' CBow CWal GGGa LHyd LMil MBal MBar MLea NBar NHol SCog SPer SPla WBod
¶ – Cremorne (g.&cl.) SExb
§ – 'Crest' CBow CSam CSco CWal GGGa GWht IOrc LHyd LKna LMil LTil MBal MBlu MGos MLea SHBN SLeo SPer SReu SSta WThu WWeb
– 'Crete' COtt GGGa LTil MAsh MGos SReu
– 'Crimson Pippin' GGGa
– Crossbill CB&S GGGa MBal NKay SLeo
– 'Crowthorne' SCog
– 'Crushed Strawberry' WBod
– 'Cunningham's Blush' GAri GGGa GWht SExb SHBN
– 'Cunningham's Sulphur' See R. ***caucasicum*** 'C.S.'
– 'Cunningham's White' CB&S CHig CSam CWal ELan GGGa GRei IJoh LKna LMil MBar MBri MGos MMor SExb SLeo SPer SReu WStI
*– 'Cupcake' GGGa
– 'Curlew' Widely available
– 'Cutie' GGGa SLeo SSta
– 'Cynthia' CB&S CHig CSam CSco CWal GGGa IJoh IOrc ISea LHyd LKna MBal MBar MBri MGos MMor NBar NWea SBod SExb SHBN SLeo SPer SReu SSta
*– 'Dagmar' GGGa
– 'Dairymaid' CWal ISea LHyd LKna SLeo SReu
– Damaris CWal SLeo
– 'Damaris Logan' See R. H. 'Logan Damaris'
*– 'Dame Edith Evans' GGGa
– Damozel (g.&cl.) CWal LRHS SCog SExb SPer WThu
– 'Dandy' LKna
– Dante CWal SLeo
– 'Daphne' SLeo
– 'Daphne Jewiss' SReu
– 'Daphne Magor' SLeo
– 'Daphnoïdes' GGGa MLea SBar
¶ – 'Dartmoor Dawn' MBal
– 'David' CWal GGGa LHyd LKna MAsh SLeo SReu
– 'David Grant' GDra
– 'David Rockefeller' SExb
*– 'Davidson' ISea
¶ – 'Dawn's Delight' ISea
– Day Dream (g.&cl.) CWal LHyd LKna SExb SReu
– 'Desert Orchid' LHyd
– 'Dexter's Spice' GGGa LTil
– 'Diana Colville' CWal
– 'Diana Pearson' SLeo
– 'Diane' LKna SExb SLeo SReu
– Dicharb CWal
¶ – 'Dietrich' SSta
– 'Diny Dee' CAbP COtt MBal MGos SExb SPla SSta
– Diva (g.&cl.) SExb
– 'Doc' CB&S CWal ELan GGGa GRei IOrc ISea LMil MBal MBar MGos MMor NBar NKay SCog SLeo SReu WStI
– 'Doctor Arnold W Endtz' MAsh MBar MMor NBar SLeo
– 'Doctor Ernst Schäle' GGGa SExb
– 'Doctor H C Dresselhuys' SHBN
– 'Doctor Stocker' CWal SExb SLeo
– 'Doctor Tjebbes' ISea
– 'Doctor V H Rutgers' MGos
– 'Doncaster' CWal EBre GRei LBre LKna MGos NHol NWea SBod SCog SExb SHBN SLeo
– 'Dopey' CBow CDoC CSco CWal EBlo GGGa GRei GWht IHos IJoh IOrc LHyd LMil MBal MBar MBri MLea MMor NBar NHol SCog SExb SHBN SLeo SPer SReu
– 'Dora Amateis' COtt CSam CWal EBre GGGa LBre LHyd LMil LTil MBal MBar MBri MGos MLea MMor NHar NHol NKay NRoo SCog SExb SLeo SPer SReu SSpi
– Dormouse LMil SExb
– 'Dorothea' CWal SLeo
– 'Dorothy Amateis' SSta
– 'Double Date' GGGa
– 'Douglas McEwan' GWht MBri
– Dragonfly CWal SExb SLeo SReu
– 'Drake's Mountain' MBar MPlt MRav
– 'Dreamland' GGGa LHyd LTil SExb SReu
– 'Duchess of Portland' CWal
– 'Dusky Dawn' CWal
– 'Dusty Miller' CAbP CDoC COtt CWal IHos ISea LMil MBal MBri MGos SCog SExb SHBN SLeo SPer SReu WBod
– 'Earl of Athlone' LHyd LKna SReu
– 'Earl of Donoughmore' CWal IDai LHyd LKna MMor SExb SPer SReu SSta
– Early Brilliant LKna
– 'Early Gem' ISea MBri
– ***edgeworthii*** × ***leucaspis*** CB&S
– × ***moupinense*** CB&S
*– 'Edith Bosley' LMil
– 'Edith Mackworth Praed' CWal
– 'Edmond Amateis' LMil
– Edmondii LHyd
– 'Egret' CDoC CSam EPot GAri GGGa GWht ITim LMil LTil MBal MBri MGos NHar NHol SExb SLeo SPer SSta WAbe WBod
*– 'Ehrengold' GGGa
– 'Eider' GCHN GGGa LTil MAsh MBal SLeo SReu

Hybrid 'Eileen' LMil SReu
– 'El Alamein' CWal SLeo
– 'El Camino' GGGa MBal MBlu MLea SExb SHBN SLeo
– 'El Greco' SLeo
– Eleanore (g.&cl.) ISea SExb
– Electra (g.&cl.) See R. ***augustinii*** E.
– 'Elisabeth Hobbie' GDra GGGa GWht LKna LMil MBal MBar MGos SCog SExb WBod
– Elizabeth Widely available
– 'Elizabeth de Rothschild' CB&S SExb
– 'Elizabeth Jenny' See R. H. 'Creeping Jenny'
– 'Elizabeth Lockhart' CBow CWal GGGa MBal MGos MLea
– 'Elizabeth of Glamis' GGGa
*– 'Elizabeth Red Foliage' GGGa
– 'Elsa Crisp' LKna
– Elsae (g.&cl.) CWal SLeo
– 'Else Frye' GGGa
– 'Elsie Straver' CDoC GWht MBal NHol SExb SHBN SPer SReu WStI
– 'Elspeth' CWal LHyd LKna
– 'Emanuela' GGGa
– 'Emasculum' CGre CSam CWal GWht LKna SPer SReu WThu
– 'Empire Day' LKna
– 'Ems' GGGa
– 'Enborne' LHyd SLeo
– 'Endre Ostbo' CWal SLeo
– 'English Roseum' GWht
– 'Ernest Inman' CWal LHyd SLeo
– Ethel (g.&cl.) CHig CWal GWht WBod
– 'Etta Burrows' GGGa LMil MBal MLea
– 'Euan Cox' GGGa MBal NHar NHol
– 'Europa' SReu
– 'Evening Glow' CDoC NHol SExb
– 'Everestianum' LKna MBar SLeo SSta
– 'Everything Nice' GGGa
– 'Exbury Albatross' LKna
– 'Exbury Fabia' SReu
§– 'Exbury Lady Chamberlain' SReu
– 'Exbury May Day' SReu
– F C Puddle (g.&cl.) SLeo
– Fabia (g.&cl.) CBow CWal GCHN GGGa GWht IJoh IOrc LHyd LKna LMil SExb SLeo SSpi
– 'Fabia Tangerine' GWht LRHS MBal SExb SReu SRms WBod
– 'Faggetter's Favourite' CWal LKna LMil MMor SLeo SReu SSta
– Fairy Light CWal LMil SExb SRms
*– 'Falkner Alison' SExb
– 'Faltho' SLeo
¶– Fancy Free (g.&cl.) SExb
– Fandango CWal
– 'Fantastica' GGGa LMil
– 'Fastuosum Flore Pleno' (d) CSco CWal GGGa ISea LHyd LKna LMil MBal MBar MBlu MBri MGos MMor NBar NWea SExb SLeo SPer SReu SSta
– Fine Feathers WBod
– Fire Bird LHyd SExb SLeo SReu
– 'Fireball' CWal
– Firedrake SReu
– 'Fireman Jeff' GGGa MBal SPer
¶– 'First Love' GGGa
– 'Fittra' GGGa
¶– 'Flamenco Dancer' (V) ERea
– Flamingo CWal
– 'Flare' CWal
– Flashlight CWal SLeo
– 'Flautando' GGGa
§– Flava (g.&cl.) CWal GGGa ISea LMil MBar MBri MGos SSta
§– 'Flavour' LKna
– 'Flirt' COtt GGGa LMil
– 'Florence Archer' MAsh SSta
– 'Floriade' LHyd LKna SExb
– Fortorb SLeo
– Fortune (g.&cl.) CWal GWht LKna SLeo
– 'Fox Hunter' LKna
– 'Fragrantissimum' CB&S CGre CTre CTrw CWal ELan ERea GGGa IOrc ISea LHyd LMil MBal MRav SExb SReu WBod
– Francis Hanger (Reuthe's) CWal GWht SExb SLeo SReu
– 'Frank Baum' GGGa MBal MBri SLeo SSta
– 'Frank Galsworthy' GGGa LKna LMil MAsh SLeo SReu SSta
– 'Fred Peste' CAbP GGGa LMil LTil MAsh MLea MMor SSpi
– 'Fred Rose' SLeo
– Fred Wynniatt (FCC) LMil SExb
– 'Frill' CTrw
– 'Frilled Petticoats' GWht LRHS MLea SLeo
– 'Frontier' GGGa LMil
– 'Frühlingszauber' CWal SExb
– 'Fuju-kaku-no-matsu' LRHS MGos
– 'Fulbrook' CWal LHyd
– 'Fulgarb' CWal SLeo
– Full House LHyd
– 'Furnivall's Daughter' CSam CSco GGGa LHyd LKna LMil MBal MBlu MBri MGos MMor SExb SLeo SReu SSta WWeb
– Fusilier (g.&cl.) CWal LHyd SExb SReu
– 'Galactic' SLeo
– Garnet CWal
– 'Gartendirektor Glocker' CSam GGGa SSta WAbe
– 'Gartendirektor Rieger' GGGa LMil MAsh NHol
– Gaul (g.&cl.) SExb
¶– 'Gemstone' SExb
– 'General Eisenhower' SReu
– 'General Eric Harrison' CWal LHyd SCog SLeo
– 'General Sir John du Cane' SExb
– 'Gene's Favourite' SReu
– 'Genghis Khan' LRHS MLea
– 'Geoffrey Millais' LMil
– 'George Hardy' CWal SExb
– 'George Johnstone' LMil MBal
– 'Georgette' CWal LHyd SLeo
– 'George's Delight' GGGa
– Gertrud Schale CWal MBal MBar MLea MPlt NHol SReu
– Gibraltar SExb
– 'Gigi' GGGa
¶– 'Gill's Crimson' SExb

Hybrid 'Ginny Gee'	CDoC CHig COtt CSam EPot GGGa GWht LHyd LMil LTil MBal MBri MGos MLea MPlt NBar NHar NHol NRoo SBar SReu SSpi SSta WAbe
– Gipsy King	SExb WThu
– 'Gipsy King Memory'	SExb
– 'Glad Tidings'	SLeo
– Gladys (g.&cl.)	SCog
– Glamour (g.&cl.)	SExb
– 'Gleam'	CWal
¶ – 'Glen's Orange'	SExb
– 'Gletschernacht'	GGGa
– 'Gloriana'	SReu
– 'Glory of Leonardslee'	SLeo
– 'Glory of Penjerrick'	CWal SLeo
– 'Gold Mohur'	SLeo SReu
– 'Golden Bee'	GGGa
– 'Golden Belle'	LMil MBal MBri MLea SLeo SPer
– 'Golden Coach'	ISea SExb
– 'Golden Fleece'	CWal LKna SExb SLeo SReu
– 'Golden Gate'	CDoC GGGa SLeo
– Golden Horn (g.&cl.)	IOrc MBal SLeo
– 'Golden Horn Persimmon'	See R. H. 'Persimmon'
– 'Golden Orfe'	CWal LHyd LMil NKay
– Golden Oriole	CB&S NHol SLeo SPer
– 'Golden Oriole Talavera'	CB&S CWal MBal SCog
*– 'Golden Princess'	GGGa LMil
§ – 'Golden Queen'	CWal
– 'Golden Star'	GGGa LMil
– 'Golden Torch'	CAbP CCla CMHG COtt CSam CSco CWal GGGa GWht IOrc LHyd LMil LNet MBal MBlu MBri MGos MLea MMor SBar SCog SExb SHBN SLeo SPer SReu SSta WWeb
– 'Golden Wedding'	CBow GGGa LMil MAsh MBal MBri MLea
– 'Golden Wit'	LRHS MBal MBri MLea SBod
– Goldfinger	MBal
*– 'Goldflimmer'	GGGa MAsh MGos
– 'Goldfort'	LKna SLeo SReu
– 'Goldika'	GGGa LMil
– 'Goldilocks'	GGGa NHar
– 'Goldkrone'	GGGa ISea LHyd LMil
– 'Goldstrike'	GGGa LMil
– 'Goldsworth Orange'	CWal GGGa LHyd LKna MBal MBar MBlu MGos MMor SLeo SPer SReu SSta
– 'Goldsworth Orange' x *insigne*	GGGa
– 'Goldsworth Pink'	LKna SReu
– 'Goldsworth Yellow'	LKna MGos SExb SLeo SReu
– 'Gomer Waterer'	CB&S CSam CSco CWal GGGa IJoh ISea LHyd LKna LMil MBal MBar MBri MGos MMor NBar NWea SBod SExb SLeo SPer SReu SSta
– 'Goosander'	NHar
– 'Grace Seabrook'	COtt GGGa GWht LHyd LMil MBlu MBri MLea SExb SLeo SPer SReu
– 'Graf Lennart'	GGGa
– 'Graf Zeppelin'	GGGa
*– 'Grafton'	SExb
*– 'Grand Pré'	GGGa
– 'Grayswood Pink'	CSam SPer
– 'Green Eye'	CWal
– 'Greensleeves'	LKna
– Grenadier (g.&cl.)	CWal GWht SExb
– 'Gretzel'	SLeo
– Grierocaster	SCog
– 'Grisette'	SExb SLeo
– 'Gristede'	GGGa LMil MAsh NHol SReu SSta WBod
– Grosclaude (g.&cl.)	CWal SCog SLeo
– 'Grouse'	EPot GGGa MBal WBod
– 'Grumpy'	CB&S CDoC CMHG CWal EBlo EBre ELan GGGa GRei GWht IHos ISea LBre LHyd LMil LNet MBal MBar MBri MLea MMor NHol SCog SHBN SLeo SPer SReu
– Guardsman	SLeo
– 'Gwen Bell'	LMil
– 'Gwillt-King'	CWal SLeo
– 'H Whitner'	SLeo
– 'Hachmann's Diadem'	GGGa
– 'Hachmann's Porzellan'	GGGa
– 'Hachmann's Rosita'	GGGa
– 'Hachmann's Violetta'	GGGa
– 'Hackmann's Marlis'	GGGa
– 'Haida Gold'	GGGa LMil MBal MBri MGos MLea NKay SExb SSta WWeb
– Halcyone	CWal SExb SLeo
– 'Halfdan Lem'	CAbP CSam GGGa LHyd LMil LTil MBal MGos MLea MMor SExb SHBN SLeo SPer SSta WWeb
– 'Hallelujah'	GGGa LMil MAsh MBal
– 'Handsworth Scarlet'	SLeo
– Happy	CWal ELan IJoh IOrc ISea SHBN
– 'Happy Occasion'	SExb
– 'Hardijzer's Beauty'	See R. Azaleodendron 'Hardijzer's Beauty'
¶ – 'Harkwood Moonlight'	LRHS
¶ – 'Harkwood Premiere'	LRHS
– 'Harry Tagg'	GGGa
– 'Harvest Moon'	CSam CWal GGGa LHyd MBal MBar MBlu MGos NKay SExb SLeo SReu SSta
– Hawk 'Crest'	See R. H. 'Crest'
*– Hawk 'Falcon'	SReu
– 'Hawk 'Jervis Bay'	See R. H. 'Jervis Bay'
¶ – Hawk 'Merlin'	SExb
– 'Haze'	SLeo
– 'Hazel'	LRHS
– 'Hazel Fisher'	LMil
– Hebe	CWal SExb
– 'Helene Schiffner'	GGGa SExb SLeo SReu
*– 'Henry Street'	SLeo
¶ – Hermes	SExb
– Hesperides	CWal
– 'High Gold'	LMil
– 'High Summer'	LMil
– 'Hilda Margaret'	SReu
– 'Hill Ayah'	CWal
– 'Hollandia'	MMor NBar SHBN
– 'Honey'	CWal LKna SLeo
– 'Honey Bee'	GGGa LMil LRHS MAsh SSta
¶ – 'Honeymoon'	SExb
– 'Hope Findlay'	LHyd

Hybrid 'Hoppy' CBow CMHG CSco CWal EBre GGGa GWht LBre MBal MBlu MBri MLea MMor SCog SExb SLeo SReu WWeb
¶– 'Horizon' LMil
– 'Horizon Snowbird' GGGa LMil
– 'Hotei' CAbP CBow CSco CWal EBlo ECar GCHN GGGa GWht IJoh ISea LHyd LMil LTil MBal MBar MBri MGos MLea MMor NKay SExb SHBN SLeo SPer SReu SSpi SSta
– 'Hugh Koster' CB&S CSam CWal LHyd LKna MGos SExb SLeo SPer
– Humming Bird CB&S CMHG CSam CSco CWal EPot GGGa GWht ISea LHyd LKna MBal MBar MBri MGos MMor MPlt NHol SExb SHBN SLeo SPer WBod WThu
– 'Hurricane' COtt LMil MBlu MBri SExb
– 'Hydon Ball' CWal LHyd SReu
– 'Hydon Ben' LHyd
– 'Hydon Dawn' CWal ECar GGGa ISea LHyd LMil MGos SCog SLeo SReu SSta
– 'Hydon Glow' CWal LHyd SLeo
– 'Hydon Gold' LHyd
– 'Hydon Hunter' CWal GGGa LHyd LMil LNet SCog SLeo SPla SReu SSta
– 'Hydon Mist' LHyd
– 'Hydon Pearl' LHyd
– 'Hydon Pink' LHyd
– 'Hydon Rodney' LHyd
– 'Hydon Salmon' LHyd SLeo
– 'Hydon Snowflake' CWal GGGa
– 'Hydon Velvet' LHyd
– Hyperion LKna SReu SSta
– Ibex (g.&cl.) CWal SExb
– Icarus CWal
– 'Ice Cream' SCog
– 'Iceberg' See R. H. 'Lodauric Iceberg'
– 'Icecream Flavour' See R. H. 'Flavour'
– 'Icecream Vanilla' See R. H. 'Vanilla'
– Idealist (g.&cl.) CWal LHyd MBri SExb SLeo SPer SReu
– 'Ightham Gold' SReu
*– 'Ightham Peach' SReu
*– 'Ightham Purple' SReu
– 'Ightham Yellow' CWal MMor SLeo SReu SSta
– 'Ilam Violet' GGGa LKna LMil
– Impi (g.&cl.) CWal LKna MBri SExb SLeo WThu
– Inamorata SExb
– Intermedium MBal
– Intrifast CWal GAri GGGa GWht LHyd LTil MBal MBri NHol NKay
– 'Isabel Pierce' CSam LMil MBal NBar SLeo SSta WWeb
– Isabella (g.&cl.) SExb
– 'Isabella Mangles' LHyd
¶– Ispahan SExb
– Italia SLeo
¶– 'Ivan D Wood' SExb
– Ivanhoe (g.&cl.) CWal ISea
– 'Ivery's Scarlet' CWal SExb
– Iviza SReu
*– 'J C Williams' CB&S
– 'J G Millais' LHyd
– 'J M de Montague' See R. H. 'The Hon. Jean Marie de Montague'
– 'Jabberwocky' LHyd
*– 'Jack' CTrw
*– 'Jack Skelton' CWal LHyd
– 'Jacksonii' CWal ISea LKna MBal MBar SLeo SReu
– Jacques SLeo SReu
– Jacquetta WBod
– 'Jade' SLeo
– Jaipur CWal
– Jalisco (g.&cl.) CWal SExb SLeo
– 'Jalisco Eclipse' CWal LKna SExb
– 'Jalisco Elect' LKna LMil SExb
– 'Jalisco Goshawk' SExb SLeo
– 'Jalisco Janet' CWal SExb
– 'Jalisco Jubilant' LHyd SExb
– 'James Barto' CWal LHyd LMil SLeo SPer SSta
– 'James Burchett' LKna LMil SLeo SPer
– 'Jan Bee' GGGa MBal
– 'Jan Dekens' SReu
– Jan Steen (g.&cl.) SExb
– 'Jancio' SExb
– 'Janet Ward' LHyd LKna
– 'Janine Alexandre Debray' SCog SLeo
– Jean SCog
– 'Jean Mary Montague' See R. H. 'The Hon. Jean Marie de Montague'
– 'Jennie Dosser' LMil
– 'Jenny' See R. H. 'Creeping Jenny'
– 'Jerez' SExb
§– 'Jervis Bay' LMil SExb
– 'Jingle Bells' GGGa
– 'Joan Scobie' CWal SLeo
– Jock CB&S CMHG LHyd
*– 'Jock's White' MBal SPer
– 'John Barr Stevenson' LHyd SLeo
– 'John Keats' CWal
– 'John Tremayne' SLeo
– 'John Walter' GRei MBar MGos SExb SPla SSta
– 'John Waterer' LKna
– Johnnie Johnston (g.&cl.) CWal SLeo
– 'Johnny Bender' MLea SExb
– 'Johnson's Impeditum' SExb
– 'Joseph Whitworth' CWal
– Josephine LMil
– 'Joyful' SExb
– 'Jubilee' LKna
– Jubilee Queen (g.&cl.) SLeo
– 'Julischka' MGos
– 'Jungfrau' SExb
– 'Juwel' CSco MGos
– 'Kalinko' GGGa MGos
– 'Karin' CSco GGGa IJoh MBal SBod SHBN
¶– Karkov (g.&cl.) SExb
– 'Kate Waterer' CWal GWht LKna MBar MGos SExb SLeo SSta
– ***keiskei*** x Carolinianum Group NHar
– Keiskrac CWal
– 'Ken Janeck' See R. ***yakushimanum yak.*** 'Ken Janeck'
N– Kewense See R. H. Loderi
– Kilimanjaro (g.&cl.) SCog SLeo SReu SSta
– 'Kimberly' GGGa
– 'Kimbeth' GGGa

Name	Suppliers
Hybrid 'Kingston'	GGGa LMil LRHS
– 'Kluis Sensation'	CB&S CSam GGGa GWht LHyd LKna MGos MMor SExb SHBN SLeo SReu
– 'Kluis Triumph'	CSco LKna SReu
– 'Koichiro Wada'	See R. ***yakushimanum*** 'Koichiro Wada'
– 'Kokardia'	GGGa LMil
– 'Lacs'	SLeo
– 'Lady Adam Gordon'	CWal SLeo
– 'Lady Alice Fitzwilliam'	CB&S CBow CGre CMHG CWal ERea GGGa GWht ISea LHop LMil MBal SLeo
– 'Lady Annette de Trafford'	LKna
¶ – Lady Berry (g.&cl.)	SExb
– Lady Bessborough (g.&cl.)	LHyd SExb SLeo
– 'Lady Bessborough Roberte'	See R. H. 'Roberte'
– 'Lady Bowes Lyon'	CWal LHyd SCog SLeo SPer SReu
– 'Lady Cathcart'	SLeo
– Lady Chamberlain (g.&cl.)	CBow CWal LMil MBal MBlu MGos SLeo SReu
– 'Lady Chamberlain Exbury'	See R. H. 'Exbury Lady Chamberlain'
– 'Lady Chamberlain Golden Queen'	See R. H. 'Golden Queen'
– 'Lady Chamberlain Salmon Trout'	See R. H. 'Salmon Trout'
– 'Lady Clementine Mitford'	CSam CWal IHos LHyd LKna LMil MBri SExb SHBN SLeo SPer SReu SSta
– 'Lady Eleanor Cathcart'	CHig CWal GGGa LKna SExb SLeo
– 'Lady Grey Egerton'	CWal LKna MMor
– Lady Jean	CWal
– Lady Linlithgow	LMil SCog SLeo
– 'Lady Longman'	CWal SSta
– 'Lady Malmesbury'	SExb
– Lady Montagu (g.&cl.)	SExb
– 'Lady of Spain'	GGGa LMil
– 'Lady Primrose'	SReu
¶ – 'Lady Romsey'	LMil SExb
– Lady Rosebery (g.&cl.)	CSam CWal GGGa MLea SLeo SReu
– 'Lady Rosebery Pink Delight'	See R. H. 'Pink Lady Rosebery'
– Ladybird (g.&cl.)	SExb SReu
– Lamellen	CWal LHyd SLeo
– 'Lampion'	GGGa
– 'Lamplighter'	LMil SLeo SReu
– 'Langworth'	LKna SReu
– 'Lascaux'	SReu
– Laura Aberconway (g.&cl.)	SLeo
– 'Laurie'	GGGa
– 'Lava Flow'	CWal LHyd NHol SCog
– 'Lavender Girl'	GRei IJoh LHyd LKna LMil MBal MGos SExb SLeo SPer SReu SSta
– 'Lavender Princess'	LMil
– 'Lavender Queen'	GWht MBlu
– 'Lavendula'	CSam GGGa LMil
– 'Lea Rainbow'	MLea
– 'Lee's Dark Purple'	IJoh ISea MBlu SExb SPer
– 'Lee's Scarlet'	LKna LMil
– 'Lemon Ice'	SCog
– 'Lem's 121'	LMil LTil SExb
– 'Lem's Cameo'	GGGa LMil SReu SSta
– 'Lem's Monarch'	GGGa LMil MGos SReu SSta
– 'Lem's Stormcloud'	GGGa LMil MLea SReu SSta
– 'Leny'	NHol SSta
– Leo (g.&cl.)	CWal SLeo
– 'Leonardslee Brilliant'	SLeo
– 'Leonardslee Giles'	SLeo
– 'Leonardslee Pink Bride'	SLeo
– 'Leonardslee Primrose'	SLeo
– Leonore (g.&cl.)	SReu
– Letty Edwards (g.&cl.)	CWal LKna SLeo SReu
– 'Lila Pedigo'	GGGa LMil MBal MLea SReu
– 'Lincill'	CWal
– 'Linda'	CSam CSco EBre GGGa GWht LBre LMil MBal MBar MBri MGos MLea NHol SBod SCog SReu
– Lionel's Triumph (g.&cl.)	CWal LHyd LMil SLeo
* – 'Lissabon Rosa'	SExb
– 'Little Ben'	MBal MBar MPlt NBar WAbe WBod
– 'Little Bert'	SLeo SReu
* – 'Little Jock'	MBal
– 'Llenroc'	ISea
– 'Loch Rannoch'	GGGa
– 'Loch Tay'	GGGa
¶ – 'Loch Tummel'	GGGa
§ – 'Lodauric Iceberg'	CWal LKna LMil SReu
* – 'Lodbrit'	SReu
N – Loderi	LMil SExb
– 'Loderi Fairy Queen'	SLeo
– 'Loderi Fairyland'	CWal LHyd SLeo
§ – 'Loderi Game Chick'	GGGa LHyd MBal SExb SLeo SPer SPla SReu SSta
– 'Loderi Georgette'	SLeo
– 'Loderi Helen'	SLeo
§ – 'Loderi Julie'	SLeo SReu
– 'Loderi King George'	CAbP CB&S CSam CSco GGGa ISea LHyd LKna LMil MBlu MBri MLea SExb SHBN SLeo SPer SReu SSta
– 'Loderi Patience'	LHyd SExb SLeo
– 'Loderi Pink Diamond'	SExb
– 'Loderi Pink Topaz'	LMil SExb SLeo
– 'Loderi Pretty Polly'	SLeo
– 'Loderi Princess Marina'	SLeo
– 'Loderi Sir Edmund'	SLeo
– 'Loderi Sir Joseph Hooker'	SExb SLeo
– 'Loderi Titan'	SReu
§ – 'Loderi Venus'	CAbP CWal GGGa IOrc LHyd LKna LMil MBal MLea SExb SHBN SLeo SPer SReu SSta
– 'Loderi White Diamond'	CWal SExb SLeo
– 'Loder's White'	CBow CWal GGGa IHos LHyd LKna LMil MBal MBlu MLea SCog SExb SLeo SPer SReu SSta
– 'Lodestar'	SExb
§ – 'Logan Damaris'	CWal LHyd SLeo SReu

Hybrid 'Loki' SLeo
¶– 'Looking Glass' CAbP SHBN
– 'Lord Roberts' CB&S CBow CHig CSam CWal EBre ELan GGGa GRei GWht IOrc LBre LKna LMil MBal MBar MBri MGos MMor SExb SHBN SLeo SPer SSta
– 'Lord Swaythling' LHyd SLeo
– 'Lori Eichelser' CSam GGGa MAsh MBal
– 'Louis Pasteur' SReu SSta
– 'Lovely William' CSam LMil MBal SExb
– *lowndesii* x Yaku Fairy SSta
– 'Lucy Lou' GGGa LTil NHar NHol SExb
– ***ludlowii*** x ***mekongense*** Viridescens Group NHol
– 'Lunar Queen' CWal LHyd
– Luscombei LHyd
– 'Madame Albert Moser' LKna
– 'Madame de Bruin' CWal LKna MBal SExb SLeo SReu
– 'Madame Masson' CDoC CHig ECar GWht MBar MGos NHol SHBN SLeo SReu SSta
– 'Madison Snow' SSta
– 'Maestro' CWal
– 'Mah Jong' GGGa
– 'Maharani' GGGa
– Mai CWal
– 'Malemute' GGGa
– 'Manda Sue' GGGa LMil LTil MBal MLea SBar SPer
– Mandalay CDoC CWal LHyd LMil MBri SExb SLeo
– 'Manderley' MAsh
– 'Mannheim' LMil
– 'Marchioness of Lansdowne' MGos
– 'Marcia' SExb SLeo
– Margaret Dunn (g.&cl.) CWal GWht SLeo
– Marie Antoinette CWal LMil
– Mariloo CWal GGGa SExb SLeo
– 'Marinus Koster' CWal LKna MBri MMor NBar
– 'Marion' LMil
– 'Marion Street' CWal LHyd LMil SCog SLeo
– 'Markeeta's Prize' GAri GGGa LMil MBri
¶– 'Marlene Peste' CAbP
– 'Mars' SReu
– Marshall CWal SExb
– 'Martha Isaacson' GGGa
– 'Mary Belle' GGGa
– 'Mary Drennen' LMil
– 'Mary Fleming' MAsh MBlu MBri NHar SBod SSta
– 'Mary Forte' SExb SLeo
*– 'Master Mariner' LHyd
– Matador (g.&cl.) CWal LHyd LMil NKay SCog SExb WBod
– May Day (g.&cl.) CB&S CBow CSam CTrw CWal GWht ISea LHyd LKna LMil MBal MBri MGos NHol NKay SCog SExb SHBN SLeo SReu SSpi SSta WAbe WBod
*– 'May Glow' MGos
*– 'Mayor Johnstone' CDoC
– Medea CWal
– Medusa CWal GGGa SReu
– 'Merganser' CDoC GGGa MAsh MBal NHar NHol SReu WBod
– Merops CWal
– 'Michael Waterer' CWal ELan GWht SBod SExb SLeo
– 'Michael's Pride' CB&S CGre CWal MBal
– 'Midsummer' GGGa SLeo
– 'Minterne Cinnkeys' MBal
§– 'Moerheim' CSam CSco CWal EBre GAbr GGGa GWht IJoh LBre MBal MBar MMor MRav NHol NKay SReu SSta WAbe WStI
§– 'Moerheim's Pink' ELan GGGa LHyd LKna LMil SPer WThu
– 'Moerheim's Scarlet' LKna
– Mohamet (g.&cl.) CWal LMil MLea SExb
– 'Molly Ann' CDoC GGGa LMil MAsh MLea SReu
– 'Molly Buckley' SExb
– 'Monaco' LMil LTil
– 'Monica' SCog SReu
– 'Monica Wellington' LHyd
– Moonbeam LKna
– Moonshine (g.&cl.) SExb SReu
– 'Moonshine Bright' GGGa LHyd SReu
– 'Moonshine Crescent' GGGa SReu
– 'Moonshine Supreme' LKna SExb SReu
– Moonstone CHig CWal EPot GAri MAsh MBal MBar MLea MPlt SCog SExb SLeo WAbe WBod
– 'Moonstone Pink' CWal SExb
*– Moonstone pink-tipped GGGa NHol
– 'Moonstone Yellow' GGGa SExb
– 'Moonwax' CSam LMil MBal
– 'Morgenrot' ('Morning Red') GGGa LMil MBri MGos SReu
– 'Morning Cloud' CAbP CBow CWal GGGa LHyd LMil MAsh MBar MBri SLeo SReu WWeb
– 'Morning Magic' CWal LHyd SCog SLeo
– 'Morvah' SLeo
¶– 'Mosaique' SExb
– 'Moser's Maroon' LKna MGos SExb SLeo
– 'Moser's Strawberry' LKna
– 'Moth' GGGa
– 'Mother Greer' GGGa MAsh
– 'Mother of Pearl' CWal GGGa LKna SCog SReu
*– 'Mother Theresa' LKna
♦– 'Mount Everest' See R. ***cinnabarinum c.*** 'M. E.'
– 'Mountain Dew' SReu
– 'Mountain Star' SLeo
– 'Mrs A T de la Mare' GGGa IDai IOrc LHyd LKna LMil MBri MMor SExb SLeo SPer SReu SSta
– 'Mrs Anthony Waterer' LKna SSta
– 'Mrs Ashley Slocock' SReu
– 'Mrs Betty Robertson' CHig MBri MLea SExb SReu
– 'Mrs C B van Nes' SPer SReu
– Mrs C Whitner SLeo
– 'Mrs Charles E Pearson' CB&S CBow CWal LHyd LKna LMil MLea SCog SExb SHBN SLeo SPer SReu
*– 'Mrs Chitton' SExb
– 'Mrs Davies Evans' LHyd LKna MBar MMor SReu SSta
– 'Mrs Donald Graham' SReu
– 'Mrs E C Stirling' LKna SExb SRms

Hybrid 'Mrs Furnival' CB&S LKna MBri MGos SExb SReu
– 'Mrs G W Leak' CSam CWal GGGa ISea LHyd LKna LMil MBri MLea MMor SCog SExb SHBN SLeo SPer SReu SSta
– 'Mrs Helen Koster' LKna
– 'Mrs Henry Agnew' SLeo
– 'Mrs J C Williams' LKna LMil SLeo
– 'Mrs J G Millais' GGGa LKna LMil SLeo
– 'Mrs James Horlick' CWal SLeo
– 'Mrs John Kelk' CWal
– 'Mrs Kingsmill' CWal SLeo
– 'Mrs Lindsay Smith' LKna
– Mrs Lionel de Rothschild (g.&cl.) CWal ELan LKna LMil SExb SReu
– 'Mrs P D Williams' LKna SExb SReu
– 'Mrs Philip Martineau' LKna
– 'Mrs R S Holford' CWal LKna SExb SLeo
– 'Mrs T H Lowinsky' MBri
– 'Mrs Tom H Lowinsky' GCHN GGGa LKna LMil MAsh MGos SExb SLeo SReu SSta WWeb
– 'Mrs W C Slocock' CWal LHyd LKna SLeo SPer SReu SSta
– 'Mrs William Agnew' LKna SLeo
– 'Muncaster Mist' LHyd LRHS SSpi
– 'Muriel' SLeo
– 'My Lady' GGGa
– 'Myrtifolium' CSco MBar SReu
– 'Mystic' CWal
– 'Nancy Evans' COtt GGGa GWht LMil LTil MAsh MBal MLea MMor SPla SSpi
– Naomi (g.&cl.) LKna LMil SExb SReu
– 'Naomi Astarte' LKna SExb SLeo
¶ – 'Naomi Early Dawn' SExb
– 'Naomi Exbury' CWal LKna LMil SExb SLeo SReu
– 'Naomi Glow' CWal LMil SExb
– 'Naomi Hope' SExb
– 'Naomi Pink Beauty' MBlu
– 'Naomi Stella Maris' CWal LMil SExb
– Naomi 'Paris See R. H. 'Paris'
– Neda WBod
¶ – Nehru SExb
– Neriihaem SLeo
– 'New Comet' LHyd LMil SReu
– 'New Moon' CWal SLeo SReu
– 'Newcomb's Sweetheart' LMil
¶ – 'Nicholas' SExb
– 'Night Sky' GGGa LMil SLeo
– 'Nightingale' LMil SReu
– 'Nimbus' LKna LMil SLeo
– Nimrod SExb SLeo
¶ – 'Noble Mountain' LMil
§ – Nobleanum GGGa ISea LHyd LKna LMil SExb SLeo SSta WThu
– 'Nobleanum Album' LHyd LKna LMil MBal SLeo SReu SSta
– 'Nobleanum Coccineum' ISea SLeo SReu
– 'Nobleanum Lamellen' CWal SLeo
– 'Nobleanum Venustum' ISea LHyd LKna LMil SReu SSta WBod
*– 'Nofretete' GGGa
– Norman Shaw (g.&cl.) LHyd
– 'Normandy' LMil
– 'Northern Star' CWal SLeo
*– 'Nosutchianum' GGGa
– 'Nova Zembla' CSam GGGa IJoh ISea MBar MBlu MGos SExb SHBN SLeo SReu SSta WStI
– 'Noyo Brave' GGGa
– 'Odee Wright' GGGa LMil MAsh MBlu MLea SExb SLeo SPer SSpi SSta
– Oklahoma SExb
– 'Old Copper' CDoC GGGa LNet MBri MLea NHol SExb
– 'Old Port' CWal SHBN SReu SSta
– Oldenburgh CWal SLeo
– 'Olga' LHyd LKna LMil SReu SSta
– 'Olga Mezitt' GGGa LHyd LMil
– 'Olin O Dobbs' LMil
– 'Olive' LHyd LKna LMil SLeo SPer SReu
– 'Olive Judson' SLeo
– 'Oliver Cromwell' SReu
– Olympic Lady CWal LHyd MLea SLeo
– Omar MBar NKay
– 'One Thousand Butterflies' COtt LMil
– 'Ooh Gina' LMil
– 'Orangengold' GGGa
– ***orbiculare* × *decorum*** CWal
– Oregonia SExb
– Oreocinn MBal
– 'Organdie' SExb
– 'Osmar' CDoC GGGa MBri MGos
¶ – 'Ostfriesland' SRms
– 'Oudijk's Favorite' MBal MBar MGos SExb
– 'Oudijk's Sensation' CSco CWal GCHN GWht IDai ISea LKna MGos MMor
*– 'Ovation' GGGa
– Oxlip SExb SLeo
– P J M CSam ISea LTil MBal MBri MLea SExb SSta
– 'P J M Elite' GGGa
– 'P J Mezitt' See R. H. 'Peter John Mezitt'
– 'Palma' See R. ***parmulatum*** 'Palma'
– 'Pamela-Louise' LHyd
– Pandora WBod
– 'Papaya Punch' LMil
– 'Paprika Spiced' GGGa LMil LRHS LTil MAsh MBal MBlu MLea
– 'Paris' LHyd SExb
– 'Parisienne' SCog SExb
– 'Party Pink' GGGa LMil
– 'Patty Bee' CSam EPot GGGa GWht LHyd LMil MBlu MBri MGos MLea NBar NHar NHol SBod SReu SSpi SSta WBod
– 'Paul Vossberg' LMil
– 'Peace' CWal GGGa LHyd MBal SLeo WAbe
– 'Pearl Diver' LHyd
– 'Peeping Tom GGGa LMil LRHS LTil MAsh SHBN SLeo
¶ – 'Pelopidas' SExb
¶ – 'Pematit Cambridge' SBod
– 'Pematit Oxford' LMil SReu
– Penelope SReu
– 'Penheale Blue' CTre CWal GGGa ISea LMil LTil MBri SGil SLeo WBod WWeb
– Penjerrick (g.&cl.) GGGa SCog SExb
– 'Penjerrick Cream' CWal SLeo
– 'Penjerrick Pink' CWal SExb SLeo

Hybrid 'Penrose'	CB&S
– 'Percy Wiseman'	Widely available
¶– 'Perfect Lady'	LRHS
§– 'Persimmon'	CWal LKna SExb SLeo
¶– 'Peter Alan'	LMil
§– 'Peter John Mezitt'	GGGa LHyd LMil NHar SLeo SReu WThu
– 'Peter Koster'	CB&S IJoh SExb SHBN SLeo WStI
– 'Phalarope'	CSam CWal GAbr GGGa LHyd MBal MBar MBlu MGos NHol NKay SReu WBod
– 'Pheasant Tail'	SCog SLeo
– 'Philomene'	SReu
– 'Phyllis Korn'	CAbP GGGa LHyd LMil
– Pilgrim (g.&cl.)	LKna SExb
– 'Pink Bee'	LRHS
– 'Pink Bountiful'	LKna WAbe
– 'Pink Cameo'	GWht
– 'Pink Cherub'	CMHG CWal EBlo EBre ELan GGGa GWht IHos LBre MBal MBar MBri MMor NBar SCog SLeo SReu WWeb
– 'Pink Drift'	Widely available
– 'Pink Frills'	CB&S
– 'Pink Ghost'	CWal SLeo
– 'Pink Gin'	LMil
– 'Pink Glory'	SLeo
– 'Pink Leopard'	LMil LRHS
– 'Pink Pearl'	CB&S CHig CSam CSco CWal EBre ELan GGGa IDai IJoh ISea LBre LHyd LKna MBal MBar MBri MGos MMor NBar NHol NWea SBod SCog SExb SLeo SPer SReu SSta
– 'Pink Pebble'	CTrw CWal GGGa LHyd LMil SLeo SReu WBod
– 'Pink Perfection'	MGos SExb SLeo SReu
– 'Pink Petticoats'	MBlu
– 'Pink Rosette'	LKna
– 'Pink Sensation'	MBri
– 'Pinkerton'	LKna
– 'Pipaluk'	CWal LHyd
– 'Pipit'	GGGa MBal NHar NHol WAbe
– 'Piquante'	CWal
– 'Point Defiance'	MLea
– Polar Bear (g.&cl.)	CBow COtt CWal GAri GGGa LHyd LMil SLeo SPer SReu
– 'Polaris'	MGos
*– 'Polgrain'	CB&S
*– 'Polycinn'	SCog
– 'Ponticum'	See R. ***ponticum***
– 'Pook'	CWal LHyd
– 'Popacatapetl'	SReu
– 'Powder Puff'	LMil
– 'Praecox'	CB&S CSco CTrw CWal ELan GGGa GRei IDai IJoh ISea LHyd LKna LMil MBal MBar MBri MGos MMor SBar SBod SCog SExb SHBN SIng SPer SReu SSta WBod WThu
– 'Prawn'	LKna SReu
– Prelude (g.&cl.)	CWal SExb
– 'President Roosevelt' (v)	CBow CWal GGGa IHos IJoh IOrc LKna LNet MBal MGos MMor SDry SExb SHBN SLeo SPer SReu SSta
– 'Pretty Girl'	LKna
– 'Prima Donna'	LMil SReu
*– 'Primula'	GGGa
– 'Prince Camille de Rohan'	LMil SExb
– 'Princess Alice'	CB&S CGre COtt ERea GGGa ISea LHyd MBal WBod
– 'Princess Anne'	CB&S CHig CMHG CSam CSco CTrw CWal EPot GDra GGGa GRei GWht LHyd LMil MBal MBar MBri MGos MLea NKay SBod SExb SHBN SLeo SPer SReu SSpi SSta WBod WThu
¶– 'Princess Elizabeth'	SExb
– 'Professor Hugo de Vries'	LKna MGos SReu
– 'Professor J H Zaayer'	CWal IDai MGos SExb SLeo
– 'Prostigiatum'	CWal GDra GGGa GWht MGos
– Psyche	See R. H. Wega
– 'Ptarmigan'	CB&S CMHG CTrw CWal ECar EPot GGGa GWht LHyd LMil MBal MBar MBri MGos MMor MPlt NHar NHol SBod SExb SLeo SPer SReu SSta WAbe WBod WThu
– 'Puget Sound'	SLeo
– 'Puncta'	GGGa NHol
*– 'Purple Carpeter'	SReu SSta
– 'Purple Emperor'	LKna SExb
– 'Purple Gem'	GGGa GWht ISea NHar SReu
– 'Purple Splendour'	CB&S CHig CSam CSco CWal EBre GGGa ISea LBre LHyd LKna LMil MBal MBar MBlu MBri MGos MMor NBar NWea SCog SExb SHBN SLeo SPer SReu SSta
*– 'Purple Split'	ISea
– Quaver	SExb SRms
– 'Queen Alice'	SPer
– 'Queen Anne's'	GGGa LMil LRHS MBal SSpi SSta
– 'Queen Elizabeth II'	CWal LHyd LMil SReu SSta
– 'Queen Mary'	MBar MMor NBar
– 'Queen Mother'	See R. H. 'The Queen Mother'
– Queen of Hearts (g.&cl.)	CWal LHyd SExb SLeo
– 'Queen Souriya'	SReu
– 'Racil'	LHyd LKna MBal MBar MGos MLea MMor MPlt NBar SExb WAbe
*– 'Radistrotum'	GGGa
– 'Radmosum'	SSta
– 'Raeburn'	MPlt
– 'Rainbow'	GGGa LKna SExb
– 'Ramapo'	EBre ECar GGGa LBre LMil MBal MBri MGos MLea MPlt NHar NHol SPer SReu SSta WAbe WBod
– 'Raspberry Ripple'	LKna
– 'Rasputin'	GGGa
– 'Razorbill'	CSam EPot GGGa LHyd LMil MBri MGos NHar NHol SReu
– Red Admiral	CWal SExb SLeo
– Red Argenteum	SLeo
– Red Cap	CWal
– 'Red Carpet'	LMil LRHS SSta
– 'Red Delicious'	LMil LTil
– 'Red Dragon'	SLeo
– 'Red Glow'	LHyd SLeo
¶– 'Red Jack'	SFai
– 'Red Poll'	LHyd
– 'Red Riding Hood'	CWal LKna SExb

Hybrid 'Red Velour'	CAbP
– 'Red Walloper'	MBlu
*– 'Red Wood'	GGGa
– Remo	CWal MBal SLeo SReu
– Remus	CWal
– 'Renoir'	LHyd SLeo
– Repose (g.&cl.)	GGGa LKna
– 'Reuthe's Purple'	See R. ***lepidotum*** 'Reuthe's Purple'
– Rêve Rose (g.&cl.)	SCog
– Review Order	CWal SSta
– 'Revlon'	LHyd LMil SReu
– *rex* x Sincerity	SLeo
– Rickshaw	SLeo
*– 'Rimini'	SExb
– 'Ring of Fire'	LMil
– 'Rio'	GGGa LMil MAsh
– 'Ripe Corn'	LKna SExb SLeo SReu
– Riplet	EPot GAri GGGa NHar SLeo
– 'Robert Keir'	CWal LHyd SLeo
*– 'Robert Korn'	GGGa
– 'Robert Louis Stevenson'	GGGa
– 'Robert Seleger'	GGGa LMil MAsh NHar
§– 'Roberte'	CWal NKay SCog SExb
– 'Robin Redbreast'	LHyd SLeo
*– 'Robinette'	GGGa
– 'Rocket'	CAbP GWht MLea SExb WWeb
– Romany Chai	CWal LHyd LMil NKay SExb
– Romany Chal	CWal LHyd MBal SCog SExb SPer
– 'Romy'	LMil SLeo
¶– 'Rose Bud'	WThu
– 'Rose Elf'	CDoC GGGa MAsh MBal NHol WAbe WBod
– 'Roseum Elegans'	IJoh MBar SExb SLeo
– 'Rosevallon'	CWal
– 'Rosy Bell'	LKna
*– 'Rosy Cream'	SPer
¶– 'Rosy Dream'	CAbP LMil
*– 'Rosy Lea'	MLea
– 'Rothenburg'	GGGa LHyd LMil SExb SReu WThu
– 'Royal Blood'	LHyd
– Royal Flush	CB&S CWal MBlu
– Royal Flush pink form	CWal
– Royal Flush yellow form	CWal
– 'Royal Pink'	SBod
– Royalty	WBod
– 'Roza Stevenson'	CWal LHyd SLeo SPer
– Rubicon	GGGa WWeb
– Rubina	CWal SExb SLeo
– 'Ruby F Bowman'	CSam CSco MGos MLea SExb SLeo SReu
– 'Ruby Hart'	GGGa MAsh NHol SReu
– Russautinii	LMil
¶– 'Russellianum'	SExb
– 'Sacko'	GGGa NHol
– 'Saffron Queen'	CB&S CGre CTrw GGGa ISea MBal
– 'Saint Breward'	CB&S CWal GGGa LHyd MBal MBri MLea SBod SCog SExb SPer SReu WBod
– 'Saint Keverne'	CWal
– 'Saint Kew'	CWal
– 'Saint Merryn'	CWal ECar GAri GGGa LHyd LMil LTil MAsh MBri NHol SLeo
– 'Saint Michael'	SReu
– 'Saint Minver'	CWal LHyd LRHS MBri
– 'Saint Tudy'	CB&S CWal ECar LHyd LKna MBal MMor MPlt SExb SLeo SPer WAbe WBod
– 'Saint Wenn'	CWal
§– 'Salmon Trout'	CWal
– 'Salute'	CSco
– 'Sammetglut'	GGGa
– 'Sandling'	LHyd
– 'Santa Claus'	CWal
– Sapphire (g.&cl.)	CBow CWal EPot GAbr LKna LMil MBal MBar MPlt NKay SBod SExb SLeo WAbe WBod WThu
– 'Sappho'	CB&S CSco CWal ELan GGGa GWht IDai IHos IOrc ISea LHyd LKna LMil MBal MBar MGos MMor SCog SExb SHBN SLeo SReu SSta
– Sarita Loder (g.&cl.)	SLeo
– Sarled	CMHG CSam CWal EPot GDra GGGa LHyd LMil MBal MBri NHar SLeo SReu SSpi WThu WWat
¶– 'Scandinavia'	SExb
– 'Scarlet Wonder'	CB&S CSco CWal EBlo EBre ELan GGGa GRei GWht IJoh ISea LBre LKna LMil MBal MBar MBri MGos MLea MMor NBar NHol SBod SCog SExb SLeo SPer SReu SSta WBod
– 'Schneekrone'	GGGa
– 'Schneewolke'	GGGa
– 'Scintillation'	CDoC CSam CSco GGGa LMil MAsh MBal SHBN SLeo SSpi
– Seagull (g.&cl.)	SLeo
¶– 'Seattle Gold'	SExb
– 'Sea-Tac'	MLea
– 'Second Honyemoon'	LRHS MAsh MLea SHBN SSta
*– 'Senator Henry Jackson'	LMil
– 'Sennocke'	LHyd LMil SReu SSta
*– 'September Song'	CBow CDoC EBlo GGGa LHyd LMil MAsh MBal NBar SPer
– 'Sesterianum'	CMHG CWal
– Seta (g.&cl.)	CB&S CHig CWal LHyd MBal MLea MPlt SExb SLeo SReu
– 'Seven Stars'	CWal GGGa LHyd LMil SCog SExb SLeo SReu
– 'Seville'	CWal
– 'Shamrock'	CAbP CDoC CSam EPot GGGa GWht ISea MAsh MBal MBar MBri NHar SBar SPer SSpi SSta WBod
– 'Sham's Candy'	CWal
– Sheperd's Delight	CWal
– Shilsonii	CWal LHyd SExb SLeo
– 'Shrimp Girl'	CDoC CWal ELan IHos LHyd MBal MBri MLea SLeo SReu
– 'Silberwolke' ('Silver Cloud')	CBow GGGa SReu
¶– 'Silkcap'	WThu
*– 'Silky'	MBal
– 'Silver Jubilee'	GGGa ISea LHyd LMil
– 'Silver Sixpence'	CB&S CBow CDoC CMHG CSam CSco CWal IHos LMil MBal MBar MBlu MBri MLea SCog SExb SHBN SLeo SReu WWeb
*– 'Simmon's Classic'	LMil
– 'Simona'	GGGa LHyd

Hybrid 'Sinbad' SLeo
– 'Sir Charles Lemon' See R. ***arboreum*** 'Sir Charles Lemon'
– Sir Frederick Moore (g.&cl.) SCog SExb
*– 'Sir G E Simpson' SLeo
– 'Sir George Sansom' CWal
*– 'Sir John Tremayne' CWal
– Siren (g.&cl.) CWal MBal WBod
– 'Sirius' LHyd SReu
– 'Skookum' LMil SPer
– 'Sleepy' CSam CWal ELan GWht IHos MBri SCog SExb SLeo SPer SReu
§– Smithii Group CWal
– 'Sneezy' CB&S CDoC CWal ELan GGGa GRei IHos ISea LHyd MBal MBar MBlu MBri MGos SCog SLeo SReu SSta
– 'Snipe' CSam EBre ECar EPot LBre LHyd LMil MAsh MBal MBar MBri MGos NHar NHol SSta WAbe
¶– 'Snow Crown' EBlo
– 'Snow Lady' GGGa LTil MBal MBar MGos MPlt NBar NHar NKay WBod WThu
– Snow Queen (g.&cl.) LKna SExb SReu
– 'Soldier Sam' SReu SSta
– 'Solidarity' MBal WWeb
– 'Sonata' CWal GAri GGGa GWht MBal MBri NKay SReu
– 'Songbird' CBow CSam CWal EBre EPot GAbr GCHN GDra GGGa LBre LHyd LKna LMil MBal MBar MBri MLea MPlt NHol NKay SExb SReu WBod
– 'Songster' SLeo
– Souldis CWal LMil
– 'Southern Cross' LHyd LMil
– 'Souvenir de Doctor S Endtz' CWal LKna MBal MBar MMor SReu
– 'Souvenir of Anthony Waterer' LHyd LKna MBar MMor SReu SSta
– 'Souvenir of W C Slocock' LKna SHBN SLeo SReu SSta
– 'Sparkler' CCla CMHG COtt GGGa ISea LMil MBlu MLea SExb SReu WWeb
– 'Spinulosum' LHyd
– 'Spitfire' MGos MMor NBar SLeo SReu
– 'Spring Dawn' GWht
*– 'Spring Dream' LHyd
– 'Spring Glory' GGGa
– 'Spring Magic' LMil MAsh WThu
– 'Spring Parade' GWht LRHS SExb
– 'Spring Pearl' See R. H. 'Moerheim's Pink'
*– 'Spring Rose' LRHS
– 'Springbok' LHyd
*– 'Springday' CWal
¶– 'Squirrel' NHar
– Stadt Essen (g.&cl.) GGGa LMil
– 'Stanley Rivlin' CWal LHyd SCog SLeo
– 'Stanway' LMil SExb
– 'Starcross' LHyd
– 'Starfish' SReu
– 'Stella' SLeo
– 'Stephanie' MBlu
– 'Strategist' CWal
*– 'Strawberry Cream' GGGa NHol
– 'Streatley' CWal SLeo
*– 'Striped Beauty' ECar MBal
– 'Suave' GGGa
– 'Suede' SReu
– 'Sugar Pink' LMil LRHS
– 'Sumatra' GWht LTil
– 'Sumer Snow' GGGa
– 'Sunbeam' LKna SReu
¶– 'Sunny Splendour' (V) ERea
¶– 'Sunset over Harkwood' LRHS
– 'Surrey Heath' CB&S CCla CMHG COtt CWal EBlo GGGa GRei GWht ISea LHyd LMil LNet LTil MBal MBar MBri MGos MLea MMor NBar NHol SCog SExb SLeo SReu SSta WBod
– 'Susan' CWal GGGa LHyd LKna LMil MBri MMor SCog SExb SLeo SReu
– 'Sussex Bonfire' SLeo
– 'Swamp Beauty' GGGa
– 'Swansdown' LMil SPer
– 'Sweet Simplicity' LKna MBal SExb
– 'Sweet Sixteen' SLeo
– 'Sweet Sue' CWal MAsh MBal SCog SLeo SPer SReu
– 'Swen' GGGa
– 'Swift' GGGa
– Tally Ho (g.&cl.) CB&S CWal SLeo SReu
– 'Tan Crossing' SReu
– 'Tangerine' See R. H. 'Fabia Tangerine'
– 'Tara' SLeo
– Tasco SExb
– 'Taurus' COtt GGGa LMil MLea MMor SExb WWeb
– 'Teal' CDoC GGGa LMil MAsh MBal MBar MPlt NHol SLeo SReu WAbe WBod
¶– 'Teddy Bear' GGGa LMil
– Temple Belle CSam CWal ECar GGGa ISea LHyd LKna LMil MBal MBri MLea SCog SLeo
– 'Tequila Sunrise' LMil LTil MBal SLeo
*– 'Terra-Cotta' LKna
– Tessa (g.&cl.) LKna LMil MGos SBod SExb
– 'Tessa Bianca' LMil
¶– Tessa pink form SExb
– 'Tessa Roza' EPot GGGa LHyd MAsh MBri
§– 'The Hon Jean Marie de Montague CAbP CSam CWal GWht IDai LKna MBal MBri MLea MMor NBar SLeo WWeb
– 'The Lizzard' LKna
– 'The Master' CWal LHyd LKna SLeo SReu
§– 'The Queen Mother' CWal LHyd
– 'The Warrior' SExb
– Thomdeton CWal
– Thomwilliams CWal LKna MBal SExb
– Thor (g.&cl.) GGGa MMor SLeo
*– 'Thousand Butterflies' CSam GGGa ISea
– 'Thunderstorm' CDoC LKna LRHS SReu
– 'Tibet' MBal MBar NBar SHBN
– 'Tidbit' GGGa LHyd LKna LMil MAsh MBal MGos MLea SLeo
*– 'Tilford Seedling' LKna
– 'Timothy James' GGGa SReu

Hybrid 'Titian Beauty'	CB&S CMHG COtt CSam CSco CWal EBlo EBre ELan GGGa IHos LBre LHyd LMil LNet LTil MBal MBri MGos MLea MMor NBar NKay SCog SExb SLeo SReu
– 'Tolkien'	GGGa SSta
– 'Too Bee'	GGGa
– 'Top Banana'	GGGa LMil LRHS LTil MBal MLea
¶ – 'Top Brass'	CAbP
– 'Top Hat'	LMil MLea
– 'Topaz'	CDoC
– 'Topsvoort Pearl'	SReu
– 'Torch'	LKna SReu
– 'Tortoiseshell Biscuit'	CWal LMil
– 'Tortoiseshell Champagne'	See R. H. 'Champagne'
– 'Tortoiseshell Orange'	CB&S CWal LHyd LKna LMil MAsh MBri SCog SHBN SReu SSta
– 'Tortoiseshell Pale Orange'	LKna
– 'Tortoiseshell Salome'	LKna LMil SSta
– 'Tortoiseshell Scarlet'	LKna SReu
– 'Tortoiseshell Wonder'	CWal LHyd LKna LMil MBal MGos SExb SLeo SReu SSta
– 'Tottenham'	MBal
– 'Tow Head'	LMil
– Treasure	CWal GAri GDra LHyd MAsh MBal
– 'Trebah Gem'	CWal SLeo
– 'Tregedna'	SLeo
– 'Tretawn'	CWal SLeo
– 'Trewithen Orange'	CB&S CBow CSam CTrw CWal GGGa LMil MBal MBlu NHol SCog SHBN SLeo SPer WAbe
* – 'Trewithen Purple'	CTrw CWal
– 'Trianon'	LMil SExb
– 'Trilby'	GGGa LMil SLeo SReu
– 'Trude Webster'	CSam GGGa LRHS MLea SSta
– 'Tulyar'	LKna
– 'Turkish Delight'	MLea
– 'Twilight Pink'	GGGa MBlu MLea
– 'Tyermannii'	CWal SLeo
– Ungerio	SLeo
– 'Unique'	CB&S CSam CSco CWal GGGa GWht LHyd LKna LMil LNet MBal MBri MMor NKay SExb SHBN SLeo SPer SReu SSta WThu
– 'Unknown Warrior'	CWal MMor SExb SReu
* – 'V M H'	CWal
– Valaspis (g.&cl.)	SExb
– 'Valley Sunrise'	GGGa
– 'Van Nes Sensation'	LMil
– Vanessa (g.&cl.)	CWal LHyd LMil SCog SReu WBod
– 'Vanessa Pastel'	CHig CWal GGGa LHyd LMil MBal SCog SLeo SReu WBod
– Vanguard	ISea
§ – 'Vanilla'	LKna
– Varna	WBod
– 'Veldtstar'	LHyd
– 'Vellum'	SExb
– 'Venetian Chimes'	CMHG CWal ELan GGGa IHos ISea LMil LTil MBal MBri MLea SCog SExb SLeo SPer SReu WWeb
– 'Veryan Bay'	CB&S LMil
– 'Victoria de Rothschild'	SExb
¶ – 'Vienna'	SExb
– 'Vincent van Gogh'	MBlu
– 'Vinestar'	LHyd LMil
– 'Vintage Rose'	CWal ELan GGGa LMil MBal MBri MLea SCog SLeo SReu
– Virginia Richards (g.&cl.)	CDoC CHig GAri GGGa LHyd MBal MBri MGos MLea SExb SLeo SPer SSta
– 'Viscy'	GGGa LHyd LMil LRHS
– 'Vivacious'	GGGa
– Volker	See R. H. Flava
– 'Voodoo'	MBlu
– 'Vulcan'	CB&S CSco GGGa LMil MBal MLea SHBN SSta
– 'Vulcan's Flame'	GGGa MBlu
– W F H	LMil SCog SLeo
– 'Wagtail'	GGGa LRHS MAsh NHar NHol
– Walloper	SLeo SReu
– 'Wally Miller'	SExb SSta
– 'Waterfall'	MBal
– 'Wee Bee'	EPot GGGa LMil MAsh NHar WAbe
– Wega	CWal LKna
– 'Wellesleyanum'	SLeo
– 'Werei'	SLeo
¶ – 'Weston's Pink Diamond'	GGGa
– 'Weybridge'	SLeo
– 'Whisperingrose'	CSam GGGa LMil MAsh MBal NHol WAbe
– White Glory (g.&cl.)	SLeo
– 'White Gold'	GGGa
– 'White Olympic Lady'	LKna
– 'White Swan'	LKna LMil MBal MBlu SReu
– 'White Wings'	SLeo
* – 'Whitney's Best Yellow'	GGGa
– 'Whitney's Dwarf Red'	SLeo
– 'Wigeon'	GGGa LMil LRHS MAsh NHol SBar SPer
¶ – 'Wilbrit Rose'	SBod
– 'Wild Affair'	LRHS
– 'Wilgen's Ruby'	CSam CWal GGGa IJoh LKna LMil MBri MGos MMor NBar SBod SExb SHBN SPer SSta WStI
– 'Willbrit'	GGGa LHyd MBri MPlt SCog SExb
– Wilsonii	CWal GGGa
¶ – Windbeam	SBod
– 'Windlesham Scarlet'	LHyd LMil SPer
– 'Windsor Lad'	GGGa LKna SReu
– Winsome (g.&cl.)	CB&S CHig CSam CTrw CWal GCHN GGGa GWht IOrc ISea LHyd LKna LMil MBal MBar MMor NHol SCog SLeo SSta WBod WThu
– 'Wishmoor'	CWal LHyd LMil SCog SLeo SReu
– 'Witch Doctor'	GGGa GWht LRHS MBlu MBri SBod
– 'Witchery'	GGGa
– 'Wonderland'	LKna
– 'Woodchat'	GGGa
– 'Woodcock'	LHyd SPer
– 'Woodside'	CWal SLeo

Hybrid 'Wren'	CSam EPot GGGa MAsh MBal MBar MBri NHar NHol SReu WWeb
– 'Xenophile'	CWal
¶– 'Yaku Angel'	NBar
§– 'Yaku Fairy'	CWal EPot GAri LMil MBal WThu
– 'Yaku Prince'	CAbP MBri NBar SPer
– 'Yaku Princess'	CAbP GGGa MAsh MBri MLea NBar SLeo SPer WWeb
– 'Yaku Queen'	LTil MBri SBar SLeo
– ***yakushimanum***	
x ***bureaui***	MBal MLea SBar SSpi
– – x ***decorum***	MMor SReu
– – x ***lanatum***	GGGa
– – x ***pachysanthum***	GGGa
– – x ***recurvoïdes***	GGGa
– – x ***rex***	GGGa
– – x ***tsariense***	GGGa
*– 'Yellow By Trailer'	MLea
– Yellow Hammer	CB&S CMHG CSam CSco CWal ELan GGGa GWht IJoh ISea LKna LMil MBal MBar MBri MGos MMor NHol SBod SExb SHBN SIng SLeo SPer SReu SSta WBod
– 'Yellow Petticoats'	CSam GGGa IJoh ISea LMil MBri SBar SLeo
– 'Yellow Pippin'	GGGa
– 'Youthful Sin'	CWal GGGa ISea MBal WBod
– Yuncinn	CWal
– Yvonne	CWal
– 'Yvonne Dawn'	SLeo
¶– 'Yvonne Opaline'	SExb
¶– 'Yvonne Pride'	SExb
– Zelia Plumecocq (g.&cl.)	SExb
– Zuiderzee	SLeo SReu
hylaeum	SExb
– KW 6833	SLeo
hypenanthum	See R. ***anthopogon hypenanthum***
hyperythrum	CWal GGGa LHyd LMil SExb SLeo
– ssp. ***fauriei***	SLeo
hypoglaucum	See R. ***argyrophyllum hypoglaucum***
– 'Heane Wood'	See R. ***argyrophyllum h.*** 'H.W.'
impeditum	Widely available
– F 20454	LMil
§– 'Blue Steel'	COtt EBre ELan LBre LMil MBal NHar SLeo SReu WAbe WPat
– compact form	LKna
– 'Harry White's Purple'	ESis WThu
– 'Indigo'	CMHG GWht LMil NHar WThu
– 'Johnston's Impeditum'	LKna
♦– 'Moerheim'	See R. Hybrid 'M.'
– 'Pygmaeum'	WAbe
– Reuthe's form	SReu
– 'Russell's Blue'	SReu
imperator	See R. ***uniflorum imperator***
§ ***indicum*** (EA)	CWal MBal
§– 'Balsaminiflorum' (d)	CMac SReu WAbe WBod
– 'Crispiflorum'	GWht
– var. ***eriocarpum*** 'Gumpo'	See R. Azalea 'Gumpo'
inopinum	GGGa
insigne	CWal GGGa IOrc LMil MGos SExb SLeo SSpi
– Reuthe's form	SReu
x ***intermedium*** white form	GGGa
intricatum	GGGa WAbe
– KW 4184	SLeo
irroratum	CWal LMil SLeo
§– ssp. ***pogonostylum***	SLeo
– 'Polka Dot'	GGGa SExb SLeo
– white form	GGGa
iteaphyllum	See R. ***formosum formosum*** Iteaphyllum Group
japonicum Suringar (A)	GGGa LHyd
– JR 871 (A)	GGGa
– Scheneider var. ***japonicum***	See R. ***degronianum heptamerum***
– var. ***pentamerum***	See R. ***degronianum degronianum***
¶ ***jasminiflorum*** (V)	ERea GGGa
¶ ***javanicum*** Sands 74(V)	GGGa
johnstoneanum	CB&S CSam CWal GGGa ISea LMil LTil MBal SExb SLeo
¶– 'Double Diamond' (d)	CGre CWal LHyd
– 'Rubrotinctum' KW 7723	SLeo
kaempferi (EA)	CHig GGGa LHyd LMil
– 'Damio'	See R. ***k.*** 'Mikado'
– 'Eastern Fire'	LMil
– 'Firefly'	See R. Azalea 'Hexe'
– ***latisepalum***	GGGa
§– 'Mikado'	LMil LTil
keiskei	CHig CWal LMil LTil MBal SExb
– 'Cordifolium'	SLeo
– 'Ebino'	GGGa
keleticum	See R. ***calostrotum keleticum***
§ ***kendrickii***	CWal GGGa SLeo
kesangiae EGM 061	GGGa LMil
keysii	CWal GGGa LMil MBal SLeo
– 'Unicolor'	SLeo
§ ***kiusianum*** (EA)	CWal GGGa LHyd NHol SReu WAbe
– 'Album'	ECar GWht LHyd LMil SReu
– 'Benichidori'	LMil
– 'Hillier's Pink'	LMil
– 'Mountain Gem'	SReu SSta
– 'Mountain Pride'	LMil SReu
– 'Troll'	ECar
kongboense	GGGa
kotschyi	See R. ***myrtifolium***
kyawii	SLeo
§– Agapetum Group	SLeo
lacteum	CWal LMil SLeo
– SBEC 0345	GGGa
– forms	SLeo
¶ ***laetum*** (V)	GGGa
lanatum	CWal LHyd LMil SLeo
– Cooper 2148	SLeo
– DF 538	MBal
– KR 873	GGGa
– dwarf cream	GGGa
– Flinckii Group	See R. ***flinckii***
lanigerum	CWal SLeo
– KW 8251	GGGa
– 'Chapel Wood'	CWal
– pink form	SLeo
– 'Round Wood'	LHyd

– 'Round Wood'	LHyd
lapponicum	GWht
– Japanese	GGGa
§ ***latoucheae*** (EA)	MBal SLeo
laudandum	
var. ***temoense***	CWal GGGa
ledifolium 'Bulstrode'	See R. Azalea 'Bulstrode'
– 'Magnificum'	See R. Azalea 'Magnificum'
– 'Ripense'	See R. ***ripense***
lepidostylum	CB&S CHig CWal ECar EPot GAbr GGGa GWht LHyd LMil MBar MBri SExb SIng SLeo SPla SReu SSta WAbe WBod WThu
lepidotum	CGre CWal GArf GGGa GWht LHyd SLeo
– FMB 279	MBal
¶ – Elaeagnoïdes Group	GWht
§ – 'Reuthe's Purple'	GGGa MBal SLeo SReu SSta
– white form	GGGa
§ ***leptocarpum*** C&H 420	SLeo
leptothrium	CWal GGGa SLeo
leucaspis	CHig CWal EPot ERea GGGa IOrc LHyd MBal SExb SReu
– KW 7171	SLeo
liliiflorum Guiz 163	GGGa
lindleyi	CBow CWal LMil SLeo
– L&S	GGGa MBal
– 'Geordie Sherriff'	GGGa
litiense	See R. ***wardii wardii*** Litiense Group
¶ ***lochiae*** (V)	GGGa
loderi	See R. Hybrid Loderi
longesquamatum	CWal GGGa LMil SLeo
lopsangianum	See R. ***thomsonii l.***
lowndesii	GGGa
– x ***keiskei*** 'Yaku Fairy'	See R. Hybrid 'Yaku Fairy'
ludlowii	LMil MBal
lukiangense	GGGa SLeo
§ – R 11275*	SLeo
luteiflorum	CWal LMil
– KW 21040	GGGa
lutescens	CB&S CBow CGre CHig CTre CWal GWht IBlr IOrc ISea LMil MBal MBri SCog SExb SPla SReu SSpi SSta WAbe WBod WWat
– 'Bagshot Sands'	CWal GGGa LHyd LMil SReu
– 'Exbury'	CWal
– pink form	CWal
§ ***luteum*** (A)	CB&S CCla CSam CTre CWal ECar GDra GGGa GWht ISea LKna LMil MBal MBar MBri MGos MUlv SExb SLeo SReu SSta WBod WWat
§ ***lyi***	CWal SLeo
lysolepis	LMil
– KW 4456	GGGa
macabeanum	CB&S CBow CHEx CWal GGGa GWht LHyd LMil LTil MBal SLeo SReu SSpi SSta
– KW 7724	SLeo
– Reuthe's form	SReu
¶ ***macgregoriae*** (V)	ERea
¶ – P Woods 2646(V)	GGGa
¶ – yellow (V)	GGGa
macranthum	See R. ***indicum***
macrophyllum	GGGa LMil
§ ***macrosepalum*** (A)	SExb
§ – 'Linearifolium' (A)	CMac CTre CWal SLeo
§ ***macrosmithii***	CWal SLeo
maculiferum	
Guiz 120,121,148	GGGa
§ – ssp. ***anwheiense***	CWal GGGa LHyd LMil SLeo
maddenii	CGre CWal LHyd LMil SLeo
§ – ssp. ***crassum***	CTrw CWal GGGa LMil MBal
§ – – Obtusifolium Group	CWal SLeo
§ – ssp. ***maddenii***	CWal SLeo
§ – – Polyandrum Group	CWal ISea LTil MBal SLeo
– pink form	CWal
magnificum	LMil SLeo
¶ ***maius*** Herklots	GGGa
♦ ***makinoi***	See R. ***yakushimanum m.***
mallotum	CWal GGGa LHyd LMil SLeo
manipurense	See R. ***maddenii crassum*** Obtusifolium Group
martinianum	SLeo
– KW 21557	GGGa
maximum	SLeo
meddianum	CWal SLeo
– var. ***atrokermesinum***	CWal SLeo
– – F 26476	SLeo
– – KW 21006A	GGGa
megacalyx	CWal GGGa GWht LMil SLeo
megaphyllum	See R. ***basilicum***
megeratum	CB&S CWal GGGa SLeo SReu
– 'Bodnant'	WBod
mekongense	GGGa
§ – var. ***mekongense***	
Rubroluteum Group	GGGa LMil
§ – – Viridescens Group	GGGa LMil MBal
– – Viridescens Group KW 5829	CWal SLeo
– – Viridescens Group 'Doshang La'	LMil
– – 'Yellow Fellow'	LMil
§ – var. ***melinanthum***	CWal SLeo
– – Semilunatum Group	LMil
– var. ***rubrolineatum***	LMil SLeo
melinanthum	See R. ***mekongense melinanthum***
metternichii	See R. ***degronianum heptamerum***
micranthum	CWal GGGa LMil
microgynum	SLeo
– F 14242	GGGa SLeo
§ – Gymnocarpum Group	CWal LMil
microleucum	See R. ***orthocladum m.***
micromeres	See R. ***leptocarpum***
mimetes	LMil SLeo
minus	CWal LHyd LTil
§ – var. ***minus***	
Carolinianum Group	CWal GGGa LHyd
§ – – Punctatum Group	GRei MBar
mollicomum F 30940	SLeo
monosematum	See R. ***pachytrichum*** Monosematum Group
montroseanum	LMil SLeo
* – 'Baravalla'	GGGa
– 'Benmore'	GGGa
morii	CWal GGGa LHyd LMil SExb SLeo
– W A 10955	SLeo
§ ***moulmainense***	CWal SLeo
moupinense	CB&S CHig CWal ERea GGGa LHyd LMil SCog SLeo SReu WBod
– pink	GGGa

§ ***mucronatum*** (EA)	CMCN CTre GGGa LMil SLeo SPer WBod
– var. ***ripense*** (EA)	GWht
mucronulatum	CSto GGGa LHyd LMil SLeo SSpi
– 'Crater's Edge'	LMil
– 'Dwarf Cheju'	CWal
– 'Winter Brightness'	CWal
§ x ***myrtifolium***	COtt GGGa LHyd SLeo SPla
nakaharae (EA)	CWal LTil MBal SCog SLeo SReu WAbe
§ – 'Mariko'	CWal ECar EPot GGGa LHyd LMil MAsh MBal MGos NHol WAbe WPat WThu
– 'Mount Seven Stars'	CHig ECar GGGa LHyd LMil MAsh NHol SSta WPat
§ – orange form	LMil MAsh SCog SPer SReu SSta
– pink	ECar LHyd MAsh SCog SSta
– Starborough form	SSta
neriiflorum	CWal GGGa GWht ISea SCog SExb SLeo SSpi
– L&S 1352	GGGa
§ – ssp. ***neriiflorum*** Euchaites Group	SLeo
– – Euchaites Group KW 6854	CWal
– – 'Lamellen'	CWal
– – Phoenicodum Group Farrer 877	GGGa
– ssp. ***phaedropum*** C&H 422	SLeo
– – KW 6845*	SLeo
– – KW 8521	SLeo
nigroglandulosum	GGGa
nigropunctatum	See R. ***nivale boreale*** Nigropunctatum Group
nitens	See R. ***calostrotum riparium*** Nitens Group
nitidulum var. ***omeiense*** KR 185	GGGa LMil NHol
§ ***nivale*** ssp. ***boreale*** Stictophyllum Group	GGGa LMil
niveum	CWal GGGa LMil MBal SLeo SSta
– 'Nepal'	LHyd
nobleanum	See R. Hybrid Nobleanum
nudiflorum	See R. ***periclymenoïdes***
nuttallii	GGGa LMil MBal
x ***obtusum*** (EA)	CHig CWal LHyd
§ – 'Macrostemon'	WBod
occidentale (A)	CGre GGGa LMil MBal SSpi
– forms (A)	GGGa
oldhamii (EA)	CTre CWal SLeo
oleifolium 'Penheale Pink'	See R. ***virgatum o.*** 'P.P.'
orbiculare	CWal GGGa LHyd LMil SCog SLeo SSta
– W V 1519	SLeo
– Sandling Park form	SReu
oreodoxa	CWal LMil SLeo
§ – var. ***fargesii***	CWal GGGa IOrc LHyd LMil SLeo
§ – – Erubescens Group	CWal SLeo
oreotrephes	CWal IOrc LMil LTil MBal SExb SLeo SReu
– 'Davidian's Favourite'	GGGa
– Exquisitum Group	SReu
– Timeteum Group	SReu
orthocladum	CWal LHyd LMil
– F 20488	GGGa SLeo
§ – var. ***microleucum***	CWal GGGa LMil MBal SLeo WAbe
ovatum (A)	CB&S CWal SExb SLeo WBod
– W A 1391	GGGa SLeo
§ ***pachypodum***	LMil
¶ ***pachysanthum***	SSpi
– RV 72/001	CWal GGGa LMil LTil SLeo
– x ***morii***	GGGa
pachytrichum	GGGa SLeo
– Monosematum Group W V 1522	CWal SLeo
– Monosematum Group 'Blackhills'	GGGa
¶ – 'Sesame'	LMil
panteumorphum	See R. x ***erythrocalyx*** Panteumorphum Group
parmulatum	CWal LMil SLeo
– KW 5875	NHol
– mauve form	CWal
– 'Ocelot'	CWal GGGa
– pink	GGGa NHol
patulum	See R. ***pemakoense*** Patulum Group
pemakoense	CMHG CSam CWal EPot GGGa GWht LHyd LMil LTil MBal MBar MGos NKay SExb SLeo SReu WAbe WBod WThu
§ – Patulum Group	GGGa MBar MPlt NHol SLeo WPat
pendulum	GGGa LMil
pennivenium	See R. ***tanastylum p.***
pentaphyllum (A)	CWal
peregrinum	SLeo
– 'Wilson'	CWal
§ ***periclymenoïdes*** (A)	GGGa LMil
phaeochrysum	CWal GGGa SLeo
¶ – var. ***agglutinatum*** EGM 134	LMil
– Glendoick form	GGGa
§ – var. ***levistratum***	CWal GGGa
¶ – – EGM 143	LMil
– McLaren cup winner	SLeo
¶ – ***phaeochrysum*** EGM 129	LMil
pholidotum	See R. ***heliolepis brevistylum*** Pholidotum Group
§ ***piercei***	GGGa LMil SLeo
– KW 11040	SLeo
planetum	SLeo
pocophorum	CWal GGGa SLeo
– forms	SLeo
– var. ***hemidartum***	GGGa SLeo
pogonostylum	See R. ***irroratum p.***
polyandrum	See R. ***maddenii maddenii*** Polyandrum Group
§ ***polycladum***	CSam EPot GGGa GWht LHyd LKna LMil MBal MLea
– Scintillans Group	GDra MBar MBri MLea NHol SLeo WAbe WBod WThu
polylepis	GGGa SLeo
ponticum	CKin CWal GGGa IDai ISea LHyd MBar MBri MGos MMor SExb SPer
– (Azalea)	See R. ***luteum***
– AC&H 205	GGGa
– 'Cheiranthifolium'	CWal SLeo

– 'Variegatum'	CB&S CHig CWal EBre GGGa IOrc ISea LBre MBal MBar MBri MGos MMor MUlv SPer SReu SSta WThu
poukhanense	See R. ***yedoense p.***
praestans	CWal GGGa LMil SLeo
praeteritium	SLeo
praevernum	CWal GGGa GWht SReu
prattii	See R. ***faberi p.***
preptum	CWal GGGa SLeo
primuliflorum	CWal GGGa LMil
– Cephalanthoïdes Group	GGGa
principis	GGGa LMil
– Vellereum Group	CWal SLeo
♦***prinophyllum***	See R. ***austrinum***
pronum	GGGa
prostratum	See R. ***saluenense chameunum*** Prostratum Group
proteoïdes	GGGa
protistum	SLeo
– var. ***giganteum***	CWal SLeo
pruniflorum	CWal GGGa SLeo
¶***prunifolium*** (A)	LMil LTil
przewalskii	GGGa SLeo
¶– CH&M 2545	LMil
– Cox 2545	NHol
pseudochrysanthum	CBow CWal GGGa LHyd LMil LTil MBal SCog SExb SLeo SSta
– AM 1956 Form	CWal SSpi
pubescens	CWal LMil SLeo
– 'Fine Bristles'	SReu
pudorosum L&S 2752	GGGa
pumilum	GDra GGGa MBal
punctatum	See R. ***minus minus*** Punctatum Group
purdomii	SLeo
quinquefolium (A)	CCla CWal SLeo SReu
racemosum	CB&S CGre CWal GWht LMil LTil MBar SExb SIng SLeo SSpi SSta
– 'Forrest'	MBar
– 'Glendoick'	GGGa
– 'Rock Rose'	GGGa LHyd LMil
¶– 'White Lace'	LHyd
– x ***tephropeplum***	MBal MBar MLea
– – ***trichocladum*** SBEC	NHol
radicans	See R. ***calostrotum keleticum*** Radicans Group
ramsdenianum	CWal SLeo
ravum	See R. ***cuneatum*** Ravum Group
recurvoïdes	GGGa LHyd LMil SReu SSta
– KW 7184	CWal SLeo
– Keillour form	GGGa
reticulatum (A)	CWal SLeo SReu SSpi SSta
– ***dilatatum***	See R. ***d.***
– 'Sea King'	LHyd
rex	CBow CWal GGGa IOrc LHyd LMil MBal SLeo SSpi
§ – ssp. ***arizelum***	GGGa LMil SLeo
– – F 21861	CWal
– – KW 20922	CWal
– – 'Brodick'	CWal
– – Rubicosum Group	SLeo
§ – ssp. ***fictolacteum***	CWal GGGa LHyd LMil MBal SLeo SReu
– – R11043	SLeo
– – 'Cherry Tip' R 11395	SLeo
rhabdotum	See R. ***dalhousieae rhabdotum***
rigidum	CWal LHyd LMil SCog SLeo
– ***album***	CHig
ripiense	See R. ***mucronatum r.***
ririei	CWal GGGa
– Guiz 75	GGGa
– W 5254A	CWal
roseum	See R. ***austrinum***
rothschildii	GGGa LMil SLeo
roxieanum	CWal LMil SExb SLeo SReu
– R 25422	SLeo
– R11141	SLeo
– var. ***cucullatum*** SBEC 0345	SLeo
– var. ***roxieanum*** Oreonastes Group	CWal GGGa LHyd LMil SLeo SSta
– – Oreonastes Group R11312	GGGa
– – Oreonastes Group Nymans form	SReu
rubiginosum	CBow CWal GGGa GWht IOrc ISea LHyd LMil LTil MBal SLeo SReu SSta
§ – Desquamatum Group	CWal LHyd SExb SLeo
– white	LMil
rubroluteum	See R. ***mekongense m.*** Rubroluteum Group
rude	See R. ***glischrum rude***
rufum	CWal GGGa LTil SLeo
– W V 1808 *	SLeo
rupicola	CWal GDra LMil MBal
– var. ***chryseum***	GGGa LMil SLeo
– var. ***muliense***	LMil
russatum	CSam CWal GDra GGGa LHyd LMil MBri MPlt SExb SLeo
– blue black form	LMil
– 'Collingwood Ingram'	SCog
– 'Purple Pillow'	NHar
– Waterer form	LMil
saluenense	CWal GGGa LHyd LMil MBal SExb
– ssp. ***chameunum***	CWal GGGa LMil MBal SLeo
– – F 25560	NHol
– – Exbury form R 11005	LMil
§ – – Prostratum Group	GGGa MBal
– hairy form	NHol
sanctum (A)	GGGa SLeo
sanguineum	CWal GGGa LMil SLeo
§ – ssp. ***didymum***	GGGa SLeo
– ssp. ***sanguineum*** var. ***cloiophorum*** F 25521	LMil
– – var. ***cloiophorum*** R 10899	SLeo
– – var. ***cloiophorum*** R 11029	SLeo
– – var. ***cloiophorum*** R 11212	SLeo
– – var. ***didymoïdes*** R 10903	GGGa LMil SLeo
– – var. ***didymoïdes*** Consanguineum Group	SLeo

– – var.*didymoïdes* Consanguineum Group	SLeo
– – var.*didymoïdes* Consanguineum Group KW 6831	LMil
– – var.*didymoïdes* Roseotinctum Group	LMil
– – var.***haemaleum***	GGGa LMil SLeo
– – var.***haemaleum*** F 21732	SLeo
– – var.***haemaleum*** F 21735	SLeo
– – var.***haemaleum*** R 10893	SLeo
– – var.***haemaleum*** R/USDA 59303/R 10895	SLeo
– – var.***haemaleum*** R/USDA 59453/R 10938	SLeo
– – var.***himertum*** R 10906	LMil
santapaui (V)	GGGa
sargentianum	CWal MLea SLeo
– 'Maricee'	GGGa
– 'Whitebait'	GGGa
scabrifolium	SLeo
– SBEC K 160	GGGa
– var. ***spiciferum***	CWal GGGa LMil LTil MBal SLeo WAbe
schlippenbachii (A)	CGre CMCN CWal GGGa LHyd LMil MBal MBri SLeo SReu SSpi SSta WWat
– 'Sid's Royal Pink' (A)	GGGa
scintillans	See R. ***polycladum***
scopulorum	LMil SLeo
¶ – KW 6354	GGGa
– Magor's hardy form	CWal
scottianum	See R. ***pachypodum***
scyphocalyx	See R. ***dichroanthum s.***
searsiae	CWal GGGa LMil SExb SLeo
seinghkuense KW 9254	GGGa
selense	CWal
– ssp. ***dasycladum***	LMil SLeo
– ssp. ***jucundum***	GGGa LMil
– ssp. ***selense*** Probum Group	CWal
– ssp. ***setiferum***	CWal
– – F 14458	SLeo
semnoïdes	CWal GGGa GWht LMil SLeo
serotinum	CWal SLeo SReu
serpyllifolium (A)	CB&S CWal SLeo WPat
¶ – ***albiflorum***	GAri
setosum	GGGa GWht LMil MBal SLeo
shepherdii	See R. ***kendrickii***
sherriffii	CWal GGGa LHyd SLeo
– AM 1966 Form	CWal
shweliense	GGGa LMil SReu
sidereum	CWal SLeo
– KW 13649	SLeo
siderophyllum	GGGa
sikangense EGM 108	GGGa LMil
simiarum	CWal GGGa
simsii (EA)	CMac CWal SExb
sinogrande	CB&S CHEx CWal GGGa IOrc LMil MBal SLeo
– KW 21111	SLeo
smirnowii	CWal GGGa LHyd LMil MBal SLeo SSta
smithii	See R. ***macrosmithii***
– Argipeplum Group	See R. ***argipeplum***
souliei	CWal GGGa IOrc LMil SLeo
– white form	GGGa
sperabile	CWal
– F 26446	SLeo
– F 26453	SLeo
– var. ***weihsiense***	GGGa SLeo
¶ ***sperabiloïdes***	GGGa
sphaeranthum	See R. ***trichostomum***
sphaeroblastum	CWal GGGa LMil SLeo
– F 20416	SLeo
spilotum	GGGa SLeo
spinuliferum	CWal GGGa GWht LHyd LMil LTil SLeo
– 'Jack Hext'	CWal
stamineum W V 887	SLeo
stenaulum	See R. ***moulmainense***
stewartianum	CWal GGGa SLeo
stictophyllum	See R. ***nivale boreale*** Stictophyllum Group
strigillosum	CWal GGGa SLeo
– Reuthe's form	SReu
subansiriense C&H 418	CWal GGGa SLeo
succothii	CWal GGGa LHyd SLeo
¶ – EGM 086	LMil
– LS&H 21295	SLeo
sulfureum	CWal GGGa
sutchuenense	CB&S CWal GGGa LMil SLeo
taggianum	CWal
¶ – 'Cliff Hanger'	LMil
– Headfortianum Group	LMil
* ***taiwanense***	GGGa
taliense	CWal GGGa LHyd LMil SLeo
– F 6772	SLeo
– SBEC 0350	GGGa
tashiroi (EA)	CWal
tatsienense	GGGa LMil
telopeum	See R. ***campylocarpum caloxanthum*** Telopeum Group
temenium R 10909	SLeo
– var. ***dealbatum*** Glaphyrum Group F 21902	SLeo
– x ***eclecteum***	GGGa
– var. ***gilvum*** 'Cruachan' R 22272	GGGa LMil SLeo
– var. ***temenium*** F 21734	SLeo
tephropeplum	CB&S CWal LHyd SLeo
– KW 6303	SLeo
¶ – R/USDA 03914	GGGa
thayerianum	CWal GGGa LMil
thomsonii	CWal GGGa LHyd LMil SLeo SPer
– BL&M 153	MBal
– DF 540	MBal
– L&S	GGGa
– 'Balbirnie'	GGGa
§ – ssp. ***lopsangianum*** LS&T 6561	CWal SLeo
thymifolium	GGGa
tosaense 'Ralph Clarke' (EA)	SLeo

traillianum	CBow CWal GGGa LMil SLeo
– F 5881 *	SLeo
trichanthum	CHig CWal GGGa IOrc LMil SLeo
¶– W 1342	GGGa
– 'Honey Wood'	LHyd
trichocladum	CWal SLeo
– KW 21079	GGGa
§ ***trichostomum***	GGGa MLea SSpi
– Ledoïdes Group	CWal LMil SLeo SReu
– – 'Collingwood Ingram'	LMil
– Radinum Group	CWal SSta
triflorum	CWal GGGa GWht IOrc ISea LMil LTil MBal SLeo WThu
– var. ***bauhiniiflorum***	CWal LMil SLeo
– var. ***triflorum*** Mahogani Group	SLeo
tsangpoense	See R. ***charitopes t.***
tsariense	GGGa
– forms	SLeo
– var. ***trimoense***	GGGa
– 'Yum Yum'	CWal SLeo
tubiforme	See R. ***glaucophyllum t.***
ungernii	GGGa
uniflorum	CWal GGGa LMil WThu
– KW 5876	SLeo
§ – var. ***imperator***	GGGa LMil
uvariifolium	CWal GGGa SLeo
– Griseum Group LS&E 15817	GGGa
– 'Reginald Childs'	CWal LMil
– 'Yangtze Bend'	CWal GGGa
valentinianum	CB&S CSam CWal GGGa MBal SLeo
– F 24347	SLeo SReu
vaseyi (A)	GGGa LHyd LMil MBal SSpi
veitchianum	GGGa
§ – Cubitii Group	CWal GGGa SLeo
– – 'Ashcombe'	CWal LHyd
vellereum	See R. ***principis*** Vellereum Group
venator	CWal GGGa GWht SLeo
vernicosum	CWal GGGa GWht LMil SLeo
– F 5881	SLeo
verruculosum	SLeo
vesiculiferum	SLeo
vialii (A)	GGGa
virgatum	CWal
– ssp. ***oleifolium*** KW 6279	SLeo
viridescens	See R. ***mekongense mekongense*** Viridescens Group
viscidifolium	GGGa LTil
viscosum (A)	CB&S CWal GGGa LHyd LKna LMil SSpi
– ***aemulans***	LMil SReu
– 'Antilope'	See R. Azalea 'Antilope'
– 'Arpege'	See R. Azalea 'A.'
– hybrids	LMil
– f. ***rhodanthum***	LMil
wallichii	CGre GGGa GWht LMil
– LS&H 17527	CWal SLeo
walongense C&H 373	GGGa
wardii	CWal IOrc LHyd LMil LTil MBal MLea SLeo
– L&S form *	CWal GGGa SLeo SReu
– var. ***puralbum***	CWal GGGa
– var. ***wardii*** KW 4170	GGGa
§ – – Litiense Group	CWal SLeo
– yellow	GGGa
wasonii	CWal GGGa
– f. ***rhododactylum***	GGGa SLeo
– white form	SLeo
watsonii	GGGa SLeo
¶– EGM 109	LMil
¶ ***websterianum*** EGM 146	LMil
weyrichii (A)	CWal
wightii	CWal GGGa LHyd SLeo
– BM&W 153	MBal
– DF 542	MBal
– KR 877	LMil
williamsianum	CB&S CHig CSam CWal EPot GGGa ISea LHyd LMil MBal MBar MGos MLea NHol NKay SCog SExb SLeo SReu WAbe WBod WThu
– Caerhays form	CWal MPla
– 'Special'	GGGa
– white form	CWal GGGa MBal SLeo SSpi
wilsoniae	See R. ***latoucheae***
wiltonii	CWal GGGa LMil
wongii	CWal GGGa LMil
xanthocodon	See R. ***cinnabarium x.***
xanthostephanum	CWal
yakushimanum	CB&S CBow CCla CSam GGGa IOrc LKna LMil MBar MBri MGos NBar SPer SReu SSpi SSta
– 'Edelweiss'	GGGa
– Exbury form	SReu
– FCC form	MUlv SReu
§ – 'Koichiro Wada'	CWal GGGa MBal MGos NHar NHol SLeo WThu
§ – ssp. ***makinoi***	CHig CWal GGGa LHyd LMil NHol SExb SLeo SReu SSta
¶– 'Mist Maiden'	SBar
– 'Snow Mountain'	SReu
– Tremeer tall form	CWal
– ssp. ***yakushimanum*** 'Ken Janeck'	GGGa LMil LTil
yungningense	CWal LMil
yunnanense	CBow CWal EHar GGGa GWht IOrc ISea LHyd LMil SCog SLeo
– 'Diana Colville'	CWal
– Hormophorum Group	CWal
– 'Openwood'	LMil
– pink	GGGa
– selected form	SReu
– 'Tower Court'	CWal
– white	CBow GGGa SCog
¶ ***zaleucum***	GWht
¶– F 15688	GGGa
– F 27603	SLeo
– Flaviflorum Group KW 20837	SLeo

RHODOHYPOXIS (Hypoxidaceae)

'Albrighton'	CAvo CBro CRiv ELan EPot LAma NHar NHol NKay SBla SGil SHer WAbe WChr
'Appleblossom'	CAvo NHar SIng
baurii	CAvo CCla CNic CRDP CRiv CWGN ELan EPad EPot IDai MHig MTho NHar NKay NNrd NRoo NTow SGil SHer WCru WWin

– 'Alba'	CBro CCla CRDP WCru
¶– var. *baurii*	EPot NHar
¶– var. *confecta*	EPot
– 'Dulcie'	EPot NTow SWas WAbe
¶– forms	WHil
– 'Pinkeen'	WAbe
– var. *platypetala*	CRDP CRiv EPot NHar NHol NMen WAbe
– 'Susan Garnett-Botfield'	CRiv EPot WChr
'Dawn'	CAvo CRiv EPot LAma NHar NHol SBla SGil SHer WAbe WChr
'Douglas'	CAvo CRDP CRiv EPot LAma NHar NHol SGil SHer WChr
¶ 'Dusky'	EPot
'E A Bowles'	WAbe
¶ 'Emily Peel'	EPot
'Eva-Kate'	CAvo EPot LAma NHar NHol SBla SGil WChr
'Fred Broome'	CBro CCla CRiv ELan EPot LAma NHar NHol NTow SBla SGil SHer WAbe WChr
'Garnett'	CAvo CRDP EPot NHol NKay
'Great Scott'	EPot NHar WChr
'Harlequin'	CBro ELan EPot LAma NHar NHol SGil SHer WChr
¶ 'Helen'	EPot NHar NHol SBla SHer WAbe
hybrids	CKel ELan LBow SDeJ
'Knockdolian Red'	NHol
milloïdes	CRDP EPot NHar SBla WAbe WChr
'Perle'	CAvo EPot NHar NMen
'Picta'	CAvo CRDP CRiv CSam EPot LAma NHar NHol SBla SGil WAbe WChr
'Pink Pearl'	EPot NHol
'Ruth'	EPot LAma NHar NHol SBla SGil WAbe WChr
'Shell Pink'	NKay SBla
'Stella'	CAvo CRiv EPot NHol
¶ 'Susan Garnett-Bottfield	NHar
'Tetra Pink'	SHer WAbe WChr
'Tetra Red'	EPot NHar NHol SHer WAbe WChr
♦ 'Tetra White'	See R. 'Helen'
thodiana	CAvo EPot

RHODOPHIALA (Liliaceae/Amaryllidaceae)

§ *bifida*	CMon LBow
*– *spathacea*	CMon

RHODORA See RHODODENDRON

RHODOTHAMNUS (Ericaceae)

chamacistus	WCru

RHODOTYPOS (Rosaceae)

kerrioïdes	See R. ***scandens***
§ *scandens*	CBot CChu CMHG CPle MGos MPla NHol NTow SPla WBod WCru WWin

RHOEO See TRADESCANTIA

RHOICISSUS (Vitaceae)

See Plant Deletions

RHOPALOBLASTE (Palmae)

See Plant Deletions

RHOPALOSTYLIS (Palmae)

baueri	LPal NPal
sapida	CHEx LPal NPal

RHUBARB See RHEUM x *hybridum*

RHUS † (Anacardiaceae)

aromatica	LRHS MBel NHol NSal WCoo
copallina	CKni CMHG SHil SSpi WPat
cotinus	See COTINUS ***coggygria***
glabra	CB&S CDoC IJoh MBlu SPer SSta
– 'Laciniata'	CBow CCla CDoC CSco MAsh MBri MGos SHBN SPer WPat
N *hirta*	CB&S CLnd EBre ECtt ELan ENot IDai IJoh IOrc ISea LBre MBar MBri MGos MWat NNor SHBN SPer SReu SSta WAbe WDin WStI WWin
– 'Laciniata'	CB&S CBra CLnd CSco EBlo ELan ENot GRei IJoh IOrc MBar MBri MWat NBee NKay SPer WAbe WDin WPat
integrifolia	CArn
pendulina	CGre
potaninii	WWat
punjabensis	CB&S SSpi
§ *radicans*	GPoy
succedanea	CKni LRHS
toxicodendron	See R. ***radicans***
trichocarpa	CAbP CKni CMHG CPle ELan SHil SSpi
trilobata	NSal
typhina	See R. ***hirta***
verniciflua	CChu CLnd

RHYNCHELYTRUM See MELINIS

RIBES † (Grossulariaceae)

alpinum	CBow ELan ENot ESis GRei IOrc NWea SPer SPla WDin
– 'Aureum'	CCla CMHG EBre EFol ELan ISea LBre MHig MPar MPla NNor WDin WSHC
americanum 'Variegatum'	EFol ELan EPla LHop NHol SDry SFai SMad WPat
atrosanguineum	See R. ***sanguineum*** 'Atrorubens'
aureum hort.	See R. ***odoratum***
F x *culverwellii* Jostaberry	GTwe LBuc WHig
F *divaricatum* Worcesterberry	CMac CWSG GChr IJoh MBri MGos MMor NBar NRog SDea SPer WHig
fasciculatum var. *chinense*	EMon
gayanum	CGre CPle LHop SPla WCru WThu

glandulosum	CCor
glutinosum 'Albidum'	CSco ERav LHop SChu WWat
x ***gordonianum***	CB&S CBrd CChu CCor CGre CHan CMHG CPle CSco EBre EHar ERav LBre LHop MBal MRav SLon WWat WWeb
grossularia	See R. ***uva-crispa***
laurifolium	CB&S CBot CBow CChu CGre CPle CSam ELan EPla ERav GCal IOrc LAbb LTil MBal SChu SHil SPer SSpi WDin WSHC WWat
– 'Mrs Amy Doncaster'	EPla
magellanicum	CGre
F ***nigrum*** 'Amos Black'	GTwe
F – 'Baldwin'	CDoC CMac EWar GBon IJoh MBea NGrN SDea SKee SPer WStI WWeb
¶ – 'Ben Alder'	SDea
F – 'Ben Connan'	GTwe
F – 'Ben Lomond'	CSam EBre EHar EWar GBon GRei GTwe IJoh LBre LBuc MBea MBri MGos NBar NBee NElm NRog SDea SKee SPer WHig WWeb
F – 'Ben Loyal'	GTwe
F – 'Ben More'	GChr GRei GTwe LBuc MBri MGos NBar NBee NGrN SDea SKee SPer
F – 'Ben Nevis'	GRei GTwe MBea NElm NRog SDea SKee
F – 'Ben Sarek'	CSam EBre GChr GTwe LBre LBuc MBri MGos NBar SDea SKee WHig WStI WWeb
*– 'Ben Tirran'	CSut
F – 'Black Reward'	MGos
F – 'Blackdown'	SDea
F – 'Boskoop Giant'	CMac EWar NEgg NElm NRog
F – 'Daniel's September'	GTwe
F – 'Jet'	GTwe SDea SKee WHig
F – 'Laxton's Giant'	GTwe SDea
¶ – 'Loch Ness'	NBar
F – 'Malling Jet'	EHar NElm NRog SPer
F – 'Mendip Cross'	GTwe NRog
F – 'Seabrook's'	EWar WHig
F – 'Wellington XXX'	CSam EHar ESha EWar GTwe IJoh LBuc MBea MBri NBar NBee NEgg NGrN NRog SDea SKee SPer WStI WWeb
F – 'Westwick Choice'	GTwe
§ ***odoratum***	CB&S CBow CCor CMHG CPle CSam CSco ELan ENot EPla ERav GRei LAbb MBar MGos MPla NHol NWea SHBN SLon SPer SPla SSpi WStI WWat
F Pink Currant Group 'Hollande Rose'	GTwe
F – 'October Currant'	GTwe
****praecox***	CB&S
F Red Currant Group 'Fay's New Prolific'	GTwe
F – 'Jonkheer van Tets'	GRei IJoh MGos SDea SKee
F – 'Laxton Number One'	CMac CSam EBre EHar ESha GBon GChr LBre MBea MBri NBar NElm NRog SDea SKee SPer WHig
F – 'Raby Castle'	GTwe
F – 'Red Lake'	CMac EBre GBon GRei LBre LBuc MBea MBri MGos NBee NEgg NElm NRog SDea SKee SPer WStI
F – 'Redstart'	MBri NBar SDea SKee WHig
F – 'Rondom'	SDea
F – 'Stanza'	CSut SDea
F – 'Wilson's Long Bunch'	GTwe
sanguineum	CPle CSam ISea LBuc MBal MBar NNor WStI WWin
– 'Albescens'	EHar SPer
– 'Brocklebankii'	CAbP CCla CSco ECtt EHar ENot EPar EPla LHop MBar MGos MPla NHol SHBN SLon SPer SPla WAbe WSHC WWat
¶ – double	MUlv
– 'Giant White'	EPla
– 'King Edward VII'	CBow CDoC CSco ECtt IJoh MBar MBri MGos MWat NBee NNor NRoo NWea SHBN SHer SMad SPer SPla SReu WDin WWeb
– 'Lombartsii'	CShe EPla SLon
– 'Pulborough Scarlet'	CB&S CBow CDoC CSco CShe EFol ELan ENot MBri MGos MPla MRav MWat NKay WAbe WWeb
– 'Pulborough Scarlet Variegated'	EPla LHop MUlv SDry SFai
¶ – 'Red Pimpernel'	EBlo MAsh
– ***roseum***	See R. ***s.*** 'Carneum'
– 'Splendens'	GRei IDai MGos
– 'Tydeman's White'	CBow EBre ECtt LBre MBar WDin
¶ – 'White Icicle'	EBlo MAsh
speciosum	CB&S CBot CBrd CChu CCla CFis CGre CPle CSam ELan ENot EOrc EPla GCal ISea LGre LHop MBal MPla MWat SHil SPer WBod WDin WEas WKif WSHC WWat WWin
tenue	EPla
F ***uva-crispa*** var. ***reclinatum*** 'Achilles' (C/D)	GTwe
F – – 'Admiral Beattie'	GTwe NRog
F – – 'Alma' (D)	NRog
F – – 'Annelii'	SDea
– – 'Aston Red'	See R. ***u-c. r.*** 'Warrington'
F – – 'Australia'	NRog
F – – 'Bedford Red' (D)	GTwe NRog
F – – 'Bedford Yellow' (D)	GTwe
F – – 'Beech Tree Nestling'	GTwe
F – – 'Bellona' (C)	NRog
F – – 'Black Velvet'	CMac MBea MBri NBar SPer
F – – 'Blucher'	NRog
F – – 'Broom Girl' (D)	GTwe NRog
F – – 'Captivator'	GTwe
F – – 'Careless' (C)	CDoC CMac CSam EHar ESha EWar GBon GRei GTwe IOrc MBea MBri MGos NBee NElm NGrN NRog SDea SKee SPer WWeb
F – – 'Catherina'	SDea
F – – 'Champagne Red'	GTwe
F – – 'Clayton'	NRog
F – – 'Criterion' (C)	GTwe NRog
F – – 'Crown Bob' (C/D)	GTwe NRog
F – – 'Dan's Mistake' (D)	GTwe NRog
F – – 'Drill'	GTwe
F – – 'Early Sulphur' (D)	GRei GTwe IJoh NRog SDea SKee WStI
F – – 'Firbob' (D)	GTwe NRog
F – – 'Freedom' (C)	GTwe NRog
F – – 'Gipsey Queen'	GTwe

F-- 'Glenton Green' GTwe
F-- 'Golden Ball' (D) SDea
F-- 'Golden Drop' (D) GTwe
-- 'Green Gascoigne' (D) See R. ***u-c. r.*** 'Early Green Hairy'
F-- 'Green Gem' (C/D) GTwe NRog
F-- 'Green Ocean' GTwe NRog
-- 'Greenfinch' GTwe
F-- 'Greengage' (D) NRog
F-- 'Guido' GTwe NRog
F-- 'Gunner' (D) GTwe NRog
F-- 'Heart of Oak' GTwe NRog
F-- 'Hero of the Nile' (C) GTwe NRog
¶-- 'High Sheriff' (D) GTwe
F-- 'Hinnonmäki Röd' SDea
F-- 'Howard's Lancer' (C/D) GTwe NRog SDea SKee
F-- 'Invicta' (C) CDoC CMac CWSG EBre EWar GBon GChr IJoh LBre LBuc MBea MBri MGos SDea SKee WHig WStI WWeb
-- 'Ironmonger' GTwe
F-- 'Jubilee' LBuc MBri MGos NBar NRog SKee
F-- 'Keen's Seedling' (D) GTwe
F-- 'Keepsake' (C/D) GTwe NRog
F-- 'King of Trumps' GTwe NRog
F-- 'Lancashire Lad' (C/D) GTwe NRog
F-- 'Langley Gage' (D) GTwe NRog
F-- 'Leveller' (C/D) CDoC CMac CSut EBre EHar EWar GBon GTwe LBre LBuc MBea MBri MGos NBar NElm NGrN NRog SDea SKee SPer WStI WWeb
F-- 'London' (C/D) GTwe NRog
F-- 'Lord Derby' (C/D) GTwe MBri NRog
F-- 'Lord Kitchener' NRog
F-- 'Macherauch's Seedling' NRog
F-- 'Marigold' NRog
F-- 'Matchless' (D) NRog
F-- 'May Duke' (C/D) IJoh NRog SDea
F-- 'Mitre' (C) GTwe
F-- 'Pitmaston Green Gage' (D) GTwe
F-- 'Plunder' NRog
F-- 'Queen of Hearts' NRog
F-- 'Queen of Trumps' (C) GTwe NRog
F-- 'Roseberry' (D) GTwe
F-- 'Sir George Brown' (D) NRog
F-- 'Speedwell' NRog
F-- 'Spinefree' GTwe
F-- 'Sultan Juror' NRog
F-- 'Surprise' (C) GTwe NRog
F-- 'Suter Johnny' NRog
F-- 'Telegraph' GTwe
F-- 'The Leader' NRog
F-- 'Tom Joiner' GTwe
F-- 'Trumpeter' (C) NRog
F-- 'Victoria' GTwe NRog
F-- 'Warrington' (D) GTwe NRog
F-- 'Whinham's Industry' (C/D) CDoC CMac CSam CSut EHar EWar GBon GRei GTwe IJoh IOrc LBuc MBri MGos NBee NEgg NElm NGrN NRog SDea SKee SPer WHig WStI
F-- 'White Eagle' (C) NRog
F-- 'White Lion' (C/D) GTwe NRog
F-- 'White Transparent' (C) GTwe
F-- 'Whitesmith' (C/D) GRei GTwe IJoh LBuc NEgg NRog SDea SKee WHig
F-- 'Woodpecker' GTwe NRog
F-- 'Yellow Champagne' NRog
viburnifolium CGre CHan CMHG CPle NTow
F White Currant Group 'Versailles Blanche' ('White Versailles') CDoC CMac LBuc MBea MBri MGos NBar SDea SKee SPer WHig WWeb
F- 'White Grape' GTwe NElm NRog
F- 'White Pearl' GRei IJoh
F- 'White Transparent' GTwe

RICHEA (Epacridaceae)

dracophylla CSun SArc
scoparia CSun SArc SBor SSpi

RICINUS (Euphorbiaceae)

communis 'Impala' WHer

RIGIDELLA (Iridaceae)

See Plant Deletions

ROBINIA † (Leguminosae)

x ***ambigua*** 'Bella Rosea' MUlv
fertilis 'Monument' WDin
hispida CBot CBow CCla CSco EBre ELan ENot LBre LNet MUlv SHBN SMad SPer SSpi WDin WSHC
- 'Macrophylla' SHil SSpi
N- 'Rosea' CB&S CBot SPer WRus
kelseyi CPMA CSco IOrc MUlv SPer
luxurians CB&S
x ***margaretta*** 'Pink Cascade' ('Casque Rouge') CBow CCla CDoC CPMA CSPN CSco EHar LNet LPan MBri MGos MMea SChu SHBN SPer WDin
¶ ***neomexicana*** CLnd
pseudoacacia CB&S CHEx CLnd CPer ELan ENot GAri LPan WDin WNor
- 'Bessoniana' CBow CLnd CTho ENot SPer
- 'Fastigiata' See R. ***p.*** 'Pyramidalis'
- 'Frisia' CB&S CBra CCla CHEx CLnd CSam CSco CTho EBre EHar ELan ENot IOrc LBre LNet MBal MBri MGos NBar SHBN SPer SPla SReu SSta WDin WMou WWat
- 'Inermis' hort. See R. ***p.*** 'Umbraculifera'
§- 'Pyramidalis' CBow CPMA EHar ENot
- 'Rozynskiana' CTho
- 'Semperflorens' CSco

– 'Tortuosa'	CBow CBra CTho EBre EHar ELan LBre MBri MMea SHer SMad SPer
§ – 'Umbraculifera'	EBre IJoh LBre LPan MGos
– 'Unifoliola'	CLnd
x *slavinii* 'Hillieri'	CBow CCla CLnd CPMA CSco CTho ELan IOrc SHil SPer SSpi WWat

ROCHEA See CRASSULA

RODGERSIA † (Saxifragaceae)

aesculifolia	CBow CChu CGle CHEx CHad CHan CRDP CRow CSco CWGN EGol ELan ELun EPar LWad MBal MBri NDea NFai NHar NHol SBla SFis SHig SSpi WByw WCru WDav WWat
– 'Irish Bronze'	CHad EBre IBlr LBre
henrici hybrid	CChu LRHS MUlv NHol
'Parasol'	CHad ELan SSpi
pinnata	CBow CDoC CGle CHEx CHad CKel CRow CSco CWGN EBre EFol EGol ERav LBre MBal MBri MSta NDea NVic SBla SChu SHig SLon SPer WHoo WWat
– CLD 432	NHol
– 'Alba'	NHol
– 'Elegans'	CB&S CCla CHad EBre EFou ELan ELun EPar GCal LBre NHol NOrc SPer WAbe WWin
– 'Superba'	CCla CHEx CHad CSam CSco CShe EBar EBre ECha ECtt GCal IDai LBlm LBre LGro MBal MBri MBro MUlv NBee NHar NSti SBla SFis SPer SSpi WCru WHoo WKif
podophylla	CChu CCla CHEx CHad CHan CKel CRDP CWGN CWit EBre ECha EFol EGol EHon ELun LBre NDea NHol SAxl SBla SDix SHig SPer SSpi WCru WHer
– Donard form	IBlr WCot
– 'Rotlaub'	LRHS MBri MUlv
– 'Smaragd'	CRow EBre LBre MUlv
purdomii	CRow EBre LBre SSpi
sambucifolia	CChu CCla CDoC CHEx CHad CRow CShe EBre LBre MBri MFir MUlv NDea NHar NHol SFis SPer SSpi WCru WMer WWat
sp. CLD 1329	NHol
¶ sp. CLD 1432	NHol
tabularis	See ASTILBOIDES *tabularis*

ROHDEA † (Liliaceae/Convallariaceae)

japonica	SApp
¶ – 'Talbot Manor'	SApp
¶ – 'Tuneshige Rokujo'	SApp

ROMANZOFFIA (Hydrophyllaceae)

californica	See R. *suksdorfii*
sitchensis	CLew CRDP EBar NRed SMrm WHoo
tracyi	EPot WEas WThi
unalaschkensis	CNic CRiv ECar ECro ELan EPot ESis GAbr MHig MNFA NGre NMen NTow NWCA SHer SIng WAbe WOMN WPer WTyr

ROMNEYA (Papaveraceae)

coulteri	Widely available
– var. *trichocalyx*	CDoC CGre IBlr LGre
§ – 'White Cloud'	CCla SSpi
x *hybrida*	See R. *coulteri* 'White Cloud'

ROMULEA (Iridaceae)

¶ *battandieri* AB&S 4659	CMon
¶ *bifrons* AB&S 4359/4360	CMon
bulbocodium	CBro CMon CNic CRiv EBul LBow MHig
– var. *clusiana*	LAma
¶ – – SF 237	CMon
– – Serotina Group	EPot
¶ – white form	EBul
¶ *campanuloïdes*	CMon
¶ *columnae* AB&S 4659	CMon
¶ *engleri* SF 3	CMon
¶ *hirta*	CMon
¶ *ligustica* var. *rouyana* SF 360	CMon
linaresii	CNic EPot LAma
¶ – var. *graeca* CE&H 620	CMon
longituba	See R. *macowanii*
macowanii	MHig WAbe
– var. *alticola*	WOMN
minutiflora	NRog
¶ *monticola*	CMon
nivalis	LAma WChr
pratensis	CNic WThi
ramiflora	CMon
¶ – SF 63	CMon
rosea	NRog
sabulosa	CBro
¶ sp. SF 367	CMon
tempskyana	CMon
'Zahnii	CMon CSam LAma

ROSA † (Rosaceae)

'Abbandonata'	See R. 'Laure Davoust'
Abbeyfield Rose ® (HT)	CDoC GCoc LStr SJus SPer
§ 'Abbotswood' (*canina* x)	EBls
'Aberdonian' (F)	GCoc
¶ Abigaile ® (F)	NBat
Abraham Darby ® (S)	CCMG CDoC CSam EBre EWar LBre LGod LStr MAus MFry MHay MRui SPer
Ace of Hearts ® (HT)	CSan
acicularis var. *engelmannii*	CCor
– var. *nipponensis*	EBls EWar
'Adam' (T/Cl)	EBls
'Adam Messerich' (Bb)	EBls ETWh IHos MAus WHCG
'Adélaïde d'Orléans' (Ra)	CCMG EBls MAus SJus SPer SRum WAct WHCG
'Admiral Rodney' (HT)	EWar MGan MHay NBat NRog
Adolf Horstmann ® (HT)	MGan WWar
'Agatha' (G)	EBls
'Agatha Christie' (F/Cl)	CGre MMat SJus
'Agathe Incarnata' (GxD)	EWar
'Agnes' (Ru)	CCMG CSan EBls EBro ENot ETWh GCoc IHos MAus MGan MMat NSty SJus SPer SPla WAct WHCG

'Aimée Vibert' (Ra)	CBow CCMG EBls ETWh MAus SPer WAct WHCG WSHC
Air France ® (Min)	EWar
'Akebono' (HT)	MHay
'Alain Blanchard' (G)	CCor EBls MAus
N Alba Meidiland ® (GC)	EWar
x *alba*	CBow EBls NRog WWeb
§ – 'Alba Maxima' (A)	CCMG CCla CCor CHad CSan EBls ENot ETWh EWar GCoc MAus MMat NSty SFam SJus SPer WAct WHCG
– 'Alba Semiplena' (A)	CBow CCMG EBls EMFP ETWh EWar MAus NSty SJus SPer WAct WHCG
'Albéric Barbier' (Ra)	CCMG CHad CSam CSan EBls EBre EBro ETWh EWar IHos LBre LStr MAus MBri MBur MGan MHay MMat MMor NElm NRog NSty SHen SJus SPer SPla SRum WAct WHCG WWeb
'Albertine' (Ra)	Widely available
'Alchymist' (S/Cl)	CBow CCMG CCor CHad EBlo EBls EBro ETWh MAus MBri MMat SPer SPla WAct WHCG WSHC
Alec's Red ® (HT)	CB&S CCMG CDoC CGro CSan EBls ESha EWar GCoc IHos IJoh LPlm LStr MAus MBri MGan MHay MMat MMor NBar NBat NElm NRog SHen SPer WWeb
Alec's Red, Climbing ® (HT/Cl)	SPer
'Alexander Von Humbolt' (Cl)	MGan
Alexander ® (HT)	CDoC CGro CSan EBls ESha EWar GCoc IHos IJoh LGod LPlm LStr MAus MFry MGan MHay MMat MMor NBar NElm NRog SHen SPer WWar
¶ Alexandra Rose ® (S)	MRui
'Alexandre Girault' (Ra)	CCMG CCor EBls EBro ETWh MAus SJus SPer WHCG
'Alfred Colomb' (HP)	EBls
'Alfred de Dalmas' misapplied	See R. 'Mousseline'
'Alida Lovett' (Ra)	EBls MAus
'Alison Wheatcroft' (F)	SHen
§ 'Alister Stella Gray' (N)	CCMG EBls EMFP ETWh MAus MGan SFam SPer WAct WHCG WSHC
All in One ®	See R. 'Exploit'
'Allen Chandler' (HT/Cl)	EBls MAus NSty SPer WHCG
Allgold ® (F)	CB&S CGro EBls LStr MGan MMor NBar SHen SRum WStI WWeb
'Allgold, Climbing' (F/Cl)	CBow CCMG EBls ETWh EWar GCoc GGre IHos IJoh MGan MHay SRum WWeb
'Aloha' (HT/Cl)	CB&S CCMG CCla CCor CDoC CGro CSan EBls EBre ETWh IHos IOrc LBre MAus MBur MFry MGan MHay MMat MRui NBat NRog NSty SHen SJus SPer SRum WHCG
alpina	See R. ***pendulina***
Alpine Sunset ® (HT)	CCMG EBls ESha EWar GCoc LStr MAus MGan NBar NElm SPer SRum
altaica hort.	See R. ***pimpinellifolia*** 'Grandiflora'

Altissimo ® (Cl)	CCMG CHad EBls ETWh LPlm LStr MAus MBri MGan MHay MMat SPer
'Amadis' (Bs)	EBls MAus WHCG
Amanda ® (F)	LStr MBri WWar
'Amatsu-otome' (HT)	MHay
'Amazing Grace' (HT)	GGre
Amber Queen ® (F)	CDoC CGro CSan EBls ELan ESha EWar GCoc GGre IHos LGod LPlm LStr MAus MBri MBur MFry MGan MHay MMat MMor NBar NRog SHen SJus SPer SRum WWar
'Amberlight' (F)	MAus
Ambridge Rose ® (S)	EMFP MAus WWeb
'Amélia' (D)	See R. 'Celsiana'
'American Pillar' (Ra)	CB&S CCMG CDoC CGro CSan EBls EBre ESha ETWh EWar ISea LBre LGod LStr MAus MGan MHay MMat MMor NBar NBat NRog NSty SHen SJus SPer SRum WHCG
'Amy Robsart' (HSwb)	EBls ETWh MAus SJus
Anabell ® (F)	WWar
¶ 'Anaïs Ségalas' (G)	MAus
§ 'Andersonii' (*canina* x)	EBls ISea MAus WAct
'Andrea' (Min)	MHay
§ 'Andrewsii' (pimpinellifolia)	MAus WAct
§ 'Anemone' (Cl)	CCor EBls MAus SPer
anemoniflora	See R. x ***beanii***
anemonoïdes	See R. 'Anemone'
– 'Ramona'	See R. 'Ramona'
Angela Rippon ® (Min)	EBre EWar IHos LBre MFry MGan MHay MMat MRui SJus WStI
'Angela's Choice' (F)	MGan
'Angèle Pernet' (HT)	EBls MAus
'Angelina' (S)	EBls EWar GCoc MMat
Anisley Dickson ® (F)	CDoC GCoc IDic LGod LStr MGan MHay NBat SPer
'Ann Aberconway' (F)	CDoC MMat
'Anna de Diesbach' (HP)	EBls
Anna Ford ® (Min/F)	CDoC CGro CSan EWar GGre IHos LGod LPlm LStr MAus MGan MHay NBat SJus SRum WWar WWeb
Anna Livia ® (F)	IHos MMat
'Anna Olivier' (T)	EBls
'Anna Pavlova' (HT)	EBls
Anne Cocker ® (F)	CDoC EBls GCoc MGan MHay NBat
Anne Harkness ® (F)	CCMG CDoC EWar LStr MAus MGan MHay NBat NRog SJus SPer WWar
Anne Moore ® (Min)	MHay
'Anne of Geierstein' (HSwB)	EBls MAus MGan
'Anne Watkins' (HT)	EBls
Antique '89 ® (F/Cl)	MMat SJus
'Antoine Rivoire' (HT)	EBls
'Antonia d'Ormois' (G)	EBls
Anvil Sparks ® (HT)	MGan
Apothecary's Rose	See R. ***gallica officinalis***
'Apple Blossom' (Ra)	EBls EWar
'Apricot Nectar' (F)	LStr MAus MGan SPer
'Apricot Silk' (HT)	CB&S CCMG CGro EBls EWar IHos IJoh MAus MGan MHay NBar NRog SPer SRum WWeb

Apricot Sunblaze ® (Min)	CSan EBls EWar IHos NElm WWeb
Arcadian ® (F)	MMat WWar
'Archiduc Joseph' (T)	See R. 'Général Schablikine'
'Archiduchesse Elisabeth d'Autriche' (HP)	EBls WHCG
Arctic Sunrise ® (Min/GC)	MRui WWar
'Ardoisée de Lyon' (HP)	EBls
Ards Beauty ® (F)	IDic MGan
'Ards Rover' (HP/Cl)	EBls
'Arethusa' (Ch)	EBls ETWh
'Arizona Sunset' (Min)	MHay
¶ ***arkansana***	CCor
¶ – x ***moyesii***	CCor
§ – var. ***suffulta***	EBls WHCG
Armada ® (S)	GCoc MAus SPer
Arnold Greensitt ® (HT)	MHay
'Arthur Bell' (F)	CCla CMac CSan EBls EBre ESha EWar GGre IHos IJoh LBre LPlm LStr MAus MBur MGan MHay MMat NBar NBat NElm NRog SHen SPer SRum WWeb
'Arthur Bell, Climbing' (F/Cl)	NRog SJus SPer SRum
'Arthur de Sansal' (D/Po)	EBls MAus
'Arthur Hillier' (S)	CCor
'Arthur Scargill' (Min)	MHay
arvensis	CCor CKin EBls ETWh MAus SBra
'Ash Wednesday' (Cl)	EBls
'Assemblage des Beautés' (G)	EBls MAus SFam
'Astrid Späth Striped' (F)	EBls
Audrey Gardner ® (Min/Patio)	SRum
Audrey Wilcox ® (HT)	MFry
'August Seebauer' (F)	EBls MAus
'Auguste Gervais' (Ra)	EBls MAus SRum WHCG
'Augustine Guinoisseau' (HT)	EBls MAus
'Augustine Halem' (HT)	EBls
'Aunty Dora' (F)	EWar
Austrian Copper	See R. ***foetida*** 'Bicolor'
Austrian Yellow	See R. ***foetida***
'Autumn' (HT)	NRog
'Autumn Bouquet' (S)	EBls
'Autumn Delight' (HM)	EBls MAus WHCG
'Autumn Fire'	See R. 'Herbstfeuer'
'Autumn Sunlight' (HT/Cl)	EMFP EWar MBur MGan MHay SJus SPer
'Autumn Sunset' (S)	EBls
'Autumnalis' (Ra)	See R. 'Princesse de Nassau'
'Aviateur Blériot' (Ra)	EBls
Avocet ® (F)	CDoC MBri NBat SJus
¶ Avon ® (GC)	CCla EWar GCoc MBur MFry
'Awakening' (Cl)	EBls
'Ayrshire Splendens'	See R. 'Splendens'
'Baby Bio' (F)	CB&S MBri MGan NElm NRog SJus SPla SRum
'Baby Darling' (Min)	MAus MGan MRui
'Baby Faurax' (Poly)	MAus
'Baby Gold Star' (Min)	MAus MGan SPer
Baby Masquerade ® (Min)	CGro CSan EBre ELan EWar GCoc GGre IHos LAbb LBre LGod LPlm MAus MBur MGan MHay MMat MMor MRui NBar NElm NRog SJus WStI WWeb
'Baby Princess' (Min)	MRui
Baby Sunrise ® (Min)	MMat
'Bad Neuenahr' (Cl)	MGan
'Bakewell Scots Briar' (pimpinellifolia)	NSty
'Ballerina' (HM)	Widely available
'Baltimore Belle' (Ra)	EBls EWar MAus
banksiae (Ra)	CGre SPer
– ***alba***	See R. ***b. banksiae***
§ – var. ***banksiae*** (Ra/d)	CBot EMFP ERea MAus SHil
– 'Lutea' (Ra/d)	CB&S CCMG CCla CGre CHad CSam CTro EBls ELan EMFP ERea ETWh ISea LGre MAus MPar NSti NSty SBra SHil SMad SPer SPla STre SUsu WAct WHCG WSHC WWat
– 'Lutescens' (Ra)	SBra SHil
– var. ***normalis*** (Ra)	CBot MAus NSti SHil
Bantry Bay ® (HT/Cl)	CCMG CSan EBls EBro EWar LStr MGan MMat SJus SRum WWeb
'Barbara Richards' (HT)	EBls MAus
Barkarole ® (HT)	EWar LStr WWar WWeb
'Baron de Bonstetten' (HP)	EBls
'Baron de Wassenaer' (Ce/Mo)	EBls MGan
'Baron Girod de l'Ain' (HP)	CCMG EBls EBro EMFP ETWh IHos MAus NSty SPer SPla WHCG
Baron Sunblaze ®	See R. Baron Meillandina ®
'Baroness Rothschild' (HP)	See R. 'Baronne Adolph de Rothschild'
– (HT)	See R. Baronne Edmond de Rothschild ®
§ 'Baronne Adolph de Rothschild' (HP)	CCMG EMFP ETWh IHos IOrc MGan WHCG
'Baronne de Rothschild' (HP)	See R. 'Baronne Adolph de Rothschild'
Baronne Edmond de Rothchild ® (HT)	CSan EWar
'Baronne Henriette de Snoy' (T)	EBls
'Baronne Prévost' (HP)	EBls MAus SFam WAct WHCG
'Bashful' (Poly)	MGan
§ x ***beanii*** (Ra)	EMon
'Beauté' (HT)	EBls MAus MGan NElm
Beautiful Britain ® (F)	CSan EBls GCoc GGre IDic IHos LGod LStr MAus MBri MGan MHay NBar NRog SHen SJus SRum WWar
'Beauty of Rosemawr' (T/Cl)	EBls
¶ Belfast Belle ® (HT)	IDic WWar
'Belle Amour' (D x A)	CCor EBls MAus NSty WHCG
'Belle Blonde' (HT)	MGan NElm SPer
'Belle de Crécy' (G)	CBow CCMG CDoC EBls ETWh EWar GCoc IOrc MAus MMat NSty SFam SJus SPer SPla WAct WHCG

'Belle des Jardins'	See R. 'Centifolia Variegata'
'Belle Isis' (G)	CCMG CCor EBls MAus SPer
'Belle Lyonnaise' (T/Cl)	EBls
'Belle Poitevine' (Ru)	EBls MAus NSty WAct
'Belle Portugaise' (Cl)	EBls MAus
Belle Story ® (S)	MAus SPer
Belle Sunblaze ® (Min)	NElm
'Belvedere' (Ra)	MAus
'Bengal Beauty'	ELan WWat
'Bennett's Seedling' (Ra)	MAus
Benson and Hedges Gold ® (HT)	EWar MGan
Benson and Hedges Special ® (Min)	ELan MHay MMat
Bettina ® (HT)	MAus MGan NRog
Bettina, Climbing ® (HT/Cl)	EBls MAus SRum
Betty Driver ® (F)	MBri MGan SPer
'Betty Prior' (F)	GCoc MGan
'Betty Uprichard' (HT)	EBls MAus NSty
'Beyreuth' (S)	MGan
'Bharami' (Min)	MGan
Bianco ® (Patio/Min)	CSan GCoc MAus NBat SJus
Bibi Mezoon ® (S)	CCMG CDoC EWar IHos MAus MRui NBar SPer
Biddulph Grange ® (S)	MFry WWar
§ ***biebersteinii***	EBls
'Big Chief' (HT)	LGod NRog
Big Purple ® (HT)	SRum WWar
'Bishop Darlington' (HM)	EBls
'Bit o'Sunshine' (Min)	MGan MMor
'Black Beauty' (HT)	IJoh MAus NBar
'Black Ice' (F)	MGan SRum
'Black Jack' (Ce)	See R. 'Tour de Malakoff'
Black Jack ® (Min)	MHay
'Black Prince' (HP)	EBls
'Blairii Number One' (Bb)	EBls NSty
'Blairii Number Two' (Bb/Cl)	CCor EBls ETWh MAus NSty SPer WAct WHCG WSHC
'Blanche de Vibert' (DPo)	EBls MAus
'Blanche Double de Coubert' (Ru)	CCMG CCla CDoC CHad CSam EBls EHar ELan ENot ETWh EWar GCoc IHos IOrc LHol LStr MAus MFry MMat NElm NRog NSty SJus SPer SPla SRum WAct WHCG WWeb
'Blanche Moreau' (CeMo)	CCMG CSan EBls EBro IHos MAus MGan NElm NSty SPer WAct WHCG
'Blanchefleur' (Ce)	CCor EBls IHos MAus NSty WHCG
blanda	EBls
Blessings ® (HT)	Widely available
Blessings, Climbing ® (HT/Cl)	EBls
'Bleu Magenta' (Ra)	CCMG EBls EWar MAus WHCG
'Bloomfield Abundance' (Poly)	CCMG CCor CSan EBls MAus MMat NSty SPer SRum WHCG WWat
'Blossomtime' (Cl)	NRog SPer
'Blue Diamond' (HT)	MGan
Blue Moon ® (HT)	CGro CSan EBls EBre EBro ELan ESha EWar GGre IHos IJoh LBre LGod LPlm MAus MBur MFry MGan MHay MMor NBar NElm NRog SHen SPer SRum WWeb
'Blue Moon, Climbing' (HT/Cl)	MBur MGan SHen
Blue Parfum ® (HT)	MAus
Blue Peter ® (Min)	IHos MFry MRui
'Blush Boursault' (Bs)	EBls MAus
'Blush Damask' (D)	CCMG CCor EBls
'Blush Noisette'	See R. 'Noisette Carnée'
'Blush Rambler' (Ra)	CCMG EBls ETWh EWar MAus SPer WHCG
¶ 'Blushing Lucy' (Cl)	WSHC
'Bob Collard' (F)	SRum
'Bob Woolley' (HT)	NBat
'Bobbie James' (Ra)	CBow CCMG CHad CSan EBls EBre ETWh EWar IHos LBre LStr MAus MGan MHay MMat NBat NSty SJus SPer SRum WAct WHCG
'Bobby Charlton' (HT)	MFry MGan MHay NRog
'Bobolink' (Min)	GGre MGan
'Bold Bells' (S)	MAus
'Bon Silène' (T)	EBls
Bonfire Night ® (F)	CGro MGan MMat
Bonica ® (GC)	CCMG CCor CDoC EBls EBre ELan ENot GCoc IHos LBre LGod LStr MAus MBur MGan MMat SHen SJus SPer SRum
'Bonn' (HM)	CB&S MAus MGan NRog
'Bonnie Scotland' (HT)	MBur MGan
Bonsoir ® (HT)	MAus MGan MHay
'Border Coral' (F)	NRog
'Born Free' (Min)	MBur SJus
'Botzaris' (D)	CCMG EBls SFam
'Boule de Nanteuil' (G)	CCor EBls GCoc
'Boule de Neige' (Bb)	CCMG CCla CCor CHad CSan EBls EMFP ENot ETWh LHol LStr MAus MBur MMat MRav NSty SFam SJus SPer SPla WAct WHCG WWeb
'Bouquet d'Or' (N)	EBls MAus WHCG
'Bourbon Queen' (Bb)	CCMG CCor EBls ETWh MAus NSty WHCG
¶ Bow Bells ® (S)	CBow MAus
Boys' Brigade ® (Patio)	CDoC CGro EWar GCoc MAus MGan NBat SJus WWeb
§ ***bracteata***	ESha LGre MAus WWat
Breath of Life ® (HT/Cl)	CCMG CGro CSan ELan ESha EWar GGre LGod LStr MAus MBri MFry MGan MHay NBar NBat SJus SPer SPla SRum
Bredon ® (S)	CCMG MAus MBri SPer
'Breeze Hill' (Ra)	EBls MAus
§ 'Brenda Colvin' (Ra)	CBot MAus SJus
'Brennus' (Ch x)	EBls
'Briarcliff' (HT)	EBls
Bright Smile ® (F/Patio)	CDoC GCoc IDic LStr MAus MFry MGan MHay MMat NBar SPer
Bright Spark ® (Min)	MFry MRui
'Brindis' (F/Cl)	MGan
'Bristol Post' (HT)	CSan
Brother Cadfael ® (S)	EWar MAus MRui NBar SPer
Brown Velvet ® (F)	MMat WAct
'Brownie' (F)	MAus
'Browsholme Rose' (Ra)	NSty
§ ***brunonii*** (Ra)	EBls GTou MAus

§ – 'La Mortola' (Ra)	GCal MAus SPer WHCG
Buck's Fizz ® (F)	EWar GCoc MBur MGan MMat NBar
'Buff Beauty' (HM)	Widely available
'Bullata'	See R. x ***centifolia*** 'Bullata'
§ 'Burgundiaca' (G)	CBow CCMG CCor EBls ETWh MAus MPar WAct WHCG
Burgundian Rose	See R. 'Burgundiaca'
'Burma Star' (F)	ESha EWar GCoc
Burnet, Double Pink	See R. ***pimpinellifolia*** 'Double Pink'
Burnet, Double White	See R. ***pimpinellifolia*** 'Double White'
Bush Baby ® (Min)	LGod LStr MRui NBat WStI
Buttons ® (Min/Patio)	IDic IHos LStr MBur MFry MHay SJus
By Appointment ® (F)	CCMG GCoc SJus
'C F Meyer'	See R. 'Conrad Ferdinand Meyer'
'Café' (F)	MAus
'Cairngorm' (F)	ESha GCoc
'Caledonian' (HT)	NBat
californica	MAus WHCG
– 'Plena'	See R. ***nutkana*** 'Plena'
'Callisto' (HM)	EBro ETWh EWar MAus WHCG
'Camaïeux' (G)	CCMG CCor CSan EBls EBro ETWh MAus MMat SPer WAct WHCG
'Camélia Rose' (Cl)	EBls
'Cameo' (Poly)	EBls ETWh MAus MGan
'Canary Bird'	See R. ***xanthina*** 'C.B'
Candy Rose ® (S)	EWar NBar NElm SHen
canina	CKin CPer LBuc MAus MHew NSal NWea WMou
– 'Abbotswood'	See R. 'Abbotswood'
– 'Andersonii'	See R. 'Andersonii'
'Cantabrigiensis' (S)	CSam EBls ENot GCoc MAus NRog SPer WAct WWat WWeb
'Canterbury' (S)	MAus
Can-Can ® (HT)	CDoC EWar NBar SJus SRum
'Capitaine Basroger' (Mo)	EBls MAus
'Capitaine John Ingram' (Mo)	CCor CSan EBls ETWh EWar MAus NSty SFam SPer SPla
'Captain Christy, Climbing' (HT/Cl)	EBls MAus
Captain Cook ® (F)	NBat
'Captain Hayward' (HP)	EBls
'Cardinal de Richelieu' (G)	CCMG CDoC CHad EBls EBro EMFP ETWh EWar GCoc IOrc MAus MFry MMat NSty SFam SJus SPer WAct WHCG
Cardinal Hume ® (S)	EBls LStr MAus MGan MHay SPer
Carefree Beauty ® (S)	EWar
'Carmen' (Ra)	EBls MAus
§ 'Carmenetta' (S)	EBls EWar
'Carol'	See R. 'Carol Amling'
carolina	LHop
Caroline Davison ® (F)	MAus
'Caroline Testout'	See R. 'Madame Caroline Testout'
§ Casino ® (HT/Cl)	CCMG CMac CSan EBls EBre ESha EWar IJoh LBre LPlm MAus MBur MFry MGan MHay MMor MRui NElm SPer SRum WStI WWeb
Catherine Cookson ® (HT)	NBat
'Catherine Mermet' (T)	EBls MAus
'Catherine Seyton' (HSwB)	EBls
caudata	CCor
§ 'Cécile Brünner' (Poly)	CBow CCMG EBls EBro EMFP ENot ETWh EWar GCoc LHol MAus MGan MMat MPar NRar NRog NSty SFam SHen SJus SPer SPla SRum WHCG WWat
'Cécile Brünner, Climbing' (Poly/Cl)	CBow CCMG CHad CSan EBls EFol ETWh LStr MAus MHay MMat NSty SJus SPer WAct WHCG WSHC WWat
§ 'Cécile Brünner, White' (Poly)	EBls LGre MAus WHCG
§ 'Céleste' (A)	CB&S CCMG CCla CSan EBls EBro ELan EMFP ENot ETWh GCoc IHos MAus MFry MHay MMat MPar MRui NSty SFam SJus SPer SRum WAct WHCG WWeb
'Celestial'	See R. 'Céleste'
'Célina' (Mo)	CCor EBls MGan
'Céline Forestier' (N)	CCMG EBls ETWh MAus SFam SPer WAct WHCG
§ 'Celsiana' (D)	CCMG CCor EBls EWar MAus NBar SFam SPer WAct WHCG
Centenaire de Lourdes ® (F)	EBls
§ 'Centifolia Variegata' (Ce)	EBls MGan WHCG
§ x ***centifolia***	CBow CCMG EBls ETWh GCoc IOrc LHol NRog SJus WAct WHCG
§ – 'Bullata'	EBls MAus SFam
§ – 'Cristata'	CBow CCla CSan EBls EMFP ENot ETWh EWar GCoc IHos MMat NBar NRog SFam SJus SPer SPla WHCG WHer
§ – 'Muscosa'	CBow CCMG CDoC EBls EMFP ENot ETWh EWar GCoc IHos IOrc MFry MGan MMat NRog NSty SFam SJus WAct WHCG WWeb
– 'Parvifolia' (G)	See R. 'Burgundiaca'
'Centurion' (F)	MMat
cerasocarpa (Ra)	CCor ETWh
'Cerise Bouquet' (S)	CCMG CCla EBls EMFP ETWh MAus MMat NSty SJus SPer WHCG WWeb
Cha Cha ® (Patio/Min)	MBur
'Chami' (HM)	EBro
Champagne Cocktail ® (F)	EHar EWar GCoc NBat WWar WWeb
'Champion' (HT)	MAus MFry MHay NElm
'Champneys' Pink Cluster' (Ch x)	EBls WKif
Champs Elysées ® (HT)	MGan
'Chanelle' (F)	CSan EBls GCoc MAus MGan NRog SPer
Chapeau de Napoléon	See R. x ***centifolia*** 'Cristata'
'Chaplin's Pink Climber' (Cl)	CBow EBls EBro ETWh EWar MGan MHay
Chardonnay ® (HT)	MBri

Charles Austin ® (S) CCMG MAus MBri NSty SJus SPer WHCG
Charles Aznavour ® (F) EWar SJus
'Charles de Mills' (G) CCMG CCla CCor CHad CSan EBls EBro EMFP ENot ETWh MAus MFry MHay MMat NBar NSty SFam SJus SPer SPla SRum WAct WHCG WWeb
'Charles Gater' (HP) EBls
'Charles Lefèbvre' (HP) EBls
'Charles Mallerin' (HT) EBls
Charles Rennie Mackintosh ® (S) CCla EBlo EWar MAus WHCG
Charleston ® (F) MGan
Charleston '88 ® (HT) EWar SHen
'Charley's Aunt' (HT) MHay
Charmian ® (S) CCMG MAus
¶ 'Charter 700' (F) MFry
'Château de Clos-Vougeot' (HT) MGan
'Château de Clos-Vougeot, Climbing' (HT/Cl) EBls EBro MAus
Chaucer ® (S) CCMG MAus MBri
Chelsea Pensioner ® (Min) LPlm MMat
Cherry Brandy ® (HT) MBur MFry MGan SRum WWar
'Cherry Pie' (HT) MGan
'Cherryade' (S) MGan
'Cherryade, Climbing' (HT/Cl) MGan
'Cheshire Life' (HT) CSan ESha GGre LGod MAus MBur MFry MGan MMor NBar SHen SRum WStI WWeb
'Chianti' (S) CCla EBls MAus MBri NSty SPer
Chicago Peace ® (HT) CB&S CCMG EBls ESha EWar GCoc GGre IHos IJoh LGod LPlm LStr MAus MBur MFry MGan MMor NElm NRog SHen SRum WStI WWeb
Chinatown ® (F/S) Widely available
chinensis 'Mutabilis' See R. x ***odorata*** 'Mutabilis'
– 'Old Blush' See R. x ***odorata*** 'Pallida'
'Chloris' (A) EBls
'Chorus Girl' (F) MGan
Chorus ® (F) CSan
Christian Dior ® (HT) EBls MGan
'Christine Gandy' (HT) MGan
'Christine, Climbing' (HT/Cl) MAus
¶ 'Christopher' (HT) GCoc
'Chrysler Imperial' (HT) EBls MAus MGan NElm
Cider Cup ® (Min/Patio) CDoC ESha EWar GGre IDic MBur MFry NBat SJus SPer WWar
'Cinderella' (Min) CHal GAri MGan
cinnamomea See R. ***majalis***
'Circus' (F) MAus MGan
'City Light' (Patio) LGod MMat
'City of Bath' (HT) MHay
City of Belfast ® (F) CGro EBls IHos MAus MGan NElm
City of Birmingham ® (S/HT) MMat
'City of Glasgow' (HT) MHay
'City of Gloucester' (HT) MGan MHay
'City of Leeds' (F) EBls ESha EWar GGre MAus MGan MHay MMat NBar NRog SHen SPer WStI WWeb
City of London ® (F) CCMG ESha EWar LStr MBur MHay
'City of Portsmouth' (F) CB&S MBur MGan
'City of Worcester' (HT) MHay
'City of York' (Ra) EBls
Clair Matin ® (S/Cl) CCor CHad EBls ETWh MAus SPer SPla
'Claire Jacquier' (N) CCMG EBls MAus SFam SPer WHCG
Claire Rayner ® (F/Patio) LPlm MRui
Claire Rose ® (S) CCMG CSam EWar IHos MAus NBar SJus SPer
Claire Scotland ® (Patio) GCoc
Clarissa ® (Min) IHos MAus SPer
'Clementina Carbonieri' (T) EBls
'Cloth of Gold' (N) EBls MAus
Clydebank Centenary ® (F/Min) GCoc
'Clytemnestra' (HM) EBro
'Coalite Flame' (HT) MHay
Cocktail ® (S) EBls MGan
Colibre ® (Min) LGod MFry MGan
§ Colibre '79 ® (Min) CSan ELan EWar GGre LStr MHay MRui WStI WWar
Colibre '80 ® See R. Colibre '79 ®
'Colonel Fabvier' EBls
'Colonial White' See R. 'Sombreuil, Climbing'
Colorama ® (HT) MBri
'Columbian' (Cl) SPer
colvillei CCor
'Commandant Beaurepaire' (Bb) CCor EBls MAus NSty SFam SPer WHCG
Common Moss See R. x ***centifolia*** 'Muscosa'
'Compassion' (HT/Cl) Widely available
§ 'Complicata' (G) CBow CCMG CSam CSan EBls EBro ETWh EWar LHol MAus MBri MGan MMat MRav NRog NSty SFam SJus SPer WAct WHCG WWat
'Comte de Chambord' See R. 'Madame Knorr'
'Comtesse Cécile de Chabrillant' (HP) EBls MAus
'Comtesse de Lacépède' See R. 'Du Maître d'Ecole'
'Comtesse de Murinais' (D/M) CCMG CCor EBls MAus SFam
'Comtesse du Cayla' (Ch) MAus
'Comtesse Vandal' (HT) MAus
'Comtesse Vandal, Climbing' (HT/Cl) EBls MAus
¶ 'Conchita' (Poly) ETWh
§ 'Conditorum' (G) EBls SFam
Congratulations ® (HT) CSan EWar GCoc GGre IHos LGod LPlm MFry MGan MMat NElm SJus SPer WWar
§ 'Conrad Ferdinand Meyer' (Ru) CCMG EBls IHos MAus MGan NSty SHen SPer SRum WAct
Conservation ® (Min/Patio) ESha GCoc NBat
¶ 'Constance Fettes' (F) GCoc
Constance Spry ® (S/Cl) CCMG CCla CGro CHad CSan EBls EBre ENot ETWh EWar GCoc IOrc LBre LStr MAus MBri MBur MGan MMat MMor MRui NSty SJus SPer SRum WHCG WWeb

Name	Suppliers
'Cooper's Burmese'	See R. ***laevigata*** 'Cooperi'
'Copenhagen' (S)	EBls MAus MBri MBur
'Copper Delight' (F)	NRog
Copper Pot ® (F)	MBur MGan SPer
'Coral Cluster' (Poly)	EBls MAus MGan
Coral Dawn ® (HT/Cl)	EBls MAus MFry MRui
Coral Reef ® (Patio)	GCoc GGre
'Coral Satin' (Cl)	MGan
'Coralie' (D)	EBls
'Coralin' (Min)	LGod MGan MRui
'Cornelia' (HM)	Widely available
'Coronation Gold' (F)	ESha GCoc
'Coronet' (F)	WAct
'Corso' (HT)	GCoc
'Coryana'	EBls
I 'Corylus' (Ru)	See R. 'Hazel Le Rougetel'
corymbifera	EBls
corymbulosa	EBls
'Cosimo Ridolfi' (G)	EBls
'Cottage Maid'	See R. 'Centifolia Variegata'
Cottage Rose ® (S)	CBow CDoC MAus MRui
Country Heritage ® (HT)	SHen
Country Lady ® (HT)	MBur SJus
Country Living ® (S)	CBow CCMG EWar IHos MAus MRui NBar WHCG
'Country Maid' (F)	EWar
'Coupe d'Hébé' (Bb)	EBls ETWh MAus
'Cramoisi Picotée' (G)	CCor EBls MAus
'Cramoisi Supérieur' (Ch)	CCor EBls EBro ETWh MAus WHCG
'Cramoisi Supérieur Grimpant' (Ch/Cl)	EBls WHCG
Crathes Castle ® (F)	GCoc
'Crépuscule' (N)	EBls WHCG
'Cressida' (S)	CCMG MAus
Crested Moss	See R. x ***centifolia*** 'Cristata'
Cricri ® (Min)	MAus MGan
Crimson Cascade ® (Cl)	EWar MFry SJus
'Crimson Conquest' (HT/Cl)	EBls
'Crimson Damask'	See R. ***gallica officinalis***
Crimson Gem ® (Min)	MGan NBat
'Crimson Globe' (Mo)	MGan
'Crimson Glory' (HT)	EBls MAus MBur MGan
'Crimson Glory, Climbing' (HT/Cl)	EBls EBre ETWh GCoc LBre MAus MGan MHay NRog SRum
'Crimson Rambler' (Ra)	MAus
'Crimson Shower' (Ra)	EMFP ETWh EWar GGre IHos LGod LPlm MAus MGan MMat NBar NRog SPer WStI
'Cristata'	See R. ***centifolia*** 'Cristata'
'Cuisse de Nymphe'	See R. 'Great Maiden's Blush'
'Cupid' (HT/Cl)	CCMG EBls ETWh EWar MAus
Cymbeline ® (S)	MAus SPer SRum
'Cynthia Brooke' (HT)	EBls
'DAguesseau' (G)	EBls EBro MAus SPer WHCG
Daily Express ® (HT)	MFry
'Daily Mail'	See R. 'Madame Edouard Herriot'
¶ Daily Post ® (F)	MFry
Daily Sketch ® (F)	MGan SRum
'Dainty Bess' (HT)	CHad EBls EBro MAus MRav NSty
Dainty Dinah ® (Min/Patio)	GCoc MAus
'Dainty Maid' (F)	MAus
'Dairy Maid' (F)	MAus
'Daisy Hill' (***macrantha*** x)	CCMG EBls
x ***damascena bifera***	See R. x ***d. semperflorens***
§ x ***damascena semperflorens***	CCMG CSan EBls EBro ETWh IHos WHCG
N x ***damascena*** 'Trigintipetala' hort.	See R. 'Professeur Emile Perrot'
§ x ***damascena versicolor***	CCMG CGro CSan EBls ENot ETWh GCoc IHos LHol MGan NSty WAct WWeb
'Dame Edith Helen' (HT)	EBls
Dame of Sark ® (F)	ESha
Dame Wendy ® (F)	EWar LGod MAus MBri MGan MMat SJus WWar
'Danaë' (HM)	CCMG EBls EBro ETWh MAus SJus WHCG
'Danny Boy' (HT/Cl)	SRum
Danse des Sylphes ® (Cl)	EBls MHay NBat SJus
'Danse du Feu' (Cl)	Widely available
'Daphne Gandy' (F)	MGan
'Dapple Dawn' (S)	MAus MBri NBar SPer WHCG
Darling Flame ® (Min)	CGro CSan EBre ELan EWar GCoc GGre LBre MFry MGan MHay MMat MRui NElm WStI WWar
¶ 'Dart's Defender'	SLPl
David Whitfield ® (R)	MGan
davidii	EBls MAus
davurica	CCor
¶ – DF 90010	EBul
¶ 'Dawn Chorus' (HT)	EWar GCoc LGod LPlm LStr MBri MBur MFry MGan MMat SJus
'Daybreak' (HM)	EBls EBro MAus NRog WAct WHCG
¶ Daylight ® (F)	MBur
§ 'De Meaux' (Ce)	CBow CCMG CSan EBls EMFP ENot ETWh MAus MMat NSty SJus SPer WHCG
§ 'De Meaux, White' (Ce)	CCMG EBls MAus
§ 'De Rescht' (DPo)	CCMG CCla CCor CSan EBls EBro ETWh LHol MAus MBri MGan MHay SPer SPla WAct WHCG
'Dearest' (F)	CB&S CCMG CCla CDoC EWar GGre IJoh LStr MAus MBri MGan MHay MMor NElm NRog SHen SPla SRum WStI WWeb
'Debutante' (Ra)	CCMG EBls MAus
Deb's Delight ® (F)	ELan EWar GCoc MFry WWeb
'Deep Secret' (HT)	CCMG CDoC CGro CSan EBre ESha EWar GCoc GGre LBre LPlm MBur MFry MGan MMor NRog SHen SJus SPer SRum WWeb
'Delambre' (DPo)	EBls MAus
'Dembrowski' (HP)	EBls
Denman ® (HT)	SJus
'Dentelle de Malines' (S)	MAus MBri
'Deschamps' (N)	EBls
'Desprez à Fleurs Jaunes' (N)	CBow CCMG EBls ETWh MAus SPer WHCG WSHC

'Deuil de Paul Fontaine' (Mo) EBls
'Devon Maid' (Cl) WWar
'Devoniensis, Climbing' (T/Cl) CCMG CPou EBls MAus
¶ Diadem ® (F) MFry
'Diamond Jubilee' (HT) EBls MAus MHay
'Dian' (Min) SJus
'Dicbar' See R. Memento ®
'Dickson's Flame' (F) MGan
Die Welt ® (HT) MHay NBat
'Dimples' (F) NSty
'Diorama' (HT) IJoh MAus MGan NElm NRog SRum
'Directeur Alphand' (HP) EBls
Disco Dancer ® (F) IDic IHos WWar
'Doc' (Poly) MGan
'Docteur Andry' (HP) EBls
'Docteur Grill' (T) EBls MAus
'Doctor A J Verhage' (HT) MGan
Doctor Dick ® (HT) GCoc MHay NBat
'Doctor Eckener' (Ru) EBls MAus MGan
'Doctor Edward Deacon' (HT) EBls
Doctor Goldberg ® (HT) MGan
Doctor Jackson ® (S) MAus
'Doctor John Snow' (HT) MGan
Doctor McAlpine ® (F/Patio) GCoc LStr SRum
'Doctor W Van Fleet' (Ra/Cl) EBls MAus WSHC
Dollie B ® (Min) MRui
'Don Charlton' (HT) NBat
'Don Juan' (Cl) MGan
'Doncasteri' EBls MAus
'Dopey' (Poly) MGan
'Doreen' (HT) NRog
Doris Tysterman ® (HT) CDoC CGro CSan EBls EBre EBro ESha EWar GGre IHos IJoh LBre LGod LPlm LStr MAus MBur MFry MGan MHay MMor NBar NBat NElm NRog SHen SRum WWar WWeb
'Dorothy Perkins' (Ra) CB&S CCMG CDoC CGro CSan EBls EBre ETWh EWar GGre IJoh LBre LPlm LStr MAus MGan MMat MMor MRui NBar NElm NRog NSty SJus SPer SRum WAct WHCG WWeb
'Dorothy Wheatcroft' (F) ESha IHos MGan MHay MMor SHen SRum WWeb
Dortmund ® (HScB/Cl) EBls ETWh LPlm MAus MGan MHay MMat MMor SPer
Double Delight ® (HT) CGro CSan ELan ESha GCoc GGre IJoh LStr MBri MGan MHay NElm NRog SJus SPer SRum WWar
'Double Joy' (Min) MBur MHay
Dove ® (S) MAus MBri NBar
Dream Girl ® (Cl) MAus NSty
'Dream Time' (HT) MHay NBat
'Dream Waltz' (F) MHay
'Dreamglo' (Min) MHay NBat
'Dreaming Spires' (Cl) IHos MMat SJus SPer WAct
Dreamland ® (F) MFry MGan NElm
'Dresden Doll' (Min/Mo) EBls MAus MRui SPer
Drummer Boy ® (F/Patio) CSan ESha GCoc GGre LStr NBat NElm WWar
§ 'Du Maître d'Ecole' (G) CCMG CCor EBls ETWh MAus
Dublin Bay ® (Cl) CDoC CSan EBls ESha EWar IHos IJoh LGod LPlm LStr MBri MFry MGan MHay MMat NBar NRog SPer WWar
'Duc de Fitzjames' (G) EBls
'Duc de Guiche' (G) CCMG CCor CSan EBls ETWh MAus SFam SPer WHCG
'Duchess of Portland' See R. 'Portlandica'
§ Duchess of York ® (F/Patio) CDoC IDic LGod MBur
'Duchesse de Buccleugh' (G) CCor EBls MAus
§ 'Duchesse de Montebello' (G) CCMG CCor EBls ETWh MAus SPer SRms WHCG
'Duchesse de Rohan' (CexHP) EBls
'Duchesse de Verneuil' (Mo) EBls MAus SFam
'Duchesse d'Albe' (T) EBls
'Duchesse d'Angoulême' (G) CCMG CCor EBls ETWh MAus NSty
'Duchesse d'Auerstädt' (N) EBls
¶ 'Dukat' (Cl) EWar
Duke Meillandina ® (Min) MRui
'Duke of Edinburgh' (HP) EBls MAus
'Duke of Wellington' (HP) EBls WHCG
'Duke of Windsor' (HT) CDoC GGre IHos IJoh MGan NElm NRog SPer SRum
'Duke of York' (Ch) EBls
Duke Sunblaze See R. Duke Meillandina ®
'Dundee Rambler' (Ra) EBls MAus
§ 'Dunwich Rose' (pimpinellifolia) CCMG CCor EBlo EBls ENot MAus MBri MMat SPer WHCG
'Dupontii' (S) EBls MAus SFam SPer WWat
'Dupuy Jamain' (HP) EBls WAct WHCG
'Durham Prince Bishop' (HT) NBat
'Dusky Maiden' (F) CHad EBls MAus
'Dusterlohe' (R) CCor EBls
Dutch Gold ® (HT) CDoC CGro EWar LStr MAus MFry MGan MHay NElm NRog SHen SJus SPer
'Dwarf King' See R. 'Zwergkönig'
Dwarf Queen '82 ® / Zwerkönigin '82 (Min) MGan
'E H Morse' See R. 'Ernest H Morse'
'Easlea's Golden Rambler' (Ra) EBls EBre ETWh LBre MAus NSty SJus WHCG
'Easter Morning' (Min) CSan ELan GGre LGod MAus MBur MGan MRui NBar NBat NElm SPer WWeb
'Eblouissant' (Poly) MGan
ecae EBls MAus
– 'Helen Knight' See R. 'Helen Knight'
'Eclair' (HP) EBls

'Eddie's Jewel' (moyesii x) EBls MAus MGan NSty
Eden Rose ® (HT) EBls IHos MGan SRum
Eden Rose '88 ® (HT/Cl) EWar SHen SJus SPer
'Edith Bellenden' (HSwB) EBls
Edith Holden ® (F) LGod MAus MBri SJus WAct WWar WWeb
eglanteria CCMG CCor CKin CSan EBls ENot ETWh GPoy LBuc LHol MAus MHew MMat SHer SPer WAct WMou WWye
'Egyptian Treasure' (F) MGan
'Elegance' (HT/Cl) EBls MAus MGan SPer
§ ***elegantula*** CCor GAbr ILis NSal
§ – 'Persetosa' CCMG EBls EMFP ENot MAus MPar SPer WAct WHCG
§ Elina ® (HT) CCMG CSan ESha EWar IDic IHos LGod LStr MAus MFry MGan MHay MMat NElm NRog SPer WWar
Elizabeth Harkness ® (HT) EBls EWar MAus MGan SPer
Elizabeth Heather Grierson ® (HT/Cl) MMat
Elizabeth of Glamis ® (F) CCMG CDoC CGro EBls EBro ELan ESha EWar GCoc GGre IHos IJoh LStr MAus MBri MFry MGan MMat MMor NElm NRog SHen SPer SRum WWeb
'Elizabeth Philp' (F) LPlm
'Ellen Poulsen' (Poly) CBow MGan
'Ellen Willmott' (HT) EBls ETWh MAus
Ellen ® (S) MAus MBri SJus SPer
'Elmshorn' (S) CB&S CCMG CDoC CSan ENot MGan MMat WHCG
¶ 'Elsa' (HT) SRum
Elsie Warren ® (F) NBat
Emanuel ® (S) CCMG MAus SJus SPer
'Embassy' (HT) MHay
'Emily Gray' (Ra) CCMG CGro CSan EBls EBre EBro ETWh EWar IHos LBre LStr MAus MBur MGan MHay MMat MMor NBar NElm NRog NSty SPer SPla SRum WHCG WSHC
'Emma Wright' (HT) MAus
'Emmerdale' (F) ESha WStI
'Empereur du Maroc' (HP) CCMG EBls MAus MMat NSty WHCG
'Empress Josephine' See R. x ***francofurtana***
'Empress Michiko' (HT) EWar IDic MBur
Ena Baxter ® (HT) GCoc
'Ena Harkness' (HT) CGro CMac CSan EBls EBro ELan EWar GGre LStr MBur MGan NElm NRog SHen SRum WStI WWeb
'Ena Harkness, Climbing' (HT/Cl) CGro CMac EBls GCoc GGre IHos MAus MBri MBur MGan MHay NRog SPer SRum WStI WWeb
§ 'Enfant de France' (HP) EBls
English Elegance ® (S) MAus
'English Estates' (HT) NBat
English Garden ® (S) CAbP CBow CCMG CCla CSan EBre EMFP ENot ETWh EWar LBre LStr MAus MBri MMat MRui NBar SJus SPer WAct WWeb
'English Miss' (F) CBow CCMG CDoC CSan EBls EWar IHos LStr MAus MFry MGan SJus SPer SRum WStI WWeb
'Eos' (***moyesii*** x) EBls MAus
'Erfurt' (HM) CCMG EBls ETWh MAus NSty SJus SPer SPla SRms WHCG
'Ernest H Morse' (HT) EBls ESha EWar GCoc GGre IHos IJoh LStr MAus MBur MFry MGan MHay MMor NElm NRog SHen SPer SRum WWeb
'Ernest H Morse, Climbing' (HT/Cl) MGan NElm
Eroica ® (HT) EBro NRog WWeb
Escapade ® (F) EBls MAus MGan
Essex ® (GC) CCor EBre ENot EWar IHos LBre MAus MGan MMat SPer WWar
Esther Ofarim ® (F) EWar
Esther's Baby ® (Patio) MAus
Estima ® (Min) MFry MRui
Ethel Austin ® (F) MFry
'Etoile de Hollande, Climbing' (HT/Cl) CBow CCMG CSam CSan EBls EBre ETWh GCoc LBre LHol LStr MAus MRav NRog NSty SHen SJus SPer SRum WAct WHCG
'Etoile de Lyon' (T) EBls
'Etude' (Cl) CSan
'Eugène Fürst' (HP) EBls WHCG
'Eugénie Guinoisseau' (Mo) EBls EWar
Euphrates ® (persica x) MAus MGan
Europeana ® (F) CGro MAus MGan MHay SRum
'Eva' (HM) EBls
'Evangeline' (Ra) EBls MAus NSty SPer WAct
Evelyn Fison ® (Irish Wonder ®) (F) CB&S CDoC ELan EWar GCoc GGre IHos IJoh LGod LStr MAus MBur MGan MHay MMor NElm NRog SHen SPla SRum WWeb
Evelyn ® (S) CAbP CCMG CDoC EWar MAus MMat MRui SPer
'Evening Sentinel' (F) MFry
'Evening Star' (HT) IDic MAus
'Evening Telegraph' (HT) MHay
'Everest Double Fragrance' (F) EBls
'Excelsa' (Ra) CCMG CDoC CSan EBls EMFP EWar GGre IJoh LGod LStr MAus MGan MHay MMor MRui NBar NElm NRog NSty SJus SRum WStI
§ Exploit ® (Cl) EWar
Eye Paint ® (F) CSan EWar LStr MAus MGan MMat NRog
Eyeopener ® (S/GC) CGro EWar IDic MGan WWar
'F E Lester' See R. 'Francis E Lester'
§ 'F J Grootendorst' (Ru) CCMG EBls EWar IHos IOrc LGod LStr MAus MGan MMor NRog NSty SJus WAct
'Fabvier' See R. 'Colonel Fabvier'
Fair Bianca ® (S) CCMG IJoh IOrc MAus MBri WHCG
Fairy Changeling ® (Poly) MAus
Fairy Damsel ® (Poly/GC) CDoC EBls MAus
¶ Fairygold ® (Patio) MRui
Fairyland ® (Poly) EBls ESha EWar MAus

Fairysnow ® (S)	MFry
'Falkland' (pimpinellifolia)	EBls MAus
Fantan ® (HT)	MAus
'Fantin-Latour' (Ce x)	CCMG CCla CCor CHad CSan EBls EBro ELan ENot ETWh EWar GCoc IHos LStr MAus MGan MHay MMat NRog NSty SJus SPer WAct WHCG WSHC
fargesii hort.	See R. ***moyesii*** 'Fargesii'
farreri	See R. ***elegantula***
– var. ***persetosa***	See R. ***elegantula*** 'Persetosa'
'Fashion Flame' (Min)	MGan NBar
'Fashion, Climbing' (F/Cl)	EBls
Father's Day ® (Min)	NElm
Favorite Rosamini ® (Min)	MFry MRui
fedtschenkoana	CCor EBls MAus MGan NSty WHCG
'Felicia' (HM)	CCMG CCla CDoC CSam EBls EBro ENot ETWh EWar GCoc IHos LHol LStr MAus MBri MFry MHay MMat MMor MRui NBar NRog NSty SHen SJus SPer SRum WAct WHCG
'Félicité Parmentier' (A/D)	CCMG EBls EBre LBre MAus NBar NSty SJus SPer WAct WHCG
§ 'Félicité Perpétue' (Ra)	CBow CCMG CCla CCor CSan EBls EBre ETWh EWar GCoc IHos LBre LHol MAus MBri MGan MMat MRui NSty SFam SJus SPer SRum WAct WHCG
Felicity Kendal ® (HT)	CDoC LStr MBri MHay NBat
'Fellenberg' (Ch)	EBls MAus
¶ Fellowship ® (F)	GCoc LGod LStr MBur MFry WWar
'Femina' (HT)	MGan
'Ferdinand de Lesseps' (HP)	EBls
'Ferdinand Pichard' (Bb)	CBow CCMG EBls EBro EMFP ENot ETWh EWar MAus MMat NBar NSty SJus SPer WAct WHCG
Ferdy ® (GC)	CCMG CDoC EBls EBre ELan ENot ETWh EWar LBre MAus MGan MMat SHen SPer
Fergie ® (F/Patio)	MGan SJus
filipes 'Brenda Colvin'	See R. 'Brenda Colvin'
§ – 'Kiftsgate' (Ra)	Widely available
'Fimbriata' (Ru)	CCor CSan EBls EBro ETWh LGre MAus MBri SJus WAct WHCG
Financial Times Centenary ® (S)	EWar IHos MAus
Fine Gold ® (HT)	EWar
Fiona ® (S/GC)	EBls EWar IHos MBur MGan SHen SJus WHCG
'Fire Princess' (Min)	GCoc MHay MRui NBar NElm SJus WWeb
'Firecracker' (F)	EBls
Firefly ® (Min)	MRui
'First Love' (HT)	EBls MGan
'Fisher and Holmes' (HP)	EBls MAus WHCG
Fisherman's Friend ® (S)	CDoC EMFP ETWh EWar IHos MAus MHay SPer
Flaming Rosamini ® (Min)	MFry
'Fleet Street' (HT)	MHay
'Fleur Cowles' (F)	MBur
'Flora' (Ra)	EBls MAus
'Flora McIvor' (HSwB)	EBls MAus MGan
Florence Nightingale ® (F)	MBri MBur MGan SJus SPer WWeb
Flower Carpet ® (GC)	MBur MFry MMat MRui NBat SJus
§ ***foetida***	EBls MAus NSty
§ – 'Bicolor'	CCMG CCla EBls ENot ETWh MAus MMat NRog NSty SMad SPer WAct
§ – 'Persiana'	EBls MAus MGan SPer
foliolosa	EBls WHCG
Fontainebleau ® (HT)	MHay
'Forgotten Dreams' (HT)	MHay
forrestiana	CCor EBls MAus MMat
x ***fortuneana***	EBls
♦***Fortune's*** Double Yellow	See R. x ***odorata*** 'Pseudindica'
'Fosse Way' (HT)	MHay
'Fountain' (S)	CSam EBls EWar LStr MAus MFry MGan NElm SPer SRum
'Fräulein Octavia Hesse' (Ra)	CCMG EBls
Fragrant Cloud ® (HT)	CDoC CGro CMac CSan EBls EBre ESha EWar GCoc GGre IHos IJoh LBre LGod LStr MAus MBri MBur MFry MHay MMat MMor NBar NBat NRog SHen SJus SPer WWeb
Fragrant Cloud, Climbing ® (HT/Cl)	CB&S ELan MGan NElm SRum
Fragrant Delight ® (F)	CCMG CCla CSan ESha EWar GCoc IHos LPlm LStr MFry MGan NBar NBat NElm SPer WWar WWeb
Fragrant Dream ® (HT)	EWar IDic LStr MBri MBur
Fragrant Gold ® (HT)	GCoc LStr SJus SRum
'Fragrant Hour' (HT)	MGan MMat
'Francesca' (HM)	CCMG CCor EBls EBro ETWh MAus MGan NSty SPer WHCG
Francine Austin ® (S/GC)	IHos MAus MRui SPer WAct WHCG
'Francis Dubreuil' (T)	EBls
§ 'Francis E Lester' (HM/Ra)	CSam EBls EBro ETWh MAus MBri MHay NBar NSty SPer WAct WHCG
§ x ***francofurtana***	CCMG CCla EBls EBro ETWh IHos SFam WAct WHCG
'François Juranville' (Ra)	CCMG CHad CSam CSan EBls ETWh EWar LHol LStr MAus MBri MGan MMat NElm NRog SPer
'Frank Naylor' (S)	EWar MAus
'Frau Astrid Späth' (F)	NElm NRog
'Frau Karl Druschki' (HP)	CSan EBls ETWh MAus MGan MHay NSty
§ 'Frau Karl Druschki, Climbing' (HP/Cl)	EBls MGan NRog
'Fred Gibson' (HT)	MHay
'Fred Loads' (S)	EBls EMFP ENot ESha EWar MAus MFry MGan MHay MMat NBat
Freedom ® (HT)	CDoC CSan EWar GCoc IDic LGod LStr MBur MFry MGan NBat NRog WWar WWeb
'Freiherr von Marschall' (T)	EBls

'Frensham' (F)	CB&S CGro EBls LStr MGan MMat SHen SRum WStI
Fresh Pink ® (Min)	MGan
'Fringette' (Min)	MGan MMor
'Fritz Nobis' (S)	CCMG CCor CHad CSan EBls EMFP ENot ETWh EWar GCoc IHos LStr MAus MGan MHay MMat MRav NSty SJus SPer WHCG
'Frosty' (Min)	MRui
'Fru Dagmar Hastrup' (Ru)	Widely available
'Frühlingsanfang' (HScB)	EBls MAus MBri
'Frühlingsduft' (HScB)	CCor EBls ETWh NRog NSty SPer
Frühlingsgold ® (HScB)	Widely available
'Frühlingsmorgen' (HScB)	CCMG EBls ENot ETWh EWar GCoc IHos LStr MAus MBri MBur MGan MMat MMor NBar NElm NRog NSty SJus SPer WHCG WWeb
'Frühlingsschnee' (HScB)	EBls EWar
'Frühlingszauber' (HScB)	EBls
'Fulgens'	See R. 'Malton'
Fulton Mackay ® (HT)	GCoc MFry WWar
Fyvie Castle ® (HT)	GCoc MGan WWar
'Gail Borden' (HT)	ESha MAus MGan SRum
§ ***gallica***	EBls MHay
– 'Beckett's Single'	CCor
– 'Complicata'	See R. 'Complicata'
– 'Conditorum'	See R. 'Conditorum'
§ – var. ***officinalis***	CCMG CCla CCor CDoC CSan EBls EBro ENot ETWh GCoc GPoy LHol MAus MBri MMat NRog NSty SJus SPer WAct WHCG
– 'Velutiniflora'	EBls
§ – 'Versicolor'	CCla CCor CHad CSan EBls EBro EHar ELan ENot ETWh EWar GCoc LHol LStr MBri MFry MGan NRog NSty SHen SJus SPer SPla WHCG WWeb
Galway Bay ® (HT/Cl)	CSan GCoc IJoh LStr MAus MFry MGan MMat MRui SPer
¶ 'Gardener's Delight' (Ra)	NWyt
¶ 'Gardenia' (Ra)	SPer
'Garnette Carol'	See R. 'Carol Amling'
'Garnette Pink'	See R. 'Carol Amling'
'Garnette Red' (Gn)	See R. 'Garnette'
'Gary Player' (HT)	MHay
'Gateshead Festival' (HT)	NBat
'Gaujard'	See R. 'Rose Gaujard'
'Gavotte' (HT)	MHay
'Gay Vista' (S)	MGan
'Général Galliéni' (T)	EBls
'Général Jacqueminot' (HP)	EBls WAct WHCG
'Général Kléber' (Mo)	CCor EBls IHos MAus NSty SFam SPer WAct WHCG
'General MacArthur, Climbing' (HT/Cl)	EBls MAus
§ 'Général Schablikine' (T)	EBls EBro ETWh MAus WSHC WWat
N***gentiliana*** (Ra)	CCor EBls WHCG
Gentle Touch ® (Min/Patio)	CCla CDoC CGro CSan EBls EBre ESha EWar GCoc GGre IDic LBre LGod LStr MBri MBur MFry MGan MHay MMat MRui NBar NBat SHen SJus SPer SRum WWeb
'Geoff Boycott' (F)	ESha
Geordie Lad ® (HT)	NBat
'Georg Arends' (HP)	CCMG EBls MAus SFam SPer WAct WHCG
'George Dickson' (HT)	MAus SRms
'George R Hill' (HT)	NBat
'Georges Vibert' (G)	EBls MAus WHCG
Geraldine ® (F)	CDoC ESha GCoc LStr MBri MGan SJus SRum
§ 'Geranium' (***moyesii*** x)	CB&S CCMG CCla CGro CSan EBre EBro EHar ELan ENot ETWh EWar GCoc IOrc LBre MAus MBri MBur MGan NBar NElm NSty SPer SRum WAct WHCG WSHC WWeb
'Geranium Red' (F)	MAus
Gerbe d'Or ®	See R. 'Casino'
'Gerbe Rose' (Ra)	EBls MAus NSty
Gertrude Jekyll ® (S)	CCMG CDoC CHad CSam CSan EBre EMFP ENot EWar IJoh IOrc LBre LGod LPlm LStr MAus MBri MFry MMat MRui NBar SJus SPer WAct WHCG
'Ghislaine de Féligonde' (S/Ra)	CCor EBls
gigantea	EBls
– ***cooperi***	See R. ***laevigata*** 'Cooperi'
Gilda ® (F)	CSan
Gingernut ® (F/Patio)	ESha GCoc NBat
Ginny-Lou ® (Min)	MRui
'Gipsy Boy'	See R. 'Zigeunerknabe'
Glad Tidings ® (F)	CGro ESha EWar GCoc GGre LPlm LStr MBri MBur MGan MHay MMat NBar NBat SJus SPer SRum WWar WWeb
¶ Glamis Castle ® (S)	CCMG EBlo MAus MRui NBar SJus SPer
§ ***glauca***	Widely available
'Glenfiddich' (F)	CGro CSan ESha EWar GCoc GGre IHos LGod LPlm LStr MAus MBri MFry MGan MHay NBar NBat NElm NRog SHen SJus SPer SRum WStI WWeb
¶ 'Glenn Dale' (Cl)	ETWh
'Gloire de Bruxelles' (HP)	EBls
'Gloire de Dijon' (T/Cl)	CCMG CHad CSam CSan EBlo EBls EBre EBro ETWh EWar GCoc IOrc LBre LHol MAus MBri MGan MMat NBar NElm NRog NSty SFam SHen SJus SPer SRum WHCG
'Gloire de Ducher' (HP)	ETWh MAus MGan SFam WHCG
'Gloire de France' (G)	CBow CCMG CCor EBls ETWh MAus WHCG
'Gloire de Guilan' (D)	EBls MAus NSty WAct
'Gloire des Mousseuses' (Mo)	CCMG CCor CSan EBls EBro ETWh IHos MAus SFam WAct WHCG
'Gloire du Midi' (Poly)	MAus
'Gloire Lyonnaise' (HP)	CCor EBls EBro ETWh SPla
'Gloria Mundi' (Poly)	EBls MGan

§ 'Glory of Edzell' (pimpinellifolia) — EBls MAus WSHC
♦*glutinosa* — See R. ***pulverulenta***
'Godfrey Winn' (HT) — WWeb
'Goethe' (Mo) — EBls
Gold Bunny ® (F) — EWar MGan
'Gold Pin' (Min) — MMat
'Goldbusch' (S) — EBls MAus MGan SRms
'Golden Angel' (Min) — MHay
¶ Golden Celebrations ® (S) — MAus MRui NBar SJus
Golden Chersonese ® (S) — EBls MAus NRog NSty SMad
'Golden Dawn' (HT/Cl) — MAus
Golden Days ® (HT) — EWar LGod MBri MFry SJus
'Golden Glow' (Cl) — EBls MGan
Golden Jubilee ® (HT) — ELan EWar GCoc GGre LPlm LStr MBur MHay NBat
'Golden Melody' (HT) — EBls
Golden Moments ® (HT) — EWar MBur MFry NBat
'Golden Moss' (Mo) — EBls
'Golden Ophelia' (HT) — EBls MAus
¶ 'Golden Penny' (Min) — MBur
'Golden Rambler' — See R. 'Alister Stella Gray'
Golden Rosamini ® (Min) — MFry MRui
'Golden Salmon' (Poly) — MGan
'Golden Salmon Supérieur' (Poly) — EBls
'Golden Shot' (F) — ESha MGan
Golden Showers ® (Cl) — Widely available
'Golden Slippers' (F) — CB&S MAus MGan
'Golden Sunblaze' — See R. 'Rise 'n' Shine'
'Golden Times' (HT) — WWeb
¶ 'Golden Treasure' (F) — SRum
Golden Wedding ® (F/HT) — CCMG CSan EWar GCoc LGod LStr MBur MFry MGan MHay MMat NBat SJus WStI
'Golden Wings' (S) — CCMG CCla CHad EBls ENot ETWh IHos LStr MAus MBri MFry MGan MHay MMat MMor NSty SHen SJus SPer SRum WHCG
Golden Years ® (F) — EWar GCoc MAus MBur NBat
'Goldfinch' (Ra) — CBow CCMG CCor CHad CSan EBls EBre ETWh EWar GCoc LBre LGre MAus MBri NSty SPer WAct WHCG
'Goldfinger' (F) — LPlm MBri
'Goldilocks' (F) — NElm NRog
'Goldkrone' ('Gold Crown') (HT) — MGan SRum
Goldstar ® (HT) — EWar LPlm MFry MGan
'Goliath' (HT) — MHay
¶ 'Good News' — EWar
¶ 'Gordon's College' (F) — GCoc
'Grace Abounding' (F) — EWar MHay NBat
'Grace Darling' (T) — EBls
Grace de Monaco ® (HT) — EBls MAus MGan
Graham Thomas ® (S) — Widely available
Grand Hotel ® (HT/Cl) — EWar IHos LStr MBri MMat SPer
§ 'Grandiflora' (pimpinellifolia) — CCor EBls ETWh MAus SJus
'Grandpa Dickson' (HT) — CCMG EBls EBre ESha EWar GGre IHos IJoh LBre LGod LPlm MAus MBur MFry MGan MHay MMat MMor NBar NBat NElm NRog SHen SPer SRum WWeb
'Grand-mère Jenny' (HT) — EBls MGan
'Grand-mère Jenny, Climbing' (HT/Cl) — EBls
§ 'Great Maiden's Blush' (A) — CBow CSan EBls GCoc MBur MFry MMat NElm NSty WAct WWeb
'Great News' (HT) — MAus
¶ 'Great Ormond Street' (F) — EBls
'Great Western' (Bb) — EBls
'Green Diamond' (Min) — MAus MBur MFry MMat MRui
Green Snake ® (S/GC) — ELan
Greenall's Glory ® (F/Patio) — WWeb
'Greenmantle' (HSwB) — EBls MAus MGan SJus
Greensleeves ® (F) — EBls LStr MAus SPer
¶ 'Greer Garson' (HT) — GCoc
'Grootendorst Supreme' (Ru) — MAus SPer
N 'Gros Choux de Hollande' (Bb) — EBls
Grouse ® (S/GC) — CCMG CCor EBls ENot ETWh GCoc IHos MAus MGan MMat SPer WWeb
'Grumpy' (Poly) — MGan
'Gruss an Aachen' (Poly) — CCMG CCor CHad EBls ETWh LStr MAus MBri MGan NSty SPer WAct WHCG
'Gruss an Teplitz' (Ch x) — CSan EBls EBro MAus SFam WHCG
Guernsey Love ® (Min) — MRui
Guiding Spirit ® (Min/Patio) — MBur WWeb
'Guinée' (HT/Cl) — CBow CCMG CHad CMac CSan EBls EBre EBro ELan ETWh IHos LBre MAus MBur MGan MHay MMat NSty SPla WSHC
Guletta ® — See R. 'Rugul'
'Gustav Grünerwald' (HT) — EBls MAus
¶ Gwent ® (GC) — MRui
'Gypsy Boy' — See R. 'Zigeunerknabe'
'Gypsy Jewel' (Min) — CGro NBar NElm
'Gypsy Moth' (F) — SRum
'Hakuun' (F/Patio) — GCoc MAus MGan
'Hamburg Love' (F) — MBur
'Hamburger Phönix' (Ra) — CGro EBls LStr MGan NElm SPer
Hampshire ® (GC) — CCor ENot EWar IHos MAus MFry MGan MMat
Handel ® (Cl) — Widely available
Hannah Gordon ® (F) — CDoC EWar LStr MGan MHay MMat NBar NBat SJus SRum
'Hannah Hauwxell' (Patio) — NBat SRum
'Hannes' (HT) — NRog
'Hansa' (Ru) — EBls ENot IHos LBuc MAus MGan MMat
§ 'Hansestadt Lübeck' (F) — MGan
'Happy' (Poly) — MGan
'Happy Thought' (Min) — MAus SJus
Happy Wanderer ® (F) — EWar
§ x ***harisonii*** 'Harison's Yellow' (HScB) — EBls MAus SPer
§ – 'Lutea Maxima' (HScB) — EBls MAus
§ – 'Williams' Double Yellow' (HScB) — CCMG CCla CCor EBls ETWh MAus
Harkness Marigold ® (F) — CDoC

Harold Macmillan ® (F) NBat WWar
'Harry Maasz' (GC/Cl) EBls
Harry Wheatcroft ® (HT) CB&S CGro EBls ESha GGre IHos MAus MBri MGan NElm NRog
Harvest Fayre ® (F) CGro EBre GCoc GGre IDic LBre LGod LStr MAus MBri MBur MFry MGan MHay MMat NBar NBat SPer SRum WWeb
Harvest Home ® (Ru) EWar
'Harvester' (HT) MHay
'Headleyensis' CCor EBls ETWh MAus
'Heart of England' (F) MBur
'Heather' (Min) LGod
§ 'Heather Muir' (***sericea*** x) EBls MAus NSty WKif
'Heaven Scent' (F) NBat
§ 'Hebe's Lip' (D x SwB) EBls MAus
'Hector Deane' (HT) EBls MBur MGan NSty
'Heidi Jayne' (HT) MBur SRum
'Heinrich Schultheis' (HP) EBls
§ 'Helen Knight' (***ecae*** x) CSan EBls EHar MAus MBri MMat NSty SPer WHCG
'Helen Traubel' (HT) EBls MGan
helenae CCor EBls MAus SPer WHCG
Hello ® (Min/Patio) GCoc NBat
hemisphaerica EBls EMon ETWh MAus WAct
'Henri Fouquier' (G) EBls
§ 'Henri Martin' (Mo) CCMG CCor EBls IOrc MAus NRog SPer WAct WHCG
'Henry Nevard' (HP) EBls MAus
'Her Majesty' (HP) EBls
§ 'Herbstfeuer' (HSwB) CCor EBls NSty
Heritage ® (S) CCMG CDoC CSam CSan EBls EBre ELan EMFP ENot ETWh IHos LBre LGod LHol LPlm LStr MAus MBri MFry MHay MMat MRui NBar NBat SJus SPer SRum WHCG
'Hermosa' (Ch) EBls EBro ETWh MAus WHCG
Hero ® (S) MAus
Hertfordshire ® (GC) ENot EWar MMat MRui
'Hiawatha' (Ra) EBls ETWh MAus WHCG
'Hibernica' (***canina*** x) MAus
'Hidcote Gold' EBls MAus
¶ High Hopes ® (Cl) GCoc MBur MFry SJus
§ 'Highdownensis' (***moyesii*** x) CCla EBls ELan MAus MMat SPer
Highfield ® (Cl) CDoC ESha EWar LGod MAus MBri SJus SPer
Highland Laddie ® (Min) GCoc
'Highlight' (F) MGan
Hilda Murrell ® (S) MAus
§ 'Hillieri' (***moyesii*** x) EBls MAus SRms
'Hippolyte' (G) EBls MAus WSHC
Hollie Roffey ® (Min) SPer
holodonta See R. ***moyesii rosea***
Holy Rose See R. ***richardii***
'Home Sweet Home' (HT) EBls MAus
'Home Sweet Home, Climbing' (HT/Cl) MAus
'Homère' (T) EBls MAus
'Honey Bunch' (F/Patio) CDoC CSan GCoc MBri NBat
'Honey Favorite' (HT) MAus
'Honeymoon' (F) CB&S GCoc MAus MMor NElm SRum WWeb
'Honeysweet' (F) MFry
'Honorine de Brabant' (Bb) CBow CCMG CCor CHad CSan EBls ETWh EWar MAus MMat SFam SPer WAct WHCG
'Horace Vernet' (HP) EBls
horrida See R. ***biebersteinii***
'Horstmanns Rosenresli' (F) EBls
'Hot Pewter' (HT) MHay
Hotline ® (Min/Mo) MRui
'Hugh Dickson' (HP) CCMG EBls EBro ETWh MAus NSty SJus
♦***hugonis*** See R. ***xanthina h.***
'Hula Girl' (Min) CSan LGod MBur MFry MHay MRui
Hume's Blush See R. x ***odorata*** 'Odorata'
'Hunslet Moss' (Mo) EBls
'Hunter' (Ru) WAct
'Hutton Village' (HT) EWar
hypoleuca CCor
Iceberg ® (Schneewittchen ®) (F) Widely available
'Iceberg, Climbing' (F/Cl) CCMG CGro CMac EBls EBre EBro ELan ETWh EWar GGre LBre LPlm LStr MAus MGan MHay MMor NElm NRog SHen SPer SRum WAct WHCG WSHC WWeb
'Iced Ginger' (F) CCMG CSan EWar MAus MFry MGan NBar SPer WWar
¶ 'Ideal' (Poly) ETWh
'Ideal Home' (HT) MMor
'Illusion' (Cl) MGan
Ilse Krohn Superior ® (Cl) EBls
¶ Indian Summer ® (HT) CSun EWar GCoc
'Indian Sunblaze' (Min/Patio) IHos WWeb
Ingrid Bergman ® (HT) CDoC EWar GCoc LGod MBri MGan MMat NBar WWar WWeb
Inner Wheel ® (F) MFry
¶ 'Inspiration' (Cl) EWar
'Intermezzo' (HT) MBur MGan
International Herald Tribune ® (F/Patio) ESha LStr MAus
Intrigue ® (F) MHay MMat WWar
Invincible ® (F) EWar MFry MGan WWar
'Invitation' (HT) MBur MGan
'Ipsilanté' (G) CCor EBls MAus WAct WHCG
'Irene of Denmark' (F) EBls
'Irène Watts' (Ch) EBls ETWh MAus SPla WHCG
Irene's Delight ® (HT) MHay NBat
'Irish Brightness' (HT) MAus
'Irish Elegance' (HT) EBls MAus
'Irish Fireflame' (HT) EBls MAus
'Irish Fireflame, Climbing' (HT/Cl) MAus
Irish Mist ® (F) MGan
'Irish Wonder' See R. Evelyn Fison ®
'Isis' (F) MBri
'Isobel' (HT) MAus
'Ispahan' (D) CCMG CCla CCor CHad CSam EBls EBro EMFP ETWh EWar MAus NSty SFam SJus SPer SPla WAct WHCG WSHC
'Ivory Fashion' (F) EBls MAus
'Ivory Tip Top' (F) MHay

§ x ***jacksonii*** 'Max Graf'	CCMG CSan EBls ELan ENot ETWh IHos MAus MBur MGan MMat MMor NRog NSty SJus SPer SRum WAct WHCG WSHC WWeb
– Red Max Graf ® (GC)	See R. Rote Max Graf
– 'White Max Graf'	ENot IHos MMat
Jacobite Rose	See R. ***alba*** 'Alba Maxima'
Jacqueline du Pré ® (S)	CCMG EWar GCoc MAus SJus SPer WWar
¶ 'Jacquenetta' (S)	SRms
'Jacques Cartier'	See R. 'Marquise Boccella'
'James Bourgault' (HP)	EBls
'James Mason' (G)	EBls MAus
'James Mitchell' (Mo)	EBls MAus MBur SFam WHCG
'James Veitch' (DP/Mo)	EBls MAus
'Jan Guest' (HT)	MHay NBat
Jane Asher ® (Min/Patio)	CDoC SJus
'Janet's Pride' (HSwB)	EBls MAus
'Japonica' (Mo)	MAus
Jardins de Bagatelle ® (HT)	SJus
'Jayne Austin'	MAus MRui
'Jean Mermoz' (Poly)	MAus NElm NRog NSty SPer SRum
'Jean Rosenkrantz' (HP)	EBls
'Jean Sisley' (HT)	EBls
'Jeanne de Montfort' (Mo)	EBls MAus
'Jeannie Deans' (HSwB)	MAus
'Jenny Charlton' (HT)	NBat
'Jenny Duval' (G)	See R. 'Président de Sèze'
'Jenny Wren' (F)	EBls MAus
'Jersey Beauty' (Ra)	EBls
'Jiminy Cricket' (F)	EBls
'Jimmy Greaves' (HT)	MGan
Joan Ball ® (Min)	MRui
'Joan Bell' (HT)	MHay
'Joanna Hill' (HT)	EBls
'Joanne' (HT)	EWar MHay
'Jocelyn' (F)	EBls MAus
¶ 'John Cabot' (S)	WWar
'John Hopper' (HP)	EBls ETWh MAus NSty
John Hughes ® (F)	CSan
'John Waterer' (HT)	MAus SJus
Johnnie Walker ® (HT)	MFry MGan
'Josephine Bruce' (HT)	CB&S CCMG CGro CMac EBls EWar LGod MAus MBur MGan MHay NRog SHen SRum WStI
'Josephine Bruce, Climbing' (HT/Cl)	MAus MGan MHay SHen
'Josephine Wheatcroft'	See R. 'Rosina'
Joseph's Coat ® (S/Cl)	CSan EBls IHos LGod LStr MFry MGan MHay MMat MMor MRui SRum WWar WWeb
'Journey's End' (HT)	MGan
'Joybells' (F)	MAus
Joyfulness ® (F)	NElm WWeb
'Judy Fischer' (Min)	EWar LGod MHay MRui NElm WWeb
Judy Garland ® (F)	SJus
'Julia Mannering' (HSwB)	MAus
Julia's Rose ® (HT)	CCMG CGro CHad EWar LStr MAus MBur MFry MGan NElm SPer
¶ Julie Andrews ® (F)	MFry
Julie Cussons ® (F)	MFry
'Juliet' (HP)	EBls
'June Time' (Min)	MMor MRui NElm
'Juno' (Ce)	EBls EWar MAus SFam WHCG
Just Joey ® (HT)	Widely available
'Karl Foerster' (HScB)	EBls MAus
'Kassel' (S/Cl)	EBls MAus MMat SPer SRms
'Katharina Zeimet' (Poly)	EBls MAus MGan NRog NSty WAct WHCG
'Kathleen' (HM)	EBls EBro SJus
'Kathleen Ferrier' (F)	EBls MFry MGan MHay MMat MMor
'Kathleen Harrop' (Bb)	CCMG CHad EBls ENot LStr MAus MBur MMat NSty SFam SPer WHCG WSHC WWat WWeb
'Kathleen O'Rourke' (HT)	EWar
Kathryn Morley ® (F)	EWar MAus MRui
'Katie' (F/Cl)	MGan
'Kazanlik' misapplied	See R. 'Professor Emile Perrot'
Keepsake ® (HT)	LPlm MGan MHay MMat NBat NElm NRog
Kent ® (S/GC)	CCor CSan EWar IHos LGod MMat MRui SPer WWar
'Kerrygold' (F)	IJoh MFry MGan
'Kerryman' (F)	EWar MGan
'Kew Rambler' (Ra)	CBow CCMG EBls EBre ETWh EWar LBre MAus SPer WHCG
'Kiese' (canina x)	CCor
'Kiftsgate'	See R. ***filipes*** 'Kiftsgate'
'Kilworth Gold' (HT)	MGan SRum
'Kim' (Patio)	MAus NRog
King's Ransom ® (HT)	CB&S CDoC CGro CMac EBls EBro ESha EWar GGre IHos IJoh LGod LStr MAus MBur MGan MHay MMor NBar NElm SHen SPer SRum WWeb
'Kitchener of Khartoum'	See R. 'K of K'
x ***kochiana***	EBls
'Köln am Rhein' (Cl)	MGan
§ 'Königin von Dänemark' (A)	CCMG CCla CHad EBls EBro EMFP EPla ETWh GCoc MAus MBri MMat NSty SJus SPer WAct WHCG
'Korbell' (F)	MGan NBat
'Kordes Robusta'	See R. Robusta ®
Korona ® (F)	MGan NRog
'Korresia' (F)	CCMG CSan EBre EHar ESha EWar GCoc GGre IHos IJoh LBre LGod LStr MAus MBri MFry MGan MHay MMat MMor NBat NRog SJus SPer SRum WWar
Kronenbourg ® (HT)	EBls LPlm MAus MBur SRum
'Kronprinzessin Viktoria' (Bb)	CCor EBls ETWh MAus WHCG
L D Braithwaite ® (S)	CCMG CDoC CSam EBre EWar LBre LGod LPlm LStr MAus MGan MMat MRui SJus SPer WWeb
'La Belle Distinguée' (HSwB)	EBls MAus WHCG
'La Belle Sultane'	See R. 'Violacea'
'La Follette' (Cl)	EBls
'La France' (HT)	EBls EBro MAus
'La France, Climbing' (HT/Cl)	MAus
'La Jolla' (HT)	MBur
'La Mortola'	See R. ***brunonii*** 'La M.'
'La Noblesse' (Ce)	EBls WHCG

'La Perle' (Ra) MAus
'La Plus Belle des Ponctuées' (G) CCor
'La Reine' (HP) EBls NSty
'La Reine Victoria' See R. 'Reine Victoria'
'La Rubanée' See R. 'Centifolia Variegata'
La Sevillana ® (F/GC) EBls EWar NBar SHen SPer SRum
'La Ville de Bruxelles' (D) CCMG CCor EBls EBro EMFP ETWh IHos MAus MRav NSty SFam SPer WAct WHCG
'Lady Alice Stanley' (HT) EBls MAus
'Lady Barnby' (HT) EBls
'Lady Belper' (HT) EBls MAus MBur
'Lady Curzon' (Ru) EBls IHos MAus NSty
'Lady Elgin' See R. Thaïs ®
'Lady Forteviot' (HT) EBls
¶ 'Lady Gay' (Ra) MAus WHCN
'Lady Godiva' (Ra) CDoC MAus
'Lady Helen' (HT) CGro
'Lady Hillingdon' (T) CCMG EBre ETWh LBre MAus NSty
'Lady Hillingdon, Climbing' (T/Cl) CBow CCMG CSan EBls EBre EBro EMFP EWar LBre MAus MGan NSty SHen SPer WAct WHCG WSHC
'Lady Iliffe' (HT) MGan
¶ 'Lady MacRobert' (F) GCoc
'Lady Mary Fitzwilliam' (HT) EBls
Lady Mavis Pilkington ® (HT) MFry MMat
'Lady of Stifford' (F) EWar
§ 'Lady Penzance' (HSwB) CB&S CCMG CSam EBls EWar MAus MFry MGan NSty SHen SJus SPer WAct
'Lady Romsey' (F) EBls
'Lady Seton' (HT) MGan SPer
'Lady Sylvia' (HT) EBls MAus MGan NRog NSty SHen SPer WStI
'Lady Sylvia, Climbing' (HT/Cl) CCMG EBls EMFP ETWh MAus MGan NElm NRog SPer
'Lady Waterlow' (HT/Cl) CCMG EBls EBro ETWh MAus SPer WAct WHCG
laevigata CBot EBls ETWh MAus
– 'Anemonoides' See R. 'Anemone'
§ – 'Cooperi' CAbP CCMG EBls ETWh LGre MAus WSHC
'Lafter' (S) EBls
'Lagoon' (F) EBls
'Lakeland' (HT) MAus NRog
'Lamarque' (N) MAus
Lancashire Life ® (F) MBri MFry
'Lanei' (Mo) EBls
'Langdale Chase' (F) MFry
Langford Light ® (Min/GC) MBri
Laughter Lines ® (F) IDic MBri MGan WWar
Laura Ashley ® (Min/Cl) EWar LStr MBur NBat WWar
Laura Ford ® (Min/Cl) CDoC EWar LStr MBri MBur MFry MMat MRui NBat SJus SMad WWar WWeb
'Laura Jane' (HT) MGan
Laura ® (HT) EWar
'Lavender Jewel' (Min) CSan MAus MBur MHay MMat MRui SJus
'Lavender Lace' (Min) EBre LBre MAus MHay
'Lavender Lassie' (HM) EBro IOrc MAus MBur MFry MGan MHay MMat MRui SJus SRum WAct WHCG
'Lavender Pinocchio' (F) MAus WAct
Lavinia ® (Cl) EBre EWar LBre LGod LStr MBri NElm SJus SPer
'Lawrence Johnston' (Cl) CCla EBls MAus MRav NSty SPer WAct WHCG
'Le Havre' (HP) EBls
'Le Rêve' (Cl) EBls ETWh MAus
'Le Vésuve' (Ch) EBls MAus
Leander ® (S) CCMG MAus MBri
Leaping Salmon ® (HT/Cl) CCMG CDoC CGro CSan ELan EWar GCoc IHos IJoh IOrc LGod LStr MBri NBat SRum WStI
'Leda' (D) CCMG EBls EBro ETWh EWar MAus SFam SPer WAct
'Lemon Pillar' See R. 'Paul's Lemon Pillar'
Len Turner ® (F) CDoC IDic IHos MBri SJus
'Léonie Lamesch' (Poly) EBls ETWh SGil
'Léontine Gervais' (Ra) CAbP EBre LBre MAus NBar WAct WHCG
Letchworth Garden City ® (F) WWar
'Leuchtstern' (Ra) EBls
'Leverkusen' (Cl) CCMG CDoC CHad CSan EBls EBre ETWh LBre MAus MGan NElm NSty SPer SPla SRum WAct WSHC
'Leveson-Gower' (Bb) EBls
'Ley's Perpetual' (T/Cl) CCMG CCor EBls EBre ETWh LBre MAus WHCG
Lichtkönigin Lucia ® (S) WWar
'Lilac Charm' (F) CHad EBls MAus
Lilac Rose ® (S) MAus NBar
Lilian Austin ® (S) EWar IHos MAus MBri SPer
Lilli Marlene ® (F) CB&S CCMG CCla CDoC CHad EBls ESha GCoc GGre IHos IJoh LStr MAus MBur MGan MMat MMor NElm NRog SHen SPer SRum WWeb
Lincoln Cathedral ® (HT) CDoC MGan MHay NBat SPer
Lincolnshire Poacher ® (HT) NBat
Little Artist ® (Min) MHay MRui WWeb
Little Bo-Peep ® (Min/Patio) MBur MFry MMat MRui WWar
'Little Buckaroo' (Min) CGro CSan ELan EWar GCoc GGre LGod MGan MMor NBar NElm SPer WStI
'Little Dorrit' (Poly) CDoC NElm NRog
'Little Flirt' (Min) CGro EWar GCoc GGre MAus MGan MRui NBat WWeb
'Little Gem' (DPMo) EBls EBro MAus MGan
Little Jewel ® (Patio) GCoc MAus SJus
Little Marvel ® (Min) MBri MFry
Little Prince ® (F/Patio) GCoc MAus WWar
'Little Stephen' (HT) CSan
'Little White Pet' See R. 'White Pet'
'Little White Pet, Climbing' See R. 'Félicité Perpétue'
Little Woman ® (Patio) CDoC IDic IHos LStr SJus
'Liverpool Echo' (F) LPlm MHay NBat SHen
Liverpool Remembers ® (HT) EWar MBri MFry WWeb
'Living Fire' (F) EBls MGan

Lloyds of London ® (F) LGod
'Lollipop' (Min) MGan
'Long John Silver' (Cl) EBls
longicuspis Bertoloni EBls
– hort. (Ra) CBow CCMG CCla ELan ETWh ISea SJus SPer SPla WHCG WWat
– B&L 12386Bertoloni EMon
§ – *sinowilsonii* (Ra) EBls GCal MAus WHCG
Longleat ® (Min) MMat
'Lord Penzance' (HSwB) CCMG EBls ETWh MAus MGan NSty SPer WAct
L'Oréal Trophy ® (HT) CSan MAus MGan NBar WWar
'Lorraine Lee' (T) EBls
'Los Angeles' (HT) EBls
'L'Ouche' See R. 'Louise Odier'
'Louis Gimard' (Mo) EBls IHos MAus SPer WAct WHCG
'Louis Philippe' (Ch) EBls
'Louis XIV' (Ch) CHad EBls LGre WHCG
'Louise Odier' (Bb) CCMG CCla CSam EBls EBro EMFP ETWh LStr MAus MBri MMat NSty SFam SJus SPer SRum WAct WHCG
'Love Token' (F) MBur
Lovely Lady ® (HT) CDoC IDic LGod LStr MGan SJus
'Lovers' Meeting' (HT) CSan ESha GGre IJoh LPlm LStr MBri MBur MFry MGan MHay MMat NBar NBat SJus SPer WStI WWar WWeb
Loving Memory ® (HT) CSan EWar GCoc LStr MFry MGan MHay MMat SRum WWar
Loving Touch ® (Min) MHay
Lucetta ® (S) CCMG MAus SPer
luciae EBls
¶ 'Lucilla' (Patio) NBat
¶ 'Lucy Ashton' (HSwB) MAus
'Lübeck' See R. 'Hansestadt Lübeck'
'Luis Brinas' (HT) NSty
'Lutea Maxima' See R. x ***harisonii*** 'L.M.'
'Lykkefund' (Ra) CCor EBls MAus
'Lyon Rose' (HT) EBls
'Ma Perkins' (F) EBls MAus
'Ma Ponctuée' (DPMo) EBls
'Mabel Morrison' (HP) EBls MAus WHCG
Macartney Rose See R. ***bracteata***
'Macrantha' (G x) CCor EBls MAus WAct
'Macrantha Raubritter' See R. 'Raubritter'
'Macrexy' See R. Sexy Rexy ®
macrophylla CCor MAus MMat
¶ – SF 16/131 ISea
– 'Doncasteri' See R. 'Doncasteri'
§ – 'Master Hugh' EBls MAus NSty
'Madame Abel Chatenay' (HT) EBls MAus
'Madame Abel Chatenay, Climbing' (HT/Cl) CCMG EBls MAus NElm SPer WWeb
'Madame Alfred Carrière' (N) CBow CCor CHad CSam CSan EBlo EBls EMFP ETWh EWar LHol LPlm LStr MAus MGan MMat NRog NSty SFam SJus SPer SPla SRum WHCG WSHC WStI
'Madame Alice Garnier' (Ra) CCMG CSan EBls ETWh
'Madame Antoine Mari' (T) EBls
'Madame Berkeley' (T) EBls
'Madame Bravy' (T) EBls MAus
'Madame Butterfly' (HT) EBls EBro MAus MBur MGan NSty SRum
'Madame Butterfly, Climbing' (HT/Cl) CMac EBls MAus MGan SJus SPer
§ 'Madame Caroline Testout, Climbing' (HT/Cl) CBow EBls LHol MAus NRog NSty SPer WAct WSHC
'Madame de Sancy de Parabère' (Bs) EBls ETWh MAus
'Madame de Watteville' (T) EBls
'Madame Delaroche-Lambert' (DPMo) EBls MAus WAct WHCG
'Madame Driout' (T/Cl) EBls WHCG
'Madame d'Arblay' (Ra) EBls
§ 'Madame Edouard Herriot, Climbing' (HT/Cl) CCMG EBls ETWh MAus MGan SPer
'Madame Eliza de Vilmorin' (HT) EBls
'Madame Ernest Calvat' (Bb) CCMG CSan EBls MAus NSty SFam SPer WHCG
♦ 'Madame Eugène Résal' misapplied See R. 'Contesse du Cayla'
'Madame Gabriel Luizet' (HP) EBls
'Madame Georges Bruant' (Ru) EBls MAus
§ 'Madame Grégoire Staechelin' (HT/Cl) CCMG CSam CSan EBls EBro ETWh EWar MAus MBri MFry MGan MHay MMat MRui NBar NRog NSty SHen SJus SPer SRum WAct WHCG WWeb
'Madame Hardy' (D/Cl) CCMG CCla CSan EBls EBro ENot ETWh EWar GCoc LStr MAus MBri MBur MGan MHay MMat NBar NSty SFam SJus SPer WAct WHCG
'Madame Henri Guillot, Climbing' (HT/Cl) EBls
'Madame Isaac Pereire' (Bb/Cl) CCMG CCla CHad CSan EBls EBro ENot ETWh EWar GCoc IHos IOrc LHol LStr MAus MBri MBur MFry MGan MHay MMat NRog NSty SFam SJus SPer WAct WHCG WSHC WWeb
'Madame Jules Gravereaux' (T/Cl) EBls MAus
¶ 'Madame Jules Thibaud' (Poly) MAus
§ 'Madame Knorr' ('Comte de Chambord') (D/P) CBow CCMG CSan EBls EBre ETWh IHos LBre MAus NSty SJus SPer WAct
'Madame Laurette Messimy ' (Ch) CCMG EBls MAus SFam WHCG WSHC
'Madame Lauriol de Barny' (Bb) CCMG EBls ETWh MAus MGan WHCG

'Madame Legras de Saint Germain' (A/N)	CCMG CCor EBls EMFP ETWh IHos MAus NSty SFam SJus SPer WAct WHCG
'Madame Lombard' (T)	EBls
'Madame Louis Laperrière' (HT)	EBls MAus MGan NSty SPer WWeb
'Madame Louis Lévêque' (DPMo)	EBls
'Madame Pierre Oger' (Bb)	CCMG CSan EBls EBro ENot ETWh EWar IHos LHol LStr MAus MMat NSty SFam SPer SRum WAct WHCG WWeb
'Madame Plantier' (A/N)	CBow CCMG CCla CCor CHad EBls ETWh LHol MAus MMat SPer WAct WHCG
'Madame Scipion Cochet' (T)	EBls WHCG
'Madame Victor Verdier' (HP)	EBls
'Madame Wagram, Comtese de Turenne' (T)	EBls
'Madame William Paul' (PMo)	EBls
'Madame Zöetmans' (D)	CCMG EBls MAus WHCG
'Madeleine Selzer' (Ra)	EBls MAus MGan MHay
Maestro ® (HT)	EHar MAus NBar
'Magenta' (S/HT)	EBls MAus MHay SPer
Magic Carrousel ® (Min)	CGro CSan GCoc LPlm MAus MBur MFry MHay MMor MRui NBat WStI WWar WWeb
'Magna Charta' (HP)	EBls
'Magnifica' (HSwB)	EBls MAus MGan
N'Maiden's Blush' (A)	CBow CCMG CCla CDoC CHad CSam EBls EBre ELan EMFP ENot ETWh LBre LHol MAus MGan NBar SFam SJus SPer SPla SRum WHCG
'Maiden's Blush, Great'	See R. 'Great Maiden's Blush'
'Maigold' (HScB/Cl)	Widely available
§ *majalis*	CCor
'Mala Rubinstein' (HT)	IDic
'Malaga' (HT/Cl)	MMat
Malcolm Sargent ® (HT)	NBar SPer SRum
'Maltese Rose'	See R, 'Cécile Brunner'
§ 'Malton' (Chx)	EBls
'Maman Cochet, Climbing' (T/Cl)	EBls MAus
Mandarin ® (Min)	MBur MMat
'Manettii' (N)	EBls
Mannheim ® (S)	MGan
'Manning's Blush' (HSwB)	CCor EBls MAus NSty WAct
Manou Meilland ® (HT)	EWar MGan
Manuela ® (HT)	MGan
'Manx Queen' (F)	MGan
Many Happy Returns ® (F)	CDoC CSan ESha EWar LStr MBur MGan MMat NBat SJus SRum WWar WWeb
'Marbled Pink' (pimpinellifolia)	CCor MAus
'Marbrée' (D/P)	EBls MAus
'Marcel Bourgouin' (G)	CCor EBls
'Marchenland' (S)	EBls MAus
N'Marchesa Boccella' ('Jacques Cartier') (DPo)	CCMG CCla CCor CSam EBls EBro ETWh MAus MGan NBar SJus SPer WAct WHCG
'Marcie Gandy' (HT)	MGan
'Maréchal Davoust' (Mo)	EBls MAus NSty SFam
'Maréchal Niel' (N)	CCMG EBls ERea ETWh MAus MGan NSty SPer
'Margaret' (HT)	MBur MGan
Margaret Merril ® (HT/F)	CCMG CDoC CMac CSan EBls ESha EWar GCoc GGre IHos LGod LPlm LStr MAus MBri MBur MFry MGan MHay MMat NBat NElm NRog SHen SJus SPer SRum WAct WWar WWeb
Margaret Thatcher ® (HT)	CDoC MMat SRum
'Margo Koster' (Poly)	MAus NRog SJus SPer SRum
'Marguerite Guillard' (HP)	EBls
'Marguerite Hilling' (S)	CBow CCMG CHad EBls EBro ENot ETWh EWar MAus MBri MGan MMat MMor NElm NRog NSty SPer SRum WHCG WWeb
x ***mariae-graebnerae***	SLPl WBod
'Marianne Powell' (HT)	NBat
Marianne Tudor ® (HT)	MFry
'Marie de Blois' (Mo)	EBls
'Marie Louise' (D)	CCMG CCor EBls EBro ETWh IHos MAus SFam WAct WHCG
'Marie Pavié' (Poly)	EBls MAus
'Marie van Houtte' (T)	EBls MAus
'Marie-Jeanne' (Poly)	EBls MAus
'Marijke Koopman' (HT)	MFry
Marjorie Fair ® (S/GC)	CSam CSan EBls EWar LPlm LStr MAus MFry MGan MHay MMat SJus SPer SRum
'Marlena' (F/Patio)	CSan GCoc MAus MBri MFry MGan
'Marshall P Wilder' (HP)	NSty
'Martha' (Bb)	EBls MAus
'Martian Glow' (F/S)	MGan
'Martin Frobisher' (Ru)	CCor EBls MAus
'Mary' (Poly)	LStr
Mary Campbell ® (F)	NBat
Mary Donaldson ® (HT)	EWar MGan
Mary Gamon ® (Patio)	MFry
Mary Hayley Bell ® (S)	GCoc WWar WWeb
'Mary Manners' (Ru)	EBls SPer
¶ 'Mary Pope' (HT)	MMat
'Mary Queen of Scots' (pimpinellifolia)	EBls MAus NSty SRms
Mary Rose ® (S)	CCMG CCla CHad CSam CSan EBls EBre ENot ETWh EWar IHos LBre LGod LStr MAus MBri MFry MGan MHay MMat MRui NBar NBat SJus SPer SRum WHCG
'Mary Wallace' (Cl)	EBls MAus SPer
Mary Webb ® (S)	MAus MBri
'Masquerade' (F)	CB&S CGro CSan EBls EBro ESha GGre IJoh LGod LStr MAus MGan MHay MMat MMor NBar NElm NRog SHen SRum WStI WWeb

'Masquerade, Climbing' (F/Cl) CBow CSan EBls EBre EBro GGre LBre LPlm MAus MGan MHay NRog SHen SJus SRum WStI WWeb
'Master Hugh' See R. ***macrophylla*** 'M. H.'
Matangi ® (F) EWar LGod LStr MGan MHay MMat WWar
Matthias Meilland ® (F) EWar
'Max Graf' See R. × ***jacksonii*** 'Max Graf'
'Maxima' See R. ***alba*** 'Alba Maxima'
May Lyon ® (HT) LGod
'May Queen' (Ra) EBls ETWh MAus SFam SJus SPer WAct WHCG
'Mayy Woolley' (F) NBat
'McGredy's Sunset' (HT) NRog
'McGredy's Yellow' (HT) EBls MBur MGan
'McGredy's Yellow, Climbing' (HT/Cl) MGan
'Meg' (HT/Cl) CCMG CCla CHad CSan EBls ETWh MAus MBur MGan NSty SPer SRum WHCG
'Meg Merilees' (HSwB) EBls LHol MAus MGan
'Megiddo' (F) MGan WWeb
Meirov ® (Min) MGan
melina EBls
♦Melina ® (HT) See R. Sir Harry Pilkington
Melody Maker ® (F) CDoC EBre EWar GCoc GGre IDic LBre LPlm LStr MBri MBur MGan MMat NBar NBat SHen SJus SRum WWeb
§ Memento ® (F) CDoC EWar GCoc IDic MBri MGan MHay MMat WWar
'Memoriam' (HT) MGan MHay SHen
'Mermaid' (Cl) Widely available
'Merveille de Lyon' (HP) EBls
Message ® (HT) MAus MGan NBar NElm SHen
Meteor ® (F/Patio) GCoc MGan WWeb
§ 'Mevrouw G A van Rossem, Climbing' (HT/Cl) EBls MAus
§ 'Mevrouw Nathalie Nypels' (Poly) CCla CHad EBls ETWh LStr MAus SPer WAct WHCG
'Mexico' (Min) LPlm
'Michèle Meilland' (HT) EBls MAus MGan NSty SRum
× ***micrugosa*** EBls MAus
– 'Alba' EBls MAus
¶ Middlesex County ® (F) NBat
Mimi ® (Min) MGan
Mini Metro ® (Min) MFry MRui
Minijet ® (Min) EWar IHos MGan NBat
Minilights ® (Patio) CDoC EWar IDic MRui SPer
'Minnehaha' (Ra) CSan EBls EBro EMFP LGod MAus
Minnie Pearl ® (Min) MHay WWar
'Miranda Jane' (F) GCoc
mirifica stellata See R. ***stellata mirifica***
Mischief ® (HT) CDoC CSan EBls EWar GCoc GGre IJoh LPlm LStr MAus MBur MGan NElm NRog SHen SPer SRum WWeb
'Miss Edith Cavell' (Poly) EBls
Miss Harp ® (HT) MGan NElm NRog
Miss Ireland ® (HT) MGan NRog
'Miss Lowe' (Ch) CCor EBls LGre
Miss Pam Ayres ® (S) MMat WWar

§ Mister Lincoln ® (HT) CGro EBls EBro IHos LGod LStr MAus MBri MBur MGan NElm SHen SPer WWar
Modern Art ® (HT) WWar WWeb
'Modern Times' (HT) MBur MGan
'Mojave' (HT) MAus MGan
Moje Hammarberg ® (Ru) ENot IHos MMat
Molly McGredy ® (F) MGan
'Mona Ruth' (Min) MGan
'Monique' (HT) EBls MGan NSty
'Monsieur Tillier' (T) EBls
'Moon Maiden' (F) MMat
'Moonbeam' (S) MAus
'Moonlight' (HM) CCMG EBls EBro ETWh EWar IHos MAus MGan MHay MMat NElm NRog NSty SJus SPer SRum WAct WHCG
'Morgengruss' (Cl) MGan SPer
Moriah ® (HT) MGan
'Morlettii' (Bs) EBls
Morning Jewel ® (F/Cl) CB&S EWar GCoc LPlm NElm NRog SJus SPer SRum
moschata (Ra) CCMG CSan EBls ETWh MAus WAct WHCG
– ***autumnalis*** See R. 'Princesse de Nassau'
– var. ***nastarana*** See R. 'Nastarana'
– var. ***nepalensis*** (Ra) See R. ***brunonii***
Mother and Baby ® (HT) CSan
'Mothers Day' (F) ELan NElm
Mountain Snow ® (Ra) MAus MBri
Mountbatten ® (F) Widely available
§ 'Mousseline' (D/PMo) CCMG CSan EBls EBro ETWh MAus NSty SPla WAct WHCG
moyesii CBow CCMG CSam EBls ELan ENot ETWh IHos IOrc ISea MAus MFry MGan MMat MMor NRog NSty NWea WAct WHCG WStI WWeb
– 'Evesbatch' WAct
§ – var. ***fargesii*** EBls
– 'Geranium' See R. 'Geranium'
– 'Highdownensis' See R. 'Highdownensis'
– 'Hillieri' See R. 'Hillieri'
– ***holodonta*** See R. ***m. rosea***
§ – f. ***rosea*** EBls ENot
– 'Sealing Wax' See R. 'Sealing Wax'
'Mr Bluebird' (Min) EWar LGod MAus MGan MMor WStI
'Mr Chips' (HT) MBur
¶ 'Mr J C B' (S) WWar
'Mr Lincoln' See R. Mister Lincoln ®
'Mrs Aaron Ward, Climbing' (HT/Cl) EBls MAus
'Mrs Anthony Waterer' (Ru) EBls EMFP ENot IHos MAus MMat NSty SPer WAct
'Mrs Arthur Curtiss James' (HT/Cl) CCor ETWh
'Mrs Colville' (pimpinellifolia) EBls MAus
'Mrs Eveline Gandy' (HT) MGan
'Mrs G A van Rossem, Climbing' See R. 'Mevrouw G A van Rossem, Climbing'
'Mrs Herbert Stevens, Climbing' (HT/Cl) CBow CCMG EBls EMFP ETWh MAus NRog NSty WHCG

'Mrs John Laing' (HP)	CCMG EBls EBro ETWh EWar MAus NSty SFam SJus SPer WHCG
'Mrs Oakley Fisher' (HT)	CHad EBls MAus NSty WAct
'Mrs Paul' (Bb)	EBls MAus
'Mrs Pierre S du Pont' (HT)	EBls
'Mrs Sam McGredy' (HT)	MAus MBur MGan
'Mrs Sam McGredy, Climbing' (HT/Cl)	CGro EBls ETWh MAus MBri MGan MHay MMor NBar NElm NRog SPla SRum
'Mrs Walter Burns' (F/Patio)	MGan
'München' (HM)	MAus
'Mullard Jubilee' (HT)	EWar MAus MGan
mulliganii	EBls MAus
multibracteata	CCor EBls MAus MPar WHCG WWeb
multiflora	CCMG CCor EBls MAus WHCG
– 'Carnea'	EBls
– var. ***cathayensis***	EBls
§ – 'Grevillei'	EBls ETWh SPla
– 'Platyphylla'	See R. ***m.*** 'Grevillei'
– var. ***watsoniana***	See R. ***watsoniana***
– 'Wilsonii'	CSan
mundi	See R. ***gallica*** 'Versicolor'
– ***versicolor***	See R. ***gallica*** 'Versicolor'
'Munster' (S)	MGan
muriculata	CCor
'Mutabilis'	See R. x ***odorata*** 'Mutabilis'
'My Choice' (HT)	MGan SHen
'My Guy' (HT)	NBat
'My Joy' (HT)	EWar MHay
'My Little Boy' (Min)	MBur
'My Love' (HT)	GGre MBur MGan MHay WWeb
'My Love, Climbing' (HT/Cl)	MGan
My Valentine ® (Min)	EBre LBre MHay NBat
Myra ® (HT)	NBat
Myriam ® (HT)	GCoc
nanothamnus	See R. ***webbiana microphylla***
'Narrow Water' (Ra)	EBls WAct WHCG
§ 'Nastarana' (N)	EBls
'Nathalie Nypels'	See R. 'Mevrouw Nathalie Nypels'
'National Trust' (HT)	EBls ESha EWar GGre IHos LGod LStr MAus MFry MGan MHay MMat MMor NBar NElm NRog SHen SPer WStI WWeb
'Nestor' (G)	EBls MAus
'Nevada' (S)	Widely available
Neville Gibson ® (HT)	MHay
§ 'New Dawn' (Cl)	Widely available
New Horizon ® (F)	CDoC IDic
'New Look' (F)	MGan
'New Penny' (Min)	CGro EWar GGre MAus MBur MGan MMor MRui WWeb
¶ New Zealand ® (HT)	MHay NBat
News ® (F)	IHos LGod MAus MGan
'Nicola' (F)	EWar MGan MHay
Night Light ® (Cl)	CDoC EWar MBri MBur MGan SJus WWar
Nina Weibull ® (F)	MGan
'Niphetos' (T/Cl)	EBls

nitida	CBow CCor EBls EBro ELan ENot GCal IHos MAus NSty NWea SPer WHCG
§ 'Noisette Carnée' (N)	CCMG CCor CHad EBls EMFP ETWh SFam SPer WAct WHCG
'Norah Cruickshank' (HT)	GCoc
Norfolk ® (GC)	CCMG CCla CCor CSan EBre ENot EWar GCoc IHos LBre LGod LPlm LStr MAus MFry MMat SPer
Northamptonshire ® (GC)	ENot EWar LGod MMat
Northern Lights ® (HT)	GCoc
'Northumberland WI' (HT)	NBat
'Norwich Castle' (F)	EBls
'Norwich Pink' (Cl)	MAus
'Norwich Salmon' (Cl)	MAus
'Norwich Union' (F)	EBls
'Nova Zembla' (Ru)	CCMG EBls MAus NSty
'Nozomi' (GC)	CCMG CGro CSan EBls EFol ELan ENot ESha EWar GCoc GGre IHos LPlm LStr MAus MBur MFry MGan MMat MMor NBar NElm SHen SJus SPer SRum WAct WHCG WWeb
'Nuits de Young' (Mo)	CCMG CCor CHad EBls ETWh GCoc MAus MMat NSty SFam WHCG
'Nur Mahal' (HM)	EBls EBro MAus WHCG
nutkana	EBls MAus SRms
§ – var. ***hispida***	EBls
§ – 'Plena'	CCMG CCla CCor EBls ENot MAus NSty SJus
'Nymphenburg' (HM)	CCMG CCla EBls ETWh GCoc IHos MAus SPer
'Nypels' Perfection' (Poly)	MAus
'Nyveldt's White' (Ru)	CCor EBls IHos MAus
'Oakington Ruby' (Min)	CCor CHal GAri
'Octet' (S)	CCor
♦ x ***odorata*** 'Fortune's Double Yellow' (Cl)	See R. x ***o.*** 'Pseudindica'
§ – 'Mutabilis' (Ch)	CCMG CCor CGre CHad EBls EBro EMFP ENot ETWh IDai LGre MAus MMat NRar NSty SJus SPer WHCG WKif WWat
§ – 'Ochroleuca' (Ch)	EBls
§ – 'Odorata' (Ch)	EBls WHCG
§ – 'Pallida' (Ch)	CCMG CCla CCor CHad EBls EMFP ETWh IHos MMat SHen SJus SPer SPla WHCG
§ – 'Pseudindica'	EBls MAus SHil WSHC
§ – Sanguinea Group (Ch)	CHad EBls WHCG
§ – 'Viridiflora'	CSan EBls IHos LGre MAus MBur SJus SMad SRum WHCG
'Oeillet Flamand'	See R. 'Oeillet Parfait'
'Oeillet Parfait' (G)	EBls MAus
officinalis	See R. ***gallica o.***

officinalis	See R. ***gallica o.***
'Oh La La' (F)	WWeb
'Ohl' (G)	EBls
Ohshima Rose ® (HT)	GCoc
'Oklahoma' (HT)	MGan
'Old Blush China'	See R. x ***odorata*** 'Pallida'
Old Cabbage	See R. x ***centifolia***
Old Master ® (F)	MAus MBur MGan
Old Pink Moss	See R. x ***centifolia*** 'Muscosa'
Old Velvet Moss	See R. 'William Lobb'
Old Yellow Scotch	See R. x ***harisonii*** 'Williams' Double Yellow'
Olympiad ® (HT)	MBri
'Omar Khayyám' (D)	EBls ENot IHos MAus SPer
§ 'Ombrée Parfaite ' (G)	EBls
omeiensis f. *pteracantha*	See R. ***sericea pteracantha***
'Ophelia' (HT)	EBls MAus MGan NSty
'Ophelia, Climbing' (HT/Cl)	CBow EBls EBro ETWh MAus
'Orange Honey' (Min)	MBur MFry MHay SJus WWeb
§ Orange Sensation ® (F)	EBls ESha EWar GGre IJoh MAus MGan MHay MMor NElm NRog SRum WWeb
Orange Sunblaze ® (Min)	CGro EBls EWar GCoc GGre IHos IJoh LGod MGan MHay MRui NElm SHen SJus WWeb
Orange Sunblaze, Climbing ® (Min/Cl)	EWar MBri MRui WStI
Orange Triumph ® (Poly)	CCla EBls
'Orangeade' (F)	CDoC EBro MGan SHen
'Orangeade, Climbing' (F/Cl)	MGan
¶ 'Oranges and Lemons' (F)	GCoc LGod LStr MBur MFry
'Oriana' (HT)	CGro
'Orient Express' (HT)	NBat
'Ormiston Roy' (pimpinellifolia)	MAus NSty
'Orpheline de Juillet'	See R. 'Ombrée Parfaite'
Othello ® (S)	CDoC CSan EWar MAus MHay SJus SPer WHCG
Our Love ® (HT)	GGre
'Over the Rainbow' (Min)	CSan MBur MHay
'Oxfam' (HT)	MHay
Paddy McGredy ® (F)	CGro EWar GGre MAus MGan MHay NElm NRog SRum
Painted Moon ® (HT)	CDoC IDic MFry
Paint-Pot ® (Min)	MRui
'Pam Ayers' (S)	See R. Miss Pam Ayers ®
Pandora ® (Min)	MRui
'Panorama Holiday' (F)	MBur SJus
'Papa Gontier' (T)	EBls MAus
'Papa Hémeray' (Ch)	EBls
Papa Meilland ® (HT)	CB&S CGro EBls EBro MAus MGan MHay NElm NRog SPer SRum WWeb
'Papillon' (T)	EBls
Paprika ® (F)	LStr MAus MMor
'Pâquerette' (Poly)	EBls
§ 'Para Ti' (Min)	EWar MBur MGan MMat SJus SPer
'Parade' (Cl)	MAus MFry MGan MHay MMat MRui SJus
Paradise ® (HT)	MGan MMat
Parkdirektor Riggers ® (Cl)	CCMG CCla CDoC CHad CSam CSan EBls EBre EBro EWar LBre LStr MAus MBri MBur MGan MMat MMor NElm SJus SPer SRum WAct WHCG WWar
Parks' Yellow China	See R. x ***odorata*** 'Ochroleuca'
'Parkzierde' (Bb)	EBls
'Parsons' Pink China'	See R. x ***odorata*** 'Pallida'
Partridge ® (GC)	CCMG EBls ENot IHos MAus MGan MMat SPer WHCG WWeb
'Party Girl' (Min)	MHay
parvifolia	See R. 'Burgundiaca'
Pascali ® (HT)	Widely available
'Pascali, Climbing' (HT/Cl)	CB&S MGan
Patricia ® (F)	SRum
'Paul Crampel' (Poly)	EBls MAus MGan NElm NRog NSty SPer
'Paul Lédé, Climbing' (T/Cl)	CBow CCMG EBls ETWh MAus SJus
Paul McCartney ®	See R. The McCartney Rose ®
'Paul Neyron' (HP)	EBls EBro ETWh MAus MMat NSty SPer WHCG
'Paul Ricault' (CexHP)	CCor EBls MAus
Paul Shirville ® (HT)	CCMG CDoC EWar GCoc GGre IHos LPlm LStr MAus MFry MGan MHay MMat NBar NBat NRog SJus SPer WWar WWeb
'Paul Transon' (Ra)	CCMG CCor CSan EBls EMFP EMon ETWh MAus MBri SPer WAct
'Paul Verdier' (Bb)	EBls
§ 'Paulii' (Ru)	CBow CCor CSan EBls EHar ELan ENot ETWh IHos MAus MBur MMat MMor SPer WAct WHCG WWeb
'Paulii Alba'	See R. 'Paulii'
'Paulii Rosea' (Ru/Cl)	EBls MAus MBri WAct WHCG
'Paul's Early Blush' (HP)	EBls
'Paul's Himalayan Musk' (Ra)	CCMG CCla CCor CHad CSam CSan EBls EBre EBro EHar EMFP ETWh EWar LBre MAus MBri MRui NBar NSty SJus SPer WAct WHCG WKif
§ 'Paul's Lemon Pillar' (HT/Cl)	CCMG CCla EBls EBre EBro ETWh LBre MAus NRog NSty SJus SPer SRum WHCG WSHC
'Paul's Perpetual White' (Ra)	CBow EBls ETWh
'Paul's Scarlet Climber' (Ra/Cl)	CCMG CGro CSan EBls EBro ELan ETWh EWar GCoc GGre IHos IJoh LGod LPlm LStr MAus MBur MGan MHay MMat MMor NElm NSty SHen SPer SRum WSHC WWeb
'Pax' (HM)	CCMG CCla EBls EBro MAus NSty SPer WHCG
Peace ® (HT)	Widely available
Peace Sunblaze ® (Min)	EWar
Peach Blossom ® (S)	EWar MAus MRui
Peach Sunblaze ® (Min)	MRui
'Peaches 'n' Cream' (Min)	MHay
'Peachy' (HT)	MRui

'Peachy White' (Min)	MAus
Pearl Drift ® (GC)	EBls EWar LStr MAus SJus SPer WHCG
♦Peaudouce ® (HT)	See R. 'Elina'
Peek A Boo ® (Min/Patio)	CDoC EBre ELan EWar GCoc GGre IDic IHos LBre LGod LStr MAus MFry MGan MMat MRui SJus SPer WStI WWar
Peer Gynt ® (HT)	EBre ESha IHos LBre LPlm MAus MGan MMat
'Pélisson' (Mo)	EBls WHCG
§ *pendulina*	EBls MAus MPar WHCG
'Penelope' (HM)	Widely available
Penelope Keith ® (Min/Patio)	MMat
Penelope Plummer ® (F)	EBls
Pensioner's Voice ® (F)	MFry WWar WWeb
Penthouse ® (HT)	EWar
x *penzanceana*	See R. 'Lady Penzance'
Peppermint Ice ® (F)	MBur
'Percy Thrower' (HT)	SRum
Perdita ® (S)	CCMG EWar IHos IOrc MAus MBri SPer WHCG
Perestroika ® (F/Min)	MBur MMat WWar
Perfecta ® (HT)	EBls MGan MHay SRum
'Perla de Montserrat' (Min)	EWar
'Perla d'Alcañada' (Min)	EWar IHos MAus MMat
'Perle des Jardins' (T)	EBls MAus
'Perle des Panachées' (G)	EBls
'Perle d'Or' (Poly)	CCMG CCor CHad CSan EMFP ENot ETWh GCoc MAus MMat MPar NRar NRog NSty SPer SPla WAct WHCG WWat
'Perle von Hohenstein' (Poly)	EBls
Pernille Poulsen ® (F)	EBls MGan
'Persian Yellow'	See R. ***foetida*** 'Persiana'
Peter Frankenfeld ® (HT)	MHay
Petit Four ® (Min/Patio)	IDic MAus
'Petite de Hollande' (Ce)	CCMG EBls ETWh MAus NSty SPer WAct WHCG
Petite Folie ® (Min)	GGre MGan
'Petite Lisette' (Ce/D)	EBls MAus SHen SPer WHCG
'Petite Orléannaise' (Ce)	EBls
'Pharisäer' (HT)	EBls
Pheasant ® (GC)	ENot GCoc IHos MAus MGan MMat SPer WStI WWeb
'Phoebe' (S)	MRui
'Phyllis Bide' (Ra)	CBow CCMG CSan EBls EMFP ETWh EWar MAus MGan NSty SJus SPer WHCG
Picasso ® (F)	EBls MAus MGan
Piccadilly ® (HT)	CB&S CGro CSan EBls EBre ESha EWar GCoc GGre IJoh LBre LGod LPlm LStr MAus MBur MFry MGan MHay MMat MMor NBat NElm NRog SHen SPer SRum WWeb
Piccolo ® (F/Patio)	CGro EWar GGre LStr MBri MFry MGan MHay MMor WWar WWeb
'Picture' (HT)	EBls MAus MGan NRog NSty SPer
'Picture, Climbing' (HT/Cl)	EBls MAus MGan
'Pierre Notting' (HP)	EBls
Pigalle '84 ® (F)	SRum
Pillar Box ® (F)	LGod MGan WWar
§ ***pimpinellifolia***	CBow CCMG CKin EBls ENot ETWh LGre MAus MGan MMat NWea SPer WAct WHCG
– cultivars	See under cultivar names
– ***altaica*** hort.	See R. 'Grandiflora'
§ – double pink	CCor EBls WHCG
§ – double white	CBow CCMG EBls GCoc MAus WAct
– double yellow	See R. x ***harisonii*** 'Williams' Double Yellow'
– 'Harisonii'	See R. x ***harisonii*** 'Harison's Yellow'
– ***lutea***	See R. x ***harisonii*** 'Lutea Maxima'
– x ***pendula***	See R. x ***reversa***
'Pineapple Poll' (F)	MGan
Pink Bells ® (GC)	CCMG CCla CDoC CGro CSan EBls ENot EWar GCoc IHos LBuc LStr MAus MGan MMat SPer WAct WHCG WWeb
'Pink Bouquet' (Ra)	MAus
Pink Chimo ® (S/GC)	IDic
Pink Drift ® (Min/GC)	ENot IHos MMat
'Pink Elizabeth Arden' (F)	EWar SHen WWeb
'Pink Favorite' (HT)	GCoc IHos IJoh MAus MGan MHay MMor NBat NElm NRog SPer SRum WWeb
'Pink Grootendorst' (Ru)	CB&S CCMG CSan EBls ENot EWar IHos IOrc LStr MAus MGan MMat MMor NRog NSty SPer SRum WAct WHCG
'Pink Heather' (Min)	SJus
Pink La Sevillana ® (F/GC)	EWar NBar SHen SJus SRum
Pink Meidiland ® (GC)	MGan
Pink Moss	See R. ***centifolia*** 'Muscosa'
Pink Nevada ® (S)	CSan
Pink Panther ® (HT)	EWar
'Pink Parfait' (F)	CSan EBls GCoc GGre IHos IJoh LPlm LStr MAus MBur MGan MMor NBar NBat NElm NRog SHen SPer SRum WWeb
Pink Peace ® (HT)	CB&S ESha GGre MAus MMor NElm SRum WWeb
'Pink Pearl' (HT)	MBri MMat WWar
'Pink Perpétué' (Cl)	Widely available
'Pink Petticoat' (Min)	MHay WWar
Pink Posy ® (Min/Patio)	GCoc MAus
'Pink Prosperity' (HM)	CCMG EBls MAus
'Pink Showers' (HT/Cl)	WAct
Pink Sunblaze ® (Min/Patio)	CSan EWar GCoc MRui NBar NElm WWeb
Pink Surprise ® (Ru)	MAus
Pink Wave ® (GC)	ENot IHos MMat
'Pinocchio' (F)	EBls
'Pinta' (HT)	EBls
pisocarpa	CCor
'Pixie Rose' (Min)	IHos
Playgroup Rose ® (F)	NBat
Pleine de Grâce ® (S)	MAus SPer
'Plentiful' (F)	EBls MAus
Polar Star ® (HT)	EBls EHar ESha EWar GCoc IHos LGod LPlm LStr MAus MFry MGan MHay MMat NBar NBat NElm NRog SHen SJus SPer SRum WWar WWeb
'Polly' (HT)	EBls MAus MGan NElm NRog
polyantha grandiflora	See R. ***gentiliana***

pomifera	See R. ***villosa***
– 'Duplex'	See R. 'Wolley-Dod'
'Pompon Blanc Parfait' (A)	CCMG EBls MAus SFam
'Pompon de Bourgogne'	See R. 'Burgundiaca'
'Pompon de Paris, Climbing' (Ch/Cl)	CBot CCor EBls LHop MAus MPar MRav NSty SIng SPer WHCG WSHC WThu
'Pompon Panaché' (G)	CCMG EBls MAus
Portland Rose	See R. 'Portlandica'
§ 'Portlandica'	CCMG EBls ETWh SJus SPer WAct WHCG
Pot o'Gold ® (HT)	CDoC ESha GCoc IDic IHos LStr MAus MFry MGan SPer WWar
Potter and Moore ® (S)	IHos MAus
'Poulmouti'	MGan MRui
'Pour Toi'	See R. 'Para Ti'
Prairie Rose	See R. ***setigera***
prattii	CCor
'Precious Platinum' (HT)	IDic IHos LGod LStr MAus MBri MGan MHay SJus SPer WWar
§ 'Président de Sèze' (G)	CCMG CCor EBls EMFP ETWh MAus NSty SFam SHen SPer WHCG
'President Herbert Hoover' (HT)	WWat
'Prestige' (S)	NRog
Pretty Jessica ® (S)	IHos MAus WHCG
Pretty Polly ® (Min)	CGro EWar GCoc GGre LStr MFry MGan MMat MRui WWar WWeb
Pride of Park ® (F)	MFry
Prima Ballerina ® (HT)	CB&S CCMG CGro CMac CSan EBls GCoc GGre IHos IJoh LPlm LStr MAus MBur MFry MGan MHay MMat MMor NBat NElm NRog SHen SPer SRum WWeb
primula	CCMG CHad CSan EBls EBro EHar EMFP ENot ETWh IHos MAus MMat NSty WAct WHCG WKif
'Prince Camille de Rohan' (HP)	EBls MAus WHCG
'Prince Charles' (Bb)	CCMG CCor EBls ETWh MAus NSty SPla WHCG
Prince Sunblaze ® (Min)	MRui
Princess Alice ® (F)	CDoC EWar LGod MGan MHay
Princess Margaret of England ® (HT)	EWar
Princess Michael of Kent ® (F)	MGan SHen WWar
'Princess Michiko' (F)	EWar MGan MMor
¶ Princess Royal ® (HT)	GCoc IDic MFry
§ 'Princesse de Nassau' (Ra)	EBls MAus WHCG
'Princesse Louise' (Ra)	MAus
'Princesse Marie' (Ra)	EBro MBri
Priscilla Burton ® (F)	EWar MAus MGan SJus
Pristine ® (HT)	CDoC EWar GCoc IDic IHos LPlm LStr MAus MGan NBar SPer WWar
N 'Professeur Emile Perrot' (D)	CCor EBls ETWh IHos NSty SPla WHCG
'Prolifera de Redouté' misapplied	See R. 'Duchesse de Montebello'
'Prosperity' (HM)	CBow CCor CSan EBls EBre EBro ENot ETWh EWar GCoc IOrc LBre MAus MBur MFry MGan MHay MMat MRui NElm NRog SJus SPer WAct WHCG WWeb
Prospero ® (S)	CCMG ETWh MAus MBri
x ***pruhoniciana*** 'Hillieri'	See R. 'Hillieri'
Pucker Up ® (Min)	MHay
§ ***pulverulenta***	EBls
'Purity' (Ra)	CCor CSan
'Purple Beauty' (HT)	MGan
'Purple Splendour' (F)	MAus
¶ Purple Tiger ® (F)	MBur
¶ Quaker Star ® (F)	IDic
Quatre Saisons	See R. x ***damascena semperflorens***
'Quatre Saisons Blanche Mousseuse' (D/Mo)	EBls ETWh
Queen Charlotte ® (HT)	GCoc MBri MBur
♦ Queen Elizabeth ® (F)	See R. 'The Queen Elizabeth'
Queen Mother ® (Patio)	GCoc IHos LStr MBur MMat SPer WWeb
Queen Nefertiti ® (S)	IHos MAus
'Queen of Bedders' (Bb)	EBls
'Queen of Denmark'	See R. 'Königin von Dänemark'
'Queen of Hearts'	See R. 'Dame de Coeur'
Radox Bouquet ® (F)	EWar GCoc MBur
'Radway Sunrise' (S)	EBls
'Rainbow' (S)	MMat
'Rambling Rector' (Ra)	CBow CCMG CCla CCor CHad EBls EBre ELan EMFP ETWh EWar LBre LGod MAus MBri MBur MGan MRui NSty SFam SJus SPer SPla SRum WAct WHCG WSHC
§ 'Ramona' (Cl)	EBls ETWh MAus WHCG WSHC
§ 'Raubritter' (***macrantha x***)	CCMG CCla CCor CHad EBls ETWh IHos MAus MBri MMat NSty SPer WAct WHCG
Ray of Sunshine ® (Patio)	ESha GCoc GGre LPlm LStr MBri MFry NBat SJus
'Raymond Chenault' (Cl)	MGan
'Rebecca Claire' (HT)	GCoc SPer
Red Ace ® (Min)	LGod LPlm MFry MHay MRui
'Red Beauty' (Min)	MHay
Red Bells ® (Min/GC)	CCla CDoC CGro CSan EBls ENot EWar IHos LStr MAus MGan MMat SPer WHCG WWeb
Red Blanket ® (S/GC)	CGro CSan EBls ENot EWar GCoc IDic IHos LGod LStr MAus MGan MMat SJus SPer SRum WAct WWeb
'Red Coat' (F)	IHos MAus
'Red Dandy' (F)	MGan
Red Devil ® (HT)	CSan ESha EWar GGre LPlm LStr MAus MGan MHay NBar NBat NElm NRog SHen SRum
Red Dot ® (S/GC)	IDic MMat
¶ 'Red Elf' (Min)	GAri
'Red Empress' (Cl)	LStr
'Red Grootendorst'	See R. 'F J Grootendorst'
'Red Lion' (HT)	MGan MHay
'Red Max Graf'	See R. 'Rote Max Graf'
Red Minimo ® (Min)	IHos MFry MRui
Red Moss	See R. 'Henri Martin'

'Red Queen' (HT)	MHay
Red Rascal ® (Patio)	CSan EWar GCoc IDic MBri MBur
Red Rose of Lancaster	See R. ***gallica officinalis***
Red Splendour ® (F)	MHay
Red Sunblaze ® (Min)	EWar IHos IJoh NBar SJus WWar WWeb
Red Trail ® (S/GC)	EWar IDic
§ 'Red Wing' (***hugonis x***)	EBls MAus
Redgold ® (F)	GGre MGan NBar
¶ Redouté ®	MRui
Regensberg ® (F/Patio)	ESha EWar GCoc IHos LPlm LStr MAus MBri MFry MGan MHay MMat NBar NRog
'Reine des Centifeuilles' (Ce)	EBls SFam
'Reine des Violettes' (HP)	CCMG CCor CHad CSan EBls EBro ETWh EWar LStr MAus NSty SFam SJus SPer WHCG
'Reine Marie Henriette' (HT/Cl)	EBls
§ 'Reine Victoria' (Bb)	CCMG CCor CSan EBls EBro EMFP ETWh IHos LStr MAus MGan MHay NSty SJus SPer SPla WHCG
Remember Me ® (HT)	CDoC CSan ESha EWar GCoc GGre LGod LPlm LStr MFry MGan MHay MMat NBar NBat NRog SPer WWar
¶ Rémy Martin ® (HT)	LStr
'René André' (Ra)	EBls ETWh MAus SJus
'René d'Anjou' (Mo)	EBls MAus
Repens Meidiland ® (S)	EWar
'Rescht'	See R. 'De Rescht'
'Rêve d'Or' (N)	CCMG EBls ETWh MAus WSHC
'Réveil Dijonnais' (HT/Cl)	EBls MAus
'Reverend F Page-Roberts' (HT)	EBls
§ x ***reversa*** white form	MPar
'Rhodes Rose' (S)	NSty
'Richard Buckley' (F)	MBur
§ x ***richardii***	EBls MAus MBri SJus WHCG
'Richmond, Climbing' (HT/Cl)	EBls MAus
§ 'Rise 'n' Shine' (Min)	CSan EWar LGod MGan MHay MRui NBat NElm
'Ritter von Barmstede' (Cl)	MGan MMor
'Rival de Paestum' (T)	EBls MAus
Rob Roy ® (F)	CCMG GCoc MBur MGan SHen SPer
§ Robbie Burns ® (pimpinellifolia)	CHad MAus WAct
'Robert le Diable' (Ce)	CCor EBls MAus NSty SPer WAct WHCG
'Robert Léopold' (DPMo)	EBls
'Robin Hood' (HM)	EBls EBro
Robin Redbreast ® (Min/GC)	CGro EBls IDic IHos MAus SPer WWeb
§ Robusta ® (Ru)	EBls MAus MMat
'Roger Lambelin' (HP)	EBls ENot MAus MMat NSty SPer WAct
Romance ® (S)	WWeb
Rosabell ® (F/Patio)	GCoc LPlm MFry
'Rosalie Coral' (Cl)	MRui NBat SJus WWar
'Rose à Parfum de l'Hay' (Ru)	EBls
'Rose de Meaux'	See R. 'De Meaux'
'Rose de Meaux White'	See R. 'De Meaux White'
'Rose de Rescht'	See R. 'De Rescht'
'Rose des Maures'	See R. 'Sissinghurst Castle'
'Rose du Maître d'Ecole'	See R. 'Du Maître d'Ecole'
'Rose du Roi' (HP/D)	EBls MAus NSty WHCG
'Rose du Roi à Fleurs Pourpres' (HP)	EBls MAus
§ 'Rose d'Amour'	CCor EBls ETWh EWar ISea MAus SJus WHCG
'Rose d'Hivers' (D)	EBls
'Rose d'Orsay' (S)	EBls
'Rose Edouard' (Bb)	EBls
§ Rose Gaujard ® (HT)	EBls ESha EWar GGre IJoh LGod LPlm LStr MAus MBur MGan MHay MMor NElm SHen SRum WWeb
'Rosemary Gandy' (F)	MGan
Rosemary Harkness ® (HT)	CDoC EWar IHos LStr MBur MMat SPer WWar WWeb
'Rosemary Rose' (F)	EBls MAus MBri NRog SPer
'Rosenelfe' (F)	EBls
'Roseraie de l'Haÿ' (Ru)	Widely available
'Rosette Delizy' (T)	EBls MAus
§ 'Rose-Marie Viaud' (Ra)	MAus NSty SPer WHCG
¶ 'Rosie Larkin' (S)	MFry
§ 'Rosina' (Min)	EWar GCoc LPlm MGan MMat
'Rosmarin' (Min)	LPlm
'Rosy Cheeks' (HT)	GGre LPlm MBur MFry MGan WWeb
Rosy Cushion ® (S/GC)	CGro ENot EWar GCoc IDic IHos IJoh LGod LStr MAus MGan MMat SJus SPer WAct WHCG WWeb
Rosy Future ® (F/Patio)	GCoc
Rosy Gem ® (Min)	GGre
'Rosy Mantle' (Cl)	CB&S EWar GCoc LPlm MGan SPer
§ Rote Max Graf ® (GC)	EBls ENot EWar IHos LStr MMat SJus WAct
'Roundelay' (S)	EBls MAus
Roxburghe Rose ® (HT)	GCoc
roxburghii	CB&S CCla CCor CMCN GCal MMat NSty WAct WHCG
– f. ***normalis***	EBls MAus
– 'Plena'	See R. ***r. roxburghii***
§ – f. ***roxburghii***	CCor MAus
'Royal Albert Hall' (HT)	EBls GCoc MGan
Royal Baby ® (F/Min)	MBur
Royal Brompton Rose ® (HT)	See R. Yves Piaget ®
'Royal Gold' (Cl)	CCMG CGro EBls EWar IHos IJoh LPlm LStr MAus MBri MFry MGan MHay MMor MRui NElm NRog SRum WStI WWeb
'Royal Highness' (HT)	CGro EBls MGan MHay NBat SRum WWeb
Royal Meillandina ® (Min/Patio)	EWar
'Royal Occasion' (F)	SPer
Royal Romance ® (HT)	MFry SJus
Royal Salute ® (Min)	EWar MHay MMat NElm NRog
'Royal Smile' (HT)	EBls
¶ Royal Sunblaze ® (Min)	EWar
Royal Volunteer ® (HT)	GCoc

Name	Suppliers
Royal William ® (HT)	CDoC CGro CSan EHar ELan ESha EWar GCoc LGod LPlm LStr MAus MBur MGan MHay MMat MMor NBar NElm SHen SJus SPer SRum WWar WWeb
'Rubens' (HP)	EBls
rubiginosa	See R. ***eglanteria***
rubra	See R. ***gallica***
rubrifolia	See R. ***glauca***
– 'Carmenetta'	See R. 'Carmenetta'
'Rubrotincta'	See R. 'Hebe's Lip'
rubus (Ra)	MAus
'Ruby Wedding' (HT)	CB&S CCMG CSan EBre ELan EWar GCoc GGre LBre LGod LPlm LStr MAus MBri MFry MGan MHay MMat MMor NBat NElm NRog SHen SJus SPer SRum WWeb
'Ruga' (Ra)	EBls MAus
rugosa	CCor CPer CSam CSan EPla IHos ISea LBuc LHol MAus MBri WAct WStI
– 'Alba'	CB&S CCMG CCor CDoC CSan EBls ELan ETWh EWar IHos IJoh LBuc LStr MAus MBri MMat NRoo NSty SJus SPer SPla SRum WAct WHCG
– var. ***kamtschatica***	See R. ***r. ventenatiana***
– ***rubra***	CB&S CCor CDoC ETWh EWar IJoh LBuc MMat NRoo NSty SPer SRum WAct
– 'Scabrosa'	See R. 'Scabrosa'
§ – var. ***ventenatiana***	CCor
'Rugosa Atropurpurea' (Ru)	NRog
§ 'Rugul' (Min)	IHos MFry MGan MRui
'Ruhm von Steinfurth' (HP)	EBls MGan
Rumba ® (F)	MGan SHen
Running Maid ® (S/GC)	MAus WAct
'Ruskin' (Ru x HP)	EBls MAus SPer
'Russelliana' (Ra)	CCMG CCor EBls EMFP ETWh MAus WHCG
¶ 'Ruth Woodward' (Fl)	IDic
Rutland ® (Min/GC)	ENot EWar IHos MMat
'Sadler's Wells' (S)	EBls
'Safrano' (T)	EBls
Saint Boniface ® (F/Patio)	ESha MHay MMat
Saint Cecilia ® (S)	CCMG ELan ETWh EWar IHos MAus MRui NBar
Saint Dunstan's Rose ® (S)	NBat
Saint Hugh's ® (HT)	MMat
Saint John's Rose	See R. x ***richardii***
Saint Mark's Rose	See R. 'Rose d'Amour'
'Saint Nicholas' (D)	CCor EBls MAus SJus WHCG
'Saint Prist de Breuze' (Ch)	EBls
'Salet' (DPMo)	CCMG EBls EBro ETWh MAus SJus WAct WHCG
salictorum	CCor
Salita ® (Cl)	NBat WWar
Sally Holmes ® (S)	CCor CHad EBls GCoc MAus MBri MFry MGan MHay NBat
Samaritan ® (HT)	MFry
sancta	See R. x ***richardii***
'Sanders' White Rambler' (Ra)	CBow CCMG CCla CCor CDoC CSan EBls EBre EBro EMFP ETWh GGre IHos LBre MAus MGan MHay MMor NRog NSty SPer SRum WAct WHCG
'Sandringham Centenary' (HT)	EBls
'Sanguinea'	See R. x ***odorata*** Sanguinea Group
Sarabande ® (F)	MGan
Sarah ® (HT)	CCMG EWar MBur
'Sarah van Fleet' (Ru)	CCMG CGro EBls EBre EMFP ENot ETWh GCoc LBre LStr MAus MFry MGan MMat MMor MRui NElm NRog NSty SPer SRum WAct WHCG
Sarah, Duchess of York ® (F/Patio)	See R. Duchess of York ®
Satchmo ® (F)	ESha EWar IHos
Savoy Hotel ® (HT)	CCMG CSan EWar GCoc GGre LGod LStr MAus MBri MBur MFry MGan MHay MMat NBar SJus SPer WWeb
§ 'Scabrosa' (Ru)	CBow CCMG CCla CSan EBls EBro ETWh GCoc IHos MAus MGan MMat WAct WHCG
'Scarlet Fire'	See R. 'Scharlachglut'
§ Scarlet Gem ® (Min)	ELan EWar GGre LPlm MGan MMor
'Scarlet Glow'	See R. 'Scharlachglut'
Scarlet Meidiland ® (S/GC)	EWar IHos MGan MMat
¶ 'Scarlet Patio' (Patio)	MMat
'Scarlet Pimpernel'	See R. Scarlet Gem ®
Scarlet Queen Elizabeth ® (F)	CB&S CGro EBls GGre IJoh MBur MMor NElm SHen SRum WStI WWeb
'Scarlet Showers' (Cl)	MGan
Scarletta ® (Min)	GGre IHos MHay MMor
'Scented Air' (F)	MGan MMat SPer
§ 'Scharlachglut' (S/Cl)	CCMG CCla EBls ELan ENot ETWh LStr MAus MBur MGan MMat NSty SPer WAct WHCG WSHC
Scherzo ® (F)	EWar
'Schneelicht' (Ru)	EBls MAus
'Schneewittchen'	See R. 'Iceberg'
§ 'Schneezwerg' (Ru)	EBls ENot ETWh GCoc IHos IOrc MAus MGan MMat MMor NSty SPer SPla WAct WHCG WWeb
'Schoolgirl' (Cl)	Widely available
'Scintillation' (S/GC)	CCMG CCor MAus
Scotch	See R. ***pimpinellifolia***
Scottish Special ® (Min/Patio)	GCoc NBat
Sea Foam ® (S)	CDoC
'Sea Pearl' (F)	MGan MMat
'Seagull' (Ra)	CCMG CHad CSan EBls EBre EBro ELan ESha ETWh EWar GCoc LBre LGod LStr MAus MGan NElm NRog NSty SPer WAct WHCG
§ 'Sealing Wax' (***moyesii x***)	EBls MAus WAct
Selfridges ® (HT)	MMat
'Semiplena'	See R. x ***alba*** 'Alba Semiplena'
sempervirens (Ra)	CCor
'Sénateur Amic' (Cl)	EBls

Name	Suppliers
sericea	CCor MAus MBal
– 'Heather Muir'	See R. 'Heather Muir'
§ – ssp. ***omeiensis*** f.***pteracantha***	CBow CCMG CHad CPMA CSan EBls EBre EHar ELan EMFP ENot EPla ETWh EWar LBre MAus MGan MMat NRog NSty SJus SMad SPer WAct WHCG WWeb
– 'Red Wing'	See R. 'Red Wing'
'Serratipetala' (Ch)	CCor
§ ***setigera***	EBls MAus
setipoda	EBls MAus WAct WWat
'Seven Seas' (F)	MBur
Seven Sisters Rose	See R. ***multiflora*** 'Grevillei'
§ Sexy Rexy ® (F)	CGro CSan EBre ELan EWar GGre IHos IJoh LBre LStr MBri MFry MHay NBar NBat SJus SPer SRum WWeb
§ 'Shailer's White Moss' (Ce/Mo)	CBow CCMG CDoC EBls EBro ETWh EWar MAus MGan MMat NRog NSty SFam SJus WAct
Sharifa Asma ® (S)	CAbP CBow CCMG EWar MAus MMat MRui WAct WWeb
Sheila's Perfume ® (HT/F)	CDoC EWar GCoc GGre LPlm LStr MGan MHay NRog SHen SJus WWar
'Shepherd's Delight' (F)	MGan
Sheri Anne ® (Min)	MAus MBur MFry MHay MRui SJus
Shocking Blue ® (F)	LPlm MGan MMat SPer WWar
Shona ® (F)	IDic
'Shot Silk' (HT)	EBls GCoc MAus MBur MGan
'Shot Silk, Climbing' (HT/Cl)	CBow CCMG CSan EBls ETWh MAus MGan MHay SHen SJus SPer SRum
Shrewsbury Show ® (HT)	MFry
'Shropshire Lass' (S)	MAus SPer
Silver Jubilee ® (HT)	Widely available
'Silver Lining' (HT)	CMac EBls LPlm MAus MBur MHay SRum
'Silver Moon' (Cl)	CCMG EBls ETWh MAus
'Silver Tips' (Min)	MAus MGan
'Silver Wedding' (HT)	CCMG CSan EBls EBre ELan GCoc GGre LBre MBur MFry MGan MHay MMat MMor NBar NElm NRog SHen SPer SRum WStI WWeb
Simba ® (HT)	CSan GCoc LStr MBri MGan MHay MMat
Simon Robinson ® (Min/GC)	EBls
'Single Cherry' (pimpinellifolia)	EBls MAus
♦***sinowilsonii***	See R. ***longicuspis s.***
'Sir Cedric Morris' (Ra)	EBls
'Sir Clough' (S)	MAus
¶ 'Sir Edward Elgar' (Cl)	EBlo MAus
'Sir Frederick Ashton' (HT)	EBls
Sir Harry Pilkington ® (HT)	NElm
'Sir Lancelot' (F)	MGan
Sir Walter Raleigh ® (S)	EWar MAus MBri MHay
'Sir Wiliam Leech' (HT)	NBat
§ 'Sissinghurst Castle' (G)	EBls WHCG

Name	Suppliers
'Sleepy' (Poly)	MGan
Smarty ® (S/GC)	EBls ENot IDic IHos LStr MAus MGan MMat SJus SPer WAct
'Sneezy' (Poly)	MGan
'Snow Bride' (Min)	MHay
Snow Carpet ® (Min/GC)	CSan EBls ENot GCoc IHos LStr MAus MFry MGan MMat SJus SPer WAct
'Snow Dwarf'	See R. 'Schneezwerg'
'Snow Queen'	See R. 'Frau Karl Druschki'
Snow Sunblaze ® (Min)	LStr MRui
Snow White ® (HT)	CDoC LStr MBri
Snowball ® (Min/GC)	MRui
'Snowdon' (Ru)	MAus
Snowdrop ® (Min/Patio)	MFry MRui
'Snowline' (F)	EWar MGan SPer
'Soldier Boy' (Cl)	EBro WHCG
'Soleil d'Or' (HT)	MAus
Solitaire ® (HT)	EWar MBri MGan MHay WWar WWeb
§ 'Sombreuil, Climbing' (T/Cl)	CCMG CHad CSan EBls ETWh MAus MRav SJus SPer SPla WAct WHCG
'Sophie's Perpetual' (Ch/Cl)	EBls ENot MAus MGan MMat SJus SPer WHCG WWeb
Soraya, Climbing ® (HT/Cl)	MAus
soulieana (Ra)	EBls ETWh GWht MAus MMat WKif
'Soupert et Notting' (PMo)	EBls MAus SPer WHCG
'Southampton' (F)	CSan EBls EWar LStr MAus MBri MGan MHay MMat NElm NRog SPer
'Souvenir de Claudius Denoyel' (HT/Cl)	CCMG EBls ETWh MAus MMat NRog SPer WSHC
'Souvenir de François Gaulain' (T)	EBls
'Souvenir de Jeanne Balandreau' (HP)	EBls WHCG
'Souvenir de la Malmaison' (Bb)	CBow CCMG CCla CCor EBls EBro EMFP ENot ETWh GCoc IHos IOrc MAus MGan MMat NSty SPer WAct WHCG WWeb
'Souvenir de la Malmaison, Climbing' (Bb/Cl)	CBow CCMG CSan EBls ETWh MAus WAct WHCG
'Souvenir de Madame Léonie Viennot' (T/Cl)	EBls MAus
'Souvenir de Philémon Cochet ' (Ru)	EBls ETWh MAus
'Souvenir de Pierre Vibert' (DPMo)	EBls
'Souvenir de Saint Anne's' (Bb)	CCMG CHad EBls EBro ETWh MAus WAct WHCG
'Souvenir du Docteur Jamain' (HP/Cl)	CBow CCMG CHad EBls EBro EMFP ETWh LGre LStr MAus MMat NSty SFam SJus SPer WHCG
'Souvenir du Président Carnot' (HT)	EBls MAus
'Souvenir d'Alphonse Lavallée' (HP/Cl)	CSan EBls WHCG

'Souvenir d'Elise Vardon' (T)	EBls
'Souvenir d'un Ami' (T)	EBls
spaldingii	See R. ***nutkana hispida***
'Spanish Beauty' (HT/Cl)	See R. 'Madame Grégoire Staechelin'
Sparkling Scarlet ® (Ra)	EBre ELan EWar LBre LPlm MGan
'Sparrieshoop' (S/Cl)	EWar
'Spartan, Climbing' (F/Cl)	EWar MGan
'Spectabilis' (Ra)	EBls MAus WHCG
'Spek's Yellow' (HT)	CB&S EBls MGan
'Spek's Yellow, Climbing' (HT/Cl)	MAus MGan
'Spencer'	See R. 'Enfant de France'
spinosissima	See R. ***pimpinellifolia***
§ Spirit of Youth ® (HT)	SJus
§ 'Splendens' (Ra)	CCMG CCor EBls ELan ETWh
'Spong' (G)	CCMG EBls ETWh MAus WAct
Spot Minijet ® (Min)	MRui
'Stacey Sue' (Min)	MAus MBur MHay
§ 'Stanwell Perpetual' (pimpinellifolia)	CBow CCMG CCor CSam EBls EBre EMFP ENot ETWh EWar GCoc IHos LBre LStr MAus MMat NRar NSty SJus SPer WAct WHCG WWeb
Star Child ® (F)	EWar IDic
Starina ® (Min)	CSan EWar MFry MGan MHay MRui SJus WWeb
'Stars 'n' Stripes' (Min)	CSan LGod LPlm MAus MBur MFry MRui NElm SJus
Stella ® (HT)	EBls MGan SRum
§ ***stellata*** var. ***mirifica***	EBls MAus MGan MMat
'Stephanie Diane' (HT)	LPlm MHay
'Sterling Silver' (HT)	EBls LStr MAus MGan
Strawberry Fayre ® (Min/Patio)	LStr
'Strawberry Ice' (F)	IHos IJoh
'String of Pearls' (Poly)	SPer
Sue Lawley ® (F)	MBri MGan NRog WStI
Sue Ryder ® (F)	EWar MHay
Suffolk ® (S/GC)	CCMG CCor CSan EBre ENot EWar IHos LBre LGod MMat SPer
suffulta	See R. ***arkansana suffulta***
Suma ® (GC)	CSan EWar GCoc GGre LPlm LStr MFry MRui SJus WHCG WWeb
Summer Dream ® (HT)	LStr MAus MFry
Summer Fragrance ® (HT)	EWar MGan WWar
Summer Holiday ® (HT)	MBur MGan SPer WWeb
'Summer Sunshine, Climbing' (HT/Cl)	MBri NElm SHen
Summer Wine ® (Cl)	EWar IHos MBri MGan MMat NBat SJus SPer WWar
'Sun Blush' (HT)	GGre
'Sunbeam' (Min)	SJus
'Sunblaze'	See R. Orange Sunblaze ®
Sunblest ® (HT)	CSan ELan ESha GGre IHos IJoh LGod LPlm MAus MBri MBur MFry MGan MMor NRog SHen SJus WWeb
Sunderland Supreme ® (HT)	MHay NBat
Sunmaid ® (Min)	MMor MRui
Sunny Sunblaze ® (Min)	MRui
Sunset Song ® (HT)	ESha GCoc
'Sunshine' (Poly)	MGan
'Sunsilk' (F)	MBri MFry MGan
Super Star ® (HT)	CB&S CGro CMac EBls EBro ESha EWar GCoc IJoh LPlm LStr MAus MBur MFry MGan MMat MMor NBar NRog SJus SRum WWeb
Super Star, Climbing ® (HT/Cl)	CMac MAus MGan MHay MMor NElm SHen SRum
'Super Sun' (HT)	ESha MBur NElm SRum
'Surf Rider' (S)	MMor
'Surpasse Tout' (G)	EBls MAus
§ 'Surpassing Beauty of Woolverstone' (HP/Cl)	EBls WHCG
Surrey ® (GC)	CCor EBre ENot EWar GCoc IHos LBre LPlm LStr MAus MGan MMat MRui WStI
Susan Hampshire ® (HT)	EBls EWar MGan SRum
Sussex ® (GC)	CCla CCor ENot EWar LStr MBur MMat MRui SPer
'Sutter's Gold' (HT)	EBls MAus MBur MGan NElm NRog
'Sutter's Gold, Climbing' (HT/Cl)	MAus MGan SJus
'Swan Lake' (Cl)	CCMG CSan EBls EBre ELan ESha ETWh EWar IHos IJoh LBre LGod LStr MAus MBri MBur MFry MGan MHay MMat MMor NBar SPer SRum WWeb
Swan ® (S)	EWar IHos MAus
Swany ® (Min/GC)	CCMG CCla EBls EHar ELan EWar IHos LStr MAus MGan MMat SHen SJus SPer SRum WAct WHCG WWeb
'Swedish Doll' (Min)	MBur
Sweet Dream ® (Patio)	CDoC CGro CSan EBlo EBre ELan ESha EWar GCoc GGre LBre LGod LPlm LStr MAus MBri MBur MFry MGan MMor MRui NBar NBat SJus SPer SRum WWar WWeb
'Sweet Fairy' (Min)	LPlm MMat MRui
'Sweet Honesty' (Min	MBur
Sweet Juliet ® (S)	CAbP CCMG EMFP EWar LGod LPlm MAus MRui NBat WAct WWeb
Sweet Magic ® (Min/Patio)	CDoC CGro CSan EBre ESha EWar GGre IDic IHos LBre LGod LPlm LStr MBri MBur MFry MGan MMat MRui NBat NElm SHen SJus SPer SRum WWar WWeb
Sweet Nell ® (F)	LGod
Sweet Promise ® (GC)	MGan NElm
'Sweet Repose' (F)	MAus MGan
'Sweet Velvet' (F)	MGan
N Sweetheart ® (HT)	GCoc MGan NBat SJus WWar
sweginzowii	CCor MAus MMat
– 'Macrocarpa'	EBls
'Sydonie' (HP)	EBls
Sympathie ® (HT/Cl)	IHos IJoh LPlm MAus MFry MGan MMat MMor MRui SJus SPer SRum
Symphony ® (S)	EWar MAus
'Talisman' (HT)	EBls
'Talisman, Climbing' (HT/Cl)	EBls
Tall Story ® (S/GC)	EWar IDic SPer SRms SRum
'Tallyho' (HT)	EBls

'Tamora' (S) CCMG MAus MBri
Tango ® (F) EWar LPlm MMat NBat WWar WWeb
§ 'Tausendschön' (Ra) CSan EBls
'Tea Rambler' (Ra) CCor EBls NSty
Tear Drop ® (Min/Patio) GCoc IDic LStr MBur MGan NBat SJus SPer
¶ Ted Gore ® (F) NBat
Teeny Weeny ® (Min) MRui
¶ Telford's Promise ® (GC/S) NBat WWar
'Telstar' (F) MGan
'Temple Bells' (Min/GC) EBls MAus NRog
'Tenerife' (HT) ESha MBur MGan NElm SRum WStI WWeb
Tequila Sunrise ® (HT) CDoC ESha EWar GCoc IDic LPlm LStr MBri MBur MFry MGan MHay MMat NBat SJus WWar
'Texas Centennial' (HT) EBls
§ Thaïs ® (HT) EBls
'Thalia' MAus
'The Bishop' (Ce/G) EBls MAus
'The Bride' (T) EBls NSty
The Countryman ® (S) CAbP CCMG CCla CSam EWar MAus MFry MRui SJus
The Coxswain ® (HT) GCoc
The Dark Lady ® (S) IHos MAus NBar
'The Doctor' (HT) EBls MAus MGan
'The Doctor, Climbing' (HT/Cl) MGan
'The Ednaston Rose' (Cl) CCla WHCG
'The Fairy' (Poly) Widely available
The Flower Arranger ® (F) MFry
'The Friar' (S) SJus
'The Garland' (Ra) CCMG EBls ETWh MAus MMat SFam SPer SPla WHCG
'The Havering Rambler' EBro
¶ The Herbalist ® (S) MAus
'The Honorable Lady Lindsay' (S) NSty
'The Knight' (S) NSty
The Lady ® (S) GCoc MAus MBur MFry MHay NBat
'The Maid Marion' EBro
§ The McCartney Rose ® (HT) ESha EWar LStr SJus WWeb
'The Miller' (S) MAus
'The New Dawn' See R. 'New Dawn'
The Nun ® (S) IHos MAus
The Observer ® (HT) MFry
The Pilgrim ® (S) CAbP MAus MBri MRui NBar SPer
The Prince ® (S) CAbP EBlo EWar IHos MAus MRui NBar SPer
'The Prioress' (S) MAus
§ 'The Queen Elizabeth' Widely available
'The Queen Elizabeth, Climbing' (F/Cl) CCla EBls MGan SHen SRum
The Reeve ® (S) MAus WHCG
♦ 'The Royal Brompton Rose' See R. Yves Piaget ®
The Seckford Rose ® (S) ENot MMat
The Squire ® (S) MAus
The Times Rose ® (F) CDoC CSan EWar GCoc IHos LGod LStr MGan MHay MMat SPer WWar
The Valois Rose ® (R) MMat
'The Wife of Bath' (S) MAus MBri NBar SJus SPer
'Thelma' (Ra) EBls MAus
'Thérèse Bugnet' (Ru) EBls
'Thisbe' (HM) CCMG EBls EBro MAus SPer WAct WHCG
¶ Thomas Barton ® (HT) LStr
Thora Hird ® (F) MAus WWeb
'Thousand Beauties' See R. 'Tausendschön'
Threepenny Bit Rose See R. ***elegantula*** 'Persetosa'
Tigris ® (***persica*** x) (S) MAus
'Till Uhlenspiegel' (HSwB) EBls
'Tina Turner' (HT) NBat
Tip Top ® (F/Patio) CB&S CGro CMac EBls ELan EWar GCoc GGre IHos LGod LStr MBri MFry MGan MHay MMor NElm NRog SHen SPer SRum WStI WWeb
'Tipo Ideale' See R. x ***odorata*** 'Mutabilis'
'Tipsy Imperial Concubine' (T) EBls
'Toby Tristam' (Ra) WWat
'Tom Brown' (F) SJus
'Tom Tom' (F) IJoh
'Top Marks' (Min/Patio) CCla CDoC CSan ESha EWar LGod LPlm LStr MBri MBur MFry MGan MMat MRui NBat SRum WStI WWar
'Topeka' (F) SRum
Toprose ® (F) GCoc
Topsi ® (F/Patio) EWar GGre IHos IJoh LGod MAus MFry MHay MMor NElm SHen SPer SRum WWeb
Torville and Dean ® (HT) CDoC IHos NRog
§ 'Tour de Malakoff' (Ce) CCla CCor EBls ETWh MAus SFam SPer SPla WHCG
¶ Tournament of Roses ® (HT) IDic
'Toy Clown' (Min) MAus
Toynbee Hall ® (F) MMat
'Trade Winds' (HT) MGan
Tranquillity ® (HT) MBur WWar
'Treasure Trove' (Ra) CCor EBls MAus
'Tricolore de Flandre' (G) EBls GCoc MAus
Trier ® (Ra) CCor EBls ETWh MAus MMat WHCG
'Trigintipetala' misapplied See R, 'Professeur Emile Perrot'
¶ 'Triomphe de l'Exposition' (HP) MAus
'Triomphe du Luxembourg' (T) EBls MAus
triphylla See R. x ***beanii***
Troika ® (HT) CSan ESha IJoh LStr MAus MBur MFry MGan MHay MMat SPer
Troilus ® (S) CCMG MAus NBar
'Truly Yours' (HT) MGan
Trumpeter ® (F) CSan ESha EWar GCoc IHos IJoh LGod LPlm MAus MBri MFry MGan MHay MMat NBar NBat SJus SPer WWar
* 'Turkestan' WSHC
'Tuscany' (G) CHad CSan GCoc MAus SJus SPer WAct

'Tuscany Superb' (G)	CCMG CSan EBls EBre EBro EMFP ENot ETWh EWar IHos LBre LHol MAus MMat NSty SPer WAct WHCG WKif WSHC WWeb
Tynwald ® (HT)	EWar LStr MMat
'Typhoon' (HT)	MBur WWar
'Ulrich Brunner Fils' (HP)	EBls MAus SJus
ultramontana	CCor
'Uncle Bill' (HT)	EBls
Uncle Walter ® (HT)	CMac EBls ESha MMor NElm NRog SHen SRum WStI
¶ 'UNICEF' (F)	GCoc
§ 'Unique Blanche' (Ce)	CCMG EBls ETWh MAus WHCG
'Vagabonde' (F)	MGan
Valencia ® (HT)	EWar MBur MMat NBat WWar
Valentine Heart ® (F)	CDoC EBre GCoc IDic LBre SJus
'Vanguard' (Ru)	EBls MAus SPer
'Vanity' (HM)	EBls EBro IHos MAus SPer SRms WHCG
'Variegata' (pimpinellifolia)	CArn
'Variegata di Bologna' (Bb)	CBow CCMG CCla EBls EBro ETWh EWar MAus MMat NSty SFam WAct WHCG
'Veilchenblau' (Ra)	CBow CCMG CCla CHad CSan EBls EBro ELan ETWh EWar MAus MBri MBur MGan MHay NSty SJus SPer SRum WAct WHCG WKif WSHC
Velvet Fragrance ® (HT)	GCoc MAus MBur MFry SJus
'Venusta Pendula' (Ra)	EBls MAus
versicolor	See R. ***gallica*** 'Versicolor'
'Vesuvius' (HT)	MAus
'Vick's Caprice' (Bb)	EBls MAus NSty
'Vicomtesse Pierre du Fou ' (HT/Cl)	EBls MAus NSty
Victor Hugo ®	See R. Spirit of Youth ®
'Victoriana' (F)	MAus
'Village Maid'	See R. 'Centifolia Variegata'
§ ***villosa***	CMac EBls MAus MMat NSty
– 'Duplex'	See R. 'Wolley-Dod'
§ 'Violacea' (G)	CCor EBls WHCG
Violet Carson ® (F)	ESha MAus MGan
'Violette' (Ra)	CCMG EBls ETWh MAus NSty SPer WAct WHCG
'Violinista Costa' (HT)	EBls MAus
virginiana	CCor EBls ELan ETWh MAus MGan MSte SPer WHCG
– 'Plena'	See R. 'Rose d'Amour'
'Virgo' (HT)	EBls IJoh MAus SRum
'Viridiflora' (Ch)	See R. x ***odorata*** 'V.'
Vital Spark ® (F)	MGan
'Vivid' (Bb x)	EBls
'W E Lippiat' (HT)	EBls
Wandering Minstrel ® (F)	MGan
wardii var. ***culta***	MAus
'Warley Jubilee' (F)	EWar
Warm Welcome ® (Cl/Min)	CDoC EWar GCoc LStr MAus MBri MBur MFry MMat MRui NBat SJus SMad WWar
'Warrior' (F)	EWar MGan SPer WWeb
Warwick Castle ® (S)	MAus
Warwickshire ® (GC)	ENot EWar MMat
§ ***watsoniana***	EBls
webbiana	CCor EBls ETWh MAus WHCG
'Wedding Day' (Ra)	CCMG CDoC CHad CSan EBls EBre EBro ELan ETWh EWar LBre LStr MAus MBri MBur MGan MMat NSty SJus SPer SRum WAct WHCG WWeb
Wee Barbie ® (Min)	MRui NElm WWar
Wee Jock ® (F/Patio)	CDoC GCoc MAus SJus
'Wee Man' (Min)	WWeb
'Weetwood' (Ra)	CCMG MAus SPer
'Weisse aus Sparrieshoop' (S)	MGan
'Welcome Guest' (HT)	MHay
'Wembley Stadium' (HT)	MGan
'Wendy Cussons' (HT)	CB&S CCMG CDoC CGro CMac EBls EBro EWar GCoc GGre IHos IJoh LPlm LStr MAus MBur MFry MGan MHay MMor NBar NElm NRog SHen SPer SRum WWeb
'Wendy Cussons, Climbing' (HT/Cl)	CMac
Wenlock ® (S)	CSam EWar MAus SPer WHCG
Westerland ® (F/S)	ENot LPlm MGan MHay MMat WWar
'Westfield Star' (HT)	MAus
'Whippet' (HT)	MHay
'Whisky Gill' (HT)	MGan
Whisky Mac ® (HT)	Widely available
'White Bath' (CeMo)	See R. 'Shailer's White Moss'
White Bells ® (Min/GC)	CCMG CCla CCor CDoC EBls ENot EWar IHos LBuc LStr MGan MMat SPer WAct WWeb
'White Cécile Brunner'	See R. Cécile Brunner, White'
'White Christmas' (HT)	ELan MBur MGan SRum
'White Cockade' (Cl)	CB&S CCMG CDoC EBls GCoc LPlm MAus MGan NElm SJus SPer
'White Flight' (Ra)	EBls
¶ 'White Flower Carpet' (GC)	MFry
'White Grootendorst' (Ru)	EBls MAus WAct
White Meidiland ® (S/GC)	CCMG EBre EWar LBre MGan
White Moss	See R. 'Shailer's White Moss'
§ 'White Pet' (Poly)	CBow CCMG CCor CHad ETWh GCoc IHos LStr MBri MBur MGan SJus SPer SPla WAct WHCG
White Provence	See R. 'Unique Blanche'
'White Queen Elizabeth' (F)	EBls SRum
White Rose of York	See R. 'Alba Semiplena'
'White Spray' (F)	EBls
'White Wings' (HT)	CBow CCMG CHad EBls MAus MGan NSty SPer WAct
Whitley Bay ® (F)	NBat
wichuraiana (Ra)	CBow CCor EBls EBre LBre LHol MAus SRum WHCG
*– 'Variegata' (Ra)	CB&S CBow CCor CLew CPMA CRDP EBar EBro EFol EPla EPot ETWh MAus MPla NHol SDry SMad SPla WPat
*– 'Variegata Nana' (Ra)	LHop MCas
'Wickwar' (Ra)	CCor CHad EBls EFol ELan EPla GCal WAct WCot WHCG
'Wild Flower' (S)	MBri

'Wilhelm' (HM) CCor EBls EBro IHos MAus NSty SHen WHCG
'Will Scarlet' (HM) IHos LStr MAus
'Willhire Country' (F) EBls
'William Allen Richardson' (N) EBls ETWh MAus WHCG
'William and Mary' (S) EBls
'William III' (pimpinellifolia) EBls LHop MAus
§ 'William Lobb' (Mo) CCMG CCla CCor CHad CSan EBls EBro ENot ETWh EWar GCoc IDai IHos IOrc MAus MBur MGan MMat MMor NSty SFam SJus SPer SRum WAct WHCG WKif WWeb
'William R Smith' (T) EBls
William Shakespeare ® (S) CCMG EBre ELan ETWh EWar IHos LBre LStr MAus MBri SPer SPla SRum WHCG WStI WWeb
'Williams' Double Yellow' (HScB) See R. x ***harisonii*** 'W. D. Y'
willmottiae EBls MAus MGan MMat NSty SPer WAct WBod WHCG
¶ Wiltshire ® (S/GC) MFry MMat MRui
Wimi ® (HT) EWar MGan MHay NBat
Winchester Cathedral ® (S) CCMG CDoC EBre ETWh EWar LBre LGod LStr MAus MRui NBar NBat SJus SPer SPla SRum WWeb
Windrush ® (S) CCMG EMFP MAus NBar SPer WAct WHCG
¶ x ***wintoniensis*** WHCG
Wise Portia ® (S) CCMG MAus
Wishing ® (F/Patio) CCMG CDoC GCoc IDic MFry SPer WWeb
'Woburn Abbey' (F) CGro CMac EBls GGre NElm NRog
§ 'Wolley-Dod' (S) EBls SFam SJus WAct
'Woodrow's Seedling' (Cl) MMor
Woods of Windsor ® (HT) CDoC MMat SJus
§ ***woodsii*** CCor CMCN EBls MAus MBur MMat SJus SPer WHCG
– var. ***fendleri*** See R. ***woodsii***
'Woolverstone Church Rose' See R. 'Surpassing Beauty of Woolverstone'
xanthina EBls ETWh MGan MMat
§ – 'Canary Bird' CCMG CCla CDoC CGro CSam CSan EBls EBre ELan ENot EWar GCoc IJoh IOrc LBre LGod LPlm LStr MAus MBri MBur MMat NBat SJus SMad SPer SRum WAct
§ – f. ***hugonis*** CCMG CCor EBls EFol ELan ETWh MAus MGan MMat NRog SPer WAct WHCG
'Xavier Olibo' (HP) EBls
yainacensis CCor
'Yellow Beauty' (Min) NBar
'Yellow Button' (S) CCMG MAus MBri SJus WAct
Yellow Charles Austin ® (S) CCMG MAus MBri SJus SPer
'Yellow Cushion' (F) EWar MAus
¶ Yellow Dagmar Hastrup ® (Ru) CBow CCor MBri MMat MRui SJus WHCG
'Yellow Doll' (Min) CGro ELan EWar GGre IJoh MAus MGan MRui
'Yellow Pages' (HT) MAus
'Yellow Patio' (Min/Patio) LStr
'Yellow Petals' (HT) MBur
'Yellow Pixie' (Patio) LPlm
'Yellow Queen Elizabeth' (F) CCor
'Yellow Ribbon' (F) ESha
Yellow Scotch See R. x ***harisonii*** 'Williams' Double Yellow'
Yellow Sunblaze ® (Min) CSan EWar IHos NBar NElm WWeb
Yesterday ® (Poly/F/S) CCMG EBls ESha ETWh EWar LGod MAus MGan MMat SJus SPer SRum
'Yolande d'Aragon' (HP) EBls
York and Lancaster See R. x ***damascena versicolor***
Yorkshire Bank ® (HT) MFry
Yorkshire Sunblaze ® (Min) EWar
Young Quinn ® (HT) IHos MBur
§ Yves Piaget ® (HT) EWar
'Yvonne Rabier' (Poly) CBow EBls LStr MAus MMat MRui SJus SPer WAct WHCG
Zambra ® (F) CB&S
'Zéphirine Drouhin' (Bb) Widely available
§ 'Zigeunerknabe' (S) CCMG CCla CCor EBls EMFP ENot ETWh EWar MAus MMat NSty SPer WAct WHCG
Zitronenfalter ® (S) MGan
'Zola' (S) CSan
'Zweibrücken' (Cl) MGan
§ 'Zwergkönig' (Min) EWar IHos MGan

ROSCOEA † (Zingiberaceae)

alpina CRDP GDra MTho NHol NKay NWCA SBla SWas WChr WDav
auriculata CAvo CBro NHar SBla WThi
'Beesiana' ECha LAma MTho NHar WCot
capitata See R. ***scillifolia***
cautleoïdes CAvo CBro CChu CGle CRDP GArf GDra LAma LGre MPar MTho NHar NHol NKay NRog SAxl SBla SMad SSpi SUsu WChr WCru WThi
– 'Grandiflora' EPot
– 'Kew Beauty' MUlv SBla
humeana NHar SAxl SMrm
§ ***purpurea*** CBro CChu CCla CGle CHEx CPar CRDP ECro EGol ELan ELun EPar GCHN GCal LAma MFir MUlv NBir NHar NHol SAxl SPer WChr WCot WOMN WThi WWin
– ***procera*** See R. ***purpurea***
§ ***scillifolia*** CBro CRDP ECar GCal LAma NBir NHar NHol NRog WChr WThi WThu
* ***tibetica*** SAxl WHer

ROSMARINUS † (Labiatae)

angustifolius See R. ***officinalis angustissimus***
* ***calabriensis*** WCHb WHer
* ***capicanalli*** CHan
corsicus 'Prostratus' See R. ***officinalis*** Prostratus Group

♦*lavandulaceus* Noë	See R. ***eriocalyx***
♦× *lavandulaceus* hort.	See R. ***officinalis*** Prostratus Group
officinalis	Widely available
– var. *albiflorus*	CArn CCla CPMA CSFH CSev EBre ESis GPoy IBar LBre MBar MPar MPla NHHG NSti SBla SChu SLon SMad WEas WHer WHil WOMN WSHC WWye
§– *angustissimus* 'Corsican Blue'	CArn CBow SCro SPer
– 'Aureovariegatus'	See R. ***o. aureus***
§– 'Aureus' (v)	CDec CFis CLan CMer CMil CRDP EFol ELan GAbr IBlr NHHG NRar SDry SMad WCHb WEas WHer WOMN WWye
§– 'Benenden Blue'	Widely available
– 'Collingwood Ingram'	See R. ***o.*** 'Benenden Blue'
– 'Corsicus Prostratus'	CB&S
¶– 'Eden'	IEde
– 'Fastigiatus'	See R. ***o.*** 'Miss Jessopp's Upright'
– 'Fota Blue'	CDoC NHHG NSti SCro SIde
– 'Frimley Blue'	See R. ***o.*** 'Primley Blue'
– 'Guilded'	See R. ***o.*** 'Aureus'
– 'Jackman's Prostrate'	CB&S ECtt NHar NWyt WSHC
– 'Lady in White'	CLan NBar SPer
♦– *lavandulaceus*	See R. ***o.*** Prostratus Group
¶– 'Lockwood Variety'	NHHG
– 'Majorca Pink'	CB&S CBow CDec CLan CPMA CSam MPla SIde SPer WCHb WMar WOMN WPat WWat
– 'McConnell's Blue'	CDoC CLan EBre EFou ELan GAbr LBre MGos NHHG SDry WCHb WSun
§– 'Miss Jessopp's Upright'	Widely available
§– 'Primley Blue'	CArn CSam CSev MChe NHHG NHar NSel NSti SChu SHer WCHb WHer WOak WWeb
§– Prostratus Group	Widely available
– *pyramidalis*	See R. ***o.*** 'Miss Jessopp's Upright'
– *repens*	See R. ***o.*** Prostratus Group
– 'Roseus'	CArn CHan CMer CWit EBre ELan GPoy LBre LHop MChe NHHG NHar NSel NSti SBla SChu SLon SMad SUsu WHer WSHC WWat WWye
– 'Russell's Blue'	NOak WHer
– 'Severn Sea'	CArn CB&S CBot CBow CGle CHan CMea CMer CPMA CSco CSev CShe EBar ECha ECtt ELan ESis GPoy LHop MWat NHHG NNor NSti SLon SMad SPer WEas WSun WWat
– 'Sissinghurst Blue'	CArn CKni CMer CSev CShe ECha ERav ESma MSta NWyt WWat WWye
– 'Sudbury Blue'	MChe NHHG NRoo NSti WEas
– 'Trusty'	CKni ECtt LRHS NWyt
– 'Tuscan Blue'	CShe NHex SDry SIde SLon WCHb WHer WWat
– 'Variegatus'	See R. ***o.*** 'Aureus'
– 'Vicomte de Noailles'	ERea
repens	See R. ***officinalis*** Prostratus Group

ROSTRINUCULA (Labiatae)

dependens Guiz 18	CBot

ROSULARIA (Crassulaceae)

acuminata	See R. ***alpestris alpestris***
adenotricha ssp. *adenotricha*	NGre
§ *aïzoön*	MFos
alba	See R. ***sedoïdes***
alpestris	CWil MSte
– CC 327	NHol
§ – ssp. *alpestris*	WThu
§ *chrysantha*	CRiv EBur NGre NHol NMen NNrd WPer
– Number 1	CWil SMit WThu
– Number 2	CWil WThu
crassipes	See RHODIOLA ***c.***
haussknechtii	NGre
¶ *muratdaghensis*	EBur LBee MBro NMen SIng
pallida A. Berger	See R. ***chrysantha***
– Stapf	See R. ***aïzoön***
♦*platyphylla* hort.	See R. ***muratdaghensis***
rechingeri	CWil
§ *sedoïdes*	CLew CMHG CPar CRow CWil ELan EMNN EPot GCHN MBar MCas MFir SChu SMit SSmi WPer WThu WWin
§ – var. *alba*	CLew CMHG CPar CRow CWil ELan EMNN EPot GCHN MBar MCas MHig NGre SChu SIng WHoo WOMN WThu WWin
sempervivum	CWil NGre NHol NMen NNrd WThu
– ssp. *amanensis*	NGre
§ – ssp. *glaucophylla*	CWil NTow WThu
serpentinica	CWil
serrata	NGre NNrd
– from Crete	SMit
spatulata hort.	See R. ***sempervivum glaucophylla***

ROTHMANNIA (Rubiaceae)

¶ *capensis*	CTro
¶ *globosa*	CTro

RUBIA (Rubiaceae)

peregrina	CKin GPoy MHew NSal
tinctoria	CArn GPoy LHol MChe MHew NHex NSal SIde SWat WHer WWye

RUBUS † (Rosaceae)

arcticus	CGle ECar ESim ESis MBal MHig NCat SReu SSta WCru WPat WSun WThu
– ssp. *stellarcticus*	ESim
– – 'Anna'	ESim
– – 'Beata'	ESim
– – 'Linda'	ESim
– – 'Sofia'	ESim
× *barkeri*	ECou
§ 'Benenden'	CB&S CBot CCla CGle CMHG CSam CSco EBar EHar ELan ENot IDai ISea LHop MBal MBri MGos MWat NKay NNor SHBN SLon SPer SSpi WBod WDin WHal WWat WWeb WWin
'Betty Ashburner'	CDoC CHan CWit EGol EPla GCal IBar IJoh MGos WWat
biflorus	EHar EMon EPla ERav
F 'Boysenberry, Thornless'	GTwe LBuc SDea SPer WHig

♦*calycinoïdes* Hayata	See R. ***pentalobus***
¶ ***chamaemorus***	GPoy
cockburnianus	CB&S CCla CCor CGle EBre EHar ELan ENot EPar EPla IOrc LBre MBal MRav MWat NHol SPer SSpi WCru WDin WEas WWat
– Golden Vale ®	CB&S EBre EPla IJoh LBre MPla SAxl
coreanus 'Dart's Mahogany'	LRHS
crataegifolius	CBrd EPla WWat
deliciosus	CSco WDin
¶ 'Emerald Spreader'	MBri SBod
flagelliflorus	MBar
fockeanus hort.	See R. ***pentalobus***
x ***fraseri***	EPla
fruticosus	CKin
F – 'Ashton Cross'	GRei GTwe LBuc SDea WHig
F – 'Bedford Giant'	EHar GTwe MBea MGos NBar NGrN SDea SKee SPer WWeb
F – 'Black Satin'	CSam GRei GTwe MBea MBri MGos SDea SPer WWeb
¶ – 'Dart's Robertville'	SLPl
F – 'Denver Thornless'	EWar
F – 'Fantasia Blackberry'	GTwe MGos
F – 'Godshill Goliath'	SDea
F – 'Himalayan Giant'	CDoC CSam EWar GTwe MBea NRog SDea SPer
F – 'John Innes'	NElm NRog
F – 'Loch Ness'	CSam GChr GTwe LBuc MBri MGos NBar SDea WHig
F – 'Merton Thornless'	CMac EHar GTwe MBea MGos NBee NEgg NElm NGrN NRog SDea SKee
F – 'No Thorn'	SDea
F – 'Oregon Thornless'	EWar GTwe IJoh LBuc MBea MBri SDea SPer WHig WWeb
F – 'Parsley Leaved'	SDea
F – 'Thornfree'	CDoC SDea
– 'Variegatus'	CBot EFol ELan EPla LHop
¶ – 'Waldo'	CSut WHig
henryi	CBot CBrd EPla MRav WWat
– var. ***bambusarum***	CChu CDec CHan CMCN EBar ELan EPar EPla SHil SMad SSpi WWat
F 'Hildaberry'	WHig
¶ ***hupehensis***	SLPl
ichangensis	CAbb CBot CHan CMCN EPla GCal GWht ISea MBal
idaeus	CKin
F – 'Aureus'	CBos CCor ECha EFol EHal EHoe ELan EPla GCal LHop NRoo NSti SDry WRus
F – Autumn Bliss ®	CSam CSut CWSG GTwe IJoh LBuc MBri MGos MMor NBar NBee NGrN SDea SKee SPer WHig WWeb
F – 'Fallgold'	GTwe SDea SPer
F – 'Glen Clova'	CMac EHar EWar GRei GTwe IJoh LBuc NBar NBee NGrN NRog SDea SKee SPer WWeb
F – 'Glen Coe'	GTwe WHig
¶ – 'Glen Garry'	WHig
¶ – 'Glen Lyon'	GTwe
F – 'Glen Moy'	CSut CWSG GChr GRei GTwe IJoh LBuc MGos MMor NEgg NRog SKee SPer
F – 'Glen Prosen'	CSam CWSG GChr GTwe IJoh LBuc MBri MMor NBar NEgg NRog SKee SPer WHig
F – 'Golden Everest'	EWar GTwe SDea SPer
F – 'Heritage'	EHar IJoh SDea SPer
F – 'Leo'	CDoC CSut GTwe MGos NBee SDea SKee SPer WHig
F – 'Malling Admiral'	CMac EHar ESha GTwe MBri MMor NBar NRog SKee SPer
F – 'Malling Delight'	GRei GTwe MMor NRog SDea SKee SPer WHig WWeb
F – 'Malling Jewel'	EWar GTwe IJoh LBuc NBar NBee NGrN SDea SKee SPer WHig
F – 'Malling Joy'	GTwe
F – 'Malling Orion'	CMac ESha MGos MMor
F – 'Malling Promise'	EWar GTwe NBar SDea SPer
F – 'September'	EWar SPer
– 'Summer Gold'	GTwe
F – 'Zefa Herbsternte'	CMac EWar GTwe NGrN SDea SPer WWeb
F ***illecebrosus***	CCor CSun ESim WCot WPat
irenaeus	CHan
'Kenneth Ashburner'	EPla MBri WWat
¶ ***laciniatus***	EPla
lambertianus	CMCN
lineatus	CAbb CBot CBrd CPle CRDP EPla GCal MBal SDix SDry SSpi WCru WPat
F Loganberry 'LY 59'	CDoC EHar GTwe MMor NBar NElm NGrN NRog SDea SPer
F – 'LY 654'	CSam GRei GTwe LBuc MBea MBri MGos MMor NElm NGrN SDea SPer WHig WWeb
F – 'New Zealand Black'	SDea
F 'Loganberry Thornless	CMac GTwe IJoh NRog SDea
'Margaret Gordon'	IBar IJoh
microphyllus 'Variegatus'	ELan EPla IJoh SHil WAbb WPat WWeb
§ ***nepalensis***	CDoC CGle EPla ESis GWht WWat
nutans	See R. ***nepalensis***
odoratus	CDoC CHEx CSco CWit ELan SPer WCot
parviflorus	CArn CCor
¶ – 'Sunshine Spreader'	EPla
parvus	ECou
§ ***pentalobus***	CGle CHan CLew CSco CWit EGol ELan ENot EPla ESis LHop MBal MBar NHar NNor SBor SIng WAbb WAbe WCru WDin WEas WWat WWin
¶ – 'Emerald Carpet'	ESim
F ***phoenicolasius*** Japanese Wineberry	CCla CHan CMac ELan EPla ESim GTwe GWht MBri NBar NRog SDea SPer WAbb WCru WHig WPat WWat WWye
rosifolius 'Coronarius' (d)	EPla WCot
setchuenensis	CMCN SBra
F 'Silvanberry'	GTwe
spectabilis	CChu CMHG CWit EFol ELan LHop MBal MRav NHol SFis WHal
– double form	CChu CCla CMHG CPMA ELan EMon GCal LTil WPat WWeb
squarrosus	ECou EPla SDry
F 'Sunberry'	GTwe SKee WHig
F Tayberry	CMac CSam EHar EWar GChr GRei GTwe IJoh MBea MBri MGos MMor NBar NElm NGrN NRog SKee SPer WHig WWeb
F – 'Medana Tayberry'	CSut LBuc SDea

§ ***thibetanus*** CB&S CBot CCla CDoC CHan CMCN CPMA CSco EBre ECha EGol EHar ELan ENot EOrc EPla GCal LBre MBri MRav NSti SDix SDry SLon SMad SPer SUsu WDin WPat WWat
♦– 'Silver Fern' See R. ***t.***
treutleri CCor
tricolor CB&S CBra CDec CGle CHEx CHan CPle CSco CTre ECha EHar ELan ENot IHos LBuc LGro MBal MBar NHol NNor SDix SHBN SLon SPer SReu WBod WDin WEas WWat WWin
¶– 'Dart's Evergreen' SLPl
¶– 'Ness' SLPl
Tridel 'Benenden' See R. 'Benenden'
trilobus CCla SLon
ulmifolius 'Bellidiflorus' CBot CCla CSev ECar ELan ENot EPla MBal MPar NNor SChu SDix SHil WAbb
F 'Veitchberry' GTwe MMor NRog WHig
F 'Youngberry' SDea

RUDBECKIA (Compositae)

californica WPer
echinacea purpurea See ECHINACEA ***purpurea***
fulgida var. ***deamii*** CBow CGle CKel CPar EBre ECED ECha ECtt ELan ELun LBre MRav MWat NBar NKay NOak NRoo NSti SChu SCro SPer WByw WCra WEas WHoo
§ – var. ***speciosa*** CGle CKel CSco CShe ECha EJud ELan EPla IDai LWad MPit NBar NRoo SFis WOld WRus
– var. ***sullivantii*** 'Goldsturm' Widely available
gloriosa See R. ***hirta***
'Goldquelle' CGle CSco ECED EFou ELan NOrc SAxl SCro SHer SMrm SPer WWin
'Herbstsonne' ('Autumn Sun') CSco ECha IDai MWat NOrc NVic SFis SHer SMad SPer WEas WTyr
§ ***hirta*** GCra LHil WCra WWye
'Juligold' ('July Gold') EFou SMrm
laciniata CSam ELan GCal LHil NOrc SFis SMrm WByw
♦– 'Golden Glow' See R. ***l.*** 'Hortensia'
§ – 'Hortensia' CSco EMon MFir NFai
maxima ECha EMon MBri WCot
newmannii See R. ***fulgida speciosa***
occidentalis CHan WPer
¶– 'Green Wizard' ESma
purpurea See ECHINACEA ***purpurea***
subtomentosa CPou EFou EMon GCal

RUELLIA (Acanthaceae)

amoena See R. ***graecizans***
devosiana MBri SLMG
§ ***graecizans*** CTro ERea
makoyana CHal IBlr MBri SLMG

RUMEX (Polygonaceae)

§ ***acetosa*** CArn CKin CSev ECha EJud Effi GPoy IEde LHol MChe NBir NSel SIde WWye
– 'Hortensis' MBar
¶– 'Redleaf' WCot
acetosella MWil
alpinus WCot
flexuosus CHan EFol EHoe EMon GCal NBro WCot
hydrolapathum EMFW MSta NDea
montanus 'Ruber' See R. ***arifolius*** 'R.'
♦***rugosus*** See R. ***acetosa***
sanguineus
var. ***sanguineus*** CArn CElw CHun CRDP CRow EFol EHoe ELan EMon EPla LHol MTho NBro NHol NSti WHer WOak WWye
scutatus CArn CHun CSFH CSev EJud Effi GPoy IEde LHol MChe MPar MTho SIde WWye
– 'Silver Shield' CElw CRDP EFol ELan EMar EMon EPla IBlr LHil LRHS NSti SUsu WCHb WCot WCru WHer WOak WWye

RUMOHRA (Dryopteridaceae)

See Plant Deletions

RUPICAPNOS (Papaveraceae)

africanus EPot NMen NWCA SBla WAbe WOMN

RUSCHIA (Aizoaceae)

schollii pale pink LHop

RUSCUS † (Liliaceae/Ruscaceae)

aculeatus CBow CSco ECro ENot GPoy IJoh MBri MRav MUlv MWat NHol SArc SPer SSta WCru WDin WOMN WWat WWye
– andromonoecious CPMA
¶– hermaphrodite EPla
*– 'Wheeler's Variety' (f/m) CPMA SSpi
hypoglossum MUlv SHil SRms
racemosus See DANAË ***racemosa***

RUSSELIA (Scrophulariaceae)

§ ***equisetiformis*** ERea SIgm
juncea See R. ***equisetiformis***

RUTA (Rutaceae)

chalepensis CArn ELan LHol WCHb WHil
§ – 'Dimension Two' EFol EMon LHol
– prostrate form See R. ***c.*** 'Dimension Two'
corsica NTow WPer
graveolens CArn CBow CCor CGle CMer CSFH EJud IEde LGan LHol MChe NMir NOak NSel SIde WEas WHal WHer WOak WPer WStI
– 'Jackman's Blue' Widely available
– 'Variegata' CBot CBow CBre CSFH ECha EFol EFou ELan EMar EOrc EPla ERav GPoy LHop MChe NNor NOak NPer NSel NSti SPla WHer WHoo WPer WSHC
montana CBot
prostrata See R. ***chalepensis*** 'Dimension Two'

RUTTYA (Acanthaceae)

See Plant Deletions

SABAL (Palmae)

§ *mexicana*	NPal
minor	LPal NPal
palmetto	CArn LPal NPal WNor
texana	See S. ***mexicana***

SACCHARUM (Gramineae)

ravennae	EMon

SAGERETIA (Rhamnaceae)

§ *thea*	STre
theezans	See S. ***thea***

SAGINA (Caryophyllaceae)

boydii	CLew EMNN EPot GArf ITim NTow WThu
glabra 'Aurea'	See S. ***subulata*** 'Aurea'
subulata	CLew
§ – 'Aurea'	CHal CMea CNic CRiv EBar ECha EFol ELan LGro LHop MCas NVic SIng STre WEas WHal WPer WTyr WWin

SAGITTARIA (Alismataceae)

japonica	See S. ***sagittifolia***
latifolia	CHEx CRDP EMFW NDea WChe WHol
§ *sagittifolia*	CBen CRDP CRow CWGN EHon EMFW LMay MSta SHig SWat WChe WHol
– 'Flore Pleno'	CBen CRDP CRow CWGN EHon EMFW LMay MBal MSta NDea SHig SWat WChe
¶ *subulata*	CRow

SAINTPAULIA (Gesneriaceae)

See Plant Deletions

SALIX † (Salicaceae)

acutifolia	ELan ENot EPla IOrc SPla
– 'Blue Streak' (m)	CCor CMHG CSco IOrc MBal NBir SHil SSpi
– 'Pendulifolia' (m)	IOrc
adenophylla Hooker	See S. ***cordata***
'Aegma Brno' (f)	WMou
aegyptiaca	CCor CDoC CLnd ENot NWea WMou
alba	CBow CKin CLnd CPer LBuc SPer WDin WMou
– f. *argentea*	See S. ***a. sericea***
– 'Aurea'	CHan CTho EHar WMou
– var. *caerulea*	ENot NWea WMou
– 'Cardinalis' (f)	ISea
– 'Chermesina' hort.	See S. ***a. vitellina*** 'Britzensis'
– 'Hutchinson's Yellow'	EHar MBri
– 'Liempde' (m)	ENot
– 'Orange Spire'	LMer
– 'Richmond'	SPer
§ – var. *sericea*	CB&S CCor CLnd EBre EFol EGol EHar ENot EPla IOrc LBre MBal MBri MNFA MRav NNor SHBN SHil SMad SPer WDin WMou WWat
– 'Splendens'	See S. ***a. sericea***
N– 'Tristis'	CLnd ELan IJoh MBri MRav NWea SPer WDin WMou
– *vitellina*	CCor CKin CPer EBar EGol EHar ELan LBuc NHol NWea WDin WMou
§ – *vitellina* 'Britzensis'	CBow CCor CDoC CKin CLnd CMHG EHar ELan ENot GRei IOrc LBuc MBal MGos MRav NNor NWea SHBN SPer SPla SSta WDin WMou WWat
– 'Vitellina Pendula'	See S. ***a.*** 'Tristis'
– 'Vitellina Tristis'	See S. ***a.*** 'Tristis'
§ *alpina*	CShe ECar ESis GAri MBal MCas MMil MPla MPlt NHar NHol NNrd NRoo SGil SIng
apoda	ELan ESis MBal MBro NHol WHal WMou WPat WPer
§ *arbuscula*	CLew CNic CShe EBar ECar ELan EPad ESis MBal MPla NLan SSta
arctica var. *petraea*	WPat
aurita	WDin WMou
babylonica	CTho NBee NWea SHBN WDin WMou
– 'Annularis'	See S. ***b.*** 'Crispa'
§ – 'Crispa'	CCor CGre CTho EHar ELan EPla LHop SEng SHBN WMou
– var. *pekinensis* 'Pendula'	EHar SHil
– – 'Tortuosa'	CDec CLnd CSco CTho EGol EHar ELan ENot ERav IDai IJoh IOrc ISea LPan MBal MBar MGos MWat NNor NWea SHil SPer SPla SReu WThu WWat
x *balfourii*	GWht SPla WMou
§ x *bebbii* x *hastata*	WMou
bicolor Willdenow	See S. ***schraderiana***
bockii	CBra CDoC CHan ELan EPla MBar MBro MGos WPer
§ 'Bowles' Hybrid'	CCor CDoC EHar LBuc MPar MRav WMou
'Boydii' (f)	CChu CSam EBlo ECar ECtt EHar ELan EPot ESis GDra ITim LGre MBal MBri MBro NHar NHol NNor NRoo SIng WAbe WCru WOMN WPat WThu
§ 'Boyd's Pendulous' (m)	ECar EHar EPla GAri MBal MBar WDav
breviserrata	GDra
burjatica 'Germany'	WMou
– 'Korso'	WMou
x *calodendron* (f)	WMou
candida	MNFA MPar WPat
caprea	CB&S CKin CLnd CPer ENot GRei LBuc NRoo NWea WDin WMou
– 'Kilmarnock' (m)	CBra CCor CLnd CMHG CSco EHar ELan ENot GRei IDai IJoh LBuc MBar MGos MWat NBar NWea SHBN SMad SPer SPla WAbe WDin WMou
– *pendula* (f)	See S. ***c.*** 'Weeping Sally'
– – (m)	See S. ***c.*** 'Kilmarnock'
*– *variegata*	CBrd IBar SPer
capusii	LMer
cascadensis	MBal

cashmiriana	WPat WThu
'Chrysocoma'	See S. × ***sepulcralis chrysocoma***
cinerea	CB&S CDoC CKin CPer GRei NWea WDin
– 'Tricolor'	EFol WPat
– 'Variegata'	ECar EGol
× ***cottetii***	CBra CDoC ECar WMou
daphnoïdes	CDoC CLnd CSam EHar ELan ENot GRei IHos IOrc MBar NWea SHBN SPer STre WDin WMar WMou WWat
– 'Aglaia' (m)	CB&S MBal
× ***dasyclados***	WMou
'E A Bowles'	See S. 'Bowles' Hybrid'
§ ***elaeagnos***	CBrd CDoC CTho EBar ECar EPla MNFA NBee WDin WMou
§ – ssp. ***angustifolia***	CLnd EGol EHar ELan ENot EPar ERav IOrc LHop MBal MUlv NNor NWea SMad SSpi STre WAbe WWat WWin
'Elegantissima'	See S. × ***pendulina*** 'E.'
§ 'Erythroflexuosa'	CB&S CDoC CShe CTho EBlo EGol EHar ELan EPla MBri SLon SPer WDin WOak
exigua	CB&S CCla CDoC CTho EBar EBre EFol EGol EHar ELan ENot EPla IJoh IOrc LBre MBar MBri MGos MNFA NBar SDry SMad SPer SSpi WMou WPat WWat
fargesii	CBot CChu EBre EGol EHar EPla ISea LBre LHop MBal MGos MRav MUlv NHol SDix SHil SMad SPla WCru WPat WWat
§ × ***finmarchica***	MPlt
formosa	See S. ***arbuscula***
fragilis	CKin CLnd NWea WDin WMou
§ ***fruticulosa***	CGle CLew EFol GDra GGar MBal MBar NKay WPer WThu
'Fuiri-koriyanagi'	See S. ***integra*** 'Hakuro-nishiki'
♦ ***furcata***	See S. ***fruticulosa***
glauca	WMou
glaucosericea	CCor
'Golden Curls'	See S. 'Erythroflexuosa'
gracilistyla	CSco EHar WMou WWat
§ – 'Melanostachys' (m)	CAbb CB&S CBot CBra CHan CMHG EBar EGol EHar ELan EPot ERav GDra IDai ISea MBal MBar NHar NHol NNor SPer SPla STre WMou WWat WWin
× ***grahamii*** (f)	CLew MBal
– 'Moorei' (f)	ESis MBal NNrd
× ***greyi***	CSam EPla
'Hagensis'	See S. 'The Hague'
hastata 'Wehrhahnii' (m)	Widely available
helvetica	CB&S CLew CSco EBre EFol ELan ENot ESis GDra GRei IJoh IOrc LBre LHop MBal MBar MBri MGos NHar NHol NNor NRoo SHBN SPer WDin WPat WWat WWin
herbacea	GAri LRHS MBal MCas NLan NMen
♦ ***hibernica***	See S. ***phylicifolia***
× ***hirtei*** 'Reifenweide' (f)	CDoC
hookeriana	CCor EHar SSpi WMar WMou WWat
♦ ***hylematica***	See S. ***fruticulosa***
incana	See S. ***elaeagnos***
integra 'Albomaculata'	See S. ***i.*** 'Hakuro-nishiki'
§ – 'Hakuro-nishiki' (v)	Widely available
irrorata	CBot CBow CCor CMHG EHar IOrc ISea MNFA MPar WMou
'Jacquinii'	See S. ***alpina***
japonica hort.	See S. ***babylonica*** 'Lavallei'
– Thunberg	EGol
kinuyanagi (m)	ELan LHop MPar
'Kuro-me'	See S. ***gracilistyla*** 'Melanostachys'
lanata	Widely available
¶ – hybrid	NHol
– 'Stuartii'	See S. 'Stuartii'
lapponum	GAri NLan SLon SRms WPat
× ***laurina*** (f)	CMHG SPer
§ ***lindleyana***	CHan CNic CRiv EPla EPot MPla NKay NMen NOak NRoo SGil STre WWat
magnifica	CBot CChu ECar EHar ELan EPar MBal SDry SHil SMad SSpi WMou
'Mark Postill' (f)	CCor CDoC EBar ECar WWat
matsudana	See S. ***babylonica pekinensis***
– 'Tortuosa'	See S. ***babylonica pekinensis*** 'Tortuosa'
– 'Tortuosa Aureopendula'	See S. 'Erythroflexuosa'
'Melanostachys'	See S. ***gracilistyla*** 'M.'.
moupinensis	IOrc MBri SHil WMou
♦ × ***myricoïdes***	See S. × ***bebbii***
§ ***myrsinifolia***	EHar EPla MNFA
§ ***myrsinites***	NRya
– var. ***jacquiniana***	See S. ***alpina***
myrtilloïdes 'Pink Tassels' (m)	ELan ESis GAri MBal MGos SHer SIng
– × ***repens***	See S. × ***finmarchica***
nakamurana var. ***yezoalpina***	CBrd CChu CCla ECar EPla GAri LHop MBal NHol SWas WPat
nepalensis	See S. ***lindleyana***
nigricans	See S. ***myrsinifolia***
nivalis	EPot MPlt
occidentalis	See S. ***humilis***
'Onusta' (m)	CDoC NBar
× ***ovata***	EHal EMNN MPlt NRoo
pentandra	CBot CKin IOrc NWea WDin WMou WWat
§ ***phylicifolia***	CCor EGol SPer WMou
polaris	ESis MBal MPlt
procumbens	See S. ***myrsinites***
♦ ***prunifolia***	See S. ***arbuscula***
§ ***purpurea***	CB&S EHal EPad IOrc WDin WMou
– f. ***gracilis***	See S. ***p.*** 'Nana'
– 'Helix'	See S. ***p.***
– 'Howki'	WMou
– ssp. ***lambertiana***	CCor
§ – 'Nana'	CCor CPle ELan EPla MBal MGos MPar NHol SChu SPer SPla STre WBod WStI WWat
– 'Nancy Saunders' (f)	EFol EPla ERav MNFA MPar SMrm SWas
– 'Pendula'	CBra CMer CPMA EHar ENot IJoh ISea MBal MBar MBri MPla NBar NBee NHol NNor NWea SPer WDin WStI WWat
– 'Richartii' (f)	MPar
pyrenaica	ECar
pyrifolia	WMou

reinii	MNFA
repens	CNic CRiv ERav GAri LHil NCat SEng STre WDin
– var. ***argentea***	CCor CGle CMer CSco CShe ECar EGol ENot GDra IOrc MBal MBar MRav NNrd NWea SPer SSta WBod WDin WMou WWin
– 'Iona' (m)	SSou
– ***pendula***	See S. 'Boyd's Pendulous'
– Saint Kilda form	ECar
– 'Voorthuizen' (f)	ECar ESis MBri NNrd NRya
reticulata	EPot GAri GDra MBal MBro NRya NTow WPat
retusa	GAri GDra MHig MPla NHol NMen NNrd WPat
– ***pygmaea***	SSou
rosmarinifolia hort.	See S. ***elaeagnos angustifolia***
x ***rubens*** 'Basfordiana' (m)	CDoC CLnd EBar EBre EGol EHar EPla LBre WMou
x ***rubra*** 'Eugenei' (m)	CCor EHar MNFA WMou WWat WWin
sachalinensis	See S. ***udensis***
x ***sadleri***	LHil
§ ***schraderiana***	SSta
x ***sepulcralis***	EHar NWea
§ x ***sepulcralis chrysocoma***	CDoC CSco EHar ELan ENot GAri IDai LBuc MBal MGos MWat SHBN SPer
x ***sepulcralis*** 'Salamonii'	NWea
x ***sericans***	MPar WMou
serpyllifolia	CLew LHop MBal MBro MCas MHig MPlt SGil WPat WPer
♦ ***serpyllum***	See S. ***fruticulosa***
'Setsuka'	See S. ***udensis*** 'Sekka'
¶ x ***simulatrix***	GAri
N x ***smithiana***	CDoC CLnd WDin
x ***stipularis*** (f)	CMHG
§ 'Stuartii'	CSam MBar SRms WBod
subopposita	CBow CDoC CPMA ELan EPla MBar MPla NHar SHil SIng
syrticola	See S. ***cordata***
x ***tetrapla*** 'Hutchinson's Nigricans'	CNat
§ 'The Hague'	WMou
triandra	WMou
– 'Black Maul'	WMou
– 'Champion'	WMou
– 'Rouge d'Orléans'	WMou
– 'Semperflorens'	CNat
tristis	See S. ***humilis***
x ***tsugaluensis*** 'Ginme' (f)	CMHG WMou WWat
§ ***udensis***	WWat
§ – 'Sekka' (m)	CCor CDec CLnd CMer ECtt EGol EHar ELan EPar ESma IOrc MBal MBri NHol NRoo NWea SPer SPla SSta STre WMou
uva-ursi	GAri MBal SIng WMou
viminalis	CKin CPer ENot GRei NWea WDin WMou
– 'Bowles' Hybrid'	See S. 'Bowles' Hybrid'
* ***violescens***	CBot
vitellina 'Pendula'	See S. ***alba*** 'Tristis'
x ***wimmeriana***	EGol NBee SRms
'Yelverton'	MBri SPer

SALVIA † (Labiatae)

acetabulosa	See S. ***multicaulis***
aethiopis	CPle ELan EMon MNFA MSte NSti WPer
¶ ***afghanica***	WEas
§ ***africana-caerulea***	CBrd CPle
¶ – 'Kirstenbosch'	WPer
§ ***africana-lutea***	CBrk CPle CSco CTre ELan LHop SAxl WEas WHal WPer
¶ ***algeriensis***	CPle
amarissima	CPle
ambigens	See S. ***guaranitica*** 'Blue Enigma'
amplexicaulis	WPer
♦ ***angustifolia*** Cavanilles	See S. ***reptans***
♦ – Michaux	See S. ***azurea***
– Salisbury	CFis
argentea	Widely available
arizonica	CAbb CFis CHal CPle WPer
¶ ***atrocyanea***	CPle
aucheri	GCal
aurea	See S. ***africana-lutea***
austriaca	CPle MBel WByw WPer
azurea	CBrd CHan CPle ERav LHol LHop WPer
– ssp. ***pitcheri***	GCal
bacheriana	See S. ***buchananii***
barrelieri	CHan CPle
bicolor Desfontaines	See SALVIA ***barrelieri***
blancoana	CBot CBrk CHan CPle CSpe ECha EFol EMon ERav GCal LGre LHop MSte NSti SUsu WHer WPer
blepharophylla	CAbb CB&S CCan CHan CPle LHop WCot WPer
¶ ***brevilabra***	CPle
broussonetii	CPle LHil
§ ***buchananii***	CAbb CBow CBrd CCan CHal CPle ELan EMon ERea LGre LHop NOak SAga SMrm
bulleyana	CGle CHan CPle CRDP CSev EBre ECro ELan EMon GCal LBre LHol SBla SIde SMrm SUsu WAbb WCra WDav WEas WPer
cacaliifolia	CAbb CCan CFis CGre CHal CHan CMer CPle CSpe CTre ERav GCal LHil LHol LHop MSte NOak SBor SUsu WCHb WEas WHer WPer WWye
cadmica	CPle
caerulea hort.	See S. ***guaranitica*** 'Black and Blue'
♦ – Linnaeus	See S. ***africana-caerulea***
caespitosa	CPle ITim NTow NWCA SIng WAbe
campanulata	EMon
canariensis	CPle MSte
candelabrum	CHan CPle CSev GCra LGre MPar NSti SAxl WCHb WCru WHer WKif WSHC
candidissima	CPle
cardinalis	See S. ***fulgens***
¶ ***castanea***	CPle
chamaedryoïdes	CCan CPle CSpe
chapalensis	CPle
♦ ***chinensis***	See S. ***japonica***
cinnabarina	CPle
clevelandii	CPle

coccinea	CBot CPle EBar ELan EMon LHil MSte WCHb WCru WHil WPer WWye
– 'Indigo'	ELan
– 'Lactea'	CBot CPle
– pink form	CPle GCal
¶ ***columbariae***	CPle
concolor hort.	See S. ***guaranitica***
confertiflora	CAbb CCan CFis CHal CPle CWit ELan EMon GCal LHil LHop LTil MSte NRar SAxl SBor SMrm WCHb WEas WPer WWye
deserta	See S. x ***sylvestris***
* 'Devantville'	CPle
discolor	CAbb CBot CDec CFis CMea CPle CSam CSev ELan ERav ERea LHil LHol LHop MPar MRav MTho SAxl SUsu WCHb WHal WPer
dombeyi	CAbb CFis CPle
dominica	CPle
dorisiana	CFis CHan CPle CSev ELan MSte WPer
dorrii	CPle
§ ***elegans***	CCan CCla CFis CGre CHun CPle CSev EBar ERav GCal LHol MSte SAga SBor SCro SIde WOld
§ – 'Scarlet Pineapple'	Widely available
fallax	CPle
¶ ***farinacea*** 'Alba'	LGre
¶ – 'Silver'	CPle
– 'Victoria'	CPle
forsskaolii	CCMG CGle CHal CHan CPle CRDP CSev ECro ELan EMon EPad LHil MBro MFir MPar NHol SChu SCro SSvw WAbb WByw WEas WHoo WPer
frigida	CPle
§ ***fruticosa***	CArn CPle EEls LHol SIde
§ ***fulgens***	CGle CHad CPle CSam CSev ERav LHil NBro NHex SIde SMad SMrm WCHb WHal WPer WWye
gesneriiflora	CAbb CCan CHan CPle CSev GCal LHil LHol MSte SAxl SIde WPer WWye
glutinosa	CCMG CChu CHad CHal CHan CPle ECha ELan EMon GCal LGan LHol MNFA NBro NSti SAga SMrm SSvw WBon WByw WDav WPer
grahamii Bentham	See S. ***microphylla microphylla***
– hort.	See S. ***microphylla neurepia***
greggii	CBrk CFis CPle EPad ERav LHil MSte NOak SAga SPer WHil WPer WWye
– 'Alba'	CPle CSev LHil LHop SMrm WPer WWye
– 'Keter's Red'	EMon
– x ***lycioïdes***	LHil LHop SAga
– peach	CB&S CBrk CPle CSev GCal LHop NOak SAga SAxl SUsu WPer
– 'Raspberry Royal'	CPle ESma LHil LHop SAga SAxl
§ ***guaranitica***	CAbb CBot CCan CChu CFis CGle CHan CMer CPle EBre ECha ELan GCal LAbb LBre LHil LHol MRav NRar SAga SAxl SMrm SUsu WCHb WPer
§ – 'Black and Blue'	CBrd CCan CGle CPle GCal LGre MSte SBor WCot WHal WPer WWye
* – 'Black Knight'	GCal
§ – 'Blue Enigma'	CArn CB&S CBot CBrd CCan CHad CSev EFou EMon GCal LHil LHop
haematodes	See S. ***pratensis*** Haematodes Group
hians	CGle CPle EBar ECro EMar EPad GCal GCra SAga SBla WAbb WEas WPer
hierosolymitana	CPle
hispanica hort.	See S. ***lavandulifolia***
horminoïdes	CKin NMir SHer WCla WWye
horminum	See S. ***viridis***
¶ ***hypargeia***	CPle
'Indigo Spires'	CPle SAga
interrupta	EHal EMon LGre LHil SAga SChu SDix SPer SUsu WCHb WEas
involucrata	CBow CHan CMil CPle CSev GCal LHil LHol NBro SAxl SMrm WCot WEas WSHC
– 'Bethellii'	CBot CBow CCan CCla CFis CGle CMil CPle CSev CTre EBar ECha ELan EMon GCal LHop SAga SBor SHil SLon SSpi WCru WEas WOMN WOld WPer
– 'Boutin'	CCan CPle WHal WPer
– dark form	GCal MSte
§ – 'Hadspen'	CBot CCan CGle CHad CSam ECro
– 'Mrs Pope'	See S. ***i.*** 'Hadspen'
¶ ***iodantha***	CPle
x ***jamensis*** 'James Compton'	LGre MSte SAxl SIgm SMrm
– 'Pat Vlasto'	CPle LGre LHil SAga SMrm
– 'Pink Blush'	CBot CCan CPle ELan LHil LWad SWas
§ ***japonica***	CPle
jurisicii	CHan CPle MBro SUsu SWas WPer
– 'Alba'	CPle
§ ***lavandulifolia***	CArn CCla CHad CMHG CPle CSFH ECha EFou EMon LHil NSti SAxl SBor SCro SHer SLon SPer SPla SUsu WCHb WDav WEas WHer WOak WPer WSun WWat WWye
♦ ***lemmonii***	See S. ***microphylla wislizenii***
♦ ***leptophylla***	See S. ***reptans***
leucantha	Widely available
¶ ***leucophylla***	CPle
longispicata	CPle
lycioïdes	CPle SMrm
lyrata	CPle MHew NSal
¶ ***macellaria***	CPle
macrosiphon	CPle
¶ ***madrensis***	CPle
mellifera	CArn CPle
mexicana var. ***minor***	CCan CFis CHal CPle LHil WPer
microphylla	CBow CCan CCla CFis CGle CMHG CMer CPle ESma MFir NFai SAga SChu SLMG SLon WCru WPer
¶ – ***alba***	SFis
§ – var. ***microphylla***	CCan CFis CGle CHal CPle CSev ELan EOrc ESma LGre LHol MTho SBor SChu SLon SMrm SSpi WEas WOld WSHC WWat

§ – var. ***neurepia***	CB&S CFis CGle CHun CPle CSam ECro EMon ERav GCHN IMal LAbb LHol LHop NSti NTow SAga SDry SHil SPer WCHb WCru WHal WPer WSHC WSun WWye
– – 'Newby Hall'	CBrd CPle LHil WPer
♦– 'Pink Blush'	See S. x ***jamensis*** 'Pink Blush'
¶ – 'Variegata'	CPle
§ – var. ***wislizenii***	CBrd CPle LHop
moorcroftiana	CPle GCal GCra WCot WEas
§ ***multicaulis***	CHan CPle CSev ECha EFol EFou EMon EPla NTow SAxl SMrm SUsu SWas WAbb WByw WCHb WDav WOMN WOld WPer WSHC
nemorosa 'Amethyst'	EFou SWas
– 'Lubecca'	CCla CHad CPle CSco CSev CShe EBre EFou LBre SPer WOld WRus WSHC
– 'Ostfriesland' ('East Friesland')	CCla CKel CPle CSco EBre ECha ECtt EFou ELan EPla GCHN LBre MRav MSte MWat NBar NFai NKay SChu SCro SDix SMad SPer SPla WCHb WHoo WPer WRus WWin
– 'Rosenwein'	SAxl SWas
– ssp. ***tesquicola***	CBrd CHan CPle ECha GCal
¶ – 'Wesuwe'	ECha
nilotica	WHer
* ***ningpo***	CPle
¶ ***nipponica***	WPer
officinalis	CArn CHad CSFH CShe ENot Effi GPoy IEde MBal MBar MBri MChe MGos NNor NSel SHBN SLon WByw WDin WEas WOak WPer WWat WWye
– 'Alba'	See S. ***o.*** 'Albiflora'
§ – 'Albiflora'	CBot CFis CMea CMil ECha EFou LHil NSti SBla SIde WHer WPer
N– 'Aurea'	CPle GPoy MBar MFir NSel SHer SMad SUsu WWin
– 'Berggarten'	CPle ECro EFou EMon GCal LGre SWas WHer
§ – broad-leaved	CBot EJud NSti SIde WWye
¶ – 'Herrenhausen'	CPle MSte
§ – 'Icterina' (v)	Widely available
– 'Kew Gold'	ECha EFol EMon EPla LHop MRav
– ***latifolia***	See S. ***o.*** broad-leaved variety
– 'Minor'	EFou WHer
– narrow-leaved	See S. ***lavandulifolia***
– Purpurascens Group	Widely available
– 'Purpurascens Variegata'	CFis CGle CPle EFol NSti WEas
– 'Robin Hill'	LRHS WSun
– 'Rosea'	SUsu WHer
– Tomentosa Group	CArn
– 'Tricolor' (v)	Widely available
– 'Variegata'	See S. ***o.*** 'Icterina'
oppositiflora	CFis CPle ERav LHop SAga
patens	Widely available
– 'Cambridge Blue'	CBot CHad CPle CRDP CSam CSev CSun ECha EFou ELan EMon GCal LGre LHil LHol LHop MFir MRav NPer SAga SBla SBor SLon WAbe WEas WOMN WOld WPer
– 'Chilcombe'	CPle EBar LHil LHop SAga SUsu WPer
¶ – 'Guanajuato'	LGre
¶ – 'Oxford Blue'	EOrc
– 'Royal Blue'	ECha EFol ERav
¶ ***penstemonoïdes***	CPle
¶ ***polystachya***	CAbb CPle
* 'Powis Castle'	CTro
pratensis	CArn CKin CPle EFou EJud ELan EMon LWad MHew MPit NFai NSal SIde WPer WWye
§ – Haematodes Group	CCla CHad CKel CPle CSco EBre ECha ELan EMon LBre LHil MBel MFir MPar MRav NBro NKay NSti SCro SDix SPer SUsu WHil WHoo WOld WPer
– 'Lapis Lazuli'	EMon
¶ – 'Tenorei'	WPer
przewalskii	CPle EMon GCal SAga SFis SMad SUsu WPer
¶ – CLD 247	CPle NHol
¶ ***puberula***	CHan CPle
¶ – 'El Butano'	CPle
purpurea	CPle
recognita	CBot CPle LGre SUsu SWas
reflexa	CPle
regeliana	EMon GCal NBir WPer
repens	CLew CPle LHil
§ ***reptans***	CCan CFis CPle CSam CSpe LHop SAga SUsu WPer
ringens	CPle GCHN SBor
¶ ***riparia***	CPle
roemeriana	CPle WOMN WPer
'Rosentraum'	EFou
♦ ***rutilans***	See S. ***elegans*** 'Scarlet Pineapple'
* ***sariczelek tienschen***	WPer
scabra	GCal
sclarea	CArn CGle CHal CPle EJud Effi GPoy LHol LWad MChe NFai NSel SFis SIde WCHb WDav WHer WHoo WOak WPbr WPer WWye
N– var. ***turkestanica*** hort.	Widely available
sinaloensis	CPle LGre LHil LHop SAga
¶ ***sonomensis***	CPle
¶ ***spathacea***	CPle
¶ ***spinosa***	CPle
sp. Iran	WOMN
sp. T&K 550	CBot
§ ***staminea***	CPle GCal SIde
stenophylla	CPle WPer
x ***superba***	CCla CGle CHad CHal CKel CPle CShe EBre EFol ELan LBre LHil MBri MBro MWat NRoo SAxl SCro SDix SFis SSvw WEas WHoo
– 'Rubin'	EFou
– 'Superba'	CSco CSev ECha EFou SPer
§ x ***sylvestris***	CPle
– 'Blauhügel'	CCla CHad CMGP CPle CSev ECha EFou ELan GCal LGre MBri MSte NHol NRoo NVic SChu
– 'Blaukönigin' ('Blue Queen')	CGle CPar EBre ECro EFou GCHN LBre LWad MNFA MWat NMir NOak NRoo SFis WHoo WPer
– 'Indigo'	EBre EFou LBre

– 'Lye End'	CPar EBre ECtt GCal LBre MRav NBar WRus
– 'Mainacht' ('May Night')	CHad CMGP CSco EBre ECro EFou LBre MBri MSte NBar NHol NSti SChu SMrm SPer SPla WByw WEas WRus
– 'Rose Queen'	CHan CMGP CPar CPle EBre ECha EFou ELan EMon ESis GCHN LBre MNFA MSte NCat NFai NOak NOrc NRoo SFis SSvw SUsu WByw WHoo WPer
– 'Rügen'	MBri
– 'Tänzerin'	EFou MPar
– 'Viola Klose'	EFou SUsu
¶ ***taraxacifolia***	CPle
tesquicola	See S. ***nemorosa t.***
¶ ***tiliifolia***	CPle
¶ ***tingitana***	CPle
¶ ***tomentosa***	CPle
♦ ***transcaucasica***	See S. ***staminea***
transsylvanica	CMil CPle EMon SMrm WCot WPer
* ***trijuga***	CPle
triloba	See S. ***fruticosa***
uliginosa	Widely available
*– 'African Skies'	GCal
urica	CPle
verbenaca	CPle GCHN LHil MHew MWil NHol NSal WPer
¶ – pink form	CPle
verticillata	CArn CPle EBar ECha ELan EMon GCra LHil LHol NHol NNor NSal NSti WPbr WPer WWye
– 'Alba'	CBrd CPle EMon LHol MBel MPar NHol WHer
¶ – ssp. ***amasiaca***	CPle
– 'Purple Rain'	CPle EBre EFou GCal LBre LHil NSti SMrm SUsu SWas WCot
virgata	CPle
§ ***viridis***	CArn CPle LHol MChe SIde SUsu
– var. ***alba***	CPle
♦ ***viscosa***	See S. ***riparia***
¶ ***wagneriana***	CPle

SALVINIA (Salviniaceae)

braziliensis	MSta

SAMBUCUS † (Caprifoliaceae)

¶ ***adnata*** L 864	EPla
caerulea var. ***neomexicana***	EMon
canadensis	ESim
F – 'Adams'	ESim
– 'Aurea'	CDoC ELan IOrc NWea WAbe
– 'Maxima'	CCor CHEx ERav GCal
– 'Rubra'	EPla
F – 'York'	ESim
* ***coraensis***	GWht
ebulus	CKin CRow ERav
§ ***javanica***	EHal
nigra	CKin CPer EHar ENot GPoy GRei LBuc LHol MBri NNor NSel NWea SIde WMou
– 'Albomarginata'	See S. ***n.*** 'Marginata'
N – 'Aurea'	CB&S CCla CCor CFis CLnd CMHG CRow CSco EHar ELan ENot EPla ERav GRei LHol NRoo SPer WDin
– 'Aureomarginata'	CSam ELan EPla ERav GAri MBal NNor SHBN SLon
– 'Bimble' (v)	EMon
– 'Cae Rhos Lligwy'	WHer
¶ – 'Castledean'	EHal
– 'Din Dryfol' (v)	CNat
§ – 'Guincho Purple'	CBow CBra CCla CCor CFis CMHG CRow EBre EFol EFou EGol EHar EHoe ELan ERav GCal IBar IOrc LBre LHol LHop MBal MBri NNor SDix SMad SPer SSpi WSHC WWat
– 'Heterophylla'	See S. ***n.*** 'Linearis'
– 'Laciniata'	CCla CCor CMHG CRow CSam CSco EFol EHar ELan EPar EPla ERav LHol MBal NNor NWea SChu SDix SHil SMad SPer SPla SSpi SSta WMou WSHC WWat
§ – 'Linearis'	CChu CPle EBre EGol EHal ELan EPla ERav GCal LBre LTil SMad SUsu WAbe
– 'Madonna' (v)	CBow CChu CDoC CNat CPMA EHal EPla MPla NBar NBee SFai SMad SPer
§ – 'Marginata'	Widely available
– 'Nana'	EMon SLon
¶ – 'Plena'	EMon EPla
– 'Pulverulenta' (v)	CChu CDoC CRow EBlo EBre EFol EGol EHar ELan EPar EPla ERav GCal LBre LHol LHop MBri NSti SApp SDry SHil SPer SSpi WSHC
– 'Purpurea'	See S. ***n.*** 'Guincho Purple'
– 'Pygmy'	EHal EPla MPla NHol WPat
– 'Pyramidalis'	CCor EHar EMon EPla SMad WCot
*– 'Tenuifolia'	CKni LHol
– 'Variegata'	See S. ***n.*** 'Marginata'
– 'Witches Broom'	EMon EPla
racemosa	GRei
– 'Aurea'	CSco EBre GRei LBre NKay NSel
– 'Goldenlocks'	EHal NHol SPer WPat
– 'Plumosa Aurea'	CB&S CBot CMHG CRow CTrw EBre EFol EGol EHar ELan ENot IDai IJoh LBre LHop MBal MBar MBri NNor NRoo SDix SHBN SLon SMad SPer SReu SSta WDin WWin
– 'Sutherland Gold'	Widely available
– 'Tenuifolia'	CCor CPMA EHal ELan EPla MGos MPla MUlv NHol NSti SMad SPer SSpi WCru WHCG WPat WWat
sieboldiana coreana	CMCN
wightiana	See S. ***javanica***

SAMOLUS (Primulaceae)

repens	ECou

SANCHEZIA (Acanthaceae)

nobilis Hooker	CHal
♦– hort.	See S. ***speciosa***

SANDERSONIA (Liliaceae/Colchicaceae)

aurantiaca	LAma LBow NRog WChr WCru

SANGUINARIA (Papaveraceae)

canadensis	CArn CAvo CBro CChu CCla CGle CRDP EPar EPot GCal GPoy LAma LBow NBro NNor NRog SDeJ SHig WAbe WChr WCru WMar WWat
– pink form	SWas WThi
– 'Plena'	CAvo CBrd CBro CChu CCla CMea EBre EPar EPot LBre MBri MHig MTho NHar NHol NRar NRya SBla SHer SIgm SIng SPer SPou SWas WAbe WDav WEas

SANGUISORBA (Rosaceae)

albiflora	ELan EPla SMrm
benthamiana	CHEx
canadensis	CHan CRDP CRow ECha EPla GAbr GCal GPoy MFir SPer WWye
dodecandra	MPlt
hakusanensis	ELan
* ***magnifica alba***	CCla CRDP CRow EBre ECro EFou EPla GAri LBre NRoo WRus WWin
§ ***minor***	CArn CKin EEls GPoy IEde LHol MBar MChe MHew NMir NSal NSel SIde WCHb WCla WEas WHer WNdy WOak WPer WWye
obtusa	CCla CKel CRow CSco CShe ECha ECro EFol EFou GAbr GCal LHil MRav MUlv NBro NHol SFis SMad SMrm SPer WCru WEas
officinalis	CArn CLew CSev EGol Effi NLan NMir NSel WCla WNdy WWin WWye
♦***pimpinella***	See S. ***minor***
sitchensis	See S. ***stipulata***
§ ***stipulata***	GCal MUlv
tenuifolia	MUlv
¶ – 'Alba'	ECha

SANICULA (Umbelliferae)

europaea	CKin GPoy LHol WHer WWye

SANIELLA (Liliaceae/Hypoxidaceae)

verna	MHig

SANSEVIERIA (Dracaenaceae)

trifasciata 'Gigantea' (v)	CHal MBri
– 'Golden Hahnii' (v)	CDoC MBri
– 'Laurentii' (v)	CHal MBri
– 'Moonshine'	MBri

SANTOLINA † (Compositae)

§ ***chamaecyparissus***	Widely available
– var. ***corsica***	See S. ***c. nana***
– 'Lambrook Silver'	CGle CPMA ECtt ESma GAbr NH&H NHol NSel SGil WHer WWat
– 'Lemon Queen'	CArn CDoC ESis MBal MGos NH&H NSel NSti NWyt SHer SIde WCHb WOak WPer WWat
§ – var. ***nana***	CB&S CBow CSFH EBre ECha ENot EPla LBre LHop MBar NFai NH&H NNor SAxl SLon SPer WAbe WPer WWat WWye
– – 'Weston'	CLew CShe EFol MBri MCas MGos NH&H NHol NTow
– 'Pretty Carol'	CAbP CDoC CKni CSco ELan ESis MAsh NFai NH&H NHol SHer SIde SPla WWat WWeb
– 'Small-Ness'	EMon NHol SIng
¶ – ***squarrosa***	NH&H
elegans	WDav
incana	See S. ***chamaecyparissus***
'Oldfield Hybrid'	NH&H
pectinata	See S. ***rosmarinifolia canescens***
§ ***pinnata***	CBow CFis CHal CSev EMon ESma LHol NH&H WPbr WPer
– ssp. ***neapolitana***	CArn CFis CHan CMHG CPle CSFH CSev CShe ECha ELan ENot ISea LHol MBri NH&H NNor NSti SDix WBod WEas WOak WWat
– – cream form	See S. ***p. n.*** 'Edward Bowles'
§ – – 'Edward Bowles'	CCla CGle CMil EBar ECar EFol EFou EJud ELan EOrc EPad ESis GCal LHop NBir NH&H NHol NSel NSti SAxl SChu SLon SSvw WAbe WHer WSHC
– – 'Sulphurea'	CBow CDoC CFis CMer EPla LGre NCat NH&H SPer SUsu WKif WPer
rosmarinifolia	ESis NSel NSti
§ – ssp. ***canescens***	NH&H
§ – ssp. ***rosmarinifolia***	CB&S CCla CElw CFis CHan CMHG CPle CSFH CSco CSev ECha ELan ENot GCHN LHol MBri NH&H NHol NKay NSel NSti SDix STre WBod WDav WEas WSHC WWat WWin
– – 'Primrose Gem'	CB&S CLew CSam ECar ECha EFol EPad ESis IJoh LAbb LHop MBal MPla NCat NH&H NHol NSti SAxl SBod SHer SPla WPer
* ***serratifolia***	CSco LHol NH&H WPer WWye
tomentosa	See S. ***pinnata neapolitana***
virens	See S. ***rosmarinifolia rosmarinifolia***
viridis	See S. ***rosmarinifolia rosmarinifolia***

SAPINDUS (Sapindaceae)

drummondii	WCoo

SAPIUM (Euphorbiaceae)

japonicum	SSpi

SAPONARIA (Caryophyllaceae)

'Bressingham'	EBre ECha ELan EMNN EPot LBee LBre NHar NHol NTow SBla SFis SHer SIng WPat WPer WThu WWin
caespitosa	EPot GTou MHig NTow WOMN
¶ × ***lempergii*** 'Max Frei'	SUsu SWas
lutea	CNic
ocymoïdes	CB&S CFis ECha EFol EFou EHon ELan EMNN ESis GAbr GCHN IDai LAbb LGro MCas MPla NKay NRoo SIng WHil WPbr WStI WWin
– 'Alba'	ECha EHal SIng
– 'Rubra Compacta'	WAbe WPat WPer

officinalis	CArn CBre CKin CRow CSFH EJud ERav Effi GAbr GPoy IEde LHol MChe MHew NSal NSel SIde WHal WHer WNdy WOak WPer WWye
– 'Alba Plena'	CGle CHad CMil CSam ECro EMon NSti SChu WCHb WHer WPer WWin
§ – 'Dazzler' (v)	EBar EFol EHoe ELan EMon ESma LHol MTho NBir NRoo NSti SIde WCHb WCot WHal WPer
– 'Rosea Plena'	CBre CGle CHan CLew CMHG CMil CRDP CRow CSam ECro EJud ELan EMon GAbr MBri NCat NOrc SCro SMrm SPer WCHb WCot WCru WHal WPbr WPer WSun
– 'Rubra Plena'	CGle CHad CMHG CRDP ELan EMon SChu WCHb WCot WPbr WThi
– 'Variegata'	See S. ***o.*** 'Dazzler'
x ***olivana***	CPar ECha EMNN EPot LBee MHig MPla NHol NKay NMen SBod SFis WOMN WPat WPer WThu WWin
pulvinaris	See S. ***pumilio***
§ ***pumilio***	GCHN MHig NHol NWCA WPer
'Rosenteppich'	NTow SWas WPat
sicula	WPer
zawadskii	See SILENE *z.*

SARCOCAPNOS (Papaveraceae)

enneaphylla	EPot

SARCOCOCCA † (Buxaceae)

confusa	Widely available
hookeriana	CBow IOrc SHer SReu WOMN
– Sch 2396	EPla
– var. ***digyna***	Widely available
– – 'Purple Stem'	CCla EPla MGos SHil SReu SSta WDin
– var. ***hookeriana***	SSpi
– var. ***humilis***	CBow CDoC CFis CPle CSco ELan ENot EPar EPla ERav IJoh MBal MBar MBri MCas MGos MPla MWat NNor SHBN SPer SPla WBod WDin WSHC WWat
orientalis	CMCN LTil SHil
'Roy Lancaster'	EPla
ruscifolia	CB&S CBow CCla CDoC CMCN CPMA CPle CSam CSco EGol ELan ENot EPla ERav IHos IOrc MBri MGos MPla SGil SLon SPer SPla SSpi WWat
– var. ***chinensis***	CBot EPla
saligna	CB&S CCla CMCN EPla WBod

SARCOPOTERIUM (Rosaceae)

See Plant Deletions

SARRACENIA † (Sarraceniaceae)

'Ahlsii'	WMEx
alata	EPot WHal WMEx
¶ – pubescens form	WHil
¶ – 'Red Lid'	WMEx
¶ – x ***oreophila***	WMEx
x ***areolata***	WMEx
¶ 'Brook's Hybrid'	EPot
x ***catesbyi***	EPot SSpi WMEx
¶ – red form	WMEx
¶ – x ***excellens***	WMEx
¶ – x ***flava***	WMEx
– x ***popei***	WMEx
– x ***rubra***	WMEx
x ***chelsonii***	WMEx
x ***comptonensis***	WMEx
¶ x ***courtii***	WHal
'Evendine'	WMEx
x ***excellens*** x ***wrigleyana***	WMEx
x ***exornata***	WMEx
♦ x ***farnhamii***	See S. x ***readii***
flava	EPot MSte SSpi WHal WMEx
¶ – copperlid form	WHil
¶ – heavy veined form	WHil
– 'Maxima'	EPot WHal WMEx
x ***formosa*** x ***excellens***	WMEx
'Gulf Rubra'	WMEx
x ***harperi***	WMEx
¶ 'Judy'	WMEx
leucophylla	EPot MSte WHal WMEx
– x ***catesbyi***	WMEx
¶ – x ***oreophila***	WMEx
– x ***popei***	WMEx
x ***melanorhoda***	WMEx
x ***miniata***	WMEx
minor	WHal WMEx
– 'Okefenokee Giant'	MSte WMEx
¶ – x ***oreophila***	WHil
– x ***wrigleyana***	WMEx
x ***mitchelliana***	EPot WHal WMEx
x ***moorei***	WMEx
– 'Marston Select'	WMEx
¶ – x ***catesbyi***	WMEx
– x ***readii***	WMEx
oreophila	EPot
– x ***minor***	EPot WMEx
x ***popei*** x ***flava***	WMEx
– x ***purpurea venosa***	WMEx
psittacina	EPot MSte WHal WMEx
purpurea	EPot WMEx
¶ – 'Louis Burke'	WMEx
– ssp. ***purpurea***	WMEx
– ssp. ***venosa***	WHal WMEx
§ x ***readii***	WMEx
– x ***excellens***	WMEx
'Red Burgundy'	WMEx
x ***rehderi***	WMEx
rubra	WHal WMEx
¶ – ssp. ***alabamensis***	WHil
– ssp. ***gulfensis***	EPot WHal
– ssp. ***jonesii***	MSte WMEx
¶ – ssp. ***wherryi***	WHil
– x ***excellens***	WMEx
¶ – x ***alata*** 'Red Lid'	WMEx
x ***swaniana***	WMEx
¶ ***willisii*** x ***flava***	WMEx
¶ – x ***minor*** 'Giant'	WMEx

SASA † (Gramineae(Bambuseae))

borealis	See SASAMORPHA ***borealis***
¶ ***chrysantha***	EPla
♦ – hort.	See PLEIOBLASTUS ***chino***
disticha 'Mirrezuzume'	See PLEIOBLASTUS ***pygmaeus*** 'M.'.

glabra albostriata See SASAELLA *masamuneana a.*
kurilensis EPla ISta LBam SBam SDry WJun
– 'Shimofuri' EPla SBam SDry WJun
¶ – short form EPla
megalophylla 'Nobilis' SBam SDry
nana See S. *veitchii minor*
nipponica EPla SBam SDry SPla WJun
– 'Aureostriata' SBam SDry SPla
¶ *oshidensis* EPla
§ *palmata* CHad CHan ENot GAri ISta LBam NSel SBam SReu
– f. *nebulosa* CB&S CHEx EPla MUlv SArc SBam SDry WJun
¶ – 'Warley Place' (v) SBam SDry
quelpaertensis EPla GAri ISta LBam SBam SDry
senanensis EPla SBam SDry
tessellata See INDOCALAMUS *tessellatus*
tsuboiana EPla ISta LBam MUlv SBam SDry
§ *veitchii* CB&S CBow CGre CHEx CWit ECha EPar EPla ERav IOrc ISea ISta LBam LNet MBri MUlv NJap SBam SCob SDry WJun WPat WWye
§ – *minor* SBam

SASAELLA (Gramineae(Bambuseae))

bitchuensis hort. SBam SDry
glabra See S. *masamuneana*
§ *masamuneana* f. *albostriata* (v) EPla SBam SDry WJun
– f. *aureostriata* (v) EPla ISta SBam SDry
§ *ramosa* EHoe EPla GAri ISta LBam MBal NRya SBam SCob SDry SHil WJun
*– 'Tsuyu-zasa' EPla

SASAMORPHA (Gramineae(Bambuseae))

§ *borealis* GAri LBam SBam

SASSAFRAS (Lauraceae)

albidum CArn CBot CCla CHEx CMCN EHar MBri SHil SSpi
tzumu CHEx

SATSUMA See CITRUS *reticulata* Satsuma Group

SATUREJA (Labiatae)

coerulea CKel SFis SIde WPer
cuneifolia MCas
hortensis GPoy IEde ILis LHol LHop MChe NSal NSel WHer
montana CArn CHal CNic CRiv EEls ELan Effi GPoy IEde ILis LHol MBri MChe MPla NMen NRoo NSal NSel NSti SDix SIde WCHb WHer WOak WPer WWye
§ – ssp. *illyrica* CHal WThi
– prostrate white CRDP LGan
– *subspicata* See S. *m. illyrica*
parnassica WPer WWye
repanda See S. *spicigera*
seleriana LHil MHig NTow WPer WWye
§ *spicigera* CArn CHal CLew CNic CRiv CSFH EMNN EPot LHol MHig NKay NMen NTow SFis SIde WCHb WHil WPer WWin WWye
spinosa WPer

SATYRIUM (Orchidaceae)

nepalense EPot

SAURAUIA (Actinidiaceae)

subspinosa CHEx

SAUROMATUM (Araceae)

guttatum See S. *venosum*
§ *venosum* CRDP ELan LAma MBri SMad WCot WCru

SAURURUS (Saururaceae)

cernuus CBen CRDP CWGN EBre EHon ELan EMFW LBre LMay MSta NDea SRms SWat WChe WHol

SAUSSUREA (Compositae)

alpina GDra
¶ *chinophylla* WPer

SAXEGOTHAEA (Podocarpaceae)

conspicua CGre CMCN EHar EPla IBar LCon LTil SBor SLon SMad WThu

SAXIFRAGA † (Saxifragaceae)

'Aemula' (x *borisii*) (8) WAbe
aïzoïdes var. *atrorubens* (6) MBal MBro MWat NGre
*– *aurantiana* (6) NGre
aïzoön See S. *paniculata*
'Alba' (x *apiculata*) (8) CShe ELan EMNN ESis GTou MBal MBro MHig MPlt NHol NRed SBla SIng SSmi WAbe WCla WHoo WPat WThu WWin
– (x *arco-valleyi*) See S. 'Ophelia'
– (*oppositifolia*) (9) CRiv ELan EPot GTou MYat NGre NHar NNrd NRya SHer SIng SSmi WAbe WDav WThu WWin
– (*sempervivum*) See S. 'Zita'
'Albert Einstein' (x *apiculata*) (8) WAbe
'Albertii' (*callosa*) (7) CShe GTou MHig NNrd SGil SIng SSmi WWin
'Aldebaran' (x *borisii*) (8) EPot NHar
'Alfons Mucha' (8) MWat NGre NRed WAbe
¶ 'Alpenglow' (8) MWat
'Amitie' (x *gloriana*) (8) MYat NHol
* 'Anagales Sunset' WThu
andersonii (8) EPot ITim MBal MYat NGre NNrd NTow WAbe WDav
¶ – GFS 76/2(8) MWat
x *andrewsii* (3x7) LBee MDHE MFir MHig MTho NHol
§ *androsacea* (12) NTow
'Anne Beddall' (*cinerea*) (8) MWat NGre
x *apiculata* See S. 'Gregor Mendel'
♦ *aquatica* See S. *irrigua*

Name	Suppliers
'Archfield White' (*callosa*) (7)	CLew CNic NNrd
§ 'Arco' (x ***arco-valleyi***) (8)	EPot MWat NNrd WAbe
x ***arco-valleyi***	See S. 'Arco'
x ***arendsii*** (12)	MPit WEas
§ 'Aretiastrum' (x ***boydii***) (8)	EPot MYat NGre NMen NNrd WAbe WThu
aretioïdes (8)	WAbe WThu
'Ariel' (x ***hornibrookii***) (8)	LRHS MWat
* ***armstrongii***	NRed
'Assimilis' (x ***petraschii***) (8)	MBro MYat WAbe WDav WHil
'August Hayek' (x ***leyboldii***) (8)	NNrd NRed
§ 'Aureopunctata' (x ***urbium***) (3/v)	CArn CGle CKel CMil CShe CTom ECha EFol ELan EPla GCal MBal MBro MFir NGre NHol NNrd NRoo SHer SMrm WBon
'Balcana'	See S. ***paniculata orientalis***
'Baldensis'	See S. ***paniculata baldensis***
'Ballawley Guardsman' (12)	EPar IDai MBal NKay NRoo SHer SIng
§ 'Beatrix Stanley' (x ***anglica***) (8)	ECar EMNN EPot MBal MBro MYat NGre NHar NHol WAbe
¶ 'Becky Foster' (x ***borisii***) (8)	MWat
¶ 'Beechcroft White'	LBee
¶ 'Berenika' (x ***bertolonii***) (8)	MWat
'Bettina' (x ***paulinae***) (8)	WAbe
'Biegleri' (8)	EPot
'Birch Baby' (12)	SIng
'Birch Yellow'	See S. 'Pseudoborisii'
'Black Beauty' (12)	ECar LBee SGil SHer
* 'Blackhouse White'	NGre NNrd
¶ 'Blanik' (x ***borisii***) (8)	MWat
¶ 'Blanka' (x ***boresii***)	MWat
'Bob Hawkins' (12/v)	CMHG CMer ECar EFol ELan EPad EPar GDra LBee NMen NNrd NRed NVic WWin
§ 'Bodensee' (x ***hofmannii***) (8)	WAbe WPat
x ***borisii***	See S. 'Sofia'
'Boston Spa' (x ***elisabethiae***) (8)	CKel EMNN GCHN ITim MBro MCas MHig MPit MPlt MYat NGre NKay NNrd NRed NRoo NTow SGil SHer SIng WAbe WDav WHoo WPat WThu WTyr
'Bridget' (x ***edithiae***) (8)	CShe ELan ESis ITim MBal MCas NGre NRed NTow SGil SHer WAbe WDav WHil WThu
'Brookside' (***burseriana***) (8)	EPot SGil SPou WAbe
brunoniana	See S. ***brunonis***
§ ***brunonis*** (2)	EPot GTou NHar WCru
bryoïdes (5)	GTou MHig
x ***burnatii*** (7)	EPot MBro MCas MHig NKay NNrd NRed SIng WTyr
burseriana (8)	GCHN NRed NRya SIng WAbe
¶ – WPY/V1 (8)	MWat
'Buttercup' (x ***kayei***) (8)	EPot GTou MBro MWat MYat NGre NNrd NWCA WAbe WHoo WPat
caesia (7)	SRms
§ ***callosa*** (7)	EMNN GTou MBro MPla MWat NGre NHar NKay SBla WAbe WPat
§ – var. ***australis*** (7)	CNic CRiv ESis MBro MCas MHig NNrd SIng WHil
– var. ***bellardii***	See S. ***callosa***
§ – ssp. ***catalaunica*** (7)	MBro NHol SPou
– var. ***lantoscana***	See S. ***c. australis***
– ***lingulata***	See S. ***callosa.***
'Cambria Jewel' (12)	NNrd
'Cambridge Seedling' (8)	MYat
§ ***camposii*** (12)	GAbr SIng
'Camyra' (8)	MWat MYat NGre WAbe
canaliculata (12)	WDav
x ***canis-dalmatica*** (7)	CMHG ECtt EMNN ESis GGar GTou LBee MBro MHig NHar NMen NNrd SIng
§ 'Carmen' (x ***elisabethiae***) (8)	CShe ECar ELan EMNN EPot IDai ITim LBee MBro MCas MHig MYat NKay NNrd NRya SHer WAbe WThu
'Carnival' (12)	ESis
* ***carolinica***	NWCA
'Castor' (x ***bilekii***) (8)	MWat WAbe WThu
catalaunica (7)	See S. ***callosa catalaunica***
'Caterhamensis' (***cotyledon***) (7)	WEas
§ ***caucasica*** (8)	NKay
cebennensis (12)	EPad EPot NRed NRya NTow SIgm SIng SPou
– dwarf form (12)	WAbe
cespitosa (12)	NWCA
– var. ***emarginata*** (12)	MFos NHol WDav
'Chambers' Pink Pride'	See S. 'Miss Chambers'
§ ***cherlerioïdes*** (5)	EBar ELan NRed NRya SHer WCla WEas WWin
'Cherrytrees' (x ***boydii***) (8)	MCas NNrd NRed WAbe
'Chetwynd' (***marginata***) (8)	MWat WAbe
'Chez Nous' (x ***gloriana***) (8/v)	NGre
'Christine' (x ***anglica***) (8)	MWat SIng
x ***churchillii*** (7)	NKay
'Clare Island' (12)	SIng
§ 'Clarence Elliott' (***umbrosa primuloïdes***) (3)	CNic CShe ELan EPot GCal GDra MBro MCas MHig NCat NGre NHol NKay NNrd NRar NRya NVic SHer STre WCla WOMN WPat WThu
§ 'Cloth of Gold' (***moschata***) (12)	CMea CShe ECha ELan EPar EPot GDra GTou ITim LBee MBal MBar MBro MCas MPla NKay NRoo NRya NWCA SBla SBod SIng SSmi WAbe WPat WThu WWin
cochlearis (7)	CMea CShe ESis LBee MBal NNor NWCA SGil SIng SSmi WWin
* – ***probinii*** (7)	MWat SPou
¶ 'Cockscomb'	MWat
'Compacta' (***moschata***) (12)	SHer SIng
'Coningsby Queen' (x ***hornibrookii***) (8)	ITim

¶ 'Cordata' (***burseriana***) (8) — MWat
¶ 'Corona' (x ***boydii***) (8) — MWat NGre
*x ***correvensis*** — ECtt GCHN MFir NNrd WPer
'Correvoniana' (***paniculata***) (7) — CNic CPar EBre EMNN EPad ESis LBre MBar MBro NKay SIng WAbe WHoo WPer WWin
corsica ssp. ***cossoniana*** (11) — WOMN
§ ***cortusifolia*** (4) — CChu CHEx CKel MBal NHar NKay SAxl
– dwarf form — EPot LGre
– var. ***fortunei*** — See S. ***fortunei***
§ ***corymbosa*** (8) — EPad NGre NKay
cotyledon (7) — GDra LBee MPla NKay NNor SHer SIng WAbe WCla WEas WTyr
§ 'Cranbourne' (x ***anglica***) (8) — CRiv CShe EBre EMNN EPot LBre MBro MCas MYat NGre NHar NHol NMen NNrd NRed SBla SGil SHer SIng WAbe WHoo WPat WThu
'Cream Seedling' (8) — EBre LBre MBro MDHE MWat NGre NRed NRya
'Crenata' (***burseriana***) (8) — CNic EPot MBro MWat MYat NGre NHar NHol NKay NRya SSmi WAbe WHoo
'Crimson Rose' — NNrd
crispa (4) — SIng
crustata (7) — MDHE MPla NNrd SIng WThu
'Crystalie' (x ***biasolettoi***) (8) — EPot MBro NGre SPou WAbe WPat WThu
'Cultrata' (***paniculata***) (7) — NKay
cuneata (12) — NHol
cuneifolia (3) — CHEx CPar CRiv GDra MBal MCas MFir MWat NGre NRoo NSti NWCA SIng SSmi WPer
– var. ***capillipes*** — See S. ***c. cuneifolia***
§ – var. ***cuneifolia*** (3) — NKay SIng
cuscutiformis (4) — GCal LRHS MFir NCat SIng WCru
'Cwm Idwal' (***rosacea***) (12) — CNat
cymbalaria (13) — CRDP EBur SIng WCla WHil
– var. ***huetiana*** (13) — CNic
'Dainty Dame' (x ***arco-valleyi***) (8) — NGre SIng WAbe
'Dana' (x ***megaseiflora***) (8) — LBee NRed
'Dartington Double' (12) — EBre ECar GCHN GDra GTou LBee LBre MBal MCas MFir NHar NKay NMen NNrd NRed SGil
¶ 'Dawn' (8) — GTou
* ***decumbens*** — WPat
§ 'Denisa' (x ***pseudokotschyi***) (8) — MBal WAbe
densa — See S. ***cherlerioïdes***
'Dentata' (x ***geum***) (3) — CBos CRDP ECha ECro EPla GAbr GGar NVic SWas
desoulavyi (8) — MHig NNrd
¶ ***diapensioïdes*** (8) — NGre NRya
Dixter form (x ***geum***) (3) — CRDP ECha EPla
'Doctor Clay' — WAbe
'Doctor Ramsay' (7) — ECar ELan ESis ITim LBee MBro MCas MPla NKay NNrd NRed SIng WDav
'Dorothy Milne' (8) — WThu
'Drakula' (***ferdinandi-coburgii***) (8) — WAbe
'Dubarry' (12) — CPar NGre NKay SHer SIng
¶ 'Duncan Lowe' (***stolitzkae***) (8) — MWat NGre
'Edgar Irmscher' (8) — WAbe
'Edie Campbell' (12) — NGre
'Edith' (x ***edithiae***) — LRHS NNrd
'Edward Elgar' (x ***megaseiflora***) (8) — MWat NRed
'Elf' (12) — CRiv ELan LBee NKay NMen NNrd NRoo SGil SHer SIng WCla
'Eliot Hodgkin' (x ***millstreamiana***) (8) — WAbe
x ***elisbethiae*** — See S. 'Carmen'
'Ellie Brinckerhoff' (x ***hornibrookii***) (8) — NGre
'Elliott's Variety' (***urbium primuloïdes***) (3) — See S. 'Clarence Elliott'
erioblasta (12) — LRHS
¶ 'Ernst Heinrich' (x ***heinrichii***) (8) — MWat
'Esther' (x ***burnatii***) (7) — CPar CRiv EBre ELan ESis LBee LBre MHig MPit MPla NKay NNrd NRed NTow SBla SSmi WAbe WDav WThu WTyr
§ 'Eulenspiegel' (x ***geuderi***) (8) — EPot NHar NKay NNrd
exarata (12) — ITim NNrd WAbe
– ssp. ***moschata*** (12) — NGre NWCA
– ***pyrenaica*** — See S. ***androsacea***
Fair Maids of France — See S. ***granulata*** 'Flore Pleno'
'Fairy' (12) — CRDP CRiv ELan MCas
'Faldonside' (x ***boydii***) (8) — CRiv EPot MBro MWat NGre NRed SBla WAbe WHoo WPat
'Falstaff' (***burseriana***) (8) — EPot LRHS MDHE MWat MYat SBla SIng
¶ x ***farreri*** (7) — NNrd
§ 'Faust' (x ***borisii***) (8) — MBro NGre NKay NNrd SIng
federici-augusti (8) — SBla
– ssp. ***grisebachii*** (8) — CLew EPot GTou MPlt MYat NGre NRya SBar SPou WCla WDav
'Ferdinand' (x ***hofmannii***) (8) — WAbe
ferdinandi-coburgi (8) — NGre NRed NTow NWCA WAbe WDav
– var. ***pravislavia*** — See S. ***f-c. rhodopea***
– var. ***radoslavoffii*** — See S. ***f-c rhodopea***
§ – var. ***rhodopea*** (8) — EPot LRHS MCas WThu
ferruginea (1) — NTow WCru
'Findling' (12) — CMHG CMea CPar GCHN MBro MPlt NKay NRoo SBod SIng WAbe WEas WPat WTyr WWin
flagellaris (2) — WCla WHil
– ***crassiflagellata*** CC 298(2) — NTow
x ***fleischeri*** (8) — SPou
'Florissa' (***oppositifolia***) (9) — CRiv EBre GCHN LBre LRHS NHar
'Flowers of Sulphur' — See S. 'Schwefelblüte'
§ ***fortunei*** (4) — CBos CHal CRDP EPla NBir NHol SBar SIng SPer WCru WHal
'Foster's Gold' (8) — MWat SPou

'Four Winds' (12) GAbr LBee NMen SBla SHer SIng
'Francis Cade' (7) ELan ITim MDHE NGre
'Franzii' (x ***paulinae***) (8) MYat
'Friesei' (x ***salmonica***) (8) CShe EPot MBro MYat WDav
§ x ***fritschiana*** (7) MDHE NKay NNrd SPou WAbe WTyr
'Funkii' (x ***petraschii***) (8) MWat WAbe
¶ 'Gaertneri' (***mariae-theresiae***) (8) MWat
'Gaiety' (12) CPar CRiv ECar ELan ESis GDra NEgg NRoo SHer SIng
'Galaxie' (x ***megaseiflora***) (8) EPot NGre WAbe
'Ganymede' (***burseriana***) (8) SIng
x ***gaudinii*** (7) NKay
'Gem' (x ***irvingii***) (8) EPot NRya
'Geoïdes' See S. ***hirsuta paucicrenata***
¶ ***georgei*** (8) WAbe
x ***geuderi*** See S. 'Eulenspiegel'
x ***geum*** (3) ECha EPar MCas SIng
'Gladys' ELan
§ 'Glauca' (***paniculata brevifolia***) (7) MDHE NGre SIng
'Gloria' (***burseriana***) (8) CLew CNic CRiv CShe MBal MBro MCas MYat NGre NMen NNrd SBla WAbe WPat WThu
x ***gloriana*** (8) EPot
'Godiva' (x ***gloriana***) (8) EPot NHol WAbe
'Goeblii' (8) MDHE NGre SIng WAbe
'Gold Dust' (x ***eudoxiana***) (8) CRiv GTou MBro MHig MYat NKay NMen NNrd SBod WAbe WTyr WWin
'Golden Falls' (12/v) CLew EFol EPot GTou LBee LHop NHar NMen SIng
'Golden Prague' (x ***pragensis***) (8) NGre NNrd WAbe
'Grace Farwell' (x ***anglica***) (8) CRiv ECar EPot GCHN ITim MBar MBro MCas MYat NGre SGil SHer SIng WAbe WHoo
'Gracilis' (x ***geum***) (3) CNic
granulata (11) CCla CHan CNic CRDP MCas MHew NMen NMir NNrd NRed WBon WCla WGwy WOak
§ – 'Flore Pleno' (11) CElw CMil CNic CRDP GAbr GArf NBir NRya SBar SUsu WAbe
'Gratoïdes' (x ***grata***) (8) MWat MYat NGre WAbe
§ 'Gregor Mendel' (x ***apiculata***) (8) CMea CNic ELan EMNN ESis GDra GTou IDai MBal MBro MHig MPla MYat NGre NKay NRed SBla SBod SHer SIng SPla SSmi WAbe WCla WHil WThu
grisebachii See S. ***federici-augusti g.***
'Gustav Hegi' (x ***anormalis***) (8) WAbe
'Haagii' (x ***eudoxiana***) (8) CNic CRiv ELan EMNN EPot MBal MBro MCas NGre NKay NRed NTow SBla SIng SSmi WAbe WDav WHoo WWin
hallii WWin
'Hartswood White' (12) NGre SIng
x ***hausmannii*** (7x6) NKay
'Herbert Cuerdon' (x ***elisabethiae***) (8) NGre NNrd
'Highdownensis' (7) NHol
'Hindhead Seedling' (x ***boydii***) (8) ITim LRHS MDHE MWat NNrd SHer WAbe
hirsuta (3) NRya SWas WBon WHil
'Hirsuta' (x ***geum***) See S. x ***geum***
'Hirtella' (***paniculata***) (7) MDHE SIng
'His Majesty' (x ***irvingii***) (8) SIng WAbe WThu
'Hi-Ace' (12/v) CRDP ELan LBee MBar MBro MCas MPit NGre NNrd NRoo NTow SBla SBod SHer SIng SSmi WAbe WHal WHoo WPat WThu WWin
'Hocker Edge' (x ***arco-valleyi***) (8) ITim MHig MWat MYat NNrd WAbe WThu
'Holden Seedling' (12) EMNN EPot
x ***hornibrookii*** (8) NKay
hostii (7) ESis GTou ITim LBee MBro MCas MHig NHol NKay SIng WAbe WHoo
– var. ***altissima*** See S. ***h. hostii***
§ – ssp. ***hostii*** (7) EPad MDHE NTow STre
– ssp. ***rhaetica*** (7) MDHE NMen
hypnoïdes (12) GAbr GTou MPla NLan SSmi
§ – var. ***egemmulosa*** (12) MBal
'Ingeborg' (12) ECha LBee SChu SIng
iranica (8) MWat MYat NGre SIng WAbe
'Iris Prichard' (x ***hardingii***) (8) CShe EPot ITim MBro MCas MYat NGre NHar NHol NNrd SIng WAbe WHoo WThu
§ ***irrigua*** (11) GAbr WDav
x ***irvingii*** See S. 'Walter Irving'
¶ ***jacquemontii*** C&Mc 414 GTou
'James Bremner' (12) LBee MCas SBod SIng
'Jason' (x ***elisabethiae***) (8) NHol
'Jenkinsiae' (x ***irvingii***) (8) CKel CLew CPar EBre ELan EMNN EPot ESis GTou ITim LBre MBal MBro MCas MPla MYat NGre NKay NMen NNrd NWCA SBla SGil SIng WAbe WDav WHoo WPat WThu WWin
§ 'Johann Kellerer' (x ***kellereri***) (8) EPot MHig MYat NGre NNrd SIng WAbe WWin
'John Tomlinson' (***burseriana***) (8) MCas SPou
'Josef Capek' (x ***megaseiflora***) (8) EPot NGre
'Joy' See S. 'Kaspar Maria Sternberg'
'Judith Shackleton' (8) MWat NNrd SPou WAbe
'Juliet' See S. 'Riverslea'
§ ***juniperifolia*** (8) CPar ELan EMNN GCHN ITim MBro MCas MPlt NGre NHol NKay NMen NRed NRoo NRya NWCA SChu SGil SHer SIng SSmi WDav
– var. ***macedonica*** See S. ***juniperifolia***
'Jupiter' (x ***megaseiflora***) (8) LBee MWat NGre WAbe
'Karel Capek' (x ***megaseiflora***) (8) EPot LBee NGre NNrd NRed WAbe
'Karel Stivin' (***edithiae***) NGre NRed
'Karlstejn' (x ***borisii***) (8) WAbe

§ 'Kaspar Maria Sternberg' (x *petraschii*) (8) — ITim MBro NHol NKay NNrd WPat
'Kath Dryden' (x *anglica*) (8) — NNrd NRya SIng WAbe
¶ 'Kathleen' — MWat
'Kathleen Pinsent' (7) — CShe EPad EPot MBro NHar NVic SGil SHer SIng SSmi WAbe
x *kellereri* — See S. 'Johann Kellerer'
¶ 'Kelso' (x *boydii*) (8) — MWat
'Kestoniensis' (x *salmonica*) (8) — NNrd
'Kewensis' (x *kellereri*) (8) — MWat NNrd SIng WAbe
'King Lear' (x *bursiculata*) (8) — LRHS
'Kingii' — See S. *hypnoïdes egemmulosa*
'Kingscote White' — NGre SIng
'Klondike' (x *boydii*) (8) — LRHS MDHE MWat WAbe
'Knapton Pink' (12) — CMHG MCas NGre NMir NRya SIng SSmi
'Knapton White' (12) — SIng WCla
'Knebworth' (*longifolia*) (7) — SIng
§ 'Kolbiana' (x *paulinae*) (8) — MYat
'Koprvnik' (*paniculata*) (7) — MDHE NNrd SIng
kotschyi (8) — NGre WAbe WDav
'Krasava' (x *megaseiflora*) (8) — EPot LBee NGre NHar
'Kyrillii' (x *borisii*) (8) — NNrd NRed
'Labe' (x *arco-valleyi*) (8) — EPot MWat WAbe
'Lady Beatrix Stanley' — See S. 'Beatrix Stanley'
'Lagraveana' (*paniculata*) (7) — ELan LBee NGre SIng WWin
x *landaueri* — See S. 'Leonore'
'Lenka' (*byam-groundsii*) (8) — ITim NGre NHar
'Leo Gordon Godseff' (x *elisabethiae*) (8) — MBro MHig MYat NKay NRed SBla WDav
§ 'Leonore' (x *landaueri*) (8) — MWat
'Letchworth Gem' (x *urbium*) (3) — CRiv
¶ x *leyboldii* (8) — GTou
'Lidice' (8) — LBee MWat NGre NMen
lilacina (8) — CLew MWat NGre WAbe WPat
lingulata — See S. *callosa*
'Lismore Carmine' (8) — WAbe
¶ 'Lohengrin' (x *hoerhammeri*) (8) — MWat
¶ 'Lohmuelleri' (x *biasolettoi*) (8) — MWat
longifolia (7) — EBar EPad EPla NHol SPou WAbe
¶ – JJA 861600(7) — SBla
* 'Louise' (*marginata*) (8) — LRHS
¶ 'Lowndes' (*andersonii*) (8) — WAbe
'Luna' (x *millstreamiana*) (8) — WAbe
'Lusanna' (x *irvingii*) (8) — NGre
'Lutea' (*paniculata*) (7) — EMNN EPot ESis GDra GTou LBee MBal MCas NGre NHol NMen NNrd NRoo SBla SHer SIng SSmi
§ 'Luteola' (x *boydii*) (8) — EPot SPou WAbe
¶ x *luteopurpurea* AA 12(8) — MWat
¶ – AA 7(8) — MWat
luteoviridis — See S. *corymbosa*
x *macnabiana* (7) — NKay SPou
¶ 'Magdalena' (x *thomasiana*) (8) — MWat
¶ 'Magna' (*burseriana*) (8) — MWat
major lutea — See S. 'Luteola'
'Major' (*paniculata cartilaginea*) (7) — SPou WHil
– (*cochlearis*) (7) — ITim NNrd WAbe
mandschuriensis (1) — GDra NKay
'Margarete' (x *borisii*) (8) — NNrd WAbe
marginata (8) — MYat NGre WAbe WHil WThu
– var. *balcanica* — See S. *m. rocheliana*
¶ – var. *boryi* (8) — EPot MYat NGre
– var. *coriophylla* (8) — MDHE MYat NNrd NWCA WAbe
– vr. *karadzicensis* (8) — LRHS WAbe
– 'Lutea' — See S. 'Faust'
§ – var. *rocheliana* (8) — CMHG ELan EPot MCas NGre NKay NMen SIng WAbe
'Maria Luisa' (x *salmonica*) (8) — CRiv EPot MBro MCas NHol NKay NNrd WAbe WDav
'Marianna' (x *borisii*) (8) — EMNN MWat MYat NMen NNrd
'Mars' (x *elisabethiae*) (8) — MWat
¶ 'Marshall Joffre' (12) — WHil
§ 'Martha' (x *semmleri*) (8) — MWat NHol NRed
'May Queen' — MWat
media (8) — NGre
x *megaseiflora* — See S. 'Robin Hood'
mertensiana (1) — GTou NBir NHar WDav
– var. *bulbillifera* (1) — CNic
'Meteor' (8) — WAbe
'Millstream Cream' (x *elisabethiae*) (8) — EPot MDHE NNrd WAbe
'Minehaha' (x *elisabethiae*) (8) — WAbe
'Minor' (*cochlearis*) (7) — EFol EPad GDra LBee MBal MBro MCas MHig NHol NKay NVic NWCA SIng SSmi WCla WDav WHil WHoo WPat WThu
– (*paniculata*) — See S. *p. brevifolia*
'Minor Glauca' (*paniculata*) — See S. 'Glauca' (*paniculata brevifolia*)
'Minutifolia' (*paniculata*) (7) — CLew CNic EPad ESis LBee MBal MDHE SIng
¶ 'Miss Chambers' (x *urbium*) (3) — CBos SWas
'Mona Lisa' (x *borisii*) (8) — MDHE MYat SIng WAbe
§ 'Mondscheinsonate' (x *boydii*) (8) — MWat WAbe
'Moonlight' — See S. 'Sulphurea'
'Moonlight Sonata' (x *boydii*) — See S. 'Mondscheinsonate'
moschata — See S. *exarata m.*
'Mother of Pearl' (x *irvingii*) (8) — NHol WAbe

'Mother Queen' (x *irvingii*) (8)	MBro MDHE WHoo WPat
'Mount Nachi' (*fortunei*) (4)	GArf NHar SSpi SWas
'Mrs E Piper' (12)	NKay SRms WCla
'Mrs Gertie Prichard' (x *megaseiflora*) (8)	WAbe
'Mrs Helen Terry' (x *salmonica*) (8)	EPot LRHS MDHE MWat MYat NNrd NRya
'Mrs Leng' (x *elisabethiae*) (8)	NHol NMen
mutata (7)	WCru
'Myra' (x *anglica*) (8)	CRiv EMNN EPot MBro MYat NHol SPou WAbe WHoo WPat WThu
'Myra Cambria' (x *anglica*) (8)	MWat MYat NGre WAbe
'Nancye' (8)	MWat SPou
§ ***nelsoniana*** (1)	NHol
¶ ***nivalis*** (1)	NHol
'Norvegica' (*cotyledon*) (7)	GTou MDHE NGre NNrd SPou WWin
'Notata' (*paniculata*) (7)	NKay NNrd
'Nottingham Gold' (x *boydii*) (8)	NGre SPou WAbe
'Nugget' (8)	MWat SIng
¶ 'Oberon' (8)	MWat
'Obristii' (x *salmonica*) (8)	ITim NMen NNrd WAbe
§ ***obtusa*** (8)	NHol NKay WAbe
'Obtusocuneata' (*fortunei*) (4)	SWas WCru
'Ochroleuca' (x *elisabethiae*) (8)	CRiv ITim MPlt MWat NHol NRed WAbe WThu
¶ 'Old Britain' (x *boydii*) (8)	MWat
'Opalescent' (8)	MWat NGre WAbe
§ 'Ophelia' (x *arco-valleyi*) (8)	MWat NGre SIng
oppositifolia (9)	CRiv EBre GTou ITim LBre MHig MYat NKay NMir WWin
– *x biflora* (9)	NHol
– ssp. ***latina*** (9)	ELan EMNN EPot GDra GTou NHar NHol SGil WHoo WWin
*– ***pyrenaica*** (9)	EMNN EPad NHar
– Skye form (9)	NHol WAbe
'Orientalis' (*paniculata*) (7)	SIng
'Oriole' (x *boydii*) (8)	NMen
'Orjen' (*paniculata orientalis*) (7)	MDHE NHol NNrd
§ ***paniculata*** (7)	CShe ELan ESis GTou LBee MBal MBro MCas MWat NKay NRoo SHer SIng WCla WHoo
– ***backhouseana*** (7)	WAbe
§ – var. ***baldensis*** (7)	CPar ELan EMNN GDra ITim MBar MBro MCas MWat NGre NKay NNrd SBla SHer SIgm SSmi SSou WAbe WCla WDav WHoo WWin
§ – var. ***brevifolia*** (7)	CTom NHol NKay NNrd SIng SSmi
*– ***carniolica*** (7)	EFol LBee MCas MHig NRed SBla SPou WHil
§ – ssp. ***cartilaginea*** (7)	NNrd SBla SPou
*– ***eriophylla*** (7)	NKay
– ssp. ***kolenatiana***	See S. ***p. cartilaginea***
♦– ***labradorica***	See S. ***p. neogaea***
§ – ***neogaea*** (7)	MDHE NKay NNrd
§ – var. ***orientalis*** (7)	MBro MDHE SHer SSmi WAbe WCla
paradoxa (14)	MCas NBra SBla SIng
'Parcevalis' (x *finnisiae*) (8x6)	WAbe
'Parsee' (x *margoxiana*) (8)	MWat WAbe
'Paula' (x *paulinae*) (8)	NGre NKay
'Peach Blossom' (8)	MYat NGre NHol NNrd WAbe
'Pearly Gates' (x *irvingii*) (8)	MWat NGre NNrd
* 'Pearly Gold'	CMea EBar MCas MPlt NRoo SHer WThu
'Pearly King' (12)	CKel ELan ESis LBee MBal MPlt NKay NMen NVic SChu SHer WAbe
x ***pectinata***	See S. x ***fritschiana***
pedemontana (12)	EPot
¶ – ***cymosa*** (12)	NWCA WDav
'Penelope' (x *boydilacina*) (8)	EPot ITim LBee MBro MWat MYat NGre NNrd WAbe WHoo WPat WThu
¶ ***pentadactylis*** (12)	SIng
¶ 'Perle Rose' (x *anglica*) (8)	NGre
¶ 'Peter Burrow' (x *poluanglica*) (8)	MWat WAbe
'Peter Pan' (12)	CPar ELan EMNN EPot GDra ITim LBee MCas NHar NKay NMen NRoo SBod SSmi WPat
'Petra' (8)	NHol NKay NNrd WAbe
petraea (14)	ESis
x ***petraschii*** (8)	ITim MCas NRed
'Phoenix' (x *biasolettoi*) (8)	MWat
'Pixie' (12)	EBre EMNN EPar ITim LBee LBre MBal MBar MPla MWat NGre NKay NMen NNrd NRoo NRya SChu SSmi
'Pixie Alba'	See S. 'White Pixie'
'Plena' (*granulata*) (12)	ELan MCas MTho NHar NKay SIng
poluniniana (8)	ITim MBro NGre NHar NRed NWCA SPou WAbe WDav WThu
'Pompadour'	NNrd
'Popelka' (*marginata*) (8)	NRed
porophylla (8)	GDra NGre NNrd NWCA SPou WAbe WThu
– *x sempervivum* (8)	WThu
– ***thessalica***	See S. ***sempervivum stenophylla***
¶ aff. ***porophylla*** (8)	NWCA
'Portae' (*paniculata*) (7)	NKay NNrd
¶ ***portosanctana*** (12)	MWat
'Primrose Bee' (x *apiculata*) (8)	EPot MBro NKay WAbe
'Primrose Dame' (x *elisabethiae*) (8)	CRiv CSam CShe ESis ITim MBal MBro MCas MWat MYat SIng WAbe
x ***primulaize*** (6x3)	ITim MBro NGre NKay NMen NNrd SHer WOMN
'Primulina' (x *malbyana*) (8)	WAbe
'Prince Hal' (*burseriana*) (8)	EPot ITim MDHE NHar

'Princess' (***burseriana***) (8) LBee NNrd
¶ 'Prometheus' (x ***prossenii***) (8) NGre
'Prospero' (x ***petraschii***) (8) NGre NNrd NRya
x ***prossenii*** See S. 'Regina'
§ 'Pseudoborisii' (x ***borisii***) (8) EPot ITim
x ***pseudokotschyi*** See S. 'Denisa'
'Pseudosalomonii' (x ***salmonica***) (8) EPot
pubescens ssp. ***iratiana*** (12) EPot WDav WThu
punctata See S. ***nelsoniana***
'Pungens' (x ***apiculata***) (8) NKay WAbe
'Purpurea' (***fortunei***) See S. 'Rubrifolia'
§ 'Pygmalion' (x ***webrii***) (8) CRiv MPlt MYat NGre NHol NMen NRed WHil WPat WThu
'Pyramidalis' (***cotyledon***) (7) SPou SRms
¶ 'Quarry Wood' (x ***anglica***) (8) MWat
'Rainsley Seedling' (7) CElw MDHE
'Red Poll' (8) MWat NGre WAbe
§ 'Regina' (x ***prossenii***) (8) ITim MWat NNrd SIng WAbe
retusa (9) EPot NGre NNrd NWCA WAbe
'Rex' (***paniculata***) (7) EMNN MDHE NMen NNrd SIng
§ 'Riverslea' (x ***hornibrookii***) (8) CGle EPot MWat NGre NMen NNrd WAbe WPat
§ 'Robin Hood' (x ***megaseiflora***) (8) CRiv EPot ITim LRHS MWat MYat NGre NHar NKay NMen
'Rokujo' (***fortunei***) (4) LGre WEas
¶ 'Ronald Young' MWat
rosacea (12) NLan
– ssp. ***hartii*** (12) SIng
'Rosamunda' (8) WAbe
'Rosea' (***cortusifolia fortunei***) (8) SHer SSpi SWas
– (x ***stuartii***) (8) WAbe
– (***paniculata***) (7) CNic CTom GDra LBee MBal MBro MCas MFir NGre NKay NRed NRoo SBla SIng SSmi STre WAbe WCla WHoo WWin
'Rosemarie' (x ***anglica***) (8) ITim MHig MWat MYat
'Rosenzwerg' (12) LBee
'Rosina Sündermann' (x ***rosinae***) (8) EPot LRHS WAbe
rotundifolia (10) CTom WCot WCru
– ***chrysopenifolia*** (10) WCru WPer
'Rubella' (x ***irvingii***) (8) EPot MCas MWat
§ 'Rubrifolia' (***fortunei***) (8) CRDP ECha EPar NHar NRoo SSpi WCru
'Ruth Draper' (***oppositifolia***) (9) CRiv CShe EPot GCHN NGre NHar NKay NTow SBla SHer WAbe WThu
'Ruth McConnell' (12) MBro MCas NMir NNrd
'Saint John' (***caesia***) (7) CRiv EBur MDHE NNrd WHil WWin
'Salmon' (x ***primulaize***) (6x3) CLew EPot ESis MCas MHig SIng
¶ x ***salmonica*** (8) SIng
'Salomonii' (x ***salmonica***) (8) EPot ITim MHig NHol NNrd NRed WAbe WThu
sancta (8) CNic CRiv EPot MBal MBro MHig NHol NNrd SSmi WAbe WDav WThu WTyr
– var. ***macedonica*** See S. ***juniperifolia***
'Sanguinea Superba' (x ***arendsii***) (12) GDra IDai MBro NKay NNrd SIng
'Sara Sinclair' (x ***arco-valleyi***) (8) MYat NNrd
sarmentosa See S. ***stolonifera***
'Sartorii' See S. 'Pygmalion'
'Saturn' (x ***megaseiflora***) (8) NGre
scardica (8) MDHE NRed WAbe
– ***dalmatica*** (8) See S. ***obtusa***
– var. ***obtusa*** (8) See S. ***obtusa***
§ 'Schelleri' (x ***petraschii***) (8) WAbe
'Schleicheri' (x ***kellereri***) (8) MWat NKay SHer SPou
§ 'Schwefelblüte' (12) CKel CNic ECar MBal NRoo SHer SIng SSmi WAbe WPat
x ***semmleri*** See S. 'Martha'
sempervivum (8) EPot MBro SPou WDav WThu
– JCA 864.003(8) MBro
– f. ***sempervivum*** (8) WAbe
§ – f. ***stenophylla*** (8) GTou WAbe
sibirica (11) EPot GTou
* 'Silver Cushion' (v) EBre ELan ESis LBee LBre MCas MFir SIgm SIng
* 'Silver Dome' CMHG WPat
'Sir Douglas Haig' (12) NKay NNrd SIng
* 'Snowcap' (***pubescens***) (12) EPot
¶ 'Snowdon' (***burseriana***) (8) MWat
'Snowflake' (7) CNic MCas MHig WHil
§ 'Sofia' (x ***borisii***) (8) NKay WAbe
§ 'Southside Seedling' (7) CLew CRDP CRiv CShe ELan EMNN ESis MBar MBro MCas MFos MPlt MTho NHar NHol NKay NMen NNrd NRed NRoo SIng SUsu WAbe WCla WDav WEas WHoo WPat WWin
'Spartakus' (x ***apiculata***) (8) WAbe
spathularis (3) EPla NCat NRar WCot WEas WWin
¶ 'Speciosa' (***burseriana***) (8) MDHE
'Splendens' (***oppositifolia***) (9) CRiv ELan EMNN EPar EPot ITim MBal NHol NMen NRed SGil SHer SIng SRms WAbe WHil
'Sprite' (12) GCHN LBee
spruneri (8) MYat NNrd NWCA WThu
¶ – var. ***deorum*** (8) NGre
sp. BM&W 118 GDra
sp. CLD 1350 NHol
¶ sp. McB 1377 MWat
¶ sp. SEP 549 MWat
'Stansfieldii' (12) CKel CPar CRiv EBre EMNN LBre NGre NMen NNrd NRya SBod SSmi SSou WWin
§ 'Stella' (x ***stormonthii***) (8) NHol NKay SBla WDav WThu
¶ ***stellaris*** (1) GTou

Plant	Suppliers
stolitzkae (8)	CNic EPot NGre NHol NMen NRed WThu
§ ***stolonifera*** (4)	CArn CHal ELan EPla SBar SSpi
'Stormont's Variety'	See S. 'Stella'
stribrnyi (8)	EBur EPot NKay NMen
'Sturmiana' (***paniculata***) (7)	MBro NHol NKay SIng SRms
'Suendermannii' (x ***kellereri***) (8)	NWCA SIng SPou
§ 'Sulphurea' (x ***boydii***) (8)	CNic CRiv CShe EPot LBee MBro MCas MWat MYat NBra NGre NHar NNrd NWCA WAbe WHoo WPat WThu
'Superba' (***callosa australis***) (7)	GCra GDra NNrd SPou SSmi WHil
'Sylva' (x ***elisabethiae***) (8)	NGre
taygetea (10)	NMen
x ***tazetta*** (10x3)	MCas NRed SIng
tenella (12)	NNrd
'Theoden' (***oppositifolia***) (9)	MBro NHar NHol NWCA WDav
'Thorpei' (8)	ITim NNrd
'Timballii' (7)	SIng
¶ 'Timmy Foster' (x ***irvingii***) (8)	NGre WAbe
'Tom Thumb' (12)	NMen NNrd
tombeanensis (8)	NRya
'Tricolor' (***stolonifera***) (4)	EBak ELan
trifurcata (12)	GAbr SIng
'Triumph' (x ***arendsii***) (12)	CShe ECtt EMNN GCHN GDra LBee MFir NEgg NKay NMen NNrd NRoo NVic SBod
'Tulley' (x ***elisabethiae***) (8)	MBro NHol WPat
'Tumbling Waters' (7)	CGle GAbr MCas MTho NHol NKay NRya NTow SHer SIng SSmi WAbe WThu WWin
umbrosa (3)	CKel EBre EMon EPar IDai LBre LWad NGre NNor SPer STre WOak WWin
– var. ***primuloïdes*** (3)	CGle CShe MYat WEas
– ***variegata***	See S. 'Aureopunctata'
'Unique'	See S. 'Bodensee'
x ***urbium*** (3)	CPar CTom EJud ELan GAri GDra MBal NNrd NRar NSti NVic SIng WAbe WBon
'Vaccarina' (***oppositifolia***) (9)	CPar EBre GAbr LBre NVic SGil SHer WAbe
'Vaclav Hollar' (x ***gusmusii***) (8)	NGre
'Vahlii' (x ***smithii***) (8)	MWat WAbe
'Valborg'	See S. 'Cranbourne'
'Valentine'	See S. 'Cranbourne'
'Valerie Finnis'	See S. 'Aretiastrum'
¶ 'Valerie Keevil' (x ***anglica***) (8)	MWat
'Variegata' (x ***urbium***) (3)	CBos CMer ELan EPar GDra LBee LGro MBal MCas NCat NHol NNor NSti SIng SPer SSmi WAbe WCla WEas WWin
– (***cuneifolia***) (3)	CNic CRDP ECtt EFol ELan ESis GCHN MBar MCas MPlt NKay NNrd NRoo NTow NVic SIng WPer WThu
vayredana (12)	MBro SIng
veitchiana (4)	EMon EPla MHig NCat NKay NNrd WCru WHil
'Venetia' (***paniculata***) (7)	NKay NNrd SSmi
'Vesna' (x ***borisii***) (8)	EMNN MCas MFir MHig NGre NKay NNrd NRya NTow WAbe WThu WWin
'Vincent van Gogh' (x ***borisii***) (8)	ITim NKay NNrd
'Vladana' (x ***megaseiflora***) (8)	CRiv EMNN MWat NGre NHar NNrd NRed NRya WAbe
'Vlasta' (8)	MWat WAbe
'Vltava' (8)	MWat NGre
'Volgeri' (x ***hofmannii***) (8)	EPot
'W A Clark' (***oppositifolia***) (9)	MBal WAbe
'Wada' (***fortunei***) (8)	CChu CHan CRDP CWit EPar EPot GAbr GCHN MBal NBir NHar NHol NRoo SCro SPer SSpi WWin
'Waithman's Variety' (7)	NNrd
wallacei	See S. ***camposii***
'Walpole's Variety' (***longifolia***) (7)	NHar NNrd SPou WTyr
'Walter Ingwersen' (***umbrosa primuloïdes***) (3)	SIng
§ 'Walter Irving' (x ***irvingii***) (8)	MYat NNrd NRya WAbe
'Welsh Dragon' (12)	NMir WAbe
'Welsh Red' (12)	WAbe
'Welsh Rose' (12)	WAbe
wendelboi (8)	EPot MYat NGre NHol WAbe WHil WThu
'Wendrush' (x ***wendelacina***) (8)	WAbe
'Wendy' (x ***wendelacina***) (8)	NGre WAbe
'Wetterhorn' (***oppositifolia***) (9)	ITim MBal NNrd WAbe
'Wheatley Rose' (8)	LRHS
§ 'White Pixie' (12)	CMea EPar ESis ITim LBee MCas NGre NNrd SBla SHer SIng SSmi WCla
'White Spire' (12)	NNrd
'White Star' (x ***salmonica***)	See S. 'Schelleri'
'Whitehill' (7)	CPar CShe EBre ELan ESis GCHN LBee LBre MBal MBro MCas MHig MPla NEgg NGre NKay NMen NNrd SIng SSmi WAbe WHil WHoo WPat WPer WThu WWin
'Whitlavei Compacta' (***hypnoïdes***) (12)	CRiv EMNN MCas NKay
'Wilhelm Tell' (x ***malbyana***) (8)	MWat
'William Boyd' (x ***boydii***) (8)	WAbe
'Winifred' (x ***anglica***) (8)	EPot MWat NGre NNrd NRya SPou WAbe
'Winifred Bevington' (7x3)	EBre ELan EMNN ESis GDra GTou LBee LBre LHop MBro NHar NHol NMen NNrd NRed NRoo SChu SHer SIng SPla WCla WDav WHoo
'Winston Churchill' (12)	NNrd SIng
'Winter Fire' (7)	See S. 'Winterfeuer'

§ 'Winterfeuer' (*callosa*) (7) — CShe
* 'Winton' — SPou
'Wisley' (*federici-augusti grisebachii*) (8) — CNic GCHN MBal MCas NKay NNrd SPou WHoo WPat
'Wisley Primrose' — See S. 'Kolbiana'
* 'Witham's Compact' — CPar
'Yellow Rock' (8) — MWat NHol WAbe
¶ 'Your Day' — MWat
¶ 'Your Kiss' — MWat
¶ 'Your Smile' — MWat
x *zimmeteri* (7x3) — NNrd NRed NTow
* *zohlenschaferi* — NBra

SCABIOSA † (Dipsaceae)

alpina — See CEPHALARIA *alpina*
anthemifolia — CHan
atropurpurea 'Sunburst' — SMrm
'Butterfly Blue' — EBar EFol MBri MPit NCat SChu SHer
caucasica — CHad CRDP CSam ECha LAbb LGan NCat SBla WHil WHoo WOld WPer WWin
– *alba* — ECro LGre MBri NNor NRoo NTow WHil WHoo
– 'Bressingham White' — SAsh
– 'Clive Greaves' — CB&S CBow CCla CDoC CKel CMea CSco CShe ECha EFol EFou EGol ELan EOrc GCal IDai LHop MBri MBro MWat NBar NMir NNor SHer SPer SPla SUsu WEas WRus
– 'Fama' — CBow CSam EBar ECro MPit MRav NBir NRoo SBla SRms WHoo
– 'Goldingensis' — EBar NRoo WPer
– 'Kompliment' — EFou MUlv NBro
– 'Miss Willmott' — CBow CCla CDoC CGle CHad CMGP CRDP CSco CSev EFou EGol ELan GCal LHop MBri MUlv NBar NSti SHer SPer SUsu WEas WRus WTyr
– 'Moerheim Blue' — CDoC MBri MUlv
¶ – 'Mount Cook' — SAsh
– 'Penelope Harrison' — CShe
– 'Perfecta Alba' — CSco NOrc SFis WPer
– 'Stäfa' — LHop MBri MUlv SMrm SPer WRus
cinerea — WWin
columbaria — CKin MChe MHew NLan NMir NSal NTow NWCA SHer SUsu WCla WHal WHoo
– 'Nana' — NBir NMen WHoo
§ – var. *ochroleuca* — CGle CHad CHan CMea CSam EBar ECha EPla LGan MBro MPar NBir NSti SMrm SUsu SWas WWin
¶ – var. *webbiana* — WDav
– – JCA 862.850 — CLew
cretica — SUsu
farinosa — MFir WAbe WPer
gigantea — See CEPHALARIA *gigantea*
graminifolia — CHal CLew CNic EFol ELan LGan NBir NRoo NTow SBar SChu SMrm WOld
¶ – *rosea* — SCro
japonica — WPer
– var. *alpina* — EFou GDra LBlm NHol
lucida — CGle CMea CNic CSev CSun ECro ELan GDra LGan LHop MBro MCas MHig MNFA MPit NKay NMen NRoo SBla SMrm WAbe WEas WPat WPer
minoana — EMon
ochroleuca — See S. *columbaria o.*
parnassi — See PTEROCEPHALUS *perennis*
* 'Pink Mist' — CGle MBri MPit NBir SRms
pterocephala — See PTEROCEPHALUS *perennis*
rumelica — See KNAUTIA *macedonica*
succisa — See SUCCISA *pratensis*
tatarica — See CEPHALARIA *gigantea*

SCADOXUS (Liliaceae/Amaryllidaceae)

multiflorus — CKel LAma LBow MBri NRog WChr
§ – ssp. *katherinae* 'King Albert' — CMon SLMG
§ *puniceus* — NRog SLMG
¶ *rigidus* — SLMG

SCAEVOLA (Goodeniaceae)

aemula 'Blue Fan' — CBrk CSpe NWyt
¶ – 'Blue Wonder' — SHer SUsu
¶ – 'Petite' — CBrk WRus
¶ *amoena* — CTro
§ *calendulacea* — LHil
hookeri — ECou
suaveolens — See S. *calendulacea*

SCHEFFLERA (Araliaceae)

actinophylla — EBak MBri
arboricola — MBri
– 'Beauty' — MBri
– 'Compacta' — MBri
– 'Diane' — MBri
– 'Golden Capelle' — MBri
– 'Henriette' — MBri
– 'Jacqueline' — MBri
– 'Milena' — MBri
– 'Trinetta' — MBri
– 'Worthy' — MBri
digitata — CHEx SArc

SCHIMA (Theaceae)

♦ *argentea* — See S. *wallichii noronhae superba*
§ *wallichii* ssp. *noronhae* var. *superba* — CHEx WBod
– ssp. *wallichii* var. *khasiana* — CB&S ISea WBod

SCHINUS (Anacardiaceae)

polygamus — CGre

SCHISANDRA (Schisandraceae)

chinensis — CChu CHan EHal WSHC
grandiflora — EBre EOvi LBre SPer
– var. *cathayensis* — See S. *sphaerandra*
propinqua var. *chinensis* — CBot SHil SSpi

rubriflora (f)	CB&S CBow CCla EHar ELan EOvi LGre MGos SBla SBra SDix SHil SLon SPer SSpi SSta WBod WSHC WWat WWeb
– (m)	LAbb LTil SBla SDix
¶ ***rubrifolia***	SHil
sphenanthera	CCla ECar ELan EMil EOvi IJoh LGre LTil WSHC WWeb

SCHISTOSTEGA (moss)

¶ ***pennata***	LFle

SCHIVERECKIA (Cruciferae)

doerfleri	CNic
podolica	MCas WPer

SCHIZACHYRIUM (Gramineae)

§ ***scoparium***	CRow EHoe GCal

SCHIZANTHUS (Solanaceae)

¶ ***hookeri*** JCA 12492	CNic

SCHIZOCENTRON See HETEROCENTRON

SCHIZOCODON See SHORTIA

SCHIZOPHRAGMA (Hydrangeaceae)

hydrangeoïdes	CB&S CBow CChu CCla CHEx CSco EBre EHar ELan LBre MBal MBri MGos SBra SPer SSpi SSta WDin WWeb
– 'Roseum'	CChu SBla SHil SSpi
integrifolium	CB&S CBow CCla CHEx CMac CSco EHar ELan LAbb MBal MBri SBla SDix SHBN SHil SPer SSpi SSta WSHC WWat

SCHIZOSTACHYUM (Gramineae(Bambuseae))

§ ***funghomii***	SDry WJun

SCHIZOSTYLIS † (Iridaceae)

coccinea	Widely available
– ***alba***	Widely available
– 'Ballyrogan Giant'	IBlr
– 'Cardinal'	CHan CKel CPar CRow
¶ – 'Fenland Daybreak'	EBre LBre
– 'Gigantea'	See S. *c.* 'Major'
– 'Grandiflora'	See S. *c.* 'Major'
¶ – 'Hilary Gould'	SWas
– 'Jennifer'	CAvo CBro CElw CGle CMHG COtt CRDP GAbr MUlv SHer SRms SUsu WCot
¶ – 'Madonna'	CKel
– 'Maiden's Blush'	EBre ELun LBre MUlv SPer
§ – 'Major'	CB&S CBro CChu CCla CDec CGle CShe EBre ECha EGol ELun EPar GCal IDai LBre LHop MBri NHol SApp SAxl SBla SDeJ SDix SMad SPer WAbe WBod WEas WOld WWin
– 'Mrs Hegarty'	CB&S CCla CKel CMHG CSco EGol ELan EPar EPot IDai LAma LMay NBro NHol NKay NMir NRog NSti SChu SDeJ SIng SPer WBod WEas WHoo WOMN WOld WWat
– 'November Cheer'	CCla CDec CKel CMHG CRiv CRow EBre IBlr LBre MSte NFai NRoo SHer
– 'Pallida'	CRow CSam ECha ELan GCal SHer SIng
– 'Professor Barnard'	CChu CGle CMHG CRow GCal IBlr MSte SApp SAsh WHoo
– 'Salmon Charm'	CB&S CKel CRiv CRow
– 'Snow Maiden'	EBre ELun LBre SPer
§ – 'Sunrise'	CAvo CB&S CChu CFis CHan CKel CMHG CRow ECha EGol ELan ELun GCal NFai NHol NNor NRoo SAxl SBla SChu SIng SPer SSpi SWas WAbb WAbe WBod WBon WOMN WRus
– 'Sunset'	See S. *c.* 'Sunrise'
– 'Tambara'	CHan CMHG LGan LGre NCat SSpi WWat
– 'Viscountess Byng'	CB&S CBro CChu CCla CFis CGle CMil CPar CRow CShe GCal MBri MRav NFai NRog SAxl SChu SDix WBon WHal WOMN WPer WWat
– 'Zeal Salmon'	CBro CRiv CRow GAbr SApp SSpi

SCHOENOPLECTUS (Cyperaceae)

¶ ***lacustris***	EMFW WChe
– 'Albescens'	CBen CWGN EBre EHon EMFW LBre LMay MSta SHig SRms SWat WChe WHol
– ssp. ***tabernaemontani*** 'Zebrinus' (v)	CBen CPar CRDP CRiv CWGN EBre EHon ELan EMFW EWav LBre LMay MSta MUlv NDea SHig SSpi SWat WChe WHol

SCHOENUS (Cyperaceae)

pauciflorus	ECou EHoe EPar EPla LGan SFar SSpi

SCHOTIA (Leguminosae)

brachypetala	CPle

SCIADOPITYS (Sciadopityaceae)

verticillata	CB&S CChu CDoC CKen IOrc LLin LNet LPan LTil MBar MBri SEng SLim WDin WNor

SCILLA (Liliaceae/Hyacinthaceae)

adlamii	See LEDEBOURIA ***cooperi***
♦ x ***allenii***	See X CHIONOSCILLA ***a.***
amethystina	See S. ***litardierei***
amoena	CMon LAma NHol WChr
autumnalis	CAvo CMon EPot LAma LBow NHol WChr WCru WOMN WShi WThu
¶ – ***fallax*** AB&S 4345	CMon
bifolia	CAvo CBro EPar ETub LAma LBlo LBow NHol NRog
– 'Rosea'	CAvo EPar EPot LAma LBow NHol NRog SIng WPer
bithynica	LBow WWat

campanulata	See HYACINTHOIDES ***hispanica***
cilicica	CBro CMon LAma WChr
greilhuberi	CAvo NHol
¶ *haemorrhoïdalis*	
MS 923	CMon
hohenackeri	LAma
¶ – BSBE 811	CMon
¶ *hyacinthoïdes*	CMon
italica	See HYACINTHOÏDES ***i.***
japonica	See S. ***scilloïdes***
liliohyacinthus	CBro CRow SSpi
– 'Alba'	MPar WChr
¶ *lingulata* MS 320	CMon
¶ – SF 288/281	CMon
¶ – S&L 253	CMon
– *aliata*	CBro
– *ciliolata*	WChr
§ *litardierei*	CAvo CMon EPot ETub LAma MPar NEgg NHol
¶ *mauretanica* SF 65	CMon
¶ – *alba*	CMon
¶ *messeniaca*	MBro
§ *mischtschenkoana*	CAvo CBro CMon EPot ETub LAma LBlo LBow MBri MPar NRog SIng
monophyllos	LAma
¶ *morrisii* M 4015	CMon
non-scripta	See HYACINTHOIDES ***n-s.***
nutans	See HYACINTHOIDES ***non-scripta***
¶ *obtusifolia* AB&S 4410	CMon
ovalifolia	See LEDEBOURIA ***ovalifolia***
paucifolia	SLMG
persica BSBE 1054	CMon
peruviana	CAbb CAvo CB&S CBrd CBro CHEx EBre EBul EPar EPot ETub LAma LBre MTho NRog
– 'Alba'	CAvo CMon EBul LAma NRog
¶ – *elegans*	CMon
¶ – *venusta*	CMon
pratensis	See S. ***litardierei***
puschkinioïdes	CAvo EPot LAma
ramburei	EPot LAma WChr
¶ – B&S 406	CMon
¶ – MS 417	CMon
reverchonii	WChr
¶ – MS 418	CMon
rosenii	EPot WChr
§ *scilloïdes*	CBro WOMN
siberica	CAvo CCla ETub LAma LBlo LBow NEgg NRog SIng WPer
– 'Alba'	CAvo CBro CCla EPar ETub LAma LBow NEgg NRog SIng WPer
– 'Spring Beauty'	CAvo CBro CMea EPar LAma LBlo MBri NRog SIng
¶ – *taurica* M&T 4148	CMon
tubergeniana	See S. ***mischtschenkoana***
verna	CMon WAbe WShi
¶ – MS 483	CMon
vicentina	See HYACINTHOIDES ***italica vicentina***
violacea	See LEDEBOURIA ***socialis***

SCINDAPSUS (Araceae)

aureus	See EPIPREMNUM ***aureum***
pictus (v)	MBri

SCIRPOÏDES (Gramineae)

¶ *holoschoenus*	ETPC

SCIRPUS (Cyperaceae)

♦ *cernuus*	See ISOLEPIS ***cernua***
cespitosus	MBal
§ *fauriei* var. *vaginatus*	CRow ECar
¶ 'Golden Spear'	SRms
holoschoenus	See SCIRPOÏDES ***h.***
♦ *lacustris*	See SCHOENOPLECTUS ***l.***
♦ – *spiralis*	See JUNCUS ***effusus*** 'Spiralis'
mucronatus	MSta
variegatus	CBot

SCLERANTHUS (Illecebraceae)

biflorus	CLew ECar ECou ELan ESis MBro MFir NTow WPer
singuliflorus	ECou MTho WPat
uniflorus	CLew GAbr GAri NHol NWCA

SCOLIOPUS (Liliaceae/Trilliaceae)

bigelowii	SWas WDav
hallii	SWas

SCOLOPENDRIUM See **ASPLENIUM**

SCOLYMUS See **CYNARA**

SCOPOLIA (Solanaceae)

¶ *anomala*	CArn
carniolica	EMon GCal GDra GPoy NSal WCru
– forms	IBlr
– ssp. *hladnikiana*	ECro
– *podolica*	CMea WPer
lurida	CArn ECro NSal
¶ *physaloïdes*	NSal
♦ *sinensis*	See ATROPANTHE ***s.***
stramoniifolia	GDra

SCORZONERA (Compositae)

humilis	GPoy

SCROPHULARIA (Scrophulariaceae)

aquatica	See S. ***auriculata***
§ *auriculata*	LHol MHew NDea NLan NOrc NSal WWye
– 'Burdung' (v)	EMon
§ – 'Variegata'	Widely available
coccinea	EMon
¶ *macrantha*	WDav
nodosa	CArn CKin CSFH LHol MChe MHew NLan NMir NSal SIde WCla WHer WNdy
– *variegata*	See S. ***auriculata*** 'V.'
scorodonia	CKin
umbrosa	NSal
vernalis	NSti

SCUTELLARIA (Labiatae)

§ ***alpina***	CHal CRiv ESis GCHN LBee MHig NHol NSal SHer SIng WPer WWin
altissima	CGle EMon ESis NSal NWCA WDav WPer
baicalensis	CHan ESis IBlr LHil NHol WPer
canescens	See S. ***incana***
diffusa	ESis NHol WPer
galericulata	CKin CTom Effi GPoy MHew NSal WNdy
hastata	See S. ***hastifolia***
§ ***hastifolia***	CHal CNic ECar ECtt EMNN NMir SHer SIng WOMN WPer WTyr
¶ ***hyssopus***	MHew
§ ***incana***	EFou ELan EMon SBor SFis SPer WCot
indica var. ***japonica***	See S. ***indica parvifolia***
§ – var. ***parvifolia***	CHal CLew CRiv EBur ELan LBee MBro MHig MTho NTow SFis SUsu WCru WPer
¶ – – 'Alba'	LBee WDav
¶ ***integrifolia***	NSal
lateriflora	CArn CSFH ESis GPoy IEde LHol MChe NSal NSel SIde WPer WWye
minor	CKin MHew NSal WPer
novae-zelandiae	ECou WThi
orientalis	ESis LBee NGre SBla WCru WOMN WPer WWin
– ssp. ***carica***	WOMN
pontica	WPer WThi
prostrata	ESis NHol NRed SUsu WOMN WPer WThi
repens	ESis WPer
scordiifolia	CHal CKel CLew CMea CMil CNic CRiv CSam ECha EFou ELan EMNN EPot ESis MCas NKay NMen NNrd SBla WCla WHil WPer WRus WWin
serrata	CArn
supina	See S. ***alpina***
¶ ***tournefortii***	WDav

SEAKALE See CRAMBE *maritima*

SECURIGERA See CORONILLA

SEDASTRUM See SEDUM

SEDUM † (Crassulaceae)

acre	ELan GPoy LHol MBar NGre NNrd SIde WWin
– (tetraploid)	MPit
– var. ***aureum***	CHad CNic CRiv EFol ELan EPot MBar MCas MFir MWat NHol NKay NNrd NRed NVic SHer SIng WHoo WPat
– var. ***elegans***	ECtt GDra GTou MBal NGre NMen SSmi
§ – var. ***majus***	NGre NHol SIde SSmi
– 'Minus'	NGre NHol SIde SSmi
– ssp. ***neglectum***	NNrd
adolphi	CHal
aggregatum	See OROSTACHYS ***aggregata***
§ ***aïzoön***	NGre NKay NVic SChu SIde SIng WEas
– 'Aurantiacum'	See S. ***a.*** 'Euphorbioïdes'
§ – 'Euphorbioïdes'	EBre ECha ECro ECtt ELan EMon EOrc GGar LBre MRav SChu SPer WCot
– ***maximowiczii***	See S. ***aizoon***
albescens	See S. ***forsterianum purpureum***
§ ***alboroseum***	MTho NGre SCro WTyr
§ – 'Mediovariegatum'	CBot ECro EFol EGol EHoe ELan EMon EPla LGan LHop MBri NGre NOrc NRoo SCro WEas WPer
§ ***album***	CHal EBar GGar NLan NSel SIde WPer
§ – 'Chloroticum'	CRiv GGar NGre SIde SSmi
– ***clusianum***	See S. ***gypsicola glanduliferum***
– 'Coral Carpet'	CHal CNic ELan EPot GDra MBar MCas MWat NGre NHol NKay NMen NNrd SChu SHer SIng SSmi STre
– var. ***micranthum***	See S. ***a.*** 'Chloroticum'
§ – ssp. ***teretifolium*** var. ***murale***	CRiv MBar NGre NKay SIng
altissimum	See S. ***sediforme***
amplexicaule	See S. ***tenuifolium***
§ ***anacampseros***	CHEx CLew CNic CPar CRiv CSam CTom EPad GCHN NGre NHol NKay SCro SIde SIng SSmi WCla WEas WPer
anglicum	GGar NGre SIng WCla
anopetalum	See S. ***ochroleucum***
– alpine form	See S. ***ochroleucum montanum***
athoum	See S. ***album***
atlanticum	See S. ***dasyphyllum mesatlanticum***
'Autumn Joy'	See S. 'Herbstfreude'
batesii	See S. ***hemsleyanum***
§ 'Bertram Anderson'	EBre EPot ESma GAri LBre LGre LHop MBri MCas NGre NRoo NSti SMrm WMer WPer
♦ ***beyrichianum*** hort.	See S. ***glaucophyllum***
– Masters	NGre
brevifolium	CHun GGar MFir SChu WOMN
§ – var. ***quinquefarum***	NGre SSmi
§ ***caucasicum***	NGre
– DS&T 89001T	EMon
cauticola	CHal CLew CMHG CPar CShe GCal ITim MBro MCas MHig MRav NGre NKay NNor SBod SIng SSmi SSou WAbe WWin
§ – 'Lidakense'	CLew CMea CPar CRiv CSam CTom EBar EBre ECar ELan EMar EMon LBre MBar MBri NGre NHar NHol NNrd NVic SBla SSmi
clusianum	See S. ***gypsicola glanduliferum***
confusum	NHol
crassipes	See RHODIOLA ***wallichiana***
crassularia	See CRASSULA ***milfordiae***
§ ***cyaneum***	GCHN MDHE NGre NNrd
dasyphyllum	CHal CLew CMer CNic CRiv CTom ELan EPot ESis GTou MBal MBar MCas MFir MWat NGre SSmi SSou WCla WTyr
– ssp. ***dasyphyllum*** var. ***glanduliferum***	CHEx CHal SIng

– – var.*macrophyllum*	NGre
§ – – var.*mesatlanticum*	CNic CRiv NGre SSmi WThu
– *mucronatis*	NBir
– ssp. *oblongifolium* var.*riffense*	NHol
¶ *debile*	NGre
divergens	NGre SIng SSmi
douglasii	MFir NNrd SRms
'Dudley Field'	GCHN NGre
ellacombeanum	See S. ***kamschaticum e.***
♦ *erythrostichum*	See S. ***alboroseum***
§ *ewersii*	CHal CLew CMHG CNic CRiv CSam EBre ELan EMNN ESis GCHN GTou LBre MCas NGre NMen SSmi WEas
§ – var. *homophyllum*	MHig NGre NKay SSmi
§ *fabaria*	NGre WEas
farinosum	MHig SSou
floriferum	See S. ***kamtschaticum***
§ *forsterianum*	CMGP EMar MBar NGre NHol NLan SIng SSmi WCla WEas
– ssp. *elegans*	LGro
gracile	NGre SSmi
gypsicola	CHEx MDHE NGre WPer
§ – *glanduliferum*	GAbr
§ 'Herbstfreude'	CBow CCla CFis CKel CSco CShe EBre ECha EFou ELan IDai LBre LGro LHop MBal MWat NBar NGre NHol NRoo NSti SDix SHig SIng SMad SPer WBod WEas WOMN WOld
heterodontum	See RHODIOLA ***heterodonta***
hillebrandtii	See S. ***urvillei*** Hillebrandtii Group
himalensis	See RHODIOLA ***h.***
hirsutum	See RHODIOLA ***hirsuta***
§ *hispanicum*	EMNN EPar EPla ITim MFir NKay NMir SHer
– 'Albescens	CNic NGre
– var. *bithynicum*	NGre SIng
– *glaucum*	See S. ***h. minus***
§ – var. *minus*	CHun CNic ECtt GTou MBar NGre NNrd NRar SIng SSmi STre
§ – – 'Aureum'	CB&S CHun CRiv CTom ECha EPla EPot MCas MHig NGre NHol NKay NMen SBod SIng SSmi WDav
humifusum	EBur EPot MHig NMen NTow SIng SSmi WAbe WOMN WThu
hybridum	CShe NGre SIng
hyperaïzoön	NGre
integrifolium	See RHODIOLA ***rosea integrifolia***
jaeschkei	See S. ***oreades***
'Joyce Henderson'	SUsu WEas
§ *kamtschaticum*	CHal CHun MBar MBro MCas NGre
– *ellacombeanum*	CNic CRiv ELan EMNN EMon ESis IDai MPlt NGre NKay NMen NNrd SCro SIng
§ – var. *floriferum* 'Weihenstephaner Gold'	Widely available
– var. *kamtschaticum* 'Variegatum'	CHEx CPar CRDP ELan EPar GCHN LBee LHop MBar MCas MHig NGre NHol NKay NRoo SBla SBod SSmi WEas
¶ *lanceolatum*	NGre
laxum ssp. *heckneri*	NGre
– ssp. *laxum*	NHol
– *retusum* JCA 11601	CNic
lineare	ELan SLMG
– 'Variegatum'	CHal CNic MBri SIde
litorale	NGre
lydium	CHal CLew CNic CPar CRiv CTom EMNN GTou MBal MBar MCas MFir MHig MWat NGre NKay NNrd NRoo SIng SSmi SSou STre
– *aureum*	See S. ***hispanicum minus*** 'Aureum'
– 'Bronze Queen'	NMen
makinoi makinoi	SSmi
¶ – 'Variegatum'	EBre LBre
maweanum	See S. ***acre majus***
mexicanum	MBri
middendorfianum	CTom ELan EMon LBee LHop MCas MDHE MHig MWat NGre NHol NKay NNrd SBod SHer SSmi WHil WHoo WWin
– var. *diffusum*	CHal NGre SSmi
– 'Striatum'	CNic
monregalense	NGre
* 'Moonglow'	NGre SSmi
moranense	CHal CNic CRiv NGre NHol SIde SSmi
morganianum	CHal EBak MBri
multiceps	NGre SSmi
murale	See S. ***album tenuifolium murale***
N *nevii*	CLew CShe NKay
nicaeënse	See S. ***sediforme***
obtusatum	CHal MBro WHil
– ssp. *boreale*	See S. ***oreganum b.***
– ssp. *retusum*	See S. ***retusum***
§ *ochroleucum*	SIng SSmi
– 'Green Spreader'	SSmi
§ – ssp. *ochroleucum glaucum*	NGre
§ *oppositifolium*	CLew ELan ESis NCat NGre SIde SIng
§ *oreganum*	CLew CMHG CPar CTom ECha EMNN ESis GTou LHop MBar MCas MHig MWat NGre NKay NMen NNrd NRoo SBod SChu SIng WAbe WHil WHoo WWin
– 'Procumbens'	CNic NHol
– 'Variegatum'	EFol
oregonense	NGre NMen
oryzifolium minor	EBur
§ *pachyclados*	CHun EBur ECar ELan ESis GAbr LBee MDHE MPlt NBir NGre SIde SIng SSmi WCla WPat WPer
pachyphyllum	CHal
– x *treleasei*	CHal
¶ *pallidum*	NGre
palmeri	NBir NTow SIng SMrm SSmi
pilosum	CLew CRiv EBur NGre NWCA SBla WAbe WDav WOMN WThu
§ *pluricaule*	CHal CHun CMea CNic CPar EMNN GCHN MBar MCas NGre NHol NKay NMen NNrd SChu WCla
§ –	ECha EHoe EMNN EPot GCHN GDra NGre NHol NNrd SBod SFar SUsu WPat WPer
polytrichoïdes	See RHODIOLA ***komarovii***

populifolium	CLew CMHG CPar ECar ECha GCHN GCal MCas MPla NGre NHol SDry SIng SSmi STre WEas WHil WPer
praealtum	CHal EMon
§ *primuloïdes*	NGre NMen SSmi
pruinatum	NGre NKay
pruinosum	See S. ***spathulifolium p.***
pulchellum	CShe NGre SIde
purdyi	NGre NHol
quinquefarium	See S. ***brevifolium q.***
ramosissima	See VILLADIA ***r.***
reflexum	CNic CRiv EBar ELan EMon GGar NGre NHol NKay SIde SIng SSmi
¶ – 'Minus'	NGre
– 'Monstrosum Cristatum'	CLew MBal NBir SMad
¶ *retusum*	NGre
rhodiola	See RHODIOLA ***rosea***
rosea	See RHODIOLA ***rosea***
rubroglaucum	CRiv MHig NNrd
rubromucronatum	See S. sp. RBGE 736791
x *rubrotinctum*	SLMG
§ 'Ruby Glow'	Widely available
rupestre	See S. ***forsterianum***
ruprechtii	CMHG ECha EMon MBri NGre WCot WEas WPer
sarcocaule	See CRASSULA ***sarcocaulis***
sarmentosum	NGre SIng SSmi
§ *sediforme*	CHal CTom MBro NGre NKay SIde SSmi
– *nicaeense*	See S. ***sediforme***
selskianum	CLew GDra
sempervivoïdes	EBur NGre WThi
sexangulare	CLew CPar CRiv EMNN ESis GDra MBar MCas MPlt NGre NHol NKay NMen NNrd SIng SSmi
sichotense	NGre SIng
§ *sieboldii*	CHal CPar CSam LGro MBri NGre SIng SSmi SSou
– 'Mediovariegatum'	CHal ELan NGre NNrd SCro SSmi WEas WPer
'Silvermoon'	MDHE NGre NHol SIng WPer
spathulifolium	CLew ECha ELan ESis GTou MPlt NKay SChu WEas WOld
– 'Aureum'	CRiv ECtt EMNN MBar MHig MWat NGre NHol NNor SBod
N– 'Cape Blanco'	Widely available
– 'Major'	NMir SIng
§ – ssp. *pruinosum*	NGre NHol SSmi
– 'Purpureum'	Widely available
– 'Roseum'	CTom SSmi
§ *spectabile*	CArn CBow CDoC CKel CPar CRDP CRiv EJud ELan NBar NSti SPer WHil WHoo WPer WWin
¶ – 'Album'	EOrc
– 'Brilliant'	CBow CDoC CKel CSco CShe EBre ECED ECha EFou ELan EMon EPla LBre LWad MBri NGre NOrc SDix SMad SPer SPla WEas
– 'Iceberg'	CRDP EFou EMon EPla LGre SMad
– 'Indian Chief'	See H. 'Herbstfreude'
– 'Meteor'	EBar MWat SCro SPer WAbe
*– 'Mini'	ELan
¶ – 'Rosenteller'	EFou

– 'Septemberglut' ('September Glow')	EMon
– 'Stardust'	EBar ECha SIde
♦– 'Variegatum'	See H. ***alboroseum*** 'Mediovariegatum'
spinosum	See OROSTACHYS ***spinosa***
spurium	CRiv CTom EJud ELan LGro NGre NNor SBod SIng STre WEas
– *album*	See S. ***oppositifolium***
*– 'Atropurpureum'	CRDP ECha NNor NRoo SHig SPla WOld WPat
– 'Coccineum'	CRiv EMar MBar WOMN
– 'Erdblut'	EBre GGar LBre MHig NGre NMen NNrd NRoo
– 'Fool's Gold	EMon
– 'Fuldaglut'	CHal CNic EBre EHoe LBre NGre NHar NMir NRed SChu SIng WDav WPer WWin
– 'Glow'	STre
– 'Green Mantle'	ECha MPit NHol
– 'Purpureum'	CHan ELan GDra
– 'Purpurteppich' ('Purple Carpet')	CHal CPar CShe CTom EBre EPla EPot ESis LBre LGro MHig MRav NEgg NGre NHol NKay SAxl SHer SUsu WCla WThu
¶ – 'Roseum'	NHol
– 'Ruby Mantle'	CRiv GGar SIng WCot
– 'Schorbuser Blut' ('Dragon's Blood')	CHal CMea CRiv EBar EMon LHop MBal MCas MFir MWat NGre NHol NKay NRar NVic WAbe WEas WHil WHoo
– 'Tricolor'	SPla WPat WThu
§ – 'Variegatum'	Widely available
stahlii	CHal
stenopetalum 'Douglasii'	CNic NHol
stephanii	See RHODIOLA ***crassipes s.***
stoloniferum	NGre SSmi
stribrnyi	See S. ***urvillei*** Stribrnyi Group
'Sunset Cloud'	CMHG CSam NGre SPer WOld WPer
takesimense	NGre
§ *tatarinowii*	NGre WPer
§ *telephioïdes*	WCot
§ *telephium*	EBar EPla NSti SRms WCla WCot WPer
– 'Arthur Branch'	CElw EHal EMon EPla MTho SSpi WCot
– ssp. *fabaria*	See S. ***fabaria***
§ – ssp. *maximum*	ECha EMon
– – 'Atropurpureum'	CBot CGle CHad CLew CSev CWGN ECha ELan EMar EPla MBri MFir SMrm SPer WEas WHal WPer WWin
– 'Munstead Dark Red'	CMGP CRiv CSco EJud EMon MUlv NGre SFis SHig
*– 'Roseum'	EFol EMon LHop
– 'Variegatum'	CMHG COtt CSco EFol EMar MPlt NRoo SPla WHal WWin
tenuifolium	EBur GGar SSmi
§ – ssp. *ibericum*	NGre NHol
– var. *tenuifolium*	EBur
ternatum	NGre NKay
* *trollii*	MHig NGre
§ 'Vera Jameson'	CHad CKel CMHG CSco CShe EBre ECha EHoe LBre MBri MCas MFir NHol NKay NSti SBla SChu SPer SUsu WDav WEas WPer WWat

¶ *verticillatum* NGre
'Weihenstephaner Gold' See S. ***kamtschaticum floriferum*** 'W.G.'
weinbergii See GRAPTOPETALUM ***paraguayense***
yunnenense See RHODIOLA ***yunnanensis***

SEEMANNIA See **GLOXINIA**

SELAGINELLA (Selaginellaceae)

apoda MBri
braunii NMar
douglasii NMar
emmeliana See S. ***pallescens***
helvetica NHol
kraussiana CHal MBal MBri NMar WRic
– 'Aurea' CHal GGar MBri NMar
– 'Brownii' CHal MBri NMar
– 'Variegata' MBri
martensii 'Variegata' MBri
– 'Watsoniana' MBri NMar
§ *pallescens* NMar
– 'Aurea' NMar
vogelii NMar

SELAGO (Scrophulariaceae)

See Plant Deletions

SELINUM (Umbelliferae)

carvifolia SMrm SSpi
♦ *tenuifolium* See S. ***wallichianum***
§ *wallichianum* CDec CGle CHad CRDP EFou LGre MPar NSti SBar SIgm SMrm WEas WHer

SELLIERA (Goodeniaceae)

radicans forms ECou

SEMELE (Liliaceae/Ruscaceae)

androgyna CHEx

SEMIAQUILEGIA † (Ranunculaceae)

§ *adoxoïdes* CHad EDra ESma NRya SFis WAbe WPer
§ *ecalcarata* CBot CGle CMil CPar CRiv CRow EDra EFol EFou GAbr GCal LGan MBro MPlt NHar NOak SFis SMrm WCru WDav WPer WThu WWin
– 'Flore Pleno' CBos CNic CSun LBlm LGan WEas
simulatrix See S. ***ecalcarata***

SEMIARUNDINARIA † (Gramineae(Bambuseae))

§ *fastuosa* CHEx EFul EPla ISta LBam NJap SArc SBam SCob SDry WJun
– var. *viridis* EPla ISta SBam SDry WJun
¶ *kagamiana* LBam SDry WJun
¶ *makinoi* WJun
nitida See SINARUNDINARIA ***nitida***
¶ *okuboi* WJun
villosa See S. ***okuboi***
yamadorii EPla ISta SBam SDry WJun
¶ – 'Brimscombe' SDry
yashadake EPla SBam SDry WJun
¶ – *kimmei* SDry WJun

SEMPERVIVELLA See ROSULARIA

SEMPERVIVUM † (Crassulaceae)

'Abba' CWil
♦ *acuminatum* See S. ***tectorum glaucum***
'Aglow' CWil
'Alcithoë' CWil
'Aldo Moro' CWil EBar NNrd SMit SSmi
allionii See JOVIBARBA ***allionii***
'Alluring' CWil MCas SMit
'Alpha' CRiv CWil ESis LBee MCas NGre NHol NKay SIng SSmi STre
altum CWil MCas SSmi
'Amanda' CWil MDHE NMen SIng
'Ambergreen' CWil NBra SSmi
'Amtmann Fischer' NBra
andreanum CWil GAri MCas NGre NHol SIng SMit SSmi
'Apache' CWil NNrd SSmi
'Apple Blossom' CWil MCas SIng SMit SSmi
arachnoïdeum CMea CPar CSam CShe CWil EBar ELan EPot ESis GAbr LBee MBar MCas MWat NHol NNrd NRoo NWCA SBla SHer SIng SLMG SSmi WEas WHil WHoo WWin
– var. *bryoïdes* CWil GCHN NMen
– x *calcareum* CWil NGre NMen SMit SSmi
– 'Clairchen' CWil NBra
– *cristatum* NHol
– *doellianum* See S. ***a. glabrescens***
– 'Form No 1' LBee LRHS SSmi
§ – var. *glabrescens* MCas NMen SSmi
– – 'Album' CRiv WThu
– x *grandiflorum* SIng
– 'Laggeri' See S. ***a. tomentosum***
¶ – x *montanum* SIng
– x *nevadense* CRiv CWil SMit SSmi
– x *pittonii* CWil NGre NHol NMen SMit SSmi
– 'Rubrum' NBra
– 'Sultan' SSmi
N– ssp. *tomentosum* CHal CRiv CWil EBre ECro EMNN EPad EPar GCHN LBee LBre MCas MPlt NGre NHar NHol NKay NMen SIng SSmi WPer WWin
– – 'Minor' NHol SIng
§ – – 'Stansfieldii' CHal CRiv GAbr LBee MCas NGre NHol NKay NMen STre
arenarium See JOVIBARBA ***arenaria***
'Arlet' SMit
armenum CWil
– var. *insigne* from Akyarma Gecidi SMit
'Aross' CWil NBra NMen SSmi
'Arrowheads Red' MCas SSmi
arvernense See S. ***tectorum***
'Ashes of Roses' CWil NMen NTow SSmi WAbe WHal
'Asteroid' CWil SSmi
atlanticum CWil EBar NMen NNrd SIng SSmi
– 'Edward Balls' SIng

– from Oukaimaden	CWil NHol
'Atlantis'	NHol
'Atropurpureum'	CWil NBra
'Aureum'	See GREENOVIA ***aurea***
§ 'Aymon Correvon'	NBra
ballsii	CWil GAri GCHN
– from Kambeecho	SIng
– from Smólikas	NMen SSmi
– from Tschumba Petzi	SIng SSmi
'Banderi'	CWil
'Banyan'	SSmi
x ***barbulatum***	SSmi
§ x ***barbulatum barbulatum***	GCHN MCas NKay NMen SIng WAbe WHoo WThu
§ x ***barbulatum*** 'Hookeri'	CWil EPad ESis GAri MCas NHol NRoo SIng SMit SSmi WAbe
'Bascour Zilver'	CWil
'Bedivere'	CWil NGre SSmi
'Bella Meade'	CWil NGre SMit SSmi
'Belladonna'	CWil MCas NHol NMen NTow SSmi
'Bellotts Pourpre'	SMit
'Bennerbroek'	SSmi
'Bernstein'	CWil MCas NMen SIng
'Beta'	CKel MCas NHol NKay NMen NRoo SIng SSmi
'Bethany'	CWil
'Birchmaier'	CWil NMen
'Black Mini'	CWil MCas
'Black Mountain'	CWil
'Black Prince'	CWil NBra SWas
'Black Velvet'	CWil MCas
'Blari'	NBra SSmi
'Blood Tip'	CRiv ESis GAbr GAri GCHN LBee MDHE NHar SHer WHal
'Blue Boy'	CWil MCas
'Blush'	NBra SSmi
'Boissieri'	See S. ***tectorum tectorum*** 'B.'
'Booth's Red'	SSmi
borissovae	CWil GAri SIng SSmi
'Boromir'	CWil NBra SMit SSmi
'Brock'	CWil NHol
'Bronco'	CWil ELan EPad NMen SMit SSmi
'Bronze Pastel'	CWil MCas NGre NMen SMit SSmi WHil
'Bronze Tower'	SMit
'Brown Owl'	CWil
'Brownii'	GAbr NBra NMen
'Burgundy'	NBra
'Burnatii'	CWil
¶ 'Butterbur'	CWil
'Café'	CWil NNrd SSmi
x ***calcaratum***	SIng
calcareum	CWil EPar MBro NGre NKay SIng SSmi STre WHoo WThu
¶ – from Benz	CWil
– from Ceuze	CWil
– from Colle St. Michael	CWil
– from Gleize	CWil
– from Gorges du Cains	CWil SSmi
– 'Greenii'	CWil NBra NGre NMen SMit SSmi
§ – 'Grigg's Surprise'	CWil NBra NMen SMit
– from Guillaumes, Mont Ventoux	CWil NMen
– from La Mata de la Riba	SMit
– 'Limelight'	CWil SMit SSmi
– 'Monstrosum'	See S. ***c.*** 'Grigg's Surprise'
– from Mont Ventoux	SSmi
– 'Mrs Giuseppi'	CMGP CRiv EPar ESis GAbr GCHN LBee MCas NOak SChu SSmi STre WThu
– 'Nigricans'	NKay
– 'Pink Pearl'	CWil SSmi
– from Queyras	CWil SSmi
– from Route d'Annôt	CWil SSmi
– 'Sir William Lawrence'	CWil SSmi WHal WThu
– 'Spinulifolium'	SMit
– from Triora	CWil
'Canada Kate'	CWil SMit SSmi
'Cancer'	SSmi
'Candy Floss'	CWil SSmi
cantabricum	CWil SSmi
– ssp. ***cantabricum*** from Leitariegos	CWil NMen SMit
– – from Someido No 1	SMit
– ssp. ***guadarramense*** from Lobo No 1	CWil SMit SSmi
– – from Lobo No 2	SMit SSmi
– – from Morcuera No 1	SMit
– – from Morcuera No 3	SMit
– – from Navafria No 1	SMit
– – from Valvanera No 1	SMit SSmi
– from Lago de Enol	CWil
– x ***montanum stiriacum***	CWil NGre SMit SSmi WEas
¶ – from Navafria	CWil
– from Peña Prieta	SSmi
– from Piedrafita	CWil SMit SSmi
– from Riaño	CWil
– from San Glorio	CWil GAri SSmi
– from Santander	SSmi
¶ – from Ticeros	CWil
– ssp. ***urbionense*** from Picos de Urbión	CWil SMit
– from Valvernera	CWil
'Canth'	CWil NBra
'Caramel'	CWil
'Carluke'	CWil NBra
'Carmen'	CPar CWil EPar MCas SSmi
'Carneus'	NBra
'Carnival'	MCas SSmi
caucasicum	CWil NKay SSmi
'Cavo Doro'	CWil NBra NGre SSmi
'Celon'	CWil
charadzeae	SMit
'Cherry Frost'	NGre NNrd SSmi WHil
'Cherry Tart'	CWil
'Chocolate'	CWil NBra SSmi WAbe
x ***christii***	CWil NHol SSmi WThu
* ***chrysanthum***	NBra NMen
ciliosum Butus	CPar CWil NGre NKay
– from Ali Butús	MCas WThu
– var. ***borisii***	CHal CNic ESis MFir NGre NHol NMen NMir NNrd NRoo NRya NTow
– x ***ciliosum borisii***	CPar CWil
– var. ***galicicum*** 'Mali Hat'	CWil ECar NHol NMen
– x ***marmoreum***	CWil SSmi
– x ***marmoreum*** from Sveta Peta	SMit

'Circlet'	NBra SSmi
* ***cistaceum***	WEas
'Clara Noyes'	SSmi
'Clare'	NGre SSmi
'Cleveland Morgan'	CWil ECro GAbr GAri NBra NHar SSmi
'Climax'	NBra
'Cobweb Capers'	NBra
'Collage'	CWil
'Collecteur Anchisi'	NBra NGre SMit SSmi
'Commander Hay'	CRiv EPar GCal MCas NGre NHol NTow SChu STre WEas WHal WThu
'Compte de Congae'	NBra SPla
'Congo'	CWil SMit SSmi
'Cornstone'	CWil
'Corona'	MCas NBra
'Coronet'	SSmi
'Correvons'	See S. 'Aymon Correvoa'
'Corsair'	CWil NMen NNrd SIng
'Crimson Velvet'	CWil NGre SSmi
§ 'Crispyn'	CWil MBro MCas NHol NMen NMir SSmi WEas
'Cupream'	CWil NBra NGre
'Dakota'	CWil
'Dallas'	CWil
'Damask'	CWil GAbr NGre SSmi
'Dame Arsac'	SMit
'Dark Beauty'	CWil SMit WHal
'Dark Cloud'	CWil NBra SMit SSmi
'Dark Point'	CWil MCas NMen SMit SSmi
'Darkie'	CWil
'Deep Fire'	CWil
* x ***degenianum***	CWil NBra
'Delta'	MCas
densum	See S. ***tectorum***
'Director Jacobs'	CRiv CWil GAbr GCHN MCas NGre SMit SSmi WEas
dolomiticum x ***montanum***	CWil NBra NMen SMit SSmi
'Downland Queen'	CWil SMit
'Dragoness'	SMit
'Duke of Windsor'	CWil NGre SSmi
'Dusky'	CWil NBra SSmi
'Dyke'	CWil MBro MCas
dzhavachischilii	SMit
'Edge of Night'	CWil
'Educator Wollaert'	NBra
'El Greco'	CWil
'El Toro'	CWil
'Elgar'	CWil MCas SIng
'Elvis'	CWil MBro NMen SSmi
'Emerald Giant'	CWil
'Emerson's Giant'	CWil
'Engle's 13-2'	CWil NHar NHol
'Engle's Rubrum'	CLew GTou NHol NMen NRar SHer
erythraeum	CWil NGre NHol SIng
– from Pirin	NGre
– from Rila	MCas
'Excalibur'	CWil SSmi
* ***excelsum***	NKay
'Exhibita'	CWil SSmi
'Exorna'	CWil NMen SHer SSmi WEas
'Fair Lady'	NBra NMen
'Fame'	CWil MDHE SSmi
'Fat Jack'	MCas
x ***fauconnettii***	CWil NBra NHol SIng SSmi WThu
x ***fauconnettii thompsonii***	NGre NHol SSmi
'Festival'	CWil NMen
'Fiesta'	CWil
fimbriatum	See S. x ***barbulatum barbulatum***
'Finerpointe'	CWil SSmi
'Fire Glint'	CWil NBra
'Firebird'	CWil
'First Try'	NBra
'Flaming Heart'	CWil SSmi
'Flander's Passion'	LBee
'Flasher'	CWil MCas WEas
'Forden'	NBra
'Ford's Amability'	CWil NBra NGre SSmi
'Ford's Giant'	CWil
'Ford's Spring'	CWil NBra SSmi
'Frosty'	CWil NBra
'Fuego'	CWil MCas SIng
x ***funckii***	CRiv CWil ECar NBra NGre NHol NMen SIng
'Fusilier'	NBra
'Fuzzy Wuzzy'	NBra SSmi
'Gamma'	LBee NHol NMen
'Garnet'	CWil NBra
'Gay Jester'	CWil NGre SSmi
'Gazelle'	CRiv NBra
'Ginnie's Delight'	CWil SSmi
'Gipsy'	CWil
giuseppii	CRiv CShe CWil NGre NHol NMen SIng SRms SSmi WThu
– from Peña Espigüete	CWil NHol
– from Peña Prieta	CWil SMit
'Gizmo'	CWil
'Gleam'	NBra
'Gloriosum'	NGre NRoo SSmi
'Glowing Embers'	CWil SSmi
'Godaert'	CWil
'Gollum'	SMit SSmi
'Granada'	CWil NGre
'Granat'	CKel CWil MCas
¶ 'Granby'	NMen
grandiflorum	CWil EBar GAri GCHN NBra NGre NMen NRed SSmi WThu
– ***fasciatum***	CWil GAri SMit SSmi
– 'Keston'	NGre SSmi
– x ***montanum***	SIng
– x ***tectorum***	NKay
¶ 'Grape Idol'	CWil
'Grapetone'	CWil NGre SSmi
'Green Apple'	CWil NBra NGre SSmi
'Green Gables'	CWil SSmi
'Greenwich Time'	CWil MCas NMen SSmi
* ***greigii***	NNrd
'Grey Dawn'	CPar SSmi
'Grey Ghost'	CWil
'Grey Green'	CWil
'Grey Lady'	CWil NBra SSmi
'Greyfriars'	CWil NHol NMen
'Greyolla'	CWil MCas SSmi
'Gruaud Larose'	SMit
'Hall's Hybrid'	MCas NHar NKay SIng
'Happy'	CWil MCas
* 'Hart'	CWil
'Havana'	CWil
'Hayling'	CWil NHol SSmi

'Hayter's Red'	NBra
'Heigham Red'	CWil NGre NHol SMit SSmi
'Hekla'	NBra
helveticum	See S. ***montanum***
'Hester'	CWil MDHE NHar SIng SSmi
'Hey-Hey'	CRiv EPot LBee NKay
'Hidde'	CWil SSmi
'Hiddes Roosje'	SSmi
'Highland Mist'	SMit
hirtum	See JOVIBARBA ***hirta***
'Hookeri'	See S. x ***barbulatum*** 'H.'
'Hortulanus Smit'	SSmi
'Hot Peppermint'	CWil
'Hot Shot'	MCas
'Hullabaloo'	CWil SSmi
'Hurricane'	NBra
'Hyacintha'	NBra
'Icicle'	CWil MCas NGre NHol NMen SSmi
♦***imbricatum***	See S. x ***barbulatum barbulatum***
'Imperial'	CWil SSmi
ingwersenii	CWil GAri NBra NGre SSmi
– x ***marmoreum*** from Sveta Peta	SMit
'Interlace'	SSmi
'Iophon'	NBra SSmi
'Irazu'	CWil
italicum	CWil
'Itchen'	NMen SSmi
'IWO'	CWil
'Jack Frost'	CWil NGre SIng SSmi
'Jane'	NBra
¶ 'Jasper'	CWil
'Jelly Bean'	CWil
'Jet Stream'	CWil NMen SSmi
'Jewel Case'	CWil SIng SSmi
'Jolly Green Giant'	CWil SSmi
'Jo's Spark'	CWil
'Jubilee'	CHal CNic EBar ELan GAbr MCas MPlt NHol NMen NRed NRoo SSmi WEas WPer WWin
'Jubilee Tricolor'	ECar
'Jungle Fires'	MCas NBra
'Justine's Choice'	CWil
'Kalinda'	NGre SSmi
'Kappa'	CWil NHol SSmi
'Katmai'	CWil
'Kelly Jo'	CWil NGre NHar NMen SIng SSmi
'Kermit'	CWil SSmi
¶ 'Kerneri'	CWil
'Kimono'	CWil
kindingeri	CWil MCas NMen NWCA SMit SSmi WDav
'King George'	CRiv CWil ESis LBee NGre NMen SSmi
'Kip'	CWil NMen SIng SMit SSmi
'Kismet'	SSmi
'Kolibri'	GAbr MDHE
kosaninii	CWil NGre NKay NMen SSmi
– from Koprivnik	CWil SMit SSmi WAbe WCru
'Kramers Spinrad'	CWil NGre NMen SIng SMit SSmi WEas
* ***lacktugum*** 'Metaoicum'	MPlt
'Lady Kelly'	CWil SWas
'Lavender and Old Lace'	CWil GAbr GAri MCas NGre SMit
'Laysan'	CWil
'Leneca'	NBra NGre SSmi
'Lennik's Glory'	See S. 'Crispyn'
'Lennik's Time'	SSmi
'Lentezon'	CWil SSmi
'Leocadia's Nephew'	CWil
'Lilac Time'	CWil NGre SSmi
'Liliane'	SMit
'Lipari'	CWil
'Lipstick'	CWil GAbr NGre SMit
'Lively Bug'	CWil MBro MCas NNrd SSmi
'Lloyd Praeger'	See S. ***montanum stiriacum***
'Lou Bastidou'	SSmi
'Lowe's Rubicundum'	ESis
'Lynne's Choice'	CWil
macedonicum	CWil NGre SSmi
– from Ljuboten	SSmi
'Magic Spell'	SSmi
'Magical'	CWil NBra SSmi
'Magnificum'	CWil
'Mahogany'	CRiv LBee MBro MCas MPlt NHol NMen NRoo SPla WCru WHal WHoo
'Maigret'	CWil
'Majestic'	NGre SSmi
'Malabron'	CWil SSmi
* 'Malby's Hybrid'	CShe ECar MDHE NBra NHol
'Marella'	CWil
'Marijntje'	SSmi
'Marjorie Newton'	CWil
'Marmalade'	MCas SSmi
§ ***marmoreum***	CMea CWil LBee NMen SHer SIng SPla STre WEas
– var. ***angustissimum***	SMit
– var. ***blandum***	NKay
– 'Brunneifolium'	CWil ECar ESis GAri MCas NGre NHol SChu SIng SMit SSmi
– from Kanzas Gorge	NBra NGre NHol SIng SSmi
– ssp. ***marmoreum*** var.***dinaricum***	CWil
§ – – 'Rubrifolium'	CHal CShe CWil
– from Monte Tirone	CWil SSmi
– from Okol	CWil SSmi
§ – 'Ornatum'	NGre SRms SSmi WAbe WEas
– from Sveta Peta	NGre SSmi
'Mary Ente'	NBra
'Mate'	NMen SSmi
'Mauna Kea'	SSmi
'Mauvine'	NBra
'Mavbi'	NNrd
'Medallion'	CWil
'Meisse'	SSmi
'Melanie'	CWil MCas
'Mercury'	CWil MDHE NHol SIng SMit SSmi
'Merkur'	NBra
'Merlin'	CWil SSmi
'Midas'	CWil
'Mila'	CWil
'Mini Frost'	CWil MCas
¶ 'Missouri Rose'	CWil
'Moerkerk's Merit'	CWil SSmi
¶ 'Moly Harbord'	WThu
'Mondstein'	CWil
§ ***montanum***	CRiv CWil ESis MCas NMir NNrd SCro SIng
– from Anchisis	CWil
– from Arbizion	CWil

Name	Suppliers
– ssp. ***burnatii***	NGre SSmi WThu
– ssp. ***montanum*** var.***braunii***	CPar
– 'Rubrum'	See S. 'Red Mountain'
§ – ssp. ***stiriacum***	CWil EPar GAri NBra SIng
– – from Mauterndorf	SSmi
– – 'Lloyd Praeger'	CWil NGre SSmi
– from Windachtal	CWil
'More Honey'	CWil
'Mount Hood'	CWil
* 'Moyin'	SMit
'Mulberry Wine'	CWil MCas
¶ 'Myrrhine'	CWil
'Mystic'	CWil ECar NMen NNrd SIng
nevadense	CWil NGre NHol NKay NMen SRms SSmi
– ***hirtellum***	CWil SIng SSmi
– from Puerto de San Francisco	SMit
'Nico'	CWil
'Night Raven'	CWil MCas NMen SMit SSmi
'Nigrum'	See S. ***tectorum*** 'N.'
'Niobe'	CWil
'Nixes 27'	NBra
'Noir'	CRiv CWil GAbr NBra NGre NKay NMen SIng SSmi
'Norbert'	CWil
'Nouveau Pastel'	CWil SMit
'Octet'	NBra
octopodes	ESis MDHE
– var. ***apetalum***	CWil GAri MCas NBra NMen SIng SSmi
'Oddity'	CWil SMit
'Ohio Burgundy'	CWil MDHE NMir SSmi WAbe
'Olivette'	CWil SSmi
'Omega'	SIng SSmi
'Opitz'	CWil MCas
'Ornatum'	CHal NGre SSmi WAbe WEas
ossetiense	CWil SSmi
'Othello'	CHal EBre LBre MCas NVic WAbe
'Packardian'	CWil SMit SSmi
'Painted Lady'	SSmi
'Palissander'	CWil NGre SMit SSmi
'Pam Wain'	NBra
'Pastel'	CWil MCas
patens	See JOVIBARBA ***heuffelii***
'Patrician'	CWil EBre ESis GAri LBre SSmi
¶ 'Peach Blossom'	CWil
'Pekinese'	CWil EPar NNrd SIng SSmi WEas WWin
'Peterson's Ornatum'	NGre SSmi
'Pilatus'	CWil
'Pilosella'	NBra
'Pink Cloud'	CWil MCas SSmi
¶ 'Pink Dawn'	CWil
¶ 'Pink Lemonade'	CWil
'Pink Puff'	CWil SSmi
'Pippin'	CWil NBra SIng SMit
'Piran'	CWil
pittonii	CMea CWil ESis GAbr NMen SIng SSmi
'Pixie'	CNic CWil
'Plumb Rose'	CWil MCas SIng
'Pluto'	CWil SSmi
'Poke Eat'	NBra SSmi
'Polaris'	CWil MCas SSmi

Name	Suppliers
¶ 'Poldark'	CWil
'Pottsii'	CWil GAbr
x ***praegeri***	CWil
'Precious'	CWil NBra
'President Arsac'	SSmi
'Proud Zelda'	CWil SSmi
'Pseudoörnatum'	LBee
'Pumaros'	CWil NMen SSmi
pumilum	CWil MCas NBra NGre NMen
– from Adyl Su No 1	MCas SSmi
– from Adyl Su No 2	SSmi
– from Armchi	SSmi
– from Armchi x ***ingwersenii***	NMen SMit
– from El'brus No 1	NMen SSmi
– from El'brus No 2	SSmi
'Purdy'	WAbe
'Purdy's 50-6'	CWil
'Purple Beauty'	CWil NBra
'Purple King'	CWil
'Purple Passion'	NBra
'Purpurriese'	CWil
'Queen Amalia'	See S. ***reginae-amaliae***
'Query'	NBra
¶ 'Quintessence'	CWil
'R H I'	NBra
'Racy'	CWil
¶ 'Radiant'	CWil
* 'Ramis'	MCas NBra
'Raspberry Ice'	ECar MCas NHol WAbe WHal
'Red Ace'	CWil EBar NMen SSmi
'Red Beam'	MDHE NGre SSmi
'Red Cap'	NBra
'Red Delta'	CWil SSmi
'Red Devil'	CWil MBro NMen SSmi
'Red Giant'	NBra
§ 'Red Mountain'	LBee MCas MWat NKay SSmi
'Red Prince'	CWil
'Red Shadows'	CWil MCas
'Red Skin'	CWil
'Red Wings'	GAbr NGre SRms
'Regal'	NBra
'Regina'	NBra SSmi
reginae	See S. ***reginae-amaliae***
§ ***reginae-amaliae***	ELan NHol SSmi STre
– from Kambeecho No 1	CWil SSmi
– from Kambeecho No 2	CWil MCas NMen
– from Marvi Petri	CWil SIng SMit SSmi
– from Peristéri	SMit SSmi
– from Sarpun	CWil SSmi
'Reginald Malby'	CWil MCas NGre SSmi
'Reinhard'	CWil NMen NNrd SIng
'Remus'	CWil SIng
'Rex'	NBra NMen
¶ 'Rhone'	CWil
* ***richardii***	MBar
'Risque'	CWil MCas
'Rita Jane'	CWil EBar MCas SSmi
'Robin'	CWil MCas NHol NNrd
'Ronny'	CWil
x ***roseum fimbriatum***	CWil NHol SSmi WEas
'Rosie'	CMea CRiv CWil GAbr NGre NMen NRoo SIng SMit SSmi
'Rotkopf'	CWil NBra SMit
'Rotmantel'	MCas SSmi
'Rotsand'	NBra

'Rouge'	CWil SRms
'Royal Flush'	CWil SSmi
'Royal Mail'	NBra SSmi
'Royal Opera'	CWil MCas NGre SSmi
'Royal Ruby'	CWil GCHN LBee NRoo SIng SSmi
'Rubellum'	NBra
'Rubikon Improved'	NBra SChu SSmi
'Rubin'	CPar CRiv EBar EPad EPar MCas NGre NMen SCro WAbe WEas WThu
'Rubrifolium'	See S. ***marmoreum marmoreum*** 'R.'
'Rubrum Ornatum'	MCas SIng
'Rubrum Ray'	NBra SSmi
'Ruby Heart'	NGre SSmi
'Rule Britannia'	SMit
'Rusty'	CWil
'Ruth'	NBra
ruthenicum	NGre
¶ 'Saffron'	CWil
'Saga'	CWil
'Sanford's Hybrid'	NBra
'Saturn'	CWil SSmi
schlehanii	See S. ***marmoreum***
'Seminole'	CWil
'Shawnee'	CWil
¶ 'Sheila'	GAbr
'Shirley's Joy'	CHal CWil GAbr SSmi WEas
'Sigma'	NBra
'Silberspitz'	CWil NMen SIng
'Silver Jubilee'	CWil MDHE NGre SSmi
'Silver Spitz'	NBra
'Silver Spring'	NBra
'Silver Thaw'	CWil NNrd NTow SSmi WHil
♦ 'Simonkaianum'	See JOVIBARBA ***hirta***
'Sioux'	CWil GAbr NGre SIng SSmi
'Skrocki's Bronze'	CWil NBra SMit
'Slabber's Seedling'	CWil
'Smokey Jet'	CWil SSmi
'Snowberger'	CWil ESis GAbr NHar SIng
soboliferum	See JOVIBARBA ***sobolifera***
'Sopa'	CWil
sosnowskyi	CWil
'Soul'	CWil
'Spanish Dancer'	CWil SSmi
'Sparkle'	CWil
'Spherette'	CWil SIng SSmi
'Spice'	NBra
'Spinnelli'	WThu
'Spode'	SSmi
'Spring Mist'	CWil GCHN NHar SIng
'Sprite'	CWil SMit SSmi
sp. from Mont Cenis	NBra
sp. Sierra del Cadi'	NHol
stansfieldii	See S. ***arachnoideum tomentosum*** 'Stansfieldii'
'Starshine'	CWil SIng SSmi
'State Fair'	CWil MCas NGre SIng SSmi
'Strawberry Sundae'	NBra
'Strider'	MCas SMit
'Stuffed Olive'	SSmi
'Sun Waves'	NBra SSmi
'Sunkist'	SSmi
'Superama'	CWil SSmi
¶ 'Supernova'	CWil
'Tamberlane'	CWil
'Tarn Hows'	CWil
'Teck'	MCas NBra
§ ***tectorum***	CArn CNic CRiv CSFH CWil EJud ELan EPar GAbr GPoy GTou IEde MBar MDHE MFir SHer SIde SIng SMad STre WAbe WHoo WOak WWye
– ssp. ***alpinum***	CWil MCas NKay SIng SSmi
– from Andorra	CWil
– 'Atrorubens'	NBra
– 'Atroviolaceum'	CWil ESis NHol SIng SMit
§ – var. ***glaucum***	CWil ESis NKay SSmi
– from Mont Ventoux	CWil
– from Neuvéglise	SMit
– 'Nigrum'	CWil EBar ESis NBra NGre NHol NMen SIng SSmi
– 'Red Flush'	CWil NHar NMen SIng SMit SSmi
– 'Robustum'	NKay
– 'Royanum'	WEas
– from Sierra del Cadi	CWil SSmi
– 'Sunset'	CWil MCas NMen SMit SSmi WAbe WEas
¶ – ssp. ***tectorum***	NGre
§ – – 'Atropurpureum'	CWil MCas NBra SIng SSmi
§ – – 'Boissieri'	CWil NGre NKay SSmi
– – 'Triste'	CWil LBee MCas SSmi
– 'Violaceum'	SIng WAbe
'Thayne'	NBra NMen
'Theo'	SMit
thompsonianum	CWil NGre NHol NMen SIng SSmi WThu
'Tiffany'	NBra NHol
'Tina'	SSmi
'Titania'	CWil NBra NHar SIng SSmi
¶ 'Tombago'	MCas
'Topaz'	CWil LBee LRHS
'Tordeur's Memory'	CWil NBra NGre NMen SMit SSmi
'Traci Sue'	CWil SMit SSmi
transcaucasicum	CWil SSmi
'Tristesse'	CWil NMen SMit
'Tristram'	SSmi
'Truva'	CWil MCas
'Twilight Blues'	CWil
¶ 'Unicorn'	CWil
x ***vaccarii***	NBra NGre SSmi
'Vanbaelen'	CWil SSmi
'Vaughelen'	CWil NBra
'Verdo'	MCas
¶ x ***versicolor***	NHol
vicentei	CWil
'Victorian'	NBra
'Video'	CWil ECar SSmi
'Violet Queen'	CWil
'Virgil'	CWil SIng SSmi
'Virginus'	CWil
'Vulcano'	CWil
♦ ***webbianum***	See S. ***arachnoideum tomentosum***
'Webby Flame'	CWil
'Webby Ola'	NBra SSmi
'Weirdo'	CWil NBra
'Wendy'	CWil MCas NBra SSmi
'Westerlin'	CWil GAbr NGre SIng SSmi
'Whitening'	CWil NGre NMen SSmi
x ***widderi***	SSmi
'Wollcott's Variety'	GAbr NHar SIng
wulfenii	CWil NMen

¶ 'Zackenrone'	CWil
zeleborii	CHal CWil MDHE
¶ 'Zenith'	MCas
'Zenocrate'	CWil
'Zeppelin'	CWil MBro
'Zinaler Rothorn'	LRHS
¶ 'Zircon'	NMen
'Zone'	CWil SSmi
'Zulu'	CWil MCas SSmi

SENECIO (Compositae)

§ ***abrotanifolius***	GAri LHil NTow
– ***tiroliensis***	See S. ***abrotanifolius***
aquaticus	CKin
bicolor cineraria	See S. ***cineraria***
bidwillii	See BRACHYGLOTTIS ***bidwillii***
buchananii	See BRACHGLOTTIS ***b.***
chilensis	CGre
chrysanthemoïdes	See EURYOPS ***c.***
§ ***cineraria***	CFis CHEx LHil MBri
– 'Alice'	EFou
– 'Ramparts'	LHop WPer
– 'Silver Filigree'	ENot
– 'Sleights Hardy'	NPer
– 'White Diamond'	CFis CKel ECha LGro WBod WEas WWin
compactus	See BRACHYGLOTTIS ***compacta***
crassulifolius	CBot
doria	CRDP SAxl
elaeagnifolius	See BRACHYGLOTTIS ***elaeagnifolia***
formosus	CBot
¶ ***gillesii***	LGre WDav
glastifolius	CSam
¶ ***gnaphaloïdes***	SIgm
'Gregynog Gold'	See LIGULARIA 'G.G.'
greyi Hooker	See BRACHYGLOTTIS ***greyi***
♦– hort.	See BRACHYGLOTTIS 'Sunshine'
heritieri	See PERICALLIS ***lanata***
herreianus	MBri SLMG
* ***huteri***	WEas
kirkii	See BRACHYGLOTTIS ***k.***
¶ ***laciniata***	CHEx
laxifolius Buchanan	See BRACHYGLOTTIS ***laxifolia***
♦– hort.	See BRACHYGLOTTIS 'Sunshine'
'Leonard Cockayne'	See BRACHYGLOTTIS 'L.C.'
¶ ***leucophyllus***	LGre
leucostachys	See S. ***viravira***
macroglossus 'Variegatus'	CB&S CHal ERea SLMG
maritimus	See S. ***bicolor cineraria***
♦ ***mikanioïdes***	See DELAIREA ***odorata***
monroi	See BRACHYGLOTTIS ***monroi***
petasitis	CHEx CTro
¶ ***polyodon*** SH 29	CRDP
♦ ***populifolius***	See PERICALLIS ***appendiculata***
* ***populnea***	CBot
przewalskii	See LIGULARIA ***przewalskii***
pulcher	CChu CGle CHan CRDP CSam LGre SSpi WCot
reinoldii	See BRACHYGLOTTIS ***rotundifolia***
rowleyanus	CHal EBak
scandens	CB&S CGre CMac ELan EMon ERea ISea MTho NTow SHil WCru WSHC
serpens	MBri
§ ***smithii***	CChu CHan CMHG CRDP CRow ECha MSta WCru
speciosus	WCru
'Sunshine'	See BRACHYGLOTTIS 'Sunshine'
♦ ***takedanus***	See TEPHROSERUS ***t.***
tamoïdes	CPle
– 'Variegatus'	ERea
♦ ***tanguticus***	See SINACALIA ***tangutica***
§ ***viravira***	CDec CFis CGle CGre CHan CMea CPle CSpe ECha ELan ERea LHop MBel MRav SChu SHil SPer WAbe WByw WCru WHal WOld WRus WSHC WWat
♦ ***werneriifolius***	See PACKERA ***werneriifolia***

SENNA (Leguminosae)

artemisioïdes	CPle
N ***corymbosa***	CAbb CB&S CBot CHEx CPle CTre CTro ERea LAbb LHil SLMG
didymobotrya	CPle
hebecarpa	NSal
marilandica	CB&S CPle NSal WCru WSHC
obtusa Clos	See S. ***candolleana***
– (Roxb.) Wight	CGre CWit MNew SHil
¶ ***polyantha***	CGre
procumbens	CPle
¶ ***splendida***	CGre
sturtii	CPle

SEQUOIA (Taxodiaceae)

sempervirens	CB&S CBow CDoC CGre EHar EHul GAri IJoh IOrc ISea LCon LPan WCoo WDin WMou WNor
– 'Adpressa'	CBra CDoC CMHG CMac EBre EHar EHul EPla LBre LCon LLin MBal MBar MBri MGos MPla NHol SLim
– 'Prostrata'	CGre CMac EBre EHar EPla GAri GWht LBre LCon LLin LTil MBar MBri MGos

SEQUOIADENDRON (Taxodiaceae)

giganteum	CB&S CDoC CMac CSco EHar EHul ELan ENot GRei IBar IJoh IOrc ISea LCon LNet LTil MBar MBri NWea SEng SHil SMad SPer WCoo WFro WMou WNor
– 'Barabit's Requiem'	SMad WMou
– 'Glaucum'	EHar MBri WMou
– 'Pendulum'	CDoC EHar LCon MBar SEng SHil SMad WMou

SERAPIAS (Orchidaceae)

¶ ***lingua***	SBla

SERENOA (Palmae)
See Plant Deletions

SERIPHIDIUM (Compositae)

caerulescens	
ssp. ***gallicum***	EEls
¶ ***maritimum***	CTom GGar GPoy WHer
¶ – ***maritimum***	EEls
§ ***nutans***	CFis EBre EEls LBre LHil MWat NSti
tridentatum	CFis
– ssp. ***tridentatum***	EEls
– ssp. ***vaseyanum***	EEls
– ssp. ***wyomingense***	EEls
vallesiacum	CSFH CSun EEls EMon LBlm WHer

SERISSA (Rubiaceae)

foetida	See S. ***japonica***
§ ***japonica***	STre
– 'Variegata'	CGre CPle

SERRATULA (Compositae)

§ ***seoanei***	CLew CNic ECha EFol EMon LHop MCas MFir MHig MUlv MWat NNrd SDix SIng SUsu WByw
shawii	See S. ***seoanei***
tinctoria	CArn CKin NSal SIde WNdy
– ssp. ***macrocephala***	CLew WPer

SESAMUM (Pedaliaceae)

indicum	CArn

SESBANIA (Leguminosae)
See Plant Deletions

SESELI (Umbelliferae)

¶ ***dichotomum***	SIgm
¶ ***gummiferum***	SIng

SESLERIA (Gramineae)

§ ***albicans***	ETPC
§ ***argentea***	ETPC
autumnalis	ETPC
caerulea	CElw EHoe ELan EPla ETPC GCal MPar MUlv SFar
– ssp. ***calcarea***	See S. ***albicans***
cylindrica	See S. ***argentea***
glauca	EHoe WPer
heufleriana	EMon EPla ETPC LRHS
insularis	EMon EPla LRHS
nitida	CElw EHoe EMon ETPC LRHS

SETARIA (Gramineae)

¶ ***chevarlaria***	CTro

SETCREASEA See **TRADESCANTIA**

SHADDOCK See **CITRUS *grandis***

SHEPHERDIA (Elaeagnaceae)

argentea	CBot

SHERARDIA (Rubiaceae)

arvensis	MHew NSal

SHIBATAEA † (Gramineae(Bambuseae))

kumasasa	CB&S CBar CBra CCla EPla IOrc ISta LBam LNet MBal MGos MUlv NHol NJap SArc SBam SCob SDry SHil WJun
¶ – ***aureastriatus***	ISta SDry
¶ ***lancifolia***	SDry WJun

SHORTIA (Diapensiaceae)

soldanelloïdes	GDra
– dwarf form	GDra
– var. ***ilicifolia***	IBlr
– – 'Askival'	GDra
uniflora 'Grandiflora'	IBlr

SIBBALDIA (Rosaceae)

cuneata	CNic
¶ ***procumbens***	NWCA

SIBBALDIOPSIS (Rosaceae)

tridentata 'Lemon Mac'	SIng

SIBIRAEA (Rosaceae)

altaiensis CLD 781	EMon
♦ ***laevigata***	See S. ***altaiensis***

SIDA (Malvaceae)

hermaphrodita	EMon
napaea	EMon

SIDALCEA † (Malvaceae)

'Brilliant'	CGle CMGP CPar MBel NBar SGil WMer
candida	CElw CGle CHad CHan CPar CSco EFou ELan EPar EPla GAbr GCal GGar MFir MSte NRoo NSti SCro SGil SMrm SPer SUsu WBon WRus WTyr
– 'Bianca'	SFis
'Crimson King'	CSco
'Croftway Red'	CB&S CGle EBre ECED ELan LBre NRoo NVic SChu SCro SPer WTyr
'Elsie Heugh'	CDoC CHad CHan EBre EFou GCal LBre MBri MUlv NBar NBro NSti SChu SGil WBon WRus WTyr
'Interlaken'	NMir NOrc WTyr
'Loveliness'	CGle CRDP CSco ECED ELan MWat SGil SHer SPer WHal
malviflora	CBos CBre CLew MFir NNor NSti SChu WByw WEas WHoo WPer

'Monarch'	CSco
'Mrs Borrodaile'	CTom MUlv NKay
'Mrs Cadman'	SFis
'Mrs Galloway'	CSco
'Mrs T Alderson'	CGle GAbr
neomexicana	GCal
'Oberon'	CHan NHol NTow SPer WEas
'Party Girl'	CBow CDoC CSam EBre ECtt EHal LBre MNFA NRoo SGil SMad WPbr WPer WTyr
'Reverend Page Roberts'	CShe NVic SFis
'Rosanna'	WHil
'Rose Queen'	CBow CGle CKel CMGP CSco CTom EBre ECha LBre LGan LWad MWat NHol NKay NRoo SHer SPer WHoo
Stark's hybrids	MPit SRms
'Sussex Beauty'	CBos ECha EFou SChu WCot
'The Duchess'	CSco CShe
'Twixt'	SFis
'William Smith'	CGle COtt CPar CSco EBre ECED ECha GAbr LBre MWat NHol NKay NMir NOrc SGil SPer WEas WTyr

SIDERITIS (Labiatae)

hyssopifolia	WPer
scardica	WDav
syriaca	CBot ECha SIgm WDav
¶– NS 551	NWCA

SIEVERSIA (Rosaceae)

§ ***reptans***	CNic EPad GAbr GTou MFir NHol WPer WThu

SILAUM (Umbelliferae)

silaus	CKin

SILENE (Caryophyllaceae)

acaulis	CLew CNic CPar EMNN EPad EPot GCHN GTou ITim LBee MBro MCas MPla MTho NMen NRoo NWCA SFis WAbe WPat WThu WWin
– 'Alba'	CLew CPar GDra LBee MBro NHar NHol NMen NNrd NRed WDav WHil
§ – ssp. ***elongata***	NCat NHol SGil SHer SRms WPer
– ssp. ***exscapa***	WPer
¶ – 'Flore Pleno'	SGil
– 'Frances'	GAbr GArf GCHN GDra ITim MHig NHol NWCA SGil WAbe WDav
– ssp. ***longiscapa***	CMHG GAbr GDra MCas NRed SSmi
*– ***minima***	CLew
– 'Mount Snowdon'	EBre ELan EMNN EPad GArf LBee LBre MTho NHol NMen NRed NWCA SGil SHer WPat
– 'Pedunculata'	See S. ***a. elongata***
– from Pfiezujoch	NHol
♦***alba***	See S. ***latifolia***
alpestris	CGle CLew CNic ELan EMNN EPot ESis MBro MCas MFir MHig MPla MTho NGre NKay NNrd NWCA WAbe WCla WPer
– 'Flore Pleno'	CGle CShe CSun EOrc ESis LBee LBlm MHig NKay WWin
¶ ***argaea***	MBro NGre WDav
x ***arkwrightii***	See LYCHNIS x ***a.***
armeria	WHer
asterias	CHan CLew CSun EBar EJud ESma LGan LHil MBel NSti WCla WPer WWin
¶ ***californica alba***	WHil
¶ ***caryophylloïdes***	WDav
¶ ***ciliata***	EPot
§ ***compacta***	ECro WEas WKif
delavayi	NHol
dioica	CArn CGle CKin CNat CSFH ELan MChe MHew NHol NLan SWat WCla WHen WHer WNdy WWye
– ***compacta***	See S. ***d.*** 'Minikin'
§ – 'Flore Pleno'	CBot CElw CHan CRDP CSFH ECha LGan LWad MTho NBro SRms WByw WCot WEas WHoo WPer
– 'Graham's Delight' (v)	EMon
§ – 'Minikin'	ELan EMon LRHS WBon
– 'Perkin'	CNat
– 'Richmond' (d)	ECha EMon
§ – 'Rosea Plena'	CBre CChu CElw CGle CLew CMil CSam ELan EMon EOrc MTho NKay SChu SMrm WBon WByw WHer WPer
¶ – 'Rosea Plena Variegata'	WHer
♦– 'Rubra Plena'	See S. ***d.*** 'Flore Pleno'
*– 'Variegata'	EFol ELan
elisabethiae	LBee LRHS NRed NWCA SHer
– JCA 917.100	WDav
– 'Alba'	WCla
§ ***fimbriata***	CHad CHan CRDP ELan EMon MNFA MPar SAxl SWas
flavescens	NRed
foliosa	CLew NRed
frivaldskyana	CHan GCHN LGan NHol
hifacensis	EMon WCot
hookeri	CLew EPot MTho WDav WPat WPer
ingramii	GArf
italica	CKin
keiskei	CRDP ECha ELan GTou NKay NNrd NTow SBla WPer
– ***akaisialpina***	ITim
– var. ***minor***	CNic GArf MCas MTho NWCA WAbe WOMN WPer
§ ***latifolia***	CKin NMir WCla WHen WHer
lerchenfeldiana	CNic
maritima	See S. ***uniflora***
moorcroftiana	WOMN WPer
multifida	See S. ***fimbriata***
nigrescens	WCot WPer
noctiflora	CKin WCla WNdy
nutans	CKin CNat NLan NMir WHer WNdy WPer
orientalis	See S. ***compacta***
pendula 'Compacta'	CNic WPer
– ***rosea***	LHil
¶ ***petersonii petersonii***	NHol
pusilla	LGan WPer
rubra 'Flore Pleno'	See S. ***dioica*** 'F.P.'
saxatilis	NHol NKay

schafta	CMea CNic CPar ECha EFol ELan EMNN GAbr GCHN ITim LBee LGan MBro MCas MFir MPla MWat NGre NKay NNrd NRoo NWCA SIng SSvw WCla WHoo WTyr WWin
– 'Abbotswood'	See LYCHNIS x ***walkeri*** 'Abbotswood Rose'
– 'Ralph Haywood'	CGle EPot NHol
– 'Shell Pink'	EFol LBee LHop MHig WHoo WOMN WThi
sieboldii	See LYCHNIS ***coronata sieboldii***
sp. CDB 13013	EMon
sp. L 887	NHol
suksdorfii	CLew NHol WHoo
*****surortii***	WPer
tatarica	WPer
undulata	CHan
§ ***uniflora***	CGle CHan CKin ELan EMNN GAbr MFir MHew MPar NBro NGre NKay NLan NNor NOak NSti NWCA SBod WCla WHen WHer WWin
♦– 'Alba Plena'	See S. ***u.*** 'Robin Whitebreast'
§ – 'Druett's Variegated'	ECha SGil SIng
– 'Flore Pleno'	See S. ***u.*** 'Robin Whitebreast'
§ – 'Robin Whitebrest' ('Weisskehlchen')	Widely available
– 'Rosea'	CGle CTom ECha ECtt EMNN EPot NHol NNrd NRed NWCA SAxl SUsu WPer
– 'Silver Lining' (v)	ELan EMon LRHS
– 'Variegata'	See S. ***u.*** 'Druett's Variegated'
– 'White Bells'	EPad EPla NNrd WHoo WSHC
vallesia	WPer
§ ***vulgaris***	CKin CNic MChe MWil NLan NMir WNdy
– ***alpina***	See S. ***v. prostrata***
– ssp. ***maritima***	See S. ***uniflora***
wallichiana	See S. ***vulgaris***
¶ ***wrightii***	NGre
§ ***zawadskii***	EBar ITim NGre NHar NHol NTow WDav WHil WPer

SILPHIUM (Compositae)

laciniatum	EMon NSal
perfoliatum	ECro EMar GPoy NSti
trifoliatum	NSal

SILYBUM (Compositae)

marianum	CArn CFis CGle CRDP ECro EJud ELan EMar GPoy LGan LHil LHol MFir NSal NSel SIde WEas WOak WWye

SIMMONDSIA (Simmondsiaceae)

chinensis	NSal

SINACALIA (Compositae)

§ ***tanguticus***	CBre CElw CFis CGle CHEx CHan CRow CWGN ELan GGar MBal NBro NDea NSti SDix WAbb WCru

SINARUNDINARIA † (Gramineae(Bambuseae))

anceps	See YUSHANIA ***a.***
jaunsarensis	See YUSHANIA ***anceps***
maling	See YUSHANIA ***m.***
murieliae	See THAMNOCALAMUS ***spathacea***
nitida	See FARGESIA ***n.***

SINNINGIA (Gesneriaceae)

'Arion'	NMos
'Blanche de Méru'	NMos SDeJ
'Blue Wonder'	MBri
'Boonwood Yellow Bird'	NMos
§ ***canescens***	CPle
§ ***cardinalis***	CHal EBak WEfe
§ x ***cardosa***	MBri
'Cherry Belle'	NMos
'Diego Rose'	MBri
'Duchess of York'	CSut
'Duke of York'	CSut
'Etoile de Feu'	LAma MBri NMos
'Foxy Blue'	CHal
'Hollywood'	CKel LAma NMos SDeJ
'Island Sunset'	NMos
'Kaiser Friedrich'	LAma MBri NMos NRog
'Kaiser Wilhelm'	CKel LAma MBri NMos NRog
♦***leucotricha***	See S. ***canescens***
'Medusa'	NMos
'Mont Blanc'	CKel CSut LAma MBri NMos SDeJ
'Pegasus'	NMos
'Princess Elizabeth'	SDeJ
'Red Tiger'	CSut
'Reine Wilhelmine'	SDeJ
'Royal Crimson'	CSut
Royal Pink Group	CSut
'Royal Tiger'	CSut
Tigrina Group	CKel NMos SDeJ
'Violacea'	MBri NMos NRog
'Waterloo'	NMos NRog

SINOBAMBUSA (Gramineae(Bambuseae))

tootsik	SBam SDry WJun
¶ – f. ***albostriata***	SDry
– 'Variegata'	See S. ***t. albostriata***

SINOFRANCHETIA (Lardizabalaceae)

chinensis	WWat

SINOJACKIA (Styracaceae)

¶ ***rehderiana***	CMCN

SINOWILSONIA (Hamamelidaceae)

See Plant Deletions

SISYMBRIUM (Cruciferae)

§ ***luteum***	CLew

SISYRINCHIUM † (Iridaceae)

*****album***	CGle
x ***anceps***	See S. ***angustifolium*** Miller
§ ***angustifolium*** Miller	Widely available

§ ***arenarium***	CRow
atlanticum	CRDP EBur MDHE
bellum hort.	See S. ***idahoense***
bermudianum Linnaeus	See S. ***angustifolium***
♦– 'Album'	See S. ***graminoïdes*** 'A.'
'Biscutella'	CGle CHal CLew CMea CRDP CRiv CTom EBur ECtt ELan ESis GAbr LHop MFir MTho NDea NNrd SAxl SChu SIng SSmi SSvw SUsu WCla WHal WHil WOMN
* 'Blue Ice'	CLew CRDP CRiv CSpe CTom EBur MDHE NCat WHal WHoo WPat WPer
boreale	See S. ***californicum***
brachypus	See S. ***californicum*** Brachypus Group
'Californian Skies'	CBro CGle CLew CMil EBur LBee MDHE SAsh SAxl SMrm SSmi SSvw SUsu SWas WKif
§ ***californicum***	CBen CBro CFis CHan CRow CShe CWGN EBur EFol EHon EPot ESis LMay MBar MCas MFir MSta MWat NGre NHol NKay NMen NNrd SIng SSmi WCla WRus WWin
§ – Brachypus Group	CBro CCla CHal CMea EBar ECtt GAbr GCHN LHil MPit NDea NGre NMen NRed NSti SHer SWat WEas WOMN WOak WTyr
§ ***chilense***	SIng
coeleste	EBur ESis MDHE
coeruleum	See GELASINE ***coerulea***
cuspidatum	See S. ***arenarium***
demissum	CNic EBur
depauperatum	CRDP EBur ESis ESma NRed NWCA WAbe WHer WPer
♦***douglasii***	See OLSYNIUM ***d.***
'E K Balls'	CHal CLew EBur ELan EPla EPot LBee LTil MBro MTho NHar NKay NRya SHer SSmi SSou SSvw SUsu WAbe WCla WPat WSun WThu WWin
♦***filifolium***	See OLYSNIUM ***f.***
§ ***graminoïdes***	NBro WPer
§ – 'Album'	EBur NBro WCla WPer
grandiflorum	See OLSYNIUM ***douglasii***
'Hemswell Sky'	EBur MDHE NHar
§ ***idahoense***	CBro CHal CHan CNic CRDP EBar EBre EBur ECha ELan EMNN ESis ESma GArf GCHN LBee LBre MBal MCas MHig NHar NMen NRya NWCA SSou WAbe WCla WHil WOMN WPer
§ – 'Album'	Widely available
– blue	ELan SWas
♦***iridifolium***	See S. ***micranthum***
¶ ***junceum***	NHol
littorale	EBur WCla
macounii	See S. ***idahoense***
macrocarpon	CBro CLew CMea EBur EMNN EPot ESis ESma LBee MPlt NGre NHar NHol NMen NNrd NWCA SAxl SIng SMrm SSvw SWas WAbe WCla WEas WHal WOMN WPat WPer WTyr
¶ 'Marie'	ECha
'May Snow'	See S. ***idahoense*** 'Album'
§ ***micranthum***	CBro EBur LHil NCat WHoo
montanum	CCla EBur NHol WThi
'Mrs Spivey'	CNic CRiv CRow EBar EBur ECtt EMNN EPla ESis MBal MBar NGre NHol NNrd NOak WAbe WCla WHil WOMN
¶ ***narcissiflorum***	GArf
♦ 'North Star'	See S. 'Pole Star'
¶ ***nudicaule***	NHol
– x ***montanum***	CSam EBur EMNN ESis GCal ITim MCas MDHE NHar NHol NNrd WAbe WPer
patagonicum	EBur ESis NCat NNrd NRed NWCA SIng WCla WHil
§ 'Pole Star'	CNic CSpe CTom EBur ESis GTou IBlr MFir NHar NHol NMen NRed SHer SIng WHal WPer
'Quaint and Queer'	CAvo CMil CRow EBur ECha EFol EOrc EPla LGan MTho NBro SSmi WAbe WPer WRus WTyr WWin
'Raspberry'	NHol
scabrum	See S. ***chilense***
§ ***striatum***	CAvo CBro CChu CCla CFis CGle CHan CKel CPar CRDP CRow CSco EBur ECha ELan ERav GCHN NBro NDea NHol NNor NSti NWCA SIng SPer WCla WDav WEas WWin
§ – 'Aunt May' (v)	Widely available
– ***variegatum***	See S. ***s.*** 'Aunt May'
* 'Tierra del Fuego'	CRow
¶ 'Wisley Blue'	WCum
* ***yuccifolium***	NHol

SIUM (Umbelliferae)

sisarum	GPoy LHol NSal SIde WGwy WHer WOak

SKIMMIA † (Rutaceae)

anquetilia	EPla ISea LRHS WBod
x ***confusa***	EGol SRms
– 'Kew Green' (m)	CB&S EBre EPla IOrc LBre LRHS MBal MBri NHol SBla SHil SPer WWat
§ ***japonica***	CBow CBra CHEx CLan CMHG CPle CSco CShe CTrw EBre ENot ERav IDai IJoh LBre MBri MGos NKay SDix SLon SReu SSta STre WBod WStI
– 'Alba '	See S. ***j.*** 'Fructu Albo'
– 'Bowles' Dwarf Female' (f)	CChu CHig EPla MBar MBri MGos MPar MPla MRav SHer SPer WWat
– 'Bowles' Dwarf Male' (m)	CChu CCla MAsh MBar MBri MPla SPer SSpi WWat
*– 'Bronze Beauty'	SReu
– 'Bronze Knight' (m)	CDoC ECar EPla IHos NHol
– 'Cecilia Brown' (f)	LRHS WWat
¶ – 'Emerald King'	MBri SPla
N– 'Foremanii'	See S. ***j.*** 'Veitchii'
– 'Fragrans' (m)	CBra CDoC CHig CSam CSco CTrw EPla IOrc MBal MBar MBri MGos MPar MUlv NHol SHBN SHer SPer SPla SReu WBod WThu WWat
¶ – 'Fragrantissima' (m)	MBri

§ – 'Fructu Albo' (f) CB&S CDoC CPle CTrw EGol EPla GWht IBar MBar MBri MUlv SLon SPer SPla SSpi SSta WWat
– 'Highgrove Redbud' (f) MBar MBri MGos
¶ – 'Keessen' MBri
– 'Kew White' (f) CSam EBre LBre LRHS MBal NHol
– 'Nymans' (f) CBot CDoC EBre EGol IOrc ISea LBre MBal MBar MBri MRav MUlv NHol SArc SBla SHBN SHil SPer SPla SReu SSpi SSta WStI WWat
– 'Oblata' SCob
– 'Obovata' (f) EPla
– 'Pigmy' (f) CB&S
– 'Red Princess' (f) LRHS MBri
* – 'Red Riding Hood' SHil SLon
– 'Redruth' (f) CB&S CDoC CLan IOrc MBal MBar MGos MUlv SMad
§ – ssp. ***reevesiana*** Widely available
– – 'Robert Fortune' MBar WWat
– 'Rubella' (m) Widely available
– 'Ruby Dome' (m) MBar MBri NHol WWat
– 'Ruby King' CSam EPla MBal MBar MBri MGos NHol WStI
– 'Scarlet Dwarf' (f) MBri
– 'Tansley Gem' (f) LRHS MBar
– 'Thelma King' LRHS MBar MBri
§ – 'Veitchii' (f) EBre EPla ERav LBre MAsh MBar MGos NHol SHBN SPer WDin WStI
– ***viridis*** NBar
– 'Winifred Crook' (f) LRHS MBri WWat
– 'Winnie's Dwarf' CHig MGos
– 'Wisley Female' (f) ECar EGol EPla NWyt
§ ***japonica*** Rogersii Group ENot GRei IDai IHos IOrc MBal MBar MGos MPla MWat SBla SChu SLon SPla WBod WWat
– – 'Dunwood' MBar
– – 'George Gardner' MBar
– – 'Helen Goodall' (f) MBar
§ – – 'Nana Femina' (f) CSam IHos SBla
§ – – 'Nana Mascula' (m) MGos MUlv NKay SBla SSpi
– – 'Rockyfield Green' MBar
– – 'Snow Dwarf' (m) MBar MBri
laureola CDoC CMHG ENot LAbb MAsh MBal MGos NGar NHol SArc SLon SReu WSHC
– T 132 WWat
– 'Fragrant Cloud' MBar
* ***mica*** ISea
reevesiana See S. ***japonica r.***
rogersii See S. ***japonica*** Rogersii Group

SMELOWSKIA (Cruciferae)

¶ ***calycina*** WPer

SMILACINA (Liliaceae)

racemosa Widely available
stellata CAvo CBre CBro CRDP CRow EBul EPar EPot NHol NKay WChr

SMILAX (Smilacaceae)

asparagoïdes nanus See ASPARAGUS ***a.*** 'Myrtifolius'
¶ ***aspera*** CGre
china SSpi
discotis CB&S
sieboldii MRav

SMITHIANTHA (Gesneriaceae)

'Calder Girl' NMos
'Carmel' NMos
'Carmello' NMos
'Castle Croft' NMos
'Cinna Barino' NMos
'Corney Fell' NMos
'Dent View' NMos
'Ehenside Lady' NMos
'Harecroft' NMos
'Little One' NMos
'Matins' NMos
'Meadowcroft' NMos
'Multiflora' NMos
'New Yellow Hybrid' NMos
'Orange King' NMos
'Orangeade' NMos
'Pink Lady' NMos
'Sandybank' NMos
'Santa Clara' NMos
'Starling Castle' NMos
'Summer Sunshine' NMos
'Vespers' NMos
'Zebrina Hybrid' NMos

X SMITHICODONIA (Gesneriaceae)

§ 'Cerulean Mink' NMos

SMYRNIUM (Umbelliferae)

olusatrum CArn CKin CSev LHol MChe MHew NSal SIde SWat WCot WHer WOak WWye
perfoliatum CRDP EFou ELan MFir MPar WOMN

SOLANDRA (Solanaceae)

¶ ***grandiflora*** CTro
hartwegii See S. ***maxima***
§ ***maxima*** ERea MNew

SOLANUM (Solanaceae)

aviculare ERea
crispum CCla CHan CSco ELan ISea NEgg WDin WPer WStI WWat
– 'Autumnale' See S. ***c.*** 'Glasnevin'
§ – 'Glasnevin' Widely available
– 'Variegatum' NTow
dulcamara CArn CMer GPoy NSal
– var. ***album*** EMon
– 'Variegatum' CB&S CHan CMHG CMac CRow EBar EFol ELan EMon EPla IBlr IOrc ISea MBal MBri MRav NNor NSti SBra SFis SLon SPer WEas
jasminoïdes CB&S CDoC IBar SLon SPer WDin WSHC
– 'Album' Widely available
laciniatum CAbb CGle CPle CSpe CTro ERea GCal IBlr LHil LHop LRHS NHex SArc SMad
¶ ***mauritianum*** SLMG
F ***muricatum*** 'Lime' ESim

F – 'Otavalo' ESim
F – 'Quito' ESim
¶ ***nigrum*** WHer
pseudocapsicum MBri
– 'Ballon' MBri
– 'Mandarin' MBri
– 'Thurino' MBri
rantonnetii See LYCIANTHES ***r.***
'Royal Robe' CB&S CPle
sisymbriifolium GCal WKif
wendlandii CB&S CTro ERea SLMG

SOLDANELLA (Primulaceae)

alpina CNic CPar CShe ELan EPot GArf GDra MBal MBro MTho NHar NHol NMen NRya NVic SBla SGil SHer SIng WHal
austriaca NHar NHol NTow
carpatica CNic CRiv EPot GTou MBal NCat NHol NRed NRya NTow SGil WAbe
– 'Alba' CRiv EPot NNrd SSou SWas
cyanaster GArf MBal NBir NHol NNrd NRya
dimoniei ITim SSou
hungarica CNic GArf MBal MHig MTho
minima GArf MHig NNrd NRed WAbe
– 'Alba' ITim
montana CRDP CRiv GArf GDra GTou MTho NHol NKay NMen NRed SHer WAbe
pindicola CElw ECar ELan EPot ESma MBal MBro MCas NHar NHol NMen NRed NRya SGil SHer SSou WAbe
pusilla CPar GDra ITim NHol NNrd
villosa CBos CPar MBal MCas MHig MTho NHar NNrd NRed NTow SAxl WOMN

SOLEIROLIA (Urticaceae)

soleirolii CHEx CHal CMer EPot LMay MBri SIng WEas WOak
– 'Argentea' See S. ***s.*** 'Variegata'
§ – 'Aurea' CB&S CHEx CHal WOak
– 'Golden Queen' See S. ***s.*** 'Aurea'
– 'Silver Queen' See S. ***s.*** 'Variegata'
§ – 'Variegata' CB&S CHal WOak

SOLENOMELUS (Iridaceae)

chilensis See S. ***pedunculatus***
¶ ***lechlek*** NHol
¶ ***pedunculatus*** WPer WThi
sisyrinchium NHol WThi

SOLENOPSIS (Campanulaceae)

axillaris CRDP CSpe LHil LHop SSad SUsu WWin
fluviatilis ECou
¶ ***laurentia*** CTro

SOLENOSTEMON (Labiatae)

aromaticus CHal SIde
'Autumn' CBrk CHal
'Beauty' CBrk CHal
¶ 'Beauty of Lyons' CBrk
'Beckwith's Gem' CHal
¶ 'Bizarre Croton' CBrk
¶ 'Black Prince' CBrk
¶ 'Blackheart' CBrk
'Brightness' (v) CHal
¶ 'Bronze Gloriosa' CBrk
¶ 'Buttermilk' CBrk
'Carnival' (v) CBrk CHal
¶ 'Chamaeleon' CBrk
¶ 'Charles Rudd' CBrk
¶ 'Cream Pennant' CBrk
'Crimson Ruffles' (v) CBrk CHal
¶ 'Dazzler' CBrk
¶ 'Firebrand' CBrk
'Freckles' (v) CBrk CHal
¶ 'Funfair' CBrk
¶ 'Gloriosa' CBrk
'Glory of Luxembourg' CBrk
¶ 'Goldie' CBrk
¶ 'Holly' CBrk
¶ 'Inky Fingers' CBrk
¶ 'Jean' CBrk
¶ 'Joseph's Coat' CBrk
¶ 'Juliet Quartermain' CBrk
¶ 'Kentish Fire' CBrk
'Kiwi Fern' CBrk CHal
¶ 'Klondike' CBrk
¶ 'Laing's Croton' CBrk
¶ 'Lemon Dash' CBrk
'Lemondrop' CHal
¶ 'Luminous' CBrk
¶ 'Midnight' CBrk
¶ 'Mission Gem' CBrk
¶ 'Mrs Pilkington' CBrk
¶ 'Nettle' CBrk
'Paisley Shawl' (v) CHal
pentheri CHal
'Picturatum' (v) CBrk CHal
'Pineapple Beauty' (v) CBrk CHal
¶ 'Pineapplette' CBrk
¶ 'Primrose Cloud' CBrk
¶ 'Primrose Spire' CBrk
¶ 'Red Croton' CBrk
¶ 'Red Heart' CBrk
¶ 'Red Mars' CBrk
¶ 'Red Paisley Shawl' CBrk
¶ 'Red Velvet' CBrk
¶ 'Rosie' CBrk
¶ 'Royal Scot' CBrk
¶ 'Salmon Plumes' CBrk
¶ 'Scarlet Ribbons' CBrk
scutellarioïdes MBri
¶ 'Spire' CBrk
♦ ***thyrsoideus*** See PLECTRANTHUS ***t.***
¶ 'Vesuvius' CBrk
'Walter Turner' (v) CBrk CHal
¶ 'White Gem' CBrk
¶ 'White Pheasant' CBrk
'Winter Sun' CHal
¶ 'Yellow Croton' CBrk

SOLIDAGO (Compositae)

altissima See S. ***canadensis scabra***
bicolor CGre
brachystachys See S. ***cutleri***

caesia	CChu ECha EGol LRHS NKay WCot
canadensis	ELan WByw
§ – var. *scabra*	WOak
'Cloth of Gold'	CB&S CKel CLew COtt EBre ECro IDai LBre MBri NBar SHer WCot WOld
'Crown of Rays' ('Strahlenkrone')	CPar CTom EBre ECtt EFou EPla LBre MRav NBar NHol SCro WWin
§ *cutleri*	CHal CLew CNic CPar CSun ELan EMon IDai LGan MBar MPit MTho MWat NGre NKay NMen NMir NNrd NRoo NVic SIng WHoo WPat WPer WWin
§ *flexicaulis* 'Variegata'	CBos CRDP EJud ELan EMar EMon ERav GCal LHop NSti SFar WCot
glomerata	EMon
'Golden Baby' ('Goldkind')	ECtt GAbr LHil LWad MBri MFir NCat NFai NOak NOrc SFis SGil SPla SSvw WByw
'Golden Dwarf' ('Goldzwerg')	CDoC CSco EBre EFou LBre
'Golden Falls'	WOld
'Golden Rays'	See S. 'Goldstrahl'
'Golden Shower'	CKel MWat
'Golden Thumb'	See S. 'Queenie'
'Golden Wings'	LHil MWat
'Goldenmosa'	CDec CSco CShe EHal EMon MBel MWat NKay SChu SGil SPer
¶ 'Goldilocks'	NMir
§ 'Goldstrahl'	LHil SGil
graminifolia	EMon
hybrida	See X SOLIDASTER ***luteus***
latifolia	See S. ***flexicaulis***
'Laurin'	NFai NHol SFis WHoo
'Leda'	SFis
'Ledsham'	CMGP MMil SGil
'Lemore'	See X SOLIDASTER ***luteus*** 'Lemore'
'Lesden'	CSco
'Loddon'	CSco
microcephala	EMon
'Mimosa'	NHol NKay NVic
multiradiata var. *scopulorum*	NHol
odora	NSal
§ 'Queenie'	CKel CLew CMGP ECha ECro ELan ESis GCHN LHil MBri MTho MWat NKay NNor NVic SPer WHal WPer
¶ *randii*	EMon
rigida JLS 88002WI	EMon
sempervirens	EMon
'Spätgold'	EFou
¶ *spathulata nana*	WPer
– – JCA 9627	CLew MBro
'Tom Thumb'	CShe MRav SRms WEas
virgaurea	CArn CKin CRiv GPoy LHol SIde WNdy
– ssp. *alpestris* var. *minutissima*	CLew ITim MTho
– *cambrica*	WCla
– 'Praecox'	WOld
§ – 'Variegata'	EFol EHoe EPla WDav
vulgaris 'Variegata'	See S. ***virgaurea*** 'V.'

X SOLIDASTER (Compositae)

hybridus	See X S. ***luteus***
§ *luteus*	CAll CB&S CBre CHal EFou MBri SPla WEas WHal WOld
§ – 'Lemore'	CBre CChu CSco CShe EBre ECha EFou ELan EMon LBre MUlv MWat NBar NSti SAxl SPer
'Super'	EFou EMon LRHS

SOLLYA (Pittosporaceae)

fusiformis	See S. ***heterophylla***
§ *heterophylla*	CB&S CBow CChu CHEx CHan CMac CMer CPle CSam CSun CTro EBre ECou ERea GCal IJoh IOrc ISea LAbb LBre LGre MRav SBra SHil SIgm SPer SSta WSHC
– mauve form	ECou
parviflora	ECou

SONCHUS (Compositae)

palustris	CRDP EMon
platylepsis	CHEx

SOPHORA (Leguminosae)

§ *davidii*	CChu CPle SLMG
japonica	CAbP CB&S CBra CGre CLnd EHar ELan ENot GAri ISea NBee SHBN SPer WDin WFro WNor WWat
– 'Pendula'	COtt ELan LNet LPan SEng SHil WFro
'Little Baby'	CDoC EHal ERea IJoh NBar WStI
macrocarpa	CHan MUlv SMad WBod
microphylla	CGre CHan CPle ECou GAri IBar MBrk SArc SLMG SSpi WBod WCru
– 'Dragon's Gold'	ECar ECou
– 'Earlygold'	CB&S ERea
– *fulvida*	ECou
– 'Goldilocks'	CB&S IBar
– *longicarinata*	ECou
¶ *mollis*	ESma
N *prostrata*	CBot CChu ECou GAri ITim MUlv
– Pukaki form	ECar ECou
tetraptera	CAbP CB&S CBot CBow CBra CCla CDoC CGre CHEx CHan CMac CPle CWit ECar ECou IOrc ISea LHop SHer SIgm SSpi WBod
– 'Gnome'	CB&S IMal
viciifolia	See S. ***davidii***

SORBARIA † (Rosaceae)

♦ *aitchisonii*	See S. ***tomentosa angustifolia***
arborea	See S. ***kirilowii***
§ *kirilowii*	CCor CSco CShe IOrc MRav NNor SPer
lindleyana	See S. ***tomentosa***
sorbifolia	CAbP CChu CCla CDoC CSco EPla GBel MGos SLPl SPer SSta STre WDin
¶ – *stellipila*	SLPl
§ *tomentosa*	CAbP CBow CPle EBre EHal LBre MRav NBee SHBN SLon SSpi WCru WEas
¶ – var. *angustifolia*	CCla CSco EFol ELan ENot MBal MBar MBri SHil SPer WBod WWat

SORBUS † (Rosaceae)

Plant	Suppliers
§ ***alnifolia***	CLnd CMCN EHal WCoo WNor WWat
americana	CLnd CMCN GBel NWea
– 'Belmonte'	MBri
– ***erecta***	See S. ***decora***
anglica	CSam
'Apricot Lady'	CLnd SPer
aria	CBow CBra CKin CLnd CPer EBre EHar GRei LBre LBuc MBar NBee NRoo NWea SPer WDin WMou
– 'Chrysophylla'	CBar CWSG IJoh MBri SHil SMad SPer WAbe
– 'Decaisneana'	See S. ***a.*** 'Majestica'
– 'Lutescens'	CB&S CBra CLnd CSam CTho EBre EHar ELan ENot GBel GRei IDai IJoh LBre LBuc MBar MBri MGos NBar NWea SHBN SPer SReu WAbe WDin WWat
– 'Magnifica'	CDoC CTho ENot GBel WDin
§ – 'Majestica'	CDoC CLnd CTho ELan GBel MGos SPer
– 'Mitchellii'	See S. ***thibetica*** 'John Mitchell'
¶ x ***arnoldiana*** 'Chamois Glow'	CAbP
aucuparia	CB&S CBow CBra CKin CLnd CPer EHar ELan ENot GBel GRei IDai IJoh ISea LBuc MBal MBar MBri MGos NBar NRoo NWea SHBN SReu STre WAbe WDin WMou
– 'Aspleniifolia'	CB&S CBra CLnd CTho EBre ENot GBel GRei LBre MBar MGos MRav NWea SPer WAbe WDin
§ – 'Beissneri'	CBow CLnd CTho EHar GBel MBri MGos SHil WMou WWat
– 'Cardinal Royal'	MBri SHil
– 'Dirkenii'	CBar CLnd COtt IJoh WMou
– 'Edulis'	CTho ESim IOrc WDin
§ – 'Fastigiata'	CAbP CDoC CSam CTho EBre GBel IOrc LBre MBri MGos SHBN WDin WStI
§ – 'Fructu Luteo'	ENot EPla GBel MGos WDin
– gold form	MPar
¶ – 'Harvest Moon'	CAbP
– ***pluripinnata***	See S. ***scalaris***
– 'Rossica Major'	CDoC CTho
¶ – 'Rowancroft Coral Pink'	CTho
– 'Sheerwater Seedling'	CB&S CBra CDoC CLnd CTho EBre ELan ENot GBel IOrc LBre MBri MGos NBee SPer WAbe WDin
– 'Winterdown'	CNat
– 'Xanthocarpa'	See S. ***a.*** 'Fructu Luteo'
bristoliensis	CNat
'Carpet of Gold'	CLnd CTho IOrc
cashmiriana	CB&S CLnd COtt CSam CTho EBar EHar ELan EPar IBar IJoh ISea LNet MBal MBar MBri MPar NWea SHil SPer SReu SSpi SSta WAbe WNor WWat
chamaemespilus	GDra
'Chinese Lace'	CLnd CTho EBre EHar IJoh LBre MBri MGos MUlv SHBN SMad SSpi

Plant	Suppliers
§ ***commixta***	CB&S CBra CLnd CMCN CSam CTho ENot GBel GRei IJoh IOrc MBar MGos MUlv SPer WAbe WDin
– 'Embley'	CB&S CDoC CLnd CSam CTho ENot GBel IHos MBar MBri MGos NBee
– var. ***rufoferruginea***	GBel WAbe
♦ ***conradinae*** hort.	See S. ***pohuashanensis*** Hedlund
– Koehne	See S. ***esserteauana***
'Coral Beauty'	CLnd
croceocarpa	CNat
cuspidata	See S. ***vestita***
decora	CLnd CTho NBee SPer
*– 'Grootendorst'	MBri
¶ ***devoniensis***	CTho
discolor Hedlund	CBra CLnd CMCN CSam EBar ECtt ELan EPla GRei IDai MBar MGos MUlv NWea SPer SReu
– hort.	See S. ***commixta***
domestica	EHar NWea WMou WThu
– 'Maliformis'	See S. ***d. pomifera***
§ – var. ***pomifera***	EHar
§ – var. ***pyrifera***	EHar
– 'Pyriformis'	See S. ***d. pyrifera***
'Eastern Promise'	LRHS MBri SHil
esserteauana	CDoC CSam CTho ENot GBel MPar WAbe
– 'Flava'	MBri WWat
folgneri 'Lemon Drop'	LRHS SHil
forrestii	CChu CCor CSam CTho MBri SSpi WWat
fruticosa	CChu SSpi
'Ghose'	IOrc MBri SPer
glabrescens	See S. ***hupehensis***
'Golden Wonder'	CB&S CDoC CTho GBel MGos NWea WAbe
¶ ***gracilis***	CTho
hedlundii	IBlr
¶ ***hemsleyi***	SSpi
x ***hostii***	ENot SPer
§ ***hupehensis***	CBra CChu CLnd CMCN CSam CTho EFol EHar ELan GBel GRei IDai IJoh ISea MBal MBar MPar NWea SHBN SPer SSta WAbe WCoo WDin WNor WWat WWin
§ – var. ***obtusa***	CDoC CTho GAri MBlu MUlv NTow SSpi SSta WWat
– 'Pink Pagoda'	CDoC CLnd EHar MBri MGos MSta SPer
– 'Rosea'	See S. ***h. obtusa***
x ***hybrida*** hort.	See S. x ***thuringiaca***
– Linnaeus	NWea
– 'Gibbsii'	CDoC ELan MBri SHil
insignis	EBar
intermedia	CB&S CKin CLnd CPer CSam EHar ENot GRei ISea MBal MGos NBee NWea SPer WDin WStI
– 'Brouwers'	ELan GBel SEng
'Joseph Rock'	CB&S CBra CLnd CSam CTho EBre ELan GBel GDra GRei IDai IJoh ISea LBre MBal MBar MBri MGos NBar NWea SHBN SPer SReu SSta WAbe WDin WWat
§ x ***kewensis***	CBow CLnd CSam SPer SSpi
'Kirsten Pink'	CDoC CLnd MBlu MGos
koehneana	CDoC COtt EBar EHar EPla MBlu MBri MMea NHol NTow NWea SFai SReu SSpi WPat

lanata hort. — See S. ***vestita***
lancastriensis — CNat
latifolia — CLnd EHal ENot NWea WDin WThu
'Leonard Springer' — ENot SPer
'Lowndes' — CSam CTho
matsumurana — ENot IHos
megalocarpa — CSam SSpi
meliosmifolia — CSam
microphylla BM&W 98 — NHar
minima — CNat
moravica 'Laciniata' — See S. ***aucuparia*** 'Beissneri'
'November Pink' — COtt IOrc
'Pearly King' — CB&S CSam CTho
pohuashanensis hort. — See S. x ***kewensis***
– (Hance) Hedlund — CCla CSam CTho EHar IBar MBlu WNor
poteriifolia — GArf
§ *prattii* — EHar GAri NTow
– var. *tatsienensis* — See S. ***p.***
¶ *pygmaea* hort. — MFir
'Red Tip' — CDoC CLnd CTho NBar
reducta — Widely available
– CLD 297 — NHol
reflexipetala — See S. ***commixta***
rehderiana — MBal MBri WNor
– 'Pink Pearl' — WAbe
'Salmon Queen' — CLnd ECtt
sargentiana — CBot CLnd CSam CTho EBre EHar ENot IHos LBre MBri NHol NWea SHil SPer SSpi WWat
§ *scalaris* — CCor CSam CTho ECtt IJoh IOrc MBri SHil SPer SReu SSpi WWat
'Schouten' — ENot GBel MBlu MBri
scopulina hort. — See S. ***aucuparia*** 'Fastigiata'
¶ *setchuenensis* — GAri
sp. Harry Smith 12799 — CChu MBri
'Sunshine' — CDoC MBri SHil
thibetica — CGre CMCN
§ – 'John Mitchell' — CB&S CLnd CSam CTho EBar EHar ENot MBri MGos MUlv SHil SPer SPla SSpi
§ x *thuringiaca* 'Fastigiata' — CB&S CBra CDoC CLnd ENot MGos SPer WDin
torminalis — CKin CLnd CTho EHar MBri NWea SHil SPer SSta WCoo WDin WMou WThu
umbellata var. *cretica* — See S. ***graeca***
ursina — CAbP CChu CGre CLnd IOrc SMad
§ *vestita* — CLnd CMCN CTho WWat
vexans — CNat
vilmorinii — Widely available
¶ *wardii* — SHil
'White Wax' — CBow ECtt EPla MGos SHil
'Wilfrid Fox' — LTil SHBN
willmottiana — CNat
'Winter Cheer' — SHil WWat
zahlbruckneri hort. — See S. ***alnifolia***

SORGHASTRUM (Gramineae)

avenaceum — ECha EHoe EPla ETPC
nutans — See S. ***avenaceum***

SORGHUM (Gramineae)

halepense — ETPC

SPARAXIS (Iridaceae)

bulbifera — NRog
elegans — NRog
– 'Coccinea' — LBow
fragrans acutiloba — NRog
hybrids — LAma LBlo
tricolor — EPar MBri NRog
§ *variegata* — NRog

SPARGANIUM (Typhaceae)

§ *erectum* — CRow CWGN EHon EMFW LMay MSta NDea NMir SWat WHer WWye
ramosum — See S. ***erectum***

SPARMANNIA (Tiliaceae)

africana — CAbb CB&S CGre CHEx CPle CSun CTre CTro ERea ISea LBlm MBri SArc WOak

SPARTINA (Gramineae)

pectinata
'Aureomarginata' — CPar EBre ECha EFol EGol EHoe ELan EMon EPla ETPC GCHN GCal LBre MSta MSte NHol SCob SHig SPer SSpi WRus

SPARTIUM (Leguminosae)

junceum — CB&S CBow CBra CPle CSco CShe EHar ELan ENot EPla IBar IDai MBal MBri MGos MWat NKay SArc SDix SHBN SPer SPla SReu SSta WBod WCru WStI

SPARTOCYTISUS See CYTISUS

SPATHICARPA (Araceae)

See Plant Deletions

SPATHIPHYLLUM (Araceae)

'Adagio' — MBri
'Viscount' — MBri
wallisii — MBri

SPEIRANTHA (Liliaceae/Convallariaceae)

§ *convallarioïdes* — CRDP EBul EMon SSpi WCot WCru
gardenii — See S. ***convallarioïdes***

SPERGULARIA (Caryophyllaceae)

¶ *marina* — MHig
rupicola — CKin CNic CRiv

SPHACELE See LEPECHINIA

SPHAERALCEA (Malvaceae)

ambigua — ELan LGre
¶ Dixfield hybrids — CSun
fendleri — CB&S CBot CBrk CHan CMHG CMer CNic EBar EOrc ESma LGre SMrm SUsu WAbe WMar WOMN WPer
– *venusta* — ECro

malviflora	WPer
miniata	CMHG ELan LGre SMrm WMar
munroana	CBot CHan CMHG CSev CSun EOrc LAbb LGre LHil LHop MFir MPar MUlv NTow SAxl SCro SMad SMrm SUsu WByw WEas WMar WOMN WSHC WWin
– pale pink form	CSpe CSun ECtt LBlm LGre NOak SMrm SUsu WCot
parvifolia	LHop MFos
rivularis	NRar
umbellata	See PHYMOSIA ***u.***

SPHAGNUM (moss)

¶***fuscum***	LFle
¶***magellanicum***	LFle
¶***pulchrum***	LFle

SPHENOTOMA (Epacridaceae)

See Plant Deletions

SPIGELIA (Loganiaceae)

See Plant Deletions

SPILANTHES (Compositae)

acmella	NSal

SPIRAEA † (Rosaceae)

albiflora	See S. ***japonica*** 'Albiflora'
arborea	See SORBARIA ***kirilowii***
arcuata	MBri
§ 'Arguta'	Widely available
x ***arguta*** 'Bridal Wreath'	See S. 'Arguta'
– 'Compacta'	See S. x ***cinerea***
x ***arguta nana***	See S. x ***cinerea***
bella	CPle ISea MBar WHCG
betulifolia	CDoC MBri MRav SCob WHCG WPer WWeb
– var. ***aemiliana***	CCla CMHG CPle EBlo EBre ECtt EHal EPla ESis IJoh LBre MAsh MPla SLPl
x ***billiardii*** 'Macrothyrsa'	CB&S
– 'Triumphans'	ENot NNor WWin
x ***bumalda***	See S. ***japonica***
x ***bumalda wulfenii***	See S. ***japonica*** 'Walluf'
calcicola	NHol
callosa 'Alba'	See S. ***japonica*** 'Albiflora'
canescens	CNic EHal
cantoniensis	CPle
– 'Flore Pleno'	EMon
§ x ***cinerea***	SSta
– 'Grefsheim'	CB&S CDoC CShe ECtt MBel MBri SPer SPla SSta WStI
¶ – 'Variegata'	MPla
crispifolia	See S. ***japonica*** 'Bullata'
decumbens	WDin
'Dingle Gold'	EFol
douglasii	NRoo SRms
fritschiana	SHil SLPl WHCG
hendersonii	See PETROPHYTUM ***h.***
§ ***japonica***	NHol SBod
– 'Alba'	See S. ***j.*** 'Albiflora'
§ – 'Albiflora'	CB&S CPle ECar ESis MBal MPla NRoo SChu SPer
– 'Allgold'	CDoC NBee
– 'Alpina'	See S. ***j.*** 'Nana'
– 'Anthony Waterer' (v)	CB&S CBra CPle CSco CShe CTre EBre ECar ELan ENot GRei IJoh LBre MBal MBar MBri MGos MRav MWat NKay NNor NRoo NWea SHBN SLon SPer WBod WDin WSHC WWin
– 'Atrosanguinea'	WHCG
– 'Blenheim'	SGil
§ – 'Bullata'	CMHG ECar ELan MBal MBar MBri MHig MPla NKay NRoo SHil SIng SLon SPla WAbe WBod WPat WSHC WThu
¶ – 'Candle Light'	MAsh SHil
– 'Coccinea'	ECar IDai
§ – 'Crispa'	CDoC CMHG EPla MBar MBri
– 'Dart's Red'	CDoC IOrc MBri NBar SGil SHer SLPl SSta
¶ – 'Fire Light'	ELan MAsh SHil
– var. ***fortunei*** 'Ruberrima'	NKay
– 'Froebelii'	ISea LBuc
– 'Glenroy Gold'	MBal WAbe
– 'Gold Mound'	CMHG CShe EHar ELan EPla ESis IJoh MBal MBar MBel MBri MGos MRav MWat NNor NRoo SChu SHBN SHer SIng SPer SPla WHCG
– 'Gold Rush '	CMHG EBar MPla WRus
– 'Golden Dome'	ECar
– 'Golden Princess'	CCla CSco EBlo EBre ELan GRei IDai IJoh IOrc LBre MBal MBar MPla MUlv NRoo SPer SReu SSta
– 'Goldflame'	Widely available
– 'Little Maid'	CBot
– 'Little Princess'	CB&S CBra CCla CMer CPle CSco CShe ELan EMNN ENot IJoh ISea LAbb MBal MBar MBel MBri MWat NHol NRoo NWCA SMad SPer SPla SSta WDin WHCG WThu WWat
– 'Magnifica'	WHCG
§ – 'Nana'	CMHG CSco ECar ELan ENot EPla ESis LHop MBal MBar MBri MHig MPla MTho NHar NHol NKay NNor SReu WDav WEas WHCG WPat WPer WThu WWeb
– 'Nyewoods'	See S. ***j.*** 'Nana'
– 'Pamela Harper'	SPla
– 'Shirobana'	Widely available
§ – 'Walluf'	CPle NNor SLon WHCG
'Margaritae'	NKay SLPl SPer
nipponica	CB&S ESma MBar MGos WHCG
– 'Halward's Silver'	MGos SLPl
– 'June Bride'	WHCG
– 'Rotundifolia'	ISea
§ – 'Snowmound'	Widely available
– var. ***tosaensis*** hort.	See S. ***n.*** 'Snowmound'
– – (Yatabe) Makino	LHop MWat SPer SReu WBod WHCG WWat
palmata elegans	See FILIPENDULA ***palmata*** 'Elegantissima'
'Pink Ice' (v)	CAbP CBow CDoC CPMA CWit EBlo EBre EFol EHoe ELan EPla ESma IJoh LBre LGan LHop MAsh MBal MBel MBri MGos MPla NHol SLon SPer SPla WHil
prunifolia (d)	CCla CPle CSco EBre EHar ELan ENot EPla LBre LHop MPla SPer SPla WBod WHCG WWin
salicifolia	SHBN
stevenii	GAri SPla

¶ 'Summersnow'	SLPl
thunbergii	CPle CSco EHar ELan ENot EPla IOrc ISea LHop MPla MRav NNor NWea SGil SLon SPer SReu WDin
¶ – 'Mount Fuji'	EBlo
¶ *trichocarpa*	CMCN
ulmaria	See FILIPENDULA ***ulmaria***
x *vanhouttei*	CB&S ELan ENot IDai IJoh IOrc LAbb MBal MBar MBel MRav MWat NKay NNor NRoo SHBN SLon SPer WDin WStI WWin
veitchii	MBal MRav
venusta 'Magnifica'	See FILIPENDULA ***rubra*** 'Venusta'
wilsonii	CHan
'Wynbrook Gold'	NHol WPat

SPIRANTHES (Orchidaceae)

¶ *spiralis*	SSou

SPIRODELA (Lemnaceae)

¶ *polyrhiza*	SAWi

SPODIOPOGON (Gramineae)

sibiricus	EPla ETPC SApp WCot

SPOROBOLUS (Gramineae)

¶ *fertilis*	ETPC

SPRAGUEA (Portulacaceae)

¶ *umbellata*	GTou WAbe
§ – *glandulifera*	NGre

SPREKELIA (Liliaceae/Amaryllidaceae)

formosissima	CAvo CMon GCra LAma LBow LHop NRog WChr

STACHYS (Labiatae)

§ *affinis*	GPoy
alpina	CKin NLan NSal
betonica	See S. ***officinalis***
§ *byzantina*	CCla CFis CGle CHad CRow CSco CShe EBre ELan EOrc EPla GCal IDai LBre MBri MFir NBro NNor NOrc NPer SApp SCro SIng WEas WPer WTyr WWin
§ – 'Big Ears'	EMon MNFA SApp SAxl
§ – 'Cotton Boll'	CBre CMGP CMil CPar CRow ECha EFou EMon EPla GAbr GCal MTho NSti NVic SApp SPer
♦– gold leaf form	See S. ***b.*** 'Primrose Heron'
– large-leaved form	See S. ***b.*** 'Big Ears'
– 'Margery Fish'	CPar
§ – 'Primrose Heron'	CRow EBre EPla GCra GGar LBre NSti SPer WHil
– 'Sheila McQueen'	See S. ***b.*** 'Cotton Boll'
– 'Silver Carpet'	CB&S CFis CGle CHad CKel CSco CShe CTom EBre ECha EFou EGol EHoe ELan EOrc GCra LBre LGro MBri MFir NBro SApp SHer SPer
§ – 'Striped Phantom' (v)	CElw CHan CRow EFol ELan EMon NRar WPbr
♦– 'Variegata'	See S. ***b.*** 'Striped Phantom'
candida	WOMN WThi
chrysantha	LGre
citrina	ECha EMon GCal SAxl SUsu WHal WHil
coccinea	CGle CHan CMil CSun EBar GCra LGre SAxl SUsu WEas
¶ – 'El Salto'	LGre
densiflora	See S. ***monieri***
§ *discolor*	EGol MBri MCas WCru WDav WHil WPer
germanica	CNat MFir
grandiflora	See S. ***macrantha***
iva	ESis NTow
lanata	See S. ***byzantina***
lavandulifolia	NHol
§ *macrantha*	CArn CCla CKel CLew CRDP CShe EBre ECha EPla EPot GAbr LBre MFir MPar NOak NOrc NSti SAxl WDav WEas WHal WHoo WOld WTyr WWin
– 'Nivea'	EGol ELan GCal NTow WPat
§ – 'Robusta'	CGle CHan ELan EMon EPla MBri NBro SApp SMrm SPer SUsu SWas WCot
– 'Rosea'	CKel CMGP CRDP CRiv CSco EFol EFou ELan SCro SPer WEas WHoo WOld WPer
– 'Rosea Compacta'	WOld
– 'Superba'	CGle CHan CRDP EBar EPla MBri SMrm WByw WCot
§ *monieri*	EBre LBre SIgm SMrm WDav WPer
nivea	See S. ***discolor***
¶ *niveum*	WDav
§ *officinalis*	CArn CKin CSFH CSev Effi GPoy LGan LHil MChe MHew MHig NLan NMir NSal SIde SIng WCla WGwy WHal WHer WNdy WWye
– 'Alba'	CBre CFis CGle CSFH MHig NHol SIng WNdy
– 'Rosea Superba'	CBos CGle CMil ECha EGol ELan EPla SMrm WCot
olympica	See S. ***byzantina***
palustris	CKin MSta WChe
spicata	See S. ***macrantha***
sylvatica	CArn CKin GPoy MHew NLan WCla WHer
tuberifera	See S. ***affinis***

STACHYTARPHETA (Verbenaceae)

See Plant Deletions

STACHYURUS (Stachyuraceae)

chinensis	CBow CMCN EBre LBre MBri MUlv SHil WBod
– 'Magpie' (v)	CCla CSco EBre ELan ESma LBre SHil SSpi
praecox	CB&S CBot CBow CCla CDoC CFis CPMA CSco EHar ELan ENot IOrc LTil MBar MBri SHBN SPer SReu SSpi SSta WCoo WDin WSHC WWat
* *rubriflorus*	ELan
¶ *salicifolius*	CMCN

STAEHELINA (Compositae)

uniflosculosa	LGre

STANLEYA (Cruciferae)
See Plant Deletions

STAPHYLEA (Staphyleaceae)
bumalda CMCN
colchica CB&S CCla CDoC CHan CMHG IOrc SHil WKif WSHC WWat WWye
holocarpa WWat
N– var. *rosea* EHar ENot IHos MUlv WNor WSHC
N– 'Rosea' SHil
pinnata EHal ELan EPla WNor
trifolia CMCN

STATICE See LIMONIUM

STAUNTONIA (Lardizabalaceae)
hexaphylla CBow CChu CCla CDoC CHEx CSam SBra SHil SLon SPer SSpi SSta WSHC

STEIRODISCUS (Compositae)
* *euryopoïdes* CKni NSty SHer

STELLARIA (Caryophyllaceae)
graminea CKin
holostea CKin MChe MWil NLan NMir WNdy
ruscifolia ITim MHig

STENANTHIUM (Liliaceae/Melanthiaceae)
¶ *occidentale* CRDP

STENOCHLAENA (Blechnaceae)
palustris MBri

STENOMESSON (Liliaceae/Amaryllidaceae)
§ *miniatum* EPot

STENOTAPHRUM (Gramineae)
secundatum
'Variegatum' CHal CMer CSun IBlr

STENOTUS (Compositae)
§ *acaulis* CNic

STEPHANANDRA (Rosaceae)
incisa CB&S CBow CGle CLan CPle CShe IOrc MPar SChu SPla WHCG
§ – 'Crispa' CBow CGle CMHG CPMA CPle CSco EFol EGol ELan ENot GRei LHop MBar MBri MRav MWat NKay NNor SHBN SLon SPer WDin WHCG WPat WWat
¶ – 'Dart's Horizon' SLPl
– 'Prostrata' See S. *i.* 'Crispa'
tanakae CBow CCla CDoC CGle CPMA CPle CSco EGol ELan IOrc LAbb MBar MPar MUlv MWat NNor SChu SHBN SHil SLPl SLon SPer SPla STre SUsu WBod WDin WHCG

STEPHANOTIS (Asclepiadaceae)
floribunda CB&S CBow EBak LAbb MBri SLMG

STERNBERGIA (Amaryllidaceae)
candida CBro CMon LAma
§ *clusiana* CMon ELan EPot LAma SIng WChr
colchiciflora WChr
fischeriana CBro CMon EPot LAma
'John Marr' WThu
lutea CBro CHan CMHG ECha ELan EPot LAma LBlo LBow MBri MPar NRog SDix SIng SPou WChr WThu
– Angustifolia Group CMea CMon EMon SPou
¶ – *lutea* MS 971 CMon
macrantha See S. *clusiana*
sicula CBro EPot SPou
¶ – MS 796 CMon
– Dodona form WChr
¶ – var. *graeca* CMon
¶ – 'John Marr' ex JRM 3186/75 WThu

STEWARTIA † (Theaceae)
koreana See S. *pteropetidata k.*
malacodendron ELan MBri SPer SSpi WWat
monadelpha CB&S ELan SPer WCoo WNor
ovata CCla CGre SSpi WWat
N– var. *grandiflora* LRHS SPer
pseudocamellia CB&S CBow CCla CDoC CGre COtt EHar IJoh IOrc ISea LHyd MBri SEng SHBN SHil SReu SSpi SSta WBod WNor WWat
§ *pteropetiolata* var. *koreana* CCla CDoC CMCN MBri SHil SPer SReu SSpi SSta WNor WWat
serrata CB&S CCla CGre ELan MBri SHil SReu SSpi SSta WCoo WWat
sinensis CCla EHar MBri SHil SSta WNor WWat

STICTOCARDIA (Convolvulaceae)
See Plant Deletions

STIPA (Gramineae)
arundinacea CElw CHan CRow CTom EBar ECha EFol EFou EHoe EMar EPla ETPC GAbr GCal IBar IBlr LGan MFir NSti
– 'Autumn Tints' ECou
– 'Gold Hue' ECou
barbata ETPC NCat NHol SMrm
* *brachytricha* ECha EHoe EPla ETPC SGil
§ *calamagrostis* CElw CHan CWGN ECha EHoe EMon EPla ETPC GAbr GCal NCat NRar NSti SApp
¶ *calensis* ETPC
capillata EFou ETPC NHol SAxl SGil

elegantissima	ETPC SGil
extremiorientalis	ETPC
gigantea	Widely available
¶ *keylovii*	ETPC
lasiagrostis	See S. *calamagrostis*
papposa	ETPC NRar
patens	EMon
pennata	CB&S EPla ETPC GArf NHol SAxl SUsu WHoo
¶ *pulcherrima*	SWas
¶ *spartea*	ETPC
§ *splendens*	CKel EFou EMon EPla ETPC NHol NKay SDix
tenacissima	EFou EHoe EPla SMrm
tenuifolia	MBri NHol
tenuissima	CElw EBre ECha EHoe EMon ESis ETPC GAri LBre NRar SGil WCot
tirsa	EMon EPla
zalesskyi	ETPC

STOKESIA (Compositae)

laevis	CChu CDoC ECha EHal MBro NBro NNor NRoo SAxl SCro WPer WRus
– 'Alba'	CChu CRDP EBre ECha EMon EOrc LBre LGan LGre MBri NRoo SMrm SUsu WDav
– 'Blue Star'	CB&S CGle CKel CRDP CSam CSco CShe EFou EGol ELan EPar LGre MBri MFir MTho MUlv NBar NHol NOak NRoo SChu SGil SHer SMrm SPer SUsu WWin
¶ – 'Träumerei'	EFou
– 'Wyoming'	EBre LBre NOak

STRANSVAESIA See PHOTINIA

STRATIOTES (Hydrocharitaceae)

aloïdes	CBen CHEx CRow CWGN EBre EHon EMFW EWav LBre LMay MSta SAWi SWat WChe WHol WOak

X STRAVINIA See PHOTINIA

STRAWBERRY See FRAGARIA x *ananassa*

STRAWBERRY, Alpine See FRAGARIA *vesca*

STRELITZIA (Strelitziaceae)

nicolaii	CTro LPal
reginae	CCla CHEx CHal CTro ERea IBlr LPal MNew

STREPTOCARPELLA See STEPTOCARPUS

STREPTOCARPUS (Gesneriaceae)

'Albatross'	EPla SLMG WEfe
'Amanda'	WEfe
'Anna'	EPla
¶ 'Anne'	WEfe
'Athena'	WEfe
'Beryl'	WEfe
'Blue Gem'	EPla WEfe
'Blue Nymph'	EPla
¶ *buchananii*	GUzu
candidus	EPla GUzu WEfe
'Carol'	EPla MBri WEfe
caulescens	CHal GUzu WEfe
– var. *pallescens*	WEfe
'Cobalt Nymph'	EPla MBri
¶ *compressus*	GUzu
'Concord Blue'	MBri WEfe
¶ *confusus*	GUzu
'Constant Nymph' seedling	MPit WEas
¶ *cooksonii*	GUzu
¶ *cooperi*	GUzu
cyanandrus	GUzu WEfe
cyaneus	GUzu WEfe
'Cynthia'	EPla MBri WEfe
'Diana'	EPla
¶ *dunnii*	GUzu
'Elsi'	EPla WEfe
¶ *eylesii*	GUzu
¶ – ssp. *silvicola*	GUzu
'Falling Stars'	EPla MBri WEfe
fanniniae	EPla GUzu WEfe
¶ *fasciatus*	GUzu
'Festival Wales'	WEfe
'Fiona'	EPla WEfe
¶ *galpinii*	GUzu
gardenii	GUzu WEfe
glandulosissimus	GUzu WEfe
'Gloria'	EPla WEfe
grandis	CTro GUzu MNew
¶ *haygarthii*	GUzu
'Heidi'	EPla MBri WEfe
'Helen'	EPla WEfe
holstii	CHal
hybrids	LAbb
'Joanna'	MBri WEfe
johannis	EPla GUzu
'Julie'	WEfe
'Kim'	EPla WEfe
¶ *kungwensis*	GUzu
¶ *latens*	GUzu
¶ 'Lesley'	EPla
'Lisa'	CSpe EPla MBri WEfe
'Lynne'	EPla WEfe
'Marie'	EPla
¶ *meyeri*	GUzu
'Mini Nymph'	WEfe
¶ *molweniensis*	GUzu
'Myba'	MBri
'Neptune'	EPla MBri
'New Buckenham'	EPla
'Nicola'	EPla MBri WEfe
'Olga'	EPla
¶ *parviflorus*	GUzu
'Paula'	EPla MBri WEfe
¶ *polyanthus*	GUzu
¶ *primulifolius*	GUzu
– ssp. *formosus*	EPla WEfe
rexii	EPla GUzu WEfe
'Rosebud'	MPit WEfe
'Ruby'	EPla MBri WEfe
¶ 'Sally'	WEfe

'Sandra'	EPla MBri WEfe
'Sarah'	WEfe
saxorum	CHal CTro GUzu LHil MBri MNew NTow WEfe
¶ – compact form	GUzu WEfe
'Snow White'	CSpe WEfe
solenanthus	EPla GUzu
'Stella'	EPla WEfe
'Susan'	WEfe
'Tina'	EPla MBri WEfe
¶ 'Tracey'	WEfe
'Wiesmoor Red'	EPla MBri WEfe
'Winifred'	WEfe

STREPTOPUS (Liliaceae/Convallariaceae)

roseus	LAma

STREPTOSOLEN (Solanaceae)

jamesonii	CDoC CHal CPle CSev EBak ERea IBlr LAbb LHil MNew NRog SLMG WBod
– yellow form	CBrk ERea

STROBILANTHES (Acanthaceae)

atropurpureus	CBot CGle CGre CHan CLew CPle CRDP ECha EFou EHal ELan EPla GCal LAbb NSti SBor SMrm WCru WOMN WOld WPer
attenuatus	CCla
dyerianus	CHal MBri
sp. from Nepal TSS	CGle CRDP SWas WCru
violaceus	ERea LGan LHop WPer

STROMANTHE (Marantaceae)

♦***amabilis***	See CTENANTHE ***a.***
'Freddy'	MBri
sanguinea	CHal MBri
'Stripestar	MBri

STROPHANTHUS (Apocyanaceae)

¶ ***divaricatus***	CTro
¶ ***kombe***	CTro SLMG
¶ ***speciosus***	CTro

STUARTIA See **STEWARTIA**

STYLIDIUM (Stylidiaceae)

¶ ***graminifolium***	SIng

STYLOMECON (Papaveraceae)

heterophylla	WCru

STYLOPHORUM (Papaveraceae)

diphyllum	CHan CPar CPou EBre ECha EMar EMon LAma LBre NSal SBar SSpi SSvw SWas WCru WDav
lasiocarpum	CRDP EMon MBel NCat NSti SAxl SFar SUsu SWas WAbe WBon WCot WCru WHal

STYPHELIA (Epacridaceae)

colensoi	See CYATHODES ***colensoi***

STYRAX (Styracaceae)

¶ ***dasyanthus*** var. ***cinerascens***	CPMA SSpi
hemsleyanus	LHyd LTil MAsh MBri SSpi WWat
japonicus	CB&S CBra CChu CCla CGle CMCN EBre EHar ELan IJoh IOrc LBre LHyd MBal MBri MGos MUlv NPal SEng SHBN SPer SReu SSta WBod WCoo WDin WNor WPat WWat
– 'Carillon'	ELan LRHS
¶ – 'Fargesii'	LTil
– 'Pendulus'	LTil SSta
– 'Roseus'	See S. ***j.*** Benibana Group
§ ***japonicus*** Benibana Group	CCla CDoC CPMA CSco ELan LTil SPer SReu SSpi SSta
– – 'Pink Chimes'	LRHS MAsh SHil
obassia	CBra CChu CCla CGre CMCN LTil MBri SHil SReu SSpi SSta WNor WWat

SUCCISA (Dipsacaceae)

Orkney dwarf form	CSun
§ ***pratensis***	CArn CKin ITim MChe MFir MHew MHig NLan NSal WGwy WHil WNdy WOak WPer
– dwarf form	GDra MTho NGre NTow WDav WHil

SUNBERRY See **RUBUS** Sunberry

SUTERA (Scrophulariaceae)

See Plant Deletions

SUTHERLANDIA (Leguminosae)

frutescens	CPle ECro NWCA SAxl SMrm WHer WSHC WWye
– 'Prostrata'	SIgm
montana	LHil SIgm
– SH 56/61	CHan

SWAINSONA (Leguminosae)

¶ ***galegifolia*** 'Albiflora'	LGre

SWERTIA (Gentianaceae)

¶ sp. EMAK 0412	NHol
¶ sp. EMAK 0941	NHol

SYAGRUS (Palmae)

§ ***romanzoffiana***	LPal NPal

X SYCOPARROTIA (Hamamelidaceae)

semidecidua	CKni LTil SSpi SSta

SYCOPSIS (Hamamelidaceae)

sinensis	EHar NHol SBor SHil SSpi WBod WSHC
tutcheri	See DISTYLIUM ***racemosum t.***

SYMPHORICARPOS (Caprifoliaceae)

albus	CKin CMer CPer EBre ENot LBre MPlt NWea WDin WStI WWin
– 'Constance Spry'	MUlv SRms
§ – var. *laevigatus*	CB&S ENot GRei LBuc MBar NKay WDin
– 'Taff's White' (v)	CMer
– 'Turesson'	CDoC MBar
♦– 'Variegatus'	See S. *a.* 'Taff's White'
x *chenaultii* 'Hancock'	CB&S CDoC CMer CSco ELan ENot GRei MBar MBri MGos MRav MWat SHBN SPer WDin
x *doorenbosii* 'Magic Berry'	CDoC CSco ENot MBar
– 'Mother of Pearl'	CDoC CSco ECha ELan ENot MBar MGos NWea SPer WDin
– 'White Hedge'	CDoC CSco ELan ENot LBuc MWat NWea SPer WDin
orbiculatus	WThi
– 'Albovariegatus'	See S. *o.* 'Taff's Silver Edge'
– 'Argenteovariegatus'	See S. *o.* 'Taff's Silver Edge'
– 'Bowles' Golden Variegated'	See S. *o.* 'Foliis Variegatis'
§ – 'Foliis Variegatis'	CB&S CPle EHal EHar EHoe ELan EPla LHop MBal MGos MRav SHBN SPer SSpi WDin WEas WWat WWin
§ – 'Taff's Silver Edge' (v)	CFis CHan CPle CSco ELan ENot EPla IOrc ISea MBar MGos MPla NKay NNor SGil SSpi WWat
– 'Variegatus'	See S. *o.* 'Foliis Variegatis'
rivularis	See S. ***albus laevigatus***

SYMPHYANDRA † (Campanulaceae)

armena	ELan EMar GDra LGan MBro MNFA MPar NHol WPer
cretica alba	NTow
hofmannii	CCla CFis CGle CRiv EBur ELan EPad EPot ITim MPar MTho NHol NRoo NSti NWCA SIng SMrm SSvw WDav WHer WPer WWin
ossettica	CElw CGle EPad MBel MBro WPer WThi
pendula	EPad MBro NRoo SBar WPer WThi
– *alba*	CCla
wanneri	CNic CRDP EBur ECro EPad GCra LGan MPar NMen WOMN WPer WWin
zanzegurii	ECro EPad

SYMPHYTUM † (Boraginaceae)

asperum	ECha ELan EMon LRHS MHew NSal WCHb
* *azureum*	MBri
¶ 'Boking'	GAbr
caucasicum	CCla CCor CFis CHad CHan CSam CSco ECha EPad EPar ERav GPoy MBri NFai NKay NRar NSti SSpi WCHb WCru WHer WOak WSun WWye
– 'Eminence'	CRDP EMon LRHS
– 'Norwich Sky'	CBre EJud
'Gold in Spring'	EMon WCHb
§ 'Goldsmith' (v)	Widely available
grandiflorum	See S. ***ibericum***
'Hidcote Blue'	CBre ECha ELan EMon EPla ILis MBri NHol NRar NSti SChu SUsu WHal
§ 'Hidcote Pink'	CGle EBre ECha ENot EPla LBre LHol LHop NSti SChu
'Hidcote Variegated'	CGle WCHb WWye
§ *ibericum*	CArn CCla CFis CGle CHan CLew CNic CPar CSFH ECha ELun ERav Effi GPoy LGro LHol MFir MPar NRar NSel NSti SIde SSvw WCHb WCru WHal WOak WWat
– 'All Gold'	ECha EFol
– 'Blaueglocken'	ECha
♦– 'Jubilee'	See S. 'Goldsmith'
– 'Lilacinum'	CCla CFis EMar WHer WWat
– variegated form	CRow
– 'Variegatum'	See S. 'Goldsmith'
– 'Wisley Blue'	CCla CDoC
'Langthorns Pink'	ELan EMon GCal WCHb
'Mereworth' (v)	CRDP EMon WCHb
officinale	CArn CKin CSev CShe EJud Effi GPoy IEde LHol MChe MHew NFai NMir NPer NSal SIde WHer WOak WWye
¶ – *ochroleucum*	WCHb
orientale	CGle EMon WCHb
peregrinum	See S. x ***uplandicum***
'Pink Robins'	EMon WCHb
'Roseum'	See S. 'Hidcote Pink'
'Rubrum'	CCla CRDP CSco ECha ELan EOrc EPla NRoo NSti SChu SPer WCru
tuberosum	CBre CSFH EHal GPoy MFir NCat NHol NSti WCHb WHer
§ x *uplandicum*	CGle CLew CRow CSco CSev ELan Effi MHew NFai NSal NSel WCHb WOak WWin WWye
– 'Variegatum'	CArn CBot CChu CGle CHad CHan CRDP CSam CSco CSev CWGN ECha EFol EGol ELan EOrc GCal GPoy MTho MUlv NRar NRoo SPer SSpi WCHb WEas WRus WWat WWin

SYMPLOCARPUS (Araceae)

foetidus	NSal

SYMPLOCOS (Symplocaceae)

paniculata	CB&S ELan LTil SSpi WBod WWat

SYNEILESIS (Compositae)

See Plant Deletions

SYNGONIUM (Araceae)

'Jenny'	MBri
'Maya Red'	MBri
podophyllum 'Emerald Gem'	CHal
– 'Silver Knight'	MBri
– 'Variegatum'	MBri
'White Butterfly'	MBri

SYNNOTIA See SPARAXIS

SYNTHYRIS (Scrophulariaceae)

¶ *missurica*	NGre
– *stellata*	GGar SWas WCru

reniformis	IBlr

SYRINGA † (Oleaceae)

afghanica	See S. *protolaciniata*
amurensis	See S. *reticulata a.*
x *chinensis* 'Saugeana'	CDoC
x *correlata*	IOrc
¶ x *diversifolia* 'William H Judd'	EMon
emodi	CBot WHCG
– 'Aurea'	EPla IMal
¶ – 'Aureovariegata'	SSpi
'Fountain'	CBrd SHil
¶ x *hyacinthiflora*	WStI
– 'Esther Staley'	CDoC CSco ENot SFam SHil
x *josiflexa* 'Bellicent'	CSco ELan ENot ISea MBal MBar MGos MRav MUlv NSti SChu SHBN SHer SHil SMad SPer SPla SSpi WHCG WStI
– 'Lynette'	EPla
– 'Royalty'	CDoC
josikaea	CBow CCor CPMA SPer SSpi WHCG
§ x *laciniata* Miller	CBot CCla CGre CHan CPle IJoh SChu SHil SPer WHCG WKif WWat
§ *meyeri* 'Palibin'	CBot CChu CCla CHan CSam CSco EBre ENot ESis IDai LBre LHop MBar MBri MGos MPla NBar NHar NHol SBla SHBN SIng SLon SPer SSpi WDin WPat WSHC WWat
microphylla	CBow CPle CSco
– 'Superba'	CBow CCla CShe ELan ENot ERav IDai IOrc MBri MGos NBar NRoo SHBN SLon SPer SPla SSpi SSta WBod WPat WSHC WWat
palibiniana	See S. *meyeri* 'Palibin'
patula (Palibin) hort.	See S. *meyeri* 'Palibin'
§ – (Palibin) Nakai	CCla ELan IHos IOrc LNet MBal MPar MWat NBee NRoo SHer SPla WStI
– 'Miss Kim'	MGos SHBN SHil
pekinensis	CBot CMCN
x *persica*	CSco EHal ERav ISea MGos MWat SHer SHil SPer SPla WWat WWin
– 'Alba'	CBot CCla SPer SPla WSHC
x *persica laciniata*	See S. *laciniata*
pinnatifolia	CBot CBrd CHan CPle EPla
x *prestoniae* 'Audrey'	MGos SPer
– 'Elinor'	CDoC CMHG CSco ENot SHil SPer
– 'Isabella'	MGos SHil
– 'Kim'	MAsh
§ *protolaciniata*	CChu CMHG CSco EPla ESis IBar MPar MPla SHer WWeb
reflexa	CDoC CMCN EFol MBar MBel MGos MRav NKay SHil SMad
reticulata	CMCN WWat
§ – *amurensis*	CCla MBal
– var. *mandschurica*	See S. *r. amurensis*
sweginzowii	CSam MBal NHol SPer WRus WWat
– 'Superba'	SHil
tomentella	CCla
velutina	See S. *patula* (Palibin) Nakai
¶ *villosa*	CCor SSpi
vulgaris	GRei LBuc MBar NNor NWea
– 'Adelaide Dunbar' (d)	GCHN
– var. *alba*	MBar
§ – 'Andenken an Ludwig Späth'	CB&S COtt CSco ECtt ENot IJoh IOrc MBar MBri MGos NWea SDix SHBN SPer WDin
– 'Aurea'	EMon EPla MRav
– 'Belle de Nancy' (d)	CBow CPMA ECtt ELan MAsh MBri NBee SHBN WDin
– 'Charles Joly' (d)	CB&S CBra CPMA CSam CSco ELan ENot GCHN GRei IDai IHos IJoh IOrc LHol LNet MBal MBar MBri MGos MRav NBee NWea SHBN SPer WDin WStI
– 'Charm'	GCHN NRoo
– 'Condorcet' (d)	LNet
– 'Congo'	ENot GCHN NRoo SPer
– 'Edward J Gardner' (d)	SPer
– 'Firmament'	CSco ELan ENot SHBN SPer SRms
– 'Glory of Horstenstein'	See S. *v.* 'Ruhm von Horstenstein'
– 'Katherine Havemeyer' (d)	CB&S CBow CCor CDoC CSco EBre ELan ENot GRei IDai IJoh LBre MBri MGos MRav NBee SFam SHBN SPer SReu WDin WStI
– 'Madame Antoine Buchner' (d)	CSco ENot SFam SReu
– 'Madame Florent Stepman'	CDoC
– 'Madame Lemoine' (d)	CB&S CBra CPMA CSco EBre ELan ENot GCHN GRei IDai IJoh LBre LBuc LHol LNet MBal MBar MBri MGos NBee NRoo NWea SDix SFam SHBN SPer SReu WAbe WDin WStI
– 'Masséna'	ENot SFam SPer
– 'Maud Notcutt'	CSco ENot SFam SPer
– 'Michel Buchner' (d)	CB&S CBow ECtt ENot GRei IHos IJoh IOrc LHol MBar MBri NBar NBee WStI
– 'Mrs Edward Harding' (d)	EBre ECtt ENot LBre LBuc LNet MBal MBri MGos SFam SPer SReu WStI
– 'Paul Deschanel' (d)	NBee
– 'Président Grévy' (d)	IJoh NTow
– 'Primrose'	CBow CBra CCla CPMA CSco EBre ELan ENot LBre MBal NRoo SFam SPer SReu WDin
– 'Sensation'	CBow CPMA CSco ENot MAsh SHBN SMad SPer
– 'Souvenir de Louis Spaeth'	See S. *v.* 'Andenken an Ludwig Späth'
– variegated double	CCor EFol MBal
– 'Vestale'	ENot MAsh SDix SRms
yunnanensis	ELan WBod
– 'Rosea'	ISea

TACITUS See **GRAPTOPETALUM**

TAGETES (Compositae)
lucida NSal

TAIWANIA (Taxodiaceae)
See Plant Deletions

TALINUM (Portulacaceae)
calycinum NGre NHol
okanoganense ITim MFos NGre NHol NNrd NTow NWCA SIng WOMN
rugospermum EPot
spinescens NGre SIng
teretifolium NWCA WThi
'Zoe' NHar SHer WThi

TAMARIX (Tamaricaceae)
africana WWin
gallica CDoC ENot GCHN SArc
germanica See MYRICARIA *germanica*
§ *parviflora* CB&S IOrc WPat
pentandra See T. *ramosissima*
§ *ramosissima* CBow CBra CDoC CSco CShe EBre ELan ISea LAbb LBre MBri MUlv NBee SSta WDin WWeb
– 'Pink Cascade' CBow CWit ENot EPla MBri SPer WDin WStI
– 'Rubra' CDoC CSco ENot ESma IOrc MGos SLon SPer SReu WPat
tetrandra CBow CBra CMHG CSco EBre ELan ENot LBre LNet LPan MWat NNor SHBN SHer SLon SPer SReu SSta WAbe WBod WStI WWeb
– var. *purpurea* See T. *parviflora*

TAMUS (Dioscoreaceae)
communis CArn

TANACETUM † (Compositae)
§ *argenteum* IDai MAsh MTho NTow SAsh SMad SSmi
– ssp. *canum* CKni ELan MBri
§ *balsamita* CArn CHal CHun CSFH CSev EEls EJud ELan EMar EMon Effi GPoy IEde MBri MHew NHol NSal NSel SHer SSvw WOak WPer WWye
– var. *tanacetoïdes* LHol NSal NSti SIde
– *tomentosum* LHol MChe SIde WGwy
§ *capitatum* NWCA WDav
§ *cinerariifolium* CArn GPoy IEde NHol NRar WOak WPer
§ *coccineum* GPoy NSal SPer SRms WWin
– 'Alfred' ECtt ELan
– 'Brenda' EBre ECED EFou LBre MWat
– 'Eileen May Robinson' EBre ECED LBre MWat NFai WRus
¶ – 'J N Twerdy' EBlo
– 'James Kelway' LWad MBri MRav NFai SHer SRms
– 'King Size' MPit NMir WHil
¶ – 'Laurin' EBlo
¶ – 'Peter Pan' EBlo
¶ – 'Phillipa' EBlo
– 'Queen Mary' ELan
– 'Red Dwarf' ELan
– 'Robinson's Pink' NOrc NRoo SHer SRms
– 'Robinson's Red' NOrc
– 'Scarlet Glow' MWat
– 'Snow Cloud' EFou MWat
§ *corymbosum* CGle EMon GCal NCat WCot
densum LHil SHer WWeb
– ssp. *amani* ECha EFol EFou ELan EOrc EPot ERav ESis MCas MPar MPla MPlt MWat NRoo NWCA SIng SSmi WRus WThu WWin
§ *haradjanii* CFis CGle CHal CSam CSun ELan EMNN EPla GCHN LAbb LGro NKay NNor SAxl SBla SChu SGil WByw WEas WHil WHoo WPer WSHC WWye
♦ *herderi* See HIPPOLYTIA *h.*
§ *macrophyllum* EMon GCal
¶ *niveum* EMon
pallidum spathulifolium See LEUCANTHEMOPSIS *pallida spathulifolia*
§ *parthenium* CArn CHal CKin CRDP EEls EJud Effi GPoy LHol MChe NFai NMir NPer NRoo NSel SIde WHer WOak
– 'Aureum' CHal CNic CRDP CRow CTom ECha EEls EFou ELan ERav MBri MChe MFir NFai NNrd NSel NSti SIng SMad SPer WBon WEas WHal WHer WOak WPer WWin
¶ – 'Ball's Double White' SRms
– double white CHal CRDP EPad NPer
¶ – 'Golden Ball' NTow
– 'Golden Moss' LHil
– 'Plenum' CBos EPad MBri MFir NSel NSti SIng WBon WOMN WOak
§ – 'Rowallane' (d) CHan ELan EMon
– 'Selma Tetra' NRoo
– 'Sissinghurst White' See T. *p.* 'Rowallane'
– 'White Bonnet' (d) CGle CHan ECha ELan EMon ERav MFir NRar WEas
praeteritium LGre
§ *ptarmiciflorum* NBee
¶ sp. JJH 463 WDav
vulgare CArn CCor CKin CSFH CSev CTom ECtt EEls EJud Effi IEde LHol MBar MChe MHew NLan NMir NSal NSel SHer SIde SPer WByw WCla WHal WOak WWye
– var. *crispum* CHal CSFH ELan GCal MBri SIde WGwy
¶ – 'Isla Gold' EFol
– 'Silver Lace' (v) ECha EFol EMar EMon NSti

TANAKEA (Saxifragaceae)
radicans ELan EPot NHol WCru

TANGELO See **CITRUS** x *tangelo*

TANGERINE See **CITRUS** *reticulata* Tangerine Group

TANGOR See **CITRUS** x *nobilis*

TAPEINOCHILOS (Costaceae)
ananassae MNew

TARAXACUM (Compositae)

I *officinale* LHol SIde

TASMANNIA See DRIMYS

TAXODIUM (Taxodiaceae)

ascendens See T. *distichum*
§ *distichum* Widely available
– var. *nutans* EHar IOrc MBlu SHil SMad
¶ *mucronatum* WFro

TAXUS † (Taxaceae)

baccata CB&S CBra CDoC CKin CLan CPer CSco EHar ENot ERea GRei IDai ISea LBee LBuc LCon LNet MBar MBri MChe MGos NSel NWea SMad SPer SReu WDin WMou
– 'Adpressa' EBre GAri LBre
– 'Adpressa Aurea' CKen ESis MPla WMou
– 'Adpressa Variegata' EBre EHul LBre LCon MAsh SLim
– 'Aldenham Gold' CKen
– 'Amersfoort' EPla LCon SLim SSpi
– 'Argentea Minor' NHol
§ – 'Aurea' SRms
*– 'Aurea Pendula' EBre ENHC LBre
*– 'Aureomarginata' CB&S CBra ENHC WStI
– 'Compacta' EPla
– 'Corley's Copper Tip' CDoC CKen CSam EBre EHul LBre LCon LLin MBar NHol SHer
– 'David' WMou
– 'Decora' LCon MAsh
– 'Dovastoniana' CDoC CMac ISea LPan MBar NWea SHil SMad WBod WMou
– 'Dovastonii Aurea' (v) CDoC CMac EHul EPla LCon LHol MBar MBri SHil SLim SLon SMad SPer WDin WMou
– 'Drinkstone' EPla
– 'Drinkstone Gold' EHul
– 'Dwarf White' LCon MAsh
– 'Elegantissima' (v) EHul MPla NKay NWea
¶ – 'Erecta' SHBN
§ – 'Fastigiata' Widely available
– 'Fastigiata Aurea' CKen EHar EHul IHos IJoh LLin NBee NEgg NRoo SHer
– 'Fastigiata Aureomarginata' CDoC CKen CMac CSco EBre EHul GRei IDai IOrc ISea LBre LCon LHol LPan MBal MBar MBri MGos MWat NHol NKay NWea SLim SPla SSta WMou
– 'Fastigiata Robusta' EBre EPla LBre MBar NHol WMou
– 'Glenroy New Penny' MBal
– 'Gracilis Pendula' LCon
– 'Hibernica' See T. *b.* 'Fastigiata'
– 'Nutans' CKen EHul ESis LCon LLin LTil MBar
– 'Overeynderi' EHul
*– 'Pendula' MBal MRav
– 'Pumila Aurea' MAsh
– 'Pygmaea' IOrc
– 'Repandens' CDoC EBre EHul ENHC LBre MBar SHBN SPer
– 'Repens Aurea' (v) CDoC CHig CKen CSco EBlo EHul ENHC EPla GCHN LCon LLin MBar MBri MGos MPla NHol NRoo SHil SPla WEas
– 'Rushmore' NHol
– 'Semperaurea' CB&S CBra CMac EBre EHul ENHC ENot EPla GCHN IJoh LBee LBre LCon LHol MBal MBar MBri MGos NBee NWea SLim SPla SReu WDin WWin
– 'Silver Spire' CB&S CKen
– 'Standishii' CDoC CKen CSco EBlo EHar EHoe EHul ENHC EPla GCHN IJoh IOrc LBee LCon LLin LNet MBal MBar MBri MGos MPla MRav MWat NHol SHBN SLim SPer WDin WMou
– 'Strait Hedge' EHul LCon SLim WMou
– 'Summergold' (v) CBra CDoC CSco EBre EHul ENHC ENot EPla GCHN GRei IDai IJoh IOrc LBre LCon MBar MGos NBee NHol NRoo SLim SPer WStI
– 'Variegata' See T. *b.* 'Aurea'
¶ – 'Washingtonii' SHBN
brevifolia EPla
cuspidata 'Aurescens' CKen EPla LCon MAsh SRms
I – 'Brevifolia' LCon
– 'Golden Jubilee' LRHS
– 'Luteobaccata' EPla
¶ – 'Minima' EBre LBre
– var. *nana* CDoC EHul GAri LCon LLin MBar NHol
¶ – 'Robusta' LCon
x *media* 'Brownii' EHul
– 'Hicksii' CMHG CSco ECtt ENHC LNet LPan MBar NRoo SLim WMou
– 'Hillii' EHul LCon MBar

TAYBERRY See RUBUS Tayberry

TECOMA (Bignoniaceae)

capensis CB&S CHEx CPle CSun CTro EBak EMil ERea SHil SLMG
– 'Aurea' ERea SLMG
– *nyassae* ERea
ricasoliana See PODRANEA *r.*
stans CPle CTro

TECOMANTHE (Bignoniaceae)

speciosa ECou

TECOMARIA See TECOMA

TECOPHILAEA (Liliaceae/Tecophilaecaceae)

cyanocrocus CAvo EPot LAma NRog WChr
– 'Leichtlinii' CAvo LAma NRog
¶ – 'Violacea' CAvo
violiflora EPot LAma NRog

TECTARIA (Dryopteridaceae)

gemmifera NMar

TELANTHOPHORA (Compositae)

grandifolia SArc

TELEKIA (Compositae)

§ ***speciosa***	CBow CBre CCMG CHan CNic CPar CRDP CSco CWGN ELan EMon ESma MFir NBro NHol SDix SFis WByw WDav WOld WPer

TELESONIX See BOYKINIA

TELINE See GENISTA

TELLIMA (Saxifragaceae)

grandiflora	CFis CGle CMHG CSam CSun CTom EBre ECar EHon EJud ELan ELun EMon GCHN LAbb LBlm LBre LBuc LGan MFir NBee NHol NNor NNrd NRar NWCA WHen WOak WWye
– Alba Group	EGol
– Odorata Group	CBre CElw CRDP ECha EFou EPla GCal NCat NHol NSti WBon WWat WWye
– 'Perky' JLS 86282SCCA	EMon
– 'Purpurea'	See T. ***grandiflora*** Rubra Group
– 'Purpurteppich'	CGle ECha EPla
§ – Rubra Group	Widely available

TELOPEA (Proteaceae)

oreades	LBlm
speciosissima	CHEx
truncata	CHEx ISea

TEPHROSERUS (Compositae)

See Plant Deletions

TERNSTROEMIA (Theaceae)

♦***gymnanthera***	See T. ***japonica***
§ ***japonica***	LTil

TETRACENTRON (Tetracentraceae)

sinense	CAbb CB&S CChu CCla CDoC CGre CMCN CPle CWSG EHar SHil SMad SSpi WCoo WWat

TETRADIUM (Rutaceae)

§ ***daniellii***	CCla CDoC CMCN EArb EHar SHil SSpi WCoo WWat
– Hupehense Group	CMCN GCal SSpi WCoo WHCr

TETRAGONOLOBUS See LOTUS

TETRANEURIS (Compositae)

grandiflora	NHol
– JCA 11422	SBla
§ ***scaposa***	EPot LHil

TETRAPANAX (Araliaceae)

§ ***papyrifer***	CAbb CBot CHEx SArc SMad

TETRAPATHAEA See PASSIFLORA

TETRASTIGMA (Vitaceae)

voinierianum	CHEx CTro MBri

TEUCRIUM (Labiatae)

ackermannii	CHal CLew CShe ESis LHop MBro MCas NHol NVic SBla SChu SCro WHoo WPat
arduino	CPle
aroanum	GAbr MBro MHig MPla MWat NTow SBla WDav WHil
bicolor	CGre
botrys	MHew NSal
canadense	LHop
chamaedrys hort.	See T. × ***lucidrys***
– Linnaeus	MHew NHol SFis
– 'Nanum'	CLew CNic WPat WPer WWye
– 'Rose Carpet'	CMGP
– 'Variegatum'	CHan CLew CNic EFol NHol NRar SIng WCHb WCot WHer WPer
§ ***cossonii***	NRar
§ ***creticum***	WDav
* ***discolor***	CPle
flavum	LGan WHer WOMN WPer
fruticans	Widely available
– 'Album'	CGle WSHC
– 'Azureum'	CB&S CBow ERav LGre SPer SSpi WAbe WBod WPat
– 'Compactum'	CBow LHop SDry
hircanicum	CElw ELan EMon LHop LRHS SIgm
§ × ***lucidrys***	Widely available
lucidum	WCla WOak
majoricum	See T. ***polium pii-fontii***
marum	NHol
massiliense	WHer
montanum	CLew MHig WPer
musimomum	MHig NTow WHil
polium	CFis CShe EBar ESis MBro SFar SIgm WEas WPer
pulverulentum	See T. ***cossonii***
pyrenaicum	CElw CHal CMea CPar MBro MCas MHig NHol NKay NNrd NRed SIng SUsu WAbe WPat WThu
rosmarinifolium	See T. ***creticum***
scordium	CNat
* ***scoridifolia***	WPer
scorodonia	CArn CHal CKin EJud GPoy LHol MChe MHew NLan NMir NSal SIde WCla WHer WNdy WWye
– 'Crispum'	CB&S CBos CFis CHal CHan CMer CPar CRDP CRiv ELan EOrc LHil LHol MBri MFir MWat NFai SAxl SMrm WCHb WDav WKif WPer
§ – 'Crispum Marginatum' (v)	CBot CElw CLew CMea CWGN ECha ECro EFol EFou EGol EHoe ELan EPla ESis GAbr IBlr LGan LHop NFai NOak NRar NRoo NSti WBon WEas WHer WRus
– 'Winterdown' (v)	CNat
subspinosum	ITim MHig MPla NMen NTow SLon WPat WThu

THALIA (Marantaceae)

dealbata	CHEx MSta

THALICTRUM † (Ranunculaceae)

adiantifolium	See T. ***minus a.***
angustifolium	EFol ELan MNFA
aquilegiifolium	Widely available
– album	CBre CHad CMil CRDP ECha ECro EFol EFou ELan EPla GAbr GCal LGan MBri NHol NTow SChu SCro SFis SPer SSpi WEas
¶– dwarf form	ECha
*– 'Hybridum'	ECro WHil WPer
– 'Purpureum'	CSco GAbr GCal SFis SSpi
– 'Thundercloud' ('Purple Cloud')	CChu CCla CDoC EBre ECro ECtt EFou LBre MBri MUlv NBar NHol SApp SPer WAbe WMer
§ ***chelidonii***	MNFA MSte NTow
– dwarf form	GDra
coreanum	See T. ***ichangense***
§ ***delavayi***	CBos CChu CHad CKel CSco ECha EFou ELan EOrc GCal IBar MBri NHol NNor NSti SCro SDix SPer SSpi SUsu WBod WEas WHal WOMN WOld WWin
¶– CLD 0025	NHol
– 'Album'	CSco ECha ELan LGre NDea NOak SWas
– 'Hewitt's Double'	Widely available
¶– 'Sternhimmel'	NHol
diffusiflorum	ECha GDra SBla
dipterocarpum hort.	See T. ***delavayi***
flavum	CGle CHan CRDP EFou ELan NBro NDea NKay SPer
– 'Chollerton'	See T. sp. Afghanistan
§ – ssp. ***glaucum***	CBot CChu CCla CHad CRDP CSco CShe ECha ECro EFol EHoe ELan EOrc EPla GCal LGan MBri MBro MFir NHol NOak SSpi SUsu WBon WEas WOld WPer WWin
– 'Illuminator'	MBel
isopyroïdes	EBre ECro LBre NHar SBla SUsu WBon
javanicum	ECro NOak
– B&L 12327	EMon
kiusianum	CChu ECha ECro EFol EPla EPot ESis GArf LGre MTho NTow SBar SBla SPou
– Kew form	CRDP SWas
♦***koreanum***	See T. ***ichangense***
lucidum	CPou
minus	CHan CRDP ECro ELan EMon GAbr GCal MBri NLan NOak NRoo NSti WBon
§ – ***adiantifolium***	CHan ECro EJud EPla LRHS MFir MUlv NHol NOak WMer
– ssp. ***saxatile***	WPer
¶***occidentale*** JLS 86255	EMon
¶***orientale***	SBla
polygamum	MHew NSal
rochebrunanum	CBos CChu CGle CHad CHan ECro EHal ESma MUlv NHol WSHC
speciosissimum	See T. ***flavum glaucum***
§ sp. Afghanistan	CHan CLew EFol ELan EMon GTou NHol WCot
sp. CLD 564	EMon
¶sp. EMAK 0444	NHol
tuberosum	CChu EMon LGre WCot

THAMNOCALAMUS (Gramineae(Bambuseae))

¶***aristatus***	EPla
¶***crassinodus***	SDry
¶– 'Kew Beauty'	SDry WJun
¶– 'Merlyn'	SDry
*– 'Yang Tabg'	WJun
falcatus	See DREPANOSTACHYUM ***falcatum***
falconeri	See DREPANOSTACHYUM ***falconeri***
♦***funghomii***	See SCHIZOSTACHYUM ***f.***
khasianus	See DREPANOSTACHYUM ***khasianum***
maling	See YUSHANIA ***maling***
♦***spathaceus***	See FARGESIA ***spathacea***
§ ***spathiflorus***	EFul EPla ISta SBam SDry SHil WJun
§ ***tessellatus***	EFul EPla ISta LBam SBam SDry SHil WJun

THAPSIA (Umbelliferae)

¶***garganica***	SIgm

THEA See CAMELLIA

THELYPTERIS (Thelypteridaceae)

¶***limbosperma***	NHar
palustris	NMar WRic
phegopteris	See PHEGOPTERIS ***connectilis***
¶sp. from Nepal	WRic

THEMEDA (Gramineae)

¶***triandra japonica***	ETPC

THERMOPSIS (Leguminosae)

caroliniana	See T. ***villosa***
fabacea	See T. ***lupinoïdes***
lanceolata	CAbb EFou SMad
§ ***lupinoïdes***	CPle ECha ECro EFol NOrc SFis SIgm SUsu WCru WPer
mollis	EMon EPla MPlt
montana	CCla CElw CFis CHan CRDP ECro EFol EFou ELan EMon ERav NOrc NSti SChu SPer WAbb WByw WHil WRus
§ ***villosa***	CChu CGle CHan GCal MSte NSti SIgm WRus

THEVETIA (Apocynaceae)

peruviana	CTro

THLADIANTHA (Curcubitaceae)

See Plant Deletions

THLASPI (Cruciferae)

alpinum	CLew CMGP CMHG CShe ELan EMNN EPot MBro MCas MPla MWat NKay NMen NWCA WPer
– ssp. ***brevicaulis***	NKay
bellidifolium	GDra NBir
* ***biebersteinii***	GAbr
bulbosum	ESis GTou NWCA WThi

densiflorum NWCA
montanum ESis WHer
¶ *nevadense* NWCA
rotundifolium GTou NGre NWCA
– ssp. *cenisium* WOMN
– var. *limosellifolium* NKay
stylosum MSte NWCA WHil

THRINAX (Palmae)

See Plant Deletions

THUJA (Cupressaceae)

§ *koraiensis* CMHG EHar IBar ISea LCon MBar SLim WThu
occidentalis WDin
– 'Aurea' IJoh MBar
¶ – 'Aureospicata' SHil
*– 'Baurmanii' NBar
– 'Beaufort' CKen EHul EPla LBee LCon MBar MPla
– 'Caespitosa' CMHG CNic EPla ESis LCon LLin NHol
– 'Copper Kettle' EBre EHul LBre MPla
– 'Cristata Argenteovariegata' EHul EPla
– 'Cristata Aurea' CKen
– 'Cuprea' LCon
– 'Danica' CMac CSco EBlo EBre EHar EHul ENHC ENot GRei IJoh LBre LCon LLin LPan MBar MGos MPla MWat NRoo SBod SHer SLim SPer WStI WTyr
– 'Dicksonii' EHul
– 'Douglasii Aurea' CKen
– 'Ellwangeriana Aurea' ENHC LBee MGos
– 'Emerald' See T. *o.* 'Smaragd'
– 'Ericoides' CDoC EHul ENHC MBal MBar SHer SSmi WStI
– 'Europe Gold' CDoC EHul LBee MBar MBri MGos SLim
– 'Fastigiata' ISea MBar
– 'Filiformis' CKen LCon
– 'Globosa' CMac LLin MBar MGos SBod SPer
*– 'Globosa Variegata' CKen LCon LLin MBar
¶ – 'Golden Gem' LPan
– 'Golden Globe' CSco EHul ENHC ENot LCon LNet MBar MGos MWat NHol SBod SLim WDin WStI
*– 'Golden Minaret' EHul
– 'Hetz Midget' CKen EBre EHul EPla ESis LBre LCon LLin MBar MGos NHol SLim SPer SPla
– 'Holmstrup' CDoC CMac CNic EBre EHul ENHC ENot GWht LBre LCon MBal MBar MBri MWat NBee NHol SLim SPla SReu SSmi SSta WAbe WStI
– 'Holmstrup Yellow' CDoC CKen EBre EHul LBre LCon MAsh MBri MPla NHol SPla SSmi WWeb
– 'Hoveyi' EHul ENHC MBar
– 'Little Champion' EHul GRei NHol WTyr
– 'Little Gem' EHul ENHC IDai MGos NHol WDin
– 'Lutea Nana' CMac EHul ENHC LCon MBal MBar NHol SLim
– 'Lutescens' CMac EHul ENHC EPla GRei LCon MGos MPla SPer
– 'Marrison Sulphur' EBre LBee LBre LCon SLim
– 'Meinekes Zwerg' CKen EPla
– 'Milleri' EPot
– 'Ohlendorffii' CDoC CKen EHul EPla EPot GWht LCon LLin MBar MWat SSmi
– 'Orientalis Semperaurescens' See T. *orientalis* 'Semperaurea'
¶ – 'Perk Vlaanderen' MAsh
– 'Pygmaea' MBar
– 'Pyramidalis Compacta' EHul LNet
– 'Recurva Nana' CMHG EHar EHul LLin MBal MBar NBee NHol SLon
– 'Rheingold' Widely available
*– 'Silver Beauty' CMHG
§ – 'Smaragd' CSco EBlo EBre EHul ENHC ENot EPla LBre LBuc LCon LNet MBar MGos MPla NBee NEgg SBod SPer SReu WStI
*– 'Smaragd Variegated' EPla
– 'Southport' EBre LBre LCon MBri
– 'Sphaerica' MPla
– 'Spiralis' CMHG EHar MBar
– 'Stolwijk' MGos
– 'Sudworth Pumila' NHol
– 'Sunkist' CDoC CKen CMHG CMac EBre EHar EHul ENHC ENot GRei IHos IJoh LBee LBre LCon LLin LNet MBar MBri MGos MPla MWat NHol NRoo SBod SLim SPer SPla
– 'Tiny Tim' CDoC CMac EHul EPot ESis LCon LLin MBar MGos SIng SSta
– 'Trompenburg' EHul MBri
– 'Wansdyke Silver' (v) CMac EHar EHul EPla LCon MBar MPla SLim
– 'Wareana' CDoC CMac
– 'Wareana Aurea' See T. *o.* 'Wareana Lutescens'
§ – 'Wareana Lutescens' CMHG MBal MBar SHil SLim SLon
– 'Woodwardii' EHul MBar WDin WTyr
– 'Yellow Ribbon' COtt EBlo EBre EHul EPla IJoh LBre NHol SLim SPla SSta
orientalis NWea
§ – 'Aurea Nana' Widely available
– 'Beverleyensis' MBri
– 'Blue Cone' MBar
– 'Carribean Holiday' EBre LBre LCon MAsh MBri
– 'Collen's Gold' EBre EHul LBee LBre LTil MBar NHol SLim SPla
– 'Conspicua' CKen EBre EHar EHul ENHC LBee LBre LCon MBar MWat SBod
– 'Elegantissima' CMHG CMac EHul LBee LCon MBar MBri MGos SBod SGil SHil SLim WStI
*– 'Filiformis Erecta' LCon
– 'Flame' MGos
*– 'Golden Ball' MBri
– 'Golden Minaret' LRHS MBri
– 'Golden Pygmy' CKen
¶ – 'Golden Sceptre' EBlo
*– 'Golden Wonder' ENHC
– 'Juniperoides' EHul IDai LLin MBar
– 'Magnifica' EHul SLim WMou
*– 'Marrison Sulphur' EBre EHul LBre

– 'Meldensis'	CDoC CLew CMHG EHul ENHC EPla GPen LCon LLin MBal MBar WDin
– 'Miller's Gold'	See T. *o*. 'Aurea Nana'
– 'Minima'	CDoC ESis LCon MAsh MWat
¶ – 'Minima Aurea'	LTil
– 'Minima Glauca'	CKen CSco MBar
– 'Purple King'	EBre EPla LBre NHol SLim
– 'Pyramidalis Aurea'	LPan MBri
– 'Rosedalis'	CKen CMac CNic EBlo EBre EHul ENHC EPla IDai LBee LBre LCon LLin MBal MBar MBri MPla MWat SBod SLim WDin
– 'Sanderi'	EPla LBee LCon MBar MBri
§ – 'Semperaurea'	CMac
¶ – 'Shirley Chilcott'	MAsh
– 'Sieboldii'	EBre EHul LBre LCon
– 'Southport'	LLin MAsh NHol
– 'Summer Cream'	EHul MBar MGos
¶ – 'Suzie'	LLin
– 'Westmont'	EPla
plicata	CPer EHar EHul GRei GWht IDai MBal MBar MGos NEgg NWea SBod SLim SPer SPla WFro WMou WStI WWin
– 'Atrovirens'	EBre EHar ENot LBee LBre LBuc LCon LPan MBri WMou WWeb
– 'Aurea'	EHul EPla MAsh SHil SRms WMou WTyr
I – 'Cole's Variety'	CSco MBar SLim
– 'Collyer's Gold'	EHul LCon MBri SPla SRms WTyr
– 'Copper Kettle'	CKen LCon MBar MBri NHol SLim
– 'Cuprea'	CKen EHul LLin MBar
– 'Doone Valley'	CKen CMHG EHul EPla MBar NHol SLim WThu
* – 'Dura'	CDoC
– 'Fastigiata'	CMac EHar
– 'Gracilis Aurea'	EHul LCon MPla
– 'Hillieri'	EHul EPla LCon MBar NHol
– 'Irish Gold' (v)	CMac EPla SHil
– 'Rogersii'	CDoC CKen CMHG CMac CNic EBar EBlo EBre EHul EPla EPot ESis GWht IJoh LBre LCon LLin MBar MGos MPla NHol SBod SHer SLim SLon SPer SReu SSmi WAbe WThu
– 'Semperaurescens'	CSco EHar LCon WMou
* – 'Stolwyck's Gold'	EHul
I – 'Stolwyck's Variety'	MBar SLim
– 'Stoneham Gold'	CDoC CMHG CMac CSco EBre EHar EHul ENHC EPla LBee LBre LCon LLin MBar MBri MPla SBod SLim SLon SPer SSmi WTyr
* – 'Windsor Gold'	EHar
– 'Winter Pink'	CKen EPla
– 'Zebrina' (v)	CB&S CBra CDoC CMHG CMac CSco EHar EHul ENot IDai LBee LCon MBal MBar MGos MPla MWat NEgg NWea SBod SGil SLim SLon SPer SReu WWin

THUJOPSIS (Cupressaceae)

dolabrata	CGre CMer CWit EHar EHul ELan ENot GWht IBar IDai IOrc MBar NWea SHBN SHil SMad SPer WBod WWat
– 'Aurea'	CDoC CKen EBre EHar EHul LBre LCon MGos SHBN SLim
§ – 'Laetevirens'	CDoC CKen CMac CSco EHar ESis LCon LLin MBar MBri MPla SGil SLim SLon STre
– 'Nana'	See T. *d*. 'Laetevirens'
– 'Variegata'	CDoC CMac CWit EHar EHul ESis IBar LCon LLin MBal MBar NHol SLim WDin WTyr
koraiensis	See THUJA ***k.***

THUNBERGIA (Acanthaceae)

alata	MBri
erecta	MNew
¶ – 'Alba'	MNew
grandiflora	CTro LAbb MNew SLMG
– 'Alba'	CTro MNew SLMG

THYMUS † (Labiatae)

* 'Albus'	CArn GPoy LHol MChe MPla NNor WWin
'Anderson's Gold'	See T. x ***citriodorus*** 'Bertram Anderson'
* 'Aureus'	CFis CKni CSev GPoy WOak WSun
azoricus	See T. ***caespititius***
'Belle Orchard'	WEas
§ ***caespititius***	CArn CHal CShe EMon EPot GAbr GDra GGar IDai ILis LHol MBar MBro MCas MHig MSte NHol NMen NMir NNrd NSel SSmi WCHb WDav WHoo WPer
– 'Aureus'	ECha EFol GAbr LHol SIde
camphoratus	LHop NTow SIde
carnosus	NHol SFis SSmi STre WDav WEas WHil WSun
cephalotos	CHal
cilicicus	CHun ESis GCHN GPoy IEde MChe NRoo SBla SHer SIng SWas WCHb WOMN WPer WTyr WWye
x ***citriodorus***	CArn CBow CDoC CGle CSFH GAbr GCHN GPoy MChe NHol NOak WAbe WHoo WOak WPer WSun WWye
– 'Archer's Gold'	CBow CNic EBre ECar EHoe ELan EPot GAbr LBre LGro LHop MBri MCas MPit NKay NSti SHer SSmi WCHb WHil WPer
– 'Argenteus'	CKni MBro NHol
– 'Aureus'	CHal CKel CPar CSFH CSco CShe CTom EBre EMNN ESis GDra GTou IEde LBre MBal MBar MBri MBro MCas MFos NHol NKay NMen NNrd NRoo NWCA SBla SSvw WHoo
§ – 'Bertram Anderson'	CHal CMer CShe EBre ECha EFol EMNN EPot GCHN LBre LHol MBro MHig NGre NHol NKay NNrd NRed NRoo SBla WAbe WDav WEas WHil WHoo WOld WThu WWin WWye
– 'Fragrantissimus'	CSFH ESis GPoy IEde LHol MWil NRoo WPer WWye
– 'Golden King' (v)	EBre ECha ELan EPar LBre MBar MBri MChe NGre NHol NSti SHer SIng WAbe WCHb WDav WHil WHoo WPer WStI
– 'Golden Lemon'	CArn GPoy WSun WWye
– 'Golden Queen' (v)	CHun CMea CMer EMNN NHol NKay NRoo WWin
– 'Nyewoods'	CHal CSFH GAbr SIde

x ***citriodorus repanda***	SIde
x ***citriodorus*** 'Silver Posie'	See T. ***vulgaris*** 'Silver Posie'
– 'Silver Queen' (v)	CB&S CBow CGle CLew CPar CRiv CShe ECha ELan EPar GDra GPoy IDai MBal MBar MCas MHig NGre NHol NKay NNrd NRoo SIng SSmi WCla WStI
§ – 'Variegatus'	CKel CRiv CSFH EOrc ESis LGro LHol MBri MBro MChe MPla NGre NHol NKay NMen SIng WEas WWin
comosus	CNic ESis LHol NHol NTow SIde WAbe WEas WHil WHoo WPer
* ***compactus albus***	CTom MBro MPla MPlt NMen
'Desboro'	CHal GAbr NHol NNrd
doerfleri	CLew CShe ECha GAbr LHol NKay NMen NNrd SSmi WPer WWye
– 'Bressingham Pink'	CHal CMea CTom EBre ECtt EMNN GAbr LBre LGro LHol MBro MChe MHig MPla NGre NHol NKay NMen NNrd NRoo SBla WHil WHoo WPat WPer WSun WWye
'Doone Valley' (v)	Widely available
drucei	See T. ***praecox arcticus***
– ***albus***	See T. ***praecox arcticus albus***
– ***minus***	See T. ***praecox arcticus minus***
'E B Anderson'	See T. x ***citriodorus*** 'Bertram Anderson'
* ***epiroticus***	CLew CPar
erectus	See T. ***vulgaris*** 'Erectus'
* ***ericoïdes*** 'Aureus'	EHal EPot MBro WDav
herba-barona	CArn CHad CHal CNic CSFH ECha ESis GAbr GDra GPoy IEde LHol MBal MCas NHol NNor NRoo NVic SHer SIde SIng SSmi WOak WPer WWye
'Highland Cream'	EFol EPot ESis GAri GDra LRHS SAsh WWin
*	CNic
hyemalis	GPoy NSal SIde
¶ ***insertus***	MFos
lanuginosus hort.	See T. ***pseudolanuginosus***
leucotrichus	GAbr ILis LHol MHig WOMN WPat WSun WWye
longicaulis	CArn EBar ECha LGan LHol WWye
♦ ***marschallianus***	See T. ***pannonicus***
mastichina	CArn CDoC CHad ESis LHol LHop SBla SChu SFar WPer WWye
¶ ***membranaceus***	MHig
♦ ***micans***	See T. ***caespititius***
montanus Waldstein & Kitaibel	See T. ***pulegioïdes***
neicefferi	CArn CPar CSev ECha GAbr LHol MHig NTow SIde WOMN WPer
odoratissimus	See T. ***pallasianus pallasianus***
'Onyx'	EMNN NSti WPer
§ ***pallasianus*** ssp. ***pallasianus***	CHal GCal SIde WOak WSun
¶ ***pannonicus***	LHol
'Pincushion'	NHol SIng WDav WPer
praecox	GAbr LHol NHol NMir
§ – ssp. ***arcticus***	CHal CKin EEls EPot GAbr GPoy GTou IEde MFos MHew NLan NSti WPer WTyr WWye
§ – – ***albus***	ELan NCat SGil WPer
¶ – – silver form	WWye
– 'Porlock'	CDoC CHal CTom EBar ESis GPoy LHol MCas MChe NHol NKay SHer SPla SSvw WDav WHoo WPer
§ ***pseudolanuginosus***	CArn CLew CMea CPar CSFH EBar ECha EMNN Effi GTou LGro LHol MBar MBri MBro MCas NGre NHol NNrd NSel SIng SSmi WAbe WCla WHoo WOak WOld WPer
– 'Hall's Variety'	MBro
§ ***pulegioïdes***	CArn CHun CPar CSFH CSev GPoy LHol MBri SHer WOak WPer WWye
richardii ssp. ***nitidus***	CShe IDai LHol NKay STre WWye
– – ***albus***	SSmi WPer
– – 'Peter Davis'	CArn CHal CMea CShe EBar ESis LHop MCas MPla NHol NKay NMen SBla SChu SHer WDav WPer
rotundifolius	SIde
serpyllum	CRiv CSFH ELan Effi GAbr GCHN IEde LAbb MBri MChe MPla NOak NSel WOld WPer WWye
– ***albus***	CLew CPar CRiv CSFH CShe ECha EMNN EPar ESis GDra GTou MBal MBro MCas NKay NNrd NRed NVic SBla SChu SGil SIng WDav WEas WHil WHoo WOak WThu
– 'Annie Hall'	CDoC CHal CRiv CTom EBre EMNN EPot ESis GAbr LBre LGro LHol MBro MChe NHol NMen NNor NRoo NSel SBod SHer SIng SSmi WAbe WPat WWye
– ***coccineus***	Widely available
– – 'Major'	Effi GDra SIde
– – 'Minor'	GAri MChe NRoo
– 'Dartmoor'	GCal
– 'East Lodge'	MBro NHol
– 'Elfin'	CPar ECar EPar EPot GAbr GTou LHol MBri MBro NGre NMen NNrd NWCA SGil SHer SIng WCla WEas WHil WHoo WThu
– 'Flossy'	NNrd
– 'Goldstream'	CDoC CHal CLew EMNN GAbr LBuc MBar MBri MChe MFir NHol NNrd NRoo NSti STre WCHb WHal WPer WWye
– ssp. ***lanuginosus***	See T. ***pseudolanuginosus***
– 'Lemon Curd'	CDoC CHal CHun GAbr MChe NSti SHer SIde WCHb WWye
– 'Minimus'	CArn CDoC CHal CLew CRiv CSFH ECha ESis ESma GAbr LHol MBri NSti SIde WPer WWye
§ – 'Minor'	CArn CLew ELan EMNN EPot ESis GDra LHol MBro MCas MHig NHol NKay NMen NNrd NSel SIng SSmi WCla WDav WHoo WWin
– 'Minus'	See T. ***s.*** 'Minor'

– 'Pink Chintz' CFis CGle CKel CPar CShe ECha EMNN ESis GDra GTou LBuc LGro LHol MBar MBri MChe MHig MPit NHol NNrd NRed NRoo SBla SIng WAbe WHoo WOak WWin
– 'Rainbow Falls' (v) CHal CHun EMNN GAbr MChe NCat NHol NRed NRoo SHer
– 'Ruby Glow' NHol NRoo
– 'Russetings' CDoC CHal CLew CTom EMNN EOrc EPot LHol MBar MBro MCas MChe MPit NHol NKay NMen NNrd NRoo SIng WDav WOak WWin
– 'September' NHol SGil
– 'Snowdrift' CMea LHol MBar MChe NHol NSti SIde SSmi WAbe WPat WPer
– 'Variegatus' NHol NTow SGil WHil
– 'Vey' CHun EFol EMon EOrc ESis MChe NHol SHer SIng
N 'Silver Posie' See T. ***vulgaris*** 'Silver Posie'
sp. from Turkey NHol
vulgaris CMea CSFH CSev ECha GPoy IEde LAbb MBri MChe NRoo NSel SDix WEas WPer WWye
– ***albus*** SIde WSun
– ***aureus*** LGro MChe NRoo SHer
§ – 'Erectus' CArn ELan EMon LHol MCas NTow SIde SRms WHer WPer WWye
¶ – 'Lucy' SIde
¶ – 'Silver Posie' CArn CFis CHad CSev EBre EFou EHoe ELan LBre LHol NGre NSti SBla SChu SDix WDav WEas WHoo WOak
zygis CArn CHun LHol WCHb WWye

THYSANOTUS (Liliaceae/Asphodelaceae)

¶ ***patersonii*** CMon
¶ ***tuberosus*** CMon

TIARELLA (Saxifragaceae)

collina See T. ***wherryi***
cordifolia Widely available
polyphylla ECro EGol ELan EPar GAbr MRav NHol NNor NSti SWas WCla WCra WCru
– 'Moorgrün' GCal
– pink form CGle SWas
¶ 'Slick Rock' SWas
trifoliata CChu CFis ECro ELan EMon LGan SBla SUsu WRus
– 'Incarnadine' EMon
unifoliata NCat NSal
§ ***wherryi*** CBos CCla CGle CHad CRow ECha EGol ELan ELun EPar GCHN LGre MBri MTho NBro NHol NKay NNor NOak NOrc NSti SAxl SBla SPer SSpi SUsu SWas WEas WHoo WWin
¶ – 'Bronze Beauty' SWas

TIBOUCHINA (Melastomataceae)

* 'Edwardsii' MNew
organensis CB&S CPle ERea
paratropica CPle CTro
semidecandra See T. ***urvilleana***
§ ***urvilleana*** CAbb CB&S CCla CDoC CGre CHEx CPle CSPN CSpe CSun CTre CTro CWit EBak ERea IMal IOrc IReg ISea LAbb LHil MNew SArc SHil SLMG SLon SMad WBod
– 'Grandiflora' ERea IBlr WBod

TIGRIDIA (Iridaceae)

¶ ***douglasii*** WDav
¶ ***durangense*** WDav
¶ – dwarf form WDav
hybrids CSut SDeJ WCru
lutea SDeJ
pavonia CGre LAma LBow MBri NRog SBar

TILIA † (Tiliaceae)

americana CLnd CMCN ENot WMou
¶ – 'Dentata' WMou
– 'Nova' CDoC CTho WMou
– 'Redmond' CTho WMou
amurensis CMCN WMou
♦ ***begoniifolia*** See T. ***dasystyla***
caucasica WMou
'Chelsea Sentinel' SHil
chinensis WMou
¶ ***chingiana*** WMou
cordata CB&S CKin CLnd CPer EHar ELan ENot GBel GRei IOrc LBuc MBal MBri NBee NWea SHBN SPer WDin WMou WStI WWye
– 'Dainty Leaf' WMou
– 'Erecta' COtt WMou
– 'Greenspire' CDoC CTho ENot GBel IOrc LPan MBri SPer WMou
¶ – 'Len Parvin' WMou
¶ – 'Morden' WMou
¶ – 'Plymtree Gold' CTho
¶ – 'Rancho' WMou
¶ – 'Roelvo' WMou
¶ – 'Umbrella' WMou
¶ – 'Westonbirt Dainty Leaf' WMou
¶ – 'Winter Orange' WMou
¶ ***dasystyla*** WMou
¶ – WMou
x ***euchlora*** CBow CDoC CLnd EHar ENot GBel IDai LPan MBri MGos SPer WDin WMou WStI
x ***europaea*** CLnd ELan WMou
– 'Pallida' EHar GBel WMou
– 'Pendula' WMou
– 'Wratislaviensis' CDoC CTho SHil WMou
¶ – 'Zwarte Linde' WMou
x ***flavescens*** 'Glenleven' WMou
¶ 'Harold Hillier' SHil
henryana CLnd CMCN SHil WMou
¶ – var. ***subglabra*** WMou
¶ ***heterophylla*** WMou
¶ – var. ***michauxii*** WMou
insularis CMCN WMou
¶ ***intonsa*** WMou
japonica WMou
kiusiana CMCN GAri WMou
¶ ***koreana*** WMou
¶ ***ledebourii*** WMou

maximowicziana	SSta WMou
'Moltkei'	WMou
mongolica	CLnd CMCN EHar ENot GAri WMou
♦***monticola***	See T. ***heterophylla***
neglecta	WMou
oliveri	CMCN EHar SHil WMou
¶ 'Orbicularis'	WMou
¶***paucicostata***	WMou
'Petiolaris'	CBow CDoC CLnd CTho EHar ELan ENot IOrc SHBN SMad SPer SSta WDin WMou
platyphyllos	CBra CDoC CKin ENot GBel GRei IJoh LBuc MBri SPer WDin WMou
– 'Aurea'	SHil WMou
– 'Corallina'	See T. ***p.*** 'Rubra'
– ***erecta***	See T. ***p.*** 'Fastigiata'
§ – 'Fastigiata'	CTho ENot WMou
– 'Laciniata'	CTho WMou
¶ – 'Örebro'	WMou
– 'Pannonia'	WMou
– 'Prince's Street'	SHil
§ – 'Rubra'	CDoC CLnd CTho ENot IDai IOrc MBar MBri MGos NBee SPer WDin WMou
– 'Tortuosa'	WMou
– 'Vitifolia'	WMou
¶ ***tarquetii***	WMou
tomentosa	CLnd CTho EHar ENot WDin WMou
– 'Brabant'	CDoC EHar ENot IOrc SPer WMou
¶ – 'Erecta'	WMou
¶ – 'Kolkwyk'	WMou
¶ – 'Silver Globe'	WMou
tuan	WMou

TILLAEA See CRASSULA

TILLANDSIA † (Bromeliaceae)

abdita	MBri
acostae	MBri
*– ***concolor***	SPlc
argentea	MBri
baileyi	MBri
balbisiana	MBri
♦***benthamiana***	See T. ***erubescens***
brachycaulos	MBri
– var. ***multiflora***	MBri
bulbosa	MBri
butzii	MBri
caput-medusae	MBri
circinnatoïdes	MBri
cyanea	MBri
x ***erographica***	MBri
****fasciculata*** 'Tricolor' (v)	MBri
filifolia	MBri
flabellata	MBri
*– ***rubra***	SPlc
****himmorum***	SPlc
ionantha	MBri
*– 'Blushing Bride'	SPlc
*– 'Fireball'	SPlc
*– 'Fuego'	SPlc
– ***scaposa***	See T. ***kolbii***
juncea	MBri
§ ***kolbii***	MBri
lampropoda	SPlc
magnusiana	MBri
§ ***matudae***	MBri SPlc
oaxacana	MBri
x ***polita***	SPlc
polystachia	MBri
prodigiosa	SPlc
punctulata	MBri
seleriana	MBri
sphaerocephala	MBri
tenuifolia	
var. ***surinamensis***	See T. ***t. tenuifolia***
tricolor	
var. ***melanocrater***	MBri SPlc
utriculata	SPlc
♦***valenzuelana***	See T. ***variabilis***
♦***velickiana***	See T. ***matudae***
vicentina	MBri
– var. ***glabra***	SPlc
wagneriana	MBri
xerographica	MBri

TIPUANA (Leguminosae)

tipu	CPle

TITHONIA (Compositae)

rotundifolia 'Torch'	SMrm

TOFIELDIA (Liliaceae/Melanthiaceae)

calyculata	NHol

TOLMIEA (Saxifragaceae)

'Goldsplash'	See T. ***menziesii*** 'Taff's Gold'
menziesii	CB&S CBow CGle CHEx CHal CWGN EBar ECha GAri LGro MBri NHol NOrc SHer WByw WCru
– JLS 86284CLOR	EMon
– 'Maculata'	See T. ***m.*** 'Taff's Gold'
§ – 'Taff's Gold' (v)	Widely available
– 'Variegata'	See T. ***m.*** 'Taff's Gold'

TOLPIS (Compositae)

barbata	NSal

TONESTUS (Compositae)

§ ***lyallii***	CNic SBod WHil WPer WWin

TOONA (Meliaceae)

sinensis	CChu CGre CMCN CPMA CPle EHar MBri SSpi WCoo
– 'Flamingo' (v)	CB&S CDoC COtt CPMA EFol EHar LTil SSpi

TORREYA (Taxaceae)

californica	WDin
nucifera	LRHS

TORTULA (moss)

¶ ***ruralis ruraliformis***	LFle

TOVARA See PERSICARIA

TOWNSENDIA (Compositae)

'Boulder'	WEas
exscapa	WDav
florifera	MFos NWCA WHil
formosa	CNic CRiv ELan NNrd NTow SHer WHil WOMN WPer
hookeri	MFos NWCA WHil
**jonesii tumulosa*	CNic
leptotes	NWCA WDav
mensana JCA 8809	CNic
montana	NTow
parryi	CNic EPad
§ *rothrockii*	CNic LGan NGre NHol
¶ *spathulata*	WDav
wilcoxiana hort.	See T. *rothrockii*

TRACHELIUM (Campanulaceae)

§ *asperuloïdes*	SIng
caeruleum	CAbb ERea SFis WCot
¶ *jacquinii*	EPot
– ssp. *rumelianum*	EPad NTow NWCA WPat

TRACHELOSPERMUM (Apocynaceae)

§ *asiaticum*	Widely available
– 'Goshiki'	CB&S MGos
jasminoïdes	CB&S CCla CHEx CMCN CMac CPle CSam CSun CTro EMil ERea IHos IOrc LHop LPan MBri MNew MRav SArc SBla SBra SDry SPer SReu SSpi SSta WBod
– W 776	CBot CHan CMac EBre EPla ERav IOrc LBre NRar SPer SSpi SSta WSHC
§ – 'Japonicum'	GCal NSti SSpi
– 'Major'	MNew
– 'Tricolor' (v)	ERav
– 'Variegatum'	Widely available
– 'Wilsonii'	EMil MNew MSta SReu
majus hort.	See T. *jasminoïdes* 'Japonicum'
– Nakai	See T. *asiaticum*
sp. from Nanking	CHan EPla

TRACHYCARPUS (Palmae)

§ *fortunei*	Widely available
wagnerianus	LPal NPal SArc SDry

TRACHYMENE (Umbelliferae)

See Plant Deletions

TRACHYSTEMON (Boraginaceae)

orientalis	CGle CHEx CPar CRDP EBre ECha EFol EFou EGol ELan EPar EPla ERav LBre MFir MUlv SAxl SIng WCru WHal WWat WWin

TRADESCANTIA (Commelinaceae)

albiflora	See T. *fluminensis*
§ x *andersoniana*	CRiv EFol MBro MFir NNor NSal SHer SUsu WEas WHil WPer WRus WWin
– 'Bilberry Ice'	EFou NTow SFis
– 'Blaby Blue'	MUlv
– 'Blue Stone'	CNic CSco ECha MNFA NFai SRms WThi
– 'Caerulea Plena'	See T. *virginiana* 'C.P.'
– 'Croftway Blue'	SCro
– 'Innocence'	CCla CHad CMil CSco EBlo EBre ECha ECtt EFou EOrc EPla LBre LWad MBel MBri MTho MUlv NOrc SAxl SHer SPer SPla WHoo WMer WRus
– 'Iris Prichard'	CBow CHan CMGP CSco ELan EPar MWat SChu SCro
– 'Isis'	CB&S CBow CCla CMil CPar CSco EBlo ECED ECtt EFou ELan EPar EPla GCHN MBri MUlv NHol NOrc NRoo SAxl SChu SHer SLMG SPer SUsu WOld WTyr WWin
– 'J C Weguelin'	CCla CSco MBri SRms WHoo
– 'Karminglut' ('Carmine Glow')	CB&S CPar EBlo EBre ELan EOrc EPar GCHN LBre MWat NOrc NRoo NVic SHer WHoo WPbr WRus
– 'Leonora'	CDoC CSco ENot MBri NBar NFai WThi
– 'Osprey'	Widely available
– 'Pauline'	CSco EBlo EBre ECtt EFol EFou GCHN LBre MBel MRav MUlv NFai NHol NRoo SChu SUsu WHoo WWin
– 'Purewell Giant'	CKel EBre EPla LBre NBar NCat NHol SChu SPer WHoo WKif
– 'Purple Dome'	CBow CHan CKel CNic CPar CRDP CSco CTom EBre ECED EPla GCHN LBre MBri MRav NHol SChu SPla WHal WHoo WPbr WRus WTyr
– 'Rubra'	CDoC CNic MBel NDea NFai NOrc SChu SCro SFis
– 'Valour'	WHil
– 'Zwanenburg Blue'	CBow EBlo EBre ECha EFou EOrc GCHN LBre MBri MUlv NBar NHol WMer WRus
bracteata	ECar NTow
– *alba*	CPar WThi
brevicaulis	CMon CSco ECha GDra MNFA MTho NOrc SAxl SFis SLMG
canaliculata	See T. *ohiensis*
chilensis	WThi
fluminensis 'Albovittata'	CHal SLMG
– 'Aurea'	MBri
– 'Laekenensis' (v)	MBri
– 'Quicksilver' (v)	CHal MBri
multiflora	See TRIPOGANDRA *m.*
navicularis	See CALLISIA *n.*
§ *ohiensis*	LMay SAxl
§ *pallida*	CHal IBlr
pendula	See TRADESCANTIA *zebrina*
sillamontana	CHal MBri
virginiana	See also T. x *andersoniana*
– 'Alba'	CRiv CSam GCal WPer WThi
§ – 'Caerulea Plena'	ECED EFou ELan EPla MNFA NBee NKay SChu WRus WThi
– 'Rubra'	CHan CSco WThi
§ *zebrina*	CHal SLMG
*– *discolor*	CHal
– *pendula*	See T. *z.*
– 'Purpusii'	CHal
– 'Quadricolor' (v)	CHal

TRAGOPOGON (Compositae)

porrifolius	GPoy ILis
pratensis	CArn CKin MWil NMir
roseus	See T. ***ruber***

TRAPA (Trapaceae)

natans	CHEx CWGN MSta

TREVESIA (Araliaceae)

See Plant Deletions

TRICHOCOLEA (liverwort)

¶ *tomentella*	LFle

TRICHOPHORUM (Cyperaceae)

cespitosum	ETPC

TRICUSPIDARIA See **CRINODENDRON**

TRICYRTIS (Liliaceae/Convallariaceae)

¶ 'Adbane'	CBro CRDP LRHS MBri
bakeri	See T. ***latifolia***
flava	WThi
formosana	Widely available
– 'Shelley's'	SHig
§ – Stolonifera Group	CAvo CB&S CBro CChu CCla CHan CLew CPar CRDP CShe ECha EFou EGol ELan ELun EPar LHop MBal MPar MRav MUlv NDea NFai SCro SPer WPbr WRus WThi WWin
hirta	Widely available
§ – *alba*	CBro CCla CHan CRiv CWGN ECar ECro ELan EPot MBal MBro MPlt WPbr WThi WWin
– 'Miyazaki'	CHan CRDP EFou SCro WCru WPbr WThi
– 'Variegata'	CAvo CRDP ECha EFol EGol LGre WCot WCru WHal
N Hototogisu	CRDP EMon MTho
japonica	See T. ***hirta***
¶ *lambertii*	EPot
§ *latifolia*	CAvo CBro CChu CCla CRDP EBul ECar ECro ELun EPar EPot LGre MBro MNFA MPar SBla SWas WCot WCru WHoo WPer WThi
¶ 'Lilac Towers'	EPar
macrantha	MBal SHig SIng WCru WPer
– ssp. *macranthopsis*	EPot SBla SWas WCru
* *macrocarpa*	NKay
N *macropoda*	CChu CCla CGle CSam ECha ECro EPar MPar NHol WCru WHal WThi
ohsumiensis	CGle CHan CRDP ECar EPar EPot LGre MTho WCot WThi
perfoliata	LGre SWas WCot WThi
puberula	MPar
¶ 'Shimone'	CBro CRDP LRHS MBri
stolonifera	See T. ***formosana*** Stolonifera Group
¶ 'Tojen'	CBro CRDP LRHS MBri
'White Towers'	CChu CHad CSpe ECha EMon EPar LGre MNFA NSti SAxl SWas WPbr WThi

TRIENTALIS (Primulaceae)

¶ *borealis*	CNic

TRIFOLIUM (Leguminosae)

alpinum	GDra
campestre	CKin
incarnatum	SIde WHer
ochroleucum	MWil NMir
pannonicum	GCal NSti
¶ *pratense* 'Chocolate'	EPla
– 'Dolly North'	See T. ***p.*** 'Susan Smith'
¶ – 'Harlequin'	EPla
¶ – 'Ice Cool'	EPla
§ – 'Susan Smith' (v)	CGle CHan CLew CMGP CMil CRDP CRow EBre ECha EHal EJud EMar EMon GAbr IBlr LBre LHop MBel MTho NMir SUsu WByw WHer
repens	CHEx NGre
– 'Aureum'	MBal
– 'Gold Net'	See T. ***pratense*** 'Susan Smith'
– 'Good Luck'	CRow
– 'Pentaphyllum'	See T. ***r.*** 'Quinquefolium'
– 'Purpurascens'	CArn CBre CDec CHEx CHan CKel CMer CRiv CRow EFol GCal GDra ILis MBal MCas MPar NRoo NSel SAxl SDix WOak
§ – 'Purpurascens Quadrifolium'	CHal CLew CNic ECha ELan EMar EPla MBel MRav NMir SHer SIng SPer WRus WWin
– 'Quadrifolium'	EHoe EPar IBar
§ – 'Quinquefolium'	WEas WPer
– 'Tetraphyllum Purpureum'	See T. ***r.*** 'Purpurascens Quadrifolium'
*– 'Variegatum'	EFol
– 'Wheatfen' (v)	CNat EMon
stellatum	WThi
uniflorum	WThu

TRIGONELLA (Leguminosae)

foenum-graecum	CArn GPoy NSal SIde WWye

TRILLIUM † (Liliaceae/Trilliaceae)

apetalon	WChr
catesbyi	CBro ELan EPot LAma NRog NSal WChr
cernuum	CBro CWGN EPot LAma NHol NRog WChr
chloropetalum	CBro CChu GCra GDra
– *rubrum*	SWas
cuneatum	CB&S CBro CChu CMGP CWGN ELan EPar EPot LAma MNFA MTho NHol NRog NRoo SPer SSpi SUsu WChr WCru
¶ – red form	CRDP
erectum	CArn CAvo CB&S CBro CChu CCla COtt CRDP CWGN ELan EPar EPot GDra GPoy LAma LBow MBal MTho NHol NRog NSal SAxl SDeJ SIng SPer SSpi WChr
§ – f. *albiflorum*	CBro EPot LAma NHol NSal WChr WCru
– f. *luteum*	CBro LAma NHol
grandiflorum	Widely available

– *flore-pleno*	EBlo EBre LBre SPou SSpi SWas WThu
kamtschaticum	CAvo LAma NHar NHol WChr
lancifolium	WChr
§ *luteum*	CB&S CBro CChu CWGN ELan EPar EPot LAma LBow NHar NHol NKay NRog NRoo NSti SDeJ SIng SPer SUsu WChr WCru
nivale	WChr
ovatum	EPot GDra LAma WChr
– var. *hibbersonii*	CAvo CBro GArf GDra MBal SWas
pusillum var. *virginianum*	CBro LAma
recurvatum	CB&S CWGN EPar EPot LAma NHol NRog NRoo NSti SDeJ SIng SPer WChr
rivale	CBro LAma SWas WOMN WThu
rugelii	LAma NHol WChr
sessile	CAvo CCla CDoC CHEx CKel CRDP EBlo EBre ELan EPot LAma LBow LBre NHol NKay SDeJ SPer SUsu
– var. *luteum*	See T. ***luteum***
smallii	LAma NHol
stylosum	See T. ***catesbyi***
sulcatum	GDra
tschonoskii	LAma NHol WChr
undulatum	CHEx CRDP CWGN EPot LAma LBow NHol SDeJ WChr WCru
vaseyi	CBro LAma MNFA NHol WChr
viride	ELan EPot LAma NHol WChr WCru

TRINIA (Umbelliferae)

* *grandiflora*	EMon

TRIOSTEUM (Caprifoliaceae)
See Plant Deletions

TRIPETALEIA (Ericaceae)
See Plant Deletions

TRIPLEUROSPERUM (Compositae)

maritimum	See MATRICARIA ***maritima***

TRIPOGANDRA (Commelinaceae)

§ *multiflora*	CHal

TRIPTEROSPERMUM (Gentianaceae)

¶ *volubile* EMAK 0869	NHol

TRIPTERYGIUM (Celastraceae)

regelii MSF 833	SSpi

TRISTAGMA (Liliaceae/Alliaceae)

'Rolf Fiedler'	See IPHEION 'R.F.'
♦ *uniflorum*	See IPHEION ***u.***

TRISTANIA (Myrtaceae)

conferta	CPle

TRITELEIA (Liliaceae/Alliaceae)

bridgesii	EBul LBow
* *californica*	ETub WChr
¶ *grandiflora*	WPer
hyacintha	LAma LBow MFos WChr
ixioïdes ixioïdes	WChr
– var. *scabra*	WChr
¶ – 'Splendens'	ETub
§ *laxa*	CAvo CCla LAma NRog
– PJC 951	WChr
– 'Koningin Fabiola' ('Queen Fabiola')	CCla ETub LAma LBow MBri NRog WPer
§ *peduncularis*	LAma LBow MFos WChr
x *tubergenii*	EPot LAma LBow WThi
uniflora	See IPHEION ***uniflorum***

TRITICUM (Gramineae)
See Plant Deletions

TRITONIA (Iridaceae)

crocata	ETub GCal LBow NRog WByw
§ *disticha* ssp. *rubrolucens*	CB&S CBro CChu CElw CHan CRDP ECha GAri GCal IDai MBri MFir NRoo WPbr
¶ 'Orange Delight'	WCot
rosea	See T. ***distica rubrolucens***
¶ *securigera*	CMon
¶ *squalida*	WCot

TROCHETIOPSIS (Sterculiaceae)

melanoxylon	EPad

TROCHOCARPA (Epacridaceae)

¶ *thymifolia*	WThu

TROCHODENDRON (Trochodendraceae)

aralioïdes	CB&S CCla CGre EBar EGol EHar ENot MGos MUlv SArc SHil SLon SMad SReu SSta WBod WHCr WWat

TROLLIUS † (Ranunculaceae)

acaulis	CRDP GDra MTho NGre NHar NHol WHil
§ *chinensis*	CBow ECha NHol
– 'Golden Queen'	CBow CRDP CSco CWes EBlo EBre ECtt EFou ELan EMar LAbb LBre MNFA MUlv MWat NNor NRoo SFis SPer SSpi WCru WEas WHen WHil WHoo WPer
– 'Imperial Orange'	CCla CGle CMGP WTyr
x *cultorum* 'Alabaster'	CRow ECha
– 'Baudirektor Linne'	CPar CRDP EBre ECtt GCHN LBre NKay NRoo
– Bressingham hybrids	EBre LBre NRoo
– 'Canary Bird'	CBow CSco EGol ELan SHer SPer SPla SRms
¶ – 'Commander-in-Chief'	COtt
– 'Earliest of All'	CCla CDoC CGle CMGP CSco NHol NKay NRoo SHig SPla SRms
– 'Etna'	GCal MBri
– 'Feuertroll' ('Fireglobe')	CDoC CKel CPar CWGN EBlo ECha NBar SHig
– 'Golden Cup'	CCla NHol NRoo WHal
– 'Golden Monarch'	CWGN EPar
– 'Goldquelle'	EHon MWat NVic SHig
– 'Goliath'	CGle CMGP GCal NRoo

– 'Helios'	CGle CSam ECha GCal
– 'Lemon Queen'	CCla CSco CWGN CWes EPar GCal NNor SLon WRus
– 'Maigold'	MBri
– 'Orange Crest'	GCal
– 'Orange Princess'	CSam CWGN EBre GAri LBre LWad MBal NDea NHol SHig SLon SPer
– 'Prichard's Giant'	CSco
– 'Salamander'	NKay
– 'Superbus'	CCla CKel ELan EPar MBri MWat NKay NRoo SHig SPer SSpi WRus
europaeus	CBot CBow CRow CSam ECar ECha EPad EPot LWad MBal MBro MNFA NDea NMir NRoo NRya SUsu WBon WCla WHoo WSun
ledebourii hort.	See T. ***chinensis***
pumilus	CBos CGle CNic ECha ELan EMar EPad EPar LBee MHig NHol NMen NNrd NWCA SHer SIng SUsu WHil
– 'Wargrave'	NMen NNrd WEas WPer
¶ ***riederianus***	EPot
yunnanensis	CGle CRDP ELan EMon ESis GDra MBal NGre SLon

TROPAEOLUM † (Tropaeolaceae)

ciliatum	CMon CRDP EOrc GCal MTho NCat SSpi WChr WCru WHer WMar WNor
majus	CHEx LHol SIde
– 'Alaska' (v)	CRDP EMon
*– 'Clive Innes'	ERea
¶– 'Crimson Velvet'	CRDP LHil
¶– 'Empress of India'	WEas
– 'Hermine Grashoff'	CBos CElw CRDP CRow ELan ERea GCal LHil NBro SAxl SDix SMad WCru WEas
¶– 'Red Wonder'	SMad
– 'Variegatum'	EMon ERea
¶ ***nasturtium***	EMFW
pentaphyllum	CRDP CRow GCal IBlr MTho
peregrinum	MTho
speciosum	Widely available
sylvestre	LBow WCru
tricolorum	CAvo CMon CRiv EPot MTho SDix WAbe WChr
tuberosum	CB&S CCMG CGle CMHG CRiv EPot GCal GPoy MBal MFir SLon WAbe WEas
– 'Ken Aslet'	Widely available
– P J Christian's form	NRog
– 'Pilifera Sidney'	CGle CRDP IBlr NCat NTow SAxl WCru WHer

TSUGA (Pinaceae)

canadensis	CGre EHar EHul ENHC GAri IDai LCon MBar SHBN SPer WDin
– 'Abbot's Dwarf'	CKen
¶– 'Albospica'	LBee
– 'Ammerland'	LCon
– 'Aurea'	LCon MBar
– 'Bennett'	EHul EPot LCon MBar WDin
– 'Brandley'	CKen
– 'Cinnamonea'	CKen
– 'Coffin'	CKen
– 'Cole'	CKen EBre EHar LBre LCon MBar MBri NHol SHBN
– 'Compacta'	LCon
¶– 'Curley'	CKen
– 'Curtis Ideal'	CKen
– 'Dwarf Pyramid'	MBar
– 'Dwarf Whitetip'	EPla LCon
– 'Everitt Golden'	CKen
– 'Fantana'	EHul LBee LCon LLin MBar SBod SLim
– 'Gentsch Snowflake'	CKen EPla
– 'Golden Splendour'	EPla
¶– 'Greenwood Lake'	EPla
– 'Horsford'	CKen MPla
– 'Hussii'	CKen
– 'Jacqueline Verkade'	CKen
– 'Jeddeloh'	Widely available
– 'Jervis'	CKen
– 'Lutea'	CKen
– 'Minima'	MBar
– 'Minuta'	CKen EHul ESis LBee LCon NHar
– 'Nana'	CMac EHul IOrc LCon
– 'Palomino'	CKen
– 'Pendula'	CDoC CKen CSco EHar EHul ENot LBee LCon MAsh MBar MBri MWat NHar SHil SLim WThu
– 'Prostrata'	CKen
– 'Rugg's Washington'	CKen MPla
– 'Verkade Petite'	CKen
– 'Verkade Recurved'	CKen MBar
– 'Von Helms Dwarf'	CKen
*– 'Warnham'	CKen LBee LCon
caroliniana 'La Bar Weeping'	CKen
chinensis	CMCN
diversifolia	EPot
– 'Nana'	CKen
heterophylla	CBra CDoC CMCN CPer EHar ENot GAri GRei IOrc LBee LBuc LCon MBar NWea SHBN SMad SPer STre WDin
– 'Iron Spring'	CKen
menziesii	See PSEUDOTSUGA ***menziesii***
mertensiana	LRHS
I – 'Glauca Nana'	CKen

TSUSIOPHYLLUM (Ericaceae)

tanakae	GAri GGGa WAbe

TUBERARIA (Cistaceae)

guttata	CNat WCru
lignosa	ESma MBro NHol WAbe WCla WCru WDav WHil

TULBAGHIA † (Liliaceae/Alliaceae)

capensis	LGre
cepacea	EPot GCal WCot WOMN
– var. ***maritima***	CMon WThi
coddii	LGre
cominsii	LGre
♦ ***fragrans***	See T. ***simmleri***
natalensis	LGre
§ ***simmleri***	CAvo CMon CSam ITim

violacea	CAvo CChu CHan CMon CSpe EBul ERav ESma GCal IBlr LAbb LAma MTho SHer SMrm SSpi SUsu SWas
– ***pallida***	CAvo CChu LGre SAxl SWas
§ – 'Silver Lace' (v)	CAvo CChu CGle CHan CRow CSpe ECha ELan EPla ERav ERea LGre LHop MTho SIgm SMrm WCot WThi
¶ – ***tricolor***	CMon
– ***variegata***	See T. *v.* 'Silver Lace'

TULIPA † (Liliaceae/Liliaceae)

'Abu Hassan' (3)	LAma
acuminata	CBro LAma LBow SIng
'Ad Rem' (4)	LAma
'Addis' (14)	LAma
'African Queen' (3)	LBlo
aitchisonii	See T. ***clusiana***
'Aladdin' (6)	LAma LBlo NRog
'Alaska' (6)	LAma
albertii	LAma
'Albino' (3)	LAma
aleppensis	LAma
'Aleppo' (7)	LAma
'Alfred Cortot' (12)	LAma
'Ali Baba' (14)	MBri
'Alice Leclercq' (2)	LAma
'All Bright' (5)	LAma
'Allegretto' (11)	LAma NRog
altaica	EPot LAma
¶ ***amabilis*** PF 8955	CMon
'Amulet' (3)	LAma
'Ancilla' (12)	CBro LAma LBlo
'Angélique' (11)	ETub LAma LBlo MBri
'Anne Claire' (3)	LAma
'Anneke' (3)	LAma
'Antwerp' (3)	LAma
'Apeldoorn' (4)	ETub LAma LBlo MBri NRog
'Apeldoorn's Elite' (4)	LAma LBlo NRog
'Apricot Beauty' (1)	ETub LAma LBlo LBow MBri NBir NRog
'Apricot Jewel'	See T. ***linifolia*** 'A.J.'
'Apricot Parrot' (10)	LAma LBlo NRog
¶ 'Arabian Mystery' (3)	NBir
'Arie Alkemade's Memory (2)	LBlo
'Aristocrat' (5)	LAma
'Arlington' (5)	LAma
'Arma' (7)	LAma
'Artist' (8)	CAvo LAma LBlo LBow NBir
'Asta Nielsen' (5)	LAma
'Athleet' (3)	LAma
'Attila' (3)	ETub LAma LBlo NRog
aucheriana	CBro CMon EPot ETub LAma LBow SIng WChr WCot
'Aurea'	See T. ***greigii*** 'A.'
'Aureola' (3)	LAma
bakeri	See T. ***saxatilis*** Bakeri Group
'Balalaika' (5)	LAma
'Ballade' (6)	LBlo
'Bandoeng' (3)	LAma
batalinii	See T. ***linifolia*** Batalinii Group
* 'Beauty' (7)	LAma
'Beauty of Apeldoorn' (4)	LAma LBlo NRog
'Belcanto' (3)	LAma
'Bellflower' (7)	LAma
'Bellona' (1)	ETub LAma
'Berlioz' (12)	LAma LBlo
biebersteiniana	LAma WChr
§ ***biflora***	CAvo CBro EPot ETub LAma LBow NRog SIng WChr
bifloriformis	EPot WChr
'Big Chief' (4)	LAma MBri
'Bing Crosby' (3)	ETub LAma
'Black Parrot' (10)	LAma LBlo LBow
'Black Swan' (5)	LBlo
'Bleu Aimable' (5)	ETub LAma LBlo
'Blizzard' (1)	LBlo
'Blue Heron' (7)	LAma
'Blue Parrot' (10)	LAma LBlo NRog
'Bonanza' (11)	LAma
'Boule de Neige' (2)	LAma
'Bravissimo' (2)	MBri
'Brilliant Star' (1)	LAma LBlo MBri
'Bruno Walter' (3)	LAma
'Burgundy' (7)	ETub LAma
'Burgundy Lace' (7)	LAma LBlo
'Burns' (7)	LAma
butkovii	LAma
'Cabaret' (6)	LAma
'Caland' (10)	LAma
'Candela' (13)	LAma
'Cantata' (13)	CBro LAma LBlo
'Cantor' (5)	LAma
'Cape Cod' (14)	LAma NRog
'Caprice' (10)	LAma
'Captain Fryatt' (6)	LAma
carinata	LAma
'Carlton' (2)	ETub LAma NRog
'Carnaval de Nice' (11/v)	ETub LAma LBlo MBri
'Cashmir' (5)	LAma
'Cassini' (3)	LAma LBlo
§ ***celsiana***	CMon EPot ETub LAma
'César Franck' (12)	LAma
'Charles' (1)	LAma
'Charles Needham' (5)	LAma
'China Pink' (6)	CAvo ETub LAma LBlo LBow NRog
'Chopin' (12)	LAma NRog
'Christmas Marvel' (1)	ETub LAma
chrysantha	See T. ***clusiana c.***
'Clara Butt' (5)	LAma LBlo NRog
§ ***clusiana***	CAvo CBro LAma LBlo LBow SIng WChr
§ – var. ***chrysantha*** (15)	CAvo LAma LBlo LBow NRog SIng
– – 'Tubergen's Gem'	EPar LAma MBri
– ***clusianoïdes***	WChr
– 'Cynthia'	EPar EPot LAma SIng SUsu
§ – var. ***stellata***	LAma
'Compliment' (6)	LAma
'Concerto' (13)	CBro ETub LAma
'Cordell Hull' (5)	CAvo NRog
'Coriolan' (3)	LAma
'Corona' (12)	LAma
'Corrie Kok' (3)	LAma
'Corsage' (14)	LAma LBlo
'Couleur Cardinal' (1)	ETub LAma LBow NRog
* 'Crispa Pink' (7)	LAma
'Crystal Beauty' (7)	NRog
'Dancing Show' (8)	LAma

dasystemon	EPot LAma
'Daydream' (4)	LBlo
*'Delano' (3)	LAma
'Diana' (1)	ETub LAma NRog
'Diantha' (14)	LAma
didieri	CAvo LAma
'Dillenburg' (5)	LAma
'Dix' Favourite' (5)	LAma
'Doctor James Parkinson' (3)	LAma
'Doctor Plesman' (1)	LAma LBlo
'Doll's Minuet' (8)	LAma
'Don Quichotte' (3)	LAma
'Donna Bella' (14)	LAma
'Douglas Bader' (3)	CAvo LAma NRog
'Dreaming Maid' (3)	LAma LBlo
'Duke of Wellington' (5)	LAma
*'Dutch Gold' (3)	LAma
'Dyanito' (6)	CAvo LAma
'Early Harvest' (12)	LAma
'Early Light' (1)	LAma
'Easter Fire' (3)	LAma
'Easter Parade' (13)	EWal LAma
'Easter Surprise' (14)	LAma
§ ***edulis***	CAvo CMon
eichleri	See T. ***undulatifolia***
'El Toreador' (2)	LAma
'Electra' (2)	LAma MBri
'Elegant Lady' (6)	ETub
'Elizabeth Arden' (4)	ETub LAma LBlo
'Elmus' (3)	LAma
'Esperanto' (8/v)	ETub LBlo NRog
'Estella Rijnveld' (10)	LAma LBlo LBow NBir NRog
'Esther' (5)	ETub LAma
'Etude' (3)	LAma
'Fair Lady' (12)	LAma
'Fancy Frills' (7)	LBlo
'Fantasy' (10)	LAma LBlo LBow
'Fashion' (12)	LAma
ferganica	CMon EPot LAma LBow
'Feu Superbe' (13)	LAma
'Fidelio' (3)	LBlo
'Fireside'	See T. 'Vlammenspel'
'First Lady' (3)	LAma
'Flair' (1)	LAma
'Flaming Parrot' (10)	LAma LBlo LBow
'Floradale' (4)	LAma
'Florosa' (8)	LAma
'Flying Dutchman' (5)	LAma
fosteriana	MBri
'Franfurt' (3)	LAma
'Franz Léhar' (12)	LAma
'Frasquita' (5)	LAma
'Fresco' (14)	LAma
'Fringed Apeldoorn' (7)	NRog
'Fringed Beauty' (2)	ETub MBri
'Fringed Elegance' (7)	LAma
'Fritz Kreisler' (12)	LAma
fulgens	LAma
'G W Leak' (5)	LAma
'Gaiety' (12)	LAma
'Galata' (13)	LAma
galatica	LAma
'Garanza' (2)	LAma LBlo
'Garden Party' (3)	LAma LBlo
'Generaal de Wet' (1)	ETub LAma LBlo MBri
'General Eisenhower' (4)	LAma
'Georgette' (5)	ETub LAma LBlo MBri NRog
'Giuseppe Verdi' (12)	EWal LAma LBow MBri NRog
'Glück' (12)	LAma LBlo
'Gold Medal' (11)	LAma MBri
'Golden Age' (5)	LAma LBlo
'Golden Apeldoorn' (4)	ETub LAma LBlo MBri NRog
'Golden Artist' (8)	LAma LBlo MBri NRog
'Golden Eagle' (13)	LAma
'Golden Eddy' (3)	LAma
'Golden Emperor' (13)	LAma
'Golden Harvest' (5)	LAma
'Golden Melody' (3)	ETub LAma LBlo NRog
'Golden Oxford' (4)	LAma
'Golden Parade' (4)	LAma
*'Golden Show' (3)	LAma
'Golden Springtime' (4)	LAma
'Goldenes Deutschland' (4)	LAma
'Gordon Cooper' (4)	LAma
'Goudstuk' (12)	LAma
'Goya' (2)	LAma
'Graceful' (14)	LAma
'Grand Prix' (13)	LAma
'Green Eyes' (8)	LAma
'Green Spot' (8)	LAma
greigii	CBro CMon
– 'Aurea'	CMon LRHS
grengiolensis	CAvo EPot LAma
'Greuze' (5)	LAma
'Grevel' (3)	LAma
'Groenland' (8)	LAma LBlo
'Gudoshnik' (4)	LAma LBow
'Hadley' (1)	LAma
hageri	CMon ETub LAma SIng
– 'Splendens'	ETub LAma
'Halcro' (5)	ETub LAma
'Heart's Delight' (12)	CAvo CBro ETub EWal LAma LBlo LBow NRog
'Henry Ford' (5)	LAma
'Hermione' (11)	LBlo
'Hibernia' (3)	LAma
'High Society' (3)	LBlo
hissarica	EPot WChr
'Hit Parade' (13)	LAma
'Hoangho' (2)	LAma
'Holland's Glorie' (5)	LAma
'Hollywood' (8)	LAma LBlo LBow
hoogiana	LAma
§ ***humilis***	CAvo CBro EPar EPot ETub LAma LBow SIng
§ – ***pulchella*** Albocaerulea Oculata Group	EPot LAma WChr
– 'Eastern Star'	LAma
– 'Odalisque'	EPot LAma
– 'Pallida'	LRHS
– 'Persian Pearl'	EPot LAma NRog SIng
– Violacea Group	CAvo CCla EPar ETub LAma SIng
– 'Violet Queen'	LBlo
– yellow centre	LAma LBow
§ ***humilis*** Violacea Group black centre	CBro LRHS
– – dark yellow centre	CBro LRHS SIng
'Humming Bird' (8)	LBlo LBow
'Humoresque' (13)	LAma
'Hytuna' (2)	LAma NRog
'Ibis' (1)	LAma

'Ile de France' (5)	LAma
ingens	LAma LRHS
'Inglescombe Yellow' (5)	LAma
'Inzell' (3)	LAma
'Jacqueline' (6)	LAma
'James V Forrestal' (10)	LAma
'Jan Vermeer' (2)	LAma
'Jeantine' (12)	LAma
'Jewel of Spring' (4)	LAma LBlo
'Jimmy ' (3)	NRog
'Jockey Cap' (14)	LAma
'Joffre' (1)	LAma MBri
'Johann Gutenberg' (7)	LBlo
'Johann Strauss' (12)	CAvo CBro ETub LAma LBlo MBri
'Johanna' (3)	LAma
'Juan' (13)	LAma MBri
'Kansas' (3)	LAma
¶ ***karabaghensis***	CMon
'Karel Doorman' (10)	LAma LBlo
'Kareol' (2)	LAma
kaufmanniana	CAvo CBro ETub LBow NRog SIng SRms
§ 'Kees Nelis' (3)	LAma LBlo MBri NRog
'Keizerskroon' (1)	LAma LBlo NRog
'Kingsblood' (5)	LAma
kolpakowskiana	LAma MBri NRog SIng
§ 'Koningin Wilhemina' (4)	LBlo
'Kryptos' (5)	LBlo
kurdica	LAma
'La Tulipe Noire' (5)	LAma
'Lady Diana' (14)	LAma MBri
lanata	LAma LRHS
'Landseadel's Supreme' (5)	LAma LBlo
'Large Copper' (14)	LAma
'Lefeber's Favourite' (4)	LAma
'Libretto' (3)	LAma
'Lighting Sun' (5)	LBlo
'Lilac Perfection' (11)	LBlo
'Lilac Time' (6)	LAma
'Lilac Wonder'	See T. ***saxatilis*** 'L.W.'
linifolia	CAvo CMea EPar EPot ETub LAma LBlo LBow NRog SIng WAbe WChr
§ ***linifolia*** Batalinii Group	CBro EPot LAma LBow NRog SIng
§ – – 'Apricot Jewel'	CAvo CBro
– – 'Bright Gem' (15)	CAvo CBro EPot ETub LAma LBow NRog SIng WHoo
– – 'Bronze Charm'	CAvo CBro LAma
– – 'Red Gem'	CBro LAma
– – 'Yellow Jewel'	LAma
linifolia Maximowiczii Group	CBro
'London' (4)	LAma
'Longfellow' (14)	LAma
'Love Song' (12)	LAma LBlo
'Lucifer' (7)	LAma
'Lucky Strike' (3)	LAma
§ 'Lustige Witwe' (3)	LAma
§ 'Madame Lefeber ' (13)	CBro ETub EWal LAma LBlo LBow MBri
'Madame Spoor' (3)	LAma
'Magier' (5)	LAma
'Maja' (7)	LAma LBlo
'Mamasa' (5)	LAma
'March of Time' (14)	MBri
'Maréchal Niel' (2)	LAma
'Mariette' (6)	LAma LBlo
'Marilyn' (6)	ETub LBlo
'Marjolein' (6)	LBlo
marjoletii	CAvo CBro ETub LAma LBow NRog SIng
'Marquette' (2)	LAma
'Mary Ann' (14)	LAma
'Maskerade' (5)	LAma
'Maureen' (5)	ETub LAma
mauritiana	LAma
maximowiczii	LAma LBow
'Maytime' (6)	LAma LBlo
'Maywonder' (11)	LAma
'Meissner Porzellan' (3)	LBlo
'Menton' (5)	ETub
'Merry Widow'	See T. 'Lustige Witwe'
'Mickey Mouse' (1)	NRog
'Minerva' (3)	NRog
'Mirella' (5)	LBlo
'Mirjoran' (3)	LAma
'Miss Holland' (3)	MBri
§ ***montana***	CBro EPot LAma LBow WChr
'Monte Carlo' (2)	ETub LAma LBlo
'Most Miles' (5)	LAma
'Mount Tacoma' (11)	ETub LAma LBlo MBri NRog
'Mr van der Hoef' (2)	LAma MBri
'Mrs John T Scheepers' (5)	LAma LBlo
'Murillo' (2)	LAma
'Murillo Maxima' (2)	LAma
'My Lady' (4)	LAma
'Negrita' (3)	LAma
neustreuvae	WChr
'New Design' (3/v)	ETub LAma LBlo MBri NRog
'Olympic Flame' (4)	LBlo
'Olympic Gold' (4)	LBlo
'Orange Bouquet' (5)	LAma LBlo NRog
'Orange Cassini' (3)	LAma
'Orange Elite' (14)	LAma MBri
'Orange Emperor' (13)	LAma LBlo MBri NRog
'Orange Favourite' (10)	LAma LBlo LBow
'Orange Goblet' (4)	LAma
'Orange Monarch' (3)	ETub LAma
'Orange Sun'	See T. 'Oranjezon'
'Orange Triumph' (11)	MBri
'Orange Wonder' (3)	LAma
'Oranje Nassau' (2)	LAma LBlo MBri NRog
§ 'Oranjezon' (4)	LAma
'Oratorio' (14)	LAma LBlo MBri
'Oriental Beauty' (14)	LAma NRog
'Oriental Splendour' (14)	EWal LAma
'Ornament' (3)	LAma
orphanidea	EPot LAma LBow SIng
– ***flava***	CBro CMon ETub LAma
§ – Whittallii Group	CAvo CBro CMon EPot ETub LAma LBow NRog SIng
ostrowskiana	LAma
'Oxford' (4)	LAma
'Oxford's Elite' (4)	LAma
'Page Polka' (3)	LAma
'Palestrina' (5)	LAma LBlo
* 'Pandit Nehru' (3)	LAma
'Pandour' (14)	LAma MBri
'Parade' (4)	LAma MBri
'Paris' (3)	LAma

'Paul Crampel' (2) LAma
'Paul Richter' (3) LAma
'Pax' (3) LAma
'Peach Blossom' (2) ETub LAma LBlo LBow MBri NRog
¶ 'Peer Gynt' ETub
'Peerless Pink' (3) LAma
'Perfecta' (10) LBow
'Perlina' (14) LAma
persica See T. ***celsiana***
'Philippe de Comines' (5) LAma
'Picture' (5) LAma LBlo
'Pimpernel' (8) LAma
'Pink Beauty' (1) LAma LBlo
'Pink Impression' (4) LAma
'Pink Trophy' (1) LAma
'Pinkeen' (13) LAma
'Pinocchio' (14) EWal NRog
'Plaisir' (14) ETub LAma LBlo MBri
platystigma CAvo LAma LBow
'Polo' (13) LAma
polychroma See T. ***biflora***
praestans LAma
– 'Fusilier' CAvo CBro EPot ETub EWal LAma LBlo LBow MBri NRog SIng
– 'Unicum' (v) ETub LAma LBlo MBri NRog SIng WHil
– 'Van Tubergen's Variety' ETub LAma NRog
'Preludium' (3) LAma
'President Kennedy' (4) LAma
¶ ***primulina*** CMon
'Prince Karl Philip' (3) NRog
'Prince of Austria' (1) LAma
'Princeps' (13) CBro EWal LAma MBri
'Princess Elizabeth' (5) LAma
'Princess Margaret Rose' (5) LAma
'Prins Carnaval' (1) LAma
'Prinses Irene' (1) ETub LAma LBlo LBow MBri NBir
'Prinses Margriet' (1) LBlo
'Prominence' (3) LAma
pulchella See T. ***humilis pulchella***
– ***humilis*** See T. ***humilis***
§ 'Purissima' (13) CAvo CBro ETub LAma LBlo LBow
'Purple Cupland' (5) LAma
'Queen' (4) LAma
'Queen Ingrid' (14) LAma
'Queen of Bartigons' (5) LAma LBlo NRog
'Queen of Night' (5) CAvo ETub LAma LBlo LBow MBri
'Queen of Sheba' (6) LAma LBlo
'Queen Wilhelmina' See T. 'Koningin Wilhelmina'
'Recreado' (3) ETub LAma
'Red Champion' (10) LAma
'Red Emperor' See T. 'Madame Lefeber'
'Red Georgette' (5) MBri
'Red Matador' (4) LAma
'Red Parrot' (10) LAma
'Red Present' (3) LAma
'Red Riding Hood' (14) CAvo CBro EPot ETub EWal LAma LBlo LBow MBri NBir NRog
'Red Sensation' (10) LAma
'Red Shine' (6) LAma LBlo
'Redwing' (7) LBlo
'Reforma' (3) LAma
Rembrandt MBri
'Renown' (5) LAma
'Rheingold' (2) LAma LBlo
rhodopea See T. ***urumoffii***
'Rijnland' (3) LAma
'Ringo' See T. 'Kees Nelis'
'Robinea' (3) LBlo
'Rockery Beauty' (13) LAma
'Rockery Master' (14) LAma
'Rockery Wonder' (14) LAma
* 'Rose Emperor' (13) LAma
'Rosy Wings' (5) LAma LBlo
'San Marino' (5) LBlo
saxatilis CAvo CBro CCla EPot LAma MBri NRog SIng
¶ – MS 769 CMon
§ – Bakeri Group EPot LAma WChr
§ – 'Lilac Wonder' CAvo CBro CRDP LAma LBlo MBri NRog SIng
'Scarlet Cardinal' (2) LAma LBlo
'Scarlett O'Hara' (5) LAma
'Schoonoord' (2) ETub LAma MBri
schrenkii ETub LAma SIng
'Scotch Lassie' (5) LAma
'Shakespeare' (12) CBro LAma LBlo LBow NRog
'Shirley' (5) CAvo ETub LAma LBlo MBri NRog
'Showwinner' (12) CBro ETub LAma LBlo MBri
'Sigrid Undset' (5) LAma
'Silentia' (3) LAma
'Sint Maarten' (1) LAma
'Smiling Queen' (5) LAma LBlo
'Snow Queen' (2) LBlo
'Snowflake' (3) LAma
'Snowpeak' (5) LAma LBlo
sogdiana LAma
'Sorbet' (5) LAma LBlo
sosnowskyi LRHS
'Sothis' (7) LAma
'Spalding' (3) LAma
'Sparkling Fire' (14) ETub LAma
'Spectacular Gold' See T. 'Goldenes Deutschland'
sprengeri CAvo CBro CMon ELan EPar LAma SIng SSpi
– Trotter's form WCot
'Spring Green' (8) ETub LAma LBlo LBow MBri NRog
'Spring Pearl' (13) LAma LBlo
'Spring Song' (4) LAma
stellata See T. ***clusiana s.***
'Stockholm' (2) LAma LBlo
'Stresa' (12) CBro LAma LBlo
'Striped Apeldoorn' (4) LAma NRog
subpraestans EPot LAma
'Success' (3) LAma
'Summit' (13) LAma
'Sundew' (7) LAma NRog
'Sunkist' (5) LAma
'Sunray' (3) LAma
'Susan Oliver' (8) LAma
'Sussex' (5) LBlo
'Swan Wings' (7) LAma
'Sweet Harmony' (5) ETub LAma LBlo MBri NRog

'Sweet Lady' (14) LAma NRog
'Sweetheart' (13) CBro LAma LBlo NRog
sylvestris CAvo CBro EPar ETub LAma LBow NLan NRog SIng WShi
'Tamara' (3) LAma
'Tango' (14) LAma
tarda CAvo CBro CCla CNic EPar EPot ETub EWal LAma LBlo LBow MBri MBro NRog SIng WPat
'Teenager' (14) LAma
'Teheran' (3) LAma
'Tender Beauty' (13) LAma
tetraphylla LAma
'Texas Flame' (10) LAma
'Texas Gold' (10) LAma LBlo LBow
'The First' (12) CBro LAma
'Thule' (3) LAma
'Topscore' (3) LAma
'Toronto' (14) ETub LAma LBlo MBri
'Toulon' (13) MBri
'Towa' (14) LAma
'Trance' (3) LAma
'Trinket' (14) LAma
'Triumphator' (2) LAma
tschimganica LAma
tubergeniana LAma
– 'Keukenhof' LAma
turkestanica CAvo CBro CCla CNic CRDP EPar EPot ETub LAma LBow MBri NRog SIng
'Uncle Tom' (11) LAma MBri
§ ***undulatifolia*** CBro LAma LBow SIng
'Union Jack' (5) CAvo LAma LBlo
urumiensis CAvo CBro CCla EPot ETub LAma MBri MBro NRog SIng WAbe WHoo WPat
§ ***urumoffii*** LAma
'Valentine' (3) LAma LBlo
'Van der Neer' (1) LAma
'Varinas' (3) LAma
violacea See T. ***humilis*** Violacea Group
¶ ***viridiflora*** ETub
'Vivaldi' (12) LAma
'Vivex' (4) LAma
§ 'Vlammenspel' (1) LAma
'Vuurbaak' (2) LAma
vvedenskyi CBro LAma NRog SIng
– 'Blanka' EPot
– 'Hanka' EPot
– 'Lenka' EPot
– 'Tangerine Beauty' SIng
¶ 'Wallflower' (5) ETub
'West Point' (6) CAvo ETub LAma LBlo LBow
* 'White Alba' (7) LAma
* 'White Bouquet' (5) NRog
'White Dream' (3) ETub LAma LBlo
'White Emperor' See T. 'Purissima'
'White Parrot' (10) LAma LBlo NRog
'White Swallow' (3) NRog
'White Triumphator' (6) CAvo ETub LAma LBlo LBow NRog
'White Virgin' (3) LAma
whittallii See T. ***orphanidea*** Whittallii Group
'Wilhelm Kordes' (2) LAma
'Willem van Oranje' (2) LAma
'Willemsoord' (2) LAma MBri
wilsoniana See T. ***montana***
'Wim van Est' (5) LAma
'Yellow Dawn' (14) LAma
'Yellow Dover' (4) LAma
'Yellow Emperor' (13) CBro MBri
'Yellow Empress' (13) LAma
'Yellow Present' (3) LAma
'Yellow Purissima' (13) NRog
'Yokohama' (1) LAma
'Zampa' (14) LAma
zenaidae EPot
'Zombie' (13) LAma
¶ 'Zomerschoon' (5) ETub
'Zwanenburg' (5) LAma

TUNICA See PETRORHAGIA, DIANTHUS

TURRAEA (Meliaceae)

¶ ***obtusifolia*** CTro

TUSSILAGO (Compositae)

farfara CArn CKin CSFH LHol NSal SIde WHer WNdy

TUTCHERIA (Theaceae)

See Plant Deletions

TWEEDIA (Asclepiadaceae)

§ ***caerulea*** CB&S CGle CHan CPle CSam CSun CTro ELan ERea ESma GCal IBlr ISea LAbb LBlm LGan LGre LHop MNew NPer SAxl SMad SPer SUsu WEas WPer

TYPHA (Typhaceae)

angustifolia CBen CKin CRDP CRow CWGN EBre EHon EMFW EWav LBre LMay MSta SHig SWat WChe WHol WWye
latifolia CBen CHEx CRDP CRow CWGN EHon EMFW EWav LMay MSta SWat WChe WHer WWye
– 'Variegata' CBen CRDP CRow ELan EMFW MSta
§ ***laxmannii*** CBen CRiv EHon EMFW LMay MSta SRms
minima CBen CRDP CRiv CRow CWGN EBre EHon EMFW EWav LBre LMay MSta NDea SHig SWat WChe WHol
– var. ***gracilis*** ETPC
shuttleworthii IDai
stenophylla See T. ***laxmannii***

UGLI See CITRUS x *tangelo* 'Ugli'

UGNI (Myrtaceae)

§ ***molinae*** CB&S CDec CDoC CMHG CMer CPle CSam ESim GAri ISea MBal SSpi WCHb WSHC WWat

ULEX (Leguminosae)

europaeus CDoC ENot GRei WDin WMou
– 'Aureus' CB&S EBar SPer

§ – 'Flore Pleno' CB&S CDoC CPMA EMon ENot IDai IJoh MBal MGos NTow SHBN SPer WStI WWeb
– 'Plenus' See U. *e.* 'Flore Pleno'
– 'Prostratus' MBar
– 'Strictus' IJoh
gallii MPla
– 'Mizzen' ECar ESis GCal LRHS MBri
§ ***minor*** EPla ISea
nanus See U. ***minor***

ULMUS (Ulmaceae)

'Dodoens' LBuc
§ ***glabra*** CKin CPer NWea WDin WMou
– 'Camperdownii' CDoC ELan MBen WMou
¶ – 'Exoniensis' CTho
¶ – 'Gittisham' CTho
– 'Nana' NHol WPat
× ***hollandica*** 'Commelin' CDoC EMil
– 'Groeneveld' CDoC EMil
– 'Jacqueline Hillier' CChu CCla CLew CShe CTre EBre EHar ELan ESis GDra GWht LBre LHop MAsh MBal MBar MPla MWat NBar NHar NHol SChu SIng SSpi SSta STre WAbe WDav WPat WSHC
– 'Lobel' CDoC MGos
– 'Wredei' See U. ***minor*** 'Dampieri Aurea'
minor 'Cornubiensis' CDoC CTho
§ – 'Dampieri Aurea' CBot CLnd EBre ELan IJoh LBre LNet LPan MBar MBlu NBee NHol SHBN SMad SPer WDin WMou WPat
– 'Variegata' EPot
montana See U. ***glabra***
parvifolia EHal GAri SMad STre WFro WNor
– 'Frosty' (v) CKni ELan EPla EPot ESma SGil SHer
– 'Geisha' (v) CChu CPMA CWSG ECar EHar ELan ESis ESma IJoh LHop MBar MGos MPla SBla SChu SGil SGly SMad SSpi STre WPat WWeb
§ – 'Hokkaido' LGre SBla SGil WAbe WPat
– ***pygmaea*** See U. ***p.*** 'Hokkaido'
– 'Yatsubusa' EPot ESis SGil STre WPat
'Plantijn' CDoC
procera CKin STre WCoo
– 'Argenteovariegata' SMad
pumila GAri WNor
'Regal' EHar
'Sapporo Autumn Gold' EBre EHar LBre SMad

UMBELLULARIA (Lauraceae)

californica CArn CMCN IBar SArc WSHC

UMBILICUS (Crassulaceae)

erectus CChu CRDP
rupestris CNat ELan GAbr GCHN NGre NWCA SIde WCla WHer WPer WWye

UNCINIA (Cyperaceae)

clavata EPla ETPC GCal
egmontiana SSpi
ferruginea NHar
N ***rubra*** Widely available
– var. ***phallax*** EPla
uncinata ECha EHoe EPar EPla ESis ETPC MBal NHar NHol NWCA SSpi SUsu WByw

UNGNADIA (Sapindaceae)

See Plant Deletions

UNIOLA (Gramineae)

latifolia See CHASMANTHIUM ***latifolium***

URCEOLINA (Liliaceae/Amaryllidaceae)

♦ ***miniata*** See STENOMESSSON ***miniatum***

URGINEA (Liliaceae/Hyacinthaceae)

¶ ***fugax*** SF 62 CMon
maritima GPoy LAma WHer
¶ – SF 275 CMon
¶ ***undulata*** SF 2/279/323 CMon

UROSPERMUM (Compositae)

delachampii CChu CGle CSev EBar LGre SAxl SMrm SUsu WPer

URSINIA (Compositae)

See Plant Deletions

URTICA (Urticaceae)

¶ ***pilulifera dodartii*** NBro

UTRICULARIA (Lentibulariaceae)

¶ ***aurea*** EFEx
¶ ***australis*** EFEx
¶ ***caerulea*** EFEx
¶ ***capensis*** WHil
¶ ***dichotoma*** EFEx WHil
♦ ***exoleta*** See U. ***gibba***
¶ ***fibrosa*** EFEx
§ ***gibba*** EFEx WHal
¶ ***intermedia*** EFEx
¶ ***laterifolia*** EFEx WHil
¶ ***livida*** EFEx WMEx
¶ ***longifolia*** EFEx
¶ ***menziesii*** EFEx
¶ ***monanthos*** EFEx
¶ ***nephrophylla*** EFEx
¶ ***praelonga*** EFEx WHil
¶ ***pusilla*** EFEx
reniformis EFEx WHal
sandersonii EFEx WHal
¶ ***simplex*** EFEx
subulata EFEx WHal
¶ ***tricolor*** EFEx
¶ ***vulgaris*** EFEx SAWi

UVULARIA (Liliaceae/Convallariaceae)

disporum LAma
grandiflora CBro CCMG CCla CHan EBlo EBre EBul ECar ECha ELan ELun EPar EPla EPot GDra GGar LAma LBre MBri MUlv NSal NSti SBla SHig SPer SWas WChr WCru
– ***pallida*** CChu ECar EFou EPar IBlr SWas

perfoliata	CChu CHan ECar ECha EPar EPot LAma NSal SBla SPou WChr WThu WWat
pudica	See U. ***carolininana***
§ ***sessilifolia***	EBul EPar EPot LAma NSal SPou WChr

VACCINIUM (Ericaceae)

angustifolium Newfoundland form	CSto
arctostaphylos	ECar MAsh NHar NHol SSta
bracteatum	CCla
caespitosum	GDra
¶ ***consanguineum***	LTil
constablei	NHar
corymbosum	CB&S EBre ELan GWht LBre MBal MBar MGos NBee SPer SReu SSta WDin
F – 'Berkeley'	CTrh GTwe LBuc
F – 'Bluecrop'	CDoC CMac CTrh GTwe LBuc MBri MGos NBar WHig WStI WWeb
F – 'Bluetta'	GTwe
F – 'Coville'	CTrh
F – 'Goldtraube'	CDoC MBri MGos WHig
F – 'Herbert '	MGos
¶ – 'Northland'	GAri
¶ – 'Patriot'	CTrh GAri GTwe
F – 'Pioneer'	MBar
F – 'Spartan'	CTrh GAri GTwe
F – 'Trovor'	EBre ELan LBre
F ***crassifolium*** 'Well's Delight'	MAsh MBri SSpi
cylindraceum	CCla ECar SHil WBod WPat
delavayi	ECar EPot GArf GCHN GWht MBal MBar MHig SReu SSta WAbe WThu
– 'Drummondii'	NHol
deliciosum	ECar
donianum	See V. ***sprengelii***
duclouxii	CB&S
dunalianum	CB&S
* ***eriophyllum***	SSta
erythrinum	SSta
erythrocarpum	NHar NHol
floribundum	CGre CMHG EBre ECar GAbr GDra GWht LBre MBal NHar SHil SPer SSpi SSta WAbe WPat
glaucoalbum	CAbP CKni GAbr GWht IBar MBar MRav SHil SPer SReu WBod WDin
– B 173	MBal
¶ ***griffithianum***	SSta
§ ***macrocarpon***	CMac ECar ELan ESim GTwe MBal MBar MBri SSta WThu
F – 'CH'	ESim
F – 'Early Black'	ESim LBuc SSta
F – 'Franklin'	ECar ESim
F – 'Hamilton'	CNic ECar GArf GDra NHol SSta WPat WThu
F – 'Pilgrim'	ESim SSta
* 'McMinn'	ECar GAri MBal
moupinense	CCla CNic CRiv GWht IBar ITim MBal MGos SPer SPla SSta WThu
– small-leaved	MBal
¶ – 'Variegatum'	WPat
myrtillus	ECar GPoy MBal WDin
'Nimo Pink'	MBar
nummularia	EPot GDra MBal MHig NHar SSpi WAbe WBod WThu
– LS&H 17294	NHar NHol
ovatum	CCla CMHG ECar GWht IBar MBal MBar NHar SHil SPer SSpi SSta WThu
§ ***oxycoccos***	CArn MGos NLan
padifolium	CGre MBal
palustre	See V. ***oxycoccos***
parvifolium	NHar
praestans	ECar GAri GGGa ITim NHol SIng WThu
retusum	CCla CGre CTrw MBal SSpi SSta WAbe WBod
¶ ***sikkimense***	GArf
uliginosum	ECar WPat
virgatum	MBal
vitis-idaea	CNic CSto EPot GPoy GWht IJoh MBal MBar MGos MHig SHer SLon SPer SReu WHig WThu
– 'Compactum'	MBal NHar WAbe WDav
– Koralle Group	CCla EBlo EBre ECar ESis IBar LBre MBal MBar MBri MGos MRav NBar NHol SIng SPer SPla SReu SSta WAbe WPat WThu
– ssp. ***minus***	ECar ECou ESis GArf GAri MBal MHig SSta WAbe WDav WThu
– 'Red Pearl'	CDoC MAsh

VALERIANA (Valerianaceae)

'Alba'	See CENTRANTHUS ***ruber albus***
alliariifolia	EMon GCal
arizonica	CNic MTho NCat NKay
'Coccinea'	See CENTRANTHUS ***ruber***
montana	EBur GArf MCas NHol NMen NNrd NRya SIng WHal WHil
officinalis	CArn CKin CRDP CSFH Effi GPoy IEde LHol MChe MHew NBro NLan NSel SIde WHal WHer WNdy WOak WPer WWye
– ssp. ***sambucifolia***	CHan
phu 'Aurea'	CBot CGle CHan CLew ECha EFol EFou EHoe ELan ELun EOrc GCal IBlr LGan LHop MBal MBri MFir MPar MUlv NHol NNor NRoo NSti SPer SUsu WEas WPer WRus WWin
pyrenaica	EFol EMon
saxatilis	EFol NRoo NRya SRms
supina	NWCA

VALERIANELLA (Valerianaceae)

eriocarpa	EJud
§ ***locusta***	GPoy
olitoria	See V. ***locusta***

VALLEA (Elaeocarpaceae)

stipularis	IBar
– ***pyrifolia***	CGre CPle

VALLOTA See CYRTANTHUS

VANCOUVERIA (Berberidaceae)

chrysantha	ECar ECha EMon EPla SAxl SUsu SWas WCru

hexandra	CCla CHEx CNic ECar ECha EMon GCal MBal NCat NHol NKay NRya NSti SGil SSpi WCru WDav WWin
¶ ***planipetala***	CBos WHal

VEITCHIA (Palmae)
See Plant Deletions

VELTHEIMIA (Liliaceae/Hyacinthaceae)

§ ***bracteata***	CAvo CHal CMon EBak ETub IBlr LBow NRog
§ ***capensis***	SLMG
viridifolia hort.	See V. ***capensis***
– Jacquin	See V. ***bracteata***

X VENIDIOARCTOTIS See **ARCTOTIS**

VENIDIUM See **ARCTOTIS**

VERATRUM † (Liliaceae/Melanthiaceae)

album	ECha GPoy
nigrum	CBro CCla CHEx COtt EBlo EBre EFou ELan EMon ENot GDra LBre MBri MPar SBla SChu SPer WByw WCot
viride	ECha ELun IBlr MPar

VERBASCUM † (Scrophulariaceae)

acaule	NTow
* ***adzharicum***	WHoo
'Arctic Summer'	See V. ***bombyciferum*** 'Polarsommer'
arcturus	GTou MBro MSte SIgm SUsu WDav WPer
* ***bakerianum***	EBar MPit WEas
'Bill Bishop'	SIng
blattaria	CFis CGle CHan CPou CTom ELan LGan MHew MNFA NBir WEas WHer WHil WNdy
– f. ***albiflorum***	CNic EMar LGan MBro NSti SSvw WBon WHer WHoo WNdy WPer WRus WSun
¶ – pink	GAbr LWad
§ ***bombyciferum***	CSam EFol LAbb NSel NSti SRms SSvw WByw WEas
§ – 'Polarsommer'	CDoC CHad CSam GAbr LWad MBri NBir SRms WHil
– 'Silver Lining'	NNor
'Broussa'	See V. ***bombyciferum***
chaixii	CDoC ECha ECro NBir WHoo WPer
– 'Album'	CChu CCla CGle CMil ECro EFou EOrc EPar LAbb LGan LGre LHop MBri MBro MFir MUlv NBir NBro NCat NWyt SHer SMrm SUsu WHal WHen WHil WHoo WPer WRus WWin
Cotswold Hybrid Group 'Boadicea'	CSco CShe
– 'Bridal Bouquet'	CKel
– 'C L Adams'	CSco
– 'Cotswold Beauty'	CSam CSco EMon
– 'Cotswold Gem'	CSco
– 'Cotswold Queen'	CDoC CGle CHad CHan CKel CPar CSev EBre ECED ECtt EFou ELan LBre NKay NWyt SFis SMrm SPer WCra WEas WHil WRus WSun
– 'Gainsborough'	CDoC CGle CHad CKel CPar CSam CSco EBlo EBre ECha ECtt ELan LBre MBri MUlv MWat SFis SMrm SPer WCra WEas WRus WTyr
– 'Mont Blanc'	CBot CCla CGle CHad CMGP CSco EBre EFou LBre LGre SPer WRus
– 'Pink Domino'	CBow CDoC CGle CHad CKel CMGP CPar CSco EBlo EBre EFou ELan LBre MBri NSel NSti SHer SMrm SPer WCra WRus WTyr
– 'Royal Highland'	CBow CGle CHad CMGP CSco EFou ELan SHer SMrm WRus
creticum	WCla
§ ***densiflorum***	CArn CSco Effi LHol NSal SFis SIde SPer WCla WHer
dumulosum	EBre EPot GCal LBre NTow NWCA WAbe WPer
elegantissimum	CSco
'Golden Wings'	EPot GArf ITim WPat
'Helen Johnson'	CChu CGle CHad CMGP CRDP EBlo EBre ECha EFou EGol LBre LRHS MUlv NBir NSti SHer SMrm SUsu
'Jackie'	LGre SBla
'Letitia'	CGle CHad CRiv EBre ELan EPad EPot GCal LBee LBre MFir MPar MTho NHol NRar NTow SBla SIng SUsu SWas WAbe WEas WHoo WPer WThu WWin
longifolium var. ***pannosum***	See V. ***olympicum***
lychnitis	CArn WHer
nigrum	CArn CKin CSFH ECro EOrc LHil MChe MHew NSal WHer WNdy WOak
§ ***olympicum***	CGle CSam EBar ECha ELan NOak NSel NSti SFar WPer
phlomoïdes	NSal
phoeniceum	CBow CGle ELan MPit NBee NBro NMir NOak NSel NWCA SHer SSvw WCla WCra WEas WHen WPer WWin
¶ – 'Candy Spires'	WBon
¶ – hybrids	LAbb
pulverulentum	CKin
spinosum	CGle
thapsiforme	See V. ***densiflorum***
thapsus	CKin CRDP CSFH EJud GPoy GTou IEde MChe MHew NMir NNor WNdy WOak WWye
'Turkey'	NKay
'Vernale'	CBot CSco
virgatum	CKin EMon
¶ ***wiedemannianum***	WDav

VERBENA † (Verbenaceae)

'Apple Blossom'	NRar
'Aveyron'	SChu SMrm SUsu
§ ***bonariensis***	Widely available
'Boughton House'	CSpe MSte
'Bramley'	SChu
canadensis	NSal
– 'Perfecta'	EBar

'Carousel'	CB&S
chamaedrifolia	See V. ***peruviana***
corymbosa	CGre CRDP ECha LHop SChu SMrm SUsu WCot WPer WSHC
– 'Gravetye'	EHal EMon GCal
'Cupido'	CSpe MPit
* 'Foxhunter'	LAbb LHop
hastata	CHan CSev EFol EMon EOrc GCal MBel MChe NSal NSti SMrm SUsu WCot WPer
– JLS 88010WI	EMon
– 'Alba'	EHal EMon GCal MBel WCot WPer
– 'Rosea'	EFou EMon GCal
'Hidcote Purple'	CGle GCal MRav MSte NFai SAxl SMrm WEas
'Huntsman'	CGle GCal MSte NTow SAxl
N 'Kemerton'	CSev LHop
'Kurpfalz'	IHos
* 'La France'	MRav SChu SMrm SUsu
'Lawrence Johnston'	CGle EOrc GCal MRav NTow SAxl SLMG WEas WHen
'Loveliness'	CSpe GCal IBlr LHop MUlv SAxl SMrm WEas
x ***maonettii***	CBar CHal CRiv CSpe ELan EOrc LHop NTow SIng WPer
officinalis	CArn CHal CSFH EJud Effi GPoy IEde LHol MChe MHew NSel SIde WHer WNdy WOak WPer WWye
'Othello'	CSpe
patagonica	See V. ***bonariensis***
§ ***peruviana***	CBrk CHal CSam EBre ELan EOrc EPla LAbb LBre LHop MPit MRav NRar NTow SAxl SChu SCro SIng WEas WHoo WOMN WPer WWin
– 'Alba'	CBrk CRiv CSpe ELan EOrc EPla GCal LHop MPit MRav NTow SAxl SChu SCro SIde WPer
¶ ***phlogiflora***	CBrk
'Pink Bouquet'	See V. 'Silver Anne'
'Pink Pearl'	ECtt EOrc SChu
pulchella	See V. ***tenera***
'Purple Kleopat'	IHos
§ ***rigida***	CAbb CGre ECha EMon LHil NCat SIde SMrm SRms SUsu WCot WEas WPer
– 'Lilacina'	EMon
* 'Rose du Barry'	SAxl SMrm
* 'Royal Purple'	CB&S
scabrida glandulosa	WPer
§ 'Silver Anne'	CB&S CBrk CCla CGle CHad CPar CSam ECha ECtt EOrc GCal LAbb LHop MRav MUlv NFai NTow SAxl SChu SCro SDix SMrm SUsu WEas WHen WPer
§ 'Sissinghurst'	CArn CB&S CBot CBrk CCla CGle CHad CHan CMer CSam ECtt EFol EOrc GCal LAbb LHop MPit NFai NRar SAxl SCro SLMG SUsu WEas WHen WHoo WPer WRus WWin
stricta	NSal WCot
– JLS 88008WI	CRDP EMon
§ ***tenera***	CSpe LHop
'Tenerife'	See V. 'Sissinghurst'
tenuisecta	CBrk GCal SChu SDix WPer
– var. ***alba***	SChu
venosa	See V. ***rigida***
'White Cascade'	ECtt EOrc
* 'White Knight'	CB&S CBrk CCla

VERNONIA (Compositae)

crinita	ECha ECro GCal SFis
mespilifolia	ECro

VERONICA † (Scrophulariaceae)

amethystina	See V. ***spuria***
armena	CShe MBro MSte MWat SHer SIgm SMrm WThi
§ ***austriaca***	GCal
– Corfu form	LGre SAxl SBar WPer
– ***dubia***	See V. ***prostrata***
– 'Ionian Skies'	ESis MBel SChu SIgm SMrm SWas
§ – ssp. ***teucrium***	CArn EHal MBro NNor NWCA SChu SRms WPer
– – 'Blue Fountain'	MPit
– – 'Crater Lake Blue'	CB&S CHad CKel ECha ECtt EFol EFou ELan ESis ESma LGre MFir MRav NNor SMrm WByw WCot WEas WPer WWin
– – 'Kapitän'	CKel ECha EFol LHop MFir SMrm WPer
– – 'Knallblau'	EFou MBri
– – 'Royal Blue'	CBre CKel CLew CMGP CSco EFou IDai LAbb LGan NKay NSti WHoo
– – 'Shirley Blue'	See V. 'Shirley Blue'
beccabunga	CBen CKin COtt CRDP CWGN EBre EHon ELan EMFW GPoy LBre LMay MHew MSta NDea NMir NSal NSel SHig SWat WChe WHer WHol
¶ ***bellidioïdes***	GTou NGre
'Blue Spire'	LHil LWad MBro WPer
bombycina	EPot NTow NWCA SIgm SIng SPou WOMN
bonarota	See PAEDEROTA ***bonarota***
caespitosa	WDav
– Mac&W 5849	EPot
candida	See V. ***spicata incana***
x ***cantiana*** 'Kentish Pink'	EMon SPla
caucasica	EHal ELan EMon LGre NCat
chamaedrys	CKin IEde NMir
§ – 'Miffy Brute' (v)	ELan EMon
– 'Variegata'	See V. ***c.*** 'Miffy Brute'
cinerea	CShe CTom ECha EFol MBro MCas NKay NTow SIgm SSmi WAbe WDav WEas WHil WOld WPat WSun
– JCA 983.400	CNic
dabneyi	NHol SIng
* ***dichroa***	ELan
exaltata	EHal EMon LRHS MSte WCot WPer
* ***filifolia***	WHoo
filiformis	SIng
formosa	See PARAHEBE ***f.***
§ ***fruticans***	CNic EMNN NKay WCla
fruticulosa	NWCA SSmi
gentianoïdes	Widely available
– 'Alba'	EOrc GCal NSti
– 'Nana'	EBre EOrc LBre MMil
¶ – 'Robusta'	GCra
– 'Variegata'	Widely available
x ***guthrieana***	CNic MBro WCru WPer

hendersonii	See V. ***subsessilis h.***
incana	See V. ***spicata incana***
kellereri	See V. ***spicata***
kiusiana	CBot EMon MBel
liwanensis	ELan ESis GCHN MBro NTow WThi
– Mac&W 5936	EPot GDra MHig WHil
longifolia	CBre CKel EJud ELan LHil MFir NBee NCat SFis WDav WEas WOak WOld
– 'Alba'	CSco ELan EMon LGre MBel
– 'Blaue Sommer'	CPar EFou NBar SPer
§ – 'Blauriesin'	CSco ECtt EOrc GCal MBri NFai NHol SFis
♦– 'Foerster's Blue'	See V. ***l.*** 'Blauriesin'
– 'Incarnata'	EMon
¶ – 'Joseph's Coat' (v)	EMon WCot
*– 'Rosalinde'	SCro SPla WPer
¶ – 'Rose Tone'	LGre
¶ – 'Rosea'	WPer
– 'Schneeriesin'	CBre ECha ECtt EOrc MBri NHol SFis WRus
lyallii	See PARAHEBE ***l.***
montana	CKin
– 'Corinne Tremaine' (v)	WHer
nummularia	CTom ESis NRed NTow
officinalis	CKin NHol
oltensis	GArf WEas WPat
– JCA 984.150	MBro NHol NTow WDav
¶ ***orientalis***	WHil
¶ ***ornata***	ECha SMrm WPer
pectinata	CPar ESis GDra NCat NMen NSti
– 'Rosea'	CHal CMHG CNic CTom ESis GAbr GDra MCas MFir NKay NMen SBar SHer SSmi WPer WThi WWin
peduncularis	CNic CSpe EOrc LBee LRHS SBla SUsu WEas
– 'Georgia Blue'	CHan CMGP ECha ESis LGre LHil MFir MMil MSte SChu SDix SIgm SMrm SSpi SWas WAbe WCru WWat
– 'Oxford Blue'	LHop NMir WPer
perfoliata	See PARAHEBE ***perfoliata***
¶ ***petraea*** 'Madame Mercier'	SIng
¶ ***pinnata*** 'Blue Eyes'	ESis
prenja	See V. ***austriaca***
§ ***prostrata***	CSam CShe ELan EMNN EPot ESis GDra MBar MBro MCas MHig MPla MWat NGre NKay NNrd NRed NRoo SIng SSmi WDav WEas WHil WHoo WOld WWin
– ***alba***	MBro WHoo
– 'Blauspiegel' ('Blue Mirror')	SBla SIgm SWas
– 'Blue Ice'	SSmi
– 'Blue Sheen'	CTom ECtt ESis LGre MPlt SChu WWin
– 'Loddon Blue'	CKel CPar IDai MRav NVic SBla
♦– 'Miss Willmott'	See V. ***p.*** 'Warley Blue'
– 'Mrs Holt'	CMea CNic CSam CShe EBre EFol EMNN LBre LGan MCas MFir MPlt NCat NMen NNor NNrd NVic SAxl SBla SSmi WHal WPer WSun WThi WWin
– 'Nana'	EMNN EPot ESis MCas MHig MPla NKay NMen NNrd SIng
*– 'Pavlava Hills'	CNic
– 'Rosea'	CPar ELan ESis MPla NHol NKay NRed SHer SIgm SIng WHil WPer
– 'Silver Queen'	CTom SRms
– 'Spode Blue'	CMGP CMea CShe LBee LGre LHop MBro NHol NWCA SBla SHer WDav
– 'Trehane'	CHal CRiv CShe CTom EBre ECha EFol ELan EPar EPla ESis LBre LGro LHop MBro MPar MRav MWat NGre NHar NKay NNrd SUsu WDav WHal WHil WPer WThi WWin
§ – 'Warley Blue'	CKel CMGP
repens	See V. ***reptans***
§ ***reptans***	CNic EHal EMNN LHil MCas NCat NNrd SFis WPer
* 'Romany'	CB&S
'Rosalinde'	CBot EBre EOrc LBre NBee SFis
rupestris	See V. ***prostrata***
saturejoïdes	CHal GAbr MBro SRms WDav WPer
saxatilis	See V. ***fruticans***
¶ ***schmidtiana***	GTou
– ***nana***	CLew CPar MBro NHol NMir SUsu WOMN WPat
– – ***rosea***	WOMN WThi
selleri	See V. ***wormskjoldii***
§ 'Shirley Blue'	CHal CPar CShe CTom EBar EBre ECro EFou GCHN GGar LBre LWad MFir MWat NBar NMir SFis SPer WPer
§ ***spicata***	CFis CPar CRDP ELan GDra LGan MBro MHew NNor NSal SSvw WCla WCot WHal WPer WSun
– 'Alba'	SSvw WPer
– 'Barcarolle'	ELan SFis
– 'Blaufuchs' ('Blue Fox')	CMHG EBre EFou LBre
*– 'Corali'	SFis
§ – 'Erika'	ECha ECtt EFou EOrc EPla MTol NOak WCla
– 'Heidekind'	CGle CLew CMea CPar CSco CShe EBlo EBre ECha EFol EFou ELan EOrc ESis GDra LBre LHop MBri MCas MFir MWat NHar NHol NNor NVic SBla SIng WDav WEas WWin
– 'Icicle'	EFou NTow SAsh
§ – ssp. ***incana***	CCla CCor CGle CKel CPar CShe EFol EGol EHoe ELan ENot GAbr LAbb LGan MBri MBro MCas NKay NMir NNor SBla SPer WPer WRus
– – 'Mrs Underwood'	ECha
– – 'Nana'	ECha EPla ESis LGre SAxl WHal
– – 'Saraband'	CSco WCot
– – 'Silver Carpet'	CCla CMGP EBre EFou EGol EOrc EPla LBre NBar NSti SMrm WSun
– – 'Wendy'	GCal WSun
– 'Minuet'	SFis WByw
– 'Mori's Form'	WWin
¶ – 'Nana Blauteppich'	NHol
– 'Pavane'	SFis
¶ – 'Pink Damask'	EFou EMon
– 'Romiley Purple'	EFou EMon GCal MSte NBar SAxl SChu
♦– ***rosea***	See V. ***s.*** 'Erika'

– 'Rotfuchs' ('Red Fox')	CCla CGle CMGP CMHG CRDP CSam EBlo EBre ECha ECtt EFou ELan EPar LBre MRav NHol NRoo NSti SCro SHer SPer WByw WEas WHal WPer WRus WWin
*– 'Sightseeing'	CBow EHal NMir NRoo
¶ – ssp. *spicata* 'Nana'	SSmi
– *variegata*	EFol EMon NBir NRar
§ ***spuria***	EMon WPer
stelleri	See V. ***wormskjoldii***
subsessilis	GCal
¶ – 'Blau Pyramide'	LGre
§ – ***hendersonii***	EHal GCal
sumilensis	EPla
¶ ***surculosa***	SBla
tauricola Mac&W 5835	EPot SIgm
telephiifolia	CLew CMea EMNN ESis MPla MPlt NMen NMir NRed NTow NWCA SFis WHil WPat
¶ ***teucrioïdes***	WDav
teucrium	See V. ***austriaca t.***
¶ ***thessalica***	NTow
¶ ***thymoïdes***	WDav
– ***thymoïdes***	ESis SIgm
virense	CHan
virginica	See VERONICASTRUM ***virginicum***
* ***waldsteinii***	EMon
'Waterperry Blue'	ELan LGre MRav SBod
wherryi	WPer
'White Spire'	CBot
whitleyi	CHal CNic GAbr MPar NKay NNrd NOrc SFis WHil WWin
§ ***wormskjoldii***	CHal CHan CRiv EFol ELan ESis LHop MBro MHig MPar NHol NKay NMen NNrd SBla SHer SIgm WCla WDav WHil WPat WPer WWin
¶ – 'Alba'	WPer

VERONICASTRUM (Scrophulariaceae)

§ ***virginicum***	CRow ECha EFol EFou MFir NSal NSti WPer WTyr WWin
– ***album***	CBot CChu CCla CDoC CHan CKel CLew CShe EFol ELan GCal LGan MBri MBro MUlv MWat NSti SBla SCro SFis SMad SPer WEas WHoo WSun
– 'Pink Glow'	EFou
– ***roseum***	EFou LRHS MBri NSti SCro SMad WCot
– var. ***sibiricum***	EMon

VESTIA (Solanaceae)

§ ***foetida***	CB&S CBra CGre CMHG CPle CTro ELan ERea ESma GCal GWht IBlr IReg ISea LHil NBir NRar SIgm WHer WOMN WPer WTyr
lycioïdes	See V. ***foetida***

VIBURNUM † (Caprifoliaceae)

acerifolium	EPla SSpi WWat
'Allegheny'	SHil
alnifolium	See V. ***lantanoïdes***
atrocyaneum	CCla CPle SSpi
betulifolium	CB&S CBow CChu CCla CPle CTrw MBal NHol SSpi WHCG WThu WWat
bitchiuense	ELan
x ***bodnantense***	CBot CChu CPle CTrw ELan ENot GRei IDai IJoh MBel MRav MWat NHol NNor SLon WEas WStI WWat WWin
– 'Charles Lamont'	CBot CSam ECtt EHar EPla ESma IBlr MBri MGos NHol SFai SPer SSpi WBod WPat WWeb
– 'Dawn'	Widely available
– 'Deben'	EGol EHar ENot EPla MBri SPer
bracteatum	SSpi
buddlejifolium	CChu CCla EHal WHCG WWat
x ***burkwoodii***	Widely available
– 'Anne Russell'	CB&S CBow CPMA CSco CShe EBre EHar EPla IOrc LBre SHBN SHil SPer WAbe WHCG WRus
– 'Chenaultii'	EHal ELan SPer SSta
– 'Fulbrook'	EHar LTil MUlv NHol SSpi WBod
– 'Park Farm Hybrid'	CBow CChu CCla CTre EBre EGol ENot IJoh IOrc LBre LTil MBal NHol NKay SPer WBod WWat
x ***carlcephalum***	CB&S CChu CSco EBre EGol ELan ENot IDai IJoh IOrc LBre MBri MGos MRav MUlv MWat NHol NKay NNor SLon SPer SPla SReu SSpi WBod WDin WPat WSHC
carlesii	CB&S CBow CBra CPle ENot GRei IOrc LHol NBee SGil SPer SReu WStI
– 'Aurora'	CB&S CCla CPMA CSco EBre ELan ENot IDai IJoh IOrc LBre MBar MBri MGos MUlv MWat NHol NKay SHBN SHil SPer SReu SSpi SSta WBod WCru WDin WPat WWat
– 'Charis'	CMHG NBar SSpi WBod
– 'Diana'	CMHG EBre ELan LAbb LBre SGil SHil SSpi SSta
cassinoïdes	WPat
'Chesapeake'	CChu CCla EHar NTow SFai
chingii	ELan EMon WWat
cinnamomifolium	CBow CLan CSco ELan ISea LNet SArc SBor SLon SMad SPer SSpi WWat
congestum	ELan
¶ ***cotinifolium***	CChu
cylindricum	CBot ELan GWht SBor SSpi WCru WWat
dasyanthum	EPla
davidii	CBra CDec CHEx CPle CShe EBlo EBre EGol EHar ELan ENot GRei IDai IJoh ISea LBre LHop MBal MBar MBri MGos MWat NHol NNor NRoo SHBN SLon WDin WPat WWin
– (f)	CB&S CDoC CPMA CSco EHar ELan LTil MBal MGos MUlv NBee NKay SHBN SPer SPla SReu SSta WBod WPat WWat WWeb
– (m)	CB&S CDoC CSco EHar ELan LTil MBal MGos MUlv NBee SPer SPla SReu SSta WBod WWat WWeb
dilatatum	EHar ELan SSpi
– f. ***xanthocarpum***	EPla
erubescens	WWat

– var. *gracilipes*	WWat
'Eskimo'	CDoC EBlo EBre EPla LBre SHil WPat
§ *farreri*	CB&S CBra CSco CShe ELan ENot GRei ISea LBuc LHol LTil MBal MBar MGos MPla NHol NNor NRoo NWea SHBN SPer SSpi WAbe WBod WWat
– 'Album'	See V. *f.* 'Candidissimum'
§ – 'Candidissimum'	CBot CCla ECar EFol EHar ELan ENot EPla LHop MPar SPer WPat WThu
– 'Farrer's Pink'	CCla LRHS NHol WWat
– 'Nanum'	ECar EGol EPla MPar MPla NHol SChu SSta WHCG WPat WThu WWat
foetidum	WHCr
fragrans Bunge	See V. *farreri*
furcatum	CChu SHil WWat
x *globosum* 'Jermyns Globe'	CDoC CMHG CPle CSco EGol EPla IBar MBar MBri NHol SHil SLon WWat
grandiflorum	SLon WBod
harryanum	CCla CPle ECou EPla IOrc LGre MBal MUlv WCru
henryi	CChu CCla CPle EHar EPla MBri NHol SMad SPer SPla SSpi WWat
x *hillieri*	CAbP EPla MPar SLon SSpi WBod WCru WKif
– 'Winton'	CDoC CMHG ISea MAsh MBri MUlv SHBN SHil
japonicum	CChu CDoC CHEx CPle CSam SHBN SSpi WWat
x *juddii*	CB&S CBot CBow CCla CLan CPle CSco CShe EBre EHar ELan ENot IOrc LBre MBal MBar MGos MPar NHol SPer SReu SSpi SSta WBod WPat
koreanum	WBod
lantana	CKin CPer ENot IJoh IOrc LBuc MBar NWea WDin WMou
– 'Aureum'	CMHG EFol EPla
– 'Mohican'	SFai
– 'Xanthocarpum'	CSco ISea
§ *lantanoïdes*	SHil
lentago	MRav NHol
macrocephalum	SHil SSpi
mariesii	See V. *plicatum* 'Mariesii'
¶ 'Mohawk'	SMad SSpi
nudum	CCla
– 'Pink Beauty'	CChu CCla
odoratissimum	CB&S CGre CHEx CPle EPla SHBN SMad SSpi WSHC
opulus	CB&S CBow CBra CChu CKin CPer CSam ELan ENot GPoy IOrc LBuc LHol MBar MBri MWat NBee NNor NWea SHBN SPer WDin WMou
– 'Aureum'	Widely available
– 'Compactum'	CB&S CBow CCla CSco EBlo EBre EFou EGol ELan ENot IBar IJoh IOrc ISea LBre LHop MBar MBri MGos MPla MWat NHol SDix SPer SPla SReu WDin WRus WWat
N– 'Fructu Luteo'	EBre LBre
– 'Nanum'	CAbP EGol ELan EPla EPot ESis MBal MBar MBel MBri MCas MPla NHol WDin WHCG
– 'Notcutt's Variety'	CBow CSco ENot SHBN
– 'Park Harvest'	EFol EPla MUlv
§ – 'Roseum'	CB&S CBot CBow CCla CPle CSco EBre EGol ELan ENot IDai IOrc ISea LAbb LBre MBar MBel MBri MGos MPla MWat NNor NWea SHBN SPer SPla SReu SSta WBod WDin
– 'Sterile'	See V. *o.* 'Roseum'
N– 'Xanthocarpum'	CChu CCla CMHG CSam CSco EBre EGol ELan IOrc LBre LHop MBar MRav MUlv MWat NHol SLon SPer SPla WBod WOMN WSHC WWat WWin
N *plicatum*	CB&S CShe EHar ENot MBar SHer WDin
– 'Cascade'	EBlo EGol EPla SHBN SSpi
– 'Dart's Red Robin'	MBri SHer
– 'Grandiflorum'	CPle CSco EGol EHar IDai MBar NHol SBla SMad SPla SReu SSpi WBod
– 'Lanarth'	CB&S CBra CCla CPle CSam CSco CShe CTre ECtt EGol EHar ENot IOrc LHop MBri MPla SLon SPer SPla SSta WBod WDin WEas WHCG
§ – 'Mariesii'	Widely available
– 'Nanum'	See V. *p.* 'Nanum Semperflorens'
§ – 'Nanum Semperflorens'	CB&S CSco EBre ECtt EHar ELan EPla IJoh IOrc LBre LGre LHop LTil MBal MBar MBel MBri MGos MPla MUlv NHol NTow SHBN SLon SPer SSpi WHCG WKif WPat WWat
– 'Pink Beauty'	CAbP CB&S CBra CChu CCla CMHG CSco CShe EBre EGol EHar ELan IJoh LBre LHop MBal MBri MPla MWat NHol SBla SHBN SLon SPer SPla SSpi SSta WPat WSHC WWat
*– 'Prostratum'	EPla
– 'Rotundifolium'	MBri
– 'Rowallane'	CSco WBod WWat
N– 'Sterile'	EHar SHil
– 'Summer Snowflake'	CAbb CBow CCla ELan IJoh IOrc MAsh MBal MBri MPla MWat SPer SPla SSpi WWeb
– f. *tomentosum*	CBow CBra CDoC CLan EFol ELan EPla ISea NNor WStI
– 'Watanabe'	See V. *p.* 'Nanum Semperflorens'
'Pragense'	CChu CMCN EBre EGol EHar EPla LBre MBar MBri MGos SHil SLon SMad SPer SSpi
pubescens	See V. *dentatum p.*
¶ *recognitum*	CCla
x *rhytidophylloïdes*	CPle NNor WWat
– 'Dart's Duke'	MBri SLPl
rhytidophyllum	CBow CBra CChu CHEx CLan CPle CSco EBre ELan ENot GRei GWht IBar IDai IJoh ISea LBre MBal MBar MGos SHBN SLon SMad SPer SReu WBod WDin WTyr WWat WWin
– 'Roseum'	CShe WWat
– 'Variegatum'	CBot ELan EPla SDry
sargentii	IOrc
– 'Onondaga'	Widely available
– 'Susquehanna'	SPer
semperflorens	See V. *plicatum* 'Nanum Semperflorens'

sempervirens	SSpi
§ ***setigerum***	CChu CCla EPla SHil SMad
'Shasta'	CCla CDoC EHar EPla MBri NWyt SSpi SSta
sieboldii	LRHS
– 'Seneca'	SSpi
theiferum	See V. ***setigerum***
tinus	Widely available
– 'Bewley's Variegated'	CB&S IBar MGos
– 'Eve Price'	Widely available
– 'French White'	CGre EPla IJoh SGil SSpi WWat
– 'Gwenllian'	CDoC CSco EBre ECtt EGol EHar ELan ENot EPla IJoh LBre MBal MGos MPla MRav MUlv NHar NTow SHer SLon SPer SPla WAbe WBod WPat WWat WWeb
– ***hirtellum***	CTre
– 'Israel'	CB&S EGol SMad SPer
– 'Lucidum'	CB&S CSam CSco CShe MGos MUlv NNor SHBN SLon SPla SSpi WCru
– 'Lucidum Variegatum'	CLan EMon SDry
– 'Pink Prelude'	SSpi SSta
¶ – 'Prostratum'	SHBN
– 'Purpureum'	CB&S CBow CDoC EGol EHoe ELan EPla MUlv SHBN SLon SPer SReu SSpi SSta WWeb
♦– 'Pyramidale'	See V. ***t.*** 'Strictum'
§ – 'Strictum'	SLon
– 'Variegatum'	Widely available
tomentosum	See V. ***plicatum***
utile	EHal SSpi WHCG WThu WWat
wrightii	NHol WPat
– var. ***hessei***	MBri

VICIA (Leguminosae)

angustifolia	See V. ***sativa nigra***
cracca	CKin MWil NLan WNdy
§ ***sativa nigra***	CKin
sepium	CKin WNdy
sylvatica	MWil WGwy

VICTORIA (Nymphaeaceae)

regia	See V. ***amazonica***

VIGNA (Leguminosae)

¶ ***caracalla***	CPle

VILLADIA (Crassulaceae)

hemsleyana	See SEDUM ***hemsleyanum***

VILLARESIA See CITRONELLA

VILLARSIA (Menyanthaceae)

bennettii	See NYMPHOIDES ***peltata*** 'Bennettii'

VINCA † (Apocynaceae)

difformis	CCor CFis CGle CRDP CRow EBre ECha ELan EPla IDai LBre LHop NCat SDix SDry SIng SUsu WHal WHer
¶ – ***alba***	CCor
– ***bicolor*** 'Jenny's Pym'	EMon
– ssp. ***difformis***	EMon
– Greystone form	WRus
¶ – 'Oxford'	SLPl
¶ – 'Snowmound'	CMil
herbacea	EMon WEas
'Hidcote Purple'	See V. ***major*** 'Oxyloba'
major	CB&S CBow CDoC CPar CRow CSFH CSco CShe EFou ELan ENot EOrc ERav GPoy GRei IJoh ISea LBuc MBri MFir MGos MWat SBod SHBN SIng SPer SReu WDin WOak WWin
– ***alba***	CFis IBlr LHop WPer WWat WWeb
– 'Caucasian Blue'	LMer
– 'Elegantissima'	See V. ***m.*** 'Variegata'
§ – ssp. ***hirsuta***	CFis CRow CShe CTom EMon EOrc WCot
– 'Jason Hill'	ELan EMon LRHS MBel
§ – 'Maculata' (v)	CElw CGre CRDP CRow EFol ELan EMon ENot EPla GAbr IBar MBri NRoo NSti SDry SFai WAbe WCru
§ – 'Oxyloba'	CHal CNic CRow ECtt ELan EMon EPla ESma MRav SLPl SPla
– var. ***pubescens***	See V. ***m. hirsuta***
– 'Reticulata'	ELan EMon MBel NSti SDry
¶ – 'Starlight'	NSti
– 'Surrey Marble'	See V. ***m.*** 'Maculata'
§ – 'Variegata'	Widely available
minor	CBow CBra CDoC CKin CPle CRow ELan ENot EPar ERav GCHN GPoy GRei IJoh LBuc MBar MBro MFir MPar MWat SReu STre WDin WOak WTyr WWin
*– ***acutiloba***	WWye
– f. ***alba***	Widely available
– 'Alba Aureavariegata'	See V. ***m.*** 'Alba Variegata'
§ – 'Alba Variegata'	CBow CCla CGle CRDP CRow CSFH CTom EBre EGol EHoe EJud EOrc EPla IJoh LBre MBar MFir NHol NKay NNrd NRoo SPer STre WAbe WEas WHer WWat
§ – 'Argenteovariegata'	CB&S CCla CFis CGle CRDP CSco CShe ECha EFou EGol ELan ENot GDra GRei LBuc LGro MBar MBri MGos NHol NRoo SBod SIng SPer WBod WDin WEas WWat WWin
§ – 'Atropurpurea'	CB&S CCla CPar CRow CSam CSco CShe EBre ECha EGol ELan EPla IJoh LBre MBar MBri MGos NHol NKay NRoo NSti SBod SChu SHBN SPer WBon WEas WOak WWeb
– 'Aurea'	EPla
§ – 'Aureovariegata'	CB&S CBot CCla CSco ECha ELan EOrc EPla ERav GPoy IJoh MBal MBar MBri MFir MPar NNor NRoo SReu WAbe
§ – 'Azurea Flore Pleno'	CB&S CBre CCla CGle CPar CRDP CRow EOrc EPar EPla ERav GGar MBal MBar MFir MPla MPlt NHol NKay NRoo NSti SChu SHBN SPer WBon WEas WHen WHoo WWat WWeb
¶ – 'Blue Cloud'	SBod
¶ – 'Blue Drift'	SBod
– 'Bowles' Blue'	See V. ***minor*** 'La Grave'
– 'Bowles' Variety'	See V. ***m.*** 'La Grave'
– 'Burgundy'	CBre CShe EPar MBal SIng SRms WWat WWye

– 'Caerulea Plena'	See V. ***m.*** 'Azurea Flore Pleno'
– 'Dartington Star'	See V. ***major*** 'Oxyloba'
– 'Dart's Blue'	MBri
– 'Double Burgundy'	See V. ***m.*** 'Multiplex'
– 'Gertrude Jekyll'	CAbb CCla CFis CRiv CRow CSco CTom EGol ELan EPla IBar IDai MBri MPar NHol NRoo NSti SBod SChu SPer WAbe WHer WSun
– 'Grüner Teppich' ('Green Carpet')	EMon MBri SPla
§ – 'La Grave'	CB&S CBow CCla CDoC CHal CLew CRiv CRow CSco CShe EBre ECha ENot EPla GAbr LBre MBri MBro MPlt NHol NNor SBod SPer SSvw STre WBod WWat
– 'Maculata' (v)	ELan SHer
§ – 'Multiplex' (d)	CCla CGre CMil CNic CRow CTom ECtt EGol ELan EPar EPla ESma MBri NNor NRoo SFai WBod WBon WCru WWat WWeb
– 'Purpurea'	See V. ***m.*** 'Atropurpurea'
– 'Rubra'	See V. ***m.*** 'Atropurpurea'
¶ – 'Sabinka'	EMon
– 'Silver Service' (v)	CElw CMil EMon ESma LRHS WCot
– 'Variegata'	See V. ***m.*** 'Argenteovariegata'
– 'Variegata Aurea'	See V. ***m.*** 'Aureovariegata'
¶ – 'White Gold'	ESma

VINCETOXICUM (Asclepiadaceae)

§ ***hirundinaria***	GPoy NSal
nigrum	EMon EPla LRHS NSal WThi
♦ ***officinale***	See V. ***hirundinaria***

VIOLA † (Violaceae)

'Abigail' (Vtta)	SCaw
'Achilles' (Va)	SCaw
'Adelina' (Va)	SCaw
'Admiral Avallon'	See V. 'Amiral Avallon'
'Admiration' (Va)	CFul SCaw WBou
¶ ***adunca*** 'Alba'	WDav
aetolica	CPla EBar EFol NKay NWCA
'Agneta' (Va)	SCaw
'Alanta' (Va)	LGre MTho SCaw
§ ***alba***	CPla CRiv EFou ELan NHol NSti NVic SCro SHer SPla WEas WWin
albanica	See V. ***magellensis***
I 'Alcea'	SCaw
'Alethia' (Va)	SCaw
¶ 'Alexander Rayfield' (Va)	SCaw
'Alexia' (Va)	SCaw
'Alice Woodall' (Va)	SCaw
'Alma' (Va)	SHaz
altaica	SCaw
'Alwyn' (Va)	SCaw
'Alys' (Va)	SHaz
'Amelia' (Va)	CFul SCaw
'Amethyst' (C)	CDoC LHop
§ 'Amiral Avellan' (Vt)	CCot CCra CGro CPla CSmi MRob WRus
'Andrena' (Va)	SCaw
'Anita' (Va)	CFul CGle
'Ann' (ExV)	SHaz
'Ann Kean' (Vtta)	SCaw
'Ann Robb' (ExV)	SHaz
'Annabelle' (Va)	SCaw
¶ 'Annaliese' (Va)	SCaw
'Anne Mott' (Va)	SCaw
'Annette Ross' (Va)	SCaw
I 'Annona' (Va)	SCaw
'Anthea' (Va)	SCaw
'Antique Lace' (Va)	WMar
'Aphrodite' (Va)	SCaw
'Apollo' (Va)	SCaw
'Arabella' (Va)	CMHG SCaw SMrm WBou
arborescens	NHol WDav
'Ardross Gem' (Va)	CCla CFul CGle CMHG CPar CPla CRDP CSam CShe ERav GAbr GArf GCHN LBee LHop NHol NNrd NSti SCaw SHaz SMrm SPer SUsu WBou WEas WMar WWin
arenaria	See V. ***rupestris***
'Arkwright's Ruby' (Va)	EBar MFir NMen NNrd
'Artemis' (Va)	SCaw
'Aspasia' (Va)	CFul CPar LBee NHol NNrd SCaw SHaz WBou
'Atalanta' (Vtta)	SCaw
'Athena' (Va)	SCaw
'Aurelia' (Va)	SCaw
'Aurora' (Va)	SCaw
'Baby Lucia' (Va)	ELan
'Barbara' (Va)	CFul SCaw WBou
'Baronne Alice de Rothschild' (Vt)	CBre CCot CWes ERav MRob
'Beatrice' (Vtta)	CBos SHaz
§ 'Belmont Blue' (C)	CFul CGle CShe EOrc EPla LBee LHop MHig MRav NHol NMen NNrd NRoo SCaw SChu SHaz SHer SMrm WBou WDav WMar
'Benjie' (Va)	SHaz
'Berna'	WHer
§ ***bertolonii***	EBar NHol SCaw WBou WMar
'Beshlie' (Va)	LBee SCaw WBou WEas
'Bessie Cawthorne' (C)	SCaw
'Bessie Knight' (Va)	SCaw
betonicifolia	NRed WPer WThu
* – ***albescens***	NHar WDav
* – ***oblonga sagittata***	WDav
'Bettina' (Va)	SCaw
'Betty'	SHaz
'Betty Grace' (Va)	SCaw
'Bianca' (Vtta)	SCaw
biflora	CMHG CPla EPar GDra MRob MTho NGre NRya WBon WEas
'Bishop's Belle' (FP)	SHaz
'Black Ace' (Va)	SCaw
'Black Diamond' (Va)	SHaz
* 'Black Velvet'	NRed
'Blue Cloud' (Va)	SCaw
'Blue Emperor'	CGro
'Blue Lace' (Va)	SHaz
'Blue Princess'	NMen
'Blue Tit' (Va)	WBou
'Bonna Cawthorne' (Va)	SCaw
bosniaca	See V. ***elegantula b.***
'Boughton Blue'	See V. 'Belmont Blue'
'Bournemouth Gem' (Vt)	CCra CSmi MRob

§ 'Bowles' Black' (T) CArn CGle CHad CHan CMea CPar CRow ECha EFou ELan EPad GAbr NBro NRoo NSti SBla WBou WEas
'Boy Blue' (Vtta) SCaw
'Brenda Hall' (Va) SCaw
'Bronwen' (Va) SCaw
bubanii SCaw
'Bullion' (Va) SCaw SHaz WMer
'Buttercup' (Vtta) CFul LBee NRoo SCaw SHaz WBou WMar WWin
'Buxton Blue' (Va) CFul SCaw SChu SHaz
'Byrony' (Vtta) SCaw
calaminaria CHun SCaw
'Calantha' (Vtta) SCaw
calcarata ELan SCaw SHer WThu
§ – ssp. ***zoysii*** GArf GDra ITim NGre NMen
'California' (Vt) CCot MRob
'Callia' (Va) SCaw
I 'Calypso' (Va) SCaw
canadensis var. ***rugulosa*** CRDP SFis
'Candida' (Vtta) SCaw
canina CKin
'Carberry Seedling' (Va) SCaw
'Carina' (Vtta) SCaw
'Caroline' (Va) SHaz SMrm
I 'Cassandra' (Vtta) SCaw
chaerophylloïdes See V. ***dissecta c.***
'Chantal' (Vtta) SCaw
'Chantreyland' (Va) NCat SRms WHen
'Charity' (Va) SCaw
'Charlotte Mott' (Va) SCaw
'Chelsea Girl' (Va) SHaz SMrm
'Chloe' (Vtta) CFul SCaw
'Christmas' CBre CSmi
'Christobel' (Va) SCaw
'Cinderella (Va) CFul
'Cindy' (Va) SHaz
'Citrina' (Va) SCaw
'Clementina' (Va) CCot CPar EBre GAri GCHN LBre MRav NRoo NSti SCro
'Cleo' (Va) SHaz
'Clive Groves' (Vt) CGro CSmi
'Clodagh' (Va) CMHG SCaw
'Clover' (Va) SCaw
'Coeur d'Alsace' (Vt) CCot CGro CNic CPla CSmi ELan EPar ERav SHaz SSou WBon WEas WRus WSun
'Colleen' (Vtta) SCaw
'Columbine' (Va) CMHG CRDP SCaw SMrm
§ 'Comte de Brazza' (dVt) CCot CCra CPla CWes MRob SHaz
'Comte de Chambord' (dVt) MRob
'Connie' (Va) CBos SCaw SHaz
'Coralie' (Vtta) SCaw
'Cordelia' (Va) MRob SCaw
cornuta CFul CGle CHad CMea CPla EOrc LGan MBro MFir MHig NBro NKay NMen NNrd NRoo SCaw SDix SIng SMrm SPer SPla WBou WHen WHoo
– Alba Group Widely available
§ – 'Alba Minor' CFul CGle CHun CLew CNic EFol ELan MBro NMen NRoo SCaw SChu WHoo
– blue SCaw WMar WSun WWat
¶ – ***compacta*** CHan GArf
– 'Foliis Aureis' MFir
– Lilacina Group CFul CGle CPar CTom ECha NCat SCaw SChu SHaz SMrm SWas WPer WSun
– 'Minor' CFul CNic CPla CSam EPot MBro MFir NNrd SBla SCaw SHaz WBou WDav WRus
– 'Minor Alba' See V. ***c.*** 'Alba Minor'
– Purpurea Group CMea ECha WRus
– 'Rosea' CFul SCaw WMar WSun
– 'Seymour Pink' CFul
– 'Variegata' SCaw
– 'Violacea' SCaw
'Coronation' CMHG CSam
corsica SCaw
'Cox's Moseley' (ExV) SHaz
'Cream Sensation' (Va) SHaz
'Cressida' (Va) SCaw
cucullata See V. ***obliqua***
cunninghamii CPar GDra NNrd
curtisii See V. ***tricolor c.***
'Cyril Bell' (Va) SCaw
§ 'Czar' (Vt) CBre CCot CGro CPla CSmi GAbr ILis MRob NRed NRya SHaz WHen WSun
'Czar Bleu' (Vt) MRob
'Daena' (Vtta) SCaw SMrm
'Daisy Smith' (Va) CFul WBou
'Dartington Hybrid' (Va) SCaw
'Daveron' (C) SCaw
'David Wheldon' (Va) CFul SCaw SHaz
'Davina' (Va) SCaw SChu
'Dawn' (Vtta) CCot CFul LBee MMil SCaw SHaz WBou
'Decima' (Va) SCaw
'Delia' (Va) CFul SCaw WBou
'Delicia' (Vtta) CMHG SCaw
'Delmonden' (Va) SAsh
delphinantha NWCA
'Delphine' (Va) SCaw
'Demeter' (Va) SCaw
'Desdemona' (Va) CHun CMHG SHaz SUsu WBou
'Desmonda' (Va) SCaw SChu
'Dimity' (Va) SCaw
'Dione' (Vtta) SCaw
I 'Diosma' (Va) SCaw
'Dirty Molly' CGle
§ ***dissecta*** WPer
– var. ***chaerophylloïdes*** f.***eizanensis*** CCla CHad CRDP EBre ECro ESma LBre MTho WDav WHal WOMN
– var. ***sieboldiana*** EFol MRob
'Dobbie's Bronze' (Va) CFul SCaw SHaz WBou
'Dobbie's Red' (Va) SCaw WBou
'Doctor Smart' (C) SCaw
doerfleri SCaw
'Dominy' (Vtta) SCaw
'Double White' (dVt) CGle MPar MRob
dubyana SBar WOMN
'Duchesse de Parme' (dVt) CGle CGro CSmi CWes MRob SHaz WHer
'Dudine' (dVt) MRob
'Dulcie Rhoda' (Va) SHaz
'Dusk' WBou
'E A Bowles' See V. 'Bowles' Black'

'Eastgrove Blue Scented (Va) WAbe WBou WEas
'Ednaston Gem' CSam
♦*eizanensis* See V. ***dissecta chaerophylloïdes e.***
§ *elatior* CCor CFis CHun CMea CMil CPar CPla CRDP EBar ECha EMon LGan MPar MRob NHol NSti SChu SHaz SIng SWas WBon WDav WMar WPer
§ *elegantula* SCaw
– *bosniaca* SCaw WEas
¶ 'Elisha' (Va) SCaw
'Elizabeth' (Va) CFul CMGP SCaw WBou
'Elizabeth Cawthorne' (C) SCaw
'Elizabeth Robb' (FP) SHaz
'Elsie Coombs' (Vt) MRob
'Emily Mott' (Va) SCaw
'Emma' (Va) NHar SCaw
'Emma Cawthorne' (C) SCaw
'Enterea' (Va) SCaw
erecta See V. ***elatior***
'Eris' (Va) SCaw
'Eros' (Va) SCaw
'Etain' (Va) ECha SCaw
'Ethena' (Va) SCaw
'Etienne' (Va) SCaw
'Evelyn Cawthorne' (C) SCaw
eximia SCaw
'Fabiola' (Vtta) CFul LBee SCaw WBou
'Felicity' (Va) SCaw
'Finola Galway' (Va) SCaw
'Fiona' (Va) CMHG ERav NCat SCaw SUsu WBou WMar WSun
flettii NKay NTow WHal WOMN
'Florence' (Va) SCaw
'Foxbrook Cream' (C) CFul CPar SHaz SPer WBou WRus WSun
'Francesca' (Va) SCaw
'Freckles' See V. ***sororia*** 'F.'
'Gatina' (Va) SCaw
I 'Gazania' (Va) SCaw WBou
'Gazelle' (Vtta) ECha SCaw
'Gemma' (Va) SHaz
'Genesta Gambier' (Va) CFul CMHG CSam SCaw
'George Rowley' (FP) SHaz
'Georgina' (Va) SCaw
'Geraldine' (Vtta) SCaw
'Geraldine Cawthorne' (C) SCaw
'Gina' (Vtta) SCaw
'Giselle' (Va) SCaw
glabella SUsu WOMN
'Gladys Findlay' (Va) SCaw SHaz WBou WHer
'Glenroyd Fancy' (ExV) SHaz
¶ 'Gloriole' CGro
'Governor Herrick' (Vt) CShe EFou MRob
'Grace' (Va) EBar SHaz
§ *gracilis* ECha ELan SBla SCaw
– *lutea* CNic CSam SBla SMrm SSvw
*– 'Magic' CElw CRDP NTow SMrm
– 'Major' CRDP SCaw SHaz
'Grey Owl' (Va) SCaw SUsu WKif
grisebachiana CHun CPla CRDP NGre NTow
'Griselda' (Vtta) SCaw
'Grovemount Blue' (C) CElw CMea NCat NKay

§ *grypoceras* var. *exilis* CHun CNic CPla CRDP ESma NWCA WCru WHal WHoo
– 'Variegata' EFol NBir
'Gustav Wermig' (C) CBos GAbr NCat SCaw SHaz SSvw WBou
'Gwen Cawthorne' (C) SCaw
¶ 'Hadria Cawthorne' (C) SCaw
'Hansa' (C) CGle
'Haslemere' See V. 'Nellie Britton'
I 'Hebe' (Vtta) SCaw
§ *hederacea* CArn CCot CGro CHan CMHG CPla CRDP CSFH CShe ECou EFol ELan ELun EPot ESis GCHN GCal MFir MPar MRob NBro NHar SHaz SUsu WHer WOMN
– blue form CElw CPla CSpe ECou LHil SAxl SHer WHal WOMN WPer
– 'Putty' EBre ECou LBre
– *sieberi* See V. ***sieberiana***
'Helen' (Va) SHaz
'Helen W Cochrane' (ExV) SHaz
'Helena' (Va) SCaw
'Hera' (Va) SCaw
'Hespera' (Va) SCaw
I 'Hesperis' (Va) SCaw
heterophylla ssp. *epirota* See V. ***bertolonii***
'Hextable' (C) SCaw
hirta CGro CKin MRob MWil WCla
hispida SCaw
'Honey' (Va) SHaz
'Hudsons Blue' CElw
'Hugh Campbell' (ExV) SHaz
'Huntercombe Purple' (Va) CBos CCla CFul CGle CHun CSam NNrd SBla SCaw SMrm SUsu WBou WKif WPer WSun
'Hyacintha' (C) CFul
'Hyperion' (Va) SCaw
'Iantha' (Vtta) SCaw
'Iden Gem' (Va) CFul SCaw SHaz
¶ *incisa* MFos
'Inkie' (Va) CFul
'Inverurie Beauty' (Va) EJud MFir NCat SCaw WBou
'Inverurie Mauve' (Va) SCaw SUsu
'Iona' (Va) SCaw
'Irene Missen' CGle
'Irish Elegance' (Vt) CHad CRDP ERav MRob NRed WHal
'Irish Molly' (Va) Widely available
'Isata' (Va) SCaw
'Isla' (Vtta) LGre SCaw
'Ita' (Va) SCaw
'Iver Grove' (Va) SCaw
'Ivory Queen' (Va) CCla CFul SCaw
'Ivory White' (Va) SCaw WOMN
'Jack Frost' (FP) SHaz
'Jackanapes' (Va) CBot CCla CCot CFul CGle CMHG CMea CRDP CSam CShe ECha ECtt ELan ERav LHop MHig NBro NNrd NSti SCaw SHaz SMrm SSvw SUsu WBou WMar WWin
'James Christie' (FP) SHaz
'James Pilling' (Va) CFul SCaw SHaz
'Jamie' (Va) SHaz
'Jane Askew' (Va) SCaw
'Jane Mott' (Va) SCaw

'Janet' (Va)	SCaw WBou
'Janine' (Vtta)	SCaw
'Janna' (Va)	SCaw
'Jeannie' (Va)	SHaz
'Jeannie Bellew' (Va)	SCaw SChu WBou WKif WMar
'Jemma' (Va)	SCaw
'Jenelle' (Vtta)	SCaw
'Jenny' (Vtta)	SCaw
'Jersey Gem' (Va)	SCaw SHaz
'Jessie East'	WEas
'Jimmie's Dark' (ExV)	SHaz
'Joan Christie' (FP)	SHaz
'Joe Millet' (FP)	SHaz
'Joella' (Va)	SCaw
'John Raddenbury' (Vt)	CCra CGro CHal MRob
'John Yelmark' (Va)	SCaw
'John Zanini' (Vtta)	SCaw
'Johnny Jump Up' (T)	MPit
Joker strain (P)	NOak
jooi	CHun CNic GTou MPar MRob MTho NBir NMen NNrd SBla SIng WPer WThu
'Joyce Gray' (Va)	EBar SHaz SMrm
'Julia' (Va)	SCaw WBou
'Julian' (Va)	CBos CFul CHun EBar GDra NHar NKay NMen NSti SBla SIng WAbe WBou WDav WMar
'Juno' (Va)	SCaw
'Jupiter' (Va)	SCaw
'Kadischa' (Va)	SCaw
'Karen' (Va)	SHaz
'Kate' (Va)	CFul
¶ 'Katerina' (Va)	SCaw
'Kathleen Hoyle' (ExV)	SHaz
'Kathy' (Vtta)	SCaw
'Katinka' (Va)	SCaw
'Kerrie' (Va)	SCaw
'Kiki McDonough'	SCaw
'Kilruna' (Va)	SCaw
'King of the Blues' (Va)	SHaz
¶ 'Kirsty' (Va)	SCaw
'Kitty White' (Va)	SCaw
'Kizzy' (Va)	SHaz
koraiensis	MTho SPou
♦***koreana***	See V. ***grypoceras exilis***
♦***labradorica*** hort.	See V. ***riviniana*** Purpurea Group
– ***purpurea***	See V. ***riviniana*** Purpurea Group
'Lady Finnyoon' (Va)	SHaz
'Lady Jane' (Vt)	MRob
'Lady Tennyson' (Va)	CFul SBla SCaw SHaz WBou
'Lamorna' (Vtta)	SCaw
lanceolata	CPla
'Larissa' (Va)	SCaw
'Latona' (Va)	SCaw
'Laura' (C)	CFul EFol
'Lavender Lady'	CGro MRob
'Laverna' (Va)	SCaw
'Lavinia' (Va)	CPar SCaw SHaz WBou
'Leander' (Va)	SCaw
'Leda' (Va)	SCaw
'Lee' (Va)	SHaz
'Leora' (Vtta)	CFul SCaw
'Leora Hamilton' (C)	CMHG SCaw
'Lerosa' (Vtta)	SCaw
'Leta' (Vtta)	SCaw

'Letitia' (Va)	CFul NHar SCaw SHaz WAbe WBou
'Leto' (Va)	SCaw
'Lewisa' (Va)	SCaw
'Lianne' (Vt)	CCra CGro CWes MRob SHaz
'Lilac Rose' (Va)	CFul LBee WBou
'Liliana' (Va)	SCaw
'Liriopa' (Va)	SCaw
'Lisa Cawthorne' (C)	SCaw
'Little David' (Vtta)	CBos CCot CDec CFul CSam CShe LBee NNrd SCaw SHaz SMrm WBou WEas WRus
'Little Liz' (Va)	SHaz
'Livia' (Vtta)	SCaw WBou WMar
'Lola' (Va)	SCaw
'Lord Nelson' (C)	WMer
'Lord Plunket' (Va)	CFul NCat SCaw WBou
'Lorna' (Va)	SCaw SUsu
'Lorna Cawthorne' (C)	CMGP SCaw
'Lorna Moakes' (Va)	SCaw SMrm
'Louisa' (Va)	SCaw SUsu
'Louise Gemmell' (Va)	SCaw SChu
'Love Duet'	NBir
'Luca' (Va)	SCaw
'Lucinda' (Va)	SCaw
'Lucy' (Va)	SCaw
'Ludy May' (Va)	SCaw
'Lulu' (Va)	SHaz
'Luna' (Vtta)	SCaw
lutea	CShe ECha SCaw WBou
– ssp. ***elegans***	See V. ***lutea lutea***
'Luxonne' (Vt)	CBre CCot MRob SHaz
lyallii	ECou
'Lydia' (Va)	CShe SCaw SChu SHaz SMrm WBou
'Lydia Groves'	CGro MRob
'Lysander' (Va)	SCaw
macedonica	See V. ***tricolor macedonica***
'Madame Armandine Pages' (Vt)	CBre CCra ERav MRob
'Madelaine' (Va)	SCaw
'Madge' (Va)	SCaw
'Maera' (Vtta)	SCaw
§ ***magellensis***	CPla MPit
'Magenta Maid' (Va)	CFul LBee
'Maggie' (Va)	SCaw
'Maggie Mott' (Va)	CCla CCot CFul CGle CSam CShe ECha EOrc ERav GArf LHop MBri MHig NBro NNrd NSti SBla SCaw SHaz SPer SSvw SUsu WBou WEas WMar WRus WWin
'Magic'	LBee WBou
¶ 'Maid Marion'	SRms
'Majella' (Vtta)	SCaw
'Malise' (Va)	SCaw
'Malvena' (Vtta)	SCaw
mandshurica	CGro MPar WHal WThu
¶ – 'Ikedaeana'	MFos
'Margaret' (Va)	SHaz
'Margaret Cawthorne' (C)	SCaw
'Marian' (Va)	SCaw
'Marie Louise' (dVt)	CCot CCra CGro CPla CSmi EPar MRob
'Marika' (Va)	SCaw
'Mark Talbot' (Va)	CFul
'Maroon Picotee'	ELan SHer

'Mars' (Va) SCaw
'Marsland's Yellow' (Vtta) SCaw
'Martin' (Va) CBos CBre CCla CFis CFul CMHG CSam CShe ECha GCHN LBee LHop NKay SCaw SChu SHaz SHer SMrm WBou WMar WSun WWin
'Mary Cawthorne' (C) SCaw
'Mary Dawson' (Va) SCaw
'Mary Ellen' (Va) CFul
'Mattie' (Va) SHaz
'Mauve Beauty' (Va) SCaw
'Mauve Haze' (Va) CCla MTho WBou WEas WMar
'Mauve Radiance' (Va) CFul CShe NVic SCaw SHaz SSvw WBou
'Mavis Tuck' CSam
'May Mott' (Va) WAbe
'May Roberts' (ExV) SHaz
'Meena' (Vtta) SCaw
'Megumi' (Va) SCaw
'Melinda' (Vtta) SCaw WBou
I 'Melissa' (Va) CFul
'Mercury' (Va) SCaw
'Midnight' (Va) WHil
'Midnight Turk' (Va) SHaz
'Milkmaid' (Va) CFul CGle ECha GAbr LBee NBir WKif
'Mina Walker' (ExV) SHaz
'Minerva' (Va) SCaw
'Miranda' (Vtta) SCaw
'Miss Brookes' (Va) CBos CFul SCaw SMrm WBou
'Mistral' (Va) SCaw
'Mitzel' (Vtta) SCaw
'Molly Sanderson' (Va) CBot CCla CGle CMea CPar CRDP CSam ECha EFol ELan ELun EPot LBee LHop MRav NHar NMen NSti SCaw SChu SIng SMrm SUsu WAbe WBou WEas WMar WPer WWin
'Monica' (Va) SCaw
'Moonlight' (Va) CFul CGle CHad CMea CRDP CSam ECha EFol ELan EPla GCHN LBee LHop MHig NHar NKay NRoo NSti SBla SCaw SHaz SMrm SUsu WBou WHal WPer
'Moonraker' CCot NCat NKay NTow SIng
'Morvana' (Va) SCaw
'Morwenna' (Va) SCaw
'Moscaria' (Va) SCaw
'Moseley Ideal' (ExV) SHaz
'Moseley Perfection' (Va) SCaw
'Mother's Day' CGro MRob
'Mrs Chichester' (Va) LHop SCaw WBou
'Mrs David Lloyd George' (dVt) MRob
'Mrs Lancaster' (Va) CBos CFul CSam LBee SCaw WBou
'Mrs Pinehurst' (Vt) MRob
'Mrs R Barton' (Vt) CCot CCra CGro CHal CPla CSmi MRob SHaz WHen WHil
¶ 'Mrs Reid's French' ERav
'Myfawnny' (Va) CSam NRoo SCaw WBou
'Mylene' (Va) SCaw
'Myntha' (Vtta) SCaw
'Mysie' (Va) CFul
'Nadia' (Va) SCaw
'Natasha' (Va) SCaw
'Nell' (Va) CFul
§ 'Nellie Britton' (Va) CCla CFul CGle EOrc NHar NKay NNrd NSti SBla SCaw SChu SHaz SMrm SPer WAbe WBou WEas WMar WRus WWin
'Nemesis' (Va) SCaw
'Neptune' (Va) SCaw
'Nerena' (Vtta) SCaw
'Nesta' (Vtta) SCaw
♦ 'Netta Statham' (C) See V. 'Belmont Blue'
'Nicole' (Va) SCaw
'Nigra' (Va) SCaw SRms
'Nimrod' (Va) SCaw
'Nina' (Va) CHun SCaw
'Nona' (Va) SCaw
'Noni' (Vt) MRob
'Nora May' (Va) CFul
'Norah Church' (Vt) CGro CSmi CWes MRob SHaz
'Norah Leigh' (Va) CCra EBre ESis LBre NRoo WBou
¶ ***nuttallii vallicola*** MFos
§ ***obliqua*** CPar MPlt NVic SHaz WOMN
♦ **– *alba*** See V. ***a.***
§ **– *rosea*** CBre CSFH EPla
'Octavia' (Va) SCaw
'Odile' (Va) SCaw
odorata CArn CB&S CGle CGro CKin CRDP CRow EPar ERav GPoy LHol MBri MRob NKay NNrd NRoo NSal NSel NSti SIde SSou WCla WOak WWye
§ **– *alba*** CKin
– 'Alba' CBre CCla CGle CRDP CRow EFou ELan EPad EPar ERav ILis MFir MPar MRob NCat NNrd NRoo NSti SIde WBon WCla WRus WWat
– 'Alba Plena' CRDP WHer
– 'Aurea' MPar
♦ **– *dumetorum*** See V. ***alba***
– *flore-pleno* EFol EPar
– pink MPar WCla
– *rosea* WOMN
– 'Sulphurea' ELan WOMN
– 'Wellsiana' (Vt) GArf
'Olive Edmonds' (Va) SCaw
'Opera' (Vt) CCot CCra CGro MRob
'Orchid Pink' (Vt) MRob
oreades SCaw
'Oriana' (Va) SCaw
orphanidis SCaw
ossea SCaw
'Palmer's White' (Va) CFul SCaw SHaz
palustris CGro CKin CRDP CRow CShe MRob
'Pamela' (Va) SHaz
'Pamela Zambra' (Vt) MRob SHaz
'Pam's Fancy' (ExV) WBou
'Pandora' (Va) SCaw WBou
papilionacea See V. ***sororia***
'Parme de Toulouse' (dVt) MRob
'Pat Creasy' (Va) SHaz WBou
'Pat Kavanagh' SCaw
'Patricia Brookes' (Va) SCaw
pedata CBro CRDP MRob NHar NHol SSou WAbe WHil WWat

pedatifida	CCla CRiv ECro EFol ELan EMar EPla GDra MRob MTho NNrd NSti SChu SHaz SHer WHal WRus WThu
'Penny Black' (Va)	CNic ECha EMon SCaw WBou
pensylvanica	See V. ***pubescens eriocarpa***
¶***perinensis*** JCA 992.600	CNic
'Perle Rose' (Vt)	CCot CCra CGro CWes MRob
'Pete'	SChu
'Petra' (Vtta)	SCaw
'Philippa Cawthorne' (C)	SCaw
'Phoebe' (Va)	SCaw WBou
'Phyllida' (Va)	SCaw
'Pickering Blue' (Va)	CFul SCaw SHaz WBou
¶'Pilar' (Va)	SCaw
'Piper' (Va)	SHaz
'Pippa' (Vtta)	SCaw SChu
'Pixie' (Va)	SHaz
'Poppy' (Va)	SCaw
'Priam' (Va)	SCaw
'Primrose Cream' (Va)	SCaw
'Primrose Dame' (Va)	CDoC NNrd SCaw SHaz WBou WMer
'Primrose Pixie' (Va)	WBou
'Prince Henry' (T)	LAbb MPit NKay NMen
'Prince John' (T)	MPit NCat NKay NMen
'Princess Alexandra' (Vt)	MRob
'Princess Mab' (Vtta)	CFul NNrd SCaw SHaz WBou
'Princess of Prussia' (Vt)	WWat
'Princess of Wales'	See V. 'Princesse de Galles'
§ 'Princesse de Galles' (Vt)	CB&S CCra CGro CHal CSmi EPar MRob SHaz WRus
§ ***pubescens eriocarpa***	CBro CKni CRDP WPer
'Purity' (Vtta)	SCaw
'Purple Dove' (Va)	SHaz SMrm
'Purple Radiance'	CCla
'Purple Wings' (Va)	WBou
'Quatre Saisons' (Vt)	MRob
'Queen Charlotte' (Vt)	GCHN ILis MBri MRob NMen WCot
'Queen Disa' (Vtta)	CMHG SCaw
'Quink' (Va)	CFul
'Ramona' (Va)	SCaw
'Raven (Vtta)	CFul GCal WBou
'Ravenna' (Va)	SCaw
'Rawson's White' (Vt)	MRob NCat
'Rebecca' (Vtta)	CBos CCot CFul CGle CHun CLew CMHG CPla CRDP CSam EBar EFol ELan LBee NBir NCat NHar NRoo NSti NTow SCaw SChu SUsu WBou WHal WHer WKif WPer
'Rebecca Cawthorne' (C)	SCaw
'Red Charm' (Vt)	MBri
'Red Lion'	CGro
'Red Queen' (Vt)	CCot CGro MRob
reichenbachiana	ELan EPar MWil
'Reliance' (Va)	CFul
'Remora' (Vtta)	SCaw WBou
reniforme	See V. ***hederacea***
'Rhoda' (Va)	SCaw
'Richard Vivian' (Va)	SCaw
'Richard's Yellow' (Va)	CMGP SCaw
riviniana	CArn CKin CTom NLan NNrd WHer WOak
– 'Autumn White'	MPar
§ – Purpurea Group	Widely available
'Romilly' (Va)	SCaw
'Rosine' (Vt)	CCra CSmi MRob
'Rowan Hood' (ExV)	SHaz
'Rowena' (Va)	SCaw
'Royal Delft'	GCHN
'Royal Robe' (VT)	CCra MRob
'Rubra' (Vt)	MRob
rugulosa	See V. ***canadensis r.***
¶***rupestris***	CGro
– blue	MRob NCat
§ – ***rosea***	CBre CGro CHal CNic CPar CPla CRDP CTom MRob NCat NGre NRed NSti NWCA STre WBon WCla WDav WEas WHal WSun
'Russian Superb' (Vt)	CCot MRob
'Ruth Blackall' (Va)	SCaw
'Ruth Elkans' (Va)	SCaw SHaz
'Saint Helena' (Vt)	CGro MRob
'Saint Maur' (Va)	CFul
'Sally' (Vtta)	SCaw
'Samantha' (Vtta)	SCaw
'Sammy Jo' (Va)	SHaz WBou
'Sarah' (Va)	CFul SHaz
saxatilis	See V. ***tricolor subalpina***
¶***scariensis***	WDav
¶***schariensis*** JCA 993.150	CNic
'Scottish Yellow' (Va)	MRob
selkirkii	CNic CPla CRDP CRiv EFol NNrd WCot WHal WThu
¶– 'Variegata'	NBir
****sempervivoides***	WOMN
septentrionalis	CCla CCot CCra CHal CMea CMil CRDP ECha EGol ELan MCas MPar MRob NGre SAxl SHaz SSmi SSou WHal WHil WRus
– ***alba***	CFis CMHG MRob WPer WTyr
– 'Rubra'	CMil
'Septima' (Va)	SCaw
'Serena' (Va)	SCaw WBou
'Sheila' (Va)	SHaz WBou
¶***sheltonii***	MFos
'Sidborough Poppet'	EFol MBro WPer
§ ***sieberiana***	ECou
'Sigrid' (Va)	SCaw
'Sissinghurst' (Va)	SAxl SCaw
'Sky Blue' (Va)	SCaw
'Sophie' (Va)	SHaz SMrm
§ ***sororia***	CHun CRow LBlm MFir MRob SAxl WHal WOMN
– 'Albiflora'	GCal NHar WCot WDav WPer
§ – 'Freckles'	Widely available
– 'Priceana'	CCla CHad CMil CNic NRed SAxl SHaz WBon WCot WPer WWat
'Soula' (Vtta)	SCaw
¶'Spode Blue'	MHig
'Stewart William' (FP)	SHaz
'Steyning' (Va)	SCaw
stojanovii	CMea ELan EMar MBro NMen SBla SGil WEas WOMN WPer
striata	CHun WWat
'Sulphurea' (Vt)	CGro CHal CPla CWes ELan ERav MRob
'Sunshine' (Va)	CFul
'Susan' (SP)	SHaz
'Susannah' (Va)	CCot SHaz SMrm
'Susie' (Va)	SHaz
'Swanley White'	See V. 'Comte de Brazza'

'Sybil' (ExV) SHaz
'Sylvia Hart' MTho WBon
'Talitha' (Va) LBee SCaw
'Tamsin' (Va) SCaw
'Tara' (Va) SCaw
'Thalia' (Vtta) CFul SCaw SUsu WBou
'The Czar' See V. 'Czar'
'Thea' (Va) SCaw
'Thelma' (Va) SCaw
'Thetis' (Va) SCaw
'Tiffany' (Va) SCaw
'Tina' (Va) SHaz WBou
'Tina Whittaker' (Vt) MRob
'Titania' (Vtta) SCaw
'Tom Tit' (Va) SCaw WBou
'Tomose' (Va) CFul
'Tony Venison' (C/v) CBos CCot CRDP EFol EHoe EMon GArf MTho NNrd NSti SHaz WBou WHal WHer WRus
'Translucent Blue' MRob WBon
tricolor CKin CNic CRDP GPoy IEde LHol NGre NSal NSel NWCA SIde SSou WHer WSun
§ – ssp. ***curtisii*** SCaw
§ – ssp. ***macedonica*** NGre SIng
– 'Sawyer's Blue' WPer
'Tullia' (Vtta) SCaw
'Tuscany' (Vt) MRob
'Una' (Va) SCaw
'Unity' (Va) SCaw
'Velleda' (Vtta) SCaw
velutina See V. ***gracilis***
'Venetia' (Va) SCaw
'Venus' (Va) SCaw
§ ***verecunda***
var. ***yakusimana*** CMHG CNic CRDP CRiv CTom EPot ESis NGre NHol SIng
'Victoria' (Vt) See V. 'Czar Bleu'
'Victoria Cawthorne' (C) NSti SCaw SChu WHoo WMar
'Victoria Regina' (Vt) CRow MRob
'Vignette' (Va) SHaz
'Virginia' (Va) CFul SCaw SHaz WBou
'Virgo' (Va) SCaw
x ***visseriana lutea*** WKif
'Vita' (Va) CFul EBar ERav GCal LGre NNrd SCaw SChu SHaz SMrm SUsu WBou WMar WSun
'Wanda' (Va) SCaw
'Wheatley White' SPer
'White Czar' (Vt) MRob
'White Gem' (Va) LBee SHaz
'White Ladies' (Vt) See V. ***obliqua alba***
'White Pearl' (Va) WBou
¶ 'White Superior' CB&S
'White Swan' (Va) LBee NHar SCaw
'William Fife' (ExV) SHaz
'William Wallace' (Va) SCaw
'Windward' (Vt) CCot CGro MRob NCat
'Winifred Jones' (Va) SHaz
'Winifred Wargent' (Va) CMGP SCaw
'Winona' (Vtta) SCaw
'Winona Cawthorne' (C) SCaw SChu
'Woodlands Cream' (Va) SHaz
'Woodlands Gold' (Va) SHaz
'Woodlands Lilac' (Va) SCaw WBou
'Woodlands White' (Va) SCaw
'Xantha' (Va) SCaw
yakusimana See V. ***verecunda yakusimana***
yezoensis CHun CPla SBla
'Yoyo' (Va) SHaz
'Zalea' (Va) SCaw
'Zara' (Va) NHar SHaz WBou
¶ 'Zenobia' (Vtta) SCaw
'Zepherine' (Va) SCaw
'Zeta' (Va) SCaw
'Ziglana' (Va) SCaw
'Zoe' (Vtta) CFul SCaw WBou
'Zona' (Va) SCaw
zoysii See V. ***calcarata zoysii***

VISCARIA (Caryophyllaceae)

vulgaris See LYCHNIS ***viscaria***

VITALIANA (Primulaceae)

§ ***primuliflora*** CRiv GArf GTou MBro NKay WHoo
– ssp. ***praetutiana*** CNic EPot GDra ITim MBro MCas MHig NHar NHol NNrd NTow NWCA SIng WAbe WDav WPat WThu
¶ – – ***chionantha*** EPot
¶ – – ***compacta*** EPot
– ssp. ***tridentata*** WDav

VITEX (Verbenaceae)

agnus-castus CAbb CArn CB&S CCla CDoC CGre CHun CWSG EEls ELan GPoy LHol NSal SHil SMad SPer SSpi WHer WOMN WWye
– 'Blue Spire' LRHS
– 'Silver Spire' SSpi
lucens CHEx
negundo CArn CHun
– ***cannabinifolia*** See V. ***incisa***

VITIS † (Vitaceae)

F 'Abouriou' (***vinifera***) (O/B) WStA
F 'Alden' (O/W) CYea
F 'Alicante' (***vinifera***) (G/B) CB&S ERea GTwe WStA
F 'Alzey Red' (***vinifera***) (O/R) CYea
amurensis CHEx WCru WWat
F 'Angers Frontignan' (***vinifera***) (G/O/B) ERea
'Apiifolia' (***vinifera***) See V. 'Ciotat'
F 'Appley Towers' (***vinifera***) (G/B) ERea
F 'Aris' (O/W) CYea
F 'Ascot Citronelle' (***vinifera***) (G/W) ERea
F 'Aurora' (Seibel 5279) CYea
F 'Auvergne Frontignan' (***vinifera***) (G/O/W) ERea
F 'Auxerrois' (***vinifera***) (O/W) CYea WStA
F 'Bacchus' (***vinifera***) (O/W) WStA
F 'Baco Noir' (O/B) CYea GTwe WStA
'Black Alicante' (***vinifera***) See V. 'Alicante'

F 'Black Corinth' (*vinifera*) (G/B) — ERea
F 'Black Frontignan' (*vinifera*) (G/O/B) — ERea WStA
'Black Hamburgh' — See V. 'Schiava Grossa'
F 'Black Monukka' (*vinifera*) (G/B) — ERea
F 'Black Prince' (*vinifera*) (G/B) — ERea
F 'Blauburger' (*vinifera*) (O/B) — CYea WStA
'Blue Portuguese' (*vinifera*) — See V. 'Portugieser'
F 'Boskoop Glory' (*vinifera*) — CMac GTwe IJoh SDea WStA
F 'Brant' (O/B) — CB&S CBra CMac CSco CYea EBre ELan ENot ERea EWar GTwe LBre LBuc LHop MBri MGos NElm NRog SDea SHBN SPer SReu SSpi SSta WBod WStA
F 'Buckland Sweetwater' (*vinifera*) (G/W) — ERea GTwe MBri
F 'Cabernet Sauvignon' (*vinifera*) (O/B) — WStA
F ***californica*** — ERea
'Canadice' — ESim
F 'Canon Hall Muscat' (*vinifera*) (G/W) — ERea
F 'Cardinal' (*vinifera*) — ERea
F 'Cascade' (Seibel 13053) (O/B) — CYea ERea LBuc SDea WStA
F 'Chaouch' (*vinifera*) (G/W) — ERea
F 'Chardonnay' (*vinifera*) (O/W) — CYea SDea WStA
F 'Chasselas' (*vinifera*) (G/O/W) — CB&S CDoC CMac ERea EWar NGrN WStA
'Chasselas d'Or' (*vinifera*) — See V. 'Chasselas'
F 'Chasselas Rosé' (*vinifera*) (G/R) — ERea WStA
F 'Chasselas Vibert' (*vinifera*) (G/W) — ERea
F 'Chenin Blanc' (*vinifera*) (O/W) — WStA
F 'Ciotat' (*vinifera*) — EPla ERea SDea WCru WStA
coignetiae — Widely available
F 'Concord' (*labrusca*) (O/B) — ERea
F 'Cot' (*vinifera*) (O/B) — WStA
F 'Cote House Seedling' (*vinifera*) (O/W) — ERea
* 'Csabyongye' (*vinifera*) (W) — WStA
F 'Dunkelfelder' (*vinifera*) (O/R) — CYea WStA
F 'Early Van der Laan' (*vinifera*) — LHol
F 'Ehrenfelser' (*vinifera*) (O/W) — CYea WStA
F 'Elbling' (*vinifera*) (O/W) — WStA
F 'Emerald Riesling' (*vinifera*) (O/W) — CYea
F 'Espiran' (*vinifera*) — ERea
F 'Excelsior' (*vinifera*) (W) — SDea WStA
F 'Faber' (*vinifera*) (O/W) — CYea WStA
¶ ***flexuosa*** — EPla
F 'Forta' (*vinifera*) (O/W) — WStA
F 'Foster's Seedling' (*vinifera*) (G/W) — ERea GTwe NGrN SDea SKee SPer WStA
F 'Fragola' (*vinifera*) (O/R) — CMac EBre ECha EPla ERav ERea GTwe LBre SDea WStA WWat
F 'Gagarin Blue' (*vinifera*) (O/B) — CYea ERea SDea WStA
F 'Gamay Hatif' (*vinifera*) (O/B) — ERea
¶ 'Gamay Hatif des Voges' (*vinifera*) — WStA
F 'Gamay Noir' (*vinifera*) (O/B) — CYea WStA
F Gamay Teinturier Group (*vinifera*) (O/B) — WStA
F 'Gewürztraminer' (*vinifera*) (O/R) — CYea WStA
F 'Glenora' — ESim
'Glory of Boskoop' (*vinifera*) — See V. 'Boskoop Glory'
'Golden Chasselas' (*vinifera*) — See V. 'Chasselas'
F 'Golden Queen' (*vinifera*) (G/W) — ERea
F 'Goldriesling' (*vinifera*) (O/W) — WStA
F 'Grizzley Frontignan' (*vinifera*) (G/R) — ERea
F 'Gros Colmar' (*vinifera*) (G/B) — ERea
F 'Gros Maroc' (*vinifera*) (G/B) — ERea
F 'Gutenborner' (*vinifera*) (O/W) — CYea WStA
henryana — See PARTHENOCISSUS ***henryana***
F 'Himrod' (O/W) — CYea ERea ESim GTwe SDea
F 'Incana' (*vinifera*) (O/B) — CSco EPla ERav LGre SHil WCru
inconstans — See PARTHENOCISSUS ***tricuspidata***
F 'Interlaken' (*vinifera*) — ERea ESim
F 'King's Ruby' (*vinifera*) — ERea
F 'Kuibishevski' (O/R) — CYea WStA
F 'Lady Downe's Seedling' (*vinifera*) (G/B) — ERea
F 'Lady Hastings' (*vinifera*) (G/B) — ERea
F 'Lady Hutt' (*vinifera*) (G/W) — ERea
F Landot 244 (O/B) — WStA
F 'Léon Millot' (*vinifera*) (O/G/B) — CYea ERea SDea SKee WStA
F 'Lucombe' (*vinifera*) — SDea
F 'Madeira Frontignan' (*vinifera*) (G/R) — ERea
F 'Madeleine Angevine' (*vinifera*) (O/W) — CDoC CYea EBre ERea GTwe LBre NGrN SDea WStA
F 'Madeleine Royale' (*vinifera*) (G/W) — ERea WStA
F 'Madeleine Silvaner' (*vinifera*) (O/W) — CYea ERea GTwe LBuc MGos NGrN SDea SKee SPer WStA

F 'Madresfield Court' (*vinifera*) (G/B)	ERea GTwe SKee WStA
'Malbec' (*vinifera*)	See V. 'Cot'
F 'Maréchal Foch' (O/B)	CYea
F 'Maréchal Joffre' (O/B)	CYea GTwe WStA
F 'Melon de Bourgogne' (*vinifera*) (O/W)	WStA
F 'Mireille' (*vinifera*)	GTwe WStA
F 'Morio Muscat' (*vinifera*) (O/W)	CYea WStA
F 'Mrs Pearson' (*vinifera*) (G/W)	ERea
F 'Mrs Pince's Black Muscat' (*vinifera*) (G/B)	ERea
F 'Müller-Thurgau' (Riesling-Silvaner) (*vinifera*) (O/W)	CB&S CYea ECtt ERea GTwe LBuc MBri MGos NElm NGrN SDea SKee SPer WStA
'Muscadet' (*vinifera*)	See V. 'Melon de Bourgogne'
F 'Muscat Blanc à Petits Grains' (*vinifera*) (O/W)	WStA
F 'Muscat Bleu' (*vinifera*) (O/B)	ERea
F 'Muscat Champion' (*vinifera*) (G/R)	ERea
F 'Muscat Hamburg' (*vinifera*) (G/B)	ERea MGos WStA
F 'Muscat of Alexandria' (*vinifera*) (G/W)	CB&S CMac CSam ERea EWar IJoh NGrN
F 'Muscat of Hungary' (*vinifera*) (G/W)	ERea
F 'Muscat Ottonel' (*vinifera*) (O/W)	WStA
F 'Muscate de Saumur' (*vinifera*) (W)	WStA
F 'New York Muscat' (*vinifera*) (O/B)	ERea
F 'Nobling' (*vinifera*) (O/W)	CYea
F 'Noir Hatif de Marseilles' (*vinifera*) (O/B)	CYea ERea
F 'No. 69' (*vinifera*) (W)	WStA
F Oberlin 595 (O/B)	CYea WStA
F 'Oliver Irsay' (*vinifera*) (O/W)	ERea WStA
F 'Optima' (*vinifera*) (O/W)	CYea WStA
F 'Ortega' (*vinifera*) (O/W)	CYea WStA
parsley leaved	See V. 'Ciotat'
F 'Perle' (*vinifera*) (O/W)	CYea WStA
F 'Perle de Czaba' (*vinifera*) (G/O/W)	ERea
F 'Perlette' (*vinifera*) (O/W)	NGrN WStA
F 'Phoenix' (*vinifera*) (O/W)	CYea
F 'Pinot Blanc' (*vinifera*) (O/W)	CYea WStA
F 'Pinot Gris' (*vinifera*) (O/B)	CYea WStA
F 'Pinot Meunier' (*vinifera*) (O/B)	CYea
F 'Pinot Noir' (*vinifera*)	CYea WStA
F 'Pirovano 14' (O/B)	CDoC CYea ERea GTwe WStA
F 'Plantet' (O/B)	WStA
F 'Portugieser' (*vinifera*) (O/B)	CYea WStA
F 'Précoce de Bousquet' (*vinifera*) (O/W)	WStA
F 'Précoce de Malingre' (*vinifera*) (O/W)	CYea ERea
F 'Primavis Frontignan' (*vinifera*) (G/W)	ERea WStA
F 'Prince of Wales' (*vinifera*) (G/B)	ERea
'Pulchra'	WCru
F 'Purpurea' (*vinifera*) (O/B)	CB&S CBot CBra CHad CMac CSco CYea EHar EHoe ELan ENot ERav IHos MBri MGos MWat NKay SHBN SMad SPer SReu SSta WDin WPat WSHC WWat
quinquefolia	See PARTHENOCISSUS ***quinquefolia***
F 'Ramdas' (O/W)	CYea
F Ravat 51 (O/W)	WStA
F 'Regner' (*vinifera*) (O/W)	WStA
F 'Reichensteiner' (*vinifera*) (O/G/W)	CYea WStA
F 'Reine Olga' (*vinifera*) (O/R)	ERea
F 'Rembrant' (*vinifera*) (R)	WStA
F 'Riesling' (*vinifera*) (O/W)	CYea WStA
¶ ***riparia***	GAri WCru
F 'Rotberger' (*vinifera*) (O/G/B)	CYea
F 'Royal Muscadine' (*vinifera*)	See V. 'Chasselas'
F 'Saint Laurent' (*vinifera*) (G/O/W)	ERea
F 'Sauvignon Blanc' (*vinifera*) (O/W)	CYea WStA
F 'Scheurebe' (*vinifera*) (O/W)	CYea WStA
F 'Schiava Grossa' (*vinifera*) (G/B)	CB&S CMac CYea ECtt ELan ERea EWar GChr GRei GTwe ISea LHol MBri NElm NGrN NRog SDea SKee SPer WStA
F 'Schönburger' (*vinifera*) (O/W)	CYea WStA
F 'Schuyler' (O/B)	CYea
F Seibel	GTwe
Seibel 13053	See V. 'Cascade'
F Seibel 138315 (*vinifera*) (R)	WStA
F Seibel 5409 (*vinifera*) (W)	WStA
Seibel 5455	See V. 'Plantet'
¶ Seibel 7053	WStA
¶ Seibel 9549	WStA
F 'Septimer' (*vinifera*) (O/W)	CYea WStA
F 'Seyval Blanc' (Seyve Villard 5276) (O/W)	CYea ERea GTwe LBuc NGrN SDea WStA
Seyve Villard 12.375	See V. 'Villard Blanc'
F Seyve Villard 20.473 (*vinifera*) (W)	WStA

F 'Siegerrebe' (*vinifera*) (O/W) CDoC CYea ERea GTwe NGrN SDea WStA
F 'Silvaner' (*vinifera*) (O/W) CYea WStA
'Strawberry Grape' (*vinifera*) See V. 'Fragola'
§ 'Sultana' (*vinifera*) ERea WStA
F 'Syrian' (*vinifera*) (G/W) ERea
F Teinturier Group (*vinifera*) (O/B) ERea
F 'Tereshkova' (O/B) ERea WStA
'Thompson Seedless' (*vinifera*) See V. 'Sultana'
F 'Traminer' (*vinifera*) (O/W) CYea
F 'Trebbiano' (*vinifera*) (G/W) ERea
F 'Triomphe d'Alsace' (O/B) CYea NGrN SDea WStA
'Trollinger' See V. 'Schiava Grossa'
'Vanessa' ESim
'Venus' ESim
F 'Villard Blanc' (O/W) WStA
F 'West's St Peter's' (*vinifera*) (G/B) ERea
¶ *wilsoniae* WPat
F 'Wrotham Pinot' (*vinifera*) (O/B) CYea WStA
F 'Würzer' (*vinifera*) (O/W) CYea WStA
F 'Zweigeltrebe' (*vinifera*) (O/B) CYea WStA

VRIESEA (Bromeliaceae)

carinata MBri
hieroglyphica MBri
x ***poelmanii*** MBri
x ***polonia*** MBri
saundersii MBri
splendens MBri
'Vulkana' MBri

WACHENDORFIA (Haemodoraceae)

paniculata NRog
thyrsiflora CBrd CHEx IBlr NRog SAxl
– Trengwainton Form GCal

WAHLENBERGIA (Campanulaceae)

albomarginata ECou EPad GArf GCHN GGar GTou LGan NHol NMen NTow NWCA
– 'Blue Mist' ECou EPad
ceracea NNrd WDav
congesta GCHN LRHS SHer SIng WThi
gloriosa CLew CNic EPad GArf NTow SBla WAbe WCru WPat
¶ ***matthewsii*** GTou
pumilio See EDRAIANTHUS ***pumilio***
§ ***saxicola*** CLew CRiv CRow CSpe ESma NGre NHol NMen NNrd NTow NVic NWCA SMrm WCru WPer WThu
¶ ***simpsonii*** GTou
species ECou
tasmanica See W. ***saxicola***
trichogyna LBee LRHS

WALDHEIMIA See ALLARDIA

WALDSTEINIA (Rosaceae)

fragarioïdes ECro WPer
ternata Widely available

WALNUT, Common See JUGLANS *regia*

WASABIA (Cruciferae)

japonica CArn GPoy

WASHINGTONIA (Palmae)

filifera CHEx LPal MBri SArc

WATSONIA † (Iridaceae)

aletroïdes NRog
angusta CHan GCal
ardernei See W. ***borbonica a.***
beatricis See W. ***pillansii***
§ ***borbonica*** CChu IBlr IMal NRog
§ – ssp. ***ardernei*** GCal NRog
brevifolia See W. ***laccata***
bulbillifera See W. ***meriana***
coccinea Baker See W. ***spectabilis***
– Herbert ex Baker dwarf form NRog
¶ ***fulgens*** CHan
hysterantha NRog
'Indian Orange' WThi
§ ***laccata*** WThi
marginata CHan NRog
§ ***meriana*** CHan IBlr NRog WThi
§ ***pillansii*** CChu CHan CWit EBre GCal IBlr LBre SHer SSpi WThi
pyramidata See W. ***borbonica***
¶ ***socium*** CRDP
§ ***spectabilis*** NRog
¶ sp. SH 89 CHan
'Stanford Scarlet' LGre SCro WEas
'Tresco Dwarf Pink' GCal
vanderspuyae CHan NRog
versfeldii CHan

WATTAKAKA See DREGEA

WEIGELA † (Caprifoliaceae)

'Abel Carrière' CBow CSco CShe ECtt ELan ENot EPla MRav WDin WWeb
'Abel Carrière Golden' EPla
'Avalanche' ECtt MRav WStI
'Boskoop Glory' CDoC CSco MBri SPer
Briant Rubidor ® See W. Olympiade ®
'Bristol Ruby' CBra CSco CShe ELan ENot GRei IJoh LHop MBar MGos MPla NNor NRoo NWea SHBN SLon SPer SReu SSta WAbe WDin WWin
'Candida' ELan EPla MBri NHol SGil SPer SPla WBod
Carnaval ® CBow CDoC COtt MBri
'Centennial' MGos
coraeensis 'Alba' CChu GWht WSHC
¶ ***decora*** CPle
'Espérance' EPla

'Eva Rathke'	CB&S CBra CFis ELan EMar EPla ISea NWea
'Evita'	CMHG CSco ESis GRei IOrc MBar MGos MPla SPer WPat
'Féerie'	WWeb
florida	CTrw MWat
– ***alba***	CB&S MBar
*– 'Albovariegata'	CFis SMad
§ – 'Aureovariegata'	CDec CMHG CSco EPar IJoh ISea MBal NHol SLon SPer SPla WPat
– 'Bicolor'	CB&S
– 'Bristol Snowflake'	CBow CCla CDoC CSco LHop SFai SLon SReu
– 'Foliis Purpureis'	Widely available
– 'Gustave Malet'	ISea
*– 'Langtrees'	EFol
– 'Magee'	CMCN
*– 'Minuet'	EBre EPla ESis LBre SEng WPat
– 'Nana Variegata'	CBow CSco EHal ERav MBar MBri NBee NHol
– 'Pink Princess'	CDoC SCob
– 'Rubigold'	See W. Olympiade ®
– 'Suzanne'	SCob
– 'Tango'	ECtt MBri
*– 'Variegata Aurea'	See W. *f.* 'Aureovariegata'
– 'Versicolor'	CChu CCor CMHG LHop MBel
'Florida Variegata'	CB&S CBra CCla CPle CShe CTrw EBar EBre ELan ENot ERav GRei IDai LBre MBar MGos MPla MWat NRoo NWea SDix SSta WAbe WBod WEas WSHC WWat WWin
hortensis 'Nivea'	CPle
japonica Dart's Colourdream ®	CCla EBre ECtt EHal EPla ERav IOrc LBre MGos MRav SAxl SGil SLPl
'Looymansii Aurea'	CBow CChu CCla CMHG CPle CSco EBre EFol EHar ELan EPla LBre MPla NHol SGil SHil SLon SPer SPla WDin WWat
Lucifer ®	CDoC WDin WWeb
'Majestueux'	SSta
maximowiczii	CBra CCla CPle NHol SSta WHCG
§ ***middendorffiana***	CBot CBow CCla CGre CMHG CPle CSco CWit ELan ENot EPla ERav ISea MBal MBar MPla MWat NHol SHil SPer SSpi WHCG WSHC WWin
'Mont Blanc'	CBot EHal
'Newport Red'	CBow ENot IDai MRav MWat NBee SPla WStI WTyr
§ Olympiade ® (v)	CB&S EBar ECtt EFol EHoe ELan ERav IOrc MBal MBar MBel MBri MGos NHol NNor SPer SReu WBod WStI
'Praecox Variegata'	CChu CMHG EBlo EBre EHar EPla LBre LHop MBri NHol SHil SLon SPer SPla SReu SSpi SSta WCru WHCG WPat WWat WWeb
'Red Prince'	CBow LRHS MBri SCob WPat
'Rubidor'	See W. Olympiade ®
'Snowflake'	CBow CPle EBre ECtt EPla LBre MPla SRms WWeb
'Victoria'	COtt EBlo EBre ECtt EFol LBre MAsh MBel MBri NHol SCob SHil

WEINMANNIA (Cunoniaceae)

trichosperma	CHEx IBlr SArc

WELDENIA (Commelinaceae)

candida	LRHS NHar

WESTRINGIA (Labiatae)

angustifolia	ECou
brevifolia	ECou
– Raleighii Group	ECou
§ ***fruticosa***	CPle CTre CTro LHop SSad
– 'Variegata'	CPle CTre ESma LHop
rosmariniformis	See W. ***fruticosa***

WIDDRINGTONIA (Cupressaceae)

¶ ***cedarbergensis***	GAri
§ ***cupressoïdes***	GAri LTil NHol
nodiflora	See W. ***cupressoïdes***
whytei	MBri

WIGANDIA (Hydrophyllaceae)

caracasana	CHEx
urens	CHEx

WINEBERRY See RUBUS *phoenicolasius*

WISTERIA † (Leguminosae)

floribunda	CB&S CBow ELan MAsh NKay SHBN SLon WNor
§ – 'Alba'	CB&S CBow CCla CDoC CPMA CSco EBlo EBre EHar ELan GAri LBre LNet NEgg NHol SBra SHBN SHil SPer SPla SSpi SSta WDin WStI
*– 'Burford'	CDoC MAsh MMea MWat NHol
– 'Domino'	CCla CPMA LNet MMea
– 'Hichirimen'	LNet MMea
*– 'Lipstick'	CBow CCla LNet
– 'Macrobotrys'	See W. *f.* 'Multijuga'
§ – 'Multijuga'	CBow CDoC CPMA CWit EBlo EBre EHar ELan IOrc LBre LNet MBri MGos MMea MUlv MWat NHol SMad SPer SPla SSpi WWat
– 'Murasaki Noda'	MGos
¶ – 'Nana Richin's Purple'	LNet
– 'Peaches and Cream'	CB&S CBow CCla LNet MMea SMad SPer
– 'Pink Ice'	CBow CCla CDoC CPMA ELan IOrc LNet MBri MMea SMad SSpi WWat
– 'Purple Patches'	CCla CPMA LNet MMea SPer
¶ – 'Reindeer'	NHol
– 'Rosea' ('Honko')	CBow CCla CMac CPMA EBre EHar ELan ENot IOrc LBre LNet MBar MMea SBra SPer WStI
– 'Royal Purple'	MMea
– 'Snow Showers'	CCla CPMA IHos LNet MBri MMea SMad SPer SReu
– 'Violacea Plena'	MBri MMea SHBN SHil
× ***formosa***	CPMA WFro
– 'Issai'	CB&S CBow CSam ELan LNet MBar MGos MMea MUlv NEgg SPer WWat

– 'Kokkuryu' ('Black Dragon') (d)	CB&S CBow CCla CDoC CPMA ELan IOrc LNet MAsh MGos SMad SPer SPla SReu SSpi SSta WWat
frutescens	WNor
multijuga 'Alba'	See W. ***floribunda*** 'Alba'
sinensis	Widely available
– 'Alba' ('Shiro-capital')	CBow CSco CShe EHar ELan IOrc LNet MBar MBri MMea MWat SPer SSpi WBod WDin
– 'Amethyst'	CBow CCla CPMA
– 'Caroline'	CB&S CBow CDoC CPMA CSam LNet MMea MUlv SPer SReu SSpi SSta WStI
– 'Plena'	SHil
– 'Prematura'	CBow MAsh NHol SSpi
– 'Prematura Alba'	WWat
– 'Prolific'	CBow CDoC CHad MBri MMea
*– 'Rosea'	CBow
venusta	CPMA EHar ENot LNet MMea MUlv SHBN SMad SPer SSpi WWat

WITHANIA (Solanaceae)

somnifera	NSal

WITTSTEINIA (Alseuosmiaceae)

¶ ***vacciniacea***	WCru

WOODSIA (Dryopteridaceae)

¶ ***ilvensis***	NHar
¶ ***intermedia***	NBro WRic
¶ ***mollis***	WRic
obtusa	NMar

WOODWARDIA † (Blechnaceae)

¶ ***fimbriata***	SPla
martinezii	SApp
* ***orientalis formosana***	NMar SMad
radicans	CGre CHEx CTro NMar SArc
¶ ***unigemmata***	WRic
virginica	CB&S

WORCESTERBERRY See **RIBES *divaricatum***

WULFENIA (Scrophulariaceae)

carinthiaca	CNic EBar MBel MBro MHig NGre WHoo

XANTHOCERAS (Sapindaceae)

sorbifolium	CAbb CB&S CBot CChu CCla CMCN CPle ECtt EHar ELan GCal LGre SHil SIgm SMad SSpi WWat

XANTHORHIZA (Ranunculaceae)

simplicissima	CChu CCla CGle CRow MUlv SHil SPer WSHC WWat

XANTHORRHOEA (Xanthorrhoeaceae)

¶ ***preisii***	SIgm
¶ ***quadrangulata***	CGre
¶ ***thorntonii***	SIgm

XANTHOSOMA (Araceae)

lindenii	See CALADIUM ***lindenii***
sagittifolium	CHEx SLMG

XERONEMA (Liliaceae/Phormiaceae)

callistemon	EBul ECou

XEROPHYLLUM (Liliaceae/Melanthiaceae)

tenax	GDra NHol

XYLORHIZA See **MACHAERANTHERA**

YOUNGBERRY See **RUBUS**

YUCCA † (Agavaceae)

aloifolia	CCan CHEx MBri MUlv SArc SIgm
– 'Variegata'	CCan CHEx LPal
angustifolia	See Y. ***glauca***
§ ***elephantipes***	CCan CHEx MBri SArc
filamentosa	CAbb CB&S CBow CBra CCan CHEx CKel CLan CMHG CPar EFou ELan ENot IDai ISea MBal MGos MWat NBro NHol SHBN SLon SPer SReu SSpi WBod WDin WWin
– 'Bright Edge' (v)	CAbb CB&S CBow CCan CDoC CMHG CPMA CSam EBre EGol ELan EOrc IHos IOrc LBre MBri MGos MUlv NHol SArc SHBN SPla
– 'Variegata'	CB&S CBot CBow CCan CPMA CTre EBre EGol ELan ENot IBar IJoh IOrc LBre LHop MBal MBri MGos SDix SPer SSta WDin WStI
flaccida	CCan MAsh NBee SDix WThu
– 'Golden Sword' (v)	CCan CDoC CMHG CSco EBre EGol IHos IJoh IOrc LBre MBal MBri MUlv SArc
– 'Ivory'	CB&S CBow CCan CDoC CPMA CSam CSco CShe ECtt EGol ELan ENot GCal IDai IOrc ISea MBri MRav MUlv NHol NKay NWyt SPer SPla SSpi SSta STre WThu
– striated cultivar	CCan
x ***floribunda***	SArc
'Garland's Gold' (v)	CDoC CHEx COtt ELan LRHS MBri
§ ***glauca***	CB&S CBow CCan CHEx CMHG GAri GCal NHol SArc SIgm
gloriosa	CB&S CCan CDoC CHEx CPMA CSco CShe CTre ENot EPla LNet MUlv SArc SHBN SLon SPer
– 'Aureovariegata'	See Y. ***g.*** 'Variegata'
– 'Nobilis'	SDix
§ – 'Variegata'	CAbb CBot CBow CCan CDoC CHEx CPMA CSco EBre ELan ENot IBar IJoh LBre MBri MGos MUlv NWyt SArc SCro SDry SHBN SMad SPer SSpi
guatemalensis	See Y. ***elephantipes***
harrimaniae	SIgm
neomexicana	WThu
recurvifolia	CCan CHEx CLan MBal SArc
– 'Marginata'	CCan
– 'Variegata'	CCan CHEx
treculeana	SArc

*'Tricolor' CB&S
'Vittorio Emanuele II' MUlv NWyt SArc
'Vomerensis' CCan
whipplei CAbb CBot CBow CCan CDoC CGre CHEx SArc SHil SLMG SSpi WHCr
– JLS 86188LACA EMon
– var. ***parishii*** CCan

YUSHANIA (Gramineae(Bambuseae))

§ ***anceps*** CDoC CHEx CHad EPla GAri IOrc ISea ISta LBam MBri MGos MUlv SArc SBam SCob SDry SPer SReu
§ – 'Pitt White' ISta SBam SDry WJun
maculata SBam SDry WJun
§ ***maling*** EPla SBam SDry WJun

ZALUZIANSKYA (Scrophulariaceae)

ovata EPot LHop NBir NWCA SAxl SBla WMar WPer

ZAMIA (Zamiaceae)

floridana LPal WNor
furfuracea LPal

ZAMIOCULCAS (Araceae)

See Plant Deletions

ZANTEDESCHIA † (Araceae)

§ ***aethiopica*** CBen CHEx CMHG CRDP CWGN EHon ELun EWav GCal LAma LMay MSta NRog SDix SWat WChe WEas
– 'Apple Court Babe' CRow SApp
– 'Childsiana' SApp
– 'Crowborough' CAvo CB&S CBro CCla CHEx CHad CHan CKel CPar CRow CSco EBre ECha EFou EGol EHon ELan LBre MBal MBri MRav MUlv NBar SApp SDeJ SIng SLon SMad SPer WCru
– ***gigantea*** SLMG
– 'Green Goddess' CB&S CHan CMon CRDP CRiv CRow CWGN ECha ELan NBro SRms
– 'Little Gem' ECha
– 'White Sails' CRow GCal MUlv
albomaculata CAvo CMon LAma MBri NRog
– SH 35 CHan
'Best Gold' LAma LRHS MBri
'Black Magic' LAma
'Black-eyed Beauty' CBro LAma LRHS MBri NRog
'Bridal Blush' LAma LRHS
'Cameo' LAma LRHS MBri
¶ 'Candy' LRHS
'Carmine Red' MBri
'Christina' LRHS MBri
'Dominique' LRHS MBri
elliottiana CB&S CSut LAma MBri NRog
'Garnet' LRHS MBri
'Harvest Moon' CWit LAma LRHS MBri
'Helen O'Connor' SLMG
¶ 'Jubilee' LRHS
'Lavender Petite' LAma NRog
'Mango' LRHS MBri
'Maroon Dainty' LAma NRog
'Monique' MBri
¶ 'Number 13' LRHS
¶ 'Oriental Sun' LRHS
'Pacific Pink' LAma
pentlandii See Z. ***angustiloba***
'Pink Opal' LRHS MBri
rehmannii CB&S CMon CRDP LAma LRHS MBri SRms
*– ***superba*** SLMG
'Ruby' LRHS MBri
'Shell Pink ' LAma NRog
'Solfatare' LAma
'Yvonne' LRHS MBri

ZANTHORHIZA See XANTHORHIZA

ZANTHOXYLUM (Rutaceae)

ailanthoïdes EHar
¶ ***americanum*** CLnd EArb LTil
coreanum CCla
piperitum CMCN EArb EHar
simulans CB&S

ZAUSCHNERIA See EPILOBIUM

ZEBRINA See TRADESCANTIA

ZELKOVA † (Ulmaceae)

carpinifolia CMCN CTho EHar SHil WMou WNor
schneideriana CMCN
serrata CB&S CBra CDoC CLnd CMCN CTho CWSG EHar ELan IOrc MBal MBar NHol NPal NWea SEng SPer SSpi STre WDin WFro WMou WNor WWat
– 'Goblin' NHol WPat
¶ – 'Yrban Ruby' MGos
¶ ***sinica*** WNor
¶ × ***verschaffeltii*** EPla GAri

ZENOBIA (Ericaceae)

pulverulenta CAbb CB&S CChu CCla CGre CWSG CWit ELan ESis GCal IOrc MBal MBar MBri MUlv NHol SGil SHBN SHil SPer SReu SSpi SSta WDin WPat WWat

ZEPHYRANTHES (Liliaceae/Amaryllidaceae)

candida CAvo CBro ERea LAma LBow NHol NRog SDeJ SDix WAbe WThu
citrina LAma LBow NRog WAbe
flavissima CAvo CBro CMon
grandiflora LBow
robusta See HABRANTHUS ***robustus***
rosea LAma
¶ ***sulphurea*** LAma

ZIERIA (Rutaceae)
See Plant Deletions

ZIGADENUS (Liliaceae/Melanthiaceae)

elegans	CCla CGle EBre EBul ECha ECro ELun EPot ESis LBre LGre MBro MCas NHol NWCA SAsh SBla SMad WDav WHoo WThu
fremontii	EBul
leimanthoïdes	EBul
nuttallii	CLew LGre NHol
¶ ***venenosus***	CHan

ZINGIBER (Zingiberaceae)

officinale	NHex

ZINNIA (Compositae)
See Plant Deletions

ZIZANIA (Gramineae)

¶ ***aquatica***	EMFW

ZIZIA (Umbelliferae)

aptera	NSal

ZIZIPHORA (Labiatae)

¶ ***pamiroalaica***	MFos

Nursey - Code Index

Nurseries that are included in **THE PLANT FINDER** for the first time this year (or have been reintroduced) are marked in **Bold Type**.
Full details of the nurseries with a four letter Code will be found in the **Code-Nursery** Index on page 620.
Nurseries with a number are detailed in the **Additional Nursery** Index on page 678.
Nurseries marked **SEED, SUCC** or **ORCH** are listed in the
Seed Suppliers, Cacti & Succulent or **Orchid Specialist Index**

39 Steps	**WThi**
Abbey Dore Court Gardens	**WAbb**
Abbey Plants	**CAbP**
Abbot's House Garden	**LAbb**
Abbotsbury Sub-Tropical Gardens	**CAbb**
Aberconwy Nursery	**WAbe**
Abriachan Nurseries	**GAbr**
Acton Beauchamp Roses	**WAct**
Agar's Nursery	**SAga**
Misses I Allen & J Huish	**CAll**
Allwood Bros	**SAll**
Allwood Bros	**SEED**
Altoona Nurseries	**CAlt**
Jacques Amand Ltd.	**LAma**
Angus Heathers	**GAng**
Apple Court	**SApp**
Arbor Exotica	**EArb**
Anthony Archer-Wills Ltd.	**SAWi**
Architectural Plants	**SArc**
Ardfearn Nursery	**GArf**
Arivegaig Nursery	**GAri**
Arne Herbs	**CArn**
Ashenden Nursery	**SAsh**
Ashwood Nurseries	**MAsh**
Ashwood Nurseries	**SEED**
David Austin Roses Ltd.	**MAus**
Avon Bulbs	**CAvo**
Axletree Nursery	**SAxl**
B & T World Seeds	**SEED**
Steven Bailey	**SBai**
B & H M Baker	**EBak**
Ballagan Nursery	**03**
Ballalheannagh Gardens	**MBal**
Helen Ballard	**WBal**
Ballerina Trees Ltd.	**EBal**
Ballydorn Bulb Farm	**IBal**
Ballyrogan Nurseries	**IBlr**
The Bamboo Centre	**LBam**
Bamboo Nursery Ltd.	**SBam**
Barkers Primrose Nurseries & Grdn Cntr	**NBar**
Barncroft Nurseries	**MBar**
Barnhawk Nursery	**SBar**
Barnsdale Plants	**EBar**
Barons Court Nurseries	**IBar**
Barters Farm Nurseries Ltd.	**CBar**
Battersby Roses	**NBat**
Battle & Pears Ltd.	**EB&P**
John Beach (Nursery) Ltd.	**MBea**
Peter Beales Roses	**EBls**
Beamish Clematis Nursery	**NBea**
Beechcroft Nurseries	**NBee**
Beechcroft Nursery	**LBee**
R F Beeston	**86**
Beetham Nurseries	**05**
Bellhouse Nursery	**MBel**
Belwood Nurseries Ltd.	**GBel**
Michael Bennett	**MBen**
Bennett's Water Lily Farm	**CBen**
Billy's Herbs	**74**
Birkheads Cottage Garden Nursery	**NBir**
Blackmore & Langdon Ltd	**CBla**
Blackthorn Nursery	**SBla**
Blairhoyle Nursery	**GBla**
Walter Blom and Sons Ltd.	**LBlo**
Bloomsbury	**LBlm**
The Bluebell Nursery	**MBlu**
R J Blythe	**EBly**
Bodiam Nursery	**SBod**
Bodnant Garden Nursery Ltd.	**WBod**
S & E Bond	**WBon**
Bonhard Nursery	**GBon**
Borde Hill Garden Ltd.	**SBor**
Bosvigo Plants	**CBos**
The Botanic Nursery	**CBot**
Bouts Cottage Nurseries	**WBou**
Ann & Roger Bowden	**CBdn**
Rupert Bowlby	**LBow**
Bowood Garden Centre	**CBow**
J W Boyce	**SEED**
Brackenwood Nurseries	**CBra**
S & N Brackley	**SEED**
Bradley Batch Nursery	**SUCC**
J Bradshaw & Son	**SBra**
Brambling House Alpines	**NBra**
Bregover Plants	**CBre**
Bressingham Gardens Mail Order	**EBlo**
Bressingham Plant Centre	**EBre**
Bressingham Plant Centre	**LBre**
Bretby Nurseries	**09**
Bridgemere Nurseries	**MBri**

Nursery	Code
Eastgrove Cottage Garden Nursery	WEas
Eau Brink Cactus Nursery	SUCC
Eden Plants	IEde
Efenechtyd Nurseries	WEfe
Eggleston Hall	NEgg
Elly Hill Herbs	22
Elm Ridge Gardens Ltd.	NElm
Elsworth Herbs	EEls
Elworthy Cottage Garden Plants	CElw
Emorsgate Seed	SEED
English Water Garden	SEng
Equatorial Plant Co.	ORCH
Equatorial Plants	SEED
Evegate Nursery Floral Workshop	57
Evelix Daffodils	GEve
Exbury Enterprises Ltd.	SExb
Christopher Fairweather Ltd.	SFai
Fairy Lane Nurseries	NFai
Family Trees	SFam
Farmhouse Plants	SFar
Felspar Cacti	SUCC
Fernhill Nursery	IFer
Daphne ffiske Herbs	Effi
Fibrex Nurseries Ltd	WFib
Field House Nurseries	MFie
Field House Nurseries	SEED
The Firs Nursery	MFir
The Margery Fish Plant Nursery	CFis
Kaytie Fisher	SFis
M V Fletcher	LFle
Flora Exotica	EFEx
The Flower Centre	26
Foliage & Unusual Plants	EFol
Foliage Scented & Herb Plants	01
Fosse Alpines	MFos
Mr Fothergill's Seeds Ltd.	SEED
Four Counties Nursery	WFou
Four Seasons	EFou
Foxgrove Plants	LFox
Fron Nursery	WFro
The Fruit Garden	SFru
Fryer's Nurseries Ltd.	MFry
Fulbrooke Nursery	EFul
Rodney Fuller	CFul
Gandy's (Roses) Ltd.	MGan
Gannock Growers	LGan
Garden Cottage Nursery	GGar
Gardenscape	NGar
Linda Gascoigne Wild Flowers	28
W G Geissler	SUCC
Diana Gilbert	SGil
Glebe Cottage Gardens	29
Glebe Cottage Plants	CGle
Glendoick Gardens Ltd	GGGa
Glenhirst Cactus Nursery	SUCC
Glenhirst Cactus Nursery	SEED
Global Orange Groves UK	CGOG
Glyndley Nurseries	SGly
Godly's Roses	LGod
Goldbrook Plants	EGol
Goscote Nurseries Ltd	MGos
Goulding's Fuchsias	EGou
Grange Farm Nursery	32
Peter Grayson	SEED
Great Dixter Nurseries	SDix
Green Farm Plants	LGre
Green City Plants	58
Greenacres Nursery	WGre
Greenaway Orchids	ORCH
Greenhead Roses	GGre
Greenholm Nurseries	CGrh
Greenland Nurseries	NGrN
Greenslacks Nurseries	NGre
Greenway Gardens	CGre
C W Groves & Son	CGro
Growing Carpets	LGro
Gwydir Plants	WGwy
Hadspen Garden & Nursery	CHad
Halecat Garden Nurseries	NHlc
Hall Farm Nursery	EHal
Hall Farm Nursery	WHal
Halls of Heddon	NHal
Halsway Nursery	CHal
The Hannays of Bath	CHan
Hardstoft Herb Garden	NHHG
Hardy Exotics	CHEx
Harrisons Delphiniums	SEED
Harrisons Delphiniums	LHar
Hartshall Nursery Stock	EHar
Hartside Nursery Garden	NHar
Harvest Nurseries	SUCC
F Haynes & Partners Ltd.	MHay
Hayward's Carnations	SHay
Hazeldene Nursery	SHaz
C E Henderson & Son	SHen
James Henderson & Sons	SEED
Henllys Lodge Plant	WHen
The Herb Garden	WHer
Herb & Heather Centre	NH&H
The Herbary Plant Centre	SHer
The Herbary Prickwillow	35
Hergest Croft Gardens	WHCr
Herterton House Garden Nursery	36
Hewthorn Herbs & Wild Flowers	MHew
Hexham Herbs	NHex
High Banks Nurseries	SHBN
The High Garden	CHig
Higher End Nursery	SHig

Nursery	Code
Highgates Nursery	MHig
Brian Hiley	LHil
Hillier Nurseries (Winchester) Ltd	SHil
Hillview Hardy Plants	WHil
Hippopottering Nursery	NHip
Hoecroft Plants	EHoe
Holberrow Aquatics	WHol
Holden Clough Nursery	NHol
Holden Clough Nursery	SEED
Hollington Nurseries	LHol
Holly Gate Cactus Nursery	SUCC
Holly Gate Cactus Nursery	SEED
Home Meadows Nursery Ltd	EHMN
Honeysome Aquatic Nursery	EHon
Hoo House Nursery	WHoo
Hopleys Plants Ltd	LHop
Hosford's Geraniums & Garden Centr	IHos
Houghton Farm Plants	45
Diana Hull	MHul
Hull Farm	EHul
Diana Hull	SEED
Hunts Court Garden & Nursery	WHCG
Brenda Hyatt	SHya
Hydon Nurseries Ltd.	LHyd
Iden Croft Herbs	SIde
Tim Ingram	SIgm
W E Th. Ingwersen Ltd	SIng
International Acers	WAce
Island Plants	GIsl
Jackson's Nurseries	MJac
The Japanese Garden Co.	NJap
Jasmine Cottage Gardens	02
Paul Jasper (Trees & Roses)	WJas
Jersey Lavender Ltd.	CJer
Johnstown Garden Centre	IJoh
Judy's Country Garden	EJud
Jumanery Cacti	SUCC
Jungle Giants	WJun
Just Plants	34
Just Roses	SJus
K & C Cacti	SUCC
Reginald Kaye Ltd	NKay
Kayes Garden Nursery	63
Keepers Nursery	SKee
Kelways Nurseries	CKel
Kent Cacti	SUCC
Kent Street Nurseries	SKen
Kenwith Nursery (Gordon Haddow)	CKen
Kiftsgate Court Gardens	WKif
Kingsfield Conservation Nursery	CKin
Kinlochlaich House	80
Kittoch Plants	GKit
Knap Hill & Slocock Nurseries	LKna
Knightshayes Garden Trust	CKni

Nursery	Code
Laburnum Nurseries	MLab
Landford Trees	CLnd
Landlife Wildflowers Ltd.	NLan
Landlife Wildflowers Ltd.	SEED
Landscape Plants	SLPl
Langley Boxwood Nursery	SLan
Langthorns Plantery	ELan
The Lanhydrock Gardens (NT)	CLan
The Laurels Nursery	38
Layham Garden Centre	40
Lea Rhododendron Gardens Ltd.	MLea
Leonardslee Gardens	SLeo
Lewdon Farm Alpine Nursery	CLew
Lime Cross Nursery	SLim
Lincluden Nursery	LLin
Lingholm Gardens	NLin
Liscahane Nursery	07
Lisdoonan Herbs	ILis
Little Brook Fuchsias	SLBF
Little Creek Nursery	CLCN
C S Lockyer	CLoc
Long Man Gardens	SLMG
Long Man Gardens	SUCC
Longacre Nursery	41
Longstock Park Nursery	SLon
Lower Severalls Herb Nursery	CSev
Mrs Ann Lunn	ELun
Mackay's Garden Centre	SEED
Mackey's Garden Centre	98
Macpennys Nurseries	CMac
Madrona Nursery	SMad
Malahide Nurseries Ltd.	IMal
Mallet Court Nursery	CMCN
Manningford Nurseries	42
Mansell & Hatcher Ltd.	ORCH
Markham Grange Nurseries	NMGN
Marle Place Plants & Gardens	43
Marley Bank Nursery	WMar
Lesley Marshall	EMar
S E Marshall & Co Ltd.	SEED
Marshall's Malmaison	WMal
Marshford Organic Nursery	65
J & D Marston	NMar
Marston Exotics	WMEx
Martin Nest Nurseries	EMNN
J E Martin	SEED
Marwood Hill Gardens	CMHG
Frank P Matthews Ltd.	18
Mattock's Roses	MMat
Maydencroft Aquatic Nurseries	LMay
S M McArd (Seeds)	SEED
The Mead Nursery	CMea
Mears Ashby Nurseries Ltd.	MMea
Mendle Nursery	NMen

Nursery	Code
Merlin Rooted Cuttings	CMer
Merriments Nursery & Gardens	SMrm
Merrist Wood Plant Shop	LMer
Merton Nurseries	WMer
Mickfield Fish & Watergarden Centre	EMFW
Mickfield Market Garden	EMic
Mill Cottage Plants	CMil
Mill Hill Plants	MMil
Mill Race Nursery	EMil
Millais Nurseries	LMil
Mills' Farm Plants & Gardens	EMFP
Milton Garden Plants	CMGP
Mires Beck Nusery	NMir
Mary & Peter Mitchell	SMit
Monksilver Nursery	EMon
Monocot Nursery	CMon
Monocot Nursery	SEED
Morehavens	LMor
John Morley	EMor
John Morley	SEED
F Morrey & Sons	MMor
Stanley Mossop	NMos
Frances Mount Perennial Plants	EMou
Mount Pleasant Trees	WMou
Muckross Garden Centre	60
Mugswell Nursery	21
Muncaster Castle	59
Kathleen Muncaster Fuchsias	EKMF
Naked Cross Nurseries	CNCN
Natural Selection	CNat
Natural Selection	SEED
Nettletons Nursery	LNet
New Trees Nurseries	SNTN
Newington Nursery	MNew
Newton Hill Alpines	73
Nicky's Rock Garden Nursery	CNic
Norden Alpines	NNrd
Nordybank Nurseries	WNdy
Andrew Norfield Trees & Seeds	WNor
Andrew Norfield Trees & Seeds	SEED
Norfolk Lavender	ENor
Northumbria Nurseries	NNor
Norwich Heather & Conifer Centre	ENHC
Notcutts Nurseries	ENot
The Nursery Further Afield	MNFA
Oak Cottage Herb Garden	WOak
Oak Tree Nursery	NOak
Oakleigh Nurseries	SOak
Oakleigh Nurseries	SUCC
Stuart Ogg	SOgg
Stuart Ogg	SEED
Okell's Nurseries	MOke
Old Court Nurseries	WOld
The Old Manor Nursery	WOMN

Nursery	Code
The Old Mill Herbary	77
Oldbury Nurseries	SOld
Orchard House Nursery	NOrc
Orchard Nurseries	EOrc
Orchardstown Nurseries	IOrc
Orchid Sundries Ltd.	ORCH
Otter Nurseries Ltd.	COtt
Otters' Court Heathers	COCH
M Oviatt-Ham	EOvi
P M A Plant Specialities	CPMA
P W Plants	EPla
Padlock Croft	EPad
The Palm Centre	LPal
The Palm Farm	NPal
A J Palmer & Son	LPlm
Pantiles Nurseries Ltd.	LPan
Paradise Centre	EPar
Parham Nursery	CPar
J & E Parker-Jervis	MPar
Park Green Nurseries	EPGN
Parkinson Herbs	50
Chris Pattison	WPat
Pennyacre Nurseries	GPen
Perhill Nurseries	WPer
Perrie Hale Forest Nursery	CPer
Perrybrook Nursery	WPbr
Perryhill Nurseries	SPer
Perry's Plants	NPer
Pete & Ken Cactus Nursery	SUCC
Peveril Clematis Nursery	CPev
Phedar Nursery	MPhe
Phedar Nursery	SEED
A & A Phipps	SUCC
Pinks & Carnations	NPin
Pinks & Carnations	SEED
Pitts Farm Nursery	MPit
The Plant Lovers	SUCC
Plant World Botanic Gardens	CPla
Plant World Botanic Gardens	SEED
Plantables	MPlt
E L F Plants Cramden Nursery Ltd.	MPla
Plantcraft	SPlc
Plantworld	44
Plaxtol Nurseries	SPla
Pleasant View Nursery	CPle
J V Porter	NPor
Porthpean House Gardens	52
Potterton & Martin	EPot
Potterton & Martin	SEED
Roger Poulett	SPou
Roger Poulett	SEED
Pound Lane Nurseries	06
Pounsley Plants	CPou
Poyntzfield Herb Nursery	GPoy

Nursery	Code
The Torbay Palm Farm	**CTor**
Totties Nursery	**64**
Tough Alpine Nursery	**GTou**
Town Farm Nursery	**NTow**
Treasures of Tenbury Ltd	**95**
Trehane Camellia Nursery	**CTrh**
Peter Trenear	**STre**
Trewidden Estate Nursery	**CTre**
Trewithen Nurseries	**CTrw**
Tropicana Nursery	**CTro**
Van Tubergen UK Ltd.	**ETub**
Edwin Tucker & Sons	**SEED**
J Tweedie Fruit Trees	**GTwe**
Ty'r Orsaf Nursery	**WTyr**
Ulverscroft Grange Nursery	**MUlv**
Unwins Seeds Ltd.	**SEED**
Usual & Unusual Plants	**SUsu**
Uzumara Orchids	**GUzu**
Uzumara Orchids	**ORCH**
Uzumara Orchids	**SEED**
The Valley Clematis Nursery	**EVal**
The Vicarage Garden	**NVic**
Waddesdon Gardens Nursery	**LWad**
J Walkers Bulbs	**EWal**
Wall Cottage Nursery	**CWal**
Ward Fuchsias	**MWar**
Wards Nurseries	**61**
Warley Rose Garden Ltd.	**EWar**
Warners Roses	**WWar**
Washfield Nursery	**SWas**
The Water Garden Nursery	**CWGN**
Water Meadow Nursery	**SWat**
Waterperry Gardens Ltd.	**MWat**
Waterwheel Nursery	**WWat**
Waveney Fish Farm	**EWav**
Weasdale Nurseries	**NWea**
Webbs Garden Centres Ltd	**WWeb**
West Kington Nurseries Ltd.	**CWes**
West Somerset Garden Centre	**CWSG**
Westfield Cacti	**SUCC**
Westwood Nursery	**SWes**
Westwood Nursery	**ORCH**
A D & N Wheeler	**MWhe**
White Cottage Alpines	**NWCA**
Trevor White Old Fashioned Roses	**ETWh**
Whitehills Nurseries	**GWht**
Whitehouse Ivies	**EWhi**
Whitestone Gardens Ltd.	**SUCC**
The Wild Flower Centre	**54**
The Wildlife Gardening Centre	**MWil**
Wildseeds	**SEED**
K M & R J R Willoughby	**SUCC**
H & S Wills	**CWil**
H & S Wills	**SUCC**
Wingates	**NWin**
Wintergreen Nurseries	**WWin**
Wisley Plant Centre	**LRHS**
Withleigh Nurseries	**CWit**
Woodborough Garden Centre	**24**
Woodfield Bros	**MWoo**
H Woolman Ltd	**MWol**
Worth Trees	**79**
Wye Valley Herbs	**WWye**
Wytherstone Nurseries	**NWyt**
R J Yates	**MYat**
Yearlstone Vineyard	**CYea**
Roy Young Seeds	**SEED**
Roy Young Seeds	**SUCC**
Zephyrwude Irises	**NZep**

Code-Nursery Index

Please note that all these nurseries are listed in alphabetical order of their Codes. All nurseries are listed in alphabetical order of their name in the **Nursery-Code Index** on page 613.

CAbb **Abbotsbury Sub-Tropical Gardens,** Abbotsbury, Nr Weymouth, Dorset DT3 4LA
TEL: (0305) 871344/412 *CONTACT:* David Sutton
OPENING TIMES: 1000-1800 daily mid Mar-1st Nov. 1000-1500 Nov-mid Mar.
MAIL ORDER: Yes *MIN VALUE:* £10.00 + p&p *CAT. COST:* A5 Sae + £1.00
W/SALE or RETAIL: Both
SPECIALITIES: Less common & tender Shrubs. *MAP PAGE:* **2**

CAbP **Abbey Plants,** Chaffeymoor, Bourton, Gillingham, Dorset SP8 5BY
TEL: (0747) 840841 *CONTACT:* K Potts
OPENING TIMES: 1000-1300 & 1400-1700 Tue-Sat all year
MAIL ORDER: No *CAT. COST:* Free *W/SALE or RETAIL:* Retail
SPECIALITIES: Flowering Trees & Shrubs. Shrub Roses incl. many unusual varieties.
MAP PAGE: **2**

CAll **Misses I Allen & J Huish,** Quarry Farm, Wraxall, Bristol, Avon BS19 1LE
TEL: (0275) 810435 *CONTACT:*
OPENING TIMES: By appt. only.
MAIL ORDER: No *CAT. COST:* 50p + Sae *W/SALE or RETAIL:* Retail
SPECIALITIES: National Reference Collection of Aster. *MAP PAGE:* **2/4**

CAlt **Altoona Nurseries,** The Windmill, Tigley, Dartington, Totnes Devon TQ9 6DW
TEL: (0803) 868147 *CONTACT:* Paul A Harber
OPENING TIMES: Anytime by appt.
MAIL ORDER: No *CAT. COST:* Sae *W/SALE or RETAIL:* Both
SPECIALITIES: Japanese Maples. *MAP PAGE:* **1**

CArn **Arne Herbs,** Limeburn Nurseries, Limeburn Hill, Chew Magna, Avon BS18 8QW
TEL: (0275) 333399 *CONTACT:* A Lyman-Dixon & H Lee
OPENING TIMES: Most times. Check first.
MAIL ORDER: Yes *MIN VALUE:* None *CAT. COST:* 75p *W/SALE or RETAIL:* Both
SPECIALITIES: Herbs, Wild Flowers & Cottage Flowers. *MAP PAGE:* **2/4**

CAvo **Avon Bulbs,** Burnt House Farm, mid-Lambrook, South Petherton, Somerset TA13 5HE
TEL: (0460) 42177 *CONTACT:* C Ireland-Jones
OPENING TIMES: Thu, Fri, Sat mid Sep-end Oct 1992 & mid Feb-end Mar 1993 or by appt.
MAIL ORDER: Yes *MIN VALUE:* £10.00 + p&p *CAT. COST:* 4 x 2nd class
W/SALE or RETAIL: Retail
SPECIALITIES: Smaller & unusual Bulbs. *MAP PAGE:* **2**

CBar **Barters Farm Nurseries Ltd.,** Chapmanslade, Westbury, Wiltshire BA13 4AL
TEL: (0373) 832294 *FAX:* (0373) 832677 *CONTACT:* C L Walker
OPENING TIMES: 0900-1700 Mon-Sat & 1000-1700 Sun & Bank Hols. Closed Good Friday.
MAIL ORDER: No *CAT. COST:* A4 Sae *W/SALE or RETAIL:* Both
SPECIALITIES: Very wide range of Shrubs. Ground Cover, specimen Patio plants, container & open-ground Trees. Ferns, half-hardy Perennials, Bamboos & Grasses. *MAP PAGE:* **2**

CBdn **Ann & Roger Bowden,** Cleave House, Sticklepath, Okehampton, Devon EX20 2NN
TEL: (083784) 0481 *CONTACT:* Ann & Roger Bowden
◆ *OPENING TIMES:* Appt only.
MAIL ORDER: Yes *MIN VALUE:* None *CAT. COST:* 3 x 1st class *W/SALE or RETAIL:* Both
SPECIALITIES: Hosta only. *MAP PAGE:* **1**

CBen **Bennett's Water Lily Farm,** Putton Lane, Chickerell, Weymouth, Dorset DT3 4AF
TEL: (0305) 785150 *FAX:* (0305) 781619 *CONTACT:* J Bennett
OPENING TIMES: Tue-Sun Apr-Aug, Mon-Fri Sep-Mar.
MAIL ORDER: Yes *MIN VALUE:* £25.00 + p&p *CAT. COST:* 2 x 1sr class
W/SALE or RETAIL: Both
SPECIALITIES: Aquatic plants. *MAP PAGE:* **2**

CBla **Blackmore & Langdon Ltd,** Pensford, Bristol Avon BS18 4JL
TEL: (0275) 332300 *CONTACT:* J S Langdon
◆ *OPENING TIMES:* 0900-1800 daily.
MAIL ORDER: Yes *MIN VALUE:* None *CAT. COST:* Sae *W/SALE or RETAIL:* Both
SPECIALITIES: Phlox, Delphinium & Begonias. *MAP PAGE:* **2/4**

CBos **Bosvigo Plants,** Bosvigo House, Bosvigo Lane, Truro, Cornwall TR1 3NH
TEL: (0872) 75774 *CONTACT:* Wendy Perry
OPENING TIMES: 1100-1800 daily Mar-end Oct.
MAIL ORDER: No *CAT. COST:* 4 x 2nd class *W/SALE or RETAIL:* Retail
SPECIALITIES: Rare & unusual Herbaceous. *MAP PAGE:* **1**

CBot **The Botanic Nursery,** Rookery Nurseries, Cottles Lane, Atworth, Nr Melksham, Wiltshire SN12 8NU
TEL: (0225) 706597/706631 *CONTACT:* T & M Baker
OPENING TIMES: 1000-1700 daily, closed Sun in Winter.
MAIL ORDER: No *CAT. COST:* £1.50 *W/SALE or RETAIL:* Both
SPECIALITIES: Rare hardy Shrubs & Perennials for lime soils. Also Conservatory plants. Also at Bath Rd, Atworth, Melksham, Wilts. *MAP PAGE:* **2**

CBow **Bowood Garden Centre,** Bowood Estate, Calne, Wiltshire SN11 0LZ
TEL: (0249) 816828 *FAX:* (0249) 821757 *CONTACT:* Miss Charlotte Cole
◆ *OPENING TIMES:* 1000-1800 daily Apr-Oct. 1000-1700 daily Nov-Mar. Closed Xmas period.
MAIL ORDER: No *CAT. COST:* *Sae *W/SALE or RETAIL:* Retail
SPECIALITIES: Wide range of Old Fashioned Roses, unusual Rhododendrons & Magnolias, plus ever changing selection of Trees, Shrubs & Perennials. *List of Roses & Rhodos only. *MAP PAGE:* **2**

CBra **Brackenwood Nurseries,** 131 Nore Road, Portishead, Nr Bristol, Avon BS20 8DU
TEL: (0275) 843484 *CONTACT:* Mr J Maycock
OPENING TIMES: 0900-1730 daily ex Xmas period.
MAIL ORDER: No *CAT. COST:* Not available *W/SALE or RETAIL:* Both
SPECIALITIES: Trees, Shrubs, Conifers & Alpines. Many unusual varieties. *MAP PAGE:* **2/4**

CBrd **Broadleas Gardens Ltd.,** Broadleas, Devizes, Wiltshire SN10 5JQ
TEL: (0380) 722035 *CONTACT:* Lady Anne Cowdray
OPENING TIMES: 1400-1800 Wed, Thu & Sun Apr-Oct.
MAIL ORDER: No *CAT. COST:* *W/SALE or RETAIL:* Both
SPECIALITIES: General range. *MAP PAGE:* **2**

CBre **Bregover Plants,** Hillbrooke, Middlewood, North Hill, Nr Launceston, Cornwall PL15 7NN
TEL: (0566) 82661 *CONTACT:* Jennifer Bousfield
OPENING TIMES: 1100-1700 Wed-Fri Mar-mid Oct and by appt.
MAIL ORDER: Yes *MIN VALUE:* No minimum charge *CAT. COST:* 2 x 1st class
W/SALE or RETAIL: Retail
SPECIALITIES: Hardy Perennials inc. Asters, Hardy Geraniums, Primulas. Small supply of Show Auriculas, named Primroses & Violets. (Not all available by Mail Order). *MAP PAGE:* **1**

CBrk **Brockings Nursery,** Petherwin Gate North Petherwin, Cornwall PL15 8LW
TEL: (0566) 85533 *CONTACT:* Ian K S Cooke
OPENING TIMES: Tue-Sat
MAIL ORDER: Yes *MIN VALUE:* £15.00 + p&p *CAT. COST:* 3 x 1st class
W/SALE or RETAIL: Retail
SPECIALITIES: Tender Perennials, Cannas, Coleus & Conservatory plants. *MAP PAGE:* **1**

CBro **Broadleigh Gardens,** Bishops Hull, Taunton, Somerset TA4 1AE
TEL: (0823) 286231 *CONTACT:* Lady Skelmersdale
OPENING TIMES: 0900-1600 Mon-Fri for viewing ONLY. Orders collected if prior notice given.
MAIL ORDER: Yes *MIN VALUE:* None *CAT. COST:* 2 x 1st class *W/SALE or RETAIL:* Retail
SPECIALITIES: Two Catalogues. (Jan) - Bulbs in growth, (Galanthus, Cyclamen etc.) & Herbaceous. (June) - Dwarf & unusual Bulbs. *MAP PAGE:* **1**

CB&S **Burncoose & South Down Nurseries,** Gwennap, Redruth, Cornwall TR16 6BJ
TEL: (0209) 861112 *FAX:* (0209) 860011 *CONTACT:* C H Williams & D Knuckey
OPENING TIMES: 0900-1700 Mon-Sat & 1100-1700 Sun.
MAIL ORDER: Yes *MIN VALUE:* £10.00 + p&p* *CAT. COST:* £1.00 inc p&p
W/SALE or RETAIL: Both
SPECIALITIES: Extensive range of over 2000 Ornamental Trees & Shrubs and Herbaceous. 30 acre garden. *NOTE: Individual quotations for EC sales. *MAP PAGE:* **1**

CCan **Cannington College Plant Centre,** Cannington, Bridgwater, Somerset TA5 2LS
TEL: (0278) 652226 *FAX:* (0278) 652479 *CONTACT:* Steve Rudhall
OPENING TIMES: 1400-1700 daily Easter-Sep.
MAIL ORDER: Yes *MIN VALUE:* None *CAT. COST:* 50p *W/SALE or RETAIL:* Retail
SPECIALITIES: Abutilon, Argyranthemum, Ceanothus, Osteospermum, Salvia, Felicia, Diascia & Euryops *MAP PAGE:* **1/4**

CChu **Churchills Garden Nursery,** Exeter Road, Chudleigh, South Devon TQ13 0DD
TEL: (0626) 852585 *FAX:* (0626) 852585 *CONTACT:* Mr M J S Henry
OPENING TIMES: 1400-1700 Mon-Fri, 1000-1700 Sat & Sun, mid Mar-mid Oct. Also by appt.
MAIL ORDER: *MIN VALUE:* *CAT. COST:* 3 x 2nd class *W/SALE or RETAIL:* Retail
SPECIALITIES: Extensive & interesting range of garden-worthy Trees, Shrubs, Climbers & Herbaceous - many unusual. *MAP PAGE:* **1**

CCla **Clapton Court Gardens,** Crewkerne, Somerset TA18 8PT
TEL: (0460) 73220/72200 *FAX:* (0460) 73220 *CONTACT:* Capt. S Loder
◆ *OPENING TIMES:* 1030-1700 Mon-Fri, 1400-1700 Sun Mar-Oct. 1400-1700 Easter Sat only.
MAIL ORDER: No *CAT. COST:* £1.35 *W/SALE or RETAIL:* Retail
SPECIALITIES: Rare & unusual Herbaceous, Shrubs, Trees, Clematis & Roses. *MAP PAGE:* **2**

CCMG **Cranborne Manor Garden Centre,** Cranborne, Nr Wimborne, Dorset BH21 5PP
TEL: (0725) 517248 *FAX:* (0725) 517248 *CONTACT:* Miss Sandra Hewitt
OPENING TIMES: 0900-1700 Tue-Sat 1000-1700 Sun.
MAIL ORDER: Yes *MIN VALUE:* None *CAT. COST:* £1 (Roses) *W/SALE or RETAIL:* Retail
SPECIALITIES: Roses, Clematis, Herbaceous incl unusual varieties, Topiary, Fan & Espalier Fruit, Shrubs & Trees. *NOTE: Mail Order for Roses only. *MAP PAGE:* **2**

CCor **Corsley Mill,** Highfield House, High Street, Shrewton, Salisbury, Wiltshire SP3 4BU
TEL: (0980) 621396 *CONTACT:* Brigid Quest-Ritson
OPENING TIMES: By appt.
MAIL ORDER: Yes *MIN VALUE:* No minimum charge *CAT. COST:* 50p *W/SALE or RETAIL:* Both
SPECIALITIES: Roses on own root-stock. NOTE: Mail Order in winter only. *MAP PAGE:* **2**

CCot **Cottage Garden Plants Old & New,** Cox Cottage, Lower Street, East Morden, Wareham, Dorset BH20 7DL
TEL: (092945) 496 *CONTACT:* Mrs Alex Brenton
OPENING TIMES: 0900-1500 Mon & Tue Feb-Oct. Please phone to check first at other times.
MAIL ORDER: Yes *MIN VALUE:* £5.00 + p&p *CAT. COST:* 2 x 1st class
W/SALE or RETAIL: Retail
SPECIALITIES: Primroses, Cheiranthus, Viola & Violets. *MAP PAGE:* **2**

CCra **Crankan Nurseries,** New Mill, Penzance, Cornwall TR20 8UT
TEL: (0736) 62897 *CONTACT:* Mr J J Jelbert
OPENING TIMES: Daily by appt.
MAIL ORDER: Yes *MIN VALUE:* None *CAT. COST:* Sae *W/SALE or RETAIL:* Both
SPECIALITIES: Violets. *MAP PAGE:* **1**

CDec **Decorative Foliage,** Higher Badworthy, South Brent, Devon TQ10 9EG
TEL: (03647) 2768 *CONTACT:* Amanda Morris
OPENING TIMES: Mon-Wed Mar-Nov.
MAIL ORDER: Yes *MIN VALUE:* None *CAT. COST:* 2 x 1st class *W/SALE or RETAIL:* Retail
SPECIALITIES: Flower arrangers plants & rarities. *MAP PAGE:* **1**

CDoC **Duchy of Cornwall,** Penlyne Nursery, Cott Road, Lostwithiel, Cornwall PL22 08W
TEL: (0208) 872668 *CONTACT:* Andrew Carthew
OPENING TIMES: 0900-1700 Mon-Sat ex Bank Hols.
MAIL ORDER: No *CAT. COST:* £1.00 *W/SALE or RETAIL:* Retail
SPECIALITIES: Very wide range of all garden plants incl. Trees, Shrubs, Conifers, Roses, Perennials & Fruit. *MAP PAGE:* **1**

 See note on Mail Order, EC sales & Export on page 5

CElw **Elworthy Cottage Garden Plants,** Elworthy Cottage, Elworthy, Lydeard St Lawrence, Taunton, Somerset TA4 3PX
TEL: (0984) 56427 *CONTACT:* Mrs J M Spiller
OPENING TIMES: Tues & Fri afternoon & by appt mid Mar-mid Oct.
MAIL ORDER: No *CAT. COST:* 3 x 2nd class *W/SALE or RETAIL:* Retail
SPECIALITIES: Unusual Herbaceous plants esp. Penstemon & Hardy Geranium & Grasses.
MAP PAGE: **1**

CFis **The Margery Fish Plant Nursery,** East Lambrook Manor, East Lambrook, S. Petherton, Somerset TA13 5HL
TEL: (0460) 40328 *FAX:* (0460) 42344 *CONTACT:* Mr M Stainer
OPENING TIMES: 1000-1700 Mon-Sat.
MAIL ORDER: Yes *MIN VALUE:* £10.00 + p&p *CAT. COST:* 4 x 1st class
W/SALE or RETAIL: Retail
SPECIALITIES: Hardy Geranium, Euphorbia, Helleborus, Primula vulgaris, Penstemon, Salvia & Herbaceous. *MAP PAGE:* **2**

CFul **Rodney Fuller,** Coachman's Cottage, Higher Bratton Seymour, Wincanton, Somerset BA9 8DA
TEL: *CONTACT:* Rodney Fuller
OPENING TIMES: Not open.
MAIL ORDER: Yes *MIN VALUE:* £15.00 + p&p *CAT. COST:* Sae *W/SALE or RETAIL:* Retail
SPECIALITIES: Violas & Violettas. Please note that stocks are strictly limited. *MAP PAGE:*

CGle **Glebe Cottage Plants,** Pixie Lane, Warkleigh, Umberleigh, North Devon EX37 9DH
TEL: (0769) 540554 *CONTACT:* Carol Klein
OPENING TIMES: 1000-1700 Wed-Sun, please check first.
MAIL ORDER: Yesd *MIN VALUE:* £20.00 + p&p *CAT. COST:* £1.00 *W/SALE or RETAIL:* Retail
SPECIALITIES: Extensive range of hard-to-find Perennials. *MAP PAGE:* **1**

CGOG **Global Orange Groves UK,** PO Box 644, Poole, Dorset BH17 9YB
TEL: (0202) 691699 *CONTACT:* P K Oliver
◆ *OPENING TIMES:* By appointment only.
MAIL ORDER: Yes *MIN VALUE:* £30.00 + p&p *CAT. COST:* Sae *W/SALE or RETAIL:* Both
SPECIALITIES: Citrus trees & Citrus fertiliser. *MAP PAGE:*

CGre **Greenway Gardens,** Churston Ferrers, Brixham, Devon TQ5 0ES
TEL: (0803) 842382 *CONTACT:* Roger Clark (Manager)
OPENING TIMES: 1400-1700 (Nov-Feb 1630) Mon-Fri, 1000-1200 Sat, ex Bank Hols. Also by appt.
MAIL ORDER: Yes *MIN VALUE:* None *CAT. COST:* 50p *W/SALE or RETAIL:* Retail
SPECIALITIES: Unusual Trees & Shrubs particularly from temperate South America. *MAP PAGE:* **1**

CGrh **Greenholm Nurseries,** Lampley Road, Kingston Seymour, Clevedon, Avon BS21 6XS
TEL: (0934) 833350 *FAX:* (0934) 838237 *CONTACT:* John Vanderplank
◆ *OPENING TIMES:* 0900-1700 daily
MAIL ORDER: Yes *MIN VALUE:* No minimum charge *CAT. COST:* 3 x 1st class
W/SALE or RETAIL:
SPECIALITIES: Passiflora. National Collection of over 120 species & varieties. See also SEED SUPPLIER INDEX. NOTE: Retail nursery at Smallway Congresbury, Yatton, Avon. *MAP PAGE:* **2**

CGro **C W Groves & Son,** West Bay Road, Bridport, Dorset DT6 4BA
TEL: (0308) 22654 *FAX:* (0308) 420888 *CONTACT:* C W Groves
OPENING TIMES: 0830-1300 & 1400-1700 Mon-Sat, 1000-1300 & 1400-1700 Sun.
MAIL ORDER: Yes *MIN VALUE:* £50 + p&p *CAT. COST:* Free *W/SALE or RETAIL:* Retail
SPECIALITIES: Nursery & Garden Centre specialising in Parma & Hardy Viola. *MAP PAGE:* **2**

CHad **Hadspen Garden & Nursery,** Hadspen House, Castle Cary, Somerset BA7 7NG
TEL: (0963) 50939 *CONTACT:* N & S Pope
◆ *OPENING TIMES:* 0900-1800 Thu-Sun & Bank Hols. 1st Mar-1st Oct. Garden open at the same time.
MAIL ORDER: No *CAT. COST:* 2 x 1st class *W/SALE or RETAIL:* Retail
SPECIALITIES: Large leaved Herbaceous. Old fashioned and shrub Roses. *MAP PAGE:* **2**

CHal **Halsway Nursery,** Halsway, Nr Crowcombe Taunton, Somerset TA4 4BB
TEL: (09848) 243 *CONTACT:* T A & D J Bushen
OPENING TIMES: Most days - please telephone first.
MAIL ORDER: Yes *MIN VALUE:* £2.00 + p&p *CAT. COST:* Sae* *W/SALE or RETAIL:* Retail
SPECIALITIES: Coleus & Begonias (excl. tuberous & winter flowering). Also good range of Greenhouse & garden plants. *NOTE: List for Coleus & Begonias only, no nursery list.
MAP PAGE: **1**

CHan **The Hannays of Bath,** Sydney Wharf Nursery, Bathwick, Bath, Avon BA2 4ES
TEL: (0225) 462230 *CONTACT:* Mr V H S & Mrs S H Hannay
◆ *OPENING TIMES:* 1000-1700 Wed-Mon & by appt.
MAIL ORDER: No *CAT. COST:* £1.00+40p p&p *W/SALE or RETAIL:* Retail
SPECIALITIES: Unusual Perennials in specimen sizes and uncommon shrubs. *NOTE: For Export items, Certificates arranged but collection only. *MAP PAGE:* **2**

CHEx **Hardy Exotics,** Gilly Lane, Whitecross, Penzance, Cornwall TR20 8BZ
TEL: (0736) 740660 *CONTACT:* Clive Shilton & Julie Smith
OPENING TIMES: 1000-1700 daily 1st Apr-31st Oct. 1000-1600 Mon-Sat 1st Nov-31st Mar.
MAIL ORDER: Yes *MIN VALUE:* £13.50 carriage *CAT. COST:* 4 x 24p *W/SALE or RETAIL:* Retail
SPECIALITIES: Trees, Shrubs & Herbaceous plants to create tropical & desert effects. Hardy & half-Hardy for gardens patios & conservatories. *MAP PAGE:* **1**

CHig **The High Garden,** Courtwood, Newton Ferrers, South Devon PL8 1BW
TEL: (0752) 872528 *CONTACT:* F Bennett
OPENING TIMES: By appt.
MAIL ORDER: Yes *MIN VALUE:* £5.00 + p&p *CAT. COST:* 60p *W/SALE or RETAIL:* Both
SPECIALITIES: Pieris & Rhododendron. *MAP PAGE:* **1**

CJer **Jersey Lavender Ltd.,** Rue du Pont Marquet, St Brelade, Jersey, Channel Isles
TEL: (0534) 42933 *FAX:* (0534) 45613 *CONTACT:* David Christie
OPENING TIMES: 1000-1700 Mon-Sat Jun-Sep. Also by appt.
MAIL ORDER: No *CAT. COST:* Free *W/SALE or RETAIL:* Retail
SPECIALITIES: National Collection of Lavandula *MAP PAGE:* **1**

CKel **Kelways Nurseries,** Langport, Somerset TA10 9SL
TEL: (0458) 250521 *FAX:* (0458) 253351 *CONTACT:* John Landell Mills (M.D.)
OPENING TIMES: 0900-1700 Mon-Fri, 1000-1600 Sat & Sun.
MAIL ORDER: Yes *MIN VALUE:* £15.00 + p&p *CAT. COST:* Free *W/SALE or RETAIL:* Both
SPECIALITIES: (Spring) Lilium, Gladioli, Dahlias, Summer & Autumn flowering Bulbs, Border & Alpine plants. (Autumn) Peonies, Iris, Spring bulbs, Herbaceous perennials. *MAP PAGE:* **2**

CKen **Kenwith Nursery (Gordon Haddow),** The Old Rectory, Littleham, Bideford, North Devon EX39 5HW
TEL: (02372) 473752 *CONTACT:* G Haddow
◆ *OPENING TIMES:* 1000-1200 & 1400-1630 Wed-Sat & by appt.
MAIL ORDER: Yes *MIN VALUE:* £10.00 + p&p *CAT. COST:* 3 x 1st class
W/SALE or RETAIL: Retail
SPECIALITIES: All Conifer genera. Grafting a speciality. Many new introductions to UK.
MAP PAGE: **1**

CKin **Kingsfield Conservation Nursery,** Broadenham Lane, Winsham, Chard, Somerset TA20 4JF
TEL: (0460) 30070 *CONTACT:* G & J E Peacock & Y Saunders
OPENING TIMES: Please phone for details.
MAIL ORDER: Yes *MIN VALUE:* None *CAT. COST:* Free *W/SALE or RETAIL:* Both
SPECIALITIES: Native Trees, Shrubs, Wild flowers & Wild flower Seeds.. *MAP PAGE:* **1/2**

CKni **Knightshayes Garden Trust,** The Garden Office, Knightshayes, Tiverton, Devon EX16 7RG
TEL: (0884) 259010 (Shop) *CONTACT:* M Hickson
OPENING TIMES: 1030-1730 daily 1st Apr-31st Oct.
MAIL ORDER: None *MIN VALUE:* *CAT. COST:* £2.50 per list *W/SALE or RETAIL:* Retail
SPECIALITIES: Bulbs, Shrubs & Herbaceous. *MAP PAGE:* **1**

CLan **The Lanhydrock Gardens (NT),** Lanhydrock, Bodmin, Cornwall PL30 5AD
TEL: (0208) 72220 *CONTACT:* The National Trust
OPENING TIMES: Daily Easter (or Apr 1st)-31st Oct.
MAIL ORDER: No *CAT. COST:* Free *W/SALE or RETAIL:* Both
SPECIALITIES: Shrubs, especially Camellia, Azalea, Rhododendron, Magnolia, Deutzia. Philadelphus & Ceanothus. *MAP PAGE:* **1**

CLCN **Little Creek Nursery,** 39 Moor Road, Banwell, Weston-super-Mare, Avon BS24 6EF
TEL: (0934) 823739 *CONTACT:* Rhys & Julie Adams
OPENING TIMES: 1000-1630 Thu & Fri. Also most w/ends (but please check first) mid-March to mid-Sept & by appt.
MAIL ORDER: Yes *MIN VALUE:* None *CAT. COST:* 3 x 1st class *W/SALE or RETAIL:* Retail
SPECIALITIES: Species Cyclamen (from seed) & Helleborus. *MAP PAGE:* **2/4**

CLew **Lewdon Farm Alpine Nursery,** Medland Lane, Cheriton Bishop, Nr Exeter, Devon EX6 6HF
TEL: (0647) 24283 *CONTACT:* Betty Frampton
◆ *OPENING TIMES:* Daily, end Mar-end Oct. By appt. in winter.
MAIL ORDER: No *CAT. COST:* 2 x 2nd class *W/SALE or RETAIL:* Retail
SPECIALITIES: Alpines, miniature Shrubs, dwarf Conifers & herbaceous. *MAP PAGE:* **1**

CLnd **Landford Trees,** Landford Lodge, Landford, Salisbury, Wiltshire SP5 2EH
TEL: (0794) 390808 *FAX:* (0794) 390037 *CONTACT:* C D Pilkington
OPENING TIMES: 0800-1700 Mon-Fri.
MAIL ORDER: No *CAT. COST:* Free *W/SALE or RETAIL:* Both
SPECIALITIES: Deciduous ornamental Trees. *MAP PAGE:* **2**

CLoc **C S Lockyer,** Lansbury, 70 Henfield Road, Coalpit Heath, Bristol, Avon BS17 2UZ
TEL: (0454) 772219 *CONTACT:* C S Lockyer
◆ *OPENING TIMES:* Appt only. (Many open days & coach parties).
MAIL ORDER: Yes *MIN VALUE:* 6 plants + p&p *CAT. COST:* 3 x 1st class
W/SALE or RETAIL: Both
SPECIALITIES: Fuchsia. *MAP PAGE:* **2**

CMac **Macpennys Nurseries,** 154 Burley Road, Branscore, Christchurch, Dorset BH23 8DB
TEL: (0425) 72348 *CONTACT:* T & V Lowndes
OPENING TIMES: 0800-1700 Mon-Fri, 0900-1700 Sat 1400-1700 Sun.
MAIL ORDER: Yes *MIN VALUE:* No minimum charge *CAT. COST:* 50p A5 Sae
W/SALE or RETAIL: Both
SPECIALITIES: General. *MAP PAGE:* **2**

CMCN **Mallet Court Nursery,** Curry Mallet, Taunton, Somerset TA3 6SY
TEL: (0823) 480748 *FAX:* (0823) 481009 *CONTACT:* J G S & P M E Harris F.L.S.
OPENING TIMES: 0900-1300 & 1400-1700 Mon-Fri. Sat & Sun by appt.
MAIL ORDER: *MIN VALUE:* *CAT. COST:* £1.00 *W/SALE or RETAIL:* Both
SPECIALITIES: Maples, Oaks, Magnolias, Hollies & other rare and unusual plants including those from China & South Korea. *MAP PAGE:* **1**

CMea **The Mead Nursery,** Brokerswood, Nr Westbury, Wiltshire BA13 4EG
TEL: (0373) 859990 *CONTACT:* Steve Lewis-Dale
OPENING TIMES: 0900-1800 Wed-Sat, 1400-1800 Sun 1st Mar-31st Oct.
MAIL ORDER: No *CAT. COST:* 2 x 1st class *W/SALE or RETAIL:* Retail
SPECIALITIES: Perennials & Alpines incl. Bulbs. *MAP PAGE:* **2**

CMer **Merlin Rooted Cuttings,** Little Drym, Praze, Camborne, Cornwall TR14 0NU
TEL: (0209) 831 704 *CONTACT:* Liz & Roger Jackson
◆ *OPENING TIMES:* 1000-1700 Wed-Fri, 0900-1300 Sat Mar-mid Oct & by appt.
MAIL ORDER: Yes *MIN VALUE:* No minimum charge *CAT. COST:* 3 x 1st class
W/SALE or RETAIL: Both
SPECIALITIES: Rooted cuttings. *MAP PAGE:*

CMGP **Milton Garden Plants,** Milton-on-Stour, Gillingham, Dorset SP8 5PX
TEL: (0747) 822484 *CONTACT:* Sue & Richard Cumming
OPENING TIMES: Tue-Sun & Bank Hol Mons.
MAIL ORDER: No *CAT. COST:* 3 x 1st class *W/SALE or RETAIL:* Retail
SPECIALITIES: Perennnials & wide range of Trees & Shrubs. *MAP PAGE:* **2**

CMHG Marwood Hill Gardens, Barnstaple, North Devon EX31 4EB
TEL: (0271) 42528 *CONTACT:* Dr. Smart
OPENING TIMES: 1100-1300 & 1400-1700 daily.
MAIL ORDER: No *CAT. COST:* 70p *W/SALE or RETAIL:* Retail
SPECIALITIES: Large range of unusual Trees & Shrubs. Eucalyptus, Alpines, Camellia, & Bog plants. *MAP PAGE:* **1/4**

CMil Mill Cottage Plants, The Mill, Henley Lane, Wookey, Somerset BA5 1AP
TEL: (0749) 676966 *CONTACT:* Sally Gregson
OPENING TIMES: 1000-1800 Wed Mar-Sep or by appt. Ring for directions.
MAIL ORDER: Yes *MIN VALUE:* £5.00 + p&p *CAT. COST:* 2 x 1st class
W/SALE or RETAIL: Retail
SPECIALITIES: Unusual & period Cottage plants especially 'old' Pinks, Campanulas, Hardy Geraniums, Euphorbias & Ferns. *MAP PAGE:* **2**

CMon Monocot Nursery, Jacklands, Jacklands Bridge, Tickenham, Clevedon Avon BS21 6SG
TEL: CONTACT: M R Salmon
OPENING TIMES: 1000-1800 daily.
MAIL ORDER: Yes *MIN VALUE:* None *CAT. COST:* Sae *W/SALE or RETAIL:* Retail
SPECIALITIES: Rare & unusual Bulbous plants. Narcissus, Colchicum, Scilla, Crocus, Aroids, S. African & S. American species. *MAP PAGE:* **2/4**

CNat Natural Selection, 1 Station Cottages, Hullavington, Chippenham, Wiltshire SN14 6ET
TEL: (0666) 837369 *CONTACT:* Martin Cragg-Barber
OPENING TIMES: Please telephone first.
MAIL ORDER: No *CAT. COST:* 2 x 1st class *W/SALE or RETAIL:* Retail
SPECIALITIES: Unusual British natives, Pelargoniums & others. *MAP PAGE:* **2**

CNCN Naked Cross Nurseries, Waterloo Road, Corfe Mullen, Wimborne, Dorset BH21 3SR
TEL: (0202) 693256 *CONTACT:* Mr P J French & Mrs J E Paddon
OPENING TIMES: 0900-1730 daily.
MAIL ORDER: MIN VALUE: CAT. COST: Free *W/SALE or RETAIL:* Both
SPECIALITIES: Heathers and Herbaceous. *MAP PAGE:* **2**

CNic Nicky's Rock Garden Nursery, Broadhayes, Stockland, Honiton, Devon EX14 9EH
TEL: (040488) 213 *CONTACT:* Diana & Bob Dark
OPENING TIMES: 0900-dusk daily.
MAIL ORDER: No *CAT. COST:* 3 x 1st class *W/SALE or RETAIL:* Retail
SPECIALITIES: Plants for Rock gardens, Alpine house, Scree, Troughs, Banks, Walls & front of border & Dwarf Shrubs. Many unusual. *MAP PAGE:* **1**

COCH Otters' Court Heathers, Otters' Court, West Camel, Yeovil, Somerset BA22 7QF
TEL: (0935) 850285 *CONTACT:* Mrs D H Jones
OPENING TIMES: 0900-1700 Wed-Sun and by appt.
MAIL ORDER: Yes *MIN VALUE:* £3.00 + p&p *CAT. COST:* 3 x 1st class *W/SALE or RETAIL:* Both
SPECIALITIES: Lime-tolerant Heathers. *MAP PAGE:* **2**

COtt Otter Nurseries Ltd., Gosford Road, Ottery St. Mary, Devon EX11 1LZ
TEL: (0404) 815815 *FAX:* (0404) 815816 *CONTACT:* Mr K Owen
OPENING TIMES: 0800-1700 daily ex Xmas.
MAIL ORDER: No *CAT. COST:* Free *W/SALE or RETAIL:* Both
SPECIALITIES: Large Garden Centre & Nursery with extensive range of Trees, Shrubs, Conifers, Climbers, Roses, Fruit & hardy Perennials. *MAP PAGE:* **1**

CPar Parham Nursery, The Sands, Market Lavington, Wiltshire SN10 4QA
TEL: (038 081) 8427/2443 *CONTACT:* A G Penn
◆ *OPENING TIMES:* 0930-1700 Sat & Sun, Mar-Nov incl. (Dec-Feb & Aug by appt. only).
MAIL ORDER: Yes *MIN VALUE:* See Cat, for details *CAT. COST:* Free *W/SALE or RETAIL:* Both
SPECIALITIES: Wide range of Alpine & Perennial in traditional and unusual varieties.
MAP PAGE: **2**

CPer Perrie Hale Forest Nursery, Northcote Hill, Honiton, Devon EX14 8TH
TEL: (0404) 43344 *FAX:* (0404) 47163 *CONTACT:* N C Davey & Mrs J F Davey
OPENING TIMES: 0800-1630 Mon-Fri, 0800-1300 Sat. Retail sales by appt. please.
MAIL ORDER: Yes *MIN VALUE:* £5.00 + p&p *CAT. COST:* Sae *W/SALE or RETAIL:* Both
SPECIALITIES: Forest Trees, native Hedging plants & Shrubs. *MAP PAGE:* **1**

CPev **Peveril Clematis Nursery,** Christow, Exeter, Devon EX6 7NG
TEL: (0647) 52937 *CONTACT:* Barry Fretwell
OPENING TIMES: 1000-1300 & 1400-1730 Fri-Wed, 1000-1300 Sun. Dec-Mar by appt..
MAIL ORDER: No *CAT. COST:* 2 x 1st class *W/SALE or RETAIL:* Retail
SPECIALITIES: Clematis. *MAP PAGE:* **1**

CPla **Plant World Botanic Gardens,** St Marychurch Road, Newton Abbot, South Devon TQ12 4SE
TEL: (0803) 872939 *CONTACT:* Ray Brown
◆ *OPENING TIMES:* 0900-1700.
MAIL ORDER: *MIN VALUE:* *CAT. COST:* 70p *W/SALE or RETAIL:* Both
SPECIALITIES: Alpines & unusual Herbaceous plants. Choice seed list available (Meconopsis, Gentians, Primulas, Lewisias). 4 acre world botanic map. NCCPG Primula collections. *MAP PAGE:* **1**

CPle **Pleasant View Nursery,** Two Mile Oak, Nr Denbury, Newton Abbot, Devon TQ12 6DG
TEL: (0803) 813388 *CONTACT:* Mrs B D Yeo
OPENING TIMES: 1000-1700 Wed-Sat 17th Mar-end Oct. (Closed for lunch 1245-1330)
MAIL ORDER: Yes *MIN VALUE:* £10.00 + p&p *CAT. COST:* *£1.00 (coin)
W/SALE or RETAIL: Retail
SPECIALITIES: Unusual Shrubs, Salvias & Conservatory Plants. National Collection Holders of Abelia & Salvia. *NOTE: Sae for Salvia list. *MAP PAGE:* **1**

CPMA **P M A Plant Specialities,** Lower Mead, West Hatch, Taunton, Somerset TA3 5RN
TEL: (0823) 480774 *FAX:* (0823) 481046 *CONTACT:* Karan or Nick Junker
OPENING TIMES: STRICTLY by appt. only.
MAIL ORDER: Yes *MIN VALUE:* None *CAT. COST:* 4 x 2nd class *W/SALE or RETAIL:* Both
SPECIALITIES: Choice & unusual Shrubs incl. grafted Acer palmatum cvs, Cornus cvs, Hamamelis etc. *MAP PAGE:* **1**

CPou **Pounsley Plants,** Poundsley Combe, Spriddlestone, Brixton, Plymouth, Devon PL9 0DW
TEL: (0752) 402873 *CONTACT:* Mrs Jane Hollow
OPENING TIMES: By appt. only.
MAIL ORDER: No *CAT. COST:* 2 x 1st class *W/SALE or RETAIL:* Both
SPECIALITIES: Unusual Herbaceous Perennials & 'Cottage plants'. *MAP PAGE:* **1**

CRDP **R D Plants,** Homelea Farm, Tytherleigh, Axminster, East Devon EX13 7BG
TEL: (0460) 20206 *CONTACT:* Rodney Davey & Lynda Windsor
OPENING TIMES: 0900-dusk Mon-Fri & most weekends, mid Mar-end Sep. Please check first.
MAIL ORDER: No *CAT. COST:* 3 x 1st class *W/SALE or RETAIL:* Retail
SPECIALITIES: Herbaceous, Woodland, Pond & Moisture loving plants, many rare & unusual. A few choice Alpines. (Over 1,000 varieties). *MAP PAGE:* **1**

CRiv **Rivendell Alpines,** Horton Heath, Wimborne, Dorset BH21 7JN
TEL: (0202) 824013 *CONTACT:* John & Claire Horsey.
OPENING TIMES: 1000-1700 Sat-Thu Mar-Oct. Nov-Feb by appt.
MAIL ORDER: Yes *MIN VALUE:* £5.00 + p&p *CAT. COST:* Sae *W/SALE or RETAIL:* Retail
SPECIALITIES: Alpines & Aquatics. *MAP PAGE:* **2**

CRos **Royal Horticultural Society's Garden,** Rosemoor, Great Torrington, Devon EX38 8PH
TEL: (0805) 24067 *FAX:* (0805) 24717 *CONTACT:* Plant Sales Manager
OPENING TIMES: 1000-1700 1st Mar-31st Oct.
MAIL ORDER: No *CAT. COST:* None issued *W/SALE or RETAIL:* Retail
SPECIALITIES: National Cornus and part Ilex collections. Many rare & unusual plants. *MAP PAGE:* **1**

CRow **Rowden Gardens,** Brentor, Nr Tavistock, Devon PL19 0NG
TEL: (0822) 810275 *CONTACT:* John R L Carter
OPENING TIMES: 1000-1700 Sat-Sun & Bank Hols 25th Mar-end Sep. Other times by appt.
MAIL ORDER: Yes *MIN VALUE:* No minimum charge *CAT. COST:* £1.50
W/SALE or RETAIL: Both
SPECIALITIES: Aquatics, Bog, unusual & rare specialist plants. NCCPG Polygonum Collection. *MAP PAGE:* **1**

CSam **Sampford Shrubs,** Sampford Peverell, Tiverton, Devon EX16 7EW
TEL: (0884) 821164 *FAX:* (0884) 821164 *CONTACT:* M Hughes-Jones & S Proud
OPENING TIMES: 0900-1700 (dusk if earlier) Thur-Sun except 25th Dec-end Jan.
MAIL ORDER: Yes *MIN VALUE:* £15.00 + p&p *CAT. COST:* Sae *W/SALE or RETAIL:* Retail
SPECIALITIES: Common & uncommon plants. *MAP PAGE:* **1**

CSan **John Sanday (Roses) Ltd.,** Over Lane, Almondsbury, Bristol, Avon BS12 4DA
TEL: (0454) 612195 *CONTACT:* Thomas Sanday
OPENING TIMES: 0900-1700 Mon-Sat all year. 1000-1700 Sun Mar-Dec.
MAIL ORDER: Yes *MIN VALUE:* None *CAT. COST:* Free *W/SALE or RETAIL:* Both
SPECIALITIES: All types of Roses old & new. *MAP PAGE:* **2/4**

CSCl **Scott's Clematis,** Miramar, Lee, Nr Ilfracombe, North Devon EX34 8LW
TEL: (0271) 863366 *CONTACT:* John Scott
◆ *OPENING TIMES:* 1000-1700 Tue-Sun & Bank Hols Mon. Closed 25th Dec-31st Jan.
MAIL ORDER: Yes *MIN VALUE:* 3 plants £15 + p&p *CAT. COST:* A4 Sae
W/SALE or RETAIL: Both
SPECIALITIES: Clematis only. *MAP PAGE:* **1/4**

CSco **Scotts Nurseries (Merriott) Ltd,** Merriott, Somerset TA16 5PL
TEL: (0460) 72306 *FAX:* (0460) 77433 *CONTACT:* Mark Wallis
◆ *OPENING TIMES:* 0900-1700 Mon-Sat, 1000-1700 Sun.
MAIL ORDER: Yes *MIN VALUE:* £5.00 + p&p *CAT. COST:* £1.50 *W/SALE or RETAIL:* Both
SPECIALITIES: Wide general range. *MAP PAGE:* **2**

CSev **Lower Severalls Herb Nursery,** Crewkerne, Somerset TA18 7NX
TEL: (0460) 73234 *FAX:* (0460) 76105 *CONTACT:* Mary R Pring
OPENING TIMES: 1000-1700 Fri-Wed (1400-1700 Sun).
MAIL ORDER: Yes *MIN VALUE:* £10.00 + p&p *CAT. COST:* 3 x 1st class
W/SALE or RETAIL: Retail
SPECIALITIES: Herbs, Herbaceous & Conservatory plants. *MAP PAGE:* **2**

CSFH **Scotland Farmhouse Herbs,** Virginstow, Beaworthy, North Devon EX21 5EA
TEL: (040921) 585 *CONTACT:* Jean Jewels & Peter Charnley
OPENING TIMES: Anytime, but please phone first.
MAIL ORDER: No *CAT. COST:* 5 x 2nd class *W/SALE or RETAIL:* Both
SPECIALITIES: Herbs, culinary, medicinal & dye plants. Scented foliage plants & plants for the wild garden. *MAP PAGE:* **1**

CShe **Shepton Nursery Garden,** Old Wells Road, Shepton Mallet, Somerset BA4 5XN
TEL: (0749) 343630 *CONTACT:* Mr & Mrs P W Boughton
OPENING TIMES: 0930-1730 Tue-Sat and by appt.
MAIL ORDER: No *CAT. COST:* 4 x 2nd class *W/SALE or RETAIL:* Retail
SPECIALITIES: Herbaceous, Alpines & Chaenomeles. *MAP PAGE:* **2**

CSin **John Sinden,** 10 Derwentwater Road, Merley Ways, Wimbourne, Dorset BH21 1QS
TEL: (0202) 885841 *CONTACT:* John Sinden
◆ *OPENING TIMES:* 0900-1700 daily.
MAIL ORDER: Yes *MIN VALUE:* None *CAT. COST:* Sae *W/SALE or RETAIL:* Both
SPECIALITIES: Convallaria. *MAP PAGE:* **2**

CSmi **Elizabeth Smith,** Downside, Bowling Green, Constantine, Falmouth, Cornwall TR11 5AP
TEL: (0326) 40787 *CONTACT:* Elizabeth Smith
OPENING TIMES:
MAIL ORDER: Yes *MIN VALUE:* Negotiable *CAT. COST:* Sae *W/SALE or RETAIL:* Retail
SPECIALITIES: Scented Violets. Some seed available for export. NOTE: Telephone or Postal enquiries please. *MAP PAGE:*

CSpe **Special Plants,** Laurels Farm, Upper Wraxall, Chippenham, Wiltshire SN14 7AG
TEL: (0225) 891686 *CONTACT:* Derry Watkins
OPENING TIMES: Most days. Please ring first to check.
MAIL ORDER: Yes *MIN VALUE:* £10.00 + p&p *CAT. COST:* 4 x 2nd class
W/SALE or RETAIL: Retail
SPECIALITIES: Tender Perennials:- Argyranthemum, Felicia, Diascia, Lotus, Salvia, Osteospermum etc. * NOTE:- Mail Order Oct-Feb only. *MAP PAGE:* **2**

 See note on Mail Order, EC sales & Export on page 5

CSPN **Sherston Parva Nursery,** 21 Court Street, Sherston, Wiltshire SN16 0LL
TEL: (0666) 840623 *CONTACT:* Mrs M Morris
◆ *OPENING TIMES:* 1000-1300 & 1400-1700 Tue-Sat. 1200-1700 Sun Easter-Nov. Also Bank Hol Mons (closed Tue).
MAIL ORDER: Yes *MIN VALUE:* £10.00 + p&p *CAT. COST:* £1.00 *W/SALE or RETAIL:* Retail
SPECIALITIES: Clematis, wall Shrubs & Climbers. *MAP PAGE:* **2**

CSto **Stone Lane Gardens,** Stone Farm, Chagford, Devon TQ13 8JU
TEL: (064723) 311 *CONTACT:* Kenneth Ashburner
OPENING TIMES: Appt only.
MAIL ORDER: Yes *MIN VALUE:* No minimum charge *CAT. COST:* List £1.00*
W/SALE or RETAIL: Both
SPECIALITIES: Wide range of wild provenance Betula and Alnus. Also interesting varieties of Rubus, Vaccinium, Sorbus etc. *£3.00 for full descriptive & keyed Catalogue. *MAP PAGE:* **1**

CSun **Sunbeam Nurseries,** Bristol Road, Frampton Cotterell, Avon BS17 2AU
TEL: (0454) 776926 *CONTACT:* Nöel Kingsbury
OPENING TIMES: 1000-1700 Wed-Sat but please telephone first.
MAIL ORDER: Yes *MIN VALUE:* £5.00 + p&p *CAT. COST:* 6 x 1st class
W/SALE or RETAIL: Retail
SPECIALITIES: Unusual hardy & Conservatory plants, many rarities & unusual plants.
MAP PAGE: **2**

CSut **Suttons Seeds Ltd.,** Hele Road, Torquay, South Devon TQ2 7QJ
TEL: (0803) 612011 *FAX:* (0803) 616381 *CONTACT:* Mr P J McDermott
OPENING TIMES: (Office) 0830-1700.
MAIL ORDER: *MIN VALUE:* None *CAT. COST:* Free *W/SALE or RETAIL:* Both
SPECIALITIES: Over 1,200 varieties of flower & vegetable seed, bulbs, plants & sundries.
MAP PAGE:

CTho **Thornhayes Nursery,** St Andrews Wood, Dulford, Cullompton, Devon EX15 2DF
TEL: (08846) 746 *FAX:* (08846) 739 *CONTACT:* K D Croucher
OPENING TIMES: By appt. only.
MAIL ORDER: Yes *MIN VALUE:* None *CAT. COST:* £1.00 *W/SALE or RETAIL:* Both
SPECIALITIES: A broad range of forms of Broadleaved, Ornamental, Amenity & Fruit Trees, including West Country Apple varieties. *MAP PAGE:* **1**

CThr **Three Counties Nurseries,** Marshwood, Bridport, Dorset DT6 5QJ
TEL: (02977) 257 *CONTACT:* A & D Hitchcock
OPENING TIMES: Not open.
MAIL ORDER: Yes *MIN VALUE:* No minimum charge *CAT. COST:* 2 x 2nd class
W/SALE or RETAIL: Both
SPECIALITIES: Pinks & Dianthus. *MAP PAGE:*

CTom **Tomperrow Farm Nurseries,** Tomperrow Farm, Threemilestone, Truro, Cornwall TR3 6BE
TEL: (0872) 560344 *CONTACT:* Mrs S C Goodswen
OPENING TIMES: 1000-1700 Mon-Sat. Evenings & Suns by appt. Dec, Jan & Aug by appt.
MAIL ORDER: Yes *MIN VALUE:* No minimum charge *CAT. COST:* 70p inc p&p
W/SALE or RETAIL: Retail
SPECIALITIES: Wide range of hardy Herbaceous plants, some unusual. *MAP PAGE:* **1**

CTor **The Torbay Palm Farm,** St Marychurch Road, Coffinswell, nr Newton Abbot, South Devon TQ12 4SE
TEL: (0803) 872800 *FAX:* (0803) 213843 *CONTACT:* T A Eley
OPENING TIMES: 0900-1730 Mon-Fri, 1030-1700 Sat & Sun.
MAIL ORDER: Yes *MIN VALUE:* £3.80 *CAT. COST:* Free *W/SALE or RETAIL:* Both
SPECIALITIES: Cordyline australis, Trachycarpus fortuneii & new varieties of Cordyline.
MAP PAGE: **1**

CTre **Trewidden Estate Nursery,** Trewidden Gardens, Penzance, Cornwall TR20 8TT
TEL: (0736) 62087 *FAX:* (0736) 68142 *CONTACT:* Mr M G Snellgrove.
OPENING TIMES: 0800-1300 & 1400-1700 Mon-Thu & Sat. 0800-1300 & 1400-1600 Fri. Closed some Sats - please phone.
MAIL ORDER: Yes *MIN VALUE:* No minimum charge *CAT. COST:* 50p *W/SALE or RETAIL:* Both
SPECIALITIES: Camellia & unusual Shrubs. *MAP PAGE:* **1**

CTrh **Trehane Camellia Nursery,** J Trehane & Sons Ltd, Stapehill Road, Hampreston, Wimborne, Dorset BH21 7NE
TEL: (0202) 873490 *FAX:* (0202) 873490 *CONTACT:* Miss J E Trehane
OPENING TIMES: 0900-1630 Mon-Fri & weekends mid Feb-Oct.
MAIL ORDER: Yes *MIN VALUE:* £10.00 + p&p *CAT. COST:* Cat/Book £1.50
W/SALE or RETAIL: Both
SPECIALITIES: Extensive range of Camellia species, cultivars & hybrids. Many new introductions. Evergreen Azaleas, Pieris, Magnolias, Blueberries & Cranberries. *MAP PAGE:* **2**

CTro **Tropicana Nursery,** Westhill Avenue, Torquay Devon TQ1 4LH
TEL: (0803) 312618 *CONTACT:* M L Eden
OPENING TIMES: By appt. only.
MAIL ORDER: Yes *MIN VALUE:* None *CAT. COST:* 3 x 1st class *W/SALE or RETAIL:* Both
SPECIALITIES: Conservatory & sub-tropical plants. *MAP PAGE:* **1**

CTrw **Trewithen Nurseries,** Grampound Road, Truro, Cornwall TR2
TEL: (0726) 882764 *CONTACT:* M Taylor
OPENING TIMES: 0800-1630 Mon-Fri.
MAIL ORDER: No *CAT. COST:* 60p *W/SALE or RETAIL:* Both
SPECIALITIES: Shrubs, especially Camellia & Rhododendron. *MAP PAGE:* **1**

CWal **Wall Cottage Nursery,** Lockengate, Bugle, St. Austell, Cornwall PL26 8RU
TEL: (0208) 831259 *CONTACT:* Mrs J R Clark
OPENING TIMES: 0830-1700 Mon-Sat.
MAIL ORDER: Yes *MIN VALUE:* £15.00 + p&p *CAT. COST:* 60p *W/SALE or RETAIL:* Both
SPECIALITIES: Specialist Rhododendron & Azalea plus general range. *MAP PAGE:* **1**

CWes **West Kington Nurseries Ltd.,** Pound Hill, West Kington, Nr Chippenham Wiltshire SN14 7JG
TEL: (0249) 782822 *FAX:* (0249) 782953 *CONTACT:* B H Ellis
◆ *OPENING TIMES:* 1000-1700 Wed-Sun 28th Feb-1st Dec 1993 & Bank Holiday Mons.
MAIL ORDER: No *CAT. COST:* *W/SALE or RETAIL:* Both
SPECIALITIES: Herbaceous & Alpines. *MAP PAGE:* **2**

CWGN **The Water Garden Nursery,** Highcroft, Moorend, Wembworthy, Chulmleigh, Devon EX18 7SG
TEL: (0837) 83566 *CONTACT:* J M Smith
OPENING TIMES: 0800-1700 Fri-Wed Apr-Sep & by appt.
MAIL ORDER: Yes *MIN VALUE:* No minimum order *CAT. COST:* 3 x 1st class
W/SALE or RETAIL: Retail
SPECIALITIES: Plants for shade, wetlands, bog & water. *MAP PAGE:* **1**

CWil **H & S Wills,** 2 St Brannocks Park Road, Ilfracombe, Devon EX34 8HU
TEL: (0271) 863949 *CONTACT:* H Wills
OPENING TIMES: Appt only.
MAIL ORDER: Yes *MIN VALUE:* £3.00 *CAT. COST:* 3 x 1st class *W/SALE or RETAIL:* Retail
SPECIALITIES: Sempervivum, Jovibarba & Rosularia. *MAP PAGE:*

CWit **Withleigh Nurseries,** Quirkhill, Withleigh, Tiverton, Devon EX16 8JG
TEL: (0884) 253351 *CONTACT:* Chris Britton
OPENING TIMES: 0900-1730 Mon-Sat Mar-Jun, 0900-1730 Tue-Sat Jul-Feb.
MAIL ORDER: No *CAT. COST:* None available *W/SALE or RETAIL:* Retail
SPECIALITIES: Shrubs & Herbaceous. *MAP PAGE:* **1**

CWSG **West Somerset Garden Centre,** Mart Road, Minehead, Somerset TA24 5BJ
TEL: (0643) 703812 *FAX:* (0643) 706470 *CONTACT:* Mrs J K Shoulders
OPENING TIMES: 0800-1700 Mon-Sat, 1100-1700 Sun (Winter times vary, please phone).
MAIL ORDER: Yes *MIN VALUE:* None *CAT. COST:* Free *W/SALE or RETAIL:*
SPECIALITIES: Wide general range. *MAP PAGE:* **1/4**

CYea **Yearlstone Vineyard,** Chilverton, Coldridge, Crediton, Devon EX17 6BH
TEL: (0363) 83302 *CONTACT:* Miss Gillian Pearkes
OPENING TIMES: Appt only.
MAIL ORDER: Yes *MIN VALUE:* None *CAT. COST:* Sae *W/SALE or RETAIL:* Both
SPECIALITIES: Vines. *MAP PAGE:* **1**

 See note on Mail Order, EC sales & Export on page 5

EArb **Arbor Exotica,** The Estate Office, Hall Farm, Weston Colville, Cambridgeshire CB1 5PE
TEL: (0223) 290328/525 *FAX:* (0223) 290650 *CONTACT:* Rachel Harrison / Enid Capewell
◆ *OPENING TIMES:* By appt.
MAIL ORDER: Yes *MIN VALUE:* None *CAT. COST:* Free *W/SALE or RETAIL:* Both
SPECIALITIES: Hardy, rare, container grown Ornamental Trees from seed. *MAP PAGE:* **6**

EBak **B & H M Baker,** Bourne Brook Nurseries, Greenstead Green, Halstead, Essex CO9 1RJ
TEL: (0787) 472900/476369 *CONTACT:* B & H M Baker
OPENING TIMES: 0800-1630 Mon-Fri, 0900-1200 & 1400-1630 Sat & Sun.
MAIL ORDER: No *CAT. COST:* 20p+stamp *W/SALE or RETAIL:* Both
SPECIALITIES: Fuchsia & Conservatory Plants. *MAP PAGE:* **6**

EBal **Ballerina Trees Ltd.,** Maris Lane, Trumpington, Cambridgeshire CB2 2LQ
TEL: (0223) 840411 *FAX:* (0223) 842934 *CONTACT:* Richard Fairburn
OPENING TIMES: 0900-1730 (Office only).
MAIL ORDER: Yes *MIN VALUE:* *CAT. COST:* Free *W/SALE or RETAIL:* Both
SPECIALITIES: Columnar Apple Trees. NOTE: Retail trade only by Mail Order. *MAP PAGE:*

EBar **Barnsdale Plants,** Exton Avenue, Exton, Oakham, Rutland LE15 8AH
TEL: (0572) 813200 *FAX:* (0572) 813346 *CONTACT:* Mr Hamilton
OPENING TIMES: 1000-1700 1st Apr-31st Oct, 1000-1600 1st Nov-31st Mar. Closed Xmas & New Year.
MAIL ORDER: Yes *MIN VALUE:* No minimum charge *CAT. COST:* A4+3x1st class
W/SALE or RETAIL: Retail
SPECIALITIES: Choice & unusual Garden Plants & Trees. *MAP PAGE:* **6**

EBlo **Bressingham Gardens Mail Order,** Bressingham, Diss, Norfolk IP22 2AB
TEL: (0379 88) 464 *FAX:* (0379 88) 8289 *CONTACT:* Sarah O'Hara
◆ *OPENING TIMES:* 0830-1630 daily. (24-hour answering machine)
MAIL ORDER: Yes *MIN VALUE:* £15.00 + p&p *CAT. COST:* £2.00 *W/SALE or RETAIL:* Retail
SPECIALITIES: Very wide general range. Many own varieties. Focus on Hardy Ornamental plants.
MAP PAGE: **6**

EBls **Peter Beales Roses,** London Road, Attleborough, Norfolk NR17 1AY
TEL: (0953) 454707 *FAX:* (0953) 456845 *CONTACT:* Mr Peter Beales
OPENING TIMES: 0900-1700 Mon-Fri, 0900-1630 Sat, 1000-1600 Sun. Jan closed Sun.
MAIL ORDER: Yes *MIN VALUE:* None *CAT. COST:* Free *W/SALE or RETAIL:* Both
SPECIALITIES: Old fashioned Roses. *MAP PAGE:* **6**

EBly **R J Blythe,** Potash Nursery, Cow Green, Bacton, Stowmarket, Suffolk IP14 4HJ
TEL: (0449) 781671 *CONTACT:* R J Blythe
OPENING TIMES: 1000-1700 Sat, Sun & Mon mid Feb-end June.
MAIL ORDER: No *CAT. COST:* 3 x 1st class *W/SALE or RETAIL:* Retail
SPECIALITIES: Fuchsias. *MAP PAGE:* **6**

EBre **Bressingham Plant Centre,,** Bressingham, Diss, Norfolk IP22 2AB
TEL: (0379 88) 8133 *FAX:* (0379 88) 8289 *CONTACT:* Tony Fry
OPENING TIMES: 1000-1730 daily. (Direct retail Plant Centre).
MAIL ORDER: No *CAT. COST:* *W/SALE or RETAIL:* Retail
SPECIALITIES: Very wide general range. Many own varieties. Focus on Hardy Ornamental plants.
MAP PAGE: **6**

EBro **Brokenbacks Nursery,** Broxhill Road, Havering-atte-Bower, Romford, Essex RM4 1QH
TEL: (04023) 77744 *CONTACT:* A Carter
OPENING TIMES: 0900-1700 Thu-Mon.
MAIL ORDER: Yes *MIN VALUE:* None *CAT. COST:* Sae *W/SALE or RETAIL:* Retail
SPECIALITIES: Old fashioned and Hybrid musk Roses. *MAP PAGE:* **3**

EBul **Bullwood Nursery,** 54 Woodlands Road, Hockley, Essex SS5 4PY
TEL: (0702) 203761 *CONTACT:* D & E Fox
OPENING TIMES: 0930-1730 Wed-Sun.
MAIL ORDER: Yes *MIN VALUE:* *CAT. COST:* Sae *W/SALE or RETAIL:* Retail
SPECIALITIES: Mainly Liliaceae, also a wide range of other Perennials, some uncommon and rare.
MAP PAGE: **3**

EBur **Jenny Burgess,** Alpine Nursery, Sisland, Norwich, Norfolk NR14 6EF
TEL: (0508) 20724 *CONTACT:* Jenny Burgess
OPENING TIMES: Any time by appt.
MAIL ORDER: Yes *MIN VALUE:* £5.00 + p&p *CAT. COST:* 2 x 1st class *W/SALE or RETAIL:* Both
SPECIALITIES: Alpines, Sisyrinchium & Campanula. National Collection of Sisyrinchium. *NOTE: Only Sisyrinchiums by Mail Order. *MAP PAGE:* **6**

EB&P **Battle & Pears Ltd.,** Glebe Farm, Bracebridge Heath, Lincolnshire LN4 2HZ
TEL: (0522) 720121 *FAX:* (0522) 723252 *CONTACT:* D J Carmichael
OPENING TIMES: By appt. only.
MAIL ORDER: Yes *MIN VALUE:* £15.00 + p&p *CAT. COST:* 2 x 1st class
W/SALE or RETAIL: Both
SPECIALITIES: Daphne, hybrid Magnolias & other choice hardy ornamental Shrubs. *MAP PAGE:* **7**

ECar **Tim Carter,** c/o Brokenbacks Nursery, Broxhill, Havering-atte-Bower, Nr Romford, Essesx RM4 1QH
TEL: (04023) 77744 *CONTACT:* Tim Carter
OPENING TIMES: 0900-1700 Thu-Mon.
MAIL ORDER: No *CAT. COST:* Sae *W/SALE or RETAIL:* Retail
SPECIALITIES: Unusual hardy plants, Alpines, dwarf Ericaceae, Shrubs & shade Herbaceous Perennials. *MAP PAGE:* **3**

ECED **C E & D M Nurseries,** The Walnuts, 36 Main Street, Baston, Peterborough, Lincolnshire PE6 9PB
TEL: (0778 560) 483 *CONTACT:* Mrs D M Fletcher
OPENING TIMES: 0900-1800 Sat-Tue Mar-Oct & by appt.
MAIL ORDER: Yes *MIN VALUE:* See Cat. for details *CAT. COST:* 2 x 1st class
W/SALE or RETAIL: Both
SPECIALITIES: Hardy Herbaceous Perennials. *MAP PAGE:* **6**

ECha **The Beth Chatto Gardens Ltd.,** Elmstead Market, Colchester, Essex CO7 7DB
TEL: (0206) 822007 *FAX:* (0206) 825933 *CONTACT:* Beth Chatto
OPENING TIMES: 0900-1700 Mon-Sat 1st Mar-31st Oct. 0900-1600 Mon-Fri 1st Nov-1st Mar. Closed Sun & Bank Hols.
MAIL ORDER: Yes *MIN VALUE:* See Cat. for details *CAT. COST:* £2.50 incl p&p
W/SALE or RETAIL: Retail
SPECIALITIES: Predominantly Herbaceous. Many unusual for special situations. *MAP PAGE:* **6**

ECop **Copford Bulbs,** Dorsetts, Birch Road, Copford, Colchester, Essex CO6 1DR
TEL: (0206) 330008 *CONTACT:* D J Pearce
OPENING TIMES: By appt.
MAIL ORDER: Yes *MIN VALUE:* None *CAT. COST:* 50p credited *W/SALE or RETAIL:* Retail
SPECIALITIES: Daffodil bulbs & Cyclamen tubers. *MAP PAGE:* **6**

ECou **County Park Nursery,** Essex Gardens, Hornchurch, Essex RM11 3BU
TEL: (0708) 445205 *CONTACT:* G Hutchins
OPENING TIMES: 0900-dusk Mon-Sat ex Wed. 1000-1700 Sun.
MAIL ORDER: No *CAT. COST:* 3 x 1st class *W/SALE or RETAIL:* Retail
SPECIALITIES: Alpines & rare and unusual plants from New Zealand, Tasmania & Falklands. *MAP PAGE:* **3**

ECro **Croftacre Hardy Plants,** Croftacre, Ellingham Road, Scoulton, Norfolk NR9 4NT
TEL: (0953) 850599 *FAX:* (0953) 851399 *CONTACT:* Mrs V J Allen
OPENING TIMES: Most days. Please telephone first.
MAIL ORDER: Yes *MIN VALUE:* None *CAT. COST:* 3 x 1st class *W/SALE or RETAIL:* Retail
SPECIALITIES: Rare & uncommon Perennials. *MAP PAGE:* **6**

ECtt **Cottage Nurseries,** Thoresthorpe, Alford, Lincolnshire LN13 0HX
TEL: (0507) 466968 *CONTACT:* W H Denbigh
OPENING TIMES: 0900-1700 daily.
MAIL ORDER: Yes *MIN VALUE:* £5.00 + p&p *CAT. COST:* 3 x 1st class *W/SALE or RETAIL:* Both
SPECIALITIES: Wide general range. *MAP PAGE:* **7**

 See note on Mail Order, EC sales & Export on page 5

EDen **Denbeigh Heather Nurseries,** All Saints Road, Creeting St. Mary, Ipswich, Suffolk IP6 8PJ
TEL: (0449) 711220 *CONTACT:* D J & A Small
OPENING TIMES: By appt. only.
MAIL ORDER: Yes *MIN VALUE:* None *CAT. COST:* £1.00 *W/SALE or RETAIL:* Both
SPECIALITIES: Rooted Heather cuttings. *MAP PAGE:* **6**

EDon **Donington Plants,** Donington House, Main Road, Wrangle, Boston, Lincolnshire PE22 9AT
TEL: (0205) 870015 *CONTACT:* D W Salt
OPENING TIMES: 1000-1700 Wed-Sat 4th Mar-9th May & 16th Sep-31st Oct & by appt.
MAIL ORDER: Yes *MIN VALUE:* £10.00 + p&p *CAT. COST:* Sae *W/SALE or RETAIL:* Retail
SPECIALITIES: Auricula, Argyranthemum, Penstemon & Barnhaven Polyanthus. *MAP PAGE:* **7**

EDra **John Drake,** Hardwicke House, Fen Ditton, Cambridgeshire CB5 8TF
TEL: *CONTACT:* John Drake
OPENING TIMES:
MAIL ORDER: Yes *MIN VALUE:* £10.00 + p&p *CAT. COST:* 70p *W/SALE or RETAIL:* Retail
SPECIALITIES: Aquilegia. *MAP PAGE:*

EEls **Elsworth Herbs,** Avenue Farm Cottage, 31, Smith Street, Elsworth, Cambridgeshire CB3 8HY
TEL: (09547) 414 *CONTACT:* Drs J D & J M Twibell
OPENING TIMES: Advertised weekends & by appt. only.
MAIL ORDER: Yes *MIN VALUE:* £10.00 + p&p *CAT. COST:* 2 x 1st class
W/SALE or RETAIL: Retail
SPECIALITIES: Herbs, Artemisia (NCCPG Collection), & Cottage garden plants. *MAP PAGE:* **6**

EFEx **Flora Exotica,** Pasadena, South-Green, Fingringhoe, Colchester, Essex CO5 7DR
TEL: (0206) 729414 *CONTACT:* J Beddoes
OPENING TIMES: By appt. only.
MAIL ORDER: Yes *MIN VALUE:* None *CAT. COST:* Free *W/SALE or RETAIL:* Retail
SPECIALITIES: Insectivorous plants, esp. Pinguicula, Drosera & rare & exotica Flora incl. Orchids. *MAP PAGE:* **6**

Effi **Daphne ffiske Herbs,** Rosemary Cottage, Bramerton, Norwich, Norfolk NR14 7DW
TEL: (05088) 8187 *CONTACT:* D ffiske
OPENING TIMES: 1000-1600 Thu-Sun.
MAIL ORDER: No *CAT. COST:* Sae *W/SALE or RETAIL:* Retail
SPECIALITIES: Herbs including own cultivars and rarities. *MAP PAGE:* **6**

EFol **Foliage & Unusual Plants,** The Dingle Nursery, Pilsgate, Stamford, Lincolnshire PE9 3HW
TEL: (0780) 740775 *FAX:* (0780) 740838 *CONTACT:* Margaret Handley
◆ *OPENING TIMES:* 1000-1800 (dusk if earlier) daily Mar-14th Nov & Bank Hols.
MAIL ORDER: Yes *MIN VALUE:* £10.00 + p&p *CAT. COST:* 3 x 1st class
W/SALE or RETAIL: Retail
SPECIALITIES: Variegated, coloured foliage & unusual plants. *MAP PAGE:* **6**

EFou **Four Seasons,** Forncett St Mary, Norwich, Norfolk NR16 1JT
TEL: (050 841) 8344 *FAX:* (050 841) 8478 *CONTACT:* J P Metcalf & R W Ball
OPENING TIMES: No callers.
MAIL ORDER: Yes *MIN VALUE:* £15.00 + p&p *CAT. COST:* £1.00 *W/SALE or RETAIL:* Retail
SPECIALITIES: Herbaceous & Grasses *MAP PAGE:*

EFul **Fulbrooke Nursery,** 43 Fulbrooke Road, Cambridgeshire CB3 9EE
TEL: (0223) 311102 *CONTACT:* Paul Lazard
OPENING TIMES: By appt. most times.
MAIL ORDER: Yes *MIN VALUE:* £6.00 + p&p *CAT. COST:* Sae *W/SALE or RETAIL:* Both
SPECIALITIES: Bamboos *MAP PAGE:* **6**

◆ **See also Display Advertisements**

EGol **Goldbrook Plants,** Hoxne, Eye, Suffolk IP21 5AN

TEL: (037975) 770 *CONTACT:* Sandra Bond
OPENING TIMES: 1030-1800 or dusk, if earlier, Thu-Sun ex. Jan, or by appt.
MAIL ORDER: Yes *MIN VALUE:* £15.00 + p&p *CAT. COST:* 4 x 1st class
W/SALE or RETAIL: Retail
SPECIALITIES: Very large range of Hosta (over 400), Hemerocallis & Bog Iris. Interesting Hardy plants esp. for shade & bog. *NOTE: M.O. Perennials and Grasses only. *MAP PAGE:* **6**

EGou **Goulding's Fuchsias,** West View, Link Lane, Bentley, Nr Ipswich, Suffolk IP9 2DP

TEL: (0473) 310058 *CONTACT:* Mr T J Goulding
OPENING TIMES: 1000-1700 daily 2nd Jan-4th July 1993, 1st Jan-3rd July 1994.
MAIL ORDER: Yes *MIN VALUE:* See Cat. for details *CAT. COST:* 3 x 1st class
W/SALE or RETAIL: Retail
SPECIALITIES: Fuchsia - new introductions, Hardy, Encliandra, Terminal flowering (Triphylla), Species, Basket & Bedding. *MAP PAGE:* **6**

EHal **Hall Farm Nursery,** Harpswell, Nr Gainsborough, Lincolnshire DN21 5UU

TEL: (0427) 668412 *FAX:* (0427) 668412 *CONTACT:* Pam & Mark Tatam
OPENING TIMES: 0900-1800 daily. Please telephone in winter to check.
MAIL ORDER: Yes *MIN VALUE:* No minimum charge *CAT. COST:* Sae *W/SALE or RETAIL:*
SPECIALITIES: Wide range of Shrubs, Trees & Perennials. *MAP PAGE:* **7**

EHar **Hartshall Nursery Stock,** Hartshall Farm, Walsham-le-Willows, Nr Bury St Edmunds, Suffolk IP31 3BY

TEL: (0359) 259238 *FAX:* (0359) 259238 *CONTACT:* J D L & M A Wight
OPENING TIMES: 1000-1630 Tue-Sat. Ex all Bank Hols & all July.
MAIL ORDER: No *CAT. COST:* 3 x 1st class *W/SALE or RETAIL:* Retail
SPECIALITIES: Hardy Shrubs, Trees & Conifers. Wide general range & rare, esp. Acer, Betula, Fagus, Prunus, Quercus, Salix & Sorbus, Viburnum. Can deliver. *MAP PAGE:* **6**

EHMN **Home Meadows Nursery Ltd,** Martlesham, Woodbridge, Suffolk IP12 4RD

TEL: (0394) 382419 *CONTACT:* S D & M I O'Brien Baker & I D Baker
OPENING TIMES: 0800-1700 Mon-Fri, 0800-1300 Sat.
MAIL ORDER: Yes *MIN VALUE:* *CAT. COST:* Free *W/SALE or RETAIL:* Both
SPECIALITIES: Small general range plus Chrysanthemum esp. Korean. *MAP PAGE:* **6**

EHoe **Hoecroft Plants,** Severals Grange, Wood Norton, Dereham, Norfolk NR20 5BL

TEL: (0362) 844206/860179 *CONTACT:* M Lister
◆ *OPENING TIMES:* 1000-1600 Wed & Sat 30th Apr-1st Oct.
MAIL ORDER: Yes *MIN VALUE:* No minimum charge *CAT. COST:* £1.00
W/SALE or RETAIL: Both
SPECIALITIES: 240 varieties of Variegated and 300 varieties of Coloured-leaved plants in all species. 170 Grasses. *MAP PAGE:* **6**

EHon **Honeysome Aquatic Nursery,** The Row, Sutton, Nr Ely, Cambridgeshire CB6 2PF

TEL: (0353) 778889 *CONTACT:* D B Barker & D B Littlefield
OPENING TIMES: 0930-1200 Sat. Mid Apr-end Oct. Also by appt. ONLY.
MAIL ORDER: No *CAT. COST:* 2 x 1st class *W/SALE or RETAIL:* Both
SPECIALITIES: Hardy Aquatic, Bog & Marginal. *MAP PAGE:* **6**

EHul **Hull Farm,** Spring Valley Lane, Ardleigh, Colchester, Essex CO7 7SA

TEL: (0206) 230045 *FAX:* (0206) 230820 *CONTACT:* J Fryer & Sons
OPENING TIMES: 1000-1630 daily ex Xmas.
MAIL ORDER: No *CAT. COST:* 50p + Sae *W/SALE or RETAIL:* Both
SPECIALITIES: Conifers. *MAP PAGE:* **6**

EJud **Judy's Country Garden,** The Villa, Louth Road, South Somercotes, Louth, Lincolnshire LN11 7BW

TEL: (0507) 358487 *CONTACT:* M J S & J M Harry
OPENING TIMES: 0900-1800 most days Mar-Nov.
MAIL ORDER: *MIN VALUE:* *CAT. COST:* 3 x 1st class *W/SALE or RETAIL:* Retail
SPECIALITIES: Herbs, old-fashioned & unusual plants, including scarce & old varieties.
MAP PAGE: **7**

 See note on Mail Order, EC sales & Export on page 5

EKMF Kathleen Muncaster Fuchsias, 18 Field Lane, Morton, Gainsborough, Lincolnshire DN21 3BY
TEL: (0427) 612329 *CONTACT:* Kathleen Muncaster
OPENING TIMES: 1000-Dusk.
MAIL ORDER: Yes *MIN VALUE:* See Cat. for details *CAT. COST:* 2 x 1st class
W/SALE or RETAIL: Retail
SPECIALITIES: Fuchsia. *NOTE: Mail Orders to be received before April 1st. *MAP PAGE:* **7**

ELan Langthorns Plantery, High Cross Lane West, Little Canfield, Dunmow, Essex CM6 1TD
TEL: (0371) 872611 *FAX:* (0371) 872611 *CONTACT:* P & D Cannon
OPENING TIMES: 1000-1700 or dusk (if earlier) daily ex Xmas fortnight.
MAIL ORDER: No *CAT. COST:* £1.00 *W/SALE or RETAIL:* Retail
SPECIALITIES: Wide general range with many unusual plants. *MAP PAGE:* **6**

ELun Mrs Ann Lunn, The Fens, Old Mill Road, Langham, Colchester, Essex CO4 5NU
TEL: (0206) 272259 *CONTACT:* Mrs Ann Lunn
OPENING TIMES: Thu & Sat and by appt.
MAIL ORDER: *MIN VALUE:* *CAT. COST:* 3 x 1st class *W/SALE or RETAIL:* Retail
SPECIALITIES: Primula, Woodland and moisture loving plants. *MAP PAGE:* **6**

EMar Lesley Marshall, Islington Lodge Cottgae, Tilney All Saints, King's Lynn, Norfolk PE34 4SF
TEL: (0553) 765103 *CONTACT:* Lesley Marshall
OPENING TIMES: Weekends Mar-Oct & by appt.
MAIL ORDER: Yes *MIN VALUE:* £5.00 + p&p *CAT. COST:* £1 refundable
W/SALE or RETAIL: Retail
SPECIALITIES: Hardy Perennials, Grasses & Foliage plants. *MAP PAGE:* **6**

EMFP Mills' Farm Plants & Gardens, Norwich Road, Mendlesham, Suffolk IP14 5NQ
TEL: (0449) 766425 *CONTACT:* Peter & Susan Russell
OPENING TIMES: 0900-1730 Wed-Mon (Closed Jan).
MAIL ORDER: Yes *MIN VALUE:* *CAT. COST:* 2 x 2nd class *W/SALE or RETAIL:* Retail
SPECIALITIES: Pinks, Old Roses, Wide general range. *NOTE: Mail Order for Pinks& Roses only. *MAP PAGE:* **6**

EMFW Mickfield Fish & Watergarden Centre, Debenham Road, Mickfield, Stowmarket, Suffolk IP14 5LP
TEL: (0449) 711336 *FAX:* (0449) 711018 *CONTACT:* Mike & Yvonne Burch
◆ *OPENING TIMES:* 0900-1700 daily.
MAIL ORDER: Yes *MIN VALUE:* No minimum charge *CAT. COST:* 50p *W/SALE or RETAIL:*
SPECIALITIES: Hardy Aquatics, Nymphaea & moisture lovers. *MAP PAGE:* **6**

EMic Mickfield Market Garden, The Poplars, Mickfield, Stowmarket, Suffolk IP14 5LH
TEL: (0449) 711576 *CONTACT:* Mr & Mrs R L C Milton
◆ *OPENING TIMES:* Sat & Sun 29th May-31st Oct or telephone for appt.
MAIL ORDER: Yes *MIN VALUE:* See Cat. for details *CAT. COST:* £1 refundable
W/SALE or RETAIL: Retail
SPECIALITIES: Hostas, over 375 varieties mostly from USA. *MAP PAGE:* **6**

EMil Mill Race Nursery, New Road Aldham, Colchester, Essex CO6 3QT
TEL: (0206) 242324 *FAX:* (0206) 241616 *CONTACT:* Bill Mathews
OPENING TIMES: 0900-1730 daily.
MAIL ORDER: Yes *MIN VALUE:* None *CAT. COST:* Sae *W/SALE or RETAIL:* Both
SPECIALITIES: Climbing & many unusual plant varieties. Range of hardy & half hardy plants. *MAP PAGE:* **6**

EMNN Martin Nest Nurseries, Grange Cottage, Harpswell Lane, Hemswell, Gainsbor'o, Lincolnshire DN21 5UP
TEL: (0427) 668369 *FAX:* (0427) 668080 *CONTACT:* M & M A Robinson
OPENING TIMES: 1000-1600 daily
MAIL ORDER: Yes *MIN VALUE:* No minimum order *CAT. COST:* 3 x 2nd class
W/SALE or RETAIL: Both
SPECIALITIES: Alpines especially Auricula, Primula, Lewisia, & Saxifraga. *MAP PAGE:* **7**

EMon **Monksilver Nursery,** Oakington Road, Cottenham, Cambridgeshire CB4 4TW
TEL: *CONTACT:* Joe Sharman & Alan Leslie
OPENING TIMES: 1000-1600 Fri & Sat 1st Apr-30th Jun.
MAIL ORDER: Yes *MIN VALUE:* £10.00 + p&p *CAT. COST:* 6 x 1st class
W/SALE or RETAIL: Retail
SPECIALITIES: Herbaceous plants, Grasses, Anthemis, Arum, Helianthus, Lamium, Nepeta, Monarda, Salvia, Vinca, Sedges & Variegated plants. Many NCCPG 'Pink Sheet' plants.
MAP PAGE: **6**

EMor **John Morley,** North Green Only, Stoven, Beccles, Suffolk NR34 8DG
TEL: *CONTACT:* John Morley
OPENING TIMES: By appt. ONLY.
MAIL ORDER: Yes *MIN VALUE:* Details in catalogue *CAT. COST:* £1.00 + stamp
W/SALE or RETAIL: Retail
SPECIALITIES: Galanthus, species & hybrids. *MAP PAGE:*

EMou **Frances Mount Perennial Plants,** 1 Steps Farm, Polstead, Colchester, Essex CO6 5AE
TEL: (0206) 262811 *CONTACT:* Frances Mount
OPENING TIMES: 1000-1700 Tue Wed Sat Sun & Bank Hols. 1400-1800 Fri. Check weekends & Hols.
MAIL ORDER: Yes *MIN VALUE:* £5.00 + p&p *CAT. COST:* 3 x 1st class
W/SALE or RETAIL: Retail
SPECIALITIES: Hardy Geraniums. *MAP PAGE:* **6**

ENHC **Norwich Heather & Conifer Centre,** 54a Yarmouth Road, Thorpe, Norwich, Norfolk NR7 0HE
TEL: (0603) 39434 *CONTACT:* B Hipperson
OPENING TIMES: 0900-1700 Mon Tue Wed Fri Sat, 1400-1700 Sun Mar-Dec.
MAIL ORDER: Yes *MIN VALUE:* No minimum charge *CAT. COST:* 40p *W/SALE or RETAIL:* Retail
SPECIALITIES: Conifers and Heathers. *MAP PAGE:* **6**

ENor **Norfolk Lavender,** Caley Mill, Heacham, King's Lynn, Norfolk PE31 7JE
TEL: (0485) 70384 *FAX:* (0485) 71176 *CONTACT:* Joy Warner
OPENING TIMES: 0930-1700 daily. Closed two weeks aafter Xmas.
MAIL ORDER: No *CAT. COST:* Free *W/SALE or RETAIL:* Retail
SPECIALITIES: National collection of Lavandula. *MAP PAGE:* **6**

ENot **Notcutts Nurseries,** Woodbridge, Suffolk IP12 4AF
TEL: (0394) 383344 *FAX:* (0394) 385460 *CONTACT:* J A Dyter
OPENING TIMES: 0845-1730 Mon-Sat, 1000-1700 Sun.
MAIL ORDER: Yes *MIN VALUE:* £30.00 + p&p *CAT. COST:* £3.25 *W/SALE or RETAIL:* Both
SPECIALITIES: Wide general range. *MAP PAGE:* **6**

EOrc **Orchard Nurseries,** Tow Lane, Foston, Grantham, Lincolnshire NG32 2LE
TEL: (0400) 81354 *CONTACT:* R & J Blenkinship
◆ *OPENING TIMES:* 1000-1800 daily 1st Mar-30th Sep.
MAIL ORDER: No *CAT. COST:* £1.00 *W/SALE or RETAIL:* Retail
SPECIALITIES: Unusual herbaceous & small flowered Clematis. *MAP PAGE:* **6**

EOvi **M Oviatt-Ham,** (Office) Ely House, 15 Green Street, Willingham, Cambridgeshire CB4 5JA
TEL: (0954) 60481* *CONTACT:* M Oviatt-Ham
OPENING TIMES: Sat & Sun from Easter-end Sept, other times by appt. only.
MAIL ORDER: Yes *MIN VALUE:* £10.00 + p&p *CAT. COST:* 50p *W/SALE or RETAIL:* Both
SPECIALITIES: Clematis & climbing plants. Nursery address: Black Pit Drove, Rampton Rd., Willingham. *Tel. No. (0954) 260481 from June '93. *MAP PAGE:* **6**

EPad **Padlock Croft,** 19 Padlock Road, West Wratting, Cambridge CB1 5LS
TEL: (0223) 290383 *CONTACT:* Susan & Peter Lewis
OPENING TIMES: 1000-1800 Mon-Sat 1st Mar-1st Nov. Winter by appt.
MAIL ORDER: No *CAT. COST:* 4 x 2nd class *W/SALE or RETAIL:* Retail
SPECIALITIES: National Collection of Campanula, Adenophora, Symphyandra & Platycodon. Other Campanulaceae & less common Alpines & Perennials. *MAP PAGE:* **6**

 See note on Mail Order, EC sales & Export on page 5

EPar **Paradise Centre,** Twinstead Road, Lamarsh, Bures, Suffolk CO8 5EX
TEL: (0787 269) 449 *FAX:* (0787 269) 449 *CONTACT:* Cees & Hedy Stapel-Valk
OPENING TIMES: 1000-1700 Sat-Sun & Bank Hols or by appt. Easter-1st Nov.
MAIL ORDER: Yes *MIN VALUE:* £7.50 + p&p *CAT. COST:* 4 x 1st class
W/SALE or RETAIL: Retail
SPECIALITIES: Unusual bulbous & tuberous plants including shade & bog varieties. *MAP PAGE:* **6**

EPGN **Park Green Nurseries,** Wetheringsett, Stowmarket, Suffolk IP14 5QH
TEL: (0728) 860139 *CONTACT:* Richard & Mary Ford
OPENING TIMES: 1000-1730 Thu-Sun and Bank Hol Mons.
MAIL ORDER: Yes *MIN VALUE:* None *CAT. COST:* 2 x 1st class *W/SALE or RETAIL:* Retail
SPECIALITIES: Hosta, Astilbe & Herbaceous. *MAP PAGE:* **6**

EPla **P W Plants,** Sunnyside Nurseries, Heath Road, Kenninghall, Norfolk NR16 2DS
TEL: (095 387) 8212* *CONTACT:* Paul Whittaker
◆ *OPENING TIMES:* Fridays and other times by appt.
MAIL ORDER: Yes *MIN VALUE:* No minimum charge *CAT. COST:* £1.00
W/SALE or RETAIL: Retail
SPECIALITIES: Choice Shrubs, Perennials, Grasses, Climbers, Bamboos, Hedera & Streptocarpus. Wide range of unusual hardy ornamental Shrubs. *(0953) 888212 from 25/05/93 *MAP PAGE:* **6**

EPot **Potterton & Martin,** The Cottage Nursery, Moortown Road, Nettleton, Caistor, Lincolnshire LN7 6HX
TEL: (0472) 851792 *CONTACT:*
OPENING TIMES: 0900-1700 daily.
MAIL ORDER: Yes *MIN VALUE:* None *CAT. COST:* 50p *W/SALE or RETAIL:* Both
SPECIALITIES: Alpines, Dwarf Bulbs, Conifers, & Shrubs and Carnivorous. *MAP PAGE:* **7**

ERav **Raveningham Gardens,** Norwich, Norfolk NR14 6NS
TEL: (0508 46) 222 *FAX:* (0508 46) 8958 *CONTACT:* Alison Bowell
◆ *OPENING TIMES:* 0900-1600 Mon-Sat Apr-Oct. Gardens open 1400-1700 Sun & Bank Hols 22nd Mar-13th Sep & 1300-1600 Wed.
MAIL ORDER: Yes *MIN VALUE:* No minimum order *CAT. COST:* 3 x 1st class
W/SALE or RETAIL: Retail
SPECIALITIES: Plants noted for Foliage, Berries, Bark & Texture. Variegated & coloured leaf plants & shrubs. *MAP PAGE:* **6**

ERea **Reads Nursery,** Hales Hall, Loddon, Norfolk NR14 6QW
TEL: (050846) 395 *FAX:* (050846) 359 *CONTACT:* Terence & Judy Read
◆ *OPENING TIMES:* 1000-1700 (or dusk if earlier) Tue-Sat & by appt.
MAIL ORDER: Yes *MIN VALUE:* £10.00 + p&p *CAT. COST:* 4 x 1st class
W/SALE or RETAIL: Both
SPECIALITIES: Conservatory plants, Vines, Citrus, Figs & unusual Fruits & Nuts. Wall Shrubs & Climbers. Scented & aromatic Hardy plants. Box & Yew hedging & topiary. UK grown
MAP PAGE: **6**

ERou **Rougham Hall Nurseries,** (RHN Ltd), Ipswich Road, Rougham, Bury St. Edmunds, Suffolk IP30 9LZ
TEL: (0359) 70577/70153 *FAX:* (0359) 71149 *CONTACT:* A A & K G Harbutt
OPENING TIMES: 0900-1700 daily.
MAIL ORDER: Yes *MIN VALUE:* £20.00 + p&p *CAT. COST:* £1 refundable
W/SALE or RETAIL: Retail
SPECIALITIES: Hardy Perennials. *MAP PAGE:* **6**

ER&R **Rhodes & Rockliffe,** 2 Nursery Road, Nazeing, Essex EN9 2JE
TEL: (0992) 463693 *FAX:* (0992) 440673 *CONTACT:* David Rhodes & John Rockliffe
OPENING TIMES: By appt.
MAIL ORDER: Yes *MIN VALUE:* £2.50 + p&p *CAT. COST:* Large Sae *W/SALE or RETAIL:* Both
SPECIALITIES: Begonias *MAP PAGE:* **3**

ESha **Shaw Rose Trees,** 2 Hollowgate Hill, Willoughton, Gainsborough, Lincolnshire DN21 5SF
TEL: (0427) 668230 *CONTACT:* Mr K Shaw
OPENING TIMES: Vary, please check.
MAIL ORDER: Yes *MIN VALUE:* £3.00 + p&p *CAT. COST:* Sae *W/SALE or RETAIL:* Both
SPECIALITIES: Roses. *MAP PAGE:* **7**

ESim **Clive Simms,** Woodhurst, Essendine, Stamford, Lincolnshire PE9 4LQ
TEL: (0780) 55615 *CONTACT:* Clive & Kathryn Simms
OPENING TIMES: By appt. for collection only.
MAIL ORDER: Yes *MIN VALUE:* None *CAT. COST:* 3 x 2nd class *W/SALE or RETAIL:* Retail
SPECIALITIES: Uncommon nut Trees & unusual fruiting plants. *MAP PAGE:*

ESis **Siskin Plants,** April House, Davey Lane, Charsfield, Woodbridge, Suffolk IP13 7QG
TEL: (0473 37) 567 *CONTACT:* Chris & Valerie Wheeler
OPENING TIMES: 1000-1700 Tue-Sat. Sun by appt. Please telephone first during Nov-Jan.
MAIL ORDER: Yes *MIN VALUE:* None *CAT. COST:* £1.00 *W/SALE or RETAIL:* Retail
SPECIALITIES: Extensive range of Alpines, miniature Conifers & dwarf Shrubs, esp. dwarf Hebes & plants for Troughs. *NOTE: Young plants also available by Mail Order. *MAP PAGE:* **6**

ESma **Smallscape Nursery,** 3 Hundon Close, Stradishall, Nr Newmarket, Suffolk CB8 9YF
TEL: (0440) 820336 *CONTACT:* Stephen & Leigh Sage
OPENING TIMES: Most times, but please telephone first.
MAIL ORDER: Yes *MIN VALUE:* None *CAT. COST:* 4 x 1st class *W/SALE or RETAIL:* Both
SPECIALITIES: Interesting, unusual & rare Alpines, Herbaceous, Shrubs, Trees & tender Perennials sold Mail Order as young plants & rooted cuttings. *MAP PAGE:* **6**

ESor **Trevor Sore,** Marward House, Stock Corner Farm, Bury St Edmunds, Suffolk
TEL: (0638) 712779 *CONTACT:* Trevor Sore
OPENING TIMES: 0800-1700 Mon-Fri
MAIL ORDER: Yes *MIN VALUE:* £9.00 + p&p *CAT. COST:* Sae *W/SALE or RETAIL:* Both
SPECIALITIES: Asparagus *MAP PAGE:* **6**

ESul **Brian Sulman Pelargoniums,** 54 Kingsway, Mildenhall, Bury St Edmunds, Suffolk IP28 7HR
TEL: (0638) 712297 *CONTACT:* Brian Sulman
OPENING TIMES: Not open. Mail Order only.
MAIL ORDER: Only *MIN VALUE:* £9.00 + p&p *CAT. COST:* 1 x 1st class
W/SALE or RETAIL: Retail
SPECIALITIES: Regal, Zonal, Trailing & Coloured-leaf Pelargoniums.

ETho **Thorncroft Clematis Nursery,** The Lings, Reymerston, Norwich NR9 4QG
TEL: (0953) 850407 *CONTACT:* Ruth P Gooch
OPENING TIMES: 1000-1700 Thu-Tue Easter Sat OR last Sat in March (whichever earlier) until last Sun Oct.
MAIL ORDER: No *CAT. COST:* 2 x 1st class *W/SALE or RETAIL:* Both
SPECIALITIES: Clematis. *MAP PAGE:* **6**

ETPC **Trevor Scott,** Thorpe Park Cottage, Thorpe-le-Soken, Essex CO16 0HN
TEL: (0255) 861308 *FAX:* (0255) 861308 *CONTACT:* Trevor Scott
◆ *OPENING TIMES:* By appt. only.
MAIL ORDER: Yes *MIN VALUE:* £10 + p&p *CAT. COST:* 4 x 1st class *W/SALE or RETAIL:* Retail
SPECIALITIES: Ornamental Grasses. *MAP PAGE:* **6**

ETub **Van Tubergen UK Ltd.,** Bressingham, Diss, Norfolk IP22 2AB
TEL: (0379) 888282 *FAX:* (0379) 88227 *CONTACT:* General Manager
OPENING TIMES:
MAIL ORDER: Yes *MIN VALUE:* No minimum charge *CAT. COST:* Free
W/SALE or RETAIL: Retail
SPECIALITIES: Bulbs. *NOTE: Retail sales by Mail Order only. *MAP PAGE:*

ETWh **Trevor White Old Fashioned Roses,** Chelt Hurst. 10 Sewell Road, Norwich, Norfolk NR3 4BP
TEL: (0603) 418240 *FAX:* (0603) 418240 *CONTACT:* Mr T A & Mrs V J White.
OPENING TIMES: 0900-1700 by appt only.
MAIL ORDER: Yes *MIN VALUE:* £100.00 + p&p *CAT. COST:* Free *W/SALE or RETAIL:* Both
SPECIALITIES: Old-fashioned, Shrub, Climbing & Rambling Roses *MAP PAGE:*

EVal **The Valley Clematis Nursery,** Willingham Road, Hainton, Lincolnshire LN3 6LN
TEL: (0507) 313398 *FAX:* (0507) 313705 *CONTACT:* Mr Keith Fair
◆ *OPENING TIMES:* 1000-1800 (Dusk in winter) daily. Closed Xmas to New Year.
MAIL ORDER: Yes *MIN VALUE:* £18.00 + p&p *CAT. COST:* £1.00 *W/SALE or RETAIL:* Retail
SPECIALITIES: Clematis. *MAP PAGE:* **7**

 See note on Mail Order, EC sales & Export on page 5

EWal **J Walkers Bulbs,** Washway House Farm, Holbeach, Spalding, Lincolnshire PE12 7PP
TEL: (0406) 26216 *FAX:* (0406) 25468 *CONTACT:* J W Walkers
OPENING TIMES: See Daffodil Catalogue for details of field viewing.
MAIL ORDER: Yes *MIN VALUE:* See Cat. for details *CAT. COST:* 50p *W/SALE or RETAIL:* Both
SPECIALITIES: Daffodils & Fritillarias. *MAP PAGE:*

EWar **Warley Rose Garden Ltd.,** Warley Street, Great Warley, Brentwood, Essex CM13 3JH
TEL: (0277) 221966/219344 *CONTACT:* J H G Deamer
OPENING TIMES: 0900-1730 Mon-Sat.
MAIL ORDER: Yes *MIN VALUE:* *CAT. COST:* Free-30p atshop *W/SALE or RETAIL:* Both
SPECIALITIES: Roses & container grown Nursery Stock.. *MAP PAGE:* **3**

EWav **Waveney Fish Farm,** Park Road, Diss, Norfolk IP22 3AS
TEL: (0379) 642697 *FAX:* (0379) 651315 *CONTACT:* D G Laughlin
OPENING TIMES: 1000-1700 daily.
MAIL ORDER: No *CAT. COST:* Free *W/SALE or RETAIL:* Both
SPECIALITIES: Aquatic & Marginals. *MAP PAGE:* **6**

EWhi **Whitehouse Ivies,** Brookhill, Halstead Road, Fordham, Colchester, Essex CO6 3LW
TEL: (0206) 240077 *CONTACT:* R Whitehouse
OPENING TIMES: Most days, but please telephone first.
MAIL ORDER: Yes *MIN VALUE:* £10.00 + p&p *CAT. COST:* £1 refundable
W/SALE or RETAIL: Both
SPECIALITIES: Hedera only, some 300 varieties. *MAP PAGE:* **6**

GAbr **Abriachan Nurseries,** Loch Ness Side, Inverness, Invernesshire IV3 6LA
TEL: (046 386) 232 *CONTACT:* Mr & Mrs D Davidson
OPENING TIMES: 0900-1900 daily, dusk if earlier.
MAIL ORDER: Yes *MIN VALUE:* None *CAT. COST:* 3 x 1st class *W/SALE or RETAIL:* Both
SPECIALITIES: Herbaceous, Primulas, Helianthemum & Hebe. *MAP PAGE:* **9**

GAng **Angus Heathers,** 10 Guthrie Street, Letham, Forfar, Tayside DD8 2PS
TEL: (030781) 504 *FAX:* (030781) 504 *CONTACT:* David Sturrock
OPENING TIMES: 1000-1700 daily.
MAIL ORDER: No *CAT. COST:* Free *W/SALE or RETAIL:* Both
SPECIALITIES: Heathers & Gentians. *MAP PAGE:* **9**

GArf **Ardfearn Nursery,** Bunchrew, Inverness Highland IV3 6RH
TEL: (0463) 243 250 *CONTACT:* James Sutherland
◆ *OPENING TIMES:* 0900-1700 Mon-Sat, 1300-1700 Sun Mar-Nov & by appt.
MAIL ORDER: Yes *MIN VALUE:* No minimum charge *CAT. COST:* 3 x 2nd class
W/SALE or RETAIL: Both
SPECIALITIES: Alpines & Ericaceae, rare & unusual. *NOTE: Mail Order Oct-Mar only.
MAP PAGE: **9**

GAri **Arivegaig Nursery,** Aultbea, Acharacle, Argyll, Scotland PH36 4LE
TEL: (096 785) 331 *CONTACT:* E Stewart
◆ *OPENING TIMES:* 0900-1700 daily Easter-end Oct.
MAIL ORDER: Yes *MIN VALUE:* None *CAT. COST:* 4 x 1st class *W/SALE or RETAIL:* Both
SPECIALITIES: A wide range of unusual plants, including those suited for the milder parts of the country. *MAP PAGE:* **9**

GBel **Belwood Nurseries Ltd.,** Mauricewood Mains, Penicuik, Midlothian, Scotland EH26 0NJ
TEL: (0968) 673621 *FAX:* (0968) 678354 *CONTACT:* Mrs Linda Brock
OPENING TIMES: 0800-1700 Mon-Fri. By appt. only
MAIL ORDER: Yes *MIN VALUE:* None *CAT. COST:* Free *W/SALE or RETAIL:* Both
SPECIALITIES: Semi-mature deciduous & coniferous Trees and specimen Shrubs for landscaping.
MAP PAGE: **9**

GBla **Blairhoyle Nursery,** Port of Menteith, Stirling, Central FK8 3LF
TEL: (08775) 669 *CONTACT:* B A & G W Cartwright
OPENING TIMES: 1000-dusk ex Tue & Sat Mar-Nov.
MAIL ORDER: No *CAT. COST:* Sae *W/SALE or RETAIL:* Retail
SPECIALITIES: Heathers, Alpines & Dwarf Conifers. *MAP PAGE:* **9**

GBon **Bonhard Nursery,** Murrayshall Road, Scone, Perth, Tayside PH2 7PQ

TEL: (0738) 52791 *CONTACT:* Mr & Mrs Hickman
OPENING TIMES: 1000-1800, or dusk if earlier, daily.
MAIL ORDER: No *CAT. COST:* Free *W/SALE or RETAIL:* Retail
SPECIALITIES: Herbaceous, Conifers & Alpines. Fruit & ornamental Trees. Shrub & species Roses.
MAP PAGE: **9**

GCal **Calley Gardens,** Gategouse of Fleet, Castle Douglas, Scotland DG7 2DJ

TEL: Not on phone. *CONTACT:* M C Wickenden
◆ *OPENING TIMES:* 1000-1750 Sat & Sun only from 18th Apr-17th Oct 1993
MAIL ORDER: Yes *MIN VALUE:* See Cat. for details *CAT. COST:* 3 x 1st class
W/SALE or RETAIL: Both
SPECIALITIES: Unusual perennials. Agapanthus, Crocosmia, Erodium, Eryngium, Euphorbia, Hardy Geraniums & Grasses. Some rare Shrubs, Climbers & Conservatory plants. *MAP PAGE:* **9**

GCHN **Charter House Nursery,** 2 Nunwood, Dumfries, Dumfries & Galloway DG2 0HX

TEL: (0387) 720363 *CONTACT:* John Ross
OPENING TIMES: 1200-1800 Sat & Sun.
MAIL ORDER: Yes *MIN VALUE:* None *CAT. COST:* 3 x 1st class *W/SALE or RETAIL:* Retail
SPECIALITIES: Aquileagia, Hypericum, Geranium, Erodium, Pelargonium species and Campanula. Erodium National Collection. *MAP PAGE:* **8/9**

GChr **T & W Christie (Forres) Ltd,** The Nurseries, Forres, Moray, Grampian IV36 0EA

TEL: (0309) 672633 *FAX:* (0309) 676846 *CONTACT:* Donald W Williamson
◆ *OPENING TIMES:* 0800-1200 & 1300-1700 Mon-Fri, 0800-1200 Sat.
MAIL ORDER: Yes *MIN VALUE:* £20.00 + p&p *CAT. COST:* Free *W/SALE or RETAIL:* Both
SPECIALITIES: Hedging & screening plants. Woodland & less common Trees, Shrubs & Fruit.
MAP PAGE: **9**

GCoc **James Cocker & Sons,** Whitemyres, Lang Stracht, Aberdeen, Scotland AB9 2XH

TEL: (0224) 313261 *FAX:* (0224) 312531 *CONTACT:* Alec Cocker
OPENING TIMES: 0900-1730 daily.
MAIL ORDER: No *CAT. COST:* Free *W/SALE or RETAIL:* Both
SPECIALITIES: Roses. *MAP PAGE:* **9**

GCra **Craigieburn Classic Plants,** Craigieburn House, by Moffat, Dumfriesshire DG10 9LF

TEL: (0683) 21250 *CONTACT:* Janet Wheatcroft & Bill Chudziak
OPENING TIMES: 1230-1800 Wed-Sun mid Apr-end Oct. Nov-Apr by appt.
MAIL ORDER: Yes *MIN VALUE:* £25.00 + p&p *CAT. COST:* 4 x 1st class
W/SALE or RETAIL: Retail
SPECIALITIES: Codonopsis, Digitalis, Meconopsis, Primula & Salvia *MAP PAGE:* **8/9**

GDra **Jack Drake,** Inshriach Alpine Nusery, Aviemore, Invernesshire PH22 1QS

TEL: (0540 651) 287 *FAX:* (0540 651) 656 *CONTACT:* J C Lawson
◆ *OPENING TIMES:* 0900-1700 Mon-Fri, 0900-1230 Sat.
MAIL ORDER: *MIN VALUE:* *CAT. COST:* £1.00 *W/SALE or RETAIL:* Both
SPECIALITIES: Rare and unusual Alpines & Rock plants. Especially Primula, Meconopsis, Gentian, Heathers etc. *MAP PAGE:* **9**

GEve **Evelix Daffodils,** Aird Asaig, Evelix, Dornoch, Sutherland IV25 3NG

TEL: (0862) 810715 *CONTACT:* D C MacArthur
◆ *OPENING TIMES:* By appt. only.
MAIL ORDER: Yes *MIN VALUE:* £5.00 + p&p *CAT. COST:* 3 x 1st class
W/SALE or RETAIL: Retail
SPECIALITIES: New Narcissus cultivars for garden display & exhibition. *MAP PAGE:* **9**

GGar **Garden Cottage Nursery,** Tournaig, Poolewe, Achnasheen, Highland IV22 2LH

TEL: (044 586) 339 *CONTACT:* R Rushbrooke
OPENING TIMES: 1200-1900 Mon-Sat (Mar-Oct) or by appt.
MAIL ORDER: Yes *MIN VALUE:* £10.00 + p&p *CAT. COST:* 3 x 1st class
W/SALE or RETAIL: Retail
SPECIALITIES: Large range of Herbacous & Alpines esp. Primula, Hardy Geraniums & moisture lovers. Range of West Coast Shrubs. *MAP PAGE:* **9**

 See note on Mail Order, EC sales & Export on page 5

GGGa Glendoick Gardens Ltd, Glencarse, Perth, Scotland PH2 7NS
TEL: (073 886) 205 *FAX:* (073 886) 735 *CONTACT:* P A, E P & K N E Cox
OPENING TIMES: Appt only. Garden Centre open 7 days.
MAIL ORDER: MIN VALUE: CAT. COST: £1.50 *W/SALE or RETAIL:* Retail
SPECIALITIES: Rhododendron, Azalea and Ericaceous, Primula & Meconopsis. National collection of Kalmia & Enkianthus. Many Catalogue plants available at Garden Centre. *MAP PAGE:* **9**

GGre Greenhead Roses, Greenhead Nursery, Old Greenock Road, Inchinnan, Renfrew, Strathclyde PA4 9PH
TEL: (041 812) 0121 *FAX:* (041 812) 0121 *CONTACT:* C N Urquhart
OPENING TIMES: 1000-1700 daily.
MAIL ORDER: No *CAT. COST:* Sae *W/SALE or RETAIL:* Both
SPECIALITIES: Roses. Wide general range, dwarf Conifers, Azaleas, Rhododendrons, Shrubs, Alpines, Fruit, hardy Herbaceous & Spring & Summer bedding. *MAP PAGE:* **9**

GIsl Island Plants,, The Old Manse, Knock, Point, Isle of Lewis PA86 0BW
TEL: (0851) 870281 *CONTACT:* Mr D Ferris
◆ *OPENING TIMES:* Every afternoon ex. Sun.
MAIL ORDER: Yes *MIN VALUE:* None *CAT. COST:* 1 x 1st class *W/SALE or RETAIL:* Retail
SPECIALITIES: Hebes & New Zealand plants esp. from coastal regions. *MAP PAGE:* **9**

GKit Kittoch Plants, Kittoch Mill, Busby Road, Carmunnock, Glasgow, Strathclyde G76 9BJ
TEL: 041-644 4712 *CONTACT:* Mrs P A Jordan
OPENING TIMES: Appt. only.
MAIL ORDER: No *CAT. COST:* Large Sae *W/SALE or RETAIL:* Retail
SPECIALITIES: Hostas from the Scottish National Collection. *MAP PAGE:* **9**

GPen Pennyacre Nurseries, Station Road, Springfield, Fife KY15 5RU
TEL: (0334) 55852 *CONTACT:* C P Piper
◆ *OPENING TIMES:* 1000-1700 Thu-Sun Mar-Oct.
MAIL ORDER: Yes *MIN VALUE:* No minimum charge *CAT. COST:* 2 x 1st class
W/SALE or RETAIL: Retail
SPECIALITIES: Heathers, Dwarf Conifers & Fuchsias. *MAP PAGE:* **9**

GPoy Poyntzfield Herb Nursery, Nr Balblair, Black Isle, Dingwall, Ross & Cromarty, Highland IV7 8LX
TEL: (03818) 352 evs *FAX:* (03818) 352 *CONTACT:* Duncan Ross
OPENING TIMES: 1300-1700 Mon-Sat.
MAIL ORDER: Yes *MIN VALUE: CAT. COST:* Sae&3x1st class *W/SALE or RETAIL:* Retail
SPECIALITIES: Over 330 popular, unusual & rare Herbs, esp. Medicinal. *MAP PAGE:* **9**

GRei Ben Reid and Co, Pinewood Park, Countesswells Road, Aberdeen, Grampian AB9 2QL
TEL: (0224) 318744 *FAX:* (0224) 310104 *CONTACT:* John Fraser
OPENING TIMES: 0900-1700 Mon-Sat. 1000-1700 Sun.
MAIL ORDER: Yes *MIN VALUE:* £10.00 + p&p *CAT. COST:* Free *W/SALE or RETAIL:* Both
SPECIALITIES: Trees & Shrubs. *MAP PAGE:* **9**

GSpe Speyside Heather Garden Centre, Dulnain Bridge, Highland PH26 3PA
TEL: (047 985) 359 *FAX:* (047 985) 396 *CONTACT:* D & B Lambie
OPENING TIMES: 0900-1730 daily in Summer. 0900-1700 Mon-Sat Nov-Mar. Closed Jan.
MAIL ORDER: Yes *MIN VALUE:* None *CAT. COST:* £2.25 inc. p&p *W/SALE or RETAIL:* Retail
SPECIALITIES: Heathers. *MAP PAGE:* **9**

GTou Tough Alpine Nursery, Westhaybogs, Tough, Alford, Aberdeenshire, Scotland AB33 8DU
TEL: (09755) 62783 *FAX:* (09755) 62783 *CONTACT:* Fred & Monika Carrie
OPENING TIMES: 1st Mar-31st Oct. Please check first.
MAIL ORDER: Yes *MIN VALUE:* None *CAT. COST:* 3 x 2nd class *W/SALE or RETAIL:* Both
SPECIALITIES: Alpines *MAP PAGE:* **9**

GTwe J Tweedie Fruit Trees, Maryfield Road Nursery, Maryfield, Nr Terregles, Dumfries, Dumfriesshire DG2 9TH
TEL: (0387) 720880 *CONTACT:* John Tweedie
OPENING TIMES: 0930-1430 Sat Oct-Mar & by appt.
MAIL ORDER: Yes *MIN VALUE:* None *CAT. COST:* Sae *W/SALE or RETAIL:* Retail
SPECIALITIES: Fruit trees & bushes. A wide range of old & new varieties. *MAP PAGE:* **8/9**

GUzu **Uzumara Orchids,** 9 Port Henderson, Gairloch, Rossshire IV21 2AS
TEL: (0445 83) 228 *CONTACT:* Mrs I F La Croix
OPENING TIMES:
MAIL ORDER: Only *MIN VALUE:* £5.00 + p&p *CAT. COST:* Sae *W/SALE or RETAIL:* Retail
SPECIALITIES: Streptocarpus species. African & Madagascan Orchids.

GWht **Whitehills Nurseries,** Newton Stewart, Wigtownshire Scotland DG8 6SL
TEL: (0671) 2049 *FAX:* (0671) 3106 *CONTACT:* Tony Weston
◆ *OPENING TIMES:* 0830-1630 Mon-Fri or by appt.
MAIL ORDER: Yes *MIN VALUE:* £20.00 *CAT. COST:* 50p *W/SALE or RETAIL:* Both
SPECIALITIES: Rhododendrons, Azaleas & Shrubs. *MAP PAGE:* **9**

IBal **Ballydorn Bulb Farm,** Killinchy, Newtownards, Co. Down, N Ireland BT23 6QB
TEL: (0238) 541250 *CONTACT:* Sir Frank & Lady Harrison
OPENING TIMES: Not open.
MAIL ORDER: Yes *MIN VALUE:* £15.00 + p&p *CAT. COST:* £1.00 *W/SALE or RETAIL:* Retail
SPECIALITIES: New Daffodil varieties for Exhibitors and Hybridisers. *MAP PAGE:*

IBar **Barons Court Nurseries,** Abercorn Estates, Newtownstewart, Co. Tyrone, N Ireland BT78 4EZ
TEL: (06626) 61683 *FAX:* (06626) 62059 *CONTACT:* Neville Mooney
OPENING TIMES: 1000-1630 Mon-Sat & 1400-1630 Sun.
MAIL ORDER: Yes *MIN VALUE:* £50.00 + p&p *CAT. COST:* Free *W/SALE or RETAIL:* Both
SPECIALITIES: Meconopsis 'Slieve Donard'. Specimen Trees & container grown Shrubs & Conifers.
MAP PAGE: **10**

IBlr **Ballyrogan Nurseries,** The Grange, Ballyrogan, Newtownards, Co. Down, N Ireland BT23 4SD
TEL: (0247) 810451 eves *CONTACT:* Gary Dunlop
OPENING TIMES: Not open except for collection.
MAIL ORDER: Yes *MIN VALUE:* £10.00 + p&p *CAT. COST:* 2 x 1st class
W/SALE or RETAIL: Both
SPECIALITIES: Conservatory & choice Herbaceous & Shrubs. Abutilon, Agapanthus, Crocosmia, Euphorbia, Hardy Geraniums & Grasses. *MAP PAGE:* **10**

ICar **Carncairn Daffodils,** Broughshane, Ballymena, Co. Antrim, N Ireland BT43 7HF
TEL: (0266) 861216 *CONTACT:* Mr & Mrs R H Reade
◆ *OPENING TIMES:* 1000-1700 Mon-Fri. Please phone in advance.
MAIL ORDER: *MIN VALUE:* None *CAT. COST:* Free *W/SALE or RETAIL:* Both
SPECIALITIES: Old and new Narcissus cultivars, mainly for show. *MAP PAGE:* **10**

IDai **Daisy Hill Nurseries Ltd,** Hospital Road, Newry, Co. Down, N Ireland BT35 8PN
TEL: (0693) 62474 *CONTACT:* W A Grills
OPENING TIMES: 0800-1700 Mon-Fri.
MAIL ORDER: Yes *MIN VALUE:* £5.00 + p&p *CAT. COST:* Free *W/SALE or RETAIL:* Retail
SPECIALITIES: Wide variety Trees, Shrubs, Herbaceous, Alpines & Heathers. *MAP PAGE:* **10**

IDic **Dickson Nurseries Ltd.,** Milecross Road, Newtownards, Co. Down, N Ireland BT23 4SS
TEL: (0247) 812206 *CONTACT:* A P C Dickson OBE.
OPENING TIMES: 0800-1230 & 1300-1700 Mon-Thur. 0800-1330 Fri.
MAIL ORDER: Yes *MIN VALUE:* £25.00 + p&p *CAT. COST:* Free *W/SALE or RETAIL:* Both
SPECIALITIES: Roses, especially modern Dickson varieties. *MAP PAGE:* **10**

IDun **Brian Duncan,** Novelty & Exhibition Daffodils 15 Ballynahatty Road, Omagh, Co. Tyrone, N Ireland BT78 1PN
TEL: (0662) 242931 *CONTACT:* Brian Duncan
OPENING TIMES: By appointment.
MAIL ORDER: Yes *MIN VALUE:* £20.00 *CAT. COST:* £1.00 inc p&p *W/SALE or RETAIL:* Both
SPECIALITIES: New hybrid & Exhibition Daffodils & Narcissi. *MAP PAGE:* **10**

IEde **Eden Plants,** Eden, Rossinver, Co. Leitrim, Rep. of Ireland
TEL: 010353 (0)7254122 *CONTACT:* Rod Alston
OPENING TIMES: 1400-1800 daily & by appt.
MAIL ORDER: Yes *MIN VALUE:* None *CAT. COST:* Sae for list *W/SALE or RETAIL:* Both
SPECIALITIES: Large range of hardy Herbs. NOTE: £1.00 for Catalogue & growing guide.
MAP PAGE: **10**

 See note on Mail Order, EC sales & Export on page 5

IFer **Fernhill Nursery,** Sandyford, Co. Dublin, Rep. of Ireland

TEL: (0001) 2956158 *CONTACT:* Robert Walker
OPENING TIMES: 1100-1700 Tue-Sat all year & 1400-1700 Sun Mar-Nov.
MAIL ORDER: No *CAT. COST: W/SALE or RETAIL:* Both
SPECIALITIES: Wide general range. *MAP PAGE:* **10**

IHos **Hosford's Geraniums & Garden Centr,** Cappa, Enniskeane, Co. Cork, Rep. of Ireland

TEL: 010353 (0)2339159 *FAX:* 010353 (0)2339300 *CONTACT:* John Hosford
OPENING TIMES: 0900-1800 Mon-Sat (all year inc. Bank Hols). 1430-1830 Sun Mar-Jun, 1430-1730 mid-Sep-Xmas.
MAIL ORDER: Yes *MIN VALUE: CAT. COST:* IR£1.50 *W/SALE or RETAIL:* Retail
SPECIALITIES: Hardy Geraniums, Pelargoniums, Basket & Window box plants, Bedding & Roses. NOTE: Express Courier service available within Ireland. *MAP PAGE:* **10**

IJoh **Johnstown Garden Centre,** Johnstown, Naas, Co. Kildare, Rep. of Ireland

TEL: 010353 (0)4579138 *FAX:* 010353 (0)4579073 *CONTACT:* Jim Clarke
OPENING TIMES: 1000-1800 Mon-Sat & 1400-1800 Sun.
MAIL ORDER: MIN VALUE: CAT. COST: Free *W/SALE or RETAIL:* Retail
SPECIALITIES: Very wide range of Shrubs, Conifers, Alpines, Herbs & Aquatics. Newest introductions. *MAP PAGE:* **10**

ILis **Lisdoonan Herbs,** 98 Belfast Road, Saintfield, Co. Down N Ireland BT24 7HF

TEL: (0232) 813624 *CONTACT:* Barbara Pilcher
OPENING TIMES: Most days, please phone to check.
MAIL ORDER: No *CAT. COST:* Sae *W/SALE or RETAIL:* Both
SPECIALITIES: Herbs. Plants and freshly cut herbs & salads. *MAP PAGE:* **10**

IMal **Malahide Nurseries Ltd.,** Mabestown, Malahide, Co. Dublin, Rep. of Irleand

TEL: 010353 (0)8450110 *FAX:* 010353 (0)8450872 *CONTACT:* Ann Nutty
OPENING TIMES: 0930-1300 & 1400-1730 Mon-Fri, 0900-1730 Sat & 1400-1730 Sun.
MAIL ORDER: Yes *MIN VALUE:* IR£15.00 + p&p *CAT. COST:* Free *W/SALE or RETAIL:* Retail
SPECIALITIES: Large range of Shrubs, Trees & Aquatics. *MAP PAGE:* **10**

IOrc **Orchardstown Nurseries,** 4 miles out, Cork Road, Waterford, Rep. of Ireland

TEL: 010353 (0)5184273 *FAX:* 010353 (0)5184422 *CONTACT:* Ron Dool
OPENING TIMES: 0900-1800 Mon-Sat, 1400-1800 Sun.
MAIL ORDER: Yes *MIN VALUE:* £50.00 + p&p *CAT. COST:* List IR£1.50
W/SALE or RETAIL: Retail
SPECIALITIES: Unusual hardy plants incl. Shrubs, Shrub Roses, Trees, Climbers, Rhododendron species & Water plants. *NOTE: Only SOME plants Mail Order. *MAP PAGE:* **10**

IReg **Regional Nurseries,** Rockfield House, Sandyford Road, Dundrum, Dublin 16, Rep. of Ireland

TEL: (0001) 2982667 *FAX:* (0001) 2982667 *CONTACT:* Neil Murray
OPENING TIMES: 0900-1200 Sat.
MAIL ORDER: No *CAT. COST:* Sae *W/SALE or RETAIL:* Both
SPECIALITIES: Trees & Shrubs esp. Ilex. NOTE: This is a Wholesale nursery that is only open for Retail sales on Saturday morning, or by appt. *MAP PAGE:* **10**

ISea **Seaforde Gardens,** Seaforde, Co. Down, N Ireland

TEL: (039 687) 225 *FAX:* (039 687) 370 *CONTACT:* P Forde
OPENING TIMES: 1000-1700 Mon-Fri all year. 1000-1700 Sat & 1400-1800 Sun mid Mar-end Oct.
MAIL ORDER: Yes *MIN VALUE:* None *CAT. COST:* Free *W/SALE or RETAIL:* Both
SPECIALITIES: Over 600 varieties of self-propagated Trees & Shrubs. National Collection of Eucryphia. *MAP PAGE:* **10**

ISta **Stam's Nurseries,** The Garden House, Cappoquin, Co. Waterford Rep. of Ireland

TEL: 010353 (0)58 54787 *FAX:* 010353 (0)58 54472 *CONTACT:* Peter Stam
OPENING TIMES: By appointment only.
MAIL ORDER: No *CAT. COST:* Sae *W/SALE or RETAIL:* Both
SPECIALITIES: Bamboos *MAP PAGE:* **10**

◆ **See also Display Advertisements**

ITim **Timpany Nurseries,** 77 Magheratimpany Road, Ballynahinch, Co. Down, N Ireland BT24 8PA
TEL: (0238) 562812 *CONTACT:* Susan Tindall
OPENING TIMES: 1400-1600 Tue-Fri, 1000-1700 Sat & Bank Hols.
MAIL ORDER: Yes *MIN VALUE:* None *CAT. COST:* 50p *W/SALE or RETAIL:* ·
SPECIALITIES: Celmisia, Androsace, Primula, Saxifraga, Helichrysum & Dianthus. *MAP PAGE:* **10**

LAbb **Abbot's House Garden,** 10 High Street, Abbots Langley, Hertfordshire WD5 0AR
TEL: (0923) 264946/262167 *CONTACT:* Dr Peter Tomson & Mrs Joan Gentry
OPENING TIMES: 0900-1300 & 1400-1600 Sat Mar-Oct, 0900-1300 Nov-Dec & by appt. Please check before visiting.
MAIL ORDER: Yes *MIN VALUE:* None *CAT. COST:* 3 x 2nd class *W/SALE or RETAIL:* Retail
SPECIALITIES: Conservatory, Tender and Patio plants. Flower arranger's plants. Small nursery. *NOTE: Only SOME plants by Mail Order. *MAP PAGE:* **3**

LAma **Jacques Amand Ltd.,** The Nurseries, 145 Clamp Hill, Stanmore, Middlesex HA7 3JS
TEL: (081) 954 8138 *FAX:* (081) 954 6784 *CONTACT:*
OPENING TIMES: 0900-1700 Mon-Fri, 0900-1300 Sat-Sun.
MAIL ORDER: Yes *MIN VALUE:* None *CAT. COST:* Free *W/SALE or RETAIL:* Both
SPECIALITIES: Rare and unusual species Bulbs. *MAP PAGE:* **3**

LBam **The Bamboo Centre,** 563 Upper Richmond Road West, London SW14 7ED
TEL: 081-876 3223 *FAX:* 081-876 6888 *CONTACT:* Martin Gibbons
OPENING TIMES: 1000-1800 daily.
MAIL ORDER: Yes *MIN VALUE:* £10.00 + p&p *CAT. COST:* Sae for list *W/SALE or RETAIL:* Both
SPECIALITIES: Hardy Bamboos *MAP PAGE:* **3**

LBee **Beechcroft Nursery,** 127 Reigate Road, Ewell, Surrey KT17 3DE
TEL: 081-393 4265 *CONTACT:* C Kimber
◆ *OPENING TIMES:* 1000-1700 May-Sep. 1000-1600 Oct-Apr, Bank Hols & Suns. Closed Xmas-New Year & August
MAIL ORDER: No *CAT. COST:* None *W/SALE or RETAIL:* Both
SPECIALITIES: Conifers, Alpines, Heather. *MAP PAGE:* **3**

LBlm **Bloomsbury,** Upper Lodge Farm, Padworth Common, Reading, Berkshire RG7 4JD
TEL: (0734) 700239 *CONTACT:* Susan Oakley
OPENING TIMES: 1100-1700 Thu-Sun 27th May-31st Oct & by appt.
MAIL ORDER: No *CAT. COST:* £1 or Sae list *W/SALE or RETAIL:* Retail
SPECIALITIES: Plants for terraces, glass & garden. Many rare or unusual. White Garden & mixed plantings amongst Shrubs to visit during opening times. *MAP PAGE:* **2**

LBlo **Walter Blom and Sons Ltd.,** Coombelands Nurseries, Thurleigh Road, Milton Ernest Bedfordshire MK44 1RQ
TEL: (0234) 782424 *FAX:* (0234) 782495 *CONTACT:* Deborah Munson
OPENING TIMES: 0900-1700 Mon-Fri. 0900-1200 Sat (Sep. only).
MAIL ORDER: Yes *MIN VALUE:* None *CAT. COST:* Free *W/SALE or RETAIL:* Retail
SPECIALITIES: Tulips, Lilies, Narcissus & Hyacinthus. *MAP PAGE:* **6**

LBow **Rupert Bowlby,** Gatton, Reigate, Surrey RH2 0TA
TEL: (0737) 642221 *FAX:* (0737) 642221 *CONTACT:* Rupert Bowlby
OPENING TIMES: Sat & Sun pm in Mar & Sep-Oct.
MAIL ORDER: Yes *MIN VALUE:* No minimum charge *CAT. COST:* 2 x 2nd class
W/SALE or RETAIL: Retail
SPECIALITIES: Unusual Bulbs & Corms. *MAP PAGE:* **3**

LBre **Bressingham Plant Centre,** Dorney Court, Dorney, Windsor, Bucks SL4 6QP
TEL: (0628) 669999 *CONTACT:* Tim Baylis
OPENING TIMES: 1000-1730 daily. (Direct retail Plant Centre).
MAIL ORDER: No *CAT. COST:* *W/SALE or RETAIL:* Retail
SPECIALITIES: Very wide general range. Many own varieties. Focus on Hardy Ornamental plants. *MAP PAGE:* **3**

See note on Mail Order, EC sales & Export on page 5

LBro **Mrs P J Brown,** V H Humphrey-Iris Specialist, Westlees Farm, Logmore Lane, Westcott, Dorking, Surrey RH4 3JN
TEL: (0306) 889827 *FAX:* (0306) 889371 *CONTACT:* Mrs P J Brown
◆ *OPENING TIMES:* Open days 1100-1500 Sat 15th & Sun 16th May 1993. Otherwise by appt.
MAIL ORDER: Yes *MIN VALUE:* No minimum charge *CAT. COST:* Large Sae 9x6
W/SALE or RETAIL: Both
SPECIALITIES: Dwarf Bearded, Median, Border, Intermediate, Tall Bearded, Spuria, Siberian, Pacific Coast & species Iris. *MAP PAGE:* **3**

LBuc **Buckingham Nurseries,** 14 Tingewick Road, Buckingham, Buckinghamshire MK18 4AE
TEL: (0280) 813556 *FAX:* (0280) 815491 *CONTACT:* R J & P L Brown
◆ *OPENING TIMES:* 0830-1730 (1800 in summer) Mon-Fri, 0930-1730 (1800 in summer) Sun.
MAIL ORDER: Yes *MIN VALUE:* None *CAT. COST:* Free *W/SALE or RETAIL:* Retail
SPECIALITIES: Bare rooted and container grown hedging. Trees & Shrubs. *MAP PAGE:* **2**

LCla **Clay Lane Nursery,** 3 Clay Lane, South Nutfield, Nr Redhill, Surrey RH1 4EG
TEL: (0737) 823307 *CONTACT:* K W Belton
OPENING TIMES: 0900-1800 Tue-Sun 1st Jan-31st Jul. Also Bank Hol. Mons & by appt.
MAIL ORDER: No *CAT. COST:* 2 x 1st class *W/SALE or RETAIL:* Retail
SPECIALITIES: Fuchsias. *MAP PAGE:* **3**

LCon **The Conifer Garden,** 1, Churchfield Road, Chalfont St Peter, Buckinghamshire SL9 9EN
TEL: (0850) 786310 *CONTACT:* Mr & Mrs M P S Powell
◆ *OPENING TIMES:*
MAIL ORDER: No *CAT. COST:* 2 x 2nd class *W/SALE or RETAIL:* Retail
SPECIALITIES: Conifers only. *MAP PAGE:*

LDea **Derek Lloyd Dean,** 8 Lynwood Close, South Harrow, Middlesex HA2 9PR
TEL: 081-864 0899 *CONTACT:* Derek Lloyd Dean
OPENING TIMES:
MAIL ORDER: Yes *MIN VALUE:* £5.80 + p&p *CAT. COST:* 2 x 1st class
W/SALE or RETAIL: Retail
SPECIALITIES: Regal, Angel & Ivy Pelargoniums. *MAP PAGE:*

LFle **M V Fletcher,** 70 South Street, Reading, Berkshire RG1 4RA
TEL: (0734) 571814 *CONTACT:* M V Fletcher
OPENING TIMES: By appt. only.
MAIL ORDER: Yes *MIN VALUE:* None *CAT. COST:* 2 x 1st class *W/SALE or RETAIL:*
SPECIALITIES: Specialist collection of Mosses & Hepaticas (Liverworts), mostly British, also about 100 ssp. from Southern Hemisphere. *MAP PAGE:*

LFox **Foxgrove Plants,** Foxgrove, Enborne, Nr Newbury, Berkshire RG14 6RE
TEL: (0635) 40554 *CONTACT:* Miss Louise Vockins
OPENING TIMES: 1000-1700 Wed-Sun & Bank Hols.
MAIL ORDER: Yes *MIN VALUE:* No minimum charge *CAT. COST:* 65p *W/SALE or RETAIL:* Retail
SPECIALITIES: Alpines, Foliage plants, Galanthus & Auriculas. *MAP PAGE:* **2**

LGan **Gannock Growers,** Gannock Thatch, Sandon, Buntingford, Hertfordshire SG9 0RH
TEL: (076 387) 386 *CONTACT:* Penny Pyle
OPENING TIMES: 1000-1600 Tue-Sun & Bank Hol Mons.
MAIL ORDER: Yes *MIN VALUE:* No minimum charge *CAT. COST:* 3 x 1st class
W/SALE or RETAIL: Retail
SPECIALITIES: Unusual & some rare herbaceous plants. *MAP PAGE:* **6**

LGod **Godly's Roses,** Redbourn, St Albans, Hertfordshire AL3 7PS
TEL: (0582) 792255 *FAX:* (0582) 794267 *CONTACT:* Colin Godly
OPENING TIMES: 0900-1900 Summer, 0900-dusk Winter Mon-Fri. 0900-1800 Sat & Sun.
MAIL ORDER: Yes *MIN VALUE:* £2.50 + p&p *CAT. COST:* Free *W/SALE or RETAIL:* Retail
SPECIALITIES: Roses. *MAP PAGE:* **3/6**

LGre **Green Farm Plants,** Bentley, Farnham, Surrey GU10 5JX
TEL: (0420) 23202 *CONTACT:* J Coke & M Christopher
OPENING TIMES: 1000-1800 Wed-Sat, end Mar-early Oct.
MAIL ORDER: No *CAT. COST:* 3 x 1st class *W/SALE or RETAIL:* Retail
SPECIALITIES: Small Shrubs, Alpines, Sub-shrubs and Perennials. Many uncommon.
MAP PAGE: **2/3**

LGro **Growing Carpets,** The Old Farmhouse, Steeple, Morden, Hertfordshire SG8 0PP
TEL: (0763) 852417 *CONTACT:* Mrs P D Milne
OPENING TIMES: 1100-1300 & 1400-1800 daily.
MAIL ORDER: No *CAT. COST:* 3 x 1st class *W/SALE or RETAIL:* Retail
SPECIALITIES: Wide range of Ground-covering plants. *MAP PAGE:* **6**

LHar **Harrisons Delphiniums,** Newbury Cottage, Play Hatch, Reading, Berkshire RG4 9QN
TEL: (0734) 470810 *CONTACT:* Len Harrison
◆ *OPENING TIMES:* 0900-1630 Sat & Sun Apr-Sep.
MAIL ORDER: Yes *MIN VALUE:* £5.00 *CAT. COST:* 1st class *W/SALE or RETAIL:* Both
SPECIALITIES: Delphiniums *MAP PAGE:* **2/3**

LHil **Brian Hiley,** 25 Little Woodcote Estate, Wallington, Surrey SM5 4AU
TEL: (081) 647 9679 *CONTACT:* Brian & Heather Hiley
OPENING TIMES: 0900-1700 Wed-Sat (ex Bank Hols). Please check beforehand.
MAIL ORDER: Yes *MIN VALUE:* £15.00 + p&p *CAT. COST:* 3 x 1st class
W/SALE or RETAIL: Both
SPECIALITIES: Penstemon, Alpines, Herbaceous, tender & unusual plants. *MAP PAGE:* **3**

LHol **Hollington Nurseries,** Woolton Hill, Newbury, Berkshire RG15 9XT
TEL: (0635) 253908 *FAX:* (0635) 254990 *CONTACT:* S & J Hopkinson
OPENING TIMES: 1000-1700 Mon-Sat, 1100-1700 Sun & Bank Hols Apr-Sep. 1000-dusk Mon-Fri Oct-Mar.
MAIL ORDER: *MIN VALUE:* *CAT. COST:* Sae *W/SALE or RETAIL:* Both
SPECIALITIES: Herbs, Thymes, Old fashioned Roses & Salvia. Cool conservatory plants.
MAP PAGE: **2**

LHop **Hopleys Plants Ltd,** High Street, Much Hadham, Hertfordshire SG10 6BU
TEL: (0279 84) 2509 *FAX:* (0279 84) 3784 *CONTACT:* Aubrey Barker
OPENING TIMES: 0900-1700 Mon & Wed-Sat. 1400-1700 Sun. Closed Jan & Aug.
MAIL ORDER: Yes* *MIN VALUE:* No minimum charge *CAT. COST:* £1.00
W/SALE or RETAIL: Both
SPECIALITIES: Wide range of Hardy & Half-hardy Shrubs & Perennials. *NOTE:- Mail Order in Autumn only. *MAP PAGE:* **3/6**

LHyd **Hydon Nurseries Ltd.,** Clock Barn Lane, Hydon Heath, Godalming, Surrey GU8 4AZ
TEL: (0483) 860252 *FAX:* (0483) 419937 *CONTACT:* A F George
◆ *OPENING TIMES:* 0800-1700 Mon-Sat. (Closed 1245-1400). Sun by appt. only.
MAIL ORDER: Yes *MIN VALUE:* None *CAT. COST:* £1.50 *W/SALE or RETAIL:* Both
SPECIALITIES: Large and dwarf Rhododendron, Yakushimanum hybrids & evergreen Azaleas.
MAP PAGE: **3**

LKna **Knap Hill & Slocock Nurseries,** Barrs Lane, Knaphill, Woking, Surrey GU21 2JW
TEL: (0483) 481212/5 *FAX:* (0483) 797261 *CONTACT:* Mrs Joy West
OPENING TIMES: 0900-1700 Mon-Sat & 1000-1700 Sun.
MAIL ORDER: Yes *MIN VALUE:* No minimum charge *CAT. COST:* 50p *W/SALE or RETAIL:* Both
SPECIALITIES: Wide variety Trees & Shrubs especially Rhododendron, Azalea & Ericaceous.
MAP PAGE: **3**

LLin **Lincluden Nursery,** Bisley Green, Bisley, Woking, Surrey GU24 9EN
TEL: (0483) 797005 *FAX:* (0483) 474015 *CONTACT:* Mr & Mrs J A Tilbury
◆ *OPENING TIMES:* 0930-1630 Tue-Sat 2nd Mar-22nd Dec. 1000-1600 Tue-Fri Jan-Feb. Other times by appt. only.
MAIL ORDER: Yes *MIN VALUE:* None *CAT. COST:* 3 x 1st class *W/SALE or RETAIL:* Both
SPECIALITIES: Dwarf, slow-growing & unusual Conifers. *MAP PAGE:* **3**

LMay **Maydencroft Aquatic Nurseries,** Maydencroft Lane, Gosmore, Hitchin, Hertfordshire SG4 7QD
TEL: (0462) 456020 *FAX:* (0462) 422652 *CONTACT:* P Bromfield
OPENING TIMES: 0900-1300 & 1400-1730 daily Feb-Oct. 1000-1300 Sat-Sun Nov-Jan.
MAIL ORDER: Yes *MIN VALUE:* £1.00 + p&p *CAT. COST:* 50p *W/SALE or RETAIL:* Both
SPECIALITIES: Water Lilies, Marginals, Bog, Alpines, dwarf Conifer. *MAP PAGE:* **6**

 See note on Mail Order, EC sales & Export on page 5

LMer **Merrist Wood Plant Shop,** Merrist Wood College, Worplesdon, Guildford Surrey GU3 3PE
TEL: (0483) 232424 *FAX:* (0483) 236518 *CONTACT:* Danny O'Shaughnessy
OPENING TIMES: 0900-1700 Mon-Fri
MAIL ORDER: Yes *MIN VALUE:* £5.00 + p&p *CAT. COST:* *W/SALE or RETAIL:* Retail
SPECIALITIES: *MAP PAGE:* **3**

LMil **Millais Nurseries,** Crosswater Lane, Churt, Farnham, Surrey GU10 2JN
TEL: (0252) 792698 *FAX:* (0252) 792526 *CONTACT:* David Millais
◆ *OPENING TIMES:* 1000-1300 & 1400-1700 Tue-Sat. Also daily in May & June.
MAIL ORDER: Yes *MIN VALUE:* £20.00 + p&p *CAT. COST:* 5 x 2nd class
W/SALE or RETAIL: Both
SPECIALITIES: Rhododendron & Azalea. *MAP PAGE:* **3**

LMor **Morehavens,** 28 Denham Lane, Gerrards Cross, Buckinghamshire SL9 0EX
TEL: (0494) 873601 *CONTACT:* B Farmer
OPENING TIMES: Only for collection.
MAIL ORDER: Yes *MIN VALUE:* £16.50 + p&p *CAT. COST:* Free *W/SALE or RETAIL:* Both
SPECIALITIES: Camomile 'Treneague'. *MAP PAGE:* **3**

LNet **Nettletons Nursery,** Ivy Mill Lane, Godstone, Surrey RH9 8NF
TEL: (0883) 742426 *CONTACT:* Jonathan Nettleton
OPENING TIMES: 0830-1300 & 1400-1730 Mon Tue Thu-Sat, 1000-1300 Sun Mar-Jun. Bank Hols by appt.
MAIL ORDER: Yes *MIN VALUE:* £100.00 *CAT. COST:* 2 x 1st class5 *W/SALE or RETAIL:* Both
SPECIALITIES: Trees & Shrubs. Especially Conifers, Azalea, Camellia, Rhododendron, Vines, Climbers. 100 Japanese Acers. 16 Wisteria. *MAP PAGE:* **3**

LPal **The Palm Centre,** 563 Upper Richmond Rd West, London SW14 7ED
TEL: (081) 876 3223 *FAX:* (081) 876 6888 *CONTACT:* Martin Gibbons
OPENING TIMES: 1000-1800 daily.
MAIL ORDER: Yes *MIN VALUE:* £10.00 *CAT. COST:* £1.95/£1.85 *W/SALE or RETAIL:* Both
SPECIALITIES: Palms & Cycads, exotic & sub-tropical, hardy, half-hardy & tropical. Seedlings to mature trees. Two cats., one for Palms & one for Cycads. *MAP PAGE:* **3**

LPan **Pantiles Nurseries Ltd.,** Almners Road, Lyne, Chertsey, Surrey KT16 0BJ
TEL: (0932) 872195 *FAX:* (0932) 874030 *CONTACT:* Brendan Gallagher
◆ *OPENING TIMES:* 0900-1730 daily.
MAIL ORDER: No *CAT. COST:* Sae *W/SALE or RETAIL:* Both
SPECIALITIES: Large Trees, Shrubs & climbers in containers. *MAP PAGE:* **3**

LPlm **A J Palmer & Son,** Denham Court Nursery, Denham Court Drive, Denham, Uxbridge, Middlesex UB9 5PG
TEL: (0895) 832035 *CONTACT:* Sheila Palmer
OPENING TIMES: 0900-dusk Jul-Oct daily. 0900-1700 Mon-Sat, 0900-1300 Sun Nov-Jun.
MAIL ORDER: Yes *MIN VALUE:* None *CAT. COST:* Free *W/SALE or RETAIL:* Both
SPECIALITIES: Roses. *MAP PAGE:* **3**

LPri **Priorswood Clematis,** Priorswood, Widbury Hill, Ware, Hertfordshire SG12 7QH
TEL: (0920) 461543 *CONTACT:* G S Greenway
OPENING TIMES: 0800-1700 Tue-Sun & Bank Hol Mondays..
MAIL ORDER: *MIN VALUE:* *CAT. COST:* 65p + Sae *W/SALE or RETAIL:* Both
SPECIALITIES: Clematis & other climbing plants. *MAP PAGE:* **3/6**

LRHS **Wisley Plant Centre,** RHS Garden, Nr Ripley, Woking, Surrey GU23 6QB
TEL: (0483) 211113 *FAX:* (0483) 211932 *CONTACT:*
◆ *OPENING TIMES:* 1000-1830 daily Summer, 1000-1730 Winter.
MAIL ORDER: *MIN VALUE:* *CAT. COST:* None issued *W/SALE or RETAIL:* Retail
SPECIALITIES: Very wide range, many rare & unusual. *MAP PAGE:* **3**

LStr **Henry Street,** Swallowfield Road Nursery, Arborfield, Reading, Berkshire RG2 9JY
TEL: (0734) 761223 *FAX:* (0734) 761417 *CONTACT:* Mr M C Goold
OPENING TIMES: 0900-1730 daily.
MAIL ORDER: *MIN VALUE:* *CAT. COST:* Free *W/SALE or RETAIL:* Both
SPECIALITIES: Roses. *MAP PAGE:* **2/3**

LSur **Surrey Primroses,,** Merriewood, Sandy Lane, Milford, Godalming, Surrey GU8 5BJ
TEL: (0483) 416747 *CONTACT:* Val & Geoff Yates
OPENING TIMES:
MAIL ORDER: Yes *MIN VALUE:* None *CAT. COST:* Sae *W/SALE or RETAIL:* Retail
SPECIALITIES: Primroses, old named varieties. *MAP PAGE:* **3**

LTil **Tilgates Garden Nursery,** Little Common Lane, Bletchingley, Surrey RH1 4QF
TEL: (0883) 744881 *CONTACT:* Graham Rankin
OPENING TIMES: 1000-1700 Mon-Fri all year, 1000-1700 Sat & Sun Apr-Oct.
MAIL ORDER: No *CAT. COST:* *W/SALE or RETAIL:* Retail
SPECIALITIES: Magnolias & rare Trees & Shrubs. *MAP PAGE:* **3**

LWad **Waddesdon Gardens Nursery,** Queen Street, Waddesdon, Buckinghamshire HP18 0JW
TEL: (0296) 658586 *FAX:* (0296) 658852 *CONTACT:*
OPENING TIMES: 0830-1730 daily Apr-Sep, 0930-1700 Oct-Mar (ex. Xmas).
MAIL ORDER: No *CAT. COST:* Sae *W/SALE or RETAIL:* Both
SPECIALITIES: Increasing range of choice & unusual herbaceous Perennials, Shrubs, Bedding, Conservatory & Houseplants. *MAP PAGE:* **2/3**

MAsh **Ashwood Nurseries,** Greensforge, Kingswinford, West Midlands DY6 0AE
TEL: (0384) 401996 *CONTACT:* John Massey & Philip Baulk
◆ *OPENING TIMES:* 0900-1800 Mon-Sat & 0930-1800 Sun. ex Xmas & Boxing day.
MAIL ORDER: No *CAT. COST:* A5 Sae *W/SALE or RETAIL:* Both
SPECIALITIES: Lewisias (Holder of NCCPG Collection). Also large range of hardy plants. Extensive range of dwarf Conifers. Mail Order for SEEDS only. *MAP PAGE:* **5**

MAus **David Austin Roses Ltd.,** Bowling Green Lane, Albrighton, Wolverhampton, West Midlands WV7 3HB
TEL: (0902) 373931 *FAX:* (0902) 372142 *CONTACT:* D Austin
OPENING TIMES: 0900-1700 Mon-Fri, 1000-1800 Sat, Sun & Bank Hols. Until dusk Nov-Mar.
MAIL ORDER: Yes *MIN VALUE:* No minimum charge *CAT. COST:* Free *W/SALE or RETAIL:* Both
SPECIALITIES: Roses, Paeonia, Iris & Hemerocallis. Also Herbaceous perennials at Nursery. *MAP PAGE:* **5**

MBal **Ballalheannagh Gardens,** Glen Roy, Lonan, Isle of Man
TEL: (0624) 861875 *CONTACT:* Clif & Maureen Dadd
OPENING TIMES: 1000-1300 & 1400-1700 or dusk if earlier in Winter. Closed w/ends Nov-Mar. Please telephone first.
MAIL ORDER: Yes *MIN VALUE:* £10.00 + p&p *CAT. COST:* £1.50 *W/SALE or RETAIL:* Retail
SPECIALITIES: Rhododendrons & Ericaceous Shrubs. Small number of rare trees and shrubs for callers not in catalogue. *NOTE: Mail Order on some items only. *MAP PAGE:* **4**

MBar **Barncroft Nurseries,** Dunwood Lane, Longsdon, Nr Leek, Stoke-on-Trent, Staffordshire ST9 9QW
TEL: (0538) 384310/372111 *CONTACT:* R & S Warner
OPENING TIMES: 0900-1900 or dusk if earlier Fri-Sun.
MAIL ORDER: No *CAT. COST:* None issued *W/SALE or RETAIL:* Both
SPECIALITIES: Very large range of Heathers, Conifers & Shrubs. *MAP PAGE:* **5**

MBea **John Beach (Nursery) Ltd.,** (Office) 9 Grange Road, Wellesbourne, Warwickshire CV35 9RL
TEL: (0926) 624173 *CONTACT:* John Beach
◆ *OPENING TIMES:* 1000-1300 & 1430-1700 Mon-Sat Mar-Oct. 1000-1300 Mon-Sat Nov-Feb.
MAIL ORDER: Yes *MIN VALUE:* 2 plants + p&p *CAT. COST:* 6 x 2nd class
W/SALE or RETAIL: Retail
SPECIALITIES: Clematis, Trees & Shrubs inc. Fruiting plants. NOTE: Nursery address:- Thelsford Farm, Charlecote, Warwick. *MAP PAGE:* **2**

MBel **Bellhouse Nursery,** Bellhouse Lane, Moore, Nr Warrington, Cheshire WA4 6TR
TEL: (0925) 740307* *FAX:* (0925) 740672 *CONTACT:* Elaine Soens & Doreen Scott
OPENING TIMES: 1000-1700 Wed-Mon Mar-Oct. 1000-1600 Wed-Mon 1st Nov-20th Dec & Feb. Closed 21st Dec-end Jan.
MAIL ORDER: *MIN VALUE:* *CAT. COST:* 3 x 1st class *W/SALE or RETAIL:* Retail
SPECIALITIES: Wide range of Herbaceous plants & Shrubs. Good selection of unusual varieties. *NOTE: Ask for nursery. *MAP PAGE:* **5/4**

 See note on Mail Order, EC sales & Export on page 5

MBen **Michael Bennett,** Long Compton, Shipston-on-Stour, Warwickshire CV36 5JN
TEL: (060 884) 676 *CONTACT:* Michael Bennett
OPENING TIMES:
MAIL ORDER: Yes *MIN VALUE:* £5.00 + p&p *CAT. COST:* Sae *W/SALE or RETAIL:* Both
SPECIALITIES: Asparagus & Globe Artichoke. Ulmus glabra 'Camperdownii' *MAP PAGE:*

MBlu **The Bluebell Nursery,** Blackfordby, Swadlincote Derbyshire DE11 8AJ
TEL: (0283) 222091 *CONTACT:* Robert & Suzette Vernon
OPENING TIMES: 0900-1700 (or dusk if earlier) daily. Closed 25th Dec-2nd Jan.
MAIL ORDER: Yes *MIN VALUE:* No minimum charge *CAT. COST:* 50p+2x1st class
W/SALE or RETAIL: Retail
SPECIALITIES: Uncommon Trees, Shrubs & Climbers. *MAP PAGE:* **5**

MBri **Bridgemere Nurseries,** Bridgemere, Nr Nantwich, Cheshire CW5 7QB
TEL: (09365) 381/239 x 157 *FAX:* (09365) 215 *CONTACT:* Keith Atkey
OPENING TIMES: 0900-2000 Mon-Sat, 1000-2000 Sun summer, until 1700 in winter.
MAIL ORDER: No *CAT. COST:* *W/SALE or RETAIL:* Both
SPECIALITIES: Largest variety of Plants, Bulbs & Seeds on one site in UK. Especially dwarf Rhododendrons, Conifers, Heathers, Alpines, Trees & Shrubs. *MAP PAGE:* **5**

MBrk **Brinkley Nurseries,** Fiskerton Road, Southwell, Nottinghamshire NG25 0TP
TEL: (0636) 814501 *CONTACT:* Mrs C Steven
◆ *OPENING TIMES:* 1000-1600 in winter, 1000-1700 summer.
MAIL ORDER: Yes *MIN VALUE:* £10.00 + p&p *CAT. COST:* £1.95 *W/SALE or RETAIL:* Both
SPECIALITIES: Shrubs, Conifers, small Trees. Unusual varieties our speciality. *MAP PAGE:* **5/7**

MBro **Broadstone Alpines,** 13 The Nursery, High Street, Sutton Courtenay, Abingdon, Oxfordshire OX14 4UA
TEL: (0235) 847557 *CONTACT:* J Shackleton
OPENING TIMES: 1600-1900 Fri, 1500-1900 Sat (except Show days). By appt on other days.
MAIL ORDER: No *CAT. COST:* 3 x 1st class *W/SALE or RETAIL:* Retail
SPECIALITIES: Plants for rock garden, scree, troughs & borders. Lime tolerant Alpines & unusual plants. *MAP PAGE:* **2**

MBur **Burrows Roses,** Meadow Croft, Spondon Road, Dale Abbey, Derby, Derbyshire DE7 4PQ
TEL: (0332) 668289 *CONTACT:* Stuart & Diane Burrows
OPENING TIMES: 0900-1700
MAIL ORDER: Yes *MIN VALUE:* £2.70 + p&p *CAT. COST:* 20p+1st class
W/SALE or RETAIL: Retail
SPECIALITIES: Roses *MAP PAGE:*

MCad **Caddick's Clematis Nurseries,** Lymm Road, Thelwall, Warrington, Cheshire WA13 0UF
TEL: (0925) 757196 *CONTACT:* H Caddick
◆ *OPENING TIMES:* 1000-1700 Tue-Sun 1st Feb-24th Dec. 1000-1700 Bank Hols.
MAIL ORDER: Yes *MIN VALUE:* £11.00 + p&p *CAT. COST:* 3 x 1st class
W/SALE or RETAIL: Both
SPECIALITIES: Clematis. *MAP PAGE:* **5**

MCas **Castle Alpines,** Castle Road, Wootton, Woodstock, Oxfordshire OX20 1EG
TEL: (0993) 812162 *CONTACT:* M S & F E Castle
OPENING TIMES: 1000-1700 Mon-Sat Mar 1-Sep 30. Appt only Oct 1-Feb 28.
MAIL ORDER: Yes *MIN VALUE:* £12.00 + p&p *CAT. COST:* 3 x 2nd class
W/SALE or RETAIL: Retail
SPECIALITIES: Alpines. *MAP PAGE:* **2**

MChe **Cheshire Herbs,** Fourfields, Forest Road, Nr Tarporley, Cheshire CW6 9ES
TEL: (0829) 760578 *FAX:* (0829) 760354 *CONTACT:* Mr & Mrs Ted Riddell
◆ *OPENING TIMES:* 1000-1700 daily 3rd Jan-24th Dec.
MAIL ORDER: No *CAT. COST:* 20p *W/SALE or RETAIL:* Both
SPECIALITIES: Display Herb garden & Elizabethan knot garden. *MAP PAGE:* **4/5**

MCol **Collinwood Nurseries,** Mottram St. Andrew, Macclesfield, Cheshire SK10 4QR
TEL: (0625) 582272 *CONTACT:* A Wright
OPENING TIMES: 0830-1800 Mon-Sat 1300-1800 Sun.
MAIL ORDER: Yes *MIN VALUE:* No minimum charge *CAT. COST:* Free
W/SALE or RETAIL: Retail
SPECIALITIES: Chrysanthemums (Dendranthema). *MAP PAGE:* **5**

◆ **See also Display Advertisements**

MDHE DHE Plants, Rose Lea, Darley House Estate, Darley Dale, Matlock, Derbyshire DE4 2QH
TEL: (0629) 732512 *CONTACT:* Peter M Smith
OPENING TIMES: By appt. only, essential to phone first.
MAIL ORDER: Yes *MIN VALUE:* *CAT. COST:* 2 x 1st class *W/SALE or RETAIL:* Retail
SPECIALITIES: Alpines; esp. Helianthemum, Saxifraga & Sisyrinchium. NOTE: Nursery will be moving, please check first by phone. *MAP PAGE:* **5/7**

MFie Field House Nurseries, Leake Road, Gotham, Nottingham NG11 0JN
TEL: (0602) 830278 *CONTACT:* Doug Lochhead & Valerie A Woolley
OPENING TIMES: 0900-1700 Wed-Mon or by appt.
MAIL ORDER: Yes *MIN VALUE:* None *CAT. COST:* 3 x 1st class *W/SALE or RETAIL:* Retail
SPECIALITIES: Auriculas, Primulas, Alpines & Rock plants. *NOTE: Mail Order for Auriculas, Primulas & Seeds ONLY. *MAP PAGE:* **5**

MFir The Firs Nursery, Chelford Road, Henbury, Macclesfield, Cheshire SK10 3LH
TEL: (0625) 426422 *CONTACT:* Fay J Bowling
OPENING TIMES: 1000-1700 Mon, Tue, Thu, Fri, Sat Mar-Oct.
MAIL ORDER: Yes *MIN VALUE:* £10.00 + p&p *CAT. COST:* 2 x 1st class
W/SALE or RETAIL: Retail
SPECIALITIES: Herbaceous Perennials, Alpines, Hebe, some unusual. *MAP PAGE:* **5**

MFos Fosse Alpines, 33 Leicester Road, Countesthorpe, Leicestershire LE8 3QU
TEL: (0533) 778237 *CONTACT:* T K West
OPENING TIMES: By appt. only
MAIL ORDER: Yes *MIN VALUE:* £8.00 + p&p *CAT. COST:* 30p refundable *W/SALE or RETAIL:*
SPECIALITIES: Alpines including specialist species in small quantities. *MAP PAGE:* **5**

MFry Fryer's Nurseries Ltd., Manchester Road, Knutsford, Cheshire WA16 0SX
TEL: (0565) 755455 *FAX:* (0565) 653755 *CONTACT:* Gareth Fryer
OPENING TIMES: 0900-1730 Mon-Sat & 1000-1730 Sun & Bank Hols.
MAIL ORDER: Yes *MIN VALUE:* None *CAT. COST:* Free *W/SALE or RETAIL:* Both
SPECIALITIES: Extensive Rose Nursery & Garden Centre producing over half a million bushes annually. Rose fields in bloom Jun-Oct. *MAP PAGE:* **5**

MGan Gandy's (Roses) Ltd., North Kilworth, Nr Lutterworth, Leicestershire LE17 6HZ
TEL: (0858) 880398 *CONTACT:* Miss R D Gandy
OPENING TIMES: 0900-1700 Mon-Sat & 1400-1700 Sun.
MAIL ORDER: Yes *MIN VALUE:* None *CAT. COST:* Free *W/SALE or RETAIL:* Both
SPECIALITIES: 600 Rose varieties. *MAP PAGE:* **2**

MGos Goscote Nurseries Ltd, Syston Road, Cossington, Leicestershire LE7 8NZ
TEL: (0509) 812121 *CONTACT:* D C & R C Cox
◆ *OPENING TIMES:* 0800-1630 Mon-Fri, 0900-1200 & 1400-1630 Sat, 1000-1300 & 1400-1630 Sun.
MAIL ORDER: Yes *MIN VALUE:* £10.00 + p&p *CAT. COST:* 4 x 2nd class
W/SALE or RETAIL: Retail
SPECIALITIES: Rhododendrons, Azaleas, Trees, Shrubs, Heathers, Conifers, Alpines, Herbaceous. Especially Ericaceae. *MAP PAGE:* **5**

MHay F Haynes & Partners Ltd., (Off.) 56 Gordon Street, Kettering, Northamptonshire NN16 0RX
TEL: (0536) 519836 *CONTACT:* Mr Maple
OPENING TIMES: 0800-1530 daily.
MAIL ORDER: Yes *MIN VALUE:* £50.00 + p&p *CAT. COST:* Free *W/SALE or RETAIL:* Both
SPECIALITIES: Roses, especially exhibition & miniature. NOTE: Nursery at Drayton Road, Lowick, Nr Thrapston. *MAP PAGE:* **6**

MHew Hewthorn Herbs & Wild Flowers,, Simkins Farm, Adbolton Lane, West Bridford, Nottingham NG2 5AS
TEL: (0602) 812861 *CONTACT:* Julie Scott
OPENING TIMES: Most weekdays during school term & some weekends. Please phone first.
MAIL ORDER: Yes *MIN VALUE:* No minimum charge *CAT. COST:* 3 x 1st class
W/SALE or RETAIL: Retail
SPECIALITIES: Native Wild flowers, plants for Butterfly gardens & Bees. Culinary & Aromatic Herbs, Dye plants, native Medicinal. *MAP PAGE:* **5**

 See note on Mail Order, EC sales & Export on page 5

MHig **Highgates Nursery,** 166a Crich Lane, Belper, Derbyshire DE56 1EP
TEL: (0773) 822153 *CONTACT:* R E & D I Straughan
OPENING TIMES: 1030-1630 Mon-Sat mid Mar-mid Oct. Closed Sun.
MAIL ORDER: MIN VALUE: CAT. COST: 2 x 1st class *W/SALE or RETAIL:* Retail
SPECIALITIES: Alpines. *MAP PAGE:* **5/7**

MHul **Diana Hull,** Fog Cottages, 178 Lower Street, Hillmorton, Rugby, Warwickshire CV21 4NX
TEL: (0788) 536574 after 1600 *CONTACT:* Diana Hull
OPENING TIMES: By appt. only.
MAIL ORDER: Yes *MIN VALUE:* None *CAT. COST:* Sae for list *W/SALE or RETAIL:* Retail
SPECIALITIES: Pelargonium species. See also SEED SUPPLIER INDEX *MAP PAGE:* **2**

MJac **Jackson's Nurseries,** Clifton Campville, Nr Tamworth, Staffordshire B79 0AP
TEL: (082786) 307 *CONTACT:* N Jackson
OPENING TIMES: 0900-1800 Mon Wed-Sat, 1000-1700 Sun.
MAIL ORDER: No *CAT. COST:* 2 x 1st class *W/SALE or RETAIL:* Both
SPECIALITIES: Fuchsia. *MAP PAGE:* **5**

MLab **Laburnum Nurseries,** (Off.) 6 Manor House Gardens Main Street, Humberstone Village, Leicestershire LE5 1AE
TEL: (0533) 766522 *CONTACT:* Mr W Johnson
OPENING TIMES: 0900-1600 Mon-Sat 0900-1200 Sat & Sun.
MAIL ORDER: No *CAT. COST:* 1 x 2nd class *W/SALE or RETAIL:* Both
SPECIALITIES: Fuchsia. NOTE: Nursery at Humberstone, Leicester. *MAP PAGE:* **5**

MLea **Lea Rhododendron Gardens Ltd.,** Lea, Matlock, Derbyshire DE4 5GH
TEL: (0629 534) 380/260 *FAX:* (0629 534) 260 *CONTACT:* Jon Tye
OPENING TIMES: 1000-1900.
MAIL ORDER: Yes *MIN VALUE:* £15.00 + p&p *CAT. COST:* 30p + Sae *W/SALE or RETAIL:* Retail
SPECIALITIES: Rhododendron, Azalea & Kalmia. *MAP PAGE:* **5/7**

MMat **Mattock's Roses,** The Rose Nurseries, Nuneham Courtenay, Oxford, Oxfordshire OX44 9PY
TEL: (086 738) 265 *FAX:* (086 738) 267 *CONTACT:* Mr Mark W Mattock
OPENING TIMES: 0900-1730 Mon-Sat, 1030-1730 Sun. Closes 1700 Nov-Feb.
MAIL ORDER: Yes *MIN VALUE:* £200 + p&p *CAT. COST:* Free *W/SALE or RETAIL:* Both
SPECIALITIES: Roses. *MAP PAGE:* **2**

MMea **Mears Ashby Nurseries Ltd.,** Glebe House, Glebe Road, Mears Ashby, Northamptonshire NN6 0DL
TEL: (0604) 812371/811811 *FAX:* (0604) 812353 *CONTACT:* John B & J E Gaggini
◆ *OPENING TIMES:* 0800-1700 Mon-Fri (Wholesale & Retail). 0930-1730 Sat & Sun (Retail only).
MAIL ORDER: No *CAT. COST:* £1.50 + 24p* *W/SALE or RETAIL:* Both
SPECIALITIES: Specialist growers of container Trees, Shrubs, Conifers & Fruit, esp. Wisteria. Tree Ferns. *NOTE: Please state Retail or W/sale Catalogue. *MAP PAGE:* **6**

MMil **Mill Hill Plants,** Mill Hill House, Elston Lane, East Stoke, Newark, Nottinghamshire NG23 5QJ
TEL: (0636) 525460 *CONTACT:* G M Gregory
◆ *OPENING TIMES:* 1000-1800 Wed-Sun & Bank Hols Mar-Oct & by appt.
MAIL ORDER: No *CAT. COST:* 3 x 1st class *W/SALE or RETAIL:* Retail
SPECIALITIES: General range. *MAP PAGE:* **7**

MMor **F Morrey & Sons,** Forest Nursery, Kelsall, Tarporley, Cheshire CW6 0SW
TEL: (0829) 51342 *FAX:* (0829) 52449 *CONTACT:* D F Morrey
OPENING TIMES: 0830-1730 Mon-Sat.
MAIL ORDER: No *CAT. COST:* 20p *W/SALE or RETAIL:* Both
SPECIALITIES: Azaleas, Rhododendrons & ornamental Trees. *MAP PAGE:* **4/5**

MNew **Newington Nursery,** Newington, Wallingford, Oxfordshire OX10 7AW
TEL: (0865) 891401 *CONTACT:* C J & C A Colbourne
OPENING TIMES: 1000-1600 Mon-Fri, Sat & Sun by appt.
MAIL ORDER: Yes *MIN VALUE:* According to country *CAT. COST:* £1.50
W/SALE or RETAIL: Retail
SPECIALITIES: Conservatory plants. *MAP PAGE:* **2**

MNFA **The Nursery Further Afield,** Evenley Road, Mixbury, Nr Brackley, Northamptonshire NN13 5YR
TEL: (0280) 848539 eves. *CONTACT:* Gerald Sinclair
OPENING TIMES: 1000-1700 Wed-Sat & Bank Hol Mons 20th Mar-9th Oct. 1400-1700 1st Sun of Apr-Oct & by appt.
MAIL ORDER: No *CAT. COST:* Sae *W/SALE or RETAIL:* Retail
SPECIALITIES: Hardy Perennials. *MAP PAGE:* **2**

MOke **Okell's Nurseries,** Duddon Heath, Nr Tarporley, Cheshire CW6 0EP
TEL: (0829) 41512 *FAX:* (0829) 41587 *CONTACT:* Gary & Donna Okell
OPENING TIMES: 0900-1730.
MAIL ORDER: No *CAT. COST:* Free *W/SALE or RETAIL:* Both
SPECIALITIES: Heathers. NOTE: Rooted cuttings only by Mail Order. *MAP PAGE:* **4/5**

MPar **J & E Parker-Jervis,** Marten's Hall Farm, Longworth, Abingdon, Oxfordshire OX13 5EP
TEL: (0865) 820376 *CONTACT:* E Parker-Jervis
OPENING TIMES: By appt. only.
MAIL ORDER: Yes *MIN VALUE:* £20.00 + p&p *CAT. COST:* 3 x 1st class
W/SALE or RETAIL: Retail
SPECIALITIES: Cottage garden plants, Colchicum, Galanthus & Paeonia. *MAP PAGE:* **2**

MPhe **Phedar Nursery,** Bunkers Hill, Romiley, Stockport, Cheshire SK6 3DS
TEL: (061 430) 3772 *FAX:* (061 430) 3772 *CONTACT:* Will McLewin
OPENING TIMES: Frequent, esp. in Spring but irregular. Please telephone before visiting.
MAIL ORDER: Yes *MIN VALUE:* £4.00 + p&p *CAT. COST:* A5 Sae. *W/SALE or RETAIL:* Both
SPECIALITIES: Helleborus, Paeonia, Erythronium. See also under SEED INDEX. *MAP PAGE:* **5**

MPit **Pitts Farm Nursery,** Shrewley, Warwick, Warwickshire CV35 7BB
TEL: (0926 84) 2737 *CONTACT:* Mrs J Farmer
OPENING TIMES: 1000-1800 daily.
MAIL ORDER: No *CAT. COST:* Sae *W/SALE or RETAIL:* Retail
SPECIALITIES: Perennials & Bedding. *MAP PAGE:* **2**

MPla **E L F Plants Cramden Nursery Ltd.,** Harborough Road North, Northampton, Northamptonshire NN2 8LU
TEL: (0604) 846246 Eve. *CONTACT:* E L Fincham-Nichols
OPENING TIMES: 1000-1700 Thu-Sat ex Dec & Jan.
MAIL ORDER: No *CAT. COST:* 70p *W/SALE or RETAIL:* Retail
SPECIALITIES: Dwarf and slow growing Shrubs & Conifers, many unusual. Some Alpines & Heathers. *MAP PAGE:* **2**

MPlt **Plantables,** The Old Orchard, Hall Lane, Hurst Hill, Coseley, West Midlands WV14 9RJ
TEL: (0902) 662647 *CONTACT:* Alan Rumble
OPENING TIMES: By appt. please.
MAIL ORDER: Yes *MIN VALUE:* No minimum charge *CAT. COST:* 2 x 2nd class
W/SALE or RETAIL: Both
SPECIALITIES: Alpines, Dwarf Shrubs, Dwarf Rhododendron & Hardy plants *MAP PAGE:*

MRav **Ravensthorpe Nursery,** 6 East Haddon Road, Ravensthorpe, Northamptonshire NN6 8ES
TEL: (0604) 770548 *CONTACT:* Jean & Richard Wiseman
OPENING TIMES: 1000-1800 (dusk if earlier) Tue-Sun. Also Bank Hol Mons.
MAIL ORDER: Yes *MIN VALUE:* No minimum charge *CAT. COST:* 4 x 1st class
W/SALE or RETAIL: Retail
SPECIALITIES: Over 1,600 different Trees, Shrubs, & Perennials with many unusual varieties.
MAP PAGE: **2**

MRil **Rileys' Chrysanthemums,** Alfreton Nurseries, Woolley Moor, Alfreton, Derbyshire DE55 6FF
TEL: (0246) 590320 *CONTACT:* C A & G K Riley
OPENING TIMES: 0900-1700 Mon-Fri, Mail Order only. 0900-1700 Sun Feb-May, collection only. 0900-1600 Sun in Sep.
MAIL ORDER: *MIN VALUE:* *CAT. COST:* 40p *W/SALE or RETAIL:* Both
SPECIALITIES: Chrysanthemum. *MAP PAGE:* **5/7**

 See note on Mail Order, EC sales & Export on page 5

MRob **Robinson's of Whaley Bridge,** 20 Vaughan Road, Whaley Bridge Stockport Cheshire SK12 7JT
TEL: (0663) 732991 *CONTACT:* J & D Robinson
OPENING TIMES: By appt. only.
MAIL ORDER: Yes *MIN VALUE:* None *CAT. COST:* Large Sae *W/SALE or RETAIL:*
SPECIALITIES: Violets & Iris. *MAP PAGE:*

MRui **Andrew de Ruiter (Rose Specialist),** 9 Ingersley Road, Bollington Cheshire SK10 5RE
TEL: (0625) 574389* *CONTACT:* Andrew de Ruiter
OPENING TIMES:
MAIL ORDER: Yes *MIN VALUE:* No minimum charge *CAT. COST:* 2 x 2nd class
W/SALE or RETAIL: Both
SPECIALITIES: Roses, esp. Miniature, also good range of English Roses. *NOTE: Only available before 1000 or after 1700. *MAP PAGE:*

MSmi **John Smith & Son,** Hilltop Nurseries, Thornton, Leicestershire LE67 1AN
TEL: (0530) 230331 *CONTACT:* J Smith
OPENING TIMES: 0800-1730 Mon-Sat.
MAIL ORDER: Yes *MIN VALUE:* No minimum charge *CAT. COST:* Sae *W/SALE or RETAIL:* Both
SPECIALITIES: Hardy & Half-hardy Fuchsia, dwarf Conifers, Heathers, Hardy Plants, Shrubs & Trees. *MAP PAGE:* **5**

MSta **Stapeley Water Gardens Ltd,** London Road, Stapeley, Nantwich, Cheshire CW5 7LH
TEL: (0270) 623868 *FAX:* (0270) 624919 *CONTACT:* Mr R G A Davis (Chairman)
◆ *OPENING TIMES:* 0900-1800 Mon-Fri, 1000-1800 Sat, 1000-1900 Sun & Bank Hols summer. 1000-1700 daily winter.
MAIL ORDER: Yes *MIN VALUE:* None *CAT. COST:* £1 *W/SALE or RETAIL:* Both
SPECIALITIES: World's largest Water Garden Centre. Full range of Hardy & Tropical Water Lilies, Aquatic, Bog & Poolside plants. Also large general stock. *MAP PAGE:* **5**

MSte **Steventon Road Nurseries,** Steventon Road, East Hanney, Wantage, Oxfordshire OX12 0HS
TEL: *CONTACT:* John Graham
OPENING TIMES: 1000-1600 Wed-Fri, 1000-1630 (dusk) Sat & Sun, 20th Mar-31st Oct 1993.
MAIL ORDER: No *CAT. COST:* £1 refunded *W/SALE or RETAIL:* Both
SPECIALITIES: Insectivorous plants. Tender & hardy Perennials. *MAP PAGE:* **2**

MS&S **S & S Perennials,** 24 Main Street, Normanton Le Heath, Leicestershire LE6 1TB
TEL: (0530) 62250 *CONTACT:* Shirley Pierce
OPENING TIMES: 0900-1730 daily.
MAIL ORDER: No *CAT. COST:* Sae *W/SALE or RETAIL:* Retail
SPECIALITIES: Erythronium, Fritillaria, hardy Cyclamen, Lilies & Iris. *MAP PAGE:* **5**

MTho **A & A Thorp,** Bungalow No 5, Main Street, Theddingworth, Leicestershire LE17 6QZ
TEL: (0858) 880496 *CONTACT:* Anita & Andrew Thorp
OPENING TIMES: Dawn to Dusk all year.
MAIL ORDER: No *CAT. COST:* 50p + Sae *W/SALE or RETAIL:* Retail
SPECIALITIES: Unusual plants or those in short supply. *MAP PAGE:* **2**

MTiv **Philip Tivey & Son,** 28 Wanlip Road, Syston, Leicestershire LE7 8PA
TEL: (0533) 692968 *CONTACT:*
OPENING TIMES: 1000-1500 daily.
MAIL ORDER: Yes *MIN VALUE:* £8.00 + p&p *CAT. COST:* Sae *W/SALE or RETAIL:* Both
SPECIALITIES: Dahlia. *MAP PAGE:* **5**

MTol **Tollgate Cottage Nursery,** Ladbroke, Leamington Spa, Warwickshire CV33 0BY
TEL: (0926) 814020 *CONTACT:* Brenda Timms
OPENING TIMES: 1100-1700 Fri, Sat & Sun Mar-mid Oct & Bank Hol Mons. Closed 16th Aug-5th Sep.
MAIL ORDER: Yes *MIN VALUE:* None *CAT. COST:* 2 x 1st class *W/SALE or RETAIL:* Retail
SPECIALITIES: Hardy Herbaceous, some unusual & Herbs. *MAP PAGE:* **2**

MUlv **Ulverscroft Grange Nursery,** Priory Lane, Ulverscroft, Markfield, Leicestershire LE67 9PB
TEL: (0530) 243635 *CONTACT:* Ted Brown
OPENING TIMES: From 1000 Wed-Sun Mar-Nov. Other times by appt.
MAIL ORDER: No *CAT. COST:* None isued *W/SALE or RETAIL:* Both
SPECIALITIES: Herbaceous & Shrubs, many unusual *MAP PAGE:* **5**

MWar **Ward Fuchsias,** 5 Pollen Close, Sale, Cheshire M33 3LP
TEL: (061973) 6467 *CONTACT:* K Ward
OPENING TIMES: 0930-1800 Tue-Sun Feb-Jun incl Bank Hols.
MAIL ORDER: Yes *MIN VALUE:* None *CAT. COST:* Free *W/SALE or RETAIL:* Retail
SPECIALITIES: Fuchsia. *MAP PAGE:* **5**

MWat **Waterperry Gardens Ltd.,** Waterperry, Nr Wheatley, Oxfordshire OX33 1JZ
TEL: (0844) 339226/254 *FAX:* (0844) 339883 *CONTACT:* Miss S Elliott
OPENING TIMES: 1000-1730 Mon-Fri, 1000-1800 Sat & Sun Summer. 1000-1700 Winter.
MAIL ORDER: No *CAT. COST:* 35p *W/SALE or RETAIL:* Retail
SPECIALITIES: General plus National Reference Collection of Saxifraga Porophyllum.
MAP PAGE: **2/3**

MWhe **A D & N Wheeler,** Pye Court, Willoughby, Rugby, Warwickshire CV23 8BZ
TEL: (0788) 890341 *CONTACT:* Mrs N Wheeler
OPENING TIMES: 1000-1630 1st Oct-1st Jun. 1st Jun-1st Oct please phone first for appt.
MAIL ORDER: Yes *MIN VALUE:* £2.50 + p&p *CAT. COST:* 2 x 1st class
W/SALE or RETAIL: Retail
SPECIALITIES: Fuchsia & Pelargonium. New varieties of coloured leaf & double flowers introduced each year. *MAP PAGE:* **2**

MWil **The Wildlife Gardening Centre,** Witney Road, Kingston Bagpuize, Abingdon, Oxfordshire OX13 5AN
TEL: (0865) 821660 *CONTACT:* Jenny Steel & Alan Pottinger
◆ *OPENING TIMES:* Please ring for opening times.
MAIL ORDER: Yes *MIN VALUE:* None *CAT. COST:* 3 x 1st class *W/SALE or RETAIL:* Both
SPECIALITIES: Native Wild Flowers & Shrubs, Cottage garden plants, Herbs & native Trees.
MAP PAGE: **2**

MWol **H Woolman Ltd,** Grange Road, Dorridge, Solihull, West Midlands B93 8QB
TEL: (0564) 776283 *FAX:* (0564) 770830 *CONTACT:* John Woolman
OPENING TIMES: 0730-1615 Mon-Fri.
MAIL ORDER: Yes *MIN VALUE:* None *CAT. COST:* Free *W/SALE or RETAIL:* Both
SPECIALITIES: Chrysanthemum. *MAP PAGE:* **2**

MWoo **Woodfield Bros,** Wood End, Clifford Chambers, Stratford-on-Avon, Warwickshire CV37 8HR
TEL: (0789) 205618 *CONTACT:* B Woodfield
OPENING TIMES: Weekends for plant collection only.
MAIL ORDER: Yes *MIN VALUE:* See list for details *CAT. COST:* Sae *W/SALE or RETAIL:* Both
SPECIALITIES: Carnations, Lupins & Delphiniums. *MAP PAGE:* **2**

MYat **R J Yates,** The Gardens, Roecliffe Manor, Woodhouse Eaves, Leicestershire LE12 8TN
TEL: (0533) 303422 *CONTACT:* R J Yates
OPENING TIMES: 0930-1630 Sat & Sun only.
MAIL ORDER: Yes *MIN VALUE:* £10.00 + p&p *CAT. COST:* Large Sae *W/SALE or RETAIL:* Retail
SPECIALITIES: Primulas & Kabschia Saxifrages. *MAP PAGE:* **5**

NBar **Barkers Primrose Nurseries & Grdn Cntr,** Whalley Road, Clitheroe, Lancashire BB7 1HT
TEL: (0200) 23521 *CONTACT:* W Barker
OPENING TIMES: 0830-1730 Mon-Sat, 1000-1700 Sun.
MAIL ORDER: No *CAT. COST:* 3 x 2nd class *W/SALE or RETAIL:* Retail
SPECIALITIES: Uncommon Trees & Shrubs, Roses, Perennials etc. *MAP PAGE:* **5**

NBat **Battersby Roses,** Peartree Cottage, Old Battersby, Great Ayton, Cleveland TS9 6LU
TEL: (0642) 723402 *CONTACT:* Eric & Avril Stainthorpe
OPENING TIMES: 1000-dusk most days.
MAIL ORDER: No *CAT. COST:* Sae *W/SALE or RETAIL:* Both
SPECIALITIES: Exhibition Roses. *MAP PAGE:* **7/8**

See note on Mail Order, EC sales & Export on page 5

NBea **Beamish Clematis Nursery,,** Burntwood Cottage, Stoney Lane, Beamish, Co Durham DH9 0SJ
TEL: (091) 3700202 *CONTACT:* C F Brown
OPENING TIMES: 0900-1700 Mon-Sat Feb-Oct.
MAIL ORDER: No *CAT. COST:* None issued *W/SALE or RETAIL:* Both
SPECIALITIES: 180 varieties of Clematis. *MAP PAGE:* **7/8**

NBee **Beechcroft Nurseries,** Bongate, Appleby-in-Westmorland, Cumbria CA16 6UE
TEL: (07683) 51201 *CONTACT:* Roger Brown
OPENING TIMES: 0800-1800 Mon-Sat, 1100-1800 Sun.
MAIL ORDER: Yes *MIN VALUE:* £8.00 + p&p *CAT. COST:* £1.50 *W/SALE or RETAIL:* Retail
SPECIALITIES: Hardy field-grown Trees & Shrubs. Mail Order Trees Nov-Mar only. *MAP PAGE:* **8**

NBir **Birkheads Cottage Garden Nursery,** Birkheads Lane, Nr Sunniside, Newcastle upon Tyne, Tyne & Wear NE16 5EL
TEL: (0207) 232262 *CONTACT:* Mrs Christine Liddle
OPENING TIMES: 1000-1800 Fri-Sun & Bank Hols Mar-mid Oct & by appt.
MAIL ORDER: No *CAT. COST:* None issued *W/SALE or RETAIL:* Retail
SPECIALITIES: Allium, Campanula, Digitalis, Euphorbia, Hardy Geraniums, Meconopsis, Primula & Herbs. *MAP PAGE:* **7/8**

NBra **Brambling House Alpines,** 119 Sheffield Road, Warmsworth, Doncaster, South Yorkshire DN4 9QX
TEL: (0302) 850730 *CONTACT:* Tony & Jane McDonagh
OPENING TIMES: 0900-dusk Tue-Sun.
MAIL ORDER: Yes *MIN VALUE:* £3.20 + p&p *CAT. COST:* Large Sae *W/SALE or RETAIL:* Retail
SPECIALITIES: Diascia, Saxifraga, Lewisia, Sempervivum (over 150 varieties). Unusual Alpine House plants. *MAP PAGE:* **5/7**

NBro **Brownthwaite Hardy Plants,** Fell Yeat, Casterton, Kirby Lonsdale, Lancashire LA6 2JW
TEL: (05242) 71340 *CONTACT:* Chris Benson
OPENING TIMES: Tue-Sun 1st Apr-31st Oct.
MAIL ORDER: Yes *MIN VALUE:* None *CAT. COST:* 2 x 1st class *W/SALE or RETAIL:* Retail
SPECIALITIES: Herbaceous Perennials & Grasses. *MAP PAGE:* **5/8**

NCat **Catforth Gardens,** Roots Lane, Catforth, Preston, Lancashire PR4 0JB
TEL: (0772) 690561/690269 *CONTACT:* Judith Bradshaw & Chris Moore
OPENING TIMES: 1030-1700 13th Mar-12th Sep 1993.
MAIL ORDER: No *CAT. COST:* 3 x 1st class *W/SALE or RETAIL:* Retail
SPECIALITIES: National Collection of Hardy Geraniums. Also other unusual herbaceous incl. Campanula, Euphorbia, Pulmonaria & Viola. *MAP PAGE:* **5**

NCra **Craven's Nursery,** 1 Foulds Terrace, Bingley, West Yorkshire BD16 4LZ
TEL: (0274) 561412 *CONTACT:* S R Craven & M Craven
OPENING TIMES:
MAIL ORDER: Only *MIN VALUE:* *CAT. COST:* 54p *W/SALE or RETAIL:* Both
SPECIALITIES: Show Auricula, Primula, Pinks, Alpines and specialist Seeds.

NDea **Deanswood Plants,** Pottteries Lane, Littlethorpe, Ripon, North Yorkshire HG4 3LF
TEL: (0765) 603441 *CONTACT:* Jacky Barber
OPENING TIMES: 1000-1700 Tue-Sun 1st Apr-30th Sep.
MAIL ORDER: No *CAT. COST:* £1.30 *W/SALE or RETAIL:* Retail
SPECIALITIES: Pond, Marginals & Bog plants. *MAP PAGE:* **5/7/8**

NEgg **Eggleston Hall,** Barnard Castle, Co Durham DL12 0AG
TEL: (0833) 50378 *CONTACT:* Mrs R H Gray
OPENING TIMES: 1000-1700 daily
MAIL ORDER: No *CAT. COST:* £1.50 *W/SALE or RETAIL:* Retail
SPECIALITIES: Rare & Unusual plants with particular emphasis to Flower Arrangers.
MAP PAGE: **8**

NElm **Elm Ridge Gardens Ltd.,** Coniscliffe Road, Darlington, Co Durham DL3 8DJ
TEL: (0325) 462710 *CONTACT:* Mr C Blake & M Blake
OPENING TIMES: 0800-1830 Mon-Sat Apr-Jul, 0800-1730 Aug-Mar.
MAIL ORDER: *MIN VALUE:* *CAT. COST:* Free *W/SALE or RETAIL:* Both
SPECIALITIES: Very large selection of Pot Plants for home & industry, bedding plants, cut flowers & floristry. *MAP PAGE:* **7/8/5**

NFai **Fairy Lane Nurseries,** Fairy Lane, Sale, Greater Manchester M33 2JT
TEL: 061-905 1137 *CONTACT:* John B Coxon
OPENING TIMES: 1000-1730 daily Summer, 1000-1630 daily Winter. Closed 23rd Dec-3rd Jan.
MAIL ORDER: No *CAT. COST:* None issued *W/SALE or RETAIL:* Retail
SPECIALITIES: Hardy & tender Perennials, Herbs, Hebes & less usual Shrubs. *MAP PAGE:* **5**

NGar **Gardenscape,** Fairview, Summerbridge, Nr Harrogate, North Yorkshire HG3 4DH
TEL: (0423) 780291 *CONTACT:* Michael D Myers
OPENING TIMES: By appt only. Mail Order predominantly.
MAIL ORDER: Yes *MIN VALUE:* None *CAT. COST:* 3 x 2nd class *W/SALE or RETAIL:* Both
SPECIALITIES: National Collections of Wood Anemones, Hepaticas & Primula marginata. Also Galanthus, hardy Orchids & uncommon plants. *MAP PAGE:* **7/5**

NGre **Greenslacks Nurseries,** Ocot Lane, Scammonden, Huddersfield, Yorkshire HD3 3FR
TEL: (0484) 842584 *CONTACT:* Mrs V K Tuton
OPENING TIMES: 1000-1600 Wed-Sun 1st Mar-31st Oct.
MAIL ORDER: Yes *MIN VALUE:* None *CAT. COST:* £1.00 or 2IRCs *W/SALE or RETAIL:* Both
SPECIALITIES: Unusual & Hardy plants esp. Succulents *MAP PAGE:* **5**

NGrN **Greenland Nurseries,** 11 Long Lane, Clayton West, Huddersfield, Yorkshire HD8 9PR
TEL: (0484) 865964 *CONTACT:* S R Smith
OPENING TIMES:
MAIL ORDER: No *CAT. COST:* Sae *W/SALE or RETAIL:* Both
SPECIALITIES: Vines for winemaking. Also Soft Fruit, Shrubs & dwarf Conifers. *MAP PAGE:*

NHal **Halls of Heddon,** (Off.) West Heddon Nurseries, Heddon-on-the-Wall, Newcastle-upon-Tyne, Northumberland NE15 0JS
TEL: (0661) 852445 *CONTACT:* Judith Lockey
OPENING TIMES: 0900-1700 Mon-Sat 1000-1700 Sun Oct-Mar, 0900-1800 Mon-Sat 1000-1800 Sun Apr-Sep.
MAIL ORDER: Yes *MIN VALUE:* None *CAT. COST:* 2 x 2nd class *W/SALE or RETAIL:* Retail
SPECIALITIES: Chrysanthemum & Dahlia. Wide range of Herbaceous. *NOTE: Mail Order Dahlia & Chrysanthemum only. *MAP PAGE:* **7/8**

NHar **Hartside Nursery Garden,** Nr Alston, Cumbria CA9 3BL
TEL: (0434) 381372 *CONTACT:* S L & N Huntley
◆ *OPENING TIMES:* 0900-1700 Mon-Fri, 1000-1600 Sat, 1230-1600 Sun & B/Hols 1st Mar-31st Oct. 1st Nov-28th Feb by appt.
MAIL ORDER: Yes *MIN VALUE:* No minimum charge *CAT. COST:* 3 x 2nd class
W/SALE or RETAIL: Retail
SPECIALITIES: Alpines grown at altitude of 1100 feet in Pennines. *MAP PAGE:* **8**

NHex **Hexham Herbs,** Chesters Walled Garden, Chollerford, Hexham Northumberland NE46
TEL: (0434) 681 483 *CONTACT:* Susie & Kevin White
◆ *OPENING TIMES:* 1000-1700 Easter-Oct daily. Please phone for Winter opening times.
MAIL ORDER: No *CAT. COST:* £1.50 inc. p&p *W/SALE or RETAIL:*
SPECIALITIES: Extensive range of Herbs & National Collection of Thymus & Origanums. Unusual Perennials & Wild Flowers. *MAP PAGE:* **8/9**

NHHG **Hardstoft Herb Garden,,** Hall View Cottage, Hardstoft, Pilsley, Nr Chesterfield, Derbyshire S45 8AH
TEL: (0246) 854268 *CONTACT:* Lynne & Steve Raynor
OPENING TIMES: 1000-1800 daily, 1st Mar-30th Sep.
MAIL ORDER: No *CAT. COST:* Free *W/SALE or RETAIL:* Retail
SPECIALITIES: Very wide range of Herb Plants. Over 40 Lavenders & 12 Rosemary. Scented Pelargoniums. *MAP PAGE:* **5/7**

NHip **Hippopottering Nursery,** Orchard House, Brackenhill Road, Haxey, Nr Doncaster, North Yorkshire DN9 2LR
TEL: (0427) 752185 *CONTACT:* John Gibbons
OPENING TIMES: By appt. only.
MAIL ORDER: Yes *MIN VALUE:* £15.00 + p&p *CAT. COST:* 2 x 1st class
W/SALE or RETAIL: Retail
SPECIALITIES: Uncommon grafted Acer palmatum & japonicum cultivars. Selected Acer seedlings. Bonsai starters. *MAP PAGE:* **7**

 See note on Mail Order, EC sales & Export on page 5

NHlc **Halecat Garden Nurseries,** Witherslack, Grange over Sands, Cumbria LA11 6RU

TEL: (044 852) 229 *CONTACT:* Mrs M Stanley
◆ *OPENING TIMES:* 0900-1630 Mon-Fri, 1400-1600 Sun & parties by appointment.
MAIL ORDER: No *CAT. COST:* 40p *W/SALE or RETAIL:* Retail
SPECIALITIES: Hosta, Hydrangea, Euphorbia, grey foliage and perenial border plants.
MAP PAGE: **5/8**

NHol **Holden Clough Nursery,** Holden, Bolton-by-Bowland, Clitheroe, Lancashire BB7 4PF

TEL: (02007) 615* *CONTACT:* P J Foley
◆ *OPENING TIMES:* 1300-1630 Mon-Thu, 0900-1630 Sat. 1400-1630 Sun (Apr & May only incl Easter Sun).
MAIL ORDER: Yes *MIN VALUE:* No minimum charge *CAT. COST:* £1.20*
W/SALE or RETAIL: Both
SPECIALITIES: Large general list incl. Primula, Saxifrage, Pulmonaria, Androsace, Astilbe, Gentiana & Hosta. NOTE:- Biannual catalogue. *Tel No. (0200) 447615 from Sep '93.
MAP PAGE: **5**

NH&H **Herb & Heather Centre,** West Haddlesey, Nr Selby, North Yorks YO8 8QA

TEL: (0757) 228279 *CONTACT:* Carole Starr
OPENING TIMES: 0930-1730 Thu-Tue Mar-Oct. 0930-dusk Thu-Tue Nov-Feb.
MAIL ORDER: Yes *MIN VALUE:* £20 + p&p *CAT. COST:* 3 x 1st class* *W/SALE or RETAIL:* Both
SPECIALITIES: 450 Herbs, 150 Heathers. *NOTE: Herb Catalogue & Heather Catalogue each 3 x 1st class stamps. National Collection of Santolina *MAP PAGE:* **5/7**

NJap **The Japanese Garden Co.,** Spout House, Lupton, via Carnforth, Lancashire LA6 1PQ

TEL: (05395) 67802 *CONTACT:* Keith & Susan Gott
OPENING TIMES: Mail Order only.
MAIL ORDER: Only *MIN VALUE:* No minimum charge *CAT. COST:* Sae for list
W/SALE or RETAIL: Retail
SPECIALITIES: Primula, Acer, Bamboo, Conifers & Herbaceous, mainly of oriental origin. Japanese garden design service. Booklet on design £3.75. *MAP PAGE:* **5/8!**

NKay **Reginald Kaye Ltd,** Waithman Nurseries, Silverdale, Carnforth, Lancashire LA5 0TY

TEL: (0524) 701252 *CONTACT:* J J & L M Kaye
OPENING TIMES: 0800-1230 & 1400-1700 Mon-Fri all year. 1000-1230 & 1400-1700 Sat & 1430-1700 Sun Mar-Nov only.
MAIL ORDER: No *CAT. COST:* 60p *W/SALE or RETAIL:* Both
SPECIALITIES: Hardy ferns, Alpines, Herbaceous, some Shrubs. *MAP PAGE:* **8**

NLan **Landlife Wildflowers Ltd.,** The Old Police Station, Lark Lane, Liverpool, Lancashire L17 8UU

TEL: (061) 794 9314 *FAX:* (061) 794 8072 *CONTACT:* Dr K Chambers & G Watson
OPENING TIMES: By appt for collection only.
MAIL ORDER: Yes *MIN VALUE:* None *CAT. COST:* Free *W/SALE or RETAIL:* Both
SPECIALITIES: Wild herbaceous plants. *MAP PAGE:* **4/5**

NLin **Lingholm Gardens,** Lingholm, Keswick, Cumbria CA12 5UA

TEL: (07687) 72003 Ext 17 *CONTACT:* Mr M J Swift
OPENING TIMES: 1000-1700 daily Apr-Oct. Nov-Mar by appt. only.
MAIL ORDER: No *CAT. COST:* No retail cat. *W/SALE or RETAIL:* Both
SPECIALITIES: Meconopsis & Primula. Other unusual plants from the garden. *MAP PAGE:* **8**

NMar **J & D Marston,** Culag, Green Lane, Nafferton, Driffield, East Yorkshire YO25 0LF

TEL: (0377) 44487 *CONTACT:* J & D Marston
◆ *OPENING TIMES:* 1350-1700 Easter-mid Sep, Sat, Sun & other times by appt.
MAIL ORDER: Yes *MIN VALUE:* £15.00 + p&p *CAT. COST:* £1.00 *W/SALE or RETAIL:* Retail
SPECIALITIES: Hardy & Greenhouse Ferns only. *MAP PAGE:* **7**

NMen **Mendle Nursery,** Holme, Scunthorpe, DN16 3RF

TEL: (0724) 850864 *CONTACT:* Mrs A Earnshaw
OPENING TIMES: 1000-1800 daily
MAIL ORDER: Yes *MIN VALUE:* No minimum charge *CAT. COST:* 2 x 1st class
W/SALE or RETAIL: Retail
SPECIALITIES: Alpines. *MAP PAGE:* **7**

◆ **See also Display Advertisements**

NMGN **Markham Grange Nurseries,** Long Lands Lane, Brodsworth, Nr Doncaster, South Yorkshire DN5 7XB
TEL: (0302) 722390 *FAX:* (0302) 727571 *CONTACT:* V T Nuttall
OPENING TIMES: 0900-1630 daily, later in summer.
MAIL ORDER: No *CAT. COST:* *W/SALE or RETAIL:* Both
SPECIALITIES: Fuchsia. *MAP PAGE:* **5/7**

NMir **Mires Beck Nusery,** Low Mill Lane, North Cave, Brough, North Humberside HU15 2NR
TEL: (0430) 421543 *CONTACT:* Dr I G & R Tinklin
◆ *OPENING TIMES:* 1000-1600 Wed-Sat, 1st Mar-31st Oct & by appt.
MAIL ORDER: Yes *MIN VALUE:* £15.00 + p&p *CAT. COST:* 3 x 1st class
W/SALE or RETAIL: Both
SPECIALITIES: British native plants. Yorkshire-hardy border Perennials. Foliage, Alpine & Rock Garden plants. *MAP PAGE:* **7**

NMos **Stanley Mossop,** Boonwood Garden Centre, Gosforth, Seascale, Cumbria CA20 1BP
TEL: (0946) 821817 *CONTACT:* Stanley & Gary Mossop.
OPENING TIMES: 1000-1700 daily.
MAIL ORDER: Yes *MIN VALUE:* No minimum charge *CAT. COST:* Free *W/SALE or RETAIL:* Both
SPECIALITIES: Achimenes, Achimenantha, Eucodonia, Gloxinia (incl. species) & Smithiantha.
MAP PAGE: **8/9**

NNor **Northumbria Nurseries,** Castle Gardens, Ford, Berwick-upon-Tweed, Northumberland TD15 2PZ
TEL: (0890) 820379 *FAX:* (0890) 820594 *CONTACT:* Hazel M Huddleston
◆ *OPENING TIMES:* 0900-1800 Mon-Fri all year, & 1000-1800 Sat-Sun & Bank Hols Mar-Oct & by appt. (Or till dusk).
MAIL ORDER: *MIN VALUE:* *CAT. COST:* £1.50 PO/Chq. *W/SALE or RETAIL:* Both
SPECIALITIES: Over 1000 different species of container grown hardy ornamental Shrubs, Perennials & Alpines. *MAP PAGE:* **8/9**

NNrd **Norden Alpines,** Hirst Road, Carlton, Nr Goole, Humberside DN14 9PX
TEL: (0405) 861348 *CONTACT:* Norma & Denis Walton
OPENING TIMES: 1000-1700 Sat-Sun & Bank Hols Mar-Sep, or by appt.
MAIL ORDER: No *CAT. COST:* None *W/SALE or RETAIL:* Retail
SPECIALITIES: Many unusual Alpines esp. Campanula, Primula & Saxifraga. *MAP PAGE:* **5/7**

NOak **Oak Tree Nursery,** Mill Lane, Barlow, Selby, North Yorks YO8 8EY
TEL: (0757) 618409 *CONTACT:* Gill Plowes
OPENING TIMES: 1000-1630 Tue-Sun mid Feb-end Oct.
MAIL ORDER: No *CAT. COST:* 2 x 1st class *W/SALE or RETAIL:* Retail
SPECIALITIES: Herbaceous & unusual Perennials. *MAP PAGE:* **5/7**

NOrc **Orchard House Nursery,** Orchard House, Wormald Green, Nr Harrogate, North Yorks HG3 3PX
TEL: (0765) 677541 *CONTACT:* Mr B M Corner
OPENING TIMES: 0900-1730 Mon-Sat, 1400-1700 Sun.
MAIL ORDER: No *CAT. COST:* £1.00 *W/SALE or RETAIL:* Both
SPECIALITIES: Herbaceous, Herbs, Alpines, Ferns & unusual cottage garden plants.
MAP PAGE: **5/7/8**

NPal **The Palm Farm,** Thornton Hall Gardens, Station Road, Thornton Curtis, Nr Ulceby, Humberside DN39 6XF
TEL: (0469) 31232 *CONTACT:* W W Spink
◆ *OPENING TIMES:* 1400-1700 daily ex Winter when advised to check by phone first.
MAIL ORDER: Yes *MIN VALUE:* £11.00 + p&p *CAT. COST:* 1 x 2nd class
W/SALE or RETAIL: Both
SPECIALITIES: Hardy & half-Hardy Palms, Meconopsis & unusual Trees, Shrubs & Conservatory plants. *MAP PAGE:* **7**

NPer **Perry's Plants,** The River Garden, Sleights, Whitby, North Yorks YO21 1RR
TEL: (0947) 810329 *CONTACT:* Pat & Richard Perry
◆ *OPENING TIMES:* 1000-1700 Easter to October.
MAIL ORDER: No *CAT. COST:* 3 x 1st class *W/SALE or RETAIL:* Retail
SPECIALITIES: Lavatera, Malva, Erysimum, Euphorbia, Anthemis, Osteospermum & Hebe.
MAP PAGE: **7/8**

 See note on Mail Order, EC sales & Export on page 5

NPin **Pinks & Carnations,** 22 Chetwyn Avenue, Bromley Cross, Bolton, Lancashire BL7 9BN
TEL: (0204) 306273 *CONTACT:* R & T Gillies
◆ *OPENING TIMES:* Appt only.
MAIL ORDER: Yes *MIN VALUE:* £20 + p&p *CAT. COST:* Free *W/SALE or RETAIL:* Both
SPECIALITIES: Pinks and Perpetual Flowering Carnations. *MAP PAGE:* **5**

NPor **J V Porter,** 12 Hazel Grove, Southport, Merseyside PR8 6AX
TEL: (0704) 533902 *FAX:* (07048) 32196 *CONTACT:* John Porter
OPENING TIMES: 1030-1600 Thu-Sun Jan-May & by appt. (Wholesale open all year 0800-1615)
MAIL ORDER: Yes *MIN VALUE:* £4.40 + p&p *CAT. COST:* 2 x 1st class *W/SALE or RETAIL:* Both
SPECIALITIES: Fuchsia. *MAP PAGE:* **5/4**

NRar **Rarer Plants,** Ashfield House, Austfield Lane, Monk Fryston, Leeds, North Yorkshire LS25 5EH
TEL: (0977) 682263 *CONTACT:* Anne Watson
OPENING TIMES: 1000-1600 Sun Feb-Easter for Hellebores. 0930-1530 Mon-Fri, 0930-1700 Sat & Sun Easter-15th Sep.
MAIL ORDER: No *CAT. COST:* 3 x 1st class *W/SALE or RETAIL:* Retail
SPECIALITIES: Unusual plants, variegated plants and Penstemons, Grasses & Hellebore hybrids.
MAP PAGE: **5/7**

NRed **Redhouse Nurseries,** c/o 19 Dovedale Avenue, Grangetown, Middlesbrough, Cleveland TL6 7QS
TEL: (0642) 463101 *CONTACT:* C Elliott
OPENING TIMES: No callers
MAIL ORDER: Yes *MIN VALUE:* No minimum charge *CAT. COST:* 2 x 1st class
W/SALE or RETAIL: Both
SPECIALITIES: Show Auriculas, minature Roses, Alpines (beginners & collectors) & dwarf Shrubs.
MAP PAGE:

NRog **R V Roger Ltd,** The Nurseries, Pickering, North Yorkshire YO18 7HG
TEL: (0751) 72226 *CONTACT:* J R Roger, S Peirson & A G & I M Roger
OPENING TIMES: 0900-1700 Mon-Sat, 1300-1700 Sun. Closed Dec 25th-Jan 2nd each year.
MAIL ORDER: Yes *MIN VALUE:* None *CAT. COST:* £1.00 *W/SALE or RETAIL:* Both
SPECIALITIES: General list, hardy in North of England. Co-holders of National Erodium & Erythronium Collection. *MAP PAGE:* **7/8**

NRoo **Rookhope Nurseries,** Rookhope, Upper Weardale, Co Durham DL13 2DD
TEL: (0388) 517272 *CONTACT:* Karen Blackburn
OPENING TIMES: 0830-1700 daily mid Mar-Oct, 1000-1600 most days Nov-mid Mar, please phone to check.
MAIL ORDER: No *CAT. COST:* 3 x 1st class *W/SALE or RETAIL:* Retail
SPECIALITIES: Wide range of Hardy plants grown at 1,100 feet in the northern Pennines.
MAP PAGE: **8**

NRya **Ryal Nursery,** East Farm Cottage, Ryal, Northumberland NE20 0SA
TEL: (0661) 886562 *CONTACT:* R F Hadden
OPENING TIMES: 1300-1700 Tue, 1000-1700 Sun Mar-Jul & by appt.
MAIL ORDER: Yes *MIN VALUE:* £5.00 + p&p *CAT. COST:* Sae *W/SALE or RETAIL:* Both
SPECIALITIES: Alpines & Primula. *MAP PAGE:* **8/9**

NSal **Salley Gardens,** Allergarth, Roweltown, Carlisle, Cumbria CA6 6JU
TEL: *CONTACT:* Richard Lewin
OPENING TIMES: By appt.
MAIL ORDER: Yes *MIN VALUE:* £25.00 + p&p *CAT. COST:* Sae *W/SALE or RETAIL:* Retail
SPECIALITIES: Wildflowers & Medicinal Herbs. *MAP PAGE:* **8**

NSel **Sellet Hall Gardens,** Whittington, via Carnforth, Lancashire LA6 2QF
TEL: (05242) 71865 *FAX:* (05242) 72208 *CONTACT:* Judy Gray
◆ *OPENING TIMES:* 1000-1700 daily all year. Please telephone to check winter weekend openings.
MAIL ORDER: Yes *MIN VALUE:* £5.00 + p&p *CAT. COST:* Sae *W/SALE or RETAIL:* Retail
SPECIALITIES: Herbs, Acers, Auriculas & Bamboos. *MAP PAGE:* **5/8**

NSti **Stillingfleet Lodge Nurseries,** Stillingfleet, Yorkshire YO4 6HW

TEL: (0904) 728506 *CONTACT:* Vanessa Cook
OPENING TIMES: 1000-1600 Tue Wed Fri & Sat 1st Apr-18th Oct.
MAIL ORDER: Yes *MIN VALUE:* £5.00 + p&p *CAT. COST:* 5 x 1st class
W/SALE or RETAIL: Retail
SPECIALITIES: Foliage & unusual perennials. Hardy Geraniums, Pulmonaria, variegated plants & Grasses. Holder of National Pulmonaria Collection. *MAP PAGE:* **5/7**

NSty **Stydd Nursery,** Stoneygate Lane, Ribchester, Nr Preston, Lancashire PR3 3YN

TEL: (0254) 878797 *FAX:* (0254) 878254 *CONTACT:* Mr & Mrs J A Walker
OPENING TIMES: 1330-1700 Tue-Fri, 0900-1700 Sat all year, 1400-1700 Sun 1st Apr-23rd Dec.
MAIL ORDER: Yes *MIN VALUE:* No minimum charge *CAT. COST:* 50p *W/SALE or RETAIL:* Both
SPECIALITIES: Old Roses & ornamental foliage. Half-hardy Perennials. *MAP PAGE:* **5**

NTow **Town Farm Nursery,** Whitton, Stillington, Stockton on Tees, Cleveland TS21 1LQ

TEL: (0740) 31079 *CONTACT:* F D Baker
◆ *OPENING TIMES:* 1000-1800 Fri-Mon Mar-Oct.
MAIL ORDER: Yes *MIN VALUE:* £10.00 + p&p *CAT. COST:* Sae *W/SALE or RETAIL:* Retail
SPECIALITIES: Unusual Alpines, Border Perennials & Shrubs. *MAP PAGE:* **7/8**

NVic **The Vicarage Garden,** Carrington, Urmston, Manchester, M31 4AG

TEL: (061 775) 2750 *CONTACT:* Miss M Zugor
OPENING TIMES: 1000-1800 Fri-Wed Apr-Sept. 1030-1700 Fri-Wed Oct-Mar.
MAIL ORDER: Yes *MIN VALUE:* £5.00 + p&p *CAT. COST:* £1.00 *W/SALE or RETAIL:* Both
SPECIALITIES: Herbaceous & Alpines. *MAP PAGE:* **5**

NWCA **White Cottage Alpines,** Eastgate, Rudston, Driffield, East Yorkshire YO25 0UX

TEL: (0262) 420668 *CONTACT:* Sally E Cummins
◆ *OPENING TIMES:* 1000-1700 (or dusk) Thu-Sun & Bank Hol Mons. Closed Dec & Jan.
MAIL ORDER: Yes *MIN VALUE:* None *CAT. COST:* 2 x 1st class *W/SALE or RETAIL:* Both
SPECIALITIES: Alpines. *MAP PAGE:* **7**

NWea **Weasdale Nurseries,** Newbiggin-on-Lune, Kirkby Stephen, Cumbria CA17 4LX

TEL: (05396) 23246 *FAX:* (05396) 23277 *CONTACT:* Andrew Forsyth
OPENING TIMES: 0900-1700 Mon-Fri.
MAIL ORDER: Yes *MIN VALUE:* No minimum charge *CAT. COST:* £2.30
W/SALE or RETAIL: Retail
SPECIALITIES: Hardy forest trees, hedging & ornamental Shrubs grown at 850 feet. Mail Order a speciality. *MAP PAGE:* **5/8**

NWin **Wingates,** 62A Chorley Road, Westhoughton, Bolton, Lancashire BL5 3PL

TEL: (0942) 813357 *CONTACT:* G Lambert
OPENING TIMES: 1400-dusk daily. Check during winter months.
MAIL ORDER: No *CAT. COST:* 30p *W/SALE or RETAIL:* Retail
SPECIALITIES: Mainly Heathers, also Dwarf Conifers & Shrubs, Ericaceous plants, Alpines & dwarf Rhododendrons. *MAP PAGE:* **5/4**

NWyt **Wytherstone Nurseries,** The Estate Office, Pockley, Yorkshire YO6 5TE

TEL: (0439) 71239 *FAX:* (0439) 70468 *CONTACT:* Ian Powell
OPENING TIMES: 1000-1700 Wed-Sun 1st Apr-20th Oct & Bank Hols Mon. Also by appt.
MAIL ORDER: Yes *MIN VALUE:* £10.00 + p&p *CAT. COST:* 2 x 1st class
W/SALE or RETAIL: Retail
SPECIALITIES: Rare & hard to find Perennials, Shrubs & Conservatory plants. *MAP PAGE:* **8/7/5**

NZep **Zephyrwude Irises,** 48 Blacker Lane, Crigglestone, Wakefield, West Yorkshire WF4 3EW

TEL: (0924) 252101 *CONTACT:* Richard L Brook
◆ *OPENING TIMES:* Viewing only 0900-dusk daily, variable May-June periods. Phone first, dark-2300.
MAIL ORDER: Yes *MIN VALUE:* £10.00 + p&p *CAT. COST:* A5 Sae or 1st
W/SALE or RETAIL: Retail
SPECIALITIES: Bearded Iris, dwarf, intermediate & tall, mainly modern American varieties. 700 variety trial/display garden. Delivery Jul-Sep only. Cat. available Apr-Sep. *MAP PAGE:* **5/7**

 See note on Mail Order, EC sales & Export on page 5

SAga **Agar's Nursery,** Agars Lane, Hordle, Lymington, Hampshire SO41 0FL

TEL: (0590) 683703 *CONTACT:* George & Diana Tombs
OPENING TIMES: 1000-1700 Fri-Wed Mar-Oct, 1000-1600 Fri-Wed Feb & Nov-20th Dec. Closed 20th Dec-31st Jan.
MAIL ORDER: Yes *MIN VALUE:* £10.00 + p&p *CAT. COST:* 3 x 1st class
W/SALE or RETAIL: Both
SPECIALITIES: Penstemon, Salvia & Iris. Also wide range of Hardy plants inc. Shrubs & Climbers.
MAP PAGE: **2**

SAll **Allwood Bros,** Mill Nursery, Hassocks, West Sussex BN6 9NB

TEL: (0273 84) 4229 *CONTACT:* W Rickaby
OPENING TIMES: 0900-1700 Mon-Fri.
MAIL ORDER: No *CAT. COST:* 2 x 1st class *W/SALE or RETAIL:* Both
SPECIALITIES: Dianthus, incl Hardy Border Carnations, Pinks, Perpetual & Allwoodii. Gypsophila, most available as Seed. *MAP PAGE:* **3**

SApp **Apple Court,** Hordle Lane, Hordle, Lymington, Hampshire S041 0HU

TEL: (0590) 642130 *CONTACT:* Diana Grenfell & Roger Grounds
◆ *OPENING TIMES:* Normally Thu-Mon Feb-Nov. Closed Dec & Jan & one week end-Aug. Suggest telephone first.
MAIL ORDER: Yes *MIN VALUE:* £10 + p&p *CAT. COST:* 3 x 1st class *W/SALE or RETAIL:* Retail
SPECIALITIES: Hosta, Grasses, Ferns, Hemerocallis. National Collection Woodwardia, Rohdea, Anthericum/Paradisea, Camassia & Hosta. *NOTE: MO Spring/Autumn only. *MAP PAGE:* **2**

SArc **Architectural Plants,** Cooks Farm, Nuthurst, Horsham, West Sussex RH13 6LH

TEL: (0403) 891772 *FAX:* (0403) 891056 *CONTACT:* Angus White
◆ *OPENING TIMES:* 0900-1700 Mon-Sat.
MAIL ORDER: Yes *MIN VALUE:* None. £13 min p&p *CAT. COST:* Free *W/SALE or RETAIL:* Both
SPECIALITIES: Architectural plants & hardy Exotics. *MAP PAGE:* **3**

SAsh **Ashenden Nursery,** Cranbrook Road, Benenden, Cranbrook, Kent TN17 4ET

TEL: (0580) 241792 *CONTACT:* Kevin McGarry
OPENING TIMES: 1000-1300 & 1400-1700 Mon-Sat.
MAIL ORDER: No *CAT. COST:* Sae *W/SALE or RETAIL:* Retail
SPECIALITIES: Rock garden & perennials *MAP PAGE:* **3**

SAWi **Anthony Archer-Wills Ltd.,** Broadford Bridge Road, West Chiltington, West Sussex RH20 2LF

TEL: (0798) 813204 *FAX:* (0798) 815080 *CONTACT:* Anthony Archer-Wills
OPENING TIMES: By appt. only - please telephone.
MAIL ORDER: Yes *MIN VALUE:* £15.00 + p&p *CAT. COST:* *W/SALE or RETAIL:* Both
SPECIALITIES: Ponds, Lakes & Water garden plants. *MAP PAGE:* **3**

SAxl **Axletree Nursery,** Starvecrow Lane, Peasmarsh, Rye, East Sussex TN31 6XL

TEL: (0797) 230470 *CONTACT:* D J Hibberd
OPENING TIMES: 1000-1700 Wed-Sat mid Mar-Sep.
MAIL ORDER: No *CAT. COST:* 4 x 1st class *W/SALE or RETAIL:* Retail
SPECIALITIES: Herbaceous plants, esp. Hardy Geraniums & Euphorbia. *MAP PAGE:* **3**

SBai **Steven Bailey,** Silver Street, Sway, Lymington, Hampshire SO41 6ZA

TEL: (0590) 682227 *FAX:* (0590) 683765 *CONTACT:*
OPENING TIMES: 1000-1300 & 1400-1630 Mon-Fri all year. 1000-1300 & 1400-1600 Sat Mar-Jun ex Bank Hols.
MAIL ORDER: Yes *MIN VALUE:* Quotation *CAT. COST:* 2 x 2nd class *W/SALE or RETAIL:* Both
SPECIALITIES: Carnations, Pinks & Alstroemeria. *MAP PAGE:* **2**

SBam **Bamboo Nursery Ltd.,** Kingsgate Cottage, Wittersham, Tenterden, Kent TN30 7NS

TEL: (0797) 270607 *FAX:* (0797) 270825 *CONTACT:* A Sutcliffe
OPENING TIMES: Appt only.
MAIL ORDER: Yes *MIN VALUE:* None *CAT. COST:* Sae *W/SALE or RETAIL:* Both
SPECIALITIES: Bamboo. *MAP PAGE:* **3**

SBar **Barnhawk Nursery,** Little Barn, Woodgreen, Fordingbridge, Hampshire SP6 2QX
TEL: (0725) 22213 *FAX:* (0725) 22213 *CONTACT:* R & V Crawford
◆ *OPENING TIMES:* 0900-1800 Fri & Sat, Mar to end-Oct only.
MAIL ORDER: No *CAT. COST:* 3 x 1st class *W/SALE or RETAIL:* Both
SPECIALITIES: Choice plants for peat and scree, dwarf shrubs. Two acre garden to visit during opening times. *MAP PAGE:* **2**

SBla **Blackthorn Nursery,** Kilmeston, Alresford, Hampshire SO24 0NL
TEL: (0962) 771796 *CONTACT:* A R & S B White
OPENING TIMES: 0900-1700 Fri & Sat Mar-end Oct.
MAIL ORDER: No *CAT. COST:* 3 x 1st class *W/SALE or RETAIL:* Retail
SPECIALITIES: Choice perennials, Shrubs & Alpines esp. Daphne & Helleborus. *MAP PAGE:* **2**

SBod **Bodiam Nursery,** Ockham House, Bodiam, Robertsbridge, East Sussex TN32 5RA
TEL: (0580) 830811/830649 *FAX:* (0580) 830071 *CONTACT:* Richard Biggs
OPENING TIMES: 0900-1800 or dusk.
MAIL ORDER: Yes *MIN VALUE:* £30.00 + p&p *CAT. COST:* 3 x 1st class
W/SALE or RETAIL: Both
SPECIALITIES: Heathers, herbaceous Perennials, Conifers, Azaleas, Camellias & Clematis.
MAP PAGE: **3**

SBor **Borde Hill Garden Ltd.,** Haywards Heath, West Sussex RH16 1XP
TEL: (0444) 450326 *FAX:* (0444) 440427 *CONTACT:* Emma Jackson
◆ *OPENING TIMES:* 1000-1800 daily (1000-2000 May-Jun) 9th Apr-31st Oct - same as garden.
MAIL ORDER: No *CAT. COST:* None issued *W/SALE or RETAIL:* Retail
SPECIALITIES: Rhododendron, hardy Ferns & unusual Trees & Shrubs & Penstemons.
MAP PAGE: **3**

SBra **J Bradshaw & Son,** Busheyfield Nursery, Herne, Herne Bay, Kent CT6 7LJ
TEL: (0227) 375415 *FAX:* (0227) 375415 *CONTACT:* D J Bradshaw
OPENING TIMES: Not open to public except to collect phone or letter orders.
MAIL ORDER: No *CAT. COST:* Sae *W/SALE or RETAIL:* Both
SPECIALITIES: Clematis & Climbers. Mainly wholesale. NCCPG collection of climbing Lonicera.
MAP PAGE: **3**

SBro **Jarvis Brook Geranium Nurseries,** Tubwell Lane, Jarvis Brook, Crowborough, Sussex TN6 3RH
TEL: (0892) 662329 *CONTACT:* Mrs W M Mitchell
OPENING TIMES: 1030-1730 Thu-Sun Apr-Aug.
MAIL ORDER: Yes *MIN VALUE:* None *CAT. COST:* 2 x 1st class *W/SALE or RETAIL:* Both
SPECIALITIES: Miniature & Dwarf Pelargonium. *MAP PAGE:* **3**

SCaw **R G M Cawthorne,** Lower Daltons Nursery, Swanley Village, Swanley, Kent BR8 7NU
TEL: *CONTACT:* R G M Cawthorne
OPENING TIMES: Written appt. only. Plants may be collected ex nursery during April only.
MAIL ORDER: Yes *MIN VALUE:* 24 plants + p&p *CAT. COST:* 70p *W/SALE or RETAIL:* Retail
SPECIALITIES: 450 named Violas & Violettas. (Largest collection in the world). Holder of NCCPG Viola collection. Assorted Viola Seed sent to US, Japan, China & Australasia. *MAP PAGE:*

SChu **Church Hill Cottage Gardens,** Charing Heath, Ashford, Kent TN27 0BU
TEL: (023 371) 2522 *CONTACT:* Mr & Mrs Michael Metianu.
OPENING TIMES: 1000-1700 daily Mar-May, 1000-1700 Wed-Sun 1st Jun-31st Aug. Other times by appt.
MAIL ORDER: No *CAT. COST:* 3 x 1st class *W/SALE or RETAIL:* Retail
SPECIALITIES: Unusual hardy plants, Dianthus, Alpines & Shrubs. *MAP PAGE:* **3**

SCob **Coblands Nursery,** (Off.) Trench Road, Tonbridge, Kent TN10 3HQ
TEL: (0732) 770999 *FAX:* (0732) 770271 *CONTACT:* Ken Turner
OPENING TIMES: 0830-1600 Mon-Fri.
MAIL ORDER: No *CAT. COST:* *W/SALE or RETAIL:* Both
SPECIALITIES: General range, esp. Bamboos, Grasses & Ferns. NOTE:- Nursery at Back Road, Ightham, Sevenoaks. *MAP PAGE:* **3**

See note on Mail Order, EC sales & Export on page 5

SCog **Coghurst Nursery,** Ivy House Lane, Near Three Oaks, Hastings, East Sussex TN35 4NP
TEL: (0424) 425371/437657 *CONTACT:* J Farnfield, L A & D Edgar
OPENING TIMES: 1200-1630 Mon-Fri, 1000-1630 Sun.
MAIL ORDER: Yes *MIN VALUE:* None *CAT. COST:* 2 x 2nd class *W/SALE or RETAIL:* Both
SPECIALITIES: Camellias, Rhododendrons, Azaleas & Eucryphia. *MAP PAGE:* **3**

SCou **Coombland Gardens,** Coombland, Coneyhurst, Billingshurst, West Sussex RH14 9DG
TEL: (0403) 741549 *FAX:* (0403) 741549 *CONTACT:* Mrs Rosemary Lee
◆ *OPENING TIMES:* 1400-1600 Mon-Fri. Bank Hols & other times by appt. only.
MAIL ORDER: Yes *MIN VALUE:* £10.00 + p&p *CAT. COST:* 4 x 1st class
W/SALE or RETAIL: Both
SPECIALITIES: Hardy Geranium, Erodium and choice Herbaceous. *MAP PAGE:* **3**

SCro **Croftway Nursery,** Yapton Road, Barnham, Bognor Regis, West Sussex PO22 0BH
TEL: (0243) 552121 *CONTACT:* Graham Spencer
OPENING TIMES: 0900-1730 daily. Closed Wed from 1st Nov-28th Feb.
MAIL ORDER: Yes *MIN VALUE:* None *CAT. COST:* £1.00 *W/SALE or RETAIL:* Both
SPECIALITIES: Wide general range, emphasis on Perennials. Specialists in Irises & Hardy Geraniums. *MAP PAGE:* **3**

SDea **Deacon's Nursery,** Moor View, Godshill, Isle of Wight PO38 3HW
TEL: (0983) 840750/522243 *CONTACT:* G D & B H W Deacon
◆ *OPENING TIMES:* 0800-1600 Mon-Sat.
MAIL ORDER: Yes *MIN VALUE:* None *CAT. COST:* 1 x 2nd class *W/SALE or RETAIL:* Both
SPECIALITIES: Over 200 varieties of Apple, old & new varieties. Pears, Plums, Gages, Damsons, Cherries etc. Fruit & Nut trees, triple Peaches, Ballerinas. *MAP PAGE:* **2**

SDeJ **De Jager & Sons,** The Nurseries, Marden, Kent TN12 9BP
TEL: (0622) 831235 *FAX:* (0622) 832416 *CONTACT:*
◆ *OPENING TIMES:* 0900-1700 Mon-Fri.
MAIL ORDER: Yes *MIN VALUE:* *CAT. COST:* Free *W/SALE or RETAIL:* Both
SPECIALITIES: Wide general range, esp. Bulbs. Lillium, Tulipa, Narcissus species & miscellaneous. Large range of Perennials. *MAP PAGE:* **3**

SDen **Denmead Geranium Nurseries,** Hambledon Road, Denmead, Waterlooville, Hampshire PO7 6PS
TEL: (0705) 240081 *CONTACT:* I H Chance
◆ *OPENING TIMES:* 0800-1300 & 1400-1700 Mon-Fri, 0800-1230 Sat (ex Aug), 1400-1700 Sat May-Jun & 0930-1230 Sun Apr-May
MAIL ORDER: Yes *MIN VALUE:* 6 plants + p&p *CAT. COST:* 3 x 2nd class
W/SALE or RETAIL: Both
SPECIALITIES: Pelargoniums - Zonals, Ivy-leaved, Scented, Unique, Rosebud, Stellars, Miniature, Dwarf, Swiss Balcony, Mini Cascade, Ornamental & Regals. *MAP PAGE:* **2/3**

SDix **Great Dixter Nurseries,** Northiam, Rye, East Sussex TN31 6PH
TEL: (0797) 253107 *CONTACT:* C Lloyd
OPENING TIMES: 0900-1230 & 1330-1700 Mon-Fri ex Bank Hols. 0900-1200 Sat.
MAIL ORDER: Yes *MIN VALUE:* £6.50 + p&p *CAT. COST:* 60p *W/SALE or RETAIL:* Retail
SPECIALITIES: Clematis, Shrubs and Plants. (Gardens open). *MAP PAGE:* **3**

SDry **Drysdale Nursery,** Bowerwood Road, Fordingbridge, Hampshire SP6 1BN
TEL: (0425) 653010 *CONTACT:* David Crampton
OPENING TIMES: 0930-1730 Wed-Fri, 1000-1730 Sun & Bank Hols. Closed 24th Dec-2nd Jan incl.
MAIL ORDER: Yes *MIN VALUE:* £10.00 + p&p *CAT. COST:* 3 x 1st class
W/SALE or RETAIL: Retail
SPECIALITIES: Plants for exotic & foliage effect. Plants for Mediterranean gardens. National Reference Collection of Bamboos. *MAP PAGE:* **2**

SEng **English Water Garden,** Rock Lane, Washington, West Sussex RH20 3BL
TEL: (0903) 892006/892408 *FAX:* (0903) 892006 *CONTACT:* J M Quick
OPENING TIMES: 0900-1730 daily.
MAIL ORDER: Yes *MIN VALUE:* No minimum charge *CAT. COST:* *W/SALE or RETAIL:* Both
SPECIALITIES: Specimen Trees, Shrubs, Waterplants & unusual species. Some Trees & Shrubs available in very large sizes. *MAP PAGE:* **3**

SExb **Exbury Enterprises Ltd.,** Exbury, Nr. Southampton, Hampshire SO4 1AZ
TEL: (0703) 898625/891203 *FAX:* (0703) 243380 *CONTACT:*
OPENING TIMES: 1000-1730 Plant Centre. 0900-1700 Office.
MAIL ORDER: Yes *MIN VALUE:* £15.00 + p&p *CAT. COST:* Sae *W/SALE or RETAIL:* Both
SPECIALITIES: Rhododendron, Azalea, Camellia & Pieris *MAP PAGE:* **2**

SFai **Christopher Fairweather Ltd.,** High Street, Beaulieu, Hampshire SO42 7YB
TEL: (0590) 612307 *FAX:* (0590) 612615 *CONTACT:* C Fairweather
OPENING TIMES: 0900-1700 daily.
MAIL ORDER: No *CAT. COST:* No retail Cat. *W/SALE or RETAIL:* Both
SPECIALITIES: Shrubs & Trees. *MAP PAGE:* **2**

SFam **Family Trees,** PO Box 3, Botley, Hampshire SO3 2EA
TEL: (0329) 834812 *CONTACT:* P F W House
◆ *OPENING TIMES:* 0900-1200 Wed & Sat Nov-Apr.
MAIL ORDER: Yes *MIN VALUE:* £30.00 + p&p *CAT. COST:* Free *W/SALE or RETAIL:* Retail
SPECIALITIES: Fruit & Ornamental trees. Old Roses & trained Fruit trees. Also hedgerow & woodland Trees. *MAP PAGE:* **2**

SFar **Farmhouse Plants,** Royal Farm House, Elstead, Godalming, Surrey GU8 6LA
TEL: (0252) 702460 *CONTACT:* Mrs S Cole
OPENING TIMES: By appointment.
MAIL ORDER: No *CAT. COST:* 3 x 2nd class *W/SALE or RETAIL:* Retail
SPECIALITIES: General range, esp. Grasses & Euphorbia. *MAP PAGE:* **3**

SFis **Kaytie Fisher,** The Nursery, South End Cottage, Long Reach, Ockham, Surrey GU23 6PF
TEL: (04865) 2304 *CONTACT:* Kaytie Fisher
OPENING TIMES: 1000-1700 Thu-Sun Apr-Oct. Oct-Mar by appt. only.
MAIL ORDER: Yes *MIN VALUE:* £10.00 + p&p *CAT. COST:* 3 x 1st class
W/SALE or RETAIL: Retail
SPECIALITIES: Mainly hardy Herbaceous & some Shrubs. Old Shrub Roses & Climbers.
MAP PAGE: **3**

SFru **The Fruit Garden,** Mulberry Farm, Woodnesborough, Sandwich, Kent CT13 0PT
TEL: (0304) 813454 *CONTACT:* Patricia & Peter Dodd
◆ *OPENING TIMES:* By appt. for collection of orders.
MAIL ORDER: Yes *MIN VALUE:* None *CAT. COST:* Free *W/SALE or RETAIL:* Retail
SPECIALITIES: Old & unusual quality Fruit Trees. Comprehensive backup service for customers.
MAP PAGE: **3**

SGil **Diana Gilbert,** 25 Virginia Road, South Tankerton, Whitstable, Kent CT5 3HY
TEL: (0227) 273128 *CONTACT:* Diana Gilbert
◆ *OPENING TIMES:* 1000-1800 Wed-Sat. Also welcome by appt.
MAIL ORDER: No *CAT. COST:* 2 x 1st class *W/SALE or RETAIL:* Retail
SPECIALITIES: Uncommon & interesting Shrubs, Perennials & Alpines. Foliage & Flower arrangers plants. *MAP PAGE:* **3**

SGly **Glyndley Nurseries,** Halisham Road, Pevensey, East Sussex BN24 5BS
TEL: (0323) 766165 *FAX:* (0323) 760553 *CONTACT:* F Godfrey
OPENING TIMES: Not open to public.
MAIL ORDER: Yes *MIN VALUE:* £8.00 + p&p *CAT. COST:* Free *W/SALE or RETAIL:*
SPECIALITIES: Clematis, over 150 varieties & grafted Shrubs & Trees. *MAP PAGE:*

SHay **Hayward's Carnations,** The Chace Gardens, Stakes Road, Purbrook, Waterlooville, Hampshire PO7 5PL
TEL: (0705) 263047 *CONTACT:* A N Hayward
OPENING TIMES: 0930-1700 Mon-Fri.
MAIL ORDER: Yes *MIN VALUE:* £10.00 + p&p *CAT. COST:* 1 x 1st class
W/SALE or RETAIL: Both
SPECIALITIES: Hardy Pinks & Border Carnations. Greenhouse perpetual Carnations.
MAP PAGE: **2/3**

SHaz **Hazeldene Nursery,** Dean Street, East Farleigh, Maidstone, Kent ME15 0PS
TEL: (0622) 726248 *CONTACT:* Mr W W Adams
OPENING TIMES: 1000-1500. Please ring prior to visit. Oct-Feb by appt. only.
MAIL ORDER: No *CAT. COST:* Sae *W/SALE or RETAIL:* Retail
SPECIALITIES: Pansies, Viola & Violets. *MAP PAGE:* **3**

 See note on Mail Order, EC sales & Export on page 5

SHBN **High Banks Nurseries,** Slip Mill Road, Hawkhurst, Kent TN18 5AD
TEL: (0580) 753031 *CONTACT:* Jeremy Homewood
OPENING TIMES: 0800-1700 daily
MAIL ORDER: No *CAT. COST:* Free *W/SALE or RETAIL:* Both
SPECIALITIES: Wide general range with many unusual plants. *MAP PAGE:* **3**

SHen **C E Henderson & Son,** Leydens Nursery, Stick Hill, Edenbridge, Kent TN8 5NH
TEL: (0732) 863318 *CONTACT:* K A Henderson
◆ *OPENING TIMES:* 0900-1700 daily.
MAIL ORDER: Yes *MIN VALUE:* No minimum charge *CAT. COST:* Free list
W/SALE or RETAIL: Both
SPECIALITIES: Hardy Trees & Shrubs. Roses, Heathers, Conifers, Fruit & Hedging. Wild British flowers, Cowslips, Primula & Polyanthus. Wide range of hardy Perennials. *MAP PAGE:* **3**

SHer **The Herbary Plant Centre,** 89 Station Road, Herne Bay, Kent CT6 5QQ
TEL: (0227) 362409 *CONTACT:* Mrs J R Giles
◆ *OPENING TIMES:* 1000-1700 Wed, Fri & Sat Mar-Oct.
MAIL ORDER: No *CAT. COST:* 50p *W/SALE or RETAIL:* Retail
SPECIALITIES: Plants suitable for Tufa growing. Aromatic Herbs, interesting Shrubs & Herbaceous.
MAP PAGE: **3**

SHig **Higher End Nursery,** Hale, Fordingbridge, Hampshire SP6 2RA
TEL: (0725) 22243 *CONTACT:* D J Case
OPENING TIMES: 1000-1700 Wed-Sat 1400-1700 Sun Apr-Aug.
MAIL ORDER: Yes *MIN VALUE:* £12.00 + p&p *CAT. COST:* 2 x 1st class
W/SALE or RETAIL: Both
SPECIALITIES: Water Lilies, Bog & Marginal, Hellebore, Rodgersia, Trollius, Bergenia.
MAP PAGE: **2**

SHil **Hillier Nurseries (Winchester) Ltd,** Ampfield House, Ampfield, Nr. Romsey, Hampshire SO51 9PA
TEL: (0794) 68733 *FAX:* (0794) 68813 *CONTACT:* Mrs Sheila Pack
OPENING TIMES: Office 0830-1700 Mon-Fri. Garden Centres 0900-1730 Mon-Sat, 1000-1730 Sun.
MAIL ORDER: Yes *MIN VALUE:* *CAT. COST:* 2 x 1st class *W/SALE or RETAIL:* Both
SPECIALITIES: Very large range of Trees, Shrubs, Conifers, Climbers, Roses, Fruit. *MAP PAGE:* **2**

SHya **Brenda Hyatt,** 1 Toddington Crescent, Bluebell Hill, Chatham, Kent ME5 9QT
TEL: (0634) 863251 *CONTACT:* Mrs Brenda Hyatt
OPENING TIMES: Appt only.
MAIL ORDER: Yes *MIN VALUE:* None *CAT. COST:* 49p *W/SALE or RETAIL:* Retail
SPECIALITIES: Show Auricula. NOTE: Border Auriculas not on show or held at Chatham.
MAP PAGE: **3**

SIde **Iden Croft Herbs,** Frittenden Road, Staplehurst, Kent TN12 0DH
TEL: (0580) 891432 *FAX:* (0580) 892416 *CONTACT:* Rosemary & D Titterington
OPENING TIMES: 0900-1700 Mon-Sat all year & 1100-1700 Sun & Bank Hols. 1st Mar- 30th Sep.
MAIL ORDER: Yes *MIN VALUE:* No minimum charge *CAT. COST:* £2.50*
W/SALE or RETAIL: Retail
SPECIALITIES: Herbs & Aromatic plants. National Origanum collection. Export orders undertaken for dispatch during Spring months. * Sae for plant list. *MAP PAGE:* **3**

SIgm **Tim Ingram,** Copton Ash, 105 Ashford Road, Faversham, Kent ME13 8XW
TEL: (0795) 535919 *CONTACT:* Dr T J Ingram
◆ *OPENING TIMES:* 1400-1800 Tue-Thur & Sat-Sun Mar-Oct. Nov-Feb by appt.
MAIL ORDER: Yes* *MIN VALUE:* £8.00 + p&p* *CAT. COST:* 2 x 1st class
W/SALE or RETAIL: Retail
SPECIALITIES: Unusual Perennials, Alpines & Australasian plants. Fruit & ornamental Trees.
*NOTE: Only Fruit Trees by Mail Order (Nov-Mar). *MAP PAGE:* **3**

SIng **W E Th. Ingwersen Ltd,** Birch Farm Nursery, Gravetye, E. Grinstead, West Sussex RH19 4LE
TEL: (0342) 810236 *CONTACT:* M P & M R Ingwersen
OPENING TIMES: 0900-1300 & 1330-1600 daily 1st Mar-31st Oct. 0900-1300 & 1330-1600 Mon-Fri Nov-Feb.
MAIL ORDER: Yes *MIN VALUE:* No minimum charge *CAT. COST:* £1.00 stamps*
W/SALE or RETAIL: Retail
SPECIALITIES: Very wide range of hardy plants mostly alpines. *NOTE: Mail Order only during Mar-May & Sep-Nov. Catalogue £1.50 if cheque or P.O. *MAP PAGE:* **3**

SJus **Just Roses,** Beales Lane, Northiam, Nr Rye, East Sussex TN31 6QY
TEL: (0797) 252355 *CONTACT:*
OPENING TIMES: 0900-1200 & 1300-1700 Tue-Fri & 0900-1200 & 1300-1600 Sat & Sun.
MAIL ORDER: No *CAT. COST:* Free *W/SALE or RETAIL:* Retail
SPECIALITIES: Roses *MAP PAGE:* **3**

SKee **Keepers Nursery,** 446 Wateringbury Road, East Malling, Kent ME19 6JJ
TEL: (0622) 813008 *CONTACT:* Anne & Mike Cook
OPENING TIMES: All hours by appt.
MAIL ORDER: Yes *MIN VALUE:* £10.00 + p&p *CAT. COST:* Sae *W/SALE or RETAIL:* Retail
SPECIALITIES: Old & unusual Top Fruit varieties. Wide range of Soft Fruit. Top Fruit, related ornamental varieties and Fruit seedlings propagated to order. *MAP PAGE:* **3**

SKen **Kent Street Nurseries,** Sedlescombe, Battle, East Sussex TN33 0SF
TEL: (0424) 751134 *CONTACT:* Mrs D Downey
OPENING TIMES: 0900-1800 daily all year.
MAIL ORDER: Yes *MIN VALUE:* 10 plants + p&p *CAT. COST:* A5 Sae* *W/SALE or RETAIL:* Both
SPECIALITIES: Fuchsia, Pelargonium, Bedding & Perennials. *NOTE: Separate Fuchsia & Pelargonium lists. Please specify which required. *MAP PAGE:* **3**

SLan **Langley Boxwood Nursery,** Rake, Nr Liss, Hampshire GU33 7JL
TEL: (0730) 894467 *FAX:* (0730) 894703 *CONTACT:* Elizabeth Braimbridge
◆ *OPENING TIMES:* By appt. only.
MAIL ORDER: Yes *MIN VALUE:* *CAT. COST:* 4 x 1st class *W/SALE or RETAIL:* Both
SPECIALITIES: Buxus species, cultivars & hedging. Good range of topiary. *MAP PAGE:* **2/3**

SLBF **Little Brook Fuchsias,** Ash Green Lane West, Ash Green, Nr Aldershot, Hampshire GU12 6HL
TEL: (0252) 29731 *CONTACT:* Carol Gubler
OPENING TIMES: 0900-1700 Wed-Sun 1st Jan-18th Jul.
MAIL ORDER: No *CAT. COST:* 20p + Sae *W/SALE or RETAIL:* Both
SPECIALITIES: Fuchsia old & new. *MAP PAGE:* **3**

SLeo **Leonardslee Gardens,** 1 Mill Lane, Lower Beeding, West Sussex RH13 6PX
TEL: (0403) 891 412 *CONTACT:* A J Clark
OPENING TIMES: 1000-1800 Tue Thu & Sun BY APPOINTMENT ONLY.
MAIL ORDER: Yes *MIN VALUE:* £50.00 + p&p *CAT. COST:* £2.00 *W/SALE or RETAIL:* Retail
SPECIALITIES: Rhododendron & Azalea in all sizes. *MAP PAGE:* **3**

SLim **Lime Cross Nursery,** Herstmonceux, Hailsham, East Sussex BN27 4RS
TEL: (0323) 833229 *FAX:* (0323) 833944 *CONTACT:* J A Tate
◆ *OPENING TIMES:* 0830-1700 Mon-Sat & 0930-1700 Sun.
MAIL ORDER: No *CAT. COST:* Free *W/SALE or RETAIL:* Both
SPECIALITIES: Conifers. *MAP PAGE:* **3**

SLMG **Long Man Gardens,** Lewes Road, Wilmington, Polegate, East Sussex BN26 5RS
TEL: (0323) 870816 *CONTACT:* O Menzel
OPENING TIMES: 0900-1200 & 1430-1700 Tue-Sun. Please check day before visit.
MAIL ORDER: Yes *MIN VALUE:* See list for details *CAT. COST:* Free list
W/SALE or RETAIL: Both
SPECIALITIES: Mainly conservatory plants. *MAP PAGE:* **3**

 See note on Mail Order, EC sales & Export on page 5

SLon **Longstock Park Nursery,** Stockbridge, Hampshire SO20 6EH
TEL: (0264) 810894 *FAX:* (0264) 810439 *CONTACT:* General Manager
OPENING TIMES: 0830-1630 Mon-Sat.
MAIL ORDER: Yes *MIN VALUE:* £50.00 + p&p *CAT. COST:* £1.50 inc p&p
W/SALE or RETAIL: Both
SPECIALITIES: Shrubs & Conifers. Herbaceous and moisture loving and Aquatics. *MAP PAGE:* **2**

SLPl **Landscape Plants,** Cattamount, Grafty Green, Maidstone, Kent ME17 2AP
TEL: (0622) 850245 *FAX:* (0622) 858063 *CONTACT:* Tom La Dell
OPENING TIMES: By appointment only.
MAIL ORDER: Yes *MIN VALUE:* £50.00 + p&p *CAT. COST:* 2 x 1st class
W/SALE or RETAIL: Both
SPECIALITIES: Low maintenance Shrubs. *MAP PAGE:* **3**

SMad **Madrona Nursery,** Tara Lodge, Harden Road, East Rype, Lydd, Kent TN29 9LT
TEL: (0679) 20868 *CONTACT:* Liam MacKenzie
OPENING TIMES: 1400-2000 Tue-Thu 23rd Mar-31st Oct.
MAIL ORDER: Yes *MIN VALUE:* No minimum charge *CAT. COST:* £1.00
W/SALE or RETAIL: Retail
SPECIALITIES: Unusual Shrubs, Conifers & Perennials. *MAP PAGE:* **3**

SMit **Mary & Peter Mitchell,** 11 Wingle Tye Road, Burgess Hill, West Sussex RH15 9HR
TEL: (0444) 236848 *CONTACT:* Mary & Peter Mitchell
OPENING TIMES: Appt only.
MAIL ORDER: No *CAT. COST:* Stamp *W/SALE or RETAIL:* Retail
SPECIALITIES: Sempervivum, Jovibaba, Rosularia. *MAP PAGE:* **3**

SMrm **Merriments Nursery & Gardens,** Hawkhurst Road, Hurst Green, East Sussex TN19 7RA
TEL: (0580) 860666 *FAX:* (0580) 860324 *CONTACT:* Mark & Amanda Buchele
◆ *OPENING TIMES:* 0830-1730.
MAIL ORDER: No *CAT. COST:* 50p *W/SALE or RETAIL:* Retail
SPECIALITIES: Tender & Hardy Perennials. *MAP PAGE:* **3**

SNTN **New Trees Nurseries,** 2 Nunnery Road, Canterbury, Kent CT1 3LS
TEL: (0227) 761209 *CONTACT:* P H Harding
OPENING TIMES: By appt. only.
MAIL ORDER: No *CAT. COST:* Large Sae *W/SALE or RETAIL:* Retail
SPECIALITIES: Apples, Pears, Plums, Cherries. Unusual varieties grafted to order. *MAP PAGE:* **3**

SOak **Oakleigh Nurseries,** Petersfield Road, Monkwood, Nr Alresford Hampshire SO24 0HB
TEL: (0962) 773344 *FAX:* (0962) 772622 *CONTACT:* D W H & J R Clark
OPENING TIMES: 1000-1630 Apr-Jun daily.
MAIL ORDER: Yes *MIN VALUE:* None *CAT. COST:* 3 x 1st class *W/SALE or RETAIL:* Both
SPECIALITIES: Fuchsia & Pelargonium. *MAP PAGE:* **2**

SOgg **Stuart Ogg,** Hopton, Fletching Street, Mayfield, East Sussex TN20 6TL
TEL: (0435) 873322 *CONTACT:* Stuart Ogg
OPENING TIMES: Appt. only, unless advertised in local press.
MAIL ORDER: Yes *MIN VALUE:* No minimum charge *CAT. COST:* Sae *W/SALE or RETAIL:* Retail
SPECIALITIES: Delphiniums. *MAP PAGE:*

SOld **Oldbury Nurseries,** Brissenden Green, Bethersden, Kent TN26 3BJ
TEL: (0233) 820416 *CONTACT:* Peter & Wendy Dresman
OPENING TIMES: 0930-1700 daily 1st Feb-16th Aug.
MAIL ORDER: *MIN VALUE:* *CAT. COST:* 36p *W/SALE or RETAIL:* Both
SPECIALITIES: Fuchsia. *MAP PAGE:* **3**

SPer **Perryhill Nurseries,** Hartfield, East Sussex TN7 4JP
TEL: (0892) 770377 *FAX:* (0892) 770929 *CONTACT:* P J Chapman (Manager)
OPENING TIMES: 0900-1700 daily March 1-Oct 31. 0900-1630 Nov 1-Feb 28.
MAIL ORDER: No *CAT. COST:* £1.40 *W/SALE or RETAIL:* Retail
SPECIALITIES: Over 900 Herbaceous varieties & 300 shrub & climbing roses. Wide range of Trees, Shrubs, Conifers, Rhododendron etc. Export by arrangement. *MAP PAGE:* **3**

SPla **Plaxtol Nurseries,** The Spoute, Plaxtol, Sevenoaks, Kent TN15 0QR
TEL: (0732) 810550 *CONTACT:* Tessa N & Donald M Forbes.
OPENING TIMES: 1000-1700 daily. Closed two weeks from Xmas eve.
MAIL ORDER: Yes *MIN VALUE:* £10.00 + p&p* *CAT. COST:* 2 x 1st class
W/SALE or RETAIL: Retail
SPECIALITIES: Hardy Shrubs & Herbaceous (inc. Ferns) esp. for Flower Arranger. Wide choice old-fashioned Roses, Climbers, Conifers & Heathers. *NOTE: Mail Order Nov-Mar ONLY.
MAP PAGE: **3**

SPlc **Plantcraft,** (Off.) 35 Rutland Way, Orpington, Kent BR5 4DY
TEL: (0689) 830157/836249 *CONTACT:* D Sizmur & J Dewhurst
OPENING TIMES: 1000-1700 most days. Please phone first.
MAIL ORDER: Yes *MIN VALUE:* See Cat. for details *CAT. COST:* A5 Sae
W/SALE or RETAIL: Retail
SPECIALITIES: Tillandsia & Carnivorous plants. NOTE: Nursery at Kent Cacti, Woodlands Farm, Shire Lane, Farnborough, Kent. *MAP PAGE:* **3**

SPou **Roger Poulett,** Nurse's Cottage, North Mundham, Chichester, Sussex PO20 6JY
TEL: *CONTACT:* Roger Poulett
OPENING TIMES: By arrangement only.
MAIL ORDER: *MIN VALUE:* *CAT. COST:* 3 x 1st class *W/SALE or RETAIL:* Retail
SPECIALITIES: Hepaticas, Corydalis, Crocus, Cyclamen and many unusual plants. List in June.
MAP PAGE: **3**

SReu **G Reuthe Ltd,** Crown Point Nursery, Sevenoaks Road, Ightham, Nr Sevenoaks, Kent TN15 0HB
TEL: (0732) 810694 *CONTACT:* C Tomlin & P Kindley
◆ *OPENING TIMES:* 0900-1630 Mon-Sat. 1000-1630 Sun & Bank Hols during Apr & May ONLY. Occasionally in June; check.
MAIL ORDER: Yes *MIN VALUE:* £25.00 + p&p *CAT. COST:* £1.30+30p p&p
W/SALE or RETAIL: Retail
SPECIALITIES: Rhododendrons, Azaleas, Trees, Shrubs & Conifers. *MAP PAGE:* **3**

SRms **Rumsey Gardens,** 117 Drift Road, Clanfield, Hampshire
TEL: (0705) 593367 *CONTACT:* Mr N R Giles
OPENING TIMES: 0900-1700 Mon-Sat & 1000-1700 Sun & Bank Hols.
MAIL ORDER: No *CAT. COST:* *W/SALE or RETAIL:* Both
SPECIALITIES: Wide general range. *MAP PAGE:* **2/3**

SRum **Rumwood Nurseries,** Langley, Maidstone, Kent ME17 3ND
TEL: (0622) 861477 *FAX:* (0622) 863123 *CONTACT:* Mr R Fermor
OPENING TIMES: 0800-1700 Mon-Sat 1000-1700 Sun.
MAIL ORDER: Yes *MIN VALUE:* None *CAT. COST:* Sae *W/SALE or RETAIL:* Both
SPECIALITIES: Roses & Trees. *MAP PAGE:* **3**

SSad **Mrs Jane Sadler,** Ingrams Cottage, Wisborough Green, Billingshurst, West Sussex RH14 0ER
TEL: (0403) 700234 *CONTACT:* Mrs Jane Sadler
OPENING TIMES: Irregular. Please phone first.
MAIL ORDER: No *CAT. COST:* Sae *W/SALE or RETAIL:* Retail
SPECIALITIES: Small nursery specialising in less common varieties, esp. Auriculas, Lathyrus, Lavenders & Pelargoniums. *MAP PAGE:* **3**

SSmi **Alan C Smith,** 127 Leaves Green Road, Keston, Kent BR2 6DG
TEL: (0959) 572531 *CONTACT:* Alan C Smith
OPENING TIMES: Appt only.
MAIL ORDER: No *CAT. COST:* 50p *W/SALE or RETAIL:* Retail
SPECIALITIES: Over 1000 kinds of Sempervivum & Jovibarba. *MAP PAGE:* **3**

SSmt **Peter J Smith,** Chanctonbury Nurseries, Rectory Lane, Ashington, Pulborough, Sussex RH20 3AS
TEL: (0903) 892870 *FAX:* (0903) 893036 *CONTACT:* Peter J Smith
◆ *OPENING TIMES:* By appt. only
MAIL ORDER: Yes *MIN VALUE:* £8.00 + p&p *CAT. COST:* 40- *W/SALE or RETAIL:* Both
SPECIALITIES: The Princess® & Little Princess® range of hybrid Alstroemeria for conservatory & garden. *MAP PAGE:*

 See note on Mail Order, EC sales & Export on page 5

SSou **Southfarthing Alpines,** Southfarthing, Hawkenbury, Staplehurst, Kent TN12 0ED
TEL: (0580) 892140 *CONTACT:* Ivan Smith
OPENING TIMES: By appt. Please phone first.
MAIL ORDER: No *CAT. COST:* None issued *W/SALE or RETAIL:* Retail
SPECIALITIES: Alpines. *MAP PAGE:* **3**

SSpi **Spinners,** Boldre, Lymington, Hampshire SO41 5QE
TEL: CONTACT: Mark Fillan
OPENING TIMES: 1000-1700 Wed-Sun.
MAIL ORDER: No *CAT. COST:* 4 x 1st class *W/SALE or RETAIL:* Retail
SPECIALITIES: Rare Tree and Shrubs especially for shade. Acer, Magnolia, Hosta, Hardy Geraniums, Hydrangea, Ferns etc. *MAP PAGE:* **2**

SSta **Starborough Nursery,** Starborough Road, Marsh Green, Edenbridge, Kent TN8 5RB
TEL: (0732) 865614 *CONTACT:* C Tomlin & P Kindley
◆ *OPENING TIMES:* 1000-1600 Thu-Mon. Closed Jan & Jul.
MAIL ORDER: Yes *MIN VALUE:* £25.00 + p&p *CAT. COST:* £1.25 *W/SALE or RETAIL:* Retail
SPECIALITIES: Rare and unusual Shrubs especially Daphne, Acer, Rhododendron, Azalea, Magnolia & Hamamelis. *MAP PAGE:* **3**

SSvw **Southview Nurseries,** Chequers Lane, Eversley Cross, Basingstoke, Hampshire RG27 0NT
TEL: (0734) 732206 *CONTACT:* Mark Trenear
◆ *OPENING TIMES:* 0900-1300 & 1400-1630 Thu-Sat 1st Feb-31st Oct. Nov-Jan by appt. only.
MAIL ORDER: Yes *MIN VALUE:* None *CAT. COST:* Free *W/SALE or RETAIL:* Retail
SPECIALITIES: Unusual Hardy plants, good selection of old named Pinks. *MAP PAGE:* **2/3**

STil **Tile Barn Nursery,** Standen Street, Iden Green, Benenden, Kent TN17 4LB
TEL: (0580) 240221 *CONTACT:* Peter Moore
OPENING TIMES: 0900-1700 Wed-Sat.
MAIL ORDER: Yes *MIN VALUE:* £10.00 + p&p *CAT. COST:* Sae *W/SALE or RETAIL:* Both
SPECIALITIES: Cyclamen species. *MAP PAGE:* **3**

STre **Peter Trenear,** Chantreyland, Chequers Lane, Eversley Cross, Hampshire RG27 0NX
TEL: (0734) 732300 *CONTACT:* Peter Trenear
◆ *OPENING TIMES:* 0900-1630 Mon-Sat.
MAIL ORDER: Yes *MIN VALUE:* £5.00 + p&p *CAT. COST:* 1 x 1st class
W/SALE or RETAIL: Retail
SPECIALITIES: Trees, Shrubs & Conifers. *MAP PAGE:* **2/3**

SUsu **Usual & Unusual Plants,** Onslow House, Magham Down, Hailsham East Sussex BN27 1PL
TEL: (0323) 840967 *CONTACT:* Jennie Maillard
OPENING TIMES: 1030-1430 Mon-Fri Mar-Nov other times by appt. Please ring before visiting.
MAIL ORDER: No *CAT. COST:* 1x1st + Sae *W/SALE or RETAIL:* Retail
SPECIALITIES: Small quantities of a wide variety of unusual perennials, esp. Erysimum, Euphorbia, Hardy Geraniums & Penstemon. *MAP PAGE:* **3**

SWas **Washfield Nursery,** Horn's Road (A229), Hawkhurst, Kent TN18 4QU
TEL: (0580) 752522 *CONTACT:* Elizabeth Strangman
OPENING TIMES: 1000-1700 Wed-Sat.
MAIL ORDER: No *CAT. COST:* 3 x 1st class *W/SALE or RETAIL:* Retail
SPECIALITIES: Alpine, Herbaceous & Woodland, many unusual & rare. Helleborus, Epimedium, Hardy Geranium. *MAP PAGE:* **3**

SWat **Water Meadow Nursery,** Cheriton, Nr Alresford, Hampshire SO24 0JT
TEL: (0962) 771895 *FAX:* (0962) 771895 *CONTACT:* Mrs Sandy Worth
◆ *OPENING TIMES:* 0900-1700 Fri & Sat, 1400-1700 Sun, Mar-Nov.
MAIL ORDER: Yes *MIN VALUE:* £10.00 + p&p *CAT. COST:* 3 x 1st class
W/SALE or RETAIL: Both
SPECIALITIES: Water Lilies, extensive Water Garden plants, unusual Herbaceous Perennials, aromatic & hardy Shrubs & Climbers. *MAP PAGE:* **2**

SWes **Westwood Nursery,** 65 Yorkland Avenue, Welling, Kent DA16 2LE
TEL: 081 301-0886 *CONTACT:* Mr S Edwards
OPENING TIMES: Not open.
MAIL ORDER: Yes *MIN VALUE:* None *CAT. COST:* Sae *W/SALE or RETAIL:* Retail
SPECIALITIES: Pleiones & Hardy Orchids. *MAP PAGE:*

WAbb **Abbey Dore Court Gardens,** Abbeydore, nr Hereford, Herefordshire HR2 0AD
TEL: (0981) 240419 *CONTACT:* Mrs C Ward
OPENING TIMES: 1100-1800 Thu-Tue from 3rd Sat Mar-3rd Sun Oct.
MAIL ORDER: No *CAT. COST:* None issued *W/SALE or RETAIL:* Retail
SPECIALITIES: Shrubs & hardy Perennials, many unusual, which may be seen growing in the garden. National Collection of Sedum & Euphorbia. Some Seeds available from garden.
MAP PAGE: **2/4**

WAbe **Aberconwy Nursery,** Graig, Glan Conwy, Colwyn Bay, Clwyd LL28 5TL
TEL: (0492) 580875 *CONTACT:* Dr & Mrs K G Lever
OPENING TIMES: 0900-1700 Tue-Sun.
MAIL ORDER: No *CAT. COST:* 1 x 2nd class *W/SALE or RETAIL:* Retail
SPECIALITIES: Alpines, including specialist varieties, esp. Autumn Gentians. Trees, Shrubs, Conifers & Herbaceous plants. *MAP PAGE:* **4**

WAce **International Acers,** Acer Place, Coalash Lane, Hanbury, Bromsgrove, Worcestershire B60 4EY
TEL: (0527) 821774 *CONTACT:* D L Horton
OPENING TIMES: 0900-1730 Sat & Sun and by appt.
MAIL ORDER: No *CAT. COST:* Free *W/SALE or RETAIL:* Both
SPECIALITIES: Acers. (Some cultivars in very short supply at present). *MAP PAGE:* **2**

WAct **Acton Beauchamp Roses,** Acton Beauchamp, Worcester Hereford & Worcester WR6 5AE
TEL: (0531) 640433 *FAX:* (0531) 640802 *CONTACT:* Lindsay Bousfield
OPENING TIMES: 1000-1700 Wed-Fri & 1400-1700 Sun Feb, Mar, Apr, Jun, Jul, Oct & Nov. 1000-1700 Sat-Mon Bank Hols.
MAIL ORDER: Yes *MIN VALUE:* £50.00 + p&p *CAT. COST:* 2 x 1st class
W/SALE or RETAIL: Both
SPECIALITIES: Old Rose species & hybrids. Also modern shrub, new English Roses, climbers, ramblers & ground-cover Roses. *MAP PAGE:* **2**

WBal **Helen Ballard,** Old Country, Mathon, Malvern, Worcestershire WR13 5PS
TEL: (0886 880) 215 * *CONTACT:* Helen Ballard
OPENING TIMES:
MAIL ORDER: Yes *MIN VALUE:* £15.00 *CAT. COST:* Free *W/SALE or RETAIL:* Retail
SPECIALITIES: Hellebores, mainly hybrid Orientalis. * Also (0531) 640683 *MAP PAGE:* **2**

WBod **Bodnant Garden Nursery Ltd.,** Tal-y-Cafn, Colwyn Bay, Clwyd LL28 5RE
TEL: (0492) 650460 *FAX:* (0492) 650448 *CONTACT:* Martin Puddle (Gen. Man.)
◆ *OPENING TIMES:* All year.
MAIL ORDER: Yes *MIN VALUE:* £10.00 + p&p *CAT. COST:* Sae *W/SALE or RETAIL:* Retail
SPECIALITIES: Rhododendron, Camellia & Magnolia. Wide range of unusual Trees and Shrubs.
MAP PAGE: **4**

WBon **S & E Bond,** Gardeners Cottage, Letton, Herefordshire HR3 6DH
TEL: (0544) 328422 after 6 *CONTACT:* Miss S Bond
OPENING TIMES: 1000-1800 Wed-Sat, 1300-1700 Sun, 1st Mar-31st Oct.
MAIL ORDER: No *CAT. COST:* 3 x 1st class *W/SALE or RETAIL:* Retail
SPECIALITIES: Shade plants. *MAP PAGE:* **4**

WBou **Bouts Cottage Nurseries,** Bouts Lane, Inkberrow, Worcestershire WR7 4HP
TEL: (0386) 792923 *CONTACT:* M & S Roberts
OPENING TIMES: Not open to the public.
MAIL ORDER: Yes *MIN VALUE:* *CAT. COST:* Sae *W/SALE or RETAIL:* Retail
SPECIALITIES: Viola. *MAP PAGE:*

 See note on Mail Order, EC sales & Export on page 5

WByw **Byways,** Daisy Lane, Whittington, Oswestry, Shropshire
TEL: (0691) 659539 *CONTACT:* Barbara Molesworth
OPENING TIMES: 0900-1700 Mon Mar-Nov. Please phone first.*
MAIL ORDER: No *CAT. COST:* Sae+1x2nd class *W/SALE or RETAIL:* Retail
SPECIALITIES: Asters, Campanulas, Hardy Geraniums, Pulmonarias & Salvias. *NOTE: Also at Newtown Market on Tue & Oswestry on Wed. *MAP PAGE:* **4**

WCel **Celyn Vale Nurseries,** Carrog, Corwen, Clwyd LL21 9LD
TEL: (0490) 83671 *FAX:* (0490) 83671 *CONTACT:* Andrew McConnell
◆ *OPENING TIMES:* Please telephone first. March to end-Oct.
MAIL ORDER: Yes *MIN VALUE:* 3 Plants + p&p *CAT. COST:* 1 x 1st class
W/SALE or RETAIL: Both
SPECIALITIES: Hardy Eucalyptus & Acacia. *MAP PAGE:* **4**

WCHb **The Cottage Herbery,** Mill House, Boraston, Nr Tenbury Wells, Worcestershire WR15 8LZ
TEL: (058 479) 575 *CONTACT:* K & R Hurst
OPENING TIMES: 1000-1800 Sun and by appt.
MAIL ORDER: No *CAT. COST:* 4 x 2nd class *W/SALE or RETAIL:* Retail
SPECIALITIES: Over 400 varieties of Herbs. Aromatic & scented foliage plants *MAP PAGE:* **2**

WChe **Checkley Waterplants,** The Knoll House, Checkley, Herefordshire HR1 4ND
TEL: (0432) 860672 *CONTACT:* Mrs M P Bennett
OPENING TIMES: By appt. only.
MAIL ORDER: Yes *MIN VALUE:* None *CAT. COST:* Sae *W/SALE or RETAIL:* Both
SPECIALITIES: Pond, Bog and moisture loving plants. *MAP PAGE:* **2**

WChr **Paul Christian - Rare Plants,** PO Box 468, Wrexham, Clwyd LL13 9XR
TEL: (0978) 366399 *FAX:* (0978) 366399 *CONTACT:* Dr. P Christian
OPENING TIMES: Not open.
MAIL ORDER: Yes *MIN VALUE:* None *CAT. COST:* 3 x 1st class *W/SALE or RETAIL:* Both
SPECIALITIES: Bulbs, Corms, Tubers, especially Colchicum, Crocus, Erythronium, Fritillaria, Iris, Rhodohypoxis & Trillium. Also Greenhouse bulbs. NOTE: Export to EEC only. *MAP PAGE:*

WCla **John Clayfield,** Llanbrook Alpine Nursery, Hopton Castle, Clunton, Shropshire SY7 0QG
TEL: (05474) 298 *CONTACT:* John Clayfield
OPENING TIMES: Daily, but please check first.
MAIL ORDER: No *CAT. COST:* 2 x 1st class *W/SALE or RETAIL:* Both
SPECIALITIES: Alpines & Wildflowers. *MAP PAGE:* **2/4**

WCoo **Mrs Susan Cooper,** Churchfields House, Cradley, Malvern, Worcestershire WR13 5LJ
TEL: (0886) 880223 *CONTACT:* Mrs Susan Cooper
OPENING TIMES: Appt only.
MAIL ORDER: Yes *MIN VALUE:* £20.00 + p&p *CAT. COST:* Small Sae *W/SALE or RETAIL:* Retail
SPECIALITIES: Rare & unusual Trees & Shrubs. Provenances on request. *MAP PAGE:* **2**

WCot **Cotswold Garden Flowers,** 1 Waterside, Evesham, Worcestershire WR11 6BS
TEL: (0386) 47337 *CONTACT:* Bob Brown
OPENING TIMES: Any time by prior appt.
MAIL ORDER: Yes *MIN VALUE:* None *CAT. COST:* Free *W/SALE or RETAIL:* Retail
SPECIALITIES: Easy & unusual Perennials for the Flower Garden. NOTE: Nursery at Sands Lane, Badsey. *MAP PAGE:* **2**

WCra **Cranesbill Nursery,** White Cottage, Stock Green, Nr. Redditch, Worcestershire B96 6SZ
TEL: (0386) 792414 *CONTACT:* Mrs S M Bates
OPENING TIMES: 1000-1700 Fri-Wed 15th March-mid Oct. August by appt. only.
MAIL ORDER: Yes *MIN VALUE:* None *CAT. COST:* 4 x 1st class *W/SALE or RETAIL:* Retail
SPECIALITIES: Hardy Geraniums. NOTE:- Mail Order Autumn only. *MAP PAGE:* **2**

WCru **Crûg Farm Plants,** Griffith's Crossing, Nr Caernarfon, Gwynedd LL55 1TU
TEL: (0248) 670232 *CONTACT:* Mr B Wynn-Jones
◆ *OPENING TIMES:* 1000-1800 Thu-Sun 27th Feb-26th Sep.
MAIL ORDER: Yes *MIN VALUE:* No minimum charge *CAT. COST:* Sae+1x2nd class
W/SALE or RETAIL: Both
SPECIALITIES: Plants for shade, climbers, Hardy Geraniums, Pulmonarias, rare Shrubs, Tropaeolums, Herbaceous & bulbous *MAP PAGE:* **4**

WCum Cumbermere Fuchsias, 22 Maescader Penceder, Dyfed, Wales SA39 9HQ
TEL: (0559) 384699 *CONTACT:* J Childs.
OPENING TIMES: Not open
MAIL ORDER: Only *MIN VALUE:* 75p per plant + p&p *CAT. COST:* 3 x 1st class
W/SALE or RETAIL: Both
SPECIALITIES: Fuchsias.

WDav Kim W Davis, Lingen Alpine Nursery, Lingen, Nr Bucknell, Shropshire SY7 0DY
TEL: (0544) 267720 *CONTACT:* Kim W Davis
◆ *OPENING TIMES:* 1000-1800 daily Feb-Oct. Fri-Sun Nov-Jan by appt.
MAIL ORDER: Yes *MIN VALUE:* None *CAT. COST:* Sae *W/SALE or RETAIL:* Both
SPECIALITIES: Alpines & Rock Plants, esp. Androsace, Aquilegia, Campanula, Primula & Penstemon. *MAP PAGE:* **2/4**

WDin Dingle Nurseries, Welshpool, Powys SY21 9JD
TEL: (0938) 555145 *FAX:* (0938) 554734* *CONTACT:* Ceri Hamer
OPENING TIMES: 0900-1700 Wed-Mon. (Wholesale Mon-Sat only).
MAIL ORDER: No *CAT. COST:* None *W/SALE or RETAIL:* Both
SPECIALITIES: Trees, Shrubs & Conifers. *Wholesale FAX number. *MAP PAGE:* **4**

WEas Eastgrove Cottage Garden Nursery, Sankyns Green, Nr Shrawley, Little Witley, Worcester WR6 6LQ
TEL: (0299) 896389 *CONTACT:* Malcolm & Carol Skinner
OPENING TIMES: 1400-1700 Thu-Mon 1st Apr-31st July. Closed Aug. 1400-1700 Thu, Fri & Sat 2nd Sep-15th Oct.
MAIL ORDER: No *CAT. COST:* 5 x 2nd class *W/SALE or RETAIL:* Retail
SPECIALITIES: Hardy plants displayed in 'old world country flower garden', from which all plants for sale are propagated. *MAP PAGE:* **2**

WEfe Efenechtyd Nurseries, Llanelidan, Ruthin, Clwyd LL15 2LG
TEL: (097 888) 677 *CONTACT:* R Dibley
OPENING TIMES: 0900-1700 daily May-Sept.
MAIL ORDER: Yes *MIN VALUE:* £20 + £5 p&p *CAT. COST:* Sae *W/SALE or RETAIL:* Both
SPECIALITIES: Streptocarpus, Columneas & other Gesneriads. *MAP PAGE:* **4**

WFib Fibrex Nurseries Ltd, Honeybourne Road, Pebworth, Stratford-on-Avon, Warwickshire CV37 8XT
TEL: (0789) 720788 *FAX:* (0789) 721162 *CONTACT:* H M D Key & R L Godard-Key
OPENING TIMES: 1200-1700. Hellebores only available for collection mid Jan-end Mar.
MAIL ORDER: Yes *MIN VALUE:* No minimum charge *CAT. COST:* 2 x 2nd class
W/SALE or RETAIL: Both
SPECIALITIES: Ivys, Ferns & Pelargoniums. *MAP PAGE:* **2**

WFou Four Counties Nursery, Todenham, Morton-in-Marsh, Gloucestershire GL56 9PN
TEL: (0608) 50522/50591 *FAX:* (0608) 50591 *CONTACT:* Sandra Taylor
OPENING TIMES: 0900-1800 daily Summer, 0900-1700 daily Winter
MAIL ORDER: Yes *MIN VALUE:* £20.00 + p&p *CAT. COST:* £1.00 *W/SALE or RETAIL:* Both
SPECIALITIES: Citrus & Conservatory plants, plus rare & unusual Trees & Shrubs *MAP PAGE:* **2**

WFro Fron Nursery, Fron Issa, Rhiwlas, Oswestry, Shropshire SY10 7JH
TEL: (069176) 605 *CONTACT:* Thoby Miller
OPENING TIMES: By appt. only.
MAIL ORDER: Yes *MIN VALUE:* £20.00 + p&p *CAT. COST:* Sae *W/SALE or RETAIL:* Both
SPECIALITIES: Rare and unusual Trees, Shrubs & Perennials. *MAP PAGE:* **4**

WGre Greenacres Nursery, Bringsty, Worcestershire WR6 5TA
TEL: (0885) 482206 *CONTACT:* D & M Everett
OPENING TIMES: Appt only.
MAIL ORDER: No *CAT. COST:* Free *W/SALE or RETAIL:* Both
SPECIALITIES: Heathers. *MAP PAGE:* **2**

WGwy Gwydir Plants, Plas Muriau, Betws-y-coed, Gwynedd LL24 0HD
TEL: (0690) 710201 *FAX:* (06906) 379 *CONTACT:* Mrs D Southgate & Mrs L Schärer
OPENING TIMES: 1100-1800 Tue-Sun & Bank Hols Mar-Oct.
MAIL ORDER: No *CAT. COST:* 2 x 1st class *W/SALE or RETAIL:* Retail
SPECIALITIES: Herbs, Wild flowers & Cottage garden plants including many unusual ones. *MAP PAGE:* **4**

 See note on Mail Order, EC sales & Export on page 5

WHal **Hall Farm Nursery,** Kinnerley, Nr Oswestry, Shropshire SY10 8DH
TEL: (069185) 219 *CONTACT:* Mrs C Ffoulkes-Jones
OPENING TIMES: 1000-1700 Tue-Sun 2nd Mar-31st Oct. Closed Mon ex. Bank Hols.
MAIL ORDER: No *CAT. COST:* 4 x 1st class *W/SALE or RETAIL:* Retail
SPECIALITIES: Unusual Herbaceous plants. Also Alpines & Carnivorous plants. *MAP PAGE:* **4/5**

WHCG **Hunts Court Garden & Nursery,** North Nibley, Dursley, Gloucestershire GL11 6DZ
TEL: (0453) 547440 *CONTACT:* T K & M M Marshall
◆ *OPENING TIMES:* Nursery 0900-1700 Tue-Sat ex Aug. Garden 1400-1800 ex Aug. Also by appt.
MAIL ORDER: No *CAT. COST:* 50p *W/SALE or RETAIL:* Retail
SPECIALITIES: Old Rose species & climbers. Hardy Geraniums. Shrubby Potentilla & unusual shrubs. *MAP PAGE:* **2**

WHCr **Hergest Croft Gardens,** Kington, Herefordshire HR5 3EG
TEL: (0544) 230160 *CONTACT:* Stephen Lloyd
OPENING TIMES: 1330-1830 daily Apr-Oct.
MAIL ORDER: No *CAT. COST:* None issued *W/SALE or RETAIL:* Retail
SPECIALITIES: Acer, Betula & unusual woody plants. *MAP PAGE:* **2**

WHen **Henllys Lodge Plant,** Henllys Lodge, Beaumaris, Anglesey, Gwynedd LL58 8HU
TEL: (0248) 810106 *CONTACT:* Mrs E Lane
OPENING TIMES: 1100-1700 Tue, Wed, Fri, Sat, Sun & by appt. Apr-Oct.
MAIL ORDER: No *CAT. COST:* 2 x 1st class *W/SALE or RETAIL:* Retail
SPECIALITIES: Hardy Geranium, Ground cover & cottage style Perennials. *MAP PAGE:* **4**

WHer **The Herb Garden,** Plant Hunter's Nursery, Capel Ulo, Pentre Berw, Gaerwen, Anglesey, Gwynedd LL60 6LF
TEL: (0248) 421064 *CONTACT:* Corinne & David Tremaine-Stevenson
◆ *OPENING TIMES:* 0900-dusk daily Mar-30th Sep. 1000-1700 Oct-Apr & Bank Hols & by appt. (Please ring out of season).
MAIL ORDER: Yes *MIN VALUE:* £15.00 + p&p *CAT. COST:* £2.00 List £1
W/SALE or RETAIL: Retail
SPECIALITIES: Wide range of Herbs, Wild flowers, unusual Perennials. Scented Pelargoniums, Salvia, old Roses & Hardy Geraniums. *MAP PAGE:* **2/4**

WHil **Hillview Hardy Plants,** Worfield, Nr Bridgnorth, Shropshire WV15 5NT
TEL: (074 64) 454 *CONTACT:* Ingrid Millington
OPENING TIMES: 1000-1700 Mon-Sat Mar-mid Oct. By appt. mid Oct-Feb.
MAIL ORDER: Yes *MIN VALUE:* £10.00 + p&p *CAT. COST:* 5 x 2nd class
W/SALE or RETAIL: Both
SPECIALITIES: Hardy Perennials & Alpines. Contract growing for Wholesale. *MAP PAGE:* **5**

WHol **Holberrow Aquatics,** Holberrow Green, Astwood Bank, Redditch West Midlands B96 6SB
TEL: (0386) 792521 *CONTACT:* B L Fowler
OPENING TIMES: 0830-1800
MAIL ORDER: Yes *MIN VALUE:* None *CAT. COST:* 50p *W/SALE or RETAIL:* Both
SPECIALITIES: Aquatic plants, Bog plants. Plants for pools and surrounds. *MAP PAGE:* **2**

WHoo **Hoo House Nursery,** Hoo House, Gloucester Road, Tewkesbury, Gloucestershire GL20 7DA
TEL: (0684) 293389 *CONTACT:* Robin & Julie Ritchie
◆ *OPENING TIMES:* 1400-1700 Mon-Sat.
MAIL ORDER: Yes *MIN VALUE:* £5.00 + p&p* *CAT. COST:* 3 x 1st class
W/SALE or RETAIL: Both
SPECIALITIES: Wide range of Herbaceous & Alpines - some unusual. *NOTE: Mail Order only available Oct-Mar. *MAP PAGE:* **2**

WJas **Paul Jasper (Trees & Roses),** The Lighthouse, Bridge Street, Leominster, Herefordshire HR6 8DU
TEL: *CONTACT:*
OPENING TIMES: Not open for Retail sales.
MAIL ORDER: Yes *MIN VALUE:* £25.00 + p&p *CAT. COST:* 2 x 1st class
W/SALE or RETAIL: Both
SPECIALITIES: Worthy old & modern Apple varieties grown on MM 111 (Standards), MM 106 (General) & MM 27 (Dwarfing) root stock. *MAP PAGE:*

WJun **Jungle Giants,** Plough Farm, Wigmore, Herefordshire HR6 9UW
TEL: (0568) 86708 *FAX:* (0568) 86383 *CONTACT:* Michael Brisbane
OPENING TIMES: Daily - by appt. only please.
MAIL ORDER: Yes *MIN VALUE:* £7.20 + p&p *CAT. COST:* £4.36 info.pack
W/SALE or RETAIL: Both
SPECIALITIES: Bamboo and hardy plants for tropical effect gardens. *MAP PAGE:* **2/4**

WKif **Kiftsgate Court Gardens,** Kiftsgate Court, Chipping Camden, Gloucestershire GL55 6LW
TEL: (0386) 438777 *CONTACT:* Mrs J Chambers
OPENING TIMES: 1400-1800 Wed, Thu & Sun Apr 1st-Sep 30th & Bank Hol Mons.
MAIL ORDER: No *CAT. COST:* *W/SALE or RETAIL:* Retail
SPECIALITIES: Small range of unusual plants. *MAP PAGE:* **2**

WMal **Marshall's Malmaison,** 4 The Damsells, Tetbury, Gloucestershire GL8 8JA
TEL: (0666) 502589 *CONTACT:* J M & M I Marshall
OPENING TIMES: By appt. only.
MAIL ORDER: Yes *MIN VALUE:* £10.00 + p&p *CAT. COST:* *W/SALE or RETAIL:* Both
SPECIALITIES: Malmaison Carnations. *MAP PAGE:*

WMar **Marley Bank Nursery,** Bottom Lane, Whitbourne, Worcester WR6 5RU
TEL: (0886) 21576 *CONTACT:* Roger & Sue Norman
OPENING TIMES: By appt. and as for National Garden Scheme.
MAIL ORDER: No *CAT. COST:* Sae *W/SALE or RETAIL:* Retail
SPECIALITIES: Alpines, Cyclamen, tender Perennials, Penstemon & Violas. *MAP PAGE:* **2**

WMer **Merton Nurseries,** Holyhead Road, Bicton, Shrewsbury, Shropshire SY3 8EF
TEL: (0743) 850773 *FAX:* (0743) 850773 *CONTACT:* Jessica Pannett
OPENING TIMES: 0900-1730 daily ex. Christmas & New Year
MAIL ORDER: No *CAT. COST:* 2 x 1st class *W/SALE or RETAIL:* Retail
SPECIALITIES: Hardy Perennials & Clematis *MAP PAGE:* **4/5**

WMEx **Marston Exotics,** Brampton Lane, Madley, Herefordshire HR2 9LX
TEL: (0981) 251140 *FAX:* (0432) 274023 *CONTACT:* Paul Gardner
OPENING TIMES: 0800-1630 Mon-Fri all year, 1300-1700 Sat & Sun Mar-Oct.
MAIL ORDER: Yes *MIN VALUE:* See Cat. for details *CAT. COST:* £1.00 *W/SALE or RETAIL:* Both
SPECIALITIES: Carnivorous plants. *MAP PAGE:* **2/4**

WMou **Mount Pleasant Trees,** Rockhampton, Berkeley, Gloucestershire GL13 9DU
TEL: (0454) 260348 *CONTACT:* G Locke
◆ *OPENING TIMES:* Appt only.
MAIL ORDER: Yes *MIN VALUE:* £20.00 + p&p* *CAT. COST:* 3 x 2nd class
W/SALE or RETAIL: Both
SPECIALITIES: Wide range of Trees for forestry, hedging, woodland & gardens. Selection of best lime tolerant species & varieties. * NOTE: Not all available by Mail Order. *MAP PAGE:* **2**

WNdy **Nordybank Nurseries,** Clee St Margaret, Craven Arms, Shropshire SY7 9EF
TEL: (0584 75) 322 *CONTACT:* P J Bolton
OPENING TIMES: 1000-1800 Mon, Wed & Sun Easter-mid Oct.
MAIL ORDER: No *CAT. COST:* 50p *W/SALE or RETAIL:* Retail
SPECIALITIES: Native & Hardy Herbaceous plants. *MAP PAGE:* **2/4**

WNor **Andrew Norfield Trees & Seeds,** Lower Meend, St Briavels, Gloucestershire GL15 6RW
TEL: (0594) 530134 *FAX:* (0594) 530113 *CONTACT:* Andrew Norfield
OPENING TIMES:
MAIL ORDER: Yes *MIN VALUE:* £3.00 + p&p *CAT. COST:* 1 x 1st class *W/SALE or RETAIL:* Both
SPECIALITIES: Wide range of Trees from seed. Acer, Betula, Stewartia & pregerminated seed. See also SEED supplier index. *MAP PAGE:*

WOak **Oak Cottage Herb Garden,** Nesscliffe, nr Shrewsbury, Shropshire SY4 1DB
TEL: (074381) 262 *CONTACT:* Jane & Edward Bygott.
◆ *OPENING TIMES:* Usually 1500-1800 weekdays, 1030-1800 weekends.
MAIL ORDER: Yes *MIN VALUE:* £3.50 + p&p *CAT. COST:* 30p + Sae *W/SALE or RETAIL:* Retail
SPECIALITIES: Herbs, Wild flowers, Old Roses and Cottage plants. Design of Herb Gardens.
MAP PAGE: **4/5**

 See note on Mail Order, EC sales & Export on page 5

WOld **Old Court Nurseries,** Colwall, Nr Malvern, Worcestershire WR13 6QE

TEL: (0684) 40416 *CONTACT:* Paul & Meriel Picton
OPENING TIMES: 1000-1300 & 1415-1730 Wed-Sun Apr-Oct. 1415-1700 Wed-Fri (by appt.) Nov-Mar.
MAIL ORDER: Yes *MIN VALUE:* £13.20 + p&p *CAT. COST:* 2 x 1st class
W/SALE or RETAIL: Retail
SPECIALITIES: National collection of Michaelmas Daisies. Herbaceous Perennials & Alpines. (Mail order for Asters only). *MAP PAGE:* **2**

WOMN **The Old Manor Nursery,** Twyning, Gloucestershire GL20 6DB

TEL: (0684) 293516 *CONTACT:* Mrs Joan Wilder
OPENING TIMES: 1400-1700, or dusk if earlier, Mons 1st Mar-31st Oct.
MAIL ORDER: No *CAT. COST:* 30p+A5 Sae *W/SALE or RETAIL:* Retail
SPECIALITIES: Predominately Alpines, small supply of unusual and rare varieties of other Perennial plants. *MAP PAGE:* **2**

WPat **Chris Pattison,** Brookend, Pendock, Gloucestershire GL19 3PL

TEL: (0531) 650480 *CONTACT:* Chris Pattison
◆ *OPENING TIMES:* 0900-1700 Mon-Fri. Weekends by appt. only.
MAIL ORDER: No *CAT. COST:* 3 x 1st class *W/SALE or RETAIL:* Both
SPECIALITIES: Choice & rare Shrubs and Alpines. *MAP PAGE:* **2**

WPbr **Perrybrook Nursery,** Brook Cottage, Wykey, Ruyton XI Towns, Shropshire SY4 1JA

TEL: (0939) 261120 *CONTACT:* Gayle Williams
OPENING TIMES: By appointment.
MAIL ORDER: No *CAT. COST:* 50p *W/SALE or RETAIL:* Both
SPECIALITIES: Herbaceous Perennials. Many unusual varieties available in small numbers. *MAP PAGE:* **4**

WPer **Perhill Nurseries,** Worcerster Road, Great Witley, Worcestershire WR6 6JT

TEL: (0299) 896329 *FAX:* (0299) 896990 *CONTACT:* Jon Baker & Duncan Straw
OPENING TIMES: 0900-1800 Mon-Sat 0900-1700 Sun.
MAIL ORDER: No *CAT. COST:* Sae for list *W/SALE or RETAIL:* Both
SPECIALITIES: Over 1800 varieties of rare & unusual Alpines & Herbaceous Perennials. Old fashioned Dianthus, Penstemon, Salvia, Thymes, Herbs & Pelargoniums. *MAP PAGE:* **2**

WRic **Rickard's Hardy Fern,** The Old Rectory, Leinthall Starkes, Ludlow, Shropshire SY8 2HP

TEL: (056886) 282 *CONTACT:* Hazel & Martin Rickard
OPENING TIMES: Most times but please make appt. first.
MAIL ORDER: Yes *MIN VALUE:* £6 + p&p *CAT. COST:* Sae *W/SALE or RETAIL:* Retail
SPECIALITIES: Ferns, hardy & half-hardy. National Reference Collection of Polypodium, Cystopteris & Thelypteroid ferns. *MAP PAGE:* **4/2**

WRid **Ridgeway Heather Nursery,** Park House, Plaish, Church Streeton, Shropshire SY6 7HY

TEL: (0694) 771574 *CONTACT:* Mrs N Cordingley
OPENING TIMES: 1000-1800 Tue-Sun, ex. Bank Holiday Monday.
MAIL ORDER: Yes *MIN VALUE:* None *CAT. COST:* Free *W/SALE or RETAIL:* Both
SPECIALITIES: Heathers *MAP PAGE:* **2/4**

WRus **Rushfields of Ledbury,** Ross Road, Ledbury, Herefordshire HR8 2LP

TEL: (0531) 632004 *CONTACT:* B & J Homewood
OPENING TIMES: 1100-1700 Wed-Sat.
MAIL ORDER: No *CAT. COST:* A5 Sae + £1.00 *W/SALE or RETAIL:* Both
SPECIALITIES: Unusual Herbaceous & foliage plants, incl. Euphorbias, Hardy Geraniums, Helleborus, Hostas, Osteospermum, Penstemon, Primroses & Grasses. *MAP PAGE:* **2**

WSHC **Stone House Cottage Nurseries,** Stone, Nr Kidderminster, Worcestershire DY10 4BG

TEL: (0562) 69902 *CONTACT:* J F & L N Arbuthnott
◆ *OPENING TIMES:* 1000-1800 Wed-Sat, & Sun in May & June. Appt. only in Nov. Closed Dec-Feb.
MAIL ORDER: No *CAT. COST:* Sae *W/SALE or RETAIL:* Retail
SPECIALITIES: Small general range, especially wall Shrubs, Climbers and unusual plants. *MAP PAGE:* **2**

WShi **John Shipton (Bulbs),** Y Felin, Henllan Amgoed, Whitland, Dyfed SA34 0SL
TEL: (0994) 240125 *CONTACT:* John Shipton
OPENING TIMES: By appt. only.
MAIL ORDER: Yes *MIN VALUE:* None *CAT. COST:* Sae *W/SALE or RETAIL:* Both
SPECIALITIES: Native British Bulbs & Daffodils. *MAP PAGE:* **4**

WSpr **Rosemary Spreckley,** Hailey House, Great Comberton, Pershore, Worcestershire WR10 3DS
TEL: (0386) 710733 *CONTACT:* Rosemary Spreckley
OPENING TIMES: By appt. only.
MAIL ORDER: No *CAT. COST:* Large Sae *W/SALE or RETAIL:* Retail
SPECIALITIES: Penstemons. *MAP PAGE:* **2**

WStA **St Annes Vineyard,** Wain House, Oxenhall, Newent Gloucestershire GL18 1RW
TEL: (098 982) 313 *CONTACT:* B R Edwards
OPENING TIMES: 1400-1900 Wed-Fri, 1000-1900 Weekends & Bank Hols.
MAIL ORDER: Yes *MIN VALUE:* *CAT. COST:* Sae *W/SALE or RETAIL:* Both
SPECIALITIES: Vines *MAP PAGE:* **2**

WStI **St Ishmael's Nurseries,** Haverfordwest, Pembrokeshire SA62 3SX
TEL: (0646) 636343 *FAX:* (0646) 636343 *CONTACT:* Mr D & Mrs H Phippen
OPENING TIMES: 0900-1730 daily Summer. 0900-1700 daily Winter.
MAIL ORDER: No *CAT. COST:* Sae *W/SALE or RETAIL:* Retail
SPECIALITIES: Wide general range. *MAP PAGE:* **4**

WSun **Sunnybank House Nursery,** Little Birch, Hereford, Herefordshire HR2 8BB
TEL: (0981) 540684 *FAX:* (0981) 540932 *CONTACT:* Mrs Pat Jones
OPENING TIMES: Visitors welcome but please phone first.
MAIL ORDER: Yes *MIN VALUE:* £6.00 + p&p *CAT. COST:* 2 x 1st class
W/SALE or RETAIL: Retail
SPECIALITIES: Cottage garden & Herb plants incl. Aquilegia, Pulmonaria, Primroses, Viola & hardy Geraniums. *MAP PAGE:* **2**

WThi **39 Steps,** Grove Cottage Forge Hill, Lydbrook, Gloucestershire GL17 9QS
TEL: (0594) 860544 *CONTACT:* Graham Birkin
OPENING TIMES: 1000-1600 Mon-Fri. Weekends by appt. Please phone first. (Closed 6th May-20th May 1993)
MAIL ORDER: No *CAT. COST:* 3 x 1st class *W/SALE or RETAIL:* Retail
SPECIALITIES: Alpines, shade lovers & Irises. *MAP PAGE:* **2**

WThu **Thuya Alpine Nursery,** Glebelands, Hartpury, Gloucestershire GL19 3BW
TEL: (0452) 700548 *CONTACT:* S W Bond
OPENING TIMES: 1000-dusk Sat & Bank hol. 1100-dusk Sun, Weekdays appt. advised.
MAIL ORDER: Yes *MIN VALUE:* None *CAT. COST:* 4 x 2nd class *W/SALE or RETAIL:* Retail
SPECIALITIES: Wide and changing range including rarities. *MAP PAGE:* **2**

WToa **Toad Hall Produce,** Frogmore, Weston-under-Penyard, Herefordshire HR9 5TQ
TEL: (0989) 750214 *CONTACT:* S V North
◆ *OPENING TIMES:* 1000-1800 Mon Apr-Sep.
MAIL ORDER: Yes *MIN VALUE:* None *CAT. COST:* Sae *W/SALE or RETAIL:* Retail
SPECIALITIES: Hardy Geranium & Ground cover plants. *MAP PAGE:* **2**

WTyr **Ty'r Orsaf Nursery,** Maentwrog Road (A470), Ty Nant, Nr Gellilydan, Gwynedd LL41 4RB
TEL: (076 685) 233 *CONTACT:* A G & M Faulkner
OPENING TIMES: 1000-1800 daily.
MAIL ORDER: No *CAT. COST:* *W/SALE or RETAIL:* Retail
SPECIALITIES: Hardy herbaceous, Shrubs, Alpines & Conifers. *MAP PAGE:* **4**

WWar **Warners Roses,** Greenfields, Brockton, Newport, Shropshire
TEL: (0952) 604217 *CONTACT:* Mr C H Warner
OPENING TIMES: 1000-1930 Mon-Sat, 1430-1830 Sun from 2nd week in July to 2nd week in April.
MAIL ORDER: Yes *MIN VALUE:* £10.00 + p&p *CAT. COST:* Free *W/SALE or RETAIL:* Both
SPECIALITIES: New and climbing Rose varieties. *MAP PAGE:* **5**

 See note on Mail Order, EC sales & Export on page 5

WWat **Waterwheel Nursery,** Bully Hole Bottom, Usk Road, Shirenewton, Chepstow, Gwent NP6 6SA
TEL: (02917) 577 *CONTACT:* Desmond & Charlotte Evans
◆ *OPENING TIMES:* Almost always, but best to phone to check & for directions. Closed on Sundays.
MAIL ORDER: Yes* *MIN VALUE:* No minimum charge *CAT. COST:* 3 x 1st class
W/SALE or RETAIL: Retail
SPECIALITIES: Wide range of Trees, Shrubs & Perennials - many unusual. *NOTE: Mail Order Oct-Mar only. *MAP PAGE:* **2/4**

WWeb **Webbs Garden Centres Ltd,** Wychbold, Droitwich, Worcestershire WR9 0DG
TEL: (0527) 861777 *FAX:* (0527) 861284 *CONTACT:* Mr J P Grunsell
◆ *OPENING TIMES:* 0900-1700 Mon-Sat 1000-1700 Sun Winter. 0900-1745 Mon-Sat 1000-1700 Sun Summer
MAIL ORDER: No *CAT. COST:* £1.95 *W/SALE or RETAIL:* Both
SPECIALITIES: Hardy Trees & Shrubs, Climbers, Conifers, Alpines, Heathers, Herbaceous, Herbs, Roses & Fruit. *MAP PAGE:* **2**

WWin **Wintergreen Nurseries,** Bringsty Common, Worcestershire WR6 5UJ
TEL: (0886) 21858 eves. *CONTACT:* S Dodd
OPENING TIMES: 1000-1730 Wed-Sun 1st Mar-29th Oct & by appt.
MAIL ORDER: Yes *MIN VALUE:* £5.00 + p&p *CAT. COST:* 2 x 2nd class
W/SALE or RETAIL: Both
SPECIALITIES: General, especially Alpines & Herbaceous. *MAP PAGE:* **2**

WWye **Wye Valley Herbs,** The Nurtons, Tintern, Chepstow, Gwent NP6 7NX
TEL: (0291) 689253 *CONTACT:* Adrian & Elsa Wood
◆ *OPENING TIMES:* 1030-1700 daily 1st Mar-mid Oct. Other times by appt.
MAIL ORDER: No *CAT. COST:* 3 x 1st class *W/SALE or RETAIL:* Retail
SPECIALITIES: Aromatic, Culinary, Medicinal & Dye Herbs. Unusual Perennials. *MAP PAGE:* **2/4**

Additional Nursery Index

Please note that all these nurseries are listed in ascending order of their numeric Codes.
All nurseries are listed in alphabetical order of their name in the **Nursery-Code** Index on page 613.

01 Foliage Scented & Herb Plants, Walton Poor Cottage, Crocknorth Rd, Ranmore Common, Dorking, Surrey RH5 6SX

TEL: (04865) 2273 *CONTACT:* Mrs Prudence Calvert
◆ *OPENING TIMES:* 1000-1700 Wed-Sun & Bank Hols.
MAIL ORDER: No *CAT. COST:* Free *W/SALE or RETAIL:* Retail
SPECIALITIES: Herbs, aromatic & scented plants. *MAP PAGE:* **3**

02 Jasmine Cottage Gardens, 26 Channel Road, Walton St. Mary, Clevedon, Avon BS21 7BY

TEL: (0275) 871850 *CONTACT:* Mr & Mrs M Redgrave
OPENING TIMES: Thurs. afternoon & by appt.
MAIL ORDER: No *CAT. COST:* None issued *W/SALE or RETAIL:* Both
SPECIALITIES: Rhodochiton, Asarina, Isotoma, Argyranthemum, Osteospermum. *MAP PAGE:* **1/4**

03 Ballagan Nursery, Gartocharn Road, Nr Balloch, Alexandria, Strathclyde G83 8NB

TEL: (0389) 52947 *FAX:* (0389) 52947 *CONTACT:* Mr G Stephenson
OPENING TIMES: 0900-1800 daily.
MAIL ORDER: *MIN VALUE:* *CAT. COST:* None issued *W/SALE or RETAIL:* Retail
SPECIALITIES: Home grown bedding and general nursery stock. *MAP PAGE:* **9**

04 Clonmel Garden Centre, Glenconnor House, Clonmel, Co. Tipperary Rep. of Ireland

TEL: 010353 (0)52 23294 *CONTACT:* C E Hanna
OPENING TIMES: 1000-1800 Mon-Sat, 1400-1800 Sun.
MAIL ORDER: No *CAT. COST:* *W/SALE or RETAIL:* Both
SPECIALITIES: Wide range of plants incl. many less common varieties. *MAP PAGE:* **10**

05 Beetham Nurseries, Pool Darkin Lane, Beetham, Nr Milnthorpe, Cumbria LA7 7AP

TEL: (05395) 63630 *CONTACT:* S J & A J Abbit
OPENING TIMES: 0900-1800 Summer, 0900-dusk Winter.
MAIL ORDER: *MIN VALUE:* *CAT. COST:* *W/SALE or RETAIL:* Retail
SPECIALITIES: Comprehensive range of Trees, Shrubs & Herbaceous Plants. Many unusual varieties. *MAP PAGE:* **5/8**

06 Pound Lane Nurseries, Ampfield, Nr Romsey, Hampshire SO5 9BL

TEL: (0703) 739685 *FAX:* (0703) 740300 *CONTACT:* Mr T A Holmes
OPENING TIMES: 0830-1730 Mon-Fri & 0930-1700 Sat & Sun.
MAIL ORDER: No *CAT. COST:* No retail Cat. *W/SALE or RETAIL:* Both
SPECIALITIES: Wide general range of Trees, Shrubs, Conifers, Rhododendrons & Azaleas and the unusual. *MAP PAGE:* **2**

07 Liscahane Nursery, Ardfert, Tralee, Co. Kerry, Rep. of Ireland

TEL: 010353 (0)6634222 *FAX:* 010353 (0)6634600 *CONTACT:* Dan Nolan/Bill Cooley
◆ *OPENING TIMES:* 0900-1800 Tue-Sat & 1400-1800 Sun. Closed Mon.
MAIL ORDER: *MIN VALUE:* *CAT. COST:* *W/SALE or RETAIL:* Retail
SPECIALITIES: Coastal shelter plants, Eucalyptus & Pines. *MAP PAGE:* **10**

08 Deelish Garden Centre, Skibbereen, Co. Cork Rep. of Ireland

TEL: 010353 (0)2821374 *FAX:* 010353 (0)02763187 *CONTACT:* Bill & Rain Chase
OPENING TIMES: 1000-1300 & 1400-1800 Mon-Sat, 1400-1800 Sun.
MAIL ORDER: Yes *MIN VALUE:* IR£50.00 + p&p *CAT. COST:* None *W/SALE or RETAIL:* Both
SPECIALITIES: Unusual plants for the mild coastal climate of Ireland. Conservatory plants. Sole Irish agents for Chase Organic Seeds. *MAP PAGE:* **10**

09 Bretby Nurseries, Bretby Lane, Burton-on-Trent, Staffordshire DE15 0QR

TEL: (0283) 703355 *FAX:* (0283) 704035 *CONTACT:* Mr David Cartwright
OPENING TIMES: 0900-1700 daily.
MAIL ORDER: No *CAT. COST:* 3 x 1st class *W/SALE or RETAIL:* Both
SPECIALITIES: Wide range of shrubs. *MAP PAGE:* **5**

11 Colemans Nurseries, 6 Old Ballyclare Road, Templepatrick, Ballyclare, Co Antrim, N Ireland BT39 0BJ

TEL: (08494) 32513 *FAX:* (08494) 32151 *CONTACT:* Mr Rodney Coleman
OPENING TIMES: 0900-1730 Mon-Fri, 0900-1700 Sat, 1400-1700 Sun.
MAIL ORDER: No *CAT. COST:* Free *W/SALE or RETAIL:* Both
SPECIALITIES: Over 2000 varieties of plants. *MAP PAGE:* **10**

12 Cottage Gardens, Langham Road, Boxted, Colchester, Essex CO4 5HU

TEL: (0206) 272269 *CONTACT:* Alison Smith
OPENING TIMES: 0800-1800 daily Spring & Summer. 0800-1800 Thu-Mon Jul-Feb.
MAIL ORDER: No *CAT. COST:* Free *W/SALE or RETAIL:* Retail
SPECIALITIES: 400 varieties of Shrubs, 390 varieties of Herbaceous. Huge range of Trees, Alpines, Herbs, Hedging - all home grown. Garden antiques. *MAP PAGE:* **6**

13 Cowcombe Farm Herbs, Gipsy Lane, Chalford, Stroud, Gloucestershire GL6 8HP

TEL: (0285) 760544 *CONTACT:* Mrs C M Barnett
OPENING TIMES: 1000-1700 Wed-Sat, 1400-1700 Sun, Easter Sat-end Sep or by appt.
MAIL ORDER: No *CAT. COST:* 2 x 2nd class *W/SALE or RETAIL:* Both
SPECIALITIES: Herbs, Wild flowers & Cottage garden plants. Herb and wild Seed. * NOTE:- Collection prefered. *MAP PAGE:* **2**

14 Seaside Nursery, Claddaghduff, Co. Galaway, Rep. of Ireland

TEL: 010353 (0)9544687 *FAX:* 010353 (0)9544687 *CONTACT:* Charles Dyck
OPENING TIMES: 0900-1300 & 1400-1800 Mon-Sat, 1400-1800 Sun.
MAIL ORDER: No *CAT. COST:* £1.00 *W/SALE or RETAIL:* Both
SPECIALITIES: Plants & Hedging suitable for seaside locations. Rare plants originating from Australia & New Zealand. *MAP PAGE:* **10**

15 Simpsons Nursery, The High Street, Marsham, Norwich, Norfolk NR10 5QA

TEL: (0263) 733432 *CONTACT:* Gillian Simpson
OPENING TIMES: 1000-1730 Wed-Sun & Bank Hols Easter-Christmas
MAIL ORDER: No *CAT. COST:* n/a *W/SALE or RETAIL:*
SPECIALITIES: Conifers, Shrubs & Bedding plants. *MAP PAGE:* **6**

16 Daleside Nurseries, Ripon Road, Killinghall, Harrogate, North Yorks HG3 2AY

TEL: (0423) 506450 *FAX:* (0423) 527872 *CONTACT:* Messrs Darley & Townsend.
OPENING TIMES: 0900-1700 Mon-Sat, 1000-1200 & 1330-1630 Sun.
MAIL ORDER: No *CAT. COST:* *W/SALE or RETAIL:* Retail
SPECIALITIES: Many plants & trees not generally available. Container grown Fruit, Apples, Pears & Soft Fruit. *MAP PAGE:* **5/7**

18 Frank P Matthews Ltd., Berrington Court, Tenbury Wells, Worcestershire WR15 8TH

TEL: (0584) 810214 *FAX:* (0584) 811830 *CONTACT:* N D Dunn
OPENING TIMES: 0730-1700 Mon-Fri
MAIL ORDER: No *CAT. COST:* Free *W/SALE or RETAIL:* Both
SPECIALITIES: Fruit & deciduous ornamental Trees. *MAP PAGE:* **2/4**

19 Denmans Ltd. (Denmans Garden), Clock House, Denmans, Fontwell, Nr Arundel, West Sussex BN18 0SU

TEL: (0243) 542808 *FAX:* (0243) 544064 *CONTACT:* John Brookes
OPENING TIMES: 0900-1700 daily 4th Mar-15th Dec.
MAIL ORDER: *MIN VALUE:* *CAT. COST:* £2.50 *W/SALE or RETAIL:* Retail
SPECIALITIES: Rare and unusual plants. *MAP PAGE:* **3**

21 Mugswell Nursery, Bisley, Stroud, Gloucestershire GL6 7AN

TEL: (0452) 770105 *CONTACT:* Peter Dinning
OPENING TIMES: 1000-1700 (dusk if earlier) Wed-Sun. Please check.
MAIL ORDER: No *CAT. COST:* £1.00 + A5 Sae *W/SALE or RETAIL:* Both
SPECIALITIES: Mainly Alpines and Herbaceous Perennials. *MAP PAGE:* **2**

22 Elly Hill Herbs, Elly Hill House, Barmpton, Darlington, Co. Durham DL1 3JF

TEL: (0325) 464682 *CONTACT:* Mrs Nina Pagan
OPENING TIMES: By appt. only
MAIL ORDER: No *CAT. COST:* 50p+large Sae *W/SALE or RETAIL:* Retail
SPECIALITIES: Herbs. *MAP PAGE:* **7/8**

23 Cherry Close Herbs, Meldreth Road, Whaddon Nr Royston Hertfordshire SG8 5RN

TEL: (0223) 207418 *CONTACT:* Virginia & Jim Christou
OPENING TIMES: 1000-1400 Tue-Fri, 1000-1900 Sat & Sun or by appt.
MAIL ORDER: Yes *MIN VALUE:* £5.00 + p&p *CAT. COST:* Free *W/SALE or RETAIL:* Both
SPECIALITIES: Herbs *MAP PAGE:* **6**

24 Woodborough Garden Centre,, Nursery Farm, Woodborough, Nr Pewsey, Wiltshire SN9 5PF

TEL: (0672) 851249 *CONTACT:* Els M Brewin
OPENING TIMES: 0900-1700 daily
MAIL ORDER: *MIN VALUE:* *CAT. COST:* *W/SALE or RETAIL:* Retail
SPECIALITIES: Wide range of Shrubs, Trees, Herbaceous, Alpines & Herbs. Large selection of Climbers, esp. Clematis, & spring Bulbs. *MAP PAGE:* **2**

25 Carewswood Garden Centre, Carewswood House, Castlemartyr, Co. Cork Rep. of Ireland

TEL: 010353 (0)21667283 *FAX:* 010353 (0)21667283 *CONTACT:* Neil Williams
OPENING TIMES: 0900-1800 Mon-Sat & 1200-1800 Sun.
MAIL ORDER: Yes *MIN VALUE:* £20.00 + p&p *CAT. COST:* £1.00 *W/SALE or RETAIL:* Retail
SPECIALITIES: Rare & unusual Shrubs, Alpines & Herbaceous plants. *MAP PAGE:* **10**

26 The Flower Centre, 754 Howth Road, Raheny, Dublin 5, Rep. of Ireland

TEL: 010353 (0)1327047 *FAX:* 010353 (0)1327251 *CONTACT:* Eugene Higgins
OPENING TIMES: 1000-1300 & 1430-1800 Summer, 1000-1300 & 1430-1700 Winter daily. Mon-Sat only Jan & Feb.
MAIL ORDER: No *CAT. COST:* Free *W/SALE or RETAIL:* Both
SPECIALITIES: Impatiens, Universal pansies, Fuchsia & hanging baskets. *MAP PAGE:* **10**

27 Chennels Gate Gardens & Nursery, Eardisley, Herefordshire HR3 6LJ

TEL: (05446) 288 *CONTACT:* Una Dawson
OPENING TIMES: 0900-1800 Mon, Fri & Sat Apr-Sep.
MAIL ORDER: No *CAT. COST:* None issued *W/SALE or RETAIL:* Retail
SPECIALITIES: Interesting Herbaceous. Micropropagated Roses, Clematis & Azaleas. *MAP PAGE:* **2/4**

28 Linda Gascoigne Wild Flowers, 17 Imperial Road, Kibworth Beauchamp, Leicestershire LE8 0HR

TEL: (0533) 793959 *CONTACT:* Linda Gascoigne
OPENING TIMES: By appt. only
MAIL ORDER: Yes *MIN VALUE:* £5.00 + p&p *CAT. COST:* 50p *W/SALE or RETAIL:* Retail
SPECIALITIES: Wide range of attractive Wild Flowers & Wildlife plants. No peat used. *MAP PAGE:* **5**

29 Glebe Cottage Gardens, Church Lane, Stockerston, Oakham, Leicestershire LE15 9JD

TEL: (0572) 821253 *CONTACT:* A V Burwood
OPENING TIMES: 1000-1700 Sat, Sun & Bank Hols, Mar-Sep or by appt. Closed Aug 1st-14th.
MAIL ORDER: No *CAT. COST:* 3 x 1st class *W/SALE or RETAIL:* Retail
SPECIALITIES: Alpines & Cottage garden plants. Only small quantities of each, please check availability. *MAP PAGE:* **6**

31 Cold Harbour Nursery, (Off.) 19 Hilary Road, Poole, Dorset BH17 7LZ

TEL: *CONTACT:* Steve Saunders
OPENING TIMES: 1400-1800 Sat, 1000-1800 Sun & Bank Hols (dusk if earlier) Mar-Oct.
MAIL ORDER: No *CAT. COST:* Sae *W/SALE or RETAIL:* Retail
SPECIALITIES: Herbaceous Perennials, incl. hardy Geraniums & Wild Flowers. NOTE:- Nursery at Bere Road, (opp. Silent Woman Inn), Wareham, Dorset. *MAP PAGE:* **2**

32 Grange Farm Nursery, Guarlford, Malvern, Worcestershire WR13 6NY

TEL: (0684) 562544 *CONTACT:* Mrs C Nicholls
◆ *OPENING TIMES:* 0900-1730 daily Summer. 0900-1700 daily Winter. ex Xmas & 2 weeks in Jan.
MAIL ORDER: No *CAT. COST:* Free pamphlet *W/SALE or RETAIL:* Retail
SPECIALITIES: Wide general range of container grown hardy Shrubs, Trees, Conifers, Heathers, Alpines & Herbaceous. Shrub, climbing & bush Roses. *MAP PAGE:* **2**

34 Just Plants, The Birches, Top Row, Wreningham, Norfolk NR16 1AR

TEL: (050841) 296 *CONTACT:* Joy McCarthy
OPENING TIMES: 1400-1700 Wed, Thu & Sat Apr-Sep. 1000-1700 Bank Hols & by appt.
MAIL ORDER: No *CAT. COST:* 2 x 1st class *W/SALE or RETAIL:* Retail
SPECIALITIES: Unusual varieties of hardy Perennials & Alpines. *MAP PAGE:* **6**

 See note on Mail Order, EC sales & Export on page 5

35 **The Herbary Prickwillow,** Ely, Cambridgeshire CB7 4SJ
TEL: (0353 88) 456 *FAX:* (0353 88) 451 *CONTACT:* Peter Petts
OPENING TIMES: 0800-1500 Mon-Thu all year.
MAIL ORDER: Yes *MIN VALUE:* £15.00 + p&p *CAT. COST:* Free *W/SALE or RETAIL:* Both
SPECIALITIES: Culinary Herbs. Will propagate any not on list; minimum of 12 plants. *MAP PAGE:* **6**

36 **Herterton House Garden Nursery,** Hartington, Cambo, Morpeth, Northumberland NE61 4BN
TEL: (067074) 278 *CONTACT:* Mrs M Lawley & Mr Frank Lawley
OPENING TIMES: 1330-1730 Mon Wed Fri-Sun 1st April-mid Oct. (Earlier or later in the year weather permitting).
MAIL ORDER: No *CAT. COST:* None issued *W/SALE or RETAIL:* Retail
SPECIALITIES: Achillea, Aquilegia, Geum, Geranium, Polemonium. *MAP PAGE:* **8/9**

37 **Claytons' Garden Nursery,** 5 Pine Hey, Neston, South Wirral, Cheshire L64 3TJ
TEL: (051 336) 3006 *CONTACT:* Mary Clayton
OPENING TIMES: Most times, but please ring first.
MAIL ORDER: No *CAT. COST:* 50p *W/SALE or RETAIL:* Retail
SPECIALITIES: Unusual hardy & half-hardy Perennials. *MAP PAGE:* **4/5**

38 **The Laurels Nursery,** Benenden, Cranbrook, Kent TN17 4JU
TEL: (0580) 240463 *CONTACT:* Mr P H Kellett
OPENING TIMES: 0800-1700 Mon-Thu, 0800-1600 Fri, 0900-1200 Sat, Sun by appt. only.
MAIL ORDER: *MIN VALUE:* *CAT. COST:* Free *W/SALE or RETAIL:* Both
SPECIALITIES: Flowering Cherries, open ground ornamental Trees & Shrubs *MAP PAGE:* **3**

40 **Layham Garden Centre,** Lower Road, Staple, Canterbury, Kent CT3 1LH
TEL: (0304) 813267 *FAX:* (0304) 615349 *CONTACT:* L W Wessel
OPENING TIMES: 0900-1700 Mon-Sat 1000-1700 Sun.
MAIL ORDER: No *CAT. COST:* Free *W/SALE or RETAIL:* Both
SPECIALITIES: Roses, Herbaceous, Shrubs, Trees, Conifers, Liners & Whips. Aquatic plants. *MAP PAGE:* **3**

41 **Longacre Nursery,** Perry Wood, Selling, Nr Faversham, Kent ME13 9SE
TEL: (0227) 752254 *CONTACT:* Dr & Mrs G G Thomas
◆ *OPENING TIMES:* 1400-1700 daily, 1st Apr-31st Oct.
MAIL ORDER: No *CAT. COST:* 25p + stamp *W/SALE or RETAIL:* Retail
SPECIALITIES: Hardy Herbaceous only. *MAP PAGE:* **3**

42 **Manningford Nurseries,** Manningford Abbots, Nr Pewsey, Wiltshire SN9 5PB
TEL: (0672) 62232 *CONTACT:* Peter Jones
OPENING TIMES: 0830-1700 Mon, Tue, Thu, Fri & Sat, 1030-1300 & 1400-1700 Sun.
MAIL ORDER: Yes *MIN VALUE:* £10 + p&p *CAT. COST:* None issued *W/SALE or RETAIL:* Both
SPECIALITIES: Plants of the 18th & 19th century. Digitalis, Penstemon, Hemerocallis, Nepeta, Aconitum volubile, Maurandya. *MAP PAGE:* **2**

43 **Marle Place Plants & Gardens,** Marle Place, Brenchley, Nr Tonbridge, Kent TN12 7HS
TEL: (0892 72) 2304 *FAX:* (0732) 464466 *CONTACT:* Mrs L M Williams
OPENING TIMES: Easter-end Oct. Gardens open 1000-1730.
MAIL ORDER: Yes *MIN VALUE:* No minimum charge *CAT. COST:* *W/SALE or RETAIL:* Both
SPECIALITIES: Herbs & Wild Flowers. *MAP PAGE:* **3**

44 **Plantworld,** Burnham Road, South Woodham Ferrers, Chelmsford, Essex CM3 5QP
TEL: (0245) 320482 *FAX:* (0245) 320482 *CONTACT:* F Waterworth
◆ *OPENING TIMES:* 1000-1700 daily. Please phone first if travelling.
MAIL ORDER: *MIN VALUE:* *CAT. COST:* £2.00 *W/SALE or RETAIL:* Both
SPECIALITIES: Tropaeolum speciosum & wide range of hardy plants. *MAP PAGE:* **3**

45 **Houghton Farm Plants,** Houghton (B2139), Arundel, West Sussex BN18 9LW
TEL: (0798) 831327 *FAX:* (0798) 831183 *CONTACT:* M J & R Lock
OPENING TIMES: 1000-1700 Mon-Fri & 1400-1730 Sun Apr-Oct.
MAIL ORDER: Yes *MIN VALUE:* £10.00 + p&p *CAT. COST:* 3 x 1st class *W/SALE or RETAIL:* Retail
SPECIALITIES: Euphorbia, Geranium & unusual Herbaceous. *MAP PAGE:* **3**

46 Cilwern Plants, Cilwern, Talley, Llandeilo, Dyfed SA19 7YH

TEL: (0558) 685526 *CONTACT:* Anne Knatchbull-Hugessen
OPENING TIMES: 1100-1800 Sat-Thu. Closed Fri.
MAIL ORDER: Yes *MIN VALUE:* £10.00 + p&p *CAT. COST:* 50p *W/SALE or RETAIL:* Retail
SPECIALITIES: Hardy Perennials, esp. Geraniums & Penstemon. *MAP PAGE:* **4**

47 Sue Robinson, 21 Bederic Close, Bury St Edmunds, Suffolk IP32 7DN

TEL: (0284) 764310 *CONTACT:* Sue Robinson
OPENING TIMES: By appt. only.
MAIL ORDER: No *CAT. COST:* None issued *W/SALE or RETAIL:* Retail
SPECIALITIES: Variegated & Foliage plants. Garden open. Lectures at Clubs & Societies, group bookings welcome.

48 Simply Plants, 17 Dunloe Brook, Eaton Socon Cambridgeshire PE19 3DW

TEL: (0480) 475312 *CONTACT:* Christine Dakin
OPENING TIMES: By appt. only
MAIL ORDER: No *CAT. COST:* *W/SALE or RETAIL:* Both
SPECIALITIES: Ornamental Grasses, Sedges & Bamboos. Also range of Shrubs & Perennials
MAP PAGE: **6**

50 Parkinson Herbs, Barras Moor Farm, Perran-ar-Worthal, Truro, Cornwall TR3 7PE

TEL: (0872) 864380 *FAX:* (0872) 864380 *CONTACT:* Elizabeth Parkinson
OPENING TIMES: 0900-1700 daily.
MAIL ORDER: Yes *MIN VALUE:* £5.00 + p&p *CAT. COST:* Free *W/SALE or RETAIL:* Retail
SPECIALITIES: Herbs. *MAP PAGE:* **1**

52 Porthpean House Gardens, Porthpean, St. Austell, Cornwall PL26 6AX

TEL: (0726) 72888 *CONTACT:* Mrs Petherick
OPENING TIMES: 0900-1700 Mon-Fri. Sat & Sun by appt.
MAIL ORDER: No *CAT. COST:* None issued *W/SALE or RETAIL:* Both
SPECIALITIES: Camellia & Shrubs for acid soils. *MAP PAGE:* **1**

53 The Priory, Kemerton, Tewkesbury, Gloucestershire GL20 7JN

TEL: (038689) 258 *CONTACT:* Mrs P Healing
OPENING TIMES: Thurs afternoons.
MAIL ORDER: No *CAT. COST:* None issued *W/SALE or RETAIL:* Retail
SPECIALITIES: Rare and unusual plants. *MAP PAGE:* **2**

54 The Wild Flower Centre, Church Farm, Sisland, Loddon, Norwich, Norfolk NR14 6EF

TEL: (0508) 20235 *CONTACT:* D G Corne
OPENING TIMES: 0900-1700 daily
MAIL ORDER: Yes *MIN VALUE:* £3.50 + p&p *CAT. COST:* 30p *W/SALE or RETAIL:* Retail
SPECIALITIES: British native and naturalised Wild Flower plants. *MAP PAGE:* **6**

56 Ryans Nurseries, Lissivigeen, Killarney, Co. Kerry, Rep. of Ireland

TEL: (0001) 6433507 *CONTACT:* Mr T Ryan
OPENING TIMES: 0900-1800 Mon-Sat 1400-1800 Sun.
MAIL ORDER: No *CAT. COST:* *W/SALE or RETAIL:* Retail
SPECIALITIES: Camellias, Pieris, Azaleas, Acacia, Eucalyptus, Dicksonia & many tender & rare plants.
MAP PAGE: **10**

57 Evegate Nursery Floral Workshop, Evegate Farm Complex, Station Road, Smeeth, Nr Ashford, Kent TN25 6SX

TEL: (0303) 813775 *CONTACT:* M C Dickerson
OPENING TIMES: 0930-1700 Tue-Sat, 1000-1700 Sun.
MAIL ORDER: No *CAT. COST:* 10p *W/SALE or RETAIL:* Retail
SPECIALITIES: Plants for Foliage & Floral effect, many of interest to the flower arranger.
MAP PAGE: **3**

58 Green City Plants, The Nursery, Cow Lane, Laverstock, Nr Salisbury, Wiltshire SP1 2RS

TEL: (0722) 339940 *FAX:* (0722) 339940 *CONTACT:* H V & J E Dooley
OPENING TIMES: 0930-1800 Fri & Sat 19th Mar-3rd Oct.
MAIL ORDER: Yes *MIN VALUE:* £5.00 + p&p *CAT. COST:* Sae *W/SALE or RETAIL:*
SPECIALITIES: Rare & Unusual plants esp. for chalkland. *MAP PAGE:* **2**

 See note on Mail Order, EC sales & Export on page 5

59 Muncaster Castle, Ravenglass, Cumbria CA18 1RQ

TEL: (0229) 717357 *FAX:* (0229) 717010 *CONTACT:* Peter Howarth
OPENING TIMES: 0900-1700 28th Mar-31st Oct. (Gardens open 1100-1700).
MAIL ORDER: No *CAT. COST:* None issued *W/SALE or RETAIL:* Retail
SPECIALITIES: Rhododendrons & Camellias. *MAP PAGE:* **8**

60 Muckross Garden Centre, Muckross. Killarney, Co. Kerry, Rep. of Ireland

TEL: 010353 (0)6434044 *FAX:* 010353 (0)6431114 *CONTACT:* John R Fuller B.Ag.Sc.(Hort.)
OPENING TIMES: 1000-1800 Tue-Sat & 1415-1800 Sun. Jan & Feb please check first.
MAIL ORDER: No *CAT. COST:* *W/SALE or RETAIL:* Retail
SPECIALITIES: Many rare & unusual plants. *MAP PAGE:* **10**

61 Wards Nurseries, Dawes Lane, Sarratt, Nr Rickmonsworth, Hertfordshire WD3 6BQ

TEL: (0923) 263237 *FAX:* (0923) 270930 *CONTACT:* M F Rawlins
OPENING TIMES: 0800-1700 Mon-Sat, 0900-1700 Sun & Bank Hols.
MAIL ORDER: No *CAT. COST:* Sae* *W/SALE or RETAIL:*
SPECIALITIES: Shrubs & Climbers, fragrant & aromatic plants. *State interest when asking for lists.
MAP PAGE: **3**

62 Southwick Country Herbs, Southwick Farm, Nomansland, Nr Tiverton, Devon EX16 8NW

TEL: (0884) 861099 *CONTACT:* Martin & Tricha Menist
OPENING TIMES: 1000-1730 Mon-Sat, 1100-1730 most Sun. Please phone first for directions.
MAIL ORDER: Yes *MIN VALUE:* £6.00 + p&p *CAT. COST:* Sae *W/SALE or RETAIL:* Both
SPECIALITIES: Over 200 Herbs & small selection of Wild Flowers. *MAP PAGE:* **1**

63 Kayes Garden Nursery, 1700 Melton Road, Rearsby, Leicestershire LE7 4YR

TEL: (0664) 424578 *CONTACT:* J E & Hazel Kaye
OPENING TIMES: 1000-1730 Wed-Sat & Bank Hols 1000-1200 Sun Mar-Oct. 1000-1600 Fri & Sat Nov, Dec & Feb. Closed Jan.
MAIL ORDER: No *CAT. COST:* 2 x 1st class *W/SALE or RETAIL:* Retail
SPECIALITIES: Herbaceous inc. Campanula, Nepeta, Potentilla, Pulmonaria, Sedum, Digitalis, Euphorbia. Geranium, Lathyrus, Viola etc. *MAP PAGE:* **5**

64 Totties Nursery, Greenhill Bank Road, New Mill, Holmfirth, West Yorkshire HD7 1UN

TEL: (0484) 683363 *FAX:* (0484) 688129 *CONTACT:* David A Shires
OPENING TIMES: 0900-1915 Mon-Fri & 0900-1800 Sat & Sun Summer. 0900-1700 daily Winter.
MAIL ORDER: No *CAT. COST:* None issued *W/SALE or RETAIL:* Both
SPECIALITIES: Large selection of ornamental Trees, field and container grown Conifers. Rhododendron & Azalea. Huge range of herbaceous Perennials. *MAP PAGE:* **5**

65 Marshford Organic Nursery, Churchill Way, Northam, Bideford, North Devon EX39 1NS

TEL: (0237) 477160 *CONTACT:* Mrs V M Ebdon
OPENING TIMES: 0900-1800
MAIL ORDER: No *CAT. COST:* *W/SALE or RETAIL:* Retail
SPECIALITIES: Herbaceous Perennials, Herbs & Organic Vegetables. *MAP PAGE:* **1**

67 Stockerton Nursery,, Kirkcudbright, Galloway, Scotland DG6 4XS

TEL: (0557) 31266 *CONTACT:* Martin Gould
OPENING TIMES: Mail Order only. Visits by arrangement.
MAIL ORDER: Only *MIN VALUE:* £3.00 + p&p *CAT. COST:* 3 x 1st class *W/SALE or RETAIL:* Both
SPECIALITIES: Native British species. *MAP PAGE:* **9!**

69 Rivendell Nursery, Menagerie Farm, Escrick, York Yorkshire YO4 6EH

TEL: (0904) 629872/728690 *CONTACT:* Gareth Hughes & Dave Fryer
OPENING TIMES: Sundays & by appt.
MAIL ORDER: No *CAT. COST:* 2 x 1st class *W/SALE or RETAIL:* Both
SPECIALITIES: Shrubs, Alpines, Conifers, & Heathers. All home gown & 100% Organic.
MAP PAGE: **7/5**

73 Newton Hill Alpines, 335, Leeds Road, Newton Hill, Wakefield, Yorkshire WF1 2JH

TEL: (0924) 377056 *CONTACT:* Sheena Vigors
OPENING TIMES: 0900-1700 Fri-Wed all year. Closed Thur. Please phone first.
MAIL ORDER: No *CAT. COST:* 50p *W/SALE or RETAIL:* Both
SPECIALITIES: Alpines, esp. Saxifrages, also Heathers, Conifers & dwarf Shrubs. *MAP PAGE:* **5/7**

74 Billy's Herbs, Manor Farm, Stradbroke, Diss, Norfolk IP21 5NJ
TEL: (0379 384) 319 *CONTACT:* W Serjent
OPENING TIMES: 0930-1600 Tue-Fri.
MAIL ORDER: Yes *MIN VALUE:* £5.00 + p&p *CAT. COST:* 2 x 2nd class *W/SALE or RETAIL:* Both
SPECIALITIES: Herbs. *MAP PAGE:* **6**

77 The Old Mill Herbary, Helland Bridge, Bodmin, Cornwall PL30 4QR
TEL: (020 884) 206 *FAX:* (020 884) 206 *CONTACT:* Mrs B Whurr
OPENING TIMES: 1000-1700 Apr-Oct
MAIL ORDER: No *CAT. COST:* £1.50 *W/SALE or RETAIL:* Retail
SPECIALITIES: Culinary, Medicinal & Aromatic Herbs, Shrubs, Climbing & Herbaceous plants.
MAP PAGE: **1**

79 Worth Trees, Fleet Estate Office, Fleet, Spalding, Lincolnshire PE12 8LR
TEL: (0406) 22778 *FAX:* (0406) 25402 *CONTACT:* Stuart Gray
OPENING TIMES: 0800-1730
MAIL ORDER: Yes *MIN VALUE:* £20.00 + p&p *CAT. COST:* Free *W/SALE or RETAIL:* Both
SPECIALITIES: Native Trees in all sizes from Seed & containerised Shrubs. *MAP PAGE:* **6**

80 Kinlochlaich House, Garden Plant Centre, Appin, Argyll PA38 4BD
TEL: (063 173) 342 *FAX:* (063 173) 482 *CONTACT:* D E Hutchison M.I.Hort.
OPENING TIMES: 0930-1730 Mon-Sat 1030-1730 Sun Apr-Oct, 0930-1700 Mon-Sat Nov-Mar.
MAIL ORDER: No *CAT. COST:* None issued *W/SALE or RETAIL:* Retail
SPECIALITIES: Wide general range of Shrubs & Perennials (over 2000 plants varieties). Particularly suitable for West coast locations i.e. damp and acid. *MAP PAGE:* **9**

84 Crocknafeola Nursery, KIllybegs, Co. Donegal, Rep. of Ireland
TEL: 010353 (0)7351018 *CONTACT:* Andy McKenna
OPENING TIMES: 0900-2100 Mon-Sat & 1200-1900 Sun in Summer. Until dusk in winter.
MAIL ORDER: No *CAT. COST: W/SALE or RETAIL:* Both
SPECIALITIES: Hardy Shrubs, Trees & Hedging suitable for exposed areas. *MAP PAGE:* **10**

86 R F Beeston, (Office) 294 Ombersley Rd., Worcestershire WR3 7HD
TEL: (0905) 53245 *CONTACT:* R F Beeston
OPENING TIMES: 1000-1300 & 1400-1700 Wed-Fri Mar 1-Oct 31 & by appt.
MAIL ORDER: Yes *MIN VALUE:* No minimum charge *CAT. COST:* Sae *W/SALE or RETAIL:* Retail
SPECIALITIES: Rare Alpines, esp. Androsace, Dionysia, Primula, Saxifraga,Gentiana & Daphne.
NOTE: Nursery at Bevere Nursery, Bevere, Worcester. *MAP PAGE:* **2**

95 Treasures of Tenbury Ltd, Burford House Gardens, Tenbury Wells, Worcestershire WR15 8HQ
TEL: (0584) 810777 *FAX:* (0584) 810673 *CONTACT:* Nicholas Hall
◆ *OPENING TIMES:* 1000-1800 daily. Until dusk in Winter
MAIL ORDER: Yes *MIN VALUE:* £4.95 + p&p *CAT. COST:* 95p *W/SALE or RETAIL:* Retail
SPECIALITIES: Clematis and Herbaceous, many unusual. Newsletter issued quarterly. *NOTE: Clematis plants ONLY by Mail Order. *MAP PAGE:* **2/4**

98 Mackey's Garden Centre, Castlepark Road, Sandycove, Co. Dublin, Rep. of Ireland
TEL: (0001) 2807385 *FAX:* (0001) 2841922 *CONTACT:* Breda Roseingrave
OPENING TIMES: 0900-1730 Mon-Sat. 1400-1730 Sun & Public Hols.
MAIL ORDER: Yes *MIN VALUE:* No minimum charge *CAT. COST:* Free *W/SALE or RETAIL:* Retail
SPECIALITIES: Roses, Trees, Houseplants, Alpines, Shrubs & Aquatics. *MAP PAGE:* **10**

 See note on Mail Order, EC sales & Export on page 5

Seed Suppliers

Allwood Bros, Hassocks, West Sussex BN6 9NB

TEL: (0273) 844229 *CONTACT:* W Rickaby *CAT. COST:* 2 x 1st class *MIN. ORDER:* None
SPECIALITIES: Carnations, Pinks & Dianthus. See also in Nursery Index under Code 'SAll'.

Ashwood Nurseries, Greensforge, Kingswinford, West Midlands DY6 0AE

TEL: (0384) 401996 *CONTACT:* John Massey & Philip Baulk *CAT. COST:* 2 x 1st class *MIN. ORDER:*
◆*SPECIALITIES:* Lewisias, Cyclamen & Auriculas. See also in Nursery Index under Code 'MAsh'

B & T World Seeds, Whitnell House, Fiddington, Bridgwater, Somerset TA5 1JE

TEL: (0278) 733209 *FAX:* (0278) 733209 *CONTACT:* David Sleigh *CAT. COST:* £10 (Europe)*
MIN. ORDER:
SPECIALITIES: Master list contains some 30,000 items. *£14 to non-European destinations. Sub-lists available.

J W Boyce, 40 Fordham, Ely, Cambridgeshire CB7 5JU

TEL: (0638) 721158 *CONTACT:* Mr Roger Morley *CAT. COST:* Free *MIN. ORDER:* 75p under £7.50
SPECIALITIES: Pansy & Vegetables seed and plants, Onion 'Oakey'. Wide range of separate colours for cut flowers, bedding & drying.

S & N Brackley, 117 Winslow Road, Wingrove, Aylesbury, Buckinghamshire HP22 4QB

TEL: (02960 681384 *CONTACT:* *CAT. COST:* Sae *MIN. ORDER:*
◆*SPECIALITIES:* Gold Medal Sweet Peas & Exhibition Vegetables

Bullwood Nursery, 54 Woodlands Road, Hockley, Essex SS5 4PY

TEL: (0702) 203761 *CONTACT:* D & E Fox *CAT. COST:* Sae *MIN. ORDER:*
SPECIALITIES: Many Liliaceae. Also wide range of common and rare Perennials. See also in Nursery Index under Code 'EBul'.

Carters Seeds Ltd., Hele Road, Torquay, Devon TQ2 7QJ

TEL: (0803) 616156 *FAX:* (0803) 615747 *CONTACT:* D G Arnold *CAT. COST:* Free *MIN. ORDER:*
SPECIALITIES: General range.

Chase Organics (GB) Ltd., Coombelands House, Addlestone, Weybridge, Surrey KT15 1HY

TEL: (0932) 820958 *FAX:* (0932) 821258 *CONTACT:* *CAT. COST:* *MIN. ORDER:*
SPECIALITIES: 'The Organic Gardening Catalogue' offers Vegetable, Herb & Flower seeds & garden sundries especially for Organic gardeners.

Cheshire Herbs, Fourfields, Forest Road, Little Budworth, Cheshire CW6 9ES

TEL: (0829) 760578 *CONTACT:* Mr & Mrs Ted Riddell *CAT. COST:* 20p *MIN. ORDER:*
◆*SPECIALITIES:* Herbs. See also in Nursery Index under Code 'MChe'.

Chiltern Seeds, Bortree Stile, Ulverston, Cumbria LA12 7PB

TEL: (0229) 581137 *FAX:* (0229) 54549 *CONTACT:* *CAT. COST:* 3 x 2nd class *MIN. ORDER:* None
◆*SPECIALITIES:* Nearly 4,000 items of all kind - Wild Flowers, Trees, Shrubs, Cacti, Annuals, Houseplants, Vegetables & Herbs.

Cowcombe Farm Herbs, Gipsy Lane, Chalford, Stroud, Gloucestershire GL6 8HP

TEL: (0285) 760544 *CONTACT:* Mrs C M Barnett *CAT. COST:* 2 x 2nd class *MIN. ORDER:*
SPECIALITIES: Herbs & Wild flowers. See also in Nursery Index under Code '13'

Craven's Nursery, 1 Foulds Terrace, Bingley, West Yorkshire BD16 4LZ

TEL: (0274) 561412 *CONTACT:* S R Craven & M Craven *CAT. COST:* Sae *MIN. ORDER:* £5.00
SPECIALITIES: Seeds of Show Auriculas, Primulas, Pinks & Alpines. See also in Nursery Index under Code 'NCra'.

B & D Davies, 2 Wirral View, Connah's Quay, Deeside, Clwyd CH5 4TE

TEL: *CONTACT:* Mr B Davies *CAT. COST:* 50p refunded *MIN. ORDER:* £6.00
SPECIALITIES: Trees & Shrubs especially Conifers.

Samuel Dobie & Sons Ltd., Broomhill Way, Torquay, Devon TQ2 7QW
TEL: (0803) 616281 *CONTACT:* Mr T J Sharples *CAT. COST:* Free *MIN. ORDER:* Add 50p under £5.00
SPECIALITIES: Flower & Vegetable seeds, Plants, Bulbs & Garden sundries.

Jack Drake, Inshriach Alpine Nursery, Aviemore, Invernesshire PH22 1QS
TEL: (0540 651) 287 *FAX:* (0540 651) 656 *CONTACT:* J C Lawson *CAT. COST:* *MIN. ORDER:*
◆*SPECIALITIES:* Rare & unusual Alpines & Rock Plants especially Primulas, Gentians & many others. See also in Nursery Index under Code 'GDra'.

Emorsgate Seed, Terrington Court, Terrington St Clement, Kings Lynn Norfolk PE34 4NT
TEL: (0553) 829028 *FAX:* (0553) 829028 *CONTACT:* Donald MacIntyre *CAT. COST:* Free
MIN. ORDER: None
SPECIALITIES: Wild British Flowers & Grasses.

Equatorial Plants, 7 Grey Lane, Barnard Castle, Co. Durham DL12 8PD
TEL: (0833) 690519 *FAX:* (0833) 690519 *CONTACT:* Richard Warren PhD. *CAT. COST:* Free
MIN. ORDER: £5.00
SPECIALITIES: Orchid seed.

Field House Nurseries, Leake Road, Gotham, Nottingham NG11 0JN
TEL: (0602) 830278 *CONTACT:* Doug Lochhead & Valerie A Woolley *CAT. COST:* 3 x 1st class
MIN. ORDER: None
SPECIALITIES: Primulas & Alpines. See also in Nursery Index under Code 'MFie'.

Mr Fothergill's Seeds Ltd., Gazeley Road, Kentford, Newmarket, Suffolk CB8 7QB
TEL: (0638) 751161 *FAX:* (0638) 751624 *CONTACT:* Gillie Gray or Ann Loads *CAT. COST:* Free
MIN. ORDER:
SPECIALITIES: Annuals, Biennials, Perennials, Herbs, Vegetables, plus Bulbs, Plants, soft Fruit and Garden Sundries.

Glenhirst Cactus Nursery, Station Road, Swineshead, Nr Boston, Lincolnshire PE20 3NX
TEL: (0205) 820314 *CONTACT:* N C & S A Bell *CAT. COST:* 2 x 1st class *MIN. ORDER:*
SPECIALITIES: Extensive range of Cacti & Succulent seeds. See also under Cacti & Succulent Specialists Index.

Peter Grayson, Sweet Pea Seedsman, 34 Glenthorne Close, Brampton, Chesterfield Derbyshire S40 3AR
TEL: (0246) 278503 *CONTACT:* Peter Grayson *CAT. COST:* Sae *MIN. ORDER:* None
SPECIALITIES: Lathyrus species & cultivars. (Sweet Peas).

Harrisons Delphiniums, Newbury Cottage, Play Hatch, Reading, Berkshire RG4 9QN
TEL: (0734) 470810 *CONTACT:* Len Harrison *CAT. COST:* 1 x 1st class *MIN. ORDER:* No minimum order
◆*SPECIALITIES:* Delphiniums. See also in Nursery Index under Code 'LHar'.

James Henderson & Sons, Kingholm Quay, Dumfries DG1 4SU
TEL: (0387) 52234 *FAX:* (0387) 62302 *CONTACT:* J H & R J Henderson *CAT. COST:* Free
MIN. ORDER:
SPECIALITIES: Over 30 varieties of Scottish Seed Potatoes

Holden Clough Nursery, Holden, Bolton-by-Bowland Clitheroe Lancashire BB7 4PF
TEL: (02007) 615* *CONTACT:* Peter Foley *CAT. COST:* Sae *MIN. ORDER:* None
◆*SPECIALITIES:* Alpines & hardy Perennials. See also in Nursery Index under Code 'NHol'. *NOTE: (0200) 447615 from Sept 1993.

Holly Gate Cactus Nursery, Billingshurst Road, Ashington, West Sussex RH20 3BA
TEL: (0903) 892 930 *CONTACT:* Mr T M Hewitt *CAT. COST:* 2 x 2nd class
MIN. ORDER: £2UK/£2.50O/Sea inc.
SPECIALITIES: Cacti & Succlulents.

Diana Hull, Fog Cottages, 178 Lower Street, Hillmorton, Rugby, Warwickshire CV21 4NX
TEL: (0788) 536574 after *CONTACT:* Diana Hull *CAT. COST:* Sae for list *MIN. ORDER:* None
SPECIALITIES: Pelargonium species. See also Nursery Index under Code 'WHul'.

Landlife Wildflowers Ltd., The Old Police Station, Lark Lane, Liverpool, Merseyside L17 8UU
TEL: (051 728) 7011 *FAX:* (051 728) 8413 *CONTACT:* Gillian Watson *CAT. COST:* Free
MIN. ORDER: None
SPECIALITIES: Native Herbaceous plants. See also in Nursery Index under Code 'NLan'.

Mackay's Garden Centre, Castlepark Road, Sandycove, Co. Dublin, Rep. of Ireland
TEL: (0001) 2807385 *FAX:* (0001) 2841922 *CONTACT:* Breda Roseingrave *CAT. COST:* Free
MIN. ORDER: None
SPECIALITIES: See also in Nursery Index under Code '98'.

S E Marshall & Co Ltd., Wisbech, Cambridgeshire PE13 2RF
TEL: (0945) 583407 *FAX:* (0945) 588235 *CONTACT:* *CAT. COST:* Free *MIN. ORDER:* None
SPECIALITIES: Vegetable seed, Onion Sets & Shallots, seed Potatoes.

J E Martin, 4 Church Street, Market Harborough, Leicestershire LE16 7AA
TEL: (0858) 462751 *FAX:* (0858) 434544 *CONTACT:* *CAT. COST:* Free (List) *MIN. ORDER:* £7.00 inc. p&p
SPECIALITIES: Over 30 varieties of Scotch & Dutch Seed Potatoes.

S M McArd (Seeds), 39 West Road, Pointon, Sleaford, Lincolnshire NG34 0NA
TEL: (0529) 240765 *CONTACT:* Susan McArd *CAT. COST:* 2 x 2nd class *MIN. ORDER:*
SPECIALITIES: Unusual & giant Vegetables. Seeds & Plants.

Monocot Nursery, Jacklands, Jacklands Bridge, Tickenham, Clevedon Avon BS21 6SG
TEL: *CONTACT:* M R Salmon *CAT. COST:* Sae *MIN. ORDER:* None
SPECIALITIES: Rare & unusual Bulbous & Tuberous plants

John Morley, North Green Only, Stoven, Beccles, Suffolk NR34 8DG
TEL: *CONTACT:* John Morley *CAT. COST:* 50p + stamp *MIN. ORDER:*
SPECIALITIES: Small specialist range of Galanthus, Allium, Fritillaria and choice shrubs. See also in Nursery Index under Code 'EMor'

Natural Selection, 1 Station Cottages, Hullavington, Chipenham, Wiltshire SN14 6ET
TEL: (0666) 837369 *CONTACT:* Martin Cragg-Barber *CAT. COST:* A5 Sae *MIN. ORDER:*
SPECIALITIES: Unusual British natives. See also in Nursery Index under Code 'CNat'.

Andrew Norfield Trees & Seeds, Lower Meend, St Briavels, Gloucestershire GL15 6RW
TEL: (0594) 530134 *FAX:* (0594) 530113 *CONTACT:* Andrew Norfield *CAT. COST:* 1 x 1st class
MIN. ORDER: None
SPECIALITIES: Germinated & pretreated Seed of hardy Trees, Shrubs, Herbaceous & House plants. See also in Nursery Index under Code 'WNor'.

Stuart Ogg, Hopton, Fletching Street, Mayfield, East Sussex TN20 6TL
TEL: (0435) 873322 *CONTACT:* Stuart Ogg *CAT. COST:* Sae *MIN. ORDER:* None
SPECIALITIES: Delphiniums. See also in Nursery Index under Code 'SOgg'.

Phedar Nursery, Bunkers Hill, Romiley, Stockport, Cheshire SK6 3DS
TEL: (061 430) 3772 *FAX:* (061 430) 3772 *CONTACT:* Will McLewin *CAT. COST:* Sae+1x1st class
MIN. ORDER: None
SPECIALITIES: Helleborus. Species seed wild collected. Hybrid seed in colour & spotting categories. All supplied fresh only in Aug & Sep. See also under 'MPhe'

Pinks & Carnations, 22 Chetwyn Avenue, Bromley Cross, Nr Bolton, Lancashire BL7 9BN
TEL: (0204) 306273 *CONTACT:* Ruth & Tom Gillies *CAT. COST:* *MIN. ORDER:*
◆ *SPECIALITIES:* Perpetual Flowing Carnations, Border Carnations, Allwoodii Alpinus & Knappii - (The Yellow Pink). See also in Nursery Index under Code 'NPin'.

Plant World Botanic Gardens, Seed Dept. (PF) St Marychurch Road, Newton Abbot, Devon TQ12 4SE
TEL: (0803) 872939 *CONTACT:* Ray Brown *CAT. COST:* 3 x 1st class *MIN. ORDER:* £6.00
◆ *SPECIALITIES:* Meconopsis, Gentiana, Primula, Aquilegia, Campanula, Viola, Lewisia, Salvia, Eryngium. See also in Nursery Index under Code 'CPla'.

Potterton & Martin, The Cottage Nursery, Moortown Road, Nettleton, Caister, Lincolnshire LN7 6HX

TEL: (0472) 851792 *CONTACT:* *CAT. COST:* Sae *MIN. ORDER:*

SPECIALITIES: Alpines & dwarf Bulbs. Seed list sent out in November. See also in Nursery Index under Code 'EPot'.

Roger Poulett, Nurse's Cottage, North Mundham, Chichester, Sussex PO20 6JY

TEL: *CONTACT:* Roger Poulett *CAT. COST:* 3 x 1st class* *MIN. ORDER:*

SPECIALITIES: Cyclamen, Corydalis, Helleborus, Hepatica etc. for summer sowing, June to Sept only. *Seed list included in plant Catalogue. See also under 'SPou'.

W Robinson & Sons Ltd., Sunny Bank, Forton, Nr Preston, Lancashire PR3 0BN

TEL: (0524) 791210 *FAX:* (0524) 791933 *CONTACT:* Miss Robinson *CAT. COST:* Free *MIN. ORDER:*

SPECIALITIES: Mammoth Vegetable seed.

R V Roger Ltd, The Nurseries, Pickering, North Yorkshire YO18 7HG

TEL: (0751) 72226 *CONTACT:* J R Roger, S Peirson & A G & I M Roger *CAT. COST:* *MIN. ORDER:*

SPECIALITIES: Bulbs & Seed Potatoes. See also in Nursery Index under Code 'NRog'.

Salley Gardens, Allergarth, Roweltown, Carlisle, Cumbria CA6 6JU

TEL: *CONTACT:* Richard Lewin *CAT. COST:* Sae *MIN. ORDER:* None

SPECIALITIES: Wildflower & Medicinal Herbs. See also in Nursery Index under Code 'NSal'.

The Seed House, 9a Widley Road, Cosham, Portsmouth, PO6 2DS

TEL: (0705) 325639 *CONTACT:* Mr R L Spearing *CAT. COST:* 4 x 1st class *MIN. ORDER:* £5.00

SPECIALITIES: Australian seeds suitable for the European climate.

Seeds by Size, 45 Crouchfield, Boxmoor, Hemel Hempstead, Hertfordshire HP1 1PA

TEL: (0422) 251458 *CONTACT:* Mr John Robert Size *CAT. COST:* Free *MIN. ORDER:* 55p if under £5.00

SPECIALITIES: Flowers & Vegetables. 1,100 varieties of Vegetable, (155 Cabbage, 93 Cauliflower, 65 Onion) & 3000 flowers such as 230 varieties of Sweet Pea.

Stewart's (Nottingham) Ltd., 3 George Street, Nottingham NG1 3BH

TEL: (0602) 476338 *CONTACT:* Brenda Lochhead *CAT. COST:* Sae *MIN. ORDER:* None

SPECIALITIES: Large general range esp. Vegetables.

Suttons Seeds Ltd., Hele Road, Torquay, Devon TQ2 7QJ

TEL: (0803) 614455 *FAX:* (0803) 615747 *CONTACT:* Customer Services *CAT. COST:* Free *MIN. ORDER:*

SPECIALITIES: Wide general range of Flowers, Vegetables & Tomatoes. Also cutting raised items in 'Suttons Plus' Catalogue. See also in Nursery Index under Code 'CSut'.

Thompson & Morgan, London Road, Ipswich, Suffolk IP2 0BA

TEL: (0473) 688821 *FAX:* (0473) 680199 *CONTACT:* Martin Thrower *CAT. COST:* Free *MIN. ORDER:* None

SPECIALITIES: Largest illustrated Seed catalogue in the world.

Thuya Alpine Nursery, Glebelands, Hartpury, Gloucestershire GL19 3BW

TEL: (0452) 700548 *CONTACT:* S W Bond *CAT. COST:* Sae *MIN. ORDER:* None

SPECIALITIES: General range. See also in Nursery Index under Code 'WThu'.

Edwin Tucker & Sons, Brewery Meadow, Stonepark, Ashburton, Newton Abbot, Devon TQ13 7DG

TEL: (0364) 652403 *FAX:* (0364) 654300 *CONTACT:* Geoff Penton *CAT. COST:* Free *MIN. ORDER:* None

SPECIALITIES: Over 40 varieties of Seed Potatoes. Wide range of Vegetables, Green Manures & sprouting seeds in packets.

Unwins Seeds Ltd., Mail Order Dept. Histon, Cambridge, Cambridgeshire CB4 4ZZ

TEL: (0945) 588522 *FAX:* (0945) 475255 *CONTACT:* *CAT. COST:* Free *MIN. ORDER:* None

SPECIALITIES: Wide general range particularly Sweet Peas.

Uzumara Orchids, 9 Port Henderson, Gairloch Rosshire IV21 2AS

TEL: (0445 83) 228 *CONTACT:* Mrs I F La Croix *CAT. COST:* Sae *MIN. ORDER:*

SPECIALITIES: Streptocarpus species. African & Madagascan Orchids. See also in Nursery Index under Code 'GUzu'

Wildseeds, Branas Llandderfel, Gwynedd LL23 7RF

TEL: (06783) 427 *CONTACT:* Mr M Thorne *CAT. COST:* Free *MIN. ORDER:* None

SPECIALITIES: Wild Flower seeds.

Roy Young Seeds, 23 Westland Chase, West Winch, King's Lynn, Norfolk PE33 0QH

TEL: (0553) 840867 *CONTACT:* Mr Roy Young *CAT. COST:* 2nd cls/3xIRC *MIN. ORDER:* None

SPECIALITIES: Cactus & Succulent seeds only

Cacti & Succulent Suppliers

Bradley Batch Nursery, 64 Bath Road, Bridgwater, Somersetshire TA7 9QJ
TEL: (0458) 210256 *CONTACT:* J E White
OPENING TIMES: 1000-1800 Tue-Sun. *W/SALE or RETAIL:* Both
MAIL ORDER: No *CAT. COST:* None issued
SPECIALITIES: Echeverias, Haworthias, Lithops & Cacti.

Bridgemere Nurseries, Bridgemere, Cheshire CW5 7QB
TEL: (09365) 381/239 x 138 *FAX:* (09365) 215 *CONTACT:* Jim Speed
OPENING TIMES: 0900-2000 Mon-Sat, 1000-2000 Sun, in summer, until 1700 winter.
W/SALE or RETAIL: Retail
MAIL ORDER: No *CAT. COST:*
SPECIALITIES: General range of Cacti & other Succulents incl. specimen plants.

Connoisseurs' Cacti, (Off.) 51 Chelsfield Lane, Kent BR5 4HG
TEL: (0689) 837781 *CONTACT:* John Pilbeam
OPENING TIMES: 1030-1430 but please phone first. *W/SALE or RETAIL:* Both
MAIL ORDER: Yes *MIN VALUE:* No minimum charge *CAT. COST:* Sae
SPECIALITIES: Mammillaria, Sulcorebutia, Gymnocalycium, Rebutia, Haworthia, Conophytum, Asclepiads etc. NOTE: Nursery at, Woodlands Farm, Shire Lane, Nr Farnborough, Kent.

Croston Cactus, 43 Southport Road, Lancashire PR7 6ET
TEL: (0257) 452555 *CONTACT:* John Henshaw
OPENING TIMES: Evenings & Weekends. Please phone before visit. *W/SALE or RETAIL:* Retail
MAIL ORDER: Yes *MIN VALUE:* None *CAT. COST:* Sae
SPECIALITIES: Mexican Cacti, Echeveria hybrids & some Bromeliads.

Cruck Cottage Cacti, Cruck Cottage, Pickering, North Yorkshire YO18 8PJ
TEL: (0751) 72042 *CONTACT:* R J A Wood
OPENING TIMES: 0900-sunset daily. Please ring first. *W/SALE or RETAIL:* Retail
MAIL ORDER: *MIN VALUE:* *CAT. COST:*
SPECIALITIES: Large range of all Cacti & Succulent. Nursery in a garden setting.

East Midlands Cactus Nursery, Manor Close, Milton Keynes, Buckinghamshire MK10 9AA
TEL: (0908) 665584 *CONTACT:* Mike & Eileen Watson
OPENING TIMES: 0900-1800 Wed-Mon *W/SALE or RETAIL:* Retail
MAIL ORDER: Yes *MIN VALUE:* None *CAT. COST:* Large Sae
SPECIALITIES: Cacti, Succulents & Carnivorous plants.

Eau Brink Cactus Nursery, Tilney All Saints, Norfolk PE34 4SQ
TEL: (0553) 617635 *CONTACT:* Derek Bowdery
OPENING TIMES: 0900-dusk Thu-Tue *W/SALE or RETAIL:* Retail
MAIL ORDER: Yes *MIN VALUE:* £10.00 + p&p *CAT. COST:* Sae for list
SPECIALITIES: Agaves, Ferocactus, Cereus, Mammillaria & Aloe.

Felspar Cacti, 20 Reawla Lane, Hayle, Cornwall TR27 5HQ
TEL: (0736) 850321 *CONTACT:* Mrs M Negus
OPENING TIMES: 1000-1700 Mon, Tue & Thu 1300-1700 Fri. *W/SALE or RETAIL:* Retail
MAIL ORDER: Yes *MIN VALUE:* £2.50 + p&p *CAT. COST:* Sae
SPECIALITIES: Cacti & Succulents. Some Fuchsias from nursery only.

W G Geissler, Winsford, Slimbridge, Gloucestershire GL2 7BW
TEL: (0453) 890340 *CONTACT:* W G Geissler
OPENING TIMES: 0900-1700 (2000 in summer) Mar-Nov. *W/SALE or RETAIL:* Retail
MAIL ORDER: No *CAT. COST:*
SPECIALITIES: Hardy Cacti & Succulents & related books.

Glenhirst Cactus Nursery, Station Road, Nr Boston, Lincolnshire PE20 3NX
TEL: (0205) 820314 *CONTACT:* N C & S A Bell
OPENING TIMES: 1000-1730 Wed-Sun 1st Mar-31st Oct. Other times by appt. *W/SALE or RETAIL:* Retail
MAIL ORDER: Yes *MIN VALUE:* None *CAT. COST:* 2 x 1st class
SPECIALITIES: Extensive range of Cacti & Succulent plants & seeds. All stock fully described on lists.

 See note on Mail Order, EC Sales & Export on page 5

Harvest Nurseries, Harvest Cottage, Iden, Nr Rye Sussex TH31 7QA
TEL: (0797) 280 493 *CONTACT:* D A Smith
OPENING TIMES: *W/SALE or RETAIL:* Retail
MAIL ORDER: Only *MIN VALUE:* £30 + p&p *CAT. COST:* 2 x 1st class
SPECIALITIES: Cacti & Succulents.

Holly Gate Cactus Nursery, Billingshurst Road, West Sussex RH20 3BA
TEL: (0903) 892 930 *CONTACT:* Mr T M Hewitt
OPENING TIMES: 0900-1700 daily. *W/SALE or RETAIL:* Both
MAIL ORDER: Yes *MIN VALUE:* £5.00 + p&p *CAT. COST:* 50p + 28p p&p
SPECIALITIES: Cactus, Succulents & Pelargoniums.

Jumanery Cacti, St Catherine's Lodge, Whaplode St Catherine, Lincolnshire PE12 6SR
TEL: (0406 34) 373 *CONTACT:*
OPENING TIMES: 0900-1700 Sun-Fri. Closed Sat. *W/SALE or RETAIL:* Retail
MAIL ORDER: Yes *MIN VALUE:* None *CAT. COST:* Free
SPECIALITIES: Rare cacti & rare other succulents, particularly Euphorbia, Pachypodiums, Asclepiads & Caudiciformis. 4 lists per year.

K & C Cacti, Fern Cottage, Barnstaple, Devon EX32 0SF
TEL: (0598) 760393 *CONTACT:* Keith & Jane Comer
◆ *OPENING TIMES:* Phone first please. *W/SALE or RETAIL:* Retail
MAIL ORDER: Yes *MIN VALUE:* £10 + p&p *CAT. COST:* Sae or IRC
SPECIALITIES: Echeveria, Euphorbia, Haworthia, Conophytum, Adromischus, Crassula, Gasteria, Sulcorebutia & dwarf Opuntia.

Kent Cacti, (Off.) 35 Rutland Way, Kent BR5 4DY
TEL: (0689) 836249/837781 *CONTACT:* Mr D Sizmur & Mr Pilbeam
OPENING TIMES: 1000-1700 most days. Please phone first. *W/SALE or RETAIL:* Retail
MAIL ORDER: Yes *MIN VALUE:* See Cat. for details *CAT. COST:* A5 Sae
SPECIALITIES: Agaves, Astrophytums, Conophytums, Crassulas, Echeverias, Echinocereus, Mammillaria etc. NOTE: Nursery at Woodlands Farm, Shire Lane, Farnborough, Kent.

Long Man Gardens, Lewes Road, Polgate, East Sussex BN26 5RS
TEL: (0323) 870816 *CONTACT:* O Menzel
OPENING TIMES: 0900-1300 & 1430-1800 Tue-Sun. *W/SALE or RETAIL:* Both
MAIL ORDER: Yes *MIN VALUE:* See list for details *CAT. COST:* Free list
SPECIALITIES: Agaves, Echiverias, Euphorbias, etc.

Oakleigh Nurseries, Petersfield Road, Nr Alresford, Hampshire SO24 0HB
TEL: (0962) 773344 *FAX:* (0962) 772622 *CONTACT:* Mr D Clark
OPENING TIMES: 1000-1630 Apr-Jun daily *W/SALE or RETAIL:* Both
MAIL ORDER: Yes *MIN VALUE:* None *CAT. COST:* 3 x 1st class
SPECIALITIES: Epiphyllums.

Pete & Ken Cactus Nursery, Saunders Lane, Nr Canterbury, Kent CT3 2BX
TEL: (0304) 812170 *CONTACT:* Ken Burke
OPENING TIMES: 0900-1800 daily. *W/SALE or RETAIL:* Retail
MAIL ORDER: Yes *MIN VALUE:* £3.00 + p&p *CAT. COST:* Sae for list
SPECIALITIES: Cactus, Succulents, Lithops (Living stones).

A & A Phipps, 62 Samuel White Road, Bristol, Avon BS15 3LX
TEL: (0272) 607591 *CONTACT:* A Phipps
OPENING TIMES: All times, but prior phone call ESSENTIAL. *W/SALE or RETAIL:* Both
MAIL ORDER: Yes *MIN VALUE:* £20.00 + p&p *CAT. COST:* Sae or 2 IRC
SPECIALITIES: Rebutias & Mammillarias.

The Plant Lovers, Candesby House, Spilsby, Lincolnshire PE23 5RU
TEL: (0754) 85256 *CONTACT:* Tim Wilson
OPENING TIMES: Daily, but please phone first. *W/SALE or RETAIL:* Both
MAIL ORDER: No *CAT. COST:* None issued
SPECIALITIES: Wide range of Cacti and other Succulents. Brochure in course of preparation.

Succulent Supplierss

Preston-Mafham Collection, 2 Willoughby Close, Alcester, Warwickshire B49 5QJ
TEL: (0789) 762938 *FAX:* (0789) 762938 *CONTACT:* Jean Preston-Mafham
OPENING TIMES: 1030-1730 Mon-Fri. Weekends by appt. only. 1st Apr-31st Oct.
W/SALE or RETAIL: Retail
MAIL ORDER: *MIN VALUE:* *CAT. COST:*
SPECIALITIES: Wide range of Cacti and other Succulents.

Chris Rodgerson, 35 Lydgate Hall Crescent, Sheffield South Yorkshire S10 5NE
TEL: (0742) 685533 *CONTACT:* Chris Rodgerson
OPENING TIMES: *W/SALE or RETAIL:* Retail
MAIL ORDER: Yes *MIN VALUE:* £15.00 + p&p *CAT. COST:* Sae or IRC
SPECIALITIES: Conophytum & Adromischus propagated from original wild material with locality data.

Robert Scott, 78 Bousley Rise, Surrey KT16 0LB
TEL: (0932) 872667 *FAX:* (0932) 872667 *CONTACT:* Robert Scott
OPENING TIMES: By appt. only. *W/SALE or RETAIL:* Both
MAIL ORDER: No *CAT. COST:*
SPECIALITIES: Seed raised plants from many families & large specimen plants.

Southfield Nurseries, Bourne Road, Nr Bourne Lincolnshire PE10 0RH
TEL: *CONTACT:* Mr & Mrs B Goodey
OPENING TIMES: 1000-1230 & 1330-1600 daily (ex Xmas & New Year). *W/SALE or RETAIL:* Both
MAIL ORDER: Yes *MIN VALUE:* £50.00 + p&p *CAT. COST:* 1 x 1st class
SPECIALITIES: A wide range of Cacti & Succulents including some of the rarer varieties all grown on our own nursery.

Toobees Nursery, 20 Inglewood, Woking, Surrey GU21 3HX
TEL: (0483) 722600 *FAX:* (0483) 722600 *CONTACT:* Bob Potter
OPENING TIMES: By appt. only, *W/SALE or RETAIL:* Retail
MAIL ORDER: Yes *MIN VALUE:* None *CAT. COST:* Sae
SPECIALITIES: South African & Madagascan Succulents. Many rare & unusual species.

Westfield Cacti, Kennford, Devon EX6 7XD
TEL: (0392) 832921 *CONTACT:* Ralph & Marina Northcott
OPENING TIMES: 1000-dusk daily. *W/SALE or RETAIL:* Both
MAIL ORDER: Yes *MIN VALUE:* £20 + £10 p&p *CAT. COST:* 50p
SPECIALITIES: Epiphytes & Sempervivum.

Whitestone Gardens Ltd., The Cactus Houses, Thirsk, Yorkshire YO7 2PZ
TEL: (0845) 597467 *CONTACT:* Roy Mottram
OPENING TIMES: Daylight hours Sat-Thu. *W/SALE or RETAIL:* Retail
MAIL ORDER: Yes *MIN VALUE:* None *CAT. COST:* 4 x 2nd class
SPECIALITIES: Cacti & other Succulents, Books & Sundries.

K M & R J R Willoughby, Willows Mead, Whittle-le-Woods, Lancashire PR6 7DJ
TEL: (0257) 262107 *CONTACT:* K M & R J R Willoughby
OPENING TIMES: 0800-1700 summer & 0900-1600 winter. Advise telephone first.
W/SALE or RETAIL: Both
MAIL ORDER: No *CAT. COST:*
SPECIALITIES: Cacti and other Succulents.

H & S Wills, 2 St Brannocks Park Road, Devon EX34 8HU
TEL: (0271) 863949 *CONTACT:* H Wills
OPENING TIMES: Appt. only *W/SALE or RETAIL:* Retail
MAIL ORDER: Tes *MIN VALUE:* £3.00 + p&p *CAT. COST:* 3 x 1st class
SPECIALITIES: Sempervivum, Jovibarba & Rosularia.

Roy Young Seeds, 23 Westland Chase, King's Lynn, Norfolk PE33 0QH
TEL: (0553) 840867 *CONTACT:* Mr Roy Young
OPENING TIMES: Not open. *W/SALE or RETAIL:* Both
MAIL ORDER: Only *MIN VALUE:* None *CAT. COST:* 2nd cls/3xIRC
SPECIALITIES: Cactus & Succulent SEEDS only.

 See note on Mail Order, EC Sales & Export on page 5

Orchid Specialists

Bridgemere Nurseries, Bridgemere, Cheshire CW5 7QB
TEL: (09365) 381/239 x 138 *FAX:* (09365) 215 *CONTACT:* Jim Speed
OPENING TIMES: 0900-2000 Mon-Sat, 1000-2000 Sun in summer, until 1700 in winter. *W/SALE or RETAIL:* Retail
MAIL ORDER: No *CAT. COST:*
SPECIALITIES: Cymbidium, Paphiopedilum, Phalaenopsis, Miltonia, Odontoglossum.

Burnham Nurseries, Forches Cross, Devon TQ12 6PZ
TEL: (0626) 52233 *FAX:* (0626) 62167 *CONTACT:*
OPENING TIMES: 0900-1700 Mon-Fri & 1000-1600 Sat & Sun. *W/SALE or RETAIL:* Both
MAIL ORDER: Yes *MIN VALUE:* £10.00 + p&p *CAT. COST:* £2 + vouchers
SPECIALITIES: All types of Orchid.

Equatorial Plant Co., 7 Gray Lane, Co. Durham DL12 8PD
TEL: (0833) 690519 *FAX:* (0833) 690519 *CONTACT:* Richard Warren PhD
OPENING TIMES: By appt. only. *W/SALE or RETAIL:* Retail
MAIL ORDER: Yes *MIN VALUE:* None *CAT. COST:* Free
SPECIALITIES: Laboratory raised Orchids only.

Greenaway Orchids, Rookery Farm, Nr Weston-super-Mere, Avon BS24 6TL
TEL: (0934) 820448 *FAX:* (0934) 820209 *CONTACT:* Robert Dadd
OPENING TIMES: 0800-1800 Tue-Sun *W/SALE or RETAIL:* Retail
MAIL ORDER: No *CAT. COST:* None issued
SPECIALITIES: Large selection of tropical Orchid species & hybrids. Flask seed raising, seedling to flowering size including endangered species.

Mansell & Hatcher Ltd., Cragg Wood Nurseries, Rawdon, Leeds LS19 6LQ
TEL: (0532) 502016 *CONTACT:* Mr Allan Long
OPENING TIMES: 0900-1700 Mon-Fri. *W/SALE or RETAIL:* Both
MAIL ORDER: Yes *MIN VALUE:* None *CAT. COST:* £1.00
SPECIALITIES: Odontoglossum, Cymbidium, Masdevallia, Miltonia & Cattleya.

Orchid Sundries Ltd., New Gate Farm, Gillingham, Dorset SP8 5LT
TEL: (0747) 838368 *FAX:* (0747) 838308 *CONTACT:* N J Heywood
OPENING TIMES: 0800-1300 & 1400-1700 Mon-Fri, Sat by appt. only. *W/SALE or RETAIL:*
MAIL ORDER: Yes *MIN VALUE:* £10.00 + p&p *CAT. COST:* Sae
SPECIALITIES: Hardy Orchids & Disa.

David Stead Orchids, Langley Farm, Lofthouse, Yorkshire WF3 3PA
TEL: (0924) 822011 *FAX:* (0924) 822011 *CONTACT:* David Stead
OPENING TIMES: 0900-1700 Mon-Fri but please phone first. Weekends by appt. only. *W/SALE or RETAIL:* Retail
MAIL ORDER: Yes *MIN VALUE:* None *CAT. COST:* 1 x 1st class
SPECIALITIES: Orchids.

Uzumara Orchids, 9 Port Henderson, Rosshire IV21 2AS
TEL: (0445 83) 228 *CONTACT:* Mrs I F La Croix
OPENING TIMES: *W/SALE or RETAIL:*
MAIL ORDER: Only *MIN VALUE:* *CAT. COST:* Sae
SPECIALITIES: Streptocarpus species. African & Madagascan Orchids. See also in Nursery Index under Code 'GUzu'

Westwood Nursery, 65 Yorkland Avenue, Kent DA16 2LE
TEL: 081 301-0886 *CONTACT:* Mr S Edwards
OPENING TIMES: Not open *W/SALE or RETAIL:* Retail
MAIL ORDER: Yes *MIN VALUE:* None *CAT. COST:* Sae
SPECIALITIES: Pleione & Hardy Orchids.

Reverse Synonyms

In order to assist users to establish from which Genera an unfamiliar plant name may have been transferred, the following list of reverse synonyms may help.

Acacia - Racosperma
Acanthocalyx - Morina
Acca - Feijoa
Achillea - Anthemis
Acinos - Calamintha
Acinos - Micromeria
Acinos - Thymus
Actinidia - Kiwi-fruit
Aeonium - Sempervivum
Aethionema - Eunomia
Agapetes - Pentapterygium
Agarista - Leucotho
Agastache - Cedronella
Ageratina - Eupatorium
Agyrocytisus - Cytisus
Aichryson - Aeonium
Albizia - Acacia
Allardia - Waldheimia
Allocasuarina - Casuarina
Aloysia - Lippia
Alsobia - Episcia
Alyogyne - Hibiscus
Alyssum - Ptilotrichum
x Amarygia - Amaryllis
Ampelopsis - Vitis
Amsonia - Rhazya
Anaphalis - Gnaphalium
Anchusa - Lycopsis
Androsace - Douglasia
Anisodontea - Malvastrum
Anomatheca - Lapeirousia
Anomyrtus - Myrtus
Anredera - Boussingaultia
Antirrhinum - Asarina
Antirrhinum - Maurandya
Aphanes - Alchemilla
Arctotis - x Venidioarctotis
Arctotis - Venidium
Arecastrum - Cocos
Arenga - Didymosperma
Argyranthemum - Anthemis
Argyranthemum - Chrysanthemum
Argyrocytisus - Cytisus
Armoracia - Cochlearia
Arundinaria - Clavinodum
Arundinaria - Thamnocalamus
Asarina - Antirrhinum
Asarina - Maurandya
Asparagus - Smilax
Asperula - Galium
Asphodeline - Asphodelus
Asplenium - Phyllitis
Aster - Crinitaria
Aster - Microglossa
Astilboides - Rodgersia
Aurinia - Alyssum
Austrocedrus - Libocedrus
Ayapana - Eupatorium
Azorella - Bolax

Balsamita - Chrysanthemum
Balsamita - Tanacetum
Bambusa - Arundinaria
Bartlettina - Eupatorium
Bellevalia - Muscari
Blechnum - Lomaria
Bolax - Azorella
Boykinia - Telesonix
Brachyglottis - Senecio
Bracteantha - Helichrysum
Brimeura - Hyacinthus
Brodiaea - Triteleia
Brugmansia - Datura
Brunnera - Anchusa
Buglossoides - Lithospermum
Bulbine - Bulbinopsis
Buphthalmum - Inula
Caladium - Xanthosoma
Calamintha - Clinopodium
Callisia - Phyodina
Callisia - Tradescantia
Calocedrus - Libocedrus
Calomeria - Humea
Caloscordum - Nothoscordum
Calytrix - Lhotzkya
Camellia - Thea
Camptosorus - Asplenium
Cardamine - Dentaria
Carica - Pawpaw
Carya - Pecan
Cassiope - Harrimanella
Castanea - Chestnut, Sweet
Catapodium - Desmazeria
Cayratia - Parthenocissus
Centaurium - Erythraea
Centranthus - Kentranthus
Centranthus - Valeriana
Cephalaria - Scabiosa
Ceratostigma - Plumbago
Cercestis - Rhektophyllum
Ceterach - Asplenium
Chaenomeles - Cydonia
Chaenorhinum - Linaria
Chamaecyparis - Cupressus
Chamaecytisus - Cytisus
Chamaedaphne - Cassandra
Chamaemelum - Anthemis
Chasmanthium - Uniola
Chiastophyllum - Cotyledon
Chimonobambusa - Arundinaria
Chimonobambusa - Arundinaria
Chimonobambusa - Quiongzhuea
Chimonobambusa - Thamnocalamus
Chionohebe - Pygmaea
Chlorophytum - Diuranthera
Chondrosum - Bouteloua
Cicerbita - Lactuca
Cionura - Marsdenia
Cissus - Parthenocissus

x Citrofortunella - Calamondin
x Citrofortunella - Citrus
Citrus - Orange, Bittersweet
Citrus - Citron
Citrus - Grapefruit
Citrus - Lime
Citrus - Mandarin
Citrus - Pummelo
Citrus - Lime, Rangpur
Citrus - Satsuma
Citrus - Orange, Sour or Seville
Citrus - Shaddock
Citrus - Mandarin, Sour
Citrus - Tangelo
Citrus - Tangerine
Citrus - Tangor
Citrus - Ugli
Clarkia - Godetia
Clavinodum - Arundinaria
Claytonia - Calandrinia
Claytonia - Montia
Clematis - Atragene
Cleyera - Eurya
Clinopodium - Acinos
Clinopodium - Calamintha
Clytostoma - Pandorea
Cnicus - Carduus
Cocos - Coconut
Coffea - Coffee
Consolida - Delphinium
Cordyline - Dracaena
Cornus - Chamaepericlymenum
Coronilla - Securigera
Cortaderia - Gynerium
Corylus - Nut, Cob & Filbert
Cosmos - Bidens
Cotinus - Rhus
Cotula - Leptinella
Crassula - Sedum
Crassula - Tillaea
Crinodendron - Tricuspidaria
Crocosmia - Antholyza
Crocosmia - Curtonus
Crocosmia - Montbretia
Cruciata - Galium
Ctenanthe - Calathea
Ctenanthe - Stromanthe
x Cupressocyparis - Chamaecyparis
Cyathodes - Leucopogon
Cyathodes - Styphelia
Cyclosorus - Pneumatopteris
Cydonia - Quince
Cymbalaria - Linaria
Cynara - Scolymus
Cyperus - Mariscus
Cyrtanthus - Vallota
Cytisus - Lembotropis
Daboecia - Menziesia
Dacrycarpus - Podocarpus

Dactylorhiza - Orchis
Daiswa - Paris
Dana - Ruscus
Darmera - Peltiphyllum
Davallia - Humata
Delairea - Senecio
Delosperma - Lampranthus
Delosperma - Mesembryanthemum
Dendranthema - Chrysanthemum
Derwentia - Hebe
Derwentia - Parahebe
Derwentia - Veronica
Desmodium - Lespedeza
Dianthus - Tunica
Dichelostemma - Triteleia
Dicliptera - Justicia
Dietes - Moraea
Disporopsis - Polygonatum
Dolicothrix - Helichrysum
Dracaena - Pleomele
Dracunculus - Arum
Dregea - Wattakaka
Drepanostachyum - Arundinaria
Drepanostachyum - Thamnocalamus
Drimys - Tasmannia
Duchesnea - Fragaria
Dunalia - Acnistus
Echinacea - Rudbeckia
Edraianthus - Wahlenbergia
Elatostema - Pellionia
Eleutherococcus - Acanthopanax
Elliottia - Botryostege
Elliottia - Cladothamnus
Elymus - Agropyron
Elymus - Leymus
Ensete - Musa
Epilobium - Chamaenerion
Epilobium - Zauschneria
Epipremnum - Philodendron
Epipremnum - Scindapsus
Episcia - Alsobia
Eranthis - Aconitum
Erica - Calluna
Erigeron - Aster
Erigeron - Haplopappus
Erybotrya - Loquat
Erysimum - Cheiranthus
Euryops - Senecio
Euryops - Ursinia
Fallopia - Bilderdykia
Fallopia - Polygonum
Farfugium - Ligularia
Fargesia - Arundinaria
Fargesia - Thamnocalamus
Fatsia - Aralia
Felicia - Agathaea
Felicia - Aster
Fibigia - Farsetia
Ficus - Fig
Filipendula - Spiraea
Foeniculum - Ferula
Fortunella - Citrus
Fragaria - Strawberry
Galium - Asperula
Gaultheria - Chiogenes
Gaultheria - x Gaulnettya
Gaultheria - Pernettya
Gelasine - Sisyrinchium
Genista - Chamaespartium
Genista - Cytisus
Genista - Echinospartum
Genista - Teline
Gentianopsis - Gentiana
Gladiolus - Acidanthera
Gladiolus - Homoglossum
Gladiolus - Petamenes
Glechoma - Nepeta
Gloxinia - Sinningia
Goniolimon - Limonium
Graptopetalum - Sedum
Graptopetalum - Tacitus
Greenovia - Sempervivum
Gymnospermum - Leontice
Habranthus - Zephyranthes
x Halimiocistus - Cistus
x Halimiocistus - Halimium
Halimium - Cistus
Halimium - x Halimiocistus
Halimium - Helianthemum
Halocarpus - Dacrydium
Haplopappus - Isocoma
Hedyscepe - Kentia
Helichrysum - Gnaphalium
Helichrysum - Ozothamnus
Helictotrichon - Avena
Helictotrichon - Avenula
Hepatica - Anemone
Hermodactylus - Iris
Heterocentron - Schizocentron
Heterotheca - Chrysopsis
Hibbertia - Candollea
Hieracium - Andryala
Himalayacalamus - Arundinaria
Himalayacalamus - Drepanostachyum
Hippeastrum - Amaryllis
Hippeastrum - Rhodophiala
Hippocrepis - Coronilla
Hippolytia - Achillea
Hippolytia - Tanacetum
Hoheria - Plagianthus
Homalocladium - Muehlenbeckia
Houstonia - Hedyotis
Howea - Kentia
Hyacinthoides - Endymion
Hyacinthoides - Scilla
Hylotelephium - Sedum
Hymenocallis - Elisena
Hymenocallis - Ismene
Hymenoxys - Actinella
Hyophorbe - Mascarena
Indocalamus - Sasa
Indocalamus - Thamnocalamus
Ipheion - Beauverdia
Ipheion - Tristagma
Ipheion - Triteleia
Ipomoea - Mina
Ipomoea - Pharbitis
Ipomopsis - Gilia
Ischyrolepis - Restio
Isolepis - Scirpus
Jovibarba - Sempervivum
Juglans - Walnut, Common
Justicia - Beloperone
Justicia - Jacobinia
Justicia - Libonia
Kalanchoe - Kitchingia
Kalimeris - Aster
Kalimeris - Boltonia
x Kalmiothamnus - Kalmiopsis
Kalopanax - Eleutherococcus
Keckiella - Penstemon
Knautia - Scabiosa
Kunzea - Leptospermum
Lablab - Dolichos
Lagarosiphon - Elodea
Lagarostrobos - Dacrydium
Lamium - Galeobdolon
Lamium - Lamiastrum
Lampranthus - Mesembryanthemum
Lampranthus - Oscularia
Laurentia - Hippobroma
Laurentia - Isotoma
Lavatera - Malva
Ledebouria - Scilla
X Ledodendron - Rhododendron
Ledum - Rhododendron
Lembotropis - Cytisus
Leptinella - Cotula
Leucanthemella - Chrysanthemum
Leucanthemella - Leucanthemum
Leucanthemopsis - Chrysanthemum
Leucanthemopsis - Tanacetum
Leucanthemum - Chrysanthemum
Leucopogon - Cyathodes
Leucoraoulia - Raoulia
Leuzea - Centaurea
Lhotzkya - Calytrix
Libocedrus - Austrocedrus
Ligularia - Senecio
Ligustrum - Parasyringa
Lilium - Nomocharis
Limonium - Statice
Linanthus - Linanthastrum
Lindelofia - Adelocaryum
Lindera - Parabenzoin
Liriope - Ophiopogon
Lithocarpus - Quercus
Lithodora - Lithospermum
Lobelia - Pratia
Lophomyrtus - Myrtus
Lotus - Dorycnium
Ludwigia - Jussiaea
Luma - Myrtus
Lycene - Lychnis
Lychnis - Agrostemma
Lychnis - Silene
Lychnis - Viscaria
Lytocaryum - Cocos
Lytocaryum - Microcoelum
Macfadyena - Bignonia
Macfadyena - Doxantha
Mackaya - Asytasia

Macleaya - Bocconia
Macropiper - Piper
Mahonia - Berberis
Maianthemum - Smilacina
Malus - Apple
Malvastrum - Modiolastrum
Mandragora - Atropa
Mariscus - Cyperus
Matricaria - Chamomilla
Matricaria - Tripleurospermum
Maurandya - Asarina
Melicytus - Hymenanthera
Melinis - Rhynchelytrum
Mentha - Preslia
Merremia - Ipomoea
Mespilus - Medlar
Microcoelum - Cocos
Mimulus - Diplacus
Minuartia - Arenaria
Moltkia - Lithodora
Moltkia - Lithospermum
Montia - Claytonia
Morus - Mulberry
Mukdenia - Aceriphyllum
Musa - Banana
Muscari - Hyacinthus
Muscari - Leopoldia
Muscari - Muscarimia
Muscari - Pseudomuscari
Myrceugenia - Myrtus
Myricaria - Tamarix
Myrteola - Myrtus
Nectaroscordum - Allium
Nemesia - Diascia
Nemesia - Diascia x Linaria
Neopaxia - Claytonia
Neopaxia - Montia
Neoregalia - Nidularium
Nepeta - Dracocephalum
Nepeta - Origanum
Nipponanthemum - Chrysanthemum
Nipponanthemum - Leucanthemum
Nymphodes - Villarsia
Oemleria - Osmaronia
Olearia - Pachystegia
Olsynium - Phaiophleps
Olsynium - Sisyrinchium
Ophiopogon - Convallaria
Orchis - Dactylorrhiza
Orostachys - Sedum
Osmanthus - x Osmarea
Osmanthus - Phillyrea
Osteospermum - Dimorphotheca
Othonna - Hertia
Othonna - Othonnopsis
Ozothamnus - Helichrysum
Pachyphragma - Cardamine
Packera - Senecio
Paederota - Veronica
Papaver - Meconopsis
Parahebe - Hebe
Parahebe - Veronica
Paraserianthes - Albizia
Parthenocissus - Ampelopsis
Parthenocissus - Ampelopsis
Parthenocissus - Vitis
Passiflora - Passion Fruit
Passiflora - Granadilla
Passiflora - Tetrapathaea
Paxistima - Pachystema
Pecteilis - Habenaria
Pelargonium - Geranium
Peltoboykinia - Boykinia
Penstemon - Chelone
Pentaglottis - Anchusa
Pericallis - Senecio
Persea - Avocado
Persea - Machilus
Persicaria - Aconogonon
Persicaria - Aconogonum
Persicaria - Polygonum
Persicaria - Tovara
Petrocoptis - Lychnis
Petrophytum - Spiraea
Petrorhagia - Tunica
Petroselinum - Carum
Phanerophlebia - Cyrtomium
Phegopteris - Thelypteris
Phlebodium - Polypodium
Phoenicaulis - Parrya
Phoenix - Date
Photinia - Heteromeles
Photinia - Stransvaesia
Photinia - x Stransvinia
Phuopsis - Crucianella
Phyla - Lippia
Phymosia - Sphaeralcea
Physalis - Gooseberry, Cape
Physoplexis - Phyteuma
Physostegia - Dracocephalum
Pieris - Arcterica
Pilosella - Hieracium
Pisonia - Heimerliodendron
Platycladus - Thuja
Plecostachys - Helichrysum
Plectranthus - Coleus
Plectranthus - Solenostemon
Pleioblastus - Arundinaria
Pleioblastus - Sasa
Podranea - Tecoma
Polianthes - Bravoa
Polygonum - Persicaria
Polygonum - Tovara
Polystichum - Cyrtomium
Poncirus - Aegle
Poranea - Tecoma
Potentilla - Comarum
Prumnopitys - Podocarpus
Prunus - Almond
Prunus - Amygdalus
Prunus - Apricot
Prunus - Bullace
Prunus - Damson
Prunus - Nectarine
Prunus - Peach
Prunus - Plum
Prunus - Cherry, Sweet
Pseudocydonia - Chaenomeles
Pseudofumaria - Corydalis
Pseudofumaria - Fumaria
Pseudopanax - Metapanax
Pseudopanax - Neopanax
Pseudopanax - Nothopanax
Pseudosasa - Arundinaria
Pseudotsuga - Tsuga
Pseudowintera - Drimys
Psidium - Guava
Pteracanthus - Strobilanthes
Pterocephalus - Scabiosa
Ptilostemon - Cirsium
Pulsatilla - Anemone
Punica - Pomegranate
Pyrenaria - Tutcheria
Pyrothropsis - Argyranthmum
Pyrothropsis - Chrysanthemopsis
Pyrothropsis - Leucanthemopsis
Pyrothropsis - Leucanthemum
Pyrus - Pear
Reineckea - Liriope
Retama - Genista
Reynoutria - Polygonum
Rhapis - Chamaerops
Rheum - Rhubarb
Rhodiola - Sedum
Rhododendron - Azalea
Rhododendron - Azaleodendron
Rhododendron - Rhodora
Rhodophiala - Hippeastrum
Ribes - Gooseberry
Ribes - Currant, Black, Red, White
Ribes - Worcesterberry
Rorippa - Nasturtium
Rosularia - Cotyledon
Rosularia - Sedum
Rosularia - Sempervivella
Rubus - Blackberry
Rubus - Boysenberry
Rubus - Wineberry, Japanese
Rubus - Loganberry
Rubus - Marionberry
Rubus - Nectarberry
Rubus - Raspberry
Rubus - Sunberry
Rubus - Tayberry
Rubus - Youngberry
Ruellia - Dipteracanthus
Saccharum - Erianthus
Sagina - Minuartia
Sambucus - Elderberry
Sanguisorba - Dendriopoterium
Sanguisorba - Pimpinella
Sanguisorba - Poterium
Sasa - Arundinaria
Sasaella - Arundinaria
Sasaella - Sasa
Sasamorpha - Sasa
Sauromatum - Arum
Scadoxus - Haemanthus
Schefflera - Dizygotheca
Schizostachyum - Arundinaria
Schoenoplectus - Scirpus
Sedum - Crassula

Sedum - Sedastrum
Semiaquilegia - Aquilegia
Semiaquilegia - Paraquilegia
Semiarundinaria - Arundinaria
Sempervivella - Rosularia
Senecio - Cineraria
Senecio - Ligularia
Senna - Cassia
Seriphidium - Artemisia
Shortia - Schizocodon
Sibbaldiopsis - Potentilla
Sieversia - Geum
Silene - Lychnis
Silene - Saponaria
Sinacalia - Ligularia
Sinacalia - Senecio
Sinarundinaria - Arundinaria
Sinarundinaria - Semiarundinaria
Sinningia - Gloxinia
Sinningia - Rechsteineria
Sisymbrium - Hesperis
Sisyrinchium - Phaiophleps
Soleirolia - Helxine
Solenopsis - Isotoma
Solenostemon - Coleus
x Solidaster - Aster
x Solidaster - Solidago
Sorbaria - Spiraea
Sphaeralcea - Iliamna
Spraguea - Calyptridium
Stachys - Betonica
Stachys - Betonica
Steirodiscus - Gamolepsis
Stenomesson - Urceolina
Stenotus - Haplopappus
Stewartia - Stuartia
Stipa - Achnatherum
Stipa - Lasiagrostis
Streptocarpus - X Streptocarpella
Strobilanthes - Pteracanthus
Succisa - Scabiosa
Syagrus - Cocos
Tanacetum - Balsamita
Tanacetum - Chrysanthemum
Tanacetum - Matricaria
Tanacetum - Pyrethrum
Tasmannia - Drimys
Tecoma - Tecomaria
Telekia - Buphthalmum
Tephroserus - Senecio
Tetradium - Euodia
Tetraneuris - Actinella
Tetraneuris - Hymenoxys
Tetrapanax - Fatsia
Thamnocalamus - Arundinaria
Thamnocalamus - Fargesia
Thamnocalamus - Sinarundinaria
Thlaspi - Hutchinsia
Thlaspi - Noccaea
Tonestus - Haplopappus
Toona - Cedrela
Trachelium - Diosphaera
Trachycarpus - Chamaerops
Tradescantia - Rhoeo
Tradescantia - Setcreasea
Tradescantia - Zebrina
Tripetaleia - Elliotia
Tripogandra - Tradescantia
Tristagma - Beauverdia
Tristagma - Ipheion
Triteleia - Brodiaea
Tritonia - Crocosmia
Tritonia - Montbretia
Tuberaria - Helianthemum
Tulipa - Amana
Tweedia - Oxypetalum
Ugni - Myrtus
Ursinia - Euryops
Uvularia - Oakesiella
Vaccinium - Blueberry
Vaccinium - Cranberry
Vaccinium - Oxycoccus
Verbascum - Celsia
Verbascum - x Celsioverbascum
Verbena - Lippia
Veronicastrum - Veronica
Villadia - Sedum
Viola - Erpetion
Vitaliana - Androsace
Vitis - Grape
Weigela - Diervilla
Weigela - Macrodiervilla
Xanthorhiza - Zanthorrhiza
Zantedeschia - Calla

Plant Deletions

Plants marked with a '7', '8', '9', '0', '1' or '2' were listed in the 1987, '88, '89, '90/91, '91/92 or '92/93 editions respectively.
Back editions of **THE PLANT FINDER** may be obtained from Lakeside, Whitbourne, Worcester, WR6 5RD. Price £6.00 each inclusive of p&p.

ABELMOSCHUS
0 ***esculentus***
2 ***moschatus*** 'Mischief'

ABIES
2 ***amabilis*** 'Spreading Star'
1 x ***arnoldiana***
7 ***chensiensis chensiensis***
0 ***cilicica***
9 ***concolor*** 'Aurea'
2 – var. ***lowiana***
7 ***durangensis coahuilensis***
2 ***fargesii***
2 – var. ***faxoniana***
9 ***firma***
2 ***forrestii***
7 x ***insignis*** 'Beissneriana'
9 ***koreana*** 'Prostrate Beauty'
2 ***magnifica*** 'Glauca'
0 ***nebrodensis***
8 ***procera*** 'Noble'
7 ***recurvata***
7 x ***shastensis***

ABROMEITIELLA
9 ***brevifolia***

ABROTANELLA
0 ***emarginata***
0 ***forsterioïdes***

ABUTILON
2 'Cynthia Pike' (v)
9 'Lopen Red'
2 ***ochsenii***
1 'Orange Glow' (v)
1 x ***suntense*** 'Gorer's White'
2 – 'White Charm'
7 'White Swan'

ACACIA
0 ***adunca***
1 ***decurrens***
1 ***farnesiana***
7 ***implexa***
9 ***jonesii***
9 ***myrtifolia***
0 ***neriifolia***

ACAENA
9 'Greencourt Hybrid'

ACALYPHA
0 ***godseffiana***

ACANTHOLIMON
2 ***acerosum***
8 ***confertiflorum***

ACANTHUS
2 ***caroli-alexandri***

ACER
9 ***capillipes morifolium***
2 ***japonicum*** 'Filicifolium'
1 ***palmatum*** 'Atropurpureum'
7 – var. ***dissectum*** 'Dissectum Rubrifolium'
0 – 'Hamaotome'
8 – 'Junihitoye'
9 – 'Koshimino'
2 – 'Maimori'
9 – 'Sango-nishiki'
1 ***platanoïdes*** 'Summershade'
1 ***rubrum*** 'Columnare'
1 ***saccharum grandidentatum***
9 ***tataricum ginnala*** 'Durand Dwarf'

ACHILLEA
2 'Forncett Tapestry'
8 ***hausmannii***
0 'Heidi'
9 ***millefolium*** 'Purpurea'
1 – 'Rougham Beauty'
0 ***oxyloba***
7 x ***prichardii***
1 'Rougham Salmon'

ACHIMENES
2 ***antirrhina***
2 – 'Redcap'
2 'Ballerina'
2 'Blue John'
2 'Bright Jewel'
1 'Cameo Lilac'
2 'Camille Pink'
2 'Carmencita'
2 'Carnelian'
2 ***cettoana***
2 – 'Tiny Blue'
2 'Coral Cameo'
2 'Crystal'
2 'Diadem'
2 ***erecta*** 'Mexican Dwarf'
2 – ***rosea***
2 'Erlkönig'
2 'Fascination'
2 'Flamboyant'
2 'Garnet'
2 'Glacier'
1 ***grandiflora***
2 'India Hybrid'
2 'Jewel Glow'
2 'Lady Lyttelton'
2 'Lavender Jade'
2 'Leonora'
2 'Madame Gehune'
2 'Mair's White'
2 'Margarita'
2 'Mauve Delight'
2 ***mexicana***
2 'Miniata'
2 'National Velvet'
2 'Opal'
2 'Painted Lady'
1 'Pearly Grey'
2 ***pedunculata***
2 'Purple Queen'
2 'Purple Triumph'
2 'Red Riding Hood'
2 'Schneewittchen' ('Snow White')
2 ***skinneri***
2 'Sunburst'
9 'Tetra Altrote Charm'
2 'Tetra Blauer Planet'
9 'Tetra Dark Violet Charm'
2 'Tetra Orange Star'
2 'Tetra Purpur Elfe'
9 'Tetra Rokoko Elfe'
2 'Tetra Rosa Queen'
2 'Tetra Verschaffelt'
2 'Tetra Weinrote Elfe'
2 'The Monarch'
2 'Tiger Eye'
2 'Topaz'
2 'Tresco'
2 ***warscewicziana***
2 'White Giant'
2 'White Knight'
2 'White Marvel'
2 'Yellow Beauty'

ACIPHYLLA
0 ***congesta***
2 ***crenulata***
8 ***dobsonii***
0 ***ferox***
8 ***lecomtei***
0 ***montana***
8 – ***montana***
2 ***similis***
9 ***spedenii***

ACONITUM
2 ***anthora***
1 ***carmichaelii*** Wilsonii Group 'Kelmscott Variegated'
9 ***chasmanthum***
2 ***falconeri***
8 ***heterophyllum***
9 ***hookeri***
2 ***kirinense***

ACORUS
1 ***calamus*** 'Purpureus'
0 ***graminifolius tanguticus***

ACTINIDIA
1 ***arguta*** 'Ananasnaja' (f)
1 – 'Meader No 2' (f)
1 – 'Stamford' (f)
9 ***callosa***
8 ***deliciosa*** 'Abbot' (f)
8 – 'Matura' (m)
2 ***giraldii***
8 ***purpurea***

ADENOPHORA
2 ***kurilensis***

ADIANTUM
0 ***raddianum*** 'Goldelse'
2 – 'Lady Geneva'
2 ***tenerum*** 'Scutum Roseum'
1 ***trapeziforme***

ADONIS
2 ***chrysocyathus***

AECHMEA
0 ***blumenavii***
0 ***cylindrata***
0 ***fulgens discolor***
0 ***gamosepala***
0 ***lueddemanniana***
9 ***recurvata recurvata***
2 ***servitensis***

AESCHYNANTHUS
0 'Black Pagoda'

AESCULUS
1 ***hippocastanum*** 'Hampton Court Gold'
7 x ***hybrida***
9 ***wilsonii***

AETHIONEMA
9 ***armenum*** 'Mavis Holmes'
8 ***stylosum***

AGAPANTHUS
1 ***campanulatus*** pale form
9 – 'Slieve Donard Variety'
7 ***inapertus pendulus***
9 ***praecox*** 'Albiflorus'

AGAPETES
2 ***serpens*** 'Scarlet Elf'

AGARISTA
2 ***populifolia***

AGASTACHE
2 ***barberi*** 'Tutti-Frutti'
2 ***foeniculum*** 'Alba'

AGAVE
1 ***colorata***
1 ***ferdinandi-regis***
1 ***funkiana***
1 ***mitriiformis***
9 ***parviflora***
1 ***potatorum verschaffeltii***
1 ***sebastiana***
0 ***shawii***
1 ***sobria sobria***
1 ***toumeyana***
1 – var. ***bella***
2 ***utahensis discreta***
1 – var. ***eborispina***

2 – var. ***nevadensis***

AGLAONEMA

0 ***commutatum maculatum***
0 – 'Pseudobracteatum'
0 ***nitidum*** 'Curtisii'
1 'Silver King'

AGROSTIS

2 ***nebulosa***

AGROSTOCRINUM

1 ***scabrum***

AJUGA

1 ***chamaepitys***
2 ***reptans*** 'Burgundy Metallica'

ALANGIUM

1 ***platanifolium macrophyllum***

ALBUCA

1 ***setosa***
0 ***spiralis***

ALCEA

0 ***rosea*** single white
0 – 'Sutton's Single Brilliant'

ALCHEMILLA

1 ***bulgarica***
9 ***hoppeana***
2 ***mollis*** 'Variegata'

ALKANNA

9 ***aucheriana***

ALLAMANDA

2 ***schottii***

ALLIUM

0 ***auctum***
1 ***barszczewskii***
9 ***campanulatum***
9 ***carinatum pulchellum*** dwarf
8 ***douglasii***
9 ***griffithianum***
2 'Laxton Sunset'
0 ***nutans***
2 ***splendens***
1 ***victorialis***
2 ***virgunculae***

ALLOCASUARINA

2 ***verticillata***

ALNUS

9 ***acuminata arguta***
7 ***hirsuta sibirica***
0 ***lanata***

ALOCASIA

0 × ***argyraea***
0 × ***chantrieri***
0 ***cuprea***
0 'Green Velvet'
0 ***korthalsii***
0 ***longiloba***
0 ***macrorrhiza***
0 ***watsoniana***
0 ***wentii***

ALONSOA

2 ***acutifolia*** coral form
2 ***incisifolia***
2 ***meridionalis*** 'Shell Pink'

ALSTROEMERIA

9 Annabel ®
9 Appelbloesem ®
0 Atlas ® / 'Stalrama'
1 Butterfly hybrids
0 Canaria ® / 'Stagelb'
1 'Furie'
2 ***haemantha***
0 Isabella ® / 'Stalis'
1 'Jolicoeur'
0 Jubilee ® / 'Stalilas'
0 Libelle ® / 'Stalbel'
0 Mandarin ® / 'Stalrin'
0 Mona Lisa ® / 'Stablaco'
0 Monika ® / 'Stalmon'
0 Pink Triumph ® / 'Stapink'
0 Ramona ® / 'Stadaram'
0 Red Sunset ® / 'Stamarko'
0 'Regina'
0 Rita ® / 'Zelido'
1 Rosello ® / 'Stalrobu'
0 Rosita ® / 'Starosello'
0 Samora ® / 'Stalsam'
1 'Sweetheart'
0 Tango ® / 'Staltang'
1 Walter Fleming ®
0 Zebra ® / 'Stazeb'

ALYSSUM

2 ***cappadocicum***
0 ***markgrafii***
8 ***montanum*** 'Prostratum'
1 ***scardicum***
9 ***troodii***

AMARYLLIS

1 ***amethystina***
1 ***bella-donna*** 'Bloemfontein'
1 – 'Hathor'
1 – 'Purpurea'
1 – 'Windhoek'

AMELANCHIER

2 ***alnifolia semiintegrifolia***
2 ***asiatica***
9 – ***sinica***

AMPELOPSIS

8 ***bodinieri***
8 ***chaffanjonii***
2 ***glandulosa brevipedunculata citrulloïdes*** f.

AMSONIA

1 ***illustris***

ANAGALLIS

1 ***arvensis caerulea***
1 ***monelli*** 'Caerulea'

ANANAS

0 ***comosus***

ANAPHALIS

9 ***keriensis***

ANCHUSA

1 ***azurea*** 'Blue Ball'

ANDROMEDA

8 ***polifolia angustifolia***
2 – 'Compacta Alba'

ANDROSACE

9 ***alpina***
1 ***carnea brigantiaca*** 'Myer's form'
2 ***chamaejasme***
8 – ***lehmanniana***
0 × ***heeri*** pink form
9 ***lactiflora***
0 ***lehmannii***
0 ***nivalis***
8 ***rotundifolia*** 'Elegans'
9 ***saximontana***
2 ***sempervivoïdes*** dark form
0 ***tapete***
8 ***wulfeniana***

ANEMONE

1 ***apennina albiflora***
2 – 'Petrovac'
0 ***biflora***
0 ***blanda*** 'Blue Pearl'
8 – ***scythinica***
2 ***bucharica***
1 ***coronaria*** De Caen Group 'Excelsior'
2 – 'His Excellency'
8 ***elongata***
2 ***eranthoïdes***
9 'French Hill'
1 × ***lipsiensis*** forms
0 ***lithophila***
1 ***nemorosa*** 'Currie's Pink'
0 ***nikoensis***
7 ***obtusiloba patula***
0 ***pavonina ocellata***
2 ***petiolulosa***
2 ***polyanthes***
9 ***raddeana***
2 ***sylvestris*** 'Macrantha'

ANEMONELLA

1 ***thalictroïdes*** pink form
1 – semi-double white form

ANETHUM

9 ***sowa***

ANIGOZANTHOS

1 ***bicolor***
1 ***flavidus*** green form
1 – grey form
1 – orange form
1 ***gabrielae***
1 ***viridis***

ANISOTOME

2 ***aromatica***
2 ***flexuosa***

ANOMATHECA

1 ***laxa alba-maculata***

ANTENNARIA

9 ***plantaginifolia***

ANTHOCERCIS

1 ***littorea***

ANTHRISCUS

1 ***sylvestris roseus***

ANTHURIUM

0 ***andreanum album***
0 – 'Aztec'
0 – 'Brazilian Sunrise'
0 – 'Nova'
0 ***crystallinum***
0 × ***ferrierense***
0 ***leuconeurum***
0 ***magnificum***
0
0 – ***minimum***
0 – 'Rothschildianum'
0 – 'Wardii'
0 ***veitchii***
9 ***warocqueanum***

ANTHYLLIS

9 ***barba-jovis***

APHELANDRA

0 'Snow Queen'

APIUM

9 ***nodiflorum***

APONOGETON

0 ***desertorum***

AQUILEGIA

9 ***bernardii***
2 ***brevicalcarata***
1 ***brevistyla***
8 ***caerulea daileyae***
1 ***chrysantha hinckleyana***
7 'Edelweiss'
2 ***formosa*** Nana Group
1 Harbutt's hybrids
9 ***hirsutissima***
8 Langdon's Rainbow hybrids
0 ***longissima*** 'Flore Pleno'
1 ***ottonis amaliae***
2 ***vulgaris*** 'Crystal Star'
2 – double purple
9 – 'Millicent Bowden'

ARABIS

2 ***aubrietioïdes***
2 ***blepharophylla*** 'Alba'
9 ***breweri***
1 ***bryoïdes olympica***
7 ***caucasica*** 'Snowflake'
1 ***ferdinandi-coburgii*** 'Reversed'
2 ***koehleri***
1 ***procurrens***
9 ***pumila***
1 ***scopoliana***
1 ***serrata japonica***
1 ***turrita***

ARAIOSTEGIA

1 ***pseudocystopteris***

ARALIA

2 ***spinosa***

ARBUTUS

7 × ***alapensis***
1 ***unedo*** 'Merriott'

ARCHONTOPHOENIX
2 ***alexandrae***

ARCTOSTAPHYLOS
8 ***auriculata***
0 'Emerald Carpet'
2 ***manzanita***

ARCTOTIS
1 x ***hybrida*** 'White'

ARECA
2 ***aliceae***
2 ***triandra***

ARENARIA
2 ***fendleri***
0 ***procera***
0 ***purpurascens*** 'Elliott's Variety'

ARENGA
9 ***caudata***

ARGEMONE
9 ***ensifolia***
0 ***platyceras***

ARGYRANTHEMUM
1 ***adauctum***
1 – ***gracile***
1 'Brontes'
1 ***sundingii***

ARISAEMA
8 ***kiushianum***
1 ***robustum***
8 ***thunbergii***

ARISTEA
2 ***major***

ARISTOLOCHIA
8 ***colchica***
2 ***heterophylla***
2 ***sempervirens***

ARMERIA
9 ***alliacea*** 'Grandiflora'
0 – ***plantaginea***
7 ***arctica***
9 'Bloodgood'
0 ***maritima*** 'Birch Pink'
7 – ***sibirica***

ARNICA
2 ***angustifolia alpina***
0 ***cordifolia***
2 ***unalaschkensis***

ARRHENATHERUM
2 ***elatius***

ARTEMISIA
7 ***absinthium*** 'Poland's Variety'
2 ***genipi***
2 ***judaica***
7 ***lactiflora*** 'Variegata'

ARTHROPODIUM
9 ***cirrhatum*** bronze form
2 – pink form

ARUM
0 ***byzantinum***
0 ***maculatum*** 'Pleddel'

ARUNCUS
0 ***dioicus*** 'Aphrodite'

ASARUM
2 ***hartwegii*** 'Silver Heart'

ASPARAGUS
1 ***scandens***

ASPLENIUM
2 ***aethiopicum***
0 ***dalhousieae***
7 ***fontanum***
0 ***scolopendrium*** 'Apple Court'
0 ***squamulatum***

ASTELIA
7 ***nivicola***
1 – 'Red Gem'

ASTER
9 ***ageratoïdes***
0 ***alpinus dolomiticus***
2 ***amellus*** 'Butzemann'
2 – 'Danzig'
2 – 'Doktor Otto Petschek'
2 – 'Glücksfund'
7 – 'Mrs Ralph Woods'
8 – 'Rotfeuer'
0 – 'September Glory'
2 ***asteroïdes***
1 ***bellidiastrum***
2 'Christine'
0 ***cordifolius***
2 ***ericoïdes*** 'Schneetanne'
0 ***falconeri***
2 ***flaccidus albus***
2 ***laevis*** 'Blauschleier'
0 'Lovely'
0 ***nana*** 'Variegatus'
0 ***novi-belgii*** 'Amethyst'
1 – 'Ashwick'
9 – 'Autumn Princess
2 – 'Barker's Double'
2 – 'Beechwood Lady'
0 – 'Blue Jacket'
0 – 'Blue Orb'
1 – 'Camerton'
0 – 'Candelabra'
0 – 'Catherine Chiswell'
0 – 'Charmwood'
1 – 'Coombe Delight'
0 – 'Desert Song'
0 – 'Dunkerton'
1 – 'Emma'
2 – 'F M Simpson'
0 – 'Fair Trial'
8 – 'Gayborder Rapture'
8 – 'Gayborder Rose'
1 – 'Gayborder Supreme'
9 – 'Glorious'
0 – 'Goblin Coombe'
0 – 'Grey Lady'
1 – 'Happiness'
2 – 'Jezebel'
2 – 'Jugendstil'
2 – 'Kassel'
1 – 'Kilmersdon'
1 – 'Leona'
1 – 'Lucille'
1 – 'Maid of Athens'
1 – 'Malvern Castle'
0 – 'Minster'
1 – 'Mittelmeer'
0 – 'Moderator'
0 – 'Monkton Coombe'
2 – 'Nesthäkchen'
0 – 'Newton's Pink'
2 – 'Norma Chiswell'
1 – 'Owen Tudor'
1 – 'Owen Wells'
2 – 'Pacific Amarant'
1 – 'Peaceful'
1 – 'Penelope'
2 – 'Petunia'
0 – 'Pink Bonnet'
1 – 'Pink Cascade'
1 – 'Pitcott'
0 – 'Powder Puff'
0 – 'Princess Marie Louise'
9 – 'Queen of Sheba'
1 – 'Real Pleasure'
0 – 'Red King'
2 – 'Rosemarie Sallman'
0 – 'Rosy Dreams'
0 – 'Ruby Glow'
0 – single blue
1 – 'Taplow Spire'
1 – 'The Urchin'
1 – 'Vice Regal'
0 – 'Walkden's Pink'
1 – 'Winsome Winnie'
1 ***tongolensis*** 'Leuchtenburg'
2 ***yunnanensis***

ASTILBE
1 ***chinensis davidii***
0 x ***crispa rosea***
2 'Intermezzo' (***chinensis***)
1 ***koreana***
2 'Mainz' (***japonica x***)
1 'Peter Pan' (x ***crispa***)
9 'Purple Splendour' (x ***arendsii***)
2 'Queen of Holland' (x ***arendsii***)
0 'Robinson's Pink'

ASTRAGALUS
1 ***alopecuroïdes***
0 ***arnotii***
9 ***crassicarpus paysonii***
2 ***falcatus***
1 ***kentrophyta implexus***
1 ***purpureus***
2 ***purshii purshii***
1 ***vexilliflexus nobilis***

ASTRANTIA
2 ***major involucrata*** 'Moira Reid'
0 ***maxima alba***

ASYNEUMA
0 ***linifolium***
9 – ***eximium***

ATHAMANTA
0 ***turbith***

ATHYRIUM
0 ***distentifolium***

ATRAPHAXIS
0 ***billardierei tournefortii***

AUBRIETA
2 'Aurea'
2 'Barker's Double'
7 'Bridesmaid'
1 'Bright Eyes'
8 'Crimson Bedder'
7 'Crimson Queen'
7 'Eileen Longster'
9 Eversley hybrids
0 'Godstone'
2 ***gracilis***
8 'Graeca Superba'
7 'Purple Splendour'
8 'Rosanna Miles'
9 'Rose Cascade'
2 'Vindictive'
2 'Violet Queen'

AUCUBA
9 ***japonica*** 'Dentata'
2 – 'Wykehurst'

AURINIA
1 ***saxatilis*** 'Nelly Reuben' (v)

AZARA
2 ***uruguayensis***

AZORELLA
2 ***filamentosa***

BABIANA
1 ***cedarbergensis***

BACCHARIS
1 ***patagonica*** prostrate form

BAECKEA
2 ***virgata***

BALLOTA
9 ***frutescens***

BAMBUSA
1 ***multiplex*** 'Chinese Goddess'

BANKSIA
1 ***caleyi***
2 ***occidentalis***
1 ***serratifolia***

BARTSIA
2 ***alpina***

BAUERA
0 ***rubioïdes***

BEGONIA
0 ***acutifolia***
1 ***amoena***
0 'Aruba'
1 'Bali Hi' (T)
8 'Bertinii'
1 'Bertinii Compacta'
0 'Black Velvet'
0 ***bowerae nigramarga***
0 'Bow-Mag'
0 ***burle-marxii***
0 'Camouflage'
0 'Chimbig'
0 'Chumash'
1 'City of Ballarat' (T)
0 'Clifton'
1 'Corona' (T)
0 ***dichroa*** (C)
1 'Dorothy White' (T)
1 'Elaine Tarttelin' (T)
0 'Enchantment'

1 'Falstaff' (T)
1 'First Love' (T)
0 *formosana*
0 'Fuscomaculata'
0 *grandis* 'Claret Jug'
1 'Guardsman' (T)
2 x *hiemalis* 'Aida'
2 – 'Aphrodite Pink'
2 – 'Arosa'
2 – 'Barbara'
2 – 'Christel'
2 – 'Elatior'
2 – 'Elfe'
2 – 'Heidi'
2 – 'Ilona'
2 – 'Korona'
2 – 'Lara'
2 – 'Lorina'
2 – 'Mandela'
2 – 'Mark Rosa'
2 – 'Nelly'
2 – 'Nelson'
2 – 'Nixe'
2 – 'Nymphe'
2 – 'Pia Elise'
2 – 'Radiant'
2 – 'Rosalea'
2 – 'Schwabenland'
2 – 'Schwabenland Mini'
2 – 'Schwabenland Red'
2 – 'Schwabenland Rosa'
2 – 'Schwabenland White'
2 – 'Schwabenland Yellow'
2 – 'Silvia'
2 – 'Sirène'
2 – 'Toran'
0 *hispida cucullifera*
0 'Holmes Chapel'
0 'Ingramii'
1 'Joy Towers' (T)
0 'Lexington'
0 'Linda Harley'
0 'Linda Myatt'
0 'Mac MacIntyre'
2 'Margaritae'
1 'Mrs T White' (T)
0 'Panther'
0 'Paul Harley'
1 'Peach Melba' (T)
0 *plagioneura*
0 'Queen of Olympus'
1 'Rose Princess' (T)
0 'Royal Lustre'
0 *shepherdii*
0 'Silbreen'
1 'Snow Bird' (T)
1 'Sunburst' (T)
0 x *superba* (C)
2 'Tigerlash'
0 'Universe'
1 'Zoe Colledge' (T)

BELLIS
2 *perennis* 'Bunter Teppich'
2 – 'Chevreuse'
2 – 'Dawn Raider'
2 – 'Double Bells'
2 – 'Lilliput Rose'
2 – 'Pink Buttons'
9 – 'Red Alice'
2 – 'Roggli'
2 – 'Shrewley Gold' (v)
2 – 'String of Pearls'
2 – 'Tuberosa Monstrosa'
9 *sylvestris*

BERBERIS
0 *amurensis* 'Flamboyant'
1 – *latifolia*
2 *approximata*
1 *brevipaniculata* Schneid.
2 x *carminea* 'Bountiful'
1 *concinna*
9 *dumicola*
8 *erythroclada*
9 *francisci-ferdinandii*
2 x *frikartii* 'Mrs Kennedy'
2 'Haalboon'
2 *hakeoïdes*
9 *hookeri viridis*
0 *ilicifolia*
2 x *interposita*
1 *koreana* 'Harvest Fire'
2 *linearifolia* 'Jewel'
2 x *mentorensis*
2 *montana*
2 *morrisonensis*
9 *orthobotrys canescens*
7 *poiretii*
8 x *stenophylla* 'Cornish Cream'
1 – 'Etna'
9 – 'Pendula'
2 – 'Prostrata'
7 – 'Semperflorens'
2 *thunbergii* 'Coronita'
7 – 'Dart's Red Devil'
0 – 'Pearly Queen'
9 *valdiviana* x *darwinii*
2 *wilsoniae guhtzunica*
2 – var. *stapfiana*
2 *yunnanensis*

BERGENIA
9 *crassifolia pacifica*
9 'Milesii'
7 'Perfect'
0 'Summer Mountain'
7 'White Dwarf'

BESSEYA
0 *wyomingensis*

BETULA
7 *austrosinensis*
1 *ermanii saitoana*
0 *fontinalis* 'Inopina'
9 *fruticosa*
9 *luminifera*
9 *nana* 'Walter Ingwersen'

BILLARDIERA
1 *longiflora* blue berried

BILLBERGIA
0 *bucholtzii*
0 *chlorosticta*
0 *distachia*
0 *leptopoda*
0 'Santa Barbara'

BLECHNUM
0 *moorei*

BOENNINGHAUSENIA
0 *albiflora*

BOMAREA
2 *hirtella*

BORNMUELLERA
2 *tymphaea*

BOUGAINVILLEA
1 'Alabama Sunset'
2 'Alison Davey'
1 'Canezzla Fiesta'
1 'Coral'
1 double red
1 double white
2 *floribunda*
1 'Helen Johnson'
1 'Jamaica Orange'
1 'Jamaica Red'
2 'Jawhuri'
2 Mahara forms
2 'Manila Red'
1 'Maureen Hatten'
2 'Mini-Thai'
1 'Rainbow Gold'
1 'Rose Parme'
1 'Roy Walker'
1 'Royal Purple'
1 *spectabilis* 'Alison Davey'
1 – 'Lateritia'
1 – 'Speciosa Floribunda'
2 'Sunfire Jennifer'
1 'Tropical Bouquet'
1 'Vicky'
1 yellow

BOUVARDIA
1 'Jourhite'
1 'Lichtrose'
1 'Roxane'
1 'Torosa'
1 'Zywerden'

BOYKINIA
8 *orientalis*

BRACHYGLOTTIS
0 *kirkii* 'Variegatus'

BRACHYSCOME
0 *diversifolia*
1 *multifida dilatata*
1 *stolonifera*

BRACTEANTHA
2 *bracteata*

BREYNIA
2 *nivosa*

BRIMEURA
0 *fastigiata*

BRIZA
7 *subaristata*

BROUSSONETIA
8 *papyrifera* 'Laciniata'

BUDDLEJA
8 *caryopteridifolia* 'Variegata'
2 *crispa* 'Variegata'
1 *davidii* 'Bluegown'
7 – 'Opéra'
9 – 'Pink Pearl'
2 – 'Salicifolia'
7 – 'Southcombe Splendour'
7 – 'Widecombe'
7 – 'Windtor'
9 *fallowiana* 'Town Foot'
8 *latifolia*
0 *nevinii*
7 x *weyeriana* 'Golden Tassels'

BULBINELLA
2 *setosa*

BUPLEURUM
9 *triradiatum*

BUXUS
0 *microphylla rugulosa*
1 *sempervirens* 'Bullata'
9 – 'Elegans'

CAESALPINIA
2 *decapetala japonica*

CALADIUM
0 *bicolor* 'John Peel'
0 – 'June Bride'
0 – 'Mrs Arno Nehrling'
0 – 'Pink Beauty'
0 – 'Postman Joyner'
0 – 'Rosebud'
0 *candidum*

CALANDRINIA
2 *discolor*

CALATHEA
0 *carlina*
0 *eximia*
0 *insignis*
0 *leopardina*
0 *louisae*
0 *majestica* 'Sanderiana'
0 *micans*
0 *musaica*
0 *rotundifolia* 'Fasciata'
0 *rufibarba*
0 *vittata*

CALCEOLARIA
9 *corymbosa*
1 *fiedleri*
2 *fothergillii* x *darwinii*
1 *tripartita*

CALLIANDRA
1 *eriophylla*

CALLIANTHEMUM
9 *angustifolium*
1 *kernerianum*

CALLICARPA
1 *japonica*
0 *mollis*

CALLISTEMON
0 *citrinus* purple form
2 *glaucus*
2 'King's Park Special'
9 *macropunctatus*
9 *montanus*
2 *pachyphyllus*
0 *pallidus* lilac form
2 *shiressii*
1 *viminalis*

CALLUNA
8 *vulgaris* 'Alba'
2 – 'Alba Carlton'
8 – 'Ariadne'
2 – 'Baby Wicklow'
8 – 'Beoley Crimson Variegated'
2 – 'Darleyensis'
8 – 'Dart's Squirrel'
8 – 'Diana'
8 – 'Discovery'
8 – 'Elegantissima Lilac'
8 – 'Elkstone White'
8 – 'Glentock Silver'
8 – 'Gnome'
0 – 'Gold Carmen'
0 – 'Gold Charm'
9 – 'Goldsworth Purple'
8 – 'Gynodioica'
8 – 'Harten's Findling'
8 – 'Hayesensis'
8 – 'Heidberg'
8 – 'Heidezwerg'
8 – 'Hetty'
8 – 'Hollandia'
8 – 'Holstein'
8 – 'Ingrid Bouter'
8 – 'Japanese White'
8 – 'Joseph's Coat'
8 – 'Karin Blum'
8 – 'Lemon Queen'
8 – 'Lime Gold'
0 – 'L'Ancresse'
2 – 'Malanie'
8 – 'Mallard'
8 – 'Manitoba'
9 – 'Minty'
8 – 'Monstrosa'
9 – 'Orange Beauty'
8 – 'Parson's Gold'
1 – 'Pepper and Salt'
0 – 'Platt's Surprise'
8 – 'Procumbens'
9 – 'Rannoch'
8 – 'Red Max'
8 – 'Rica'
0 – 'Rivington'
2 – 'Rotfuchs'
9 – 'Sedlonov'
1 – 'September Pink'
0 – 'Sonja'
8 – 'Spicata Nana'
8 – 'Spook'
8 – 'Stranger'
8 – 'Talisker'
8 – 'Tomentosa'
2 – 'Tremans'
8 – 'Winter Fire'

CALOCHORTUS
2 *kennedyi*
2 *weedii*

CALOTHAMNUS
1 *quadrifidus*
1 *sanguineus*

CALTHA
0 *sagittata*

CALYCANTHUS
2 *fertilis laevigatus*
2 – 'Purpureus'

CALYTRIX
9 *glutinosa*
8 *rhomboidea*
1 *tetragona*

CAMASSIA
2 *cusickii* 'Zwanenburg'
2 *leichtlinii* Atroviolacea Group
1 – var. *suksdorfii*

CAMELLIA
9 'Alba Superba' (*japonica*)
9 'Alta Gavin' (*japonica*)
9 'Anna Bruneau' (*japonica*)
9 'Anna M Page' (*japonica*)
9 'Anne Smith' (*japonica*)
2 'Apollo 14' (*japonica*)
1 'August Delfosse' (*japonica*)
0 'Australis' (*japonica*)
1 'Baronne Leguay' (*japonica*)
9 'Billie McCaskill' (*japonica*)
0 'Bride's Bouquet' (*japonica*)
7 'Candy Stripe' (*japonica*)
9 'Captain Folk' (*japonica*)
7 'Cardinal Variegated' (*japonica*)
9 'Centenary' (*japonica*)
7 'Charlean Variegated' (x *williamsii*)
9 'Charlotte Bradford' (*japonica*)
9 'Clark Hubbs' (*japonica*)
9 'Coccinea' (*japonica*)
7 'Coral Pink Lotus' (*japonica*)
7 'Coral Queen' (*japonica*)
8 'Cornish Cream' (*saluenensis* x *cuspidata*)
9 *crapnelliana*
0 'Dainty Dale' (hybrid)
2 'De Notaris' (*japonica*)
2 'Diddy Mealing' (*japonica*)
7 'Dorothy James' (hybrid)
9 'Drama Girl Variegated' (*japonica*)
9 'Dream Castle' (*reticulata* x *japonica*)
1 'Edith Linton' (*japonica*)
1 'Eleanor Hagood' (*japonica*)
7 'Elena Nobili' (*japonica*)
2 'Elizabeth de Rothschild' (x *williamsii*)
9 'Emmett Barnes' (*japonica*)
1 'Etherington White' (*japonica*)
1 'Etoile Polaire' (*japonica*)
7 'Evelyn' (*japonica*)
1 'Ezo-nishiki' (*japonica*)
9 'Fanny Bolis' (*japonica*)
0 'Fortune Teller' (*japonica*)
9 'Gay Marmee' (*japonica*)
9 'Geisha Girl' (*japonica*)
2 'Général Leclerc' (*japonica*)
9 'Goshoguruma' (*japonica*)
7 'Grand Prix Variegated' (*japonica*)
9 'Grand Sultan' (*japonica*)
7 'Gus Menard' (*japonica*)
9 'Hassaku-shibori' (*japonica*)
7 'Helen Bower' (*japonica*)
9 'High, Wide 'n' Handsome' (*japonica*)
9 'Hishikaraito' (*japonica*)
9 'Hody Wilson' (*reticulata*)
2 'Iwane-shibori' (*japonica*)
9 'Jennifer Turnbull' (*japonica*)
9 'Judge Solomon' (*japonica*)
7 'Julia Drayton' (*japonica*)
7 'Katherine Nuccio' (*japonica*)
2 'King Size' (*japonica*)
1 'Koyoden' (*japonica*)
9 'La Belle France' (*japonica*)
2 'La Pace' (*japonica*)
2 'Lady Gowrie' (x *williamsii*)
9 'Lady Kay' (*japonica*)
2 'Latifolia Variegated' (*japonica*)
2 'Leonora Novick' (*japonica*)
9 'Lillian Rickets' (*japonica*)
9 'Lisa Gael' (*reticulata*)
9 'Lois Shinault' (*reticulata* x *granthamiana*)
9 'Louise Wilson' (*japonica*)
9 'Lucinda' (*sasanqua*)
7 'Mabel Blackwell' (*japonica*)
9 *maliflora*
7 'Margaret Rose' (*japonica*)
9 'Margaret Short' (*japonica*)
7 'Marian Mitchell' (*japonica*)
9 'Marjorie Magnificent' (*japonica*)
8 'Mary Agnes Patin' (*japonica*)
0 'Mary Williams' (*reticulata*)
7 'Masterpiece' (*japonica*)
9 'Mildred Pitkin' (*reticulata*)
0 'Mine-no-yuki' (*sasanqua*)
9 'Miss Anaheim' (*japonica*)
9 'Miss Betty' (*japonica*)
2 'Miyakodori' (*japonica*)
1 'Monsieur Faucillon' (*japonica*)
1 'Moonlight' (*japonica*)
2 'Moshe Dayan' (*japonica*)
9 'Mrs Baldwin Wood' (*japonica*)
9 'Mrs George Bell' (*japonica*)
9 'Mrs Swan' (*japonica*)
7 'Mrs Tingley' (*japonica*)
1 'Mrs William Thompson' (*japonica*)
9 'Nancy Bird' (*japonica*)
9 'Paulette Goddard' (*japonica*)
1 'Pearl Harbor' (*japonica*)
9 'Phyl Doak' (*saluenensis* x *reticulata*)
1 'Pink Ball' (*japonica*)
1 'Pink Cherub' (x *williamsii*)
9 'Pink Sparkle' (*reticulata* x *japonica*)
0 'Premier' (*japonica*)
8 'Prince Murat' (*japonica*)
9 'Princess Lear' (*japonica*)
9 'Purple Swirl' (*japonica*)
0 'Queen's Escort' (*japonica*)
9 'Red Elephant' (*japonica*)
9 'Richard Nixon' (*japonica*)
0 'Richfield' (*japonica*)
9 'Rosemary Elsom' (*japonica*)
0 'Rosina Sobeck' (*japonica*)
1 'Sacco Vera' (*japonica*)
7 'Sawada's Dream' (*japonica*)
9 'Sheridan' (*japonica*)
1 'Shin-azuma-nishiki' (*sasanqua*)
9 'Shiro Chan' (*japonica*)
9 'Simeon' (*japonica*)
8 'Snow Chan' (*japonica*)
7 'Spring Fever' (*japonica*)

1 'Suibijin' (*japonica*)
2 'Sunset Oaks' (*japonica*)
9 'Terrell Weaver' (*reticulata* x *japonica*)
9 'Touchdown' (*japonica*)

0 x *vernalis*
9 'Ville de Nantes' (*japonica*)
7 'Waltz Time' (x *williamsii*)
9 'Waverley' (*japonica*)
0 'White Giant' (*japonica*)

9 'Wild Silk' (*reticulata*)
9 'Wildwood' (*japonica*)
1 'William Bull' (*japonica*)

CAMPANULA
7 'Abundance'
0 *alliariifolia* x *makaschvilii*
1 *argaea*
0 *arvatica* x *cochleariifolia*
0 *barbata* deep blue
9 *carpatica* 'Albescens'
9 – 'Jingle Bells'
7 – 'Loddon Bell'
7 – var. *turbinata* 'Grandiflora'
2 *cenisia*
7 *cochleariifolia* 'Patience Bell'
1 – very pale blue
9 *davisii*
1 *garganica* 'Major'
9 *glomerata* 'Wisley Supreme'
8 *hawkinsiana*
2 *hierosolymitana*
2 *hypopolia*
7 'Iceberg'
8 *lactiflora* 'Superba'
1 *latifolia* 'Lavender'
2 *morettiana*
2 – 'Alba'
2 *pallida tibetica*
0 *persicifolia* 'Curiosa'
2 *poscharskyana* 'Blue Gown'
1 – dark form
0 *pulla alba*
2 *punctata* 'Nana Alba'
0 *pyramidalis* 'Aureovariegata'
2 *scouleri*
2 *stevenii*
7 'Warley Gem'

CAMPYLOTROPIS
8 *macrocarpa*

CAPPARIS
2 *spinosa*

CARAGANA
2 *aurantiaca*
1 *pygmaea*

CARDIOSPERMUM
1 *halicacabum*

CARDUNCELLUS
1 *mitissimus*
2 *rhaponticoïdes*

CAREX
0 *buxbaumii*
1 *fraseri*
2 *solandri*

CARPINUS
8 *caroliniana virginiana*
1 *cordata*
2 *henryana*
2 *laxiflora macrostachya*
2 *tschonoskii*

CARYA
2 *aquatica*
9 *reticulata*

CASSINIA
9 *quinquefaria*
1 *sturtii*

CASSIOPE
1 *hypnoïdes*
2 *lycopodioïdes* 'Rokujo'
2 *mertensiana ciliolata*
9 *wardii*
1 – x *fastigiata* Askival Strain

CATALPA
2 *fargesii duclouxii*
9 *speciosa* 'Pulverulenta'

CAYRATIA
2 *thomsonii*

CEANOTHUS
1 'Blue Boy'
0 *burfordiensis*
1 *griseus*
0 'Mary Lake'
9 x *pallidus* 'Plenus'

CEDRUS
8 *deodara* 'Glauca Pendula'
1 – 'Golden Jubilee'
2 – 'Inversa Pendula'
0 – Paktia Group
0 – 'Polar Winter'
2 – 'Prostrata'
1 *libani brevifolia* 'Horizon'

CELASTRUS
2 *hypoleucus*

CELMISIA
0 *armstrongii*
0 *asteliifolia*
2 *glandulosa*
0 *haastii*
0 *holosericea*
2 *hookeri*
2 *lyallii*
9 *ramulosa tuberculata*
0 *spectabilis argentea*

CELTIS
7 *caucasica*
9 *tournefortii*

CENTAUREA
1 *babylonica*
2 *candidissima* Lamarck
1 *chilensis*
0 *ruthenica*
7 *triumfettii stricta alba*

CENTAURIUM
8 *chloodes*

CENTRANTHERA
1 *intermedium*

CEPHALOTAXUS
2 *harringtonia*

CERASTIUM
8 *biebersteinii*

CERATONIA
8 *siliqua*

CERATOSTIGMA
0 *minus*
1 *ulicinum*

CERCIS
7 *chingii*
2 *occidentalis*
9 *siliquastrum* 'Rubra'

CHAENACTIS
9 *alpina*
9 *jamesii*

CHAENOMELES
2 *japonica* 'Orange Beauty'
1 *speciosa* 'Atrococcinea Plena'
2 – 'Brilliant'
1 x *superba*
0 – 'Alba'
2 – 'Ernst Finken'
1 – 'Vesuvius'

CHAMAECYPARIS
1 *lawsoniana* 'Barry's Bright'
9 – 'Booth'
7 – 'Boy Blue'
9 – 'Darleyensis'
0 – 'Ellwoodii Glauca'
8 – 'Ellwood's Prize'
0 – 'Gold Lace'
2 – 'Gold Pyramid'
2 – 'Goldfinger'
1 – 'Grayswood Bronze'
8 – 'Green Monarch'
8 – 'Holden Gold'
0 – 'Juvenalis Stricta'
0 – 'Lemon Pillar'
8 – 'Lissellii'
2 – 'Merrist Wood'
0 – 'Moerheimii'
0 – 'Shawii'
8 – 'Suffolk Belle'
7 – 'Tilgate'
7 – 'Trentham Gold'
9 – 'Van Eck'
8 – 'Watereri'
2 *nootkatensis* 'Aurea'
9 – 'Tatra'
1 *obtusa* 'Bronze Elegance'
9 – 'Goldspire'
0 – 'Heinrich'
2 – 'Nana Pyramidalis'
2 – 'Repens'
9 – 'Tetragona'
0 *pisifera* 'Compacta'
2 – 'Nana Variegata'
8 – 'Plumosa Floral Arts'
2 – 'Plumosa Teddy Bear'
2 – 'Tsukumo'
8 *thyoïdes* 'Marwood'
2 – 'Purple Heather'
2 – 'Red Star'

CHAMAECYTISUS
2 *hirsutus*

CHAMAEDOREA
0 *elegans* 'Bella'

CHASMANTHIUM
0 *latifolium* 'Variegatum'

CHEILANTHES
2 *alabamensis*
0 *distans*
2 *guanchica*

CHELIDONIUM
2 *majus* 'Laciniatum'

CHELONE
1 *lyonii*
8 *obliqua* 'Praecox Nana'

CHENOPODIUM
8 *ambrosioïdes*
9 *bonus-henricus* 'Variegatum'
2 *foliosum*

CHEVREULIA
0 *lycopodioïdes*

CHIMAPHILA
1 *umbellata*

CHIMONANTHUS
7 *nitens*
1 *praecox* 'Mangetsu'

CHIONODOXA
1 *albescens*
2 *forbesii* 'Tmoli'

CHIONOHEBE
1 *ciliolata*
0 *takatima*

CHIRONIA
1 *baccifera*

CHLOROPHYTUM
2 *majus*

CHORISIA
1 *speciosa*

CHRYSANTHEMUM
2
7 *cordifolium*
9 *praeteritium*

CHRYSOCOMA
1 *coma-aurea*

CHRYSOLEPIS
2 *chrysophylla*

CHRYSOTHAMNUS
0 *nauseosus*

CICERBITA
2 *alpina*

CICUTA
9 *virosa*

CIONURA
2 *erecta*

CISTUS
0 'Elma Colicte'
0 x *glaucus*
0 *heterophyllus*
0 *ladanifer* 'Albiflorus'
0 x *nigricans*
2 *ochreatus*
1 x *platysepalus*
1 *salviifolius* 'Sienna'
0 *varius*

X CITROFORTUNELLA
0 *floridana*

X CITRONCIRUS
9 *webberi*

CITRUS
1 x *tangelo* 'Ugli'

CLADRASTIS
2 *sinensis*

CLAYTONIA
2 *megarhiza*

CLEMATIS
8 *alpina* 'Prairie River'
2 *armandii* Trengwainton form
1 *barbellata* 'Betina' (A)
9 'Blue Diamond'
0 'Elizabeth Foster'
8 *florida*
2 *fremontii*
0 *grata argentilucida*
2 *hookeriana*
9 *lanuginosa*
2 'Lincolnshire Lady'
0 'Lucey'
9 *macropetala* 'White Lady'
2 'Mercury'
7 *occidentalis occidentalis*
2 *ochotensis* (A)
1 *parviflora*
9 – *depauperata*
2 'Pennell's Purity' (L)
0 'Perryhill Pearl'
1 'Pruinina' (A)
8 'Ruby'

CLERODENDRUM
1 *cyrtophyllum*

CLETHRA
0 *alnifolia* 'Nana'

CLINTONIA
0 *uniflora*

CLUSIA
9 *rosea*

CNEORUM
1 *tricoccon*

COCCULUS
7 *trilobus*

CODIAEUM
0 *variegatum pictum* (v)
0 – – 'Excellent' (v)
0 – – 'Gold Star (v)
0 – – 'Norma' (v)

X CODONATANTHUS
1 'Fiesta'
2 'Vista'

CODONOPSIS
9 *bhutanica*

COLCHICUM
9 'Lilac Bedder'
1 *szovitsii*

COLLOMIA
2 *grandiflora*

COLOBANTHUS
0 *strictus*
0 *subulatus*

COLOCASIA
0 *esculenta antiquorum*

COLUMNEA
1 *fendleri*
0 'Mercury'
0 *microphylla*

COLUTEA
2 *arborescens* 'Pendula'
0 – 'Variegata'

CONIUM
2 *maculatum*

CONVALLARIA
9 *majalis* 'Flore Pleno'
1 *montana*
1 *transcaucasica*

CONVOLVULUS
2 *boissieri*
2 *cantabrica*

COPROSMA
9 *ciliata*
0 *serrulata*
0 *spathulata* (m)
0 *viridiflora* (f)

COPTIS
2 *laciniata*

CORDYLINE
0 *banksii* 'Purpurea'
1 *baueri*
0 *fruticosa*
0 – 'Negri'
0 *parryi purpurea*
9 *pumilio*

CORIARIA
0 *angustissima*

CORIS
1 *monspeliensis*

CORNUS
2 *bretschneideri*
0 *drummondii*
0 *florida* 'Barton's White'
2 *hongkongensis*
0 *kousa chinensis* 'Rosea'
2 – 'Robert'
0 – 'Variegata'
9 x *unalaschkensis*

COROKIA
1 x *virgata* 'Bronze Knight'
1 – 'Pink Delight'

CORREA
8 'Kane's Hybrid'

CORYDALIS
2 *afghanica*
1 *aitchisonii*
2 *ambigua* Chamiss & Schlecht
9 *cava blanda*
9 – – *alba*
9 *conorhiza*
2 *darwasica*
2 *lineariloba*
2 *popovii*
2 *saxicola*
1 *scouleri*
2 *solida solida*
9 *vittae*

CORYLOPSIS
9 *himalayana griffithii*
7 *koreana*

CORYLUS
2 *maxima* 'Garibaldi'
2 – 'Neue Riesennuss' ('New Giant')
2 – 'Waterloo'

COTINUS
9 *coggygria* 'Drinkstone Form'

COTONEASTER
2 *affinis*
2 *apiculatus*
2 *buxifolius* blue form
0 *frigidus* 'Saint Monica'
2 *glabratus*
1 *henryanus* 'Anne Cornwallis'
2 *microphyllus* 'Inermis'
1 *nitens*
2 *nummularius*
2 *prostratus*
2 *racemiflorus*
0 'Saldam'
2 *salicifolius* 'Avonbank'
1 – 'Klampen'
9 – 'Perkeo'
0 *schlechtendalii* 'Eastleigh'
2 *sikkimensis* Lowndes
9 x *suecicus* 'Greensleeves'
8 – 'Jürgl'
7 *tomentosus*
2 'Valkenburg'
7 x *watereri* 'Inchmery'

COTULA
2 *coronopifolia* 'Cream Buttons'

COWANIA
2 *mexicana*

CRASPEDIA
2 *globoïdes*
2 *incana*
2 *uniflora*

CRASSULA
0 *lactea*
7 *rigginsiana*

CRATAEGUS
9 *laevigata* 'Cheal's Crimson'
9 – 'Masekii'
9 – 'Punicea'
9 – 'Rosea'
2 *mollis*
1 *stipulacea*

CREMANTHODIUM
9 *oblongatum*
2 *reniforme*

CRINUM
0 *campanulatum*

CROCOSMIA
2 x *crocosmiiflora* 'Brightest and Best'
2 – 'Météore'
2 – 'Sir Matthew Wilson'
2 – 'Vesuvius'
9 'Orange Flame'
1 'Saracen'
1 *williamsii*

CROCUS
1 *biflorus* 'Bowles' Blue'
2 – ssp. *melantherus*
8 – ssp. *weldenii*
1 *candidus*
1 *corsicus albus*
9 *imperati* 'form'
1 *korolkowii* forms
9 – 'Unicoloratus'
1 *kotschyanus hakkariensis*
0 *niveus* 'Cape Mataplan'
9 *reticulatus*
1 – ssp. *hittiticus*
2 *sieberi sublimis*
9 *speciosus* 'Globosus'
0 *tommasinianus* forms
9 *vernus* 'Early Perfection'
0 – 'Flower Record'
9 – 'King of the Striped'
2 *versicolor*

CROTALARIA
2 *grevei*

CROWEA
1 *angustifolia*
8 *exalata* x *saligna*

CRYPTANTHUS
0 *acaulis*
2 – var. *ruber*
2 – – 'New Coster's Favorite'
2 *beuckeri*
0 *bivittatus* 'Minor'
2 Black Mystic
0 *bromelioïdes* 'Tricolor' (v)
2 Carnival
2 Feuerzauber
2 *fosterianus*
2 'It'
2 Italy
2 'Red Star'
0 x *rubra lueddemannii*
2 Silber Lila
2 *zonatus*
0 – 'Zebrinus'

X CRYPTBERGIA
0 *rubra*

CRYPTOMERIA
1 *japonica* 'Dacrydioides'
9 – 'Elegantissima'
2 – 'Fasciata'
0 – 'Knaptonensis'
2 – 'Little Diamond'
0 – 'Spiraliter Falcata'
1 – 'Tansu'
9 – 'Viridis'

CTENANTHE
0 *kummeriana*
0 *oppenheimiana* 'Tricolor'

CUNILA
1 *origanoïdes*

CUNNINGHAMIA
8 *lanceolata* 'Glauca'

CUPHEA
1 *llavea* 'Firefly'
0 'Mickey Mouse'
2 *platycentra*
1 *viscosissima*

X CUPRESSOCYPARIS
2 *leylandii* 'Haggerston Grey'
0 – 'Leighton Green'

CUPRESSUS
1 *arizonica glauca* 'Silver Smoke'
1 – 'Variegata'
1 *chengiana*
2 *gualdalupensis forbesii*
1 *macrocarpa* 'Coneybearii Aurea'
1 – 'Golden Flame'
1 – 'John Keown'
9 – 'Pendula'
1 *sempervirens* 'Stricta Aurea'
8 *tortulosa* 'Vladivostock'
8 *torulosa*

CYANANTHUS
2 *integer*
2 *lobatus* C&Mc 315
8 – 'Inshriach Blue'

CYATHEA
0 *cuninghamii*
0 *kermadecensis*

CYCLAMEN
0 *cilicium* patterned leaf
9 *coum coum caucasicum album*
1 – 'Dazzle'
2 – TK form
9 *hederifolium* x *africanum*
0 – Corfu form

CYDONIA
1 *oblonga* 'Broadview'

CYMBIDIUM
9 *goeringii*

CYMBOPOGON
0 *flexuosus*

CYMOPHYLLUS
1 *fraseri*

CYNARA
1 *cardunculus* Scolymus Group 'Brittany Belle'
0 – 'Glauca'

CYNOGLOSSUM
2 *amabile* 'Album'
2 *wallichii*

CYPELLA
2 *coelestis* 'Platensis'

CYPERUS
9 *ustulatus*

CYPRIPEDIUM
1 *calceolus pubescens*
1 *guttatum*

CYRTANTHUS
2 *mackenii cooperi*

CYRTOSPERMA
0 *johnstonii*

CYSTOPTERIS
8 *fragilis* 'Cristata'

CYTISUS
9 'Baronscourt Amber'
9 'Boskoop Ruby'
2 'C E Pearson'
7 'Charmaine'
7 'Donard Seedling'
7 'Eastern Queen'
8 *jeffsii*
2 'Johnson's Crimson'
9 'Lady Moore'
9 *maderensis magnifoliosus*
0 *monspessulanus*
2 'Mrs J Rodgers'
7 'Orange Arch'
7 x *praecox* 'Buttercup'
7 'Southcombe Apricot'
9 *subspicatus*
2 *supranubius*

DABOECIA
8 *azorica*
8 *cantabrica blummii*
8 – 'Creeping White'
8 – 'Globosa Pink'
8 – 'Harlequin'
8 – 'Heraut'
8 – 'Pink Blum'
8 – 'Rodeo'
2 – 'White Blum'
8 – 'Wijnie'
8 x *scotica* 'Red Imp'
8 – 'Robin'

DACTYLORHIZA
0 *sambucina*
1 'Tinney's Spotted'

DAHLIA
2 'Abridge Ben' (MinD)
2 'Abridge Fox' (MinD)
2 'Abridge Taffy' (MinD)
1 'Ace of Hearts'
0 'Aladdin' (SD)
8 'Alfred C' (GSC)
2 'Alltami Alpine' (MD)
9 'Alltami Coral' (MSC)
9 'Alltami Ruby' (MSC)
2 'Alva's Doris' (SC)
0 'Amanda' (SC)
9 'Amaran Guard' (LD)
2 'Amaran Pico' (MD)
2 'Amaran Relish' (GD)
8 'Amelisweerd' (MSC)
7 'Anchorite' (SD)
8 'Andries' Orange' (MinSC)
8 'Ann Hilary' (SD)
8 'Anniversary Doc'
2 'Appetizer' (SSC)
9 'Apple Blossom' (MC)
8 'Armgard Coronet'
9 'Arthur Lashlie' (MC)
2 'Bacchus' (MSC)
9 'Bach' (MC)
7 'Barbara Schell' (GD)
2 'Barbarry Flush' (MinD)
0 'Baseball' (MinBa)
1 'Bassingbourne Beauty' (SD)
2 'Bella Rose' (SSC)
2 'Belle Epoque' (MC)
9 'Belle of Barmera' (GD)
0 'Bettina' (SSC)
8 'Betty Ann' (Pom)
7 'Birchwood'
7 'Bitsa' (MinBa)
0 'Blaisdon Red' (SD)
7 'Bob Fitzjohn'
9 'Bonne Esperance ' (Sin)(Lil)
2 'Bright'
9 'Brookfield Dierdre (MinBa)
9 'Brownie' (Sin)(Lil)
2 'Brunton' (MinD)
9 'Bulls Pride' (GD)
9 'Bushfire' (Pom)
1 'Café au Lait' (LD)
2 'Cameo' (WL)
8 'Cantab Symbol' (MSC)
8 'Carol Channing'
9 'Caroussel' (MC)
8 'Cefn Glow' (SSC)
8 'Centenary Symbol' (MSC)
8 'Cherida' (MinBa)
0 'Cherry Wine' (SD)
8 'Chiltern Amber' (SD)
7 'Chinese Lantern' (SD)
0 'Chorus Girl' (MinD)
1 'Christine'
2 'Clair de Lune' (Col)
8 'Claire' (Misc)
0 'Cocktail' (SC)
9 'Color Spectacle' (LSD)
2 'Conway' (SSC)
1 'Coral Puff'
7 'Corfu'
8 'Corrine'
7 'Cortez Silver'
2 'Cream Kerkrade' (SC)
2 'Cream Linda' (SD)
0 'Cream Pontiac' (SC)
1 'Crichton Cherry' (MinD)
0 'Crossfield Sceptre' (MSC)
9 'Cryfield Jane'
9 'Cryfield Max' (SC)
7 'Cryfield Rosie' (SBa)
9 'Curiosity' (Col)
8 'Dad's Delight' (MinD)
7 'Daleko Adonis' (GSC)
0 'Daleko Tangerine' (MD)
9 'Daleko Venus' (MSC)
8 'Dana Audrey' (MinC)
8 'Dana Judy' (SSC)
9 'Dana Peerless'
8 'Dancing Queen'
8 'Dandy' (Sin)(Lil)
7 'Danum Cupid'
2 'Dauntless' (GSC)
9 'Davenport Lesley' (MinD)
8 'Dedham' (SD)
2 'Defile' (MD)
9 'Delectus' (SD)
9 'De-la-Haye' (MSC)
1 'Diamant'
2 'Diana Gregory' (Pom)
0 'Doctor John Grainger' (MinD)
0 'Donald van de Mark' (GD)
8 'Doris Knight' (SC)
0 'Dorothy Whitney Wood' (SSC)
7 'Downham Royal' (MinBa)
8 'Duncan'
1 'Earl Marc' (SC)
0 'Early Bird' (SD)
0 'Eastwood Pinky' (MSC)
7 'Eastwood Star' (MSC)
8 'Eden Marc'
2 'Eileen Denny' (MSC)
8 'Elizabeth Hammett' (MinD)
0 'Elizabethan' (SD)
0 'Elmbrook Rebel' (GSC)
2 'Emmerdale' (SC)
9 'Exotic Dwarf' (Sin)(Lil)
2 'Fernhill Champion' (MD)
9 'Flying Picket'
9 'Formby Perfection' (MD)
0 'Fred Sheard' (MinD)
0 'Free Lance' (MSC)
9 'Gale Lane' (Pom)
2 'Garden News' (SD)
0 'Gerald Grace' (LSC)
0 'Ginger Nut' (Pom)
8 'Ginger Willo'
8 'Glenafton' (Pom)
8 'Glenbank Honeycomb'
2 'Golden Festival'
0 'Golden Fizz' (MinBa)
0 'Golden Hope' (MinD)
2 'Hallmark' (Pom)
0 'Hamari Saffron' (MSC)
0 'Hamari Sunset' (MSC)
2 'Hamilton Lilian' (SD)
0 'Haseley Cameo' (SD)
0 'Haseley Pearl' (DBa)
0 'Haseley Triumph' (SD)
8 'Hazel' (Pom)
0 'Hazel's Surprise' (SD)

1 'Heljo's Flame' (SC)
8 'Higherfield Crown' (SC)
0 'Highgate Lustre' (MSC)
8 'Highgate Torch' (MSC)
8 'Hilda Clare' (Col)
0 'Holland Herald' (LSC)
7 'Horn of Plenty' (MinD)
0 'Hot Spot' (MinD)
8 'Ice Queen' (SWL)
9 'Imp' (Sin)(Lil)
7 'Inca Metropolitan' (LD)
9 'Inflammation' (Sin)(Lil)
9 'Invader' (SC)
2 'Jaldec Jerry' (GSC)
9 'Jancis' (MinSC)
8 'Jane Horton' (Col)
8 'Janet Clarke' (Pom)
2 'Jean Bailiss' (MSC)
2 'Jean Fairs' (MinWL)
8 'Jescot Jess' (MinD)
0 'Jescot Jim' (SD)
8 'Jescot Nubia' (SSC)
8 'Jill Day' (SC)
9 'Jill Doc' (MD)
1 'John Street' (SWL)
9 'Joy Bennett' (MD)
9 'Joyce Green' (GSC)
8 'Jo's Choice' (MinD)
9 'Kenn Emerland'
8 'Kenora Carousel'
8 'Kenora Sunburst'
2 'Kenora Valentine' (GD)
2 'Kenora Wildfire' (GD)
8 'Kimi' (O)
0 'Kim's Marc' (SC)
9 'Kiwi Nephew' (SSC)
9 'La Cierva' (Col)
9 'La Corbiere' (DwBa)
0 'Lady Orpah' (SD)
8 'Lady Sunshine' (SSC)
0 'Laurence Fisher' (MSC)
0 'Lavendale' (MinD)
7 'Lavender Leycett'
2 'Lavender Nunton Harvest' (SD)
0 'Lavender Pontiac' (SC)
2 'Le Vonne Splinter' (GSC)
8 'Lemon Hornsey' (SD)
0 'Leverton Chippy' (SD)
2 'Leycett' (GD)
2 'Lilac Athalie' (SC)
7 'Limited Edition'
2 'Lipoma' (MinBa)
8 'Little Conn' (Pom)
9 'Little Dorrit' (Sin)(Lil)
0 'Little Sally' (Pom)
9 'Lloyd Huston' (GSC)
7 'Louise Bailey'
9 'Love's Dream' (SWL)
9 'Lula Pattie' (GD)
8 'Madame Vera' (SD)
7 'Madelaine Ann' (GD)
2 'Magic Moment' (MSC)
2 'Magnificat' (MinD)
2 'Majestic Athalie' (SC)
2 'Majestic Kerkrade' (SC)
2 'Majjas Symbol' (MSC)
7 'Margaret Duross' (GD)
7 'Margaret Jean' (GD)
8 'Mariposa' (Col)
2 'Mark Willo' (Pom)
8 'Masons' (SWL)
8 'Mauvine'
8 'Meiktila' (SWL)
0 'Melanie Jane' (MSC)
9 'Melton' (MinD)
9 'Merriwell Topic' (MD)
0 'Millbank Inferno' (SD)
8 'Minley Iris' (Pom)
2 'Miramar' (SD)
0 'Miranda' (MSC)
1 'Miss Swiss' (SD)
2 'Mistill Beauty' (SC)
8 'Moonlight' (SD)
9 'Morley Lady' (SD)
0 'Morley Lass' (SSC)
7 'Mrs Silverston' (SD)
9 'Nescio' (Pom)
0 'Nettie' (MinBa)
8 'Neveric' (LSC)
0 'Newby' (MinD)
2 'Night Editor' (GD)
8 'Norm Williams'
9 'Omo' (Sin)(Lil)
7 'Onslow Linda Ann'
8 'Ornamental Rays' (SC)
8 'Pamela' (SD)
0 'Pastel Pontiac' (SC)
0 'Pat Seed' (MD)
0 'Patti-Pink' (SSC)
2 'Paul's Delight' (SD)
9 'Peace Pact' (SWL)
0 'Peach Pontiac' (SC)
9 'Peachette' (Misc)(Lil)
0 'Pearl Hornsey' (SD)
9 'Pearl Sharpwean' (MSC)
2 'Pensford Willo' (Pom)
2 'Peters Glorie' (MD)
9 'Pink Leycett' (GD)
2 'Pink Vaguely Noble' (SBa)
0 'Pink Worton Ann' (MinD)
8 'Pippa' (SC)
2 'Polar Sight' (GC)
2 'Polyand' (LD)
7 'Pop Stretton' (GSC)
7 'Poppa Jim'
8 'Porcelain' (SWL)
9 'Pot Black' (MinBa)
8 'Primrose Bryn' (SSC)
0 'Promise' (MSC)(Fim)
2 'Purbeck Lydia' (LSC)
0 'Purple Doris Day' (SC)
7 'Purple Joy' (MD)
7 'R Nash'
8 'Rachel's Place'
7 'Raffles' (SD)
2 'Raisa' (LD)
8 'Rani'
0 'Readley' (SWL)
8 'Red Admiral' (MinBa)
8 'Red Delight' (Col)
9 'Red Dwarf' (Sin)(Lil)
9 'Red Lotus'
8 'Red Schweitzer'
8 'Regal Kerkrade' (SC)
0 'Robbie Huston' (LSC)
8 'Roberta' (LD)
8 'Rokesley Mini' (MinC)
9 'Rosalie' (Pom)
1 'Rosalinde'
2 'Rose Cupid' (MinBa)
9 'Rose Newby' (MinD)
7 'Rose Symbol'
8 'Rose Willo' (Pom)
8 'Rosewood' (SSC)
8 'Rotonde' (SC)
2 'Ruskin Belle' (MSC)
9 'Ruskin Emil' (SC)
8 'Ruskin Melody'
9 'Saint Croix' (GSC)
7 'Salmon Athalie'
7 'Salmon Kerkrade'
2 'Salmon Symbol' (MSC)
9 'Samantha' (DwB)
0 'Sandra Chapman' (MSC)
0 'Sango' (MinBa)
8 'Scarborough'
9 'Scaur Princess' (SD)
9 'Scott's United' (MinD)
7 'Senzoe Jenny'
9 'Sharowean Pride' (MSC)
9 'Sherwood Sunrise' (SD)
1 'Shoreline' (D)
2 'Shy Lass' (SC)
9 'Shy Princess' (MC)
2 'So Dainty' (MinSC)
1 'Spencer' (SD)
9 'Stoke Festival '86' (SSC)
9 'Stoneleigh Cherry' (Pom)
8 'Stoneleigh Joyce' (Pom)
8 'Strawberry Gem'
7 'Stump Cross'
8 'Sue Willo' (Pom)
8 'Suffolk Punch' (MD)
0 'Sugar Candy' (MSC)
1 'Sultan'
8 'Sunburst' (Col)
2 'Sunray Symbol' (MSC)
0 'Supermarket' (MSC)
9 'Sure Thing' (MC)
7 'Swallow Falls'
2 'Sweet Symbol' (MSC)
9 'Sweetheart' (SD)
7 'Symbol Jim'
1 'Tango' (SD)
8 'Teatime' (MSC)
0 'The Bride' (SC)
0 'Tinker's White' (SD)
9 'Tiny Tot' (Misc)(Lil)
9 'Topaz Puff'
0 'Tourbillon' (LC)
0 'Trelawny' (GD)
7 'Twiggy' (SWL)
2 'Twilight Time' (MD)
0 'Val Saint Lambert' (MC)
2 'Vazon Bay' (MinB)
8 'Vicky Crutchfield' (SWL)
7 'Vicky Jackson' (SWL)
9 'Vidal Rhapsody' (MSC)
8 'Vidal Tracy' (SSC)
0 'Vigor' (SWL)
8 'Walter Hardesty'
8 'Weston Aramac'
9 'Weston Forge' (SC)
2 'Whale's Rhonda' (Pom)
2 'White Aster' (Pom)
2 'White Klankstad' (SC)
8 'White Lady Linda' (SD)
7 'White Marc'
8 'William Gregory'
2 'William 'B'' (GD)
8 'Willo's Fairy'
8 'Willo's Flame'
8 'Winston Churchill' (MinD)
8 'Winter Dawn' (SWL)
2 'Wittem' (MD)
9 'Wood Plumpton'
8 'Wootton Amber'
2 'Worton Ann' (MinD)
8 'Worton Bluestreak' (SSC)
7 'Worton Ruth' (SD)
7 'Wyndal Horizon'
2 'Yellow Cheer' (SD)(DwB)
8 'Yellow Jubilee'
8 'Yellow Symbol' (MSC)
8 'Yelno Harmony' (SWL)

DAPHNE

2 ***aurantiaca***
2 x ***burkwoodii*** 'Lavenirii'
9 ***cneorum*** 'Major'
2 – 'Ruby Glow'
1 – var. ***verlotii***
2 ***euboica***
2 ***gnidium***
0 ***jasminea*** forms
2 ***kamtschatica***
0 ***kiusiana***
0 'Louis Mountbatten'
2 x ***mantensiana*** 'Manten'
0 ***mezereum*** 'Variegata'
0 ***petraea***
1 – 'Flore Pleno'
9 'Rosetii'
2 'Silver Y'
1 ***tangutica*** 'Aureomarginata'

DASYLIRION

2 ***texanum***

DELOSPERMA

9 ***deschampsii***
9 ***ornatulum***

DELPHINIUM

8 'Antares'
8 'Aphrodite'
1 'Apollo'
1 'Baby Doll'
2 ***barbeyi***
1 x ***belladonna*** 'Blue Bees'
9 – 'Capri'
1 – 'Lamartine'
1 – 'Orion'
1 ***bellamania***
8 'Blue Springs'
1 'Blue Triumph'
8 'Ceylon'
8 ***cheilanthum***
0 'Cinderella'
8 'Claire'
1 'Creamcracker'
1 'Dairymaid'
9 ***denudatum***
7 ***glareosum***

1 ***grandiflorum*** 'Azure Fairy'
8 'Great Expectations'
1 'Hilda Lucas'
0 'Horizon'
1 'Icecap'
0 'Jennifer Langdon'
0 'Jo Jo'
2 'Julia Medcalf'
0 'Jumbo'
0 'Lady Eleanor'
8 'Loch Lomond'
0 'Loch Maree'
0 'Loch Morar'
1 'Loch Nevis'
1 'M Farrand'
0 'Magic Moment'
0 ***menziesii***
8 'Moody Blues'
2 'Mount Everest'
2 ***oxysepalum***
0 'Patricia'
1 'Patricia Lady Hambleden'
0 'Peacock'
2 'Percival'
0 'Peter Pan'
0 'Rev E Lascelles'
1 'Rosina'
8 'Rosy Future'
0 'Round Table'
1 'Royal Wedding'
1 'Sarabande'
8 'Sarah Edwards'
0 'Savrola'
1 'South Seas'
1 'Stardust'
1 'Summer Wine'
2 'Summerfield Viking'
2 'Taj Mahal'
1 'Thelma Rowe'
2 'Tiny Tim'
1 'Turridu'
8 'Wheatear'
1 'William Richards'
1 'Xenia Field'
8 'Zeus'

DENDRANTHEMA
9 'Alf Price' (25b)
7 'Alice Fitton' (7b)
9 'Alison McNamara' (3b)
1 'Allison '88' (Rub)
1 'Allswell' (24b)
7 'Amanda' (11)
8 'Amber Chessington' (25a)
7 'Amber Leading Lady' (25b)
7 'Amy Fitton' (4a)
8 'Ann Dickson' (25a)
7 'Apricot Harry Gee' (1)
1 'Apricot New Stylist' (24b)
0 'Arcadia'
9 'Ark Royal' (24b)
9 'Arkle' (25a)
7 'Arnold Fitton' (1)
0 'Arthur' (25a)
1 'Bambi' (24b)
9 'Bambino' (29c)
7 'Barbara Hall' (23a)
7 'Barker's Wine' (24c)
7 'Barnsley' (5a)
8 'Batley Centenary' (25b)
7 'Beaujolais' (24b)
7 'Bergerac' (24b)
9 'Betty Saxton' (24a)
2 'Bill Florentine' (3b)
2 'Birchwood' (24b)
7 'Birmingham' (2)
7 'Blanche Poitevine' (5b)
8 'Bonus' (24a)
7 'Bowers Jim'
7 'Breakaway'
2 'Brideshead' (13b)
8 'Brighton' (25b)
7 'Broadway Flare' (29c)
7 'Broadway Magic' (19e)
7 'Broadway Peach' (29c)
7 'Broadway Royal' (29c)
7 'Bronze Eda Fitton' (23a)
8 'Bronze Emilia' (29c)
9 'Bronze Juweeltje'
7 'Bronze Miss World' (24a)
9 'Bronze Nathalie' (29c)
7 'Bronze Shoesmith Salmon (4a)
0 'Bronze Venice' (24b)
1 'Bronze Wessex Charms' (29d)
2 'Bronze World of Sport' (25a)
1 'Buckland' (25c)
2 'Buff Courtier' (24a)
1 'Buff Margaret' (24b)
7 'Candy' (7a)
9 'Capulet' (3b)
8 'Carmine Margaret' (24b)
9 'Carol Moonlight' (29b)
7 'Carrie' (25a)
2 'Chamoirose'
7 'Chanelle' (25a)
0 'Chatsworth' (29c)
7 'Cheltenham Show' (25a)
1 'Chempak Crimson' (24b)
9 'Cherry Chintz' (24a)
7 'Chesswood Beauty' (7b)
8 'Chintz' (24b)
8 'Chippendale' (24a)
9 'Christina' (25b)
8 'Clarette'
2 'Cloth of Gold' (24b)
7 'Conderton' (15a)
1 'Contour' (24a)
0 'Copper Rylands Gem' (24b)
8 'Copper Spoon'
9 'Countdown' (5a)
7 'Countryman' (24b)
7 'Cranforth' (24b)
1 'Cream Pennine Pink' (29c)
9 'Crimson Daily Mirror' (5a)
0 'Crimson Purple Glow' (5a)
9 'Crimson Venice' (24b)
7 'Crimson Woolman's Glory ' (7a)
0 'Crown Derby' (15a)
9 'Daily Mirror' (5a)
7 'Dark Eve Gray' (24b)
8 'Dark Pennine Pink' (29c)
1 'Darlington Jubilee' (25a)
2 'David Higgins' (3b)
1 'Dee Prince' (29c)
2 'Denise Oatridge' (5a)
2 'Distinction' (3b)
2 'Dolly' (9c)
0 'Doreen Bircumshaw' (24a)
8 'Dorridge Jewel' (15a)
1 'Dorridge Lady' (24b)
1 'Dorridge Snowball' (3b)
1 'Dorridge Sun' (3b)
0 'Dragoon' (9c)
0 'Early Bird' (24b)
9 'Early Red Cloak' (24b)
7 'Eda Fitton' (23a)
7 'Edith Goodall' (24a)
9 'Elsie Prosser' (1)
8 'Emilia' (29c)
1 'Enbee Sunray' (29d)
7 'Enid Whiston' (4b)
1 'Eugene' (25b)
9 'Eve Gray' (24b)
1 'Evelyn' (25a)
9 'Fairisle' (24b)
0 'Fairway' (15a)
7 'Far North' (5a)
0 'Fiona Lynn' (24a)
9 'Flambard' (24b)
9 'Flo Cooper' (25a)
7 'Forest Flare' (24b)
1 'Frank Taylor' (15a)
7 'Fred Raynor'
9 'Gemma Jones' (5b)
7 'Gerrie Hoek' (29c)
2 'Gerry Milner' (23b)
2 'Gillette' (23b)
7 'Gillian Gore' (23b)
0 'Ginger' (30)
2 'Gladys Sharpe' (25a)
9 'Glorie'
2 'Glorietta' (4b)
1 'Gold Coin' (7b)
9 'Goldcrest' (25b)
9 'Golden Echo' (4a)
7 'Golden Elegance' (5a)
9 'Golden Oyster' (25b)
9 'Golden Salter'
7 'Golden Shoesmith Salmon (4a)
0 'Golden Stardust' (24b)
7 'Golden Woolman's Glory' (7a)
7 'Goldway' (25b)
9 'Granny Gow' (29d)
9 'Graphic' (23b)
9 'Green Goddess' (1)
9 'Greensleeves' (11)
0 'Hamburg' (25a)
8 'Harford'
7 'Harry Whiston' (1)
2 'Havelsonne'
9 'Hayley Boon' (25b)
2 'Hazel Macintosh' (5a)
0 'Hekla'
1 'Helen' (29K)
9 'Highland Skirmish' (29d)
9 'Honey Margaret' (29e)
0 'Horace Martin'
2 'International' (3a)
1 'Isabel' (15b)
2 'Isabellrosa' (29K)
2 'Jack Wood' (25a)
0 'James Hall' (5a)
1 'Jessica' (29c)
7 'Jessie Gilmour' (23a)
9 'Jessie Habgood' (1)
2 'Jessie Raynor'
1 'Jill Collins' (24b)
7 'Jinx' (7b)
2 'John Statham' (23b)
7 'John Wood' (5a)
1 'Joy Hughes' (4b)
1 'Joyce Stevenson' (24b)
1 'Jubilee' (9c)
7 'Julie Ann' (25b)
1 'Juliet' (24b)
7 'Just Tom' (24b)
2 'Kampfhahn'
7 'Kissy'
8 'Lady Anna' (25a)
7 'Lapley Blush' (29b)
7 'Lapley Bracken' (29d)
7 'Lapley Hallmark' (29c)
7 'Lapley Princess' (29c)
7 'Lapley Rose' (29b)
7 'Lapley Snow' (29d)
7 'Lapley Sunset'
1 'Legend'
0 'Lemon Drop' (23a)
2 'Lemon Rynoon' (9d)
1 'Lemon Tench' (29K)
2 'Liberty' (15a)
7 'Linda Young' (5b)
7 'Lipstick' (28)
7 'Littleton'
9 'Lovely Charmer' (7b)
7 'Lydia' (25a)
9 'Madge Welby' (25b)
0 'Manito'
7 'Margaret Fitton' (23b)
0 'Marian Gosling' (24b)
9 'Marie Taylor' (29c)
1 'Mark Slater' (2)
0 'Martina' (24b)
2 'Mary Blomfield' (4a)
0 'Mary Dyer' (24a)
7 'Mason's Golden'
2 'Medallion' (9c)
8 'Michael Fish' (25b)
7 'Michael Pullom' (25a)
7 'Mosquito' (28b)
8 'Mrs Farley'
8 'Munsel'
9 'Muriel Foster' (29d)
7 'My Jeanie' (25a)
7 'Naden Pound'
9 'Ned Holdaway' (25b)
7 'Nora Brook'
8 'Olga Williams' (25b)
7 'Olwyn' (4b)
0 'Orchid Helen'
8 'Orlando' (25a)
9 'Oyster' (25b)
1 'Oyster Fairweather' (3b)
2 'Pacific' (15a)
8 'Paint Box' (24b)
7 'Pandora' (5a/ 12a)
7 'Pat Amos' (23a)
9 'Peach Chessington' (25a)

9 'Peach Juweeltje'
0 'Pelsall Imperial' (3a)
7 'Pelsall Lady' (25a)
0 'Pennine Air' (29d)
9 'Pennine Alfie' (29f)
1 'Pennine Angel' (29a)
9 'Pennine Ann' (29a)
9 'Pennine Belle' (29d)
9 'Pennine Brandy' (29c)
8 'Pennine Brighteye' (29c)
8 'Pennine Bronze' (29c)
9 'Pennine Cadet' (29a)
2 'Pennine Cameo' (29a)
8 'Pennine Champ' (29c)
9 'Pennine Chorus' (29c)
9 'Pennine Chum' (29d)
2 'Pennine Dancer' (29d)
0 'Pennine Dandy' (29c)
9 'Pennine Darkeye' (29c)
9 'Pennine Dew' (29c)
9 'Pennine Dixie' (29d)
9 'Pennine Dream' (29d)
8 'Pennine Echo' (29d)
9 'Pennine Elf' (29c)
1 'Pennine Ember' (29d)
8 'Pennine Fairy' (29c)
9 'Pennine Flirt' (29b)
2 'Pennine Flute' (29f)
9 'Pennine Gem' (29c)
9 'Pennine Globe' (29a)
8 'Pennine Gloss' (29d)
7 'Pennine Gold' (29c)
2 'Pennine Ivory' (29d)
0 'Pennine Jewel' (29f)
2 'Pennine Lemon' (29c)
2 'Pennine Lotus' (29c)
9 'Pennine Marvel' (29c)
2 'Pennine Mary' (29d)
2 'Pennine Mist' (29c)
8 'Pennine Model' (29c)
1 'Pennine Orchid' (29d)
8 'Pennine Penny' (29d)
1 'Pennine Pet' (29f)
2 'Pennine Phyllis' (29b)
9 'Pennine Plume' (29d)
8 'Pennine Polka' (29c)
1 'Pennine Poppet' (29a)
9 'Pennine Prince' (29c)
9 'Pennine Prize' (29a)
9 'Pennine Quiver' (29d)
9 'Pennine Rave' (29a)
7 'Pennine Red' (19c)
9 'Pennine Rose' (29c)
0 'Pennine Salute' (29d)
8 'Pennine Sand' (29c)
7 'Pennine Shell' (29c)
9 'Pennine Shield' (29c)
2 'Pennine Silver' (29c)
8 'Pennine Smile' (29c)
8 'Pennine Solo' (29d)
2 'Pennine Spice' (29c)
0 'Pennine Sweetheart' (29c)
9 'Pennine Tan' (29c)
9 'Pennine Torch' (29d)
2 'Pennine Trinket' (29c)
8 'Pennine Tune' (29a)
1 'Pennine Vista' (29c)
7 'Penny Lane' (25b)
9 'Peter Pan' (24b)
0 'Phil Oultram' (5b)
7 'Pilsley Queen' (29c)
2 'Pink Chessington' (25a)
9 'Pink Gambit' (24a)
7 'Pink Mason' (7b)
7 'Plushred' (4b)
1 'Polar Queen' (3b)
7 'Poppet' (28a)
0 'Port Stanley' (5b)
2 'Primrose Doreen Bircumshaw' (24a)
2 'Primrose Fairweather' (3b)
1 'Primrose Heide' (29c)
7 'Primrose Olwyn' (4b)
1 'Pure Silk' (14b)
2 'Purple Pennine Wine' (29c)
1 'Ralph Lambert' (1)
0 'Rebecca Walker' (25a)
2 'Red Cassandra' (5b)
9 'Red Claire Louise' (24b)
8 'Red Cropthorne'
0 'Red Early Bird' (24b)
7 'Red Fair Lady' (5a)
7 'Red Glory' (7a)
1 'Red Lilian Hoek' (29c)
2 'Red Pennine Jade' (29d)
1 'Red Resilient' (4b)
9 'Redwing' (4b)
2 'Reg Pearce' (15a)
1 'Resilient' (4b)
1 'Rheingold' (29c)
2 'Robert Earnshaw' (3b)
7 'Romany' (2)
7 'Ronald Rowe' (24b)
8 'Rose Madeleine' (29c)
7 'Rosedew' (25a)
1 'Rosette' (29c)
2 'Rumpelstilzchen'
0 'Rutland' (24a)
1 'Rybronze' (9d)
7 'Rychart' (9d)
7 'Rychoice' (9d)
0 'Ryfire' (9d)
1 'Rystar' (9d)
9 'Sally Ball' (29a)
0 'Sally Duchess' (25a)
0 'Salmon Allouise' (25b)
7 'Salmon Chessington' (25a)
2 'Salmon Margaret Riley' (25a)
0 'Salmon Orpheus' (1)
2 'Salmon Pennine Gambol' (29a)
1 'Salmon Pennine Pink' (29c)
2 'Salmon Pennine Wine' (29c)
7 'Salmon Primrose'
8 'Salmon Rutland' (24a)
0 'Sassen'
0 'Scarlet Pennine Crimson' (29c)
2 'Schaffhausen'
1 'Sentry' (24b)
7 'Seychelle' (2)
0 'Sheffield Anniversary' (24a)
1 'Sheffield Centenary' (3b)
1 'Sheila Morgan' (5b)
9 'Sherwood Forester' (24a)
9 'Shirley Imp' (3b)
1 'Shirley Sunburst' (3a)
1 'Shirley Victoria' (25a)
7 'Sierra' (25b)
1 'Skater's Waltz' (5a)
9 'Skylark'
2 'Snooker' (23b)
7 'Snow Elf' (28)
9 'Snowcap' (14a)
7 'Snowdon' (5b/9c)
0 'Soccer' (25a)
2 'Solitaire' (24a)
0 'Southway Seville' (29c)
8 'Spartan Bronze' (29c)
2 'Spartan Yellow' (29c)
9 'Standby' (24b)
0 'Stardust' (24b)
1 'Stuart Shoesmith' (4b)
9 'Sun Blaze' (29a)
0 'Suncharm Orange' (22a)
7 'Sunflash' (5b/12a)
8 'Sunset Rylands Gem' (24b)
0 'Susan Freestone' (24b)
9 'Susan Pullom' (25a)
9 'Sydenham Girl' (24b)
2 'Talbot Classic' (29c)
7 'Terry Morris' (7b)
7 'Tiara' (28a)
9 'Tom Stillwell'
2 'Tone Dragon' (29a)
1 'Tone Girl' (29a)
9 'Tone Glow' (29a)
9 'Tone Sail' (29a)
2 'Tone Tints' (29a)
2 'Tone Yellow' (29a)
2 'Trudie Bye' (3b)
2 'Twinkle' (28)
2 'Vanessa Lynn' (24b)
0 'Vanity Apricot'
0 'Vanity Yellow'
1 'Violet Lawson' (15a)
1 'Vitax Victor' (25a)
9 'Wagtail' (22a)
1 'Wessex Charms' (29d)
2 'Wessex Opal' (29d)
1 'Wessex Pearl' (29d)
2 'Wessex Prince' (29d)
2 'Wessex Royal' (29d)
0 'Wessex Sentry' (29d)
0 'Wessex Shell' (29d)
2 'Wessex Tune' (29d)
8 'White Len Futerill' (25a)
0 'White Sally Duchess' (25a)
7 'Winter Queen' (5b)
9 'Woody's Choice' (5b)
2 'Woolman's Celebration' (23b)
9 'Worcester' (14b)
1 'Xenia Noelle' (4b)
2 'Yellow Allouise' (25b)
0 'Yellow Broadway Sovereign' (29c)
1 'Yellow Cassandra' (15b)
9 'Yellow Chessington' (25a)
2 'Yellow Cornish' (25b)
7 'Yellow Cricket' (25b)
8 'Yellow Emilia' (29c)
2 'Yellow Fair Lady' (5a)
2 'Yellow Jack Wood' (25a)
9 'Yellow Jemma Wilson' (23b)
8 'Yellow Juweeltje'
0 'Yellow Pamela' (29c)
1 'Yellow Pennine Pink' (29c)
1 'Yellow Resilient' (5b)
9 'Yellow Salter'
7 'Yellow Sam Vinter' (5a)
2 'Yellow Shirley Imp' (3b)
2 'Yellow Vitax Victor' (25a)
9 'Yorkshire Television' (5a)

DENDROMECON
2 ***rigida***

DESCHAMPSIA
9 ***cespitosa*** 'Tardiflora'
9 – 'Tauträger'

DEUTZIA
0 'Avalanche'
2 ***crenata nakaiana***
1 ***forrestii***
1 x ***hybrida*** 'Reuthe's Pink'
9 x ***kalmiiflora*** 'Pom Pom'
1 x ***maliflora***
8 ***purpurascens***
1 'Rosea Plena'
2 x ***rosea*** 'Rosea'
1 ***scabra*** 'Watereri'
8 ***vilmoriniae***

DIANTHUS
2 'Achievement' (p)
9 'Alfriston' (b)
2 'Allspice Sport' (p)
0 ***alpinus*** 'Adonis'
9 – 'Ascreavie Form'
0 – x ***callizonus***
1 – 'Cherry Beauty'
9 – 'Ruby Venus'
2 'Alyson' (p)
0 ***angulatus***
1 'Anna' (pf)
9 'Anne Jones' (b)
9 'Anthony' (p)
9 'Apollo' (b)
2 'Autumn Glory' (b)
2 'Autumn Tints' (b)
8 'Avoca Purple' (p)
9 'Barbara Norton' (p)
9 'Barton's Pink' (p)
9 'Belle of Bookham' (b)
7 'Beryl Giles' (pf)
1 ***biflorus***
2 Black and White Minstrel's Group (p,a)
2 'Bookham Beau' (b)
2 'Bookham Prince' (b)
9 'Bressingham Pink' (p)
2 ***brevicaulis***
9 'Brilliance' (p)
1 'Buckfast Abbey' (p)
2 'Candy' (p)
0 ***carthusianorum*** Atrorubens Group

1 – 'Nanus'
1 'Castleroyal Princess' (p)
2 'Celestial' (b)
9 'Charles Edward' (p)
7 'Cherry Heldenbrau' (pf)
9 'Cherry Pie' (p)
1 'Clarabelle' (b)
1 'Coleton Fishacre'
2 'Countess of Lonsdale ' (b)
9 'Cranborne Seedling' (p)
9 'Crimson Clove' (p)
9 'Crimson Treasure' (p)
0 'Crusader' (b)
2 'Dainty' (b)
1 'Dainty Dame' (p)
2 'Daphne' (p)
2 'Delicata'
1 ***deltoïdes*** 'Hilltop Star'
9 – 'Steriker' (p)
2 – 'Vampir'
2 'Desert Song' (b)
7 'Diane Marie' (pf)
9 'Dianne' (pf)
9 'Dicker Clove' (b)
2 'Diplomat' (b)
0 'Doctor Danger'
8 'Donizetti' (p)
1 'Dot Clark' (b)
0 'Double Devon' (p)
2 double mauve
1 'Douglas Fancy' (b)
9 'Downs Souvenir' (b)
9 'Downs Unique' (b)
2 'Dusty Sim' (pf)
9 'Edenside Glory' (b)
9 'Eileen Neal' (b)
9 'Elizabeth Jane' (p)
2 'Eve' (p)
1 'Fancy Monarch' (b)
0 'Favourite Lady' (p)
9 'Fay' (p)
0 'Firefly' (b)
9 'Flanders' (b)
1 'Forest Violet' (b)
1 'Fragrans' (pf)
2 'Fred Sutton' (pf)
9 'Gaiety' (p)
1 'Gaydena' (b)
8 'George Vernon' (pf)
9 'Glenda' (p)
9 'Glory'
2 'Glory Lyonnaise' (p)
9 'Goblin' (p)
9 'Grace How' (b)
0 'Grace Mather' (p)
1 ***gracilis***
7 'Grandad' (p)
1 ***graniticus***
0 ***gratianopolitanus* × *subacaulis***
1 'Green Lane' (p)
9 'Grey Dove' (b)
2 'Greystone' (b)
9 'Grome' (p)
2 'Hambledon' (p)
7 'Hardwicke's Pink' (p)
9 'Heldenbrau' (pf)
9 'Helen Keates' (b)
9 'Helga' (p)
2 'Herbert's Pink' (p)
9 'Highland Gem' (p)
2 'Hollycroft Rose' (p)
1 'Hound Tor'
8 'Houstan House' (p)
8 'Ipswich Crimson' (p)
0 'Irish Pink' (p)
2 'Isobel Templeton' (b)
8 'Jack Wood' (pf)
9 'Jack's Lass' (pf)
0 'Jacqueline's Delight' (p)
9 'Jane Bowen' (p)
1 'Janet' (p)
1 'Janet Walker' (p)
2 'Jester' (p)
9 'John Malcolm' (p)
2 'Judy' (p)
9 'Kathleen Hitchcock' (b)
9 'Katy' (b)
1 'Kesteven Kirkstead'
2 'King of the Blacks' (p,a)
1 'Kitty Jay'
2 'Kobusa' (pf)
2 'Laddie Sim' (pf)
2 'Lancing Lass' (p)
2 'Lena' (pf)
2 'Leuchtkugel'
9 'Lily Lesurf' (b)
9 'Little Beauty' (pf)
2 'Little Miss Muffet' (p)
2 'Lord Grey' (b)
9 'Lord Nuffield' (b)
9 'Maggie' (p)
9 'Maisie Neal' (b)
9 'Margaret Curtis' (p)
2 'Mark' (p)
2 'Mary Livingstone' (b)
2 'Mary Murray' (b)
2 'Maurice Prichard' (p)
2 'Melody' (pf)
9 'Messines White' (p)
8 'Monarch' (pf)
9 'Mrs Blarney's Old Pink' (p)
8 'Mrs Dunlop's Old Pink '
1 'Mrs Holt' (p)
2 'Mrs Perkins' (b)
2 'Murray's Laced Pink' (p)
1 'Murton' (p)
1 'Nora Urling Clark' (pf)
2 'Oakwood Bill Ballinger' (p)
7 'Oakwood Dainty' (p)
9 'Oakwood Dorothy' (p)
2 'Oakwood Sparkler' (p)
0 'Old Crimson Clove' (b)
9 'Orchid Lace' (p,a)
2 'Pallas' (b)
1 ***pavonius albus***
9 – 'Roaschia'
9 'Peter Adamson' (b)
9 'Peter Wood' (b)
1 ***petraeus petraeus***
9 'Petula' (p)
1 'Pink Baby' (p)
9 'Pink Bouquet' (p)
0 'Pink Delight' (p)
0 'Plum Diadem' (p)
9 'Pluto' (p)
9 'Portrait Sim' (pf)
2 'Portsdown Sunset' (b)
2 'Prichard's Variety' (p)
8 'Pride of Ayrshire' (p)
8 'Raeden Pink' (p)
1 'Ralph Gould' (p)
9 'Raspberry Ripple' (p)
2 ***repens***
9 'Richard Pollak' (b)
9 'Robert Douglas' (b)
9 'Robert Smith' (b)
2 'Rose Bradwardine' (b)
0 'Ruth' (p)
9 'Sacha' (pf)
2 'Sally's Mauve'
9 'Salmon Fragrant Ann' (p)
9 'Salmon Queen' (b)
2 'Sandra' (p)
2 ***serotinus***
1 'Sevilla' (pf)
2 'Shaston Delight' (b)
9 'Shaston Supreme' (b)
9 'Sheila Short' (pf)
0 'Sheila Weir' (b)
9 'Show Ideal' (p)
9 'Shrimp' (b)
2 ***simulans***
0 'Snowshill Fringed' (p)
2 ***spiculifolius***
2 'Spindrift' (b)
2 'Sprite' (b)
0 ***superbus longicalycinus***
2 'Surrey Clove' (b)
2 'Sway Breeze' (p)
9 'Syston Beauty' (p)
1 'Timothy' (p)
1 'Tom Bradshaw' (pf)
9 'Tom Welborn' (p)
9 'Tony Cutler' (b)
2 'Trevor' (p)
1 'Truly Yours' (pf)
2 'Vanda' (p)
2 'Water Nymph' (b)
1 'Welland' (p)
8 'Welwyn' (p)
1 'White Bouquet' (p)
9 'Whitesmith' (b)
2 'William Newell' (b)
9 'William of Essex' (p)
9 'Wisp' (p)
0 ***xylorrizus***
9 'Zephyr' (b)

DIAPENSIA
9 ***lapponica obovata***

DIASCIA
1 ***capensis***
2 ***rigescens*** 'Variegata'
2 ***stricta***
2 ***tugelensis***

DICENTRA
2 ***formosa*** 'Sweetheart'
1 ***pauciflora***
0 ***peregrina***
8 – ***alba***

DICKSONIA
0 ***lanata***

DICOMA
2 ***zeyheri***

DIEFFENBACHIA
0 × ***bausei*** (v)
0 'Janet Weidner' (v)
0 ***seguine*** 'Exotica' (v)
0 – 'Jenmanii' (v)
0 'Wilson's Delight' (v)

DIETES
7 ***grandiflora***

DIGITALIS
2 ***lamarckii*** Ivanina
9 ***lutea*** 'Sarah'
1 ***obscura*** dwarf form
0 ***purpurea nevadensis***

DIONYSIA
9 ***archibaldii***
9 ***aretioïdes*** 'Paul Furse'
0 ***bryoïdes***
0 ***curviflora***
0 ***denticulata***
0 ***janthina***
0 ***michauxii***
0 ***revoluta canescens***
0 – ***revoluta***
0 ***tapetodes***

DIOSPYROS
7 ***glaucifolia***

DIPELTA
2 ***yunnanensis***

DIPSACUS
1 ***laciniatus***

DISCARIA
0 ***toumatou***

DISPORUM
8 ***sessile yakushimense***
2 ***smilacinum***

DISTYLIUM
9 ***myricoïdes***

DODECATHEON
1 ***alpinum purpureum***
2 ***integrifolium***
1 ***redolens***
2 'Sooke's Variety'

DOLICOTHRIX
2 ***ericoïdes***

DORYANTHES
1 ***excelsa***

DRABA
8 ***alpina***
2 ***asprella***
1 ***borealis***
1 ***carinthiaca***
2 ***cinerea***
8 ***fladnizensis***
2 ***mollissima* × *longisiliqua***
0 ***oreibata***
1 ***paysonii paysonii***
0 ***setosa***
1 ***sibirica***
1 ***stellata***
2 ***streptocarpa***
2 ***yunnanensis***

DRACAENA
0 ***deremensis*** 'Compacta'
0 ***fragrans*** 'Lindenii'
0 ***reflexa***

DRACOCEPHALUM
0 ***heterophyllum***
2 ***imberbe***

9 *integrifolium*
2 *nutans*

DRACOPHYLLUM
1 *fiordense*
2 *pronum*

DRIMYS
1 *winteri* 'Fastigiata'
2 – var. *winteri*

DRYAS
9 *octopetala lanata*

DRYOPTERIS
1 *filix-mas* 'Crispatissima'

DRYPIS
1 *spinosa* 'Jacquiniana'

DUDLEYA
1 *brittonii*

ECHINACEA
1 *purpurea* 'The King'

ECHINOPS
0 *chantavicus*
1 *tournefortii albus*

EDRAIANTHUS
1 *serbicus*

EHRETIA
0 *dicksonii*

ELAEAGNUS
0 *angustifolia orientalis*
8 x *ebbingei* 'Tricolor' (v)
2 *pungens*

ELAEOCARPUS
9 *decipiens*
1 *hookerianus*
0 *pusillus*

ELEUTHEROCOCCUS
9 *henryi*

ELLIOTTIA
9 *racemosa*

ELYMUS
1 *interruptus*

EMINIUM
1 *stipitatum*

EMPETRUM
8 *hermaphroditum*
8 *nigrum* 'Bernstein'
8 – 'Compactum'
8 – 'Smaragd'

ENGELMANNIA
0 *pinnatifida*

ENKIANTHUS
0 *cernuus*
9 *serrulatus*

EPACRIS
0 *pauciflora*

EPHEDRA
1 *affinis intermedia*
0 *intermedia*

EPILOBIUM
1 *arizonicum*
9 *canum* 'Splendens Plenum'
0 *glabellum* 'Roseum'
9 *gunnianum*

EPIMEDIUM
1 *elongatum*
0 *grandiflorum* 'Rose Glow'
1 – 'White Beauty'

EQUISETUM
9 *telmateia*

EREMAEA
1 *purpurea*

EREMURUS
2 Himrob Group

ERICA
8 *andevalensis*
2 *baccans*
2 *bauera*
8 *carnea* 'Amy Backhouse'
8 – 'Margery Frearson'
8 – 'Mayfair White'
8 – 'Mr Reeves'
8 – 'Urville'
8 – 'Winter Red'
8 *ciliaris alba*
8 – 'Jennifer Anne'
8 – 'Maweana'
8 – 'Ram'
8 – 'Rock Pool'
2 – 'Stapehill'
2 *cinerea* 'A E Mitchell'
8 – 'Alette'
0 – 'Angarrack'
8 – 'Anja Blum'
8 – 'Aquarel'
8 – 'Atrorubens Daisy Hill'
8 – 'Atrosanguinea Reuthe's Variety'
2 – 'Bucklebury Red'
9 – 'Creel'
8 – 'Discovery'
0 – 'Electra'
8 – 'Guernsey Pink'
8 – 'Heatherbank'
8 – 'Heathfield'
9 – 'Hutton Pentreath'
8 – 'Hutton Seedling'
8 – 'Iberian Beauty'
7 – 'Lankidden'
0 – 'Lilian Martin'
8 – 'Marina'
2 – 'Old Rose'
8 – 'Pallida'
1 – 'Pink Lace'
2 – 'Providence'
0 – 'Rock Ruth'
8 – 'Rose Gem'
8 – 'Uschie Ziehmann'
8 – 'Violetta'
2 – 'Wine'
0 – 'Yvonne'
0 x *darleyensis*
2 *erigena* 'Rubra'
2 'January Sun'
8 *mackayana* 'Donegal'
8 *maderensis*
1 *mammosa*
1 *multiflora*
2 'Netherfield Orange'
8 *oatesii*
8 *perlata*
0 *scoparia*
9 – *azorica*
2 'Sneznick'
9 x *stuartii* 'Nacung'
8 *taxifolia*
1 *tetralix* 'Afternoon'
8 – 'Alba Praecox'
2 – 'Darleyensis'
8 – 'Humoresque'
8 – 'Mary Grace'
2 – 'Pink Glow'
8 – 'Rosea'
2 – 'Swedish Yellow'
9 *vagans* 'Alba Nana'
8 – 'Bianca'
8 – 'Elegant Spike'
2 – 'Rosea'
9 *verticillata*
8 *vestita*
1 x *watsonii*
2 x *williamsii*

ERIGERON
1 *allocatus*
2 *caespitosus*
1 *chrysopsidis brevifolius*
2 *delicatus*
0 *glabellus*
1 *glaucus* 'Sennen'
1 *humilis*
9 *myosotis*
8 *roylei*
9 *speciosus* 'Roseus'
2 'Viridis'
9 'White Quakeress'

ERINUS
2 *alpinus* pink form

ERIOCEPHALUS
8 *africanus*

ERIOGONUM
1 *flavum xanthum*
9 *giganteum*
2 *ovalifolium nivale*

ERIOPHORUM
0 *brachyantherum*
1 *scheuchzeri*

ERODIUM
0 'Bedderi'
2 'Crimson Glow'
2 *petraeum petraeum*
9 *romanum*
2 *sibthorpianum*

ERYNGIUM
2 *billardierei*
2 'Calypso' (v)
1 *nivale*
7 *serra*
7 x *zabelii* 'Spring Hills'

ERYSIMUM
1 'Bicolor'
1 *cheiri* double yellow
0 *linifolium glaucum*
2 *nivale*
9 *odoratum*
1 *sempervirens*

ERYTHRINA
2 *princeps*

ERYTHRONIUM
2 *grandiflorum chrysandrum*
2 – var. *pallidum*
2 *mesochoreum*
2 'Miss Jessopp'

ESCALLONIA
2 'Bantry Bay'
2 'Donard Glory'
2 'Greenway'
0 *laevis* 'Gold Ellen'
0 'Lord Headfort's Seedling'
0 'Red Guard'
0 *rubra macrantha* 'Sanguinea'
0 'William Watson'
0 'Wintonensis'

EUCALYPTUS
2 *alpina*
2 *amygdalina*
2 *bridgesiana*
8 *lehmannii*
8 *maculata*
2 *moorei*
9 *ovata*
9 *populnea*
8 *preissiana*
0 *pulchella*
1 *radiata*
8 *rodwayi*
9 *rossii*
8 *tenuiramis*

EUCODONIA
2 *ehrenbergii*
2 *verticillata*

EUCOMIS
2 *autumnalis autumnalis*

EUCRYPHIA
1 x *hillieri*

EUONYMUS
2 *americanus*
8 x *buxifolius* 'Nanus'
2 *europaeus* 'Brilliant'
0 – 'Chrysophyllus'
1 *fortunei*
2 – 'Carrierei'
0 – 'Dart's Covergirl'
2 – 'Emerald Charm'
2 – 'Highdown'
9 – *radicans*
1 – 'Sarcoxie'
9 *hamiltonianus maackii*

EUPATORIUM
2 *album*
1 *coelestinum*

EUPHORBIA
2 *acanthothamnos*
8 *dendroïdes*
0 'Goldburst'
0 *macrostegia*
1 *marginata*
9 *millotii*
2 *regis-jubae*
1 *tenuissimus*

EUPTELEA
2 ***pleiosperma***
EURYA
2 ***japonica***
EURYOPS
2 ***linearis***
EVOLVULUS
1 ***passerinoïdes***
EXOCHORDA
7 ***giraldii***
FAGUS
0 ***moesiaca***
2 ***orientalis***
2 ***sylvatica latifolia***
2 – 'Rohan Obelisk'
2 – var. ***variegata***
FALLOPIA
0 ***elliptica***
FALLUGIA
9 ***paradoxa***
FARGESIA
9 ***nitida*** 'Chenevieres'
FELICIA
1 ***filifolia***
FERULA
1 ***purpurea***
FICUS
0 ***elastica***
1 – 'Schrijveriana' (v)
0 ***natalensis leprieurii***
0 ***religiosa***
FORSYTHIA
9 × ***intermedia*** 'Phyllis'
FORTUNEARIA
1 ***sinensis***
FRAGARIA
2 × ***ananassa*** 'Cantata'
2 – 'Domanil'
2 – 'Gento'
1 – 'Grandee'
1 – 'Hedley'
2 – 'Maxim'
2 – 'Rabunda'
2 – 'Serenata'
1 – 'Sweetheart'
1 – 'Tantallon'
2 – 'Vigour'
2 ***vesca*** 'Delicious'
8 – 'Reine des Vallées'
FRASERA
2 ***speciosa***
FRAXINUS
9 ***bungeana***
7 ***cuspidata***
2 ***dipetala***
9 ***excelsior*** 'Argenteovariegata'
2 ***lanuginosa***
0 ***paxiana***
9 ***pennsylvanica subintegerrima***
2 – 'Summit'
7 ***quadrangulata***
7 ***rotundifolia*** 'Flame'
0 'Veltheimii'
FRITILLARIA
1 ***affinis*** 'Wayne Roderick'
8 ***alfredae platyptera***
9 ***ariana***
0 ***caucasica caucasica***
1 ***eduardii***
2 ***forbesii***
1 ***gibbosa***
8 ***imperialis*** 'Sulphurino'
1 ***japonica***
9 ***meleagris*** 'Jupiter'
9 – 'Poseidon'
9 – 'Purple King'
9 – 'Saturnus'
2 ***olgae***
2 ***orientalis***
1 ***pluriflora***
2 ***roylei***
FUCHSIA
0 'Aad Franck'
9 'Aber Falls'
9 'Abt. Koloman Holzinger'
9 'Airball'
2 'Al Stettler'
0 'Aladna's Marina'
0 'Aladna's Sander'
1 'Alan's Joy'
0 'Albert H'
0 'Albertina'
1 'Alexandra Dyos'
0 'Alma Hulscher'
1 'Althea Green'
0 'American Prelude'
9 ***americana elegans***
8 ***ampliata***
9 'Angela'
0 'Anjo'
1 'Ann Margaret'
0 'Ann Pacey'
0 'Anne Howard Tripp'
0 'Anniek Geerlings'
0 'Anthea Bond'
0 'Anthonetta'
1 'Antonella Merrills'
0 'Arc en Ciel'
9 'Architect Ludwig Mercher'
0 'Arels Fleur'
2 'Aubrey Harris'
0 'Avon Gold'
2 'Avril Lunn'
0 'Axel of Denmark'
2 'Baby Face'
2 'Baby Lilac'
0 'Baby Love'
0 'Baby Veerman'
1 'Barbara Anne'
1 'Barbara Edwards'
0 'Barry Sheppard'
1 'Beacon Kon'
0 'Belinda Allen'
2 'Bella Madina'
1 'Benjamin Pacey'
0 'Berbanella'
1 'Berba's Delight'
0 'Berba's Fleur'
0 'Berba's Francis Fenke'
0 'Berba's Impossible'
0 'Berba's Ingrid'
0 'Berba's Love'
0 'Berba's Trio'
0 'Bernard Rawdin'
2 'Bernisser Stein'
9 'Beryl's Jewel'
0 'Betma Whitison'
2 'Betty Wass'
0 'Blue Ranger'
9 'Bosun's Superb'
1 'Boy Blue'
9 'Bridal Pink'
0 'Brunette'
1 'Carlisle Bells'
9 'Carmen'
0 'Caroline Imp'
0 'Catherine Claire'
0 'Cecil Glass'
0 'Cees van Braunschott'
9 'Chance Encounter'
2 'Charles Edward'
0 'Chartwell'
0 'Chatsworth'
1 'Cherry Pie'
0 'Chris'
0 'Chris van der Linden'
0 'Christine Clements'
2 'Christine Pugh'
0 'Cindy Robijn'
0 'Cinnabarrina'
0 'Cinnamon'
2 'Cliff's Supreme'
9 'Clipper'
9 'Coconut Ice'
2 'Concord'
2 'Contamine'
1 'Coral Rose'
9 'Country Girl'
0 'Crown Derby'
2 'Cupcake'
0 'Dark Spider'
0 'Dark Treasure'
9 'Deben Petite'
2 'Deben Rose'
1 'Deborah Louise'
2 'Deborah Young'
2 'Debra Imp'
2 'Dee Star'
0 'Delta's Fellow'
2 'Delta's Glorie'
2 'Delta's Rien'
0 'Delta's Robijn'
0 'Derby Belle'
0 'Derby Countess'
0 'Derby Star'
2 'Diabolo'
9 'Diana Wright'
9 'Diana's Calypso'
1 'Diane Christiansen'
0 'Didi'
0 'Diny Hetterscheid'
9 'Donauweibchen'
9 'Dorothy Woakes'
2 'Dove Cottage'
2 'Drooping Lady'
1 'Duchess of Cornwall'
9 'Duchess of Petitport'
2 'Dunrobin Bedder'
0 'Dutch Firebird'
0 'Dutch Flamingo'
0 'Earre Barre'
1 'Eden Dawn'
1 'Edwin Miles'
0 'El Matador'
9 'Elisabeth Nutzinger'
2 'Elizabeth Brown'
0 'Elsine'
2 'Emile Zola'
0 ***encliandra tetradactyla***
2 'English Rose'
9 'Enstone'
2 'Erica Memlis'
9 'Erika Köth'
0 'Eroica'
0 'Ethel Weeks'
9 'Ethel Wilson'
0 'Eva Watkins'
2 'Fair Play'
0 'Fatima'
2 'Fenrother Fairy'
2 'Firecracker'
0 'Firenzi'
2 'First Kiss'
9 'Flamingo'
9 'Flarepath'
9 'Flim Flam'
0 'Flirt'
2 'Fluffy Frills'
2 'Fly-by-Night'
0 'Francois Villon'
0 'Frank Veerman'
0 'Frauke'
0 'Fred Standen'
9 'Fred's First'
0 'Freestyle'
2 'Frosted Amethyst'
0 'Frosty Bell'
1 'Gabriel Rose'
0 'Garden Beauty'
0 'Gazette'
0 'Geertien'
0 'Geertje'
0 'Général Negrier'
0 'Geoff Barnett'
9 'Georg Bornemann'
2 'George Bunstead'
2 'George Robinson'
0 'George Roe'
0 'Gidding'
0 'Gillian Shepherd'
2 'Glendale'
9 'Gleneagles'
0 'Gold Leaf'
1 'Golden Lustre'
0 'Golden Lye's Favourite'
0 'Golden Spade'
0 'Gondolier'
1 'Goose Girl'
0 'Grace'
9 'Grace Groom'
1 'Granada'
9 'Grand Duke'
9 'Grayrigg'
0 'Guurtje'
9 'H M S Victorious'
0 'Harbour Bridge'
9 'Harlequin'
0 'Harriet Lye'
1 'Haylettes Gold'
0 'Heather'
2 'Helen McDermott'
0 'Helene Houwen Claessen'
8 'Henriette Ernst'
0 'Hiawatha'

1 'High Peak'
2 'Hilda Fitzsimmons'
1 'Hill Top'
0 'HMS Victorious'
9 'Hobson'
1 'Humpty Dumpty'
0 'Ina Buxton'
2 'Ingram Maid'
0 'Irene van Zoeren'
2 'Irish Wedding'
0 'Ivan Gadsby'
1 'Ivor Moore'
1 'Jack Horner'
0 'Jack King'
1 'Jack Sprat'
9 'James Shurvell'
0 'Jan Bremer'
0 'Jan Houtsma'
2 'Jane Elizabeth'
1 'Janet Williams'
2 'Jason Slaney-Welch'
0 'Jaspers Donderslag'
0 'Je Maintiendrai'
9 'Jean Burton'
1 'Jean Ewart'
9 'Jean Pidcock'
2 'Jewel'
0 'Joanne'
0 'Joan's Delight'
0 'Johannes Novinski'
1 'John Waugh'
0 'Joker'
0 'Jolanda Weeda'
2 'Jolly Jorden'
1 'Joseph Holmes'
2 'Julie Adams'
0 'Julie Horton'
0 'Karen'
0 'Kathleen'
0 'Kathy Louise'
9 'Kentish Belle'
0 'Kentish Maid'
1 'Kim Hampson'
0 'King George V'
2 'King of Siam'
0 'Klein Beekestein'
9 'Kocarde'
0 'Kolibrie'
9 'Komeet'
2 'Kursal'
2 'La Bergère'
0 'Lady Bower'
9 'Lady Dorothy'
1 'Lady Pamela Mountbatten'
0 'Larissa'
0 'Lavender Thumb'
9 'Lechlade Fairy'
0 'Lechlade Maiden'
0 'Lechlade Potentate'
0 'Leo Goetelen'
9 'Liemers Lantaern'
0 'Lila Sunsa'
1 'Lilac Sceptre'
0 'Lilian Windsor'
2 'Lilo Vogt'
9 'Linda Pratt'
0 'LIngenue'
9 'Little One'
0 'Liver Bird'
0 'Lonneke'
0 'Look East'
2 'Lord Leverhulme'
1 'Lorna Doone'
2 'Loulabel'
0 'Love in Bloom'
9 'Love It'
0 'Loverdale'
1 'Lucie Harris'
2 'Lucy Harris'
1 'Lunter's Klokje'
9 'Lustre Improved'
1 'Lycioides'
0 'Lye's Elegance'
0 'Lye's Perfection'
0 'Lynhurst'
2 'Mabel Grey'
0 'Madame Danjoux'
0 'Madame Lanteime'
1 'Madame Theobald'
0 'Madurodam'
0 ***magdalenae***
1 ***magellanica conica***
9 – 'Ghostly Pink'
9 – 'Longipedunculata'
2 – var. ***macrostema***
8 – ***myrtifolia***
2 – ***purpurea***
0 'Margaret Thatcher'
9 'Margie'
1 'Marie Julie'
0 'Marja'
1 'Marta Frädrich'
0 'Martha Franck'
0 'Martyn Smedley'
2 'Mary Ellen'
2 'Matthew Welch'
2 'Maudena'
0 'Max Jaffa'
1 'Mazarine'
2 'Mediterranean'
9 'Medusa'
0 'Melissa Heavens'
0 'Mendocino Rose'
7 'Mephisto'
9 'Mercurius'
2 'Merry England'
0 'Mia van der Zee'
0 'Millie Butler'
2 'Miranda Morris'
1 'Miss Muffett'
0 'Mistique'
2 'Misty Haze'
0 'Mon Ami'
9 'Monsieur Joule'
0 'Mosedale Hall'
9 'Mrs John D Fredericks'
9 'My Love'
0 'Nanne'
9 'Naomi Adams'
0 'Nemerlaer'
0 'Nettala'
2 'New Constellation'
2 'Nicola White'
0 'Nicolina'
0 'Night and Day'
0 'Oddfellow'
0 'Olympia'
2 'Omar Giant'
1 'Orange Cocktail'
1 'P J B'
1 'Pale Beauty'
0 'Pamela Hutchinson'
0 'Panylla Prince'
2 'Paramour'
0 'Patricia Bardgett'
0 'Patricia Ewart'
1 'Paula Baylis'
1 'Pauline Flint'
9 'Pèredrup'
9 'Petit Point'
1 'Phyllis Stevens'
0 'Piet G Vergeer'
9 'Pink Cornet'
2 'Pink Domino'
1 'Pink Haze'
9 'Pink Trumpet'
2 'Pink Veil'
0 'Piquant'
0 'Playboy'
1 'Pole Star'
1 'Polly Flinders'
9 'Präsident Walter Morio'
9 'Prince Syray'
2 'Princess Saranntoe'
0 'Pukkie'
9 'Puttenden Manor'
0 'R L Lockerbie'
0 'Rachel Catherine'
9 'Rading's Michelle'
2 'Raintree Legend'
0 'Rambo'
2 'Ratae Beauty'
9 'Ravensbarrow'
1 'Rebecca Louise'
0 'Recy Holmes'
0 'Red Rain'
0 'Red Rover'
9 'Red Rum'
0 'Reflexa'
2 ***regia***
0 'Regina van Zoeren'
0 'Revival'
0 'Rhanee'
9 'Riccartonii Variegated'
2 'Rigoletto'
0 'Robert Hall'
0 'Robert Lutters'
2 'Robin Pacey'
2 'Rolts'
1 'Ron's Pet'
0 'Rosabell'
1 'Rose Lace'
0 'Rosedale'
1 'Rosetta'
2 'Roslyn Lowe'
9 'Rothbury Beauty'
9 'Royal Ruby'
9 'Royal Sovereign'
2 'Royal Splendour'
1 'Ruby Glow'
2 'Rutland Water'
1 'Santa Claus'
9 'Severn Queen'
0 'Shady Blue'
2 'Shanley'
9 'Sheila Hobson'
2 'Sheila Joy'
0 'Sherwood'
2 'Shining Knight'
0 'Shower of Stars'
0 'Showtime'
0 'Shy Look'
2 'Silver Jubilee'
1 'Simple Simon'
0 'Skyway'
0 'Slender Lady'
9 'Snowcap Variegated'
1 'Snowfall'
0 'Snowflake'
2 'Soldier of Fortune'
8 'Spangles'
2 ***splendens*** 'Karl Hartweg'
9 'Spotlight'
2 'Spring Bells'
9 'Steve Wright'
1 'Storm'
0 'Storm Petrel'
0 'Summer Mist'
0 'Summer Night'
2 'Summer Snow'
0 'Sundance'
2 'Sunny Jim'
0 'Susan Allen'
2 'Susan Young'
0 'Sweet Revenge'
2 'Tahiti'
9 'Ted's'
8 'Telegraph'
1 'Temple Bells'
0 'Tempo Doelo'
0 ***tetradactylla***
2 'The Observer'
0 'Thomos'
9 ***thymifolia thymifolia***
1 'Tillmouth Lass'
0 'Tina Head'
2 'Tolemac'
2 'Tom Silcock'
1 'Tommy Tucker'
0 'Topsin'
2 'Torotino'
9 'Tourtonne'
0 'Toven'
0 'Traviata'
9 'Tresco'
2 'Troutbeck'
0 'Trubell'
0 'Ultralight'
1 'Uncle Jinks'
1 'Valamay'
0 'Valerie Cotterell'
2 'Vera Stuart'
1 'Vi Whitehouse'
1 'Violet Lace'
2 'Violet Mist'
1 'Vivien Harris'
0 'W F C Kampionen'
0 'Waltraud Strumper'
0 'Walz Blaukous'
0 'Walz Bugel'
0 'Walz Doedelzak'
0 'Walz Gitaar'
0 'Walz Gong'
0 'Walz Hobo'
0 'Walz Kalebas'
0 'Walz Kattesnoor'
0 'Walz Meermin'
0 'Walz Piano'
0 'Walz Ratel'
0 'Walz Tam Tam'
0 'Walz Toeter'
0 'Walz Viool'
9 'Waveney Unique'
0 'Wee Lass'
2 'Wee One'
2 'Wendy Blythe'
0 'Wentelwieck'
2 'Westergeest'

0 'Whistling Rufus'
0 'White Falls'
8 'White Gem'
1 'White Haven'
1 'White Swan'
0 'Whiteknights Glister'
0 'Whiteknights Ruby'
8 'Wicked Lady'
9 'Wild Glove'
0 'Wilf Tolley'
1 'Willy Winky'
0 'Wilma Versloot'
9 'Winifred'
0 'Wise Choice'
2 'Woodnook'
0 'Yankee Clipper'
1 'Yolanda Franck'
0 'Zaanlander'

FURCRAEA
1 ***foetida***

GAHNIA
0 ***grandis***

GAILLARDIA
9 'Aurea'
7 'Bremen'
9 'Chloe'
9 'Fackelschein' ('Torchlight')
1 'Golden Queen'
2 x ***grandiflora*** 'Nana Nieske'
8 'Ipswich Beauty'
1 'Tokajer'

GALANTHUS
2 ***caucasicus*** late form
0 'Desdemona'
0 ***elwesii*** 'Whitallii'
2 'Lavinia' (d)
9 'Maidwell C'
2 'Melvillei'
2 ***plicatus*** 'Beth Chatto'

GALEGA
1 'Her Majesty'

GALIUM
2 ***firmum***

GALTONIA
9 ***princeps praecox***

GARDENIA
0 ***augusta*** 'Belmont'

GARRYA
0 ***laurifolia macrophylla***
2 x ***thuretii***

GAULTHERIA
9 ***cordifolia***
2 ***coriacea***
2 ***cumingiana***
2 ***depressa novae-zelandiae***
9 ***erecta***
2 ***mucronata angustifolia***
9 – 'Goldsworth Pink'
9 – 'Goldsworth Red'
0 ***procumbens*** 'Darthuizer'
2 ***semiinfera***
0 ***wardii***

GAYLUSSACIA
1 ***ursinum***

GAZANIA
8 ***rigens*** 'Torquay Silver'
1 'Vinner's Variegated'

GENISTA
8 ***berberidea***
0 ***falcata***
2 ***sericea***
2 ***tinctoria*** 'Golden Plate'

GENTIANA
2 ***acaulis*** 'A G Week's Form'
9 – 'Leith Vale'
8 – 'Nora Bradshaw'
2 ***affinis***
0 ***algida igarishii***
9 ***alpina*** Trotter's form
2 ***altaica***
2 ***angustifolia*** from Priin Mountains
2 – from Scoulor Pass
8 'Bucksburn Azure'
9 ***burseri***
2 ***clusii alba***
2 – ***corbariensis***
8 – 'Mount Rax'
8 ***cruciata phlogifolia***
2 ***dinarica*** 'Harlin'
2 ***divisa***
2 'Drumcairn White'
8 'Elizabeth Brand'
1 ***frigida***
0 'Inverdevon'
9 'Mount Everest'
9 ***occidentalis***
1 ***olivieri***
2 ***prolata*** Beer form
2 – forms
2 – McBeath form
2 ***przewalskii***
9 ***pyrenaica***
7 'Queen of the Blues'
0 ***sceptrum***
1 ***straminea***
7 'The Souter'
0 ***tianschanica***
1 'Tweeddale Strain'
9 'Utterby Seedling'
1 ***verna tergestina***
1 ***villosa***
1 'Wendy Jean'
9 ***wilsonii***

GENTIANOPSIS
0 ***crinita***

GEOGENANTHUS
0 ***undatus***

GERANIUM
2 ***caeruleatum***
8 x ***cantabrigiense*** 'Ingwersen'
9 – 'Ridsko'
2 ***dahuricum***
9 ***divaricatum***
1 ***drakensbergense***
9 ***himalayense*** 'Frances Perry'
1 x ***lindavicum***
1 – 'Alanah'
0 – 'Lissadel'
2 ***lingreum***
9 ***mascatense***
1 'Maxwelton'
0 ***napuligerum***
1 ***peloponnesiacum***
2 ***pratense*** x ***himalayense***
0 – pale mauve form
2 – 'Plenum Album'
9 ***sanguineum*** 'Hadspen'
2 ***viscosissimum viscosissimum***

GEUM
1 ***calthifolium***
2 – var. ***nipponicum***
1 ***elatum***
1 ***japonicum***
2 ***macrophyllum sachalinense***
9 ***rivale*** cream form
1 ***rossii***
7 ***triflorum campanulatum***

GIBASIS
9 ***linearis***

GLADIOLUS
7 'Ali Baba' (B)
2 'Andorra' (B)
2 'Anglia' (B)
9 'Blue Conqueror' (L)
2 'Campanella' (B)
0 ***cardinalis***
2 'Carmen' (L)
9 'Chanson'
9 'City Lights'
2 'Confetti' (B)
2 'Deciso' (L)
2 Dream Party ® (L)
1 'Dutch Parade' (L)
2 'Erin' (Min)
2 'Essex' (P/S)
2 'Friendship' (L)
2 'Greenland' (L)
1 'Gypsy Baron' (G)
9 ***imbricatus***
2 'Introspection' (L)
9 'Invitation'
1 ***italicus***
2 'Little Darling' (P)
2 ***longicollis***
2 'Lorena' (B)
1 Love Letter ® (M)
9 'Lovely Day' (G)
2 'Madonna' (L)
2 'Madrilene' (B)
9 'Merry'
2 'Misty Eye' (L)
2 'Pandion' (G)
2 'Piccolo' (B)
2 'Pink Lady' (L)
9 'Pink Pearl' (S)
1 Pink Perfection ® (L)
9 'Plum Tart' (L)
9 'Prosperity'
2 'Queen of Night' (L)
2 'Royal Beauty' (G)
2 'Royal Violet' (G)
2 Sancerre ® (B)
9 'Scout'
2 'Shamrock' (L)
9 'Shell Pink'
9 'Shocking Pink'
9 'Spring Gem'
2 'Storiette' (B)
2 Sundance ®
2 'Treasure' (P)
2 'Yellow Special' (P)

GLAUCIDIUM
0 ***palmatum leucanthum***

GLEDITSIA
2 ***triacanthos*** 'Bujotii'
2 – 'Shademaster'

GLOBULARIA
2 ***aphyllanthes***
7 ***vulgaris***

GNAPHALIUM
0 ***andicolum***

GOODENIA
9 ***lunata***
2 ***repens***

GOSSYPIUM
1 ***sturtianum***

GRAPTOPETALUM
1 ***paraguayense bernalense***

GRATIOLA
2 ***nana***

GREVILLEA
9 ***aspleniifolia*** 'Robin Hood'
9 – 'Robyn Gordon'
1 ***banksii forsteri***
1 ***bipinnatifida***
7 'Claret'
1 ***fasciculata***
7 ***jephcottii***
1 ***juniperina*** prostrate yellow form
8 ***lanigera***
1 ***pilulifera***
2 'Red Cloud'

GRISELINIA
2 ***littoralis*** 'Gold Edge' (v)
9 ***lucida*** 'Variegata'

GUICHENOTIA
2 ***ledifolia***
2 ***macrantha***

GUZMANIA
2 'Atilla'
2 Carine
2 'Claudine'
2 ***conifera***
2 ***donnellsmithii***
2 Gisela
2 'Golden King'
2 ***lingulata cardinalis***
2 – var. ***minor*** 'Red'
2 – – 'Vella'
2 Muriel
2 ***musaica***
2 'Nellie'
2 Rana
2 'Remembrance'
2 'Ruby'
2 ***scherzeriana***
2 ***wittmackii***

GYPSOPHILA
2 *repens* 'Monstrosa'

HAASTIA
7 *sinclairii*

HAEMANTHUS
0 *carneus*

HAKEA
0 *epiglottis*
2 *francisiana*
8 *macraeana*
2 *microcarpa*
8 *nitida*
8 *platysperma*
1 *stenocarpa*
8 *victoriae*

HALESIA
1 *parviflora*

HAMAMELIS
2 *vernalis*

HAPLOPAPPUS
9 *clementis*
1 *hirsutus*

HEBE
2 x *andersonii*
1 *armstrongii* x *selaginoïdes*
8 'Balfouriana'
8 'Barnettii'
2 'Boscawenii'
7 'Brian Kessell'
0 *buchananii* 'Major'
7 'Cilsouth'
1 'Croftway Emberglow'
2 *cupressoïdes* 'Glauca'
8 'Diamond'
9 *diosmifolia* 'Variegated'
8 'Ettrick Shepherd'
8 'Gillanders'
9 *giselli*
8 'Greenway Purple'
7 'Harlequin'
9 'Hartii'
8 'Kewensis'
1 'Lewisii'
2 'Lilac Haze'
8 'Lycing'
2 'Marlene'
7 'Obora Gold'
1 'Oratio Beauty'
2 *parviflora* (Vahl) Ckn. & Allan
7 *plano-petiolaris*
1 *propinqua* 'major'
2 *rupicola*
7 'Southcombe Pink'
1 *speciosa* 'Kapiti'
2 *stricta macroura* 'Cookiana'
0 *subsimilis*
8 *tetragona* 'Southcombe Dwarf'
8 *treadwellii*
7 'Wakehurst'
0 'Wendy'
7 'Widecombe'

HECTORELLA
8 *caespitosa*

HEDERA
0 *colchica* 'Dendroides'
0 *helix helix* 'Arrowhead'
0 – – 'Cavendishii Latina'
2 – – 'Finger Point'
1 – – 'Little Eve'
2 – – 'Minature Needlepoint'
0 – – 'Schimmer'
0 – – 'Sinclair Silverleaf'
0 – – 'Teena'
2 – – 'Victoria'

HEDYSARUM
0 *hedysaroïdes exaltatum*

HELENIUM
1 'Gartensonne'
2 'Rubinkuppel'
2 'Septemberfuchs'
8 'Tawny Dwarf'

HELIANTHEMUM
2 'Birch White'
7 'Cherry Pink'
0 'Cupreum'
2 'Fairy'
0 'Harlequin'
8 'Low Yellow'
0 'Loxbeare Gold'
8 *nummularium grandiflorum*
0 – ssp. *obscurum*
8 'Peach'
8 'Prima Donna'
7 'Rose Perfection'
8 Trenear's hybrids
8 'Wisley Yellow'

HELIANTHUS
0 *angustifolius*

HELICHRYSUM
1 *amorginum* 'Pink Bud'
1 – 'White Bud'
1 – 'Yellow Bud'
9 *bellidioïdes gracile*
9 *cooperi*
7 'Darwin Gold'
9 *dealbatum*
1 *diosmifolium*
8 *frigidum* 'Miffy Beauty'
8 *purpurascens*
9 *retortum*
0 *selaginoïdes*

HELIOPSIS
2 *helianthoïdes* 'Hohlspiegel '
8 – 'Mid West Dream'
1 – var. *scabra* 'Patula'
9 – – 'Sunburst'
2 – 'Sonnenschild'
2 – 'Spitzentänzerin'
1 – 'The Monarch'

HELIOTROPIUM
0 x *hybridum*

HELIPTERUM
9 *albicans*
1 *roseum*

HELLEBORUS
2 *argutifolius* large flowered
1 *dumetorum*
9 *foetidus* compact form
2 *multifidus* hybrids
2 *niger* 'Trotter's Form'
9 *orientalis* 'Amethyst'
1 – *antiquorum*
2 – 'Apple Blossom'
0 – 'Blowsy'
1 – 'Blue Showers'
0 – 'Blue Spray'
7 – 'Blue Wisp'
1 – 'Button'
1 – 'Citron'
9 – 'Cosmos'
2 – 'Darley Mill'
1 – 'Dawn'
9 – 'Dick Crandon'
7 – 'Dotty'
9 – 'Ernest Raithby'
2 – 'Freckleface'
9 – 'Garnet'
1 – 'Hazel Key'
9 – 'John Cross'
0 – 'Laura'
9 – 'Lynne'
8 – 'Mercury'
9 – 'Nocturne'
9 – 'Parrot'
9 – 'Peggy Ballard'
2 – 'Philip Wilson'
1 – 'Rembrandt'
1 – 'Richard Key'
9 – 'Rosa'
9 – 'Rossini'
0 – 'Rubens'
1 – 'Sarah Ballard'
1 – 'Saturn'
0 – 'Sylvia'
1 – 'Tom Wilson'
2 – 'Tommie'
0 – 'Upstart'
2 – 'Vulcan'
9 – 'Yellow Button'
9 x *sternii* dwarf form
0 *torquatus* ex Nero
1 – 'Pluto'

HEMEROCALLIS
8 'A la Mode'
8 'After Glow'
2 'Amazon Amethyst'
8 'Angel Face'
2 'Ann Kelley'
7 'Apollo'
8 'Applause'
1 'Apple Tart'
9 'Ariadne'
2 'Arkansas Post'
9 'Atlas'
9 'Atomic Age'
8 'August Pink'
1 'Ava Michelle'
2 'Avanti'
2 'Azor'
1 'Bald Eagle'
0 'Bees Rose'
8 'Belinda'
8 'Bellringer'
1 'Bitsy'
2 'Blaze of Fire'
8 'Bold Ruler'
8 'Bonnie Rose'
8 'Bourbon Prince'
8 'Bright Charm'
1 'Bright Spangles'
8 'Brilliant Red'
9 'Broad Ripples'
9 'Brunette'
1 'Buffy's Doll'
8 'Buried Treasure'
1 'By Myself'
2 'Cadence'
9 'Candle Glow'
8 'Candy Fluff'
8 'Capri'
8 'Carriage Trade'
7 'Chantilly Lace'
8 'Charlotte Holman'
1 'Chestnut Lane'
8 'Chetco'
1 'Chicago Cameo'
1 'Chicago Sugar Plum'
8 'Childscraft'
2 'Chorus Line'
9 'Christmas Isle'
9 'Claret Cup'
8 'Coquinna'
2 'Corsican Bandit'
2 'Cosmic Hummingbird'
2 'Crimson Icon'
7 'Cuddlesome'
1 'Curls'
8 'Dauntless'
8 'Dawn Supreme'
9 'Delft Rose'
2 'Delicate Splendor'
8 'Demure'
0 'Deva'
1 'Double Coffee'
0 'Double Firecracker'
2 'Double Grapette'
9 'Double Pleasure'
1 'Dutch Beauty'
8 'Dynamo'
2 'Edelweiss'
8 'Eden'
9 'Esther Murray'
1 'Fairy Delight'
8 'Far Afield'
2 'Far East'
2 'Fashion Model'
8 'Felicity'
8 'Finlandia'
8 'First Romance'
7 'Flair'
8 'Fond Caress'
8 'Fortyniner'
9 'Fox Grape'
8 'Gay Music'
8 'Georgia Peach'
2 'Gold Dust'
9 'Golden Dewdrop'
9 'Golden Glory'
8 'Goldensong'
8 'Grecian Gift'
2 'Green Puff'
1 'Hemlock'
8 'High Glory'
8 'High Time'
8 'Hippity Hop'
1 'Holiday Harvest'
0 'How About That'
8 'Illinois'
2 'Indian Serenade'
8 'Inlaid Gold'
8 'Irene Felix'
1 'Iron Gate Iceberg'

8 'Jack Frost'
9 'Jake Russell'
8 'Janet'
8 'Joan Durelle'
8 'July Gold'
8 'June Royalty'
1 'Kathleen Ormerod'
0 'Kathleen Woodbury'
2 'Kecia'
2 'Kelly's Girl'
2 'Kinfolk'
9 'King Haiglar'
1 'Late Advancement'
8 'Late Date'
8 'Laurel Anne'
8 'Lester Pastel'
7 'Lilac Chiffon'
7 'Lilly Dache'
2 'Littlest Angel'
9 'Lusty Leland'
9 'Mantra'
1 'Marcus Perry'
0 'Margaret Perry'
8 'Mary Anne'
9 'Mascot'
8 'Melotone'
1 'Michele Coe'
1 'Mikado'
2 'Ming Porcelain'
8 'Momento'
1 'Mormon Spider'
9 'Mrs B F Bonner'
9 'Multinomah'
8 'Nehoiden'
1 'Night Hawk'
2 'North Star'
8 'Northfield'
7 'Old Vintage'
1 'Ophir'
1 'Oriontio'
2 'Peach Supreme'
8 'Pecheron'
7 'Pink Perfection'
8 'Polar Bear'
8 'Powder Puff'
9 'Precious'
0 'President'
0 'Purple Water'
2 'Queen of May'
7 'Radiant'
8 'Rare China'
1 'Raspberry Pixie'
9 'Rose Motif'
8 'Rosetta'
8 'Roseway'
0 'Royal Robe'
2 'Ruffled Apricot'
8 'Satin Glass'
7 'Sawanne Belle'
7 'Sea Gypsy'
8 'Shell Cameo'
8 'Sherwood'
2 'Siloam Rose Dawn'
8 'Sleeping Beauty'
8 'Snappy Rhythm'
1 'Soft Whisper'
2 'Soledad'
9 'Star Ruby'
2 'Stoke Poges'
2 'Stolen Hours'
8 'Sweetheart Supreme'
9 'Taj Mahal'
8 'Temple Bells'
8 'Theresa Hall'
1 'Tinker Bell'
7 'Tiny Tex'
8 'Torpoint'
8 'War Clouds'
8 'Whir of Lace'
8 'Yellow Beacon'
2 'Zampa'

HEPATICA
1 ***nobilis*** 'Tabby'
2 ***transsilvanica*** 'Ada Scott'

HESPERIS
0 ***matronalis*** pink double form

HEUCHERA
7 'Damask'
8 'Edge Hill'
7 'Freedom'
9 ***glabra***
1 'Gloriana'
7 'Lady Romney'
8 'Pruhoniciana'
1 ***sanguinea*** dwarf form
0 – 'Superba'
8 – 'Variegata'
1 'Shere Variety'

HIBISCUS
1 ***diversifolius***
8 ***moscheutos palustris***
0 ***rosa-sinensis*** 'Colombo'

0 – 'Nairobi'
0 – 'Paramaibo'
0 – rose
9 ***sabdariffa***
9 ***syriacus*** 'Caeruleus Plenus'
1 – 'Dixie Belle'
2 – 'Hinomaru' (d)
2 – 'Totus Albus'
0 – 'Violet Clair'

HIERACIUM
1 ***mixtum***
8 x ***rubrum***

HIPPEASTRUM
1 'Amadeus'
1 'Bright Red'
1 'Cantate'
1 'Christmas Gift'
1 'Dark Red'
1 'Minerva'
1 'Orange Souvereign'
1 'Orange Star'
1 'Salmon Beauty'
1 'Star of Holland'
1 'Valentine'
1 'Wonderful'

HOHERIA
2 ***populnea*** 'Alba Variegata'
7 – ***sinclairii***

HOMOGYNE
1 ***alpina***

HOSTA
2 'Anne Arett' (v)
1 'Baby Blue' (x ***tardiana***)
1 'Besançon' (***ventricosa***)
1 'Blue Fan Dancer'
1 'Blue Piecrust'
1 'Claudia'
2 'Dark Victory'
2 'Emma Foster' (***montana***)
1 'Eric Smith Gold'
1 'Fond Hope' (***sieboldiana***)
1 'Freising'
2 'Gold Streak' (***tardiflora***)
2 'Granary Gold' (***fortunei***)
1 'Green Formal'
2 'Green Ripples'
1 'Grenfell's Greatest' (***sieboldiana***)
1 'Hadspen Dolphin' (x ***tardiana***)
2 'Hadspen Nymphaea'
2 'Helen Field Fischer' (***fortunei***)
1 'June Beauty' (***sieboldiana***)
2 'Leviathan'
1 'Little Fatty'
7 'Midwest Gold'
2 ***minor alba*** Maekawa
1 'Neat Splash' (v)
8 'Pixie Power'
2 'Primrose' (***kikutii***)
2 ***rohdeifolia aureomarginata***
1 'Royal Lady' (***sieboldii***)
1 'Royal Tiara' (***nakaiana***) (v)
2 'Sea Sprite' (v)
1 'Sentinels'
1 ***sieboldiana mira***
2 ***sieboldii spathulata***
2 – f. ***subcrocea***
1 'Sprengeri'
1 'Susy'
2 ***tardiva***
9 ***tsushimensis***
2 'Variegata' (***longissima***)
1 'Verte' (***sieboldii***)
1 'Viette's Yellow Edge' (***fortunei***) (v)
1 'Willy Nilly'
2 'Yakushima-mizu' (***gracillima***)
2 'Zager White Edge' (v)

HOUSTONIA
2 ***michauxii***
7 ***serpyllifolia***

HOWEA
9 ***belmoreana***

HUGUENINIA
9 ***tanacetifolia***

HUMULUS
1 ***lupulus*** variegated

HYACINTHELLA
0 ***leucophaea***

HYACINTHOÏDES
0 ***hispanica*** 'Rose'
2 ***italica vicentina***

HYACINTHUS
1 ***orientalis*** 'Blue Ice'
9 – 'Cote d'Azur'
9 – 'Eros'
1 – 'General Köhler' (d)
2 – 'Madame Sophie' (d)
2 – 'Tubergen's Scarlet'
9 – 'Yellow Hammer'

HYDRANGEA
9 ***arborescens discolor***
0 – ssp. ***radiata*** 'Robusta'
9 ***aspera*** 'Rosthornii'
2 ***heteromalla*** 'Morrey's Form'
2 – ***wilsonii***
2 'Impératrice Eugénie'
9 ***longipes***
1 ***macrophylla*** 'Adria'
9 – 'Covent Garden'
9 – 'Draps Pink' (H)
9 – 'Fargesii'
1 – 'Fischers Silberblou' (H)
2 – 'Gertrude Glahn' (H)
8 – 'Max Löbner'
8 – 'Mousseline' (H)
8 – 'Oamacha'
1 – 'Prinses Beatrix'
0 – 'Queen Elizabeth'
1 – 'Red Emperor' (H)
7 – 'Ursula'
7 – 'Val de Loire'
9 – 'Yodogawa'
1 ***paniculata*** 'Everest'
1 – 'Greenspire'
2 ***quercifolia*** 'Sike's Dwarf'
0 – sterile
2 – 'Tennessee Clone'
2 ***serrata koreana***
2 'Thomas Hogg'

HYDROCLEYS
1 ***nymphoïdes***

HYPERICUM
8 ***canariense***
2 ***cerastioïdes meuselianum***
2 'Eastleigh Gold'
8 ***hircinum albimontanum***
9 x ***inodorum*** 'Hysan'
9 – 'Summer's End'
1 ***nanum***
0 ***oblongifolium***
9 ***pallens***
1 ***patulum***
8 ***pulchrum procumbens***
9 'Summer Sunshine'
9 ***xylosteifolium***

HYPOCHAERIS
2 ***variegata***

HYPOLEPIS
2 ***rugulosa***

HYPOXIS
2 ***hirsuta***

HYPSELA
9 ***rivalis***

HYSSOPUS
0 *officinalis officinalis*

IBERIS
0 *sempervirens* 'Correifolia'
7 – 'Garrexiana'
8 – 'Gracilis'
7 – 'Zwergschneefloke' ('Snowdrift')

ILEX
7 x *altaclerensis* 'Balearica'
1 – 'Howick' (f)
9 – 'Maderensis'
1 – 'Moria' (f/v)
2 – 'Mundyi' (m)
2 – 'Purple Shaft' (f)
1 – 'W J Bean' (f)
1 *aquifolium* 'Angustimarginata Aurea' (m)
1 – 'Apricot' (f)
1 – 'Cookii' (f)
1 – 'Grandis'
1 – 'Green Sentinel' (f)
1 – 'Heterophylla Aurea Marginata' (m)
2 – 'Maderensis Variegata' (m)
7 – 'Ovata' (m)
1 – 'Weeping Golden Milkmaid' (f/v)
2 *buergeri*
0 *chinensis*
0 *corallina*
1 *crenata* 'Firefly' (m)
1 – var. *paludosa*
8 'Dazzler'
2 *dipyrena*
1 'Elegance' (f)
1 *glabra leucocarpa*
1 – 'Nana'
1 *integra*
0 – *leucoclada*
2 x *meserveae*
1 – 'Blue Stallion' (m)
1 *opaca* 'Natalie Webster' (f)
2 *pernyi* 'Jermyns Dwarf' (f)
2 *vomitoria*

IMPATIENS
2 'Ballerina'
2 'Cardinal Red'
2 'Evening Blush'
9 *glandulifera* white form
2 'Salmon Princess'
2 *scabrida*
2 'Strawberry Ripple'

INCARVILLEA
2 *mairei* pink form

INDIGOFERA
2 *australis*
9 *decora alba*

INULA
2 *candida*
9 *obtusifolia*
2 *rhizocephala rhizocephaloïdes*

IOCHROMA
1 *coeleste*
1 *purpurea*

IPHEION
1 *sellowianum*

IPOMOEA
0 *coccinea*

IPOMOPSIS
2 *aggregata*
2 – *macrosiphon*

IRIS
9 'Ablaze' (DB)
1 *acutiloba lineolata*
9 'Airy Fancy' (Spuria)
1 *albomarginata*
9 'Already' (MDB)
7 'Amber' (TB)
8 'Arab Chief' (TB)
2 'Astralite' (SDB)
0 'Autumn Primrose' (TB)
1 *babadagica*
1 'Ballerina'
2 'Barnett Anley'
9 *barnumae urmiensis*
9 'Belief' (Spuria)
9 'Bellboy' (MTB)
0 'Belvi Queen' (TB)
8 'Benton Yellow' (TB)
8 'Bibelot' (BB)
1 'Black Forest' (TB)
2 'Black Magic' (*sibirica*)
2 'Black Onyx' (TB)
0 'Blue Beret' (MDB)
1 'Blue Brilliant' (*sibirica*)
2 'Blue Frost' (DB)
2 'Blue Petticoat' (TB)
8 'Blue Valley' (TB)
1 'Bright Spring' (DB)
8 'Britomas' (TB)
9 'Bronze Charm' (TB)
2 'Brown Doll' (IB)
8 'Buster Brown' (DB)
0 'Butter Cookie' (IB)
9 'Calypso Clown' (AB)
1 'Camberley' (*sibirica*)
2 'Candy Apple' (SDB)
8 'Candy Cane' (BB)
2 'Cape Town' (TB)
2 'Cappucino' (CH)
0 'Catani' (SDB)
0 'Chain White' (SDB)
1 'Chione' (Aril)
1 'Christmas Rubies' (TB)
1 *chrysographes* yellow form
1 'Chubby Cherub' (MDB)
9 'Cinnamon Roll' (Spuria)
9 'Cinnamon Stick' (Spuria)
9 'Circlette' (SDB)
9 'City of Lincoln' (TB)
8 'Clotho' (Aril)
0 'Clouded Moon' (*sibirica*)
2 'Combo' (SDB)
9 'Confetti' (TB)
8 'Constance Meyer' (TB)
8 'Craithie' (TB)
2 'Crispette' (TB)
2 'Crystal Bright' (SDB)
1 'Dainty Belle' (MDB)
2 'Daisy Powell' (TB)
2 'Dark Fairy' (SDB)
2 'Dark Fury' (TB)
2 'Debra Jean' (TB)
2 'Doll Dress' (TB)
9 'Doll House' (MDB)
2 'Dotted Swiss'
9 *douglasiana* 'Apple Court White'
2 'Driftwood' (Spuria)
2 'Ecstatic Night' (TB)
2 'Egret Snow' (MDB)
2 'Ellen Manor' (TB)
2 'Elusive Quest' (IB)
2 'Emerald Fountain' (TB)
0 *ensata* aff. SEP 6
9 – 'Balathea'
9 – 'Buri-cho'
9 – 'Chidori'
9 – 'Chigesyo'
2 – 'Koko-no-iro'
2 – ruby form
1 'Eric the Red' (*sibirica*)
2 'Esther Fay' (TB)
0 'Ethel Hope' (Spuria)
1 'Fairy Footsteps' (SDB)
2 'Fantasy Faire' (TB)
2 'Fashion Show' (TB)
2 'Flirty Mary' (SDB)
2 'Foggy Dew' (TB)
0 'Fourfold White' (*sibirica*)
9 'Frenchii' (BB)
2 'Galillee' (TB)
2 'Gemini' (BB)
9 'Gentle Grace' (SDB)
1 *germanica* 'Kochii'
0 – 'Spartan'
2 'Gilston Guitar' (TB)
2 'Gingerbread Castle' (TB)
2 'Gleaming Gold' (SDB)
9 'Golden Chocolate' (Spuria)
2 'Golden Chord' (TB)
9 'Golden Glow' (TB)
2 'Golden Hind' (TB)
2 'Gosau' (TB)
8 'Grace Sturtevant' (TB)
2 'Gringo' (TB)
1 'Gudrun' (TB)
1 'Gypsy Eyes' (SDB)
2 'Gypsy Jewels' (TB)
8 'Gypsy Smoke' (IB)
1 *hartwegii columbiana*
8 *haynei*
2 'Helen Traubel' (TB)
8 *hermona*
8 'Hipermestra' (Aril)
1 *histrioïdes*
1 – 'Lady Beatrix Stanley'
2 'Honeydip' (SDB)
9 *hoogiana* 'Noblesse'
2 *hookeriana*
2 'Immortal Hour'
1 'Impelling' (BB)
0 'In the Buff' (IB)
0 *innominata* 'Alba'
1 'Instructor'
2 'Invisible Ink' (MDB)
1 'Iris King' (TB)
2 'Irish Lullaby' (TB)
0 'I'm Yellow' (SDB)
2 *japonica* 'Martyn Rix'
1 'Jill Welch' (MTB)
7 'Jirovette' (*sibirica*)
8 'Joanna' (TB)
2 'Joyce Terry' (TB)
2 'Just So' (SDB)
9 *korolkowii* 'Concolor'
2 'La Senda' (Spuria)
1 *laevigata* 'Monstrosa'
9 – 'Murakumo'
1 'Langport Kestrel' (IB)
2 'Lavanesque' (TB)
9 'Lavender Light' (*sibirica*)
1 'Lavender Ribbon'
1 'Lemon Charm' (SDB)
2 'Lemon Duet'
1 'Lemon Flame'
1 'Lighten Up' (SDB)
2 'Lilac Festival' (TB)
2 'Lima Colada' (SDB)
2 'Lime Ripples' (IB)
2 'Little Sheba' (AB)
9 'Little Swinger' (BB)
2 'Little Wonder' (IB)
8 'Llita' (TB)
2 'Los Angeles'
8 'Louvois' (TB)
2 'Lovely Letty' (TB)
1 *lutescens* 'Nancy Lindsay'
0 – white
1 'Mabel Cody' (*sibirica*)
2 'Mademoiselle Yvonne Pelletier' (TB)
2 *magnifica alba*
9 'Mariposa Tarde' (Spuria)
0 'Mary B' (MDB)
9 'Masked Ball' (TB)
2 'May Thirty-First' (SDB)
2 'Mill Pond' (MDB)
0 'Mini Plic' (MDB)
8 'Miss Underwood' (*sibirica*)
2 'Morning Sunlight' (TB)
7 'Mountain Lake' (*sibirica*)
1 'Mrs Perry' (*sibirica*)
2 'Murmuring Morn' (TB)
0 'Nancy's Khaki' (TB)
9 'Of Course' (IB)
8 'Oracle' (BB)
1 'Orangerie'
1 *orchioïdes*
1 *pamphylica*
1 'Panda' (MTB)
1 *paradoxa choschab*
1 *parvula*
1 'Pearl Queen' (*sibirica*)
9 'Pepper Mill' (SDB)
8 'Pink Charm' (TB)
2 'Playgirl' (TB)
9 *polakii*
2 'Primrose Drift' (TB)
2 'Princely' (TB)
0 'Princess of Love' (SDB)
1 *pseudacorus* 'Mandshurica'

2 'Pussycat' (MDB)
1 'Rainbow Rock'
2 'Raspberry Ripples' (TB)
8 'Real Gold' (AB)
2 'Red Atlast' (MDB)
2 'Red Rufus' (TB)
2 'Redwood Falls' (Spuria)
2 'Regal Splendour'
9 'Reuthe's Bronze' (CH)
2 'Revved Up' (IB)
9 'Ripe Wheat' (Spuria)
8 'Rippling Waters' (TB)
2 'Risque' (TB)
2 'Roanoke's Choice' (*sibirica*)
2 'Rumbling Thunder' (TB)
2 'Runaway' (IB)
9 'Sahara Sands' (Spuria)
2 'Saint Teresa' (IB)
2 'Saintbury' (SDB)
8 ***samariae***
1 × ***sambucina***
2 'San Leandro' (TB)
1 'Shawsii'
2 'Sherborne' (SDB)
8 'Silver Shower' (TB)
8 'Snow Princess' (*sibirica*)
0 'Southcombe Velvet'
0 'Sparkling Water' (TB)
2 'Spring Fern' (SDB)
9 'Spring Reverie (Spuria)
2 'Sterling Silver' (TB)
9 'Steve' (*sibirica*)
2 'Strawberry Sundae' (TB)
8 'Sugar Pie' (BB)
2 'Sunrise Point' (TB)
1 'Symphony' (Dutch)
2 'Tea Rose' (TB)
2 'Techny Chimes' (TB)
1 'Tender Tears' (SDB)
0 'Tetra-white Rose' (*sibirica*)
1 'The Gower'
1 'Thelma Perry' (*sibirica*)
8 'Three Oaks' (TB)
1 ***timowejewii***
2 'Ting-a-Ling' (MTB)
0 Tol-Long
1 'Triple Crown'
1 'Tulare' (BB)
9 'Turquoise Cup' (*sibirica*)
2 'Two Bits' (MTB)
2 'Ultrapoise' (TB)
1 'Velvet Toy' (MDB)
1 ***versicolor alba***
1 ***vicaria***
2 'Violet Bouquet' (MTB)
0 ***virginica***
9 'Wedgwood' (Dutch)
2 'Wigit' (IB)
2 'Wild Ginger' (TB)
2 ***willmottiana***
9 'Wine Wings' (*sibirica*)
2 'Winged Melody' (TB)
2 'Winkieland' (IB)
0 'Witch Doctor' (TB)
2 'Wyckhill' (SDB)
2 ***xiphium lusitanica***
2 'Yellow and White'
9 'Yellow Queen' (Dutch)

ISOPOGON
2 ***anethifolius***

JASIONE
8 ***laevis orbiculata***
9 ***tuberosa***

JASMINUM
1 ***dispermum***

JEFFERSONIA
2 ***dubia alba***

JOVIBARBA
2 ***heuffelii*** 'Blaze'
2 – 'Bolero'
2 – 'Brandaris'
0 – 'Cameo'
2 – 'Capricorn'
2 – 'Cinnabar'
2 – 'Cythera'
9 – var. ***glabra*** from Sapka
2 – 'Iason'
2 – 'Iobates'
2 – 'Mont Rose'
2 – 'Nannette'
2 – 'Passat'
2 – var. ***patens***
2 – 'Purple Light'
2 – 'Starlight'
2 – 'Sylvan Memory'
9 – 'Wotan'
0 – 'Xanthoheuff'
2 × ***kwediana*** 'Pickwick'
2 × ***nixonii*** 'Stefan'
2 × ***smithii*** 'Ritz'

JUANIA
0 ***australis***

JUANULLOA
1 ***mexicana***

JUNCUS
1 ***concinnus***
0 ***pusillus***

JUNIPERUS
0 ***chinensis*** 'Belvedere'
0 – 'Kuriwao Mist'
0 ***communis*** 'Edgbaston'
8 – 'Effusa'
7 – 'Gimborn'
2 – 'Hibernica Variegata'
7 – 'Inverleith'
9 – 'Nana Aurea'
0 – ***oblonga***
1 – 'Oblonga Pendula'
2 – 'Prostrata'
2 – 'Prostrata Nana'
2 – 'Repanda' Waddon clone
0 – 'Windsor Gem'
2 ***drupacea***
8 ***flaccida***
2 ***horizontalis*** 'Coast of Maine'
1 – 'Jade Spreader'
1 – 'Petraea'
1 – 'Prostrata'
0 – 'Schoodic Point'
9 × ***media*** 'Arctic'
1 – 'Gold Star'
1 – 'Mathot'
1 ***pinchotii***
9 ***sabina*** 'Knap Hill'
1 – 'Von Ehren'
0 ***salturaria***
1 ***scopulorum*** 'Blue Pyramid'
0 – 'Hillborn's Silver Globe'
8 – 'Lakewood Globe'
2 – 'Tolleson's Weeping'
0 ***silicicola***
8 ***squamata*** 'Blue Spreader'
7 – 'Forrestii'

JUSTICIA
1 ***plumbaginifolia***

KALANCHOË
2 ***blossfeldiana*** 'Annetta'
2 – 'Attraction'
2 – 'Bali'
2 – 'Beta'
2 – 'Calypso'
2 – 'Caprice'
2 – 'Charm'
2 – 'Cinnabar'
2 – 'Flores'
2 – 'Fortyniner'
2 – 'Inspiration'
2 – 'Lucky Island'
2 – 'Pollux'
2 – 'Regulus'
2 – 'Sensation'
2 – 'Sentosa'
2 – 'Seraya'
2 – 'Siam'
2 – 'Singapore'
2 – 'Yellow Nugget'
8 ***uniflora***

KECKIELLA
2 ***antirrhinoïdes***
1 – 'Microphylla'

KENNEDIA
0 ***beckxiana***
0 ***eximia***
2 ***prostrata***
0 – West Australian form
0 – West Coast form
0 ***rubicunda***

KERNERA
9 ***saxatilis***

KNIPHOFIA
2 'Apricot'
7 'David'
7 'Earliest of All'
2 ***elegans***
1 ***ensifolia***
9 'Firefly'
2 ***foliosa***
1 'H E Beale'
9 'Lye End'
2 'Nancy's Red'
9 'Ross Sunshine'
1 'Rougham Beauty'
8 'Saturn'
8 'Sunset'
8 'Timothy'
0 'Tubergeniana'
0 'Underway'

KOBRESIA
9 ***simpliciuscula***

KOELERIA
2 ***alpina***

KOHLERIA
2 'Linda'
1 'Longwood'

KUMMEROWIA
8 ***stipulacea***

KUNZEA
1 ***ambigua***
8 ***capitata***
1 ***ericifolia***
1 ***muelleri***
1 ***parvifolia***

LABICHEA
1 ***punctata***

LABLAB
1 ***purpureus***

LABURNUM
2 ***anagyroïdes*** 'Aureum'

LACCOSPADIX
2 ***australasica***

LACHENALIA
2 ***aloïdes*** 'Pearsonii'
0 ***arbuthnotiae***
0 ***bachmanii***
1 ***liliiflora***
2 ***orchioïdes glaucina***
9 ***unifolia***
9 'Violet Queen'

LACTUCA
0 ***macrantha***
1 ***sibirica***
8 ***tenerrima***
0 ***virosa***

LAGENOPHORA
9 ***pumila***

LAGERSTROEMIA
0 ***indica*** 'Berlingot Menthe'
1 – 'Little Chief'
1 – Petite Orchid ®
1 – Petite Red ®
1 – 'Watermelon'

LALLEMANTIA
2 ***canescens***

LAMARCKIA
2 ***aurea***

LAMIUM
2 'Alan Leslie'
2 ***garganicum*** 'Golden Carpet' (v)

LANTANA
2 ***camara*** 'Arlequin'
1 – 'Drap d'Or' ('Cloth of Gold')
0 – 'Miss Tibbs'
2 – 'Naide'
2 'Sunkiss'

LARIX
0 ***griffithiana***
2 ***kaempferi*** 'Blue Haze'

9 ***occidentalis***
2 ***principis-rupprechtii***

LATHYRUS
9 ***aphaca***
0 ***sativus caeruleus***

LAVANDULA
1 ***angustifolia*** 'Jackman's Dwarf'
7 – 'Nana Rosea'
8 – 'Norfolk'

LAVATERA
9 ***cretica***

LAWSONIA
1 ***inermis***

LEEA
0 ***rubra***

LEIOPHYLLUM
0 ***buxifolium hugeri***

LEONOTIS
2 'Staircase'

LEONTICE
2 ***leontopetalum***
1 – ***ewersmannii***

LEONTOPODIUM
1 ***discolor***
2 ***leontopodioïdes***

LEPECHINIA
1 ***chamaedryoïdes***

LEPTINELLA
2 ***albida***
2 ***goyenii***

LEPTODACTYLON
1 ***pungens***

LEPTOSPERMUM
1 ***arachnoïdes***
2 ***glaucescens***
2 ***liversidgei*** x ***scoparium***
8 ***micromyrtus***
1 ***minutifolium***
7 ***scoparium*** 'Big Red'
8 – 'Flore Pleno'
9 – 'Gaiety'
0 – Jervis Bay form
1 – 'Karekare'
7 – ***nanum*** 'Elizabeth Jane'
9 – – 'Ruru'
9 – 'Pink Pearl'
2 – 'Roland Bryce'
2 – 'Rosy Morn'
1 ***squarrosum***

LESPEDEZA
2 ***juncea***

LESQUERELLA
9 ***kingii sherwoodii***
1 ***multiceps***

LEUCANTHEMOPSIS
7 ***pallida spathulifolia***

LEUCANTHEMUM
0 x ***superbum*** 'Flore Pleno'
0 – 'Juno'
1 – 'Marion Collyer'
1 – 'Mayfield Giant'
9 – 'Moonlight'

LEUCOPOGON
9 ***collinus***

LEUCOSPERMUM
2 ***cordifolium*** yellow

LEUCOTHOË
0 ***keiskei*** 'Minor'

LEWISIA
8 'Chastity'
2 ***cotyledon cotyledon***
1 'Edithiae'
2 'Joyce Halley'
2 'Karen'
2 ***oppositifolia*** 'Richeyi'
2 ***rediviva*** pink form
1 ***stebbinsii***
2 'Susan'
2 ***tweedyi*** Mount Wenatchee form

LIATRIS
1 'Snow Queen'

LICUALA
0 ***spinosa***

LIGUSTRUM
2 ***japonicum*** 'Macrophyllum'
0 ***lucidum*** 'Macrophyllum'

LILIUM
1 'Achilles' (Ia)
2 'Amber Gold' (Ic)
1 ***amoenum*** (IX)
9 'Anne Boleyn' (Ia)
9 'Apricot' (Ia)
9 'Apricot Beauty' (Ib)
2 ***auratum*** 'Red Band'
9 Aurelian hybrids (VIIa)
2 'Beckwith Tiger' (Ic)
2 Bellmaid hybrids (IV)
2 'Bright Beauty' (Ia)
1 'Bull's Eye' (Ib)
1 Burgundy (Ic)
2 'Cambridge' (Ic)
8 ***concolor*** (IX)
2 'Connecticut Yankee' (Ic)
1 'Crimson Sun' (VIb)
9 'Damson' (VIa)
2 'Electric' (Ia)
9 'Escapade' (Ia)
2 'Esther' (Ia)
2 'Eurovision' (Ia)
2 'Genève' (Ia)
2 'Gold Medal' (Ia)
0 Golden Clarion (VIa)
2 'Hallmark' (Ic)
2 Imperial Crimson (VIIc)
0 x ***imperiale*** (VIa)
2 'Joanna' (Ia)
9 'John Dix' (Ib)
2 ***kelleyanum*** (IX)
0 'Langtry' (Ic)
1 ***lankongense*** (IX)
2 ***longiflorum*** 'Casa Rosa'
2 Mabel Violet (VIa)
9 'Magic Fire' (VId)
1 'Manuella' (Ia)
2 'Marilyn Monroe' (Ia)
1 ***martagon*** x ***hansonii*** (II)
2 'Maxwill' (Ic)
9 ***michiganense*** (IX)
0 Mid-Century Hybrids (Ia)
2 ***nanum flavidum*** (IX)
2 'Nell Gwyn'
1 'Orestes' (Ib)
1 'Pan' (Ic)
2 'Passat' (Ia)
2 ***philadelphicum*** (IX)
2 'Phoebus' (Ia)
2 Pink Pearl Trumpets (VIa)
2 'Pink Tiger' (Ib)
1 ***polyphyllum*** (IX)
2 'Prins Constantijn' (Ib)
1 'Purple Sensation' (Ia)
1 'Red Fox' (Ic)
0 ***regale*** yellow (IX)
2 'Rosepoint Lace' (Ic)
2 'Roter Cardinal' ('Red Knight') (Ia)
8 ***rubellum*** (IX)
2 'Sirocco' (Ia)
1 ***speciosum*** 'Twinkle' (IX)
9 'Staccato' (Ia)
2 'Sunset' (Ia)
2 'Tropicana' (Ia)
1 'Unique' (Ia)
9 'Vermilion Brilliant' (Ia)
1 'White Henryi' (VId)
2 'White Prince' (Ia)

LIMONIUM
7 ***chilwellii***

LINANTHUS
2 ***nuttallii***

LINARIA
0 ***anticaria***
2 x ***dominii***
7 ***lilacina***
1 ***maroccana*** 'Fairy Bouquet'
8 ***nobilis***
2 ***triornithophora*** cream form
1 ***tristis***
0 – ***lurida***
8 ***vulgaris*** 'Flore Pleno'

LINDELOFIA
1 ***spectabilis*** 'Hartington White'

LINDERA
8 ***praecox***
0 ***triloba***

LINUM
9 ***narbonense album***
0 ***perenne*** dwarf form
1 ***usitatissimum***

LIRIOPE
0 ***koreana***
2 ***muscari*** 'Paul Aden'

LITHOCARPUS
2 ***henryi***

LITHODORA
2 ***oleifolia*** 'Barker's Form'

LIVISTONA
0 ***rotundifolia***

LOASA
9 ***nana***

LOBELIA
2 ***alata***
9 ***angulata*** 'Tennyson'
9 ***begonifolia***
1 ***fulgens*** 'Illumination'
2 x ***gerardii*** 'Alba'
2 'Huntsman'
9 ***linnaeoïdes*** 'Dobson'
1 ***nicotinifolia***
9 ***pedunculata*** 'Tunnack'
0 ***physaloïdes***
8 ***puberula***
1 ***tenuior***
0 ***villosa***

LOISELEURIA
0 ***procumbens***

LOMATIA
1 ***myricoïdes*** glaucous form

LONICERA
2 ***acuminata***
7 ***alpigena***
0 ***discolor***
9 ***morrowii***
9 ***myrtillus***
8 ***nitida*** 'Hohenheimer Findling'
1 ***obovata***
2 ***tatarica*** 'Rosea'
7 ***trichosantha***
2 – var. ***deflexicalyx***
9 ***utahensis***

LOPHOMYRTUS
1 'Pinkalina'

LOTUS
2 ***pentaphyllus pentaphyllus***

LUCULIA
1 ***gratissima rosea***

LUDWIGIA
1 ***longifolia***
1 ***octovalvis***

LUMA
7 ***apiculata*** purple form

LUNARIA
0 ***annua*** purple stem

LUPINUS
2 ***albifrons collinus***
9 'Cherry Pie'
9 'Comet'
9 'Daydream'
0 'Freedom'
9 'Guardsman'
1 'Halina'
9 'Harlequin'
9 'Harvester'
0 ***hirsutissimus***
9 'Joy'

2 *lepidus*
9 'Lilac Time'
9 'Limelight'
0 *longifolius*
2 Mirakel hybrids
9 'Mystic Charm'
1 'Orangeade'
9 'Pat Baird'
2 *rivularis*
8 'Rougham Beuaty'
9 'Serenade'
0 *succulentus*
7 *texensis*

LUZULA
0 *banksiana*
1 *canariensis*
1 *celata* NZ Ohau
1 'Mount Dobson'
2 *sylvatica* 'Select'

X LYCENE
0 *kubotae*

LYCHNIS
0 *viscaria* 'Splendens Rosea'

LYCIUM
8 *pallidum*

LYCORIS
8 *radiata*
8 *squamigera*

LYONIA
9 *lucida*
1 *mariana*

LYTHRUM
1 *salicaria* 'Red Gem'

MACHAERANTHERA
9 *bigelovii*

MAGNOLIA
2 *campbellii* 'Darjeeling'
2 – 'Ethel Hillier'
7 – 'Visa'
2 *campbellii* Raffillii Group 'Princess Margaret'
2 – 'Wakehurst'
2 'Coral'
9 *dawsoniana* 'Caerhays'
2 *denudata* 'Purple Eye'
1 'Freeman'
2 'Glow'
0 *grandiflora* 'Edith Bogue'
0 – 'Rosemoor'
2 – 'Undulata'
2 x *highdownensis*
2 'Michael Rosse'
7 *nitida*
2 'Orchid'
1 'Pickard's Maime'
2 'Pickard's Opal'
1 'Pickard's Pearl'
1 x *proctoriana* 'Slavin's Snowy'
2 'Ruby'
7 x *soulangeana* 'Purple Dream'
1 – 'Rose Superb'
9 – 'Triumphans'
9 *sprengeri elongata*

X MAHOBERBERIS
2 *neubertii*

MAHONIA
2 *aquifolium* 'Donewell'
0 – dwarf form
2 'Cantab'
2 *higginsiae*
2 x *media* 'Arthur Menzies'
1 – 'Hope'
2 *napaulensis*
2 – 'Maharajah'
2 *repens* 'Rotundifolia'
0 x *wagneri*
2 – 'Hastings Elegant'
0 – 'Vicaryi'

MAIANTHEMUM
1 *bifolium* Yakushima form

MALPIGHIA
9 *glabra* 'Fairchild'

MALUS
1 'Coralburst'
2 *domestica* 'Bolingbroke Beauty' (D)
2 – 'Compact Mac'
2 – 'Compact Sue'
2 – 'Red Bramley' (C)
2 – 'Red Jonagold'
1 – 'Shortymac' (D)
9 'Elise Rathke'
0 *hupehensis rosea*
1 'Red Flash'
9 *sikkimensis*
9 *tschonoskii* 'Bonfire'
1 'Weeping Red Jade'
2 *yunnanensis veitchii*

MALVA
1 *sylvestris* 'Alba'
0 – 'Mest'

MALVASTRUM
7 *peruvianum*

MARANTA
0 *leuconeura massangeana*

MATRICARIA
1 *maritima*

MATTHIOLA
8 East Lothian
1 *fruticulosa*
1 *scapifera*

MAURANDYA
1 *erubescens* white form

MAYTENUS
2 *magellanica*

MAZUS
9 *miquelii*

MECONOPSIS
2 *betonicifolia* Harlow Carr strain
2 *horridula alba*
2 – Rudis Group
2 *latifolia*
2 *sherriffii*
0 'White Swan'

MEDICAGO
1 *falcata* 'Cambot'
9 *intertexta*

MELALEUCA
1 *biconvexa*
9 *citrina*
1 *coccinea*
1 *diosmatifolia*
1 *ericifolia*
1 – *nana*
1 *glaberrima*
9 *halmaturorum*
1 *lateritia*
1 *scabra*
1 *spathulata*
1 *striata*

MELIANTHUS
8 *comosus*

MELIOSMA
7 *cuneifolia*
2 *parviflora*
1 *pinnata oldhamii*

MENISPERMUM
7 *davuricum*

MENTHA
1 *angustifolia* 'Variegata'
2 x *piperita officinalis*

MERENDERA
1 *robusta*

MERTENSIA
8 *alpina*
2 *viridis*

METASEQUOIA
2 *glyptostroboïdes* 'Emerald Feathers'

METROSIDEROS
1 *kermadecensis* 'Radiant' (v)

MICHELIA
0 *champaca*
7 *maudiae*

MICROMERIA
0 *cristata*
2 *croatica*

MICROSERIS
1 *lanceolatus alpinus*

MILLIGANIA
8 *densiflora*

MIMOSA
2 *pudica*

MIMULUS
2 'Caribbean Cream'
9 'Fire King'
8 'Firedragon'
9 *minimus*
2 'Royal Velvet'
1 'Shep'
1 'Tigrinus Queen's Prize'
7 'Wildwood's'
8 'Yellow Velvet'

MINUARTIA
2 *imbricata*

2 *juniperina*
2 *kashmirica*
2 *laricifolia*
2 *recurva*
1 *verna caespitosa*

MISCANTHUS
1 *litoralis* 'Zuneigung'
2 *nepalensis*

MITELLA
9 *pentandra*

MONARDA
8 'Cerise Pink'
2 'Donnerwolke'
1 *russeliana*

MONARDELLA
2 *odoratissima*

MONSTERA
0 *obliqua*
0 – *expilata*

MONTIA
1 *chamissoi*

MORINA
9 *coulteriana*
1 *ramallyi*

MORUS
2 *alba* 'Nana'
1 *australis*

MUSA
1 *acuminata* (AAA Group) 'Dwarf Cavendish'

MUSCARI
1 *armeniacum* 'Cantab'
1 *bourgaei*
8 *parviflorum*

MUTISIA
2 *brachyantha*

MYOSOTIS
9 *alpestris*
8 – 'Nana'
9 *arvensis*
8 *azorica*
0 *forsteri*
2 *macrantha*
9 *petiolata*
7 *pulvinaris*
1 *pygmaea*
2 *saxosa*
2 *sylvatica*
9 *symphytifolia*
2 *uniflora*

MYOSURUS
9 *minimus*

MYRCEUGENIA
2 *exsucca*

MYRICA
2 *cerifera*

MYRICARIA
2 *germanica*

MYRIOPHYLLUM
2 *elatinoïdes*

NANDINA
0 ***domestica*** 'Little Princess'
9 – 'Umpqua Chief'

NARCISSUS
9 'Albacrest' (3)
9 'Aldringham' (2)
9 'Alray' (1)
9 'Andrew Marvell' (9)
9 'Ann Cameron' (2)
9 'April Message' (1)
9 'Arctic Flame' (2)
2 'Arragon' (2)
1 'Avalon' (2)
9 'Backchat' (6)
9 'Balalaika' (2)
9 'Ballyroan' (2)
9 'Bandolier' (2)
9 'Bar None' (1)
1 'Barnby Moor' (3)
9 'Ben Hee' (2)
9 'Ben Rinnes' (3)
2 'Big Cycla' (6)
9 'Birdalone' (2)
9 'Brave Adventure' (2)
9 'Bright Spark' (3)
0 'Brindisi' (2)
9 'Cairngorm' (2)
2 'Canasta' (11)
1 'Canford' (3)
9 'Capstan' (2)
9 'Caracas' (2)
9 'Carrara' (3)
9 'Carrickmannon' (2)
9 'Celtic Gold' (2)
2 'Charity Fair' (6)
2 'Chiloquin' (1)
9 'Citronita' (3)
9 'City Lights' (2)
9 'Colblanc' (11)
9 'Cold Overton' (2)
9 'Coral Ribbon' (2)
9 'Coylum' (3)
9 'Crater' (2)
2 'Curly' (2)
1 'Cushendun' (3)
1 'Cyclope' (1)
9 'Dalinda' (1)
9 'Dawncrest' (2)
9 'Debbie Rose' (2)
9 'Delightful' (3)
9 'Deseado' (1)
9 'Dorada Dawn' (2)
9 'Dress Circle' (3)
1 'Dulcie Joan' (2)
9 'Dumbleton' (1)
1 'Dunlambert' (2)
9 'Earlicheer' (4)
9 'Earthlight' (3)
9 'El Camino' (6)
9 'Elmley Castle' (1)
1 'Fairmaid' (3)
9 'Fiery Flame' (2)
0 'Fontmell' (1)
1 'Fortissimo' (2)
1 'Fourways' (3)
9 'Galahad' (1)
9 'Gambler's Gift' (2)
9 'Gay Record' (4)
9 'Gay Symphony' (4)
9 'Glandore' (2)
9 'Glenside' (2)
1 'Golden Rupee' (1)
1 'Golden Sand' (1)
1 'Green Peace' (3)
9 'Gunsynd' (2)
1 'Hartington' (2)
2 'High Church' (2)
9 'High Tower' (3)
1 'Hot Sun' (3)
1 'Ida May' (2)
1 'Irish Charm' (2)
9 'Irish Minstrel' (2)
9 'Irish Rover' (2)
9 'Ivory Crown' (2)
1 'Karelia' (1)
9 'Kelpie' (6)
9 'Kentucky Cardinal' (2)
1 'Ken's Favourite' (2)
9 'King's Ransom' (1)
9 'Kipling' (3)
9 'Knowehead' (2)
9 'Lancelot' (1)
9 'Leader' (2)
9 'Leonora' (3)
9 'LInnocence' (8)
1 'Lisbane' (3)
9 'Loch Brora' (2)
2 'Louise de Coligny' (2)
9 'Lucky Star' (3)
1 'Lysander' (2)
9 'Maid of Ulster' (2)
9 'Mandolin' (2)
9 'Matapan' (3)
9 'May Queen' (2)
9 'Milestone' (2)
9 'Mill Grove' (2)
0 'Mint Julep' (3)
2 'Mistral' (11)
9 'Modest Maiden' (2)
9 'Moonlight Sonata' (1)
9 'Mrs Ernst H Krelage' (1)
9 'Music Hall' (1)
9 'My Love' (2)
9 'Navarone' (1)
9 'Norval' (2)
9 'Ocean Spray' (7)
9 'Ohio' (2)
2 'Olympic Gold' (1)
9 'Owston Wood' (1)
9 'Papua' (4)
9 'Park Royal' (2)
9 'Parkdene' (2)
9 'Parkridge' (2)
1 'Pearly King' (1)
9 'Perky' (6)
9 'Pimm' (2)
9 'Polonaise' (2)
9 'Privateer' (3)
2 ***pseudonarcissus pallidiflorus***
9 'Queen of Spain' (10)
9 'Queensland' (2)
0 'Ramada' (2)
9 'Raspberry Ring' (2)
1 'Rathowen Flame' (2)
9 'Rathowen Gold' (1)
9 'Red Curtain' (1)
9 'Red Hot' (2)
9 'Red Mars' (2)
9 'Red Rum' (2)
1 'Revelry' (2)
9 'Revenge' (1)
9 'Rich Reward' (1)
1 'Richhill' (2)
9 'Right Royal' (2)
9 'Rimski' (2)
9 'Rimster' (2)
1 'Ringway' (3)
1 'Rose Noble' (2)
1 'Royal Oak' (1)
9 'Rubythroat' (2)
9 'Rutland Water' (2)
2 'Sabik' (2)
2 'Samba' (5)
9 'Santa Rosa' (2)
9 'Scarlet Thread' (3)
1 'Sea Dream' (3)
1 'Sea Princess' (3)
9 'Sealed Orders' (3)
9 'Sedate' (2)
9 'Shell Bay' (2)
9 'Silent Cheer' (3)
9 'Silent Morn' (3)
9 'Silversmith' (2)
9 'Sir Ivor' (1)
9 'Snow Magic' (3)
1 'Southgrove' (2)
9 'Spring Fashion' (2)
9 'Standfast' (1)
9 'Star War' (2)
9 'Suave' (3)
9 'Sunapee' (3)
2 'Sunlover' (2)
2 'Sweet Harmony' (2)
9 'Tara Rose' (2)
9 'The Prince' (2)
9 'Timandaw' (3)
1 'Tingford' (3)
1 'Tollymore' (2)
9 'Tomphubil' (2)
9 'Torch Bearer' (2)
9 'Touch of Silver' (2)
9 'Trelay' (3)
0 'Troon' (2)
2 'Troutbeck' (3)
2 'Tweedsmouth' (9)
9 'Verve' (2)
9 'Viennese Rose' (4)
2 'Vincent van Gogh' (1)
9 'White Prince' (1)
9 'Woodland Splendour' (3)
1 'Woodvale' (2)

NEMATANTHUS
1 'Bijou'

NEMOPANTHUS
8 ***mucronatus***

NEOLITSEA
0 ***caerulea***

NEOPAXIA
2 ***australasica*** 'Arthur'
2 – 'Lomond'

NEOREGELIA
2 ***carolinae*** Meyendorffii Group
2 – f. ***tricolor*** 'Perfecta' (v)
0 ***concentrica*** 'Plutonis'
9 ***cyanea***
2 Picta
0 ***spectabilis***
0 ***tristis***

NEPENTHES
1 ***alata*** × ***merrilliana***
1 – × ***ventricosa***
1 ***albomarginata***
1 ***ampullaria***
1 ***bicalcarata***
1 ***hirsuta***
1 ***leptochilia***
1 ***maxima***
1 ***merrilliana***
1 ***mirabilis***
1 ***rafflesiana***
1 – × ***ampullaria***
1 – ***gigantea***
1 ***reinwardtiana***
0 ***stenophylla***
1 – × ***reinwardtiana***
1 ***ventricosa***

NEPETA
1 ***floccosa***
0 'Valerie Finnis'

NEPHROLEPIS
2 ***cordifolia*** 'Plumosa'
2 ***exaltata***
2 – 'Whitmanii'

NERINE
2 'Hera'
1 'Joan'
0 'Lady de Walden'
2 'Lady Llewellyn'
0 'Miss France Clarke'
0 'Mrs Cooper'
0 'Mrs Dent Brocklehurst'
2 'Rushmere Star'

NICANDRA
9 ***physalodes violacea***

NICOTIANA
1 'Hopley's'
0 'Sissinghurst Green'

NIDULARIUM
0 ***billbergioïdes*** 'Flavum'
0 ***burchellii***
0 ***fulgens***
0 ***regelioïdes***

NOLANA
2 ***paradoxa***

NOMOCHARIS
1 × ***finlayorum***

NOTHOFAGUS
1 ***antarctica*** 'Benmore'

NYMPHAEA
2 'Chateau la Rouge'
2 'Emily Grant Hutchings' (T/N)
2 'Queen of the Whites' (H)
2 'Radiant Red' (T/D)

NYSSA
2 ***aquatica***
9 ***sylvatica*** 'Sheffield Park'

OENOTHERA
1 ***fruticosa*** 'Hoheslicht' ('Highlight')
9 – 'Sundrops'
2 – 'Youngii'

OLEARIA
2 ***bidwellii***
1 ***erubescens***
9 ***megalophylla***
9 ***minor***
9 ***phlogopappa*** 'Comber's Mauve'
1 ***viscosa***

OMPHALODES
1 ***cappadocica*** 'Bridget Bloom'
2 ***luciliae alba***
2 ***nitida***

OMPHALOGRAMMA
9 ***elegans***
7 ***minus***

ONONIS
7 ***crispa balearica***
2 ***fruticosa***

ONOPORDUM
1 ***acaule***

ONOSMA
2 ***albopilosa***
0 ***aucheriana***
1 ***pyramidalis***

OPHIOPOGON
2 ***japonicus*** 'Minor'
2 ***planiscapus*** green

OPITHANDRA
1 ***primuloïdes***

OREOBOLUS
8 ***pauciflorus***

ORIGANUM
2 x ***applei***
0 'French'
0 'Gold Splash'
2 ***minutiflorum***
9 'Roding'
2 ***scabrum pulchrum***
0 ***vulgare*** 'Curly Gold'

ORNITHOGALUM
2 ***sigmoïdeum***

OROSTACHYS
2 ***furusei***

ORYZOPSIS
2 ***hymenoïdes***

OSMANTHUS
1 ***delavayi*** 'Latifolius'
2 ***heterophyllus*** 'Myrtifolius'

OSMUNDA
1 ***regalis*** 'Gracilis'

OSTEOSPERMUM
1 'Cannington Sally'
0 'Croftway Whirlydots'
0 ***ecklonii*** x ***jucundum***
1 'Goulds'
8 'Lilac Beauty'
0 'Pink Whirls' low form
2 'Trailing Whirl'
1 'Valerie Finnis'

OSTROWSKIA
2 ***magnifica***

OTANTHUS
2 ***maritimus***

OTHONNA
7 ***coronopifolia***

OURISIA
9 ***breviflora***
8 ***macrocarpa***
9 ***racemosa***

OXALIS
2 ***enneaphylla*** 'Ruth Tweedie'
0 ***laciniata*** blue form
2 ***latifolia***
1 ***pes-caprae***
0 ***rubra***

OXYLOBIUM
0 ***parviflorum***

OXYTROPIS
2 ***adamsiana***
2 ***campestris***
2 ***lagopus***
2 ***lambertii***
2 ***splendens***
2 ***todomoshiriensis***
1 ***uralensis***

OZOTHAMNUS
2 ***selago*** 'Major'
2 – ***tumidus***

PAEONIA
9 ***anomala intermedia***
2 ***beresovskii***
2 ***californica***
9 ***chamaeleon***
0 ***clusii***
2 'Defender'
1 'Empress of India'
2 'Jenny'
0 ***lactiflora*** 'Amo-no-sode'
2 – 'Auten's Pride'
0 – 'Break o' Day'
0 – 'Carolina Moon'
0 – 'Charles' White'
0 – 'Cheddar Cheese'
2 – 'Dandy Dan'
0 – 'Do Tell'
0 – 'Emma Klehm'
0 – 'Fuji-no-mine'
8 – 'General Wolfe'
2 – 'Germaine Bigot'
0 – 'Gloriana'
0 – 'Glory Hallelujah'
0 – 'Grace Loomis'
0 – 'Honey Gold'
7 – 'James Kelway'
8 – 'Kestrel'
0 – 'King Midas'
0 – 'La France'
0 – 'Lake of Silver'
0 – 'Largo'
2 – 'Louis Barthelot'
2 – 'Madame Jules Dessert'
2 – 'Madame Lemoine'
0 – 'Marguérite Gerard'
0 – 'Marietta Sisson'
0 – 'Mary Brand'
2 – 'Matilda Lewis'
1 – 'Minnie Shaylor'
0 – 'Mister Ed'
9 – 'Moon River'
0 – 'Moonglow'
0 – 'Mr Thim'
2 – 'Mrs F J Hemerik'
0 – 'Mrs J V Edlund'
0 – 'My Pal Rudy'
1 – 'Nancy Nicholls'
0 – 'Nice Gal'
1 – 'Nymph'
0 – 'Philippe Rivoire'
9 – 'President Wilson'
1 – 'Snow Mountain'
0 – 'Souvenir d'A Millet'
0 – 'The Moor'
0 – 'Thérèse'
0 – 'Toro-no-maki'
0 – 'Victoria'
0 – 'Wilbur Wright'
1 – 'Zuzu'
2 'Laddie'
2 x ***lemoinei*** 'Alice Harding' (S)
1 ***suffruticosa*** 'Gosho-zakura' ('Cherries of Imperial Palace') (S)
1 – 'Kaoh' (S)
1 – 'No-kagura' ('Knight's Dance') (S)
1 – 'Yatsu-kazishi' (S)
0 ***tenuifolia*** 'Plena'
2 ***wittmanniana wittmanniana***

PALIURUS
0 ***ramosissimus***
2 ***spina-christi***

PANDANUS
0 ***veitchii***

PANICUM
2 ***virgatum*** 'Rotstrahlbusch'

PAPAVER
7 ***aprokinomenton***
2 ***corona-sancti-stephani***
1 ***dubium***
2 ***fauriei***
2 ***kluanense***
7 ***kwanense***
2 ***lateritium***
7 ***nudicaule*** Meadhome Strain
1 ***orientale*** 'Constance Finnis'
0 – 'Lavender Girl'
9 – 'Lighthouse'
2 – 'Mrs George Stobart'
7 – 'Salome'
7 – 'Snowflame'
7 – 'Stormtorch' ('Sturmfackel')
0 ***pyrenaicum degenii***
2 ***radicatum***
0 ***rhoeas*** 'Whispering Fairies Group'
2 ***sendtneri***
1 ***suaveolens***
9 ***thianschanicum***

PARAHEBE
2 x ***bidwillii*** 'Rose Hybrid'
1 ***birleyi***
2 ***catarractae*** dwarf form
1 – 'Tiny Tot'
0 ***hookeriana compacta***

PARONYCHIA
8 ***cephalotes***

PARROTIA
1 ***persica*** 'Prostrata'

PARTHENOCISSUS
8 ***inserta***

PASSIFLORA
2 ***bryonioïdes***
2 ***caerulea rosea***
2 x ***caponii*** 'John Innes'
2 ***cinnabarina***
2 ***cirrhiflora***
2 x ***decaisneana*** 'Innesii'
2 ***edulis*** 'Alice'
2 'Hartwiesiana'
2 ***helleri***
2 ***rubra*** forms
8 x ***tresederi*** 'Lilac Lady'
2 ***trifoliata***
2 ***truxillensis***
1 'Wilcrowl'

PECTEILIS
2 ***radiata***

PELARGONIUM
1 'Ada Sutcliffe' (Min)
2 'Aida' (R)
1 'Ainsdale Beauty' (Z)
1 'Ainsdale Eyeful' (Z)
1 'Ainsdale Happiness' (Z/ d)
1 'Ainsdale Sixty' (Z)
2 Alba ® (Z/ d)
1 'Alex Kitson' (Z)
2 'Alison Jill' (Z/ d)
2 'Always' (Z/ d)
1 'Amour' (R)
2 'Andenken an Emil Eschbach' (I/ d)
9 'Annette Kellerman' (Z)
2 'Aquarell' (R)
0 'Autumn Haze' (R)
2 'Avenida' (Z)
2 'Baby Snooks' (A)
2 'Barbara Rice' (Z/ d)
1 Barock ® (I)
2 'Beau Geste' (R)
2 'Belvedere' (R)
2 'Bengal Fire' (Z/ C)
2 'Blackcurrant Sundae'
2 'Blossomtime' (Z/ d)
1 'Blushing Emma' (Z)
1 'Bodey's Picotee' (R)
1 'Bold Romance' (Z)
9 'Bold Sunrise' (Z)
0 'Bovey Beauty'
2 'Brick Giant'
2 'Brilliant' (Dec)
1 'Brookside Betty' (Dw/ C/ d)
1 'Brookside Bolero' (Z)
1 'Brookside Jupiter' (Z)
1 'Brookside Serenade' (Z)

1 Brun ® (Z)
1 'Burge' (R)
0 'Cardinal Pink' (Z/ d)
2 'Carefree' (U)
1 'Carol Ann' (Z)
1 'Carol Cooper' (Fr/ d)
2 'Carole Munroe' (Z/ d)
2 'Carol's Treasure' (Z/ C)
2 'Carousel' (Z/ d)
0 'Cézanne' (I/ d)
1 Champagne ® (Z)
1 'Chang' (Z)
9 'Clown' (R)
0 'Copper Flair' (Z/ C)
1 'Coral Island' (Z/ d)
2 'Coronia' (Z/ Ca)
0 'Corot' (I/ d)
2 'County Girl' (Z)
2 'Creed's Seedling' (Z/ C)
1 ***crispum*** 'Minor'
2 'Dame Anna Neagle' (Dw/ d)
2 'Danielle' (Z)
2 'Dark Lady' (Sc)
0 'David Gamble' (Z)
2 'Delilah' (Z)
0 'Desert Dawn' (Z/ C)
1 'Diana Palmer' (Z/ d)
1 'Dibbinsdale' (Z)
0 'Double Skies of Italy' (Z/ C/ d)
2 'Duke of Devonshire' (Z/ d)
1 'Earl of Chester' (Min/ d)
1 'Earth Magic' (Z/ v)
1 'Edgar Chisnall' (Z)
2 'Elizabeth Iris' (Dw)
0 'Emily De Sylva' (I/ d)
0 'Fabel' (Z)
1 'Faircop' (Sc)
1 'Fandango' (Z/ St/ d)
2 'Feuerriese' (Z)
2 'Fire Cascade' (I)
2 'Firebrand' (Z/ d)
1 'First Love' (Z)
2 'Flamboyant' (I/ d)
2 Flirtpel ® (Z/ d)
2 'Fortuna' (Z)
1 Fortuna ® (Z)
9 'Fraulein Gruss' (R)
2 'Freckles' (Z/ d)
1 'Friesian Beauty' (Z)
0 'Frosty Petit Pierre'
2 'Gallant' (Z/ d)
9 'Gaudy' (Z)
2 'Gemstone' (Sc)
2 'Gilda' (Z)
2 'Gladys Washbrooke' (Z/ d)
2 'Gleam' (Z/ d)
2 'Glen' (Z/ d)
2 'Glenys Carey' (Z/ d)
2 'Gloria' (Z/ d)
1 'Golden Magaluf' (I/ d/ C/ v)
1 'Golden Mirage' (Z/ v)
2 'Golden Mist' (Dw/ C/ d)
1 'Gottweig' (Z)
1 'Grasmere Beauty' (Z)
0 'Great Blakenham' (Min)
1 'Greetings' (Min/ v)
2 'Grenche Belle' (I/ d)
2 'Grollie's Cream'
1 'Guernsey'
2 'Hans Rigler' (Z/ d)
2 'Harlequin Hilda Day' (I)
0 'Harvest Moon' (Z)
1 'Hayley Clover'
1 'Hazel Blake' (R)
1 'Hazel Candy' (R)
1 'Hazel Dream' (R)
1 'Hazel Fire' (R)
1 'Hazel Orchid' (R)
1 'Hazel Peach' (R)
1 'Hazel Saga' (R)
0 'Hazel White' (R)
1 'Henri Joignot' (Z/ C/ d)
2 'Henry's Rose' (Z/ C)
1 'High Glow' (R)
2 'Highfields Ballerina' (Z/ d)
2 'Highfields Cameo (Z/ d)
2 'Highfields Candy Floss' (Z/ d)
2 'Highfields Charisma' (Z/ d)
2 'Highfields Concerto' (Z)
9 'Highfields Dazzler' (Z)
2 'Highfields Delight' (Z)
2 'Highfields Fashion' (Z)
0 'Highfields Fiesta' (Z)
2 'Highfields Flair' (Z/ d)
2 'Highfields Flash' (Z/ d)
9 'Highfields Glory' (Z)
9 'Highfields Glow' (Z/ d)
2 'Highfields Harmony' (Z)
2 'Highfields Jazz' (Z/ d)
2 'Highfields Orange' (Z)
2 'Highfields Pearl' (Z)
2 'Highfields Peerless' (Z)
2 'Highfields Perfecta' (Z)
2 'Highfields Pink' (Z)
2 'Highfields Progress' (Z)
2 'Highfields Romance' (Z)
2 'Highfields Salmon' (Z/ d)
2 'Highfields Sensation' (Z)
2 'Highfields Serenade' (Z)
2 'Highfields Sonata' (Z/ d)
0 'Highfields Supreme' (Z)
2 'Highfields Symphony' (Z)
2 'Highfields Vogue' (Z)
1 'Honeywood Hannah' (R)
1 'Honeywood Jonathan' (R)
1 'Honeywood Margaret' (R)
2 'Hula' (U)
2 'Improved Goertz'
2 'Improved Rubin' (Z/ d)
2 'Ione' (Z/ d)
2 'Irene Hardy' (Z/ d)
2 'Isaac Middleton' (Z)
2 'Jack Cox' (Dw/ d)
2 'Jack of Hearts' (I)
1 'Jack Wood' (Z/ d)
9 'Janet Hofman' (Z/ d)
2 'Jean Beatty' (Dw/ d)
2 'Jean Viaud' (Z/ d)
1 'Jim Small' (Z/ C)
2 'Jim's Delight' (Z/ C)
2 'John's Dilys'
2 'John's Pride'
2 'Joseph Haydn' (R)
1 'Joy Thorp' (I)
2 'Joyden'
9 'Joyrider' (Z/ d)
2 'Judith Thorp' (R)
2 'Juniper' (Sc)
2 'Karen Gamble Improved' (Z)
2 'Kathleen Gamble Improved' (Z)
0 'Katina' (Z)
2 'Keith Vernon' (Fr/ d)
9 'Kelly's Eye' (Z/ C)
9 'Kelvendon Wonder' (Min)
1 'Lady Mavis Pilkington' (Z/ d)
1 'Lanham Royal' (Min/ d)
2 'Lara Jester' (Sc)
2 'Lara Nomad' (Sc)
2 'Lara Starshine' (Sc)
0 'Lee Gamble' (Z)
1 'Legende' (R)
2 'Lerchenmuller' (Z/ d)
1 'Lesando' (Z)
0 'Lesley Kefford' (Z)
1 'Lilac Gemma' (R)
2 'Lilian Woodberry' (Z)
1 'Little Dandy'
1 'Loveliness' (Z)
0 'Lyrik' (Z/ d)
2 'Madame Irene' (Z/ d)
1 'Madeline Crozy'
2 'Mandarin' (Z)
9 'Mary Screen' (Min)
0 'May Rushbrook' (Z)
1 'Meill Jamison' (Min)
2 'Memories' (Z/ d)
1 'Mere Casino' (Z)
9 'Mere Ripon' (R)
1 'Mere Seville' (Z)
2 'Mickey' (R)
2 'Mikado' (R)
0 'Milka' (R)
1 'Mill Wine' (I/ d)
1 'Mrs Margaret Thorp' (R)
1 'Mrs Mayne'
1 'Mutzel' (I/ v)
2 'My Choice' (R)
2 'Mystery' (U)
0 'Nanette' (Z)
2 'Orange' (Z/ St)
2 'Orange Fizz' (Z/ d)
1 'Ostergruss' (R)
0 'Otley Slam' (R)
0 'Our Jim' (Z)
1 'Paisley Red' (Z/ d)
9 'Pam Screen'
1 'Partisan' (R)
0 'Pearl Necklace' (Z/ d)
1 Pearl Necklace ® (Z)
1 'Petronella' (Z/ d)
0 'Phyllis Variegated'
2 'Picardy' (Z/ d)
1 'Pier Head' (Z)
2 'Pink Aurore' (U)
2 'Pink Cloud' (Z/ d)
1 'Pink Delight' (Z/ d)
1 'Pink Floral Cascade' (Fr/ d)
2 'Pink Lady' (Z)
1 'Pink Lady Harold' (Z)
1 'Pink Pandora' (T)
0 'Poetic' (Z)
2 'Polka' (U)
2 Polka ® (Z/ d)
2 'Portsmouth' (R)
2 Prelude ® (Z)
1 'Radio' (Z/ d)
1 'Rads Star' (Z/ St)
1 'Ragamuffin' (Min/ d)
2 'Raola Lemon'
2 'Rebecca' (R)
2 'Red Capri' (Sc)
9 'Red Doll'
2 'Red Dollar' (Z/ C)
0 'Red Grande' (I)
1 'Red Ice' (Z)
0 'Red Patricia Andrea' (T)
2 'Red Star' (Z)
1 'Ric-Rac'
2 Rio ® (Z)
0 'Robin Hood' (Dw/ d)
1 'Roi des Balcons Rouge' (I)
2 'Roller's David' (I)
2 Romy ® (I)
0 'Ron' (R)
0 'Ron's Delight' (R)
2 Rosais ® (I/ d)
1 'Rose Lady Lexington' (I/ v)
0 'Rose Star' (Z/ d)
2 'Rose Startel' (Z/ St)
1 Rospen ® (Z)
1 'Rouge' (R)
9 'Royal Pageant'
2 'Royal Sovereign' (Z/ d/ v)
1 'Ruben' (I/ d)
1 'Rubin' (Z/ d)
2 'Ruth Bessley'
2 'Sabrina' (Z/ d)
0 'Salmon Kovalevski' (Z)
2 'Salmon Satifaction' (Z)
2 x ***salmoneum***
1 'Sarkie' (Z/ d)
2 'Scarlet Galilee' (I/ d)
2 Schöne Helena ® (Z/ d)
2 'Schwarzwalderin' (I)
0 'Sea Mist' (Min)
2 'Senorita' (R)
2 'Serenade' (Z/ d)
2 'Shrubland Rose' (Sc)
2 'Silipen' (Z/ d)
0 'Silver Monarch'
2 'Silvia' (R)
2 'Simon Portas' (I/ d)
2 'Simplicity' (Z)
9 'Single New Life' (Z)
1 'Southampton' (Z)
9 'Spray Paint' (Min)
2 'Star of Persia' (Z/ Ca)
0 'Stellar Pixie Rose' (St)
0 'Stellar Red Devil' (Z/ St/ d)
9 'Stellar Snowflake' (Z/ St)

2 'Stuart Gamble' (Z/ d)
9 'Sugar Plum Fairy' (I)
1 'Summer Idyll'
1 'Sunday's Child'
1 'Sundridge Moonlight' (Z/ C)
1 'Sundridge Surprise' (Z)
2 'Sunset' (Z)
0 'Suntrap' (Z/ C)
2 'Susan Jane' (Z/ d)
2 'Susie' (Z/ C)
1 'Swan Song' (Z)
1 'Sweet Miriam' (Sc)
2 'Swing' (Z)
1 'The Mary Rose' (R)
0 'Treasure' (Z/ d)
0 'Treasure Trove' (Z/ v)
0 'Twist' (Z)
2 Twist ® (Z/ I)
2 'Valerie' (Z/ d)
1 'Variegated Oak' (Sc/ v)
0 'Velley Court' (I/ v)
1 Velvet ® (I)
1 'Vera Vernon' (Z/ v)
1 'Victoria' (Z/ d)
2 'Volcano' (Z)
2 'Wallace Fairman' (R)
1 'Wallace's Pink' (Fr)
1 Waltz ® (Z)
2 'Wedding Royale' (Dw/ d)
1 'Wembley Gem' (Z)
0 'Whistling Dancer' (Z/ C)
0 'White Startel' (Z)
2 'Winford Festival'
1 'Wirral Cascade' (Fr/ d)
1 'Wirral Target' (Z/ d)
0 'Zoe Washbrooke' (Z/ d)

PENNISETUM
2 ***alopecuroïdes*** 'Weserbergland'

PENSTEMON
1 ***acaulis***
2 ***albertinus***
2 ***caryi***
8 'Claret'
2 ***comarrhenus***
1 ***compactus***
0 ***crandallii***
0 ***digitalis nanus***
1 ***dissectus***
8 'Eva'
2 'Fairy Bouquet'
1 ***federici-augusti***
2 ***fruticosus scouleri*** f. ***roseus***
2 – – 'Amethyst'
8 – – 'Boulder'
8 'Greencourt Purple'
9 ***grinnellii***
2 ***harvardii***
9 ***hirsutus*** 'Darnley Violet'
2 ***humilis*** 'Albus'
1 ***impressus***
2 ***labrosus***
2 ***lanceolatus***
1 ***laricifolius***
2 – ssp. ***exilifolius***
1 ***leonardii***
0 'Lilactime'
8 ***mexicanus***
2 ***mucronatus***
2 ***newberryi berryi***
8 'Newbury Gem'
2 ***nitidus***
2 ***pachyphyllus***
2 ***parryi***
2 ***paysoniorum***
2 ***procerus procerus***
2 ***pseudospectabilis***
2 'Rajah'
2 'Red Knight Number 2'
2 ***rubicundus***
2 ***speciosus***
1 – ssp. ***kennedyi***
2 ***stenophyllus***
0 ***strictus*** 'Bandera'
2 ***subulatus***
2 ***thurberi***
2 ***traceyi***
2 ***virens*** pale blue
1 ***virgatus asa-grayi***
8 'Waterloo'
2 ***whippleanus*** dark form

PENTAS
0 ***lanceolata*** 'Kermesina'
0 – 'Quartiniana'

PEPEROMIA
2 ***caperata*** 'Luna'
2 ***columbiana***
2 – 'Carnival'
2 ***deppeana***
0 ***fraseri***
2 'Green Valley'
2 ***maculosa***
2 ***miqueliana***
0 ***obtusifolia*** 'Variegata'
2 ***obtusifolia*** Magnoliifolia Group
2 'Pauline'
2 ***pereskiifolia***
2 ***puteolata***
2 ***rubella***
2 'Teresa'
2 'Tine'
2 ***tristachya***

PEREZIA
1 ***linearis***

PERIPLOCA
8 ***sepium***

PERSEA
0 ***thunbergii***

PERSICARIA
9 ***affinis*** 'George Taylor'
0 ***amplexicaulis oxyphylla***
1 ***emodi*** 'George Taylor'
7 ***mollis***

PETASITES
1 ***japonicus***

PETROCOSMEA
2 ***kerrii***

PETROMARULA
0 ***pinnata***

PETROPHYTUM
2 ***cinerascens***

PHILADELPHUS
1 ***argyrocalyx***
2 'Atlas'
7 'Burkwoodii'
0 ***coronarius*** Threave form
9 'Etoile Rose'
2 'Falconeri'
2 x ***lemoinei*** 'Lemoinei'
0 ***microphyllus*** 'Superbus'
0 'Mrs Reid'
7 'Norma'
1 'Pentagon'
9 ***pubescens***
0 ***purpurascens***
1 x ***purpureomaculatus***
1 ***satsumi***
9 ***schrenkii***
0 ***sericanthus***
2 'Snowbelle'
2 ***tenuifolius***

PHILLYREA
2 ***angustifolia rosmarinifolia***

PHILODENDRON
0 ***bipennifolium*** 'Variegatum'
0 ***ilsemannii***
0 ***imbe*** 'Variegatum'
0 ***ornatum***
0 'Painted Lady'

PHLEUM
9 ***alpinum***

PHLOMIS
1 ***orientalis***
2 ***rigida***

PHLOX
8 'Boris'
0 'Chequers'
0 ***diffusa***
0 – 'Octopus'
0 ***douglasii*** 'Petra'
1 – 'Star Dust'
1 'Geddington Cross'
2 ***hoodii glabra***
2 ***kelseyi***
9 'Lee Raden'
0 ***missoulensis***
8 'Moonlight'
1 ***nana*** 'Lilacina'
1 ***ovata***
7 ***paniculata*** 'Ann'
2 – 'Anthony Six'
2 – 'Blue Mist'
0 – 'Blue Moon'
1 – 'Buccaneer'
9 – 'Denny'
0 – 'Eclaireur'
2 – 'Frau Antonin Buchner'
7 – 'Glow'
1 – 'Inspiration'
0 – 'Jules Sandeau'
0 – 'Little Lovely'
1 – 'Pink Gown'
7 – 'Scheerausch'
9 – 'Silver Salmon'
1 – 'Snowball'
1 – 'The King'
8 'Snowflake'
9 ***stolonifera*** 'Pink Ridge'
0 ***subulata*** 'Brilliant'
7 – 'Jill Alexander'
2 – 'Kimono'
7 – 'Pink Delight'
0 – pink seedling
0 – 'White Drift'

PHOENIX
2 ***reclinata***
9 ***rupicola***

PHORMIUM
1 'Burgundy'
1 ***tenax*** 'Veitchianum' (v)
0 'Tom Thumb'

PHOTINIA
0 ***lasiogyna*** Hangzhou 11818
0 ***villosa longipes***

PHRAGMITES
2 ***australis altissimus***

PHYLICA
0 ***ericoïdes***

PHYLLOSTACHYS
8 ***bambusoïdes*** 'Kronberg'
8 ***edulis subconvexa***
7 ***elegans***

PHYSALIS
2 ***peruviana***

PHYSARIA
0 ***alpina***
1 ***bellii***
2 ***chambersii***
1 ***didymocarpa***
1 ***vitulifera***

PHYTEUMA
2 ***globulariifolium***
9 ***ovatum***

PICEA
7 ***abies*** 'Gregoryana Parsonsii'
2 – 'Humilis'
0 – 'Mariae Orffiae'
0 – 'Pseudoprostrata'
2 – 'Rubrospicata'
0 ***glauca*** 'Densata'
2 – 'Elf'
2 ***glehnii***
0 ***mariana*** 'Beissneri'
1 ***morrisonicola***
1 ***omorika*** 'Glauca'
1 – 'Gnom'
2 ***orientalis*** 'Skylands Prostrate'
9 ***pungens*** 'Compacta'
2 – 'Pendula'
2 – 'Rovellis Monument'
1 – 'Schovenhorst'
2 – 'Spek'
1 ***schrenkiana tianschanica***
2 ***spinulosa***
2 ***wilsonii***

PIERIS
2 ***floribunda*** 'Elongata'

2 *formosa forrestii* 'Ball of Fire'
0 *japonica* 'Crispa'
2 – 'Crystal'
1 – 'Rosalinda'
0 – 'Stockman'
9 – 'Valley Fire'
9 – 'Whitecaps'

PILEA
2 *involucrata*
2 – 'Bronze'
2 – 'Moon Valley'

PIMELEA
2 *ferruginea* 'Magenta Mist'

PINGUICULA
2 *oaxaca*

PINUS
1 *attenuata*
7 *balfouriana*
7 *banksiana* 'Schoodic'
2 – 'Uncle Fogy'
8 *bhutanica*
7 *densata*
7 *flexilis* 'Van der Woolf's Pyramid'
7 *gordoniana*
9 *greggii*
2 *halepensis*
2 x *holfordiana*
2 x *hunnewellii*
0 *koraiensis* 'Silver Mop'
2 *kwangtungensis*
1 *luchuensis*
7 *mugo* 'Hesse'
7 – 'Spingarn's Form'
2 – 'Trompenburg'
1 – 'Yellow Point'
0 *nigra caramanica* 'Pyramidata'
7 – 'Globosa'
7 – 'Strypemonde'
2 *parviflora* 'Blue Giant'
7 – 'Fukusumi'
7 – 'Ka-Ho'
0 – 'Shikoku'
7 *peuce* 'Nana'
1 *ponderosa scopulorum*
0 *pungens*
0 *resinosa*
9 *rudis*
7 *strobus* 'Compacta'
2 – 'Macopin'
2 – 'Pendula'
2 – 'Prostrata'
7 – 'Pumila'
7 – 'Umbraculifera'
7 *sylvestris* 'Corley'
0 – 'Iceni'
2 – 'Mongolia'
7 – 'Nana Compacta'
2 – *prostrata*
2 – 'Pyramidalis Compacta'
7 – 'Scott's Dwarf'
7 – 'Umbraculifera'
2 – 'Vera Hayward'
2 – 'Viridis Compacta'
7 *tabuliformis mukdensis*
2 *thunbergii* 'Oculus Draconis'
7 *wincesteriana*

PIPER
2 *ornatum*

PITTOSPORUM
9 *chathamicum*
2 *cuneatum*
1 'Green Flame'
9 *heterophyllum*
0 – *aculeatum*
2 *tenuifolium* 'All Gold'
0 – 'Silver Sheen'
9 – 'Snowflake'

PITYROGRAMMA
2 *chrysophylla*
2 *triangularis*

PLAGIANTHUS
7 *divaricatus*

PLANERA
2 *aquatica*

PLANTAGO
1 *arborescens maderensis*
2 *argentea*
1 *barbata*

PLATANUS
1 x *hispanica* 'Pyramidalis'

PLATYCERIUM
2 *superbum*

PLECTRANTHUS
0 *coleoïdes*

PLEIOBLASTUS
8 'Chigogasa'

PLEIONE
0 *formosana* 'Blush of Dawn'
1 *hookeriana*
2 *scopulorum*
0 Shantung 'Ducat'
0 – 'Muriel Harberd'
2 Tongariro

POA
9 *flabellata*

PODOCARPUS
0 *latifolius*
7 *macrophyllus* 'Aureus'
9 *nivalis* dwarf form
2 *nubigenus*

PODOPHYLLUM
9 *pleianthum*

POGOSTEMON
2 *heyneanus*

POLEMONIUM
2 *caeruleum grandiflorum*
0 *californicum*
8 *lanatum*
9 *pulcherrimum calycinum*
2 *reptans* 'Firmament'
0 x *richardsonii* 'Album'

POLYGALA
2 *vayredae*

POLYGONATUM
9 x *hybridum* 'Flore Pleno'
9 – 'Nanum'
9 *involucratum*
9 *oppositifolium*
9 *orientale*
2 *racemosum*

POLYMNIA
0 *sonchifolia*

POLYPODIUM
1 *aureum*
0 – 'Glaucum'
0 – 'Undulatum'

POLYPOGON
2 *monspeliensis*

POLYSCIAS
0 *filicifolia*

POLYSTICHUM
9 *lonchitoïdes*
8 *setiferum* Divisilobum Group 'Oakfield'
2 – 'Gracile'
9 – Perserratum Group 'Schroeder'
9 – 'Thompsoniae'

POPULUS
0 x *canescens* 'Macrophylla'
9 *ciliata*
2 x *generosa*
9 *grandidentata*
9 *koreana*
9 *szechuanica*
8 *tomentosa*

POTENTILLA
2 *bifurca*
1 *brauniana*
9 *crantzii ternata*
9 'Cyril'
9 'Daphne'
9 *fruticosa* 'Daisy Hill Variety'
1 – 'Macpenny's Cream'
1 – 'Orangeade'
2 – 'Pink Queen'
2 – 'Pyrenaica'
1 – 'Yellow Carpet'
0 – 'Yellow Dome'
0 *gracilis nuttallii*
9 *multifida*
2 *nepalensis* 'Salmon Seedling'
2 *nitida* 'Alannah'
2 – 'Lissadell'
8 'Orange Glow'
0 *pamirica*
8 *pensylvanica*
9 'Roulette'
8 'Southcombe White'

PRIMULA
1 *allionii* 'Clarkes' (2)
0 – 'Elizabeth Earle' (2)
2 – 'Jane' (2)
9 – 'Joan Hughes' (2)
1 American Pink Hose-in-Hose (Prim)
1 'Amethyst' (Poly)
2 *apennina* (2)
2 'April Snowflake' (Prim)
9 *atrodentata* (9)
2 *aurantiaca* hybrids (4)
1 *aureata fimbriata* (21)
1 *auricula* 'A Delbridge' (A)
2 – A74 (A)
1 – var. *albocincta* (2)
9 – 'Alpine Violet' (A)
2 – 'Archer' (D)
9 – 'Aubergine' (B)
1 – 'Balihai' (S)
9 – 'Barnhill' (D)
1 – 'Black Ice' (S)
9 – 'Blackcock' (S)
1 – 'Blue Bonnet' (A)
0 – 'Blue Lagoon' (S)
2 – 'Brass Dog' (S)
2 – 'Carcerot' (A)
9 – 'Carolina Duck' (S)
2 – 'Chamois' (B)
1 – 'Cherie' (S)
2 – 'Citron' (S)
9 – 'Crackley Seashell' (D)
2 – 'Cream Blush' (D)
9 – 'Desert Dawn' (A)
9 – 'Desert Magic' (A)
9 – 'Desert Peach' (A)
9 – 'Desert Queen' (A)
9 – 'Desert Rose' (A)
9 – 'Desert Sands' (A)
9 – 'Desert Star' (A)
2 – 'Downlands' (S)
2 – 'Dunlin' (S)
9 – 'Elizabeth Saunders' (D)
9 – 'Firecrest' (S)
2 – 'Frank Faulkner' (A)
2 – 'Girlguide' (S)
2 – 'Gnome' (B)
2 – 'Graisley' (S)
1 – 'Green Edge Pin Eye'
2 – 'Green Woodpecker' (S)
2 – 'Greenfinch' (S)
1 – 'Grey Edge'
9 – 'Grey Lady' (S)
9 – 'Holne' (A)
1 – 'Ida' (A)
2 – 'Janie Hill' (A)
1 – 'K H B' (S)
9 – 'King Cole' (S)
2 – 'Light Sussex' (S)
1 – 'McWatt's Blue'
0 – 'Milk Chocolate' (S)
2 – 'Monoglow' (S)
0 – 'Moonlight' (S)
2 – 'Mrs C Warne'
1 – 'Old Mustard'
2 – 'Parchment' (S)
2 – 'Pat Berwick' (A)
0 – 'Pathan' (A)
0 – 'Peach Blossom'
9 – 'Pennant's Parakeet' (S)
2 – 'Philip Green' (S)
9 – 'Purple Heron' (S)
9 – 'Purple Lake' (S)
7 – 'Queen Alexandar' (B)
2 – 'Radiance' (A)
2 – 'Redstart' (B)
2 – 'Ruffles' (S)

0 – 'Sam Gordon'
9 – 'Scarlet Ibis' (S)
9 – 'Scarlet Lancer' (S)
2 – 'Senorita' (A)
9 – 'Shaheen' (S)
2 – 'Shako' (A)
2 – 'Shogun' (A)
8 – 'Show Red' (S)
2 – 'Spitfire' (S)
9 – 'Sunburst' (S)
9 – 'Sungold' (S)
2 – 'Sunny Boy' (S)
0 – 'Tiphareth' (A)
1 – 'Tony Murloch'
2 – 'Turnbull' (A)
9 – 'Velvet Knight' (B)
9 – 'Violetta' (S)
2 – 'Wexland' (S)
9 – 'Woodpigeon' (S)
2 – 'Yellow Hammer' (S)
1 'Barrowby Gem' (Poly)
1 'Beamish Foam' (Poly)
2 x ***berninae*** (2)
0 'Blue Diamond'
2 'Blue Triumph'
1 'Bon Accord Cerise' (D.Poly)
1 'Bon Accord Lavender' (D.Poly)
1 'Bon Accord Lilac' (D.Poly)
1 ***boothii alba*** (21)
1 Bressingham (4)
9 'Butter-pat' (Prim)
9 ***calderiana strumosa*** (21)
2 ***capitellata*** (11)
2 x ***caruelii*** (2)
2 ***cawdoriana*** (8)
2 'Charlotte' (Prim)
9 'Charmian' (D.Prim)
9 'Cheerleader'
9 'Cherry Pie' (Prim)
9 'Coerulea' (Prim)
2 'Crimson Beauty' (D.Prim)
1 'Crispii' (Prim)
2 ***cuneifolia*** (8)
1 dark scarlet (Prim)
1 'David Green' (Prim)
8 ***denticulata*** 'Prichard's Ruby' (9)
2 ***deorum*** (2)
7 ***deuteronana*** (21)
1 'Doctor Mary' (Prim)
1 'Doctor Molly' (Prim)
1 'Double Red' (D.Poly)
8 ***duthieana*** (18)
2 'E R Janes' (Prim)
1 'Early Irish Yellow' (Prim)
1 'Eastgrove's Gipsy' (Poly)
2 ***edgeworthii alba*** (21)
1 ***elatior ruprechtii*** (30)
1 'Elizabeth Dickey' (D.Poly)
0 ***ellisiae alba*** (21)
1 'Enchantress' (Poly)
0 ***erythrocarpa*** (9)
1 'Evonne' (D.Poly)
2 'Exhilaration'
9 x ***facchinii*** (2)
0 ***fedtschenkoi*** (11)
1 'Fife Yellow' (D.Poly)
1 'Finesse' (Prim)
1 x ***floerkeana biflora*** (2)
1 – ***alba*** (2)
2 'Gartenmeister Bartens' (Prim)
1 'Gloria' (Prim)
2 ***griffithii*** 'Fantail' (21)
2 'Helge' (Prim)
9 ***hidakana*** (24)
0 'Highland Jewel' (D.Prim)
1 'Hipperholme'
0 ***ianthina*** (4)
2 ***integrifolia*** (2)
2 ***japonica*** 'Apple Blossom' (4)
9 'Jubilee' (D.Prim)
2 'Ladybird' (Prim)
9 'Lambrook Peach' (Poly)
1 'Lambrook Pink' (Poly)
0 ***latifolia*** cream form (2)
0 – f. ***cynoglossifolia*** (2)
7 ***latisecta*** (7)
2 'Lee Myers' (2)
2 'Lemon Soufflé' (Prim)
1 lilac purple (D.Poly)
2 ***luteola*** (11)
1 ***marginata*** 'Longifolia' (2)
2 – maritime form (2)
1 – 'Sharp's Variety' (2)
2 'Matthew Pixton'
2 'Mauve Queen' (Prim)
9 ***minutissima*** (16)
2 ***modesta alba*** (11)
9 – 'Flore Pleno' (11)
9 x ***muretiana dinyana*** (2)
2 ***nipponica*** (8)
2 ***pedemontana*** 'Alba' (2)
1 'Penlan Cream' (D.Poly)
2 'Pink Gem' (D.Prim)
1 'Pink Lady'
1 'Pink Profusion' (Prim)
9 'Pink Ruffles' (Prim)
2 x ***pubescens*** 'Old Rose' (2)
2 – 'Pink Freedom' (2)
7 – 'The Fawn' (2)
0 ***pulverulenta*** Pyramid Pinks Group (4)
2 'Pyramid Pink' (4)
9 'Quarry Wood' (4)
1 'Queen of the Whites' (Prim)
1 'Red Warbler' (Prim)
2 ***reidii*** hybrids (28)
2 'Rhapsody' (D.Prim)
2 ***roxburghii*** (25)
9 'Royal Purple' (Prim)
9 'Ruby Button' (Prim)
0 'Schneekissen Improved' (Prim)
1 'Shocking Pink'
1 ***sieboldii*** 'Cherokee' (7)
0 – 'Chinese Mountain' (7)
7 – 'Deechin' (7)
7 – 'Hakutsuri' (7)
7 – 'Harunuyuki' (7)
9 – 'Shironyi' (7)
7 – 'Sunrokumare' (7)
9 – 'Tsu-no-motana' (7)
9 – 'Ykiguruma' (7)
1 Silver Dollar Group (Poly)
1 'Silverwells' (4)
1 single green (Prim)
2 'Sir Galahad' (Prim)
1 ***sonchifolia*** Tibetan form
2 'Soup Plate' (21)
9 'Stardust' (Prim)
9 ***stricta*** (11)
0 ***tanneri*** (21)
1 – ssp. ***tsariensis alba***
2 Tartan Reds Group (Prim)
9 'The Bride' (Poly)
0 'Tina' (Prim)
9 'Tinney's Apple Blossom' (21)
7 'Tinney's Dairymaid'
0 ***tyrolensis*** (2)
2 x ***venusta*** Askival hybrids (2)
2 ***villosa commutata*** (2)
2 'Wanda Cherry Red' (Prim)
2 Wanda Group
1 'Wanda Improved' (Prim)
1 'Wedgwood'
1 'Westmorland Blue' (Prim)
2 'Whipped Cream'

PRINSEPIA
7 ***utilis***

PRITCHARDIA
2 ***pacifica***

PROSOPIS
2 ***glandulosa***

PROSTANTHERA
7 ***caerulea***
9 ***chlorantha***
2 ***eurybioïdes***
2 ***lasianthos coriacea***
8 ***stricta***

PROTEA
2 ***burchellii***

PRUNUS
8 ***americana***
2 x ***amygdalopersica***
0 ***armeniaca ansu*** 'Flore Pleno'
1 ***avium*** 'Grandiflora'
0 ***cerasifera*** 'Mirage'
8 – 'Woodii'
7 ***davidiana*** 'Alba'
7 – 'Rubra'
1 ***domestica*** 'Pixy'
2 ***dulcis*** 'Roseoplena'
2 'Edo-zakura'
2 'Fugenzô'
9 'Gyoiko'
7 'Hilling's Weeping'
2 ***hirtipes*** 'Semiplena'
0 ***incisa*** 'Rubra'
2 x ***juddii***
1 ***laurocerasus*** 'Barmstedt'
1 – 'Goldglanz'
2 – 'Greenmantle'
1 – 'Holstein'
2 'Ojôchin'
1 ***persica*** 'Alboplena'
1 – 'Cardinal' (d)
7 – 'Crimson Cascade'
2 – 'Eros'
9 – 'Foliis Rubris'
2 – 'Klara Mayer' (d)
0 – 'New Award'
0 – 'Pink Peachy'
0 – 'Weeping Flame'
2 ***rufa***
2 ***salicifolia***
2 ***serrulata hupehensis***
2 'Uzu-zakura
7 ***virginiana***
1 x ***yedoensis*** 'Erecta'
7 – 'Moerheimii'

PSEUDOMERTENSIA
9 ***moltkioïdes***

PSEUDOPANAX
2 ***davidii***
2 ***laetivirens***

PSEUDOTSUGA
7 ***guinieri***
2 ***macrocarpa***
2 ***menziesii flahaultii***
9 – 'Knap Hill Seedling'
8 – 'Oudemansii'
7 ***rehderi***

PSILOSTROPHE
1 ***tagentinae***

PTELEA
1 ***nitens***

PTERIS
2 ***cretica*** 'Major'
0 – 'Wilsonii'
0 ***longifolia*** 'Mariesii'
2 ***vittata***

PTEROCELTIS
9 ***tatarinowii***

PTEROCEPHALUS
1 ***pinardii***

PTILOSTEMON
2 ***afer***
2 ***diacantha***

PTYCHOSPERMA
2 ***macarthurii***

PULMONARIA
1 ***rubra alba***
0 ***saccharata*** 'White Barn'
9 – 'Wisley White'

PULSATILLA
0 ***albana armena***
2 ***campanella***
9 ***halleri*** 'Budapest'
9 ***montana australis***
0 ***turczaninovii***
1 ***vulgaris*** Balkan form
8 – 'Barton's Pink'
2 – Heiler hybrids
2 – 'Mrs Van der Elst'

PUSCHKINIA
2 ***scilloïdes***

PUYA
2 *lanata*
PYCNOSTACHYS
0 *urticifolia*
PYRACANTHA
0 *augustifolia variegata*
1 *crenulata*
2 'Fiery Cascade'
0 *fortunei*
2 'Knap Hill Lemon'
2 *koidzumii* 'Victory'
2 'Lavinia Rutgers'
X PYRACOMELES
8 *vilmorinii*
PYRUS
1 *communis* 'Green Pear of Yair' (D)
2 – 'Gros Blanquet' (D)
1 – 'Marquise' (D)
2 – 'Martin Sec' (C/D)
2 – 'Merton Star' (D)
2 – 'Messire Jean' (D)
1 – 'Pierre Corneille'
2 – 'Swan's Egg' (D)
2 – 'Windsor' (D)
QUERCUS
2 x *hispanica* 'Ambrozyana'
2 *hypoleucoïdes*
0 Macon
2 *pontica*
2
2 *teucotrichophora*
QUESNELIA
0 *liboniana*
RAMONDA
0 *myconi alba*
2 *nathaliae* 'Alba'
RANUNCULUS
2 *adoneus*
9 *amplexicaulis* 'Grandiflorus'
2 *anemoneus*
1 *asiaticus* white form
1 *cadmicus*
7 *eschscholtzii*
1 *ficaria* 'Hoskins Miniature'
1 – 'Hoskins Spider'
2 – 'Wyatt's White'
0 *hirtellus*
9 *insignis*
9 *lappaceus*
9 *macrophyllus*
9 *muelleri brevicaulis*
1 *pygmaeus*
0 *traunfellneri*
RANZANIA
2 *japonica*
RATIBIDA
2 *columnifera*
REEVESIA
9 *pubescens*
REGELIA
1 *cymbifolia*
1 *inops*
1 *megacephala*
1 *velutina*
REINECKEA
2 *carnea* 'Variegata'
RESEDA
1 *odorata*
RHAMNUS
2 *alaternus*
2 *citrifolius*
2 *procumbens*
RHEUM
1 'Green Knight'
2 x *hybridum* 'Early Albert'
2 – 'Strawberry'
2 *webbianum*
RHODIOLA
1 *hirsuta*
1 – Baetica Group
1 *kirilovii*
0 *komarovii*
1 *wallichiana stephanii*
RHODODENDRON
0 *alabamense*
9 *alutaceum*
1 *ambiguum* best form
1 *arboreum delavayi* var. *peramoenum*
9 – 'Patterson'
9 Azalea 'Agamujin' (E)
9 – 'Alice de Stuers' (M)
9 – 'Ambush'
8 – 'Anne van Hoeke'
1 – 'Anthony Koster' (M)
9 – 'Apollo' (E)
2 – 'Ardeur'
9 – 'B Y Morrison' (E)
0 – 'Bulstrode' (E)
2 – 'Carmel' (E)
2 – 'Cavalier' (E)
0 – 'Challenger' (E)
2 – 'Cherokee'
0 – 'Chichibu' (E)
2 – 'Chinsai' (E)
1 – 'Colleen' (E)
9 – 'Comte de Gomer' (M)
9 – 'Comte de Papadopoli' (M)
1 – 'Con Amore' (E)
1 – 'Conversation Piece' (E)
0 – 'Coquille'
9 – 'Crepello'
0 – 'Crystal Violet'
2 – 'Dandy' (E)
1 – 'Daphne' (E)
7 – 'Dart' (K)
0 – 'Dawn's Chorus' (K)
0 – 'Dayspring' (E)
9 – 'Devon' (K)
9 – Diamant Group (salmon pink) (E)
1 – 'Directeur Moerlands' (M)
2 – 'Doctor Reichenbach' (M)
1 – 'Dorothy Rees' (E)
2 – 'Easter Parade' (E)
2 – 'Edward M Boehm' (E)
2 – 'Eisenhower' (K)
9 – 'Embley Crimson' (K)
1 – 'Eucharis' (E)
0 – 'Everbloom' (E)
2 – 'Explorer' (E)
1 – 'Favor Major' (K)
1 – 'Ferndown Beauty' (E)
2 – 'Feuerwerk' (K)
0 – 'Flaire' (K)
1 – 'Freya' (R/d)
7 – 'Garden Beauty' (E)
2 – 'Gardenia' (E)
2 – 'Gaugin'
0 – 'Geisha' (E)
0 – 'Glacier' (E)
2 – 'Gnome' (E)
2 – 'Gold Dust' (K)
2 – 'Golden Hind'
1 – 'Gosho-zakura' (E)
2 – 'Greenwood Yukon' (E)
2 – 'Greeting' (E)
0 – 'Gretchen' (E)
9 – 'Gwynidd Lloyd' (E)
1 – 'Hachika-tsugi' (E)
9 – 'Hanio-no-shion' (E)
2 – 'Harkwood Orange'
2 – 'Haru-no-yuki'
9 – 'Harwell' (K)
9 – 'Hershey's Bright Red'
9 – 'Hikkasen' (E)
1 – 'Hinode-no-taka' (E)
9 – 'Hollandia' (G)
2 – 'Hopeful' (E)
2 – 'Hugh Wormald' (K)
9 – 'Igneum Novum' (G)
0 – 'Imazuma' (E)
9 – 'Imperator' (M)
9 – 'Jan Steen' (M)
1 – 'Janet Baker'
1 – 'Jeff Hill' (E)
0 – 'Joho-ngodor-akako'
2 – 'Kasumi-gaseki'
2 – 'Kormesing'
1 – 'Krishna'
9 – 'Kumoidori' (E)
1 – 'Kumo-no-ito' (E)
1 – 'Kurai-no-himo' (E)
9 – 'La France' (E)
1 – 'Lady Louise' (E)
1 – 'Lady Robin' (E)
2 – 'Litany' (E)
1 – 'Little Beauty' (E)
7 – 'Louisa Hill'
2 – 'Louise Gable' (E)
1 – 'Mahler' (E)
0 – 'Matsukasa Pink'
9 – 'Medway' (K)
9 – 'Midsummer Beauty' (E)
9 – 'Miyagino' (E)
2 – 'Modesty' (E)
1 – 'Moira' (E)
2 – 'Multatuli' (M)
1 – 'Naniwagata' (E)
1 – 'Natalie Coe Vitetti' (E)
1 – 'Niphetos' (E)
1 – 'Noordtianum' (E)
2 – 'Opal' (E)
1 – 'Oregon Trail'
1 – 'Otome' (E)
1 – 'Panaché'
2 – 'Papineau' (E)
8 – 'Peter Koster' (M)
1 – 'Pickard's Gold'
0 – 'Picotee' (E)
2 – 'Pink Mimosa' (Vs)
9 – 'Pink Treasure' (E)
2 – 'Psyche' (E)
8 – 'Pure Gold' (K)
1 – 'Purple Velvet'
2 – 'Quaker Maid' (K)
2 – 'Rhapsody' (E)
0 – 'River Belle'
1 – 'Robin Hill Congo' (E)
7 – 'Rogue River Belle' (O)
2 – 'Rosalie' (E)
9 – 'Rosella' (K)
2 – 'Rubinstern' (E)
9 – 'Salmon Queen' (M)
9 – 'Satrap' (E)
2 – 'Seikai' (E)
1 – 'Sherbrook' (E)
7 – 'Shinto' (E)
1 – 'Shin-utena' (E)
2 – 'Spek's Brilliant' (M)
9 – 'Spinoza' (M)
0 – 'Splendens' (E)
0 – 'Sui-yohi' (E)
8 – 'Sunset Boulevard' (K)
0 – 'Superbum' (O)
9 – 'Tamarind'
1 – 'Tama-no-utena' (E)
1 – 'Tay' (K)
1 – 'Tebotan' (E/d)
9 – 'Tyrian Rose' (E)
0 – 'Viscosepalum' (G)
9 – 'Wadai-akasuba' (E)
9 – 'Wada's Pink Delight'
1 – 'Wee Willie' (E)
1 – 'Werrington'
2 – 'White Jade' (E)
1 – 'White Moon' (E)
0 – 'Wye' (K)
1 – 'Yaye-giri' (E)
2 – 'Yaye-hiryu' (E)
0 – 'Yellow'
9 – 'Yokohama' (E)
0 – 'Yokora'
1 – 'Yorozuyo' (E)
0 Azaleodendron 'Tottenham'
9 *brachycarpum brachycarpum* Tigerstedii Group
2 *bureaui* 'Berg'
2 *campanulatum campanulatum* 'Roland Cooper'
0 *campylogynum* Brodick form
0 – 'Crushed Strawberry'
1 – 'Hillier's Pink'
1 *camtschaticum* Murray-Lyon form
9 *caucasicum* 'Cunningham's Sulphur'
7 *cinnabarinum* 'Caerhays Yellow'
1 – 'Magnificum'
1 – ssp. *xanthocodon* Exbury AM form

1 ***cookeanum***
8 ***cuneatum*** Ravum Group
9 ***degronianum heptamerum*** 'Oki Island'
0 – – 'Wada'
9 – Kyomaruense Group
1 x ***detonsum*** Edinburgh select form
9 ***ferrugineum*** 'Ascreavie'
8 – 'Plenum'
0 ***fittianum***
9 ***forrestii*** 'Branklyn'
0 ***fortunei*** 'Lu-Shan'
0 ***fulgens*** Leonardslee form
0 ***glaucophyllum*** 'Prostratum'
1 ***hanceanum*** x ***lutescens***
2 ***hippophaëoïdes hippophaëoïdes*** 'Sunningdale'
2 – 'Inshriach'
2 Hybrid 'Abe Arnott'
0 – Aladdin (g.&cl.)
2 – 'Albatross Townhill White'
1 – 'Album'
9 – 'Alice Martineau'
1 – Alix (g.&cl.)
1 – 'Ann Aberconway'
2 – 'Anne Dring'
1 – 'Annette'
2 – 'Arctic Snow'
9 – 'Arlie'
1 – 'Babylon'
2 – 'Bach Choir'
9 – 'Balta'
0 – 'Beefeater'
1 – 'Bishopsgate'
9 – 'Black Beauty'
0 – 'Bray'
1 – 'Brightwell'
1 – Calrose
1 – Campirr
0 – 'Candi'
1 – 'Caperci Special'
0 – 'Carex White'
2 – 'Carita Charm'
1 – 'Catalode'
1 – Chanticleer
0 – 'Chelsea'
1 – 'Chippewa'
2 – 'Cool Haven'
0 – 'Cunningham's Album Compactum'
1 – 'Dayan'
1 – 'Dido'
0 – 'Director Dorsman'
1 – 'Dollar Princess'
9 – 'Duchess of Teck'
9 – Duke of Cornwall (g.&cl.)
9 – Dusky Maid
2 – Eldorado
0 – Elena
0 – Emerald Isle
1 – 'Endsleigh Pink'
0 – 'Esveld Select'
1 – Exburiense
0 – 'Exbury Matador'
1 – 'Fabia Roman Pottery'
2 – 'Fabia Waterer'
9 – 'Feespite'
9 – 'Flip'
0 – 'Gladys Rose'
1 – Goblin (g.&cl.)
0 – 'Goldbukett'
1 – 'Golden Spur'
2 – 'Goldfee'
1 – Goldfinch
9 – 'Good News'
1 – Grenadine (g.&cl.)
1 – Gretia (g.&cl.)
1 – 'Grilse'
7 – 'Halopeanum'
0 – 'Hansel'
0 – Hawk (g.&cl.)
8 – Hawk 'Buzzard'
9 – 'Helen Johnson'
0 – hemsleyanum x 'Polar Bear'
8 – 'Hillcrest'
9 – Huntsman
1 – 'Hydon Harrier'
0 – 'Ightham White'
1 – Indiana
0 – 'Inshriach Blue'
1 – Intrepid
2 – 'Irene'
2 – 'J H Agnew'
1 – 'J H van Nes'
2 – Janet
2 – 'Janet Blair'
1 – 'Jasper Pimento'
9 – Joanita
0 – 'July Fragrance'
2 – Jutland
2 – 'Kathleen'
9 – Kiev (g.&cl.)
0 – 'Lemon Grass'
8 – 'Leonard Messel'
2 – 'Lillian Peste'
0 – 'Limbatum'
0 – Linswegeanum
2 – Lodauric
1 – 'Lucy Lockhart'
8 – 'Madame Carvalho'
2 – 'Madame Fr V Chauvin'
2 – Major
1 – 'March Sun'
1 – 'Margaret Falmouth'
0 – Margaret Findlay (g.&cl.)
2 – 'Mariner'
0 – 'Mayfair'
0 – 'Melpomene'
9 – 'Melville'
9 – 'Midsummer Snow'
1 – 'Molly Miller'
1 – 'Montreal'
1 – 'Mortimer'
2 – 'Mrs A M Williams'
2 – 'Mrs Alfred Taubman'
9 – 'Mrs Mary Ashley'
9 – 'Mrs Tom Agnew'
1 – 'Multiflorum'
8 – 'Multimaculatum'
9 – 'Mum'
0 – 'Nancy Fortescue'
9 – 'Naomi Nautilus'
2 – 'Nero'
9 – 'Nimrod Scheherezade'
9 – 'Oporto'
9 – Orestes
0 – 'Ostbo's Low Yellow'
0 – 'Overstreet'
2 – 'Parsons' Gloriosum'
1 – 'Patricia's Day'
9 – 'Peekaboo'
0 – 'Pink Beauty'
1 – 'Pink Lady Rosebery'
9 – 'Platinum Pearl'
9 – 'Polly Clarke'
1 – Portia (g.&cl.)
1 – 'Princess Juliana'
8 – 'Prinses Marijke'
0 – 'Prosti'
2 – 'Purple Lace'
9 – 'Purpureum Grandiflorum'
9 – Quaker Girl
1 – 'R W Rye'
9 – 'Raoul Millais'
9 – 'Red Bells'
0 – 'Red Rum'
1 – 'Rijneveld'
1 – 'Rosa Regen'
1 – Rosalind (g.&cl.)
9 – Rouge (g.&cl.)
1 – 'Royal Purple'
0 – 'Royal Windsor'
0 – 'Schneebukett'
0 – 'Serena'
2 – Snow White
2 – Solent Queen
1 – Soulking
0 – 'Souvenir de D A Koster'
0 – 'Spring Song'
7 – Stonehurst hybrids
9 – 'Susan Everett'
1 – 'Tensing'
1 – 'Tiger'
0 – 'Travis L'
2 – 'Van'
2 – 'Van Weerden Poelman'
1 – 'Veesprite'
1 – Vega
1 – 'Venapens'
7 – 'Violette'
0 – 'Virgo'
0 – 'Viscount Powerscourt'
1 – 'Wantage'
0 – 'Wavertree'
0 – 'William Fortescue'
9 – 'Windle Brook'
1 – 'Windsor Hawk'
1 ***imberbe***
2 ***impeditum*** 'Drake's Hybrid'
1 – Litangense Group
9 ***kaempferi*** 'Hall's Red'
9 – 'Troll'
1 ***keiskei*** Windsor Great Park form
0 ***kiusianum*** 'Chidori'
1 – 'Tenshi'
0 ***lepidotum*** Obovatum Group
2 ***lysolepis*** 'Woodland Purple'
1 ***minus chapmanii***
9 – var. ***minus*** Carolinianum Group 'Album'
9 ***mollicomum***
1 ***moupinense*** white form
0 ***mucronulatum*** best form (EA)
1 – Reuthe's form
0 ***nakaharae*** 'Benenden'
1 ***nivale***
2 – ssp. ***boreale*** Nigropunctatum Group
2 ***niveum*** 'Clyne Castle'
1 ***oblongifolium*** (A)
1 ***paradoxum***
0 ***parmulatum*** 'Palma' ex KW 5875
1 ***parryae***
9 ***pingianum***
1 ***polycladum*** Compactum Group
1 ***ponticum*** 'Gilt Edge'
0 ***pseudochrysanthum*** dwarf form
1 ***russatum album***
9 – 'Hill of Tarvit'
9 – 'Keillour'
2 – tall form
1 ***sargentianum*** Leonardslee form
1 ***seinghkuense***
1 ***serrulatum*** (A)
1 ***simsii*** double form
0 ***sinogrande*** Trewithen form
1 ***tanastylum pennivenium***
0 ***tapetiforme***
0 ***telmateium*** Drumonium Group
8 ***temenium***
1 ***thomsonii lopsangianum***
2 ***trichostomum*** deep form
1 ***virgatum album***
8 – ssp. ***oleifolium*** 'Penheale Pink'
1 ***williamsianum*** 'Exbury White'
2 – x ***martinianum***
0 ***yedoense poukhanense***
0 – – ***album***
2 ***yungningense*** Glomerulatum Group

RHODOHYPOXIS

0 'Bety's Carmine'
0 'Margaret Rose'
0 'Monty'

RHODOPHIALA

2 ***rosea***

RHOICISSUS

0 ***capensis***

RHOPALOBLASTE

1 ***ceramica***

RIBES

0 ***alpinum*** 'Pumilum'

2 ***burejense***
1 ***glutinosum***
2 ***henryi***
9 ***leptanthum***
1 ***menziesii***
2 ***nigrum*** 'Green's Black'
1 – 'Tsema'
2 Red Currant Group 'Rovada'
1 ***roezlii cruentum***
9 ***sanguineum*** 'Atrorubens'
9 – 'Carneum'
1 ***uva-crispa reclinatum*** 'Admiral Beattie'
1 – – 'Angler'
1 – – 'Antagonist'
1 – – 'Beauty'
1 – – 'Beauty Red' (D)
1 – – 'Belle de Meaux'
1 – – 'Berry's Early Giant' (C)
1 – – 'Black Seedling'
1 – – 'Bobby'
1 – – 'Bright Venus' (D)
1 – – 'British Oak' (D)
1 – – 'Brown's Red' (D)
1 – – 'Champion'
1 – – 'Coiner'
1 – – 'Colossal'
1 – – 'Conquering Hero'
1 – – 'Cook's Eagle' (C)
1 – – 'Early Green Hairy' (D)
1 – – 'Echo' (D)
1 – – 'Edith Cavell'
1 – – 'Emerald' (D)
1 – – 'Faithful' (C)
1 – – 'Fascination'
1 – – 'Forester' (D)
1 – – 'Forever Amber' (D)
1 – – 'Gautrey's Earliest'
1 – – 'Gem' (D)
1 – – 'Glencarse Muscat' (D)
1 – – 'Globe Yellow'
1 – – 'Golden Lion'
1 – – 'Green Overall' (C)
1 – – 'Green Walnut'
1 – – 'Gretna Green'
1 – – 'Grüne Flashen Beere'
1 – – 'Grüne Kugel' (C)
1 – – 'Grüne Reisen' (C)
1 – – 'Guy's Seedling' (D)
1 – – 'Hebburn Prolific' (D)
1 – – 'Hedgehog' (D)
1 – – 'Helgrüne Samtbeere' (C)
1 – – 'Highlander' (D)
1 – – 'Höning Früheste' (D)
1 – – 'Hot Gossip'
1 – – 'Hough's Supreme'
1 – – 'Hue and Cry' (C)
1 – – 'Improved Mistake'
1 – – 'Independence'
1 – – 'Ingal's Prolific Red' (C)
1 – – 'Jenny Lind'
1 – – 'Jolly Angler'
1 – – 'Jolly Potter'
1 – – 'Katherina Ohlenburg' (C)
1 – – 'Kathryn Hartley' (C)
1 – – 'Lady Delamere' (C)
1 – – 'Lady Haughton' (D)
1 – – 'Lady Leicester' (D)
1 – – 'Langley Green' (C)
1 – – 'Lauffener Gelbe'
1 – – 'Laxton's Amber' (D)
1 – – 'Leader' (C)
1 – – 'Lily of the Valley'
1 – – 'Lloyd George'
1 – – 'Lord Audley' (D)
1 – – 'Lord Elcho'
1 – – 'Lord George'
1 – – 'Marmorierte Goldkugel' (D)
1 – – 'Maurer's Seedling' (D)
1 – – 'Mertensis'
1 – – 'Mischief'
1 – – 'Monarch' (D)
1 – – 'Montgomery'
1 – – 'Mrs Westlon'
1 – – 'Muttons' (D)
1 – – 'Nailer'
1 – – 'Napoléon le Grand' (D)
1 – – 'Norden Hero' (D)
1 – – 'Ostrich' (C)
1 – – 'Pixwell'
1 – – 'Plain Long Green'
1 – – 'Postman'
1 – – 'Pottage'
1 – – 'Preston's Seedling' (D)
1 – – 'Prince Charles'
1 – – 'Profit'
1 – – 'Railway'
1 – – 'Ries von Kothen' (C)
1 – – 'Rifleman' (D)
1 – – 'Roaring Lion'
1 – – 'Robustenda'
1 – – 'Rushwick Seedling' (C)
1 – – 'Scotch Red Rough' (D)
1 – – 'Scottish Chieftan' (D)
1 – – 'Sensation' (C)
1 – – 'Shiner'
1 – – 'Slap Bang' (C)
1 – – 'Smaragdbeere' (C)
1 – – 'Smiling Beauty' (C)
1 – – 'Snow'
1 – – 'Snowdrop' (C)
1 – – 'Souter Johnny'
1 – – 'Stockwell'
1 – – 'Sulphur' (D)
1 – – 'Talfourd' (D)
1 – – 'Thatcher'
1 – – 'Viper' (C)
1 – – 'Weisse Riesen'
1 – – 'Weisse Volltriesen' (C)
1 – – 'Werdersche Frühemarkt' (D)
1 – – 'White Fig' (C)
1 – – 'White Swan' (C)

RICINUS

2 ***communis***

RIGIDELLA

0 ***orthantha***

ROBINIA

2 x ***ambigua*** 'Decaisneana'
9 ***boyntonii***
2 x ***margaretta***
0 ***pseudoacacia*** 'Sandraudiga'

RODGERSIA

2 ***podophylla*** 'Pagode'

ROMANZOFFIA

2 ***suksdorfii***

ROMULEA

1 ***bulbocodium leichtliniana***

ROSA

1 'Abundance' (F)
2 ***acicularis***
0 'Aglaia' (Ra)
9 'Alamein' (F)
2 Allotria ® (F)
0 'Amarillo' (HT)
2 'Améthyste' (Ra)
0 'Amorette' (Patio)
1 'Andrea, Climbing' (MinCl)
0 'Andrew's Rose' (F)
2 Anna Zinkeisen ® (S)
2 Anneka ® (F)
0 'Appreciation' (HT)
2 Apricot Spice ® (HT)
0 'Apricot Wine' (F)
2 'Arabesque' (F)
0 'Artistic' (F)
9 'Ascot' (F)
2 'Baby Gold' (Min)
1 Baccará ® (HT)
2 'Bambino' (Min)
2 Baron Meillandina ®
2 Basildon Bond ® (HT)
2 Beauty Queen ® (F)
2 'Beauty Secret' (Min)
1 'Bel Ange' (HT)
2 Benevolence ® (HT)
9 'Berlin' (S)
2 Beryl Bach ® (HT)
2 Bill Slim ® (F)
2 Bischofsstadt Paderborn ® (S)
2 'Blaze Away' (F)
9 Blue Peter, Climbing ® (Min/Cl)
0 'Bountiful' (F)
0 'Brandy Butter' (HT)
2 'Bridgwater Pride' (F)
2 Bright Eyes ® (F)
2 'Buccaneer' (HT)
1 'Burning Love' (F)
0 'Capistrano' (HT)
1 'Carol Amling' (Gn)
1 Carol Ann ® (F)
2 Charles de Gaulle ® (HT)
2 'Charm of Paris' (HT)
2 'Chatterbox' (F)
2 'Children's Rose' (F)
2 Christingle ® (F)
1 'Chuckles' (F)
2 City of Bradford ® (F)
2 'Clio' (HP)
9 'Cologne Carnival' (HT)
1 'Comtesse d'Oxford' (HP)
2 'Comtesse O'Gorman' (HP)
2 Conqueror's Gold ® (F)
1 'Coral Star' (HT)
2 Corsair ® (F)
2 'Countryman' (S)
2 'Crarae' (HT)
1 Crimson Wave ® (F)
0 'Culverbrae' (Ru)
2 Curiosity ® (HT/v)
2 'Dale Farm' (F/Patio)
2 'Dame de Coeur' (HT)
2 Dame Vera Lynn ® (F)
9 'Dekorat' (HT)
1 Diamant ® (F)
9 'Doctor F L Skinner'
1 'Dornröschen' (Cl)
2 Dwarf Favourite ® (Patio)
1 'Eiffel Tower' (HT)
0 'Eleanor' (Min)
2 Elegant Pearl ® (Min/Patio)
2 'Ellen Mary' (HT)
2 'Ellinor LeGrice' (HT)
1 'Ellinor LeGrice, Climbing' (HT/Cl)
9 'Else Poulsen' (Poly)
2 'Embassy Regal' (HT)
2 'Emily Carter'
2 Emily Louise ® (Patio)
1 Eminence ® (HT)
2 Esperanto Jubileo ®
9 'Eve Allen' (HT)
1 'Eyecatcher' (F)
2 'Fairlight' (F)
2 'Fairy Prince' (GC)
1 'Fashion' (F)
9 ***fedtschenkoana*** 'Flore Pleno'
1 ***filipes*** 'Toby Tristram' (Ra)
1 'Fillette' (F)
0 'Firecrest' (F)
0 'Firecrest, Climbing' (F/Cl)
2 Flanders Field ® (F)
9 'Flashlight' (F)
1 'Florida von Scharbeutz' (F)
2 Freddy ® (F)
2 Friction Lights ® (F)
9 'Frost Fire' (Min)
1 'Garden Princess'
2 'Garnette' (Gn)
2 'Garnette Apricot' (Gn)
1 'Garnette Golden' (Gn)
2 'Garnette Rose' (Gn)
1 'Garnette Salmon' (Gn)
2 'Garnette Yellow' (Gn)
2 Gary Lineker ® (F)
2 'Gay Gordons' (HT)
2 Gentle Maid ® (F/Patio)
1 Glowing Embers ® (F)
2 'Gold Coin' (Min)
2 'Gold Marie' (F)

1 Gold Topaz ® (F)
0 'Golden Autumn' (HT)
9 'Grace Kimmins' (F)
1 'Granadina'
2 'Grandpa's Delight' (F)
2 'Grey Dawn' (F)
0 'Hadspen Arthur'
0 'Hadspen Eleanor'
2 'Halley's Comet' (F)
0 x ***hardyi***
2 'Harriny' (HT)
2 'Harry Edland' (F)
1 'Hazel Le Rougetel' (Ru)
2 Heather Honey ® (HT)
2 Heidelberg ® (S)
2 Heidi ® (Min/ Mo)
2 Helga ® (HT/ F)
1 'Help the Aged' (HT)
0 ***hemsleyana***
2 Hiroshima's Children ® (F)
2 Ice Fairy ® (GC)
2 'Ice White' (F)
1 IGA '83 München ® (GC)
2 ***iliensis***
9 'Incense' (HT)
0 Indian Song ® (HT)
2 Iris Webb ® (F)
2 'Isabel de Ortiz' (HT)
2 'Isobel Harkness' (HT)
2 'Janice Tellian' (Min)
2 'Jean Thomson Harris' (F)
9 Jennie Robinson ® (Min/ Patio)
2 'Jenny's Dream' (HT)
2 Jimmy Savile ® (F)
2 'John Abrams' (F)
2 'Jules Margottin' (HP)
2 Juliet Anne ® (Min)
1 'June Bride' (F)
1 'June Park' (HT)
9 'Junior Miss' (F)
0 'K of K' (HT)
1 'Korona, Climbing' (F/ Cl)
2 'Korp' (F)
9 'Kumbaya' (F)
0 'Lady Hamilton' (pimpinellifolia)
2 Lady Meillandina ® (Min)
2 Lady Mitchell ® (HT)
2 Lady Taylor ® (F/ Patio)
0 Lakeland Princess ® (HT)
1 'Laure Davoust'
2 Laurence Olivier ® (F)
2 'Lemon Delight' (Min/ Mo)
1 'Lemon Yellow' (F)
1 'Liberty Bell' (HT)
2 Lilac Airs ® (HT)
2 Little One ®
1 Little Russel ® (Min)
2 'Lively Lady' (F)
2 Lolita ® (HT)
2 Lordly Oberon ® (S)
2 'Love Affair' (Min)
9 'Madame Caroline Testout' (HT)
2 'Madame Jules Bouché, Climbing' (HT/ Cl)
1 'Mainzer Wappen' (HT)
2 'Malmesbury' (HT)
2 Mandy ® (HT)
2 'Marchioness of Salisbury' (HT)
2 Marion Harkness ® (HT)
2 Maritime Bristol ® (HT)
2 Marty ® (F)
2 'Mary Barnard' (F)
2 Mary Jean ® (HT)
2 Mary Sumner ® (F)
2 Midas ® (HT)
9 'Midget' (Min)
2 'Mission Supreme' (HT)
1 'Montezuma' (HT)
2 'Mood Music' (Min)
0 ***moyesii*** 'Nassau'
0 'Mrs Reynolds Hole' (T)
0 'Mrs Wakefield Christie-Miller' (HT)
0 'Mrs Wemyss Quin' (HT)
2 Muriel ® (F/ Patio)
2 'Naomi' (HT)
2 Nigel Hawthorne ® (S)
1 'Nikki' (F)
2 Nimbus ® (F)
2 ***nitida*** 'Kebu'
2 Nona ® (F)
9 'Nymph'
1 x ***odorata*** 'Bengal Crimson'
1 – 'Miss Willmott's Crimson China'
0 'Ohio' (S)
2 Olive ® (F)
2 Olympic Spirit ® (F)
2 'Only You' (HT)
2 'Opera' (HT)
1 'Orange Goliath' (HT)
0 Orange Minimo ® (Min)
0 'Orange Mother's Day' (F)
2 Pacemaker ® (HT)
2 Paint Box ® (F/ Min)
2 Pallas ® (Min)
2 Pat James ® (F)
2 'Penny' (F)
9 'Petula Clarke' (HT)
2 Phoebe ® (R)
2 Phoenix ® (Min)
9 'Pink Cloud' (HT/ Cl)
2 'Pink Fountain' (F)
1 'Pink Meteor' (F)
2 Playboy ® (F)
2 Potton Heritage ® (HT)
0 'Poulbright' (F)
2 Pride of Maldon ® (F)
2 'Prince Charming' (Min)
1 Prins Claus ® (HT)
2 Proud Titania ® (S)
1 'Purple Elf'
2 'Queen Esther' (HT)
0 'Queenie' (F)
2 'Ralph Tizzard' (F)
2 'Red Maid' (F)
0 'Red Planet' (HT)
1 'Red Sprite' (F)
2 'Redcliffe' (F)
1 Rediffusion Gold ® (F)
2 'Redland Court' (F)
2 'Ripples' (F)
2 'Robin' (Min)
2 Rochester Cathedral ® (S)
2 Roddy McMillan ® (HT)
1 'Rosamini Gold' (Patio)
1 'Rosamini Orange' (Patio)
1 'Rosamini Pink' (Patio)
1 'Rosamini Red' (Patio)
1 'Rosamini White' (Patio)
2 'Rose of Clifton' (F)
1 'Rose of Tralee' (F)
2 'Royal Bath and West' (F)
0 'Royal Conquest' (F)
2 'Royal Lavender' (HT/ Cl)
1 'Saga' (F)
2 'Salmon Sprite' (F)
0 'Sandra Marie' (HT)
0 'Santa Catalina' (FCl)
1 'Saul' (HT)
2 Save the Children ® (F/ Patio)
2 Seafarer ® (F)
1 Seaspray ® (F)
2 ***serafinii***
1 'Serenade' (HT)
2 ***sericea omeiensis*** f. ***pteracantha*** 'Atrosanguinea'
0 Shalom ® (F)
2 Sheila Macqueen ® (F)
1 'Shepherdess' (F)
2 Shire County ® (HT)
2 Showman ® (HT)
2 'Silver Charity' (F)
2 'Snowflake' (Ra)
1 'Snowgoose' (Min)
2 'Sonatina' (F)
1 'Souvenir di Castagneto'
1 'Spartan' (F)
9 'Spica Red'
2 Spirit of Pentax ® (F)
1 'Stanley Duncan' (Min)
2 'Stephen Langdon' (F)
2 'Stirling Castle' (F)
1 'Stromboli' (F)
2 'Sugar Sweet' (F)
1 Summer Love ® (F)
2 Summer Sérénade ® (F)
1 'Summer Song' (F)
1 'Sunday Times' (F)
9 'Sunny Queen'
1 'Sunny South' (HT)
2 Suspense ® (HT)
2 'Swinger' (Min)
9 'Sylvian Dot'
1 Tender Night ® (F)
2 The Fisherman's Cot ® (F)
2 'The Queen Alexandra' (Ra)
2 'The Yeoman' (S)
1 'Tiara' (HSwB)
1 'Tinker Bell' (Min)
9 'Toddler' (F)
2 Tonight ® (HT)
2 'Tricia's Joy' (Cl)
2 'Twinkles' (Min)
2 'Typhoo Tea' (HT)
1 'Tyrius' (HT)
9 'Tzigane' (HT)
9 'Una' (Ra)
2 'Uncle Joe' (HT)
1 'Vanda Beauty'
2 'Velvet Hour' (HT)
2 Velvia ® (F)
2 'Vesper' (F)
2 Volunteer ® (F)
1 Wagbi ® (F)
1 ***webbiana microphylla***
9 'White Dick Koster'
1 'White Sunblaze' (Min)
1 'Winefred Clarke' (HT)
9 'Wisbech Gold' (HT)
9 With Love ® (HT)
1 'Woburn Gold' (F)
1 Young Venturer ® (F)
1 'Zorina' (F)

ROSMARINUS

9 ***creticus***
7 ***officinalis angustissimus***
7 – 'Pat Vlasto'
9 – 'Suffolk Blue'

ROSULARIA

2 ***globulariifolia***
0 ***libanotica*** from Kaypak
0 ***radiciflora glabra*** from Beyas Dag
0 – ***radiciflora*** from Bitlis
2 ***serpentinica*** from Sandras Dag
0 ***stylaris***

RUBUS

2 ***fruticosus*** 'Sylvan'
2 'King's Acre Berry'
9 ***lasiostylus***
2 'Tummelberry'
0 ***ulmifolius***

RUDBECKIA

1 ***hirta*** 'Irish Eyes'

RUMEX

9 ***arifolius*** 'Ruber'

RUMOHRA

2 ***adiantiformis***

RUSCHIA

2 ***putterilii***

RUTTYA

2 ***fruticosa***

SAINTPAULIA

2 'Alexander'
1 'Alma'
2 'Barnados'
1 'Bella'
1 'Bertini'
1 'Blue Nymph'
2 'Bright Eyes'
2 'Celebration'
2 'Centenary'
2 'Colorado'
2 'Delft'
2 'Emma Louise'
2 'Fred'
1 'Fusspot'
2 'Garden News'
2 'Gisela'

2 'Gredi'
2 'Ice Maiden'
2 'Iona'
2 'Jupiter'
2 'Kim'
1 'Lotte'
2 'Lupus'
1 'Ma Cherie'
2 'Maria'
2 'Meteor Trail'
2 'Midnight Trail'
1 'Miki'
2 'Orion'
2 'Phoenix'
2 'Porcelain'
2 'Rococo Pink'
1 'Sarah'
1 'Silver Milestone Star'
2 'Starry Trail'
2 'Susi'
1 'Wonderland'

SALIX

8 ***alba*** 'Dart's Snake'
2 ***babylonica pekinensis***
1 ***caprea*** 'Weeping Sally' (f)
9 ***cordata***
2 ***daphnoïdes*** 'Oxford Violet'
0 x ***ehrhartiana***
0 x ***erdingeri***
0 ***eriocephala*** 'American Mackay'
0 x ***gillotii***
0 ***glabra***
0 ***gooddingii***
7 'Harlequin'
2 ***humilis***
0 ***kitaibeliana***
1 ***lucida***
0 ***mackenzieana***
9 x ***meyeriana***
2 'Micrugosa' (m)
1 ***myrtilloïdes***
9 ***pendulina elegantissima***
0 ***repens*** 'Pygmaea'
0 ***retusoïdes***
0 ***schwerinii***
0 x ***sirakawensis***
7 ***thibetica***
1 ***waldsteiniana***

SALVIA

9 ***apiana***
2 ***farinacea*** 'Porcelain'
0 ***huberi***
1 ***nelsonii***
1 ***nemorosa***
1 ***nubicola***
1 ***officinalis*** 'Cedric'
2 – 'Grete Stolze'
1 ***prostrata***
2 ***rosifolia***
2 ***semiatrata***
2 ***sessei***

SALVINIA

9 ***auriculata***

SAMBUCUS

2 ***alba*** 'Variegata'
9 ***caerulea***
1 ***canadensis*** 'Hidden Springs'
1 – 'John's'
1 ***mexicana***
2 ***nigra*** 'Albovariegata'
2 – 'Fructu Luteo'

SAPONARIA

2 x ***boissieri***
7 ***ocymoïdes*** 'Splendens'

SARCOPOTERIUM

9 ***spinosum***

SARRACENIA

9 ***alata*** x ***minor***
9 x ***excellens***
9 ***flava*** x ***alata***
9 x ***formosa***
9 x ***gilpinii***
9 ***psittacina*** x ***alata***
8 x ***wrigleyana***

SATUREJA

1 ***thymbra***

SAUSSUREA

2 ***ceratocarpa***

SAXIFRAGA

2 'Aladdin' (x ***borisii***) (8)
2 'Alan Hayhurst'
8 'Albida' (***callosa***) (7)
2 'Aphrodite' (***sempervivum***) (8)
2 'Apple Blossom' (12)
2 'Arabella' (x ***edithiae***) (8)
0 'Armida' (x ***boeckeleri***) (8)
2 'Avoca Gem'
2 'Balkan' (***marginata rocheliana***) (8)
2 'Beauty of Letchworth'
0 'Bellisant' (x ***hornibrookii***) (8)
1 'Ben Lawers' (***oppositifolia***) (9)
8 'Big MD' (***andersonii***) (8)
2 ***bronchialis*** (5)
1 'Buchholzii' (x ***fleischeri***) (8)
0 'Buster' (x ***hardingii***) (8)
2 'Cervinia' (***oppositifolia***) (9)
0 'Chelsea Pink' (x ***urbium***) (3)
2 ***cinerea*** (8)
1 'Clare' (x ***anglica***) (8)
2 'Crinkle' (3)
2 ***crustata vochinensis*** (7)
2 'Diana' (x ***lincoln-fosteri***) (8)
7 ***diversifolia*** (2)
0 'Dulcimer' (x ***petraschii***) (8)
0 'Felicity' (x ***anglica***) (8)
1 ***flagellaris flagellaris*** (2)
7 'Forsteriana' (***petraea***)
2 'Grace'
2 'Grandiflora' (***burseriana***) (8)
0 ***grisebachii montenegrina*** (8)
1 'Harlow Car' (8)
2 'Harry Marshall' (x ***irvingii***) (8)
8 ***hirsuta paucicrenata***
0 ***hypostoma*** (8)
0 'Intermedia' (***marginata***) (8)
2 'Josef Mánes' (x ***borisii***) (8)
0 'Jubilee' (x ***edithiae***) (8)
2 'Kew Green'
2 'Knapton Red' (12)
1 ***latepetiolata*** (11)
2 'Lismore Pink' (8)
2 'Loeflingii' (x ***grata***) (8)
0 ***lolaensis***
0 'London Cerise' (x ***urbium***) (3)
2 ***lyallii*** (1)
2 'Mangart' (***burseriana***) (8)
2 x ***mariae-theresiae*** (8)
8 ***michauxii*** (1)
2 'Midas' (x ***elisabethiae***) (8)
1 'Minor' (***marginata coriophylla***) (8)
2 'Monika' (***webrii***) (8)
7 ***mucronulata*** (2)
2 'Muffet' (***burseriana***) (8)
1 'Multipunctata' (***paniculata***) (7)
9 'Nana' (***bronchialis***) (5)
7 ***nipponica*** (4)
7 ***oppositifolia grandiflora*** (9)
0 – Iceland form (9)
2 – ssp. ***rudolphiana*** (9)
2 ***paniculata punctata*** (7)
1 x ***patens*** (6x7)
0 ***pedemontana cervicornis*** (12)
7 'Pike's Primrose' (12)
7 'Pike's White' (12)
2 'Pilatus' (x ***boydii***) (8)
2 'Pollux' (x ***boydii***) (8)
1 'Priestwood White' (12)
2 x ***pseudoforsteri*** (3)
2 'Pseudofranzii' (x ***paulinae***) (8)
1 'Pseudokellereri' (8)
2 'Pseudopaulinae' (x ***paulinae***) (8)
2 'Pseudopungens' (x ***apiculata***) (8)
2 'Pseudoscardica' (x ***wehrhahnii***) (8)
0 ***pulvinaria*** (8)
2 'Romeo' (x ***hornibrookii***) (8)
2 'Roy Clutterbuck'
2 'Russell Vincent Prichard' (x ***irvingii***) (8)
2 ***scardica erythrantha*** (8)
2 'Seissera' (***burseriana***) (8)
2 ***squarrosa*** (7)
8 'Subluteiviridis' (x ***gusmusii***) (8)
2 'Suendermannii Major' (x ***kellereri***) (8)
7 'Theresia' (x ***mariae-theresiae***)
8 ***vandellii*** (8)
1 'Variegata' (***exarata moschata***) (12)
7 'Wargrave Rose' (12)
8 'Waterperry' (***sempervivum***) (8)
2 'White Imp' (8)
9 'Zita' (8)

SCABIOSA

2 ***atropurpurea*** dark form
9 ***caucasica*** 'Backhouse'
2 – 'Floral Queen'
2 ***japonica*** 'Alba'
9 ***pseudograminifolia***
2 ***speciosa***

SCADOXUS

2 ***multiflorus multiflorus***

SCAEVOLA

1 'Blue Jade'

SCHEFFLERA

1 ***elegantissima***
1 – 'Castor'
1 – 'Castor Variegata'
0 'Starshine'

SCHIMA

9 ***yunnanensis***

SCHINUS

0 ***molle***
0 ***patagonicus***

SCHISANDRA

2 ***sphaerandra***

SCHIZOSTYLIS

8 ***coccinea*** 'Rosalie'
8 – 'Rose Glow'

SCILLA

0 ***bifolia danubialis***
2 ***litardierei hoogiana***
2 ***monanthos***
8 ***nivalis***
2 ***siberica*** 'Taurica'
1 ***vvedenskyi***

SCINDAPSUS

0 ***pictus argyraeus***

SCLERANTHUS

2 ***brockiei***

SCROPHULARIA

2 ***grandiflora***

SCUTELLARIA

0 ***albida***
2 ***alpina*** 'Alba'
1 ***ovata***
2 ***ventenatii***

SEDUM

1 ***album album balticum***
1 – ***ibizicum***
1 – ssp. ***teretifolium*** var. ***turgidum***
1 ***alfredii nagasakianum***
1 ***allantoïdes***
1 ***alsinifolium fragrans***
1 ***amecamecanum***
1 ***anglicum anglicum hibernicum***

1 – ***microphyllum***
1 – ssp. ***pyrenaicum***
1 ***apoleipon***
2 x ***battandieri***
1 ***borissovae***
1 ***borschii***
1 ***brevifolium induratum***
1 – var. ***novum***
1 ***brissemoretii***
1 ***burrito***
1 ***caducum***
0 ***cauticola*** 'Robustum'
1 ***cepaea gracilescens***
1 ***chontalense***
1 ***clavatum***
1 ***cockerellii***
1 ***commixtum***
1 ***compactum***
1 ***compressum***
1 ***craigii***
1 ***dasyphyllum oblongifolium***
1 – ***suendermannii***
1 ***decumbens***
1 ***dendroïdeum***
1 ***diffusum***
2 'Eleanor Fisher'
1 ***ewersii cyclophyllum***
2 – ***hayesii***
1 ***forsterianum purpureum***
1 ***frutescens***
1 ***furfuraceum***
1 ***fusiforme***
1 ***greggii***
1 'Harvest Moon'
1 ***hemsleyanum***
1 ***hispanicum*** 'Pewter'
1 ***indicum densirosulatum***
1 – ***yunnanense***
1 ***japonicum***
1 – var. ***senanense***
1 ***kostovii***
1 ***laconicum***
1 ***lancerottense***
1 ***laxum***
1 ***liebmannianum***
9 ***lineare*** 'Major'
1 'Little Gem'
1 ***longipes***
1 ***lucidum***
1 – 'Obesum'
1 x ***luteolum***
1 x ***luteoviride***
1 ***magellense***
1 ***moranii***
1 ***multiflorum***
1 ***nanifolium***
1 ***nussbaumerianum***
1 ***nutans***
1 ***oaxacanum***
1 ***obcordatum***
1 ***ochroleucum montanum***
2 ***oreades***
9 ***oreganum boreale***
1 ***oryzifolium***
1 ***oxycoccoïdes***
1 ***oxypetalum***
2 ***parvum***
9 ***pluricaule*** 'Rosenteppich' ('Rose Carpet')
1 ***potosinum***
9 ***reflexum albescens***
8 – 'Major'
1 – 'Viride'
1 ***reptans***
1 – ***carinatifolium***
1 ***rosulatobulbosum***
1 ***rubens***
1 – ***praegeri***
1 x ***rubrotinctum*** 'Aurora'
1 ***rupifragum***
1 ***ruwenzoriense***
9 ***sediforme*** 'Gran Canaria'
1 ***serpentinii***
1 ***sexangulare elatum***
1 ***sieboldii ettyuense***
1 ***spectabile*** 'Carmen'
2 – 'Green Ice'
1 – 'Humile'
1 ***spurium*** 'Bronze Carpet'
1 – ***carneum***
1 – ***salmoneum***
1 ***stefco***
1 ***stelliforme***
1 ***stenopetalum***
1 ***subtile***
1 ***treleasei***
9 ***tschernokolevii***
1 ***tuberiferum***
1 ***urvillei***
1 – Hillebrandtii Group
1 – Sartorianum Group
1 – Stribrnyi Group
1 ***versadense***
1 – ***villadioïdes***
0 ***yabeanum***
1 ***yesoense***
1 ***zentaro-tashiroi***

SELAGINELLA
2 ***lepidophylla***
2 ***sanguinolenta***

SELAGO
2 ***thunbergii***

SEMPERVIVUM
1 'Alaric'
9 'Big Red'
1 'Blue Moon'
0 ***calcareum*** 'Benz'
0 'Caliph's Hat'
8 ***ciliosum*** x ***leucanthum***
8 'Clipper'
0 ***davisii***
1 'Disco Dancer'
1 ***dolomiticum***
0 'Dunstan'
1 ***erythraeum*** 'Red Velvet'
2 'Ford's Shadows'
2 'Georgette'
2 ***glabrifolium***
0 ***globiferum***
1 'Haullauer's Seedling'
9 'Jubilation'
9 'Jungle Shadows'
8 'Kolagas Mayfair'
9 'Kristina'
1 'Kubi'
1 Le Clair's Hybrid No 4
0 ***leucanthum***
0 'Madame Arsac'
8 ***marmoreum***
x ***dinaricum*** from Karawanken
0 ***minus***
0 ***montanum carpaticum*** 'Cmiral's Yellow'
9 'Mors'
8 'Mount Usher'
0 'Mrs Elliott'
7 ***pumilum***
x ***arachnoïdeum***
0 'Purdy's 90-1'
9 'Red Planet'
0 'Red Rum'
9 'Roosemaryn'
1 x ***roseum***
1 'Rotund'
2 'Rubrum Ash'
8 'Ruby'
8 'Samba'
9 'Sponnier'
9 'Syston Flame'
8 ***tectorum cantalicum***
9 'Wega'
9 'Witchery'
0 ***zeleborii*** x ***kosaninii*** from Koprivnik

SENECIO
0 ***adonidifolius***
1 ***canus***
1 ***confusus***
8 ***doronicum***
0 ***hypochionaeus argaeus***
1 ***incanus carniolicus***
1 ***jacquemontianus***
9 ***littoralis***
2 ***natalensis***
2 ***pectinatus***

SENNA
8 ***acutifolia***
2 ***candolleana***
1 ***retusa***

SERENOA
0 ***repens***

SESBANIA
2 ***punicea***

SHORTIA
0 ***galacifolia***
0 – ***brevistyla***
9 x ***interdexta*** 'Wimborne'
0 ***soldanelloïdes magna***
0 – ***minima***
1 ***uniflora***
9 – ***kantoensis***

SIBBALDIOPSIS
2 ***tridentata***

SIDALCEA
0 'Rose Bouquet'

SILENE
0 ***acaulis variegata***
1 ***altaica***
1 'Bill Mackenzie'
0 ***burchellii***
1 ***caryophylloïdes echinus***
0 ***dioica*** 'Tresevern Gold'
9 ***hookeri bolanderi***
2 ***laciniata***
8 'Pink Bells'
1 ***rupestris***
9 ***saxifraga***
8 ***schafta*** 'Robusta'
1 ***scouleri***
1 ***vulgaris prostrata***

SINNINGIA
2 'Brilliant Scarlet'
2 'Royal Purple'

SINOJACKIA
2 ***xylocarpa***

SINOWILSONIA
2 ***henryi***

SISYMBRIUM
9 ***officinale***

SISYRINCHIUM
2 ***californicum*** British Columbia form
2 ***convolutum***

SKIMMIA
9 ***japonica*** 'Stoneham Red'
0 ***multinervia***

SMYRNIUM
9 ***perfoliatum rotundifolium***

SOLANUM
1 ***aculeatissimum***
0 ***capsicastrum*** 'Variegatum'
0 ***elaeagnifolium***
1 ***muricatum*** 'Ryburn'
0 ***valdiviense***
1 – 'Variegatum'

SOLDANELLA
2 x ***ganderi***

SOLENOPSIS
1 ***erianthum***

SOLIDAGO
9 'Goldenplume'
2 'Goldwedel'
8 'Leraft'
0 ***multiradiata***
2 'Septembergold'
0 ***spathulata***
0 ***ulmifolia***

SOPHORA
9 ***japonica*** 'Violacea'
1 ***tetraptera*** 'Goughensis'
2 – 'Grandiflora'

SORBUS
8 ***aucuparia*** 'Pendula'
2 'Ethel's Gold'
2 ***folgneri***
1 ***graeca***
1 ***hupehensis obtusa*** 'Rufus'
0 ***mougeotii***

2 *randaiensis*
2 'Red Marbles'
2 'Signalman'
2 'Tundra'

SPARTINA
1 *pectinata* 'Variegata'

SPATHICARPA
0 *sagittifolia*

SPATHIPHYLLUM
0 *cannifolium*
0 *cochlearispathum*
0 *cuspidatum*
0 *floribundum*
0 'Mauna Loa'
0 'McCoy'
0 *patinii*

SPHENOTOMA
1 *gracilis*

SPIGELIA
2 *marilandica*

SPIRAEA
2 *trilobata*

STACHYS
7 *corsica*

STACHYTARPHETA
1 *jamaicensis*

STACHYURUS
9 *himalaicus*
1 *leucotrichus*
9 *spinosus*

STANLEYA
0 *pinnata*
8 *pinnatifida*

STENANTHIUM
9 *robustum*

STENOTUS
8 *andersonii*

STICTOCARDIA
2 *beraviensis*

STIPA
1 *atropurpurea*
2 *turkestanica*

STREPTOCARPUS
2 'Eira'

STREPTOPUS
0 *axillaris*
1 *simplex*

STROBILANTHES
2 *urticifolius*

STROMANTHE
0 *porteana*

STYRAX
9 *americana*
2 *dasyanthus*
0 *officinalis*
2 *wilsonii*

SUCCISA
9 *pratensis rosea*

SUTERA
2 *pristisepala*

SWAINSONA
1 *procumbens*

SWERTIA
0 *longifolia*
1 *petiolata*

SYMPHORICARPOS
2 x *doorenbosii* 'Erect'

SYMPHYANDRA
2 *ossettica* hybrids

SYMPHYTUM
1 *officinale* 'Bohemicum'

SYNEILESIS
1 *palmata*

SYNGONIUM
0 *podophyllum*

SYNTHYRIS
0 *pinnatifida lanuginosa*

SYRINGA
9 x *chinensis*
2 x *henryi*
7 x *hyacinthiflora* 'Alice Eastwood'
2 – 'Blue Hyacinth'
8 – 'Buffon'
2 – 'Clarke's Giant'
2 *julianae*
0 'Minuet'
0 'Miss Canada'
9 *oblata*
9 x *persica* 'Gigantea'
1 x *prestoniae* 'Coral'
9 – 'Desdemona'
9 – 'Hiawatha'
1 – 'James Macfarlane'
1 – 'Nocturne'
1 – 'Redwine'
1 *reticulata* 'Ivory Silk'
9 *vulgaris* 'Alphonse Lavallée' (d)
9 – 'Ambassadeur'
9 – 'Charles X'
2 – 'Ellen Willmott' (d)
9 – 'Etna'
9 – 'General John Pershing' (d)
7 – 'Lavaliensis'
9 – 'Maréchal de Bassompierre' (d)
9 – 'Maréchal Foch' (d)
0 – 'Marie Legraye'
7 – 'Monique Lemoine' (d)
7 – 'Night'
2 – 'Paul Thirion' (d)
7 – 'Réaumur'
9 – 'Ruhm von Horstenstein'
9 – 'Souvenir d'Alice Harding' (d)
0 – 'William Robinson' (d)
0 *wolfii*

TAIWANIA
2 *cryptomerioïdes*

TALINUM
1 *okanoganense* pink stem form
2 *parviflorum*

TANACETUM
9 *bipinnatum*
9 *coccineum* 'Bees' Pink Delight'
2 – 'Jubilee Gem'
0 – 'Kelway's Glorious'
9 – 'Langport Scarlet'
0 – 'Marjorie Robinson'
8 – 'Red King'
2 – 'Salmon Beauty'
1 – 'Sam Robinson'
7 – 'Silver Challenger'
7 *corymbosum clusii*
9 *dolichophyllum*
2 *parthenium* 'Snowball' (d)
2 – 'Spirit'
2 – 'Sundew'

TARAXACUM
1 *albidum*

TAXODIUM
2 *distichum* 'Pendens'

TAXUS
0 *baccata* 'Cavendishii'
1 – 'Cheshuntensis'
1 – 'Glauca'
2 – 'Grayswood Hill'
2 – 'Lutea'
7 – 'Nana'
9 – 'Prostrata'
0 – 'Pyramidalis'
9 *cuspidata*
7 – 'Densa'
0 x *hunnewelliana* 'Richard Horsey'
0 x *media* 'Halloran'
1 – 'Kelseyi'
1 – 'Skalborg'

TECOMA
1 *garrocha*

TELLIMA
1 *grandiflora* 'Perky'
0 – 'Pinky'

TEPHROSERUS
2 *takedanus*

TETRADIUM
7 *velutinum*

TETRANEURIS
1 *acaulis caespitosa*
0 – *glabra*
2 – *ivesiana*

TEUCRIUM
9 *polium pii-fontii*
8 *subspinosum roseum*
2 *webbianum*

THALICTRUM
8 *delavayi* 'Amethystine'
2 *ichangense*
8 *petaloïdes*
2 *reniforme*

THELYPTERIS
9 *dentata*

THLASPI
9 *alpinum auerswalde*

THRINAX
0 *parviflora*

THUJA
7 *occidentalis* 'Cloth of Gold'
8 – 'Columbia'
2 – 'Globosa Compacta Nana'
2 – 'Indomitable'
1 – 'Madurodam'
2 – 'Malonyana'
0 – 'Mastersii'
0 – 'Robusta'
8 – 'Semperaurea'
2 – 'Vervaeneana'
1 *orientalis* 'Berckman'
1 – 'Green Cone'
9 – 'Hillieri'
2 – 'Madurodam'
2 *plicata* 'Extra Gold'
8 – 'Savill Gardens'
2 *standishii*

THYMUS
2 *carnosus* 'Argenteus'
0 *corsicus*
1 *hirsutus*
1 *hyemalis* 'Albus'
7 *praecox arcticus minus*
2 *serpyllum* 'Carol Ann' (v)
7 – 'Little Heath'
1 – 'Pink Ripple'
2 – 'Silver Dew'
8 – 'Winter Beauty'
7 'Southcombe Spreader'
9 *striatus*
9 'Widecombe'
8 'Wintergold'

TIGRIDIA
2 *van-houttei*

TILIA
1 x *flavescens*

TILLANDSIA
2 *achyrostachys*
2 *aëranthos*
2 *albertiana*
2 *albida*
2 *anceps*
2 *andreana*
2 *andrieuxii*
2 *araujei*
2 *arhiza*
2 *atroviridipetala*
2 *bartramii*
2 *bergeri*
2 *cacticola*
2 *capitata* 'Peach'
2 – 'Rubra'
2 *carlsoniae*
2 *chiapensis*
2 *complanata*
2 *compressa*
2 *concolor*
2 *crocata*
2 *disticha*
2 *duratii*
2 *ehlersiana*
2 *elizabethiae*
2 *erubescens*
2 *exserta*

2 *fasciculata*
2 *festucoïdes*
2 *flexuosa*
2 *floribunda*
2 *funckiana*
2 *gymnobotrya*
2 *hammeri*
2 *harrisii*
2 *incarnata*
2 *ionantha stricta*
2 – var. *vanhyningii*
2 *ixioïdes*
2 *jaliscomonticola*
2 *kautskyi*
2 *kirchhoffiana*
2 *latifolia divaricata*
2 *leiboldiana*
2 *loliacea*
2 *lucida*
2 *macdougallii*
2 *makoyana*
2 *mallemontii*
2 *massiliense vivipara*
2 *mauryana*
2 *meridionalis*
2 *mima*
2 *mitlaensis*
2 *monadelpha*
2 *multicaulis*
2 *multiflora*
2 *myosura*
2 *neglecta*
2 *paleacea*
2 *paucifolia*
2 – *prolifera*
2 *plagiotropica*
2 *plumosa*
2 *pruinosa*
2 *pseudobaileyi*
2 *pueblensis*
2 *purpurea*
2 *recurvata*
2 *roland-gosselinii*
2 *schatzlii*
2 *schiedeana glabrior*
2 – *major*
2 *setacea*
2 *straminea*
2 *streptocarpa*
2 *streptophylla*
2 *stricta*
2 *tectorum*
2 *tenuifolia*
2 – var. *saxicola*
2 – var. *tenuifolia*
2 *tricholepis*
2 *tricolor*
2 *usneoïdes*
2 *variabllis*
2 *vernicosa*
2 *viridiflora*

TITHONIA
2 *rotundifolia*

TONESTUS
1 *pygmaeus*

TORREYA
0 *grandis*
0 *nucifera* 'Spreadeagle'

TOWNSENDIA
1 *eximia*
1 *grandiflora*
0 *hirsuta*
2 *incana*

TRACHYMENE
0 *humilis*

TRADESCANTIA
0 x *andersoniana* 'Lilacina Plena'
8 – 'Purple Glow'
9 – 'Taplow Crimson'
7 *brevicaulis caerulea*
0 *spathacea*
2 *tabulaemontana*

TRAGOPOGON
0 *ruber*

TREVESIA
9 *palmata* 'Micholitzii'

TRICYRTIS
2 *affinis*
9 *formosana* 'Variegata'
0 *hirta* dwarf form
1 *japonica* 'Kinkazan'

TRIENTALIS
2 *europaea rosea*

TRILLIUM
2 *decumbens*
2 *discolor*
2 *erectum roseum*
9 *flexipes*
2 *nervosum*
2 *pusillum*
2 *rugelii* pink form

TRIOSTEUM
1 *erythrocarpum*

TRIPETALEIA
2 *bracteata*

TRITICUM
2 *spelta*

TROCHOCARPA
2 *gunnii*

TROLLIUS
8 x *cultorum* 'Byrne's Giant'
0 – 'Empire Day'
0 – 'Glory of Leiden'
0 – 'Meteor'
0 – 'Orange Glow'
0 – 'Orangekönig'
0 – 'Oranje Nassau'
0 – 'T Smith'
0 – 'Yellow Beauty'
0 *stenopetalus*

TROPAEOLUM
1 *polyphyllum*

TSUGA
7 *canadensis* 'Dawsonia'
7 – 'Essex'
7 – 'Gentsch Variegated'
2 – 'Nana Gracilis'
2 *caroliniana*
7 *chinensis tchekiangensis*
7 *dumosa*
2 *heterophylla* 'Greenmantle'
2 – 'Laursen's Column'
2 *mertensiana* 'Glauca'
0 *sieboldii*
9 *yunnanensis*

TUBERARIA
9 *globulariifolia*

TULBAGHIA
1 *capensis* 'Variegatus'

TULIPA
9 'Aga Khan'
1 'Akela' (3)
9 'Annie Salomons' (14)
1 'Astarte' (3)
2 *aximensis*
1 'Baby Doll' (2)
1 'Ballerina' (6)
1 'Baronesse' (3)
1 Beauty Queen ® (1)
1 *biflora* forms
1 'Bird of Paradise' (10)
1 'Black Diamond' (5)
9 'Blushing Beauty' (5)
9 'Blushing Bride' (5)
1 *buhseana*
9 'Chatham' (5)
1 'China Lady' (14)
1 'Christmas Dream' (1)
1 *clusiana chrysantha* 'Diplomate' (4)
9 'Compostella' (14)
9 'Dante' (2)
9 'Demeter' (5)
9 'Dreamboat' (14)
1 'Dreamland' (5)
9 'Dutch Princess' (3)
1 Early Glory ® (3)
9 'Ellen Willmott' (6)
1 Fire Queen ® (1)
1 'Françoise' (5)
1 'Gerbrand Kieft' (11)
9 'Gold Coin'
8 *goulimyi*
1 'Hamilton' (7)
2 'Happy Family' (3)
9 'Hocus Pocus' (5)
1 'Ivory Floradale' (4)
1 'Jenny' (1)
1 *julia*
1 'Juri Gagarin' (14)
1 'Lady Montgomery' (11)
1 'Laverock' (7)
1 'Leen van der Mark' (3)
9 'Lutea Major' (10)
1 'Majestic' (14)
1 'Modern Style' (5)
9 'Musical' (3)
9 'Niphetos' (5)
1 'Noranda' (7)
8 'Orange Boy' (12)
1 'Orange King' (5)
2 'Orange Toronto' (14)
0 *orphanidea* 'Splendens'
1 'Oscar' (3)
9 Peacock strain (*greigii* x *kaufmanniana*)
9 'Pink Emperor' (13)
0 *planifolia*
9 'Primrose' (12)
9 'Prince Charles' (3)
2 'Princesse Charmante' (14)
1 'Red Reflection' (14)
2 'Rhodos' (5)
1 'Rococo' (10)
1 'Rosanna' (14)
1 'Rosella' (5)
1 'Rosy Queen' (2)
1 'Salmon Parrot' (10)
9 'Show Girl' (5)
1 'Smyrna' (14)
1 'Sun Dance' (14)
2 'Sylvia Warder' (14)
9 'Tambour Maître' (3)
9 'Tarakan' (5)
1 'Temple of Beauty' (5)
9 'Timay'
1 'Treasure' (14)
1 Trendsetter ® (3)
8 *vvedenskyi* 'Josef Marks'
0 – 'Orange Sunset'
9 'Water Lily'
1 'Wienerwald' (3)
1 'Wirosa' (11)
1 'Yellow Parrot' (10)
9 'Yellow River'

TUTCHERIA
9 *spectabilis*

UGNI
0 *molinae* 'Variegata'

ULEX
2 *europaeus* 'Dubloon'

ULMUS
9 *glabra* 'Lutescens'
2 – 'Pendula'
2 'Louis van Houtte'
0 *minor* 'Sarniensis'

UNGNADIA
7 *speciosa*

URSINIA
2 *chrysanthemoïdes*
1 *sericea*

UVULARIA
2 *caroliniana*

VACCINIUM
2 *angustifolium*
2 *corymbosum* 'Blue Ray'
2 – 'Earliblue'
9 – 'Tifblue'
9 – 'Woodward'
2 *membranaceum*
2 *myrsinites*
1 *nubigenus*
9 *ovalifolium*
2 *sprengelii*

VEITCHIA
2 *merrillii*

VERBASCUM
2 Cotswold Hybrid Group 'Hartleyi'
9 'Golden Bush'
9 *pestalozzae*
1 *undulatum*

VERBENA
2 *bipinnatifida*
2 'Cardinal'
1 'Heckter'

1 ***peruviana*** Japanese form

VERONICA
7 ***armena rosea***
8 ***cusickii***
7 x ***cynarium***
0 'Green Mound'
0 ***kotschyana***
0 ***nipponica***
0 ***tauricola*** Ala Dag
8 ***virgata***

VIBURNUM
7 'Aldenhamensis'
1 ***burejaeticum***
1 ***calvum***
1 ***dentatum***
1 – var. ***pubescens*** 'Longifolium'
9 ***dilatatum*** 'Erie'
0 ***erosum***
2 ***grandiflorum*** Foetens Group
2 ***hupehense***
1 ***ichangense***
1 ***kansuense***
2 ***lobophyllum***
1 ***mullaha***
1 ***opulus*** 'Andrews'
1 – 'Apricot'
2 – 'Flore Pleno'
1 – 'Hans'
2 – 'Harvest Gold'
9 – 'Wentworth'
1 ***parvifolium***
2 ***plicatum*** 'Rosace'
2 – 'Roseum'
2 ***propinquum***
2 ***prunifolium***
2 ***rigidum***
2 ***setigerum sulcatum***
2 ***tinus*** 'Little Bognor'
2 ***trilobum***
1 ***veitchii***

VICIA
9 ***bithynica***
0 ***orobus***

VICTORIA
0 ***amazonica***
0 ***cruziana***

VILLADIA
1 ***ramossisima***

VINCA
2 ***difformis argentea***

VIOLA
0 'Adam's Gold' (Va)
1 ***adunca***
2 'Agnes Susannah'
1 'Anna' (Va)
9 'Arlington' (C)
9 ***arvensis***
2 'Avalanche' (Va)
2 'Avril Lawson'
2 'Baby Blue'
2 'Baby Franjo'
2 'Bambini' (Va)
0 'Barbara Swan' (ExV)
0 'Beth'
0 ***betonicifolia*** white flowered form
9 ***blanda***
2 'Blue Carpet' (Va)
2 'Blue Heaven' (Va)
2 'Blue Perfection' (Va)
1 'Blue Ripple'
2 'Blue Skies' (C)
0 'Blue Waves'
7 'Bob's Bedder'
1 'Bonnie Heather' (Va)
9 ***camschatalorum***
9 ***canina montana***
9 'Captivation'
2 'Carnival' (Va)
2 'Cat's Whiskers'
2 'Cendrillon' (Vt)
9 ***cenisia***
9 'Chandler's Glory'
0 'Cheekie Chappie'
2 'Colwall' (C)
2 'Constellation'
0 ***cornuta*** pale blue
1 – ***rotundiflora***
9 ***crassiuscula***
2 'Cuty' (Va)
2 CW 5021
2 'Devon Cream' (Va)
2 'Double Blue' (dVt)
2 'Double Russian' (dVt)
1 'Evelyn Jackson' (Va)
0 'Fairy Tales' (Va)
9 ***gracilis*** x ***cornuta***
0 'Haze' (Va)
1 'Horrie' (Va)
1 'Irina' (Va)
8 'Jane' (Va)
0 'Jenny Wren' (Va)
8 'Joanna' (Va)
1 'John Rodger' (SP)
1 'Josie'
0 'Kathleen Williams' (ExV)
0 ***keiskii***
8 'Lady May'
0 'Lady Saville'
2 'Lindy'
2 'Little Johnny' (Va)
1 'Lizzie's Favourite' (Va)
2 ***lutea lutea***
9 'Magic Lantern'
7 'Major'
0 ***mandshurica triangularis bicolor***
0 'Mandy Miller' (Va)
2 'Marquis de Brazais' (Vt)
2 'Mayfly' (Va)
2 'Melita'
9 'Moonshadow'
2 'Moonshine'
1 'Moseley Bedder'
0 'Mrs Alex Forrest' (ExV)
7 'Nickie's Blue' (C)
0 ***odorata*** blue double
0 – 'Caerulea Plena'
9 'Old Blue'
8 'Old Jordans'
2 'Oxbrook Cream'
0 'Peggy Brookes' (FP)
0 'Roem van Aalsmeer'
2 'Royal Picotee'
1 ***sempervirens***
1 'Spey' (C)
2 'Sulphur Queen'
2 'Sybil Cornfield'
1 'The Clevedon Violet' (Vt)
9 ***tricolor subalpina***
9 'Triumph' (Vt)
1 'Tropical Waves'
2 x ***visseriana***
0 'Wendy' (SP)
1 'White Waves'

VITALIANA
2 ***primuliflora cinerea***
2 – silver-leaved form

VITEX
7 ***agnus-castus*** 'Albus'
2 ***incisa***
1 ***negundo heterophylla***

VITIS
2 ***betulifolia***
2 ***davidii***
1 – var. ***cyanocarpa***
8 'Isabella' (***vinifera***)
1 'Madame Mathias Muscat' (***vinifera***)
8 ***piasezkii***
1 'Wabetta' (***vinifera***)

VRIESEA
2 ***barclayana barclayana***
2 – var. ***minor***
2 ***cereicola***
2 ***espinosae***
2 'Favorite'
0 ***fenestralis***
0 ***fosteriana***
0 – 'Red Chestnut'
0 ***gigantea***
2 Hitchcockiana
2 'Margot'
0 ***platynema***
0 – 'Variegata'
2 ***rauhii***
1 ***splendens*** 'Fire'
2 ***tequendamae***
2 Tiffany
2 ***zamorensis***

WAHLENBERGIA
7 ***cartilaginea***
1 ***gloriosa*** white form
2 ***lobelioïdes***
2 ***undulata***

WALDSTEINIA
2 ***rosaceae***

WASHINGTONIA
0 ***lindenii***

WATSONIA
0 ***fourcadei***
1 ***marginata alba***
7 'Starspike'
2 ***tabularis***
2 Tresco hybrids

WEIGELA
9 'Conquête'
2 ***florida venusta***
8 ***japonica***
7 'Kosteriana Variegata'
1 ***lonicera***
2 ***praecox***
0 'Stelzneri'
9 ***subsessilis***
9 'Van Houttei'

WISTERIA
9 ***floribunda*** 'Kuchi-beni'

WOODWARDIA
0 ***orientalis***

WULFENIA
2 ***amherstiana***
2 ***baldaccii***
2 x ***suendermanii***

XANTHOSOMA
0 ***violaceum***

YUCCA
0 ***aloifolia*** 'Purpurea'
9 ***brevifolia***
2 ***filamentosa*** 'Schneefichte'
9 ***gloriosa*** 'Albovariegata'

ZAMIOCULCAS
0 ***zamiifolia***

ZANTEDESCHIA
1 ***angustiloba***
2 'Aztec Gold'
2 'Dusky Pink'
1 'Galaxy'
2 'Golden Affair'
1 'Golden Sun'
1 'Lady Luck'
2 'Majestic Red'
1 'Treasure'

ZANTHOXYLUM
2 ***schinifolium***

ZENOBIA
7 ***pulverulenta nitida***

ZEPHYRANTHES
1 ***drummondii***

ZIERIA
8 ***arborescens***

ZIGADENUS
9 ***glaberrimus***
1 ***muscitoxicus***

ZINNIA
1 ***grandiflora***

Hardy Plant Society Search List

The following plants, for which no source is known in the British Isles, are being sought by the Hardy Plant Society. If any one knows the whereabouts of any items, seed or plant, on this list, in the British Isles or overseas, would they please contact:-
Mrs Jean Sambrook, Garden Cottage, 214 Ruxley Lane, West Ewell, Surrey KT19 9EZ

ABRONIA
umbellata

ACAENA
caesiiglauca 'Frikart'

ACONITUM
delavayi
fletcherianum
paniculatum
– 'Nanum'
pulchellum

ADENOPHORA
takedae 'Alba'

ADONIS
dahurica 'Pleniflora'

AGAPANTHUS
'Dorothy Palmer'
nutans
praecox
'Aureovariegatus'
'Rosemary'
'Victoria'

AGERATUM
orientale 'Leichtlinii'
– 'Pallidum'

AJUGA
genevensis 'Pink Beauty'
reptans 'Silver Beauty'
– 'Silver Carpet'

ALLIUM
protensum
regelii

ALSTROEMERIA
'Afterglow'
'Ballerina'
caryophyllea
– 'Alba'
haemantha 'Parigo Charm'
pelegrina 'Alba'
'Sonata'
violacea

AMARYLLIS
bella-donna 'Barberton'
– 'Cape Town'
– 'Elata' ('Pallida')
– 'Jagersfontein'
– 'Maxima'
– 'Rosea'
– 'Rosea Perfecta'
– 'Spectabilis' ('S. Tricolor')

ANEMONE
glauciifolia
hupehensis 'Crispa'
x ***hybrida*** 'Beauté Parfait'

– 'Brilliant'
– 'Collerette'
– 'Herbstrose'
– 'Herzblut'
– 'Lady Ardilaun'
– 'Lord Ardilaun'
– 'Magdalena Uhink'
– 'Magenta'
– 'Mignon'
– 'Stuttgard'
– 'Treasure'
– 'Turban'
– 'Vase d'Argent'
nemorosa 'Rubra Plena'
tenuifolia

ANTHEMIS
tinctoria 'Moonlight'
– 'Perry's Variety'

ARISAEMA
angustina

ARISTOLOCHIA
moupinensis

ARMERIA
maritima white foliage

ARTEMISIA
ifranensis

ARUM
besserianum
longispathum
orientale danicum

ASARUM
shuttleworthii 'Callaway'

ASCLEPIAS
tuberosa 'Gerbe d'Or'

ASPARAGUS
officinalis pseudoscaber 'Spitzenschleier'
tenuifolius

ASPHODELINE
amurensis 'Flore Pleno'
lutea 'Flore Pleno'

ASTER
amellus 'Bessie Chapman'
paternus
sedifolius canus
sericeus
thomsonii 'Winchmore Hill'

ASTILBE
x ***crispa*** 'Pygmaea Rosea'

'Gladstone' (x ***arendsii***)
'King Albert' (x ***arendsii***)

'Mars' (x ***arendsii***)
'Queen Alexander' (x ***arendsii***)

ASYNEUMA
campanuloïdes

ATHYRIUM
vidalii

AUBRIETA
'Aileen'
'King of the Purples'
'Purple Splendour'

BAPTISIA
alba
perfoliata

BEGONIA
grandis 'Maria'
– 'Simsii'

BELLIS
perennis 'Eliza'
– 'Helichrysiflora'
– 'Lutea'
– 'Madame Crousse'
– 'Mavourneen'
– 'Mount Etna'
– 'Rubriflora'
– 'Victoria'

BERGENIA
crassifolia 'Variegata'
'Distinction'
'Walter Kienli'

BERKHEYA
macrophylla

BETA
vulgaris 'Variegata'

BOMAREA
andimarcana
carderi

BRASSICA
Four Seasons Cabbage

BRUNNERA
macrophylla 'Blaukuppel'

BULBINELLA
modesta

BUPLEURUM
ranunculoïdes 'Canalease'

CACCINIA
macrantha

CALCEOLARIA
alba
integrifolia white form

CALTHA
laeta alpestris
leptosepala 'Grandiflora'
– var. ***leptosepala*** blue flowered form
novae-zelandiae
palustris Elata Group
– 'Pallida Plena'
– 'Pleurisepala'
– 'Purpurascens'
– 'Semiplena'
– Silvestris Group

CALYSTEGIA
gigantea

CAMASSIA
leitchtlinii 'Orion'

CAMPANULA
'Fergusonii'
'Gremlin'
'Pamela'
persicifolia 'Blue Bell'
– 'Spetchley'
'Profusion'
rapunculoïdes 'Plena'
trachelium 'Versicolor'
'Woodstock'
zoysii alba

CANNA
'Feuerzauber'
x ***generalis*** 'America'
'Liebesglut'

CARDAMINE
nemorosa 'Plena'

CATANANCHE
caerulea 'Perry's White'

CENTAUREA
atropurpurea 'Alba'

CENTRANTHUS
ruber 'Bragg's Variety'

CHAEROPHYLLUM
hirsutum 'Rubriflorum'

CHASMANTHE
intermedia

CHELONE
obliqua 'Praecox Nana'

CIMICIFUGA
simplex 'Braunlaub' variegated form

CLEMATIS
recta 'Plena'

COCHLEARIA
officinalis 'Variegata'

COLCHICUM
callicymbium 'Danton'
guadarramense
'Mr Kerbert'
'President Coolidge'
triphyllum

CONVALLARIA
majalis 'Gigantea'
– 'Robusta'
– 'Rosea Plena'

CONVOLVULUS
pentapetaloïdes

COREOPSIS
grandiflora 'Perry's Variety'
CORTADERIA
selloana 'Bertini'
– 'Monstrosa'
COSMOS
scabiosoïdes
CRAMBE
pinnatifida
CRINUM
x *powellii* 'Krelagei'
– 'Variegatum'
CROCOSMIA
'Mephistopheles'
CROCUS
'Albidus'
chrysanthus 'Al Jolson'
– 'Andromeda'
– 'Atom'
– 'Aubade'
– 'Belle Jaune'
– 'Bloemfontein'
– 'Blue Beauty'
– 'Blue Bonnet'
– 'Blue Butterfly'
– 'Blue Jacket'
– 'Blue Jay'
– 'Blue Princess'
– 'Blue Rock'
– 'Blue Throat'
– 'Bullfinch'
– 'Bumble-bee'
– 'Buttercup'
– 'Constellation'
– 'Crescendo'
– 'Cum Laude'
– 'Cupido'
– 'Curlew'
– 'Dandy'
– 'Distinction'
– 'Golden Pheasant'
– 'Golden Plover'
– 'Goldene Sonne'
– 'Grand Gala'
– 'Grey Lady'
– 'Harlequin'
– 'Ivory Glory'
– 'Ivory Glow'
– 'Jester'
– 'Johan Cruyff'
– 'Khaki'
– 'Koh-i-Nor'
– 'Lemon Queen'
– 'Lentejuweel'
– 'Lilette'
– 'Lilliputaner'
– 'Magic'
– 'Mannequin'
– 'Mariette'
– 'Marion'
– 'Marlene'
– 'Morning Star'
– 'Mrs Moon'
– 'Mystic'
– 'Nanette'
– 'Olympiade'
– 'Opal'
– 'Palette'
– 'Parade'
– 'Paradiso'
– 'Plaisir'
– 'Reverence'
– 'Rising Sun'
– 'Ruby Gown'
– 'Shot'
– 'Siskin'
– 'Solfatare'
– 'Solo'
– 'Sorrento'
– 'Spotlight'
– 'Spring Song'
– 'Sulphur Glory'
– 'Sunset'
– 'Sunshine'
– 'Susie'
– 'Symphonia'
– 'Topolino'
– 'Trance'
– 'Uschak Orange'
– 'White Egret'
– 'White Splendour'
– 'Winter Gold'
– 'Yellow Gem'
– 'Yellow Hammer'
– 'Yellow Queen'
vernus 'Blue Ribbon'
CYPRIPEDIUM
arietinum
candidum
montanum
tibeticum
x *ventricosum*
DACTYLIS
glomerata aurea
DACTYLORHIZA
elata white form
majalis 'Glasnevin'
DAHLIA
'Emperor Franz-Joseph'
DEINANTHE
caerulea alba
DELPHINIUM
brachycentrum
grandiflorum white form
DENDRANTHEMA
'Anna Hay' (30)
'Apollo'
'Ceres'
'Jean Harlowe'
pacificum 'Silver & Gold'
'Tiny'
'Venus' (30k)
DIANTHUS
'Beverley Pink' (p)
'Black Prince' (p)
'Evelyn'
'Granado' (b)
'Lambrook Beauty' (p)
'Lincolnshire Lass' (p)
'Lucy Glendill' (b)
'Old Man's Head' (p)
'Ruth Fischer' (p)
DICENTRA
'Appleblossom'
'Paramount'
'Queen of Hearts'
'Silver Smith'
DIOSCOREA
balcanica
DISPORUM
menziesii
DORONICUM
pardalianches 'Goldstrauss'
DRACOCEPHALUM
isabellae
rupestre
tanguticum
ECHINACEA
purpurea 'Abendsonne'
ECHINOPS
exaltatus albus
EPILOBIUM
angustifolium variegatum
EPIMEDIUM
x *youngianum* Yenomoto form
ERAGROSTIS
spectabilis
EREMURUS
afghanicus
aitchisonii 'Dawn'
x *isabellinus* 'Highdown Dwarf'
– 'Highdown Gold'
kaufmannii
'Lady Falmouth'
olgae
'Primrose'
robustus tardiflorus
spectabilis
'Sunset'
ERIGERON
'Double Beauty'
glaucus 'B Ladhams'
pulchellus 'Meadow Muffin'
ERYNGIUM
floribundum
horridum
lassauxii
planum 'Blue Diamond'
x *zabelii* 'James Ivory'
ERYSIMUM
'Miss Massey' (d)
EUPATORIUM
coelestinum 'Cori'
fistulosum 'Gateway'
purpureum 'Album'
FRAGARIA
vesca 'Alpina Scarletta'
FRANCOA
rupestris
FRITILLARIA
imperialis 'Flore Pleno'
GAILLARDIA
x *grandiflora* 'Ipswich Beauty'
GALANTHUS
'Allen's Perfection'
'Cupid'
'Jenny Wren'
'Rebecca'
'Romeo'
'Tomtit'
'Valentine'
'White Swan'
GALEGA
officinalis compacta
GENTIANA
asclepiadea 'Caelestina'
– 'Phaeina'
x *japonica*
GERANIUM
renardii 'Walter Ingwersen'
sanguineum double
GEUM
x *ewenii*
pentapetalum 'Plenum'
GLADIOLUS
x *brenchleyensis*
GLYCERIA
maxima 'Pallida'
GUNNERA
tinctoria 'Nana'
HEDYCHIUM
'F W Moore'
HELENIUM
autumnale 'Aurantiacum'
'Baronin Linden'
'Chanctonbury'
'Flammenrad'
'Goldlackzwerg'
'Goldreif'
'July Sun'
'Spätrot'
'Wonadonga'
HELIANTHUS
decapetalus 'Soleil d'Or
x *laetiflorus* 'Miss Mellish'
tomentosus
HELIOPSIS
helianthoïdes scabra 'Venus
HELLEBORUS
niger 'Mr Poë's Variety'
HEMEROCALLIS
'Aurantiaca Major'
'E A Bowles'
fulva rosea
'Gay Music'
HETEROTHECA
mariana
HEUCHERA
'Crimson Cascade'
'Gaiety'
'Honeybells'
'June Bride'
'Lady Warwick'
'Montrose'
'Mount St Helens'
'Orphei'
'Oxfordii'

'Painted Lady'
'Rose Cavalier'
'Rufus'
'Scarlet Beauty'
'Souvenir of Wolley-Dod'

'Tattletale'
'The Rocket' ('Rakete')

HIDALGOA
wercklei

HYPERICUM
olympicum minus
'Schwefelperle'

IBERIS
sempervirens 'Plena'

IMPERATA
cylindrica 'Major'

IRIS
'Barcarole' (Regeliocyclus)
'Big Blue' (***sibirica***)
'Blue Reverie' (***sibirica***)
'Camilla' (Regeliocyclus)
'Clara' (Regeliocyclus)
cristata 'Abbey's Violet'
'Dance Ballerina' (***sibirica***)
'Dorothea'
'Dress Circle' (Spuria)
'Emily Grey'
ensata 'Benibotan'
– 'Kegoromo'
– 'Kumazumi'
– 'Lady in Waiting'
– 'Pin Stripe'
– 'Reign of Glory'
– 'Sky Mist'
– 'Tinted Cloud'
– 'Warei Hotei'
'Highline Halo' (Spuria)
'Ice Blue'
'Little White' (***sibirica***)
'Lutetas' (Regeliocyclus)
'Marshmallow Frosting' (***sibirica***)
'Medea' (Regeliocyclus)
'Mercurius' (Regeliocyclus)
'Myddelton Blue'
orientalis 'Snowflake'
pseudacorus 'Gigantea'
'Shirley Pope' (***sibirica***)
'Teal Velvet' (***sibirica***)
tectorum 'Lilacina'
Tollong Group
Toltec Group
unguicularis 'Bowles' White'
– 'Ellis's Variety'
wilsonii
'Zwanenburg Beauty'

JEFFERSONIA
dubia 'Flore Pleno'

KNIPHOFIA
'Adam'
'Amberlight'
'Bees' Flame'
'Bees' Orange'
'Bees' Yellow'
'Bressingham Gleam'
'Bressingham Glow'
'Bressingham Torch'
'Burnt Orange'
'Buttercrunch'
'C M Prichard' Prichard
'Canary Bird'
'Chartreuse'
'Cleopatra'
'Cool Lemon'
'Enchantress'
'Florella'
'Green Lemon'
'Honeycomb'
'Hortulanus Laren'
'Indian'
leichtlinii 'Aurea'
'Lemon Queen'
'Maxima'
parviflora
'Primulina' hort.
rogersii
'Russell's Gold'
'Slim Coral Red'
'Slim Orange'
'Snow Maiden'
'Spanish Gold'
'The Rocket'

KNOWLTONIA
capensis

LATHYRUS
chrysanthus
japonicus maritimus
latifolius 'Rose Queen'
– violet form
ornatus
undulatus

LAVANDULA
'Backhouse Purple'
'Glasnevin Variety'

LEONTOPODIUM
haplophylloïdes

LEUCANTHEMUM
x ***superbum*** 'Beauté Anversoise'

LEUZEA
rhapontica

LIATRIS
pycnostachya 'Alba'
scariosa
– 'White Spire'
spicata 'Picador'
– 'Silvertips'
– 'Snow Queen'

LIGULARIA
altaica
dentata 'Dunkellaubig'
– 'Golden Queen'
– 'Moorblut'
persica
sibirica racemosa
stenocephala 'Globosa'

LIGUSTICUM
mutellina

LILIUM
arboricola
brownii australe
candidum 'Peregrinum'
– purple-spotted flowers
x ***maculatum*** 'E A Bowles'
x ***princeps*** 'Myddelton House'
sherriffiae

LIMONIUM
platyphyllum 'Blue Cloud'
– f. ***roseum***

LINARIA
aeruginea
'Aureopurpurea'

LINUM
hirsutum
narbonense 'June Perfield'
– 'Six Hiils'

LITHOSPERMUM
canescens

LOBELIA
fulgens 'Blinkfeuer'
– 'Elmfeuer'
kalmii
'Mrs Humbert'
x ***speciosa*** 'Anne'
'Twilight Time'
'Wildwood Splendour'

LUPINUS
'Betty Astell'
'Billy Wright'
'Blue Jacket'
'City of York'
'George Russell'
ornatus
'Pink Pearls'
polyphyllus 'Downer's Delight'
'Tom Reeves'

LYCHNIS
chalcedonica 'Alba Plena'
coronaria 'Flore Pleno'
coronata 'Speciosa'
flos-cuculi 'Adolph Muss'

LYSIMACHIA
leschenaultii

MATELEA
carolinensis

MECONOPSIS
x ***cookei***
grandis 'Keillour Crimson'
– 'Miss Dickson'
x ***sheldonii*** 'Archie Campbell'
– 'Springhill'
torquata

MELITTIS
melissophyllum
'Variegata'

MIMULUS
lewisii 'Albus'
– 'Sunset'

MONARDA
'Gardenway Red'
'Magnifica'
'Violet Queen'

MULGEDIUM
giganteum

MYOSOTIS
dissitiflora
'Elegantissima' (v)

NARCISSUS
'Alpha of Donard' (1)
'Astron' (2)
'Gog'
'Golden Miller' (1)
'Golden Thought'
'Green Mantle' (3)
'Lucinda'
'Magistrate' (1)
'Precentor' (1)
'Red Light' (2)
'Saint Dorothea' (1)
'Slieve Bernagh' (1)
'Slieve Donard' (1)
'Solid Gold' (1)

NEPETA
x ***faassenii*** 'Blue Wonder'
– 'White Wonder'

NERINE
bowdenii 'Blush Beauty'

OENOTHERA
fruticosa 'Best Red'
– 'Sonnenwende'

ORCHIS
militaris

ORIGANUM
vulgare 'Bury Hill'

PAEONIA
lactiflora 'Coral Charm'
– 'Doris Cooper'
– 'Jean Bockstoce'
– 'Sea Shell'
– 'Sword Dance'
mascula arietina 'Hilda Milne'
officinalis 'Phyllis Prichard'
– 'Red Ensign'
– 'Splendens'
Saunders hybrid 'Archangel'
– 'Argosy'
– 'Black Douglas'
– 'Black Pirate'
– 'Chalice'
– 'Constance Spry'
– 'Cytherea'
– 'Daystar'
– 'Early Bird'
– 'Early Windflower'
– 'Good Cheer'
– 'Legion of Honour'
– 'Little Dorrit'
– 'Moonrise'
– 'Roman Gold'
– 'Rose Garland'
– 'Victoria Lincoln'
– 'White Innocence'
suffruticosa 'Bijou de Chusan'
– 'Elizabeth'
'Sybil Stern'
tenuifolia 'Rosea'

'Windchimes'
wittmanniana nudicarpa

PANICUM
'Squaw'
'Warrior'

PAPAVER
orientale 'Ameliore'
– 'Atrosanguineum Maximum'
– 'Australia's Orange'
– 'Barr's White'
– 'Blush Queen'
– 'Bobs'
– 'Border Beauty'
– 'Brightness'
– 'Burgundy'
– 'Cavalier'
– 'Cerise Bedder'
– 'China Boy'
– 'Colonel Bowles'
– 'Corina'
– 'Countess of Stair'
– 'Crimped Beauty'
– 'Crimson Pompon'
– 'Curtis's Strain'
– 'Dégas'
– 'Delicatum'
– 'Duke of Teck'
– 'E A Bowles'
– 'Edna Perry'
– 'Enchantress'
– 'Enfield Beauty'
– 'Ethel Swete'
– 'Fire King'
– 'Fringed Beauty'
– 'Gibson's Salmon'
– 'Goldschmidt'
– 'Grenadier'
– 'Henri Cayeux Improved'
– 'Hewiit's Old Rose'
– 'Humphrey Bennett'
– 'Ida Brailsford'
– 'Immaculatum'
– 'Iris Perry'
– 'Ivy Perry'
– 'Jeannie Mawson'
– 'Joyce'
– 'Kleine Tänzerin'
– 'Lady Haig'
– 'Lady Haskett'
– 'Lady Roscoe'
– 'Lavender Glory'
– 'Little Prince'
– 'Lovely'
– 'Magnificence'
– 'Mahony'
– 'Mahony Ameliore'
– 'Margherite'
– 'Marie Studholme'
– 'Masterpiece'
– 'Max Leichtlin'
– 'May Curtis'
– 'May Saddler'
– 'Medusa'
– 'Menelik'
– 'Minimum'
– 'Miss Julia'
– 'Mogul'
– 'Mrs Carl Skinner'
– 'Mrs John Harkness'
– 'Mrs Lockett Agnew'
– 'Mrs M Bevan'
– 'Mrs Marsh'
– 'Olympia'
– 'Orange King'
– 'Orange Queen'
– 'Oriental King'
– 'Oriental Queen'
– 'Oriflamme'
– 'Pale Face'
– 'Parkmanii'
– 'Perry's Blush'
– 'Perry's Favorite'
– 'Perry's Pigmy'
– 'Perry's Unique'
– 'Persepolis'
– 'Peter Pan'
– 'Prince of Orange'
– 'Princess Ena'
– 'Princess Mary'
– 'Purity'
– 'Queen Alexander'
– 'Rose Queen'
– 'Royal Prince'
– 'Royal Scarlet'
– 'Ruby Perry'
– 'Salmon Beauty'
– 'Salmon Perfection'
– 'Salmon Queen'
– 'Sass Pink'
– 'Semiplenum'
– 'Silberblick'
– 'Silver Queen'
– 'Silverblotch '
– 'Snoflame'
– 'Sonata'
– 'Souvenir'
– 'Splendens'
– 'Suleika'
– 'Sungold'
– 'Surprise'
– 'The King'
– 'The Queen'
– 'Thora Perry'
– 'Tom Tit'
– 'Toreador'
– 'Van der Glotch'
– 'Vuurkogel'
– 'Winnie'
– 'Wurtemburgia'

PENNISETUM
'Cassian's Choice'

PENSTEMON
'Prairie Dawn'
'Prairie Dusk'

PEROVSKIA
'Longin'

PERSICARIA
mollis

PHLEUM
pratense 'Aureum'

PHLOX
amoena 'Pinstripe'
– 'Snowdrift'
– 'Vein Mountain'
buckleyi
carolina forms
caryophylla
dolichantha
floridana
– ssp. *bella*
glaberrima
idahoensis
maculata 'Schneelawine'
paniculata 'Antoine Mercier'
– 'David'
– 'Hochgesang'
– 'Landhochzeit'
– 'Sandra'
pulchra
stansburyi

PHORMIUM
'Aurora'
tenax 'Goliath'
– 'Purple Giant'
– 'Yellow Queen'

PHYSALIS
alkekengi franchetii dwarf forms
– – monstrous forms

PHYTOLACCA
variegated forms

PIMPINELLA
saxifraga 'Rosea'

PODOPHYLLUM
pleianthum

POLEMONIUM
carneum 'Rose Queen'
laxiflorum

POLYGONATUM
x *hybridum* 'Flore Pleno'

POLYGONUM
coriaceum

POTENTILLA
alba 'Snow White'
'Arc-en-Ciel'
'Congo'
'Hamlet'
'Mont d'Or'
ovalis
'Volcan'

PRIMULA
'Donard Gem'

PULMONARIA
officinalis immaculata

RANUNCULUS
aconitifolius 'Luteus Plenus'
alpestris 'Flore Pleno'
parnassiifolius 'Semiplenus'

RATIBIDA
pinnata

RESEDA
odorata 'Parson's White'

RHEUM
'Dr Baillon'
palmatum 'Atropurpureum Dissectum'

RHEXIA
mariana
– f. *purpurea*

RIGIDELLA
flammea
orthantha

ROMNEYA
coulteri 'Butterfly'

ROSCOEA
cautleoïdes 'Bees' Dwarf'

RUDBECKIA
laciniata 'Foliis Variegatis'

RUTA
graveolens 'Blue Beauty'
– 'Blue Mound'

SACCHARUM
strictum

SALVIA
beckeri
ceratophylla
cryptantha
dichroa
doyamae
eichleriana
fercanensis
formosa
'Glory of Stuttgart'
guaranitica 'Costa Rica'
– 'Indigo Blue'
– 'Purple Splendor'
ianthina
indica
napifolia
pinnata
teddii
valentina
yunnanensis

SANGUISORBA
officinalis 'Shiro-fukurin'

SAXIFRAGA
pensylvanica
virginiensis 'Flore Pleno'

SCABIOSA
caucasica 'Blue Mountain'
– 'Challenger'
– 'Constancy'
– 'Diamond'
– 'Isaac House'
– 'Loddon White'
– 'Mrs Isaac House'
– 'Penhill Blue'
– 'Rhinsburg Glory'
fischeri

SENECIO
cineraria 'Hoar Frost'

SIDALCEA
'Donard Queen'
'H Blanchard'
malviflora double form
'Puck'
'Rosy Gem'
'Scarlet Beauty'

SILENE
dioica 'Alba Plena'

SILPHIUM
'Carpenter's Cup'

TANACETUM
coccineum 'A M Kelway'
– 'Allurement'
– 'Avalanche'
– 'Beau Geste'
– 'Bishop of Salisbury'
– 'Bridal Pink'
– 'Bright Boy'
– 'Charming'
– 'China Rose'
– 'Comet'
– 'Countess Poulett'
– 'Duke of York'
– 'Kelway's Lovely'
– 'Kelway's Magnificent'
– 'Langport Scarlet'
– 'Lorna'
– 'Mrs Bateman Brown'
– 'Progression'
– 'Radiant'
– 'Somerset'
– 'White Madeleine'

TELEKIA
speciosissima

TEUCRIUM
polium 'Album'

THLADIANTHA
dubius (f)
oliveri (f)

TIARELLA
cordifolia 'Montrose'

TRADESCANTIA
'Charlotte'

TRILLIUM
catesbyi album
erectum blandum
– f. ***cahnae***
– f. ***polymerum***
– var. ***sulcatum***
gracile
'Hokkaido'
japonicum
kamtschaticum 'Tsuzuki'
kurabayashii
ovatum 'Edith'
– 'Kenmore'
– f. ***roseum***
– 'Tillicum'
persistens
petiolatum
reliquum
rivale 'Del Norte'
– 'Verne Ahiers'
texanum
tschonoskii violaceum
vaseyi album

TROLLIUS
asiaticus aurantiacus
lilacinus
'Miss Mary Russell'
ranunculinus

VERATRUM
stenophyllum
wilsonii
yunnanense

VERNONIA
angustifolia
noveboracensis

VERONICA
'Blue Charm'
spicata 'Gina's Pale Blue'

VIOLA
'Red Giant'

XEROPHYLLUM
asphodeloïdes

ZANTEDESCHIA
aethiopica 'Compacta'

The National Council For The Conservation Of Plants& Gardens (NCCPG) Collections

All or part of the following Genera are represented by a National Collection.

Full details of these collections are contained in the *National Plant Collection Directory 1993* available from: R A W Lowe, NCCPG General Secretary, The Pines, c/o Wisley Gardens, Woking, Surrey GU23 6QB. Price £2.50 including post & packing.

Abelia
Abies
Abutilon
Acacia
Acanthus
Acer
Achillea
Actinidia
Adenophora
Adiantum
Aechmea
Aesculus
Agapanthus
Alchemilla
Allium
Alnus
Alstoemeria
Amelanchier
Ampelopsis
Anemone
Aquilegia
Arabis
Araceae
Arbutus
Argyranthemum
Artemisia
Arundinaria
Asphodelus
Asplenium
Aster
Astilbe
Athyrium
Aubrieta
Azara
Bambusa
Begonia
Bellis
Berberis
Bergenia
Betula
Borago
Borzicactinae
Brachyglottis
Buddleja
Buxus
Calamintha
Calathea
Calceolaria
Callistemon
Calluna
Caltha
Camassia
Camellia
Campanula
Canna
Carpinus
Carya
Caryopteris
Cassiope
Castanea
Catalpa
Cautleya
Ceanothus
Ceratostigma
Cercidiphyllum
Chamaecyparis
Chionodoxa
Chusquea
Cimicifuga
Cistus
Citrus
Clematis
Codiaeum
Colchicum
Colutea
Conifers
Convallaria
Coprosma
Cordyline
Coreopsis
Cornus
Cortaderia
Corylopsis
Corylus
Cotinus
Cotoneaster
Crocosmia
Crocus
Cyclamen
Cystopteris
Cytisus
Daboecia
Dahlia
Daphne
Delphinium
Dendranthema
Dendrobium
Deutzia
Dianella
Dianthus
Diascia
Dicentra
Dicksoniaceae
Diervilla
Digitalis
Dodecatheon
Doronicum
Dracaena
Dryopteris
Echeveria
Echinocerus
Elaeagnus
Embothrium
Enkianthus
Epimedium
Erica
Erigeron
Erodium
Eryngium
Erysimum
Erythronium
Escallonia
Eucalyptus
Eucryphia
Euonymus
Euphorbia
Fagus
Fallopia
Ficus
Filicales
Forsythia
Fragaria
Fraxinus
Fritillaria
Fuchsia
Galanthus
Garrya
Gaultheria
Genista
Gentiana
Geranium
Geum
Gladiolus
Grevillea
Halimium
Hamamelis
Hebe
Hedera
Hedychium
Helenium
Helianthemum
Helianthus
Helichrysum
Heliopsis
Helleborus
Hemerocallis
Hepatica
Hesperis
Heuchera
Hibiscus
Hosta
Hoya
Hyacinthus
Hydrangea
Hypericum
Ilex
Inula
Iris
Jasminum
Juglans
Juniperus
Kalmia
Kniphofia
Lamium
Larix
Lathyrus
Lavandula
Leptospermum
Leucanthemum
Leucojum
Lewisia
Libertia
Ligustrum
Linum
Liriodendron
Liriope
Lithocarpus
Lobelia
Lonicera
Lupinus
Lycaste
Lychnis
Lysimachia
Magnolia
Mahonia
Malus
Meconopsis
Mentha
Monarda
Muscari
Narcissus
Nepeta
Nerine
Nothofagus
Nymphaea
Oenothera
Olearia
Ophiopogon
Origanum
Osmunda
Osteospermum
Ourisia

Oxalis
Ozothamnus
Paeonia
Papaver
Paphiopedilum
Paradisea
Parahebe
Parthenocissus
Passiflora
Pelargonium
Penstemon
Pernettya
Persicaria
Philadelphus
Phlomis
Phlox
Phormium
Photinia
Phyllodoce
Phyllostachys
Picea
Pieris
Pinguicula
Pinus
Pittosporum
Pleiblastus
Platanus
Platycodon
Pleione
Polemonium
Polygonum
Polypodium
Polystichum
Populus
Potentilla
Primula
Prunus
Pseudopanax
Pteridophyta
Pulmonaria
Pyracantha
Pyrus
Quercus
Ranunculus
Rheum
Rhododendron
Rhus
Ribes
Robinia
Rodgersia
Rohdea
Rosa
Roscoea
Rosmarinus
Rubus
Ruscus
Salix
Salvia
Sambucus
Santolina
Sarcococca
Sarracenia
Sasa
Saxifraga
Scabiosa
Schizostylis
Sedum
Semiaquilegia
Semiarundinaria
Sempervivum
Shibataea
Sidalcea
Sinarundinaria
Sisyrinchium
Skimmia
Slieve Donard
Sorbaria
Sorbus
Spiraea
Sir F Stern
Stewartia
Styracaceae
Symphyanda
Symphytum
Syringa
Tanacetum
Taxus
Thalictrum
Thelyptaceae
Thymus
Tilia
Tillandsia
Trillium
Trollius
Tropaeolum
Tulbaghia
Tulipa
Variegated
Veratrum
Verbascum
Verbena
Veronica
Viburnum
Vinca
Viola
Vitis
Watsonia
Weigela
Wisteria
Woodwardia
Yucca
Zantedeschia
Zelkova
Zingiberaceae

Bibliography

International Plant Finders

Australia

Nursery Plants Buyers Guide. Hills Growers Group, PO Box 12, The Patch 3792, Victoria, Australia.

Canada

The Canadian Plant Source Book (1992). Anne & Peter Ashley, 93 Fentiman Avenue, Ottawa, ON, CANADA K1S OT7. $17 (Canadian or US) inc. p&p. Add $5 for airmail. 14,000 hardy plants available at retail and wholesale nurseries across Canada, including those who ship to US. English names & English & French cross-indexes.

France and Belgium

25,000 Plantes, où et comment les acheter. (1993). Société National d'Horticulture de France, 84 rue de Grenelle, Paris 75007. ISBN 2-7066-1731-4. Contains details of about 25,000 plants and 350 nurseries in France.

Germany

Pflanzen-Einkaufsführer. (1990) Anne & Walter Erhardt. Verlag Eugen Ulmer, PO Box 70 05 61, D-70574 Stuttgart. ISBN 3-8001-6393-4. Some 14,000 plants from German nurseries.

Ireland

Irish Hardy Nursery Stock. (1992). Irish Trade Board, Merrion Hall, Strand Road, Sandymount, Dublin 4. Ireland. Details of about 130 Irish nurseries and over 5,000 plants

Switzerland

Der Stauden Finder. Balz Schneider, Im Veltlin 38, CH-8706 Meilen, Switzerland. Lists about 5,000 herbaceous perennials from over 40 nurseries in Switzerland.

United Kingdom

Find That Rose. Rose Growers' Association, 303 Mile End Road, Colchester, Essex CO4 5EA Over 2,000 Roses and 70 growers.

The Vegetable Finder. HDRA, Ryton-on-Dunmore, Coventry CV8 3LG. Nearly 2,000 different Vegetable seeds from 36 suppliers

USA

The Andersen's Horticultural Library's Source List of Plants and Seeds. Andersen Horticultural Library, Minnesota Landscape Arboretum, 3675 Arboretum Drive, Box 39, Chanhassen, MN 55317 USA. Compiled by Richard Isaacson. (1989). Approx. 40,000 plants and seeds from 400 retail & wholesale outlets in the US & Canada. All are prepared to ship interstate. Does not include Orchids, Cacti or Succulents. New revision due autumn 1992.

Combined Rose List. (1993) Beverly R Dobson & Peter Schneider, PO Box 16035, Rocky River, Ohio 44116. Lists over 8,100 roses from 211 nurseries In US, Canada & Overseas.

Cornucopia - A Source Book of Edible Plants. (1990). Stephen Facciola, Kampong Publications, 1870 Sunrise Drive, Vista, California 92084. ISBN 0-9628087-0-9. A very substantial and comprehensive volume, (678 pages), which documents 3,000 species of edible plants & 7,000 cultivars available in the US and abroad. An Electronic version will be available mid-1993.

Fruit, Berry and Nut Inventory. (1993). Ed. Kent Whealy. Seed Saver Publications, 3076 North Winn Road, Decorah, Iowa 52101. An inventory of all fruit, berry and nut varieties available from over 250 mail-order nurseries in the US.

Garden Seed Inventory. (1992). Ed. Kent Whealy. Seed Saver Publications, 3076 North Winn Road, Decorah, Iowa 52101. List every non-hybrid vegetable variety available from 223 mail-order seed companies in the USA and Canada with description and sources for each.

Gardening by Mail (1990). 3rd ed. Barbara J Barton. Tusker Press, PO Box 1338, Sebastopol, California 95473. A directory of mail order resources for gardeners in the USA and Canada, including seed companies, nurseries, suppliers of all garden necessaries and ornaments, horticultural and plant societies, magazines, libraries and books.

Hortus Source List. (1992). Bailey Hortorium, 462 Mann Library, Cornell University, Ithaca, 14853 NY, USA. Over 22,000 plant entries from 63 nurseries, most in New York State.

Hortus Northwest: A Pacific Northwest Native Plant Directory. (Issue 3 - 1992). ed. Dale Shank. Hortus Northwest, PO Box 955, Canby, OR 97013. 100 native plant nurseries in Oregon, Washington, British Columbia and northern California.

Northwind Farm's Herb Resource Directory. (1992-93 edition). ed. Paula Oliver. Northwind Farm Publications, Route 2, Box 246, Shevlin, MN 56676-9535. Over 1,100 sources & resources for herb growers & enthusiasts. Bi-monthly journal also available.

Nursery Sources, Native Plants and Wild Flowers. New England Wild Flower Society, Garden in the Woods, 180 Hemenway Road, Framingham, MA 01701-2699. Over 200 native North American wild flowers, ferns, grasses and shrubs. Details of 45 nurseries

Perennials: A Nursery Source Manual (1989). ed. Barbara Pesch. Brooklyn Botanic Garden, 1000 Washington Avenue, Brooklyn, NY 11225-1099. ISBN 0 945352 48 4. List 320 nurseries and some 4000 perennials.

Taylor's Guide to Speciality Nurseries (1993). Houghton Miffin Co., 2 Park Street, Boston, MA 02108, USA. Over 300 nursereis in the US selliung ornamental garden plants, all of which will ship.

General

The following list of bibliographic sources and references is by no means exhaustive, but lists some of the more useful and available works used in the preparation of **THE PLANT FINDER.**

The Plantsman is published regularly by The Royal Horticultural Society, Vincent Square, London SW1P 2PE

Armitage, A M. 1989. *Herbaceous Perennial Plants.* Varsity Press, Athens, Georgia.

Bailey, L H Bailey, E Z et al. 1976. *Hortus Third.* Macmillan, New York.

Bean, W J. 1970-1988. *Trees and Shrubs Hardy in the British Isles* (8th ed. edited Sir George Taylor & D L Clarke & Supp. ed. D L Clarke). John Murray, London.

Beckett, K A. 1987. *The RHS Encyclopaedia of House Plants.* Century Hutchinson, London.

Blundell, M. 1992. *Wild Flowers of East Africa.* Collins, London.

Bond, P & Goldblatt, P. 1984. *Plants of the Cape Flora.* Journal of South African Botany. (Sup. Vol. No 13). Kirstenbosch.

Bramwell, D & Z. 1974. *Wild Flowers of the Canary Islands.* Stanley Thomas, London, 1974.

Brickell, C D (ed.) et al. 1980. *International Code of Nomenclature for Cultivated Plants.* Utrecht.

Brickell, C D (ed.) 1989. *Gardeners' Encyclopaedia of Plants and Flowers.* Dorling Kindersley, London.

Brummitt, R K & Powell, CE. 1992. *Authors of Plant Names.* Royal Botanic Gardens, Kew.

Brummitt, R K. 1992. *Vascular Plant Families and Genera.* Royal Botanic gardens, Kew.

Bryan, J E 1989. *Bulbs* (Vols I & II). Christopher Helm, Bromley, Kent.

Chittenden, F J (ed.). 1965. *The Royal Horticultural Society Dictionary of Gardening* (2nd ed.). Oxford University Press.

Clausen, R R & Ekstrom, N H. *Perennials for American Gardens.* Random House, New York.

Clayton, W D & Renvoize, S A. 1986. *Genera Graminum.* HMSO, London

Cribb, P & Bailes, C. 1989. *Hardy Orchids.* Christopher Helm, Bromley, Kent.

Davis, P H et al. (ed.). 1965-1988. *Flora of Turkey* (Vols 1-10). University Press, Edinburgh.

Flora of New Zealand. (Vols. I-III). 1961-80. Wellington, New Zealand.

Du Plessis, N and Duncan, G. 1989. *Bulbous Plants of Southern Africa.* Tafelberg, Cape Town, South Africa.

Forrest, M. (ed. Nelson, E C.) 1985. *Trees and Shrubs Cultivated in Ireland.* Boethius Press for An Taisce, Dublin.

Galbraith, J. 1977. *Field Guide to the Wild Flowers of South-East Australia.* Collins, London.

Graf, A B. 1981. *Tropica* (2nd ed.). Roehrs, New Jersey.

Grierson, A J C & Long D G. 1983-91. (Vols. 1 Pt I-III & Vol. 2 Pt. I) *Flora of Bhutan.* Royal Botanic Garden Edinburgh.

Harkness, M G & D'Angelo, D. 1986. *The Bernard E Harkness Seedlist Handbook*. Timber Press, Portland, Oregon.

Heath, R E. 1981. *Collectors Alpines*. Collinridge, Twickenham, UK.

Hillier Manual of Trees and Shrubs. (6th ed.). 1991. David & Charles, Newton Abbot.

Hogg, R. 1884. *The Fruit Manual*. (5th ed.). Journal of Horticulture Office, London.

Huxley, A (ed). 1992. *The New Royal Horticultural Society Dictionary of Gardening*. Macmillan, London.

Index Kewensis (Vols. I-IV & Supps. I-XIX). 1893-1991. Clarendon Press, Oxford.

Innes, C F. 1985. *The World of Iridaceae*. Holy Gate International Ashington, Sussex.

Jacobsen, H. 1973. *Lexicon of Succulent Plants*. Blandford, London.

Jellitto, L & Schacht, W. *Hardy Herbaceous Perennials*. (3rd ed. edited by W. Schacht & A Fessler). Timber Press, Portland, Oregon, USA.

Johns, R J. 1991. *Pteridophytes of Tropical East Africa*. Royal Botanic Gardens, Kew.

Jones, D L. 1987. *Encyclopaedia of Ferns*. Lothian, Melbourne, Australia.

Krussmann, G. (English ed. trans. M E Epp). 1984-1986. *Manual of Cultivated Broadleaved Trees & Shrubs* (Vol I-III). Batsford, London.

Laar, H J van de. 1989. *Naamlijst van Houtige Gewassen*. Proefstation voor de Boomteelt en het Stedelijk Groen, Boskoop, Holland.

Laar, H J van de & Fortgens, Ing. G. 1988. *Naamlijst van Vaste Planten*. Proefstation voor de Boomkwekerij, Boskoop, Holland.

Lewis, J. ed. Leslie, A C. 1987 & 1989. *The International Conifer Register*. Pt.I (*Abies* to *Austrotaxus*), Pt.II (*Belis* to *Pherosphaera* (excluding Cypresses and Junipers). Pt.III: *Cypresses*. Royal Horticultural Society, London.

Mabberley, D J. 1987. *The Plant-Book*. Cambridge University Press.

McGregor, R L, Barkley, T M et al. 1986. *Flora of the Great Plains*. University Press of Kansas, USA.

Metcalf, L J. 1987. *The Cultivation of New Zealand Trees and Shrubs*. Reed Methuen, Auckland, New Zealand.

Ohwi, J. (ed F G Meyer & E H Walker). 1965. *Flora of Japan*. Smithsonian Institute, Washington.

Phillips, R. & Rix, M. *Shrubs*. 1989. Pan Books, London.

Phillips, R. & Rix, M. 1991/2. *Perennials*. Pan Books, London.

The Plantsman. The Royal Horticultural Society, Vincent Square, London SW1P 2PE.

Polunin, O & Stainton, A. 1984. *Flowers of the Himalaya*. Oxford University Press.

Rehder, R. 1940. *Manual of Cultivated Trees & Shrubs Hardy in North America*. (2nd ed.) Macmillan, New York.

Stafleu, F A et al. 1978. *International Code of Botanical Nomenclature*. Bohn, Scheltema & Holkema, Utrecht.

Stace, C A. 1992. *New Flora of the British Isles*. St Edmundsbury Press, Bury St Edmunds, Suffolk.

Stainton, A. 1988. *Flowers of the Himalaya: A Supplement*. Oxford University Press.

Stearn, Prof. W T. *Botanical Latin*. David & Charles. Newton Abbot, England.

Stearn, Prof. W T. 1992. *Stearn's Dictionary of Plant Names for Gardeners*. Cassell, London.

Thomas, G S. 1990. *Perennial Garden Plants*. (3rd ed.) J M Dent & Sons, London.

Trehane, R P. 1989. *Index Hortensis*. Quarterjack Publishing, Wimborne, Dorset.

Tutin, T G. 1964-1980. *Flora Europaea* (Vols I-V). Cambridge University Press.

Tutin, T G et al. 1993. *Flora Europaea* (2nd ed. Vol I). Cambridge University Press.

Uhl, N J. & Dransfield, J. 1987. *Genera Palmarum*. Alan Press, Lawrence, Kansas, USA.

Walters, S M (ed.) et al. 1984, 1986 & 1989. *The European Garden Flora*. (Vols I-III). Cambridge University Press, UK.

Willis, J C. 1973. *A Dictionary of the Flowering Plants and Ferns* (8th ed.) revised H K Airy Shaw. Cambridge University Press.

Wilson, H D. 1978. *Wild Plants of Mount Cook National Park*. Christchurch, New Zealand.

Van Scheepen, J. 1991. *International Checklist for Hyacinths and Miscellaneous Bulbs*. KAVB, Hillegom, Netherlands.

Genera

Acacia

Simmons, MH. 1987. *Acacias of Australia* (2nd ed). Nelson, Melbourne, Australia.

Acer

De Jong, P C et al. *International Dendrology Society Year Book 1991*. London.

Harris, J G S. 1983. *The Plantsman*. (Vol 5 Pt I).

Vertrees, J D. 1978. *Japanese Maples*. Timber Press, Oregon.

Adiantum

Goudry, C J. 1985. *Maidenhair Ferns in Cultivation*. Lothian, Melbourne, Australia.

Aeschynanthus

Dates, J D. *The Gesneriad Register 1990: Check List of Aeschynanthus*. American Gloxinia and Gesneriad Society, Galesburg, Illinois.

Aesculus

Wright, D. 1985. *The Plantsman*. (Vol 7 Pt IV).

Agapetes

Argent, G C G & Woods, P J B. 1988. *The Plantsman*. (Vol 8 Pt II).

Ajuga

Adam, C G. *Alpine Garden Society Bulletin*. (Vol 50 Pt I).

Allium

Davies, D. 1992. *Alliums*. Batsford, London.

Alnus

Ashburner, K. *The Plantsman*. (Vol 8 Pt III).

Androsace

Smith, G F & Lowe, D B. 1977. *Androsaces*. Alpine Garden Society.

Anemone, Japanese

McKendrick, M. 1990. *The Plantsman*. (Vol 12 Pt III).

Anemone nemorosa

Toubol, U. 1981. *The Plantsman*. (Vol 3 Pt III).

Aquilegia

Munz, P A. 1946. *Aquilegia: The Cultivated and Wild Columbines. Gentes Herbarum* (Vol VII Fasc I). Bailey Hortorium, New York.

Araceae

Bown, D. 1988. *Aroids*. Century Hutchinson, London.

Argyranthemum

Humphries, C J. 1976. *A Revision of the Macaronesian Genus Argyranthemum*. The Bulletin of the British Museum (Natural History) Botany Vol. 5 No. 4, London.

Arisaema

Mayo, J J. 1982. *The Plantsman*. (Vol 3 Pt IV).

Pradhan, UC. 1990. *Himalayan Cobra-lilies (Arisaema): Their Botany and Culture*. Primulaceae Books, Kalimpong, West Bengal, India.

Aster

Ranson, E R. 1947. *Michaelmas Daisies*. Garden Book Club.

Aubrieta

International Registration Authority Checklist. Weihenstephan.

Bamboos

McClintock, D. 1992. *The Plantsman*. (Vol 14 Pt 3).

Wang Dajun & Shen Shao-Jin. 1987. *Bamboos of China*. Timber Press, Oregon.

Begonia

Ingles, J. 1990. *American Begonia Society Listing of Begonia Cultivars* (Revised Edition Buxton Checklist).

Wall, B. 1989. *The Plantsman*. (Vol 11 Pt I).

Thompson, M L. & Thompson, E J. 1981. *Begonias: The Complete Reference Guide*. Times Books, New York.

Betula

Ashburner, K. 1980. *The Plantsman.* (Vol 2 Pt I).

Ashburner, K & Schilling, A D. 1985. *The Plantsman.* (Vol 7 Pt II).

Bougainvillea

Bor, N L. & Raizada, M B. 1982. *Some Beautiful Indian Climbers and Shrubs.* (2nd ed.) pp 291-304. Bombay Natural History Society.

Gillis, W T. 1976 *Bougainvilleas of Cultivation. Baileya.* Vol 20(1) pp34-41. New York.

MacDaniels, L H. 1981. *A Study of Cultivars in Bougainvillea. Baileya.* Vol 21(2) pp77-100. New York.

Bromeliaceae

Beadle, D A. 1991. *A Preliminary Listing of all the known Cultivar and Grex Names for the Bromeliaceae.* Bromeliad Society, Corpus Christi, Texas, USA.

Luther, H E & Sieff, E. 1991. *An Alphabetical List of Bromeliad Binomials.* Bromeliad Society, Orlando, Florida, USA.

Rauh, W. 1979. *Bromeliads.* Blandford Press, Dorset.

Buddleja

Maunder, M. 1987. *The Plantsman.* (Vol 9 Pt II)

Bulbs

Grey-Wilson, C & Matthew, B. 1981. *Bulbs.* Collins, London.

Innes, C. 1985. *The World of Iridaceae.* Hollygate International, Sussex.

Rix, M & Phillips, R. 1981. *The Bulb Book.* Pan Books, London.

Buxus

Batdorf, L R. 1989. *Checklist of Buxus.* American Boxwood Society.

Camellia

Savige, T J. 1993. *The International Camellia Register.* The International Camellia Society, Wirling, Australia.

Campanula

Lewis, P & Lynch, M. 1989. *Campanulas.* Christopher Helm, Bromley, Kent.

Carnivorous Plants

Pietropaulo, J & Pietropaulo, P. 1986 *Carnivorous Plants of the World.* Timber Press, Oregon.

Slack, A. 1988. *Carnivorous Plants.* (rev. ed.). Alphabooks, Sherbourne, Dorset.

Carpinus

Rushforth, K. 1986. *The Plantsman* (Vol 7 Pts III & IV).

Caryopteris

Pattison, G. 1989. *The Plantsman* (Vol 11 Pt I.)

Cassiope

Blake, F S. *Alpine Garden Society Bulletin.* (Vol 53 Pt I).

Starling, B. 1989. *The Plantsman.* (Vol 11 Pt II).

Cestrum

Beckett, K A. 1987. *The Plantsman.* (Vol 9 Pt III).

Chrysanthemum (Dendranthema)

British National Register of Chrysanthemums. National Chrysanthemum Society. 1964-1991.

Chaenomeles

Weber, C. 1963. *Cultivars in the Genus Chaenomeles.* Arnoldia. (Vol 23 No 3) Arnold Arboretum, Harvard, Massachusetts.

Cimicifuga

Compton, J. 1992. *The Plantsman.* (Vol 14 Pt 2).

Cistus

Page, R G. 1991. *The Plantsman.* (Vol 13 Pt III).

Clematis

Fisk, J. 1989. *Clematis, the Queen of Climbers.* Cassell, London.

Fretwell, B. 1989. *Clematis.* Collins, London.

Grey-Wilson, C. 1986. *The Plantsman.* (Vol 7 Pt IV).

Hutchins, G. 1990. *The Plantsman.* (Vol 11 Pt IV).

Lloyd, C & Bennett, T H. 1989. *Clematis.* Viking, London.

Snoeijer, W. 1991. *Clematis Index.* Fopma, Boskoop, Netherlands.

Codonopsis

Alpine Garden Society Bulletin. (Vol 48 Pt 2).

Grey-Wilson, C. 1990. *The Plantsman.* (Vol 12 Pt II).

Conifers

Krussmann, G. (English trans. M E Epp). 1985. *Manual of Cultivated Conifers.* Batsford, London.

Ouden, P. den & Boom, B K. 1965. *Manual of Cultivated Conifers.* Martinus Nijhorff, The Haque, Netherlands.

Welch, H J. 1979. *Manual of Dwarf Conifers.* Theophrastus, New York.

Welch, H J. 1990. *The Conifer Manual.* Vol I. Kluwer Academic Publishers, Dordrecht, Holland.

Cornus

Howard, R A. 1961. Registration Lists of Cultivar Names in *Cornus* L., Arnoldia. (Vol 21 No 2). Arnold Arboretum, Harvard, Massachusetts.

Corydalis

Lidn, M and Zetterlund, H. 1988. A.G.S. Bulletin. (Vol 56 No 2).

Corylopsis

Wright, D. 1982. *The Plantsman.* (Vol 4 Pt I).

Crocosmia

Kostelijk, P J. 1984. *The Plantsman.* (Vol 5 Pt IIII).

Cyclamen

Grey-Wilson, C. 1988. *The Genus Cyclamen.* Christopher Helm, Bromley, Kent.

Grey-Wilson, C. 1991. *The Plantsman.* (Vol 13 Pt I).

Cynara

Wiklund, A. 1992. *The Genus Cynara.* Botanical Journal of the Linnean Society. (Vol 109 No 1).

Cyrtanthus

Holford, F. 1989. *The Plantsman.* (Vol 11 Pt III).

Daphne

Brickell, C D & Mathew, B. 1976. *Daphne.* Alpine Garden Society.

Deutzia

Taylor, J. 1990. *The Plantsman.* (Vol 11 Pt II).

Dianthus

Leslie, A C. 1983-93. *The International Dianthus Register.* (2nd ed. & supps. 1-10). Royal Horticultural Society, London.

Diascia

Benham, S. 1987. *The Plantsman.* (Vol 9 Pt I).

Dierama

Hilliard, O M. & Burtt, B L. 1990. *The Plantsman.* (Vol 12 Pt II).

Hilliard, O M and Burtt, B L. 1991. *Dierama.* Acorn Books CC. Johannesburg, South Africa.

Dionysia

Grey-Wilson, C. 1989. *The Genus Dionysia.* Alpine Garden Society, Woking, Surrey.

Dodecatheon

Mitchem, C M. 1991. *The Plantsman.* (Vol 13 Pt III).

Episcia

Arnold, P. *The Gesneriad Register 1977: Episcia.* American Gloxinia and Gesneriad Society, Binghamton, New York.

Erodium

Bacon, L. 1990. *A.G.S. Bulletin.* (Vol 58 No 1).

Leslie, A C. 1980. *The Plantsman.* (Vol 2 Pt III).

Erythronium
Mathew, B. 1992. *A Taxonomic and Horticultural Review of Erythronium.* Botanical Journal of the Linnean Society. (Vol 109 No 4)

Eucomis
Compton, J. 1990. *The Plantsman.* (Vol 12 Pt III).

Eucryphia
Wright, D. 1983. *The Plantsman.* (Vol 5 Pt III).

Euonymus
Lancaster, R. 1981. *The Plantsman.* (Vol 3 Pt III).

Euphorbia
Turner, R & Radcliffe-Smith, A. 1983. *The Plantsman.* (Vol 5 Pt III).

Fagus
Wyman, D. 1964. Registration List of Cultivar Names of *Fagus* L., Arnoldia. (Vol 24 No 1). Arnold Arboretum, Harvard, Massachusetts.

Ferns
Kaye, R. 1968. *Hardy Ferns.* Faber & Faber, London.
Rush, R. 1984. *A Guide to Hardy Ferns.* The British Pteridological Society, London.

Festuca
Wilkinson, M J. & Stace, C A. 1991. *A new taxonomic treatment of the Festuca ovina aggregate in the British Isles.* Botanical Journal of the Linnean Society. (Vol 106 No 4). London.

Fremontodendron
McMillan Browse, P. 1992. *The Plantsman.* (Vol 14 Pt 1).

Fritillaria
Turrill, W B & Seely, J R. 1980. *Studies in the Genus Fritillaria.* Hooker's Icones Plantarum, (Vol XXXIX Pts I & II), Royal Botanic Gardens, Kew.

Fuchsia
Boullemier, L B. 1991. *The Checklist of Species, Hybrids & Cultivars of the Genus Fuchsia.* (2nd ed.). Blandford Press, Dorset, UK.

Gaultheria (inc. Pernettya)
Middleton, D J. 1990/91 *The Plantsman.* (Vol 12 Pt III & Vol 13 Pt III).
Middleton, D J. 1991. *Infrageneric Classification of the Genus Gaultheria.* Botanical Journal of the Linnean Society. (Vol106 No 3).

Gentiana
Bartlett, M. 1975. *Gentians.* Blandford Press, Dorset.
Wilkie, D. 1950. *Gentians.* (2nd ed.) Country Life, London.

Geranium
Clifton, R T F. 1992. *Geranium Family Species Checklist* ed IV pt 2: Geranium. The Geraniaceae Group of the British Pelargonium and Geranium Society, Kent.
Yeo, P F. 1985. *Hardy Geraniums.* Croom Helm, London.

Gesneriaceae
Dates, J D. *The Gesneriad Register 1986: Check List of Intergeneric Hybrids in the tribe Gloxinieae.* American Gloxinia and Gesneriad Society, Sugar Grove, Illinois.
Dates, J D. *The Gesneriad Register 1987: Check List of Bucinellina, Columnea, Dalbergaria, Pentadenia, Trichantha and Intergeneric Hybrids.* American Gloxinia and Gesneriad Society, Galesburg, Illinois.
Dates, J D. *The Gesneriad Register 1990: Appendix C: Registered Gesneriads 1957-90.* American Gloxinia and Gesneriad Society, Galesburg, Illinois.

Gladiolus
Lewis, G J & Obermeyer, A A & Barnard, T T. 1972. *A Revision of the South African Species of Gladiolus.* (Sup. Vol. 10). Journal of South African Botany, Purnell, Cape Town.
List of Gladiolus Cultivars. The British Gladiolus Society.

Gleditsia *triacanthos*
Santamour, F S Jr & McArdle, A J. 198?. *Checklist of Cultivars of Honeylocust.* USA.

Gramineae (Bambuseae)
Wang Dajun & Shen Shap-Jin. 1987. *Bamboos of China*. Timber Press, Portland, Oregon.
Grasses
Grounds, R. 1979. *Ornamental Grasses*. Pelham Books, London.
Haemanthus
Snijman, D. 1984. *A Revision of the Genus Haemanthus. Journal of South African Botany*. Supplementary Vol 12. National Botanic Gardens, Kirstenbosch.
Hamamelidaceae
Wright, D. 1982. *The Plantsman*. (Vol 4 Pt I).
Heathers
Small, D. and Small, A. 1992. *Handy Guide to Heathers*. Debeigh Heather Nurseries, Suffolk, England.
Hebe
Hayter, T (ed.) 1986-92. *Hebe News*. Macclesfield, Cheshire, UK.
Hutchins, G. 1979. *Hebe and Parahebe Species in Cultivation*. County Park Nursery, Essex.
Chalk, D. 1988. *Hebes and Parahebes*. Christopher Helm, London.
Hedera
Rose, P Q. 1980. *Ivies*. Blandford Press, Dorset, UK.
McAllister, H. 1988. *The Plantsman*. (Vol 10 Pt I).
McAllister, H A. & Rutherford, A. 1990. *Hedera helix & H. hibernica in the British Isles*. Watsonia Vol 18.
Hedychium
Schilling, A D. 1982. *The Plantsman*. (Vol 4 Pt III).
Helichrysum
Hilliard, O M & Burtt, B L. 1987. *The Garden*. (Vol 112 Pt VI). Royal Horticultural Society, London.
Heliconia
Berry, F & Kress, WJ. 1991. *Heliconia: An Identification Guide*. Smithsonian Institution Press, Washington.
Helleborus
Mathew, B. 1981. *The Plantsman*. (Vol 3 Pt I).
Hemerocallis
Kitchingman, R M. 1985. *The Plantsman*. (Vol 7 Pt II).
Munson, R W. 1989. *Hemerocallis, The Daylily*. Timber Press, Oregon.
Webber, S. (ed.) 1988. *Daylily Encyclopaedia*. Webber Gardens, Damascus, Maryland, USA.
Hibiscus
Beers, L. & Howie, J. 1990. *Growing Hibiscus*. (2nd ed.). Kangaroo Press, Kenthurst, Australia.
Hippeastrum
Alfabetische Lisjt van de in Nederland in cultuur zijnde Amaryllis (Hippeastrum) Cultivars. 1980. Koninklijke Algemeene Veereniging voor Bloembollencultur, Hillegom, Netherlands.
Hosta
Grenfell, D. 1985. *The Plantsman*. (Vol 7 Pt IV).
Grenfell, D. 1990. *Hosta*. Batsford, London.
Hensen, K J W. 1985. *The Plantsman*. (Vol 7 Pt I).
Schmid, W G. 1991. *The Genus Hosta*. Timber Press, Oregon.
Hoya
Innes, C. 1988. *The Plantsman*. (Vol 10 Pt III).
Hydrangea
Haworth-Booth, M. 1975. *The Hydrangeas*. Garden Book Club, London.
Mallet, C. 1992. *Hydrangeas*. Centre d'Art Floral, Varengeville-sur-Mer, France
Hypericum
Robson, N K B. 1980. *The Plantsman*. (Vol 1 Pt IIII).

Ilex

Andrews, S. 1983. *The Plantsman.* (Vol 5 Pt II).

Andrews, S. 1984. *The Plantsman.* (Vol 6 Pt III).

Andrews, S. *The Garden.* (Vol 110 p11). Royal Horticultural Society, London.

Dudley, T R & Eisenbeiss, G K. 1973 & 1992. *International Checklist of Cultivated Ilex* Pt1: *Ilex opaca*; Pt 2: *Ilex crenata.* US Department of Agriculture, US National Arboretum, Washington.

Impatiens

Grey-Wilson, C. 1983. *The Plantsman.* (Vol 5 Pt II).

Iris

Hoog, M H. 1980. *The Plantsman.* (Vol 2 Pt III).

Mathew, B. 1981. *The Iris.* Batsford, London.

Iris (Series Unguculares)

Service, N. 1990. *The Plantsman.* (Vol 12 Pt I).

Kniphofia

Taylor, J. 1985. *The Plantsman.* (Vol 7 Pt III).

Kohleria

Dates, J D (ed.). *The Gesneriad Register 1985: Check List of Kohleria.* American Gloxinia and Gesneriad Society, Lincoln Acres, California.

Lachenalia

Duncan, G D. 1988. *The Lachenalia Handbook. Annals of Kirstenbosch Botanic Gardens.* Vol 17. Republic of South Africa.

Lantana

Howard, R A. 1969. A Check List of Cultivar Names used in the Genus *Lantana Arnoldia.* (Vol 29 No 11). Arnold Arboretum, Harvard, Massachusetts.

Larix

Horsman, J. 1988 *The Plantsman.* (Vol 10 Pt I).

Lavandula

Tucker, A O. & Hensen, K J W. 1985. *The Cultivars of Lavender and Lavandin.* Baileya. Vol 22(4) pp168-177. New York.

Leptospermum

Nomenclature Committee of the Royal New Zealand Institute of Horticulture. 1963. *Check List of Leptospermum Cultivars.* Journal of the Royal New Zealand Institute of Horticulture. (Vol V No V).

Leucojum

Elliott, J. 1992. *The Plantsman.* (Vol 14 Pt 2).

Lewisia

Elliott, R. 1978. *Lewisias.* Alpine Garden Society, Woking.

Mathew, B. 1989. *The Genus Lewisia.* Christopher Helm, Bromley, Kent.

Liliaceae

Mathew, B. 1989. *The Plantsman.* (Vol 11 Pt II).

Lilium

Leslie, A C. 1982-93. *The International Lily Register.* (3rd ed. & supps. 1-10). Royal Horticultural Society, London.

Lonicera

Bradshaw, D. 1991. *The Plantsman.* (Vol 13 Pt II).

Wright, D. 1983. *The Plantsman.* (Vol 4 Pt IV).

Magnolia

Holman, N. 1979. *The Plantsman.* (Vol 7 Pt I).

Treseder, N G. 1978. *Magnolias.* Faber & Faber, London.

Malus

Parfitt, B. 1965. *Index of the Apple Collection at the National Fruit Trials.* Ministry of Agriculture, Fisheries and Food, Faversham, Kent.

Taylor, H V. 1948. *The Apples of England.* Crosby Lockwood, London.

Meconopsis

Cobb, J L S. 1989. *Meconopsis*. Christopher Helm, Bromley, Kent.

Grey-Wilson, C. 1992. *The Plantsman.* (Vol 14 Pt 1).

Moraea

Goldblatt, P. 1986. *The Moraeas of Southern Africa.* National Botanic Gardens of South Africa.

Narcissus

Blanchard, J W. 1990. *Narcissus*. Alpine Garden Society, Woking, Surrey.

Kington, S. 1989-93 (2nd ed.) *The International Daffodil Checklist.* (2nd ed. & supps. 14-18). Royal Horticultural Society, London.

Throckmorton, T D (ed.). 1985. *Daffodils to Show & Grow and Abridged Classified List of Daffodil Names.* Royal Horticultural Society and American Daffodil Society, Hernando, Mississippi.

Nematanthus

Arnold, P. *The Gesneriad Register 1978: Check List of Nematanthus.* American Gloxinia and Gesneriad Society,

Nerium

Pagen, F J J. 1987. *Oleanders.* Agricultural University, Wageningen, Holland.

Nothofagus

Hill, R S. & Read, J. 1991. *Botanical Journal of the Linnean Society.* (Vol 105 No 1).

Nymphaea

Swindells, P. 1983. *Waterlilies.* Croom Helm, London.

Ostrya

Rushforth, K. 1986. *The Plantsman.* (Vol 7 Pts III & IV).

Paeonia

Haw, S G. 1991. *The Plantsman.* (Vol 13 Pt II).

Haworth-Booth, M. 1963. *The Moutan or Tree Peony.* Garden Book Club, London.

Kessenich, G M. 1976. *Peonies.* (Variety Check List, Pts 1-3). American Peony Society.

Passiflora

Vanderplank, J. 1991. *Passion Flowers.* Cassell, London.

Pelargonium

Baggust, H. 1988. *Miniature and Dwarf Geraniums.* Christopher Helm, Bromley, Kent.

A Checklist and Register of Pelargonium Cultivar Names. Part 1 (1978) and Part 2 (unpublished). Australian Geranium Society, Sydney.

Clifford, D. 1958. *Pelargoniums.* Blandford Press, London.

Complete Copy of the Spalding Pelargonium Checklist. Unpublished. USA.

Van der Walt, J J A et al. 1977-88. *Pelargoniums of South Africa.* (Vols I-III). National Botanic Gardens, Kirstenbosch, Republic of South Africa.

Philadelphus

Taylor, J. 1990. *The Plantsman.* (Vol 11 Pt IV).

Wright, D. 1980. *The Plantsman.* (Vol 2 Pt II).

Phlox

Wherry, E T. 1955. *The Genus Phlox.* Morris Arboretum Monographs III, Philadelphia, Penn.

Phormium

Heenan, P B. 1991. *Checklist of Phormium Cultivars.* Royal New Zealand Institute of Horticulture, Canterbury, New Zealand.

Phygelius

Coombes, A J. 1988. *The Plantsman.* (Vol 9 Pt IV).

Pieris

Bond, J. 1982. *The Plantsman.* (Vol 4 Pt II).

Wagenknecht, B L. 1961. Registration List of Names in the Genus *Pieris.* D. Don, Arnoldia Vol 21 No 8. Arnold Arboretum, Harvard, Massachusetts.

Pinus

Muir, N. 1992. *The Plantsman.* (Vol 14 Pt 2).

Podocarpus

Hutchins, G. 1991. *The Plantsman.* (Vol 13 Pt II).

Potentilla

Brearley, C. 1991. *The Plantsman.* (Vol 13 Pt I).

Brearley, C. 1992. *A.G.S. Bulletin.* (Vol 60 Nos 3 & 4).

Davidson, C G. & Lenz, L M. 1989. *Experimental Taxonony of Potentilla fruticosa. Canadian Journal of Botany.* (Vol 67 No 12) pp3520-3528.

Potentilla (Shrubby)

Brearley, C. 1987. *The Plantsman.* (Vol 9 Pt II)

Primula

Fenderson, G K. 1986. *A Synoptic Guide to the Genus Primula.* Allen Press, Lawrence, Kansas.

Green, R. 1976. *Asiatic Primulas.* The Alpine Garden Society,Woking.

Halda, J J. 1992. *The Genus Primula.* Tethys Books, Colorado.

Hecker, W R. 1971. *Auriculas & Primroses.* Batsford, London.

Smith, G F, Burrow, B & Lowe, D B. 1984. *Primulas of Europe and America.* The Alpine Garden Society, Woking.

Wemyss-Cooke, T J. 1986. *Primulas Old and New.* David & Charles, Newton Abbot.

Primula allionii

Marcham, A J. 1992. *A.G.S. Bulletin.* (Vol 60 No 3).

Prunus

Bultitude, J. *Index of the Plum Collection at the National Fruit Trials.* Ministry of Agriculture, Fisheries & Food, Faversham, Kent.

Grubb, N H. 1949. *Cherries.* Crosby Lockwood, London.

Index of the Cherry Collection at the National Fruit Trials. 1986. Ministry of Agriculture, Fisheries & Food, Faversham, Kent.

Jefferson, R M & Wain, K K. 1984. *The Nomenclature of Cultivated Flowering Cherries (Prunus): The Sato-zakura Group.* U S D A.

Smith, M W G. 1978. *Catalogue of the Plums at the National Fruit Trials.* Ministry of Agriculture, Fisheries & Food, Faversham, Kent.

Taylor, H V. 1949. *The Plums of England.* Crosby Lockwood, London.

Pulmonaria

Mathew, B. 1982. *The Plantsman.* (Vol 4 Pt II).

Pyrus

Parfitt, B. 1981. *Index of the Pear Collection at the National Fruit Trials.* Ministry of Agriculture, Fisheries & Food, Faversham, Kent.

Smith, M W G. 1976. *Catalogue of the British Pears.* Ministry of Agriculture, Fisheries & Food, Faversham, Kent

Quercus

Miller, H A & Lamb, S H. 1985. *Oaks of North America.* Naturegraph Publishers, Happy Camp, California, USA.

Raoulia

Hutchins, G. 1980. *The Plantsman.* (Vol 2 Pt II).

Rhododendron

Chamberlain, D F. 1982. *Notes from the Royal Botanic Garden Edinburgh.* (Vol 39 No 2). H M S O, Edinburgh.

Chamberlain, D F. & Rae, S J. 1990. *A Revision of Rhododendron IV Subgenus Tsutsusi* (in Edinburgh Journal of Botany Vol 47 No 2). HMSO, Edinburgh.

Cox, P A & Cox, K N E. 1988 *Encyclopaedia of Rhododendron Hybrids.* Batsford, London.

Cullen, J. 1980. *Notes from the Royal Botanic Garden Edinburgh.* (Vol 39 No 1). H M S O, Edinburgh.

Davidian, H H. 1982, 1989 & 1992. *The Rhododendron Species.* (Vol I-III). Batsford, London.

Galle, F C. 1987. *Azaleas.* Timber Press, Portland, Oregon.

Lee, F P. 1958. *The Azalea Book.* D Van Nostrand, New York.

Leslie, A C. (compiler). 1980. *The Rhododendron Handbook.* Royal Horticultural Society, London.

Leslie, A C. 1989 *The International Rhododendron Register: Checklist of Rhododendron Names registered 1989-1993 & supps 28-32. Royal Horticultural Society, London.*

Salley, H E & Greer, H E. 1986. *Rhododendron Hybrids.* Batsford, London.

Ribes

Index of the Bush Fruit Collection at the National Fruit Trials. 1987. Ministry of Agriculture, Fisheries & Food, Faversham, Kent.

Romneya

McMillan Browse, P. 1989. *The Plantsman.* (Vol 11 Pt II)

Rosa

Austin, D. 1988. *The Heritage of the Rose.* Antique Collectors' Club, Woodbridge, Suffolk.

Beales, P. 1992. *Roses.* Harvill, London.

Bean, W J. 1900-1988 (rev. D L Clarke & G S Thomas) *Rosa* in *Trees and Shrubs Hardy in the British Isles* 8th ed. (Vol IV & Supp.)

McCann, S. 1985. *Miniature Roses.* David & Charles, Newton Abbot, Devon.

Pawson, A. 1992. *Find That Rose (10th ed).* Rosegrowers' Association, Colchester, Essex.

Phillips, R & Rix, M. 1988. *Roses.* Macmillan, London.

Thomas, G S. 1955 (rev. 1983). *The Old Shrub Roses.* Dent, London.

Thomas, G S. 1962. *Shrub Roses of Today.* Dent, London.

Thomas, G S. (rev. ed 1978). *Climbing Roses Old and New.* Dent, London.

Rosularia

Eggli, U. 1988. *A monograph study of the genus Rosularia.* (*Bradleya*, Vol 6 Suppl.). British Cactus & Succulent Society, Bury, Lancashire, UK.

Salix

Newsholme, C. 1992. *Willows.* Batsford, London.

Saxifraga

Horn, R. Webr, K M & Byam-Grounds, J. 1986. *Porophyllum Saxifrages.* Byam-Grounds Publications, Stamford, Lincolshire, UK.

Kohlein, F. 1984. *Saxifrages and Related Genera.* Batsford, London.

Webb, D A & Cornell, R J. 1989. *Saxifrages of Europe.* Christopher Helm, Bromley, Kent.

Sedum

Evans, R L. 1983. *Handbook of Cultivated Sedums.* Ivory Head Press Motcombe, Dorset.

Hensen, K J W & Groendijk-Wilders, N. 1986. *The Plantsman.* (Vol 8 Pt I).

Sempervivum

Mitchell, P J. 1985. *International Cultivar Register for Jovibarba, Rosularia, Sempervivum.* The Sempervivum Society, W Sussex.

Shortia

Barnes, P G. 1990 *The Plantsman.* (Vol 12 Pt I).

Sinningia

Dates, J D. *The Gesneriad Register 1988: Check List of Sinningia.* American Gloxinia and Gesneriad Society, Galesburg, Illinois.

Skimmia

Brown, P D. 1980. *The Plantsman.* (Vol 1 Pt IV).

Solenostemon

Pedley, W K. & Pedley, R. 1974. *Coleus - A Guide to Cultivation and Identification.* Bartholemew, Edinburgh.

Sorbus

McAllister, H. 1985. *The Plantsman.* (Vol 6 Pt IV).

Rushforth, K. 1991. *The Plantsman.* (Vol 13 Pt II).

Rushforth, K. 1992. *The Plantsman.* (Vols 13 Pt 4 & 14 Pt 1).

Wright, D. 1981. *The Plantsman.* (Vol 3 Pt II).

Streptocarpus

Arnold, P. *The Gesneriad Register 1979: Check List of Streptocarpus.* American Gloxinia and Gesneriad Society, Binghamton, New York.

Sutherlandia

Schrire, BD & Andrews, S. 1992. *The Plantsman.* (Vol 14 Pt 2).

Syringa

Fiala, Fr J L. 1988. *Lilacs.* Christopher Helm, Bromley, Kent.

Rogers, O M. 1976. *Tentative International Register of Cultivar Names in the Genus Syringa.* University of New Hampshire.

Taylor, J. 1990. *The Plantsman.* (Vol 11 Pt IV).

Vrugtman, F. 1976-83. *Bulletin of the American Association of Botanical Gardens and Arboreta.*

Tilia

Muir, N. 1984. *The Plantsman.* (Vol 5 Pt IV).

Muir, N. 1988. *The Plantsman.* (Vol 10 Pt II).

Tillandsia

Kiff, LF. 1991. *A Distributional Checklist of the Genus Tillandsia.* Botanical Diversions, Encino, California.

Tricyrtis

Matthew, B. 1985. *The Plantsman.* (Vol 6 Pt 4).

Trillium

Mitchell, R J. 1989. *The Plantsman.* (Vol 10 Pt IV, Vol 11 Pts II & III, Vol 12 Pt I).

Mitchell, R J. 1992. *The Plantsman.* (Vol 13 Pt 4).

Tulipa

Classified List and International Register of Tulip Names. 1987. Royal General Bulbgrowers' Association, Hillegom, Holland.

Ulmus

Green, P S. 1964. Registration of the Cultivar Names in *Ulmus.* Arnoldia, Vol 24 Nos 608, Arnold Arboretum, Harvard, Massachusetts.

Veratrum

Mathew, B. 1989. *The Plantsman.* (Vol 11 Pt I).

Viola

Coombs, R E. 1981 *Violets.* Croom Helm, London.

Farrar, E. 1989. *Pansies, Violas & Sweet Violets.* Hurst Village Publishing, Reading.

Fuller, R. 1990. *Pansies, Violas & Violettas* Crowood Press, Marlborough, Wiltshire.

Vitis

Pearkes, G. 1989. *Vine Growing in Britain.* Dent, London.

Robinson, J. 1986. *Vines, Grapes and Wines* Mitchell Beazley, London.

Watsonia

Goldblatt, P. 1989. *The Genus Watsonia.* National Botanic Gardens, Republic of South Africa.

Weigela

Howard, R A. 1965. A Check-list of Cultivar Names in *Weigela.* Arnoldia, Vol 25 Nos 9-11. Arnold Arboretum, Harvard, Massachusetts.

Taylor, J. 1990. *The Plantsman.* (Vol 12 Pt IV).

Wisteria

McMillan-Browse, P. 1984. *The Plantsman* (Vol 6 Pt II).

Zauschneria (now Epilobium)

Raven, P H. 1976. *Annals of the Missouri Botanic Garden.* (Vol 63 pp326-340).

Zelkova

Ainsworth, P. 1989. *The Plantsman.* (Vol 11 Pt II).

Muir, N. 1991. *The Plantsman.* (Vol 13 Pt II).

INDEX MAP

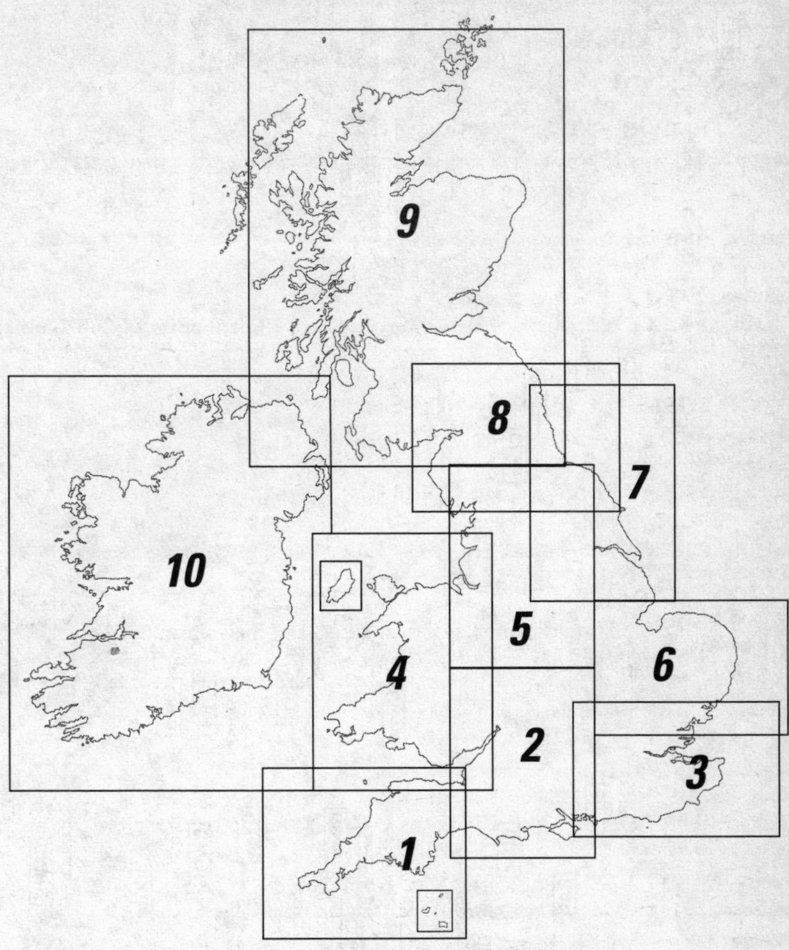

Motorways

Primary routes

Other routes

The maps on the following pages show the *approximate* location of the nurseries whose details are listed in this directory.

Details of nurseries with letter Codes in boxes CRow are given in the CODE-NURSERY Index.

Details of nurseries with number Codes in circles (20) are given in the ADDITIONAL NURSERY Index.

Maps prepared by à la carte

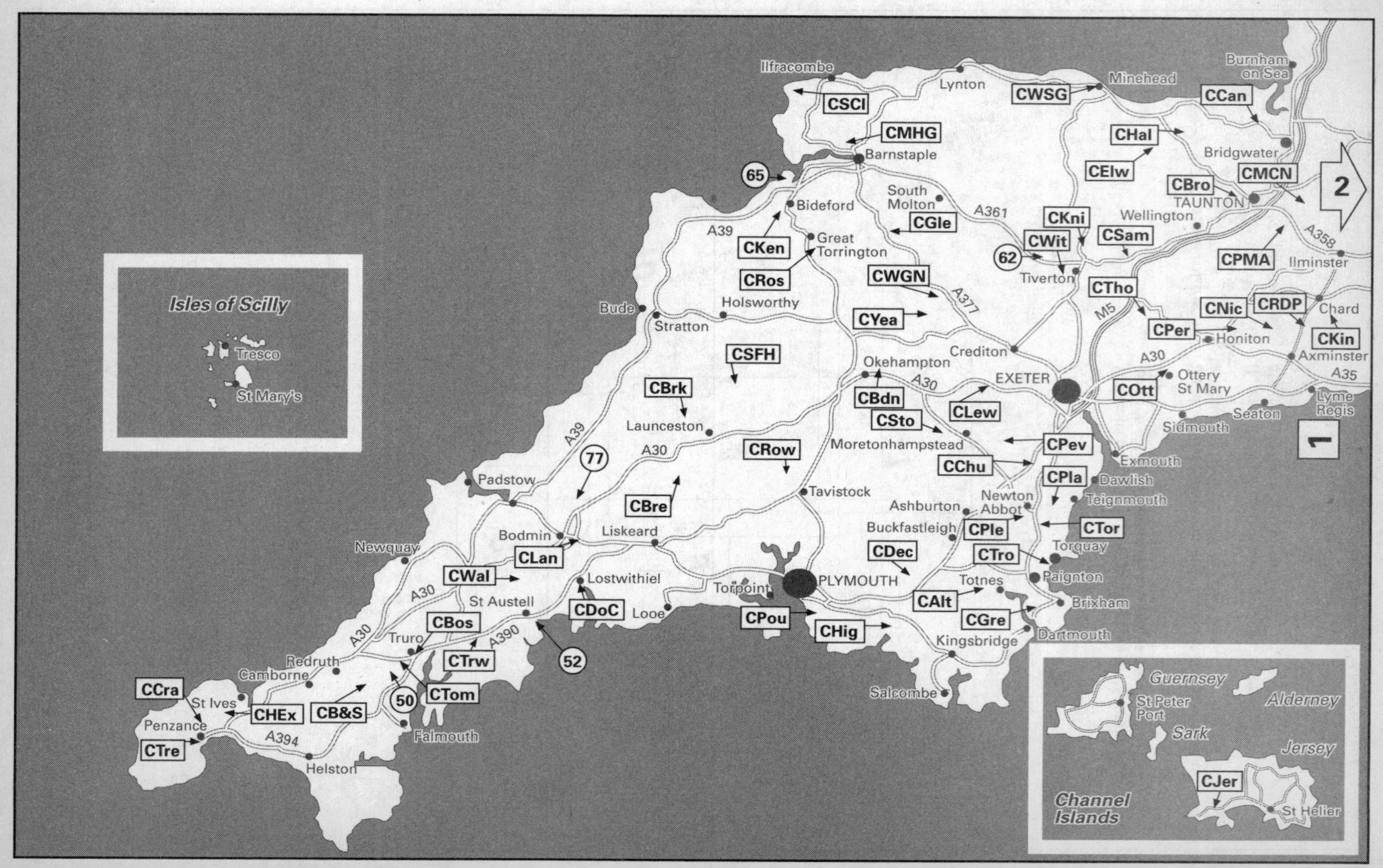

Isles of Scilly
Tresco
St Mary's
Ilfracombe
Lynton
Minehead
Burnham on Sea
Barnstaple
Bridgwater
Bideford
South Molton
A361
Wellington
TAUNTON
A39
Great Torrington
Tiverton
A358
Ilminster
A377
Bude
Stratton
Holsworthy
M5
Chard
Honiton
Okehampton
Crediton
Axminster
A30
EXETER
Ottery St Mary
A35
Lyme Regis
Launceston
Seaton
Sidmouth
A39
Moretonhampstead
Exmouth
Padstow
Tavistock
Dawlish
Newton Abbot
Teignmouth
Ashburton
Buckfastleigh
Bodmin
Liskeard
Torquay
Newquay
PLYMOUTH
Paignton
Lostwithiel
Torpoint
Totnes
St Austell
Brixham
Looe
Truro
A390
Kingsbridge
Dartmouth
Redruth
Camborne
St Ives
Penzance
A394
Falmouth
Helston
Salcombe
Guernsey
St Peter Port
Alderney
Sark
Jersey
St Helier
Channel Islands
CSCl
CMHG
CWSG
CCan
CHal
CElw
CBro
CMCN
CKni
CGle
CWit
CSam
CKen
CRos
CWGN
CPMA
CTho
CYea
CNic
CRDP
CPer
CKin
CSFH
CBrk
CBdn
COtt
CLew
CSto
CRow
CPev
CChu
CPla
CBre
CTor
CPle
CDec
CTro
CLan
CWal
CDoC
CAlt
CPou
CGre
CHig
CBos
CTrw
CTom
CCra
CHEx
CB&S
CTre
CJer
65
62
77
52
50
1
2

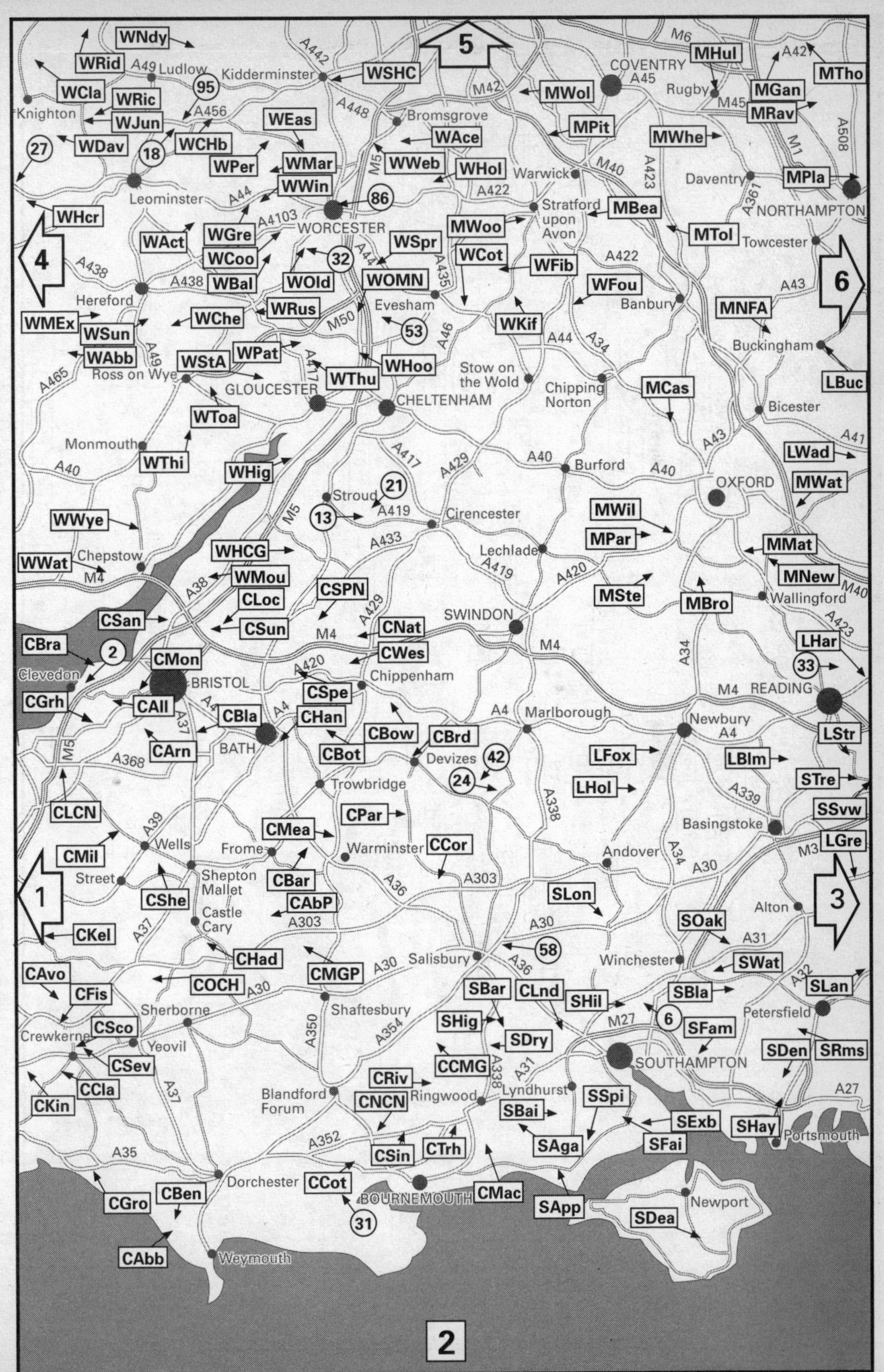
5
4
6
1
3
Ludlow
Kidderminster
Knighton
Bromsgrove
COVENTRY
Rugby
Warwick
Daventry
NORTHAMPTON
Leominster
WORCESTER
Stratford upon Avon
Towcester
Hereford
Evesham
Banbury
Buckingham
Ross on Wye
GLOUCESTER
CHELTENHAM
Stow on the Wold
Chipping Norton
Bicester
Monmouth
Burford
OXFORD
Stroud
Cirencester
Chepstow
Lechlade
Wallingford
SWINDON
Clevedon
BRISTOL
Chippenham
READING
BATH
Marlborough
Newbury
Devizes
Trowbridge
Basingstoke
Wells
Frome
Warminster
Andover
Street
Shepton Mallet
Castle Cary
Alton
Salisbury
Winchester
Sherborne
Shaftesbury
Petersfield
Crewkerne
Yeovil
SOUTHAMPTON
Lyndhurst
Blandford Forum
Ringwood
Portsmouth
Dorchester
BOURNEMOUTH
Newport
Weymouth
WNdy
WRid
WCla
WRic
WJun
WDav
WCHb
WEas
WPer
WMar
WWin
WSHC
WAce
WWeb
WHol
WHcr
WAct
WGre
WCoo
WBal
WOld
WSpr
WOMN
WCot
WRus
WChe
WMEx
WSun
WAbb
WStA
WPat
WThu
WHoo
WToa
WThi
WHig
WWye
WWat
WHCG
WMou
WKif
WFib
WFou
WWoo
MWol
MPit
MHul
MGan
MRav
MTho
MWhe
MPla
MBea
MTol
MNFA
MCas
LBuc
LWad
MWat
MWil
MPar
MMat
MNew
MSte
MBro
LHar
CSPN
CLoc
CSun
CSan
CBra
CMon
CNat
CWes
CGrh
CAll
CBla
CSpe
CHan
CArn
CBow
CBrd
CBot
LFox
LHol
LStr
LBlm
STre
SSvw
LGre
CLCN
CMea
CPar
CCor
CMil
CBar
CShe
CAbP
SLon
SOak
CKel
CHad
SWat
CAvo
CFis
COCH
CMGP
SBar
CLnd
SHil
SBla
SLan
CSco
SHig
SDry
SFam
CSev
CCMG
SDen
SRms
CCla
CKin
CRiv
CNCN
SSpi
SBai
SExb
SHay
SFai
SAga
CSin
CTrh
CGro
CBen
CCot
CMac
SApp
SDea
CAbb
95
18
27
86
32
53
21
13
2
33
42
24
58
6
31
M6
M42
M45
M1
A508
A427
M40
A45
A423
A442
A49
A456
A448
M5
A422
A44
A4103
A361
A438
A435
A46
M50
A417
A43
A465
A429
A40
A41
A419
A433
A420
M4
A38
A34
A4
A37
A368
A338
A339
M3
A39
A36
A303
A30
A31
A32
A350
A354
A27
A35
A352

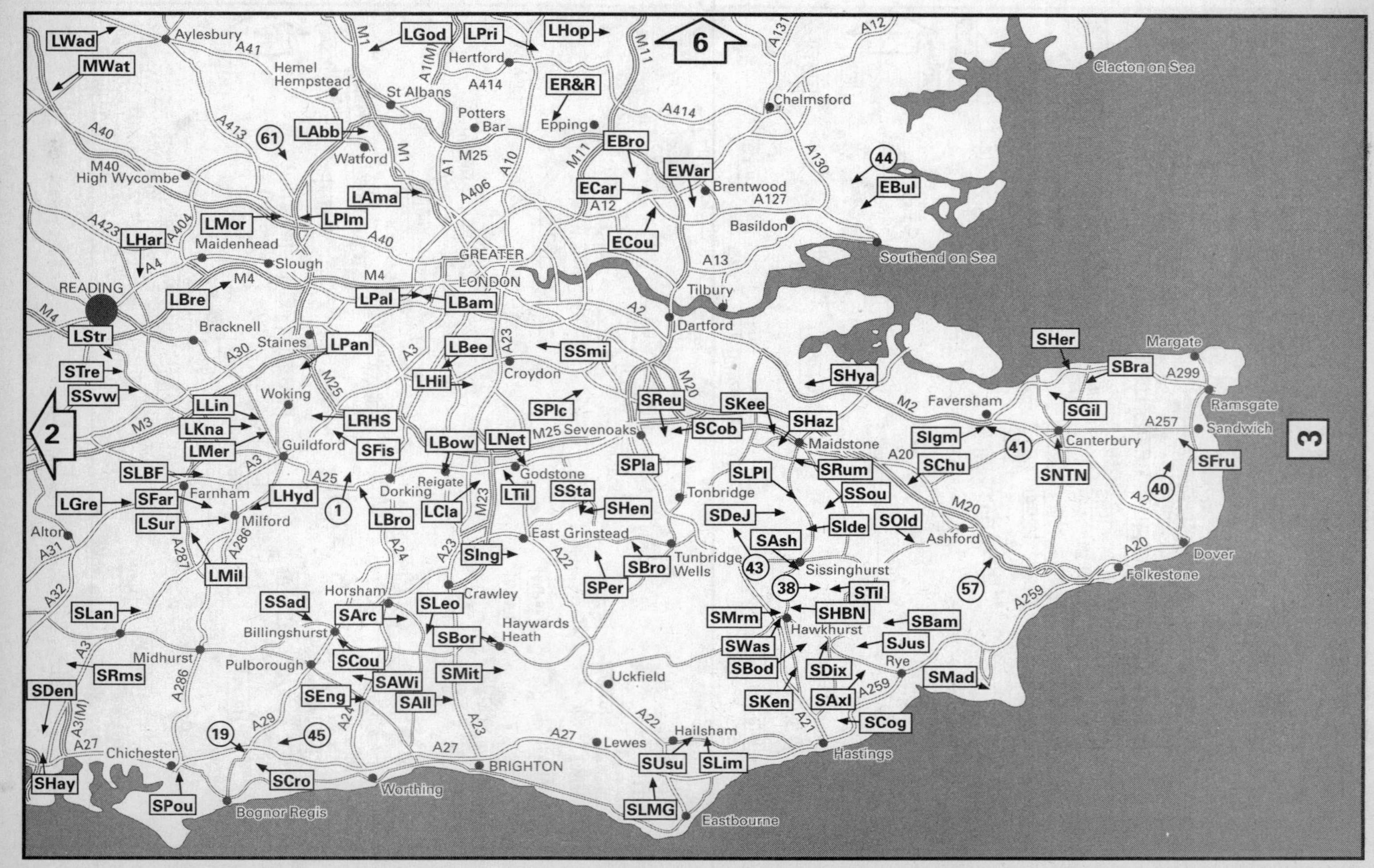

3
2
6
READING
Aylesbury
Hemel Hempstead
St Albans
Hertford
Potters Bar
Epping
Chelmsford
Clacton on Sea
Watford
High Wycombe
Maidenhead
Slough
Brentwood
Basildon
Southend on Sea
GREATER LONDON
Tilbury
Dartford
Bracknell
Staines
Woking
Guildford
Croydon
Sevenoaks
Godstone
Reigate
Dorking
Farnham
Milford
Alton
Tonbridge
Maidstone
Faversham
Canterbury
Margate
Ramsgate
Sandwich
Dover
Folkestone
Ashford
East Grinstead
Tunbridge Wells
Sissinghurst
Hawkhurst
Rye
Hastings
Crawley
Horsham
Haywards Heath
Billingshurst
Pulborough
Midhurst
Uckfield
Lewes
Hailsham
Eastbourne
BRIGHTON
Worthing
Chichester
Bognor Regis
LWad
MWat
LGod
LPri
LHop
ER&R
LAbb
61
EBro
EWar
ECar
ECou
44
EBul
LAma
LPlm
LMor
LHar
LBre
LPal
LBam
LStr
STre
SSvw
LPan
LBee
SSmi
LHil
LLin
LKna
LMer
LRHS
SFis
SLBF
LGre
SFar
LSur
LMil
LHyd
1
LBro
LBow
LNet
LCla
LTil
SPlc
SReu
SCob
SKee
SHaz
SHya
SHer
SBra
SGil
SIgm
41
SNTN
SFru
40
SChu
SRum
SLPl
SPla
SSta
SHen
SSou
SDeJ
SIde
SOld
SAsh
43
38
STil
SHBN
SMrm
SBam
SJus
SWas
SBod
SDix
SMad
SAxl
SKen
SCog
57
SIng
SPer
SBro
SLan
SSad
SArc
SLeo
SBor
SCou
SRms
SAWi
SMit
SDen
SEng
SAll
19
45
SHay
SPou
SCro
SUsu
SLim
SLMG
M4
M40
M1
A1(M)
A1
M25
A10
M11
A414
A41
A40
A413
A406
A12
A13
A127
A130
A131
A423
A404
A4
A2
A3
A30
M3
M20
M23
A23
A25
A24
A22
A20
M2
A257
A299
A259
A21
A27
A29
A31
A32
A286
A287
A3(M)

Ramsay
Kirk Michael
MBal
Douglas
Castletown
Isle of Man
PRESTON
Southport
NPor
M6
NWin
LIVERPOOL
M62
Birkenhead
MBel
NLan
37
MMor
M56
A54
CHESTER
MChe
Llandudno
Rhyl
A55
WHen
WHer
A5
Holyhead
Menai Bridge
Bangor
WAbe
A470
WBod
WCru
WGwy
Mold
MOke
A51
Ruthin
A494
WEfe
Betws y Coed
A41
Corwen
Llangollen
WCel
Whitchurch
WFro
WByw
5
Oswestry
WPbr
Portmadoc
Ffestiniog
WTyr
WOak
A442
WHal
Dolgellau
WDin
WMer
Shrewsbury
A458
A488
A49
M54
Welshpool
A483
Machynlleth
Newtown
WRid
Church Stretton
Caersws
WNdy
Bishop's Castle
A44
95
Aberystwyth
Llangurig
Knighton
WCla
Ludlow
18
WDav
Rhayader
27
WJun
WRic
Tregaron
Llandrindod Wells
Kington
Leominster
WHcr
A4112
A487
Builth Wells
A438
Hereford
A465
Cardigan
A475
Lampeter
WBon
2
A485
46
Llandovery
WMEx
A40
Brecon
A479
WAbb
Ross on Wye
St David's
WShi
Carmarthen
Llandeilo
Haverfordwest
A48
Monmouth
Merthyr Tydfil
Abergavenny
WWye
WStl
Hirwaun
WWat
Milford Haven
Pembroke
Llanelli
Chepstow
CSan
CMon
Newport
CBra
BRISTOL
M4
CARDIFF
Bridgend
Clevedon
CAll
CGrh
CArn
CBla
Weston Super Mare
CLCN
M5
Minehead
A39
A371
CSCl
4
CWSG
CCan
Bridgwater
CMHG

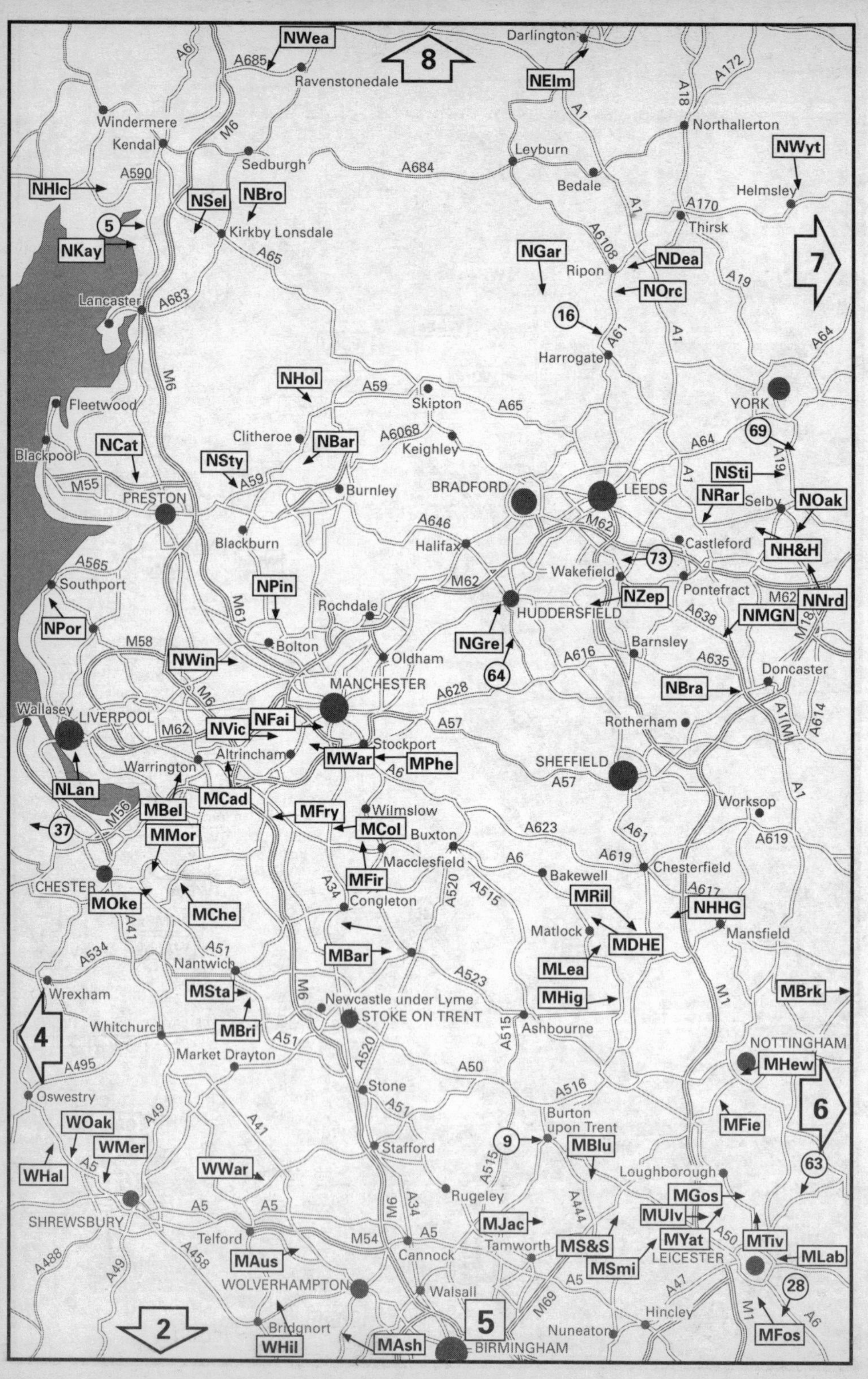
8
NWea
A6
A685
Ravenstonedale
Darlington
NElm
A1
A18
A172
Northallerton
Windermere
Kendal
M6
Sedburgh
Leyburn
A684
Bedale
NWyt
Helmsley
A590
NHlc
NSel
NBro
5
Kirkby Lonsdale
NKay
A65
A170
Thirsk
7
NGar
NDea
Ripon
A6108
NOrc
A19
Lancaster
A683
16
A61
A1
A64
Harrogate
NHol
A59
Skipton
A65
YORK
Fleetwood
NCat
Clitheroe
NBar
A6068
Keighley
69
A64
Blackpool
NSty
NSti
A19
M55
PRESTON
A59
Burnley
BRADFORD
LEEDS
NRar
Selby
NOak
A646
M62
Blackburn
Halifax
Castleford
NH&H
A565
73
Wakefield
Southport
NPin
M62
Pontefract
M62
NNrd
Rochdale
NZep
HUDDERSFIELD
A638
NMGN
NPor
M61
M18
M58
Bolton
Barnsley
NWin
Oldham
NGre
A616
A635
64
Doncaster
M6
MANCHESTER
A628
NBra
Wallasey
LIVERPOOL
NFai
A1(M)
A614
M62
NVic
A57
Rotherham
Stockport
Altrincham
MWar
MPhe
Warrington
A6
SHEFFIELD
NLan
A57
A1
MCad
M56
MBel
MFry
Wilmslow
Worksop
37
MMor
MCol
Buxton
A623
A619
A61
A6
CHESTER
Macclesfield
A619
Chesterfield
MFir
A515
Bakewell
A34
A520
A617
MOke
MRil
Congleton
NHHG
MChe
A41
Matlock
MDHE
Mansfield
A534
A51
MBar
Nantwich
MLea
A523
M1
Wrexham
MSta
MHig
MBrk
M6
Newcastle under Lyme
4
MBri
STOKE ON TRENT
A515
Whitchurch
Ashbourne
A51
NOTTINGHAM
Market Drayton
A520
MHew
A495
A50
Oswestry
Stone
A516
6
A49
A51
WOak
Burton upon Trent
MFie
A41
WMer
9
MBlu
WHal
Stafford
A515
63
A5
WWar
Loughborough
A444
MGos
Rugeley
A5
A5
MUlv
SHREWSBURY
M6
A34
MJac
MYat
A50
MTiv
Telford
M54
A5
Tamworth
MS&S
LEICESTER
A488
A458
MAus
Cannock
MSmi
MLab
A49
WOLVERHAMPTON
A5
A47
28
Walsall
M69
M1
2
5
Hinckley
A6
Bridgnorth
Nuneaton
WHil
MAsh
BIRMINGHAM
MFos

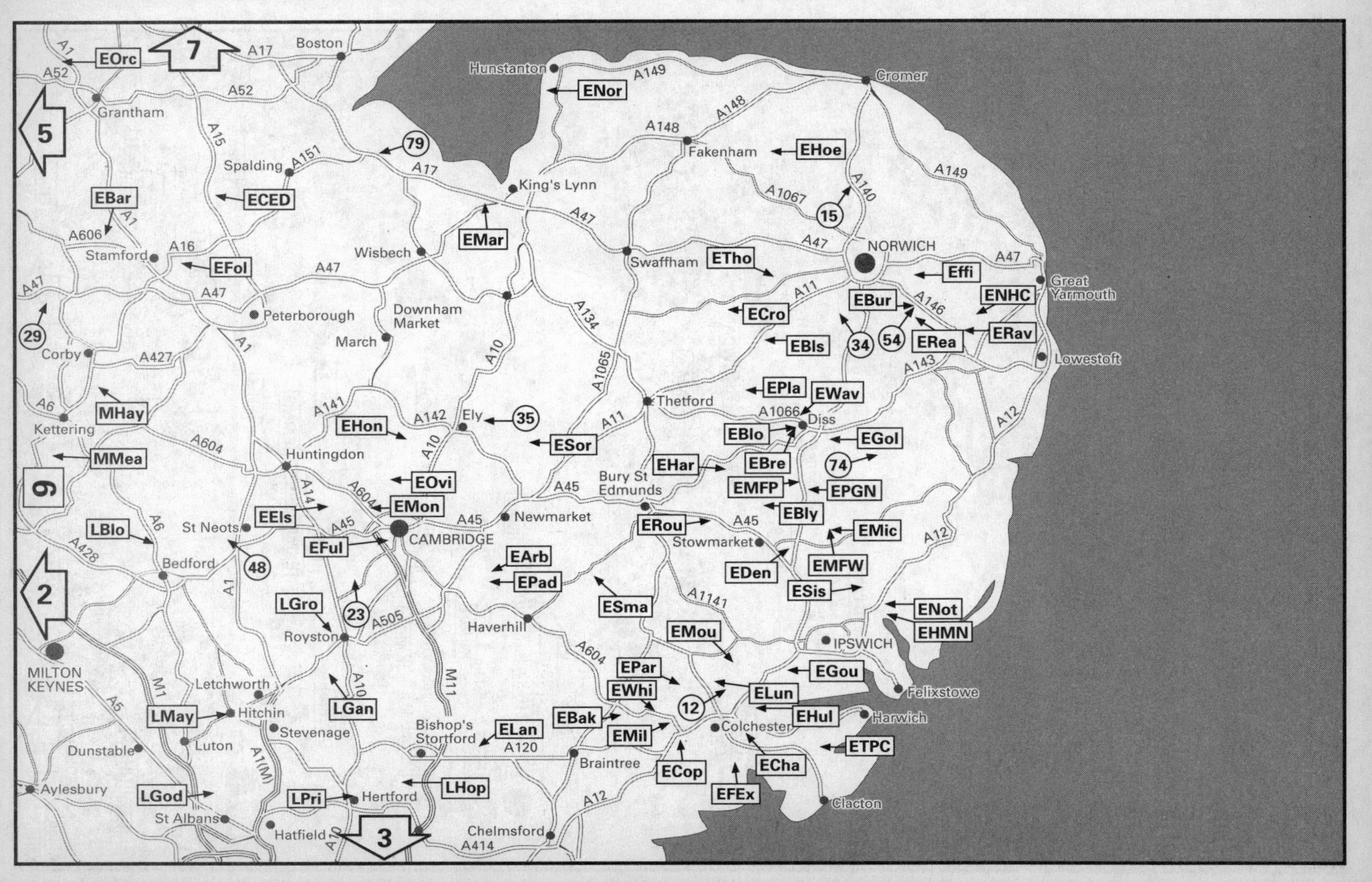

7
5
2
3
6
Boston
Hunstanton
Cromer
Grantham
Spalding
King's Lynn
Fakenham
NORWICH
Great Yarmouth
Lowestoft
Stamford
Wisbech
Swaffham
Peterborough
Downham Market
March
Corby
Kettering
Thetford
Ely
Diss
Huntingdon
Bury St Edmunds
Newmarket
St Neots
CAMBRIDGE
Stowmarket
Bedford
Royston
Haverhill
IPSWICH
Felixstowe
MILTON KEYNES
Letchworth
Hitchin
Stevenage
Luton
Bishop's Stortford
Colchester
Harwich
Dunstable
Braintree
Aylesbury
Hertford
St Albans
Hatfield
Chelmsford
Clacton
EOrc
ENor
EHoe
EBar
ECED
EMar
EFol
ETho
Effi
EBur
ENHC
ECro
ERea
ERav
EBls
EPla
EWav
EHon
ESor
EBlo
EGol
EHar
EBre
EOvi
EMFP
EPGN
EMon
EBly
EEls
ERou
EMic
LBlo
EFul
EArb
EPad
EDen
EMFW
ESis
ENot
EHMN
LGro
ESma
EMou
EGou
EPar
ELun
EWhi
EHul
LMay
LGan
EBak
ELan
EMil
ETPC
ECop
ECha
LGod
LPri
LHop
EFEx
MHay
MMea
79
29
15
34
54
35
74
48
23
12

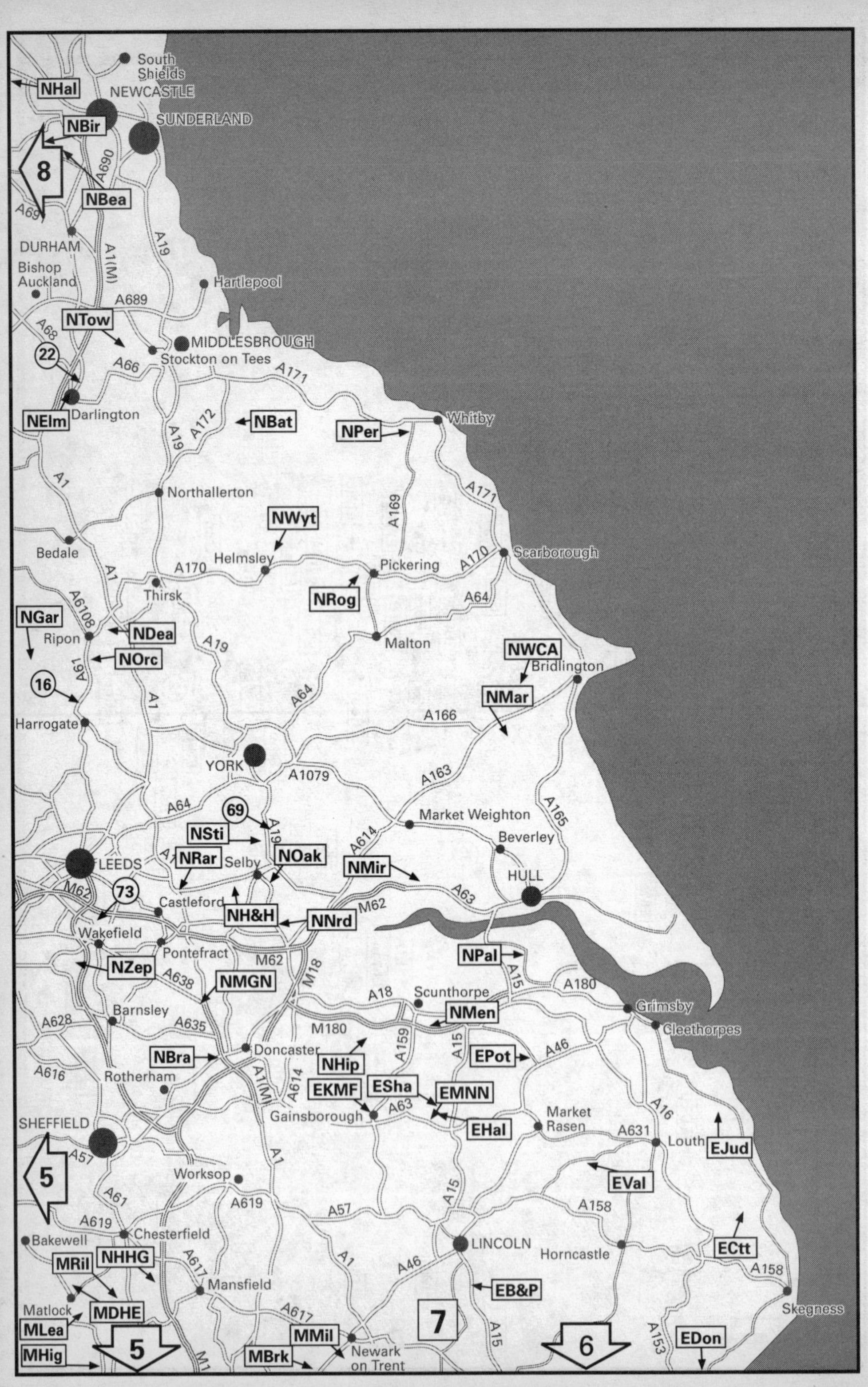

South Shields
NHal
NEWCASTLE
SUNDERLAND
NBir
8
NBea
A690
A69
DURHAM
A1(M)
A19
Bishop Auckland
Hartlepool
A689
NTow
A68
22
MIDDLESBROUGH
Stockton on Tees
A66
A171
NElm
Darlington
NBat
Whitby
NPer
A19
A172
A1
Northallerton
A171
A169
NWyt
Bedale
Helmsley
A170
Pickering
A170
Scarborough
A1
A170
Thirsk
NRog
A64
A6108
NGar
Ripon
NDea
Malton
NWCA
NOrc
A19
Bridlington
A61
16
NMar
A1
A64
A166
Harrogate
YORK
A1079
A163
A64
69
A165
NSti
A19
Market Weighton
A614
Beverley
LEEDS
NRar
Selby
NOak
NMir
HULL
M62
73
Castleford
A63
NH&H
NNrd
M62
Wakefield
Pontefract
M62
NPal
NZep
A638
NMGN
M18
A15
A180
A18
Scunthorpe
Barnsley
Grimsby
NMen
A628
A635
M180
Cleethorpes
A616
NBra
Doncaster
A159
A15
EPot
A46
NHip
Rotherham
A614
A1(M)
EKMF
ESha
EMNN
A16
Gainsborough
A63
Market Rasen
EHal
SHEFFIELD
A631
Louth
EJud
A57
5
A1
Worksop
EVal
A61
A619
A57
A15
A158
A619
Bakewell
Chesterfield
LINCOLN
Horncastle
ECtt
MRil
NHHG
A617
A1
A46
A158
Mansfield
EB&P
Matlock
MDHE
Skegness
A617
7
MLea
A15
A153
MMil
EDon
5
6
MHig
MBrk
Newark on Trent
M1

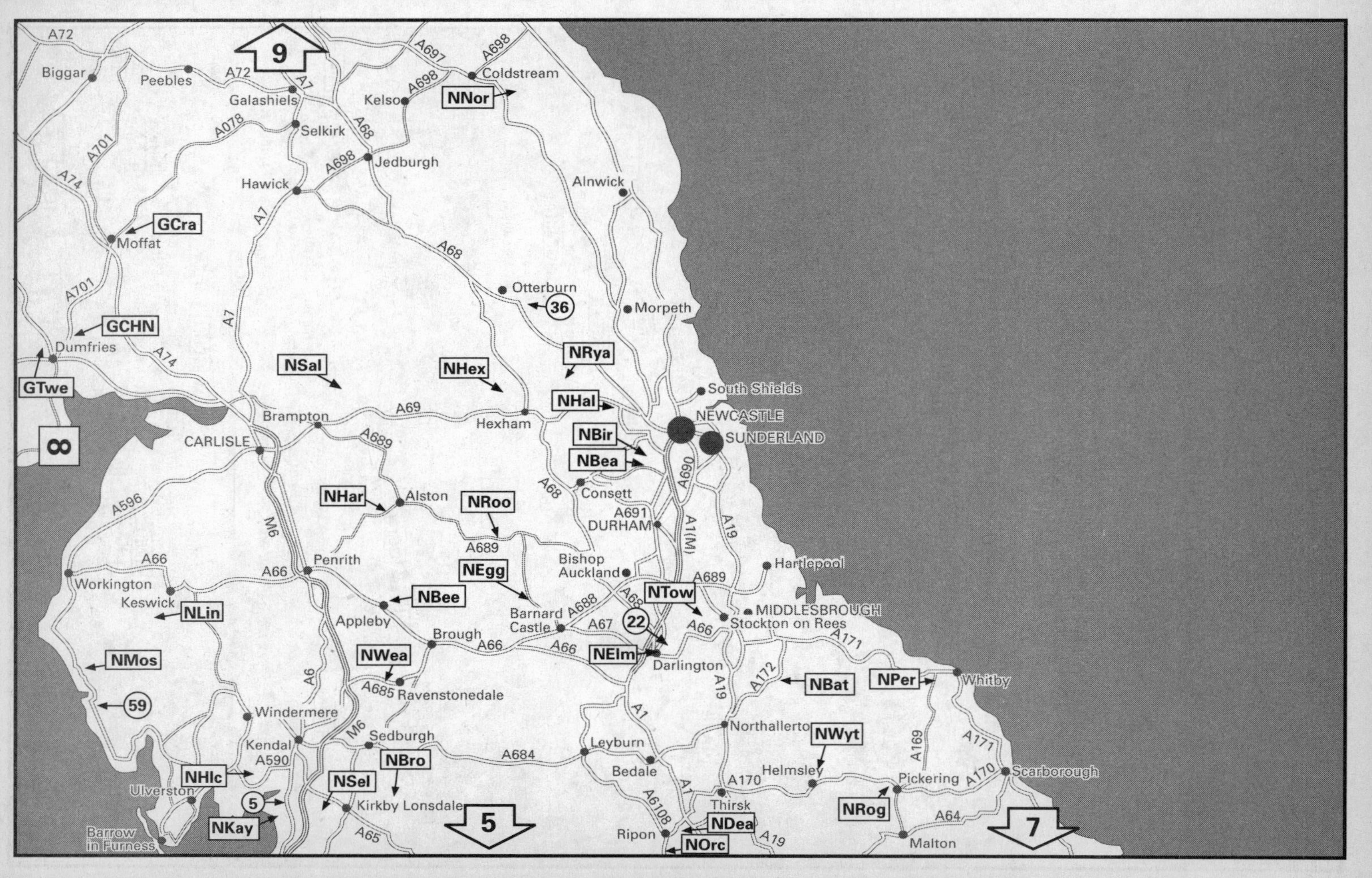
9
8
5
7
Biggar
Peebles
Galashiels
Selkirk
Kelso
Coldstream
Jedburgh
Hawick
Alnwick
Moffat
Otterburn
Morpeth
Dumfries
South Shields
NEWCASTLE
SUNDERLAND
Brampton
Hexham
CARLISLE
Alston
Consett
DURHAM
Penrith
Bishop Auckland
Hartlepool
Workington
Keswick
Appleby
Barnard Castle
MIDDLESBROUGH
Stockton on Rees
Brough
Darlington
Whitby
Ravenstonedale
Windermere
Northallerto
Kendal
Sedburgh
Leyburn
Bedale
Helmsley
Pickering
Scarborough
Ulverston
Kirkby Lonsdale
Thirsk
Barrow in Furness
Ripon
Malton
GCra
GCHN
GTwe
NNor
NSal
NHex
NRya
NHal
NBir
NBea
NHar
NRoo
NEgg
NTow
NBee
NLin
NMos
NWea
NElm
NBat
NPer
NWyt
NHlc
NSel
NBro
NKay
NRog
NDea
NOrc
36
22
59
5
A72
A697
A698
A7
A68
A078
A701
A74
A69
A689
A596
A66
A6
A685
A590
A65
A684
A691
A1(M)
A690
A19
A688
A67
A172
A171
A169
A170
A64
A1
A6108
M6

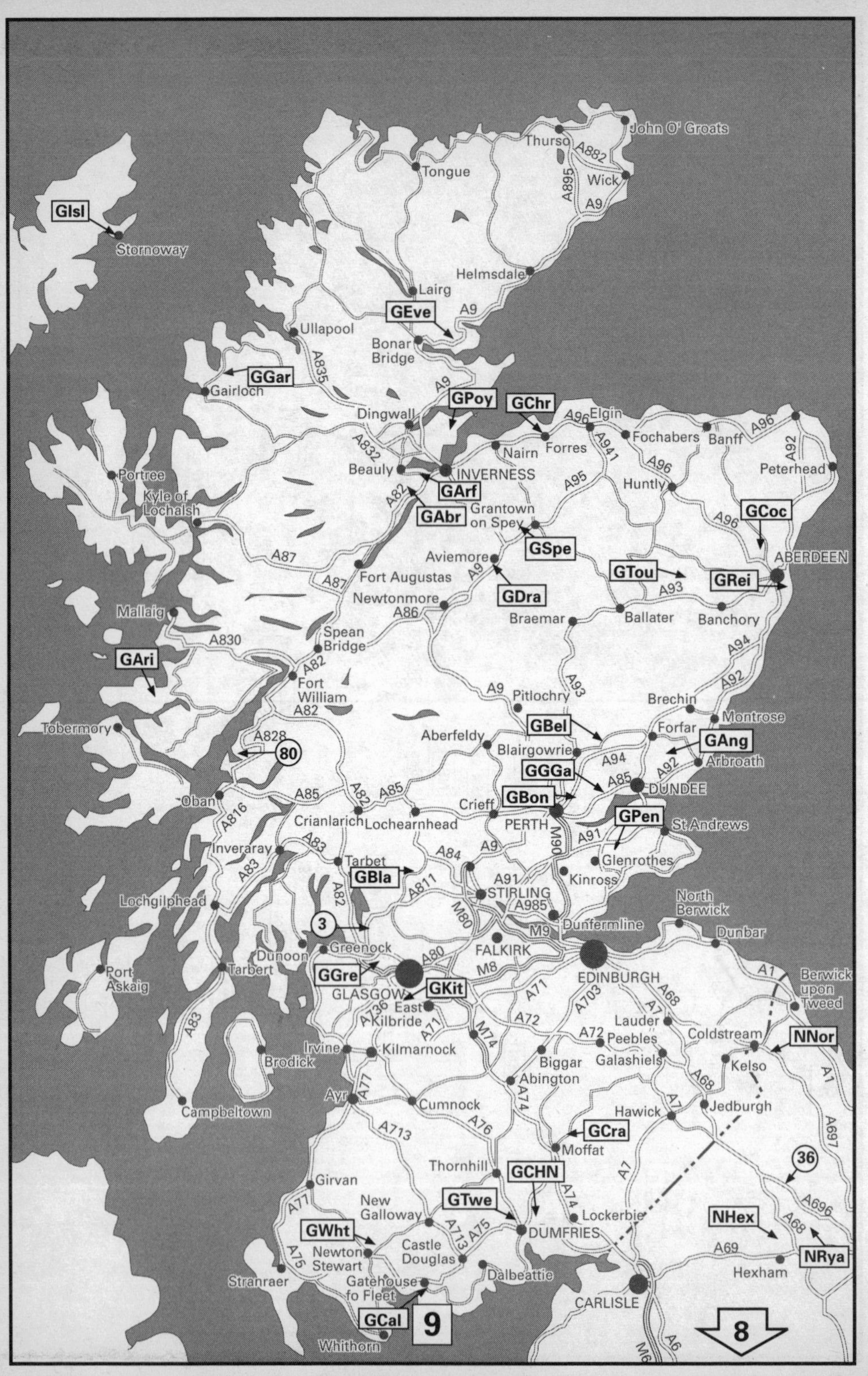

John O' Groats
Thurso
A882
Tongue
A895
Wick
A9
GIsl
Stornoway
Helmsdale
Lairg
GEve
A9
Ullapool
Bonar Bridge
GGar
A835
Gairloch
A9
GPoy
GChr
Dingwall
A96
Elgin
A832
Nairn
Forres
A941
Fochabers
Banff
A96
A92
Beauly
INVERNESS
A96
Peterhead
Portree
GArf
A95
Huntly
Kyle of Lochalsh
A82
GAbr
Grantown on Spey
GCoc
A96
GSpe
ABERDEEN
A87
Aviemore
A9
Fort Augustas
GTou
GRei
A87
GDra
A93
Newtonmore
Mallaig
A86
Braemar
Ballater
Banchory
Spean Bridge
A830
A94
GAri
A82
Fort William
A9
Pitlochry
A93
A92
Brechin
A82
Montrose
Tobermory
GBel
Forfar
A828
Aberfeldy
GAng
80
Blairgowrie
Arbroath
A94
GGGa
A92
A85
DUNDEE
Oban
A85
A82
A85
GBon
Crieff
A816
Crianlarich
Lochearnhead
PERTH
GPen
St Andrews
M90
A91
Inveraray
A83
A9
A84
Glenrothes
A83
Tarbet
GBla
A91
Kinross
A82
A811
STIRLING
Lochgilphead
M80
A985
North Berwick
3
M9
Dunfermline
Dunbar
Dunoon
Greenock
FALKIRK
A80
Port Askaig
Tarbert
GGre
M8
EDINBURGH
A1
Berwick upon Tweed
GLASGOW
GKit
A71
A7
A68
East Kilbride
A703
A736
A72
Lauder
A71
A72
Coldstream
A83
M74
Peebles
NNor
Irvine
Kilmarnock
Brodick
Biggar
Galashiels
Kelso
A1
Abington
A68
Ayr
A77
Cumnock
A74
A7
Jedburgh
Campbeltown
Hawick
A697
A713
A76
GCra
Moffat
A7
36
Thornhill
GCHN
Girvan
A74
A696
A77
New Galloway
GTwe
Lockerbie
NHex
A68
GWht
A713
A75
DUMFRIES
A75
Newton Stewart
Castle Douglas
A69
NRya
Stranraer
Dalbeattie
Hexham
Gatehouse fo Fleet
CARLISLE
GCal
9
8
Whithorn
M6
A6

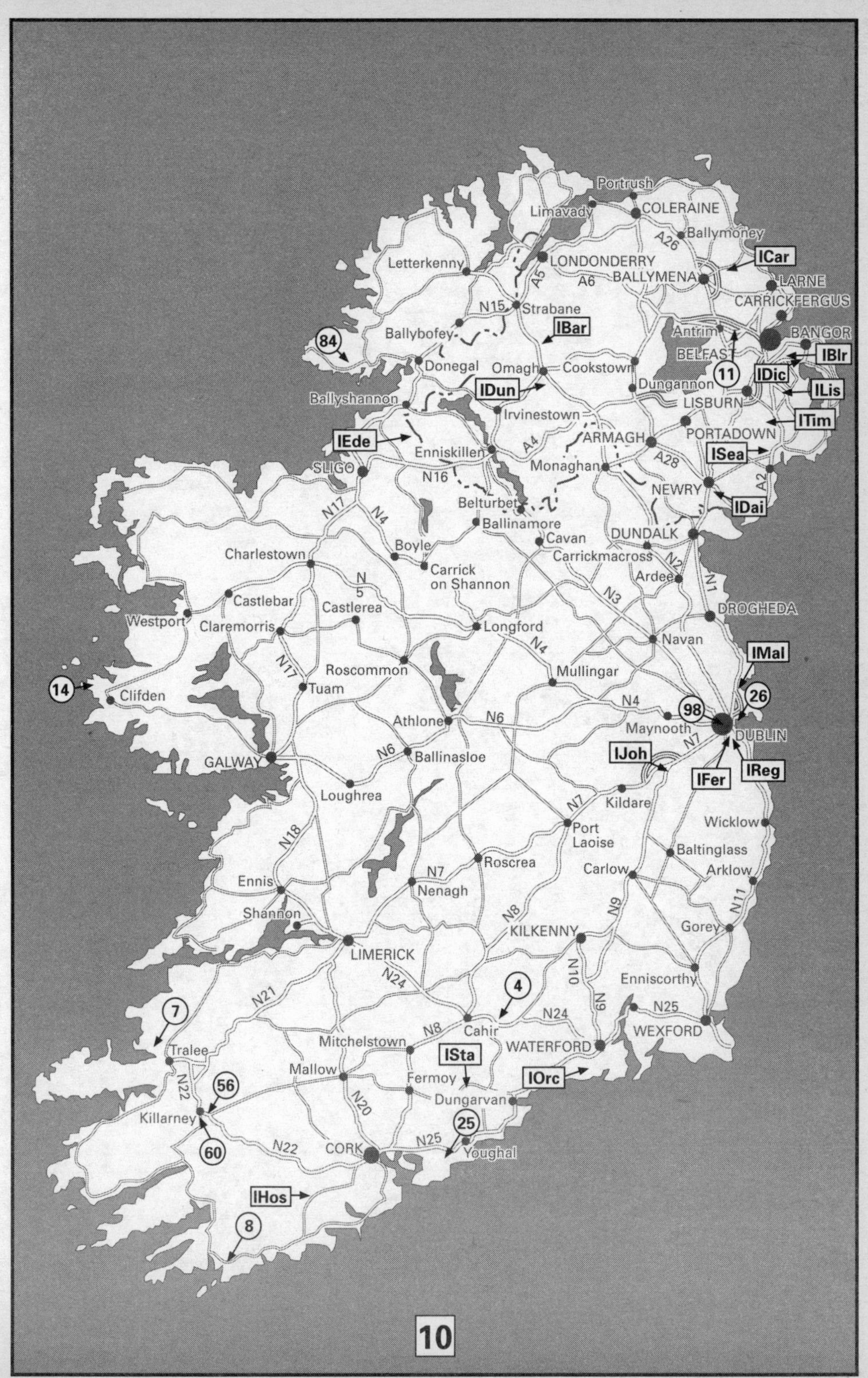
Portrush
COLERAINE
Limavady
Ballymoney
A26
Letterkenny
LONDONDERRY
ICar
A5
A6
BALLYMENA
LARNE
N15
Strabane
CARRICKFERGUS
IBar
Antrim
BANGOR
84
Ballybofey
BELFAST
IBlr
Donegal
Omagh
Cookstown
11
IDic
IDun
Dungannon
ILis
Ballyshannon
LISBURN
Irvinestown
ITim
IEde
ARMAGH
PORTADOWN
A4
A28
ISea
Enniskillen
SLIGO
Monaghan
N16
A2
NEWRY
N17
Belturbet
IDai
N4
Ballinamore
DUNDALK
Cavan
Boyle
Carrickmacross
Charlestown
N2
Carrick on Shannon
Ardee
N 5
N1
N3
Castlebar
Castlerea
DROGHEDA
Westport
Claremorris
Longford
N4
Navan
IMal
N17
Roscommon
Mullingar
14
Tuam
Clifden
26
N4
98
Athlone
N6
Maynooth
DUBLIN
N7
N6
Ballinasloe
IJoh
GALWAY
IFer
IReg
Loughrea
Kildare
N7
Wicklow
N18
Port Laoise
Baltinglass
Roscrea
Carlow
Arklow
N7
Ennis
Nenagh
N9
N11
N8
Shannon
KILKENNY
Gorey
LIMERICK
N10
N24
Enniscorthy
4
N9
N21
N24
N25
7
N8
Cahir
WEXFORD
Mitchelstown
WATERFORD
Tralee
ISta
Mallow
Fermoy
IOrc
N22
56
N20
Dungarvan
Killarney
25
N25
N22
Youghal
CORK
60
IHos
8
10

ADD MAGIC TO YOUR GARDEN WITH WATER
and get advice and supplies from aquatics specialists at the World's Largest Water Garden Centre.
Stapeley Water Gardens
For FREE 8-page price list just send large S.A.E.
For both price list and 40 page full-colour handbook send £1 Cheque or P.O.
Professional advice and quality aquatic plants will put you well on your way to creating a beautiful and successful garden pond or water feature of your own.
Why not plan a visit to our 53 acre complete Garden Centre in lovely rural Cheshire, just minutes from junction 16 off the M6? You'll find acres of display gardens to fire your imagination, three departments exclusively devoted to aquatic plants, healthy fish, fountains, pumps and pond liners and experts available everyday to answer your questions.
If you aren't able to visit us, send for our 40 page, full colour handbook packed with the largest range of plants and supplies and all the information you'll need to help you create your own water magic.
Visit us!
For FREE 8-page price list just send large S.A.E.
For both price list and 40-page full-colour handbook send £1 cheque or P.O.
If you do not wish to receive direct mail from companies other than Stapeley Water Gardens please tick.
Name
Address
Stapeley Water Gardens Limited Dept. PLFDR
London Road, Nantwich Cheshire. Tel: 0270 628111.

EVERYTHING UNDER THE SUN
FOR YOUR GARDEN
The actual sunshine is beyond us but we can provide everything else a gardener could wish for; seeds, bulbs, shrubs, trees, furniture, house plants, rockery, paving, aquatics and advice. All beautifully set out for your selection.
(Another ray of sunshine: Our Thatched Restaurant for coffee, lunch or afternoon tea.)
Webbs
OF WYCHBOLD
WYCHBOLD DROITWCH
TELEPHONE 0527 861777
On the A38 between Bromsgrove & Droitwich Junction 5, M5

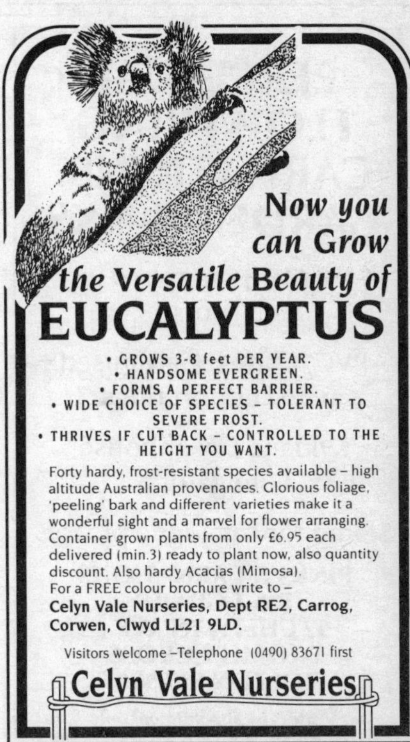

Now you can Grow the Versatile Beauty of
EUCALYPTUS
• GROWS 3-8 feet PER YEAR.
• HANDSOME EVERGREEN.
• FORMS A PERFECT BARRIER.
• WIDE CHOICE OF SPECIES – TOLERANT TO SEVERE FROST.
• THRIVES IF CUT BACK – CONTROLLED TO THE HEIGHT YOU WANT.
Forty hardy, frost-resistant species available – high altitude Australian provenances. Glorious foliage, 'peeling' bark and different varieties make it a wonderful sight and a marvel for flower arranging. Container grown plants from only £6.95 each delivered (min.3) ready to plant now, also quantity discount. Also hardy Acacias (Mimosa).
For a FREE colour brochure write to –
Celyn Vale Nurseries, Dept RE2, Carrog, Corwen, Clwyd LL21 9LD.
Visitors welcome –Telephone (0490) 83671 first
Celyn Vale Nurseries

Est. over 40 years
HEDGING, TREES, SHRUBS, CONIFERS,
ORNAMENTAL & FRUIT TREES
Over 150 different varieties of hedging plants and young trees to choose from, plus fruit trees, soft fruit and ground cover plants.
Telephone or write for your FREE COLOUR BROCHURE
Buckingham Nurseries
14 Tingewick Rd. Buckingham MK18 4AE
Tel:(0280) 813556 Fax:(0280) 815491

SCOTT'S CLEMATIS NURSERY

Lee
Nr. Ilfracombe
North Devon
EX34 8LW

Tel: 0271 863366

★ Wholesale and Retail
★ Extensive range, including rare and unusual
★ Catalogue on request. A4 sae
★ Open Tuesday – Sunday. Bank Holidays 10-6pm
★ Closed 24 December – 1st February
★ Set in charming valley – just ten minutes from the sea
★ **Visit Scotts . . . The Specialists**

TOAD HALL PRODUCE

FROGMORE,
WESTON-UNDER-PENYARD
HEREFORDSHIRE
LEA 0989 750 214

HARDY GERANIUMS and GROUND COVER PLANTS

Come and visit any MONDAY from APRIL to OCTOBER. (Other times by arrangement),

Send S.A.E. for Plant List.

From Ross-on-Wye take A40 through Weston-under-Penyard; turn right to Pontshill, keep to the right – the Nursery is 1 mile from A40.

Ferns and Fountains

We have probably the widest range of ferns for outdoors and conservatories in the country. In our display areas they are combined with high quality handmade leadwork in: Fountains, Tubs and Planters.

Catalogue £1 Open weekends
Weekdays by Appointment
J&D Marston, Culag, Green Lane, Nafferton, East Yorkshire YO25 0LF

FROM PALMS TO POPPIES
from

The Palm Farm

an unusual range of palms from subtropical species to hardy trees and shrubs from one nursery in South Humberside

Mail order service (14p stamp for list) or nursery customers welcome

Open 7 days, 2-5pm (Ring ahead in winter)

STATION ROAD, THORNTON CURTIS,
Nr ULCEBY, SOUTH HUMBERSIDE DN39 6XF
TEL. 0469 31232

JACK DRAKE

Proprietor: John C. Lawson

Dept PF, Inshriach Alpine
Plant Nursery
Aviemore
Inverness-shire
PH22 1QS

Situated on B970

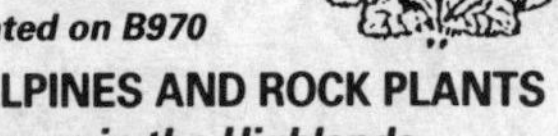

HARDY ALPINES AND ROCK PLANTS

Grown in the Highlands

Tel: 0540 651 287
Fax: 0540 651 656

Kenwith Nursery

THE OLD RECTORY, LITTLEHAM, DEVON EX39 5HW
Telephone: BIDEFORD 0237 473752

England's leading postal nursery in rare dwarf conifers. Send 3 x 1st class stamps for our catalogue.

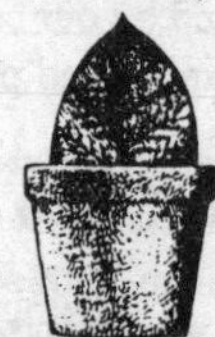

SELLET HALL GARDENS

Kirkby Lonsdale LA6 2QF

3½ acres of gardens planted with wide variety of Acers, Herbs and other interesting plants. Open daily 10-5pm. Group visits welcome by prior appointment. Tea & refreshments available at nursery shop

Tel. 05242 71865

V. H. HUMPHREY

Iris Specialist

Westlees Farm, Logmore Lane, Westcott, Dorking, Surrey RH4 3JN. Tel. 0306 889827 Fax. 0306 889371

Proprietor: Mrs P J Brown

Visits by appointment only

DWARF BEARDED, MEDIAN, BORDER, INTERMEDIATE, SPURIA, SIBIRICA, PACIFIC COAST, SPECIES

Large SAE for catalogue

BRINKLEY NURSERIES

Fiskerton Road, Southwell, Notts. NG25 0TP Tel: (0636) 814501

This nursery is well known for its high quality plus fast and efficient personal service. We have an outstandingly wide range with a speciality for the rare and unusual. It is definitely to be recommended for a visit to see and, if you wish, choose for yourself.

'JUST GIVE US A CALL AND WE WILL DO THE REST!'

LISCAHANE NURSERY

A general nursery offering a selection of coastal shelter plants including trees and shrubs.

Open Tues-Sat 9-6pm. Sun 2-6pm. CLOSED EACH MONDAY

LISCAHANE NURSERY, ARDFERT, TRALEE, CO. KERRY. TEL: 066 34222

CARNCAIRN DAFFODILS LTD

Our bulbs are known and grown all over the world. Gold Medal winners at the R.H.S. Vincent Square Shows.

Details from:- **Broughshane, Ballymena, Co. Antrim, BT43 7HF, N. Ireland Tel. 0266 861216**

QUALITY FRUIT TREES

A wide range of varieties both old and new. Write or telephone for our catalogue

THE FRUIT GARDEN

Mulberry Farm, Sandwich, Kent CT13 0PT

Telephone 0304 813 454

THE HERBARY PLANT CENTRE

89 Station Road, Herne Bay, Kent CT6 5QQ

Telephone 022 736 2409

Selection of plants to attract butterflies and bees to your garden. Aromatic shrubs, plants for TUFA.

Open Wed, Fri, Sat, 10am-5pm

MARCH UNTIL OCTOBER

CALLY GARDENS

Gatehouse of Fleet, Castle Douglas, Scotland DG7 2DJ Specialist grower of the scarcer perennials, grasses, shrubs and climbers. Please send 3 x 1st class stamps for the mail-order catalogue, opening times included.

Desmond & Charlotte Evans

Waterwheel Nursery

7 miles from Severn Bridge

Trees, shrubs and perennials, many unusual (see WWat)

Bully Hole Bottom, Usk Road, Shirenewton, Chepstow NP6 6SA Tel. 02917 577

CHRISTIES OF FORRES

One of the oldest established Scottish Nurseries, trading continuously since 1826.

We offer an extremely wide range of plants for gardeners, landscapers and foresters.

T. & W. CHRISTIE (FORRES) LTD

The Nurseries, Forres, Grampian. Tel. (0309) 672633. Fax. (0309) 676846. *Do send for our catalogue*

UNUSUAL HARDY HERBACEOUS PLANTS

PERRY WOOD, SELLING, NEAR FAVERSHAM, KENT

Tel: (0227) 752254

OPEN DAILY – 2.00pm-5.00pm APRIL to OCTOBER

PLANTS WANTED

Any forms or cultivars of Double Convallaria 'Lily of the Valley'

John Sinden, 'Hostas', 10 Derwent Water Road, Merley Ways, Wimborne, Dorset

Telephone: 0202 885841

PETER TRENEAR

TREES, SHRUBS, CONIFERS

For Garden or Bonsai. List free. Mail order or callers welcome 9 – 4.30. Closed Sundays

Tel. 0734 732300

Chequers Lane, Eversley Cross, Hants

WHITE COTTAGE ALPINES

Over 500 different species for the rock garden

FIND US off the B1253 York to Bridlington road, 30 miles north of Hull

For details see NWCA classification

THE WILDLIFE GARDENING CENTRE

Specialist growers of wildflowers and cottage garden plants. We also have a range of herbs, annuals, native trees, shrubs and climbers. Nursery open 10-5 (dusk in winter) Wed-Mon Catalogue 3 x 1st class stamps

Witney Road, Kingston Bagpuize, Abingdon, Oxon OX13 5AN. Tel. 0865 821660

EVERYTHING FOR THE WILDLIFE GARDENER

INDEX OF ADVERTISERS

INDEX OF ADVERTISERS

For further information concerning Display Advertisements in future editions, please write to:- Leslie Morris, c/o The Plant Finder, Lakeside, Whitbourne, Worcester WR6 5RD. Tel. 0903 505049

Notes

Notes

Notes

THE HARDY PLANT SOCIETY

The Hardy Plant Society was formed to foster interest in hardy herbaceous plants on the widest possible scale. It aims to give its members information about the wealth of both well known and little known hardy plants, how to grow them to the best advantage and where they may be obtained. It also aims to ensure that all worthy hardy plants remain in cultivation and have the widest possible distribution.

Further information may be obtained from:

The Administrator
Mrs Pam Adams
Little Orchard
Great Comberton
Pershore
Worcs. WR10 3DP
Tel No. (0386) 710317

Regional and Local Groups

Members may join any of the growing number of local groups organising many events in their own area including plant sales, garden visits, demonstrations and lectures. Most groups issue their own newsletter. The Groups form a basis for friendly exchange of information and plants and are an invaluable way of meeting other keen plantsmen locally. There is also a Correspondents Group for those not able to get out and about.

Genus and special Groups

Members may also join any of the specialised groups within the Society which will put them in touch with other members having similar interests. At present there are eight such groups covering 'Variegated Plants', 'Geraniums', 'Grasses', 'Paeony', 'Half-Hardy', 'Bellflowers' 'Pulmonarias' & 'Violas'.

Publications and Slide Library

The Society's Journal 'The Hardy Plant' is currently issued twice a year containing major illustrated articles on a wide variety of plants and gardens. Regular newsletters keep members informed of current events. A central collection of slides is available for loan to members wishing to compile illustrated lectures.

Seed Distribution

Each year members are encouraged to collect seed from plants in their gardens for the Seed Distribution which produces a printed list of all available seed, much of which comes from overseas. This currently lists over 2,000 varieties of seed, the majority of which is not available from commercial sources and, for a nominal sum members may select a number of packets from this.

Plant Sales and Shows

At organised meetings, both national and local, members bring interesting and unusual plants which are sold to aid the Society's funds. The Society puts on displays at the Royal Horticultural Society and other shows around the country and members can be involved by helping with the stands or by supplying plants to be shown.

Propagation and Wants scheme

This is run by the Southern Counties Group which propagates material from rarer or more difficult plants to ensure that the plants have the widest possible distribution. Some groups regularly issue lists of plants that members want but have been unable to locate. Word of mouth often helps locate wanted plants.

Conservation

The Society is most concerned about the conservation of garden plants. Countless fine plants have totally disappeared from cultivation and remain but a memory. In close cooperation with the National Council for the Conservation of Plants and Gardens, the Society is making efforts to ensure that all worthy plants are kept in cultivation.

For MEMBERSHIP APPLICATION FORM see over

HARDY PLANT SOCIETY

MEMBERSHIP APPLICATION FOR 1993

The Annual Subscriptions are as follows:

Single Membership **£8.50**
Joint Membership (any two members living at the same address) **£10.00**

Subscriptions are renewable annually on January 1st. Subscriptions of members joining after October 1st are valid until the end of the following year.
Overseas members are requested to remit by International Money Order in Sterling or by Credit Card (Visa/MasterCard/Eurocard/Access).

APPLICATION FORM

IMPORTANT: If you are renewing a past membership please tick box ☐

I wish to apply for Membership for 1993

NAME . . . .

ADDRESS . . . .

. . . .

. . . . POSTCODE . . . .

and would like to apply for the following type of membership

SINGLE	£8.50	. . . . .
JOINT (2 members at one address)	£10.00	. . . . .
Airmail postage	£3.00	. . . . .

	TOTAL	
		========

I enclose an International Money Order or Eurocheque in Pounds Sterling payable to **THE HARDY PLANT SOCIETY** (Please DO NOT send cheques in Foreign Currency)

OR
Please debit my Visa/MasterCard/Eurocard/Access

CARD NUMBER ☐☐☐☐ ☐☐☐☐ ☐☐☐☐ ☐☐☐☐

EXPIRY DATE ☐☐☐☐ Your name as on Card . . . .

SIGNATURE . . . . DATE . . . .

Please print name and address clearly, tear out the page and send to:

THE ADMINISTRATOR
Mrs Pam Adams
Little Orchard
Pershore
Great Comberton
Worcs. WR10 3DP

For further details of the Society please see previous page